TABLE OF ATOMIC WEIGHTS

Names	Symbol	Atomic Number	Atomic Weight
Actinium	Ac	89	227.0278
Aluminum	Al	13	26.98154
Americium	Am	95	(243)
Antimony	Sb	51	121.75
Argon	Ar	18	39.948
Arsenic	As	33	74.9216
Astatine	At	85	(210)
Barium	Ba	56	137.33
Berkelium	Bk	97	(247)
Beryllium	Be	4	9.01218
Bismuth	Bi	83	208.9804
Boron	B	5	10.811
Bromine	Br	35	79.904
Cadmium	Cd	48	112.41
Calcium	Ca	20	40.078
Californium	Cf	98	(251)
Carbon	C	6	12.011
Cerium	Ce	58	140.12
Cesium	Cs	55	132.9054
Chlorine	Cl	17	35.453
Chromium	Cr	24	51.9961
Cobalt	Co	27	58.9332
Copper	Cu	29	63.546
Curium	Cm	96	(247)
Dysprosium	Dy	66	162.50
Einsteinium	Es	99	(252)
Erbium	Er	68	167.26
Europium	Eu	63	151.96
Fermium	Fm	100	(257)
Fluorine	F	9	18.998403
Francium	Fr	87	(223)
Gadolinium	Gd	64	157.25
Gallium	Ga	31	69.723
Germanium	Ge	32	72.59
Gold	Au	79	196.9665
Hafnium	Hf	72	178.49
Helium	He	2	4.002602
Holmium	Ho	67	164.9304
Hydrogen	H	1	1.00794
Indium	In	49	114.82
Iodine	I	53	126.9045
Iridium	Ir	77	192.22
Iron	Fe	26	55.847
Krypton	Kr	36	83.80
Lanthanum	La	57	138.9055
Lawrencium	Lr	103	(260)
Lead	Pb	82	207.2
Lithium	Li	3	6.941
Lutetium	Lu	71	174.967
Magnesium	Mg	12	24.305
Manganese	Mn	25	54.9380
Mendelevium	Md	101	(258)
Mercury	Hg	80	200.59
Molybdenum	Mo	42	95.94
Neodymium	Nd	60	144.24

Names	Symbol	Number	Weight
Neon	Ne	10	20.179
Neptunium	Np	93	237.0482
Nickel	Ni	28	58.69
Niobium	Nb	41	92.9064
Nitrogen	N	7	14.0067
Nobelium	No	102	(259)
Osmium	Os	76	190.2
Oxygen	O	8	15.9994
Palladium	Pd	46	106.42
Phosphorus	P	15	30.97376
Platinum	Pt	78	195.08 ± 3
Plutonium	Pu	94	(244)
Polonium	Po	84	(209)
Potassium	K	19	39.0983
Praseodymium	Pr	59	140.9077
Promethium	Pm	61	(145)
Protactinium	Pa	91	231.0359
Radium	Ra	88	226.0254
Radon	Rn	86	(222)
Rhenium	Re	75	186.207
Rhodium	Rh	45	102.9055
Rubidium	Rb	37	85.4678
Ruthenium	Ru	44	101.07
Samarium	Sm	62	150.36
Scandium	Sc	21	44.95591
Selenium	Se	34	78.96
Silicon	Si	14	28.0855
Silver	Ag	47	107.8682
Sodium	Na	11	22.98977
Strontium	Sr	38	87.62
Sulfur	S	16	32.066
Tantalum	Ta	73	180.9479
Technetium	Tc	43	(98)
Tellurium	Te	52	127.60
Terbium	Tb	65	158.9254
Thallium	Tl	81	204.383
Thorium	Th	90	232.0381
Thulium	Tm	69	168.9342
Tin	Sn	50	118.710
Titanium	Ti	22	47.88
Tungsten	W	74	183.85
Unnilennium	Une	109	—
Unnilhexium	Unh	106	(263)
Unniloctium	Uno	108	—
Unnilpentium	Unp	105	(262)
Unnilquadium	Unq	104	(261)
Unnilseptium	Uns	107	(262)
Uranium	U	92	238.0289
Vanadium	V	23	50.9415
Xenon	Xe	54	131.29
Ytterbium	Yb	70	173.04
Yttrium	Y	39	88.9059
Zinc	Zn	30	65.39
Zirconium	Zr	40	91.224

A value in parentheses is the mass number of the isotope of longest half-life.

Values in this table are from the 1983 Report of the International Union of Pure and Applied Chemistry (IUPAC).

Organic Chemistry

Organic Chemistry

A. DAVID BAKER
Queens College

ROBERT ENGEL
Queens College

WEST PUBLISHING COMPANY
St. Paul New York Los Angeles San Francisco

Copyediting	Pamela McMurry
Composition	Syntax, International
Film	Syntax, International
Text Design	Janet Bollow
Artwork	J/B Woolsey Associates
Proofreading	Luana Richards
Indexing	Pamela McMurry
Cover design	Janet Bollow
Cover image	The belief that molecular-level prototypes can be constructed to mimic familiar macroscopic objects has been the inspiration for many intensive and successful synthetic efforts. Inspired by the beauty and efficiency of branching networks found in *Bryoza* colonies, a new class of precise macromolecules referred to as Starburst™ dendrimers (cascade molecules) has been synthesized (D. A. Tomalia, A. M. Naylor and W. A. Goddard III, *Angewandte Chemie, International Edition in English 29* (1990), 138). Just as Nature controls macroscopic three-dimensional space with this branching motif, so can the synthetic chemist control molecular level (nanoscopic) space.

Production, Prepress, Printing, and Binding
all by West Publishing Company

99 98 97 96 95 94 93 92 8 7 6 5 4 3 2 1 0

Library of Congress Cataloging-in-Publication Data

Baker, Arthur D.
Organic chemistry/A. David Baker, Robert Engel.
p. cm.
ISBN 0–314–93000–0 (hard)
1. Chemistry, Organic. I. Engel, Robert. II. Title.
QD251.2.B345 1992
547–dc20 91–32670
∞ CIP

West's Commitment to the Environment

In 1906, West Publishing Company began recycling materials left over from the production of books. This began a tradition of efficient and responsible use of resources. Today, up to 95 percent of our legal books and 70 percent of our college texts are printed on recycled, acid-free stock. West also recycles nearly 22 million pounds of scrap paper annually—the equivalent of 181,717 trees. Since the 1960s, West has devised ways to capture and recycle waste inks, solvents, oils, and vapors created in the printing process. We also recycle plastics of all kinds, wood, glass, corrugated cardboard, and batteries, and have eliminated the use of styrofoam book packaging. We at West are proud of the longevity and the scope of our commitment to our environment.

To nine special people:

My parents, Arthur and Catherine Baker
My wife, Peggy, and her parents, Norman and Aimée
My children, Philip and Stephen
My brother, Mark, and his wife, Soumaya

A. David Baker

To my family, for their patience:

My wife, Liz
My children, Cheryl and Erik

Robert Engel

Brief Contents

Contents

Preface

When we began writing this text in 1986, our goal was to produce a student-oriented text that would introduce the main aspects of modern organic chemistry in a clear and thorough fashion. Our teaching experience had alerted us to the topics and the concepts that prove to be difficult for many students, and we felt that some of the novel approaches that worked well in our lectures would also work in a textbook presentation. Some of the ideas we had at the beginning have remained unchanged, while others have been refined and improved during the years in which this textbook matured from a primitive draft to its present form.

Features

EARLY EMPHASIS ON STRUCTURE AND BONDING

It is crucial that students quickly become adept at drawing Lewis structures, understand the use of resonance-contributing forms, learn to assign formal charges accurately, understand the hybridization model, and understand the basic ideas of molecular orbital theory. Therefore we give a thorough systematic treatment of these topics in Chapter 1 and provide constant reinforcement in later chapters. We also introduce the useful curved-arrow formalism at the beginning of the text and continue to use it throughout.

LARGE SELECTION OF PROBLEMS

Problem solving is the key to success in organic chemistry; thus it is essential that a text offer a wide selection of problems of different types. We have given much thought to the selection of good problems. A large number of problems are included in the main text and at the end of each chapter, and additional drill problems are given in the accompanying study guide and solutions manual. The problems vary in difficulty, and many of them require students to review material from earlier in the course. Solutions to all problems are given in the *Study Guide and Solutions Manual.*

EARLY TREATMENT OF ALCOHOL CHEMISTRY

We begin our treatment of alcohols in Chapter 5. We feel that alcohol chemistry offers much appeal as a way of introducing students to organic reactions. For example, many aspects of alcohol chemistry can be related to topics that students learn about in their introductory chemistry courses, including acid-base chemistry, redox chemistry, and the importance of hydrogen bonding.

Also, of course, alcohols are among the most important of organic compounds—they play such a central role in organic chemistry that an early emphasis on their chemistry is certainly appropriate. We use the reactions of alcohols to introduce mechanistic principles and to acquaint students with nucleophiles, leaving groups, carbocations, and oxonium ions. Many ideas first introduced in the context of alcohols are then reemphasized in different contexts in subsequent chapters. An additional advantage of introducing alcohols early is that laboratory experiments based on alcohols can be initiated early in the first semester.

EARLY EMPHASIS ON THE CONTRAST BETWEEN HALOALKANES AND ORGANOMETALLIC COMPOUNDS

In Chapter 11 we introduce the contrasts in chemistry resulting from the different directions of polarity in carbon-metal and carbon-halogen bonds. The idea of *umpolung* is introduced here and used again later in the text.

REPEATED EMPHASIS OF BASE BEHAVIOR VERSUS NUCLEOPHILIC BEHAVIOR

The competition between base behavior and nucleophilic behavior pervades organic chemistry. We introduce the idea very early and constantly reemphasize it, adding new aspects and new discussion at each stage.

THOROUGH TREATMENT OF STEREOCHEMISTRY

Stereochemistry is often the hardest topic for students. It is therefore crucial that students be given clear instructions so that they can master the basic skills needed to manipulate stereochemical drawings, assign configurations, and predict the products of stereospecific reactions. We therefore emphasize these basics in Chapter 8. We give detailed explanations of how to work with molecular models (and include some problems for students to solve) and with the different types of stereochemical projection drawings. We also use analogies to help students envisage some of the more difficult aspects of the topic.

USE OF PICTORIAL MOLECULAR ORBITAL THEORY

Applications of molecular orbital theory often seem obscure to students, so we have made a great effort to present this material in a novel and clear fashion. First, the basic principles are introduced in Chapter 1 in a rather traditional fashion. Following Chapter 1, aspects of molecular orbital theory are introduced in the context of the topic being discussed. Usually this information is found in sections entitled "Molecular Orbital Analysis," which are designed to give additional insight into the immediately preceding material. We introduce students to some of the principles that are becoming ever more important in the analysis of organic reactions—the correlation of reactivity with the energies of either or both the HOMO and the LUMO and the correlation of stereospecificity in a reaction with the orientation of orbitals. Two chapters are devoted almost entirely to molecular orbital theory—Chapter 16, which deals with conjugated π systems and aromaticity, and Chapter 30, which focuses on concerted reactions. In Chapter 16 we introduce a simple pictorial method of relating the energies of the π orbitals of cyclic conjugated systems to those of their open-chain analogs. This method gives a particularly clear rationalization of the periodicity of aromaticity of cyclic conjugated molecules expressed by the Huckel $(4n + 2)$ rule.

EXTENSIVE TREATMENT OF SPECTROMETRIC DETERMINATION OF STRUCTURE

Over our years of teaching, we have found that the ideal time to begin this topic is near the beginning of the second semester. Accordingly, we introduce IR and NMR techniques in Chapter 17. We know that some faculty prefer to introduce these topics sooner, so this chapter is self-contained and can be covered earlier. Our treatment of IR and NMR is thorough. Enough information is given so that students can understand how spectra are obtained, appreciate the underlying theory, and extract structural information from spectra. Many sample spectra are analyzed, and flow charts and other aides are used to guide students in the task of interpreting a spectrum. UV and mass spectrometry are covered in Chapter 25. These topics are placed later in the book because many instructors do not find time to cover them in the typical sophomore-level course. However, for the most part, the book has been written so that the order in which chapters are covered can be somewhat flexible to accommodate the needs of different instructors.

INTEGRATION OF SYNTHETIC STRATEGY THROUGHOUT THE TEXT

We discuss why it is important to have more than one method for effecting many functional group transformations. Retrosynthetic analysis is also introduced, and there are several discussions about protecting groups. The use of natural products as sources of optically pure chiral reagents for synthesis is introduced in the course of the discussion of carbohydrates.

APPLICATIONS TO BIOLOGY, MEDICINE, TECHNOLOGY, AND OTHER AREAS ARE FOUND THROUGHOUT THE TEXT

We believe that it is important to stress the relevance of organic chemistry to other areas and to point out some of the more interesting features of organic compounds. We have addressed this need in various ways. Some topics are worked into the main discussion or into problems. Others are described in "Special Topic" sections. "Compound Capsule" features, which focus on a particular chemical or a group of chemicals that has interesting properties or applications, are scattered through the text.

Pedagogy

- Each chapter begins with a short introduction explaining what is to be covered and relating the topic to material covered in earlier chapters.
- We have attempted to make the writing style student-friendly. Transitions between topics are smooth, and we consistently relate new topics to earlier topics, pointing out common mechanisms or properties.

- A phased-in approach is used for several topics. The topic is introduced in one chapter and then reexamined later in light of new material.
- Mechanisms are presented in a consistent format in the "Mechanism of Reaction" features. Each mechanism is presented in a step-by-step format with appropriate annotations. Curved arrows are used throughout the mechanisms, and electrons that are shifted are color-coded for clarity.
- Extensive use is made of four-color art to help students visualize structural and mechanistic relationships.
- There is a summary of key terms at the end of each chapter. There is also a summary of important reactions at the end of appropriate chapters. These reactions are numbered consecutively throughout the text to help instructors identify for the students the reactions that they need to learn thoroughly and to help students organize their studies.
- In the early part of the book, reaction maps are provided at the end of each chapter to summarize how the reactions introduced up to that point can be used to bring about conversions among the different classes of organic compounds. Students are encouraged to continue these reaction maps throughout the course.

Acknowledgements

We wish to express our appreciation to the many people who aided us in completing what often seemed to be an endless task. Our science editors, first Jay Ricci, then Ron Pullins, guided us through the maelstrom of conflicting reviewer comments and encouraged us that with each new draft the book was improving. We are especially grateful to Ron, who took over the project at a critical time and immediately made all the right decisions to get the book on track for publication in 1992. His help and suggestions are greatly valued. We also thank Sharon Adams and Denise Bayko, who served as our developmental editors. They were always ready to offer whatever support we needed, and their friendly cooperation was a major plus. Once the book entered into production, a new and hectic phase of operations began, guided by our production editor, Tom Hilt. Our contacts with Tom have only been by telephone, but the quiet competent way he went about his work was quite evident, and he has been a calming influence for us. The beautiful artwork for the book was produced by John and Bette Woolsey of J/B Woolsey Associates; we gratefully acknowledge their expertise. We also thank Pamela McMurry, who efficiently handled the copyediting. On so many occasions, she found just the right way to express a complicated idea. We also thank Miss Karin Melkonian and Mr. Joseph Badalamenti for their help in measuring some the ^{1}H NMR spectra. Last, but not least, we thank our families for their patience and understanding throughout the period when we were writing.

The ^{13}C NMR spectra used in this book are printed with permission from John Wiley, Inc. Items appearing in various editions of the Encyclopaedia Britannica *Yearbook of Science and the Future* provided ideas for some of the "Compound Capsules." An article by Drs. A. M. Ingham and R. C. Henson (*Journal of Chemical Education* 61, (1984): 704) suggesting the use of flowcharts for the systematic interpretation of spectra served as the basis for the flowcharts presented in Chapter 17.

Finally, we wish to thank the reviewers who added valuable input to the project:

David M. Howell	*Northeastern University*
R. Gerald Bass	*Virginia Commonwealth University*
Larry Bray	*Miami Dade University/South Campus*
Gary P. Crowther	*James Madison University*
Raymond C. Fort, Jr.	*University of Maine*
Peter A. Wade	*Drexel University*
Michael W. Rathke	*Michigan State University*
David W. Boykin	*Georgia State University*
Harry Ungar	*Cabrillo College*
Marye Anne Fox	*University of Texas/Austin*
Asbot Merijanian	*The William Patterson College of New Jersey*
Thomas G. Waddell	*The University of Tennessee at Chattanooga*
Robert Boxer	*Georgia Southern*
Byron L. Hawbecker	*Ohio Northern University*
Timothy F. Crimmins	*University of Wisconsin/Oshkosh*
E. P. Papadopoulos	*University of New Mexico*
Charles W. Spangler	*Northern Illinois University*
Joseph Landesberg	*Adelphi University*
James F. Wolfe	*Virginia Tech*
Lawrence K. Montgomery	*Indiana University*
Russell C. Petter	*University of Pittsburgh*
Roy Garvey	*North Dakota State*
George H. Wahl, Jr.	*North Caroline State University*
Ken Turnbull	*Wright State University*
Daniel H. O'Brien	*Texas A & M University*
George Kraus	*Iowa State University*
George B. Clemans	*Bowling Green State University*
James B. Ellern	*University of Southern California*
James M. Tanko	*Virginia Polytechnic Institute and State University*
Winfield M. Baldwin	*University of Georgia*
John L. Hoss	*Texas A & M University*
Suzanne T. Purrington	*North Caroline State University*
David Goldsmith	*Emory University*
Carl T. Wigal	*Idaho State University*
W. F. Berkowitz	*Queens College*
Kenneth E. Kolb	*Bradley University*
J. W. Timberlake	*University of New Orleans*
Mark L. McLaughlin	*Louisiana State University*
James L. Lyle	*California State University/Dominquez Hill*
William F. Bailey	*University of Connecticut*
James Seidel	*University of Wisconsin/Oshkosh*
Edward Turos	*SUNY/Buffalo*
Ronald L. Marhenke	*California State University/Fresno*
William A. Donaldson	*Marquette University*
Walter S. Trahanovsky	*Iowa State University*

Introduction

I.1 Origins and History of Organic Chemistry

The study of chemistry as a scientific discipline began in Europe during the seventeenth and eighteenth centuries. Pioneering work by scientists such as Boyle, Cavendish, Priestley, and Lavoisier led to new insights into chemical phenomena. Their efforts sowed the seeds for Dalton's development of atomic theory in the first decade of the nineteenth century.

Of necessity, most early scientific inquiry involved studies of substances that were plentiful and easily isolated from the environment. These materials included water, the atmospheric gases, some minerals and salts, and substances isolated from biological materials. Some of these substances were known to be present both in living organisms and in materials generally not described as living. Of particular interest, however, were substances found only in living organisms. These substances were classified as *organic* to distinguish them from *inorganic* substances (those found in nonliving materials).

Careful investigations of organic materials uncovered a further common characteristic. Antoine Lavoisier, a French chemist, discovered quite early that all organic materials are composed of carbon in combination with other elements. The other elements present are most often hydrogen, oxygen, and nitrogen, although other elements are also found in some organic materials.

It was widely believed by these early scientists that organic substances could be generated only within living organisms. Even as late as 1820, all attempts to synthesize organic materials from inorganic substances had failed. These fruitless attempts indirectly supported the notion of the time that a *vital force*, supposedly only present in living organisms, was required for the generation of organic materials.

By the mid-nineteenth century, however, it had become clear that the vital force concept was incorrect. In 1828 Friedrich Wohler succeeded in using an inorganic substance, ammonium cyanate, to synthesize urea, an organic material previously found only as a constituent of urine.

$$\underset{\text{ammonium cyanate}}{NH_4^{+}\ {}^{-}OCN} \xrightarrow{\text{heat}} \underset{\text{urea}}{H_2\ddot{N}-\overset{\overset{:O:}{\|}}{C}-\ddot{N}H_2}$$

Soon afterwards, Hermann Kolbe accomplished the synthesis of acetic acid from elemental sources. Acetic acid had previously been isolated only from materials of biological origin. After exposure to the atmosphere, fermented fruit juices (i.e., wines) were found to produce vinegar, from which pure acetic acid could be isolated. (Acetic acid is the component of vinegar that gives it its characteristic odor and taste.)

$$H_3C-\overset{\overset{:O:}{\|}}{C}-\ddot{\underset{..}{O}}H$$

acetic acid

Soon chemists began achieving remarkable success in the new art of synthesis of organic compounds. In 1856 at the age of 18, William Henry Perkin synthesized the dye aniline purple (mauveine) from coal tar. Coal and related products of biological decay have since proven to be rich sources of carbon-containing materials for organic syntheses. Within a year the new dye was marketed. For the first time, a development in an organic chemistry laboratory had led to the establishment of a new industry, the coal-tar–derived dye industry.

In 1895 another landmark in the growth of applied chemistry was established at the Baeyer company in Germany. Salicylic acid, which can be isolated from the bark of willow trees, was known to be a natural analgesic. Willow bark had been chewed for the relief of minor pain since the time of the ancient Romans. Baeyer prepared aspirin (acetylsalicylic acid) from the natural salicylic acid, and the laboratory-produced derivative proved to be superior to the naturally occurring substance because its use involved less irritation to the stomach while still providing the analgesic effect. Baeyer's enormous success with aspirin spawned the pharmaceutical industry.

salicylic acid

acetylsalicylic acid

The source of most starting materials for laboratory-generated organic compounds has been and continues to be biologically derived materials. The main reason for this is the sheer abundance of carbon compounds present in living organisms and substances derived from them. Included, of course, are the petrochemicals derived from biological materials decaying over eons. With the drilling of the first oil wells in 1859 in Pennsylvania, a cheap and abundant source of carbon-containing compounds became available. Today the petrochemical industry supplies organic compounds from this biologically derived source for the manufacture of thousands of substances, including dyes, pharmaceuticals, explosives, plastics, fibers, fuels, and agricultural chemicals.

Organic compounds are, of course, the "stuff of life," the foundation materials of biological organisms, and advances in organic chemistry have had a profound effect in increasing our understanding of heredity, nutrition, disease, and other physiological phenomena.

In the early days of organic chemistry, progress was slow in these areas because of the inherent complexity of most of the organic compounds that are involved in biological processes. Until quite recently, analytical and structural determinations of complex, biochemically important substances were seriously hindered by a lack of adequate techniques. However, spectacular advances have now been made in this area. As a result, extraordinary insights have been obtained into the structure and function of proteins, carbohydrates, drugs, vitamins, and other biologically important molecules. Furthermore, a chemical basis for heredity has been established, and it has become possible to modify structurally the nucleic acids responsible for carrying the genetic information. Organisms can thus be reprogrammed to produce new and useful chemicals, and it is even possible to create new organisms through this genetic engineering. These techniques open up entire new vistas for scientific study. Indeed, a new high-tech industry based on genetic engineering has begun to assert itself.

The early vital force concept was inevitably doomed to be replaced by an understanding of organic materials on a chemical basis. Fundamental to this understanding was the recognition that organic compounds contain carbon as a fundamental constituent and exhibit characteristic chemical reactions. Organic chemistry is in fact now defined as the chemistry of carbon compounds, rather than the chemistry of "compounds derived from living organisms." This modified definition is sensible because it includes the chemistry of compounds structurally and chemically related to those from biological systems; many of these compounds do not actually exist anywhere in the plant or animal kingdoms. The underlying chemistry of natural (from biological sources) and synthetic carbon compounds is the same. The chemical and physical properties of a compound of a particular structure are identical whether that material is generated in a living bush or a glass laboratory flask. Pure vitamin C isolated from an orange is indistinguishable from pure vitamin C synthesized in glassware in laboratory. No scientific purpose is served by making an artificial definition of the two sources.

I.2 Organic Compounds as the Basis of Life

Having noted that organic chemistry had its origins in the study of biological systems, we might ask why biological processes are based on the chemistry of carbon rather than on some other element. At the risk of oversimplification, the answer would seem to be found in a few main issues. Probably most significant is the unique ability of carbon to form long, stable sequences of covalent bonds to other carbon atoms. This characteristic of carbon allows the formation of large, highly complex molecules that are capable of innumerable highly specific interactions with each other. Since any carbon atom in a neutral, stable (isolable, unreactive) molecule must form a total of four bonds, there is a wide scope for structural variation in these large molecules, depending on the other atoms or groups of atoms that are bonded to the carbon atoms.

Biological organisms generate a vast number of compounds that participate in a wide variety of complicated processes. From the tremendous variety of possible carbon compounds, biological organisms utilized those with suitable properties for each task. Thus, in order to sustain itself, a living organism must constantly generate the specific carbon compounds it needs but cannot get readily from outside sources.

Plant and animal species circulate a delicately balanced mix of the proper carbon compounds needed for their continued existence. Plants utilize carbon dioxide as a carbon source and convert it into more complex molecules. Many of the biological organic syntheses involved in this process have been well studied and are now reasonably understood on a chemical basis. Animals obtain their carbon starting materials by the consumption of plants or other animals that are plant eaters. Life requires a wide variety of chemical compounds. Carbon provides this variety as no other element can.

I.3 The Structure and Scope of the Science of Organic Chemistry

During the nineteenth century a fundamental order was brought to the new science of organic chemistry. It was recognized that compounds exhibiting similar chemical characteristics have similar arrangements of atoms, so compounds were classified on the basis of their structural features. This classification by *functional group* persists today because of its general utility and our study of organic chemistry is organized on this basis of functional group.

It is clear from these few examples that organic chemistry is a broad scientific field. It involves basic studies of the structure and reactivity of carbon compounds. In addition to the elucidation of the structures of natural products and the study of their role in biological processes, organic chemistry is concerned with the development of a wide variety of synthetic substances.

Much remains today to be done with organic chemistry, in regard to both biological and nonbiological endeavors. What can be done with organic chemistry is limited only by our imagination. Perhaps today's organic chemistry student will determine the chemical basis of memory or develop methods to remedy genetic diseases. Current students of the science may participate in the development of molecular-sized electronic components or organic materials that will conduct electricity as well as (or better than) copper. Some organic chemists will be concerned with the theoretical aspects of the science rather than the laboratory work. We can anticipate fundamental breakthroughs that will affect the ways we view many aspects of the discipline.

The aim of this text is to prepare you for these or other new adventures in organic chemistry by presenting the fundamentals of the subject in a systematic, reasoned, and clear fashion.

Organic Chemistry

CHAPTER 1 Bonding in Organic Compounds

1.1 Introduction

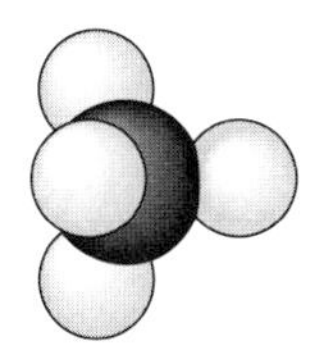

In this chapter, we begin to address an issue that is of fundamental importance for the study of all organic chemistry: the **structure** of organic molecules. First, you might ask, what exactly is meant by the term *structure* when applied to molecules? This term usually means the arrangement in space of the atoms and bonds making up a molecule. Chemists normally represent structure with drawings, in which case certain conventions are followed for depicting atoms, their arrangement in space, and the bonded interactions among them. Molecular models of various kinds are also useful. In the opening chapters we will introduce some basic ideas and conventions that will be followed throughout the text.

Organic chemists spend much of their time striving to understand as fully as possible the many aspects of structure. Through knowledge of the molecular structure of a substance, we are able to understand and predict its chemical, physical, and even biological properties. Knowledge of the structure of a substance requires at the most basic level the determination of the identity of the atoms present in a molecule of the substance and a determination of the sequence or arrangement of these atoms. We obtain this information by using experimental techniques that provide a probe of molecular structure. These techniques include spectroscopic methods that rely on the absorption of light or other electromagnetic radiation by the compound or other analytical techniques. We will describe many of these methods as we proceed through the text. Often organic chemists, faced with a new material for which a structure needs to be determined, will rely on both spectroscopic and chemical analyses.

Once the gross arrangement of atoms in a molecule has been determined, we need to fine-tune our knowledge. We might want to know about details of the structure, such as bond lengths (the distances between bonded atoms), or bond angles (the angles between a pair of bonds), or we might want to know about the stability of the structure relative to other structures we know about. Many of these questions are intimately related to a knowledge of the bonding within the molecule. In order to understand bonding, we need to combine fundamental theories or models of chemical bonding with experimental data. A fruitful place for us to begin is by considering various aspects of chemical bonding.

1.2 The Chemical Bond

We say that a bond is present between a pair of atoms when they take up positions close to one another because of a mutual attraction. Whenever bonding occurs, there is some particular distance between the atoms at which the atoms associate more strongly than at any other distance. At this separation the *energy* of the system is at a relative minimum. Energy would have to be

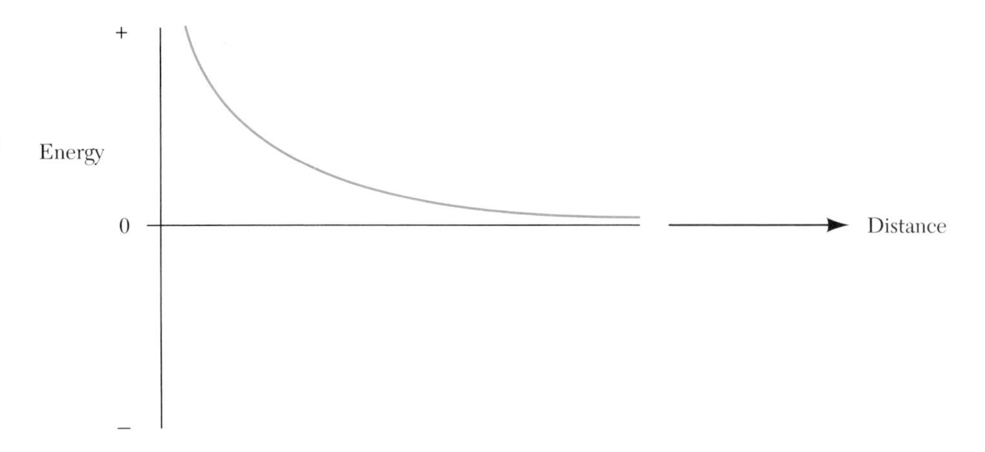

Figure 1.1 Relative energy associated with a pair of protons as a function of the internuclear distance. As the protons approach, greater energy is required to keep them from moving apart. They repel each other.

supplied to separate the two bonded partners. Consider two examples, one that involves the formation of a chemical bond and one that does not.

Suppose we consider two protons. Recall that a proton is a fundamental atomic particle having a positive charge. A proton is also the nucleus of a hydrogen atom. When the two protons are far apart, there is a very small repulsive interaction between them as a result of electrostatics (like charges repel each other). If we wish to have these two protons approach each other, we find that it is necessary to provide energy—we need to push them together. The closer we wish them to be, the greater the amount of energy we must provide to them (see Figure 1.1). This energy is needed to overcome the natural tendency of the two protons to repel one another and push apart. There is no bond between the two protons. They mutually repel at all distances of separation.

Now consider a pair of hydrogen *atoms*. Each hydrogen atom has a proton as its nucleus and an electron situated outside the nucleus. Imagine now the hydrogen atoms coming closer and closer together. In terms of energy, we see something quite different (Figure 1.2) from what we just described for the ap-

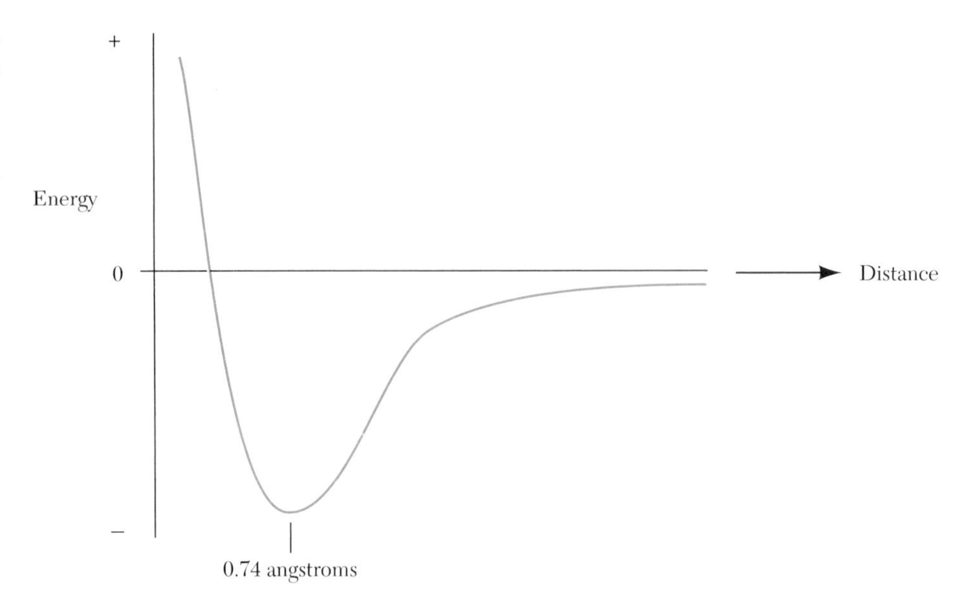

Figure 1.2 Relative energy associated with a pair of hydrogen atoms as they approach from a large distance. A relative energy minimum occurs when they are 0.74 angstrom apart. This energy minimum represents a chemical bond between them.

proach of two protons. First, the hydrogen atoms increasingly *attract* each other as the distance between them decreases. In consequence, the energy of the two-atom system steadily decreases to a minimum (and the stability increases to a maximum). This energy minimum occurs when the hydrogen atoms are 0.74 angstrom apart (1 angstrom = 10^{-10} m). However, at shorter distances the energy again rises. We would need to push the hydrogen atoms together if we wished them to be closer than 0.74 angstrom, as illustrated in Figure 1.2. We see that over some range of distances the hydrogen atoms tend to stick together, that is, they form a bond. At 0.74 angstrom distance the hydrogen atoms have no tendency to push apart or to move closer together. We say that the hydrogen atoms are separated by their *equilibrium bonding distance*. (Actually, the two hydrogen atoms in a hydrogen molecule do not remain *exactly* 0.74 angstrom apart. They vibrate about this distance, sometimes being slightly closer together and sometimes being slightly farther apart. All atoms in bonds behave this way; see Chapter 17 for more detail.)

Whenever we speak of bonds of any type in chemistry, we always recognize that the distance between the bonded atoms corresponds to an *energy minimum*. For there to be an energy minimum, the bonded partners must exert both attractive and repulsive forces on each other. If the force were attractive only, they would coalesce into a single particle, and if the force were repulsive only, they would fly apart. At the equilibrium bonding distance, the repulsive and attractive forces just balance.

All types of chemical bonds are electrostatic in nature, that is, they depend on the attraction of positively and negatively charged entities. In a hydrogen molecule, the attractive forces are the electrostatic interactions between the positively charged nuclei and the negatively charged electrons, and the repulsive forces, again electrostatic, are those between particles of like charge, that is, proton-proton and electron-electron interactions.

Although all chemical bonds do have a common origin, it is convenient to divide bond types into various subgroups. Bonds that exist between atoms *within* a given molecule or formula unit are classified as either **covalent** or **ionic.** Bonds that exist between a pair of atoms belonging to *different* molecules are said to be *intermolecular*. Intermolecular bonds are generally weaker than ionic or covalent bonds but are nevertheless important for a number of reasons. In this opening chapter, we will focus on ionic and covalent bonds, giving special attention to the latter type, because covalent bonds are much more common than ionic bonds in organic substances. A little later, in Chapter 3, we will discuss intermolecular bonds, which can also be subdivided into various types: dipole-dipole interactions, van der Waals forces, hydrogen bonds, and so forth.

1.3 Ionic and Covalent Bonds

The *exact* description of any given bond obviously requires an exact knowledge of all the electrostatic attractions and repulsions present. Unfortunately, our description must be a compromise because mathematical complexity is imposed by the number of charged entities present and because our knowledge about the location of electrons has an inherent limit imposed by the Heisenberg uncertainty principle. Nevertheless, our models of bonding do provide very powerful ways of examining bonds. Actually a hierarchy of bonding models exists. The simplest have the advantage of being easy to apply, while nevertheless giving useful information for a wide range of bonds. They have the disadvantage of being only qualitative and sometimes inaccurate. More sophisticated models are called upon when the simplest models cannot provide the required information.

The simplest models of ionic and covalent bonding can be traced back to the pioneering ideas of G. N. Lewis and W. Kossel. In 1916 these chemists made the first attempts to correlate bonding with the arrangement of electrons in the species undergoing bonding. They knew that some substances, for example, sodium chloride and other salts, have very strong bonds and that these strong bonds, along with other properties of salts such as electrical conduction when melted or in aqueous solution, are consistent with the presence of ions—that is, charged atoms or molecules. Accordingly, the ionic bond is simply the attraction of a positive and a negative ion. The ions can be considered as forming by the transfer of one or more electrons from one of the parent atoms to another, for example, transfer of an electron from a sodium atom to a chlorine atom produces an Na^+ ion and a Cl^- ion. Ionic bonding is found most commonly when the partners in the bond are a metallic and a nonmetallic element.

Lewis and Kossel were aware that many substances (including most organic substances) are not ionic in nature. They proposed that the type of bonding present in these substances is of a different type, known as covalent, and that the covalent bond results when a pair of electrons is shared between two atoms. A covalent bond is represented in a structure by a line (—) or a pair of dots (:). For example the hydrogen molecule described above can be represented as H—H or as H:H. In this simple view of the covalent bond, each hydrogen atom is considered as sharing its electron with the other atom. Although this simple model does not specifically address the issues as to the attractive and repulsive forces present in a covalently bonded molecule and is only qualitative, the notion that a covalent bond is an electron-pair bond is remarkably successful in helping us correlate much information about bonding. The basic model also serves as a starting point for more sophisticated treatments.

1.4 Electronic Configuration and Bonding—Standard Valences

There are important correlations between bonding and electronic configuration. By the **electronic configuration** of an atom, we mean a description of the number of electrons present and an accounting of the atomic orbitals that the electrons occupy. To deduce the electronic configuration of an atom, we first need to know how many electrons are present, then we need to determine which orbitals the electrons occupy. The following rules are used in assigning electronic configurations:

- ***The aufbau principle.*** Orbitals are filled in order of increasing energy, that is, orbitals of lower energy are filled before orbitals of higher energy. The order of the energies of the atomic orbitals increases as follows:

$$1s < 2s < 2p < 3s < 3p < 4s < 3d < 4p < 5s < 4d < 5p$$

- ***The Pauli exclusion principle.*** A maximum of two electrons can occupy a single orbital. If two electrons do occupy an orbital, their spins must be opposite.

- ***Hund's rule.*** When placing electrons into a set of orbitals of equal energy (for example, the three $2p$ orbitals), we add one electron to each orbital until each orbital of the set contains one electron, before pairing up electrons in any one orbital.

Using these principles, we can deduce the electronic configuration of any atom. For example, consider an oxygen atom. From the Periodic Table (see inside cover), we find that the atomic number of oxygen is 8. Thus an oxygen atom has eight protons in its nucleus and eight electrons outside the nucleus. To assign these eight electrons to orbitals, we follow the principles just given to arrive at the electronic configuration depicted in Figure 1.3. Usually we are interested in just the outer-shell electrons, as it is these electrons that participate in bonding. The outer shell is also known as the valence shell. For oxygen, a total of six electrons are present in the valence shell, which includes the $2s$ and $2p$ levels.

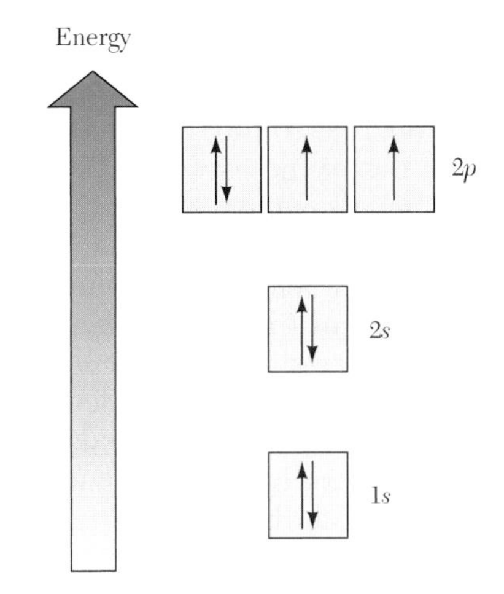

Figure 1.3 A representation of the electronic configuration of an oxygen atom. In this type of diagram, each box represents an orbital and each arrow represents an electron. The direction of the arrows indicate spin. Two electrons in the same orbital must have opposite spins, so they are represented by arrows pointing in opposite directions. We can write the electronic configuration of oxygen as $1s^2 2s^2 2p^4$. The superscripts indicate the total number of electrons in each level.

A most important way in which electronic configuration relates to bonding is embodied in the **noble gas rule.** This rule states that atoms forming bonds donate, receive, or share electrons so as to achieve the electronic configuration of a noble gas.

Consider again an oxygen atom. An oxygen atom needs two more electrons to achieve the configuration of the noble gas neon. One way for this to happen is through the *complete* transfer of two electrons to the oxygen from one or more other atoms. When two electrons are completely transferred to it, the oxygen atom becomes an oxide ion, O^{2-}. For example, a magnesium atom will transfer two electrons to oxygen. By doing so, both the magnesium atom and the oxygen atom achieve the configuration of a noble gas. The result is an ionic compound, magnesium oxide, consisting of Mg^{2+} and O^{2-} ions.

In organic compounds, covalent bonding is more common than ionic bonding. In covalent bonding, electrons are not completely transferred from one atom to another, but are shared between the atoms. The shared electrons are considered to belong to both partners in the bond, and we can count them as contributing toward the electronic configurations of both atoms in the bond. Thus in our trivial example of H—H, the two electrons in the covalent bond are considered to provide *both* hydrogen atoms with a noble gas configuration (that of helium).

There are exceptions to the noble gas rule. Generally, however, we find that compounds containing atoms lacking a noble gas arrangement of electrons are especially reactive. For example, many transient species formed in organic reactions have fewer electrons than required for a noble gas electron configuration. These are species that form in the course of a reaction, exist for only a brief period of time, and react further to form the observed products of the reaction. We will have much to say about such **reaction intermediates** in due course, as an understanding of their structures and properties is crucial to a full comprehension of organic reactions.

We also find that even stable compounds of boron, aluminum, and several other elements have incomplete noble gas electronic configurations. This characteristic is important for their chemistry. A number of highly useful reactions for compounds of these elements can be correlated with the lack of a complete noble gas configuration, as we will find in our later discussions.

A noble gas configuration is often called an *octet*, because all the noble gases except helium have eight electrons in their outermost shell. Some atoms are able to accommodate *more* than an octet of electrons in their valence shell. Sulfur and phosphorus are two important examples for organic chemists. However, elements in the first row of the Periodic Table (that is, Li to F) can never have more than an octet of valence level electrons.

Although a hydrogen atom can form just one covalent bond to one other atom in a stable compound, other atoms, for example, oxygen, can covalently bond simultaneously to more than one atom. By observing large numbers of molecules, we can make generalizations. We find that most atoms always form the same number of covalent bonds in stable compounds. We use the term **valence** to describe the number of bonds formed. The usual valences we find for atoms commonly present in organic molecules are shown in Table 1.1.

Table 1.1 Standard Valences for Common Elements in Organic Compounds
The standard valence is the usual number of *bonds formed by the atom* rather than the number of attached atoms or ligands. (A ligand is an attached atom or group of atoms.)

Atom	Standard Valence
H	1
O, S	2
N	3
C	4
P	3, 5
F, Cl, Br, I	1

These standard valences describe the *usual* number of covalent bonds formed by the atoms in stable, neutral organic compounds. For example, oxygen forms two covalent bonds in its stable compounds such as water, H—O—H. Each covalent bond in a water molecule consists of an electron pair, one of the electrons being donated by the central oxygen atom and the other electron by hydrogen.

A few simple examples are shown in Table 1.2 to illustrate these valences for the common elements in some covalently bonded organic compounds. A line (—) between the elemental symbols indicates a single covalent bond, a double line (=) represents a double bond (four shared electrons) and a triple line (≡) represents a triple bond (six shared electrons). Structural representations like those shown in Table 1.2 are known as **Lewis structures.**

Look at one of the oxygen atoms in the carbon dioxide molecule in Table 1.2. Notice that we show it to be involved in a double bond to the central carbon atom and also to have two *unshared pairs* of electrons, sometimes called *lone-pairs,* represented as pairs of dots above and below the O symbol for oxygen. How do we know that we should place *two* unshared electron pairs on the oxygen atoms of carbon dioxide, just *one* on the nitrogen atom of methyleneimine, *three* on the bromine atom of bromomethane, and none on any of the carbon atoms shown in the table?

The answers to these questions again depend on an application of the noble gas rule. We assume that the oxygen atom of carbon dioxide achieves a noble gas electronic configuration by bonding to carbon. Thus the electronic configuration about the oxygen atom must be like that of neon, that is, eight valence electrons that can be counted toward the valence shell electronic configuration must be present. We see that the oxygen atom of carbon dioxide is involved in a double bond. All four electrons in this double bond can count toward the noble gas configurations of both partners in the bond. Thus oxygen has four valence electrons from this source. Four *more* are needed to satisfy a rare gas configuration, and these are shown as the two unshared pairs. Similarly, the central carbon atom of carbon dioxide is shown with no unshared electron pairs (no pair of dots near the C symbol), since it is forming two double bonds, and the eight electrons from the two double bonds constitute the needed octet.

Although most atoms in almost all neutral organic compounds do obey the noble gas rule, we will conclude this section with a word of caution. There *are* some exceptions to the noble gas rule (see earlier discussion) that must be

Table 1.2 Examples of Valence of Atoms in Neutral, Stable Molecules
Each type of atom forms the indicated number of bonds: carbon, 4; hydrogen, 1; chlorine, 1; bromine, 1; oxygen, 2; nitrogen, 3.

Formula	Name	Bonding Arrangement	
CH_4	Methane	H—C(H)(H)—H	Main component of natural gas
CH_2Cl_2	Dichloromethane	H—C(:C̈l:)(:C̈l:)—H	Common solvent
CH_5N	Methylamine	H—C(H)(:N—H, H)—H	Gas with an odor similar to ammonia
CH_3Br	Bromomethane	H—C(:B̈r:)(H)—H	Simplest bromine-containing organic molecule; it is a toxic gas, used as an agricultural pesticide
CH_4O	Methanol	H—C(H)(:Ö—H)—H	A common solvent, "wood alcohol"
C_2H_3N	Acetonitrile	H—C(H)(C≡N:)—H	A common solvent
C_2H_2	Acetylene	H—C≡C—H	Gas used as fuel in welding
CO_2	Carbon dioxide	Ö=C=Ö	Photosynthetic precursor to organic compounds in plants
C_2H_4	Ethylene	H₂C=CH₂	Gas that acts as a plant hormone to ripen fruit
CH_2O	Formaldehyde	H—C(=:O:)—H	Gas, commonly used as aqueous solution for biological storage
CH_3N	Methyleneimine	H—C(=:N—H)—H	Reactive organic intermediate derived from formaldehyde

kept in mind when drawing Lewis structures. Sometimes there are insufficient electrons to give every atom a noble gas configuration. In neutral organic compounds, this electron deficiency is encountered most often in boron and aluminum compounds. Boron and aluminum atoms form three bonds in neutral compounds (accounting for six electrons), but have no unshared pair to make up a noble gas configuration. The most common examples of atoms having *more* electrons than are required for a noble gas configuration occur in some sulfur and phosphorus compounds. We will have more to say about these exceptions later.

PROBLEM 1.1 How many valence level unshared electron pairs are present in each of the following molecules?

a. water
b. ammonia (NH_3)
c. hydrogen cyanide (HCN)

PROBLEM 1.2 Draw Lewis structures showing all bonds and valence level unshared electron pairs for each of the following compounds (the atoms are connected in the order indicated):

a. BrCN
b. OCO
c. NN
d. H_3COH
e. H_3COCH_3
f. $BrCH_2CH_2OH$
g. FF
h. H_2CO

Steps to Solving the Problem

Solution to Problem 1.2a

1. First, we must know the order of connection, either by experimental determination or as given in the problem. Here the order is Br—C—N.
2. Next, we consider the valences of each atom. Bromine, with a standard valence of 1, will share one of its valence shell electrons to form one covalent bond to the central carbon atom. Carbon has a standard valence of 4, so it will form four bonds. Since only one bond is to bromine, the other three must be to nitrogen. So we can write a partial structure directly from standard valences.

Br—C≡N

3. Finally, we add unshared pairs so as to provide all atoms with noble gas configurations. Bromine requires six more electrons, so we add three unshared pairs. Carbon already has a noble gas configuration—no extra electrons are required. The nitrogen atom needs two more electrons, so we show one unshared pair. The final structure is:

:B̤̈r—C≡N:

PROBLEM 1.3 For each of the following molecular formulas, write structures based on the common valences for each of the atoms present. Remember that hydrogen never forms more than one bond.

a. C_2H_3Br b. C_2HCl_5 c. N_2H_4
d. Cl_2CO e. C_2N_2

For stable *ions* we find valences that are different from those in neutral molecules. Some examples of ions containing nitrogen or oxygen are shown in Figure 1.4.

Occasionally we find that even stable molecules may contain atoms with unusual valences. For example, carbon and oxygen both form three bonds to each other in carbon monoxide (**1.1**). Also, in the neutral molecule nitromethane (**1.2**) (a laboratory solvent and racing fuel), we write a structure with four bonds to nitrogen and only one to one of the oxygen atoms. As in the structures in Figure 1.4, we place a positive charge on the nitrogen atom with four bonds, and a negative charge on the oxygen with only one bond.

$^{-}$:C≡O:$^{+}$

carbon monoxide
1.1

H_3C—N^+(=O:)—$\ddot{O}$:$^-$

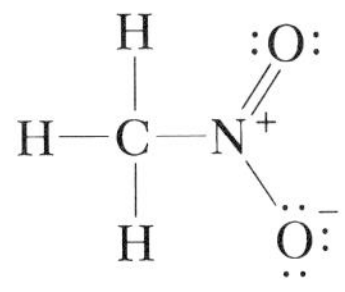

nitromethane
1.2

FORMAL CHARGES

The charges indicated in structures 1.1 and 1.2 and those in Figure 1.4 are known as *formal charges*. How would you know whether a given structure had any charges? As we just noted, one guideline is the presence of an unusual number of bonds to a given atom. There is, however, a simple bookkeeping method that allows us to calculate formal charges in a straightforward manner.

First, we can define formal charge in terms of the difference between the number of valence electrons owned by an atom when *free* and the number owned when it is part of a molecule or ion. In deciding ownership of electrons in molecules or ions, we count any unshared valence level electrons as belonging *solely* to the parent atom, and we evenly distribute any electrons in bonds between the two atoms forming the bond. To calculate the formal charge associated with a given atom in a Lewis structure, we subtract from the number of valence electrons in the free atom the number of its unshared electrons and the number of bonds it forms. Thus, formal charges for atoms in molecules or

Figure 1.4 Structures for some common ions. Notice that oxygen has a valence of one in negative ions and three in positive ions, while nitrogen has a valence of four in positive ions and two in negative ions.

H—$\ddot{O}$:$^-$
hydroxide ion, as in sodium hydroxide, NaOH

H—$\ddot{O}^+$(H)—H
hydronium ion, as in the solution of an acid (such as HCl) in water

H—N^+(H)(H)—H
ammonium ion, as in ammonium chloride, NH_4Cl

H—$\ddot{N}^-$—H
amide ion, as in sodium amide, $NaNH_2$

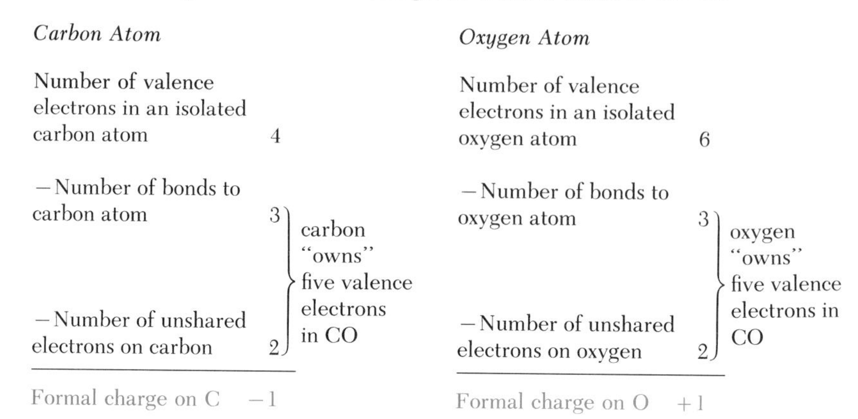

Assignment of Formal Charges to C and O atoms of :C≡O:
Carbon Atom
Number of valence electrons in an isolated carbon atom 4
−Number of bonds to carbon atom 3
−Number of unshared electrons on carbon 2
carbon "owns" five valence electrons in CO
Formal charge on C −1
Oxygen Atom
Number of valence electrons in an isolated oxygen atom 6
−Number of bonds to oxygen atom 3
−Number of unshared electrons on oxygen 2
oxygen "owns" five valence electrons in CO
Formal charge on O +1

Figure 1.5 Calculation of formal charges in the carbon monoxide molecule. The molecule has a formal charge of −1 on carbon and of +1 on oxygen.

ions can be calculated using the equation:

Formal charge = (number of valence shell electrons for the atom when isolated, i.e., not part of a molecule)
− (number of bonds it shares in the compound)
− (number of unshared valence electrons it has in the compound)

This calculation is illustrated in Figure 1.5 for the carbon monoxide molecule.

PROBLEM 1.4 Assign formal charges to every atom in the following Lewis structures:

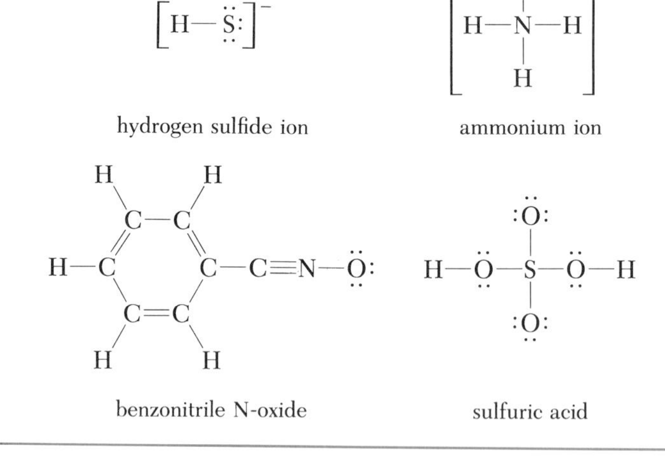

A SYSTEMATIC METHOD FOR DRAWING LEWIS STRUCTURES

For most molecules, it is possible to arrive at a correct Lewis structure by using the standard valences given above. However, there is an obvious need for a systematic method for constructing Lewis structures that works whether or not the atoms form their usual number of bonds. Here we outline a five-step procedure and then illustrate it by working out the Lewis structure of carbon monoxide.

Procedure

1. Calculate the total number of valence level electrons in the molecule by adding the contribution from each atom. The number of valence electrons for each atom is given by the number of the element's group in the Periodic Table.* In fact, you should *memorize* the number of valence electrons for all the elements commonly found in organic compounds, that is, H, B, C, N, O, P, S, and the halogens.
2. For ions, add one electron to the total for each negative charge; subtract one for each positive charge.
3. Each pair of atoms must be connected by *at least* a single bond, which requires one pair of electrons. Accordingly, first construct a partial structure showing single bonds between all connected pairs of atoms. Then calculate the remaining number of valence electrons still to be placed.
4. Determine the total number of electrons that the atoms in the partial structure are short of noble gas configurations. The difference between this total and the actual number of electrons remaining to be placed (from Step 3) gives the number of electrons that must be placed in *additional* (i.e., additional to those already placed in the partial structure) covalent bonds. Placement of additional bonds will of course result in *multiple* (double or triple) bonds in the structure.
5. Draw a structure with the appropriate number of multiple bonds as calculated in Step 4 above, and if possible distribute the remaining electrons as unshared pairs so as to give all atoms a noble gas configuration. (Sometimes there are not enough electrons to give *all* atoms a noble gas configuration, for example, in organic boron compounds.)

Now we will work out the Lewis structure of carbon monoxide using this approach.

- *Step 1.* We first calculate a total of ten valence level electrons (carbon has four valence level electrons and oxygen has six.)
- *Step 2.* Carbon monoxide is uncharged, so we can proceed directly to Step 3.
- *Step 3.* We place a single bond between C and O and write the partial structure: C:O. Step 3 also calls for us to calculate how many electrons still remain to be placed: there are eight (the ten original electrons minus the two already placed in the partial structure of Step 2).
- *Step 4.* Both the carbon and oxygen atoms in the partial structure are short of octets by six electrons, giving a total deficiency of 12 electrons. This means that four ($12 - 8 = 4$) must be shared between the two atoms in additional

* IUPAC, the International Union of Pure and Applied Chemistry, has recommended a new Periodic Table in which the groups are numbered 1–18 right across the chart; for example, the halogens constitute Group 17 in this new presentation. If you use this table, you must realize that the equivalence of the number of valence level electrons and group number is sometimes lost. You will need to rely on your knowledge of the electronic configurations of atoms to deduce the number of valence level electrons.

covalent bonds. Thus two new covalent bonds must be placed between C and O (remember that each bond accounts for two electrons). Along with the bond already placed in the partial structure, these two new bonds give an overall total of three bonds between carbon and oxygen—a triple bond.

- *Step* 5. We are now ready to draw the complete Lewis structure:

:C:::O: or :C≡O:

Finally, formal charges should be computed and any nonzero values indicated.

PROBLEM 1.5 Draw Lewis structures for the following, showing all unshared electrons and indicating all nonzero formal charges:

a. diimide, N_2H_2
b. perchlorate ion, ClO_4^- (central Cl atom surrounded by four O atoms)
c. sulfur dioxide, SO_2 (sequence of atoms is OSO)
d. ozone, O_3(O—O—O)
e. formyl cation, HCO^+

Sometimes you will find that you can write *more* than one Lewis structure by application of the procedure outlined above. We will take up the significance of these alternative structures, which are known as resonance structures, a little later in the chapter.

1.5 The Arrangement of Atoms Bound to Carbon

In the *Introduction* (read it now if you haven't already done so), we pointed out that organic chemistry is the chemistry of carbon compounds. Thus as organic chemists, we are particularly interested in the bonding about carbon atoms. Here we discuss the geometrical arrangements of atoms bonded to carbon.

Figure 1.6 Tetrahedral geometry of bonding about carbon when it forms bonds to four other atoms. In (*a*), the shape of a tetrahedron is shown. In (*b*), a carbon atom at the center of the tetrahedron, is linked by four covalent bonds to the four hydrogen atoms at the four corners. In (*c*), another useful view is given of a tetrahedral arrangement of bonds about a central atom—the four bonds are directed from the central atom to the four indicated corners of the cube.

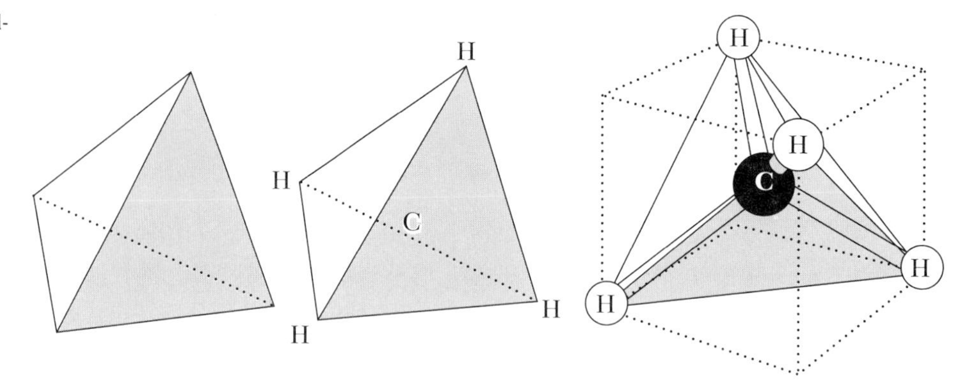

A regular tetrahedron

(*a*)

A regular tetrahedron with a carbon atom placed at the center and hydrogen atoms at each of the corners

(*b*)

A useful view of a tetrahedral arrangement of bonds. The bonds are directed from the central atom to four corners of the cube.

(*c*)

CARBON BONDED TO FOUR OTHER ATOMS

Experimentally we find that a carbon atom with four bonds to four other atoms has a **tetrahedral geometry.** That is, the carbon atom is located at the center of a regular tetrahedron and the four bonded atoms are at the corners. A regular tetrahedron is a four-sided polyhedron in which all four sides are congruent equilateral triangles. The tetrahedral bonding arrangement for methane is illustrated in Figure 1.6. Notice that a good perspective view of a tetrahedral arrangement of bonds is obtained by imagining the central atom at the center of a cube, and the four bonded atoms at four non-adjacent corners of the cube.

The observed tetrahedral arrangement of bonds is fully consistent with predictions we would make using the **valence shell electron pair repulsion** (**VSEPR**) model. According to the VSEPR model, valence level electrons (bonding and unshared electron pairs) tend to be arranged about an atom as far apart as possible so as to minimize electrostatic repulsions.

With regular tetrahedral geometry, the angles between any pair of carbon-hydrogen bonds in the methane molecule are 109°28′ (approximately 109.5°), as shown in Figure 1.7.

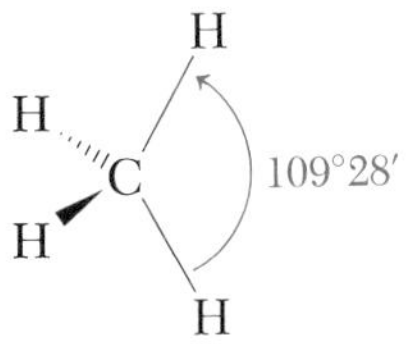

H H C H H 109°28′

Figure 1.7 Tetrahedral bond angle in the methane molecule. In this figure we introduce a convention regarding bonds. Bonds shown as a solid wedge are imagined as projecting forward from the plane of the paper toward the viewer, while those shown as broken wedges indicate a bond going behind the plane of the paper, away from the viewer.

PROBLEM 1.6 How many H—C—H bond angles are there in a methane molecule? Draw a molecule of methane showing each tetrahedral H—C—H bond angle.

PROBLEM 1.7 Consider the structure of methane shown in Figure 1.7. Choose any two hydrogen atoms along with the central carbon atom and note the plane defined by these three points. (Remember from geometry that three points define a plane.) Another plane is defined by the remaining two hydrogen atoms and the carbon atom. What is the angle between these two planes? Based on your answer, would you expect the two rings of spiropentane (C_5H_8, shown below) to be in the same plane, or to be tilted relative to each other at some angle? At what angle would they be tilted?

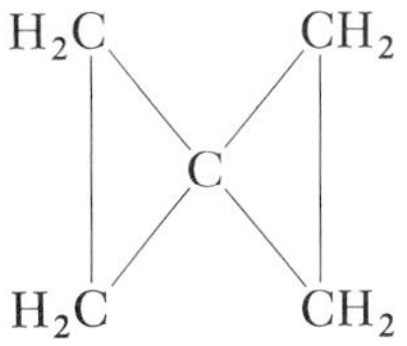

H_2C CH_2 C H_2C CH_2

Most carbon atoms bonded to four other atoms in organic compounds are characterized by a tetrahedral or nearly tetrahedral geometry. We do, however, sometimes encounter deviations, which will be discussed as needed. Several molecules from Table 1.2 are shown in Figure 1.8, which illustrates the tetrahedral arrangement of atoms about carbon.

CARBON BONDED TO THREE OTHER ATOMS

When a carbon atom is bonded to *three* other atoms with four bonds, the VSEPR model suggests a different geometry (**trigonal planar geometry**)—one

Figure 1.8 Tetrahedral geometry about the carbon atom. The ethane molecule has two tetrahedral carbon atoms. *Space-filling* models of each of the molecules are shown. Molecular models will be discussed further in Chapter 2.

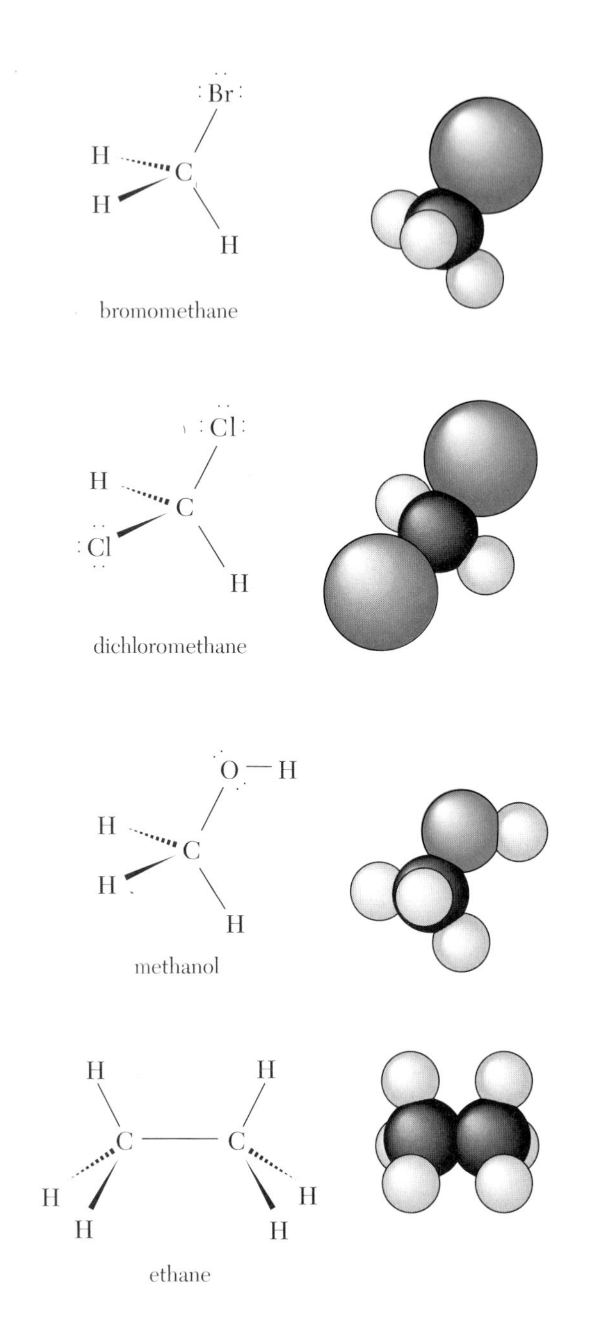

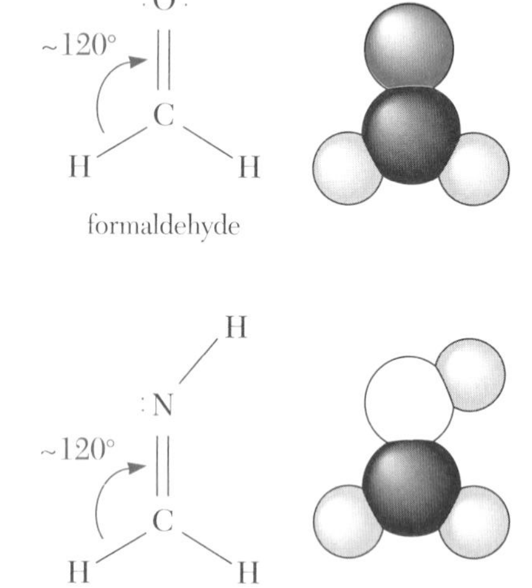

Figure 1.9 Trigonal planar geometry of carbon bound to three other atoms. All atoms shown lie in the plane of the paper.

in which the carbon and the atoms directly attached to it all lie in the same plane. The bond angles are 120° (or close to it). The experimentally determined geometries of such molecules match this description quite closely. The geometries of two such molecules from Table 1.2 are shown in Figure 1.9.

CARBON BONDED TO TWO OTHER ATOMS

For carbon bound to only two other atoms, VSEPR predicts that a linear arrangement of the three atoms will minimize repulsions. This arrangement again matches experimentally determined geometries. Figure 1.10 illustrates

Figure 1.10 Geometry associated with carbon bonded to two atoms.

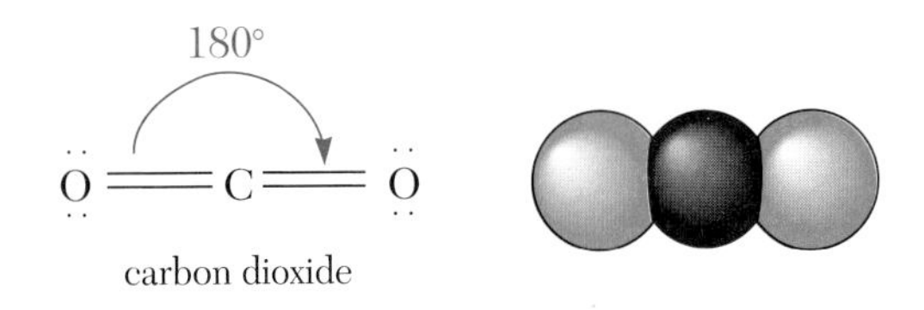

180°
H_3C—C≡N:
acetonitrile

the shapes of carbon dioxide and acetonitrile (CH_3CN, see Table 1.2) molecules.

Throughout this discussion of the observed geometries of bonding about carbon atoms we have made no mention of *how* carbon forms four bonds with these geometries. In the next section we will begin to consider the orbital structure of carbon in relation to the geometries of its compounds. With consistent rationalizations of the experimentally observed structural data, we hope to make predictions regarding the chemistry of organic molecules.

PROBLEM 1.8 Draw a structure representing the acetonitrile molecule (Figure 1.10) showing *all* of the bond angles with their approximate values.

PROBLEM 1.9 Draw the structure of each of the following molecules with the proper geometries about all carbon atoms, and indicate the size of all bond angles:

a. $H_3C—CH_2—CH_3$ **b.** $H_3C—C(=\ddot{O}:)—CH_3$

c. $H_2C═CH—C≡C—H$

1.6 Atomic Orbital Interactions and Covalent Bonding

We can gain a more complete understanding of organic bonding and structure by considering the orbitals that the electrons occupy. In the **valence bond model** we consider interactions of electrons in the **atomic orbitals** of each of the atoms that have come together.

We can think of an atomic orbital as a description of a region of space that can be occupied by one or two electrons of the atom in question. Although no experiment can measure anything *directly* about an orbital, we *can* use the theory of orbitals to predict many properties of atoms. Because these predictions do agree with experimental observations, the orbital model is a useful one.

Descriptions of orbitals are obtained by solving the Schrödinger wave equation that provides information about electrons in atoms. According to the wave equation, each orbital has not only a spatial form but a precise energy as well. We derive an electronic description of the ground state of an atom by allowing its electrons to occupy the lowest energy spaces (orbitals) available. Only two electrons can occupy any one orbital, so larger atoms must make use of higher energy orbitals to accommodate their greater numbers of electrons. This filling of successively higher energy orbitals with increasing atomic number was referred to earlier as the *aufbau principle*.

Although we can not use any experimental methods to measure anything about orbitals per se, we *can* make measurements on electrons. For example, we can measure the energy needed to move an electron from one energy level (an orbital) to another. We can also measure the energy needed to eject an electron completely from an atom. From these experimental measurements, we can *infer* much about the relative energies of the orbitals that the electrons occupy. We find that energies calculated by the wave equation conform well to the results of experimental measurements. This correlation suggests that our theoretical description of orbitals is a useful one.

The valence bond model suggests that bonding occurs when orbitals of two atoms come together with two electrons. If certain criteria are met, a bond results and the energy of the system decreases. These criteria are:

1. The two interacting orbitals are of approximately the same energy.
2. The spins of the two electrons are paired.
3. The overlap of the involved orbitals is efficient.

An efficient overlap of the orbitals involves both the overlap of a significant portion of each orbital in question and an increase in the region of space in which the associated electrons can move. *The larger the region of space (a "box") in which a charged particle (e.g., an electron) is allowed to move, the lower is its energy*. (This point is extremely important here and in understanding a number of concepts that will be developed in this course.)

Consider a hydrogen molecule forming through the approach of two hydrogen atoms, each with a 1*s* electron. As they approach, the electrons in their orbitals interact with each other and with *both* of the nuclei. As a result, the electron from one atom may be near the nucleus of the other atom—this is a major determinant in the formation of a bond.

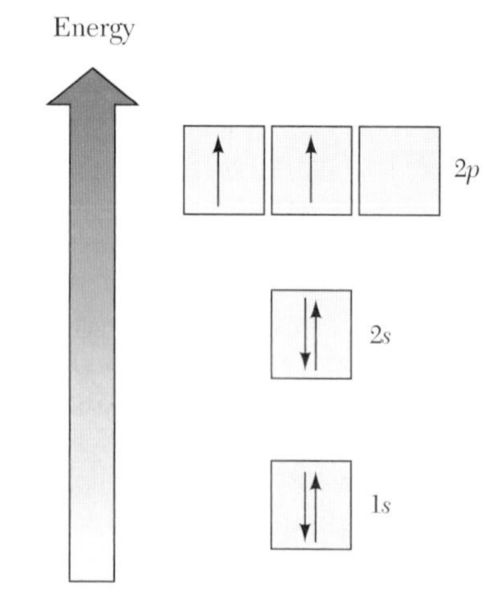

Figure 1.11 Ground state electronic configuration of a carbon atom.

VALENCE BOND MODEL APPLIED TO CARBON

The valence bond model equates the formation of a covalent bond with the pairing of two electrons with opposite spins in the region between the nuclei. This model suggests that there should be a correlation between the number of unpaired electrons in the atom and the valence of the atom. Indeed, we find such correlations. Hydrogen, with one unpaired electron, forms one covalent bond, and nitrogen ($1s^22s^22p^3$), with three unpaired electrons, forms three covalent bonds. However, there is no such correlation for carbon. The ground state carbon atom has the electronic configuration shown in Figure 1.11.

There are only *two* unpaired electrons in the valence level of a carbon atom. On this basis we might predict that carbon would form just two covalent

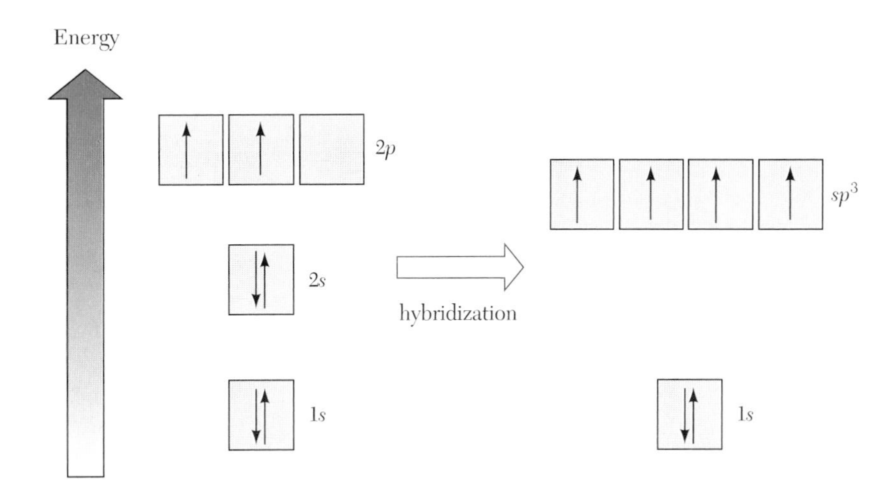

Figure 1.12 Mixing of 2*s* and three 2*p* orbitals of a carbon atom to generate four sp^3 carbon orbitals, each with energy intermediate between 2*s* and 2*p* orbitals.

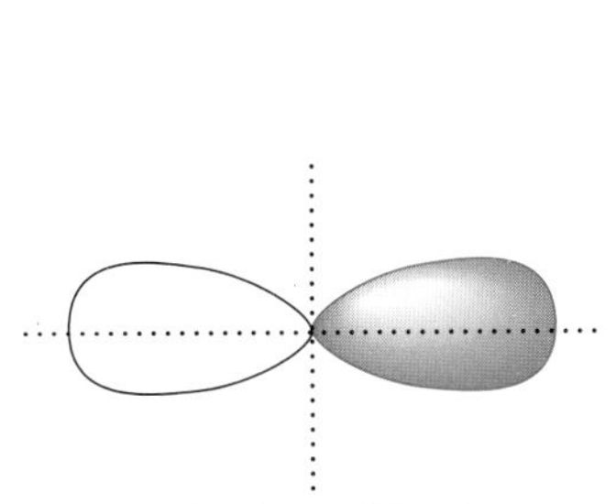

A 2*p* orbital–Bond formation (e.g., with a hydrogen atom) can occur with equal likelihood at either end of this orbital.

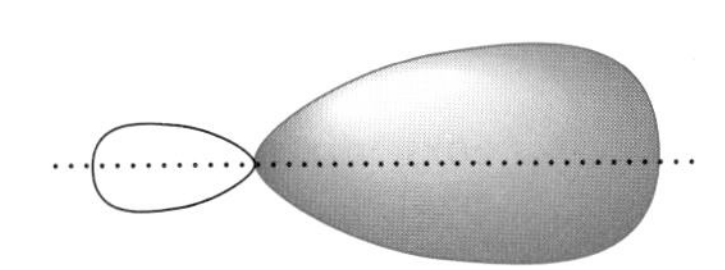

An sp^3 hybrid orbital–Bond formation to a hydrogen atom occurs using the larger (major) lobe only.

Figure 1.13 Comparison of unhybridized *p* and sp^3 hybridized orbital shapes. The atomic nucleus is at the junction of the lobes in each case.

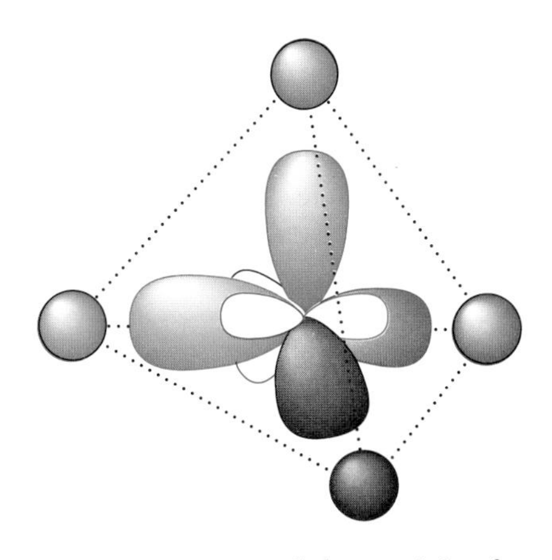

Figure 1.14 Directional characteristics of sp^3 hybrid orbitals of carbon and the formation of C—H bonds in methane CH_4. The hybrid orbitals point toward the corners of a regular tetrahedron. Hydrogen 1*s* orbitals are illustrated in position to form bonds by overlap with the major lobes of the hybrid orbitals.

bonds. Yet, from experimental observations we know that carbon generally forms *four* bonds in neutral, stable molecules.

Linus Pauling (1954 winner of the Nobel Prize in chemistry) developed a useful model for dealing with this conflict. It requires us to consider a modified form of the carbon atom. Pauling found that mathematical mixing of the four available atomic orbitals of carbon could produce four new, *equivalent* orbitals. Each new orbital is directed from the carbon atom to one of the corners of a regular tetrahedron. This process of mixing orbitals by mathematical combination of their wave functions is known as **hybridization.** It is shown schematically in Figure 1.12.

The **hybrid orbitals** are intermediate in character between *s* and *p*. Each **sp^3 hybrid orbital** is considered to contain a single electron available for covalent bond formation. Each hybrid orbital has a two-lobed shape, similar to the shape of a *p* orbital but with different sized lobes, as shown in Figure 1.13. Moreover, each hybrid orbital points toward the corner of a regular tetrahedron, as shown in Figure 1.14.

In the illustrations of the *p* and sp^3 orbitals, one lobe is shown as shaded while the other is clear in order to illustrate a characteristic of orbitals. We can think of the difference between the two regions in terms of wave properties. One region represents a peak of the wave while the other represents a trough. An alternative way of thinking about this is to consider the mathematical expression relating the position and energy of the electrons (the wavefunction) of the orbital as changing sign from one region to the other. The point at which the peak turns to a trough (the sign changes) is referred to as a **node.** (A node is a region where there is zero probability of finding an electron. The 1*s* orbital has *no* node.) These aspects of the orbitals are illustrated in Figure 1.15.

THE GEOMETRY OF BONDS FORMED USING HYBRID ORBITALS

Each carbon-hydrogen bond in methane can be viewed as arising from an end-on overlap of a C(sp^3) and a H(1*s*) orbital. The electron density associated with the bond is *cylindrically symmetrical* with respect to the internuclear axis,

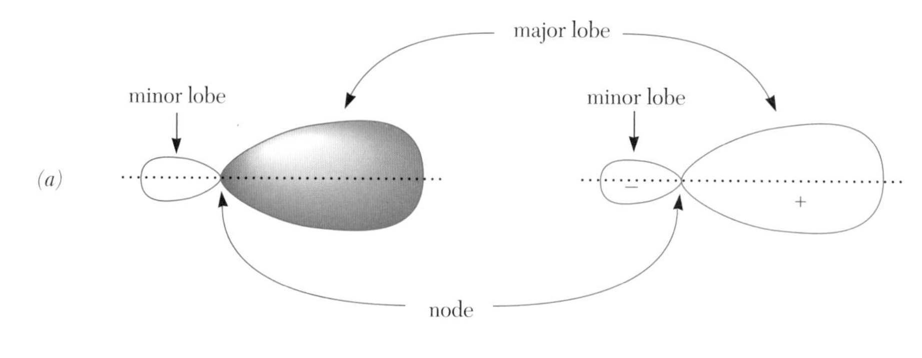

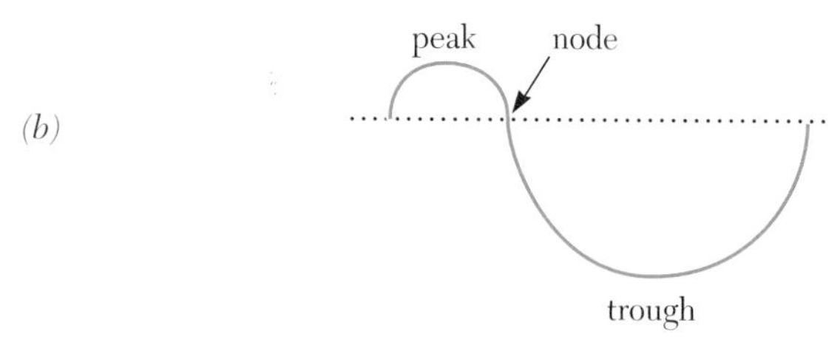

Figure 1.15 (*a*) **Representations of sp^3 hybrid orbitals showing major and minor lobes and point of zero electron density (node) at the nucleus.** (*b*) **Representation of the wavefunction for the sp^3 hybrid orbital showing peak and trough.** The square of the wavefunction is used in calculating the electron density. Although the wavefunction may be positive or negative, the square, relating to the electron density, is always positive.

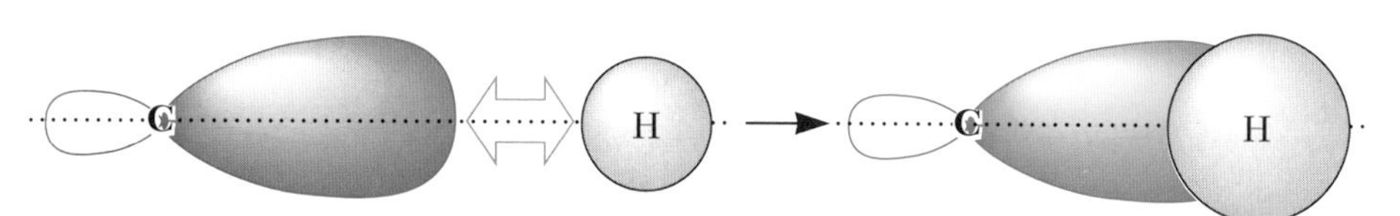

Figure 1.16 Direction of approach for bond formation between carbon sp^3 hybrid orbital and hydrogen 1*s* orbital.

Efficient direction of approach for overlap–Bond formation occurs when orbitals meet on this line of approach. The line of approach, the internuclear axis (dotted line), is an axis of symmetry for the electron pair of the bond.

as shown in Figure 1.16. (Examples of everyday items having cylindrical symmetry include baseball bats, plastic soda bottles, and drinking goblets. If we view any of these objects from a direction perpendicular to its axis, we can rotate the object about that axis and will see no change in the object with rotation.) Bonds of this type are referred to as **σ bonds.** A methane molecule is thus said to have four carbon-hydrogen σ bonds aligned along directions pointing from the center to the corners of a regular tetrahedron.

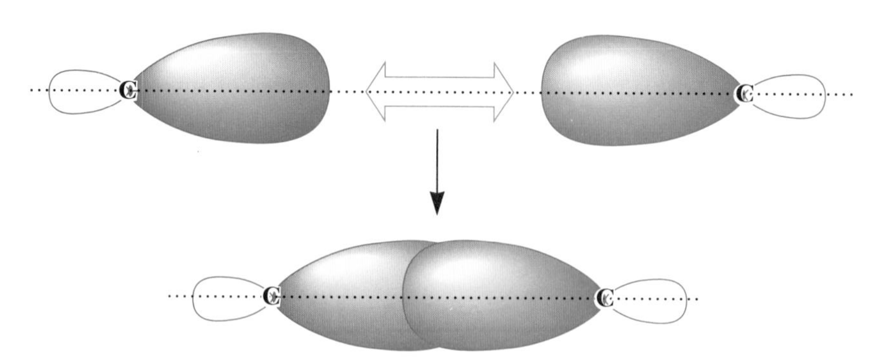

Figure 1.17 Formation of a carbon-carbon bond using hybrid orbitals.

The electron density of the bond formed between two carbon atoms using hybrid orbitals is cylindrically symmetrical about the internuclear axis.

Similarly, bonds formed between carbon atoms by overlap of hybrid orbitals are σ bonds. End-on interaction of the hybrid orbitals provides the most efficient overlap for bond formation (see Figure 1.17).

PROBLEM 1.10 Draw the orbitals used for each of the bonds present in the ethane molecule (see Figure 1.8).

PROBLEM 1.11 The ammonium ion, NH_4^+, is known to have tetrahedral geometry. Describe the orbitals used in the formation of the four N—H bonds.

MULTIPLY BONDED CARBON

The participation of carbon in double or triple bonds requires a different type of hybridization model. The guiding rule we follow in understanding carbon bonding in stable molecules is that we need as many hybrid orbitals as there are attached atoms and unshared pairs of electrons. For example, consider the molecule formaldehyde, $H_2C{=}O$.

Carbon is bonded to only *three* atoms (two hydrogens and one oxygen). It requires just three hybrid orbitals to form three σ bonds (one to each bonded atom). To get three hybrids, we mix just *two* of the $2p$ orbitals with the one $2s$ orbital. (Whenever we combine or mix n simple atomic orbitals to generate new orbitals, we end up with n new orbitals.) One $2p$ orbital is left unhybridized.This hybridization is illustrated schematically in Figure 1.18.

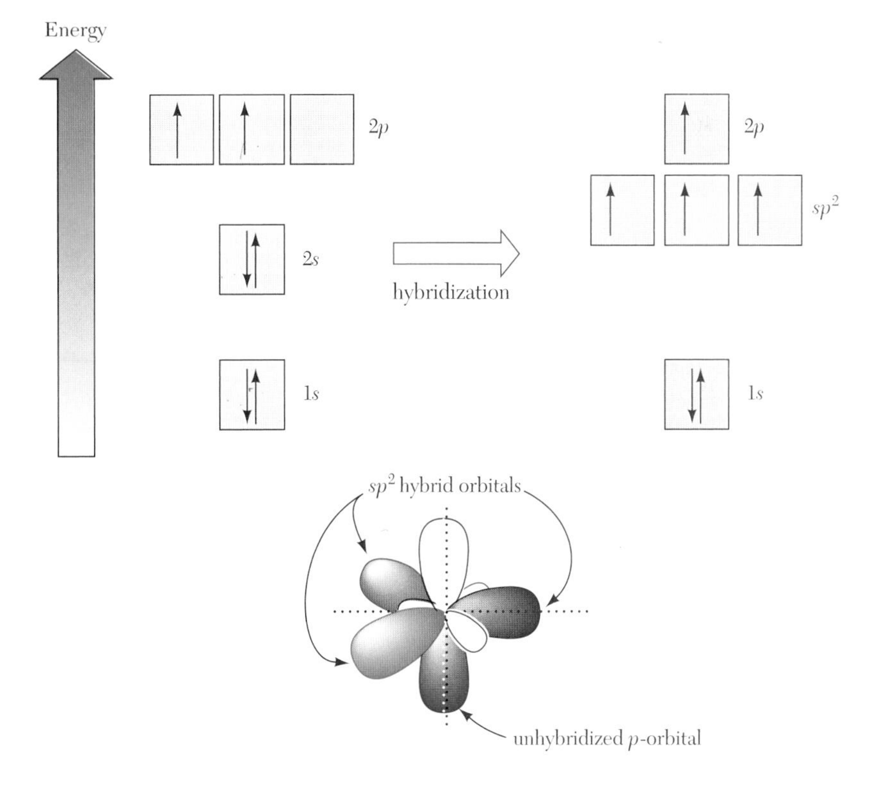

Figure 1.18 Schematic representation of sp^2 hybridization of carbon. The hybridization mixes two of the $2p$ orbitals with the single $2s$ orbital to produce three sp^2 hybrid orbitals. One $2p$ orbital is not involved in the hybridization process and remains unchanged. The three sp^2 hybrids project out from the carbon atom in a single plane. The unhybridized $2p$ orbital is in a plane perpendicular to that occupied by the three hybrids.

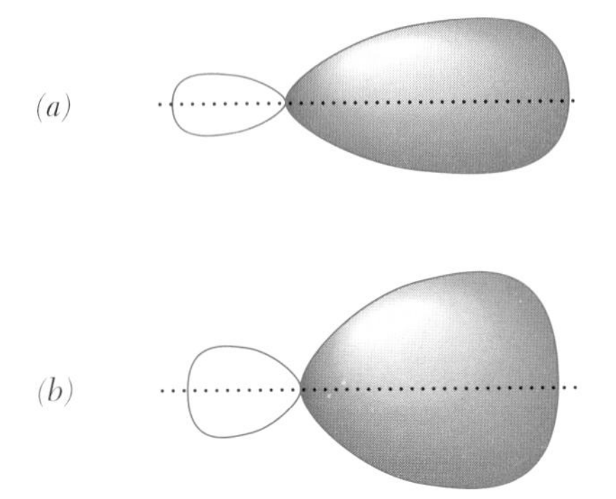

Figure 1.19 ***(a) sp*^{3} hybrid orbital. *(b) sp*^{2} hybrid orbital.** The greater *s* character of the sp^2 hybrid orbital makes it slightly shorter and fatter than the sp^3 hybrid orbital, which has a greater *p* character. Both of these orbitals (and the σ bonds they form) have an axis of symmetry shown by the dotted line. The electron density is cylindrically symmetrical about this axis.

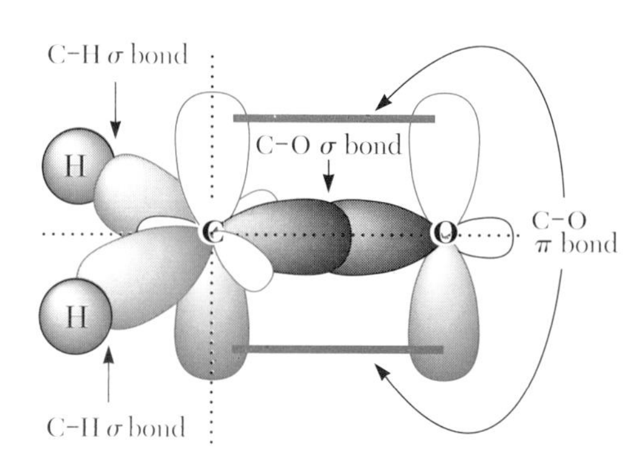

Figure 1.20 Orbitals involved in bonding in formaldehyde. Three σ bonds are present. Two of these are between carbon and the hydrogen atoms (the carbon uses two sp^2 hybrid orbitals). The third σ bond is between carbon and oxygen; each atom uses sp^2 hybrid orbitals. A *fourth* bond (a π bond) is generated by a side-to-side overlap of the remaining unhybridized *p* orbital on carbon and a *p* orbital on oxygen (see text discussion below). Other orbitals on oxygen are not shown for simplicity.

An sp^2 hybrid has approximately the same shape as an sp^3 hybrid orbital but is slightly shorter and fatter (see Figure 1.19), owing to the mix of atomic orbitals it uses. It has greater *s* character (33.3%) than does an sp^3 orbital (25%), thus it is a little more like an *s* orbital than is an sp^3 hybrid. As a result, any electron in an sp^2 orbital is held closer to the nucleus than it would be in an sp^3 hybrid. This is reflected in the shorter and fatter shape of the orbital. In spite of this difference, sp^2 hybrids form bonds in the same way as do sp^3 hybrids. End-on overlap with orbitals from other atoms yields σ bonds. However, the bonds formed by **sp^2 hybrid orbitals** are *shorter* (and stronger) than the corresponding bonds formed by sp^3 hybrid orbitals, again because of their more *s*-like character.

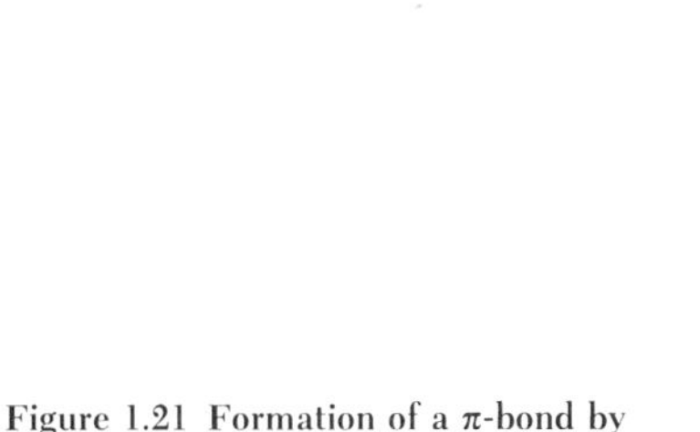

The use of sp^2 hybrids in the formation of the three σ bonds in formaldehyde is illustrated in Figure 1.20. The unhybridized *p* orbital of the carbon is used to form a carbon-oxygen π bond. The **π bond** has a side-to-side overlap with a *p* orbital on oxygen. This second bond is different from the other bonds (σ bonds) in the formaldehyde molecule. It does not have an axis of symmetry but does have a *plane* of symmetry (see Figure 1.21).

Consider now an acetylene molecule, H—C≡C—H. Each carbon is involved in a triple bond. We can rationalize the bonding in acetylene using the

Figure 1.21 Formation of a π-bond by side-to-side overlap of *p*-orbitals. When carbon forms four bonds to three other atoms, one bond will be a π bond with the symmetry characteristics shown here. The indicated plane of symmetry for the π bond is the plane in which the σ bonds lie.

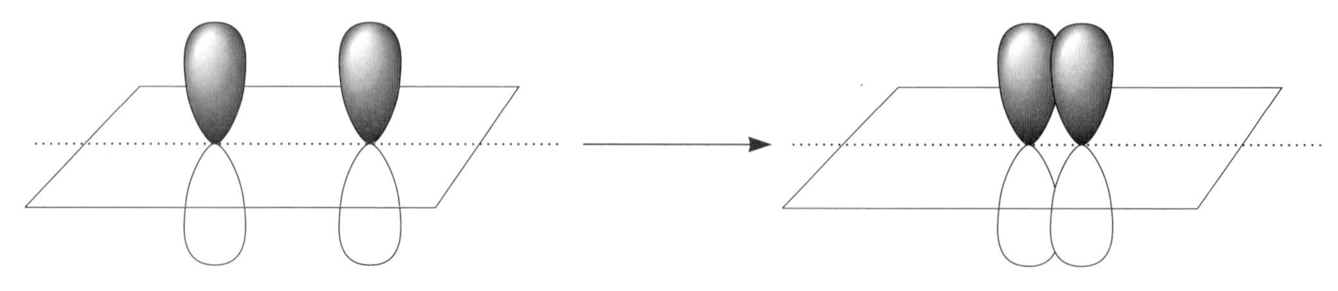

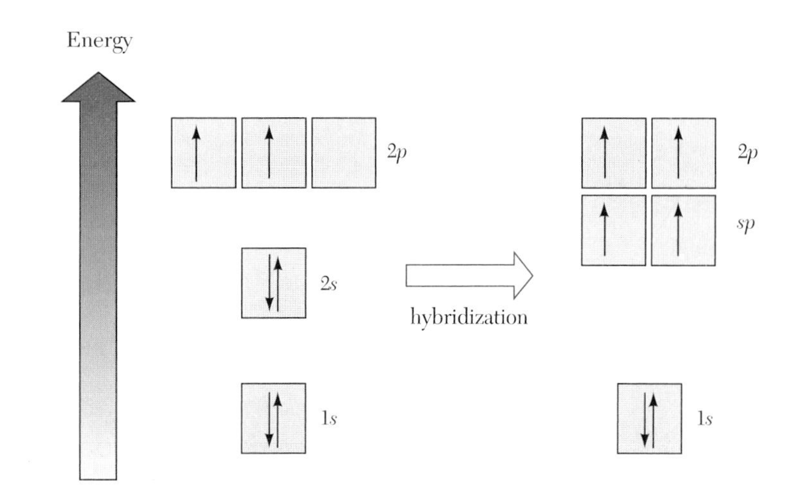

Figure 1.22 Construction of *sp* hybrid orbitals. The *sp* hybrids are constructed by mixing one of the $2p$ orbitals with the $2s$ orbital. Two $2p$ orbitals are uninvolved in the hybridization process.

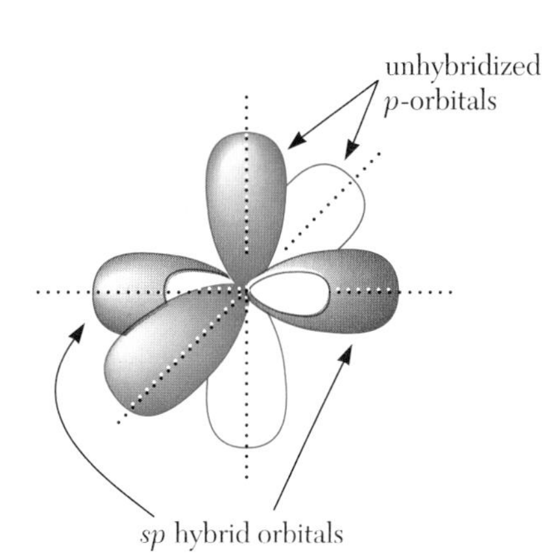

Figure 1.23 Relative orientation of *sp* hybrids and unhybridized 2*p* orbitals. The *sp* hybrids are used to form σ bonds, and the unhybridized *p* orbitals are used to form π bonds.

hybridization guidelines we have been following. Figure 1.22 shows the mixing of orbitals to generate two *sp* hybrid orbitals per carbon atom; these two **sp hybrid orbitals** are required for the formation of the two σ bonds.

Figure 1.23 shows the geometric relationship among the two *sp* hybrids and the two unhybridized $2p$ orbitals. The two *sp* hybrids point in opposite directions along a straight line. The unhybridized *p* orbitals are at right angles to the *sp* hybrids. The hybrid orbitals, as usual, form *only* σ bonds, and the unhybridized *p* orbitals form *only* π bonds. We consider the acetylene molecule as having one σ bond and two π bonds joining the two carbon atoms. In general, we always assume that only the *first* bond between two atoms is a σ bond and that any other bonds are π bonds.

PROBLEM 1.12

Describe the bonds, the orbitals used to form them, any unshared electron pairs, and the molecular geometry of each of the following molecules:

a. ethylene ($H_2C{=}CH_2$) **b.** methyleneimine ($H_2C{=}\ddot{N}H$)

c. acetylene ($HC{\equiv}CH$)

Steps to Solving the Problem

Solution to Problem 1.12a

1. First consider the orbital hybridization used by each atom. Although each of the carbon atoms forms four bonds, it is attached to only three other atoms. The hybridization scheme we use to describe each must therefore be sp^2 with a single unhybridized *p* orbital.
2. Next consider what kinds of bonds are formed with each orbital. The six hybrid orbitals are used to form σ bonds, one to each of the four hydrogens of the molecule (which themselves use $1s$ atomic orbitals) and two to form the carbon-carbon σ bond. The second bond between the two carbon atoms is formed by side-to-side overlap of the unhybridized *p* orbitals and is a π bond. It has a plane of symmetry in which all five of the σ bonds lie.
3. Finally construct the appropriate bonds with the available orbitals and decide on the geometry of the molecule. In order to have the two *p* orbitals

overlap efficiently to give the π bond, the σ bonds must remain rigidly in the same plane. The six atoms of the molecule therefore all lie in the same plane, as shown in the illustration.

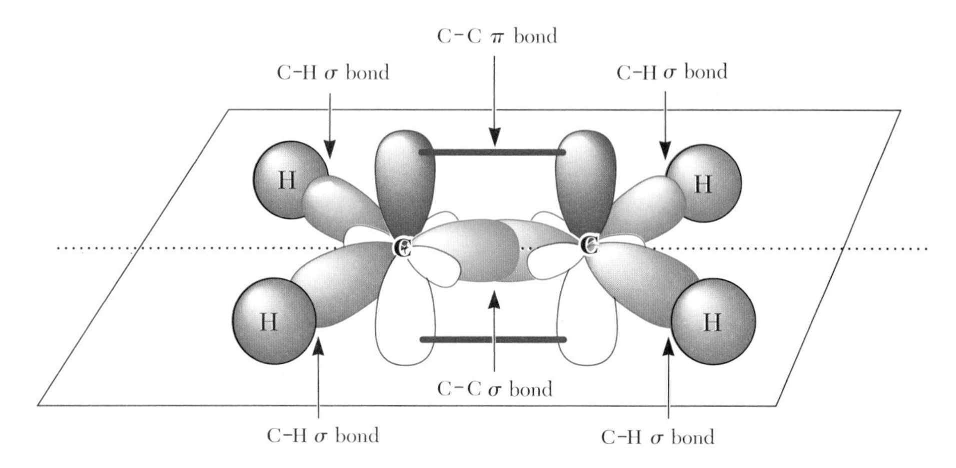

PROBLEM 1.13 What is the percentage *s* character in the hybrids used by carbon in each of the molecules in Problem 1.12? Which molecule do you predict will have the shortest C—H bond?

1.7 Resonance Structures

By following the procedures given earlier in the chapter, we can write a unique Lewis structure for every molecule considered thus far. These descriptions compare well with the descriptions we infer from experimental probes of structure.

What do we do when we can draw more than one Lewis structure? Consider, for example, the carbonate ion, CO_3^{2-}. We know from experimental probes of structure that this ion consists of a central carbon atom joined to three oxygen atoms. Now, consider the picture we obtain from theory. If we follow the procedure outlined earlier (Section 1.4) for drawing a Lewis structure, we find that there must be two carbon-oxygen single bonds and one carbon-oxygen double bond. We also find that we can draw *three* Lewis structures obeying our guidelines—they differ only in which carbon-oxygen linkage we designate a double bond, as shown in Figure 1.24.

Are these representations correct? That is, do they correspond to the real carbonate anion? The answer is given by comparing *experimental* data on the carbonate anion with the Lewis structures we have drawn: we find that the Lewis structures we draw are *not* good reflections of the experimentally found structure. Experimental measurements tell us that all three carbon-oxygen bonds in the carbonate anion are equivalent. There is *not* one double bond and two single bonds. We know this because our observations of bond lengths in molecules tell us that carbon-oxygen double bonds are shorter than carbon-oxygen single bonds, and experiments tell us that all of the carbon-oxygen bonds in the carbonate anion have the *same* length.

An interesting situation exists when we can draw several Lewis structures for a molecule or ion. Although none of the Lewis structures is individually a good representation of the true structure, an *average* of the structures usually provides a good description.

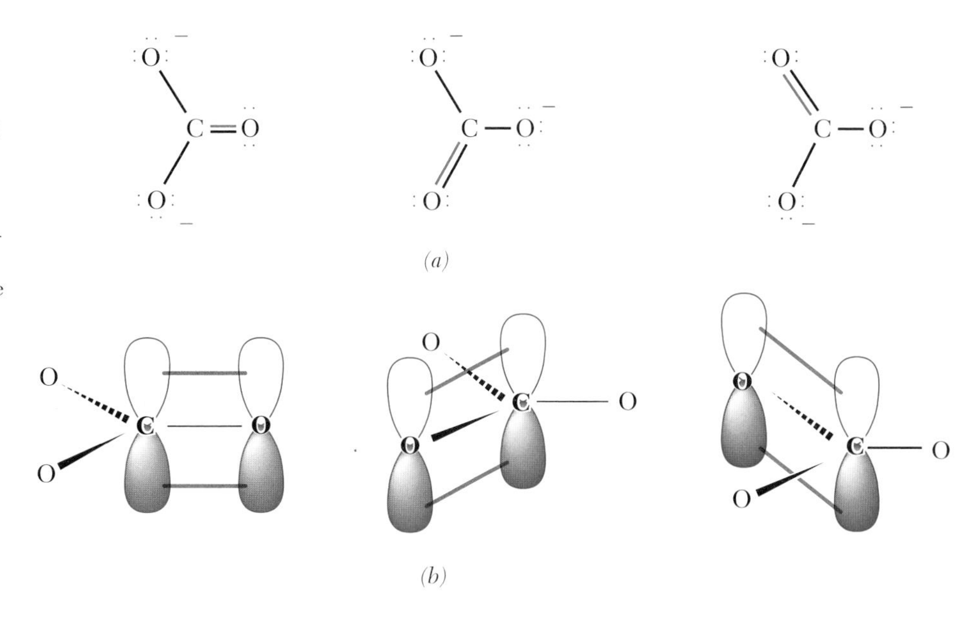

Figure 1.24 ***(a)* Lewis representations of electron distribution in the carbonate anion.** Bonds are shown with lines and unshared electron pairs with dots. Formal charges are shown where appropriate on the oxygen atoms. ***(b)* π bonding in the carbonate anion.** The unhybridized *p* orbital on the carbon atom is shown interacting with a *p* orbital on the attached oxygen atom. Each structure relates to the Lewis structure shown directly above it. (Unshared electron pairs are omitted for clarity.)

We generally represent this by writing the individual Lewis structures separated by a double-headed arrow, as shown in Figure 1.25. We call the individual structures **resonance contributing forms.** When we use a blend of resonance structures to describe bonding, we say we are using a resonance hybrid description of that bonding. We understand the true structure to be an average or a blend of the individual structures. Attempts to show the true structure (as an average of the resonance contributing forms) are illustrated in Figure 1.26. Notice that the resonance hybrid description implies that each carbon-oxygen bond is partway between single and double. We find that this

Figure 1.25 Representing the carbonate anion using three Lewis structures. The double-headed arrow between the individual structures indicates that the true description is an average of the individual structures.

Figure 1.26 Representing the carbonate anion as a resonance structure average.

Partial double bonds between carbon and oxygen are designated by the broken lines. Formal charges are shown with the oxygen atoms. Unshared electron pairs not shown.

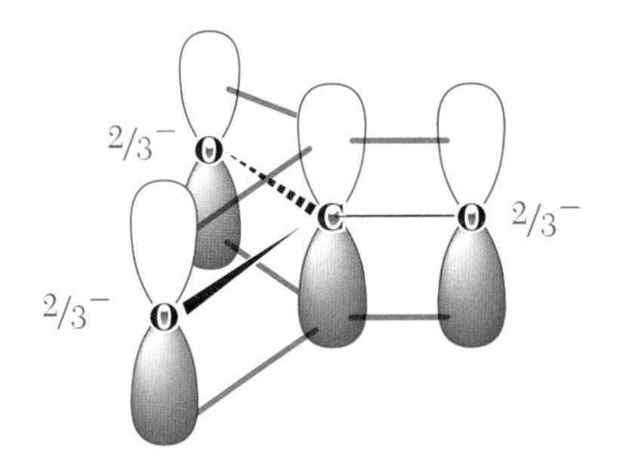

The π bonding between carbon and oxygen is shown by *p* orbital overlap. Formal charges are shown at oxygen, but unshared electron pairs are not shown.

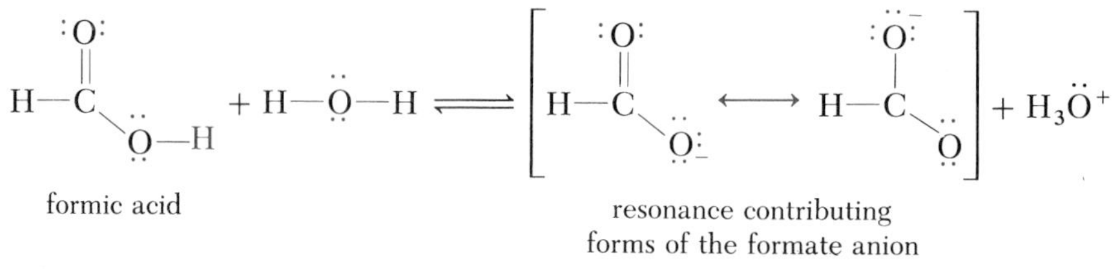

$$\mathrm{H{-}C({=}\ddot{O}{:}){-}\ddot{O}{-}H} + \mathrm{H{-}\ddot{O}{-}H} \rightleftharpoons \left[\mathrm{H{-}C({=}\ddot{O}{:}){-}\ddot{O}{:}^-} \longleftrightarrow \mathrm{H{-}C({-}\ddot{O}{:}^-){=}\ddot{O}}\right] + \mathrm{H_3\ddot{O}^+}$$

formic acid

resonance contributing forms of the formate anion

Figure 1.27 Resonance contributing forms for the formate anion. Neither structure adequately describes the formate anion, whose charge is equally distributed between the oxygens and which has equal distances for the two carbon-oxygen bonds. A better description of the formate anion is given by the average or a blending of the two structures.

description matches very well with the evidence we obtain from experimental probes of the structure of the carbonate anion.

The blending of resonance contributing forms implies a greater delocalization of the involved electrons than is present in any one of the individual structures. This example illustrates a concept introduced in the beginning of our discussion of the valence bond model of bonding—the larger the region of space in which a charge is allowed to exist, the lower its energy—and it leads to a useful rule of thumb: structures for which we can draw more than one Lewis structure are usually more stable than we would expect for any one of the structures.

Consider now another example of an ion that is better described by contributing resonance forms than by a single Lewis structure. The formate anion is produced by the dissociation of formic acid in aqueous solution, as shown in Figure 1.27. Experiments show that the formate anion (but *not* formic acid itself) has two identical carbon-oxygen bonds. This result is consistent with our ability to write two equivalent resonance structures for formate ion but not for formic acid.

PROBLEM 1.14

Write two resonance structures for each of the following molecules, showing formal charges on the atoms where appropriate. (*Note:* The formal charge on a given atom is not *necessarily* the same in all resonance structures of a particular molecule).

a. H_2CNN (diazomethane, a yellow, toxic, potentially explosive gas sometimes used in organic synthesis)

b. HNNN (hydrazoic acid, the parent acid of azide salts)

THE CURVED-ARROW FORMALISM

A simple procedure for writing alternative resonance contributing forms involves first writing *one* structure showing all valence level electrons. We then shift these electrons in pairs about the structure. However, only certain types of movements of the electrons are acceptable. We may move unshared electron pairs *as a pair* to form an additional bond to an adjacent atom. Electrons from multiple bonds may be moved, again as pairs, either to form another bond to a different adjacent atom, or onto one of the atoms connected by the multiple bond, where they become an unshared pair. We represent these electron pair shifts using curved arrows in the **curved-arrow formalism.** The application of

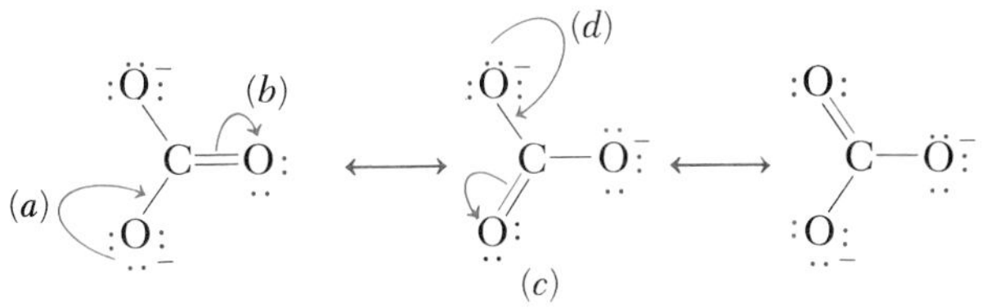

Figure 1.28 Curved-arrow formalism in writing resonance structures of the carbonate anion. The locations of the formal charges change with the electron pair shifts. Movements of electrons are coordinated so that electrons are not piled up in any given site. The head of the arrow indicates the destination of the electron pair, and the arrow tail the source of the electron pair.

(*a*) An unshared pair is moved from oxygen to form a π bond between oxygen and carbon.

(*b*) A bonding pair (the π bonding pair) is moved onto the oxygen as an unshared pair.

(*c*) A π bonding pair is moved from between carbon and oxygen to become an unshared pair on oxygen.

(*d*) An unshared pair is moved from oxygen to form a π bond between oxygen and carbon.

this procedure to writing resonance structures for the carbonate anion is illustrated in Figure 1.28.

PROBLEM 1.15

a. For the three resonance structures of the carbonate anion as shown in Figure 1.28, start with the structure shown on the *right* and illustrate how the structures in the center and on the left can be generated from it using the curved-arrow formalism.

b. One resonance structure for the isocyanate ion, NCO^- is shown below.

$$:N{\equiv}C{-}\ddot{\underset{\cdot\cdot}{O}}:^-$$

Use curved arrows to deduce a second resonance structure. Draw the second structure, clearly showing formal charges.

Several general rules must be followed to assess the acceptability of resonance structures that might be written. Contributing resonance structures are significant if they are all energetically similar. Higher energy structures contribute less to the hybrid (blended) picture of an ion or molecule's electronic structure than do lower-energy forms. The general rules for considering the acceptability of contributing resonance structures are outlined below.

General Guidelines for Writing Resonance Structures and Assessing Their Relative Energies

1. The relative positions of the nuclei must be the same in all structures. For example, $H{-}C{\equiv}N:$ and $H{-}N{\equiv}C:$ are *not* resonance structures because the bonded atoms have different sequences.
2. Charge separation in a resonance-contributing form generally causes its energy to be higher than that of similar structures with no charge separation. For example, consider carbon dioxide. Following the usual procedure for developing a Lewis structure, we deduce that eight electrons are to be shared.

We could draw a Lewis structure with two double bonds (O═C═O) or one with one triple bond and one single bond (O—C≡O). When we assign formal charges, we see that the structure with the triple bond has separated charges:

$$^{-}\!:\ddot{\underset{..}{O}}-C\equiv O:^{+}$$

The structure with two double bonds has no atoms with formal charges, and it therefore is the better structure. It corresponds more closely to the true structure of carbon dioxide. This structure also agrees with the one we would draw using the standard valences.

3. If possible, all atoms should obey the noble gas rule. Special cases arise when there are not sufficient electrons to provide every atom with a noble gas configuration; this situation occurs for some reaction intermediates, some boron compounds, and odd-electron species (radicals, see Chapter 7).
4. When we use the curved-arrow formalism to derive a second structure from the first, we must be careful to correlate the electron movements so that we do not accumulate more than the noble gas number on any one atom.
5. The relative importance of various resonance structures depends on the nature of the atoms carrying charges and the number and type of bonds present. Two structures may *both* be significant (have similar number and types of bonds and have similar charge separations) but not be exactly equivalent. Consider, for example, the two resonance structures shown below.

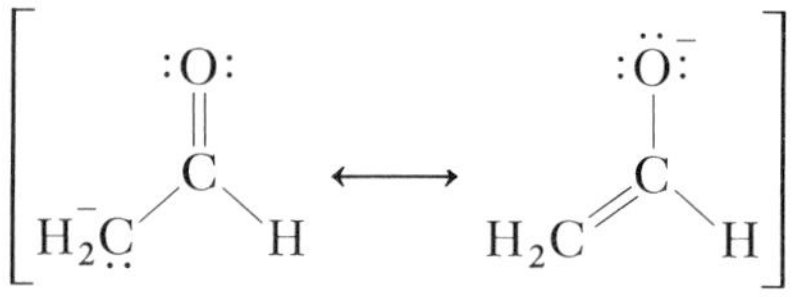

$$\left[H_2\bar{C}{:}-C(=\ddot{O}{:})-H \longleftrightarrow H_2C{=}C(-\ddot{O}{:}^{-})-H \right]$$

These two structures have the same number of bonds, and each has one formal negative charge. The two are of *similar* but not exactly the same energy. In such a case we find that the structure that best matches the experimental evidence is, as usual, a hybrid of the two. However, this best structure is not a 50/50 mix of the two resonance forms. One resonance form is closer to the real structure than the other. The weighting of the individual structures depends on the atom that best accommodates the negative charge (oxygen rather than carbon) and the relative strengths of the bonds in the structures. Usually there is no need for us to try to quantify these effects. We simply realize that the resonance hybrid is somewhere between the two individual forms but closer to one than the other.

PROBLEM 1.16 Using the curved arrow formalism, write contributing resonance Lewis structures for each of the following ions:

a. nitrite anion (ONO^-)   b. acetate anion ($H_3C—CO_2^{\ -}$)

c. thiocyanate ion (SCN^-)

PROBLEM 1.17 In each case, what is the outcome of the curved-arrow operation on the Lewis structure shown? Does it lead to another acceptable resonance structure?

a. S^{2+} with $=\ddot{O}:$, $:\ddot{O}:^-$, $:\ddot{O}:^-$ b. $^-:C{\equiv}N:$ c. $^-:C{\equiv}N:$

d. $H_2C{=}\overset{+}{N}{=}\ddot{N}^-$ e. $(H_3C)_2C{=}\ddot{O}$ f. $H_3C{-}\ddot{O}{-}\overset{+}{N}H_3$

PROBLEM 1.18 Consider the use of a base to remove one hydrogen as a proton (H^+) from the molecule shown below to form an anion of formula $C_6H_{11}O^-$. Suppose the anion is formed by the removal of a proton from the $-CH_3$ group shown on the left side of the molecule. Give a Lewis structure for this anion. Is there a second significant resonance structure you could write for this anion? If there is, draw it. Suppose the anion is formed by the removal of a proton from one of the three $-CH_3$ groups shown on the right side of the molecule. Write a Lewis structure for this anion. Are there any other resonance structures you could write for this particular anion? If so, draw them. From which side of the molecule would you anticipate a proton to be removed more readily by a base if you were to perform the experiment? Explain your prediction.

$H_3C{-}C({=}\ddot{O}{:}){-}C(CH_3)_2{-}CH_3$

PROBLEM 1.19 As in Problem 1.18, consider the use of a base to remove a hydrogen as a proton from the structure shown below. There are three types of hydrogen atoms in this molecule. Which would you expect to be attacked more readily by a base? Explain your prediction.

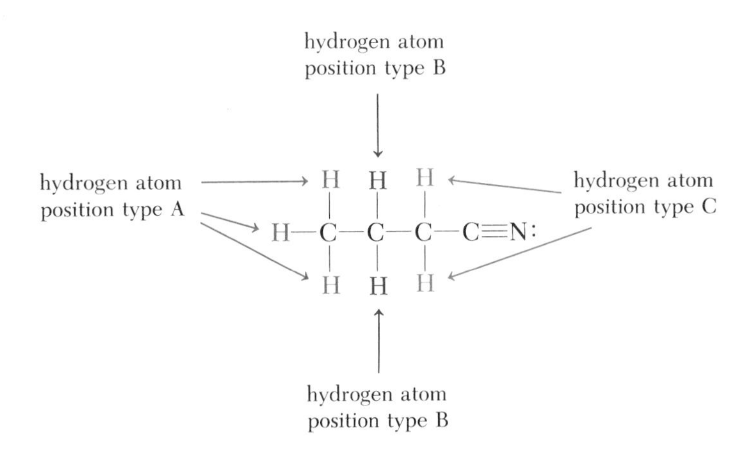

PROBLEM 1.20 Use the curved-arrow formalism to show any other contributing resonance structure(s) for the benzene molecule, for which one structure is shown below.

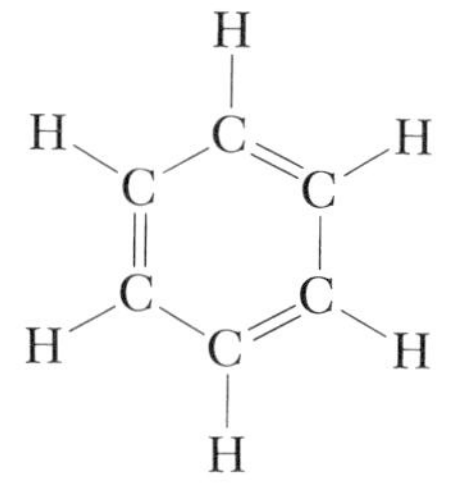

PROBLEM 1.21 Using the Lewis structure for the benzene molecule in the previous problem, state the orbital type used by the atoms in each of the bonds and the types of bonds they form. What geometry would be expected for this molecule?

1.8 When the Valence Bond Model Gives the Wrong Answer

At its most basic level, the valence bond model requires the drawing of Lewis structures. Occasionally we find that Lewis structures drawn according to the guidelines set down earlier are totally at odds with experimental measurements. Also we find that the valence bond approach simply does not (and cannot) give us answers to *all* of the questions we may have regarding bonding and the chemistry of molecules.

We must always keep in mind that experimental reality directs theory. Our theories are good only so long as they provide us with answers in accord with experiment and allow us to make correct predictions of experiments. There exist many molecules for which simple valence bond theory does not give us an adequate description. We must remember that valence bond theory is only a method we use to describe experimental reality and make predictions. Atoms and molecules "do their own thing" without any recourse to our theories. Theories, including the valence bond model for describing molecules, are for our convenience and do not direct what molecules do.

Similarly, the concepts of hybridization and resonance are our creations to help us to understand experimental results. Even the concepts of hybridization and valence bond theory break down if we begin to look at the electronic spectra of molecules. Hybridization is a mathematical method useful to us for certain purposes, but not for others. We can use hybridization and valence bond theory as long as they give us answers in accord with experimental reality. When they do not give us correct answers, we must go to a different model or theory. Hybridization and resonance are two modifications of the basic valence bond model that we use for considering bonding in molecules. These modifications allow us to rationalize *much* of chemistry in terms of the valence bond model. However there are exceptions. For example, consider the oxygen molecule, O_2. Experimental observations are in clear conflict with the standard Lewis structure for the oxygen molecule shown in Figure 1.29.

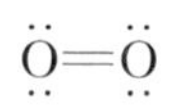

Figure 1.29 Lewis structure of the oxygen molecule. Although this Lewis structure is drawn in accordance with all usual guidelines such as the noble gas rule, it is *not* in accord with the experimentally measured properties of oxygen.

The oxygen molecule is found by experiment to be *paramagnetic*. (Liquid oxygen is strongly attracted to the poles of a magnet.) Further, we find that the observed paramagnetism points to the presence of *two* unpaired electrons in the O_2 molecule. The Lewis structure of Figure 1.29 suggests that all of the oxygen molecule's electrons are paired. On the basis of the Lewis structure, we would not predict any paramagnetic properties for O_2.

The valence bond model also fails at the most basic level to explain the existence of the hydrogen molecular ion, H_2^+, or the helium molecular ion, He_2^+. It is not even possible to write a standard Lewis structure for these ions.

In the following sections we discuss a different way of viewing the bonding in molecules, the *molecular orbital model*. The main advantage of the molecular orbital model is that it always gives a description of bonding in accord with experiment, *if* we can solve the appropriate wave equations and derive a proper orbital description.

The main disadvantage of the molecular orbital model is that it is considerably more difficult to apply than is the valence bond model. At the most rigorous level, major computations using computers are necessary. However, organic chemists usually work with the molecular orbital model at a simpler, more pictorial level, and it is at this level that we will focus in this text.

The molecular orbital and valence bond models should be regarded as complementary. For example, Lewis structures generally provide us with a "quick and dirty" but highly useful method for viewing the basic bonding in molecules. In fact, organic chemists advanced their science for many years using only this simplified model.

For more detailed views of bonding and to handle molecules such as O_2, for which the valence bond model fails, we need to turn to more sophisticated models of bonding, such as the molecular orbital model.

Our usual approach in organic chemistry is to use the simplest possible model of bonding that will rationalize experimental facts and accurately predict observable phenomena. Most of the time we do very well with Lewis structures, but at times we must resort to higher-level models. This philosophy will be followed in this text. The following sections provide an introduction to the molecular orbital model.

MOLECULAR ORBITAL ANALYSIS

1.9 The Molecular Orbital Model for Bonding

THE DEFINITION OF MOLECULAR ORBITALS

We have already defined atomic orbitals as regions of space in an atom in which one or two electrons can exist with a particular energy. A **molecular orbital** is a region of space in a molecule in which one or two electrons can exist. Associated with each molecular orbital is a particular, precisely defined energy. The basic precept of the molecular orbital model is that every molecule has a set of molecular orbitals. Although all atoms have the same basic set of atomic orbitals (1*s*, 2*s*, 2*p*, etc.), different molecules have different sets of molecular orbitals. For example, the molecular orbitals of methane are quite different from those of hydrogen.

MOLECULAR ORBITAL DESCRIPTIONS

The usual method for constructing a molecular orbital description of a molecule begins with the atomic orbitals of the constituent atoms. The mathematical functions describing these atomic orbitals are combined so as to yield the set of molecular orbitals. This process is known as the method of **linear combination of atomic orbitals (LCAO).**

At the most rigorous level, complex mathematical calculations are performed, using a computer, to provide a solution to the appropriate equations describing the energy and spatial relationship of electrons and nuclei. We thereby obtain a mathematical description of a set of molecular orbitals. However, organic chemists often find that a less quantitative, more pictorial (and time-saving) approach is able to provide extremely useful information.

A fundamental premise underlying the LCAO approach is that the combination of a given number of atomic orbitals will yield the same number of molecular orbitals. (We saw this same premise in the construction of hybrid orbitals from simple atomic orbitals.) For example, if we wish to describe the hydrogen molecule using molecular orbitals, we use two atomic orbitals, one from each of the atoms involved. The LCAO procedure produces two molecular orbitals for the hydrogen molecule. Placing the nuclei at the normal internuclear distance for the hydrogen molecule, we combine the wavefunctions in the two available ways (addition and subtraction) to generate two molecular orbital wavefunctions as shown in Figure 1.30. These molecular orbitals also have particular shapes, as shown in Figure 1.31.

Figure 1.30 Construction of molecular orbitals from two hydrogen 1*s* atomic orbitals. The combination of two atomic orbitals (ϕ_a and ϕ_b) produces two molecular orbitals. One of these (ψ_1), resulting from the addition of the atomic orbital wavefunctions, is lower in energy than either of the atomic orbitals, and the other (ψ_2), resulting from subtraction, is correspondingly higher in energy.

Atomic 1*s* orbitals:

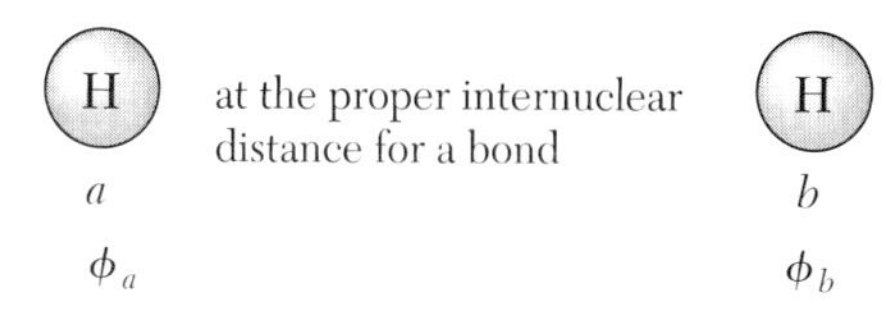

Combining atomic 1*s* orbitals:

$$\Psi_1 = \phi_a + \phi_b$$
$$\Psi_2 = \phi_a - \phi_b$$

Ψ_1 and Ψ_2 represent the wavefunctions for the newly created molecular orbitals.

The relative energies of the atomic orbitals and the newly created molecular orbitals can then be shown in an energy diagram:

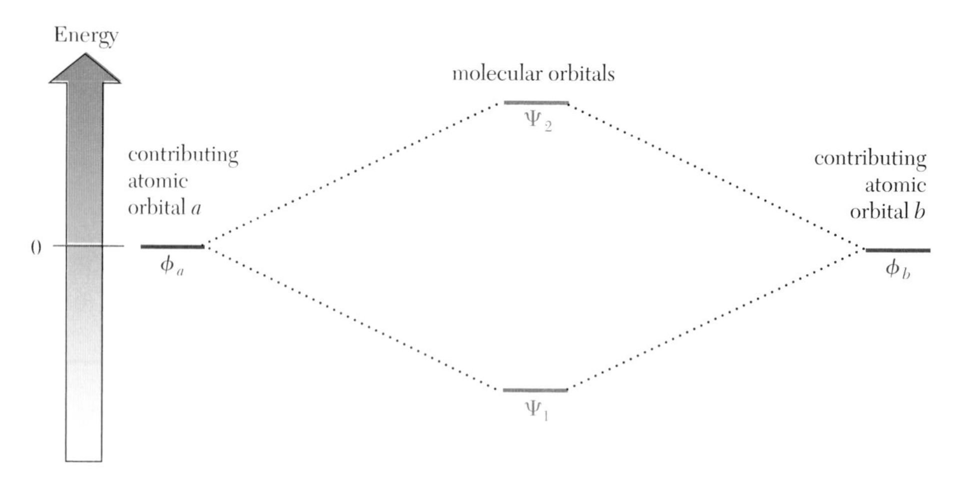

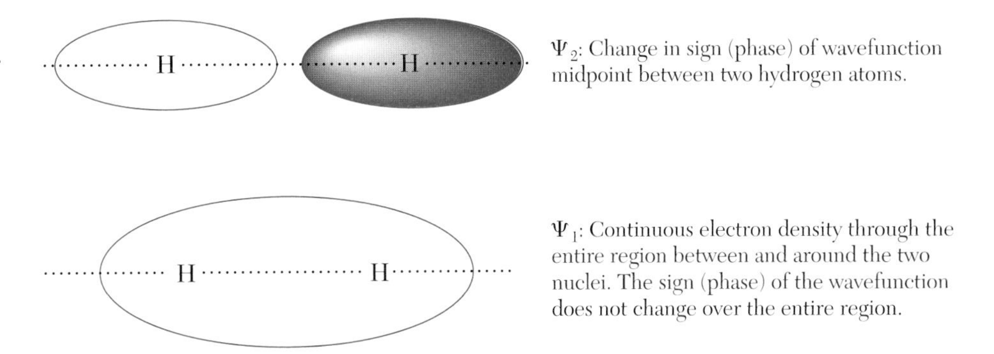

H
H
Ψ_2: Change in sign (phase) of wavefunction midpoint between two hydrogen atoms.
H
H
Ψ_1: Continuous electron density through the entire region between and around the two nuclei. The sign (phase) of the wavefunction does not change over the entire region.

Figure 1.31 Shapes of molecular orbitals created from atomic hydrogen 1s orbitals. Both orbitals have an axis of symmetry about which they are cylindrically symmetrical. We thus call them σ molecular orbitals.

DEFINING A BOND WITH MOLECULAR ORBITALS

When using the molecular orbital model, we first obtain a description of the molecular orbitals without initially thinking about the electrons that can occupy them. In this way our approach is quite different from that used in the valence bond model. Once we have a picture of the orbitals, we *then* add the appropriate number of electrons to the available molecular orbitals, as shown in Figure 1.32 for the H_2 molecule.

An electron in a bonding molecular orbital provides stabilization because it is simultaneously associated with more than one nucleus. It provides continuous electron density between the nuclei and shields their normal proton-proton repulsions. An electron in an antibonding molecular orbital does *not* provide a continuum of electron density between the nuclei. Thus, it cannot shield the normal proton-proton repulsions, and the sum of the electron-proton attractions is smaller.

The bond energy and the electron distribution of the ordinary hydrogen molecule as shown by the molecular orbital pictures (Figures 1.31 and 1.32) are essentially the same as would be given by the valence bond model. If we wish simply to describe the energy and electron distribution of a ground state hydrogen molecule, either approach gives us an adequate result. For certain other considerations, however, the molecular orbital view is superior.

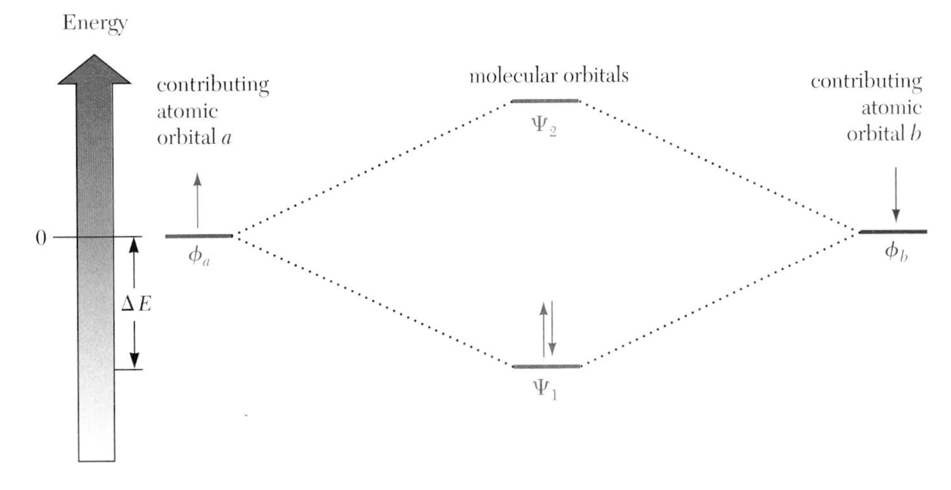

Figure 1.32 Electrons associated with molecular orbitals in the hydrogen molecule. Two electrons from the participating hydrogen atoms are placed in the lowest-energy molecular orbital (the aufbau principle). We thus place both electrons in the ψ_1 molecular orbital. Compared with the energy of the electrons in the original orbitals (ϕ_a and ϕ_b), the energy of the electrons in the lower-energy molecular orbital is stabilized by an amount equal to $2\Delta E$. Because ψ_1 is lower in energy than the original atomic orbitals and electrons are stabilized by placing them there, ψ_1 is called a **bonding molecular orbital.** The molecular orbital ψ_2, being higher in energy than the original atomic orbitals, is called an **antibonding molecular orbital.** If electrons were placed in it, the system would be *less* stable than if they were associated with the isolated atoms. The bond energy in a hydrogen molecule is 104 kcal/mole, so ΔE is approximately 52 kcal/mole.

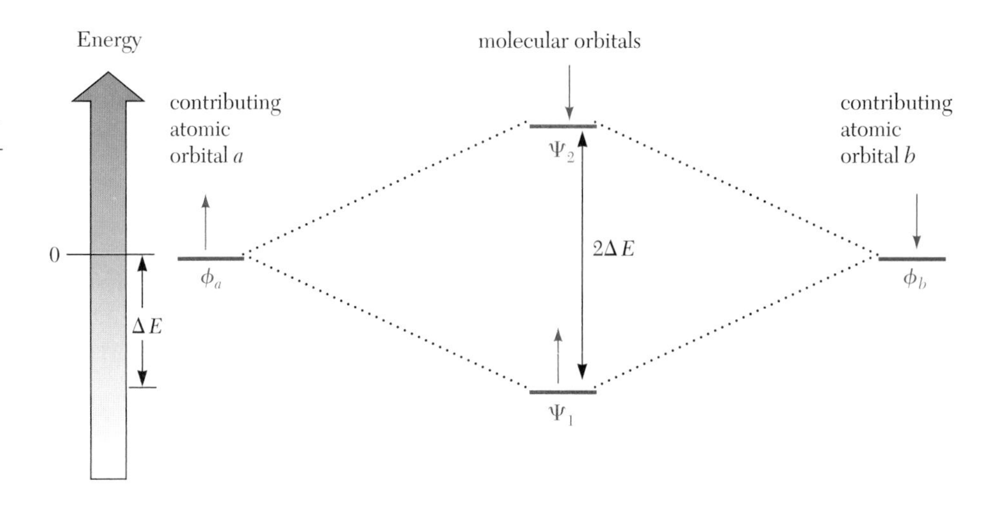

Figure 1.33 Excitation of a hydrogen molecule. An electron is energized by light absorption from the bonding to the antibonding orbital. The net bonding stabilization of the system is zero—one electron in the antibonding level destabilizes the system to the same extent as one electron in the bonding level stabilizes it. The molecule would dissociate under these conditions—in accord with the observed photolysis (cleavage by light) of hydrogen molecules.

COMPLICATIONS ON THE HYDROGEN SYSTEM

An Energized Hydrogen Molecule Suppose we put energy into a hydrogen molecule by shining light on it. We know that we can excite the electrons of atoms to higher energy orbitals in this manner. We might expect that we could do the same with molecules.

With a valence bond model of bonding we do not get any specific notion of higher energy orbitals to which an electron might be excited. However, with the molecular orbital model, we have available a higher energy orbital to which an electron could be excited. The excitation process is illustrated in Figure 1.33.

The molecular orbital model of bonding in the hydrogen molecule allows us to understand this process more easily than does the valence bond model.

The Hydrogen Molecular Ion Consider two hydrogen nuclei with only one associated electron. The valence bond model would predict that no bond exists between the two nuclei since the model requires the sharing of a pair of electrons between nuclei. However, the hydrogen molecular ion (H_2^+) is

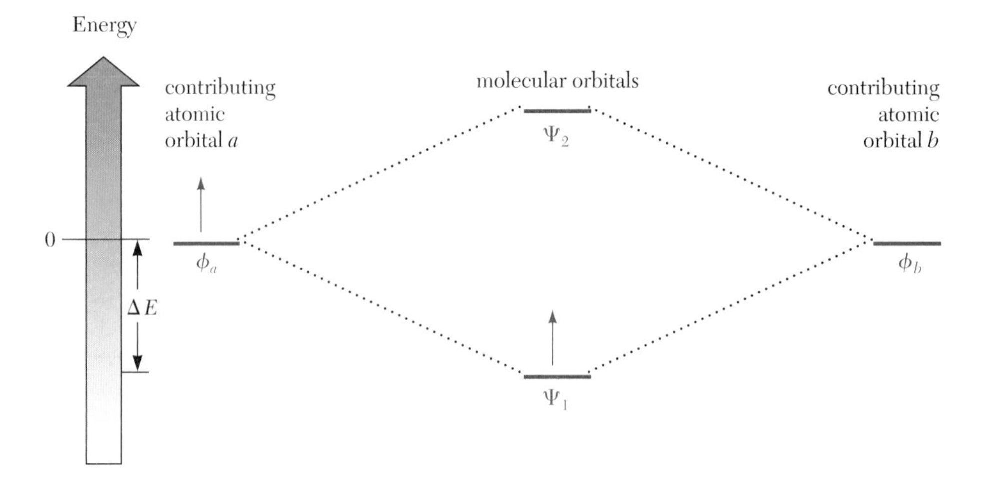

Figure 1.34 Bonding in the hydrogen molecular ion. One electron occupies the bonding molecular orbital, providing a stabilization of ΔE. The bonding stabilization is half that of the hydrogen molecule.

known to exist. (*Caution:* The hydrogen molecular ion is *not* something we can prepare and put in a bottle as the cationic component of a salt, as sodium ion in NaCl is. It exists as a transient species only.) We can understand its bonding (and its existence) by the molecular orbital model as shown in Figure 1.34.

PROBLEM 1.22

Consider the bond formed when a proton (H^+) reacts with a hydride ion ($H:^-$). Is this bond any different from the bond formed by the combination of two hydrogen atoms?

PROBLEM 1.23

Suppose we add a third electron to a hydrogen molecule, attempting to generate the H_2^- species. Describe the bonding in this species and estimate the bond energy in kcal/mole. (See Figure 1.32)

PROBLEM 1.24

Use the molecular orbital model to describe the bonding (if any) in the following species:

a. He_2 **b.** He_2^+ **c.** Li_2 **d.** Li_2^+

Steps to Solving the Problem

Solution to Problem 1.24a

1. First construct the molecular orbital energy diagram for this system. The atomic orbitals from which a pair of molecular orbitals for the He_2 molecule would be constructed are the same as for the H_2 molecule. Thus, we have the same molecular orbital energy diagram.
2. We next consider the number of electrons to occupy these levels. A total of *four* electrons must be placed, and they will occupy the molecular orbitals as shown.

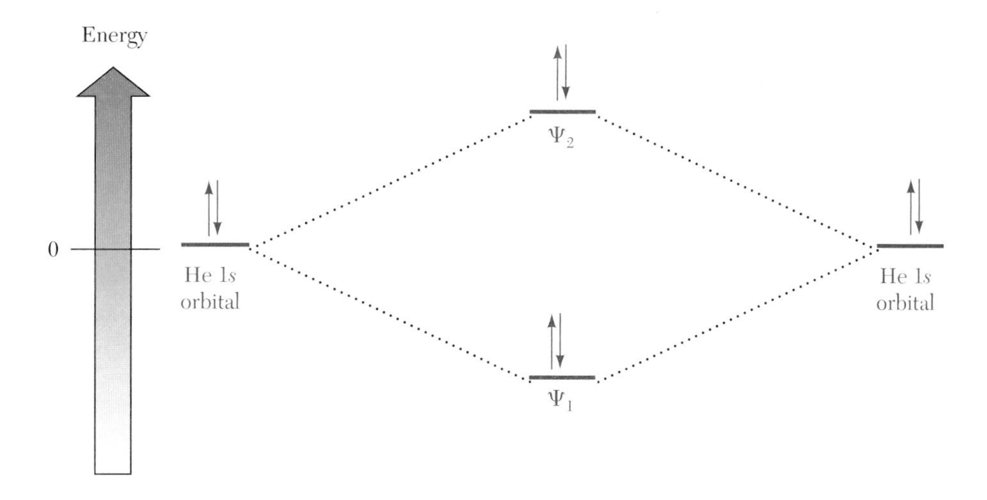

3. Consider the stability of this electronic configuration. The pair of electrons in the antibonding level cancels any stabilization from the electrons in the bonding level so that no overall bond exists. No He_2 molecule has in fact ever been detected, a result we would predict from the molecular orbital analysis just given.

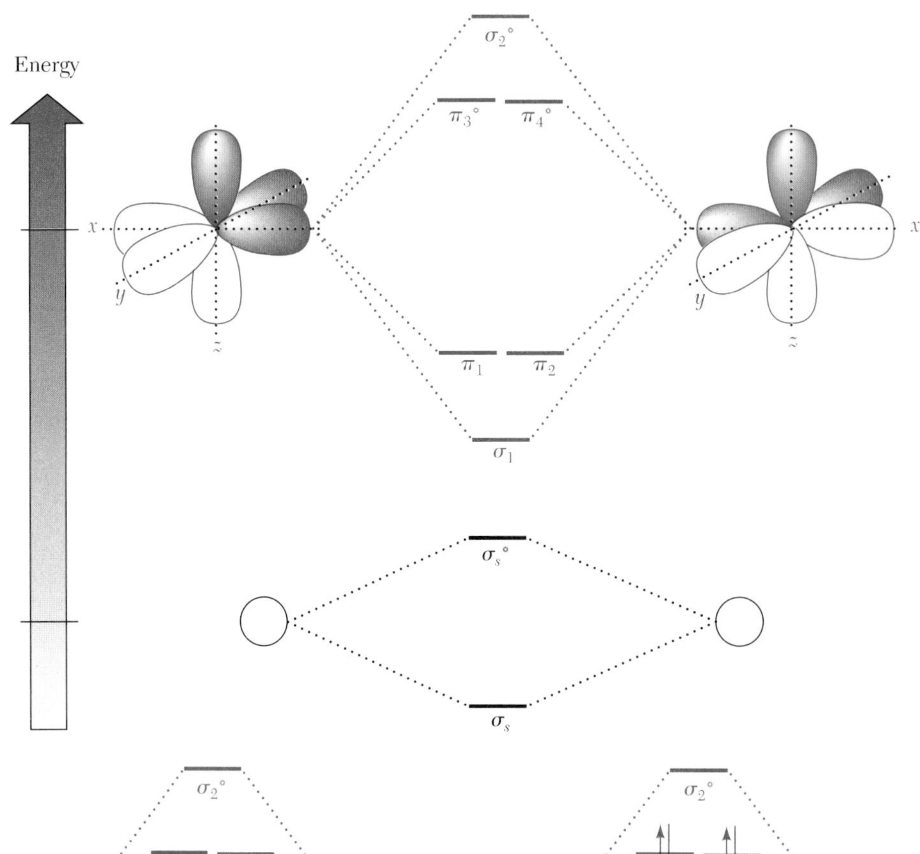

Figure 1.35 Construction of molecular orbitals from 2*s* and 2*p* atomic orbitals. The 2*s* orbitals, shown at the bottom, lead to bonding (σ) and antibonding (σ^*) molecular orbitals entirely analogous to those of the hydrogen system. The $2p_x$ orbitals also lead to σ and σ^* molecular orbitals. Combination (addition and subtraction) of the $2p_y$ and $2p_z$ orbitals leads to a pair of degenerate π (bonding) and a pair of degenerate π^* (antibonding) molecular orbitals. (*Degenerate* orbitals are those having the same energy.) In some molecules (N_2, for example), the σ_1 level is above the π_1 and π_2 levels.

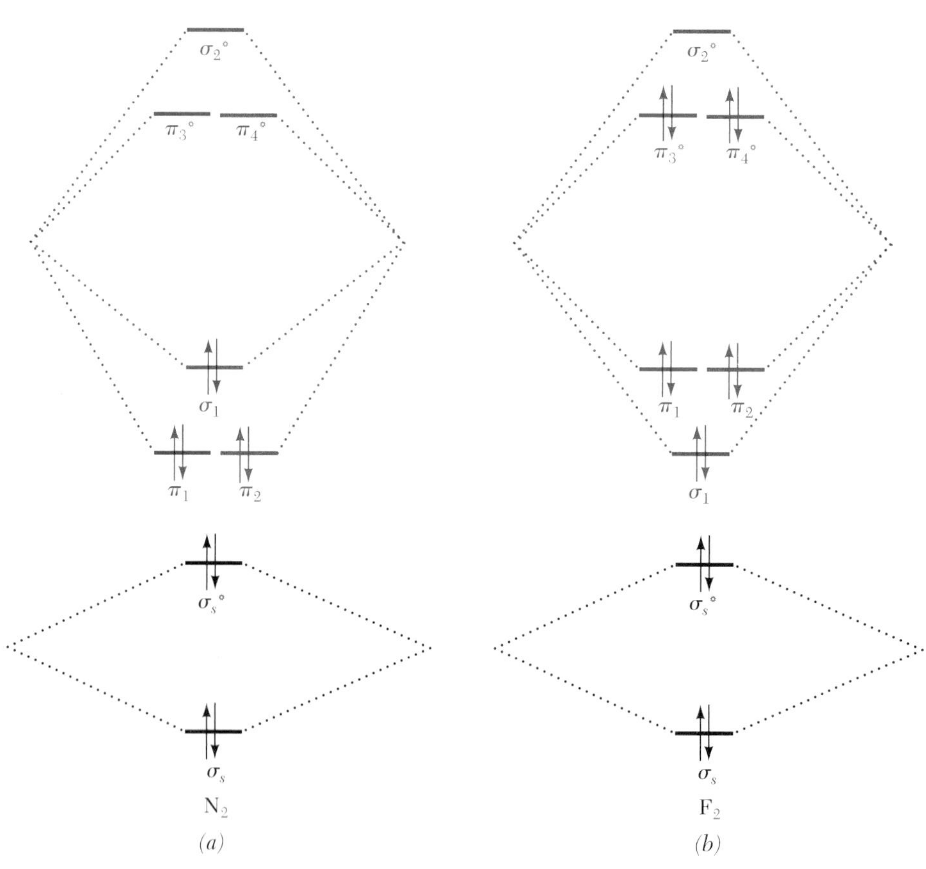

Figure 1.36 (*a*) Valence shell molecular orbital description of the N_2 molecule. The 1*s* electrons from each atom are not shown. We place the ten valence shell electrons in successively higher energy orbitals in accord with the aufbau principle. The filling of σ_s^* offsets the filling of σ_s such that this pair produce no net bonding. The filling of the three higher levels results in a net bond order of three (one σ and two π bonds). **(*b*) Valence shell molecular orbital description of the F_2 molecule containing 14 valence electrons.** Again, the 1*s* electrons from each atom are not shown. In addition to the levels filled in the N_2 system, two higher π^* levels are filled, leading to a total bond order of one (one σ and zero π bonds.)

DIATOMIC MOLECULES OF THE SECOND PERIODIC ROW

Constructing a Molecular Orbital Picture The main difference between constructing molecular orbitals for the hydrogen molecule and constructing molecular orbitals for molecules involving atoms of the second periodic row is the inclusion of the $2p$ orbitals. Since s atomic orbitals are spherical, they can be combined in only two ways to give σ molecular orbitals. With p orbitals there are two possible directions of approach. Addition and subtraction of the wavefunctions with an end-on approach leads to σ molecular orbitals, but a sideways approach leads to π molecular orbitals. For the $2s$ and $2p$ orbitals of second-row elements, the molecular orbitals are approximately as illustrated in Figure 1.35.

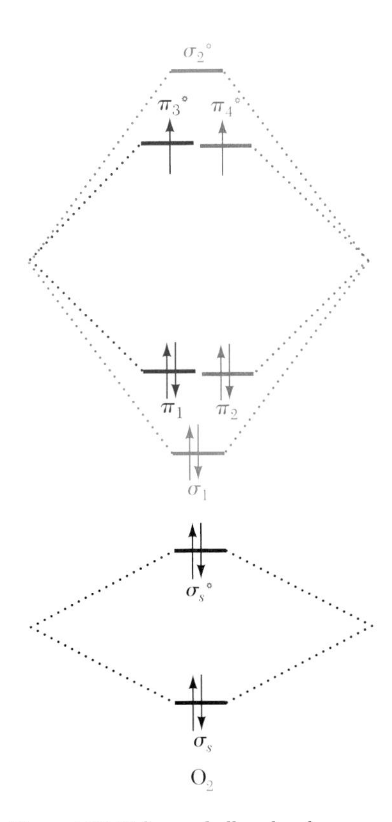

Figure 1.37 Valence shell molecular orbital system for the O_2 molecule. The two $1s$ orbitals from each atom are not shown. Following the aufbau principle for the filling of orbitals, the 12 valence shell electrons are placed in orbitals of progressively increasing energy. The last two electrons are placed according to Hund's rule. That is, when several electrons are to be placed in degenerate levels, we locate one in each of the degenerate orbitals (π^*) with the same spin and do not begin pairing them in any of the orbitals until each orbital is occupied by one electron. The molecular orbital model thus predicts that the oxygen molecule will have two unpaired electrons, in agreement with experimental measurements.

Nitrogen and Fluorine Suppose we now place in this molecular orbital system the appropriate number of electrons for a homonuclear diatomic (the two atoms are of the same element) molecule of the second periodic row. Two examples are illustrated in Figure 1.36, the nitrogen molecule (N_2) and the fluorine molecule (F_2).

The concept of **bond order** is slightly different in the valence bond model than in the molecular orbital model. In the valence bond model, bond order is simply the number of electron pairs shared between a pair of atoms. With the molecular orbital model we need to consider both the bonding and the antibonding electrons. The bond order is given by:

$$\text{bond order} = (\text{number of bonding electrons} \\ - \text{number of antibonding electrons})/2$$

The molecular orbital description of bonding in both the nitrogen and the fluorine molecule is essentially identical to that obtained from the valence bond model.

The Oxygen Molecule If we look at the oxygen molecule with a molecular orbital model (Figure 1.37), we see a quite different result from that produced by the valence bond model.

The molecular orbital model accounts for the paramagnetic nature of the oxygen molecule. There is one σ bond and one (net) π bond. The molecular orbital model is better for the oxygen molecule than is the valence bond model since it gives us a description more in accord with experimental observations.

PROBLEM 1.25 Does the molecular orbital model predict a strengthening or weakening of the nitrogen-nitrogen bond when an electron is removed from N_2 to give N_2^+? Consider the fluorine-fluorine bond strength upon removal of an electron from F_2 to give F_2^+. Is the bond stronger or weaker? Describe the bond order in F_2^+ according to the molecular orbital model.

PROBLEM 1.26 Consider adding energy to the nitrogen molecule (electronic excitation) to move the highest-energy electron to the next available level. Draw the molecular orbital energy diagram for this excited nitrogen molecule. What is the bond order of the species?

PROBLEM 1.27 The salt O_2PtF_6 is one of an interesting group of materials that contain the O_2^+ ion. Give the molecular orbital description of the bonding in this ion. Is the oxygen-oxygen bond stronger or weaker in O_2^+ as compared to O_2? Explain.

1.10 Molecular Orbitals for Organic Molecules

Organic molecules are more complex than the homonuclear diatomics discussed in the previous section. Organic chemists normally are not concerned with all of the bonds in a molecule but limit their attention to those bonds that are undergoing change in the chemical reaction of interest. The remainder of the molecule remains much the same after the reaction as before. Rather than considering the molecular orbitals of the entire molecule, organic chemists usually are concerned with molecular orbitals that describe only the region undergoing change. We normally make the approximation of considering each σ bond to be localized. The bonding and antibonding orbitals associated with that linkage are constructed by mixing two atomic orbitals, one from each of the connected atoms. This procedure is very similar to the one we used with the diatomics.

For example, if we wish to focus on the carbon-fluorine σ bond of CH_3—F, we construct σ and σ^* molecular orbitals for it by mixing the appropriate atomic orbitals from carbon and fluorine only, as illustrated in Figure 1.38.

When we mixed atomic orbitals to generate the molecular orbitals of the carbon-fluorine linkage, we used atomic orbitals of different energies. (We make estimates of the differences in atomic orbital energies from the electronic spectra of atoms.) Orbitals of unequal energy do not mix as efficiently as do two orbitals of the same energy, and thus there is a smaller gain in covalent bonding than when the two orbitals involved are of the same energy.

We also use this partially localized molecular orbital model for looking at other organic molecules. Single bonds between carbons (or carbon and other

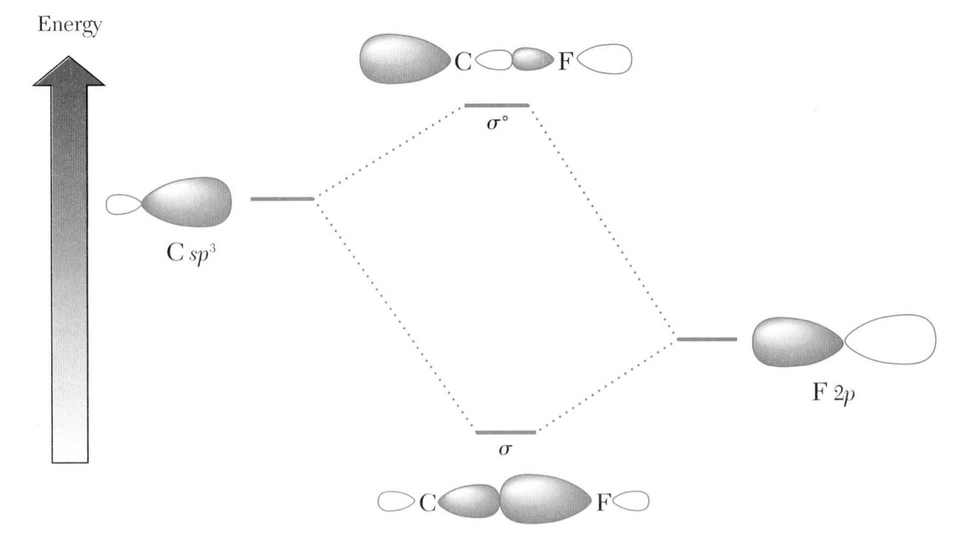

Figure 1.38 Creation of molecular orbitals for a carbon-fluorine bond. This is a simplification of the full molecular orbital description of the molecule, but it is usually adequate for making chemical predictions.

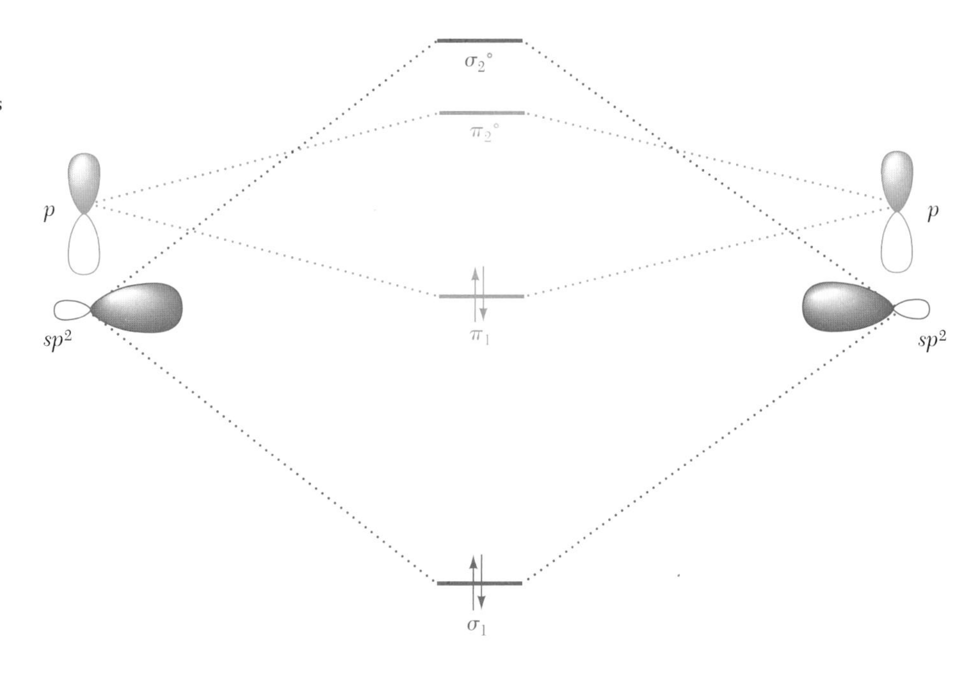

Figure 1.39 Molecular orbital diagram for the carbon-carbon double bond of ethylene. Both sp^2 orbitals lie along axes that are perpendicular to the p orbitals and thus do not interact with them. The orbitals described are localized over adjacent atoms. Other atomic orbitals present in the system are considered not to interact with those shown but do interact with each other to provide the remaining carbon-hydrogen molecular orbitals.

atoms) are viewed in an entirely analogous manner to that described above for CH_3—F. When multiple bonds are present, we describe the π portion separately from the σ portion. For example, we describe the carbon-carbon double bond in ethylene ($H_2C{=}CH_2$; see Table 1.2) using the molecular orbital picture shown in Figure 1.39. We generate the σ portion using only two sp^2 hybrid orbitals and the π portion using only the two unhybridized p-orbitals. The shapes of these molecular orbitals are shown in Figure 1.40.

Throughout this text we will continue to use the simplification that σ molecular orbitals are localized between adjacent atoms. We will consider

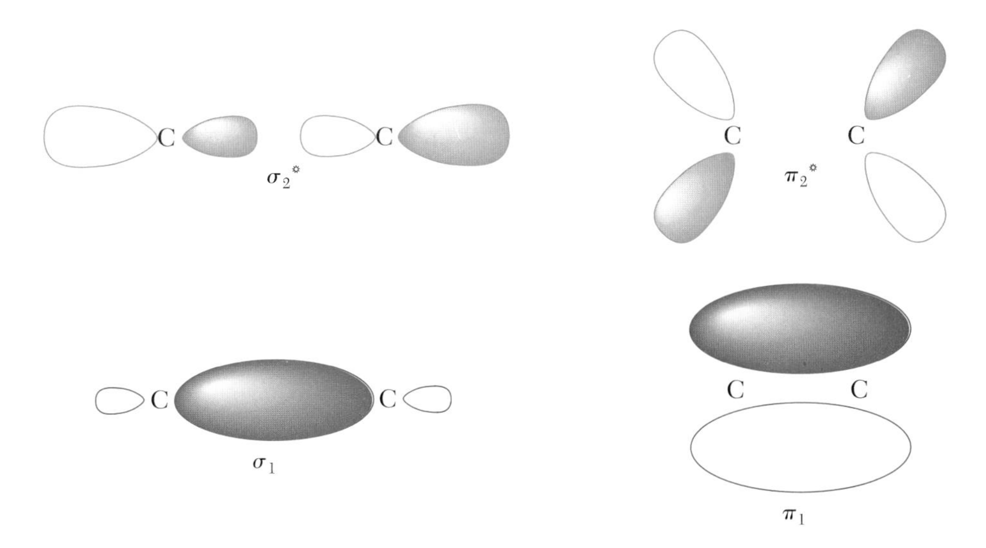

Figure 1.40 Shapes of molecular orbitals associated with a carbon-carbon double bond.

extended interactions, that is, those beyond adjacent atoms, only for certain π systems to be discussed later.

PROBLEM 1.28 Use the molecular orbital model to describe the carbon-carbon bond in ethane (Figure 1.8). How does this description differ from a valence bond model description of the molecule?

PROBLEM 1.29 Give a description of the bonding in the carbon-nitrogen linkage in acetonitrile (Figure 1.10) using the molecular orbital model.

The views we get of bonds in organic molecules from the valence bond model and from the molecular orbital model are usually very similar. The major difference between the two methods is that the molecular orbital model reveals information about antibonding molecular orbitals. The valence bond model tells us nothing about space for electrons other than those that are part of the electron-pair bond. If we wish simply to describe the bond(s) of a molecule at rest, this description is often sufficient. However, the concept of other spaces or energy levels for electrons is often useful for understanding what happens when molecules undergo changes such as electronic excitations or chemical reactions.

Summary

- In the vast majority of cases, the bonds in organic molecules are best described as covalent bonds, that is, they involve a *sharing* of electrons between the nuclei.
- The valence bond model for describing covalent bonds in organic molecules is historically associated with Lewis structures (electron-dot pictures). It considers the overlap of orbitals containing a pair of electrons between them in such a way that there is a partial exchange of electrons associated with each nucleus, resulting in a bond between the atoms. This classical model of the electron-pair covalent bond is a simple model to use, and it generally provides good descriptions of bonds in molecules in their ground states.
- Hybrid orbitals are useful for describing the bonding in organic molecules, that is, bonding occurs using a mixture of two or more simple atomic orbitals from a given atom.
- For certain molecules the description provided by the valence bond model is inadequate. Another way of understanding chemical bonds is through the molecular orbital model.
- In the molecular orbital model, wavefunctions for the atomic orbitals of the interacting atoms are combined to generate new wavefunctions associated with both of the interacting atoms at the same time. For each atomic orbital used, a new molecular orbital is created. Molecular orbitals that are lower in energy than the atomic orbitals from which they were created are called *bonding molecular orbitals*. Electrons occupying them will stabilize the association between the involved atoms. Those molecular orbitals higher in energy than the starting atomic orbitals are known as *antibonding molecular orbitals*. If electrons occupy these orbitals, the association between the involved atoms is weakened.
- Organic chemists usually use both the valence bond model and the molecular orbital model to describe the bonding in organic compounds and the reactions between these compounds.

Terms to Remember

The following list contains the terms emphasized and defined in this chapter. It is useful to understand these terms and be able to use them when discussing bonding in organic chemistry.

structure
covalent bond
ionic bond
electronic configuration
aufbau principle
Pauli exclusion principle
Hund's rule
noble gas rule
reaction intermediate
valence
Lewis structure
formal charge
tetrahedral geometry
VSEPR model
trigonal planar geometry
valence bond model
atomic orbital
hybridization
sp^3 hybrid orbitals
node
σ bond
sp^2 hybrid orbitals
π bond
sp hybrid orbitals
resonance contributing forms
curved-arrow formalism
molecular orbital
LCAO
bonding molecular orbital
antibonding molecular orbital
bond order

Additional Problems

Problems relating to the sections on molecular orbitals are marked with an *.

1.30 Write Lewis structures for each of the following molecules, inferring the presence of unshared valence electron pairs:
a. HOOH b. H_2NNH_2 c. CH_3SH d. $(CH_3)_2NH$

1.31 Write Lewis structures for each of the following ions. Show all valence electrons and all formal charges.
a. $(CH_3)_2NH_2^+$ b. HCO_3^- c. $CH_3CH_2O^-$ d. F^-

1.32 Assign formal charges to all atoms in each of the following Lewis structures, and give the charge of the overall molecule or ion.

a.
```
    H  H
    |  |    ..
 H—C—C—O—H
    |  |  |
    H  H  H
```

b.
```
      :O:
       ||   ..
   H—C—C—H
           |
           H
```

c.
```
      H        H
      |        |
  H—C—C—C—H
      |   |    |
      H   |    H
          |
       H—C—H
          |
          H
```

1.33 For each of the compounds listed in Table 1.2, give the hybridization of each carbon atom present and the geometry of the bonding about that carbon atom.

1.34 Give the hybridization of each of the carbon atoms in each of the following molecules:

a.
```
   :O:
    ||
    C
   / \
  H   CH3
```

b.
```
            ..
 H2C=C=O
            ..
```

c. $H_3C-CH_2-CH_2-\underset{\displaystyle H}{\underset{|}{C}}=CH_2$ d. $:N\equiv C-CH_2-CH_3$

1.35 How many valence level unshared electron pairs are there in each of the following:
a. carbon dioxide b. methanol c. amide anion

1.36 Give a Lewis structure for each of the following neutral molecules. Show the presence of unshared valence electron pairs and multiple bonds:
a. CH_3NH_2
b. CH_3CHCH_2
c. CH_3OCH_3
d. $(CH_3)_3B$ (*Note:* There are not sufficient electrons to provide every atom with a noble gas configuration. Boron has only six valence level electrons in this compound.)
e. $(NO)^+$

1.37 For each molecule or ion in Problem 1.34, give a structure showing the complete geometry.

1.38 The bond angle in water is observed to be 104.5°. Explain this observed angle in terms of the orbitals used to form the oxygen-hydrogen bonds and to hold the unshared electron pairs.

1.39 One acceptable resonance structure of each of the molecules or ions is shown below. Use the curved arrow formalism to deduce any other acceptable resonance structures.

a. 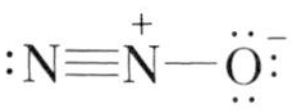 $:N\equiv\overset{+}{N}-\ddot{\underset{\cdot\cdot}{O}}:^-$ b. 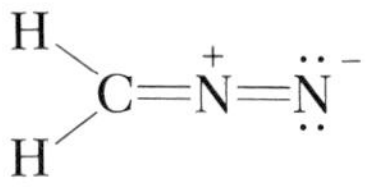 $H_2C=\overset{+}{N}=\ddot{\underset{\cdot\cdot}{N}}^-$

c. 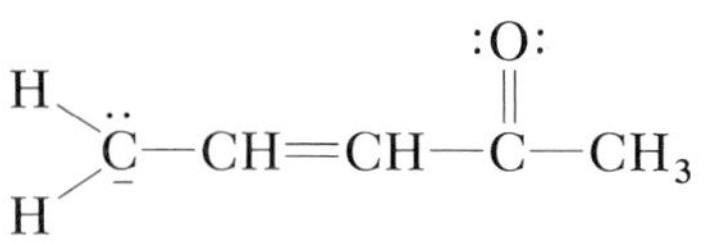 $H_2\overset{-}{\ddot{C}}-CH=CH-\overset{\overset{:O:}{\|}}{C}-CH_3$ d. 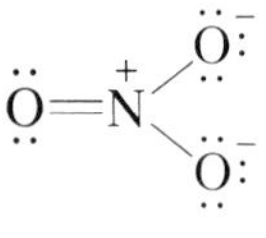 $\ddot{\underset{\cdot\cdot}{O}}=\overset{+}{N}(-\ddot{\underset{\cdot\cdot}{O}}:^-)-\ddot{\underset{\cdot\cdot}{O}}:^-$

1.40 It is possible to remove a proton from a methyl acetate molecule by treating it with a strong base. There are two different anions (shown below) that could possibly be formed in this reaction. Assuming that the proton will be removed to give the *more stable* of the two possible anions, predict which will actually be formed. Use the concept of resonance stabilization to support your answer.

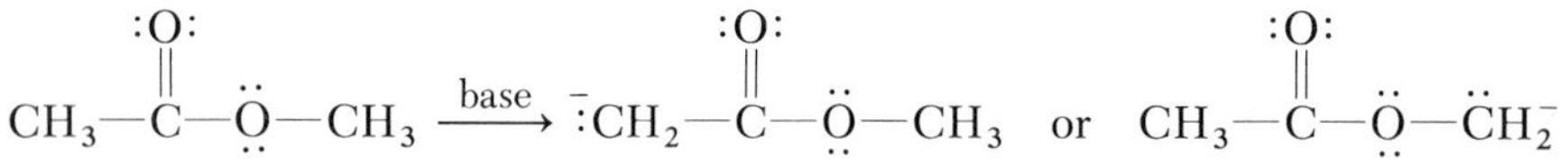

$$\underset{\text{methyl acetate}}{CH_3-\overset{\overset{:O:}{\|}}{C}-\ddot{\underset{\cdot\cdot}{O}}-CH_3} \xrightarrow{\text{base}} \overset{-}{:}CH_2-\overset{\overset{:O:}{\|}}{C}-\ddot{\underset{\cdot\cdot}{O}}-CH_3 \quad \text{or} \quad CH_3-\overset{\overset{:O:}{\|}}{C}-\ddot{\underset{\cdot\cdot}{O}}-\ddot{C}H_2^-$$

1.41 Dimethyl sulfoxide is a common organic solvent often represented by the structure:

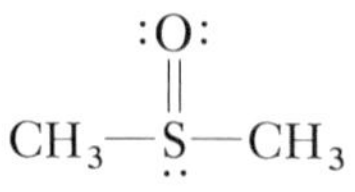

$$CH_3-\underset{\cdot\cdot}{\overset{\overset{:O:}{\|}}{S}}-CH_3$$

a. How many electrons are present in the valence level of the sulfur atom as shown?
b. Draw a Lewis structure for dimethyl sulfoxide, including formal charges, such that sulfur does *not* violate the octet rule.

1.42 A series of resonance structures for the pyrazine molecule are shown below. Which of these are acceptable resonance structures for pyrazine? Explain why or why not for each structure.

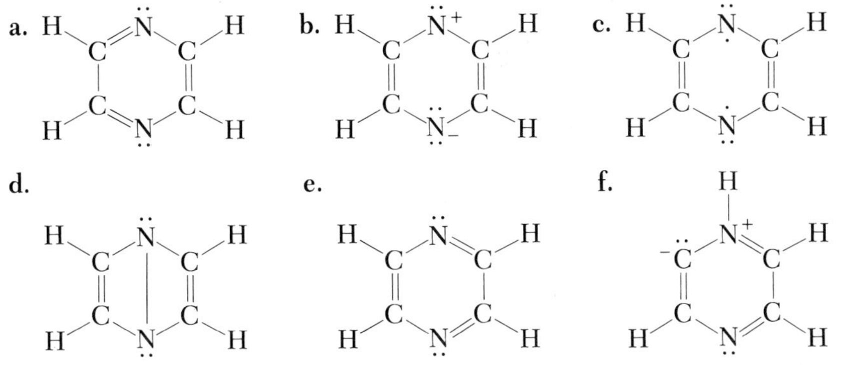

a. b. c.

d. e. f.

1.43 The nitrite ion (NO_2^-) has a different shape from the nitronium ion (NO_2^+). What are the two shapes? Which ion would be expected to have the longest (and thereby the weakest) nitrogen-oxygen bonds? Explain your reasoning. (*Hint:* First draw Lewis structures for the two ions, inferring the number of unshared valence electron pairs and bonds present.)

1.44 Do you expect the azide ion (N_3^-) to be linear or bent? Why? Are there any resonance structures you can write for the azide ion? Draw a Lewis structure for the hydrazoic acid molecule (HNNN) and show all bond angles.

1.45 Draw a Lewis structure for the ozone molecule (O_3). Can you write any resonance structures for it? Predict the bond angle in ozone and give your reasoning for your prediction.

1.46 Consider the Lewis structure shown below. Does it represent a stable neutral molecule, an ion, or a free radical? Explain your reasoning.

$$H_2C{=}CH{-}\underset{\displaystyle CH_3}{\underset{|}{C}}{-}CH_3$$

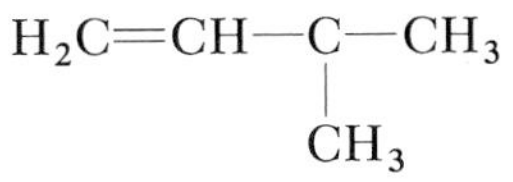

1.47 Consider the structure of propene shown below. Compare the different negative ions that would be obtained by removing a proton from carbon 1 or from carbon 3. One of these anions is more stable than the other. In the more stable of the two anions, the two carbon-carbon bond lengths are found to be identical. Which is the more stable of the two anions? How do you know? Why are two identical carbon-carbon bond lengths found in this anion, while two different carbon-carbon bond lengths are found in the less stable anion?

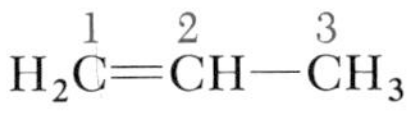

$$\overset{1}{H_2C}{=}\overset{2}{CH}{-}\overset{3}{CH_3}$$

propene

1.48 Draw the two resonance structures for the anion produced by removal of a proton (H^+) from one of the two CH_3 groups of acetone, shown below.

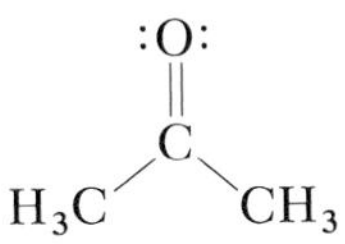

$$H_3C{-}\overset{\displaystyle :O:}{\overset{\|}{C}}{-}CH_3$$

1.49 Draw a Lewis structure for boron trifluoride (BF_3) in which the boron has only a sextet of electrons. Now draw a resonance structure in which *all* the atoms obey the octet rule. Assign formal charges. It is observed that the B—F bond length of BF_3 is shorter than that in the BF_4^- ion. Does this suggest that the second resonance structure you drew for BF_3 has any significance? Explain your answer. Would you expect the B—F bonds of BF_3 to be of equal lengths or to be of different lengths? Explain your answer.

*1.50 Use the molecular orbital model to deduce the bond order in each of the following molecules or ions:
a. C_2 b. CO c. NO d. C_2^-

*1.51 Use the molecular orbital model to describe the indicated bond in each of the following molecules:
a. $H_3C—C{\equiv}C—H$ (the $C{\equiv}C$ bond) b. $H_2C{=}O$ (the $C{=}O$ bond) c. H_3CI (the C—I bond)

*1.52 In our molecular orbital model of the nitrogen molecule (N_2) we ignored the 1*s* atomic orbitals from each atom. Consider including these atomic orbitals for generation of the molecular orbitals. Does it change the net bonding picture? Explain your reasoning.

Introduction to Organic Compounds: Functional Groups, Nomenclature, and Representations of Structure

2.1 Introduction

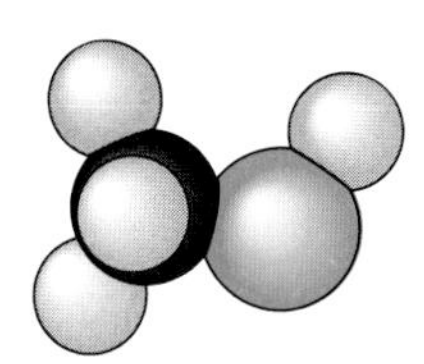

FUNCTIONAL GROUPS

The number of known organic compounds is vast, and many new organic compounds are discovered every year in nature or are synthesized in the laboratory. However, a unique molecular structure can be assigned to each, and considerable order is brought to the discipline of organic chemistry by using systematic methods to classify and name organic compounds on the basis of their structures. These methods are introduced in this chapter.

Early organic chemists quickly recognized that compounds containing similar structural features usually have chemical similarities. They began to classify compounds on the basis of common structural arrangements known as **functional groups.** This classification system continues to be useful. You will find that by studying the chemistry of simple compounds containing just one functional group, you will accumulate knowledge that can be extended to more complex compounds containing several functional groups.

ALKANES

The simplest organic compounds contain only carbon atoms and hydrogen atoms connected by single bonds. Such compounds are classified as **alkanes** and contain no functional group as such. Having no functional group, alkanes have a rather limited chemistry. However, the alkane structure constitutes the canvas upon which the chemistry of the more colorful functional groups is painted.

All *open-chain* alkanes share the general formula

$$C_nH_{2n+2}$$

where n is an integer (the number of carbon atoms present). An open-chain alkane is one in which no rings of carbon atoms are present. If one or more rings *are* present, we refer to the compound as a **cycloalkane.** Cycloalkanes have different general formulas depending on the number of rings present.

Methane (CH_4) is the simplest alkane. It is the major component of natural gas and is also produced from carbon dioxide by a class of anaerobic bacteria. This process has become an important source of atmospheric methane and may contribute to the greenhouse effect. Propane (C_3H_8) is another gaseous alkane. Propane can be liquefied under pressure with relative ease—it is the bottled gas commonly used for heating and cooking. Gasoline consists primarily of a mixture of liquid alkanes having from six to ten carbon atoms. Some open-chain alkanes occur naturally as protective coatings on the surface of fruits and vegetables. We will begin our discussion of the chemistry of alkanes in Chapter 4.

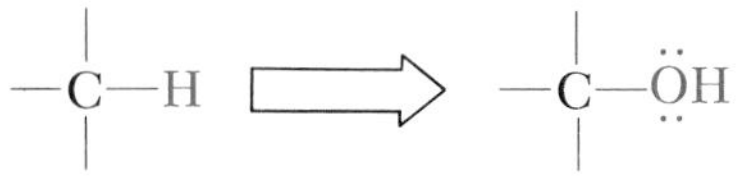

Figure 2.1 Structural relationship between an alkane and an alcohol.

—C—H ⟹ —C—ÖH

alkane alcohol

PROBLEM 2.1 Write a complete structure for the propane molecule and describe the bonding in the carbon-hydrogen and carbon-carbon bonds using valence bond model terms.

PROBLEM 2.2 Upon analysis of an alkane we find its molecular weight to be 198 g/mole. What is the molecular formula of this alkane?

ALCOHOLS

Imagine a hydroxyl group (—ÖH) in place of one of the hydrogen atoms of an alkane, as shown in Figure 2.1. Such a compound is called an **alcohol.** All alcohols contain a hydroxyl group attached to an sp^3 hybridized carbon atom. The simplest alcohols are methanol (**2.1**) and ethanol (**2.2**). We will study in detail the alcohols as a family of compounds in Chapters 5 and 6. Their chemistry is particularly rich and illustrates many important general principles of organic chemistry.

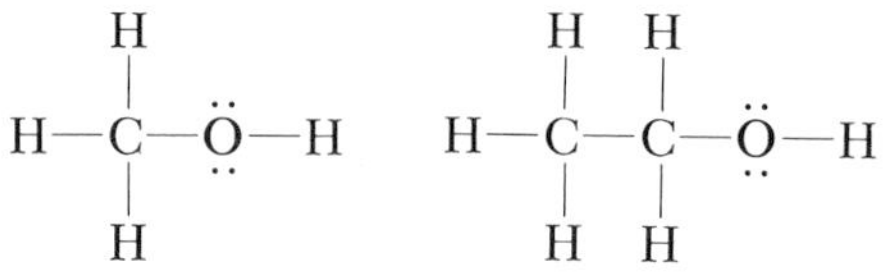

methanol (methyl alcohol) **2.1** — $H_3C–\ddot{O}–H$

ethanol (ethyl alcohol) **2.2** — $H_3C–CH_2–\ddot{O}–H$

OTHER FUNCTIONAL GROUPS

Other families of compounds contain different functional groups. Some important functional groups and the names of compounds containing them are summarized in Table 2.1. The chemistry of these and other functional groups will be studied in depth as we proceed through this course.

PROBLEM 2.3 The following compounds each contain more than one functional group. List the functional groups you find in each compound.

a. 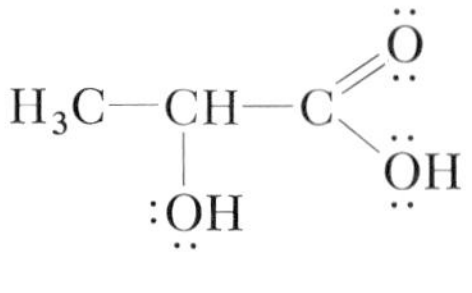 $H_3C–CH(\ddot{O}H)–C(=\ddot{O})–\ddot{O}H$ lactic acid (present in sour milk)

b. $H_3C-CH(CH_3)-CH(NH_2)-C(=O)OH$ valine (an essential amino acid for humans)

c. $H_2C{=}CH-O-CH{=}CH_2$ divinyl ether (an inhalation anesthetic)

d. $(H_3C)_2C{=}CH-CH_2-CH_2-C(CH_3){=}CH-CH_2OH$ geraniol (obtained from geraniums and roses)

e. prostaglandin E_1 (plays a role in controlling blood pressure and other functions in humans)

Table 2.1 Common Functional Groups

Functional Group	Name of Group	Example (Compound Containing Group)	Class of Compound
$-OH$	hydroxyl	CH_3OH	alcohol
$-X:$	halogen (F, Cl, Br, I)	$CH_3Br:$	haloalkane (or alkyl halide)
$-NH_2$	amino	CH_3NH_2	amine
$-C{\equiv}N:$	cyano or cyanide	$CH_3C{\equiv}N:$	nitrile
$>C{=}C<$	carbon-carbon double bond	$H_2C{=}CH_2$	alkene
$-C{\equiv}C-$	carbon-carbon triple bond	$HC{\equiv}CH$	alkyne
$>C{=}O$	carbonyl	$H_2C{=}O$	aldehyde or ketone
$-C(=O)OH$	carboxyl	HCO_2H	carboxylic acid
$-O-C-$	alkoxyl	CH_3OCH_3	ether*

* The oxygen atom of an ether is connected to two carbon atoms.

2.2 Naming and Representing Structures of Organic Compounds

INTRODUCTION

Chemists have devised methods for naming organic compounds that permit the name to be deduced from the structure. Similarly, the structure can be deduced from the name. This type of nomenclature is said to be *systematic*. The most widely used systematic method of nomenclature was devised by a committee of the International Union of Pure and Applied Chemistry (IUPAC). The **IUPAC method** is based on a set of rules to be introduced later in this chapter.

However, the IUPAC method is not the only method that is followed in naming organic compounds. *Common* or *trivial* names (names that may convey little or no structural information) are often used by chemists in their everyday conversations. Sometimes these names are older ones that have persisted because of their widespread use in the laboratory, classroom, commerce, and communications media. Common names are also invented for new compounds if their IUPAC names are so cumbersome as to be unsuitable for everyday use; for example, the IUPAC name for *cubane* (**2.3**), a compound synthesized only a few years ago, is shown below.

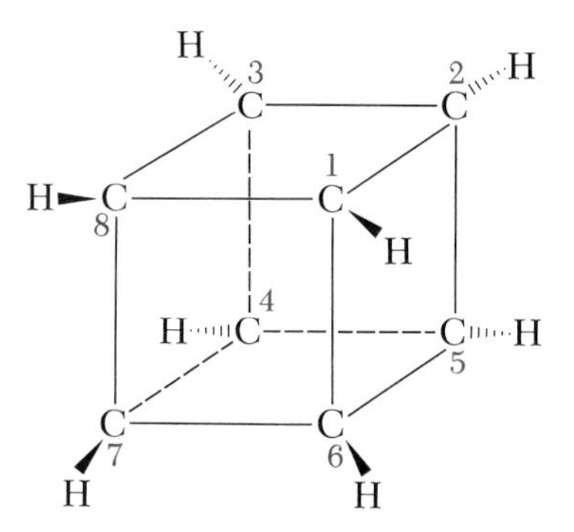

cubane
pentacyclo[4.2.0.0^{2,5}.0^{3,8}.0^{4,7}]octane
2.3

A main advantage of the IUPAC system is that it provides a systematic organization and documentation of organic chemistry. Imagine that you are a chemist who has isolated a compound from a plant and deduced its structure. You would like to know what (if anything) is recorded in the chemical literature about this and related compounds. Knowing the structure, you can use the IUPAC rules to provide a systematic name for the compound. Using the same name as any other chemist would give to this compound enables you to search the documented literature in a systematic way. Even if you find the compound to be previously unknown, giving it a systematic name specifies its structure for other chemists.

Before the IUPAC system was introduced, other attempts had been made to systematize the naming of organic compounds. Some of the names that evolved remain in common usage. The IUPAC rules often allow some rudiments of the earlier systems to be incorporated into an IUPAC name.

Table 2.2 Names of Straight-Chain Alkanes with One to Ten Carbon Atoms

Structure	IUPAC Name	Formula
CH_4	*Meth*ane	CH_4
CH_3CH_3	*Eth*ane	C_2H_6
$CH_3CH_2CH_3$	*Prop*ane	C_3H_8
$CH_3CH_2CH_2CH_3$	*But*ane	C_4H_{10}
$CH_3(CH_2)_3CH_3$	*Pent*ane	C_5H_{12}
$CH_3(CH_2)_4CH_3$	*Hex*ane	C_6H_{14}
$CH_3(CH_2)_5CH_3$	*Hept*ane	C_7H_{16}
$CH_3(CH_2)_6CH_3$	*Oct*ane	C_8H_{18}
$CH_3(CH_2)_7CH_3$	*Non*ane	C_9H_{20}
$CH_3(CH_2)_8CH_3$	*Dec*ane	$C_{10}H_{22}$

STRAIGHT-CHAIN ALKANES

A **straight-chain alkane** is one in which all of the carbon atoms are connected in a continuous sequence. There is no branching of the chain. The names of the first ten straight-chain alkanes are given in Table 2.2. These names must be learned, because they form the basis for naming other compounds using the IUPAC method.

STRUCTURAL REPRESENTATIONS

We can represent the structures of organic molecules in various ways. For example, consider hexane, shown in Figure 2.2. We *could* draw a complete structure with all carbon-carbon and carbon-hydrogen bonds shown. Usually, however, more condensed structures are preferred. They are quicker to draw, occupy less space, and are less cluttered in appearance. One shorthand notation (as in Table 2.2) uses parentheses to show a succession of methylene ($—CH_2—$) groups. An alternative method uses a zigzag line to represent the carbon skeleton. When this method is used, each break in the zigzag line represents a carbon atom.

When viewing a condensed structure of the zigzag or skeletal type, we keep in mind that all carbon atoms form four bonds in stable molecules. If the zigzag structure shows fewer than four bonds for a particular carbon atom, the remaining bonds of that carbon are understood (by default) to be to hydrogen. For example, in Figure 2.2, the far left-hand carbon of the zigzag structure of hexane has only one bond shown to it. It is understood that this carbon is also bound to three hydrogens. Similarly, just two bonds are shown to each of the

Figure 2.2 Representations of the structure of hexane.

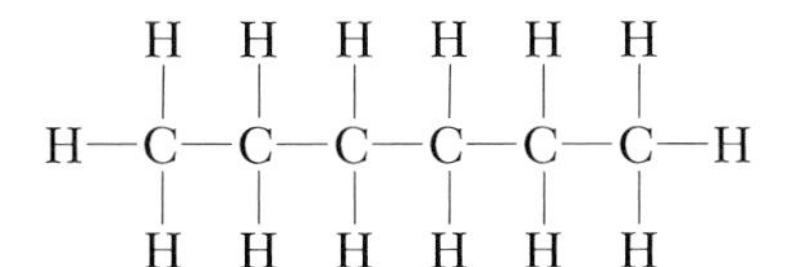

$CH_3CH_2CH_2CH_2CH_2CH_3$ $CH_3(CH_2)_4CH_3$

Figure 2.3 Examples of condensed structures and their equivalent abbreviated or skeletal representations.

$CH_3CH_2\ddot{O}CH_2CH_3$ ⇒ (skeletal)

$CH_3CHCH_2CH_3$ with :ÖH ⇒ (skeletal)

$CH_3-C(=O:)-CH_2CH_3$ ⇒ (skeletal)

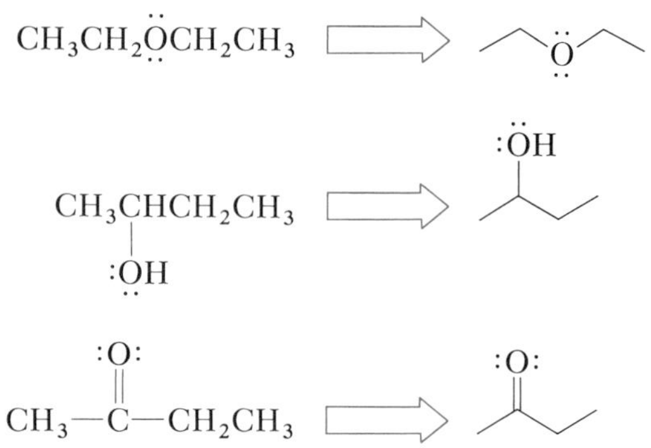

internal carbons. It is understood that these carbons form the remainder of their four bonds to hydrogen.

There are other conventions that we follow when using skeletal representations. Atoms other than carbon and hydrogen must be shown specifically, and hydrogen atoms attached to atoms other than carbon must also be shown. Further examples of skeletal representations are shown in Figure 2.3.

PROBLEM 2.4 Provide formulas ($C_xH_yO_z$) for the substances represented by the following skeletal representations:

a.

b. Ö

c. :ÖH

d. ÖH

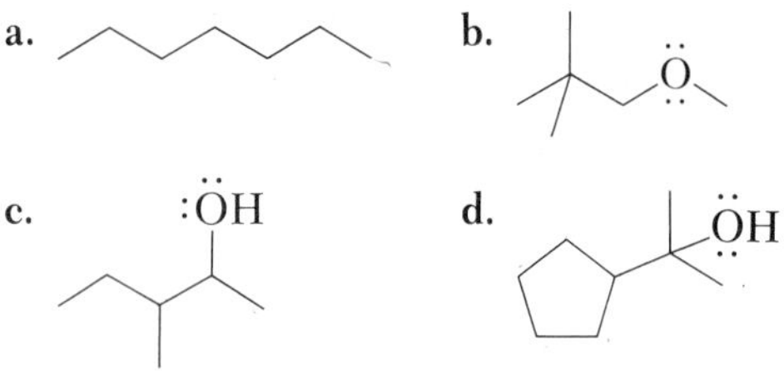

We also use parentheses to designate branches along a chain. For example, the four structures shown in Figure 2.4 all represent the same molecule, 3-methylpentane.

The limitations of a two-dimensional page result in organic structures being presented as flat. Real organic molecules are usually *not* flat. Therefore, you should exercise particular caution when looking at structures. Two-dimensional representations of three-dimensional structures often do not even show the correct bond angles of the molecule. Later, we will see examples that illustrate this need for caution in handling these two-dimensional representations.

Figure 2.4 Representations of the 3-methylpentane molecule.

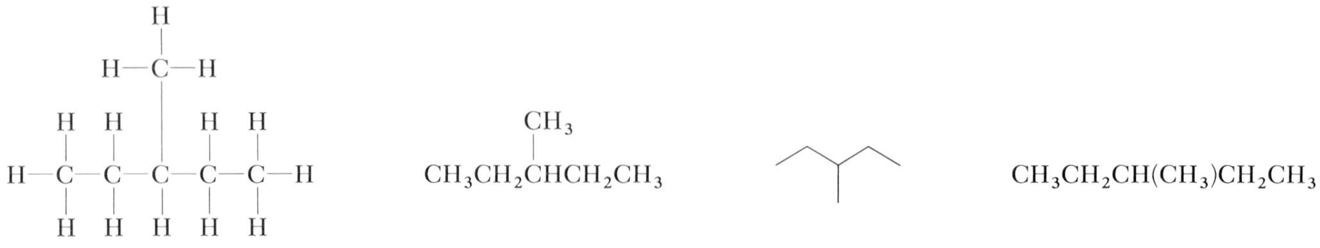

(full structural formula)

$CH_3CH_2CHCH_2CH_3$ with CH_3 branch

(skeletal)

$CH_3CH_2CH(CH_3)CH_2CH_3$

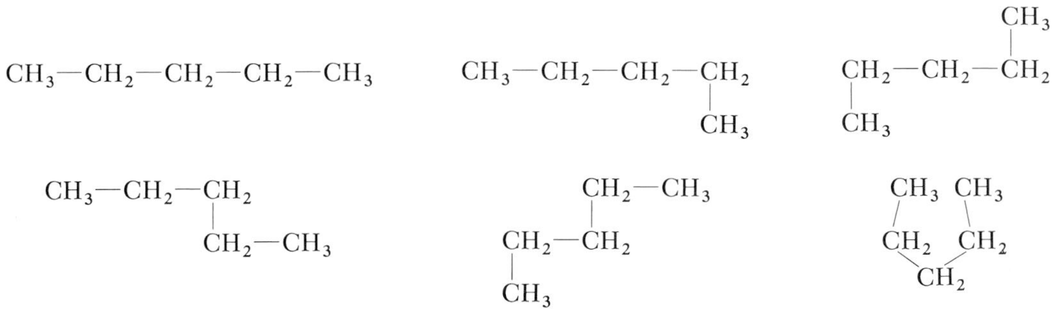

$$CH_3{-}CH_2{-}CH_2{-}CH_2{-}CH_3$$

$$CH_3{-}CH_2{-}CH_2{-}\underset{\textstyle CH_3}{\underset{|}{CH_2}}$$

$$\underset{\textstyle CH_3}{\underset{|}{CH_2}}{-}CH_2{-}\overset{\textstyle CH_3}{\overset{|}{CH_2}}$$

$$CH_3{-}CH_2{-}\underset{\textstyle CH_2{-}CH_3}{\underset{|}{CH_2}}$$

$$\underset{\textstyle CH_3}{\underset{|}{CH_2}}{-}\overset{\textstyle CH_2{-}CH_3}{\overset{|}{CH_2}}$$

$$\begin{array}{ccc} CH_3 & & CH_3 \\ / & & \backslash \\ CH_2 & & CH_2 \\ & \diagdown CH_2 \diagup & \end{array}$$

Figure 2.5 Representations of the pentane molecule.

A common problem for beginners in organic chemistry is recognizing that different diagrams actually represent the same compound. For example, all six structural diagrams in Figure 2.5 represent pentane. We can recognize that all these structures are equivalent by realizing that all show exactly the *same connectivity* (i.e., the same sequence of bonded atoms). For example, all six have a continuous sequence of five carbon atoms. One way you can see this connectivity is by starting at one end of the structure with a pencil point and continuing to the other end without lifting the pencil. In each case you pass through five carbon atoms in going from one end to the other. All of these structures represent pentane. Some may simply be more convenient than others for showing a particular aspect of the structure or chemistry of pentane.

PROBLEM 2.5 Which structure in each set does not represent the same molecule as the other two?

a. (i) $CH_3CH_2CH_2CH(CH_3)_2$ (ii) 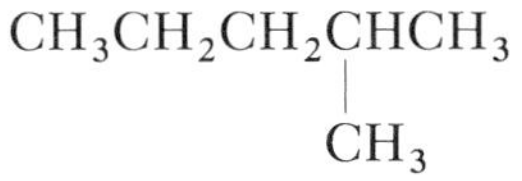 $CH_3CH_2CH_2\underset{\textstyle CH_3}{\underset{|}{C}}HCH_3$

(iii) 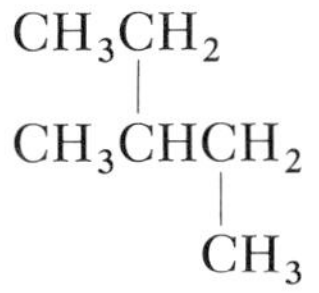
$$\begin{array}{l} CH_3CH_2 \\ \quad\quad\;\; | \\ CH_3CHCH_2 \\ \quad\quad\quad\;\; | \\ \quad\quad\quad CH_3 \end{array}$$

b. (i) 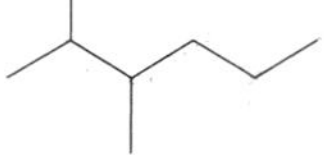 (ii) 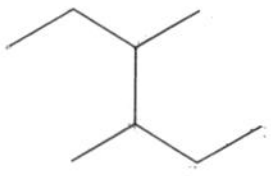 (iii)

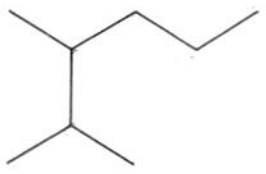

MODELS OF ORGANIC MOLECULES

It is especially useful to work with molecular model kits to help you understand the intricacies of organic structure. Models allow us to view the full shape of molecules from all directions. As you become more experienced in viewing and working with organic structures, you will find that you need models less frequently than at the beginning. Even so, it is always useful to have them at hand, since they are invaluable for understanding the more subtle points of organic structure.

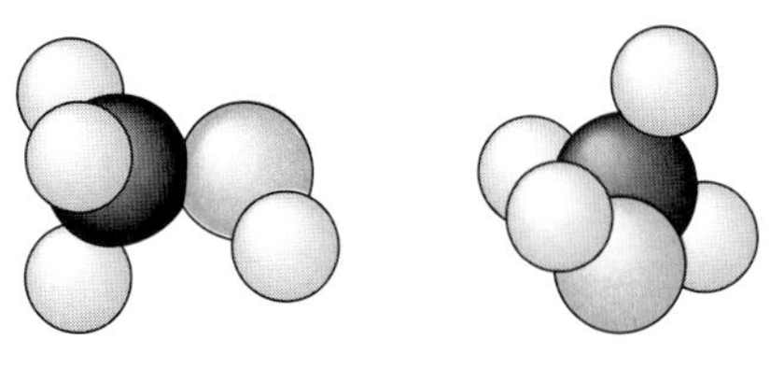
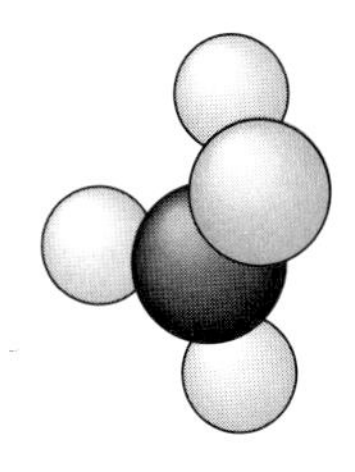
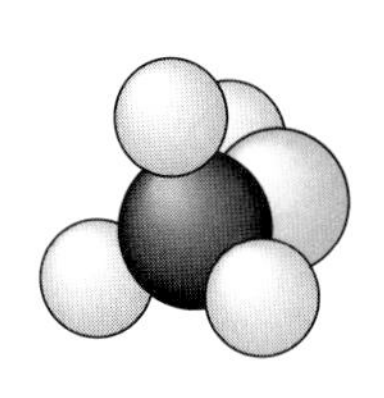

Figure 2.6 Space-filling models of methanol. Several views of the same model are shown.

The simplest models are nothing more than ball-and-stick representations of molecules. The ball portion represents an atom, and the stick represents a bond between atoms. With more sophisticated models (e.g., space-filling models), the sticks are shortened in an attempt to represent the proper scale of internuclear distances, and the ball becomes a truncated sphere representing the actual volume occupied by a particular atom. Several views of a space-filling model of methanol are shown in Figure 2.6. We saw one of these views earlier in Chapter 1. You will probably find that the simpler models are more useful at the onset of your studies.

SIMPLE ALKYL GROUPS

A group obtained by removing a hydrogen from an alkane is known as an **alkyl group.** In simple cases such groups are named by dropping the -ane ending from the alkane name and replacing it with -yl, for example:

CH_4 (methane) ⇨ CH_3— (methyl group)

CH_3CH_3 (ethane) ⇨ CH_3CH_2— (ethyl group)

Alkyl groups are *not* molecules, but rather represent *portions* of molecules. We have already seen the use of alkyl group names as parts of IUPAC names of branched alkanes (e.g., 3-*methyl*pentane in Figure 2.4). In 3-methylpentane a methyl group (CH_3) is substituted for a hydrogen along the pentane (five-carbon) chain.

ALKYL GROUPS WITH THREE AND FOUR CARBON ATOMS

Two different alkyl groups can be produced by removing a hydrogen atom from propane. Removal of a hydrogen atom from one of the terminal carbon atoms (those at the ends of the molecule) creates one alkyl group. A different alkyl group results from removal of a hydrogen atom from the central carbon. We use the names *propyl* and *isopropyl* to describe these groups, as shown in Figure 2.7.

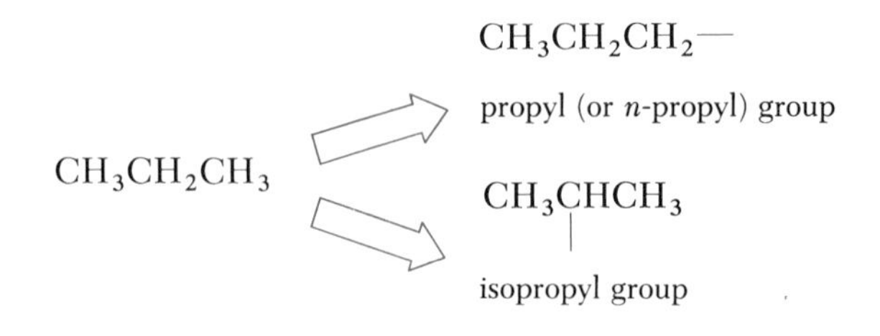

Figure 2.7 The propyl and isopropyl groups. The triply connected carbon in each alkyl group has a line drawn to it indicating an *open valence*. A fourth group can be bonded to the carbon through this open valence. The isopropyl group may also be referred to as 1-methylethyl (see Table 2.3 and later discussion).

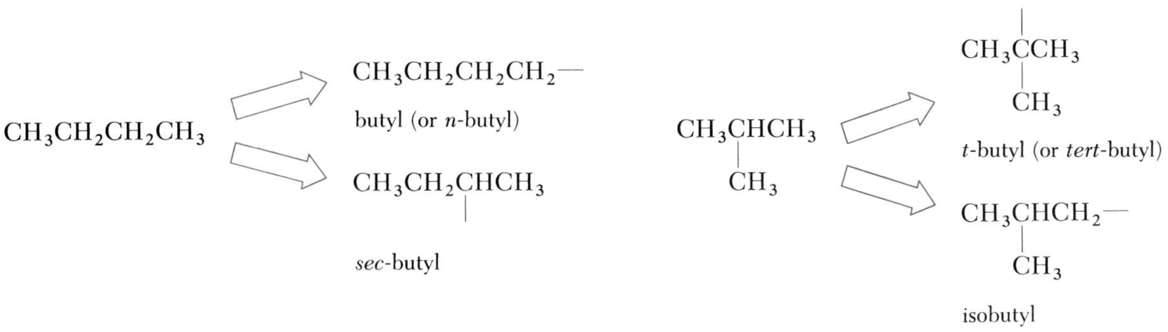

$CH_3CH_2CH_2CH_3$ → $CH_3CH_2CH_2CH_2$— butyl (or *n*-butyl); $CH_3CH_2\underset{|}{C}HCH_3$ *sec*-butyl

CH_3CHCH_3 (with CH_3 on the central carbon) → $CH_3\overset{|}{C}CH_3$ (with CH_3 on the central carbon) *t*-butyl (or *tert*-butyl); CH_3CHCH_2— (with CH_3 on the CH) isobutyl

Figure 2.8 Alkyl groups of formula C_4H_9. Alternative names are given in Table 2.3 (see page 56).

With groups of four carbon atoms there is a further complication. There are two different alkanes of formula C_4H_{10}. Molecules having the same molecular formula but different structures are called **isomers.** (This term is the source of the name *isopropyl group*—it is an *iso*mer of the *propyl* group.) We need to consider both isomeric alkanes of formula C_4H_{10}: butane (**2.4**) and 2-methylpropane (**2.5**), also known as *isobutane*.

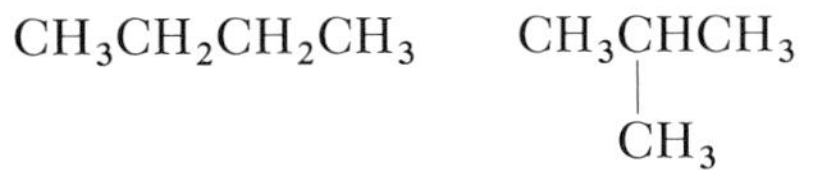

$CH_3CH_2CH_2CH_3$ — butane **2.4**

CH_3CHCH_3 (with CH_3 on the central carbon) — 2-methylpropane **2.5**

To find all possible alkyl groups for C_4H_9—, it is necessary to consider both structures. Each can give rise to two different alkyl groups upon removal of a hydrogen. Thus, altogether there are four different butyl groups, as shown in Figure 2.8.

The term *n*-butyl is short for *normal*-butyl, the term *sec*-butyl is short for *secondary*-butyl, and *t*-butyl (or *tert*-butyl) is short for *tertiary*-butyl. For the present these names should be learned as labels. We will have more to say about them later.

PROBLEM 2.6 Show the structures for all of the alkanes of each of the following formulas:
a. C_5H_{12} **b.** C_6H_{14} **c.** C_7H_{16}

Steps to Solving the Problem

Solution to Problem 2.6a

1. Construct the straight-chain alkane structure first. To do this, arrange the five carbon atoms in one continuous chain. Then add hydrogens to each carbon atom to make it tetracoordinated. This gives us the first isomer of structure

$$CH_3CH_2CH_2CH_2CH_3$$

2. Now we must construct the branched-chain alkane structures. Start by reducing the number of carbons in the continuous chain by one. Then attach the remaining carbon atom to one of the internal carbon atoms of the chain

and add hydrogen to make each of the carbon atoms tetracoordinated. This gives a second isomer of structure

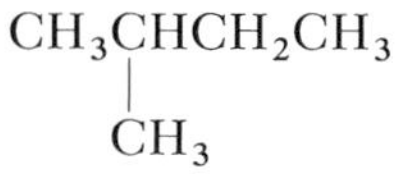

$$\begin{array}{l} CH_3\underset{|}{C}HCH_2CH_3 \\ \quad\; CH_3 \end{array}$$

Caution! Placing the extra carbon on the *other* internal position yields a structure entirely equivalent to the one shown. We can see this by using the pencil connectivity method described in the discussion of Figure 2.5. (*Question:* What would be the result of attaching a $—CH_3$ group to the first or to the last carbon atom of the four-carbon chain?)

3. We now need to see if there are any further isomeric structures. We do this by reducing to three the number of carbons in the continuous chain. We attach the remaining two carbons to the internal carbon of the three-carbon chain. We then add hydrogens to make each carbon tetracoordinated, giving the structure

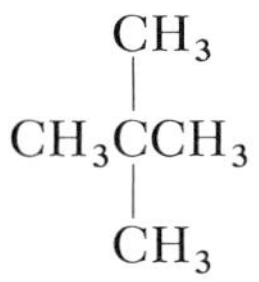

$$\begin{array}{c} CH_3 \\ | \\ CH_3CCH_3 \\ | \\ CH_3 \end{array}$$

4. As we consider further possibilities, we see that we have in fact already drawn all possible unique structures of C_5H_{12}. Thus we have a total of three isomers that share the formula C_5H_{12}.

   Caution! Be careful that you do not reconstruct an isomer that you previously counted. For example, the structure shown below is equivalent to the one deduced in Step 2.

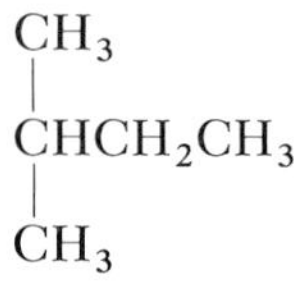

$$\begin{array}{l} CH_3 \\ | \\ CHCH_2CH_3 \\ | \\ CH_3 \end{array}$$

PROBLEM 2.7 Based on your answers to Problem 2.6, deduce the number of different alkyl groups with the formula:

a. $C_5H_{11}—$ **b.** $C_6H_{13}—$

Draw structures for each of the different alkyl groups.

Compounds containing functional groups are often named as combinations of an alkyl group and the functional group. Several examples are shown in Figure 2.9.

Figure 2.9 Common names for some simple organic compounds.

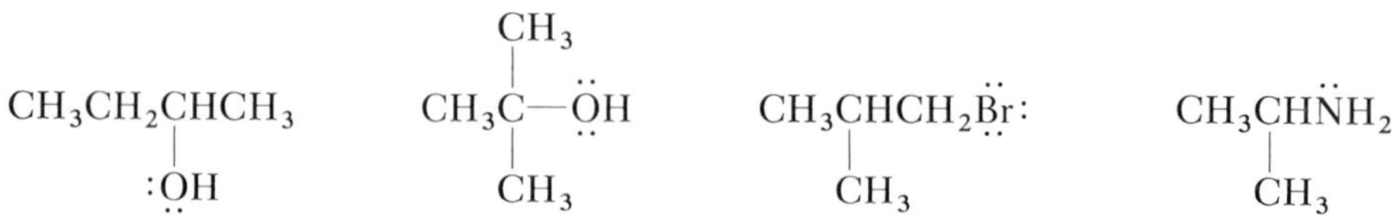

$CH_3CH_2\underset{\large :\ddot{O}H}{\underset{|}{C}}HCH_3$	$CH_3\overset{CH_3}{\underset{CH_3}{C}}—\ddot{\underset{..}{O}}H$	$CH_3\underset{CH_3}{\underset{|}{C}}HCH_2\ddot{\underset{..}{Br}}:$	$CH_3\underset{CH_3}{\underset{|}{C}}H\ddot{N}H_2$
sec-butyl alcohol	*t*-butyl alcohol	isobutyl bromide	isopropylamine

PROBLEM 2.8 How many different alcohols are there for each of the following formulas? Show the structure of each and provide each with a common name using the system described above.

a. C_3H_8O **b.** $C_4H_{10}O$

THE NAMING OF BRANCHED ALKANES

IUPAC Rules—The Basics We must follow a standard procedure to give IUPAC names to branched alkanes. The steps are summarized as follows:

1. Identify the longest continuous sequence of carbon atoms. A convenient way to do this is by using the pencil connectivity approach noted earlier (see the discussion relating to Figure 2.5). The route that proceeds through the greatest number of carbon atoms represents the longest continuous chain present. This sequence provides the root for naming the compound. For example, if the longest continuous chain of carbon atoms is five, the compound is named as a derivative of pentane. (Recall that *pentane* is the name of the straight-chain alkane with five carbon atoms.)
2. Locate and name the substituents (alkyl groups) along this sequence of carbon atoms. Number the positions at which the substituents are located. The IUPAC name contains a prefix number to indicate the position of the alkyl group, a dash, the name of the alkyl group, and the root name. Two examples are shown in Figure 2.10.
3. A chain could be numbered starting from either end. In both of the examples in Figure 2.10, it does not matter which end we choose because the substituent is bonded to the central carbon atom. We would get the same name regardless of whether we number from right to left or left to right. However, in general it *does* matter. The IUPAC rules stipulate that the chain should be numbered beginning at the end that results in a lower number for the carbon at which a branch (i.e., a substituent) first appears. Two examples are shown in Figure 2.11.
4. Multiple branching is indicated by naming all of the functional groups and showing their positions along the chain. We begin numbering the chain from the end providing the *lower* of the possible numbers for the substituent(s)

Figure 2.10 Names of branched chain alkanes. The root chain is outlined with a broken line for each compound.

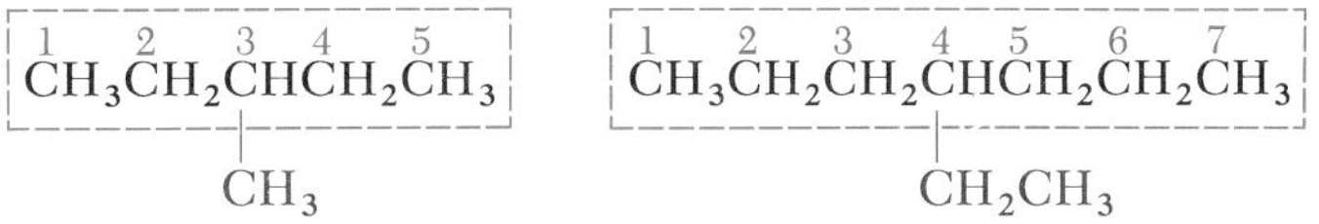

1 2 3 4 5
$CH_3CH_2CHCH_2CH_3$ (with CH_3 on C3)
3-methylpentane

1 2 3 4 5 6 7
$CH_3CH_2CH_2CHCH_2CH_2CH_3$ (with CH_2CH_3 on C4)
4-ethylheptane

Figure 2.11 Numbering positions in the IUPAC nomenclature system.

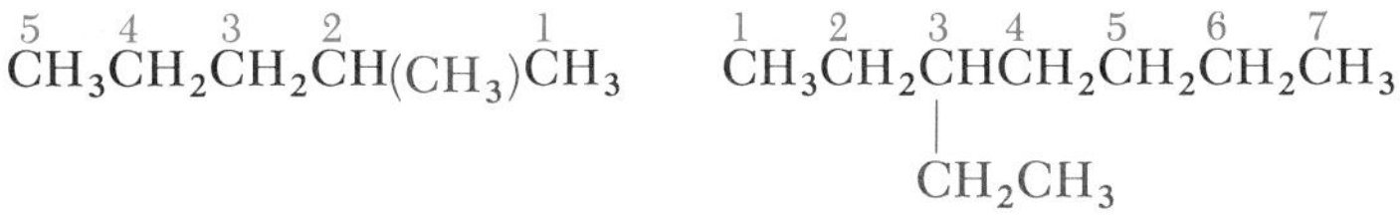

5 4 3 2 1
$CH_3CH_2CH_2CH(CH_3)CH_3$

correct: 2-methylpentane
incorrect: 4-methylpentane

1 2 3 4 5 6 7
$CH_3CH_2CHCH_2CH_2CH_2CH_3$ (with CH_2CH_3 on C3)

3-ethylheptane
5-ethylheptane

Figure 2.12 Naming multiply branched alkanes by the IUPAC system.

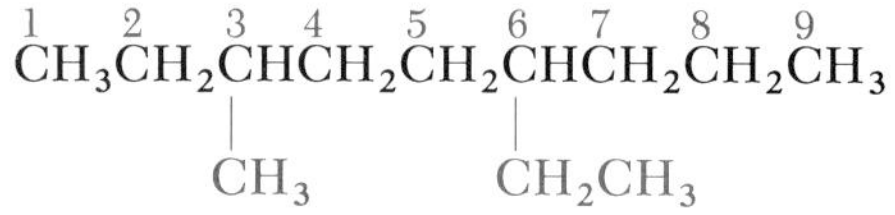

1 2 3 4 5 6 7 8 9
$CH_3CH_2CHCH_2CH_2CHCH_2CH_2CH_3$ (with CH_3 on C3 and CH_2CH_3 on C6)

6-ethyl-3-methylnonane

Figure 2.13 Further examples of IUPAC names for multiply branched alkanes.

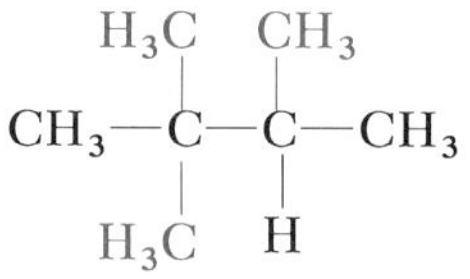

$CH_3-C(CH_3)_2-CH(CH_3)-CH_3$

2,2,3-trimethylbutane

$CH_3CH(CH_3)CH_2CH(CH(CH_3)CH_3)CH(CH_3)CH_2CH_3$

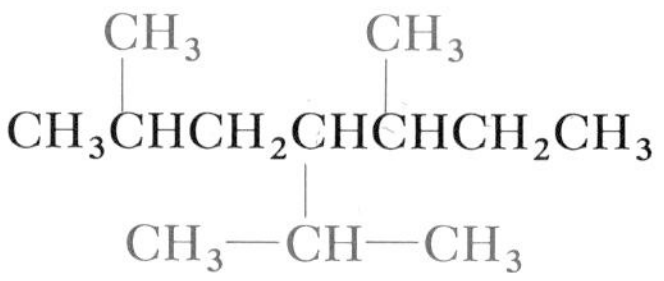

4-isopropyl-2,5-dimethylheptane

Figure 2.14 Naming alkanes with different substituents in equivalent positions.

$CH_3CH_2CH(CH_2CH_3)CH_2CH_2CH(CH_3)CH_2CH_3$

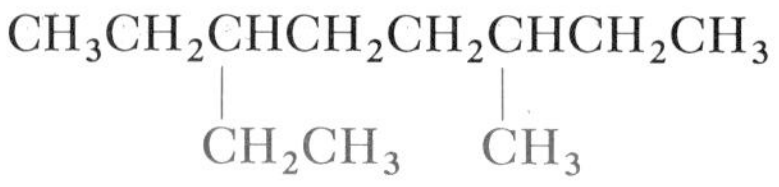

correct: 3-ethyl-6-methyloctane
incorrect: 6-ethyl-3-methyloctane

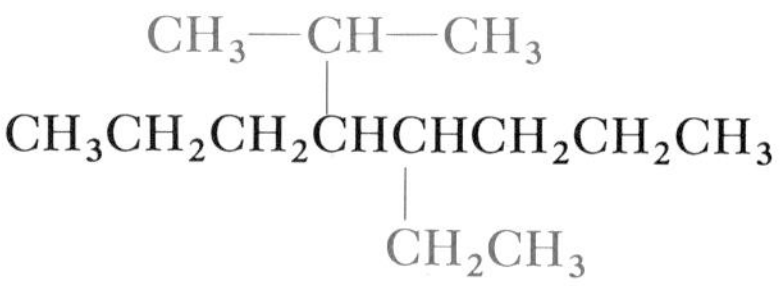

$CH_3CH_2CH_2CH(CH(CH_3)CH_3)CH(CH_2CH_3)CH_2CH_2CH_3$

4-ethyl-5-isopropyloctane
4-isopropyl-5-ethyloctane

at the first branch point. The substituent groups are listed alphabetically. An example is shown in Figure 2.12.

5. If the same substituent appears more than once, its name is not repeated. Instead, the following prefixes are used:

di-	two identical substituents
tri-	three identical substituents
tetra-	four identical substituents
penta-	five identical substituents
hexa-	six identical substituents

In alphabetizing the substituents, these prefixes are *not* considered. We still look to the fundamental name of the alkyl group. Two examples in Figure 2.13 illustrate this point.

6. If two substituents are found in equivalent positions, the lower number is assigned to the one coming first in the alphabetical listing. Two examples are shown in Figure 2.14.

7. At times we find that two (or more) chains qualify for selection as the longest. In this case we select the chain that has the greater number of substituents on it to be the root chain. An example is shown in Figure 2.15.

Figure 2.15 Naming branched alkanes. The chain enclosed in dashed lines in the right-hand structure has more substituents than the left-hand chain for purposes of IUPAC naming. The chain indicated has a greater number of substituents than the chain of equivalent length shown in the left-hand structure. The proper name of the compound is 5-butyl-4,4-dimethylnonane.

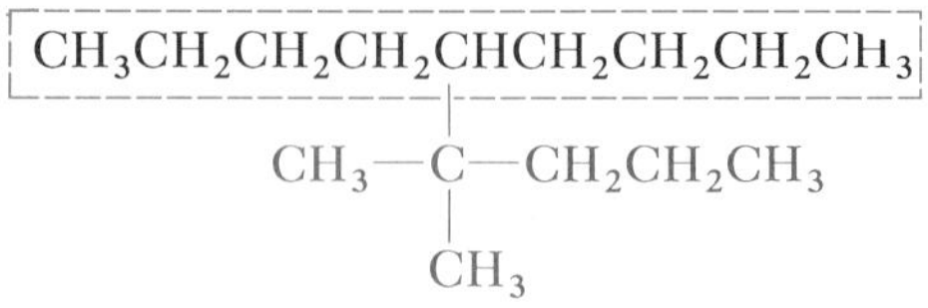

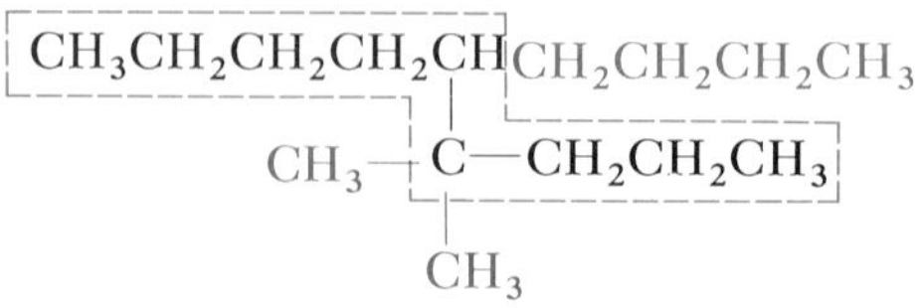

$CH_3CH_2CH_2CH_2CHCH_2CH_2CH_2CH_3$ with $CH_3-C(CH_3)-CH_2CH_2CH_3$ attached

$CH_3CH_2CH_2CH_2CH$ $CH_2CH_2CH_2CH_3$ with $CH_3-C(CH_3)-CH_2CH_2CH_3$ attached

PROBLEM 2.9 Provide IUPAC names for each of the folowing compounds:

a. $(CH_3)_3CCH_2CH(CH_3)_2$

b. $CH_3CH_2CH(CH_3)CH(CH_2CH_3)CH_2CH_2CH_3$

c. $CH_3(CH_2)_4CH(CH(CH_3)_2)CH(CH_2CH_3)CH_2CH_2CH_3$

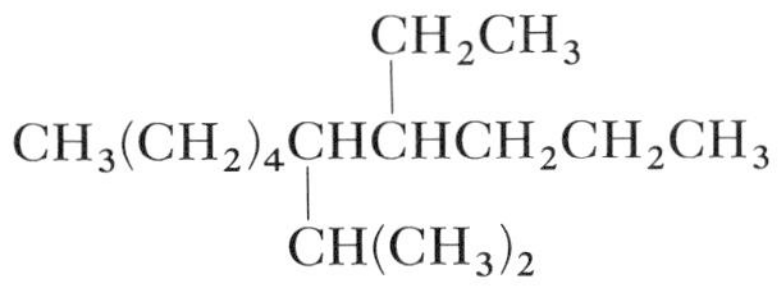

d. $(CH_3)_2CHCH(CH_2CH_3)CH_2CH_2CH_3$

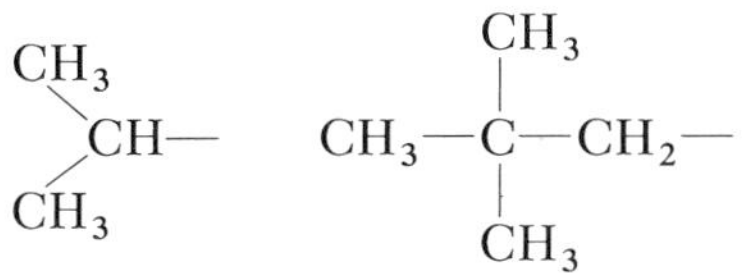

$(CH_3)_2CH—$ iso-

$CH_3—C(CH_3)_2—CH_2—$ neo-

Figure 2.16 Structures of the isopropyl and neopentyl groups.

The Use of Iso- and Neo- We commonly encounter the prefixes iso- and neo- in both IUPAC and non-IUPAC nomenclature systems. These prefixes indicate the presence of structural units of the type shown in Figure 2.16. Before the IUPAC rules were devised, these prefixes were used in naming some branched alkanes. These names have continued in common usage as alternatives to the systematic IUPAC names for compounds such as isohexane (**2.6**) and neohexane (**2.7**). Another very common usage of iso- and neo- is for compounds with functional groups, such as isobutyl alcohol (**2.8**) and neopentyl chloride (**2.9**).

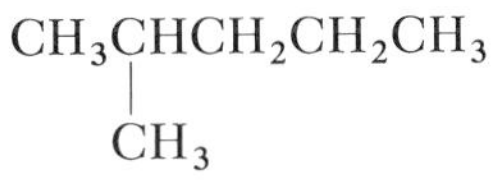

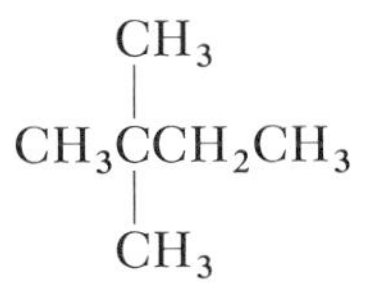

	$CH_3CH(CH_3)CH_2CH_2CH_3$	$CH_3C(CH_3)_2CH_2CH_3$
common name:	isohexane	neohexane
IUPAC name:	2-methylpentane	2,2-dimethylbutane
	2.6	**2.7**

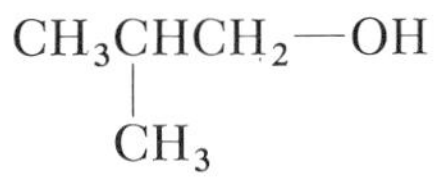

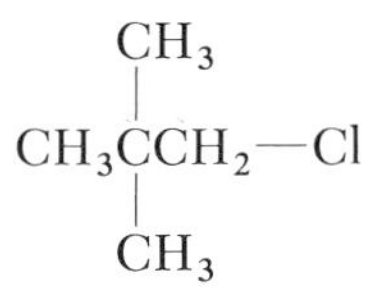

	$CH_3CH(CH_3)CH_2—OH$	$CH_3C(CH_3)_2CH_2—Cl$
common name:	isobutyl alcohol	neopentyl chloride
	2.8	**2.9**

When we alphabetize the substituents in a name, we consider the terms iso- and neo- to be part of the fundamental name of the alkyl group. However, the prefixes *sec-* and *tert-* are *not* considered to be part of the fundamental name of the alkyl group and are ignored for the purposes of alphabetizing.

The IUPAC system does have a set of rules for the systematic naming of alkyl groups. However, it also permits the use of iso- and related common prefixes for describing alkyl group substituents along the longest sequence of carbon atoms, as long as these groups are not further substituted. Some acceptable IUPAC names incorporating these prefixes are shown in Figure 2.17.

Systematic Naming of Branched Alkyl Groups—IUPAC Method Although IUPAC rules under certain circumstances allow the use of the older common

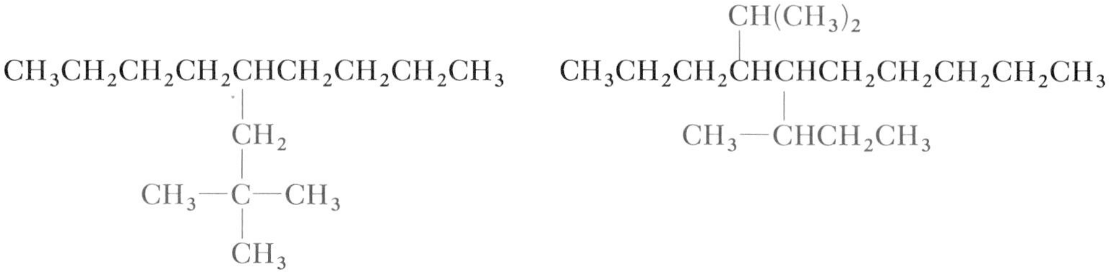

$$\begin{array}{c} CH_3CH_2CH_2CH_2CHCH_2CH_2CH_2CH_3 \\ | \\ CH_2 \\ | \\ CH_3-C-CH_3 \\ | \\ CH_3 \end{array}$$

5-neopentylnonane

$$\begin{array}{c} CH(CH_3)_2 \\ | \\ CH_3CH_2CH_2CHCHCH_2CH_2CH_2CH_2CH_3 \\ | \\ CH_3-CHCH_2CH_3 \end{array}$$

5-*sec*-butyl-4-isopropyldecane

Figure 2.17 Use of common prefixes in IUPAC names.

prefixes for several types of branched alkyl groups, there *is* a set of rules for their systematic nomenclature, and you should learn these rules along with the common names. The rules we use are similar to those for naming branched alkanes. The main difference is that the carbon atom with the open valence is numbered 1 for the alkyl group. Two examples are shown in Figure 2.18.

For simple alkyl groups many people use the older names (e.g., isobutyl, *sec*-butyl) rather than the systematic IUPAC names. Table 2.3 summarizes the alternative names for branched alkyl groups of five or fewer carbon atoms.

PROBLEM 2.10 Provide systematic names for each of the following alkyl groups:

a. $CH_3CH(CH_3)CH(CH_3)CH_2-$ b. $CH_3CH_2CH(CH_3)\underset{|}{C}(CH_3)_2$

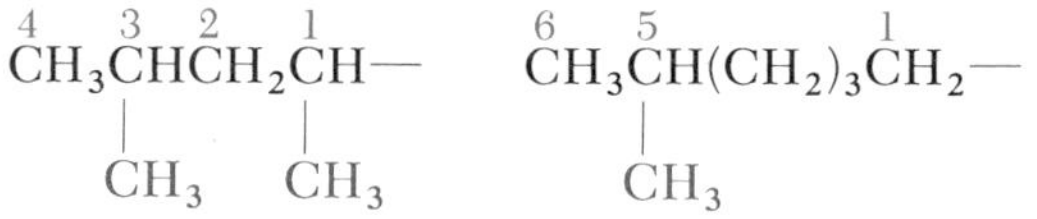

Figure 2.18 IUPAC names for alkyl groups.

$$\begin{array}{c} ^4CH_3\,^3CH\,^2CH_2\,^1CH- \\ |\quad\quad | \\ CH_3\quad CH_3 \end{array}$$

1,3-dimethylbutyl-

$$\begin{array}{c} ^6CH_3\,^5CH(CH_2)_3\,^1CH_2- \\ | \\ CH_3 \end{array}$$

5-methylhexyl-

Table 2.3 Common and Systematic Names for Branched Alkyl Groups

Structure	Common Name	Systematic Name
$(CH_3)_2CH-$	isopropyl-	1-methylethyl-
$(CH_3)_2CHCH_2-$	isobutyl-	2-methylpropyl-
$CH_3CH_2\underset{|}{C}HCH_3$	*sec*-butyl-	1-methylpropyl-
$(CH_3)_3C-$	*t*-butyl-	1,1-dimethylethyl-
$(CH_3)_2CHCH_2CH_2-$	isopentyl-	3-methylbutyl-
$(CH_3)_3CCH_2-$	neopentyl-	2,2-dimethylpropyl-
$CH_3CH_2\underset{|}{C}(CH_3)_2$	*t*-pentyl-	1,1-dimethylpropyl-

Table 2.4 Names of Common Substituent Groups Other than Alkyl

Group	Name
—F:	fluoro
—Cl:	chloro
—Br:	bromo
—I:	iodo
—C≡N:	cyano
$—NO_2$	nitro
$—OCH_3$	methoxy
$—NH_2$	amino
—D	deuterio

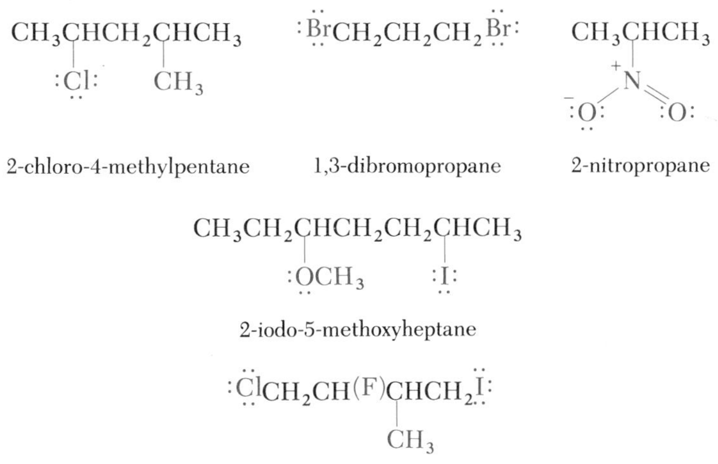

$CH_3CH(Cl)CH_2CH(CH_3)CH_3$ — 2-chloro-4-methylpentane

$:BrCH_2CH_2CH_2Br:$ — 1,3-dibromopropane

$CH_3CH(NO_2)CH_3$ — 2-nitropropane

$CH_3CH_2CH(OCH_3)CH_2CH_2CH(I)CH_3$ — 2-iodo-5-methoxyheptane

$:ClCH_2CH(F)CH(CH_3)CH_2I:$ — 1-chloro-2-fluoro-4-iodo-3-methylbutane

Figure 2.19 IUPAC names of substituted alkanes.

NAMING SUBSTITUENTS OTHER THAN ALKYL GROUPS

We name compounds other than alkanes by following guidelines very similar to those given for branched alkanes. In later chapters, as we discuss each class of compounds according to functional group, we will cover specific details of nomenclature as they apply to those compounds. For the present you should learn the method for naming several common groups as substituents on a carbon chain. The common substituent names are summarized in Table 2.4. Several examples of compounds containing these groups are shown in Figure 2.19, along with their names.

PROBLEM 2.11 Provide IUPAC names for each of the following:

a. $CH_3CH_2CCl_2CH(CH_3)_2$ b. $(CH_3CH_2)_2CHCH_2CH_2C{\equiv}N:$

c. $H_2\ddot{N}CH_2CH_2\ddot{N}H_2$

2.3 Classification as Primary, Secondary, Tertiary, or Quaternary

We often use the terms primary, secondary, tertiary, and quaternary (written as 1°, 2°, 3°, and 4°) in organic chemistry. The rules for applying these terms differ somewhat according to the type of assignment being made.

CARBON ATOMS

Carbon atoms are classified on the basis of the number of other carbon atoms bound to them. A *primary* carbon atom has only one other carbon attached to it. A *secondary* carbon atom has two other carbon atoms attached to it, and

$CH_3CH_2\ddot{C}l:$ $(CH_3)_2CH\ddot{O}H$ $(CH_3)_3C\ddot{B}r:$

a primary chloroalkane | a secondary alcohol | a tertiary bromoalkane

Figure 2.20 Alcohols and haloalkanes classified according to the carbon attached to the functional groups.

so forth. Thus the alkane 2-methylbutane (**2.10**) contains three primary, one secondary, and one tertiary carbon atom.

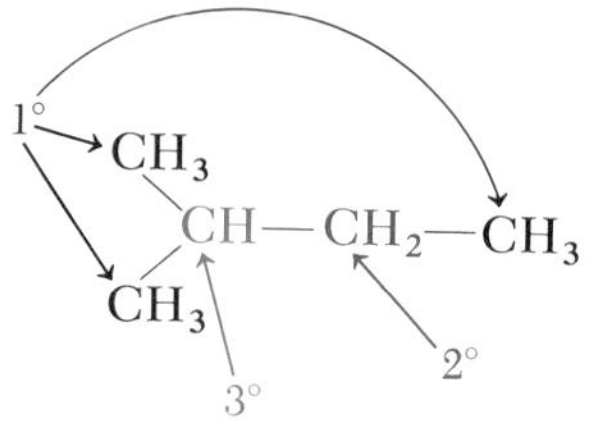

$$\begin{array}{l} CH_3 \\ \quad \backslash \\ \quad CH—CH_2—CH_3 \\ \quad / \\ CH_3 \end{array}$$

1° → both CH_3 groups on CH and terminal CH_3; 2° → CH_2; 3° → CH

2-methylbutane
2.10

HYDROGEN ATOMS

A hydrogen atom attached to a carbon atom has the same classification as the carbon atom. Thus, there are nine 1° hydrogens, two 2° hydrogens, and one 3° hydrogen in a molecule of 2-methylbutane.

ALCOHOLS AND HALOALKANES

These compounds are classified on the basis of the carbon atom to which the functional group is attached. Several examples are shown in Figure 2.20.

PROBLEM 2.12 Classify all carbon atoms of neopentane as primary, secondary, tertiary, or quaternary. How many primary, secondary, and tertiary hydrogen atoms are there per molecule of neopentane?

PROBLEM 2.13 Draw structures for all tertiary alcohols of the formula $C_6H_{14}O$.

2.4 Projection Drawings and Conformations

THE WEDGE REPRESENTATION

There are various methods to impart three-dimensional information to two-dimensional drawings. One common method was introduced in Chapter 1, and we will take a further look at it here. Consider a molecule having four bonds distributed about a central carbon atom in the usual tetrahedral manner. It is possible to rotate this molecule in space such that the central carbon and two of the attached atoms lie in a vertical plane. When these atoms lie in the plane of the paper, one of the remaining attached atoms points toward the viewer and the other points away from the viewer. (Work with a molecular model to

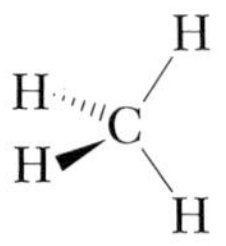

Figure 2.21 Wedge projection view of the methane molecule.

make certain you follow this discussion.) The latter two atoms and the central carbon atom lie also in a horizontal plane (see Figure 2.21).

In a **wedge representation,** bonds in the plane of the paper are shown by a simple solid line. Bonds pointing toward the viewer are shown by a solid wedge, and those pointing away from the viewer are indicated by a broken wedge. A wedge projection of methane is shown in Figure 2.21. Space-filling and ball-and-stick models of the methane molecule are shown in Figure 2.22, using the same view as for the wedge projection in Figure 2.21.

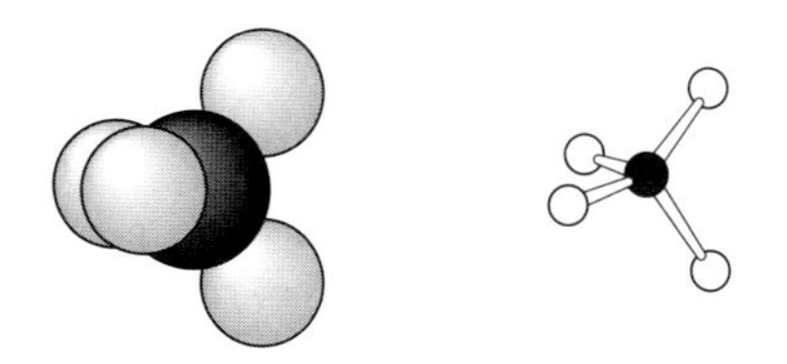

Figure 2.22 Models of the methane molecule. The space-filling model is shown on the left, with the ball-and-stick representation on the right.

THE SAWHORSE PROJECTION: CONFORMATIONS

When you work with a ball-and-stick molecular model of the ethane molecule, you find that it can be manipulated to take a form similar to that of a sawhorse. Figure 2.23 shows such a structure, along with a corresponding space-filling model and a **sawhorse projection** diagram.

Sawhorse projections are often used to convey information about the spatial arrangement of atoms bonded to two adjacent carbon atoms. Using a model of ethane, one can rotate the two ends of the molecule (the two connected methyl groups) relative to each other, producing a different form of the same molecule. Different forms of a molecule that can be obtained by rotation about single bonds are known as **conformations** or **conformational isomers.** Figure 2.24 shows sawhorse projections for two different conformations of the ethane molecule (one was shown in Figure 2.23), along with models of these conformations.

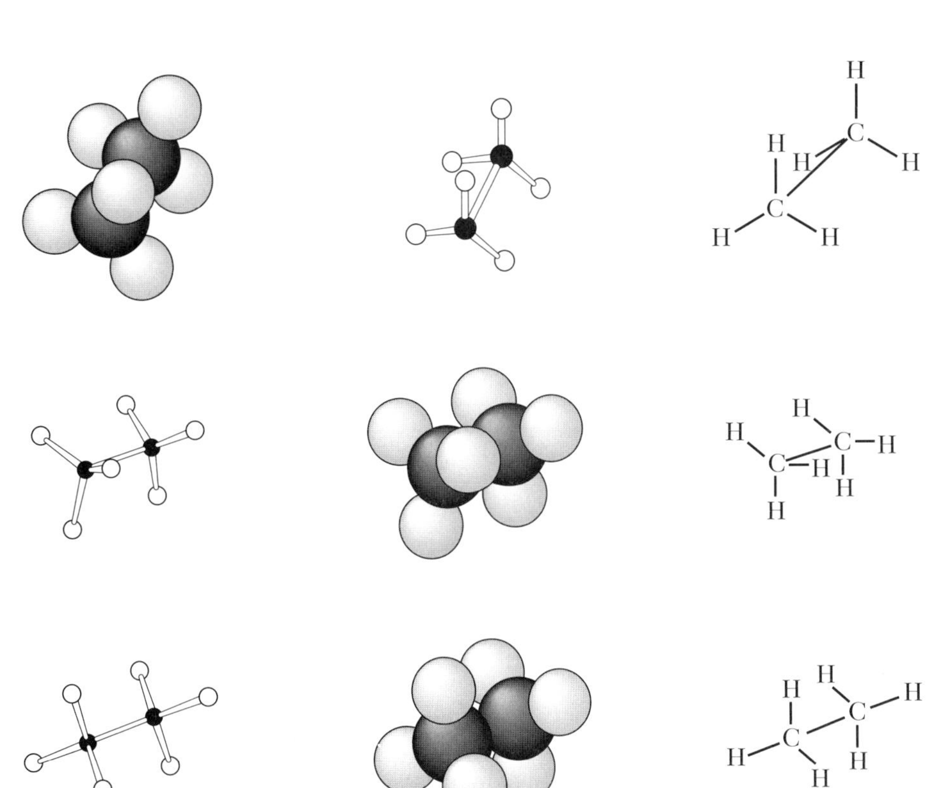

Figure 2.23 Space-filling, ball-and-stick, and sawhorse projections of the ethane molecule.

Figure 2.24 Conformations of ethane. In the **eclipsed conformation** (shown at the top) the hydrogens attached to the front carbon are closer to the hydrogens attached to the rear carbon than they are in the **staggered conformation** (shown at the bottom).

PROBLEM 2.14

Draw a sawhorse projection for each of the following molecules, showing all of the atoms present and emphasizing the bonds indicated:
a. propane (C1—C2) **b.** butane(C2—C3)
c. 2-methylpentane (C2—C3)

NEWMAN PROJECTIONS

Newman projections provide an alternative to the sawhorse or wedge projection for looking at the relationship of groups on adjacent carbon atoms. The Newman projection is obtained by viewing the molecule *along* a particular bond. In this way we see the front atom of the bond while the rear atom is hidden behind it. Newman projections use a circle to represent the atoms of the bond. Bonds reaching to the center of the circle represent linkages to the front carbon atom, and bonds reaching only to the perimeter of the circle represent linkages to the rear carbon atom. Figure 2.25 shows wedge projections of ethane conformations as they are viewed to produce Newman projections. We can view the natures of eclipsed and staggered conformations more easily with Newman projections than we can with the other methods.

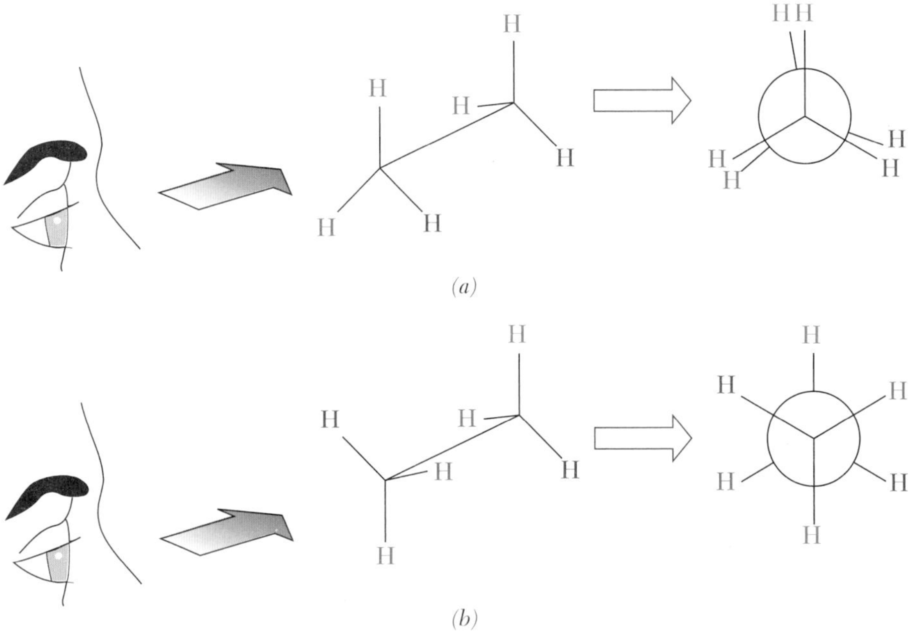

Figure 2.25 Newman projections of ethane. With the Newman projections, the relationships of hydrogens on adjacent carbon atoms are clearly shown. (*a*) An eclipsed ethane molecule, shown by a wedge projection, is viewed along the carbon-carbon bond. The view obtained is given by the Newman projection on the right. In an eclipsed conformation, atoms attached to adjacent carbon atoms are directly behind each other in the Newman projection. (b) A similar view is taken of a staggered ethane conformation to produce a Newman projection. In the staggered conformation, atoms attached to adjacent carbon atoms are as far from each other as possible.

(*a*)

(*b*)

PROBLEM 2.15

Draw a Newman projection representing each of the following:
a. a propane molecule viewed along a carbon-carbon bond
b. a butane molecule viewed along the *central* carbon-carbon bond
c. a 2-methylpentane molecule viewed along the bond between the second and third carbons in the chain

PROBLEM 2.16 Using a set of molecular models, construct and draw Newman projections of *all* eclipsed and staggered conformations of the 2-methylbutane molecule as viewed along the bond between the second and third carbon atoms in the chain.

FISCHER PROJECTIONS

We can always view an atom with tetrahedral geometry with two bonds pointing away from the viewer and two bonds pointing toward the viewer. (Confirm this by working with a molecular model.) A **Fischer projection** is in essence a simplified wedge projection that makes use of this type of view. The tetrahedral atom is placed such that the two bonds coming toward the viewer are in the horizontal plane while the two bonds directed away from the viewer are in the vertical plane. With a Fischer projection, the central atom is indicated only by a cross, with the arms of the cross representing the bonds. Vertical bonds are *always* understood as being directed away from the viewer while horizontal bonds are *always* understood as being directed toward the viewer, as illustrated in Figure 2.26 with wedge and Fischer projections of 2-chlorobutane.

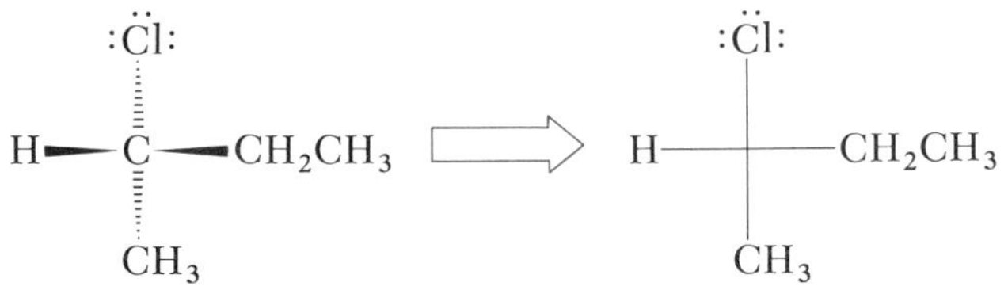

Figure 2.26 Fischer projection of 2-chlorobutane. To draw a Fischer projection we must view the molecule in a standard way, with the horizontal bonds pointing toward the viewer and the vertical bonds pointing away from the viewer, as shown in the wedge projection. The Fischer projection is a stylized version of the wedge projection.

:Cl:
H—C—CH_2CH_3 ⟹ H—+—CH_2CH_3
CH_3

One way of thinking about the Fischer projection is to imagine the molecule, in its standard orientation, placed in front of a screen. Now imagine the molecule illuminated from the front, so that it casts a shadow on the screen. The shadow is the Fischer projection. Fischer, wedge, and other types of projection drawings will be used extensively in connection with our studies. We will return to consider conformations and their importance in organic chemistry in detail in Chapter 4 and later chapters.

PROBLEM 2.17 Construct molecular models for each of the Fischer projections shown below. (Use different-colored spheres to represent the different halogens.) Compare the models. Is it possible to rotate the models in space so that they look identical? What is necessary to make the models identical? What conclusion can you draw about possible isomeric forms of bromochlorofluoroiodomethane?

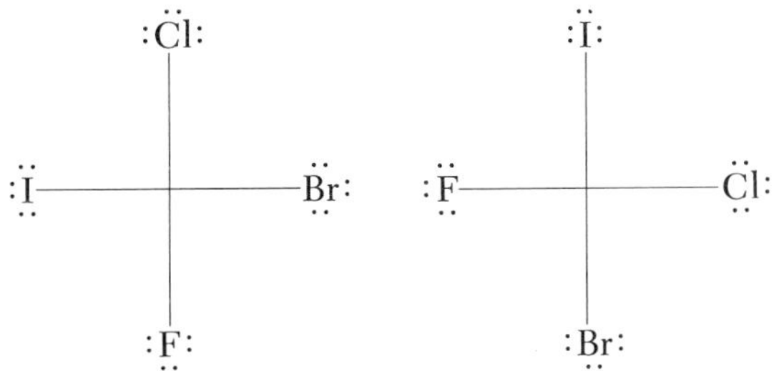

:Cl: (top), :I (left), Br: (right), :F: (bottom)

:I: (top), :F (left), Cl: (right), :Br: (bottom)

PROBLEM 2.18 Repeat Problem 2.17 for the two Fischer projections shown below.

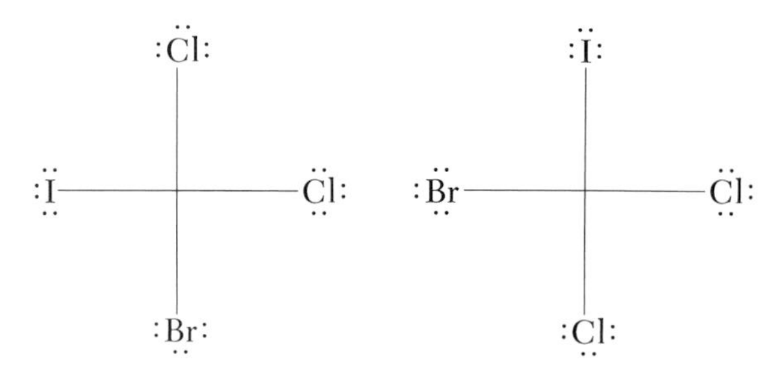

Summary

- The vast body of information we refer to as organic chemistry requires a method of organization if we are to understand it and use it.
- Arrangements of atoms that give compounds a characteristic chemistry are referred to as functional groups. Our study of organic chemistry is organized as a study of the chemistry of each type of functional group.
- The systematic nomenclature of organic compounds is critical if we are to communicate information regarding their chemistry. The primary system of nomenclature currently in use is that developed by the IUPAC. This system of nomenclature allows each organic structure to be assigned a descriptive name that will completely distinguish it from any other structure.
- The basis for naming organic compounds in a systematic manner is the set of names assigned to the straight-chain alkanes.
- Names of branched-chain alkanes and molecules containing other functional groups are derived from the straight-chain alkane names.
- In the process of studying and doing organic chemistry it is important to visualize the relationships among atoms and functional groups within a molecule.
- Molecular models provide a supersized analogue of the actual molecule and can be manipulated to view the desired relationships. When it is not convenient to use such models, two-dimensional representations of the three-dimensional molecules can be used.
- When we use two-dimensional drawings of organic molecules, we use agreed-upon conventions for depicting three-dimensional relationships. These conventions include the use of wedge representations of bonds and the use of sawhorse, Newman, and Fischer projections.

Terms to Remember

functional group
alkane
cycloalkane
alcohol
IUPAC method
straight-chain alkane
alkyl group
isomers
wedge representation
sawhorse projection
conformational isomers
eclipsed conformation
staggered conformation
Newman projection
Fischer projection

Additional Problems

2.19 Write structures for all molecules satisfying the following descriptions:
 a. an alkyne of formula C_5H_8
 b. a carboxylic acid of formula $C_5H_{10}O_2$

c. an alcohol of formula $C_6H_{14}O$
d. a compound of formula $C_5H_{10}O$ containing a carbonyl group
e. an chloroalkane of formula $C_6H_{13}Cl$
f. a molecule of formula $C_4H_{10}O$ that contains an ether functional group

2.20 Give the IUPAC name for each of the following:
a. $CH_3CH_2C(CH_3)_3$
b. $CH_3CH_2CH(CH_2CH_3)C(CH_3)_2CH_2CH_3$
c. $CH_3CH_2C(CH_2CH_3)_2CH(CH_3)CH(CH_2CH_2CH_3)_2$
d. $CH_3CH_2CH_2C(CH_2CH_2CH_3)_3$
e. $CH_3CH_2CH(CH_3)CH(CH_2CH_3)CH_2CH_2CH_3$
f. $CH_3CH_2CH_2CHCH_2CH_2CH_2CH_3$
$\qquad\qquad\quad |$
$\qquad\qquad CH(CH_3)_2$
g. $CH_3CH_2CH(CH_3)CH(CH_2CH_2CH_3)CH_2CH_3$
h. $(CH_3)_2CHCH_2CH_2CH(CH_3)_2$

2.21 Classify all the carbon atoms of the compounds in Problem 2.20 as primary, secondary, tertiary, or quaternary.

2.22 Provide IUPAC names for:
a. an alkane that has the formula C_5H_{12} and contains only primary hydrogens
b. all isomers of formula C_8H_{18} that do not contain any secondary hydrogens

2.23 Provide IUPAC names for each of the following:
a. neopentyl chloride b. isohexyl bromide c. isohexane
d. *sec*-butyl bromide e. *t*-butyl bromide

2.24 Each of the following is an incorrect IUPAC name. Explain what is wrong, draw the intended structure, and provide a correct IUPAC name for each.
a. 4,4-dimethylhexane b. 2,2-diethylpentane c. 2-*sec*-butyloctane
d. 7-ethyl-2-methyloctane e. 3-propylhexane f. 5-(2,2-dimethylbutyl)-3-ethyldecane

2.25 Provide molecular formulas and IUPAC names for the compounds represented by the following skeletal structures:

a. 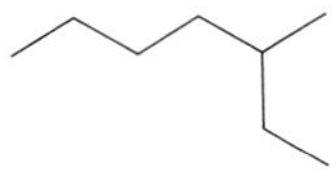 b. 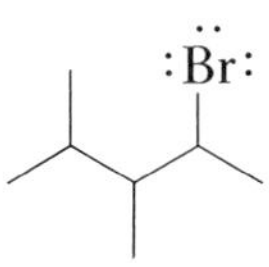 :Br: c.

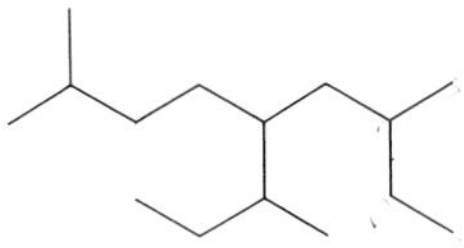

d. 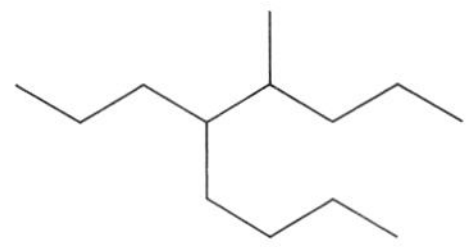 e.

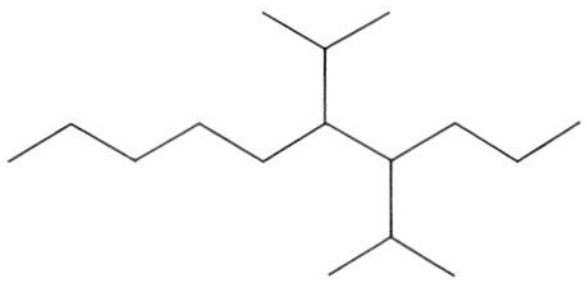

2.26 Show skeletal representations of structure for each of the following:
a. 3-ethyl-4-methylhexane
b. 2,3-dimethylpentane
c. 3-isopropyl-2,2-dimethylhexane
d. 2,2,3,4-tetramethylpentane
e. neopentyl alcohol
f. the smallest possible amine that has three different alkyl groups attached to nitrogen

2.27 Draw Newman projections for conformations of 1-chloro-2-iodoethane in which:
- a. Cl and I are eclipsed with each other
- b. Cl and I are each eclipsed with hydrogen
- c. Cl and I are as far apart as possible
- d. any other staggered conformation

2.28 Draw a Newman projection of a conformation of 2-bromo-1-chloropropane (viewing along the carbon-carbon bond between the first and second carbon atoms) in which the two halogens are as far apart as possible.

2.29 Give IUPAC names for the compounds represented by each of the following Newman projections:

a. $CH(CH_3)_2$; H, H; H, H; CH_3

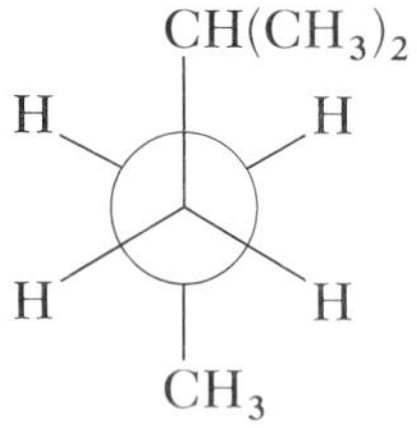

b. CH_3; H_3C, $\ddot{B}r$:; H, $\ddot{B}r$:; $CH_2CH_2CH(CH_3)_2$

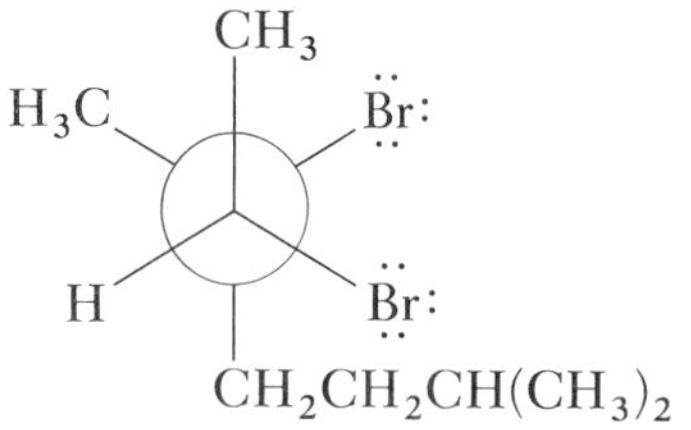

c. H; :$\ddot{B}r$, CH_3; H, H; CH_3

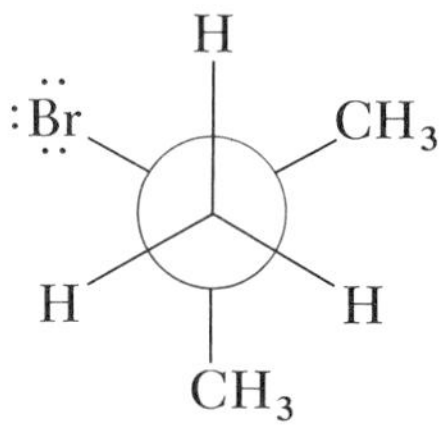

2.30 Represent each of the compounds in Problem 2.29 with a skeletal structure.

2.31 Use a set of molecular models to construct the butane molecule. Once constructed, rotate one of the carbon atoms connected by the central carbon-carbon bond. Consider the two conformations in which the distance from carbon-1 to carbon-4 are greatest and least. What is the (approximate) ratio of these two distances?

CHAPTER 3 Intermolecular and Acid-Base Interactions

3.1 Introduction

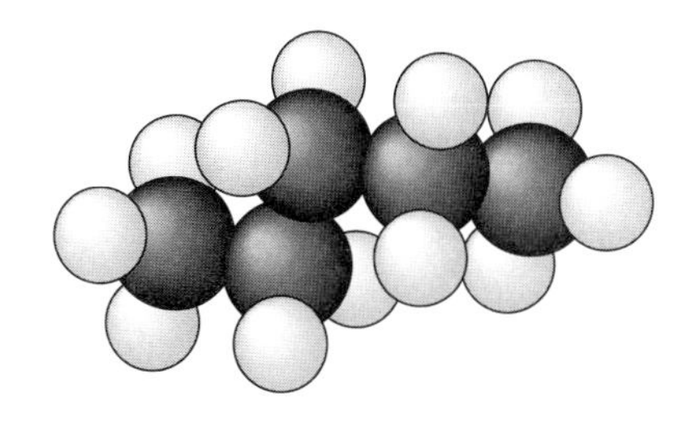

In this chapter we begin to consider relationships between molecules. In particular, we focus on the attractive forces that all molecules are able to exert on their neighbors and feel in return. We will also consider the nature of acid-base interactions in organic chemistry.

For a pure substance, interactions among its constituent molecules are reflected in physical properties such as melting and boiling temperatures. For mixtures of substances, the degree of interaction among the molecules influences properties such as the solubility of one substance in another, and ultimately determines whether a reaction between the molecules will occur.

All molecules have some tendency to stick together. For any given substance, this tendency diminishes on going from the solid phase to the liquid phase and again going from the liquid phase to the gas phase. In fact, for most purposes the molecules of gas can be regarded as separate, nonaggregated entities. Melting and boiling temperatures provide useful information about the tendency of molecules to stick together and thus about the forces that exist among molecules. Forces between molecules are referred to as **intermolecular forces.** They are usually subdivided into the following categories:

1. Ionic interactions between charged particles (ions)
2. Dipole-dipole interactions, which cause polar molecules to aggregate
3. van der Waals forces, which cause nonpolar molecules to aggregate
4. Hydrogen bonding interactions, which bring about the aggregation of molecules containing a hydrogen atom covalently bound to an electronegative atom.

We discuss these interactions in the following sections.

3.2 Ionic Interactions

Solid ionic compounds consist of crystal lattices. A crystal lattice is a very ordered collection of ions. The positive and negative ions arrange themselves to give the most stable possible structure; that is, they maximize the attractive interactions between ions of unlike charge and minimize repulsive interactions between ions of like charge. Generally, there is a large net attractive interaction. Considerable energy must be expended to break up the crystal lattice.

Many inorganic compounds are salts that exist in crystal lattices. A typical example is common salt, sodium chloride, whose crystal lattice is shown in Figure 3.1. Sodium chloride melts only at the high temperature of 801 °C. Organic salts also have structured crystal lattices and tend to melt at higher temperatures than do substances not composed of ions.

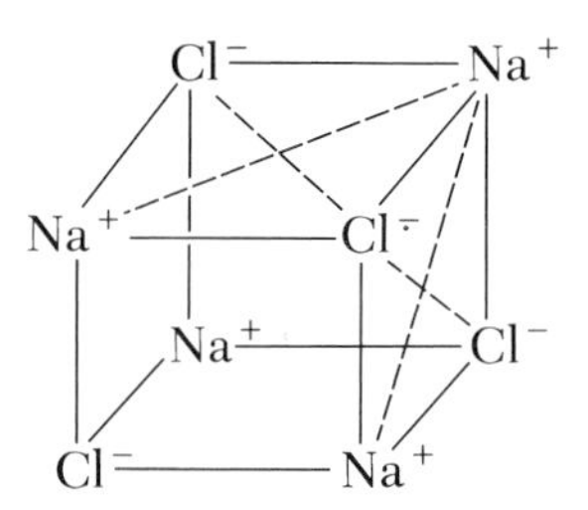

Figure 3.1 A portion of the sodium chloride ionic lattice. Attractive interactions are shown by the solid lines. Repulsive interactions along two sides of the lattice are shown by the dashed lines. The lattice continues in three dimensions, with Na^+ and Cl^- ions alternating along any given direction.

PROBLEM 3.1 Refer to the illustration of the sodium chloride lattice in Figure 3.1. The distance between nearest neighbor Na^+ and Cl^- ions is 2.66 angstrom. If the lattice is extended in three dimensions, how many nearest-neighbor Cl^- ions surround each Na^+ ion? What is the distance of closest approach of two Na^+ ions in this lattice? Again, extending the lattice in three dimensions, how many Na^+ ions surround each Na^+ ion at this distance of closest approach?

3.3 Dipole-Dipole Interactions

BOND POLARITY

The bond of the hydrogen chloride molecule is covalent. However, since hydrogen and chlorine have different abilities to attract the electron pair of the bond, the bond is also polar. We say that these atoms (hydrogen and chlorine) have different **electronegativities** (i.e., different abilities to attract an electron pair in a bond). Chlorine is significantly more electronegative than is hydrogen. Thus the electron pair of the hydrogen-chlorine covalent bond is partially skewed toward the chlorine end of the bond, as illustrated in Figure 3.2.

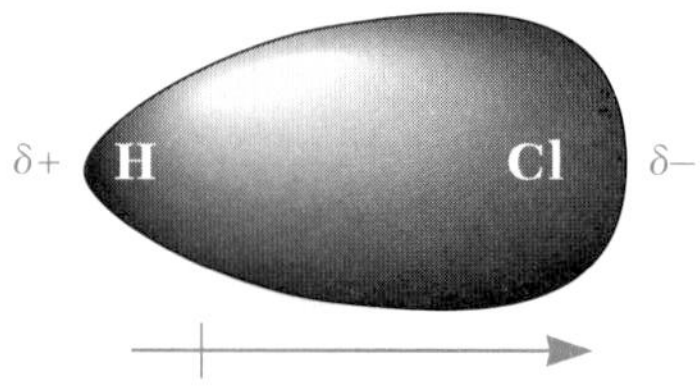

Figure 3.2 The bonding molecular orbital of HCl. The electron density is skewed toward the chlorine end of the bond. The arrow indicates the direction of the **bond dipole,** the head representing the negative end. The polarity of a bond is related to the electronegativity difference of the bound atoms. The orbital shown contains a pair of electrons.

Two main influences on an element's electronegativity are its ionization potential and its electron affinity. The ionization potential of an atom is the energy per unit charge needed to remove an electron from the atom to an infinite distance, as shown by:

$$\text{energy} + \underset{\text{atom}}{M} \longrightarrow \underset{\text{cation}}{M^+} + \underset{\text{electron}}{e^-}$$

The electron affinity of an atom is the energy *released* when the neutral atom captures an electron, as shown by:

$$\underset{\text{atom}}{M} + \underset{\text{electron}}{e^-} \longrightarrow \underset{\text{anion}}{M^-} + \text{energy}$$

An atom with a large ionization potential will resist giving up electron density to the other partner in a bond. An atom with a high electron affinity will tend to compete effectively for electron density in a bond. The electronegativity of an atom thus depends on its ionization potential and its electron affinity. Usually, electronegativities are assigned values on a scale of 0–4 devised by Linus Pauling. The most electronegative atom is fluorine (it has a relatively high ionization potential and a high exothermic electron affinity). Fluorine is assigned an electronegativity of 4 on the Pauling scale, and other

Table 3.1 Pauling Electronegativities for Atoms Commonly Found in Organic Compounds

Atom	Electronegativity
H	2.1
P	2.1
C	2.5
S	2.5
I	2.5
Br	2.8
N	3.0
Cl	3.0
O	3.5
F	4.0

atoms have smaller electronegativities. Electronegativities of some common atoms are listed in Table 3.1.

A bond dipole is a measure of the separation of charge between two bonded nuclei. Quantitatively, the bond dipole (μ) is given by the product of the distance (r) between the centers of positive and negative charge and the magnitude of charge (q) at each center.

$$\mu = (r)(q)$$

The bond dipole is represented by an arrow with the tail at the center of positive charge and the head at the center of negative charge, as shown for hydrogen chloride in Figure 3.2.

For molecules more complex than diatomics, the **dipole moment** is the vector sum of all of the individual bond dipoles in the molecule. Since hydrogen chloride contains only one bond, the bond dipole is also the dipole moment.

The dipole moment of a compound can be measured by placing it between the plates of a capacitor for which the capacitance is known. When the material between the plates has a dipole moment, it causes discharge of the capacitor to occur at a lower potential (voltage) than in the absence of that material. The difference in capacitance measured by the two experiments (with and without the polar material) indicates the magnitude of the dipole moment of the material.

Experimental measurement of individual bond dipoles is impossible unless the molecule is a simple diatomic such as hydrogen chloride. For molecules more complex than diatomics, experimental measurement provides the overall dipole moment, which represents the vector sum of all of the bond dipoles present. The vector sum takes into account not only the *magnitudes* of the individual bond dipoles but also their *directions*.

A molecule may be nonpolar even though it contains individual polar bonds. The molecule is nonpolar if the vector sum of the bond dipoles is zero. This phenomenon is observed with numerous molecules such as carbon dioxide (linear) and boron trifluoride (planar trigonal), which are shown in Figure 3.3. In both of these molecules the center of positive charge happens to coincide with the center of negative charge.

O=C=O   carbon dioxide

:F—B(—F:)(—F:)   boron trifluoride

Figure 3.3 Bond dipoles contributing to the dipole moment of molecules. Both carbon dioxide and boron trifluoride have zero net dipole moments, although they have nonzero bond moments. The individual bond moments are in directions such that they cancel each other.

Unshared pairs of electrons contribute to the overall dipole moment of a molecule. Consider the ammonia molecule as an example. In addition to three bond dipoles, one for each nitrogen-hydrogen bond, it also has a so-called **atomic dipole** associated with the unshared electron pair. An unshared electron pair on nitrogen has a directional character associated with it. The observed dipole moment is a vector sum of the three nitrogen-hydrogen bond dipoles and the single atomic dipole moment, as shown in Figure 3.4.

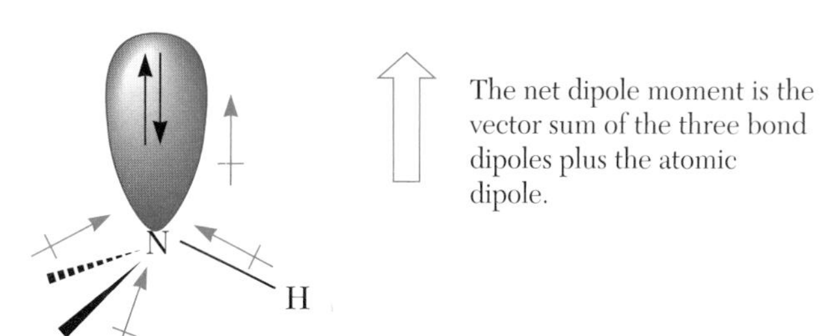

N
H
The net dipole moment is the vector sum of the three bond dipoles plus the atomic dipole.

Figure 3.4 Dipole moment of the ammonia molecule. The geometry of the ammonia molecule is similar to that of methane, with the unshared electron pair in place of one of the hydrogens of methane.

PROBLEM 3.2 Which of the following molecules has a net dipole moment? For each molecule, show the bond dipoles contributing to the net dipole.

a. Cl_3CH **b.** CCl_4 **c.** $H_2C{=}C{=}CH_2$ **d.** $H_2C{=}O$

Steps to Solving the Problem

Solution to Problem 3.2a

1. View the molecule with its proper three-dimensional geometry. The arrangement of groups about carbon is tetrahedral:

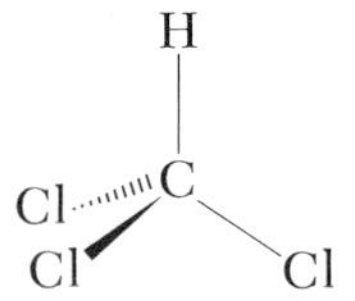

2. What is the polarity of each bond? Each carbon-chlorine bond is significantly polar with the chlorine being the negative end of the dipole. The carbon-hydrogen bond is only very weakly polar. The molecule with bond dipoles is drawn as follows:

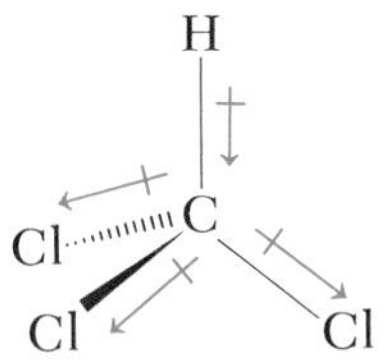

3. Consider the vector sum of these dipoles. We can resolve each of the three carbon-chlorine dipoles into a horizontal and a vertical component, as shown below for one of the carbon-chlorine bonds.

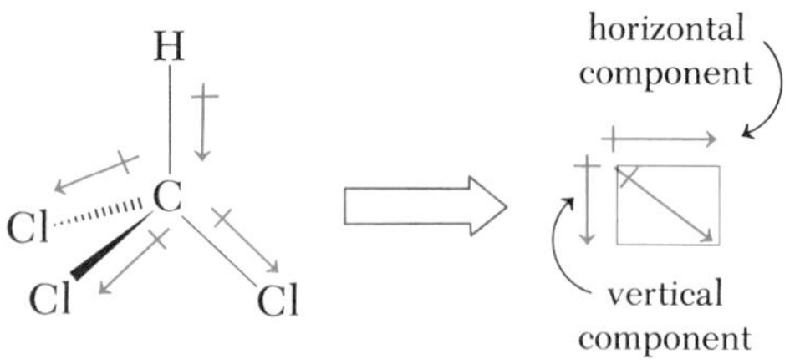

horizontal component

vertical component

The horizontal components of the carbon-chlorine bond dipoles nullify each other. Only the vertical components add to give a nonzero result. The net molecular moment is along the vertical axis, pointing away from the carbon in the direction opposite the carbon-hydrogen bond, as shown below.

net dipole moment

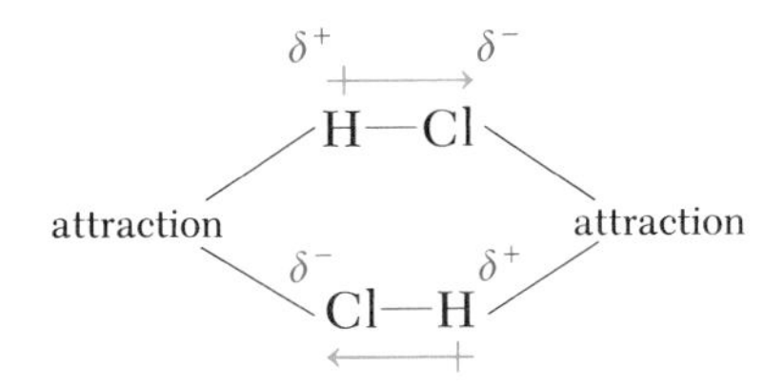

Figure 3.5 Interaction of dipoles in hydrogen chloride. Centers of opposite charge associate with each other due to electrostatic interactions.

INTERACTIONS OF DIPOLES

An important consequence of bond polarity is that it tends to impose a degree of order on a collection of molecules. The positive center of one molecule tends to become associated with the negative center of a neighboring molecule. For example, there are sizable interactions among neighboring hydrogen chloride molecules as a result of dipole-dipole interactions, as shown in Figure 3.5.

Although they are much weaker than the electrostatic interactions in an ionic lattice, dipole-dipole interactions are very important. We usually find appreciably higher melting and boiling temperatures for polar covalent materials compared with nonpolar materials of similar molecular weight. For example, we find that hydrogen chloride, of molecular weight 36, has a boiling temperature of −85 °C. The nonpolar molecules of oxygen (molecular weight 32) and fluorine (molecular weight 38) have boiling temperatures about 100 C° lower (−183 °C for oxygen and −188 °C for fluorine).

There are some exceptions to the general rule. If one end of a dipole is buried or shielded, it is difficult for the molecule to associate with neighboring molecules through dipole-dipole interactions. In fact, like poles of two adjacent molecules can then cause a repulsive interaction. This effect is seen if we compare the properties of some organic compounds with their perfluorinated analogues (i.e., compounds in which all of the hydrogens have been replaced by fluorines). Compare, for example, acetone (**3.1**) and hexafluoroacetone (**3.2**) (the locations of partial charges are shown).

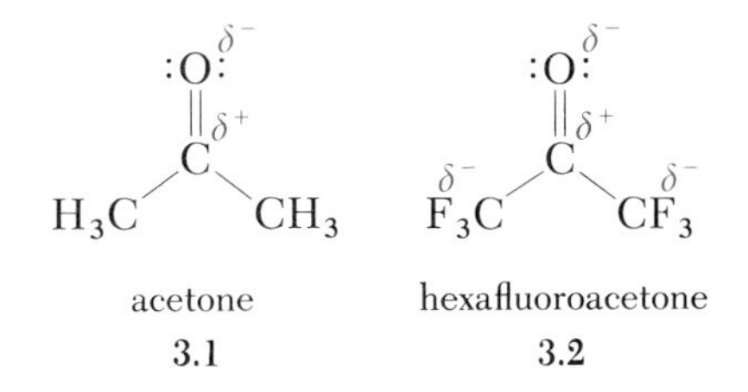

The fluorinated compound has a periphery of electronegative atoms constituting a sheath of negative charge. The more electropositive carbon is buried inside. The result is that neighboring molecules feel a repulsive interaction between their negative sheaths. Hexafluoroacetone is more volatile than is acetone, in spite of its higher molecular weight and highly polar bonds. In fact, hexafluoroacetone has a boiling temperature of −26 °C at 1 atm pressure and so is a gas under normal laboratory conditions, while acetone (boiling point 56 °C at 1 atm pressure) is a liquid. Similar differences in volatility are often found between pairs of molecules that differ in having all the hydrogen atoms replaced by fluorine atoms.

PROBLEM 3.3 In each of the following pairs of molecules (of similar molecular weight), predict which one will have the higher boiling point:

a. $(H_3C)_2C{=}\ddot{\underset{..}{O}}$ or $(H_3C)_2C{=}CH_2$

b. $CH_3\ddot{\underset{..}{O}}CH_3$ or $CH_3CH_2CH_3$

c. $CH_3CH_2CH_3$ or $CH_3CH_2\ddot{\underset{..}{F}}\!:$

3.4 van der Waals Forces

Nonpolar molecules aggregate because of attractive **van der Waals forces.** These forces arise from the transient attraction of electrons of one molecule to the nuclei of another.

The electron clouds surrounding the nuclei of a molecule (or the nucleus of an atom) are in constant oscillation. As the electrons oscillate in space, the nuclei can become slightly exposed. Electrons on a nearby molecule then experience an electrostatic attraction toward the exposed nucleus, as is illustrated schematically in Figure 3.6.

These van der Waals attractive forces exist in all samples of matter, not just those composed on nonpolar molecules, although they are often weak in comparison with other types of intermolecular forces (and therefore they are *relatively* unimportant). These van der Waals forces become dominant in the absence of other forces.

In general, the greater the number of electrons in a molecule or atom, the more easily polarized (distorted) they are. Atoms (or ions or molecules) with

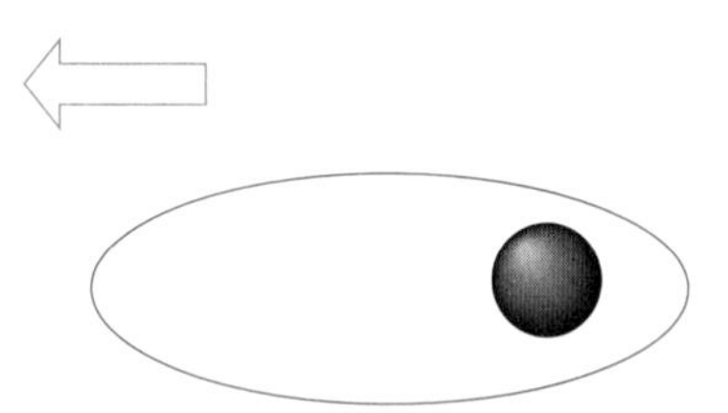

Normal electron oscillation causes a nonsymmetrical electron distribution, partially exposing the nucleus on one side.

Electrons about a nearby nucleus are momentarily attracted to the partly exposed nucleus, distorting their distribution about their own nucleus.

Figure 3.6 Transient polarization of electrons about a nucleus. Normal electron oscillations cause the temporary displacement of the electrons surrounding the nucleus on the left, resulting in an attractive force on the electrons of the molecule to the right. The weak force thus holding the molecules together is called the van der Waals force.

large numbers of electrons (*diffuse* collections of electrons) are said to be easily **polarizable.** The van der Waals forces become more important with increasing molecular weight and often with increased surface area of the molecule, because increased molecular weight is associated with an increased number of electrons. For this reason, molecules of similar structure (e.g., the straight chain alkanes) exhibit increasing boiling points with increasing molecular weight.

PROBLEM 3.4 Arrange the following ions in order of increasing polarizability:

$$Br^-, F^-, I^-, Cl^-$$

THE INFLUENCE OF SHAPE ON VAN DER WAALS INTERACTIONS

The van der Waals attractive forces depend not only on the number of electrons in a molecule but also on the area of contact of a molecule with its neighbors. For example, molecular hydrogen exhibits a boiling temperature some 16 C° higher than does helium. Both a hydrogen molecule (H_2) and a helium atom contain two electrons, but the helium atom has a spherical symmetry while the hydrogen molecule is elongated. The elongated form of the hydrogen molecule makes its electron pair more diffuse, resulting in a greater contact area with neighboring molecules. We can use a simple analogy to illustrate this point. Imagine gluing two spheres together. There can be only one point of contact, and the glue joint will be weak. In contrast, if we glue two cylinders along their lengths, there are many points of contact and the glue joint is much stronger. If we glue together two boards, an extremely strong joint results because of the very high surface area and multiple contact points.

We see this effect with organic compounds. Consider two isomers of the formula C_5H_{12}, pentane (**3.3**) and neopentane (**3.4**).

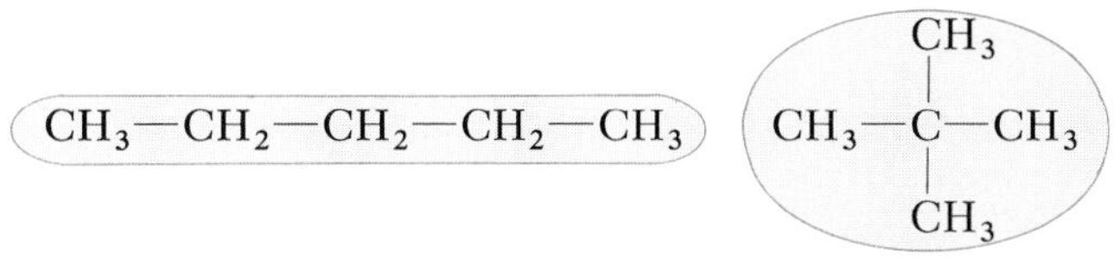

$$CH_3{-}CH_2{-}CH_2{-}CH_2{-}CH_3$$

pentane
3.3

$$CH_3{-}\underset{CH_3}{\overset{CH_3}{\overset{|}{\underset{|}{C}}}}{-}CH_3$$

neopentane
(2,2-dimethylpropane)
3.4

Neopentane is more compact than is pentane. It is virtually spherical in its electron distribution, whereas pentane is elongated. We find that pentane has a boiling temperature 26 C° higher than that of neopentane. For each molecule, the relative surface areas available for van der Waals interactions are illustrated schematically in Figure 3.7.

We find an interesting crossover in the order of melting temperatures for pentane and neopentane. Of the two molecules, pentane has a considerably

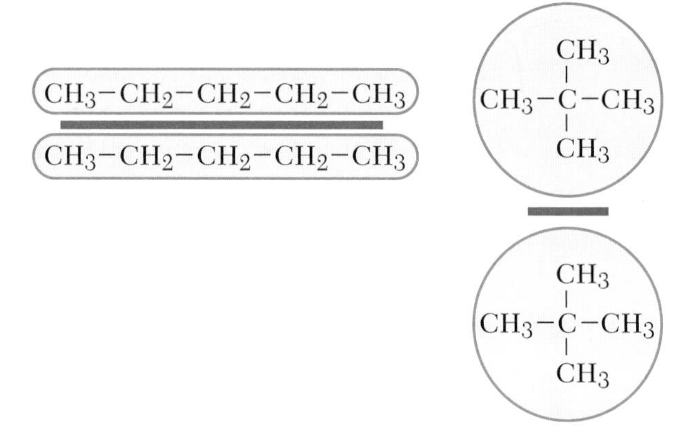

Figure 3.7 Relative surface areas for van der Waals attractive interaction. The pentane molecules on the left have a much greater surface area for interaction than do the neopentane molecules on the right.

lower melting temperature (−129.8 °C, compared with −16.8 °C for neopentane). The reason for the crossover lies in the improved ability of the more spherical neopentane to pack into a crystal lattice. Neopentane molecules are *always* spherical. Pentane molecules, on the other hand, can twist into a variety of shapes (try this with your molecular models). A collection of objects with identical shapes packs more efficiently than does a collection with a variety of shapes. The improved packing of neopentane molecules results in a more stable crystal, which requires a higher temperature to melt.

PROBLEM 3.5 Write the structures for all of the isomeric C_6H_{14} alkanes. Predict the order of their boiling points, from lowest to highest.

3.5 Hydrogen Bonds

Some compounds containing hydrogen exhibit a powerful type of attractive force on neighboring molecules. This phenomenon, known as **hydrogen bonding,** is of particular importance for compounds containing hydrogen that is covalently bound to small, highly electronegative atoms. That is, it is most important when the hydrogen is bound to oxygen, nitrogen, or fluorine.

A hydrogen bond is weaker than either an ionic or a covalent bond, but it can be much stronger than dipole-dipole or van der Waals interactions. Its strength can be as much as ten percent of the strength of an ordinary covalent bond. As a result, hydrogen bonds can significantly influence both the physical and chemical characteristics of molecules. Aside from effects on boiling point and solubility (see Section 3.6), hydrogen bonds play particularly important roles in biological processes.

We can view a hydrogen bonding interaction in the following way. When hydrogen forms a covalent bond with a more electronegative atom, the shared electron pair is greatly distorted toward the more electronegative end. This concentration of electron density at the negative pole was discussed earlier for hydrogen chloride and shown in Figure 3.2. In an extreme case, the hydrogen end of the bond is largely denuded of electron density and shows a permanently exposed proton nucleus. It can then act as a *hydrogen bond donor*, since the exposed proton is able to exert a large attractive force on electron-rich atoms of neighboring molecules. However, for hydrogen bonding to occur, there must be a *hydrogen bond acceptor* on the neighboring molecule. The neighboring atoms most likely to function as hydrogen bond acceptors are the strongly electronegative oxygen, nitrogen, and fluorine atoms.

SPECIAL TOPIC

Hydrogen Bonding in Biological Systems

Intermolecular hydrogen bonds play a profound role in the behavior of biological molecules. Not only are hydrogen bonds important for influencing the interactions of cellular water with the polar functional groups of a variety of biological molecules, but hydrogen bonding also occurs *between* biological molecules themselves. One of the most important examples of hydrogen bonding between biological molecules is in the interactions of nucleic acid molecules. Deoxyribonucleic acids (DNA) are extremely large molecules composed of linear chains of four similar units (nucleotides) with distinguishing structural characteristics. The DNA of a cell provides a chemical blueprint for the ultimate construction of enzymes, the catalysts of biological processes.

DNA exists as an associated pair of complementary nucleic acid chains, that is, a given nucleotide unit in one chain is matched by a particular nucleotide in its accompanying chain. The chains are paired through hydrogen bonds that link portions of the nucleotide units. The hydrogen bonding illustrated below shows the two sets of pairings that occur among the four types of nucleotide units. The heterocyclic bases thymine and adenine are complementary. They are coupled by two well-placed hydrogen bonds (dotted lines). Each hydrogen bond can provide about 5 kcal/mole of stabilization. The heterocyclic bases cytosine and guanine are also complementary. They are coupled by three hydrogen bonds (dashed lines).

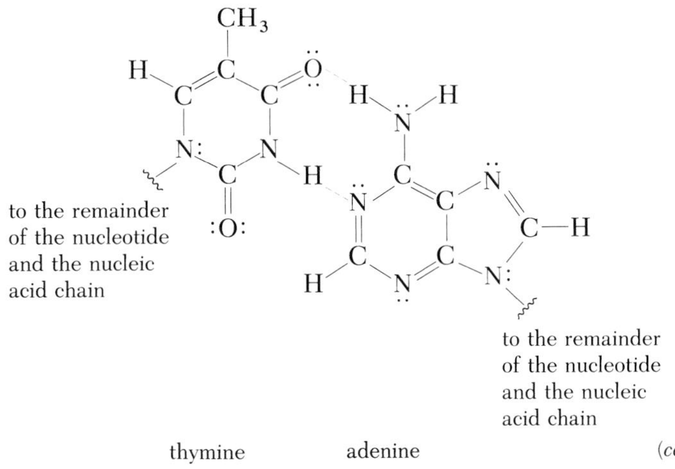

CH_3 H C C C O H N H N: C N H N C C N C H :O: C C N N: H

to the remainder of the nucleotide and the nucleic acid chain

to the remainder of the nucleotide and the nucleic acid chain

thymine adenine

(continued)

(*continued from previous page*)

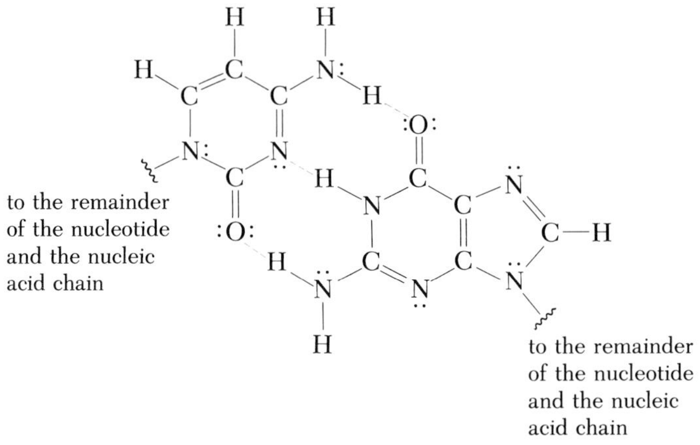

to the remainder of the nucleotide and the nucleic acid chain

to the remainder of the nucleotide and the nucleic acid chain

cytosine guanine

If a pairing other than thymine to adenine or cytosine to guanine is attempted, the association is inefficient. For example, thymine and guanine are not complementary and they pair poorly. They are coupled by only one hydrogen bond (dashed line). Furthermore, there are repulsive interactions (broad lines) where other hydrogen bonds would be located with favorable pairings.

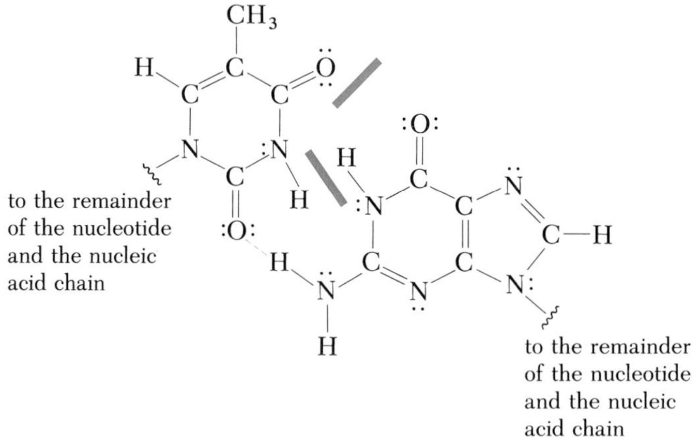

to the remainder of the nucleotide and the nucleic acid chain

to the remainder of the nucleotide and the nucleic acid chain

thymine guanine

The hydrogen bonding and base-pairing interactions shown here are of the Watson-Crick type. Other types of interactions between DNA chains are known. Nucleic acids will be discussed in detail in Chapter 28.

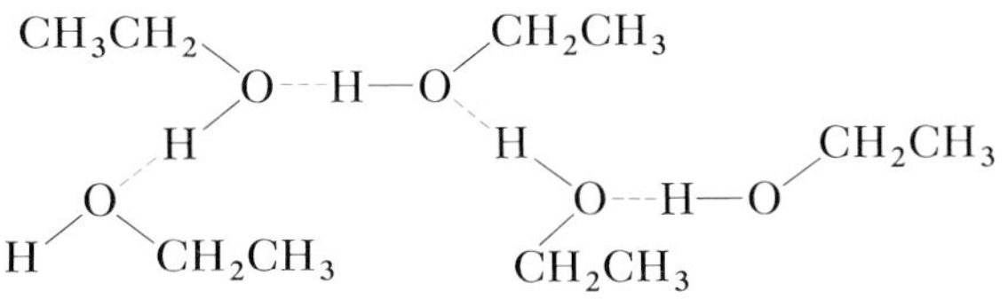

Figure 3.8 **Hydrogen bonding among ethanol molecules.** The dashed lines, represent the hydrogen bonds. The interactions extend in three dimensions; only one plane is shown here for the sake of clarity.

CH_3CH_2—O···H—O—CH_2CH_3 ; H···O ; H—O—CH_2CH_3 ; H···O···H—O—CH_2CH_3 ; CH_2CH_3

Hydrogen bonding in liquid ethanol is illustrated in Figure 3.8. In this case one ethanol molecule functions as the hydrogen bond donor, and a neighboring molecule acts as a hydrogen bond acceptor.

Hydrogen is unique in that it is the only atom that, although bound in a molecule, can be virtually denuded of neighboring electron density by attachment to an electronegative atom. Not surprisingly, no analogues of hydrogen bonds are found when atoms other than hydrogen are bonded to electronegative atoms.

Substances whose molecules can associate by hydrogen bonding show significantly higher boiling temperatures than substances of similar molecular weight that do not hydrogen bond. For example, the boiling temperature of water (100 °C) is 267 C° above that of nonpolar methane, and it is 167 C° above that of hydrogen bromide, despite the much higher molecular weight of the latter.

PROBLEM 3.6 Arrange the following molecules of similar molecular weight in order of increasing boiling point:

$CH_3CH_2CH_2CH_2CH_3$ $CH_3CH_2CH_2CH_2OH$ $CH_3CH_2OCH_2CH_3$

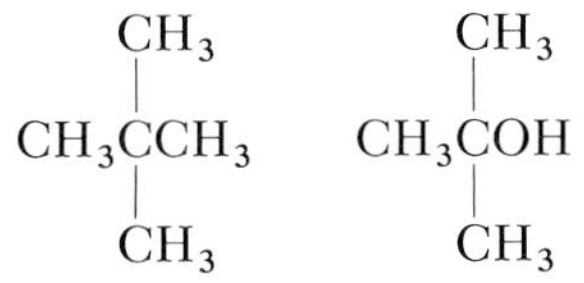

$(CH_3)_3CCH_3$ (CH_3CCH_3 with two CH_3 groups) $(CH_3)_3COH$ (CH_3COH with two CH_3 groups)

3.6 Solubilities

TYPES OF SOLVENT

A solution is a homogeneous mixture of two or more substances. We generally refer to the substance present in the greater amount as the **solvent.** Other substances present in the solution are referred to as **solutes.** In organic chemistry, we are usually concerned with liquid solvents, since most reactions are performed in the liquid phase.

Consider a salt or a highly polar substance dissolved in a liquid solvent. Oppositely charged ions dispersed throughout the solvent experience a mutual attraction. Similarly, the opposite ends of highly polar substances tend to associate. The ability of a solvent to separate oppositely charged ions (i.e., shield them from each other) is measured by its **dielectric constant,** given the symbol ε. More rigorously, the dielectric constant is defined by Equation 3.1, where the force of interaction, F, of two charged particles is related to the magnitude of the charges (q_1 and q_2) and to the distance separating them (r).

Eqn. 3.1

$$F = (q_1 q_2)/\varepsilon r^2$$

The higher the value of ε, the lower the force of attraction (or repulsion for like charges) at a given distance. If only empty space separates a pair of charges, then ε has the value of unity. Polar solvents have relatively high dielectric constants (above 20) and include water, simple alcohols, and dimethylsulfoxide. Apolar solvents have small dielectric constants. Included in this category are hexane, tetrachloromethane, and acetic acid. The dielectric constants of a series of common solvents are listed in Table 3.2.

Liquid solvents are often classified in several ways. In this context, the following terms are frequently used:

- Polar solvent—a solvent that has a high dielectric constant
- Apolar solvent—a solvent that has a low dielectric constant
- Protic solvent—a solvent that contains molecules that can act as hydrogen bond donors (in these solvents hydrogen atoms are bound to oxygen or nitrogen; examples include water, methanol, and liquid ammonia).
- Aprotic solvent—a solvent whose molecules cannot act as hydrogen bond donors (common examples are acetone and dimethyl sulfoxide).

A polar solvent is defined in terms of its dielectric constant and not in terms of the polarity of its molecules. While the two characteristics are related, there are many examples of low dielectric solvents (by definition, apolar) that have polar molecules, such as acetic acid. When we refer to the polarity of a *molecule*, we consider its dipole moment. When we consider the polarity of a material acting as a *solvent*, we consider its dielectric constant.

THE SOLUTION PROCESS

Consider the process of common salt dissolving in water. Solid sodium chloride consists of a very ordered crystal lattice of sodium and chloride ions. This lattice is very stable. We must heat sodium chloride to a temperature in excess of 800 °C to melt it, yet sodium chloride dissolves spontaneously in liquid water. Although we provide no heat energy, the crystal lattice breaks up and the sodium and chloride ions become dispersed in solution. What is it about the dissolved state of sodium chloride that provides the driving force for the solution process? Why does sodium chloride *not* dissolve in hexane, while many organic substances dissolve in hexane but not in water? In order to answer these and other questions about the dissolved state, we must consider the solution process in some detail.

Consider a liquid solvent. Although the molecules are in motion, there is an order to the system. Intermolecular bonding is present as a result of hydrogen bonding, dipole-dipole attractions, or van der Waals forces. With hydroxylic solvents (e.g., alcohols, water), hydrogen bonding is quite important. In alkane solvents, the weaker van der Waals forces are the major source of intermolecular attractions.

In order to have a solute molecule dissolve in the liquid solvent, it must make and then occupy a hole in the collection of solvent molecules. The creation of such a hole in the solvent requires that intermolecular attractions among some solvent molecules be broken. This is an energy-requiring process.

Table 3.2 Dielectric Constants of a Series of Common Solvents

Name	Structure	Dielectric Constant (ε)
hydrogen cyanide	$H{-}C{\equiv}N{:}$	114 (20 °C)
water	$H{-}\ddot{\underset{..}{O}}{-}H$	78.5 (25 °C)
formic acid	$H{-}C({=}\ddot{O}{:}){-}\ddot{O}H$	58 (16 °C)
dimethyl sulfoxide	$H_3C{-}\ddot{S}({=}\ddot{O}{:}){-}CH_3$	47 (25 °C)
dimethyl formamide	$H{-}C({=}\ddot{O}{:}){-}\ddot{N}(CH_3)_2$	37 (20 °C)
nitrobenzene	$C_6H_5{-}N^{+}({=}\ddot{O}{:})({-}\ddot{O}{:}^{-})$	34.8 (25 °C)
methanol	$CH_3\ddot{O}H$	32.6 (25 °C)
ethanol	$CH_3CH_2\ddot{O}H$	24.3 (25 °C)
acetone	$H_3C{-}C({=}\ddot{O}{:}){-}CH_3$	20.7 (20 °C)
1-propanol	$CH_3CH_2CH_2\ddot{O}H$	20.1 (25 °C)
1-butanol	$CH_3CH_2CH_2CH_2\ddot{O}H$	17.8 (20 °C)
pyridine	$C_5H_5N{:}$	12.3 (25 °C)
chloroacetic acid	$ClCH_2{-}C({=}\ddot{O}{:}){-}\ddot{O}H$	12.3 (60 °C)
acetic acid	$CH_3{-}C({=}\ddot{O}{:}){-}\ddot{O}H$	6.2 (20 °C)
diethyl ether	$CH_3CH_2\ddot{O}CH_2CH_3$	4.3 (20 °C)
tetrachloromethane	CCl_4	2.2 (20 °C)
hexane	$CH_3(CH_2)_4CH_3$	1.89 (20 °C)

If it is to occur, then at some point in the overall dissolution there must be an energy-releasing process to compensate for it.

There is a similar requirement for the solute. Solute molecules, in the process of dissolving, must become separated from neighboring solute molecules in the original pure sample—this again is an energy-requiring process. This energy requirement can be very large if an ionic substance such as sodium chloride is to dissolve. Again we see that there is a need for an energy-releasing process at some point in the dissolution so that the overall process is favorable in terms of energy.

The energy-releasing process occurs as the solute is placed in the solvent hole. New, energy-releasing intermolecular attractions can occur between solute and solvent. The efficiency of these energy-releasing interactions determines whether a particular solute will dissolve in a given solvent. These individual components of the total dissolution process are illustrated schematically in Figure 3.9.

By considering the structure of organic compounds and the nature of their intermolecular attractions, we can predict which solutes are likely to dissolve in particular solvents. The general rule of thumb is that *like dissolves like*. For example, alkanes are good solvents for other materials that also associate primarily by van der Waals forces. Much more polar materials, such as water or inorganic salts, are not soluble in alkanes. There is negligible energy release upon placing the water molecule or inorganic ion in the alkane hole. It does not compensate for the energy requirement of breaking up the order of the liquid water structure or the ionic lattice.

Similarly, water is a poor solvent for medium-sized or large alkanes and other nonpolar organic compounds. Although the alkane molecules are separated with relative ease, there is insufficient energy release upon placing the alkane in the water to compensate for making the hole in the liquid water. However, water is a good solvent for many salts and for polar organic molecules such as some alcohols, aldehydes, ketones, and carboxylic acids.

Organic molecules become both more versatile solutes and more versatile solvents if they contain certain types of polar functional groups. For example,

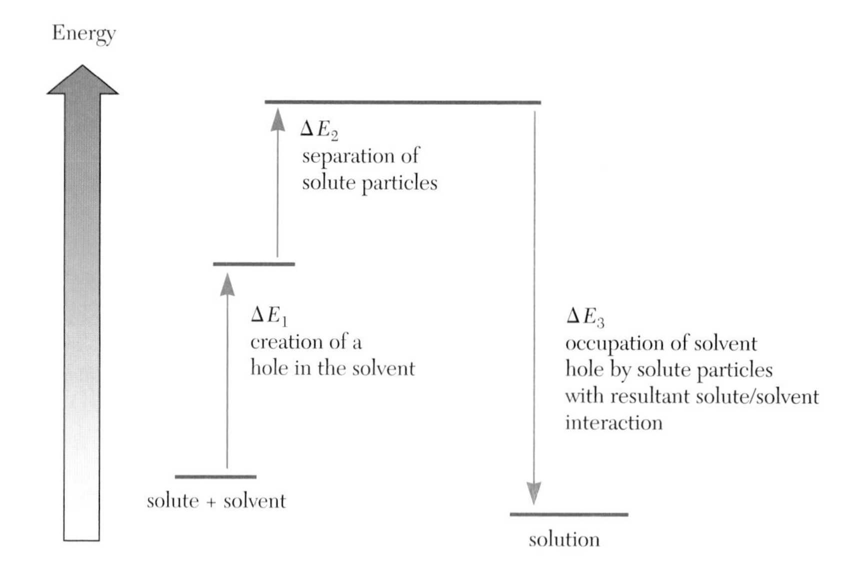

Figure 3.9 Energetics of dissolution. The energy requiring processes (ΔE_1 and ΔE_2) and energy releasing process (ΔE_3) are shown. If $-\Delta E_3$ is small compared to $(\Delta E_1 + \Delta E_2)$, dissolution is unfavorable. These energy terms include both bond energy (enthalpy) and organizational (entropy) factors.

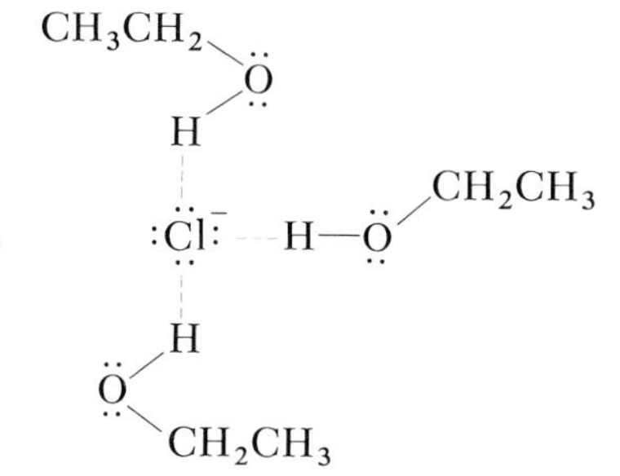

hydroxyl groups and other functional groups that bear unshared electron pairs increase the solvent power of organic molecules. Polar functional groups allow dipole-dipole interactions to occur as well as van der Waals forces. Hydroxyl groups provide hydrogen-bonding capabilities for the organic compound, as is illustrated in Figure 3.10 for interaction of ethanol with an inorganic anion.

Unshared electron pairs serve as potential binding sites for electron-deficient species, either cations or hydrogens capable of hydrogen bonding. The interaction between the unshared electron pairs on the oxygen atom in ethanol and a sodium ion is shown in Figure 3.11.

CH_3CH_2—Ö—H ⋯ :Cl:$^-$ ⋯ H—Ö—CH_2CH_3; :Cl:$^-$ ⋯ H—Ö—CH_2CH_3

Figure 3.10 Interaction of ethanol as a solvent with chloride anion. Only a portion of the total (three-dimensional) interactions are shown to preserve clarity in the illustration.

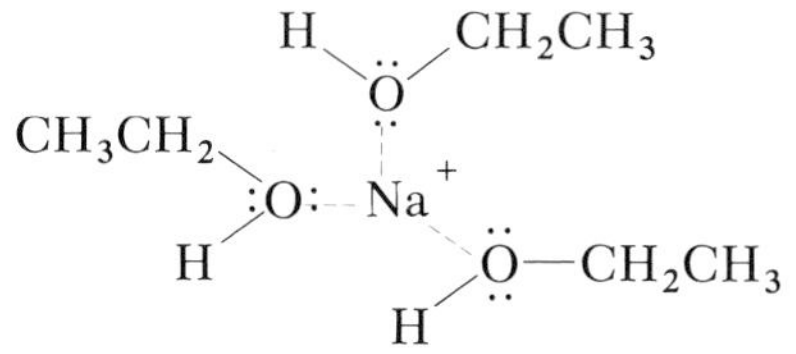

The sodium ion in Figure 3.11 is said to be **solvated** by ethanol molecules. The ethanol molecules interact with the sodium ions in the specific way shown. This interaction is actively involved in keeping the ion in solution.

We see from this analysis that ethanol has a much broader power as a solvent than does hexane. Ethanol is able to participate in hydrogen bonding to stabilize other hydroxylic solutes, such as water. Even many inorganic salts have sizable solubilities in ethanol. Yet its own intermolecular attractive forces are sufficiently weak that an effective hole can be created for a weakly interacting solute (such as hexane).

Hexane, on the other hand, can act as a solvent only for relatively weakly interacting solutes. It can provide no stabilization for solute molecules or ions that themselves have strong interactions.

Molecules such as organic ethers have intermediate solvent characteristics. The unshared electron pairs are able to interact to a limited extent as receptors for hydrogen bonding. With ordinary ethers, however, the unshared electron pairs are insufficient to allow most inorganic salts to dissolve to any significant extent. Exceptions are found when the salt is a strong Lewis acid (next section), for example, $MgCl_2$ and $AlCl_3$ are quite soluble in simple ethers. Molecules containing several ether linkages also have unusual solvating abilities (see "Supramolecular Effects" later in this chapter).

Na^+ surrounded by three ethanol molecules (CH_3CH_2(H)Ö:, H(Ö)CH_2CH_3, H—Ö—CH_2CH_3) coordinated through oxygen

Figure 3.11 Interaction between the oxygen of ethanol and a sodium ion. Again, only some interactions are shown to preserve clarity.

3.7 Acids and Bases

LEWIS ACIDS AND BASES

We classify molecules that serve as electron-pair donors as **Lewis bases** and molecules that serve as electron-pair acceptors as **Lewis acids.** In Figure 3.12 we illustrate a reaction in which ammonia behaves like a Lewis base and aluminum chloride behaves like a Lewis acid. The curved-arrow formalism introduced in Chapter 1 is used in this figure to illustrate the electron-pair donation.

BRØNSTED ACIDS AND BASES

Substances that serve as proton donors are classified as **Brønsted acids,** and substances that serve as proton acceptors are classified as **Brønsted bases.** Since a Brønsted base must use an electron pair to bind the proton it accepts, it follows that it is also a Lewis base. *All Brønsted bases are Lewis bases.*

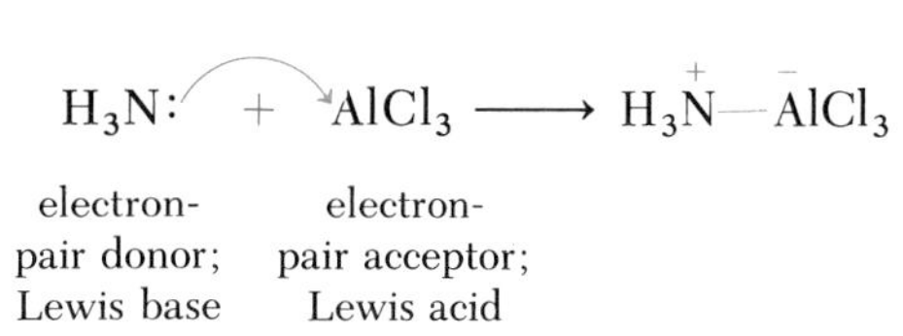

$$H_3N: + AlCl_3 \longrightarrow H_3\overset{+}{N}—\overset{-}{Al}Cl_3$$

electron-pair donor; Lewis base — electron-pair acceptor; Lewis acid

Figure 3.12 Reaction of a Lewis acid and a Lewis base to form a Lewis acid-base complex. The donation of the electron pair is illustrated using the curved-arrow formalism.

However, the converse is *not* true. For example, the ammonia molecule in Figure 3.12 is *not* behaving as a Brønsted base since it is *not* accepting a proton. We see that our classification depends on the way a compound behaves in a particular reaction. Sometimes ammonia does behave as a Brønsted base, as when it accepts a proton from hydrogen chloride to form ammonium chloride, and sometimes it does not, as in the reaction above. Therefore we should not say that ammonia *is* or *is not* a Brønsted base, but rather that it either *does* or *does not* behave as a Brønsted base in some particular reaction.

The unqualified use of the terms *acid* and *base* is usually taken to mean a Brønsted acid or base. If we mean a Lewis acid or base, this should be specified.

$$\text{Acid}_1 + \text{Base} \xrightleftharpoons{K_1} \text{Product}_1$$

$$\text{Acid}_2 + \text{Base} \xrightleftharpoons{K_2} \text{Product}_2$$

$$K_2 > K_1$$

Figure 3.13 Comparison of acid strengths. Using the same base, the acid that causes the equilibrium to lie farther to the right is called the stronger acid. As K_2 is greater than K_1, Acid_2 is stronger than Acid_1.

MEASUREMENT OF ACID AND BASE STRENGTHS

We commonly speak of the strengths of acids and bases. The strength of a Lewis acid in general is a measure of its ability to serve as an electron-pair acceptor. Similarly, the strength of a base is related to its relative ability to serve as an electron-pair donor. If we wish to compare the relative strengths of two acids, we do so by looking at their reaction with some Lewis base that acts as a standard for comparison. The acid that causes the equilibrium in Figure 3.13 to lie farther to the right is called the stronger acid.

When we compare Brønsted acids, we generally use water as the standard base. The relative acid strengths are then determined as shown in Figure 3.14.

$$HA_1 + H_2O \xrightleftharpoons{K_1} H_3O^+ + A_1^-$$

$$HA_2 + H_2O \xrightleftharpoons{K_2} H_3O^+ + A_2^-$$

$$K_2 > K_1$$

$$pK_a = -\log K_a \qquad pK_2 < pK_1$$

Figure 3.14 Comparison of strengths of Brønsted acids. Water is used as the standard base in this comparison. HA_2 is a stronger acid than is HA_1. We often use pK_a rather than K_a to denote the strength of an acid. The stronger acid is the one that has the smaller (less positive) pK_a.

For each of the reactions shown in Figure 3.14, the reverse process is also an acid-base reaction. For the reverse processes the acid is the hydronium ion (H_3O^+) and the base is the anion derived from the original acid (A_n^-). The species A_n^- is called the **conjugate base** of the acid HA_n. The stronger the acid HA_n, the weaker is its conjugate base A_n^-. If we compare the two acids HA_n and H_3O^+, the equilibrium lies to the side of the weaker acid.

We use a similar notation for the comparison of base strengths. We compare two bases by looking at their reaction with a given acid. The base that causes the equilibrium to lie farther to the right is the stronger base, as shown in Figure 3.15.

$$B_1\!: + H_2O \xrightleftharpoons{K_1} B_1H^+ + HO^-$$

$$B_2\!: + H_2O \xrightleftharpoons{K_2} B_2H^+ + HO^-$$

$$K_2 > K_1$$

$$pK_b = -\log K_b \qquad pK_2 < pK_1$$

Figure 3.15 Comparison of base strengths by reaction with a common acid (water. The larger the value of K_b, the stronger the base. Thus $B_2\!:$ is a stronger base than $B_1\!:$.

The reverse of each reaction in Figure 3.15 is also an acid-base reaction. For the reactions shown, the species B_nH^+ is referred to as the **conjugate acid** of the base $B_n\!:$. The stronger the base, the weaker the conjugate acid. If we compare the two related bases $B_n\!:$ and HO^- in these reactions, the equilibrium lies to the side of the weaker base. *In general, all acid-base equilibria lie to the side of the equation containing the weaker acid and the weaker base.* This is a very important generalization that you should commit to memory.

It has become common practice to express both acid and base strengths in terms of pK_a values. For a base, we work with the pK_a of the conjugate acid. For example, the base strength of ammonia is expressed in terms of the pK_a of its conjugate acid, the ammonium ion. Table 3.3 lists the strengths of a series of common acids expressed in terms of pK_a values.

We can make some generalizations regarding acid strength based on the element to which the hydrogen is bound in the acid. Within a given period of the Periodic Table, acidity increases going to the right for acids of the type HA. For example, we observe the following relative acid strengths:

$$H_4C < H_3N < H_2O < HF$$

Table 3.3 pK_a Values for a Series of Acids

Compound	Structure	pK_a
perchloric acid	$HClO_4$	−10
hydrogen chloride	HCl	−7
formic acid	HCO_2H	3.7
acetic acid	CH_3CO_2H	4.7
ammonium chloride	NH_4Cl	9.2
phenol	HO—C_6H_5 (benzene ring)	9.9
2-chloroethanol	$ClCH_2CH_2OH$	14
water	H—O—H	16
methanol	CH_3OH	16
ethanol	CH_3CH_2OH	17
2-propanol	$CH_3CH(OH)CH_3$	18
2-methyl-2-propanol	$(CH_3)_3C$—OH	19
acetylene	HC≡CH	25
ammonia	NH_3	34
ethane	H_3CCH_3	42

Organic derivatives of these molecules show the same trend in acidity, that is, alcohols are more acidic than amines, which are more acidic than alkanes.

Similarly, going down a given column of the Periodic Table, the acidity increases for acids of the type HA. For example:

$$HF < HCl < HBr < HI$$

We will go on to make more extensive correlations of acidity and structure as we meet different families of organic compounds.

BASIC SITES ON SOLVENTS

Solvents that bear an unshared electron pair can have stabilizing interactions with solutes by donating that electron pair. The solute must have an electron-deficient site to interact with the electron pair from the solvent. The solvent behaves as a Lewis base, and the solute behaves as a Lewis acid.

Organic molecules that have such unshared electron pairs include the amines, ethers, alcohols, and carbonyl compounds (aldehydes and ketones). Of

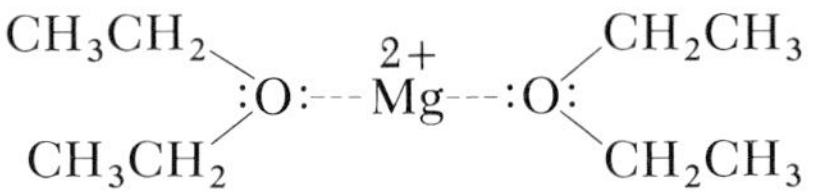

$$\begin{array}{l} CH_3CH_2 \quad\quad\quad\quad\quad CH_2CH_3 \\ \quad :\ddot{O}:\text{---}\overset{2+}{Mg}\text{---}:\ddot{O}: \\ CH_3CH_2 \quad\quad\quad\quad\quad CH_2CH_3 \end{array}$$

Figure 3.16 Interaction of unshared electron pairs on oxygen of diethyl ether with magnesium ion.

these, the amines (with an unshared electron pair on nitrogen) are the most basic. Although ethers have two unshared electron pairs per oxygen, they are significantly less basic than amines. They can, however, interact with Lewis acids, including inorganic cations, as shown in Figure 3.16.

LEWIS ACID SITES ON SOLVENTS

A Lewis acid site is one that is electron deficient. For purposes of solvation, it is not necessary that such a site be a strong acid (as we think of strong mineral acids in inorganic chemistry). Rather, it need only be a site that is moderately electron deficient due to the presence of a more electronegative atom. The hydroxylic proton of an alcohol is such an acidic site. It is capable of interacting with sites that can donate an electron pair. Alcohols thus contain both acidic and basic sites, and this feature is a major factor in their serving as good solvents.

Carbonyl compounds also bear electron-deficient sites but are somewhat less efficiently solvated than the alcohols. They are capable of interacting with basic reagents both as solvents and as substrates for chemical reactions.

PROBLEM 3.7 Point out the most electron-deficient and most electron-rich sites in each of the following molecules:

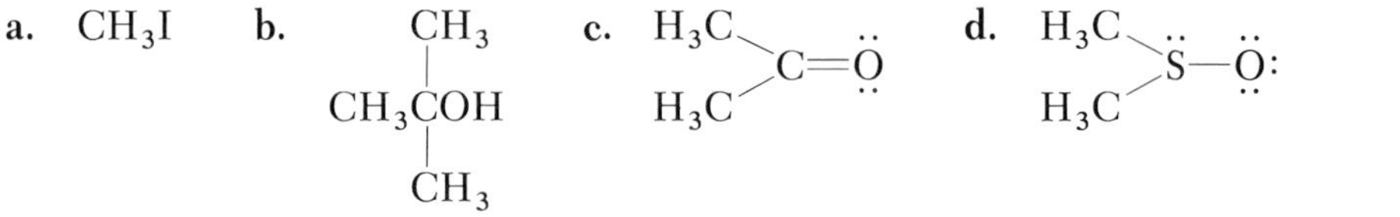

a. CH_3I

b. $(CH_3)_3COH$ (drawn as $CH_3\overset{CH_3}{\underset{CH_3}{C}}OH$)

c. $(H_3C)_2C{=}\ddot{\underset{..}{O}}$

d. $(H_3C)_2\ddot{S}{-}\ddot{\underset{..}{O}}:$

SPECIAL TOPIC

Supramolecular Effects

The attractive interactions among molecules in a condensed phase, in contrast to the covalent bonds within molecules, are a simple form of what has been termed *supramolecular effects*. Supramolecular effects are the transient interactions of two or more molecules that allow other bonding changes to occur. The attractive intermolecular forces that we have been discussing in this chapter are the source of these supramolecular effects, which have long been recognized to occur in the enzyme-substrate interactions of biological systems. However, it is only in recent years that these effects have been applied to the performance of laboratory synthetic procedures. The efforts of Charles J. Pedersen, Donald J. Cram, and Jean-Marie Lehn in this area of chemistry over the past 25 years led to their receiving the 1987 Nobel Prize in chemistry.

(*continued*)

(*continued from previous page*)

Most inorganic salts are insoluble in most organic solvents. However, a major area of investigation of supramolecular effects has involved the development of *ionophores*, organic compounds that bind strongly to inorganic cations. Strong binding of the cation of an inorganic salt to an ionophore allows the entire salt to dissolve in organic solvents. Although the cation is bound by the ionophore, the anion of the salt is relatively free to float as a *naked anion* through the organic solution. This freedom enhances its reactivity and allows it to participate in reactions with organic materials dissolved in the medium that would otherwise not be possible.

The molecule shown below is an example of such an ionophore. It contains six ether-type oxygens in a particular spatial relationship, and it is able to capture a potassium cation and bind it strongly.

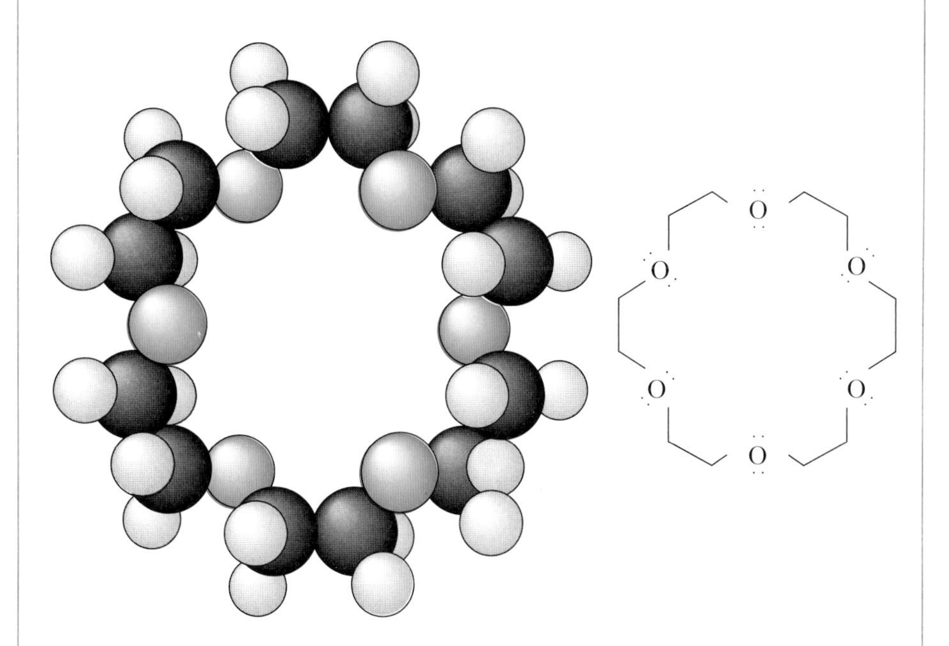

While we might expect other cations to bind to this ionophore, potassium ion is just the right size to fit in the cavity. The anion originally associated with the potassium cation then becomes free (naked) in the organic solvent to perform reactions.

The generation of the naked anion would not be possible using a simple ether in the solution. Simple ethers do not have the structural organization to provide sufficient interaction with the potassium cation to remove it completely from the anion. It requires several electron-pair donating sites acting in concert to provide the full binding potential. With the ionophore, the necessary organization is already present prior to interaction with the cation.

MOLECULAR ORBITAL ANALYSIS

FRONTIER MOLECULAR ORBITALS

Much of organic chemistry can be understood in terms of Lewis acid–Lewis base reactions. One reagent donates a pair of electrons, and another reagent accepts the pair of electrons. A new bond is generated in the process. At the same time, other old bonds may be broken. A molecular orbital analysis of such reactions is often useful for providing insights beyond those given by simple valence bond theory.

The product of a Lewis acid-base reaction has its own set of molecular orbitals, distinct from those of either reactant. A useful way to consider these orbitals is to look at the ways in which the orbitals of the reactants can interact.

Suppose we focus on the molecular orbitals immediately involved in the bond-breaking/making process. Specifically, in a Lewis acid-base reaction we consider the interaction of the **highest occupied molecular orbital** (**HOMO**) of the Lewis base and the **lowest unoccupied molecular orbital** (**LUMO**) of the Lewis acid. In a simple sense, we can think of the Lewis base HOMO as being the source of the donated electron pair. Similarly, the Lewis acid LUMO is the acceptor of the donated electron pair. More rigorously, we consider that the HOMO–LUMO interaction will lead to two new molecular orbitals. The more stable of these two molecular orbitals will hold the electrons of the new bond formed.

Collectively, the interacting HOMO and LUMO are referred to as **frontier molecular orbitals.** Frontier molecular orbital considerations are based on the interactions of these orbitals. In all cases we consider the interaction of a *filled* orbital of one molecule (its HOMO) and an *empty* orbital of the other (its LUMO).

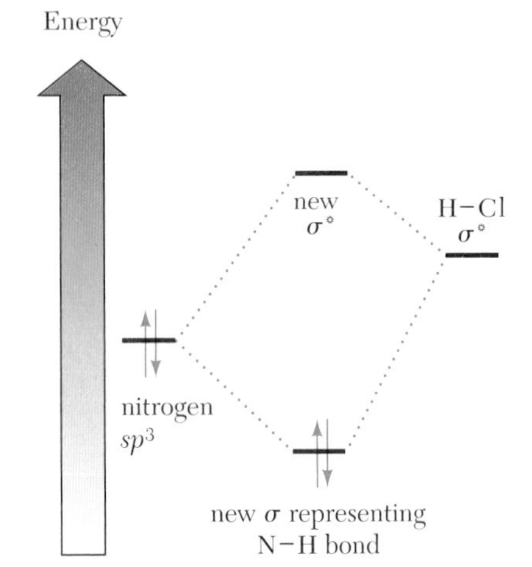

Figure 3.17 Molecular orbital representation of new bond formation in the reaction of ammonia with hydrogen chloride. Notice that both electrons are more stable in a nitrogen-hydrogen bonding orbital of the ammonium ion than in the parent nitrogen sp^3 orbital of ammonia. This improvement in stability is reflected in the driving force of the reaction.

Consider the reaction of ammonia with hydrogen chloride. Ammonia acts as the base in this reaction. The HOMO is an sp^3 orbital of nitrogen containing the unshared electron pair. For the hydrogen chloride molecule, the LUMO is the σ^* orbital associated with the hydrogen-chlorine bond. This interaction leads to new nitrogen-hydrogen σ and σ^* orbitals as shown in Figure 3.17. The two available electrons enter the σ bonding orbital associated with the new nitrogen-hydrogen bond in the product (NH_4^+).

Notice that the two electrons originally in the nitrogen sp^3 HOMO end up in a more stable orbital in the ammonium ion product. You should also appreciate that the improvement in stability depends on the degree of HOMO–LUMO interaction. The larger the interaction, the more highly stabilized is the molecular orbital of the product relative to the frontier orbitals of the reactants. In many cases we find that the efficiency of HOMO–LUMO interaction is a determining factor in governing whether a reaction can occur and/or how fast it occurs. In fact, one of the main uses of frontier molecular orbital considerations is to make predictions about the relative rates within families of related reactions. In further sections we will see how such predictions work and will also use other frontier orbital considerations to provide more useful predictive abilities.

Summary

- In addition to the covalent bonds holding the atoms together in molecules, there are intermolecular attractions that hold molecules together in condensed phases. These intermolecular attractions have three fundamental sources:
  - hydrogen bonding
  - dipole-dipole interactions
  - van der Waals forces
- Intermolecular forces have a profound influence on the solution characteristics of organic compounds. For a given substance, they define the types of materials that will dissolve readily in it.
- Intermolecular forces also define how a given substance will behave as a solute, determining the solvents in which it will dissolve readily.
- Using the Lewis concept of acids as electron-pair acceptors and bases as electron-pair donors, we can understand the nature of many transient intermolecular interactions.
- The Lewis concept also allows us to understand the nature of many reactions involving changes in covalent bonding in organic molecules.

Terms to Remember

intermolecular forces
electronegativity
bond dipole
dipole moment
atomic dipole
van der Waals forces
polarizable
hydrogen bonding
solvent
solute
dielectric constant
solvated
Lewis base
Lewis acid
Brønsted acid
Brønsted base
conjugate base
conjugate acid
HOMO
LUMO
frontier molecular orbital

Additional Problems

3.8 Show the contributing bond dipoles for each of the following molecules, and indicate the direction of any resultant net dipole moment for the molecule.
a. CH_2Cl_2 **b.** CS_2 **c.** CH_3OH **d.** $Cl_2C{=}O$

3.9 Arrange the substances in each set in order of decreasing boiling temperature.
a. pentane, hexane, heptane
b. isopentane, neopentane, pentane
c. octane, 2-methylheptane, 2,2,3,3-tetramethylbutane, diethyl ether
d. tetrachloromethane, tetrabromomethane
e. 3,3-diethylpentane, nonane

3.10 Write the structures for all of the isomeric C_7H_{16} alkanes. Arrange them in order of increasing boiling temperature.

3.11 For each pair of molecules, choose the one with the higher boiling temperature.
a. $CH_3CH_2CH_2CH_2\ddot{\underset{\cdot\cdot}{O}}H$ or $CH_3CH_2\ddot{\underset{\cdot\cdot}{O}}CH_2CH_3$
b. $CH_3CH_2CH_2CH_2CH_3$ or $CH_3CH_2CH_2\ddot{N}H$ (with CH_3 on N)

c. $CH_3CH_2C(=O)CH_3$ or $CH_3CH_2OCH_2CH_3$

d. $CH_3CH_2C(=O)CH_3$ or $CH_3CH_2CH_2CH_2OH$

3.12 Which molecules from the following list have a dipole moment?

a. CH_4 b. CH_3Cl: c. $CHCl_3$ d. CCl_4 e. NO_2

f. SO_2 g. CF_2Cl_2 h. NH_3 i. BCl_3 j. CS_2

3.13 Which molecule has the higher dipole moment, $CHCl_3$ or CH_2Cl_2? Explain your answer.

3.14 Suggest a reason for the low observed dipole moment of NF_3 compared to that of NH_3. Both molecules have bonds of comparable polarities, and both have the pyramidal shape.

3.15 Explain how dipole moment measurements can be used to distinguish whether a molecule X—Y—X is linear or bent. Draw a Lewis structure for ozone, O_3. Predict the shape of this molecule, and predict whether it has a dipole moment.

3.16 What are the conjugate acid and conjugate base for each of the following:

a. bicarbonate ion, HCO_3^-

b. bisulfate ion, HSO_4^-

3.17 For each of the following acid-base equilibria, show which is the acid and which is the base. Also identify their conjugate acid and conjugate base.

a. $(CH_3CH_2)_3N\!: + HOCH_2CH_3 \rightleftharpoons (CH_3CH_2)_3\overset{+}{N}H + {}^-\!:OCH_2CH_3$

b. $HOCH_2CH_3 + HOCH_2CH_3 \rightleftharpoons H_2\overset{+}{O}CH_2CH_3 + {}^-\!:OCH_2CH_3$

c. $H_2O + HOCH_2CH_3 \rightleftharpoons H_3O^+ + {}^-\!:OCH_2CH_3$

3.18 Each of the following equilibria lies to the right-hand side as shown:

$$HC{\equiv}N\!: + HO\!:^- \rightleftharpoons H_2O + :C{\equiv}N\!:^-$$

$$H_3PO_4 + :C{\equiv}N\!:^- \rightleftharpoons HC{\equiv}N\!: + H_2PO_4^-$$

List in decreasing order of strength (i.e., strongest first) all of the species involved as Brønsted acids in these equations.

3.19 For each pair of molecules, choose the one with the greater acidity.

a. CH_3CH_2OH or $CH_3CH_2NH_2$ b. CH_3CH_3 or CH_3CH_2OH

c. CH_3CH_2OH or CH_3CH_2SH

3.20 Consider the reaction of hydroxide ion acting as a Lewis base and ethanol acting as a Lewis acid. Write the acid-base equilibrium process. What are the conjugate acid and conjugate base in this equilibrium?

3.21 Arrange the following ions in order of increasing polarizability:

$$CH_3S\!:^-, \quad CH_3O\!:^-, \quad CH_3Se\!:^-$$

3.22 Consider the same ions as in Problem 3.21. Arrange them in order of increasing basicity.

3.23 Diethyl ether, $(CH_3CH_2)_2O$, and boron trifluoride, BF_3, react in a Lewis acid-base sense. Write the structure of the product, showing all formal charges.

3.24 The K_b for ammonia is 1.8×10^{-5}. Calculate K_a for the conjugate acid, NH_4^+.

3.25 The K_a for $CH_3NH_3^+$ is 2.5×10^{-11}. Calculate the K_b for the conjugate base, $CH_3\ddot{N}H_2$.

3.26 Two acids, HA and HB, have respective pK_a values of 4 and 6.
a. Which acid is stronger?
b. What is the ratio of the larger to the smaller K_a?
c. Which base is stronger, A^- or B^-?
d. Could you prepare HA by treating NaA with HB? Explain.

3.27 Find the most electron-deficient and electron-rich sites in each of the following molecules:
a. $CH_3CH_2CH_2CH_2\ddot{B}r$: b. $CH_3CH_2\ddot{S}H$ c. $(CH_3)_2C{=}\ddot{N}CH_3$

3.28 Sodium iodide is much more soluble in both water and ethanol than is sodium fluoride. What type of solvent-solute interactions occur in these solutions? Draw structures showing these interactions. What type of interactions occur in NaF and NaI? Explain the greater solubility of NaI compared to NaF.

***3.29** Consider the molecular orbital diagrams for each of the molecules listed below (refer to Chapter 1). What are the HOMO and the LUMO of each?
a. H_2 b. N_2 c. $H_2C{=}CH_2$ (carbon-carbon linkage only)

3.30 Ethanol and hexane are completely miscible with each other. (They mix to form a solution in any proportions used.) Explain how you could use water to separate the ethanol from the hexane.

3.31 Two conformations of the molecule glyoxal are shown below. (The molecule can rotate about the carbon-carbon bond.) Which of the two conformations would you expect to be the more stable, based on the supposition that minimization of electrostatic repulsions is the dominant consideration? What dipole moment would you expect for glyoxal on this basis?

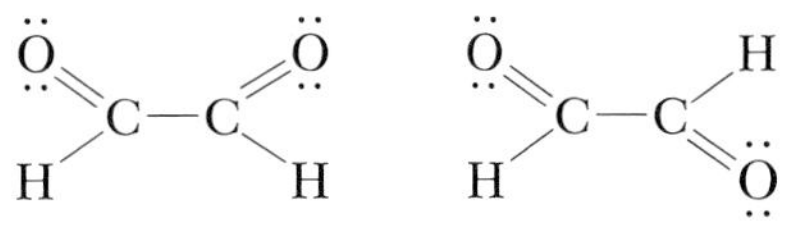

3.32 Give structures for the conjugate bases of ethanol and acetic acid. Which of these conjugate bases would you expect to:
a. have the longer carbon-oxygen bond lengths
b. be more stable
c. be a weaker base

3.33 Hydrogen chloride is a stronger acid than acetic acid. Which of the following preparations would you predict to be successful:
a. the preparation of acetic acid by the treatment of sodium acetate with hydrochloric acid
b. the preparation of hydrochloric acid by the treatment of sodium chloride with acetic acid
Explain your answer. Use the curved-arrow formalism to depict the reaction you choose.

3.34 One of the following species, on being added to water, produces a gas that dissolves in the water. Explain why only one compound reacts in this way. Write an equation for the reaction, and use the curved-arrow formalism to depict the process.
a. KNH_2 b. KF

3.35 Hydrogen chloride is a stronger Brønsted acid in hexane solution than it is in water. Suggest a reason for this behavior.

3.36 If 100 mL of water and 100 mL of ethanol are mixed, the total volume of the solution is less than 200 mL. Suggest an explanation for this behavior.

3.37 Of the four isomeric $C_4H_{10}O$ alcohols, $(CH_3)_3COH$ is by far the most soluble in water. Explain why.

3.38 Explain why the conjugate base of formic acid has two equivalent carbon-oxygen bonds while formic acid has one long and one short carbon-oxygen bond.

3.39 If 2,4-pentanedione is treated with a base, a hydrogen is removed (as a proton) from the central carbon atom rather than from one of the terminal carbon atoms.

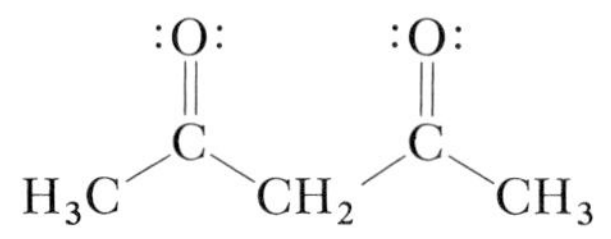

$$H_3C-\overset{\overset{:\ddot{O}:}{\|}}{C}-CH_2-\overset{\overset{:\ddot{O}:}{\|}}{C}-CH_3$$

2,4-pentanedione

a. Draw the conjugate base that is actually formed.

b. Compare it with the conjugate base that would be formed by removal of a proton from a terminal carbon atom. Explain why the reaction proceeds the way that it does.

3.40 It is possible to prepare hydrogen chloride by heating chloride salts with sulfuric acid. Which acid, sulfuric or hydrochloric, would you conclude is the stronger? Explain your answer.

3.41 When hydride salts (salts containing the H^- ion) are added to water, a violent reaction occurs in which hydrogen gas is produced. Write a reaction describing the reaction of sodium hydride with water. Identify the Lewis acid and Lewis base in this reaction. Are these substances also behaving as Brønsted acids and bases? Use the curved-arrow formalism to show the electron pair shifts in this reaction.

***3.42** If you were applying frontier orbital considerations to the reaction in Problem 3.41, for which species would you need to consider the HOMO and for which would you need to consider the LUMO?

CHAPTER 4 Alkanes and Cycloalkanes I. An Introduction to Structure and Reactions

4.1 Introduction

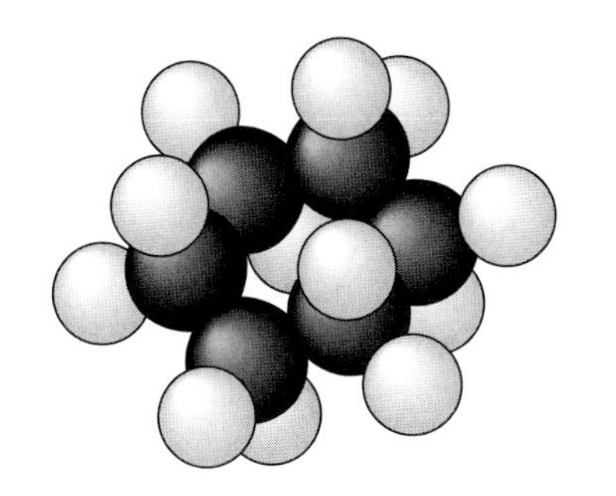

In this chapter we begin our discussion of the chemical and physical properties of alkanes and their cyclic analogues, cycloalkanes. Alkanes and cycloalkanes are examples of *hydrocarbons*—substances composed only of carbon and hydrogen. Alkanes are also referred to as being **saturated hydrocarbons** since each carbon atom is bonded to the maximum possible number (four) of attached atoms. Reaction can occur only if some carbon-carbon single bond or carbon-hydrogen bond (or bonds) is broken so that a new bond can be formed. Alkanes are inert to most reagents since their bonds are broken only under rather extreme conditions. Their inert character makes some of the simpler alkanes excellent choices as solvents in which reactions of nonpolar molecules can be performed.

Cycloalkanes have properties that are usually very similar to those of open-chain alkanes with the same number of carbon atoms. There are, however, three special characteristics of cycloalkanes. The first of these concerns their molecular formulas. *A cycloalkane contains two fewer hydrogen atoms than does an open-chain alkane having the same number of carbon atoms.* As a result, while alkanes have the general formula C_nH_{2n+2}, cycloalkanes have the general formula C_nH_{2n} (see Figure 4.1).

For a hydrocarbon of formula C_nH_x, the number of double bonds or rings may be calculated as follows:

$$\text{Number of rings or double bonds} = (2n + 2 - x)/2$$

For example, a compound with the formula $C_{12}H_{20}$ contains $(26 - 20)/2 = 3$ rings and/or double bonds.

PROBLEM 4.1 What is the general formula for each of the types of compounds listed below? (Refer to Chapter 2 if necessary to remind yourself of the structural particulars of each functional group.)

a. an open-chain alkene **b.** a cycloalkene
c. an open-chain alkyne

PROBLEM 4.2 A cycloalkane has the formula C_4H_8. There are two possible structures for this compound. What are they?

PROBLEM 4.3 A hydrocarbon containing no alkene or alkyne linkages has the formula $C_{10}H_{16}$. How many rings are present in this compound?

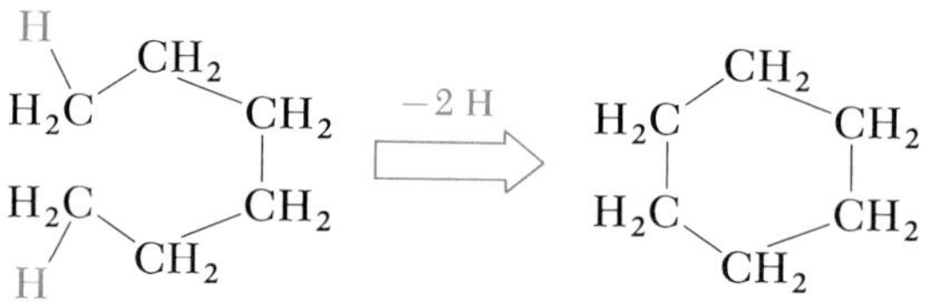

Figure 4.1 Molecular formula of cycloalkanes. Cyclohexane has two fewer hydrogen atoms than does hexane. In general, the formula for an open-chain alkane is C_nH_{2n+2}, whereas that for a cycloalkane is C_nH_{2n}.

-2 H

hexane C_6H_{14}
C_nH_{2n+2}

cyclohexane C_6H_{12}
C_nH_{2n}

The second special characteristic of cycloalkanes (and other cyclic compounds) relates to the cleavage of the bonds that make up the ring. If we break a carbon-carbon bond in an open-chain alkane, we produce two fragment species. On the other hand, cleavage of a cycloalkane bond yields a single open-chain compound, as is illustrated schematically in Figure 4.2.

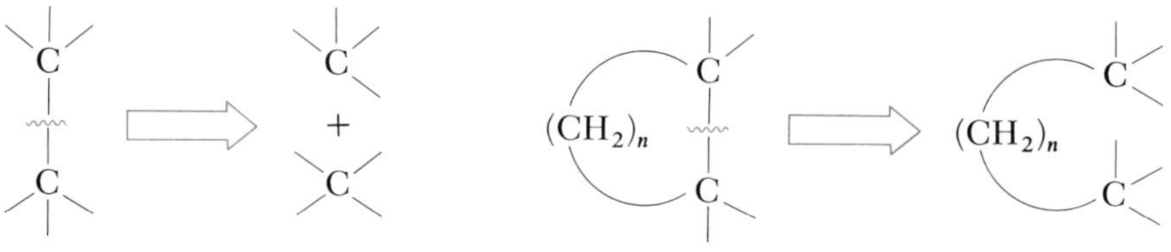

Figure 4.2 Cleavage of open-chain and cyclic compounds. (*a*) The cleavage of one bond of an open-chain compound gives *two* molecular fragments. (*b*) The cleavage of a bond that is part of a ring leaves all remaining parts of the original molecule still connected, resulting in a single product molecule.

(*a*) (*b*)

The final special characteristic of cycloalkanes is their relative lack of conformational freedom compared with open-chain molecules. In Chapter 2 we briefly discussed the interconversion of conformational isomers by rotation about single bonds. The freedom of the ring bonds of cycloalkanes to rotate is much more restricted than is the case with open-chain compounds. In extreme cases, the bonds forming the ring may be so rigid that *no* rotation is possible, as, for example, in cyclopropane, which contains a three-membered ring. More often *some* rotation is possible about ring single bonds, but the number of conformational forms a cyclic molecule is able to adopt is limited. We will discuss the conformational properties of simple alkanes in this chapter and of cycloalkanes and other cyclic molecules in Chapter 13.

4.2 Nomenclature of Alkanes and Cycloalkanes

OPEN-CHAIN COMPOUNDS

The IUPAC nomenclature of alkanes was introduced in Chapter 2. Let us quickly review the steps involved in determining the IUPAC systematic name for an open-chain alkane.

1. Identify the longest continuous sequence of carbon atoms in the compound. This sequence provides the root or parent alkane for naming the compound.
2. Locate and name any alkyl substituents along this sequence of carbon atoms. Identify the positions of these substituents by numbering the atoms of the root sequence beginning at one end.

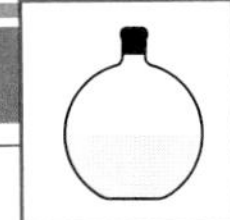

COMPOUND CAPSULE

$(CH_3)_2CH(CH_2)_{14}(CH_3)$

2-methylheptadecane

This alkane plays an important role in the courtship of tiger moths. The female produces the compound in her body. In order to attract a mate, she releases a small amount into the air. The male detects the compound and is able to locate the female. As such, this chemical is a sex attractant. Sex attractants constitute one class of *pheromones*—chemicals used by animals, insects, and plants for communication purposes. We will introduce other pheromones later. Sex attractants are quite prevalent in the matings of insects and also some mammals. Many sex attractants have rather simple structures, making it possible to synthesize them at the laboratory bench. (In 1983 there was published a claim of an apparent human sex attractant, but as yet the claim has not been confirmed.)

3. Begin numbering the root sequence at the end that results in a lower number for the carbon at which a branch first appears. The name of the compound consists of the number of the carbon bearing the substituent followed by a hyphen, the name of the substituent, and the name of the root sequence.
4. Indicate multiple substituents by designating the site of attachment and name of each, listed alphabetically as a prefix to the name of the root sequence.
5. If the same substituent is present at more than one site, indicate the site of attachment of each, but do not repeat the name of the substituent. Instead, use a prefix to the substituent name to indicate how many are present.
6. If two substituents are in equivalent positions on the root sequence, assign the lower number to the one coming first in the alphabetical listing.
7. If two or more chains qualify as being the longest, choose as the root sequence the one with the greater number of substituents.

PROBLEM 4.4 Provide IUPAC names for each of the following:

a. $(CH_3)_2CHCH_2CH_2\underset{\displaystyle CH_3}{\underset{|}{C}}HCH_2CH_2CH_3$

b. $(CH_3)_3CCH_2CH_2CH_2C(CH_3)_3$

c. $(CH_3)_2CH\underset{\displaystyle CH_2CH_2CH_3}{\underset{|}{C}}HCH(CH_3)_2$

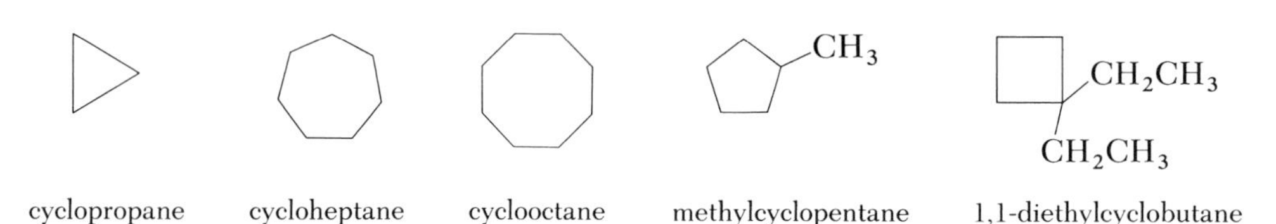

Figure 4.3 Names of simple cycloalkanes. The skeletal structures shown are commonly used for cycloalkanes.

SIMPLE CYCLIC COMPOUNDS

Cyclic compounds are named in a similar way to their open-chain counterparts. The main differences between the two types of names are the addition of the prefix *cyclo-* to the root name and, at times, a need to specify the geometric relationship of the substituents. Several examples of cycloalkanes are shown in Figure 4.3 along with their names.

When substituents are present on more than one atom of the ring, we often need to specify the spatial relationship of those substituents. The derivatives of cyclopropane shown in Figure 4.4 provide an example. In the two compounds (isomers) shown, the methyl substituents have different spatial relationships. In one isomer, the two methyl substituents are on the *same* side of the plane of the ring. We refer to this arrangement as a ***cis*** **relationship** of the substituents and to the compound as *cis*-1,2-dimethylcyclopropane. In the other isomer the two methyl groups are on *opposite* sides of the plane of the ring. We refer to this arrangement as a ***trans*** **relationship** and to the compound as *trans*-1,2-dimethylcyclopropane.

Isomers that differ in this way are known as **geometric isomers.** This type of isomerism exists not only with cyclopropane derivatives but with *all* cyclic systems. Other examples of cycloalkanes with more than one substituent are shown in Figure 4.5.

Figure 4.4 Dimethylcyclopropanes having *cis* and *trans* relationships for the methyl substituents.

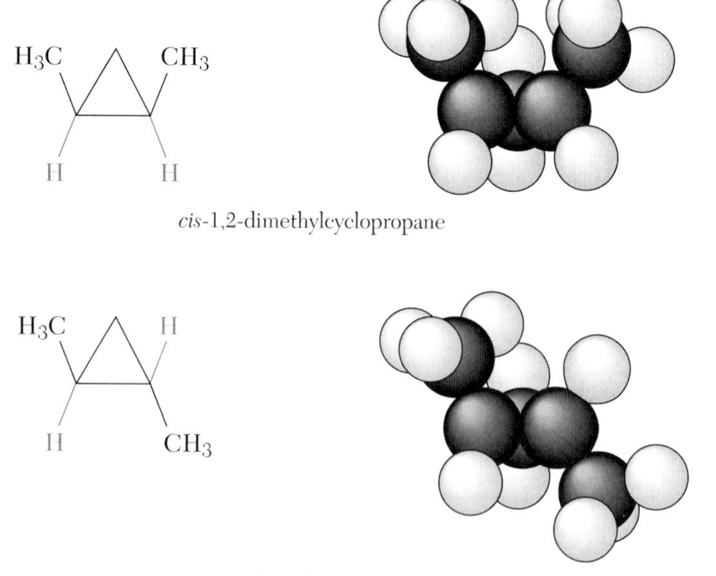

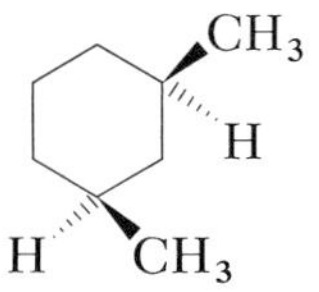

Figure 4.5 Cycloalkanes with more than one substituent. For the first example, we use the wedge representation introduced in Chapter 2 to indicate the *cis/trans* relationship of the substituents.

CH_3 H H CH_3

cis-1,3-dimethylcyclohexane

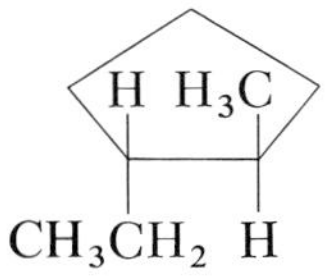

H H_3C CH_3CH_2 H

trans-1-ethyl-2-methylcyclopentane

PROBLEM 4.5 There is a third dimethylcyclopropane compound (in addition to those shown in Figure 4.4). Draw its structure and provide its IUPAC name.

PROBLEM 4.6 Write the structure and provide an IUPAC name for all cycloalkanes of the formula C_6H_{12}.

PROBLEM 4.7 Give the IUPAC name for each of the following cycloalkanes:

a. CH_2CH_3 CH_3

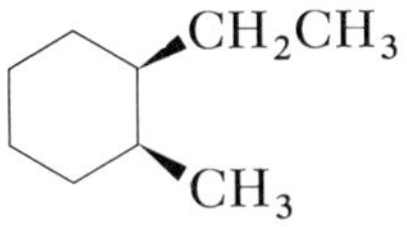

b. CH_3 CH_3 CH_3

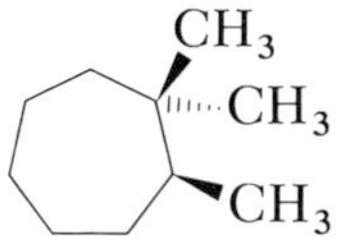

c. CH_2CH_3 CH_2CH_3

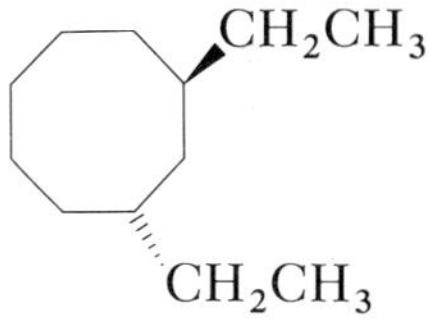

COMPOUNDS WITH MORE THAN ONE RING

Separated Rings Separated rings are part of the same molecule but share no common atoms. In naming such compounds we usually list one or more of the rings as substituents joined to a parent molecule. Two simple examples in which rings are substituents of an alkane are shown in Figure 4.6.

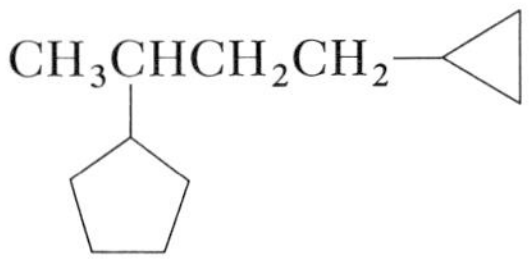

Figure 4.6 Nomenclature of compounds with separated rings.

$CH_3CHCH_2CH_2$—

3-cyclopentyl-1-cyclopropylbutane

—CH_2CH_2—

1-cyclobutyl-2-cyclohexylethane

Rings Sharing a Single Common Atom **Spiranes** are compounds containing a single carbon atom that is common to two rings. We name spiranes by adding the prefix *spiro* to the name of the open-chain alkane bearing the same number of carbon atoms, and we indicate the size of each of the rings by specifying the number of atoms of each ring *other than* the one held in common by the two rings. These numbers are placed in brackets in increasing order as shown in Figure 4.7.

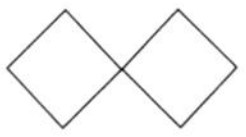

spiro[3.3]heptane 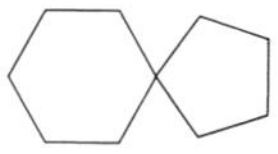 spiro[4.5]decane

Figure 4.7 Nomenclature of spiranes.

Other Types of Multiring Compounds Further aspects of the nomenclature of multiring compounds will be described in Chapter 13.

4.3 Introduction to the Reactions of Alkanes

OXIDATION OF ALKANES

Equation 4.1 is the general equation for the combustion of a hydrocarbon. This is one of the most important chemical reactions of modern society. It is the major route by which we provide energy for a wide range of purposes.

Eqn. 4.1

$$C_xH_y + \left(x + \frac{y}{4}\right) O_2 \longrightarrow x\ CO_2 + \frac{y}{2} H_2O + \text{heat}$$

The heat liberated during combustion is substantial. We make use of it in our homes and factories when we burn natural gas, kerosene, and other hydrocarbons.

We can make important deductions about the relative stabilities of hydrocarbons by comparing their **heats of combustion.** The heat of combustion is the energy liberated when a compound is burned completely. Compare the heats of combustion of the two isomers, pentane and 2-methylbutane (or isopentane), which are, respectively, 845.2 kcal/mole and 843.5 kcal/mole. The mass balance equations for the combustion of these two isomers are the same, as shown in Equation 4.2.

Eqn. 4.2

$$C_5H_{12}(g) + 8\ O_2(g) \longrightarrow 5\ CO_2(g) + 6\ H_2O(g) + \text{heat}$$

$$\Delta H^\circ = -845.2 \text{ kcal/mole (3536 kJ/mole) for pentane}$$

$$\Delta H^\circ = -843.5 \text{ kcal/mole (3529 kJ/mole) for 2-methylbutane}$$

The combustion of pentane releases 1.7 kcal/mole more heat than does 2-methylbutane. Since the products of both combustion reactions are the same, we infer that pentane has a higher energy content than does 2-methylbutane (by 1.7 kcal/mole), and we conclude that 2-methylbutane is thermodynamically more stable than pentane by 1.7 kcal/mole. This comparison is illustrated in Figure 4.8.

We interpret this result as indicating that 2-methylbutane has stronger bonds than does pentane. Stronger bonds correlate with greater stability. An important general point to keep in mind throughout our discussion is that energy content and thermodynamic stability correlate *inversely*. The higher the energy content, the lower the thermodynamic stability. Thermodynamically *less* stable compounds react *more* exothermically in the combustion reaction than do their more stable isomers.

PROBLEM 4.8 Write a balanced equation for the complete combustion of each of the following compounds:

a. hexane **b.** cyclohexane **c.** methylcyclohexane

Differences in energy content between isomers of ordinary open-chain alkanes are usually quite small, as in the comparison above. The principal

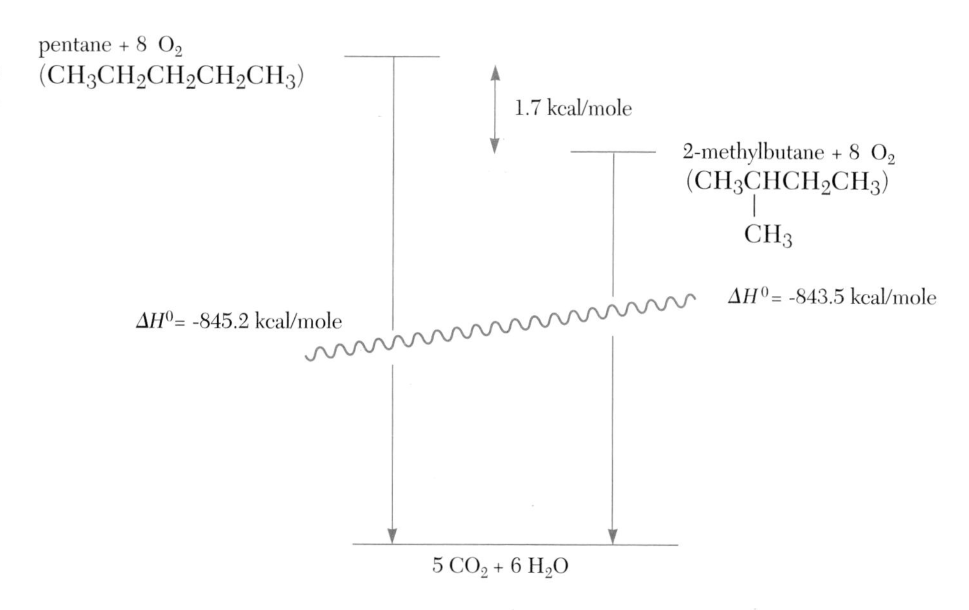

Figure 4.8 Energy changes on combustion of pentane and 2-methylbutane. Pentane has a more exothermic heat of combustion than does 2-methylbutane. We infer that pentane has a higher energy content than does 2-methylbutane, that is, pentane is thermodynamically less stable than 2-methylbutane.

theme that emerges from many comparisons is that branching generally leads to an increase in stability. We find more significant and revealing differences when we compare the heats of combustion of cycloalkanes.

Heats of Combustion and the Stabilities of Cycloalkanes In cyclic substances the efficiency of orbital interaction in the bonds of the ring can be disturbed by the geometrical constraints imposed by the ring structure. The different heats of combustion associated with rings of various sizes correlate with this effect. In general, we would expect the heat of combustion to increase (become more exothermic) if the bonds of the cycloalkane are weakened and to decrease (become less exothermic) if the bonds are strengthened. However, we must be careful in making comparisons. Let us briefly digress to analyze this need for caution.

All the combustion reactions we will discuss are exothermic, because the products of the reactions (carbon dioxide and water) are, in every case, more stable than the reactants (the alkanes or cycloalkanes plus oxygen). This difference in stability in turn reflects the greater net strength of the bonds of the products compared with those of the starting materials. Now consider the following extremely important point: as we go to alkanes or cycloalkanes of higher molecular weight, their combustion reactions will become progressively more exothermic simply because *more* moles of products (with their net stronger bonds) are produced per mole of alkane or cycloalkane starting material. These changes will overshadow any changes due to weakening or strengthening of bonds in the alkane or cycloalkane starting material. Thus we cannot expect to use heats of combustion by themselves to probe in any straightforward way the relative strengths of the bonds in cycloalkanes and alkanes containing *different* numbers of carbon atoms. To compare bond strengths, we need to factor out the contribution made to the heat of combustion by increasing molecular weight. In fact, a simple way to remove the influence of molecular

Table 4.1 Heats of Combustion per $-CH_2-$ Group for Cycloalkanes

Hydrocarbon	Number of Carbon Atoms	Heat of Combustion per $-CH_2-$ Group (kcal/mole)	Deviation from Open-Chain (kcal/mole)
n-alkane	—	157.4*	—
cyclopropane	3	166.6	9.2
cyclobutane	4	164.0	6.6
cyclopentane	5	158.7	1.3
cyclohexane	6	157.4	0
cycloheptane	7	158.3	0.9
cyclooctane	8	158.6	1.2
cyclononane	9	158.8	1.4
cyclodecane	10	158.6	1.2
cycloundecane	11	158.4	1.0
cyclododecane	12	157.6	0.2
cyclotridecane	13	157.8	0.4
cyclotetradecane	14	157.4	0

* This value is obtained from the difference between the heats of combustion of two straight-chain alkanes differing by a single methylene unit, e.g., hexane and pentane, or decane and nonane.

Source: Thermochemical data from S. Kaarsemaker and J. Coops, *Rec. trav. Chim.* 71, (1952): 261 and J. Coops, H. van Kamp, W. A. Lambgrets, B. J. Visser, and H. Dekker, *Rec. trav. Chim.* 79, (1960): 1226.

weight is to compare heats of combustion per $-CH_2-$ (**methylene group**). These values are shown in Table 4.1.

If the bonds in all cycloalkanes were of equal strength, all cycloalkanes would have the same heat of combustion per methylene group. However Table 4.1 shows that the heat of combustion per methylene group is significantly greater for the small rings (cyclopropane and cyclobutane) than for the larger cycloalkanes, suggesting that the small rings have weaker bonds than other cycloalkanes. Furthermore, we can conclude from the data that most cycloalkanes have a higher energy content per methylene group than open-chain alkanes. We refer to the extra energy content as *strain*. Notice, however, that cyclohexane is *unstrained*. It has the same energy content per methylene group as an open-chain alkane. We also find that the strain per methylene group is quite small or zero for rings of 12 or more members. We will now focus on understanding these trends and the sources of strain in the molecules.

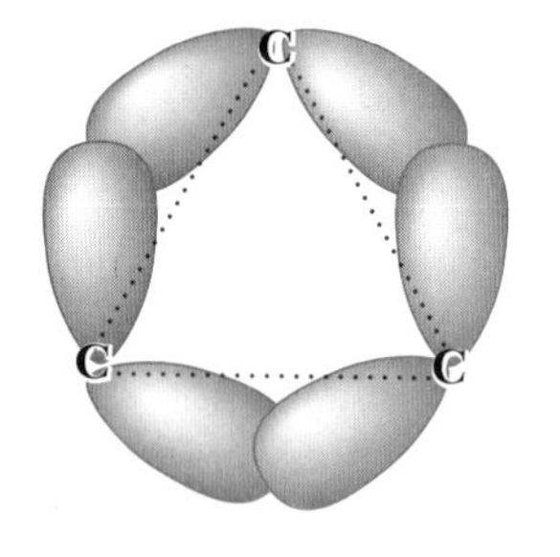

Figure 4.9 Strain in cyclopropane. The angle between sp^3 hybrid orbitals is 109°28′. However, because the carbon atoms of cyclopropane define an equilateral triangle, the C-C-C bond angles are necessarily 60°. The strain in cyclopropane correlates with this mismatch in angles.

First, consider the extreme case of cyclopropane. The cyclopropane ring is of necessity an equilateral triangle with carbon-carbon-carbon internuclear angles of 60°. This angle is significantly smaller than the standard tetrahedral angle (109°28′) that we normally find with tetracoordinated carbon. If we envision ordinary sp^3 bonding in cyclopropane, we conclude that it is impossible for the orbitals to overlap along the internuclear axes. The diminished overlapping of these orbitals is shown schematically in Figure 4.9. We can now make a prediction: diminished overlap should result in weaker (less stable) bonds and a correspondingly higher energy content (again we stress the *inverse* correlation between energy content and stability). This prediction correlates with the experimentally observed heat of combustion.

It was once believed that all rings in organic molecules were planar. Heat of combustion data allow us to refute this notion. If all rings were planar, the maximum thermodynamic stability per methylene group would be found with cyclopentane because a regular pentagon has internal angles of 108°, very close to the tetrahedral value.

Actually, cyclopentane is thermodynamically less stable per methylene group than is cyclohexane. We infer the latter molecule to be unstrained from combustion data. This lack of strain is not consistent with a planar structure for cyclohexane. A regular hexagon has internal angles of 120°, significantly larger than the tetrahedral angle of 109°28′, so we would expect a planar cyclohexane molecule to be quite strained.

Combustion data on large rings also suggest that the concept of planar rings is false. Strain would increase with increasing ring size, because the internal bond angles would be forced to be larger. As we do not find this to be the case, we conclude that these rings are not planar. Other studies, including X-ray analysis, confirm the nonplanarity of cycloalkane rings other than cyclopropane.

The preceding discussion raises some important questions. What are the sources of strain in cyclic compounds? What effect does strain have on the properties of a cyclic compound? We will begin to discuss these questions later in this chapter (Section 4.4) and will consider them in greater detail in Chapter 13.

The Combustion Analysis of Organic Compounds The reaction illustrated in Equation 4.1 easily goes to completion and thus it is useful for the quantitative analysis of the elemental composition of organic compounds.

Before we can make progress in understanding the properties of a substance, we need to know its molecular structure. The structures of the simple alkanes and cycloalkanes were elucidated many years ago. Nevertheless, aspects of the thought processes and experimental strategies used to determine their structures are still of interest and relevance now.

The first step in a structure elucidation is generally the determination of an empirical and then a molecular formula. The empirical formula of a substance is usually determined by quantitative elemental analysis. Subsequent determination of the molecular weight (usually by mass spectrometry, Chapter 25) then allows the molecular formula to be deduced. Organic chemists normally submit samples of unknown materials to an analytical laboratory where combustion (and sometimes other) analyses are performed to determine the elemental percentage composition. In combustion analysis, a carefully weighed sample of the compound is burned in a stream of oxygen. The water and carbon dioxide produced are collected and weighed. From these weights, the weights and weight percentages of carbon and hydrogen in the original sample can be calculated (see Problem 4.9).

Once we have determined the percentage composition of carbon and hydrogen, it is a simple matter to calculate the relative number of atoms of the two elements in the sample. We divide each weight percentage by the atomic mass of the element to find the relative number of that type of atom. This procedure leads to an empirical formula. We must then determine the molecular weight in order to calculate the molecular formula.

PROBLEM 4.9 Combustion of a sample of 11.40 mg of butane produces 17.69 mg of water and 34.52 mg of carbon dioxide. Measurement of the molecular weight of butane shows its molecular weight to be ~58 g/mole. Show that these data lead to the molecular formula C_4H_{10} for butane.

Steps to Solving the Problem

Solution to Problem 4.9

1. First calculate the fraction of the weight of a water molecule that is hydrogen and the fraction of the weight of a carbon dioxide molecule that is carbon.

$$\begin{aligned}\%\text{ H in water} &= 100 \times (\text{weight of H in water/molecular weight of water}) \\ &= 100 \times (2 \times 1.008)/[(2 \times 1.008) + (15.999)] \\ &= 11.19\%\end{aligned}$$

$$\begin{aligned}\%\text{ C in carbon dioxide} &= 100 \times (\text{weight of C in } CO_2/\text{molecular weight of } CO_2) \\ &= 100 \times (12.011)/[(12.011) + (2 \times 15.999)] \\ &= 27.29\%\end{aligned}$$

2. Now calculate the weight of hydrogen and the weight of carbon in the sample. Remember, 11.19% of the water formed is hydrogen coming from the sample, and 27.29% of the carbon dioxide is carbon coming from that same sample.

$$\begin{aligned}\text{Weight of H in sample} &= (0.1119)(17.69) \\ &= 1.98 \text{ mg}\end{aligned}$$

$$\begin{aligned}\text{Weight of C in sample} &= (0.2729)(34.52) \\ &= 9.42 \text{ mg}\end{aligned}$$

These two components add up to 11.40 mg, the weight of the original sample.

3. Compute the relative number of carbon and hydrogen atoms by dividing each weight by the atomic weight of the element.

$$\begin{aligned}\text{Relative number of H atoms} &= (1.98 \text{ mg H})/(1.008 \text{ mg H/mmol H}) \\ &= 1.96 \text{ mmol H}\end{aligned}$$

$$\begin{aligned}\text{Relative number of C atoms} &= (9.42 \text{ mg C})/(12.011 \text{ mg C/mmole C}) \\ &= 0.78 \text{ mmol C}\end{aligned}$$

4. We now need the smallest ratio of integers for this relative number of atoms. Begin by dividing through by the smaller number of mmol present, that is, 0.78.

$$\text{Ratio H/C atoms} = 1.96 \text{ mmol H}/0.78 \text{ mmol C}$$
$$= 2.5 \text{ mmol H}/1.0 \text{ mmol C}$$
$$= 2.5 \text{ mol H}/1.0 \text{ mol C}$$

Next we multiply through by an integer (2 here) that will make the result a ratio of two whole numbers:

$$\text{H/C} = (2.5 \text{ mol H}/1.0 \text{ mol C}) \times 2 = 5 \text{ mol H}/2 \text{ mol C}$$

The empirical formula is thus C_2H_5.

5. Finally, calculate the molecular formula for the sample. To do this we first calculate the weight of the empirical formula, C_2H_5.

$$\text{C} \quad 12 \times 2 = 24$$
$$\text{H} \quad 1 \times 5 = 5$$
$$\text{weight of empirical formula} = 29$$

This weight is just half of the determined molecular weight of 58 g/mole. Thus we need to multiply the empirical formula by 2 to obtain the molecular formula, C_4H_{10}.

PROBLEM 4.10 A sample of 8.50 mg of a saturated hydrocarbon of unknown structure yields 26.67 mg of carbon dioxide and 10.90 mg of water upon complete combustion. Determination of the molecular weight of this material shows its molecular weight to be ~70 g/mole. What is the molecular formula of the unknown? Is it an open-chain alkane or a cycloalkane?

THE REACTION OF ALKANES WITH HALOGENS

Alkanes and cycloalkanes undergo only a relatively few types of reactions. Combustion, as discussed previously, is one type. A second type is reaction with halogens (X_2 molecules). This type of reaction is a **substitution** reaction, with an atom of the halogen molecule (X of X_2) *replacing* (i.e., substituting for) a hydrogen of the alkane. The basic reaction is illustrated in Figure 4.10.

Only two of the halogens (bromine and chlorine) are of practical use in this reaction with alkanes. Iodine reacts too slowly to be of use, while the reaction with fluorine is very difficult to control and hence seldom used.

Figure 4.10 A substitution reaction of an alkane. Overall, a halogen atom substitutes for a hydrogen atom of an alkane. The symbol R designates an alkyl group, and the symbol $h\nu$ is used to designate light.

$$\underset{\text{alkane}}{\text{R—H}} + \underset{\text{halogen}}{\text{X—X}} \xrightarrow[\text{light } (h\nu)]{\text{heat or}} \underset{\text{hydrogen halide}}{\text{H—X}} + \underset{\text{haloalkane}}{\text{R—X}}$$

In order to cause an alkane to react with chlorine or bromine, we need to heat the reaction mixture to approximately 110 °C or shine light (ultraviolet or visible) on it. An example of this reaction is shown in Equation 4.3.

Eqn. 4.3

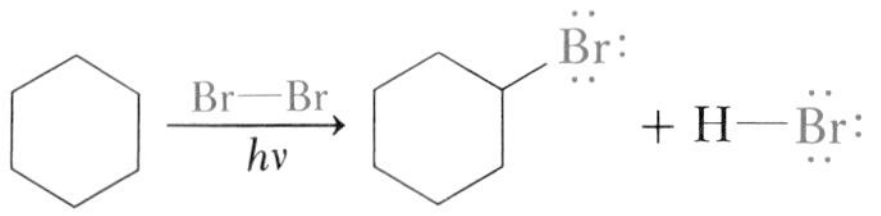

$$\text{cyclohexane} \xrightarrow[h\nu]{Br-Br} \text{bromocyclohexane } (-\ddot{\underset{..}{Br}}:) + H-\ddot{\underset{..}{Br}}:$$

90% yield

Why would reaction occur when we shine light on the mixture? Experimentally we find that the light is involved in initiating the reaction, like the match that lights the fire. To discover something about how this happens, we can subject a halogen and an alkane to light separately. When we do this, we find that only the halogen molecules are affected. Although light has no effect on an alkane or cycloalkane, it does split some of the halogen molecules into highly reactive halogen atoms. We infer that these halogen atoms bring about reaction with an alkane. Heating the reaction mixture is another way of splitting halogen molecules into halogen atoms to initiate the reaction.

$$:\ddot{\underset{..}{X}}-\ddot{\underset{..}{X}}: \xrightarrow{h\nu} :\ddot{\underset{..}{X}}\cdot + \cdot\ddot{\underset{..}{X}}:$$

halogen molecule — halogen atoms

Figure 4.11 Homolytic bond cleavage of a halogen molecule.

The first event in the overall reaction is thus the cleavage of the halogen-halogen bond so as to produce two halogen atoms. Of the two electrons originally constituting the halogen-halogen bond, one goes with each of the halogen atoms. We refer to this process, illustrated in Figure 4.11, as **homolytic bond cleavage** (further discussed in Chapter 7).

When we unravel all of the individual events in a reaction, we say that we know the *mechanism* of the reaction. A mechanism is simply a step-by-step accounting of an overall reaction. A knowledge of reaction mechanisms is crucial to our ability to make rational progress in the understanding of organic reactions. From knowledge of many reaction mechanisms we make generalizations that help us to predict new reactions. Moreover, we are able to predict experimental conditions that will optimize a reaction (e.g., produce a desired product more quickly or more efficiently.)

The cleavage of the halogen-halogen bond is merely the first step in the mechanism of the reaction of a halogen with an alkane. We will explore the remaining steps and discuss their implications in Chapter 13. We delay our discussion of the entire mechanism until we have covered several further concepts that will help us to appreciate fully the implications of the reaction mechanism.

While the halogen substitution reaction may appear to be a useful chemical conversion, there are actually several limitations. Two of these are illustrated in Figure 4.12. If all of the carbon-hydrogen bonds in the molecule are *not* the same, more than one product can result. We say that reactions that produce

Figure 4.12 The lack of selectivity in the halogenation reaction of alkanes.

$$CH_3CH_2CH_2CH_3 \xrightarrow[h\nu]{Cl_2} :\ddot{\underset{..}{Cl}}CH_2CH_2CH_2CH_3 + CH_3\underset{:\underset{..}{Cl}:}{\underset{|}{C}}HCH_2CH_3$$

$$CH_4 \xrightarrow[h\nu]{Cl_2} CH_3Cl + CH_2Cl_2 + CHCl_3 + CCl_4$$

more than one product are not *selective*. Moreover, more than one hydrogen atom in a molecule of alkane may be substituted by a halogen atom, leading to di-, tri-, and further halogenated products, another manifestation of the lack of selectivity.

PROBLEM 4.11 How many different products of formula $C_8H_{17}Cl$ can be obtained by monochlorination of each of the compounds listed below? Draw the structure of each product and name it.

a. 2,2,3,3-tetramethylbutane **b.** 2,5-dimethylhexane

4.4 The Sources of Strain

We have seen that cyclopropane has a higher energy content per methylene group than other cycloalkanes. Using our orbital model, we rationalized the high energy content of cyclopropane in terms of strain associated with inefficient orbital overlap in the small ring. We refer to this type of strain as **angle strain.** We now need to discuss other types of strain present in alkanes and cycloalkanes.

TORSIONAL STRAIN

In Chapter 2 we discussed the different conformations that can be adopted by an ethane molecule. Of the extreme conformations, staggered and eclipsed, the staggered is more stable by about 3.0 kcal/mole. We describe the eclipsed conformation as having 3.0 kcal/mole of strain energy. This type of strain is known as **torsional strain.** The major factor producing torsional strain in eclipsed ethane is the eclipsing interactions of three pairs of carbon-hydrogen bonds. The repulsion of the electrons in a pair of carbon-hydrogen bonds when they are at the minimal distance destabilizes the molecule by about 1.0 kcal/mole compared with their maximal separation, as is illustrated in Figure 4.13.

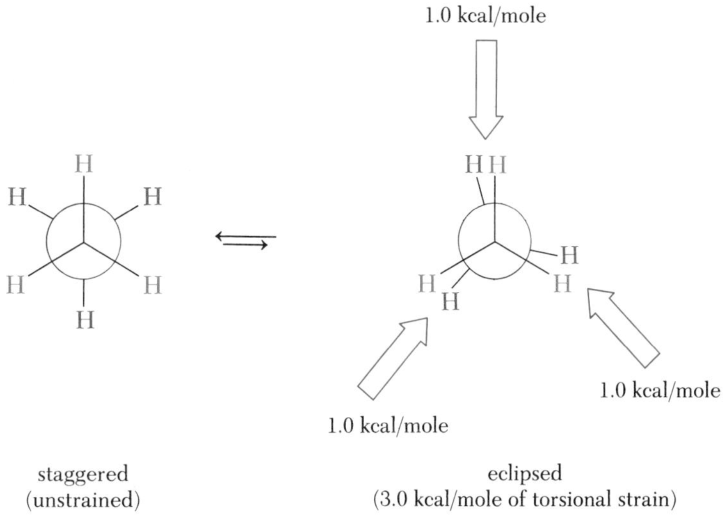

Figure 4.13 Energetics of ethane conformations. Each hydrogen-hydrogen interaction destabilizes the conformation by about 1.0 kcal/mole (4.2 kJ/mole).

Figure 4.14 Conformations of propane. The staggered and eclipsed forms differ in energy by 3.4 kcal/mole (14.2 kJ/mole).

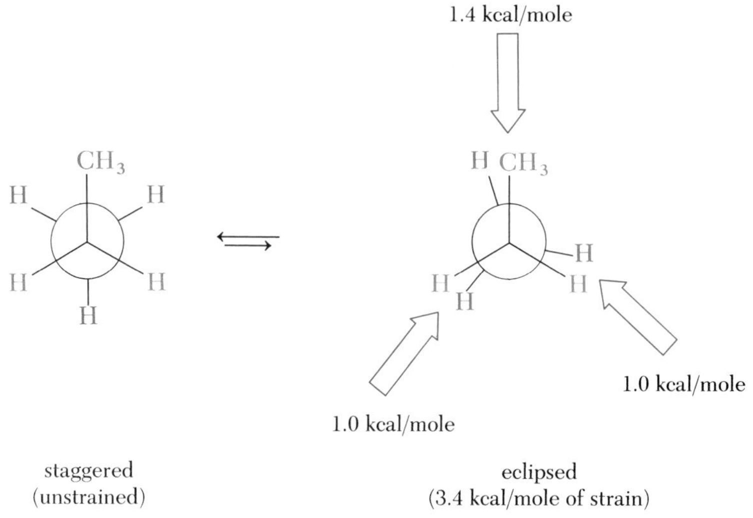

1.4 kcal/mole

CH_3 H H H H H

H CH_3 H H H H

1.0 kcal/mole

1.0 kcal/mole

staggered
(unstrained)

eclipsed
(3.4 kcal/mole of strain)

STERIC STRAIN

The staggered and eclipsed conformations of propane differ in stability by 3.4 kcal/mole. In the eclipsed conformation of propane there are two hydrogen-hydrogen and one methyl-hydrogen eclipsing interactions, as illustrated in Figure 4.14.

Notice that the methyl-hydrogen interaction imposes 0.4 kcal/mole of additional strain on top of the 1.0 kcal/mole torsional strain we have learned to associate with eclipsing interactions. This additional strain is referred to as **steric strain.** Steric strain results when two atoms or groups approach within a distance shorter than the sum of their van der Waals radii. The **van der Waals radius** of an atom or group is defined as one half of the distance between two equivalent atoms or groups when they are separated by the distance giving the minimum energy. It is a measure of the effective size of the group.

Earlier (in Chapter 3) we discussed van der Waals *attractive* forces, which account for the tendency of atoms and molecules to stick together. If the molecules are *too* close to each other (closer than the sum of the van der Waals radii), however, these forces become repulsive. The repulsive interaction of their overlapping electron clouds offsets any attractive forces. In general, as two atoms (or molecules) approach, there will be an increasing van der Waals attractive interaction until, at a distance corresponding to the sum of the van der Waals radii, an energy minimum (stability maximum) is attained. Closer approach of the atoms or molecules results in a repulsion from destabilizing overlap of their filled electron orbitals. Some representative values of van der Waals radii are given in Table 4.2.

When the propane molecule is in an eclipsed conformation, the methyl group and the hydrogen do happen to approach closer than the sum of their van der Waals radii, thus accounting for the additional 0.4 kcal/mole of strain.

We encounter important examples of steric strain in both alkanes and cycloalkanes. Let's look at butane as an example. We will focus on conformations

Table 4.2 van der Waals Radii for Selected Atoms and Groups

Atom or Group	van der Waals Radius (angstroms)
H	1.2
F	1.35
O	1.4
N	1.5
Cl	1.8
S	1.85
P	1.9
CH_2	2.0
CH_3	2.0

that arise through rotation about the central carbon-carbon bond. With butane, as with ethane, there are staggered and eclipsed conformations. With ethane, all eclipsed conformations have the same energy, and all staggered conformations have the same energy. However, the butane molecule is more complicated. Figure 4.15 shows an energy diagram for the various conformations of ethane. A corresponding energy diagram for butane is shown in Figure 4.16.

Figure 4.15 Potential energy as a function of bond rotation in ethane.

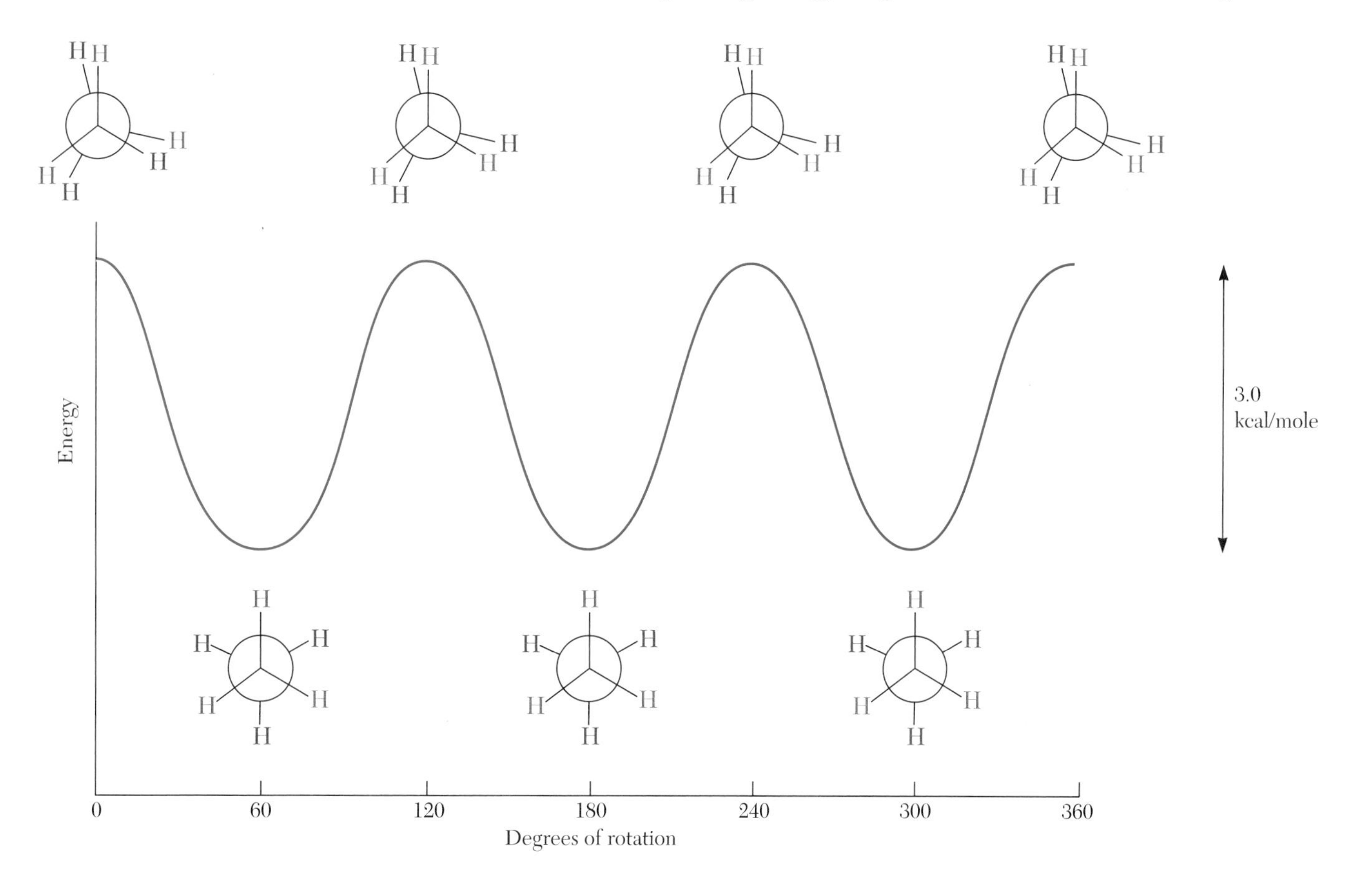

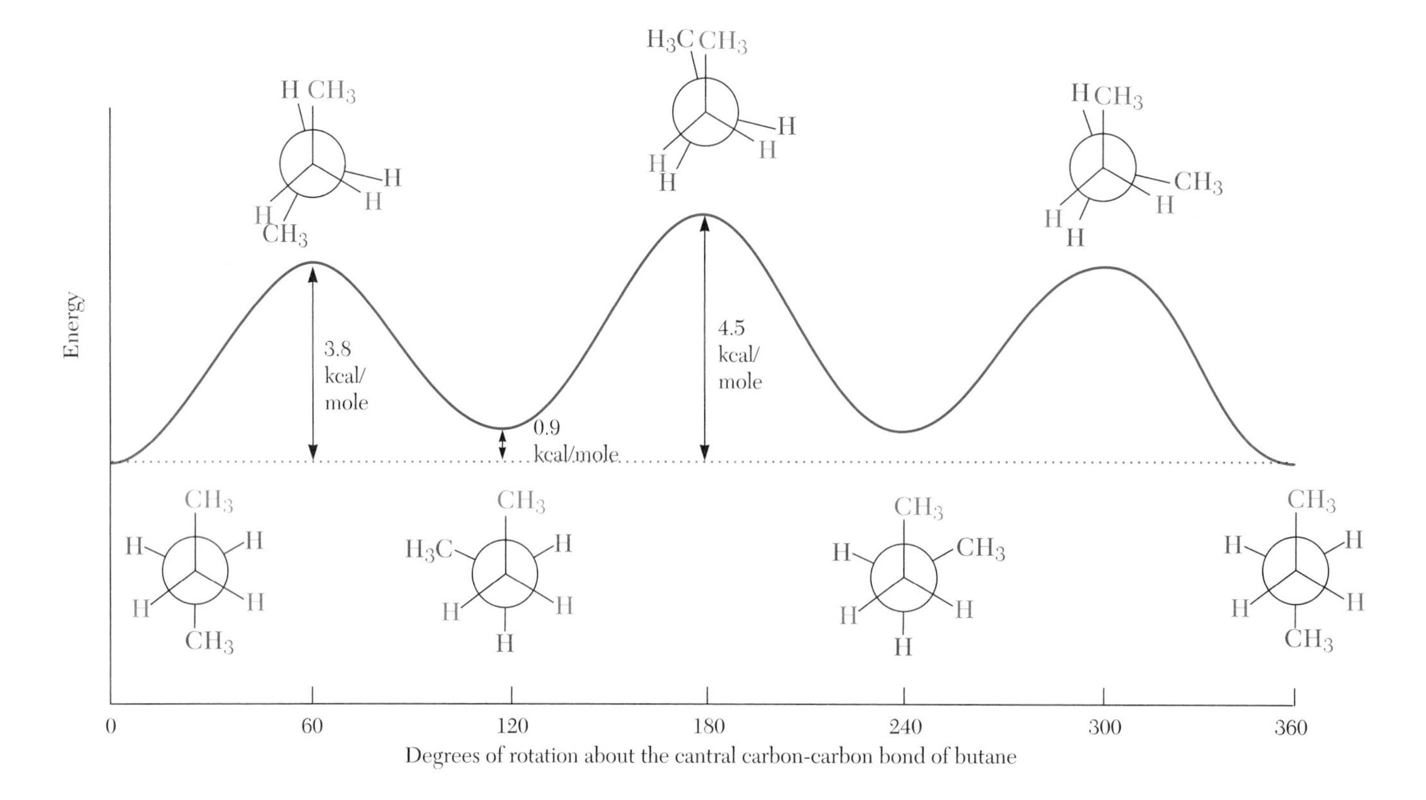

Figure 4.16 Change in potential energy plotted against the degree of rotation about the central carbon-carbon bond of butane.

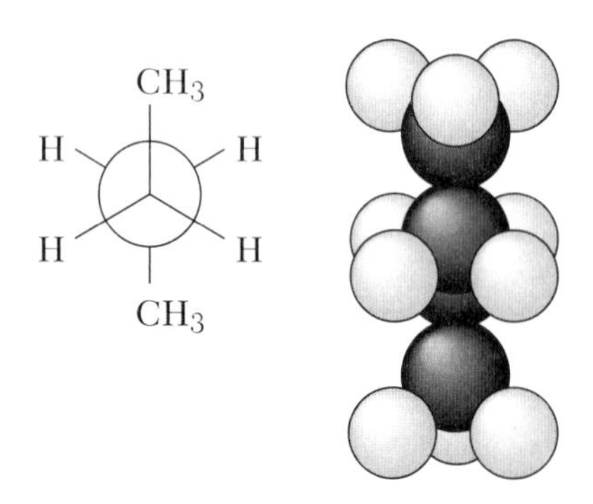

Figure 4.17 The anti conformation of butane. The methyl groups are as far apart as possible in this conformation.

The lowest energy form of butane is a staggered conformation in which the two largest groups (methyl groups) are as far apart as possible. This particular staggered conformation is known as an *anti conformation,* and it is illustrated again in Figure 4.17.

If we rotate the rear carbon through 60°, while holding the front carbon steady, we generate an eclipsed conformation in which there is one carbon-hydrogen/carbon-hydrogen torsional strain interaction, and two carbon-methyl/carbon-hydrogen torsional/steric interactions. This conformation is shown in Figure 4.18. Using the 1.0 kcal/mole and 1.4 kcal/mole values we deduced earlier for these types of interactions, we predict that this eclipsed form is more strained than the anti conformation by 3.8 kcal/mole (15.9 kJ/mole), and this prediction agrees with the experimentally determined value.

If we continue to rotate through another 60° we arrive at a different staggered conformation. We find this particular staggered conformation, which we refer to as a **gauche** conformation, to be 0.9 kcal/mole less stable than the anti conformation. It is strained, even though it contains no eclipsing interactions. The strain is steric in origin. The methyl groups approach within a distance less than the sum of their van der Waals radii. The gauche structure is shown in Figure 4.19.

We can also analyze other conformations resulting from further rotation about the carbon-carbon bond. The least stable butane conformation has associated with it 4.5 kcal/mole of strain. It is an eclipsed conformation in which the two methyl groups are as close as possible. We deduce that the methyl-methyl eclipsing interaction is destabilizing by about 2.5 kcal/mole, significantly

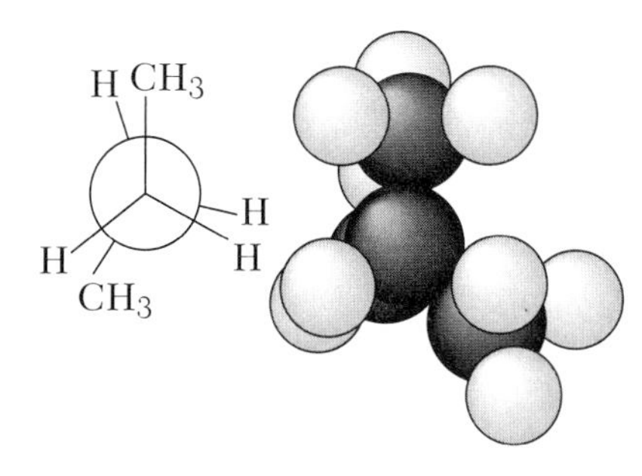

Figure 4.18 An eclipsed conformation of butane. This eclipsed conformation is 3.8 kcal/mole (15.9 kJ/mole) higher in energy than the anti conformation of butane.

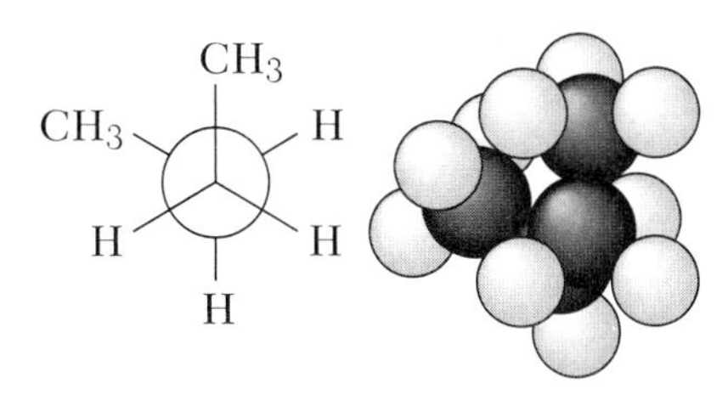

Figure 4.19 The gauche conformation of butane. There is 0.9 kcal/mole steric strain associated with the methyl-methyl interaction.

larger than any interaction we have seen thus far. The value is large because it reflects two types of strain that are additive. There is torsional strain due to the eclipsing interaction, and there is steric strain due to the closeness of the methyl groups. In our further discussions we will consider in detail the effects of these types of strain on the shapes of cycloalkanes. We will also consider the chemical reactions of alkanes in greater detail.

As we have noted, the *known* chemistry of alkanes is rather limited, compared with that of other types of organic compounds. For example, there is no good general method for the direct conversion of an alkane to an alcohol or a carbonyl compound. Biological systems, however, illustrate what is possible. In certain biological organs, such as the human liver, enzymes bring about conversions that we cannot effect efficiently in the laboratory. For example, cyclohexane is converted to cyclohexanol in virtually quantitative (that is, 100%) yield. The development of catalysts or reaction systems that mimic what occurs in cells is an area that is ripe for further exploration. In fact, at elevated temperatures we *can* use oxygen in the presence of a cobalt catalyst to oxidize certain alkanes directly to alcohols, such as cyclohexane to cyclohexanol. This is an important industrial reaction that can be effected in high yield. Unfortunately, the efficiency of the reaction is not good for *all* alkanes so the reaction is not of general use.

We will now move to the study of a functional group that abounds with interesting chemistry, the hydroxyl group of the alcohols. In the following two chapters we will study not only some interesting chemistry, but we will also consider how we learn about chemistry and make generalizations for other functional groups.

Summary

- Alkanes and cycloalkanes show many similarities in their physical properties and chemical reactions.
- Heat of combustion measurements are of great use for comparing the relative stabilities of isomeric alkanes. We find that many molecules are strained.
- Strain can be subdivided into torsional strain, angle strain, and steric strain.
- Torsional strain results when groups that are bound to neighboring atoms are in an eclipsed relationship. Torsional strain is related to the mutual repulsion of the electron clouds of the bonds.
- Angle strain occurs when the bond angles in a molecule are forced to be different from normal values, resulting in poorer overlap of the participating orbitals and weaker bonds than in unstrained molecules.
- Steric strain occurs when two groups approach within a distance that is smaller than the sum of their van der Waals radii. An important example of steric strain is the gauche interaction of two methyl groups in butane.
- For cycloalkanes, profound differences are found when heats of combustion per methylene group are compared. These differences result from various combinations of the several types of strain.
- Alkanes and cycloalkanes undergo substitution reactions with bromine or chlorine under thermal or photochemical conditions. In many such reactions, mixtures of products are formed.

Terms to Remember

saturated hydrocarbons
cis relationship
trans relationship
geometric isomers
spirane
heat of combustion
methylene group
substitution
homolytic bond cleavage
angle strain
torsional strain
steric strain
van der Waals radius
gauche

Additional Problems

4.12 Give systematic IUPAC names to each of the compounds listed below. Specify *cis-* or *trans*-geometry where appropriate.

a. $(CH_3)_2CHCH_2CH(CH_3)_2$

b. Newman projection: front carbon CH_3 (top), H, H; back carbon H, H, CH_2CH_3 (bottom)

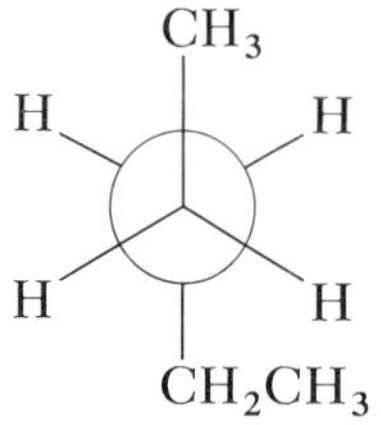

c. Newman projection: front carbon CH_3 (top), H, H; back carbon CH_3, H, CH_2CH_3 (bottom)

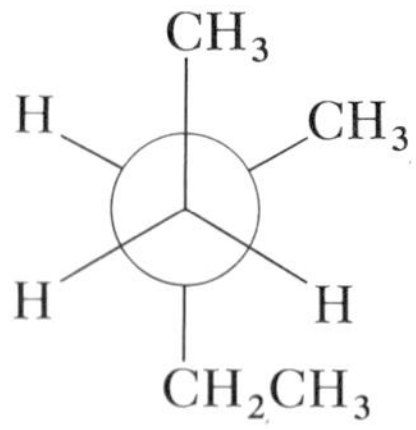

d. $CH_3CH_2CH_2CH_2\underset{|}{C}HCH_2CH_2CH_3$ with $CH(CH_3)_2$ on the branching carbon

e. (spiro compound of two five-membered rings)

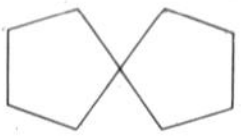

f. (spiro compound of a six-membered ring and a three-membered ring)

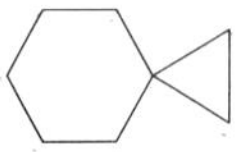

g. cyclopentane with $CH(CH_3)_2$ (wedge) and $CH(CH_3)_2$ (dash)

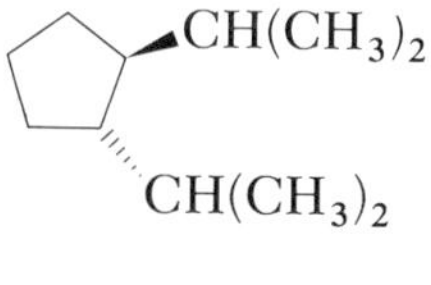

h. cyclobutane attached to CH_2CHCH_3, with cyclohexane on the CH_2

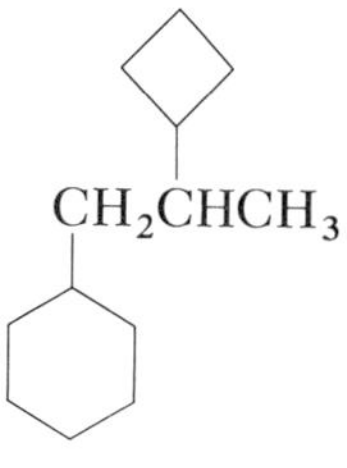

i. $(CH_3CH_2)_2CHCH_2CHCH_3$ with $C(CH_3)_2CH_2CH_3$ on the CH

j. cyclobutane bearing $CH_3CH_2CH(CH_3)$ (wedge) and $CH(CH_3)CH_2CH_3$ (wedge)

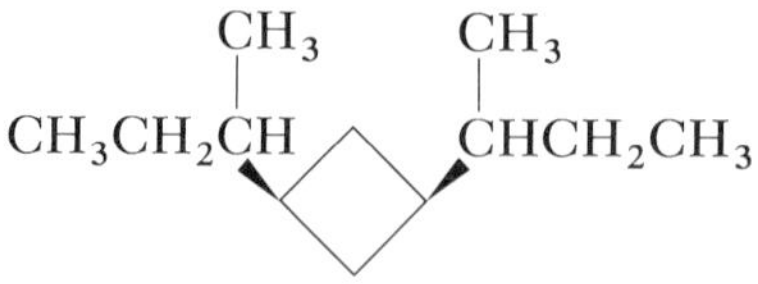

4.13 Consider the alkanes of the general structure R—R, where R is each of the groups listed below. Name each of these alkanes by the IUPAC method (review Chapter 2 if necessary).

a. isobutyl b. *sec*-butyl c. *tert*-butyl

4.14 Suggest structures and give names for alkanes or cycloalkanes having the following characteristics:
 a. C_5H_{10}; contains a quaternary carbon atom
 b. C_5H_{12}; contains nine primary, two secondary, and one tertiary hydrogen atoms
 c. a compound that reacts with bromine in a substitution reaction to give a *single* monobrominated product of formula $C_5H_{11}Br$
 d. the C_5H_{12} isomer with the lowest boiling point
 e. contains four carbon atoms and *only* secondary hydrogen atoms

4.15 Use a Newman projection to show 3,4-dimethylhexane in a staggered conformation as viewed along the central carbon-carbon bond (C_3—C_4) with two hydrogen atoms in an anti relationship.

4.16 Draw all possible cycloalkane structures that have the following characteristics:
 a. C_6H_{12}; contains one ring and has an isopropyl group
 b. C_7H_{14}; contains one ring and has an isobutyl group
 c. C_7H_{14}; contains one ring and has an isopropyl group
 d. C_6H_{12}; contains one ring and has two methyl groups

4.17 From each pair of compounds, choose the one with the indicated property, and give an explanation of your choice.
 a. higher boiling point: nonane or 3,3-diethylpentane
 b. higher heat of combustion: hexane or isohexane
 c. higher heat of combustion: butane or methylcyclopropane
 d. most hydrogen atoms per molecule: cyclopentane or spiropentane
 e. contains only secondary hydrogen atoms: cyclobutane or butane
 f. higher heat of combustion: *cis-* or *trans*-1,2-dimethylcyclopropane

4.18 Consider the conformations of octane produced by rotation about the central carbon-carbon bond. Use Newman projections to depict each of the following:
 a. the conformation of lowest energy **b.** a gauche conformation
 c. the conformation of highest energy **d.** an anti conformation

4.19 Show all structures and give an IUPAC name for all of the compounds having the general name trimethylcyclobutane.

4.20 A chemist allows hexane to react with chlorine under irradiation with light. She isolates three isomers of formula $C_6H_{13}Cl$. Give the IUPAC name for each of these compounds.

4.21 Draw a set of Newman projections for 2-methylpentane in 60° increments as viewed along the C_2—C_3 bond. Graph the potential energy changes during a complete cycle of rotation (360°).

4.22 Calculate the percentages (by mass) of carbon and hydrogen present in each of the following compounds:
 a. cyclooctane **b.** spiropentane

4.23 Calculate the empirical formula of a hydrocarbon that yields 8.94 mg of water and 31.18 mg of carbon dioxide on combustion of a 9.61 mg sample. Is this empirical formula also the molecular formula? How do you know?

4.24 Could you distinguish between cyclohexane and cyclononane on the basis of their combustion analysis? Why or why not?

4.25 Consider again the octane molecule, which was discussed in Problem 4.18. Using molecular models, view the model of the conformation described in part c. Does it represent a conformation having a *single* specific energy (relative to the other conformations), or are there several possible relationships (with different energies) for the propyl groups attached to the viewed atoms? Explain your answer.

CHAPTER 5 Methanol and Ethanol

5.1 Introduction

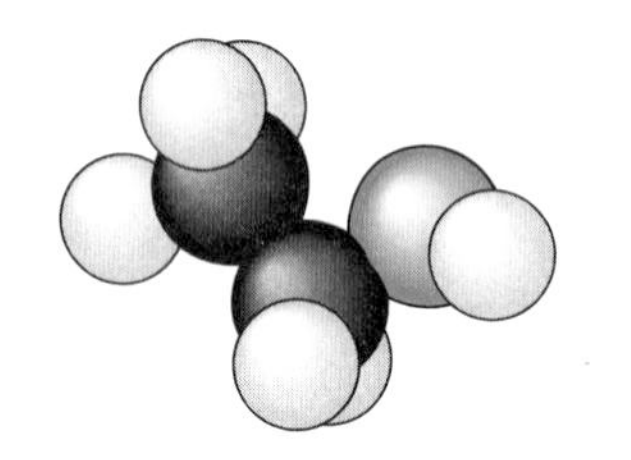

Alcohols are represented by the general formula R—OH, where R indicates an alkyl group. The two simplest members of the alcohol family, methanol ($R = CH_3$) and ethanol ($R = CH_3CH_2$), are among the oldest known organic compounds to have been purified. Both can be obtained from natural sources or synthesized commercially, and both find widespread use in industry and in the laboratory.

The **hydroxyl group** ($-\ddot{O}H$), the functional group of alcohols, is also present in water ($H-\ddot{O}H$). There are important similarities (and differences) in the properties of water and alcohols. This chapter provides an introduction to the chemistry of the alcohols by focusing on methanol and ethanol and by comparing and contrasting them with water.

5.2 Methanol: Manufacture and Use

Methanol can be manufactured from wood by a process known as destructive distillation. Wood is heated to temperatures above 250 °C in the absence of air. Under these conditions the large molecules present in wood are split (degraded) into smaller ones. One of these smaller molecules is methanol. Methanol has a relatively low boiling temperature and volatilizes under the destructive distillation conditions. It is collected by allowing it to distill into a receiving vessel, where it condenses as a colorless liquid. Because this process was once a standard manufacturing procedure, the name *wood alcohol* is sometimes used to describe methanol. (This process is no longer of commercial significance.)

A different procedure is now used to manufacture methanol on the large scale needed for industry (about 10 million tons per year). Carbon monoxide and hydrogen are heated in the presence of a catalyst in a high-pressure reaction vessel. The reaction is shown in Equation 5.1.

Eqn. 5.1

$$CO + 2\,H_2 \xrightarrow[400\,°C,\ 150\ atm]{ZnO/Cr_2O_3} CH_3OH$$

Most manufactured methanol is converted into other useful chemicals. However, some is used for gasoline feedstocks, and it is a useful solvent. Methanol has also been used in the commercial production of proteins. Some yeasts and bacteria are able to use methanol as a carbon source for synthesizing proteins (Chapter 26). The protein synthesis is performed in an aqueous nutrient solution that contains appropriate nitrogen, sulfur, and phosphorus compounds. The proteins produced have been used as a feed supplement for animals. Methanol itself is highly toxic and causes blindness or death if taken internally.

5.3 Ethanol: Manufacture and Use

Ethanol is the principal alcohol present in alcoholic beverages. (Depending on the type and brand, small amounts of other alcohols are also present.) Ethanol has been prepared by the yeast fermentation of aqueous solutions of sugars and starches and used as a component of beverages since ancient times. Common fermentation sources for ethanol production are corn, blackstrap molasses (the residue remaining after the purification of cane sugar), rice, potatoes, and grain (hence the term *grain alcohol*), grape and other fruit juices, and certain vegetables. The process of fermentation of sugars (carbohydrates, Chapter 24) proceeds under the catalytic influence of enzymes. Many steps are involved, and different enzymes catalyze the different steps. Under fermentation conditions yeast acts on an aqueous solution of the sugar or starch. As the reaction proceeds, carbon dioxide is evolved and ethanol is formed. The maximum concentration of alcohol produced in the solution by this method is in the range 12–15%. (Higher concentrations are toxic to yeast.)

Ethanol, like methanol, is a bulk industrial chemical. The usual sources of industrial ethanol are fermentation (described above) and synthesis. The usual starting material for synthesizing ethanol is ethylene ($H_2C{=}CH_2$), which is in turn prepared (in billions of pounds per year) from natural gas. Regardless of the method of production, ethanol is obtained mixed with water. When this mixture is distilled, an azeotrope (a constant boiling mixture) of approximately 95% ethanol and 5% water is obtained. This mixture is satisfactory for many purposes, but there is sometimes a need for pure (100%) ethanol, which is also known as *absolute ethanol.*

Various methods are available to decrease the water content from the 5% level to zero. One method involves adding quicklime (calcium oxide, CaO), which reacts with water to produce calcium hydroxide but has no effect on the ethanol. Ethanol dried in this way is purified by a simple distillation.

Another approach involves the formation of a minimum-boiling ternary azeotrope of water, ethanol, and cyclohexane. When the water has been removed, a binary azeotrope of cyclohexane and ethanol distills until pure ethanol remains.

Ethanol has many uses. Like methanol, it can be used as a fuel. Mixtures of gasoline and ethanol are referred to as *gasohol*. Ethanol is used as the starting material for the manufacture of other important organic substances, and, like methanol, can serve as a carbon source for biological protein synthesis. Ethanol is also used commonly as a solvent. It has a dissolving ability for a wide range of solutes. It is significantly less toxic than methanol, but it is addictive. In its role as an addictive drug, ethanol is responsible for millions of dollars of damage per year worldwide.

5.4 Determination of Molecular Structure

We can perform quantitative elemental analyses of methanol, ethanol, and other compounds in the same manner we described in Chapter 4 for hydrocarbons.

Qualitative elemental determinations indicate that three elements (carbon, hydrogen, and oxygen) are present in both methanol and ethanol. Combustion analysis yields the amount of carbon and hydrogen only. Usually no direct analysis for oxygen is performed on organic compounds due to experimental difficulties. Instead, we normally analyze for all other elements and then assume that any weight unaccounted for is oxygen. Such analysis leads to the formulas CH_4O and C_2H_6O for methanol and ethanol, respectively.

PROBLEM 5.1 Combustion of a 10.16-mg sample of methanol produces 11.43 mg of water and 13.96 mg of carbon dioxide. Molecular weight measurements show the molecular weight of methanol to be 32 g/mole. Show that these analytical data lead to the molecular formula CH_4O for methanol.

PROBLEM 5.2 A sample of 4.00 mg of vitamin C is subjected to combustion analysis, which produces 6.00 mg of carbon dioxide and 1.63 mg of water. Other analyses reveal that carbon, hydrogen, and oxygen are the only elements present, and mass spectrometric analysis reveals a molecular weight of 128 g/mole for vitamin C. Find the molecular formula for vitamin C.

The molecular formula CH_4O for methanol is consistent with just one structure (CH_3OH) in which all atoms form their usual number of bonds. However, the molecular formula of ethanol, C_2H_6O is shared by two isomeric structures, CH_3OCH_3 and CH_3CH_2OH. One of them must correspond to the structure of ethanol, but which one?

Early chemists observed striking similarities in the properties of water, methanol, and ethanol (these similarities will be discussed in the following sections of this chapter). These observations led to the conclusion that the three materials had a common structural unit, the hydroxyl group (—OH), and the choice of the structure CH_3CH_2OH for ethanol.

Chemical similarities are still used occasionally by chemists to help in structure determinations. However, physical methods such as infrared and nuclear magnetic resonance spectrometry have now assumed the central role in molecular structure elucidation. (These techniques will be described in Chapter 17). For the present let us simply note that the infrared spectra of all alcohols (and water) exhibit characteristic signature patterns that we associate with the O—H bond.

5.5 Water, Methanol, and Ethanol: Physical Similarities

Some common physical properties of methanol, ethanol, and water are listed in Table 5.1. Methanol and ethanol are both volatile, flammable liquids that are less dense than water.

Table 5.1 Some Physical Properties of Methanol and Ethanol

Property	Methanol	Ethanol	Water
Boiling Temperature (°C)	64.65	78.5	100
Melting Temperature (°C)	−97.8	−117.3	0
Density (g/mL, 20 °C)	0.7914	0.7893	0.9982
Refractive Index	1.33118	1.36242	1.333
Water Solubility	miscible	miscible	—
*Flash Point (°C)	52	55	—
†Ignition Temperature (°C)	725	689	—
Lethal Dose (lowest recorded oral, human) (mg/Kg)	340	2000	—

* The lowest temperature at which vapors of a substance will ignite momentarily upon application of a flame in air.

† The lowest temperature at which combustion begins and continues upon heating in air.

Table 5.2 Boiling Temperatures of Water, Simple Alcohols, and Alkanes of Similar Molecular Weights

Compound	Molecular Weight (g/mole)	Boiling Temperature (°C)
$H\ddot{O}H$	18	100
CH_4	16	−161
$CH_3\ddot{O}H$	32	64.65
CH_3CH_3	30	−89
$CH_3CH_2\ddot{O}H$	46	78.5
$CH_3CH_2CH_3$	44	−45

Water, methanol, and ethanol are all colorless liquids under normal conditions. That all three are liquids is revealing because many compounds of similar molecular weight are gases at ordinary temperature and pressure. Comparisons of the three compounds with alkanes of similar molecular weight are shown in Table 5.2.

The relatively high boiling temperatures of water and these alcohols result from hydrogen-bonding interactions among neighboring molecules. It is particularly noteworthy that even methanol, the simplest alcohol, is a liquid. The simplest members of most classes of organic compounds are gases at room temperature, as can be seen in Table 5.3.

Table 5.3 Comparison of the Simplest Members of Several Classes of Organic Compounds

Class	Simplest Member	Boiling Temperature (°C)	Physical State (20 °C)
Alkane	CH_4	−161	gas
Alcohol	$CH_3\ddot{O}H$	65	liquid
Alkene	$H_2C{=}CH_2$	−104	gas
Alkyne	$HC{\equiv}CH$	−84 (sublimes)	gas
Ether	$CH_3\ddot{O}CH_3$	−24	gas
Aldehyde	$H_2C{=}\ddot{O}$	−21	gas
Amine	$CH_3\ddot{N}H_2$	−7	gas
Fluoride	$CH_3\ddot{F}:$	−79	gas
Chloride	$CH_3\ddot{Cl}:$	−24	gas
Acid	$H{-}C({=}\ddot{O}){-}\ddot{O}H$	100.7	liquid

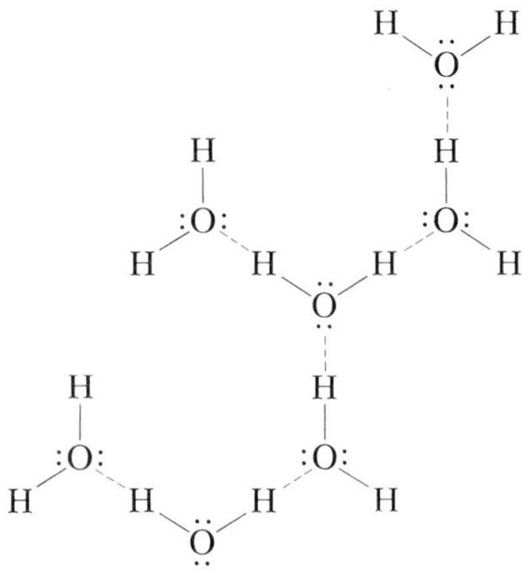

Figure 5.1 Hydrogen bonding among molecules in liquid water. Each water molecule can participate in hydrogen bonding using both hydrogen atoms. The effect continues in three dimensions. Some of the possible hydrogen bonds to each oxygen are omitted in the interest of clarity.

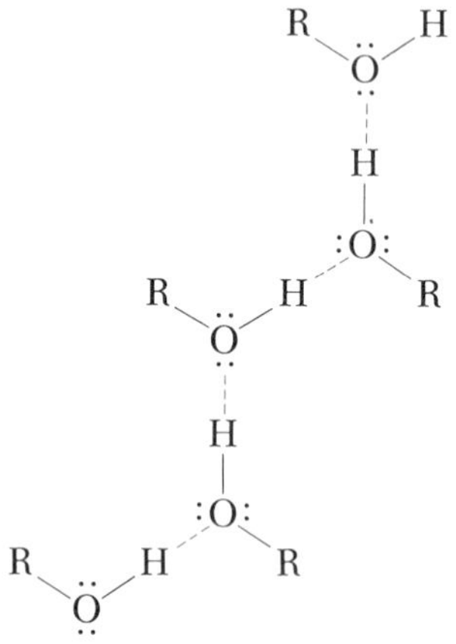

Figure 5.2 Hydrogen bonding among alcohol molecules. The alkyl groups cannot participate in hydrogen bonding. Again, some of the possible bonds to each oxygen are omitted.

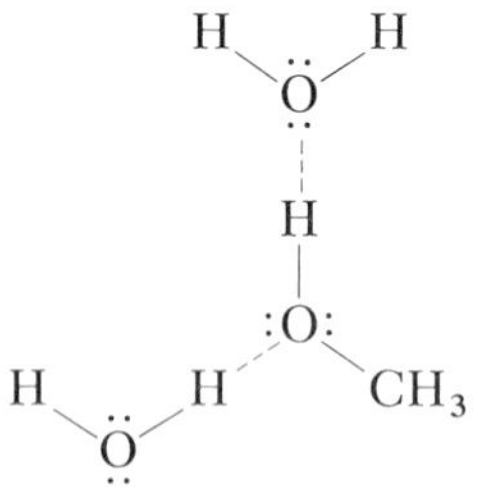

Figure 5.3 Formation of hydrogen bonds between water and methanol molecules. This hydrogen bonding plays a key role in the miscibility of the two substances. Again, some of the possible hydrogen bonds are omitted.

Of the compounds listed in Table 5.3, only two (methanol and formic acid) are liquids at room temperature. Both compounds have strong intermolecular associations through hydrogen bonding (see Chapter 3).

Consider boiling temperatures in a little more detail. The boiling temperature of water (mol wt 18) is 261 C° higher than that of methane (mol wt 16). However, the boiling temperature of methanol (mol wt 32) is only 154 C° above that of ethane (mol wt 30). The extra-high boiling temperature of water can be attributed to more efficient hydrogen bonding. Both the hydrogen atoms and the oxygen atom of water participate in hydrogen bonding, as illustrated in Figure 5.1.

By contrast, an alcohol molecule has only one hydrogen that can participate in hydrogen bonding with other alcohol molecules, as shown in Figure 5.2. Its alkyl group cannot participate in hydrogen bonding since it lacks a hydrogen atom directly attached to a highly electronegative atom.

Because their hydrogen bonding is more extensive, water molecules form larger aggregates than do alcohol molecules, and greater amounts of energy are required to break up larger aggregates. As a result, water has a higher boiling temperature than either methanol or ethanol, in spite of the higher molecular weights of the alcohols.

Methanol and ethanol are miscible with water. That is, mixing water with methanol or ethanol in any proportion produces a solution. For alcohols in general, two factors compete in governing their solubility properties. The polar hydroxyl group tends to favor associations with other polar molecules through hydrogen bonding and dipole-dipole interactions. The nonpolar alkyl group of an alcohol tends to favor associations with nonpolar molecules through van der Waals interactions. For the lower molecular weight alcohols, the nonpolar alkyl group plays a relatively minor role. Methanol and ethanol are fully water soluble because their molecules can form hydrogen bonds as or more effectively with water molecules than with similar alcohol molecules, as shown in Figure 5.3.

Water molecules are able to surround fully alcohol molecules that contain small alkyl groups. The entire molecule can become encapsulated in the water structure, as shown in Figure 5.4.

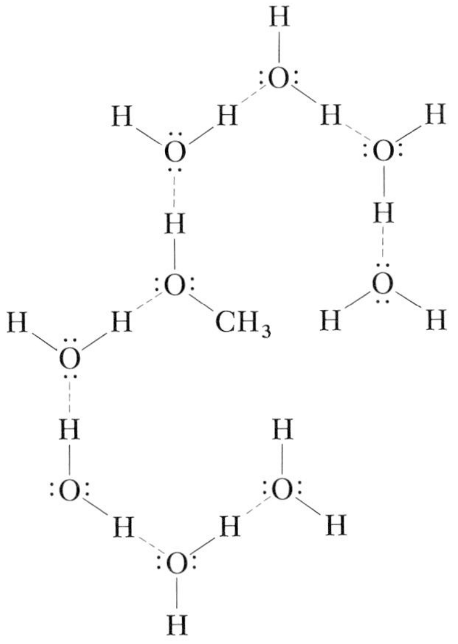

Figure 5.4 Dissolution of methanol in water. The entire methanol molecule can be surrounded by water molecules without appreciably disturbing the continuum of favorable hydrogen bonding interactions. The effect continues in three dimensions.

COMPOUND CAPSULE

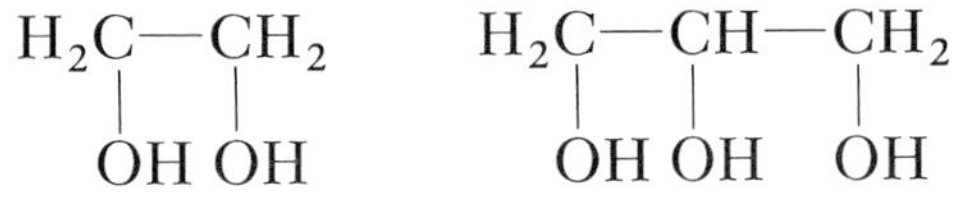

$H_2C{-}CH_2$ with OH on each carbon — **Ethylene Glycol**

$H_2C{-}CH{-}CH_2$ with OH on each carbon — **Glycerol**

Diols and triols are substances that contain two and three hydroxyl groups, respectively. The simplest diol is ethane-1,2-diol, usually known as ethylene glycol, and the simplest triol is propane-1,2,3-triol, commonly known as glycerine or glycerol. Both of these substances are oily, viscous materials. Their viscosity results from the ability of the molecules to hydrogen bond to neighbors through more than one hydroxyl group. As a result of their hydrogen-bonding capabilities, these compounds are miscible with water. Ethylene glycol is commonly used as an antifreeze in the cooling systems of automobiles. Its miscibility with water allows us to prepare aqueous solutions having very low freezing temperatures, while at the same time having relatively high boiling temperatures.

Some insects use glycerol as their own antifreeze. Such insects accumulate glycerol in their cells (up to 15%) during the fall to protect themselves from low temperatures during the winter months by avoiding damage to cells from ice crystal formation. With a glycerol content of 15%, eggs of the moth *Alsophilia pomentaria* can be cooled to temperatures as low as −45 °C before fatal ice crystal formation occurs.

Larger alkyl groups prevent this type of encapsulation and greatly disturb the continuum of hydrogen-bonding interactions, as shown in Figure 5.5. The solubility in water of alcohols with large alkyl groups is greatly decreased. (Solubilities of heavier alcohols in water are listed in Chapter 6.)

Figure 5.5 Association of water and 1-heptanol molecules. The water cannot completely surround the 1-heptanol molecule without appreciable loss of favorable hydrogen bonding among water molecules. 1-Heptanol has a very low water solubility.

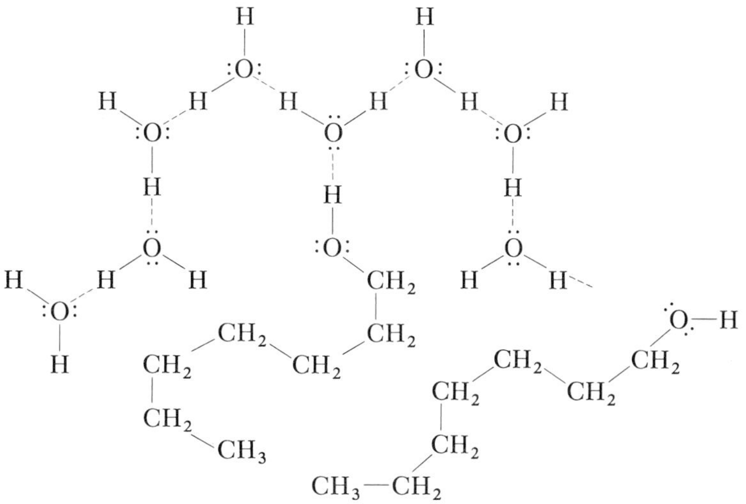

5.6 Water, Methanol, and Ethanol: Chemical Similarities

REACTIONS WITH ACTIVE METALS

The effect of dropping a small pellet of sodium or potassium into water is quite spectacular. A vigorous reaction takes place during which hydrogen gas is evolved. With potassium the reaction is sufficiently violent to ignite the hydrogen immediately, as it is if a large amount of sodium is used. The metal is reduced to a cation that goes into solution. This reaction is described in Equation 5.2 for sodium.

Eqn. 5.2

$$H_2\ddot{O} + Na\cdot \longrightarrow Na^+(aq) + H\ddot{O}\colon^-(aq) + \tfrac{1}{2}H_2(g)$$

Evaporation of the resultant aqueous solution yields pure sodium hydroxide as a white solid.

If sodium metal is added to methanol or to ethanol, very similar experimental observations are made. The reaction is less vigorous, but hydrogen gas is again evolved. On evaporation of the excess alcohol, a white solid is obtained. This white solid is an **alkoxide salt.** The reaction of sodium with methanol is described in Equation 5.3.

Eqn. 5.3

$$CH_3\ddot{O}H + Na\cdot \longrightarrow Na^+(solv) + CH_3\ddot{O}\colon^-(solv) + \tfrac{1}{2}H_2(g)$$

On evaporation of the excess methanol, the salt sodium methoxide ($NaOCH_3$) is obtained. Notice the nomenclature used for the anion of this salt—it reflects the structural similarity between HO^- (hydroxide) and CH_3O^- (methoxide).

PROBLEM 5.3 A compound with a molecular weight of approximately 60 g/mole gives the following result on combustion analysis:

%C in sample = 60.02

%H in sample = 13.33

The compound is found to contain only carbon, hydrogen, and oxygen, and it does *not* react with sodium metal. Give the molecular structure of the compound.

ALCOHOLS AS ACIDS

An alkoxide ion, RO^-, is the conjugate base of an alcohol, ROH. We therefore anticipate that reaction of a suitable base with an alcohol should yield an alkoxide ion. We find this indeed to be true. The alcohol in such a reaction behaves as a Brønsted acid, donating a proton to the base, as is illustrated in Equation 5.4.

Eqn. 5.4

$$CH_3\ddot{O}H + [Base]^- \rightleftharpoons Base{-}H + CH_3\ddot{O}\colon^-$$

In Chapter 3 we noted that the position of equilibrium in such reactions is to the side of the equation containing the weaker acid and weaker base. In order to push the equilibrium to favor the formation of methoxide ion, it is necessary to use a base appreciably stronger than the methoxide ion. The base most common to students of introductory chemistry is hydroxide ion. However, the strengths of the hydroxide ion and the methoxide ion as bases are rather similar. The methoxide ion is actually somewhat stronger than the hydroxide ion. Accordingly, hydroxide ion is not the best choice for a base to use in preparing methoxide ion from methanol. The equilibrium for the reaction shown in Equation 5.5 lies somewhat to the left in aqueous solution.

Eqn. 5.5

$$\underset{\text{weaker acid}}{CH_3\ddot{O}H} + \underset{\text{weaker base}}{H\ddot{O}:^-} \rightleftharpoons \underset{\text{stronger base}}{CH_3\ddot{O}:^-} + \underset{\text{stronger acid}}{H_2\ddot{O}}$$

In organic chemistry we often need to use bases that are appreciably stronger than hydroxide ion in order to achieve an efficient reaction. In Chapter 3 we introduced several guidelines for estimating the strength of bases and acids. One base that is stronger than hydroxide ion is the amide ion (NH_2^-). We find that when potassium amide (KNH_2) is added to methanol, the reaction proceeds dominantly to the right-hand side, as shown in Equation 5.6.

Eqn. 5.6

$$\underset{\text{stronger acid}}{CH_3\ddot{O}H} + \underset{\text{stronger base}}{\ddot{N}H_2^-} \rightleftharpoons \underset{\text{weaker base}}{CH_3\ddot{O}:^-} + \underset{\text{weaker acid}}{:NH_3(g)}$$

Note that methoxide ion reacts with water to form hydroxide ion (the reverse reaction of Equation 5.5.) This reaction illustrates a fundamental aspect of acid-base equilibria. *The strongest base that can exist in a solvent is the conjugate base of the neutral solvent.* Any stronger base added to the solvent converts it predominantly to its conjugate base.

PROBLEM 5.4

Methyllithium (CH_3Li) behaves as a source of the strong base methide ion ($H_3C:^-$). Write an equation for the reaction that you would predict when methyllithium is added to each of the substances listed below. Illustrate each reaction using the curved-arrow formalism.

a. water **b.** methanol **c.** ethanol

ALCOHOLS AS BASES

Within the hydroxyl group of alcohols is an oxygen atom with two unshared pairs of electrons. Alcohols can thus function as Brønsted bases, using one of the two unshared electron pairs to bind a proton (H^+) from some suitable donor. In doing so the oxygen atom acquires a third bond and a formal positive charge. Positive ions with three bonds to oxygen are known as **oxonium ions.**

When methyl alcohol accepts a proton, the methyloxonium ion is formed, as shown in Equation. 5.7.

Eqn. 5.7

$$CH_3—\ddot{\underset{..}{O}}—H + H^+ \longrightarrow CH_3—\overset{+}{\ddot{O}}\begin{matrix}H \\ H\end{matrix}$$

methyloxonium ion

Because alcohols are very weak bases, no significant concentration of oxonium ions is produced in aqueous solution. However, strong acids such as HCl and H_2SO_4 efficiently protonate alcohols. The oxonium ions produced in this way are quite reactive and often go on to react with other species in solution. We will discuss one such reaction later in this chapter (Section 5.8).

5.7 The Oxidation of Methanol and Ethanol

Most manufactured methanol is converted into formaldehyde using the reaction shown in Equation 5.8.

Eqn. 5.8

$$CH_3\ddot{\underset{..}{O}}H + O_2 \xrightarrow[600–700\,°C]{\text{Ag catalyst}} H_2C{=}\ddot{\underset{..}{O}} + H_2\ddot{\underset{..}{O}}$$

Approximately two million tons of formaldehyde are prepared annually by this route. Most of this formaldehyde is used to manufacture plastics. Formaldehyde, like methanol, is a significantly toxic material (see "Biological Oxidations" later in this chapter).

The conversion of methanol to formaldehyde is an **oxidation.** Oxidation and **reduction** are usually defined in terms of the loss (oxidation) or gain (reduction) of electrons. In introductory chemistry courses students learn how to use oxidation numbers to keep track of species undergoing oxidation and reduction. We commonly use the standard values of +1 and −2 as the oxidation numbers of hydrogen and oxygen atoms, respectively, in organic compounds. We can use these values, along with the rule that the sum of the oxidation numbers equals the charge on the molecule or ion as a whole, to derive oxidation numbers for the carbon atoms of methanol and formaldehyde as −2 and 0, respectively, as shown in Figure 5.6.

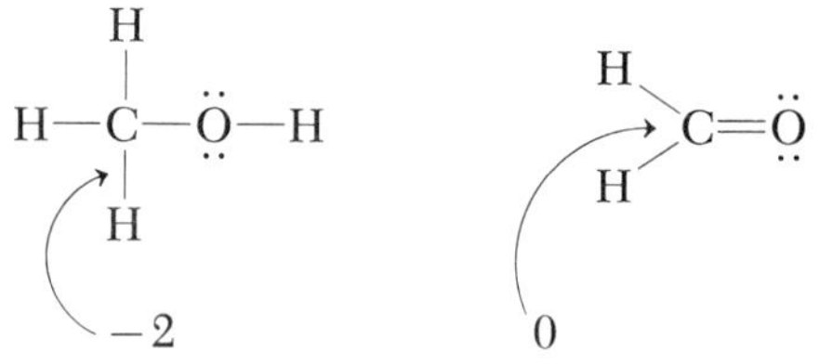

H—C(H)(H)—Ö—H → −2 H₂C=Ö → 0

Figure 5.6 Oxidation numbers for the carbon atoms of formaldehyde and methanol. The values are derived by assigning to hydrogen and oxygen their customary oxidation numbers of +1 and −2, respectively. Since the sum of oxidation numbers within each molecule must be zero (each molecule has an overall charge of zero), it follows that the oxidation number of the carbon atom in methanol is −2 and in formaldehyde is 0. The conversion of methanol to formaldehyde is therefore an oxidation, because the oxidation number of the carbon has increased.

Oxidation numbers are used only occasionally by organic chemists, who instead recognize the oxidation state of a compound by its structure. It *usually* suffices to think of oxidation as the addition of oxygen to or the removal of hydrogen from a molecule. More specifically, oxidation involves the breaking of carbon-hydrogen (or sometimes carbon-carbon) bonds and the making of carbon-oxygen bonds at the functional carbon. Correspondingly, reduction is

SPECIAL TOPIC

Biological Oxidations

The human body, along with other organisms, is able to oxidize alcohols. It does so in a series of steps utilizing a biological oxidizing agent. A compound known as nicotinamide adenine dinucleotide (NAD^+) plays the pivotal role as the oxidizing agent. The reaction occurs in the presence of a catalyst, an enzyme known as alcohol dehydrogenase. For example, ethanol is oxidized to acetaldehyde in the following process:

$$CH_3CH(H)\ddot{O}H + \text{NAD}^+ \xrightleftharpoons[\text{dehydrogenase}]{\text{alcohol}} CH_3CH{=}\ddot{O} + \text{NADH} + H^+$$

NAD⁺ (pyridinium ring bearing H, $C(=O)NH_2$, and N^+–R)

NADH (dihydropyridine ring with CH_2 (H, H), $C(=O)NH_2$, and N–R)

In humans this process occurs in the liver. The R group of NAD^+ (and NADH) is complex; it is related to the nucleotide systems described in Chapter 3 regarding hydrogen bonding and nucleic acids. While the R group structure is important for recognition and binding with the biological catalyst, it is not directly involved in the oxidation-reduction depicted here.

The NAD^+ that serves as the oxidizing agent becomes reduced to the NADH (nicotinamide adenine dinucleotide–reduced), which can serve as a reducing agent for the reverse reaction.

Further oxidation of the acetaldehyde to acetic acid and ultimately to carbon dioxide also occurs. The drug Antabuse, used in the treatment of severe alcoholism, inhibits the alcohol dehydrogenase, leading to temporary, violent illness upon ingestion of ethanol.

Methanol is oxidized as well in biological systems. The immediate product of oxidation is formaldehyde, which is further oxidized to formic acid. These oxidation products are highly poisonous to humans and account for the high toxicity of methanol. Acetaldehyde, formed in the oxidation of ethanol, is also toxic. However, it is less toxic than either formaldehyde or formic acid. (There will be a further discussion of NAD^+ and NADH in Chapter 28.)

Figure 5.7 Hierarchy of oxidation states for several classes of organic compounds containing oxygen.

Class of Compound (Increasing oxidation state ↓)	C_1 Example	C—H Bonds	C—O Bonds
Alkane	CH_4	4	0
Alcohol	CH_3OH	3	1
Aldehyde	$H_2C{=}O$	2	2
Carboxylic Acid	HCO_2H	1	3
Carbon Dioxide	$O{=}C{=}O$	0	4

the adding of hydrogen or the taking away of oxygen from a molecule. A hierarchy of oxidation states for organic compounds containing one carbon atom is summarized in Figure 5.7.

Many kinds of oxidizing and reducing agents are used in organic chemistry. Drastic conditions (e.g., combustion) cause the oxidation of alcohols and other compounds to proceed all the way to carbon dioxide. Controlled oxidation procedures must be used to stop the oxidation at the level of a carbonyl or carboxyl group. We will see that the development of reagents that bring about controlled oxidations and reductions is a very important part of organic chemistry. The search for *selective* reagents to accomplish the entire range of chemical transformations will continue to occupy the time and thinking of research chemists.

PROBLEM 5.5 The alcohol 1-propanol ($CH_3CH_2CH_2OH$) can be oxidized to yield either a carbonyl compound or a carboxylic acid, depending on the reaction conditions used. Draw structures for each of these possible products.

PROBLEM 5.6 An important reaction in the biological degradation of sugars is the oxidation of lactic acid [$CH_3CH(OH)CO_2H$] by NAD^+. The products of this reaction are NADH and pyruvic acid ($C_3H_4O_3$). Suggest a structure for pyruvic acid.

5.8 Reaction of Methanol and Ethanol with Hydrogen Bromide

THE REACTION

When methanol or ethanol is heated with hydrogen bromide (HBr), a reaction occurs in which a bromine atom takes the place of the hydroxyl group, as shown in Equation 5.9.

Eqn. 5.9

$$CH_3CH_2\ddot{O}H + H\ddot{B}r{:} \longrightarrow CH_3CH_2\ddot{B}r{:} + H_2\ddot{O}$$

Hydrogen chloride (HCl) and hydrogen iodide (HI) react similarly. This reaction is another example (see Chapter 4) of a **substitution reaction.** A substitution reaction is one in which one atom or group of atoms takes the place of some other atom or group of atoms. Here a halogen takes the place of a hydroxyl group.

THE MECHANISM OF A REACTION

Our understanding of organic reactions depends on our ability to unravel the sequence of events that happens between the time the reactants come together and the time the product or products are formed. This sequence of events is referred to as the **mechanism** of the reaction. (We briefly mentioned the concept of a reaction mechanism in Chapter 4.) We usually describe a mechanism by writing equations for a series of individual steps that lead to the product(s). To write a complete mechanism, each step must be listed.

We are, of course, unable to observe directly what is happening at the molecular level in any reaction. We must infer what is happening through interpretation of experimental observations and logical application of the best theory. Once a mechanism has been proposed, it must be carefully tested. First, the proposed mechanism is used to make predictions of what would happen in reactions not yet observed. These reactions are then carried out so that the predictions can be tested. If the experimental observations are different from those predicted, then the mechanism must be changed. Only when the proposed mechanism is found to predict new experimental results correctly does it have validity.

Organic chemists constantly find new ways to test mechanisms. Sometimes previously accepted mechanisms are changed on the basis of new results. Many mechanisms have been so thoroughly tested that they are generally assumed to be correct. Included in this category is the reaction of methanol and ethanol (and other primary alcohols) with hydrogen bromide.

THE MECHANISM OF THE HBr REACTION WITH METHANOL AND ETHANOL

The mechanism deduced from a series of experiments consists of two steps, which are illustrated here for the reaction of hydrogen bromide with ethanol.

MECHANISM OF REACTION

Step 1 An acid-base reaction occurs in which HBr protonates the oxygen of the ethanol to form an oxonium ion.

$$CH_3CH_2{-}\ddot{\underset{..}{O}}{-}H + H{-}\ddot{\underset{..}{Br}}: \longrightarrow CH_3CH_2{-}\overset{+}{\ddot{O}}H_2 + :\ddot{\underset{..}{Br}}:^-$$

Step 2 The bromide ion displaces a molecule of water from the oxonium ion. The product bromoethane is thus formed.

$$:\ddot{\underset{..}{Br}}:^- + CH_3CH_2{-}\overset{+}{\ddot{O}}H_2 \longrightarrow :\ddot{\underset{..}{Br}}{-}CH_2CH_3 + :\ddot{O}H_2$$

PROBLEM 5.7 Write the mechanism for the reaction of methanol with HI using the curved-arrow formalism.

We will now consider this mechanism in the context of experimental observations. For example, what happens if we mix ethanol and hydrogen bromide while keeping the reaction mixture cold? Experimentally we find that *no* bromoethane is formed. The initial acid-base reaction occurs as rapidly as the reagents are mixed, but the second step of the mechanism does not occur.

Suppose we heat ethanol with sodium bromide (NaBr). Experimentally, we find that no reaction of any kind occurs under these conditions. We infer that a bromide ion is not able to displace a hydroxide ion from an alcohol.

On the basis of these and other observations, we conclude that bromoethane is formed by the reaction of bromide ion with the protonated ethanol (i.e., the ethyloxonium ion). We also find that an elevated temperature is needed for this reaction to occur. Although many alcohols other than methanol and ethanol also react according to the same mechanism, there are some categories of alcohols that react by a different mechanism. We will look at the experimental evidence supporting this contention in Chapter 7, where we will consider the question of alternative mechanisms by which structurally different alcohols react.

Now let us introduce some important terms that relate to this reaction. Bromide ion is said to function as a **nucleophile** in the reaction described. A nucleophile is a molecule or ion that supplies a pair of electrons to form a bond to an atom other than hydrogen. A nucleophile is thereby a type of Lewis base. Lewis bases can in general behave either as nucleophiles or as Brønsted bases (see Figure 5.8). As the latter, they supply a pair of electrons to bond to a proton. The same Lewis base may function as a nucleophile in one reaction and a Brønsted base in another reaction. Therefore we should not say that a bromide ion *is* a nucleophile, but rather that it *functions* as a nucleophile in certain reactions.

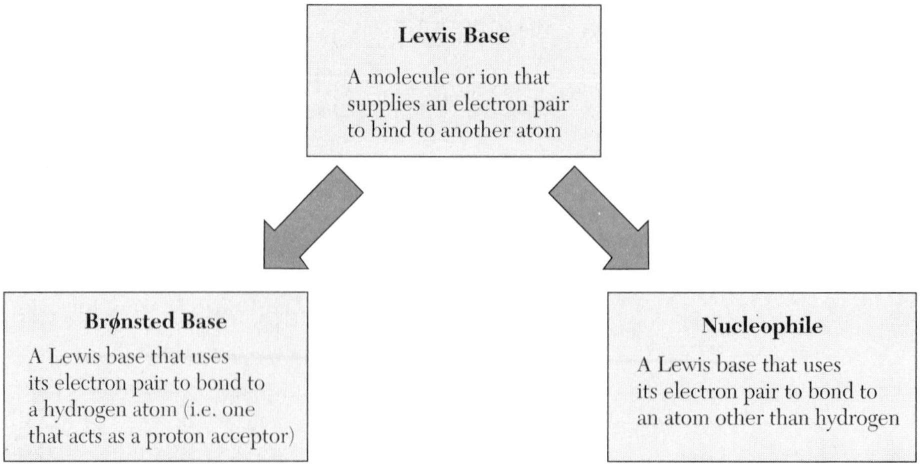

Figure 5.8 Subdivisions of Lewis bases. Any molecule that supplies an electron pair for bond formation is a Lewis base. Lewis bases can be classified as Brønsted bases or as nucleophiles, depending on the atom to which they bind.

Lewis Base
A molecule or ion that supplies an electron pair to bind to another atom

Brønsted Base
A Lewis base that uses its electron pair to bond to a hydrogen atom (i.e. one that acts as a proton acceptor)

Nucleophile
A Lewis base that uses its electron pair to bond to an atom other than hydrogen

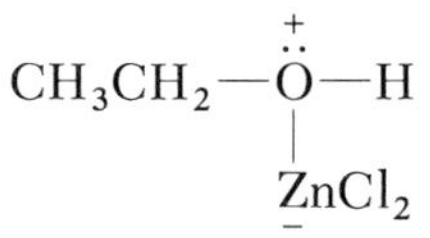

$$CH_3CH_2-\overset{+}{\ddot{O}}-H$$
$$|$$
$$\underset{-}{ZnCl_2}$$

Figure 5.9 Intermediate in the reaction of ethanol with the Lucas reagent.

The water molecule that is displaced in the second step of the reaction is called a **leaving group.** We further say that it is a *good* leaving group since it is readily displaced. (In later chapters we will accumulate knowledge that allows us to predict which groups are good leaving groups and which are poor.) The reaction of methanol, ethanol, and other primary alcohols (see Chapter 6) with HCl is aided by the addition of $ZnCl_2$. The alcohol, acting as a Lewis base, reacts with the $ZnCl_2$ to generate the intermediate shown in Figure 5.9. The net effect is to generate an even better leaving group than water. A solution of $ZnCl_2$ in hydrochloric acid is known as the **Lucas reagent.**

In due course, you will be able to recognize features in a molecule that enable it to function as an efficient nucleophile and ultimately know how to combine this with other knowledge about leaving group abilities to predict the consequences and mechanisms of **nucleophilic substitution reactions** (reactions in which a nucleophile displaces a leaving group from a reaction center). The reaction of HBr with ethanol, analyzed in the present chapter, is but one example of this most important reaction type.

MOLECULAR ORBITAL ANALYSIS

FRONTIER ORBITALS AND THE RATE OF REACTION

In a multistep reaction, the overall rate of the reaction is equal to the rate of the slowest step. We will have more to say about this topic later. The important point now is that the slow step of the reaction of hydrogen halides with methanol or ethanol is the *second* step, that is, the displacement of water from the alkyloxonium ion by halide ion. The rate of this displacement process governs the rate at which the haloalkane is formed; it is the chemical bottleneck in the conversion of alcohol to haloalkane.

There are many questions we might have about such a reaction, beyond those raised in the preceding sections. For example, we observe that HI reacts faster than HBr with both methanol and ethanol. We infer from this observation that iodide ion reacts faster with the alkyloxonium ion than does bromide ion. Why is this so? We also pointed out in the earlier discussion that halide ions do not perform displacements on the unprotonated alcohols. Only with the alkyloxonium ion does the displacement occur. How can we have a better understanding of these observations?

Organic chemists use many different approaches to improve their understanding of reactions. We will now explore one useful approach based on a frontier orbital analysis of the second step of the mechanism. Consider the reaction of bromide ion with ethyloxonium ion. When we apply the frontier molecular orbital model (see Chapter 2) we need to consider the HOMO of the Lewis base (bromide ion) and the LUMO of the Lewis acid (ethyloxonium ion). Remember that a Lewis base is an electron-pair *donor*. Thus the Lewis base orbital we need to consider is an *occupied* orbital—its HOMO. Similarly a Lewis acid is an electron *acceptor*. For it, the frontier orbital we need to consider must be *vacant*, that is, its LUMO.

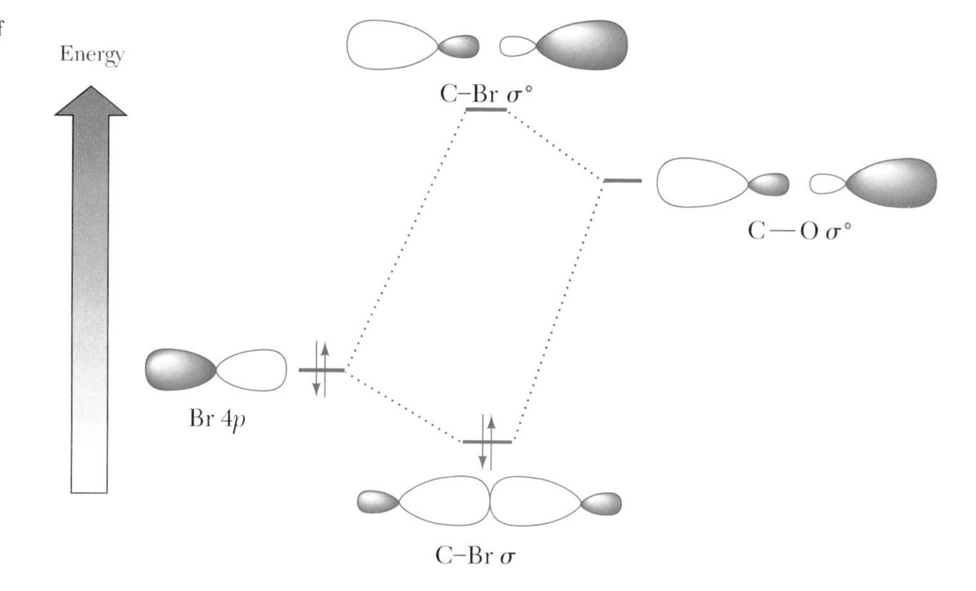

Figure 5.10 Frontier orbital interaction of the bromide ion with the ethyloxonium ion.

The HOMO of the bromide ion is a $4p$ orbital. The LUMO of the ethyloxonium ion is the σ^* orbital associated with the carbon-oxygen bond. The interaction of these orbitals leads to two new orbitals. The more stable (lower energy) new orbital is the σ orbital (bonding) associated with the new carbon-bromine bond. This orbital is shown in Figure 5.10.

By experiment we find that iodide ion reacts faster in this reaction than does bromide ion. Consider the frontier molecular orbitals involved in the reactions. The HOMO is now an iodide $5p$ orbital instead of a bromide $4p$ orbital. The iodide $5p$ orbital is higher in energy that the bromide $4p$ orbital. Thus the energy gap between the HOMO of the halide ion and the LUMO of the ethyloxonium ion is decreased, as is illustrated in Figure 5.11.

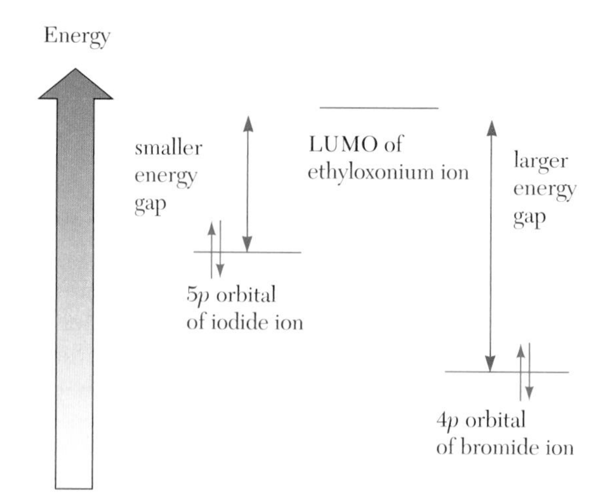

Figure 5.11 Comparison of HOMO–LUMO gap in reaction of ethyloxonium ion with halide ions. A faster reaction rate is associated with a smaller HOMO–LUMO gap.

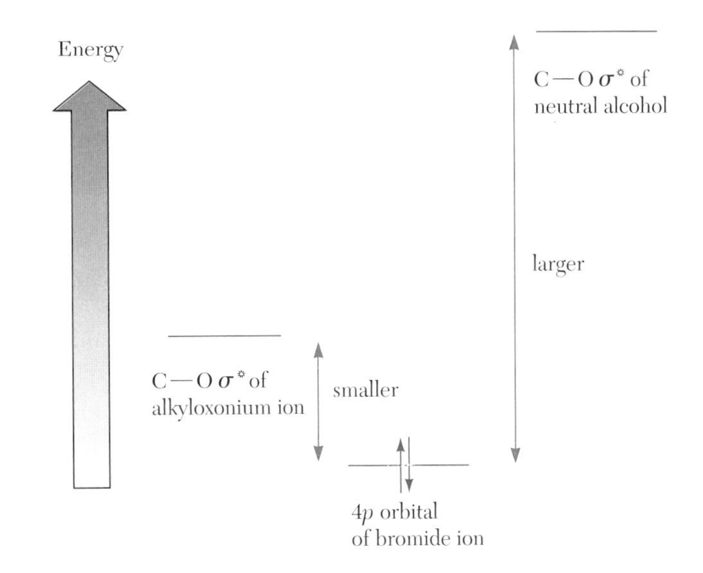

Figure 5.12 Comparison of HOMO–LUMO gap. The HOMO–LUMO gap is much larger between the bromide ion and the alcohol than it is between the bromide ion and the alkyloxonium ion. The reaction will occur much more rapidly with the alkyloxonium ion than it will with the unprotonated alcohol.

In general, we find that the efficiency of the HOMO–LUMO interaction is governed by the energy separation. We thus rationalize our observation of a faster reaction with iodide than with bromide in terms of a more efficient orbital interaction with iodide.

The frontier orbital model can also help us rationalize the experimental observation that unprotonated alcohols do not react with halide ions. The LUMO associated with the carbon-oxygen bond of an alcohol is similar to that of the oxonium ion; however, its energy is higher. The positive charge of the alkyloxonium ion lowers the energy of the LUMO compared to the parent neutral alcohol. Thus the alkyloxonium ion is a better electron acceptor (using its LUMO) than is the neutral alcohol. There is a smaller HOMO–LUMO energy gap for the reaction of a halide ion with the alkyloxonium ion than with the neutral alcohol. With the unprotonated alcohol the HOMO–LUMO gap is quite large. In fact, it is so large that interaction with a halide ion is quite inefficient (Figure 5.12). This rationalization correlates with the reaction proceeding at a negligibly slow pace.

The frontier orbital model is a greatly simplified version of molecular orbital theory. When two molecules react, *all* of their orbitals undergo interactions and change. All are transformed into new molecular orbitals of the product. The frontier orbital model focuses on only two molecular orbitals, the HOMO and the LUMO. Nevertheless, we find that this simplification often allows us to make substantial inroads into understanding or predicting important aspects of organic chemistry.

While we introduce this aspect of the frontier orbital model to introduce the idea that it can have a useful role as a predictive tool for the comparison of reaction rates in related reactions, we should stress that the size of the HOMO–LUMO gap is not the only factor governing the efficiency or rate of a reaction. Electrostatic interactions between charged sites in the reactants, steric effects, solvent effect, and other factors are often equally or more important and can overshadow the effect of HOMO–LUMO interactions.

Summary

- Methanol and ethanol are the simplest members of the class of organic compounds known as alcohols. Every alcohol contains a hydroxyl group, the functional group that is responsible for the characteristic chemistry of alcohols.
- While both methanol and ethanol can be produced directly in biological processes, other methods are normally used to synthesize them in large quantities for industrial purposes.
- Methanol and ethanol both show physical and chemical characteristics similar to those of water. We can think of alcohols as being derived from water by replacing one hydrogen in a water molecule by an alkyl group.
- The alkyl groups of methanol and ethanol are sufficiently small that the hydroxyl group is mainly responsible for not only their fundamental chemical properties but also their physical characteristics.
- The ability of both methanol and ethanol to participate in extensive hydrogen bonding is a characteristic shared with the parent water molecule.
- Methanol and ethanol also show acidic and basic characteristics similar to those of water. The hydroxyl hydrogen of each can be removed as a proton by reaction with a strong base. The result is the formation of a methoxide or ethoxide anion.
- The oxygen of the hydroxyl group, like that of water, has two unshared pairs of electrons that allow it to serve as a basic site. In the presence of sufficiently strong acids this oxygen can accept a proton to form an oxonium ion.
- Protonation of the hydroxyl oxygen of methanol, ethanol, and similar alcohols can lead to substitution reactions of the alcohol. Once an oxonium ion has been generated, the carbon bearing the oxygen is susceptible to attack by nucleophiles. Halide ions displace water to form haloalkanes.

Terms to Remember

alcohol
hydroxyl group
alkoxide salt
oxonium ion
oxidation
reduction
substitution reaction
mechanism
nucleophile
leaving group
Lucas reagent
nucleophilic substitution

Additional Problems

5.8 Calculate the weight percentages of carbon, hydrogen, and oxygen in each of the following molecules:
a. pentane **b.** 3,3-dimethylpentane **c.** 2-chloroethanol **d.** acetic acid

5.9 Find the molecular formulas of each of the following compounds. The only elements present are carbon, hydrogen, and possibly nitrogen and oxygen.
a. C 53.30%; H 11.18%; no nitrogen; mol wt ~90 g/mole
b. C 35.60%; H 4.95%; N 27.70%; mol wt ~202 g/mole
c. C 68.90%; H 4.92%; no nitrogen; mol wt ~244 g/mole
d. C 46.38%; H 5.90%; N 27.01%; mol wt ~155 g/mole

5.10 What is the empirical formula of a compound containing only carbon, hydrogen, and oxygen if 0.307 g of the compound produces 0.696 g of carbon dioxide and 0.286 g of water upon combustion analysis?

5.11 When 7.10 mg of a compound containing only carbon and hydrogen was burned in a combustion analysis, 22.96 mg of carbon dioxide and 7.43 mg of water were produced. The molecular weight of the compound was found to be 68.0 g/mole in an independent measurement. What is its molecular formula?

5.12 A protein for which the molecular weight is determined to be approximately 36,000 g/mole is known to contain 0.086% phosphorus by weight. How many atoms of phosphorus are present in each molecule of the protein?

5.13 A metalloprotein has a molecular weight of approximately 64,000 g/mole and contains 0.35% by weight iron. How many atoms of iron are present in each molecule of this protein?

5.14 A substance containing only carbon, hydrogen, and oxygen is analyzed and found to contain 70.60% C and 5.88% H. A molecular weight analysis of the material indicates the molecular weight to be 136 g/mole. Calculate the molecular formula for the compound.

5.15 Monosodium glutamate (MSG) is the sodium salt of the amino acid glutamic acid. It is used extensively in cooking. MSG contains carbon, hydrogen, nitrogen, sodium, and oxygen. Elemental analysis gives the following weight percentages: C, 35.51%; H, 4.77%; N, 8.23%; Na, 13.6%. The molecular weight of MSG is determined to be approximately 169 g/mole. Determine its molecular formula.

5.16 Combustion analysis of 0.880 g of a substance containing only carbon, hydrogen, and oxygen yields 1.760 g of carbon dioxide and 0.720 g of water. A separate determination shows its molecular weight to be approximately 88 g/mole. Calculate its molecular formula.

5.17 Explain why dimethyl ether (CH_3OCH_3) is a gas while its isomer, ethanol, is a liquid at room temperature.

5.18 Ethylene glycol ($HOCH_2CH_2OH$) has a much higher boiling temperature than butanol ($CH_3CH_2CH_2CH_2OH$) although they have approximately the same molecular weight. Explain why.

5.19 *tert*-Butyl alcohol is the only one of the isomeric $C_4H_{10}O$ alcohols to be fully miscible with water. Rationalize this observation.

5.20 Which compound in each of the following pairs do you expect to be more soluble in water:
a. ethanol or chloroethane **b.** ethanol or $CH_3CH_2CH_2CH_2CH_2OH$

5.21 Write equations for each of the following reactions:
a. ethanol + sodium **b.** methanol + sodium amide **c.** ethanol + cold HBr

5.22 Give the conjugate acid for each of the following:
a. hydroxide ion **b.** methoxide ion **c.** ethanol **d.** chloride ion

5.23 Give the conjugate base for each of the following:
a. acetic acid **b.** HBr **c.** methanol **d.** hydronium ion **e.** methyloxonium ion

5.24 Use the curved-arrow formalism to depict each of the following reactions:
a. methanol with sulfuric acid **b.** bromide ion with methyloxonium ion **c.** amide ion with ethanol

5.25 Which of the following conversions is an oxidation and which is a reduction?
a. acetic acid to acetaldehyde **b.** formic acid to carbon dioxide
c. ethylene ($H_2C{=}CH_2$) to ethane **d.** methane to methanol
e. 2-propanol to acetone, $(CH_3)_2C{=}O$

5.26 In methanol the carbon atom has a formal oxidation number of -2. Methanol can be oxidized to an oxygen-containing substance in which the oxidation number of the central carbon is $+4$. What is the structure of the compound? In another oxidation reaction, methanol is oxidized to a different product, an oxygen-containing compound in which the central carbon atom has an oxidation number of 0. What is the structure of this product?

5.27 Propose a detailed two-step mechanism to account for the formation of 1-bromobutane when 1-butanol ($CH_3CH_2CH_2CH_2OH$) is heated with sodium bromide and sulfuric acid.

5.28 Cyanide ion is the conjugate base of hydrogen cyanide, HCN. Cyanide ion functions as a nucleophile in reaction with bromoethane, displacing bromide ion as the leaving group. A new carbon-carbon bond is formed in this reaction.
a. Write Lewis structures for HCN and the cyanide ion.
b. Show a curved-arrow representation of the reaction of cyanide ion with bromoethane.

5.29 Potassium ethoxide is the alkoxide salt of ethanol. The ethoxide ion acts as a nucleophile toward iodoethane and displaces the iodide ion. Write a structure for the organic product of this reaction.

5.30 Assign a formal charge and an oxidation number to the oxygen of the hydronium ion. Is there any general relationship between formal charge and oxidation number?

5.31 On treatment with aqueous sulfuric acid, ethanol that has been isotopically labeled with ^{18}O undergoes an exchange of this isotope with the ^{16}O of the aqueous solution as indicated in the equation shown below.

$$CH_3CH_2{}^{18}\ddot{\underset{\cdot\cdot}{O}}H + H_2{}^{16}\ddot{\underset{\cdot\cdot}{O}} \xrightleftharpoons{H_2SO_4} H_2{}^{18}\ddot{\underset{\cdot\cdot}{O}} + CH_3CH_2{}^{16}\ddot{\underset{\cdot\cdot}{O}}H$$

Explain how this exchange can occur.

5.32 On addition of heavy water (D_2O) to ordinary ethanol, CH_3CH_2OH, the ethanol is rapidly converted to CH_3CH_2OD. Explain how this conversion can occur (i.e., propose a mechanism).

5.33 When CH_3CH_2OD (as produced by the reaction in Problem 5.32) is treated with sodium metal, a gas is formed. What is this gas? Write an equation for the reaction showing all the reactants and products.

5.34 For each pair of reagents show the product(s) of the acid-base reaction between them.

a. $CH_3\ddot{\underset{\cdot\cdot}{O}}H + BF_3 \longrightarrow$

b. $CH_3Li + HC{\equiv}CH \longrightarrow$

c. $CH_3CH_2\ddot{\underset{\cdot\cdot}{O}}H + LiC{\equiv}CH \longrightarrow$

d. $CH_3\ddot{\underset{\cdot\cdot}{O}}H + H_3PO_4 \longrightarrow$

5.35 A beginning organic chemistry student, attempting to prepare chloroethane from ethanol, accidentally used concentrated sulfuric acid rather than hydrochloric acid. On careful workup of the reaction, the student found that diethyl ether was formed (but, of course, no chloroethane). Explain how the diethyl ether could be formed in this reaction by writing a mechanism using the curved-arrow formalism.

$$CH_3CH_2OCH_2CH_3$$

diethyl ether

*5.36 Using orbital pictures, show the approach of a bromide ion to a methyloxonium ion for the displacement of a water molecule. Show the positions of each of the atoms in space for the following three stages of reaction:

a. as bromide ion begins to approach

b. halfway through the displacement process

c. as water is departing

*5.37 Using your answer to Problem 5.36 as a foundation, show the same changes as they would occur with the ethyloxonium ion. Which would you expect to react faster with bromide ion, the methyloxonium ion or the ethyloxonium ion? Explain your answer.

Alcohols

6.1 Introduction

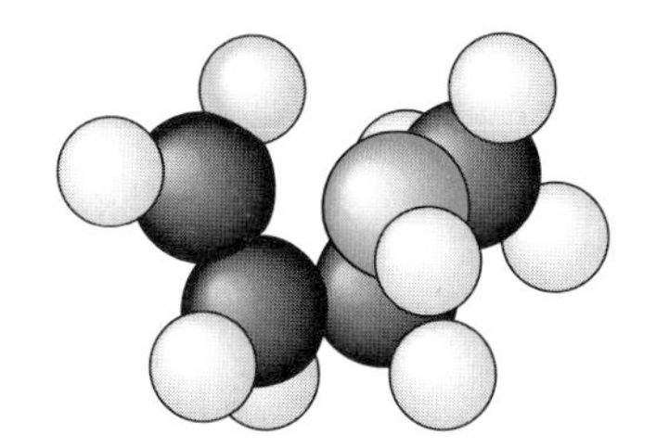

In this chapter we examine the alcohol family of compounds in more detail. For now we will focus on compounds in which a hydroxyl group is the *only* functional group present. Later in our studies we will encounter more complex molecules in which the hydroxyl group may be only one of several functional groups present. For example, allyl alcohol (**6.1**) and cholesterol (**6.2**) both contain a carbon-carbon double bond (an alkene functional group) in addition to the hydroxyl group.

$CH_2{=}CH{-}CH_2{-}\ddot{O}H$

allyl alcohol
6.1

$CH_3CHCH_2CH_2CH_2CH(CH_3)_2$, H_3C, H_3C, $H\ddot{O}$

cholesterol
6.2

These compounds are still alcohols, but they also exhibit chemistry characteristic of alkenes, as you might expect, since they both contain a carbon to carbon double bond. The presence of additional functional groups may somewhat modify the chemistry of a hydroxyl group contained in a compound; however, we can usually recognize reactions that are typical of simple alcohols.

6.2 The Classification of Substances Containing a Hydroxyl Group

For a substance to be classified as an alcohol, its hydroxyl group must be attached to an sp^3 hybridized carbon atom. Compounds that have a hydroxyl group attached to an atom other than carbon, such as dimethylhydroxylamine (**6.3**), or to a carbon atom that is *not* sp^3 hybridized are not classified as alcohols. For example, neither phenol (**6.4**) nor acetic acid (**6.5**) is classified as an alcohol

$(CH_3)_2\ddot{N}{-}\ddot{O}H$

dimethylhydroxylamine
6.3

$C_6H_5\ddot{O}H$

phenol
6.4

$CH_3C({=}\ddot{O}){-}\ddot{O}H$

acetic acid
6.5

Figure 6.1 Classification of alcohols by point of attachment of the hydroxyl group. A compound with a hydroxyl group attached to a primary carbon atom is a primary alcohol, and so forth. R represents an alkyl group.

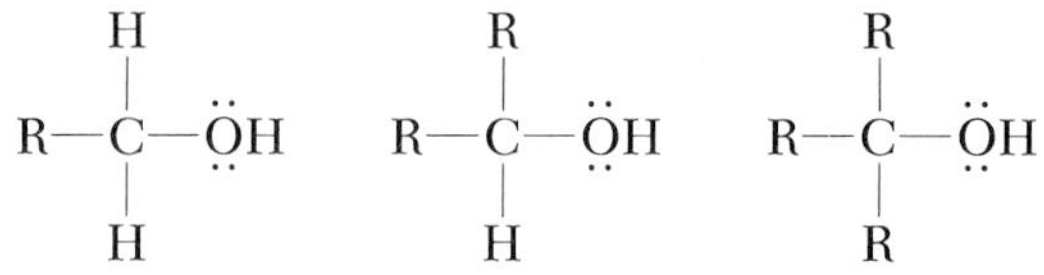

since in both cases the hydroxyl group is attached to a carbon atom that is sp^2 hybridized. The substances **6.3–6.5** do have some properties that are like those of alcohols, but they are not similar enough to be included in the alcohol family.

Alcohols are classified as primary, secondary, or tertiary (1°, 2°, or 3°) depending on the type of carbon atom to which the hydroxyl group is attached, as shown in Figure 6.1.

PROBLEM 6.1 Classify each of the following alcohols as primary, secondary, or tertiary.

a. $(CH_3)_2CHCH(OH)CH_3$ **b.** $(CH_3)_3CCH_2CH(CH_3)CH_2OH$

c. $(CH_3CH_2)_2C(OH)CH_3$ **d.** cyclohexane ring carrying H and OH on the same carbon

e. skeletal structure with OH **f.** skeletal structure with —OH

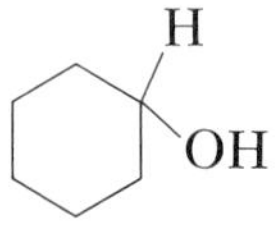

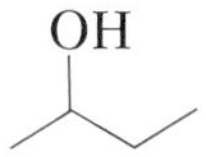

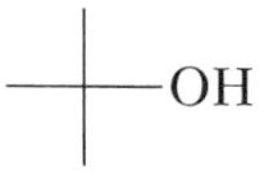

6.3 Nomenclature for Alcohols

We introduced the IUPAC system of nomenclature for organic compounds in Chapter 2. We will now see how we can use this method for the systematic naming of alcohols.

The longest continuous carbon chain to which the hydroxyl group is attached provides the root name for the alcohol. However, the alkane ending is changed by dropping the *-e* and adding *-ol*. The position of the hydroxyl group is indicated by a numerical prefix, and we number the carbon atoms of that chain beginning at the end closest to the hydroxyl group. If the hydroxyl group is at the midpoint of the chain, we number it to provide the smaller of the possible sets of numbers for other substituents. Several examples are shown in Figure 6.2.

PROBLEM 6.2 Consider all isomeric alcohols of the formula $C_6H_{14}O$. Draw their structures and name them following the IUPAC method. Classify each alcohol as primary, secondary, or tertiary.

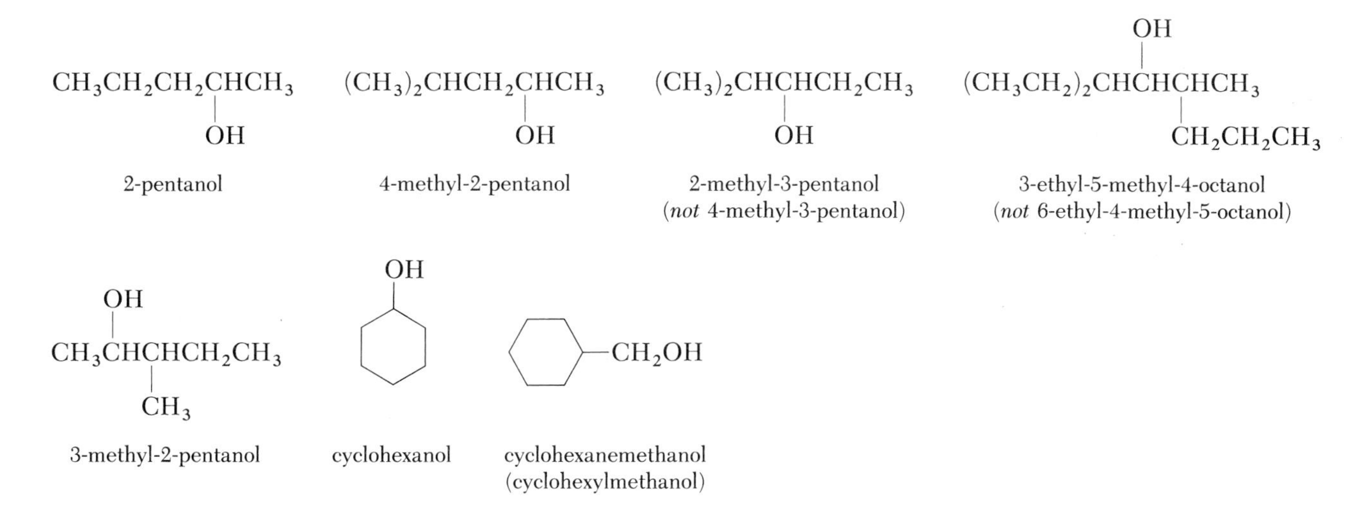

Figure 6.2 IUPAC nomenclature for alcohols.

Other naming systems are used for alcohols. One popular method (the **radicofunctional method**) is to name the alkyl group to which the hydroxyl group is attached and to follow this name with the word alcohol. Generally this system is used only for alcohols containing relatively simple alkyl groups. Several examples are shown in Figure 6.3.

Alcohols are also sometimes named as *carbinols*. The carbon atom to which the hydroxyl group is bonded is known as the carbinol carbon atom, and all attached *alkyl* groups are specified; for example, $(C_2H_5)_2CHOH$ is diethylcarbinol, and *tert*-pentyl alcohol (Figure 6.3) is named ethyldimethylcarbinol.

CH_3OH — methyl alcohol

$CH_3CH_2CH_2CH_2OH$ — *n*-butyl alcohol

$(CH_3)_2CHOH$ — isopropyl alcohol

$(CH_3)_3COH$ — *tert*-butyl alcohol

$(CH_3)_2CHCH_2OH$ — isobutyl alcohol

$CH_3CH_2CH(OH)CH_3$ — *sec*-butyl alcohol

$(CH_3)_2C(OH)CH_2CH_3$ — *tert*-pentyl alcohol (*tert*-amyl alcohol)

$(CH_3)_2CHCH_2CH_2OH$ — isopentyl alcohol (isoamyl alcohol)

Figure 6.3 Radicofunctional names for simple alcohols. This nomenclature system was discussed briefly in Chapter 2.

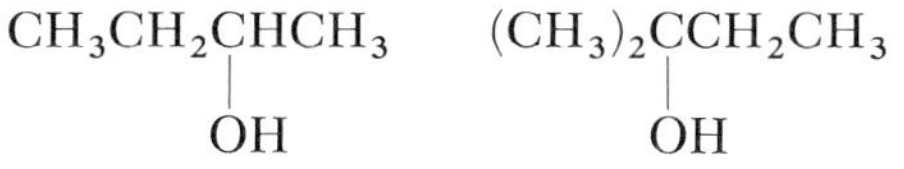

PROBLEM 6.3 Provide an alternative name for each of the alcohols listed in Figure 6.3.

6.4 Physical Properties of the Alcohols

Selected physical properties for a series of alcohols are shown in Table 6.1. Alcohols are listed according to their number of carbon atoms, with subsections based on their classification according to substitution.

BOILING TEMPERATURES

The boiling temperatures of the straight-chain primary alcohols increase in a steady manner with increasing molecular weight, as illustrated in Figure 6.4.

Table 6.1 Selected Physical Properties of Alcohols

Alcohols are listed according to their number of carbon atoms, with subsections based on their classification according to substitution.

Name	Melting Temperature (°C)	Boiling Temperature (°C)	Density (g/mL) (20 °C)	Water Solubility (g/100 mL) (20 °C)
C_1, 1°				
methanol	−93.9	65.15	0.7914	miscible
C_2, 1°				
ethanol	−117.3	70.5	0.7093	miscible
C_3, 1°				
1-propanol	−126.5	97.4	0.8035	miscible
C_3, 2°				
2-propanol	−89.5	82.4	0.7055	miscible
C_4, 1°				
1-butanol	−89.5	117.2	0.8090	8.0
2-methyl-1-propanol	−100	108	0.8018	10.0
C_4, 2°				
2-butanol	−114	99.5	0.8063	12.5
C_4, 3°				
2-methyl-2-propanol	25.5	82.3	0.7887	miscible
C_5, 1°				
1-pentanol	−79	137.3	0.8144	2.2
2-methyl-1-butanol	—	127	0.8152	—
2,2-dimethyl-1-propanol	52	113	0.812	miscible
C_5, 2°				
2-pentanol	—	110.9	0.8183	4.9
3-pentanol	—	116.1	0.8212	5.6
C_5, 3°				
2-methyl-2-butanol	−0.4	102	0.8059	miscible
C_6, 1°				
1-hexanol	−46.6	158	0.8136	0.7
C_6, 2°				
2-hexanol	—	140	0.8178	—
C_6, 3°				
3-methyl-3-pentanol	−23.6	122.4	0.8286	—
C_7, 1°				
1-heptanol	−34	176	0.822	0.2
C_8, 1°				
1-octanol	−15	195	0.825	0.05

Figure 6.4 Variation of boiling temperature of straight-chain terminal alcohols with number of carbon atoms. There is a steady increase of boiling temperature with increasing number of carbon atoms.

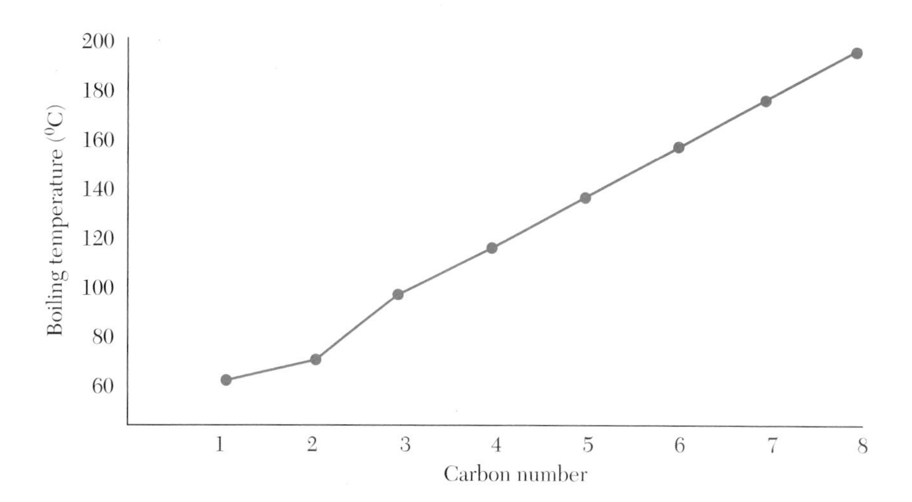

Each of these alcohols is the highest-boiling member of the group containing that number of carbon atoms.

The boiling temperature decreases with branching from the straight-chain structure. For example, 2-methyl-2-butanol (a five-carbon alcohol) is not only lower boiling than 1-pentanol, but it is also lower boiling than either 1-butanol or 2-methyl-1-propanol, both of which are four-carbon alcohols.

The boiling temperature of a substance depends on the magnitude of its intermolecular interactions. With increased branching of the carbon skeleton, the surface area of the alcohol decreases (see Chapter 3) and the molecule becomes more nearly spherical. A decrease in the van der Waals forces results from the decrease in surface area. This explanation correlates with the lower boiling temperatures found for the more highly branched alcohols.

The ability of alcohols to form hydrogen bonds has a significant effect on their physical characteristics (see Chapter 3). The relatively high boiling temperatures of alcohols compared to alkanes of similar molecular weight reflect the influence of hydrogen bonding and polarity. For example, the boiling temperatures of pentane and 1-fluorobutane (36.2 °C and 31.95°C, respectively) are far lower than that of 1-butanol (117.2 °C) in spite of their similar molecular weights.

6.5 Acidity of Alcohols

Alcohols can act as Brønsted acids, as we described in Chapter 5. The relative acidities of alcohols are found by comparing their equilibrium constants, K_a, for reaction with water (Figure 6.5). For simple alcohols the value of K_a is generally between 10^{-15} and 10^{-19}. Accordingly, alcohols are relatively weak acids compared to ordinary mineral acids or even water. Values of pK_a for several alcohols and other substances are listed in Table 6.2. Alcohols are much less acidic (by a factor of 10^7–10^{10}) than even weak inorganic acids such as HF ($pK_a = 3.5$) and weak organic acids such as acetic acid ($pK_a = 4.8$). For

Figure 6.5 Determination of the relative acidity of alcohols. The larger the value of K_a for an alcohol, the greater its acidity.

$$R—\ddot{\underset{..}{O}}—H + H_2\ddot{\underset{..}{O}} \rightleftharpoons R—\ddot{\underset{..}{O}}\colon^- + H_3\ddot{O}^+$$

$$K_a = [RO^-][H_3O^+]/[ROH]$$

Table 6.2 Approximate pK_a Values for Alcohols and Other Acids

Compound	pK_a
perchloric acid [$HClO_4$]	−10
hydrogen chloride [HCl]	−2.2
hydrogen fluoride [HF]	3.5
formic acid [HCOOH]	3.7
carbonic acid [H_2CO_3]	3.9
acetic acid [CH_3COOH]	4.8
hydrogen sulfide [H_2S]	7
ammonium chloride [NH_4Cl]	9.2
phenol [C_6H_5OH]	9.9
2-chloroethanol [$ClCH_2CH_2OH$]	14.3
water [H_2O]	15.7
methanol [CH_3OH]	15.5
ethanol [CH_3CH_2OH]	16.0
2-propanol [$CH_3CH(OH)CH_3$]	17
2-methyl-2-propanol [$(CH_3)_3COH$]	18
acetylene [$HC{\equiv}CH$]	25
ammonia [NH_3]	34
ethane [CH_3CH_3]	42

example, while aqueous solutions of acetic acid give an acidic reaction with ordinary acid-base indicators such as litmus, alcohols do not.

Variations in the acidities of alcohols demonstrate how different factors determine reactivity. Measurements of the acidities of simple alcohols in solution yield the general order of acidities:

$$\text{primary} > \text{secondary} > \text{tertiary}$$

We will now digress to examine, in a general way, the factors that are important in influencing acidity.

FACTORS INFLUENCING ACIDITY

The differing acidities of substances such as alcohols arise from the interplay of several important factors. We will now analyze some of the issues in terms of a generalized substance, HX, which behaves as an acid as shown in Equation 6.1.

Eqn. 6.1

$$HX(aq) + H_2O \rightleftharpoons H_3O^+(aq) + X^-(aq)$$

First, as we noted above, the relative strengths of acids are measured by their K_a or pK_a values, where K_a is the equilibrium constant for the reaction in Equation 6.1. Since K_a is an equilibrium constant, it can be related to the thermodynamic property ΔG° by Equation 6.2.

Eqn. 6.2

$$\Delta G^\circ = -2.303\ RT \log K_a$$

Here ΔG° is the difference between the free energy of the products and reactants in Equation 6.1. In turn, ΔG° is related to changes in enthalpy, ΔH°, and entropy, ΔS°.

Eqn. 6.3

$$\Delta G^\circ = \Delta H^\circ - T\,\Delta S^\circ$$

We see that the acid strength of a compound will in general be influenced by both enthalpy and entropy changes, since both types of change influence the value of ΔG°. Enthalpy changes relate to the strengths of bonds broken and formed in a reaction, while entropy changes relate to the extent to which the system becomes more or less disordered as the reaction proceeds from reactants to products. For a generalized acid HX, we need to consider the following important factors:

1. The enthalpy and entropy changes accompanying the breaking of the H—X bond to form H^+ and X^- ions
2. The enthalpy and entropy changes accompanying the solvation of the H^+ and X^- ions, as well as those for the parent acid
3. The stabilization (or lack thereof) of the negative charge within the X^- ion

It is particularly important to realize that we need to focus not only on the breaking of the H—X bond of the acid HX but also on the role of the solvent (water) in the reaction. Each reactant and product in Equation 6.1 is *solvated* to some degree by the aqueous solvent. By **solvation** we mean the clustering of solvent molecules around a molecule or ion. Solvation occurs because there are attractive forces (bonds) between any molecule or ion and the surrounding solvent molecules. Solvation is of major importance in many types of reactions, including acid-base reactions. Let's consider an example. We know from experimental measurements that hydrogen chloride is a strong acid. On a simplistic level, we sometimes think of the acid behavior of HCl as involving the splitting of HCl molecules into H^+ and Cl^- ions. However, we can easily realize that this is not a realistic view, since considerable energy is needed to break the H—Cl bond of hydrogen chloride. If this breaking of the H—Cl bond were the only process of importance in the behavior of HCl as an acid, we would expect HCl to be a very weak acid since so much energy is required for cleavage of this bond.

In fact, solvation is of overriding importance. The H^+ and Cl^- ions produced by the bond dissocation are much more strongly solvated (and hence stabilized) than are the parent HCl molecules. The greater solvation of the ions is a result of their charges. Because they are charged, the ions interact much more strongly with the polar water (solvent) molecules than does the uncharged HCl parent molecule. For each solvent-ion interaction or bond that forms, energy is released (ΔH is negative). In fact, the energy released by the interaction of the H^+ cations and Cl^- anions with water molecules is sufficiently great to offset the unfavorable energy associated with the H—Cl bond cleavage.

We observe experimentally that a considerable amount of heat is evolved when HCl dissolves in water. This observation is related to the increase in solvation accompanying the dissociation of HCl into solvated H^+ and Cl^- ions in aqueous solution, and it correlates with the stabilization associated with the solvation of the product ions. As always, energy is *liberated* when we go from *less stable reactants* (here, HCl gas and liquid water) to *more stable products* (here, solvated protons and chloride ions).

Eqn. 6.4
$$H\ddot{C}l{:}(g) + H_2\ddot{O}\,(l) \rightleftharpoons H_3\ddot{O}^+(aq) + {:}\ddot{C}l{:}^-\,(aq) + \text{heat}$$

Recall, however, that *both* enthalpic and entropic factors contribute to ΔG° and thus to K_a. Entropy refers to the degree of randomness in a system. When ions are solvated, there may be an ordering of the system—a decrease in entropy. In such cases, the more solvation that occurs, the greater is the decrease in entropy (i.e., ΔS is a *negative* number). However, entropic effects are usually small compared to enthalpic effects and in general only partially offset the acid-strengthening effect associated with the enthalpy of solvation.

Nevertheless, because many enthalpic and entropic terms need to be considered in an acid-base equilibrium, comparisons among acids are complicated because differences in all these terms need to be considered. Sometimes one factor does dominate the others and may be cited as the major explanation for a trend. For example, HF, with a K_a of only about 3.5×10^{-4}, is a considerably weaker acid than HCl, a strong acid. The major contributing factor is the greater amount of energy needed to break the relatively strong HF bond (about 136 kcal/mole or 569 kJ/mole) compared with the weaker HCl bond (about 103 kcal/mole or 432 kJ/mole). The extra 33 kcal/mole is reflected in a lowered tendency for HF to dissociate into ions and hence a lowered K_a.

When alcohols act as acids, the bond undergoing cleavage is the oxygen-hydrogen bond. As Table 6.2 shows, there is a significant variation in alcohol acidity with substitution of the carbinol carbon atom (the one to which the —OH group is attached). We now need to probe deeper to understand why there is such a sizable variation.

Consider an alcohol behaving as an acid, that is, as a proton donor, in the *absence* of a solvent (that is, in the *gas phase* rather than in solution). From experimental measurements, we find that all alcohols are much weaker acids in the gas phase than they are in solution. This observation tells us that solvation must have a very important influence on solution acidities. We also find that the *order* of acidities is actually reversed in the gas phase, as shown in Figure 6.6.

	Decreasing acid strength →
gas phase	$3^\circ > 2^\circ > 1^\circ > CH_3OH$
solution	$CH_3OH > 1^\circ > 2^\circ > 3^\circ$

Figure 6.6 Order of acidities of alcohols in the gas phase and in solution.

Why do alcohols have this particular order of acidities in the gas phase? Since there is no solvation involved and the cation is the same in each case, we can infer that this order of acidities reflects the *intrinsic stabilities* of the alkoxide ions, RO^-. (An increased stability of the product alkoxide ion favors its formation.) We conclude that the tertiary alkoxide ion has greater intrinsic stabilization than the others. This stabilization is provided by the additional alkyl groups bonded to the carbon atom bearing the hydroxyl group. These additional alkyl groups interact with the charged oxygen atom via a polarization mechanism (Chapter 3). The negative charge is thus stabilized as it is partly delocalized onto the attached alkyl groups.

When the ion is placed in solution, this polarization is overwhelmed by solvation effects. The alkyl groups about the alkoxide center have two effects on the solvation of the anion by water. First, their size disturbs the normal hydrogen-bonding associations within the water itself. Water cannot hydrogen bond with the alkyl groups—we say that the alkyl groups are **hydrophobic.** (Conversely, we say that materials that have a stabilizing interaction with water or waterlike substances are **hydrophilic** (see Figure 5.3)). Second, these hydrophobic portions of the molecule are close to the alkoxide center and prevent the approach of water molecules that could interact with the alkoxide site. This steric effect is related to destabilization by steric strain, as discussed in Chapter 4.

The role of solvation is of great importance in many areas of organic chemistry, and we will encounter other examples as we proceed with our discussions.

PROBLEM 6.4 Which of the following alkoxide ions would you expect to be the strongest base in aqueous solution?

$$:\ddot{Cl}CH_2CH_2\ddot{O}:^-$$

$$CH_3CH_2\ddot{O}:^-$$

$$(CH_3)_3C\ddot{O}:^-$$

Explain your choice.

PROBLEM 6.5 The enolate anion, $CH_2{=}CH{-}\ddot{O}:^-$, has an appreciably greater intrinsic stability than the alkoxide ion, $CH_3CH_2\ddot{O}:^-$. Suggest an explanation for this stability. Which of these ions would you expect to be the stronger base?

We can predict that the introduction of any substituent that provides internal stabilization to an alkoxide ion will tend to increase the acid strength of the parent alcohol. One way of achieving internal stabilization is to introduce electronegative atoms near to the hydroxyl group. The electronegative halogen in 2-chloroethanol (**6.6**) provides a way for the negative charge of the alkoxide ion to be dispersed.

$$:\ddot{Cl}{-}CH_2{-}CH_2{-}\ddot{O}H$$

2-chloroethanol

6.6

As we first noted in Chapter 1, dispersal of charge stabilizes ions. The more the charge can be dispersed, the more stable the ion. The equilibrium dissociation of the alcohol in solution then proceeds farther to the alkoxide side. In accord with our predictions, we find that 2-chloroethanol has an acid strength ($pK_a = 14.3$) that is greater than that of ethanol itself ($pK_a = 16.0$). The presence of *three* nearby halogen atoms, as in 2,2,2-trifluoroethanol (CF_3CH_2OH), further accentuates the effect. The pK_a of this compound is approximately 12.4.

The halogen atoms in the anions of 2-chloroethanol and 2,2,2-trifluoroethanol are said to exert an **inductive effect.** This term refers to the ability of an atom to polarize a bond by virtue of its electronegativity. Halogens and other electronegative atoms are said to exert an electron-withdrawing inductive effect. Thus the negative charge of the alkoxide ions is partially delocalized because of the presence of the halogen atoms. As usual, this charge delocalization correlates with an increased stability.

If a substituent is *electropositive*, its inductive effect will be electron *donating*. Such substituents stabilize positively charged but destabilize negatively charged entities.

A final word is in order. Changing from one substituent to another affects more than the inherent stability of the anion. Such a change *also* affects the enthalpy and entropy of solvation of the species involved in the acid-base equilibrium. Thus, any change in acidity caused by a substituent reflects all these changes. In fact, in some instances, enhancements of acidity accompanying substituent changes have been discovered to depend more on the difference in solvation entropy effects than on the improved stability of conjugate ions (see the discussion of relative acidities of substituted carboxylic acids in Chapter 21).

6.6 Alcohols as Bases

Alcohols have two unshared pairs of electrons on the oxygen atom of the hydroxyl group. These electrons give alcohols the potential to act as Lewis bases. This potential is realized in many of the reactions of alcohols. When one of these unshared electron pairs binds to a proton, the alcohol is acting as a Brønsted base. This reaction occurs when a strong acid such as sulfuric acid is added to the alcohol, as shown in Equation 6.5.

Eqn. 6.5
$$R\ddot{O}H + H_2SO_4 \longrightarrow R\overset{+}{O}H_2 + HSO_4^-$$

The curved-arrow formalism can be used to represent the electron-pair shifts involved in this reaction, as shown in Equation 6.6.

Eqn. 6.6
$$R{-}\ddot{O}(H){:}\;\; H{-}\ddot{O}{-}S(=O)_2{-}\ddot{O}{-}H \longrightarrow R{-}\overset{+}{\ddot{O}}(H){-}H + {:}\ddot{O}^-{-}S(=O)_2{-}\ddot{O}{-}H$$

This reaction is entirely analogous to the reaction of water with sulfuric acid, as shown in Equation 6.7.

Eqn. 6.7
$$H_2\ddot{O} + H_2SO_4 \longrightarrow H_3\ddot{O}^+ + HSO_4^-$$

Frequently, however, an unshared electron pair binds to something other than a proton. In Chapter 5 we introduced the term *nucleophile* for a Lewis base that donates an electron pair to an atom other than hydrogen. As we previously saw in the reactions of oxonium ions with halide ions, a nucleophilic substitution reaction is one in which a group is displaced from the acceptor atom by the attacking Lewis base. Another example of a nucleophilic substitution reaction is that of an alcohol with phosphorus trichloride, as shown in Equation 6.8.

Eqn. 6.8
$$R{-}\ddot{O}(H){:} \;\; \ddot{P}(Cl)_2{-}Cl \longrightarrow R{-}\overset{+}{\ddot{O}}(H){-}\ddot{P}(Cl)_2 + {:}\ddot{Cl}{:}^-$$

Phosphorus trichloride acts as a Lewis acid in this reaction. It accepts an unshared electron pair from the alcohol molecule. An oxygen-phosphorus bond is formed as a result. At the same time, a chloride ion is displaced from the phosphorus atom. It leaves with the electron pair from the (now broken) phosphorus-chlorine bond.

The cation formed in the reaction of Equation 6.8 is labile and undergoes further reaction. We shall see its fate and learn the final product of the reaction in the next section. Stay tuned!

6.7 Haloalkanes from Alcohols

The haloalkanes (alkyl halides) are a very important group of compounds. They are represented by the general formula R—X, where R is an alkyl group and X is a halogen. We can prepare haloalkanes from several other classes of organic compounds. In Chapter 5 we saw one method for preparing haloalkanes by treating methanol or ethanol with a hydrogen halide. (We also saw in Chapter 4 that reactions of alkanes with halogens can produce haloalkanes). Another particularly convenient method is the reaction of an alcohol with an appropriate inorganic halide. The inorganic halides we use for this purpose are **acid halide** derivatives of inorganic oxyacids.

Structures for some commonly used acid halides are shown in Figure 6.7 with their parent oxyacids. The acid halides differ from their parent oxyacids in having halogen atoms in place of hydroxyl groups. These acid halides are very reactive toward molecules containing hydroxyl groups. Consider the mechanism of the reaction of ethanol with phosphorus trichloride, which has the overall effect of producing chloroethane.

MECHANISM OF REACTION

Overall:

$$CH_3CH_2\ddot{O}H + PCl_3 \longrightarrow CH_3CH_2\ddot{C}l\colon + (HO)PCl_2$$

Step 1 The alcohol acts as a nucleophile, and chloride ion is displaced from the phosphorus atom.

$$CH_3CH_2{-}\ddot{O}(H)\colon + PCl_3 \longrightarrow CH_3CH_2{-}\overset{+}{O}(H){-}\ddot{P}Cl_2 + \colon\ddot{C}l\colon^-$$

ethanol

Step 2 The products, the $CH_3CH_2O(H)PCl_2^+$ and Cl^- ions, then react with each other by way of a second nucleophilic attack. This time chloride ion behaves as the nucleophile and attacks a carbon atom. In this step the leaving group is $HOPCl_2$, and a carbon-oxygen bond is broken. An oxygen bearing a positive charge has been displaced from carbon by the nucleophile. This step is completely analogous to the displacement of water from a protonated alcohol (an oxonium ion) by a halide (see Chapter 3).

$$\colon\ddot{C}l\colon^- + CH_3CH_2{-}\overset{+}{\ddot{O}}(PCl_2){-}H \longrightarrow \colon\ddot{C}l{-}CH_2CH_3 + H{-}\ddot{O}{-}PCl_2$$

Figure 6.7 Oxyacids and their acid halide derivatives. The acid halides are useful in the conversion of alcohols to haloalkanes.

Acid halide	PCl_3	$O{=}SCl_2$	$O{=}PCl_3$	$O{=}CCl_2$
	phosphorus trichloride	thionyl chloride	phosphorus oxychloride	phosgene
Parent oxyacid	$P(OH)_3$	H_2SO_3	H_3PO_4	H_2CO_3
	phosphorous acid	sulfurous acid	phosphoric acid	carbonic acid

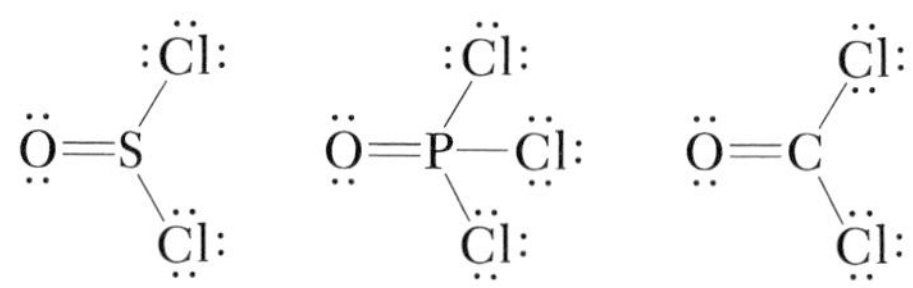

In general, this reaction produces good yields of haloalkanes from alcohols. Another example is the preparation of 1-bromobutane, as shown in Equation 6.9. Other inorganic acid halides can also be used. We will return to consider the synthetic utility of this reaction in more detail later.

Eqn. 6.9

$$\underset{\text{1-butanol}}{3\,CH_3CH_2CH_2CH_2OH} + PBr_3 \xrightarrow{25^\circ} \underset{\text{81\% yield}}{3\,CH_3CH_2CH_2CH_2Br} + (HO)_3P$$

A nucleophilic displacement reaction will occur only if the available reagents meet certain criteria. These criteria can be subdivided into requirements for the nucleophile and requirements for the reagent attacked by the nucleophile. An analysis of all of the factors involved is not simple, since different factors may work in opposite directions. We will delve more deeply into the many aspects of nucleophilic displacements later. For the present we can employ a most useful correlation between the basicity of a leaving group and its ability to be displaced: *leaving-group ability correlates inversely with the basicity of the group displaced.* The weaker the base, the more readily it serves as a leaving group. For example, we find that fluoride ion is a relatively potent base (its conjugate acid, HF, is a relatively weak acid), but it is a poor leaving group. On the other hand, iodide ion is a good leaving group—it is a relatively poor base, as its conjugate acid, HI, is a strong acid.

In the conversion of alcohols to haloalkanes using phosphorus halides, both steps of the reaction mechanism illustrate this general correlation. The leaving groups Cl^- and $HOPCl_2$ both have very strong conjugate acids (HCl and $(H_2OPCl_2)^+$, respectively).

PROBLEM 6.6

Based on the relationship between basicity and leaving group abilities, which of the following classes of compounds would you predict to undergo nucleophilic substitution reaction readily with hydroxide ion?

a. amines ($R\ddot{N}H_2$) **b.** fluoroalkanes ($R\ddot{F}$:)
c. chloroalkanes ($R\ddot{Cl}$:) **d.** nitriles ($R{-}C{\equiv}N$:)

Only a one-third molar amount of phosphorus trihalide is theoretically required to convert alcohols to haloalkanes, because each of the three halogens present can convert an alcohol to a haloalkane, as shown in Equation 6.10.

Eqn. 6.10

$$3\ CH_3CH_2CH_2OH + PBr_3 \longrightarrow 3\ CH_3CH_2CH_2Br + (HO)_3P$$

1-propanol — 78% yield 1-bromopropane

In practice, to ensure that all of the alcohol is converted to haloalkane, a slight excess of the phosphorus trihalide is used.

PROBLEM 6.7 Using the curved-arrow formalism, write out the mechanism by which the remaining two chlorine atoms of $HOPCl_2$ react with alcohol, leading to the formation of two additional molar amounts of chloroalkane and a molar amount of phosphorous acid ($(HO)_3P$).

This reaction is performed by the careful direct addition of the phosphorus trihalide to a liquid alcohol. If the alcohol is a solid, an inert solvent (an alkane or an ether) is used. The reaction provides an efficient preparation of chloroalkanes from primary, secondary, or tertiary alcohols. It also serves to prepare bromoalkanes cleanly from primary alcohols. It works less well for converting secondary or tertiary alcohols to bromoalkanes.

Other inorganic acid chlorides (Figure 6.7) can also be used to prepare chloroalkanes from alcohols. These reactions are analogous to the reaction using phosphorus trichloride.

PROBLEM 6.8 The reaction of 1-butanol with phosphorus oxychloride proceeds in a manner entirely analogous to that of 1-butanol and phosphorus trichloride. Give the products of the equation of 1-butanol and phosphorus oxychloride.

6.8 Esters from Alcohols

Acid chlorides are said to be **derivatives** of their parent acids—they differ from the acids by having a chlorine atom in place of a hydroxyl group. Another type of derivative of an acid is of great significance throughout organic and biological chemistry: the **ester.** In esters, one or more hydroxyl groups of the oxyacid have been replaced by alkoxy groups. Some examples of esters are shown in Figure 6.8.

Esters of phosphoric acid are known as phosphate esters. They are central to the chemistry of biological systems. One route for the laboratory preparation of phosphate esters involves the reaction of alcohols with the acid chloride of phosphoric acid, the same reagent we just used (in Problem 6.8) for the preparation of a chloroalkane. However, different reaction conditions (low temperature) are required to prepare the phosphate ester. The reaction of 1-butanol with phosphorus oxychloride to form tri-1-butyl phosphate is shown in Equation 6.13.

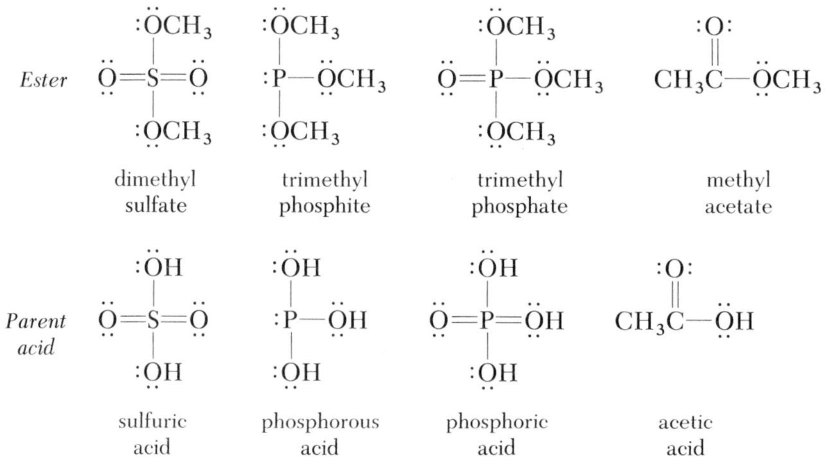

Figure 6.8 Examples of esters. Methyl acetate is an example of an organic ester, a derivative of a carboxylic acid. Such compounds are discussed in Chapters 21 and 22. The others are examples of inorganic esters, which are derived from inorganic acids.

	dimethyl sulfate	trimethyl phosphite	trimethyl phosphate	methyl acetate
Ester	$O{=}S(OCH_3)_2{=}O$	$:P(OCH_3)_3$	$O{=}P(OCH_3)_3$	$CH_3C({=}O)OCH_3$

	sulfuric acid	phosphorous acid	phosphoric acid	acetic acid
Parent acid	$O{=}S(OH)_2{=}O$	$:P(OH)_3$	$O{=}P(OH)_3$	$CH_3C({=}O)OH$

Eqn. 6.11

$$3\ CH_3CH_2CH_2CH_2OH + O{=}PCl_3 \longrightarrow O{=}P(OCH_2CH_2CH_2CH_3)_3 + 3\ HCl$$

1-butanol; tributyl phosphate (85% yield)

This reaction works well for the formation of phosphate esters using primary or secondary alcohols. Primary alcohols react faster than secondary alcohols. Tertiary alcohols also react, but complications prevent the facile isolation of phosphate ester products.

Thus we see that either a phosphate ester or a haloalkane can be obtained by the reaction of an alcohol with phosphorus oxychloride. Two types of products are possible because the chloride ion formed in the initial step can follow either of the two routes shown in Figure 6.9.

It is a recurring theme in organic chemistry that Lewis bases have available to them the competing possibilities of proton abstraction and nucleophilic attack. We can direct the reaction of an alcohol with phosphorus oxychloride by choosing different reaction conditions. For ester formation, we add the alcohol slowly to a cooled solution of the phosphorus oxychloride in an inert solvent. For the formation of a chloroalkane, we add the phosphorus oxychloride to the alcohol, often without solvent, and the reaction mixture is heated. We can understand

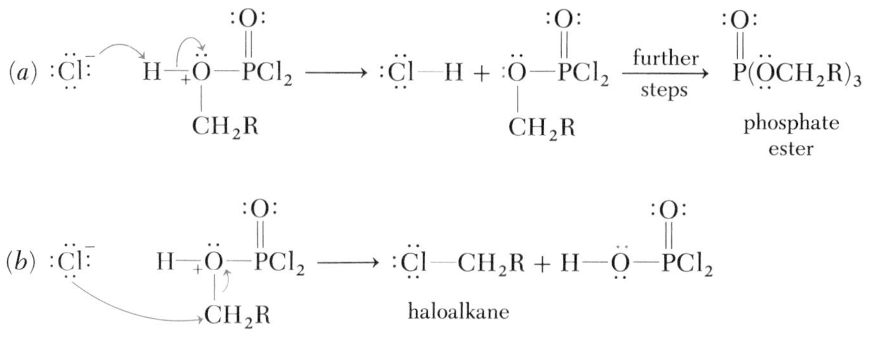

(a) $:Cl^- + H{-}\overset{+}{O}(CH_2R){-}P({=}O)Cl_2 \longrightarrow :Cl{-}H + :O(CH_2R){-}P({=}O)Cl_2 \xrightarrow{\text{further steps}} O{=}P(OCH_2R)_3$ (phosphate ester)

(b) $:Cl^- + H{-}\overset{+}{O}(CH_2R){-}P({=}O)Cl_2 \longrightarrow :Cl{-}CH_2R + H{-}O{-}P({=}O)Cl_2$ (haloalkane)

Figure 6.9 Two possible routes for chloride ion attack on the oxonium ion intermediate in the reaction of an alcohol with phosphorus oxychloride. (*a*) The chloride ion acts as a Brønsted base, abstracting a proton from the intermediate and leading to ester formation. (*b*) The chloride ion acts as a nucleophile (Lewis base), performing a displacement reaction and leading to haloalkane formation.

SPECIAL TOPIC

Phosphate Esters in Biological Systems

In biological systems, phosphate esters play a variety of vital roles. For example, in Chapter 3 we pointed out the role of hydrogen bonding between chains of DNA. Along each chain of DNA there are phosphate diester linkages holding together the individual chain components (nucleosides). (We excluded these linkages from the diagram in Chapter 3 for simplicity.) These phosphate ester linkages are emphasized in the diagram below, which shows a portion of a single DNA chain.

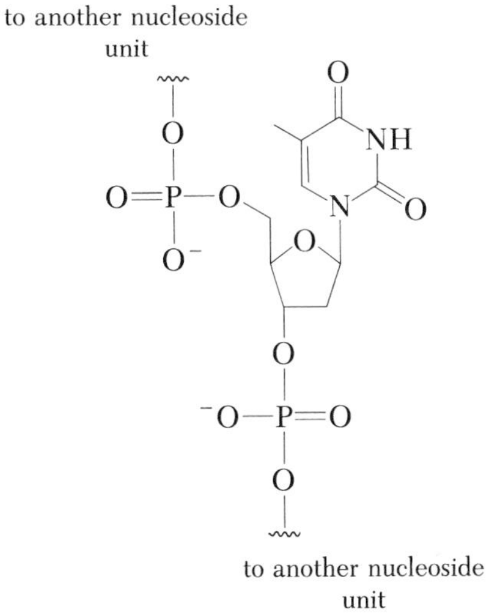

to another nucleoside unit

to another nucleoside unit

For each nucleoside in the chain, there must be a phosphate diester linkage. These linkages are phosphate *di*ester linkages because two of the acidic hydroxyl groups on phosphorus are replaced by alkoxy groups.

Nucleic acids are not the only biological molecules in which phosphate ester linkages are found. Two other important examples are shown below.

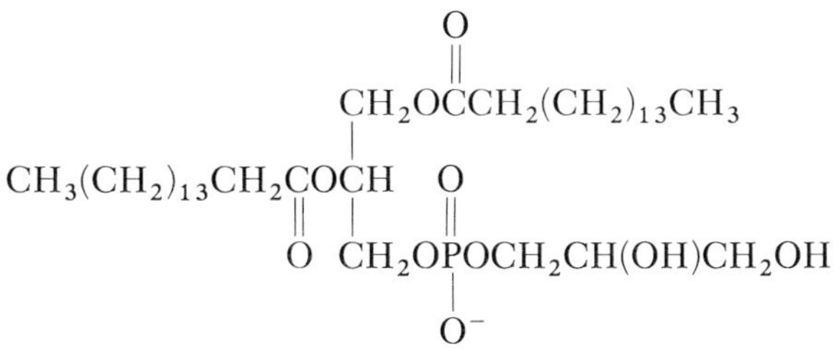

dihexadecanoylphosphorylglycerol (phosphatidyl glycerol, PG), a phospholipid constitutent of membranes of cells

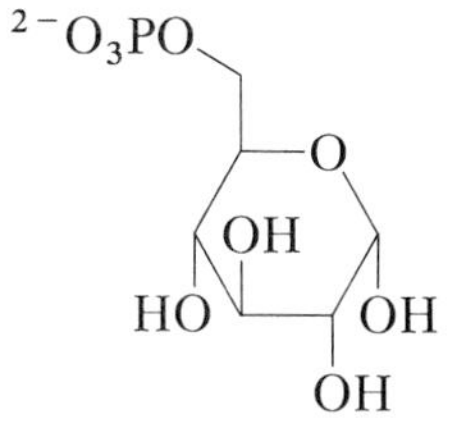

glucose 6-phosphate, an intermediate in the biological degradation of carbohydrates

(continued)

(continued from previous page)

One is an example of a phospholipid (phospholipids are major constituents of the membranes of cells), and the other is a carbohydrate derivative and is a critical intermediate in the metabolism of sugars.

This particular phospholipid contains a phosphate diester linkage, while glucose 6-phosphate contains a monophosphate ester linkage. In addition to the structures shown, there are a multitude of other critical biological molecules that contain phosphate ester linkages.

the controlling role of temperature in terms of the different **energies of activation** for the competing processes. We will introduce the fundamental idea of activation energies rather briefly here.

In chemical reactions, bonds are broken and formed. Each bond that is broken requires an energy input, and each bond that is formed releases energy to the surroundings. However, in general, energy is always needed to start reactions, even if the products are more stable (have stronger bonds) than the reactants. The energy that must be provided to initiate the reaction is the activation energy. It is a measure of the energy barrier to reaction.

Generally, Brønsted acid-base reactions are observed to have a very low energy barrier (activation energy). Nucleophilic displacement reactions have higher energy barriers. Thus, by keeping the reaction at a relatively low temperature we favor the reaction pathway with the lower energy barrier (in the present case, the proton abstraction reaction). Figure 6.10 shows energy profiles for the two types of reactions.

We will return to these ideas and enlarge upon them in later chapters after we introduce some basic principles that we will need for an in-depth discussion.

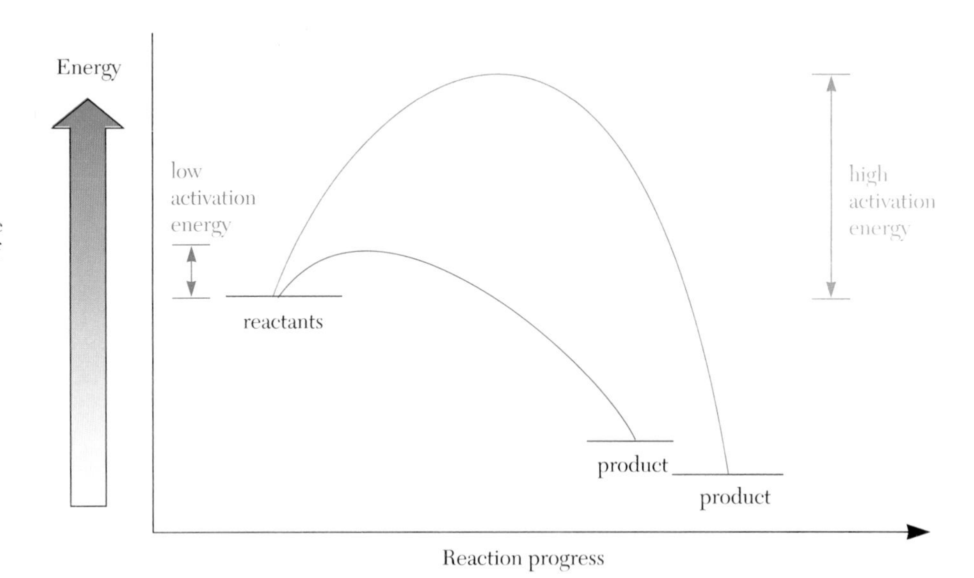

Figure 6.10 The importance of activation energy. As reactions proceed from reactants to products there is an initial *increase* in energy, followed by a fall. The extra energy that must be given to the reactants to reach the state of maximum energy is known as the activation energy. It is provided by collisions in which kinetic energy is changed into potential energy. If the reaction temperature is low, relatively few collisions will be energetic enough to allow a reaction of high activation energy to occur. Under these conditions, the reaction of lower activation energy dominates. For further discussion, see later chapters.

6.9 Oxidation of Alcohols

The reactions we discussed earlier in this chapter were *substitution* reactions; that is, they involved the *replacement* of one atom by another atom. Another important type of reaction for alcohols is oxidation. You should recall that we first introduced this type of reaction in Chapter 5. We noted, for example, that two products—formaldehyde (**6.7**) and formic acid (**6.8**)—are obtained from the oxidation of the simplest alcohol, methanol.

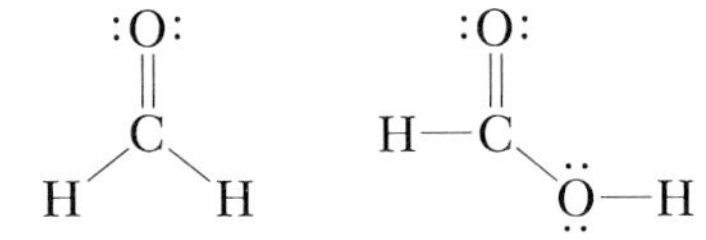

$$H_2C{=}\ddot{O}\!:\qquad\qquad H{-}C({=}\ddot{O}\!:){-}\ddot{O}{-}H$$

formaldehyde (also known as methanal) **6.7**

formic acid (also known as methanoic acid) **6.8**

The varying reactions of primary, secondary, and tertiary alcohols with oxidizing agents are summarized in Figure 6.11.

In general, susceptibility to oxidation correlates with the presence of hydrogen atoms bonded to the carbinol (C—OH) or carbonyl (C═O) carbon. For example, primary alcohols have *two* hydrogen atoms attached to the carbinol carbon. *Two* stages of oxidation occur under relatively mild conditions. The first stage involves the removal of one of the carbinol hydrogen atoms and the formation of a carbon to oxygen double bond. The product is an **aldehyde,** a compound having at least one hydrogen atom bonded to the carbonyl carbon atom. Because the aldehyde has this hydrogen, further oxidation is readily effected. The second stage of oxidation, like the first, involves the removal of a hydrogen atom, but now it is replaced by a hydroxyl group, forming a **carboxylic acid.**

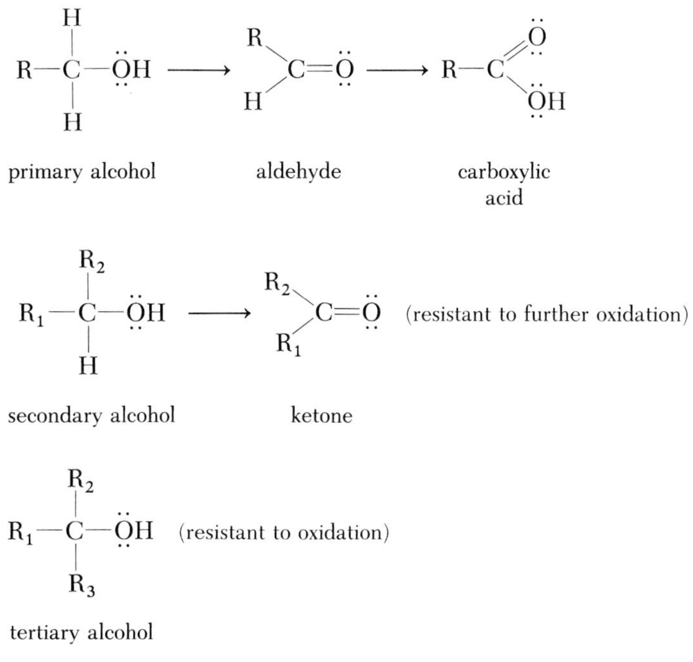

$$R{-}CH_2{-}\ddot{O}H \longrightarrow R(H)C{=}\ddot{O} \longrightarrow R{-}C({=}\ddot{O}){-}\ddot{O}H$$

primary alcohol — aldehyde — carboxylic acid

$$R_1{-}CH(R_2){-}\ddot{O}H \longrightarrow R_2(R_1)C{=}\ddot{O} \quad \text{(resistant to further oxidation)}$$

secondary alcohol — ketone

$$R_1{-}C(R_2)(R_3){-}\ddot{O}H \quad \text{(resistant to oxidation)}$$

tertiary alcohol

Figure 6.11 Action of oxidizing agents on the different classes of alcohols. *Primary* alcohols are oxidized to aldehydes, which can be further oxidized to carboxylic acids. Many common oxidizing agents convert primary alcohols directly into carboxylic acids (the intermediate aldehyde is oxidized under the conditions of the reaction). *Secondary* alcohols are oxidized to ketones, which are resistant to further oxidation. *Tertiary* alcohols are inert to most common oxidizing agents. In all these structures R, R_1, R_2, . . . represent alkyl groups.

Secondary alcohols contain only one hydrogen atom attached to the carbinol carbon atom, and only one stage of oxidation can be readily effected. As in the first oxidation of a primary alcohol, a hydrogen atom bonded to the carbinol carbon is removed, and a carbon to oxygen double bond forms. The product is a **ketone,** a compound having two alkyl groups attached to a carbonyl carbon atom. A ketone has no hydrogen atoms bonded to the carbonyl carbon, and we find it to be resistant to further oxidation. The simplest ketone is acetone (IUPAC name: 2-propanone); it is formed by the oxidation of 2-propanol, as shown in Equation 6.12.

$$(CH_3)_2CH{:}\ddot{O}H \xrightarrow[\text{agent}]{\text{oxidizing}} (CH_3)_2C{=}\ddot{O}{:}$$

isopropyl alcohol (2-propanol) → acetone (2-propanone)

In order to oxidize a ketone to a carboxylic acid, a carbon-carbon bond would have to be broken. Breaking a carbon-carbon bond requires much more severe conditions than are needed for the breaking of carbon-hydrogen bonds. Thus ketones, unlike aldehydes, are not easily oxidized to carboxylic acids. For a similar reason, tertiary alcohols are much more resistant to oxidation than are primary and secondary alcohols.

In the oxidation of an alcohol to an aldehyde or ketone, a double bond is generated between carbon and oxygen. The carbon-oxygen σ bond remains, and a new bond arises from the side-to-side π-overlap of p orbitals on the carbon and oxygen atoms. The carbon-oxygen double bond thus consists of both a σ bond and a π bond. The carbon undergoing oxidation is changed in its hybridization from sp^3 to sp^2.

PROBLEM 6.9 Draw the structures for the ketones that would be produced upon oxidation of each of the following alcohols:

a. *sec*-butyl alcohol **b.** 3-pentanol **c.** cyclohexanol

PROBLEM 6.10 Draw the structures of the carboxylic acids that would be produced by oxidation of each of the following alcohols:

a. isobutyl alcohol **b.** neopentyl alcohol **c.** 2-cyclohexylethanol

REAGENTS USED FOR THE OXIDATION OF ALCOHOLS

There are a wide variety of reagents for the controlled oxidation of alcohols. Two types of inorganic oxidizing agents will be described here, and other oxidizing agents will be introduced later.

Compounds of chromium and manganese in high oxidation states are particularly useful for the oxidation of alcohols. Rather common examples of chromium(VI) oxidizing agents are chromium trioxide (CrO_3), sometimes known as chromic anhydride, and dichromate salts ($Na_2Cr_2O_7$ or $K_2Cr_2O_7$).

A useful qualitative test for alcohols depends on the use of a Cr(VI) reagent (e.g., chromic anhydride or sodium dichromate in sulfuric acid). The Cr(VI)

reagent is added to a solution of the alcohol in acetone. If the alcohol is primary or secondary, a blue-green color appears within a few seconds. Tertiary alcohols do not give a color change with this test because they are resistant to oxidation. The test is based on the reduction of Cr(VI), which has an orange color in solution, to Cr(III), which is green in solution. When the alcohol is oxidized, the chromium reagent is reduced. This color change provides a rapid method for the detection of alcohols, and it is used in the *breathalyzer* test for ethanol intoxication.

With secondary alcohols, the reaction with oxidizing agents produces ketones. Examples are shown in Equations 6.13 and 6.14.

$$CH_3CH_2CH(OH)CH_2CH_2CH_3 \xrightarrow[\text{acetic acid}]{CrO_3} CH_3CH_2C(=O)CH_2CH_2CH_3$$

3-hexanol → 63% yield 3-hexanone

$$CH_3CH_2CH_2CH(OH)CH_3 \xrightarrow[\text{sulfuric acid}]{Na_2Cr_2O_7} CH_3CH_2CH_2C(=O)CH_3$$

2-pentanol → 74% yield 2-pentanone

The mechanism of this type of reaction involves several steps.

MECHANISM OF REACTION

Step 1 An intermediate ester of chromic acid forms.

$$(CH_3)_2CH{-}OH + HCrO_4^- + H^+ \longrightarrow (CH_3)_2CH{-}O{-}Cr(=O)_2{-}OH + H_2O$$

The formation of the ester renders the hydrogen on the original hydroxyl carbon significantly more acidic than it was prior to ester formation.

Step 2 The hydrogen on the original hydroxyl carbon is sufficiently acidic that the weak base present in the system (water) is able to remove it and thereby complete the oxidation.

$$H_2O\!: + (CH_3)_2CH{-}O{-}Cr(=O)_2{-}OH \longrightarrow CH_3C(=O)CH_3 + O{=}Cr{=}O(OH)^- + H_3O^+$$

Figure 6.12 Oxidation of 1-propanol using chromic anhydride in sulfuric acid. Either the aldehyde or the carboxylic acid can be obtained by the proper choice of reaction conditions. It is possible to isolate the aldehyde because it is relatively volatile and thus easily removed from the reaction mixture. In general, if the aldehyde is not removed from the reaction mixture, it is further oxidized to a carboxylic acid.

$$CH_3CH_2CH_2\ddot{O}H \xrightarrow[H_2SO_4]{CrO_3} CH_3CH_2\overset{\overset{:O:}{\|}}{C}H$$

1-propanol → propanal

(49% yield when the oxidizing agent is added slowly to the alcohol and the aldehyde is distilled from the reaction as it is formed)

$$CH_3CH_2CH_2\ddot{O}H \xrightarrow[H_2SO_4]{CrO_3} CH_3CH_2\overset{\overset{:O:}{\|}}{C}\ddot{O}H$$

propanoic acid

(65% yield upon isolating the acid after the completion of the reaction, with no attempt to remove the aldehyde by distillation)

Aldehydes are formed by the oxidation of primary alcohols with Cr(VI) reagents under these conditions. The mechanism is the same as shown for secondary alcohol oxidation. However, the aldehyde formed is often further oxidized to a carboxylic acid. We can isolate the aldehyde only under special conditions. Low molecular weight aldehydes can be distilled from the reaction mixture as they are formed and before they can be further oxidized, but this is usually not possible with higher molecular weight aldehydes (those containing more than five carbon atoms). The results of the CrO_3/H_2SO_4 oxidation of 1-propanol are shown in Figure 6.12.

An alternative method for the preparation of aldehydes from primary alcohols uses CrO_3 in the organic base pyridine (**6.9**) rather than in an acidic medium. Under these conditions, oxidation of both primary and secondary alcohols occurs to give carbonyl compounds. It is of particular interest that the oxidation of primary alcohols stops at the aldehyde stage. (Recall that most other oxidizing agents acting on primary alcohols yield carboxylic acids.) Equation 6.15, for example, illustrates the preparation of geranial from geraniol.

$$(CH_3)_2C{=}CHCH_2CH_2C(CH_3){=}CHCH_2OH \xrightarrow[pyridine]{CrO_3} (CH_3)_2C{=}CHCH_2CH_2C(CH_3){=}CHCHO$$

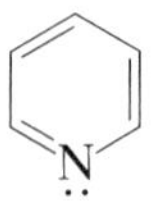

Eqn. 6.15

geraniol → geranial (66% yield)

pyridine
6.9

Care is required for the preparation of the CrO_3/pyridine oxidizing system (Sarett's reagent). Since the reaction between chromic anhydride and pyridine is quite exothermic, it is critical to add the CrO_3 to the pyridine. The reverse order of addition usually leads to the mixture catching fire. Another oxidizing agent that can be used for the same purpose as CrO_3/pyridine is pyridinium dichromate or PDC (prepared from sodium dichromate, $Na_2Cr_2O_7$ and pyridine). It is safer to use and is commercially available.

High oxidation state manganese compounds also oxidize alcohols to carbonyl compounds and carboxylic acids. Permanganate ion, MnO_4^-, in aqueous basic solution oxidizes secondary alcohols smoothly to ketones. An example is shown in Equation 6.16.

Eqn. 6.16

$$\text{cyclohexanol} \xrightarrow{KMnO_4,\ OH^-} \text{cyclohexanone}$$

cyclohexanol (a cyclic secondary alcohol)

95% yield cyclohexanone (a cyclic ketone)

Permanganate oxidizes primary alcohols initially to the aldehydes, which subsequently are oxidized further to the carboxylic acids. It is generally not possible to isolate the aldehyde intermediates in the permanganate oxidation system. An example of the permanganate oxidation of a primary alcohol is shown in Equation 6.17.

Eqn. 6.17

$$CH_3CH_2CH_2CH_2CH(CH_2CH_3)CH_2\ddot{O}H \xrightarrow[\text{2. aqueous acid}]{\text{1. } KMnO_4,\ NaOH,\ H_2O} CH_3CH_2CH_2CH_2CH(CH_2CH_3)CO_2H$$

2-ethyl-1-hexanol

74% yield 2-ethylhexanoic acid

Permanganate ion is also used at times as an oxidizing agent in acetic acid solution. However, permanganate ion does not oxidize tertiary alcohols.

The inorganic by-product in the permanganate oxidation of alcohols is manganese dioxide. Thus permanganate provides a quick visual test for the differentiation of tertiary alcohols from primary and secondary alcohols. Once a determination has been made that a sample is an alcohol (e.g., by reaction with sodium metal), oxidation with permanganate ion is attempted. The disappearance of the characteristic purple color of the permanganate solution and the formation of a brown precipitate (MnO_2) indicates the presence of a primary or secondary alcohol.

Manganese dioxide itself *slowly* oxidizes primary and secondary alcohols to the corresponding aldehydes and ketones. If this reaction is used preparatively, the alcohol is stirred with manganese dioxide in a hydrocarbon solvent such as benzene or pentane. An example is given in Equation 6.18.

Eqn. 6.18

$$CH_3CH_2CH_2CH_2\ddot{O}H \xrightarrow[\text{benzene, 1 week}]{MnO_2} CH_3CH_2CH_2CH\ddot{O}$$

1-butanol

70% yield butanal

PROBLEM 6.11 Substance *A*, of formula $C_4H_{10}O$ is known to react with sodium metal to produce hydrogen. On being heated with sulfuric acid and potassium dichromate, substance *B*,with the formula $C_4H_8O_2$, is produced. Suggest two possible structures for *A* and *B*.

6.10 Other Aspects of Alcohol Chemistry

This chapter and the previous one have introduced you to many important aspects of the chemistry of the alcohols. As we proceed, you will find that alcohols figure prominently in all our discussions of organic compounds. The chemistry you have learned so far will provide a good introduction for many of the topics we will meet, and as we explore these later topics, you will find that the newly introduced chemistry helps to reinforce the concepts and reactions already discussed and adds to your knowledge of alcohols. You will learn how to prepare alcohols from other types of compounds such as alkenes and carbonyl compounds. You will also see that the reaction types introduced in this chapter have counterparts in other areas of organic chemistry. As we continue beyond this chapter, we will introduce more reactions of alcohols that reflect their central role in the preparation of other organic compounds. We will see how alcohols can be used to prepare a whole host of compounds, including some that we met in this chapter, such as organic esters, and others that we have yet to encounter. In the following chapter, in fact, you will see some new aspects of alcohol chemistry. You will find that alcohols can be used to produce an important type of reaction intermediate known as a *carbocation*, and we will explore the chemistry of this species.

Summary

- Alcohols react with inorganic acid halides to produce haloalkanes or esters, depending on the specific reaction conditions used. These reactions proceed in a sequence of Lewis acid/Lewis base reaction steps.
- Alcohols can act as either acids or bases.
- Alcohols act as bases by using an unshared electron pair on the hydroxyl oxygen.
- When alcohols act as Brønsted bases, they accept a proton, forming protonated alcohols known as oxonium ions. They can also act as Brønsted acids by donating the hydrogen of the hydroxyl group. Loss of this hydrogen from an alcohol leads to an alkoxide ion, $R\ddot{\underset{..}{O}}{:}^-$.
- Although alcohols can act as Brønsted acids, they are *weak* acids. They require strong bases to generate sizable concentrations of the alkoxide ion in solution.
- Primary and secondary alcohols undergo facile oxidation.
- High oxidation state chromium and manganese reagents readily oxidize secondary alcohols to ketones.
- Primary alcohols can be oxidized to aldehydes using these same reagents. However, unless special precautions are taken, the oxidation proceeds further to a carboxylic acid.
- Tertiary alcohols are resistant to oxidation under normal conditions. A hydrogen attached to the carbinol carbon is required for facile oxidation.

Terms to Remember

radicofunctional method	hydrophobic	inductive effect
solvation	hydrophilic	acid halide

derivative
ester
energy of activation
aldehyde
carboxylic acid
ketone

Reactions of Synthetic Utility

Reactions of synthetic utility will be summarized at the end of each chapter in which they are introduced. These reactions are numbered sequentially throughout the entire text, and the number of the section in which they were first discussed appears to the right of the equation. For Chapters 6 through 9 these reactions are cross-referenced on a functional-group map. For reactions introduced after Chapter 9, each student should continue the development of the functional-group map in the form most convenient for his or her own use. Limitations of the reactions are given to assist in the design of synthetic procedures.

1. $ROH + PX_3 \longrightarrow RX$ **6.7**

   $X = Br$, $ROH = 1°$; $X = Cl$, $ROH = 1°, 2°, 3°$

2. $ROH + POCl_3 \longrightarrow RCl$ **6.7**

3. $ROH + SOCl_2 \longrightarrow RCl$ **6.7**

4. $ROH + COCl_2 \longrightarrow RCl$ **6.7**

5. $ROH + POCl_3 \longrightarrow O{=}P\,(OR)_3$ **6.8**

   $ROH = 1°, 2°$

6. $\underset{2°}{R_2CHOH} + CrO_3 \xrightarrow[\text{acetic acid or } H_2SO_4]{} R_2C{=}O$ **6.9**

7. $\underset{2°}{R_2CHOH} + Na_2Cr_2O_7 \xrightarrow[H_2SO_4]{} R_2C{=}O$ **6.9**

8. $\underset{1°}{RCH_2OH} + CrO_3 \xrightarrow[H_2SO_4]{} RCOOH$ **6.9**

9. $\underset{1°}{RCH_2OH} + Na_2Cr_2O_7 \xrightarrow[H_2SO_4]{} RCOOH$ **6.9**

10. $\underset{1°,\,2°}{R_2CHOH} + CrO_3 \xrightarrow[\text{pyridine}]{} R_2C{=}O$ **6.9**

    Notes: (*a*) This reaction stops at the aldehyde stage if a primary alcohol is used; most other oxidants convert primary alcohols to carboxylic acids. (*b*) PDC, pyridinium dichromate, in pyridine is a useful alternative to CrO_3 in pyridine.

11. $\underset{2°}{R_2CHOH} + KMnO_4 \xrightarrow[H_2O,\ NaOH]{} R_2C{=}O$ **6.9**

12. $\underset{1°}{RCH_2OH} + KMnO_4 \xrightarrow[H_2O,\ NaOH]{} RCOOH$ **6.9**

13. $R_2CHOH + MnO_2 \xrightarrow[\text{solvent}]{\text{hydrocarbon}} R_2C{=}O$ **6.9**

Note: Reactions 8, 9, and 12 are useful for aldehyde synthesis only with low molecular weight alcohols (*see page 146*).

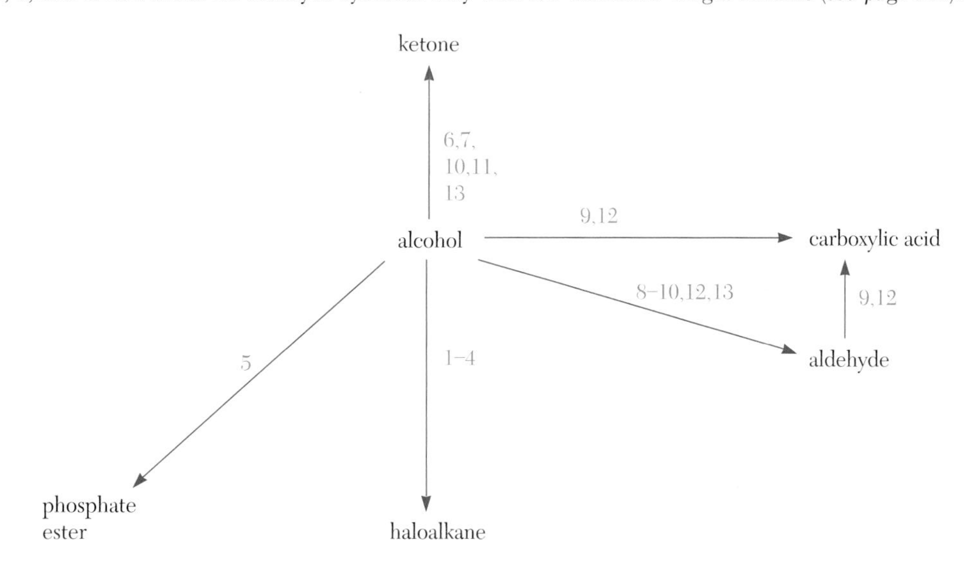

Additional Problems

6.12 Provide IUPAC names for each of the following structures:

a. $CH_3CH_2CH_2CH_2CH_2\ddot{O}H$

b.
$$\begin{array}{c} CH_3 \\ | \\ CH_3CH_2CHCHCH_2\ddot{O}H \\ | \\ CH_3 \end{array}$$

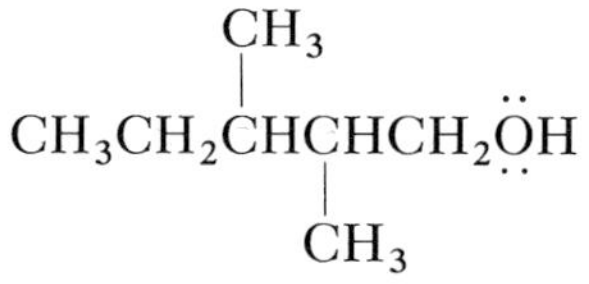

c.
$$\begin{array}{c} CH_3CH_2CH_2CH_2C(CH_3)_2 \\ | \\ :\ddot{O}H \end{array}$$

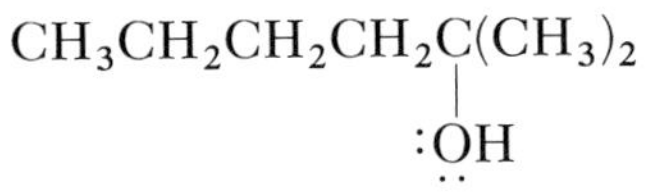

d.
$$\begin{array}{c} :\ddot{O}H \\ | \\ CH_3CH_2CHCHCH(CH_3)_2 \\ | \\ CH_3 \end{array}$$

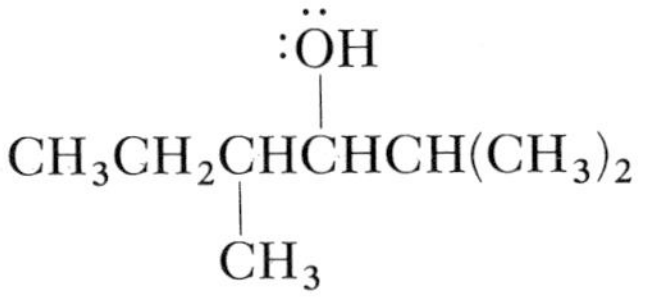

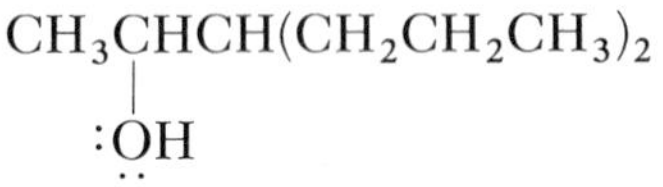

e.
$$\begin{array}{c} (CH_3CH_2)_2CHCH_2CHC(CH_3)_3 \\ | \\ :\ddot{O}H \end{array}$$

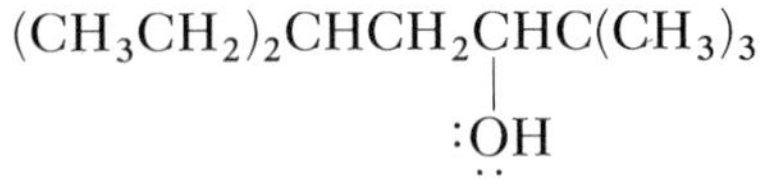

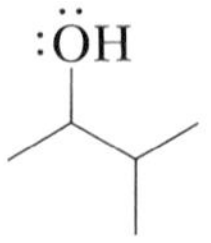

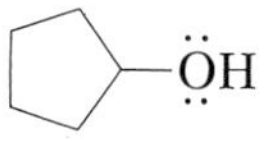

f. $(CH_3CH_2)_3CCH_2CH_2\ddot{O}H$

g.
$$\begin{array}{c} CH_3CHCH(CH_2CH_2CH_3)_2 \\ | \\ :\ddot{O}H \end{array}$$

h.
$$\begin{array}{c} :\ddot{O}H \\ | \\ (CH_3CH_2CH_2)_2CHCHCH_2CHCH_2CH_3 \\ | \\ CH_3 \end{array}$$

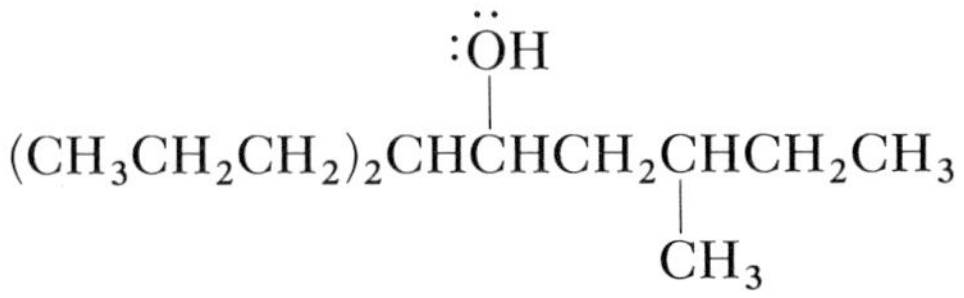

i.
$$\begin{array}{c} CH_3 \\ | \\ CH_3CH_2CCH(CH_3)CH_2CH_3 \\ | \\ H\ddot{O}: \end{array}$$

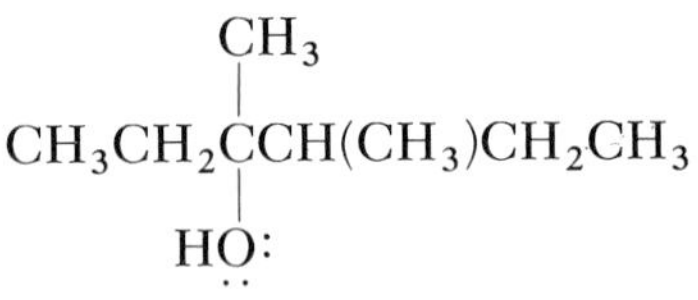

j. $(CH_3CH_2CH_2)_3C\ddot{O}H$

k.
$$\begin{array}{c} CH_3CHCH_2CHCH_3 \\ | \quad\quad | \\ :\ddot{O}H \quad :\ddot{O}H \end{array}$$

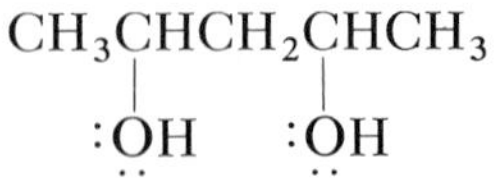

l.
$$\begin{array}{c} CH_3 \\ | \\ CH_3CH_2CHCHCH_2CH_3 \\ | \\ CH_2\ddot{O}H \end{array}$$

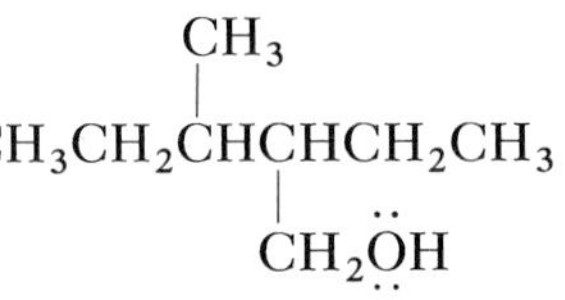

m. $:\ddot{O}H$

n. $\ddot{O}H$

o. $:\ddot{O}H$

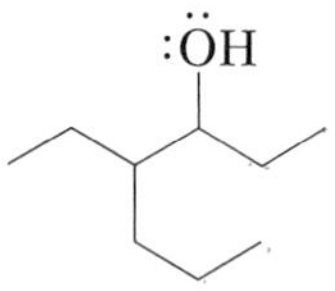

p. $\ddot{O}H$

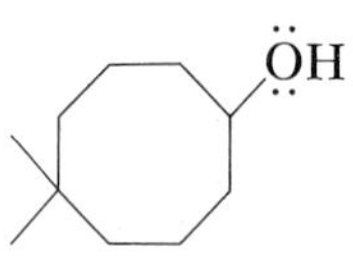

6.13 For each of the compounds in Problem 6.12, tell whether it is a primary, secondary, or tertiary alcohol.

6.14 Draw a structure for each of the following compounds:

a. 4-heptanol
b. 3,3-dimethyl-2-butanol
c. 3-ethyl-1-hexanol
d. 4-ethyl-3,3-dimethyl-4-octanol
e. 3-methyl-3-hexanol
f. 4-ethyl-2-methyl-3-heptanol
g. 3-ethyl-2,6-dimethyl-3-octanol
h. 3-propyl-1-heptanol
i. 4-isopropyl-4-octanol
j. 3-ethyl-2-methyl-3-pentanol

k. potassium ethoxide
l. sodium isopropoxide
m. potassium *tert*-butoxide
n. 4,4-di-*sec*-butylcyclohexanol

6.15 For each of the first ten compounds in Problem 6.14, tell whether it is a primary, secondary, or tertiary alcohol.

6.16 Draw all of the structural isomers of the formula $C_5H_{12}O$. Some of these do not contain the hydroxyl group and therefore are not alcohols. Give the IUPAC name of each structure that *is* an alcohol.

6.17 Draw structures for the methyl esters of each of the following acids:
a. sulfuric acid (H_2SO_4) (dimethyl ester) b. nitric acid (HNO_3) c. formic acid (HCOOH)

6.18 Give the structure of the major organic product in each of the following reactions:
a. 3-pentanol heated with thionyl chloride
b. 3-pentanol heated with potassium permanganate in aqueous sodium hydroxide solution
c. 3-methyl-1-butanol treated with chromic anhydride in pyridine
d. 2-methyl-2-hexanol treated with chromic anhydride in sulfuric acid
e. phosphorus tribromide added to 2-methyl-2-hexanol with heating
f. 2,3-dimethyl-1-butanol treated with phosgene ($COCl_2$) in pyridine
g. 2,3-dimethyl-1,4-pentanediol treated with chromic anhydride in pyridine
h. 4,4-dimethyl-1-pentanol treated with potassium permanganate in aqueous sodium hydroxide
i. excess 1-propanol added to phosphorus oxychloride at 0°C
j. 2-heptanol treated with sodium dichromate in sulfuric acid
k. 3-methyl-1-pentanol treated with sodium dichromate in sulfuric acid
l. 1,6-heptanediol treated with potassium permanganate in aqueous sodium hydroxide

6.19 Give the structure and the name of the alcohol that would be used for the preparation of each of the following compounds upon treatment with chromic anhydride in sulfuric acid:

a. 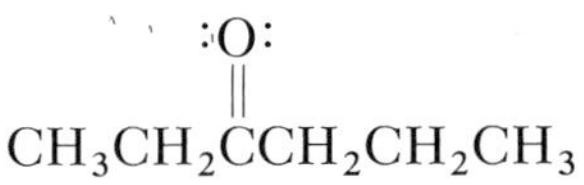
:O:
||
$CH_3CH_2CCH_2CH_2CH_3$

b. 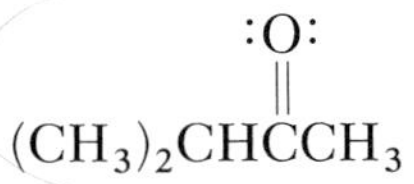
:O:
||
$(CH_3)_2CHCCH_3$

c. $(CH_3)_3CCOOH$

d. 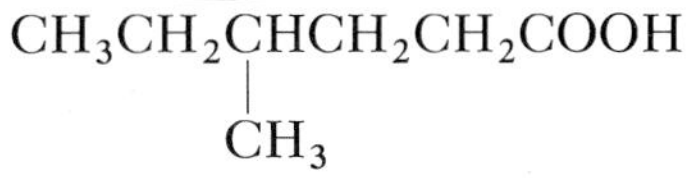 $CH_3CH_2CHCH_2CH_2COOH$
|
CH_3

e. 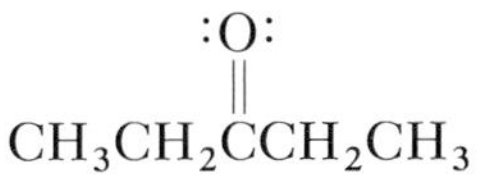
:O:
||
$CH_3CH_2CCH_2CH_3$

f. 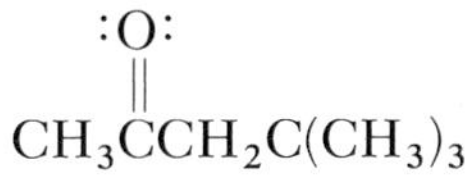
:O:
||
$CH_3CCH_2C(CH_3)_3$

g. 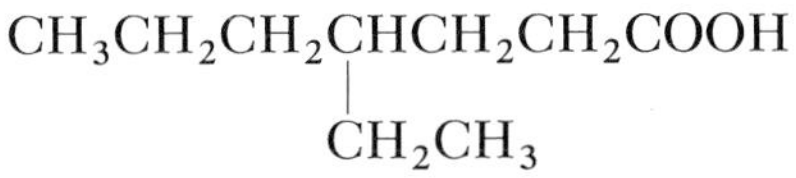 $CH_3CH_2CH_2CHCH_2CH_2COOH$
|
CH_2CH_3

h. 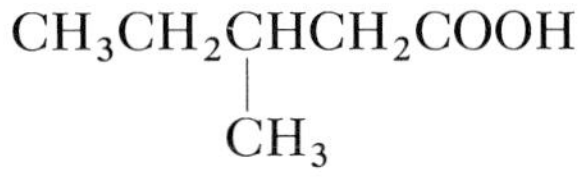 $CH_3CH_2CHCH_2COOH$
|
CH_3

i. 
:O:
||
$(CH_3CH_2)_2CHC(CH_3)_2CH_2CCH_3$

j. 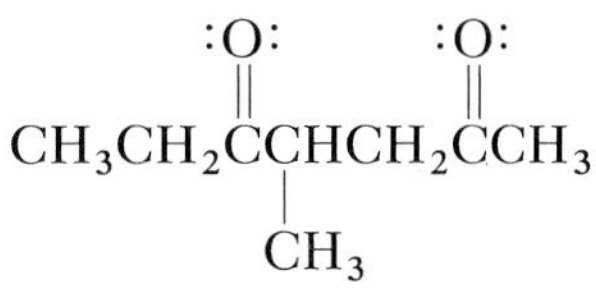
:O: :O:
|| ||
$CH_3CH_2CCHCH_2CCH_3$
|
CH_3

6.20 Give the structure and the name of the alcohol that would be heated with phosphorus trichloride to prepare each of the following compounds:

a. 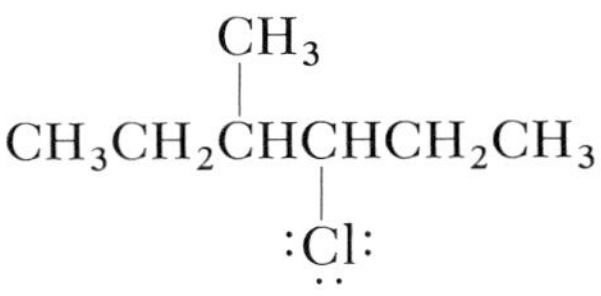
CH_3
|
$CH_3CH_2CHCHCH_2CH_3$
|
:Cl:

b. 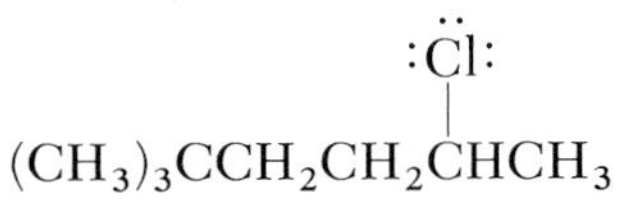
:Cl:
|
$(CH_3)_3CCH_2CH_2CHCH_3$

c. $(CH_3)_2CHCHCH_2CH_2\ddot{C}l:$ with CH_3 on the third carbon

d. $(CH_3CH_2)_2CCH_2\ddot{C}l:$ with CH_3 on the quaternary carbon

e. $CH_3CH_2CHCHCHCH_2CH_2CH_2Cl$ with $:\ddot{C}l:$ and CH_3 on the third carbon, and CH_2CH_3 on the fourth carbon

f. $(CH_3CH_2)_2CCH_3$ with $:\ddot{C}l:$ on the quaternary carbon

g. cyclobutane ring bearing an ethyl group and $\ddot{C}l:$ on the same carbon

h. cyclohexane ring bearing an ethyl group, with $:\ddot{C}l$ on the neighbouring carbon

6.21 Give the structure of the major organic product formed from each of the following alcohols upon treatment with potassium permanganate in aqueous sodium hydroxide:
a. 2,3-dimethyl-1-pentanol b. 2-methyl-2-butanol c. 2,4-dimethyl-3-hexanol
d. 2,2,6,6-tetramethyl-1-octanol e. 4-ethyl-1-hexanol

6.22 For each of the compounds in Problem 6.21, give the structure of the major organic product formed upon treatment with CrO_3 in pyridine.

6.23 For each of the compounds in Problem 6.21, give the structure of the major organic product formed upon heating with phosphorus trichloride.

6.24 Arrange the following compounds in order of increasing acidity (in solution): 2-butanol, methanol, 2,2-dichloroethanol, 2-methyl-2-hexanol. Explain your placement of the compounds in the order you choose.

6.25 Phenol (**6.4**) is a stronger acid than ethanol. Suggest an explanation for this increased acidity. (*Hint:* Consider the conjugate bases of the two hydroxyl compounds in question.)

6.26 The formation of phosphite esters ($(RO)_3P:$) by the reaction of phosphorus trichloride with alcohols (ROH) is analogous to the formation of phosphate esters from phosphorus oxychloride. Use the curved-arrow formalism to show the mechanism of this reaction.

6.27 Describe how you would distinguish, using one or more chemical reactions, between each of the following pairs of compounds. Tell exactly what you would do and what you would see.
a. 2-propanol and *tert*-butyl alcohol b. 1-methylcyclohexanol and cyclohexanol
c. propanal (CH_3CH_2CHO) and *tert*-butyl alcohol

6.28 Substance *C* has the molecular formula $C_5H_{12}O$. It reacts with sodium metal to produce hydrogen but gives no color change upon treatment with either chromic anhydride in sulfuric acid or potassium permanganate in aqueous base. Give a structure for *C* that is consistent with this data.

6.29 Undecanal ($CH_3(CH_2)_9CHO$) is the sex attractant of the greater wax moth (*Galleria mellonella*). How would you synthesize this compound from 1-undecanol?

6.30 Phosphorus trichloride reacts with three equivalents of water to give hydrogen chloride and $(HO)_3P:$ (phosphorous acid). Using the curved-arrow formalism, give a mechanism for this reaction.

6.31 Write an equation, balanced if you can, for the following reactions (or state that no reaction occurs):
a. methanol + sodium hydroxide b. 1-pentanol + hydrogen chloride
c. 2-methyl-2-butanol + hot aqueous alkaline potassium permanganate
d. ethanol + trimethylboron ($(CH_3)_3B$) e. 1-butanol + sodium
f. $CH_3CH_2OCH_2CH_3$ + sodium

6.32 Show how 1-butanol can be converted into each of the following compounds:
a. butanal ($CH_3CH_2CH_2CHO$) b. butanoic acid ($CH_3CH_2CH_2COOH$)
c. 1-chlorobutane d. 1-bromobutane

6.33 On treatment with aqueous basic potassium permanganate, both 1-heptanol and 3-heptanol react. Write the structure for the organic product of each reaction. The product from the reaction of 1-heptanol dissolves in the aqueous solution while that from reaction of 3-heptanol does not dissolve. Explain why.

6.34 You are given a mixture of 2-methyl-1-octanol and 2-methyl-2-octanol from which you must isolate the pure 2-methyl-2-octanol. Propose a method for accomplishing this. You need not worry about recovering the 2-methyl-1-octanol.

6.35 Name the reagents you would use to accomplish each of the following transformations:
a. 4,4-dimethylpentanal ($(CH_3)_3CCH_2CH_2CHO$) from 4,4-dimethyl-1-pentanol
b. tri(1-propyl) phosphate from 1-propanol
c. 2-chlorohexane from 2-hexanol
d. cyclohexanone from cyclohexanol
e. 2-methylpropanoic acid ($(CH_3)_2CHCOOH$) from isobutyl alcohol

6.36 Choose the better leaving group of each pair:
a. chloride ion or hydroxide ion
b. chloride ion or formate anion
c. HS^- or formate anion
d. hydroxide ion or amide ion (NH_2^-)
e. acetate anion or formate anion
f. acetate anion or HS^-

6.37 Compound *D* is known to have the molecular formula $C_4H_{10}O_2$. It reacts with sodium metal to form hydrogen gas. On treatment with chromic anhydride in sulfuric acid, *D* is oxidized to compound *E*, which has the formula $C_4H_6O_4$. Give structures for compounds *D* and *E*.

6.38 *F* and *G* are two compounds of formula $C_4H_{10}O_2$ (different from compound *D* in Problem 6.37). *F* and *G* also form hydrogen gas on reaction with sodium metal. However, on oxidation with chromic anhydride in sulfuric acid, *F* yields a compound *H* of formula $C_4H_6O_3$ and *G* gives a compound *I* of formula $C_4H_6O_2$. Give structures for compounds *F* through *I*.

6.39 In Problems 6.37 and 6.38 we were able to distinguish among three isomeric structures on the basis of the formulas of their oxidation products using chromic anhydride in sulfuric acid. Could we make the same distinction, using only the formulas of the oxidation products, if chromic anhydride in pyridine were used as the oxidizing agent? Explain your answer.

6.40 What is the minimum weight of PBr_3 we would need to convert 20.0 g of 1-hexanol to 1-bromohexane?

6.41 Compound *J*, of formula $C_3H_6O_2$, reacts with phosphorus tribromide to yield a compound *K* of formula C_3H_5OBr. In another reaction, upon treatment with potassium permanganate and work-up with aqueous acid, *J* yields compound *L*, of formula $C_3H_4O_4$. Give structures for the compounds *J* through *L*.

6.42 A student in an elementary organic chemistry course attempted to prepare acetic acid by the reaction shown below. Unfortunately for the student, no acetic acid could be isolated from the reaction mixture, even after prolonged heating. Explain why this approach for the preparation of acetic acid was destined to fail.

$$\underset{\text{methanol}}{CH_3\ddot{O}H} + \underset{\text{sodium acetate}}{CH_3-\overset{\overset{:O:}{\|}}{C}-\ddot{O}:^-\ Na^+} \longrightarrow \underset{\text{sodium methoxide}}{CH_3\ddot{O}:^-\ Na^+} + \underset{\text{acetic acid}}{CH_3-\overset{\overset{:O:}{\|}}{C}-\ddot{O}H}$$

6.43 Compounds *M* and *N* react with each other to yield primarily compounds *O* and *P* at low temperatures but primarily compounds *Q* and *R* at higher temperatures. Which reaction pathway has the higher energy of activation (energy barrier)?

Types of Bond Cleavage—Carbocations and Radicals as Reaction Intermediates

7.1 Introduction

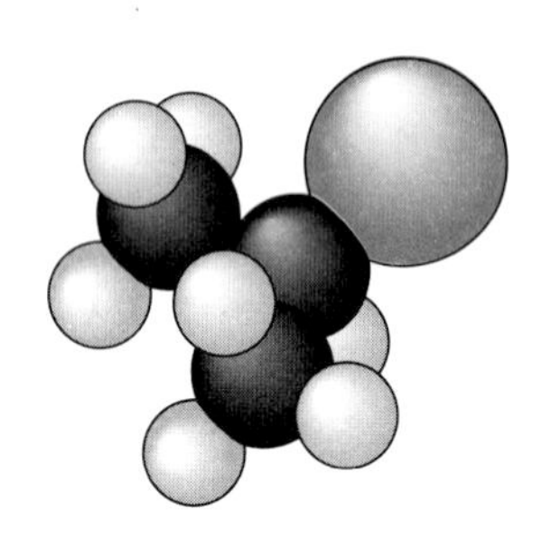

In earlier chapters we introduced the idea that many organic reactions proceed in a succession of mechanistic steps. Such reactions produce **intermediate** ions or molecules that then undergo further reactions. An intermediate in a chemical reaction is a species with a definite lifetime (usually short)—it forms and then reacts further as the reaction proceeds. Intermediates lead eventually to the formation of the product or products that we actually isolate on work-up of the reaction mixture.

Most intermediates are highly reactive and have only a fleeting existence. We often need to apply much ingenuity to learn about these intermediates and their role in a reaction. This effort is worthwhile because a thorough knowledge of the structures and reactions of intermediates allows us to understand better the variety of reactions that can occur.

We apply a wide variety of approaches to learn about the nature of intermediates. First, we are often able to learn much about the course of a reaction and its intermediates by indirect inferences. For example, we learn about the nature of a reaction by changing the reaction conditions and seeing the effect of these changes on its rate. (The **reaction rate** is a measure of how fast product is formed or reactant is consumed.)

Second, we are often able to make direct experimental measurements of reaction intermediates. Direct measurements provide us with structural data for intermediate species. We may also use thermochemical data to understand the nature of intermediates. Knowledge of bond energies and the type of bonding involved in reactants and products often allows us to make conclusions regarding intermediate species.

In this chapter we will be concerned with several types of intermediates that are common in organic reactions. We will also be concerned with the bond-breaking and bond-making processes involved in their formation and continued reaction.

7.2 The Types of Bond Cleavage

Earlier we referred to a bond as an association between atoms that is characterized by a relative energy minimum. From this description, we can understand that an input of energy is needed to break any kind of bond. In organic chemistry we are concerned primarily with the breaking of covalent bonds. These bonds can break in two fundamental ways: **homolytic bond cleavage** (or homolysis) and **heterolytic bond cleavage** (or heterolysis). The nature of each type of cleavage and the intermediates each produces are discussed in the following sections.

HOMOLYTIC BOND CLEAVAGE

A homolytic bond cleavage (homolysis) is one in which each fragment of the cleavage retains one of the electrons of the original bond. For example, if we heat hydrogen gas to a sufficiently high temperature, the molecules dissociate homolytically to hydrogen atoms. This dissociation is illustrated in Figure 7.1, where *fish hook arrows* show the fate of the two electrons of the hydrogen-hydrogen bond.

$$H{-}H \longrightarrow H^{\cdot} + H^{\cdot}$$

Figure 7.1 Homolytic cleavage of the hydrogen-hydrogen bond. Each of the hydrogen atoms takes one electron of the original bond with it upon bond cleavage. The *fishhook arrows* each indicate the fate of a single electron. (A *full-headed arrow* of the type we used in earlier chapters indicates the movement of a *pair* of electrons.)

The homolytic cleavage of hydrogen molecules is **endothermic** to the extent of 104 kcal/mole (435 kJ/mole). An endothermic reaction is one that requires energy input for the conversion of reactants to products. The products are of higher energy (and therefore less stable) than the starting materials. (An **exothermic** reaction is one that releases energy in going from reactants to products.) We say that the hydrogen-hydrogen bond dissociation energy is 104 kcal/mole. A **bond dissociation energy** is the amount of energy needed to break a bond in a homolytic fashion. It is also the amount of energy *released* when the bond *forms*. For these simple bond dissociations, the energies noted are **enthalpies,** ΔH, of the bond-breaking reaction.

Consider now an organic molecule, methane. It too undergoes a homolytic bond cleavage on being heated. The reaction, which produces a hydrogen atom and a methyl **radical,** is shown in Equation 7.1.

Eqn. 7.1

$$H{-}CH_3 \longrightarrow H^{\cdot} + {}^{\cdot}CH_3$$

A radical (sometimes called a *free radical*) is any species with one or more unpaired electrons. Radicals are produced as intermediates in many organic reactions. For example, methyl radicals are produced in high-temperature reactions of methane, such as combustion. They are also intermediates in the halogenation of methane, a reaction we introduced in Chapter 4 and will investigate in further detail in Chapter 13.

For methane, the carbon-hydrogen bond dissociation energy is about 104 kcal/mole. Other bond dissociation energies are given in Table 7.1.

PROBLEM 7.1 The reaction shown below is a free radical process that occurs in the combustion of methane. Use the bond dissociation energies given in Table 7.1 to calculate ΔH for the reaction.

$$H\ddot{\underset{..}{O}}^{\cdot} + CH_4 \longrightarrow H_2\ddot{\underset{..}{O}} + CH_3^{\cdot}$$

hydroxyl radical — methyl radical

Steps to Solving the Problem

Solution to Problem 7.1

1. We must focus on the bonds that are broken and the bonds that are formed in this process. One bond is broken (the $CH_3{-}H$ bond), and one bond is formed (the $HO{-}H$ bond). You should recall that bond breaking is *always* endothermic and bond forming is *always* exothermic.
2. Calculate the difference between the energy input required to break the carbon-hydrogen bond and the energy released on forming the hydrogen-oxygen bond. The $CH_3{-}H$ bond cleavage is endothermic to the extent of

104 kcal/mole. The HO—H bond formation is exothermic to the extent of 119 kcal/mole. The difference is the ΔH for the process:

$$\Delta H = 104 - 119 = -15 \text{ kcal/mole}$$

A negative value for ΔH means that the reaction is exothermic.

Table 7.1 Homolytic Bond Dissociation Energies (ΔH) in kcal/mole

Bond	ΔH	Bond	ΔH
Diatomics			
H—H	104	H—F	136
D—D	106	H—Cl	103
F—F	38	H—Br	87.5
Cl—Cl	58	H—I	71
Br—Br	46	I—I	36
Methyl-X			
—H	104	—F	108
—Cl	83.5	—Br	70
—I	56	—OH	91.5
—OCH_3	80	—CH_3	88
—1° C*	85	—2° C*	84
—3° C*	80		
1° C—X*			
—H	98	—F	106
—Cl	81.5	—Br	69
—I	53.5	—OH	92
—OCH_3	80	—1° C	82
2° C—X*			
—H	94	—F	105
—Cl	81	—Br	68
—I	53	—OH	92
—OCH_3	81		
3° C—X*			
—H	91	—Cl	78
—Br	63	—I	53
—OH	92	—OCH_3	77
Others			
HO—H	119	HO—OH	51
*RO—H	103	*N—H	93
*S—H	83	*C=C$\underline{H}$	108
*C=C—C$\underline{H}$	85	*C≡C—$\underline{H}$	125
*C$\underline{H}$O	87	*C—N	66

* Average values; actual values may differ from compound to compound

SPECIAL TOPIC

Free Radicals: Some Points of Interest

The Cracking of High Molecular Weight Hydrocarbons

Crude oil consists of a variety of hydrocarbons ranging from low molecular weight, low-boiling components through heavy oils and asphalt. The various components are separated by fractional distillation and are used for different purposes. The lightest fractions become gasoline and kerosene. Gasoline is a mixture of hydrocarbons boiling in the range from about 30 °C to 200 °C. The components of kerosene boil at a somewhat higher temperature.

Higher-boiling fractions are used as fuel oil in furnaces and as diesel fuel. Nonvolatile components (asphalt) are used for road surfaces, among other applications. In general, the more volatile fractions of crude oil find the most uses. Thus it is desirable to have methods for reducing the average molecular weight (and thereby increase the volatility) of heavy oils.

The fragmentation of large hydrocarbon molecules into smaller ones is performed industrially on a huge scale in a process known as *cracking*. The oldest method used for cracking involves heating the heavy oil to a sufficiently high temperature that homolysis of bonds occurs. The homolysis of carbon-carbon bonds results in the formation of radicals, which react further to form lower molecular weight alkanes or alkenes.

We can illustrate some of the processes that occur in cracking by looking at what happens to pentane when heated to a high temperature. Two carbon-carbon bond cleavages occur:

$$CH_3CH_2CH_2CH_2CH_3 \xrightarrow{\text{heat}} \begin{cases} CH_3^{\cdot} + CH_3CH_2CH_2CH_2^{\cdot} \\ CH_3CH_2^{\cdot} + CH_3CH_2CH_2^{\cdot} \end{cases}$$

The radicals then react to form alkanes or alkenes:

$$CH_3^{\cdot} + CH_3^{\cdot} \longrightarrow CH_3CH_3$$

$$CH_3^{\cdot} + CH_3CH_2^{\cdot} \longrightarrow CH_3CH_2CH_3$$

$$CH_3CH_2^{\cdot} + CH_3CH_2CH_2^{\cdot} \longrightarrow CH_3CH_3 + CH_3CH{=}CH_2$$

With higher molecular weight alkanes, more complex fragmentation routes can occur. Modern cracking methods use catalysts along with heating to allow fragmentation to occur at lower temperatures. These catalysts are primarily silica and alumina.

Aging

Radicals have been implicated in the process of aging in biological organisms. Since free radicals are very reactive, they have the potential to damage delicate living cells. Particularly vulnerable to radical action are

(*continued*)

(*continued from previous page*)
the fatty acids present in the lipids of cell membranes. Radicals can alter these lipids so that the cell is unable to rid itself completely of waste materials or to take up oxygen and nutrients efficiently. It has been argued that aging involves an increased rate of damage to cell membranes by radicals and an erosion of the ability of the cells to repair such damage.

Radicals arise naturally in the body from hydrogen peroxide (HO—OH) or organic hydroperoxides (RO—OH), which are produced by various reactions in cells. The oxygen-oxygen bonds of these molecules are weak and are susceptible to homolytic cleavage, particularly in the presence of metal ions such as Fe^{2+}, which is present in cellular fluids. Hydroxyl ($HO^{\cdot}$) and alkoxyl ($RO^{\cdot}$) radicals are produced in these reactions.

Some substances, such as vitamin E, are inhibitors of free radical processes. Experiments have demonstrated that the lifespan of rodents is increased when certain of these inhibitors are added to their daily diets. For example the lifespan of fruitflies has been increased by about 15% by the addition of vitamin E to their diet.

PROBLEM 7.2 The reaction shown below is one of the free radical steps in the reaction of methane with chlorine. Use the bond dissociation energies given in Table 7.1 to calculate ΔH for this reaction step.

$$:\ddot{\underset{..}{Cl}}\cdot + CH_4 \longrightarrow H\ddot{\underset{..}{Cl}}: + CH_3^{\cdot}$$

chlorine atom

PROBLEM 7.3 When ethers are stored for extended periods of time, they react with oxygen in the air to form organic peroxides and hydroperoxides (structures shown below). These materials are thermally unstable and present an explosion hazard. The instability is associated with the weak oxygen-oxygen bond, which undergoes facile homolysis. What species are produced by these homolyses?

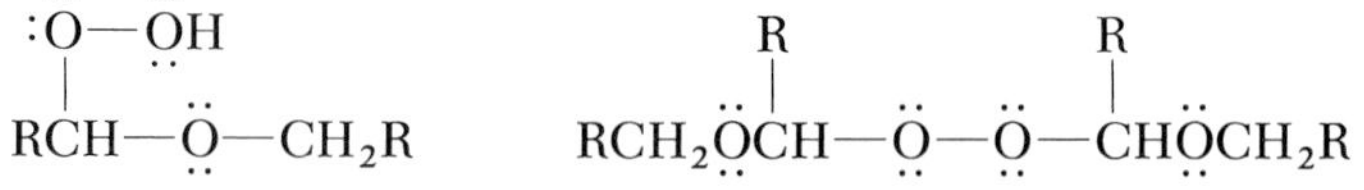

$$\underset{\text{hydroperoxide}}{RCH(OOH){-}\ddot{\underset{..}{O}}{-}CH_2R} \qquad \underset{\text{organic peroxide}}{RCH_2\ddot{\underset{..}{O}}CH(R){-}\ddot{\underset{..}{O}}{-}\ddot{\underset{..}{O}}{-}CH(R)\ddot{\underset{..}{O}}CH_2R}$$

HETEROLYTIC BOND CLEAVAGE

A heterolytic bond cleavage (or heterolysis) is one in which both electrons of the broken bond are retained by one of the fragments. Consider, for example, the heterolysis of hydrogen chloride. If the more electronegative chlorine retains both electrons of the bond, the products are a proton (H^+) and a chloride ion (Cl^-), as shown in Equation 7.2.

Eqn. 7.2

$$H{-}\ddot{\underset{..}{Cl}}: \longrightarrow H^+ + :\ddot{\underset{..}{Cl}}:^-$$

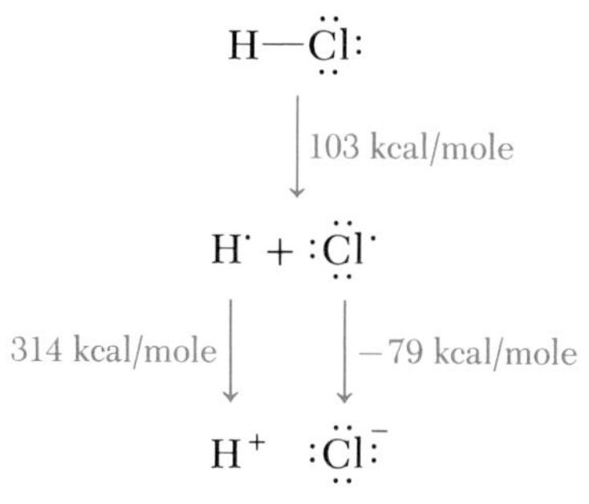

Heterolytic bond cleavages are usually unimportant in the gas phase. Homolyses require less energy input than heterolyses and therefore occur more readily in the gas phase. However, *in solution* heterolyses are of great importance. Suitable solvents stabilize the ionic fragments by solvating them, that is, by binding to them through Lewis acid/Lewis base interactions. When these interactions are possible, they make heterolysis the favored route for bond fracture.

We can calculate the energy for a bond heterolysis from the homolysis (bond dissociation) energy. For example, if we wish to calculate the ΔH associated with the reaction shown in Equation 7.2, we must correct the homolysis energy of the hydrogen-chlorine bond by the ionization potential of hydrogen and the electron affinity of chlorine. This calculation is illustrated in Figure 7.2.

H—Cl:
↓ 103 kcal/mole
H· + :Cl·
314 kcal/mole ↓ ↓ −79 kcal/mole
H^+ :Cl:$^-$

Figure 7.2 Energy of heterolysis of the hydrogen-chlorine bond. The energy for heterolysis is obtained by adding the bond dissociation energy (homolysis energy) of 103 kcal/mole (432 kJ/mole), the ionization potential of hydrogen, 314 kcal/mole (1,312 kJ/mole), and the electron affinity of chlorine, −79 kcal/mole (−332 kJ/mole). The resultant ΔH for heterolysis is 338 kcal/mole (1,414 kJ/mole). This process is highly endothermic. The electron affinity of chlorine is negative, meaning energy is released when a chlorine atom picks up an electron.

The ΔH calculated in Figure 7.2 for the heterolysis of the hydrogen-chlorine bond refers to the process occurring in the gas phase. In a polar solvent, considerable solvation of the H^+ and Cl^- product ions occurs. Solvation makes heterolysis much more favorable in solution than it would be in the gas phase, where homolysis is the favored mode of bond cleavage. In fact, we know that when hydrogen chloride gas dissolves in water, it reacts almost completely to form $H^+(aq)$ and $Cl^-(aq)$. Interactions between the water molecules and the ions provide the driving force for the overall heterolysis of hydrogen chloride. So large is the solvation of the ions that we observe the dissolution of HCl in water to be *exothermic*. The stability gained by solvation of the H^+ and Cl^- ions more than compensates for the energy needed for the heterolysis of the hydrogen-chlorine bond.

PROBLEM 7.4

Compare the energy needed for the heterolysis of hydrogen fluoride into H^+ and F^- with that needed for the heterolysis into H^- and F^+. Use the following data along with data from Table 7.1.

	Ionization Potential	Electron Affinity
H	314 kcal/mole	−17.2 kcal/mole
F	401 kcal/mole	−79.3 kcal/mole

7.3 Carbocations

A very important type of reaction intermediate is formed by the heterolytic cleavage of bonds between carbon and some other atom. Consider the example of *tert*-butyl bromide. We find that when this substance is placed in a suitable polar solvent, a few molecules undergo heterolysis of the carbon-bromine bond. Each heterolysis produces a *tert*-butyl cation and a bromide ion, as shown in Equation 7.3. For reaction to occur, we need a polar solvent to provide stabilization for the *tert*-butyl cation and the bromide ion. All other things being equal, the greater the polarity of the solvent, the more likely heterolysis will occur.

Eqn. 7.3

$$(CH_3)_3C{-}\ddot{\underset{..}{Br}}: \xrightarrow[]{\text{polar solvent}} (CH_3)_3C^+ + :\ddot{\underset{..}{Br}}:^-$$

tert-butyl cation

The term **carbocation** is used to describe an organic cation in which a carbon atom has a formal charge of $+1$ (see Figure 7.3). Notice that the positive carbon atom has a sextet rather than an octet of electrons. This lack of a complete octet of electrons is a source of reactivity. Carbocations, once formed, generally react quickly to complete the octet of electrons associated with carbon.

7.4 Classification and Stability of Alkyl Radicals and Carbocations

Alkyl radicals and carbocations are classified according to the number of carbon atoms attached to the electron-deficient carbon atom. Examples of the various classes are shown in Table 7.2.

PROBLEM 7.5 Consider carbocations of the formula $C_5H_{11}^+$. Write all structures of this formula that are:
a. primary carbocations **b.** secondary carbocations
c. tertiary carbocations

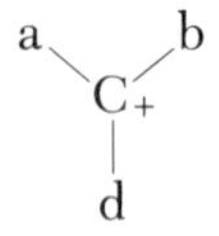

a, b, d attached to C+

Figure 7.3 A carbocation. The central carbon atom is electron deficient as it has about it only a sextet of electrons. This type of carbocation was referred to as a *carbonium ion* in earlier chemical literature. However, the use of this name has been discontinued for reasons of consistency in nomenclature. Other "onium" ions, for example, the oxonium ions of Chapter 5, have a complete octet of electrons about the positively charged atom. The name **carbenium ion** has been proposed as a replacement for *carbonium ion*, but the generic term *carbocation* enjoys widespread use.

We can use thermochemical data to estimate the relative ease of formation of radicals from their parent compounds. Consider the formation of alkyl radicals from propane by the homolysis of a carbon-hydrogen bond. Propane contains two types of carbon-hydrogen bonds. Primary carbon-hydrogen bonds are located at the ends of the molecule and secondary carbon-hydrogen bonds are located at the center. Figure 7.4 shows the bond dissociation energies associated with the homolysis of each of these bonds.

In propane, the bond cleavage that leads to a secondary radical requires a smaller energy input than the cleavage that leads to a primary radical. Both reactions have the same reactant (propane) and one identical product (a hydrogen atom). The only difference in the reactions is the type of carbon-hydrogen

Table 7.2 Classification of Radicals and Carbocations

	Methyl Species	Primary (1°) Species	Secondary (2°) Species	Tertiary (3°) Species
Radicals	$\dot{C}H_3$ methyl radical	$\dot{C}H_2CH_3$ ethyl radical	$\dot{C}H(CH_3)_2$ isopropyl radical	$\dot{C}(CH_3)_3$ *tert*-butyl radical
Carbocations	$^+CH_3$ methyl cation	$^+CH_2CH_3$ ethyl cation	$^+CH(CH_3)_2$ isopropyl cation	$^+C(CH_3)_3$ *tert*-butyl cation

$$CH_3CH_2CH_2{-}H \longrightarrow CH_3CH_2CH_2\cdot + H\cdot \qquad \Delta H = 98 \text{ kcal/mole } (410 \text{ kJ/mole})$$

$$(CH_3)_2CH{-}H \longrightarrow (CH_3)_2\dot{C}H + H\cdot \qquad \Delta H = 94 \text{ kcal/mole } (395 \text{ kJ/mole})$$

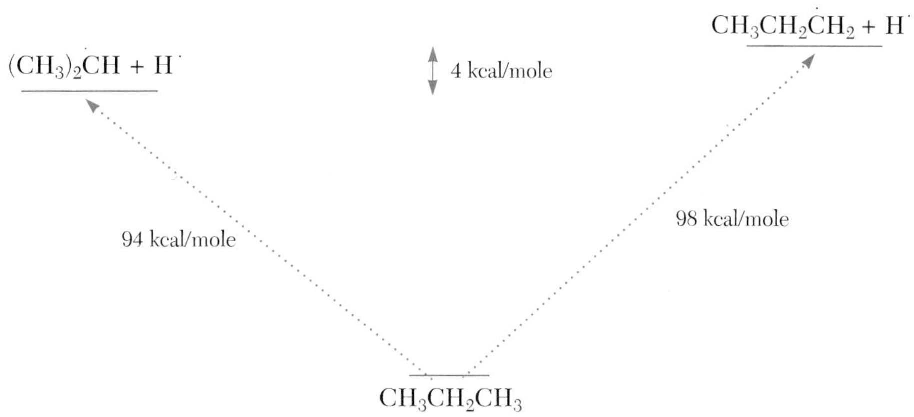

Figure 7.4 Homolysis of primary and secondary carbon-hydrogen bonds in the propane molecule.

Figure 7.5 Formation of secondary and primary radicals from propane. Because less energy is required for the formation of the secondary radical from propane, we conclude that it is more stable than the primary radical. The energy difference of 4 kcal/mole is a measure of the improved stability of the secondary radical relative to a primary radical.

bond broken. If we think about generating a different type of free radical in each reaction, we see that generation of the more stable free radical requires less energy input than generation of the less stable free radical (see Figure 7.5).

Looking at the bond dissociation energies for producing a variety of radicals, we arrive at the general order of radical stabilities:

$$3° > 2° > 1° > \text{methyl}$$

We find the *same* order of stabilities for carbocations. However, the *differences* in stability among different types of carbocations are greater than for radicals. How can we rationalize the order of stabilities?

Both radicals and carbocations are electron-deficient species, since both have a carbon atom that lacks a complete octet of electrons. In general, we find that the stability of electron-deficient species is increased by the attachment of alkyl groups. Tertiary radicals and carbocations each have three alkyl groups attached to the electron-deficient carbon, and they are more stable than secondary, primary, or methyl radicals and cations, each of which has fewer attached alkyl groups.

We rationalize the improved stability of both radicals and carbocations in terms of increased delocalization of charge. With carbocations, the formal positive charge at the central carbon is delocalized onto the attached group. With radicals there is no formal charge; however, there is an electron deficiency at the central carbon since it is one electron short of an octet. The more this electron deficiency can be delocalized, the more stable the radical will be.

The *order* of stabilities results because alkyl groups are better able than hydrogen to delocalize the charge at the central carbon atom. Charge delocalization for the *tert*-butyl cation is shown pictorially in Figure 7.6.

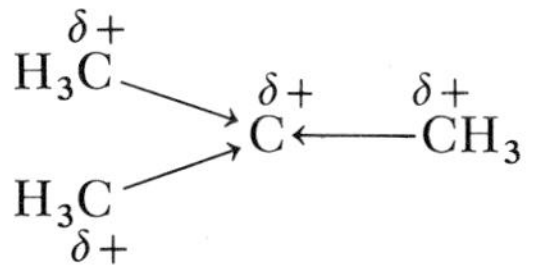

Figure 7.6 Stabilization of the *tert*-butyl cation. The three methyl groups stabilize the positive charge on the central carbon atom by pushing electron density toward it. Each carbon atom in the structure thus acquires a partial positive charge indicated by the $\delta+$ symbol. The methyl groups can be thought of as donating electron density toward the central positive carbon atom, as indicated in the diagram by the arrows on the bonds.

MOLECULAR ORBITAL ANALYSIS

The molecular orbital model predicts that orbital interactions can greatly influence the stability of carbocations. It is helpful to think in terms of an interaction between a filled orbital associated with the carbon-hydrogen bond and an empty orbital on the central carbon atom. The tricoordinated carbon atom of a carbocation is sp^2 hybridized. The three sp^2 hybrids are used to form the three σ bonds to the attached atoms. The remaining unhybridized p orbital of the atom is empty and can interact with a filled carbon-hydrogen σ orbital as shown in Figure 7.7.

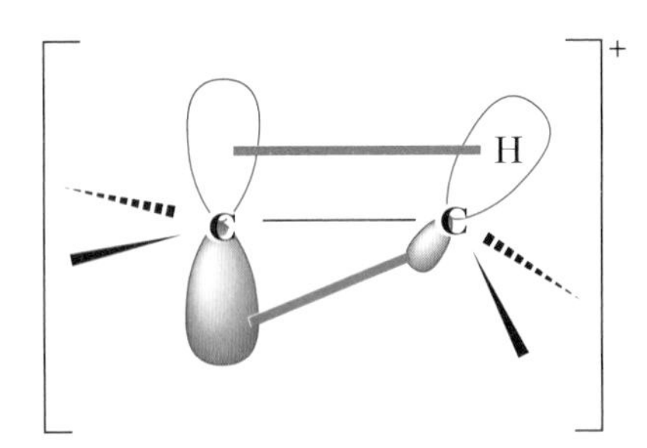

Figure 7.7 Stabilization of a carbocation. The interaction of a filled carbon-hydrogen σ orbital and an empty p orbital of the tricoordinated carbon atom leads to improved stability by providing a means for delocalization of the electron deficiency. The stabilization of carbon free radicals is entirely analogous.

This interaction is shown on an orbital energy-level diagram in Figure 7.8. The energy of the electrons is decreased by this interaction, thus making the carbocation more stable

A further result of this interaction is a weakening of the carbon-hydrogen bonds and a strengthening of the carbon-carbon bond. The carbon-hydrogen bonds are weakened because some of the bonding electron density is shifted toward the central carbon. This infusion of electron density strengthens the carbon-carbon bond. Put another way, the carbon-hydrogen bonds have a bond order somewhat less than unity, while the carbon-carbon bond has a bond-order somewhat in excess of unity. We say that the carbon-carbon bond has some double-bond character. Obviously, the greater the number of adjacent C—H or C—C bonds, the more opportunity there will be for σ bond interactions with the empty p orbital. It follows that $3° > 2° > 1°$ will be the order of stability for carbocations.

In fact, simple representations such as $(CH_3)_3C^+$ for the *tert*-butyl cation do not convey a completely accurate picture of the structure. In valence-bond terms, we often use resonance structures to compensate for deficiencies asso-

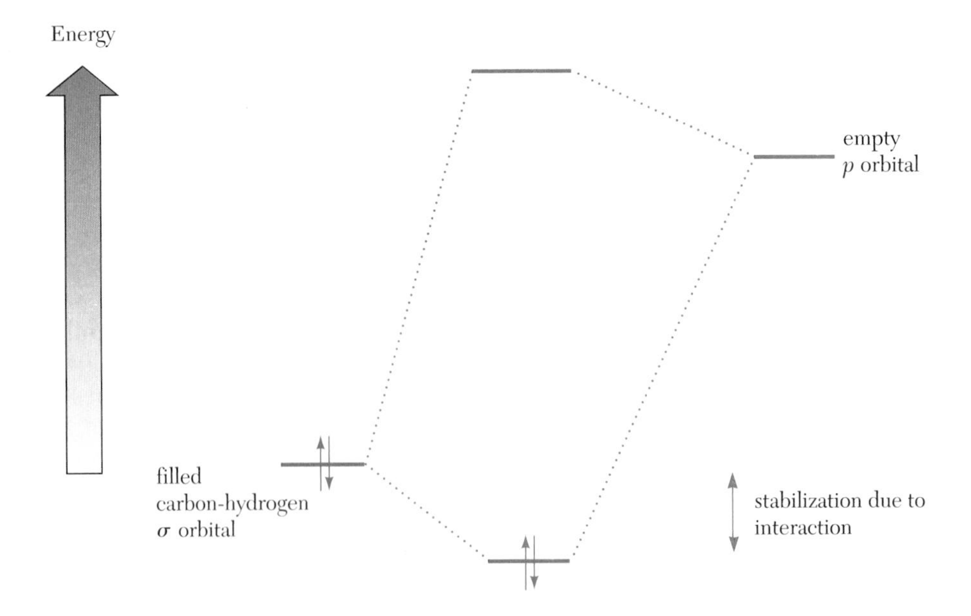

Figure 7.8 Orbital energy-level diagram depicting the stabilization of a carbocation. The energies of the orbitals from Figure 7.7 are shown. The two electrons occupy a more stable position as a result of the interaction.

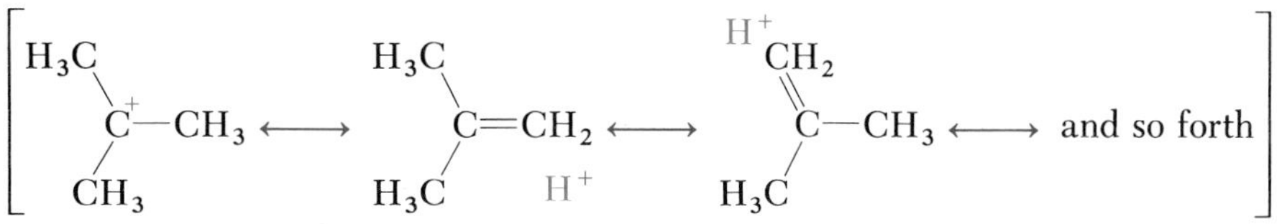

$$\left[(CH_3)_2\overset{+}{C}{-}CH_3 \longleftrightarrow (CH_3)_2C{=}CH_2\ H^+ \longleftrightarrow H^+\ CH_2{=}C(CH_3){-}CH_3 \longleftrightarrow \text{and so forth} \right]$$

Figure 7.9 Resonance structures for the *tert*-butyl cation. As usual with resonance structures, no individual structure has any real meaning. That is, under *no* conditions is a carbocation identical to an alkene with a nearby proton. However, the average of the structures reflects the structure of the real species. The type of charge delocalization represented here and the accompanying stabilization is known as "no-bond resonance" or **hyperconjugation.** Hyperconjugation refers to the resonance delocalization of σ-bonding electrons.

ciated with a single structure. For the *tert*-butyl cation, resonance structures of the type shown in Figure 7.9 are sometimes used to account for the strengthened carbon-carbon bonds, the weakened carbon-hydrogen bonds, and the delocalization of charge.

7.5 Carbocations from Alcohols

All alcohols are protonated by strong acids to produce oxonium ions, as illustrated in Equation 7.4.

Eqn. 7.4

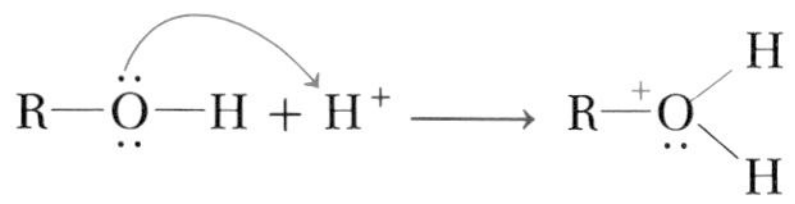

$$R{-}\ddot{O}{-}H + H^+ \longrightarrow R{-}\overset{+}{O}H_2$$

We first met oxonium ions in Chapter 5, where their reaction with nucleophiles was introduced. Here we see another facet of oxonium ion chemistry. In solution, the carbon-oxygen bond may undergo heterolysis to produce a carbocation, as shown in Equation 7.5.

Eqn. 7.5

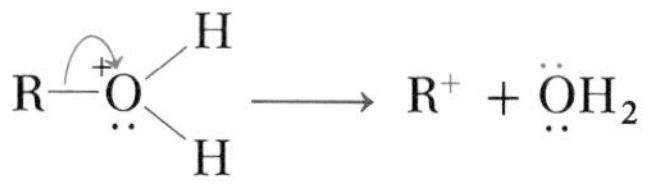

$$R{-}\overset{+}{O}H_2 \longrightarrow R^+ + \ddot{O}H_2$$

Two major factors determine whether an oxonium ion in solution will fragment into a carbocation and water. The first of these is the reactivity of the oxonium ion toward potential nucleophiles in solution. We generally find that methyl and most primary oxonium ions react faster with nucleophiles than do oxonium ions derived from secondary and tertiary alcohols. If a sufficiently potent nucleophile is present in solution, methyl and most primary oxonium ions react with it rather than decomposing to a carbocation. (In this context, review the reaction of methanol and ethanol with HBr and HI described in Chapter 5.) Secondary and tertiary oxonium ions are less reactive toward nucleophiles. The degree of branching about the original carbon bearing the hydroxyl group hinders the approach of the nucleophile. We will consider this phenomenon in more detail later.

Second, heterolysis of the carbon-oxygen bond of oxonium ions is more favorable when the carbocation product is more stable. The more highly substituted the carbon atom bonded to oxygen, the more likely it is that a carbocation will form by heterolysis of the carbon-oxygen bond.

A carbon-oxygen bond must be broken for an oxonium ion to decompose into a carbocation and a water molecule, and energy is required for this to occur. Solvents that are able to solvate the carbocation product lower this energy requirement. Intermolecular association of the carbocation and the solvent helps to compensate for the energy needed to break the carbon-oxygen bond.

Carbocations are generally very reactive. They react quickly to complete the octet of electrons on carbon, usually so quickly that we cannot observe them directly. However, under certain conditions, carbocations do persist long enough to be studied by spectrometric techniques. Studies under these conditions provide direct confirmation of the structure and properties of carbocations. Before the advent of these spectrometric techniques, structures of carbocations could be inferred only from the study of reaction kinetics and the structures of final reaction products.

7.6 Reactions of Carbocations

COMBINATION WITH NUCLEOPHILES

A Lewis base can provide an electron pair to bind to the electron-deficient carbon of a carbocation. By doing so, the Lewis base completes the octet of electrons about the carbon atom. While any substance with an unshared electron pair has the potential to act in this way, actual reaction will occur only if some other competing reaction does not occur more quickly.

Among many effective nucleophiles are chloride, bromide, and iodide ions. For example, when 2-methyl-2-propanol (*tert*-butyl alcohol) is treated with concentrated hydrochloric acid, 2-chloro-2-methylpropane is formed in a three-step mechanism.

MECHANISM OF REACTION

Overall:

$$(CH_3)_3C\ddot{\underset{\cdot\cdot}{O}}H \xrightarrow{HCl} (CH_3)_3C\ddot{\underset{\cdot\cdot}{Cl}}: + H_2\ddot{\underset{\cdot\cdot}{O}}$$

Step 1 The *tert*-butyl alcohol acts as a base to accept a proton from the acid. An oxonium ion is formed.

$$(CH_3)_3C{-}\ddot{\underset{\cdot\cdot}{O}}H + H{-}\ddot{\underset{\cdot\cdot}{Cl}}: \longrightarrow (CH_3)_3C{-}\ddot{O}^{+}(H)_2 + :\ddot{\underset{\cdot\cdot}{Cl}}:^{-}$$

Step 2 The protonated alcohol dissociates to a molecule of water and a carbocation.

$$(CH_3)_3C{-}\ddot{O}^{+}(H)_2 \longrightarrow (CH_3)_3C^{+} + \ddot{\underset{\cdot\cdot}{O}}H_2$$

Step 3 The carbocation undergoes combination with a chloride ion to give the chloroalkane product.

$$(CH_3)_3C^{+} + :\ddot{\underset{\cdot\cdot}{Cl}}:^{-} \longrightarrow (CH_3)_3C{-}\ddot{\underset{\cdot\cdot}{Cl}}:$$

85% yield
from the alcohol

Reaction of *tert*-butyl alcohol occurs readily even in the cold (0–5 °C). Shortly after mixing the alcohol and the acid, a two-layer system forms. The upper (less dense) layer is the product, 2-chloro-2-methylpropane.

Primary and secondary alcohols react less readily, and elevated temperatures are usually necessary for these reactions to occur. Their diminished reactivity reflects the lessened stability of primary and secondary carbocations, which are formed much less efficiently than are tertiary carbocations from their parent alcohols. In fact, the formation of a carbocation may be so slow that overall product formation arises by a different route. For example, we saw in Chapter 5 that a direct nucleophilic attack can occur on an oxonium ion. This type of process is particularly common for the reaction of most primary alcohols with hydrogen halides. For example, if we heat 1-butanol with hydrobromic acid (or with concentrated sulfuric acid mixed with sodium bromide) 1-bromobutane forms from direct nucleophilic attack of the bromide ion on the oxonium ion. No carbocation forms in these reactions.

MECHANISM OF REACTION

Overall:

$$CH_3CH_2CH_2CH_2\ddot{O}H \xrightarrow{HBr} CH_3CH_2CH_2CH_2\ddot{Br}: + H_2\ddot{O}$$

Step 1 The protonated alcohol (oxonium ion) forms with 1-butanol in the usual manner.

$$CH_3CH_2CH_2CH_2{-}\ddot{O}H + H^+ \longrightarrow CH_3CH_2CH_2CH_2{-}\dot{O}^+H_2$$

Step 2 A bromide ion performs a nucleophilic displacement on the oxonium ion. No carbocation intermediate is involved.

$$CH_3CH_2CH_2CH_2{-}\dot{O}^+H_2 + :\ddot{Br}:^- \longrightarrow CH_3CH_2CH_2CH_2{-}\ddot{Br}: + H_2\ddot{O}$$

95% yield from 1-butanol with sulfuric acid and sodium bromide

PROBLEM 7.6 Treatment of 1-propanol with sulfuric acid produces a compound of formula $C_6H_{14}O$ that does not react with sodium metal. Suggest a structure for this compound and a mechanism for its formation. (*Hint:* 1-Propanol can act as a nucleophile.)

DOUBLE-BOND FORMATION

We now meet for the first time an important process, the conversion of a carbocation to an alkene through the loss of a proton to a suitable Brønsted base. Brønsted bases are able to remove a proton from positions adjacent to the positive center of carbocations. Simultaneously, the electrons of the original carbon-hydrogen bond move toward the positive center to form a carbon-carbon π bond, as shown in Equation 7.6.

Eqn. 7.6

$$\overset{+}{C}-C-H \quad :Base \longrightarrow C{=}C + H-\overset{+}{Base}$$

Abstraction of the proton leaves a (formally) full orbital at the carbon adjacent to the carbocation site. As reaction proceeds, the hybridization at this carbon atom changes from sp^3 to sp^2. A free p orbital is generated, which then overlaps with the p orbital on the adjacent (positive) carbon atom to produce the carbon-carbon π bond of the alkene product.

When we convert an alcohol to an alkene by means of a carbocation intermediate, the overall reaction is an **elimination** reaction, as the elements of water (H and OH) are eliminated from adjacent carbon atoms. This reaction constitutes an important method for the preparation of some alkenes. An alcohol is heated under reflux with a concentrated acid such as sulfuric or phosphoric acid. After an hour or so, an alkene can be recovered from the reaction mixture.

MOLECULAR ORBITAL ANALYSIS

The conversion of the intermediate carbocation to the final alkene product can be viewed in terms of a base donating its electron pair to the (empty) σ^* orbital associated with the carbon-hydrogen bond of the carbocation. The (filled) σ orbital of that bond is in position to interact with the empty p orbital of the tricoordinated carbon to generate the new π bond, as illustrated in Figure 7.10.

Two examples of alkene formation from alcohols are illustrated in Equations 7.7 and 7.8.

Eqn. 7.7

$$(CH_3)_2\underset{}{C}(\ddot{O}H)CH_2CH_3 \xrightarrow{H_2SO_4} (CH_3)_2C(\overset{+}{O}H_2)CH_2CH_3 \longrightarrow$$

2-methyl-2-butanol

$$(CH_3)_2\overset{+}{C}CH_2CH_3 + H_2\ddot{O} \xrightarrow{H_2O} (CH_3)_2C{=}CHCH_3 + H_2\overset{+}{O}-H$$

82% yield
2-methyl-2-butene

Figure 7.10 Formation of a π bond by deprotonation of a carbocation. (*a*) A base approaches to interact with the empty σ^* orbital of the carbon-hydrogen bond. (*b*) The filled σ orbital of the same bond is in position to form a new π bond by interacting with the empty p orbital on the adjacent carbon atom.

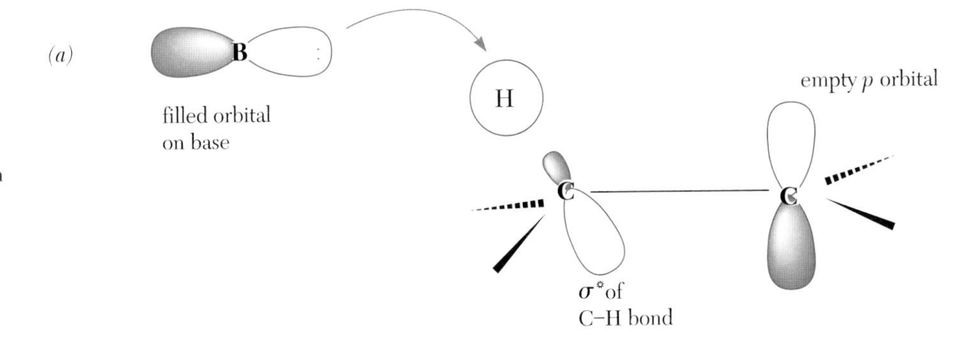

(*b*)

H
empty *p* orbital
C
C
σ of
C–H bond

Eqn. 7.8

$$\text{1-methylcyclohexanol} \xrightarrow{H_2SO_4} \text{protonated alcohol} \longrightarrow \text{carbocation} + H_2\ddot{O} \xrightarrow{H_2O} \text{1-methylcyclohexene} + H_2\ddot{O}^+\text{—H}$$

1-methylcyclohexanol

91% yield
1-methylcyclohexene

PROBLEM 7.7 Consider the reaction of 2,3-dimethyl-2-butanol with concentrated sulfuric acid in the absence of a good nucleophile. These conditions are conducive to the formation of alkenes. More than one alkene can result from this reaction. Explain how more than one alkene *could* be formed, and draw the structure of each.

The elimination reaction leading to alkene formation competes with the previously discussed substitution reactions because any potential Brønsted base can also function, in principle, as a nucleophile to form a new bond to carbon. However, not all Brønsted bases are good nucleophiles. Thus slightly different reaction conditions may be used to produce different products. For example, 2-methyl-2-propanol upon treatment with concentrated hydrochloric acid yields

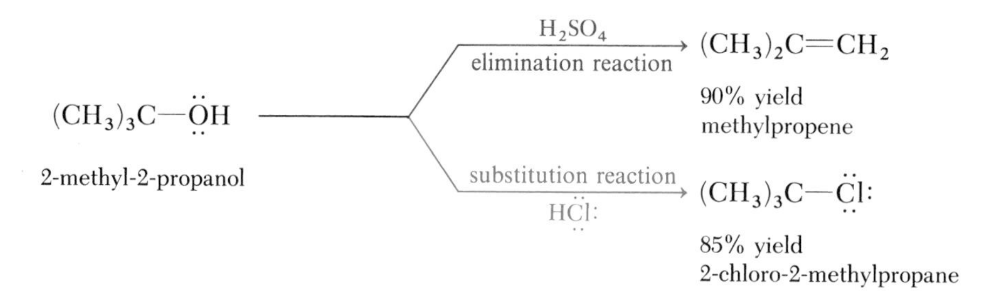

Figure 7.11 Different reactions of *tert*-butyl alcohol with sulfuric and hydrochloric acids. The bisulfate anion, HSO_4^-, formed in the initial reaction involving sulfuric acid, is not a sufficiently good nucleophile to capture (i.e., react with) the *tert*-butyl cation. It is, however, a sufficiently good Brønsted base to remove a proton and form the alkene. Chloride ion is a good nucleophile that readily captures the intermediate carbocation, but it is a weak base that does not cause elimination.

2-chloro-2-methylpropane. A *substitution* reaction has occurred, a chlorine atom having taken the place of the hydroxyl group of the original alcohol. However, when the same alcohol is treated with concentrated sulfuric acid, 2-methylpropene is the major product—*elimination* has occurred. These reactions are illustrated in Figure 7.11.

In later chapters we will learn much more regarding competing elimination and substitution reactions and the proper choice of reaction conditions. We will also consider those attributes that render a Lewis base a potent or a poor nucleophile.

7.7 Skeletal Rearrangements of Carbocations

Many carbocations have been generated and studied. Most are not stable species. That is, they cannot be isolated and stored. They readily undergo reactions that complete the octet of electrons about the positively charged carbon center, usually by reacting with a species in solution (a nucleophile or a base), as has been described in the previous sections. However, carbocations may undergo other reactions prior to completing their octet of electrons.

A common reaction that carbocations may undergo is a **skeletal rearrangement.** If such a rearrangement occurs, the product ultimately isolated from the reaction mixture has the carbon skeleton determined by the rearranged carbocation. Consider as an example the reaction of 3,3-dimethyl-2-butanol with sulfuric acid. The major product isolated is 2,3-dimethyl-2-butene, a compound whose carbon skeleton is rearranged compared with that of the starting alcohol. The product distribution is shown in Equation 7.9.

Eqn. 7.9

$$(CH_3)_3C\overset{:\ddot{O}H}{\overset{|}{C}}HCH_3 \xrightarrow{H_2SO_4} \left[\begin{array}{c} (CH_3)_2CH\underset{CH_3}{\underset{|}{C}}{=}CH_2 \\ \text{2,3-dimethyl-1-butene (31\%)} \\ + \\ (CH_3)_3CCH{=}CH_2 \\ \text{3,3-dimethyl-1-butene (3\%)} \\ + \\ (CH_3)_2C{=}C(CH_3)_2 \\ \text{2,3-dimethyl-2-butene (61\%)} \end{array}\right]$$

3,3-dimethyl-2-butanol

Mechanisms illustrating the formation of each of the products are shown on the next page.

MECHANISM OF REACTION

Step 1 Protonation of the alcohol occurs to give an oxonium ion, as in the previously examined reactions of alcohols and acids.

$$CH_3-\underset{CH_3}{\overset{CH_3}{C}}-\underset{:\ddot{O}H}{CH}-CH_3 \xrightarrow{H_2SO_4} CH_3-\underset{CH_3}{\overset{CH_3}{C}}-\underset{:\overset{+}{O}(H)-H}{CH}-CH_3$$

Step 2 *Heterolytic* cleavage of the carbon-oxygen bond of the oxonium ion occurs to form a water molecule and a secondary carbocation. This is the point of divergence for the several products.

$$CH_3-\underset{CH_3}{\overset{CH_3}{C}}-\underset{:\overset{+}{O}(H)-H}{CH}-CH_3 \longrightarrow CH_3-\underset{CH_3}{\overset{CH_3}{C}}-\overset{+}{C}H-CH_3 + H_2\ddot{O}$$

Step 3 A Brønsted base in the reaction system abstracts a proton from the carbon atom adjacent to the carbocation center, forming the *direct* elimination product. Note that only 3% of the product results from this route.

$$B: \quad CH_3-\underset{CH_3}{\overset{CH_3}{C}}-\overset{+}{C}H-\overset{H}{C}H_2 \xrightarrow{H^+ \text{ abstraction}} CH_3-\underset{CH_3}{\overset{CH_3}{C}}-CH=CH_2 + \overset{+}{B}-H$$

3% yield

Step 4 The initially formed 2° carbocation rearranges to a more stable 3° carbocation. We illustrate this rearrangement as occurring through the movement of a methyl group *with* an electron pair from one carbon atom to an adjacent one.

$$CH_3-\underset{CH_3}{\overset{CH_3}{C}}-\overset{+}{C}H-CH_3 \longrightarrow CH_3-\overset{CH_3}{\overset{+}{C}}-\underset{CH_3}{CH}-CH_3$$

Step 5 A Brønsted base in the reaction system abstracts a proton from a carbon atom adjacent to the positively charged carbon atom. The two possible ways in which this abstraction can occur are shown below.

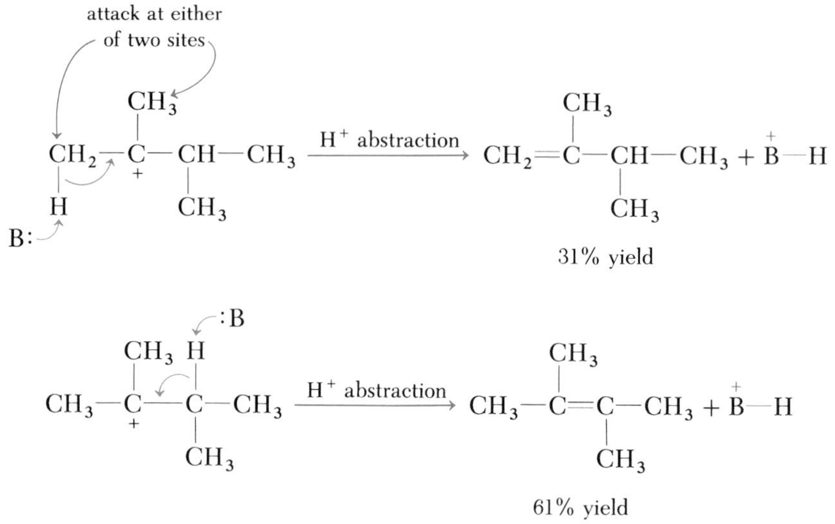

attack at either of two sites

$$CH_2(H)\text{—}\overset{+}{C}(CH_3)\text{—}CH(CH_3)\text{—}CH_3 \;\; (B:) \xrightarrow{H^+ \text{ abstraction}} CH_2{=}C(CH_3)\text{—}CH(CH_3)\text{—}CH_3 + \overset{+}{B}\text{—}H$$

31% yield

$$CH_3\text{—}\overset{+}{C}(CH_3)\text{—}C(H)(CH_3)\text{—}CH_3 \;\; (:B) \xrightarrow{H^+ \text{ abstraction}} CH_3\text{—}C(CH_3){=}C(CH_3)\text{—}CH_3 + \overset{+}{B}\text{—}H$$

61% yield

The rearrangement shown is conveniently viewed as a *migration*. A group moves to the positively charged carbon from the *immediately adjacent* carbon atom. Other, more remote groups, do not migrate. We consider the migrating group as moving *with* its bonding electron pair, leaving behind a new carbocation site.

Rearrangements are most favored if they lead to a more stable carbocation than existed initially. In the system just described, a secondary carbocation rearranged to give the more stable tertiary carbocation.

The migration that occurred was that of an alkyl group with its bonding electron pair. We refer to this migration as an **alkide shift.** In this example it was specifically a *methide shift*, since a methyl group migrated with its bonding electron pair. We sometimes illustrate such a shift as shown in Figure 7.12.

The transfer of an alkide group is not the only type of skeletal rearrangement that can occur with a carbocation. Transfer of a hydrogen along with its bonding electron pair can also occur readily. This migration is known as a **hydride shift.** Again, the transfer occurs from a carbon atom adjacent to the positively charged carbon. An example of such a shift is shown in Figure 7.13 for the rearrangement of the 3-methyl-2-butyl cation to the 2-methyl-2-butyl cation.

$$CH_3\text{—}C(CH_3)(CH_3)\text{—}\overset{+}{C}H\text{—}CH_3 \longrightarrow CH_3\text{—}\overset{+}{C}(CH_3)\text{—}C(CH_3)(CH_3)H$$

Figure 7.12 Migration of a methyl group with its bonding electron pair in a carbocation. The alkyl group moves from one carbon atom to the adjacent tricoordinated positively charged carbon taking with it the bonding electron pair originally holding it to the first carbon atom. At *no* time is a free CH_3^- group involved. The new carbocation is more stable than the original one.

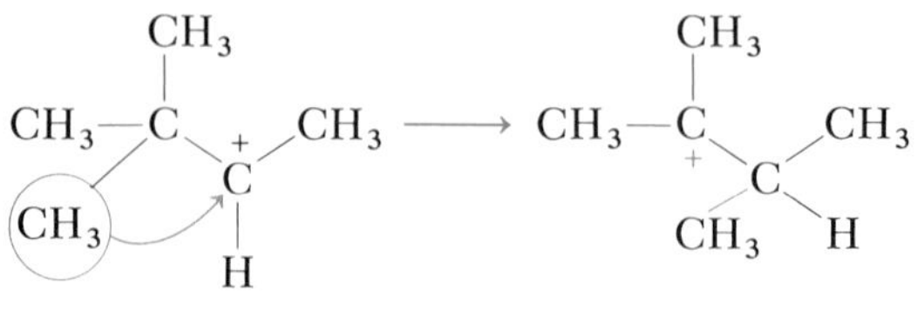

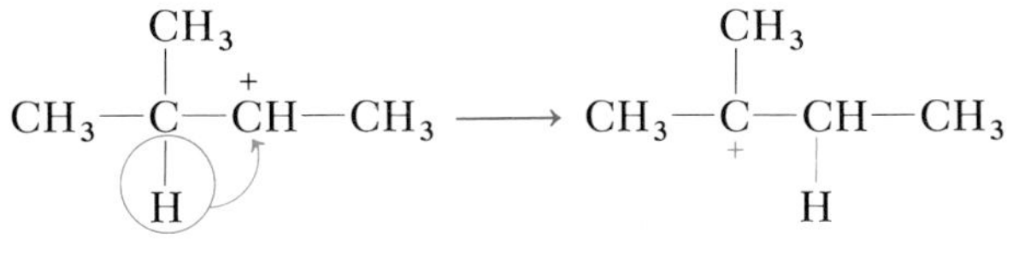

$$CH_3-\overset{\overset{CH_3}{|}}{\underset{\underset{H}{|}}{C}}-\overset{+}{C}H-CH_3 \longrightarrow CH_3-\overset{\overset{CH_3}{|}}{\underset{+}{C}}-\underset{\underset{H}{|}}{C}H-CH_3$$

Figure 7.13 Hydride shift in a carbocation rearrangement. The hydrogen moves to the original carbocation site from an adjacent carbon atom, bringing with it its bonding electron pair. At *no* time is a free hydride ion ($H:^-$) involved.

In general, an equilibrium is established between the initial and the rearranged carbocations. With highly branched alcohols, treatment with acid can lead to a considerable number of different carbocations in dynamic equilibrium with each other. The presence of several carbocations at the same time in a reaction mixture usually leads to a complex mixture of products. This situation often precludes the use of carbocation reactions for the clean preparation of a single product.

A final point is that migrations generally occur in acids that have poorly nucleophilic conjugate bases, such as sulfuric, phosphoric, and perchloric acids.

PROBLEM 7.8 A student plans to synthesize 1-pentene ($CH_2{=}CH-CH_2-CH_2-CH_3$) by heating 2-pentanol with concentrated sulfuric acid. What problems do you envision in the accomplishment of this goal?

PROBLEM 7.9 Upon treatment of 3-methyl-2-pentanol with hydrochloric acid, a carbocation is generated, and it undergoes rearrangement. Suggest a structure for the initially formed carbocation. Also give structures for the rearranged carbocation and the major product, which has the formula $C_6H_{13}Cl$. Tell whether the rearrangement occurred with an alkide shift or a hydride shift, and explain why one occurred rather than the other.

PROBLEM 7.10 Use the curved-arrow formalism to show how each of the following reactions would occur.

a. 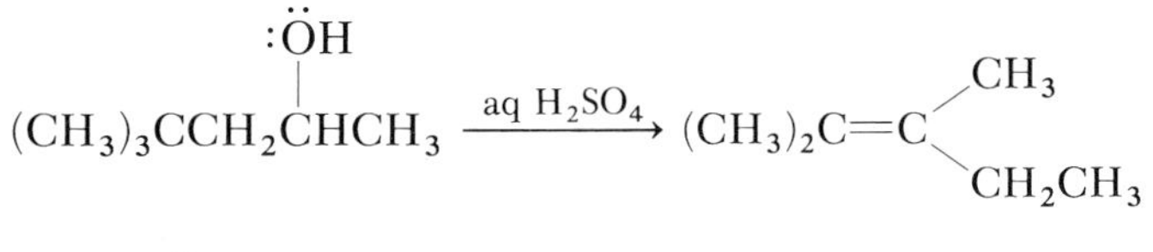 $$(CH_3)_3CCH_2\underset{}{\overset{\overset{:\ddot{O}H}{|}}{C}}HCH_3 \xrightarrow{\text{aq } H_2SO_4} (CH_3)_2C{=}C\begin{matrix}CH_3\\ CH_2CH_3\end{matrix}$$

b. 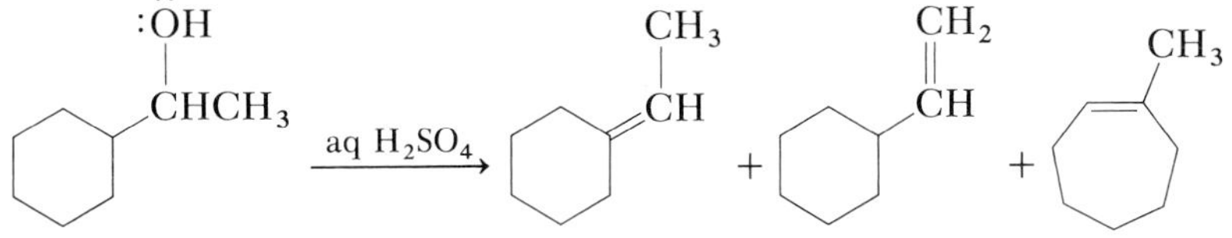 (cyclohexyl)$\overset{\overset{:\ddot{O}H}{|}}{C}HCH_3$ $\xrightarrow{\text{aq } H_2SO_4}$ (cyclohexylidene)$=\overset{\overset{CH_3}{|}}{C}H$ + (cyclohexyl)$\overset{\overset{CH_2}{||}}{C}H$ + 1-methylcycloheptene (CH_3)

Steps to Solving the Problem

Solution to Problem 7.10a

1. Decide what is happening in the overall reaction. An alcohol is converted to an alkene—overall, this is an elimination reaction. We also note that the carbon skeleton of the product is different from that of the starting alcohol. Thus a rearrangement has occurred. Under the acidic conditions of the reaction, such a rearrangement most likely proceeds through a carbocation intermediate.

2. Write the mechanistic steps leading to the formation of a carbocation from the alcohol.

$$(CH_3)_3C{-}CH_2{-}\underset{\displaystyle :\ddot{O}H}{\underset{|}{CH}}{-}CH_3 + H^+ \longrightarrow (CH_3)_3C{-}CH_2{-}\underset{\displaystyle H\,\overset{+}{:O}\,H}{\underset{|}{CH}}{-}CH_3$$

$$(CH_3)_3C{-}CH_2{-}\underset{\displaystyle H\,\overset{+}{:O}\,H}{\underset{|}{CH}}{-}CH_3 \longrightarrow (CH_3)_3C{-}CH_2{-}\overset{+}{C}H{-}CH_3 + H_2\ddot{O}$$

3. How can rearrangement occur with this carbocation? There are several rearrangements that can be envisioned directly (two hydride shifts and one alkide shift) with this carbocation. Two of these (one hydride shift and the alkide shift) lead to *less* stable carbocations (primary) than the initially formed carbocation. These shifts thus represent unlikely routes of reaction. The hydride shift that leads to another secondary carbocation occurs as shown below.

$$CH_3{-}\underset{CH_3}{\overset{CH_3}{C}}{-}\underset{H}{\overset{H}{C}}{-}\underset{H}{\overset{+}{C}}{-}CH_3 \longrightarrow CH_3{-}\underset{CH_3}{\overset{CH_3}{C}}{-}\underset{H}{\overset{+}{C}}{-}\underset{H}{\overset{H}{C}}{-}CH_3$$

We must now consider how this rearranged carbocation can lead to our observed product.

4. Can this new carbocation undergo any further rearrangement? Aside from reverting to the initial carbocation, the new carbocation is capable of undergoing a *methide shift* to form a tertiary carbocation, a more stable intermediate species:

$$CH_3{-}\underset{CH_3}{\overset{CH_3}{C}}{-}\underset{H}{\overset{+}{C}}{-}\underset{H}{\overset{H}{C}}{-}CH_3 \longrightarrow CH_3{-}\underset{CH_3}{\overset{+}{C}}{-}\underset{H}{\overset{CH_3}{C}}{-}\underset{H}{\overset{H}{C}}{-}CH_3$$

5. We now have the fundamental carbon skeleton of the observed product. Formation of that product requires only the removal of a proton from the carbon atom adjacent to the carbocation center:

$$CH_3{-}\underset{CH_3}{\overset{+}{C}}{-}\underset{H}{\overset{CH_3}{C}}{-}\underset{H}{\overset{H}{C}}{-}CH_3 \xrightarrow{:B} (CH_3)_2C{=}C\begin{matrix}CH_3\\CH_2CH_3\end{matrix} + \overset{+}{B}{-}H$$

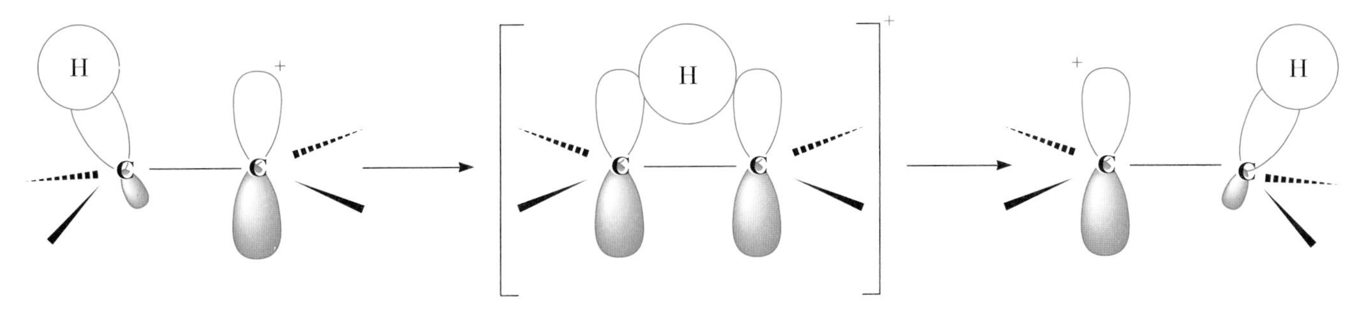

Figure 7.14 Orbital arrangement for hydride migration in a carbocation. In the structure on the left, the *p* orbital is empty and the orbital for the carbon-hydrogen bond is full, that is, it contains a pair of electrons. As the hydrogen begins to migrate (in the center view), its orbital partially interacts with both the *p* orbital of the target carbon atom and a developing *p* orbital at its original binding site. At this point *three* orbitals are interacting simultaneously with a pair of electrons among them. A positive charge is associated with the entire orbital system. This situation has sometimes been referred to as *electron deficient binding*. Finally, as the shift is completed (in the structure on the right), the hydrogen is completely bound to the target carbon, leaving an empty *p* orbital at its original site.

MOLECULAR ORBITAL ANALYSIS

We might ask *how* alkide and hydride shifts actually do occur in carbocations. We know that the free anions do *not* separate from the main skeleton and then recombine with it. Rather, the alkide or hydride somehow migrates along the intervening σ bond without becoming totally removed from that bond. We can draw orbital pictures that illustrate this migration. Figure 7.14 illustrates this orbital arrangement for a hydride shift.

PROBLEM 7.11 Construct an orbital picture, analogous to that shown in Figure 7.14, for the migration of a methyl group in a rearranging carbocation.

7.8 Driving Force for Rearrangement of Carbocations—The Lack of Rearrangement with Radicals

There is an important difference between carbocations and the structurally related free radicals. The rearrangements described for carbocations do *not* occur with radicals. If radicals are produced in a reaction, the eventual product has the same carbon skeleton as the reactant.

This fact is interesting, because carbocation rearrangements are sometimes observed even if the newly formed carbocation is less stable than its precursor, that is, even if the rearrangement is "uphill" in terms of the overall energy change. Such uphill rearrangements are commonly observed when the newly formed carbocation can itself rearrange to something more stable than its predecessors (e.g., Problem 7.10a). Radicals, on the other hand, do not undergo rearrangements even when the product radical is more stable. The difference between radicals and carbocations cannot, then, be attributed to the magnitude of the overall energy change but rather must be due to the magnitude of the *energy barriers* to the two types of rearrangements, that is, to the different activation energies (see Chapter 6). We can infer that radical rearrangements have higher activation energies than do carbocation rearrangements.

We can analyze this difference a little further. For both types of rearrangements, we can imagine the migrating group transferring from one atom

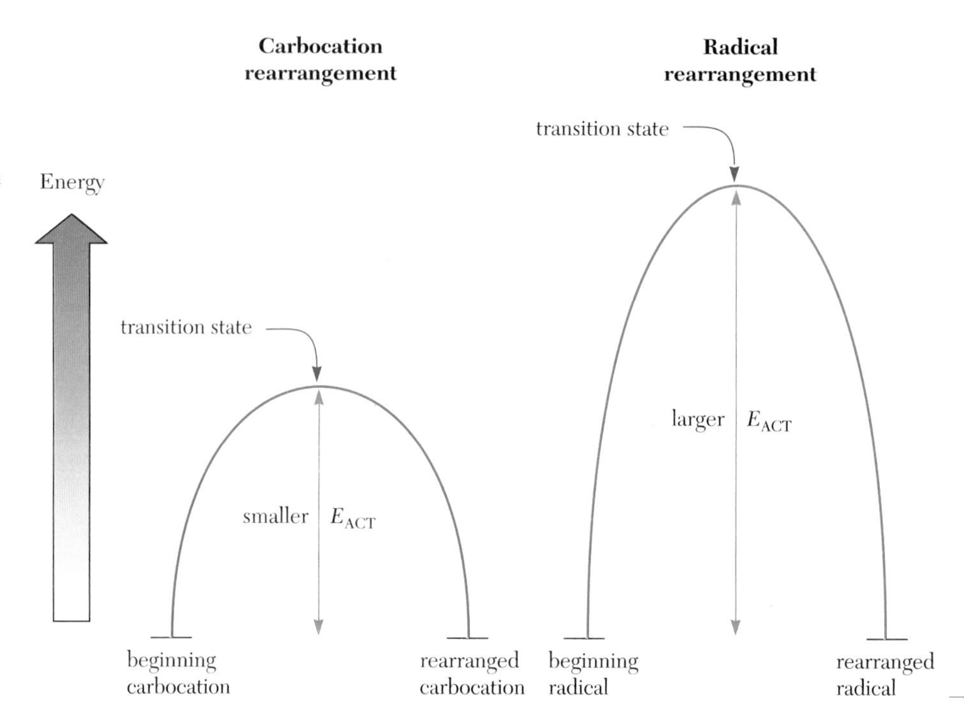

Figure 7.15 Carbocation and radical rearrangements. The energy changes accompanying the migration of a group are shown in these diagrams. Energy rises as migration begins, reaching a maximum value at the transition state. The transition states are similar for cations and radicals of identical carbon skeletons undergoing rearrangement; in particular, they have similar orbitals. However, a radical has one electron more than does the corresponding carbocation. In the transition state, this extra electron occupies a higher-energy orbital, which correlates with an increased transition state energy. The activation energies for radical rearrangements are larger than those for the corrresponding carbocation rearrangements. Radical rearrangements are not observed under usual laboratory conditions. (The energies of the beginning and rearranged radicals are shown as equal here only for convenience. Generally, they are not equal).

to a neighboring atom. As the group begins to migrate, the bond to its original point of connection must begin to weaken, and the energy content of the system will accordingly increase. We can imagine that the energy will continue to rise until the migrating group is midway between the initial and final points of attachment. The energy of the system is now at a maximum, and the increase in energy from the original energy is the activation energy for the process. As the migration continues, the energy content of the system will progressively decrease as bonding develops between the migrating group and its new point of attachment.

The structure corresponding to the state of highest energy content is known as the **transition state** or **activated complex** for the rearrangement. Now make a mental comparison of the transition states for rearrangements of a carbocation and a radical of identical carbon skeletons. We can imagine that the transition states would be quite alike in many ways. In particular, we would expect the orbital structure of both transitions states to be similar. However, a radical *contains one more electron than the corresponding carbocation,* and this additional electron must occupy a higher-energy molecular orbital. Occupation of this higher-energy orbital correlates with the higher energy for the transition state of a radical rearrangement over a carbocation rearrangement for structurally related species. We infer that the activation energies for radical rearrangements are too high to allow the reaction to progress at any significant rate under normal laboratory conditions. Figure 7.15 summarizes these arguments.

7.9 The Shapes of Carbocations and Radicals

Simple VSEPR theory predicts that carbocations should have a trigonal planar shape. Indeed, we find that the properties of carbocations are completely consistent with such a shape. If planarity is prevented for any reason, loss of stability results. In the extreme case, we find that it is virtually impossible to

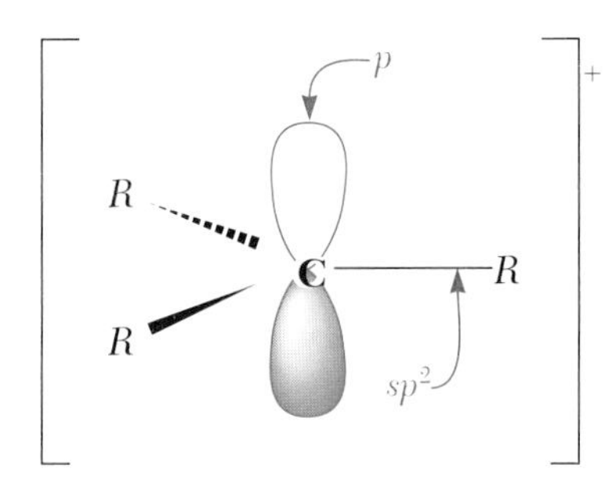

Figure 7.16 Carbocation structure. The central carbon atom is sp^2 hybridized. The attached groups are present in a planar trigonal array about the positive carbon site. The unhybridized p orbital is empty.

generate a carbocation if it cannot be planar. In later discussions we will look at some examples of this phenomenon.

We describe carbocations as having sp^2 hybridization. The hybrid orbitals form the σ bonds to adjoining atoms, and the unhybridized p orbital is empty. We commonly picture carbocations as shown in Figure 7.16.

The geometry about the central carbon in free radicals is not as well defined as about a carbocation site. There are examples of free radicals in which the geometry is planar and others in which the geometry is *not* planar. More will be said about the consequences of nonplanar structures after additional concepts of molecular shape are developed in the next chapter.

Summary

- Carbocations can be generated from certain alcohols by treating them with acids. The more highly substituted the alcohol on the carbinol carbon, the more readily it will form a carbocation.
- Tertiary carbocations are more stable than secondary carbocations, which are more stable than primary carbocations, which are more stable than the methyl cation.
- Once generated, carbocations are capable of undergoing a variety of reactions.
- Carbocations are capable of forming a new covalent bond by reaction with a Lewis base. Either an anion or a neutral Lewis base (an electron-pair donor) has the fundamental ability to form a covalent bond to a carbocation center. Potent nucleophiles will form this new bond more rapidly than poor nucleophiles.
- Carbocations can undergo other reactions before or instead of combining with a nucleophile, particularly if no potent nucleophile is present.
- Carbocations may undergo an alkide or a hydride shift from an adjacent carbon atom to generate a new carbocation. Generally these rearrangements generate a more stable carbocation than the original one.
- Carbocations may react with Brønsted bases to lose a proton from a carbon atom adjacent to the carbocation site and produce an alkene.
- A free radical is a neutral species with a single electron in a non-bonding orbital on carbon.
- Although carbocations and free radicals are both electron-deficient species, they exhibit quite different chemistry.
- Carbocations are formed by heterolysis of bonds. With protonated alcohols, the carbon-oxygen bond undergoes heterolysis.
- Free radicals are generally formed by homolysis of a bond.
- While carbocations readily undergo rearrangement, free radicals rarely do.

Terms to Remember

intermediate
reaction rate
homolytic bond cleavage
heterolytic bond cleavage
endothermic
exothermic
bond dissociation energy
enthalpy
radical
carbocation
carbenium ion
hyperconjugation
elimination
skeletal rearrangement
alkide shift
hydride shift
transition state
activated complex

Reactions of Synthetic Utility

The reactions summarized below are noted as being useful for either tertiary or primary alcohols. Secondary alcohols may also be used with certain of these reactions, but rearrangements often decrease their synthetic utility significantly.

14. $R_3COH \xrightarrow{HX} R_3CX$ **7.6**

$3°$; X = Cl, Br, I

15. $R_2C(OH)-CHR_2 \xrightarrow[H_2O]{H_2SO_4} R_2C{=}CR_2$ **7.6**

$3°$

16. $RCH_2OH \xrightarrow[MX]{acid} RCH_2X$ **7.6**

(H_2SO_4 with NaBr, or H_3PO_4 with KI)

17. $RCH_2CH_2OH \xrightarrow[H_2O]{H_2SO_4} RCH{=}CH_2$ **7.6**

Note: The dehydration of 1° (and 2°) alcohols to alkenes may be complicated by rearrangement of the intermediate carbocation.

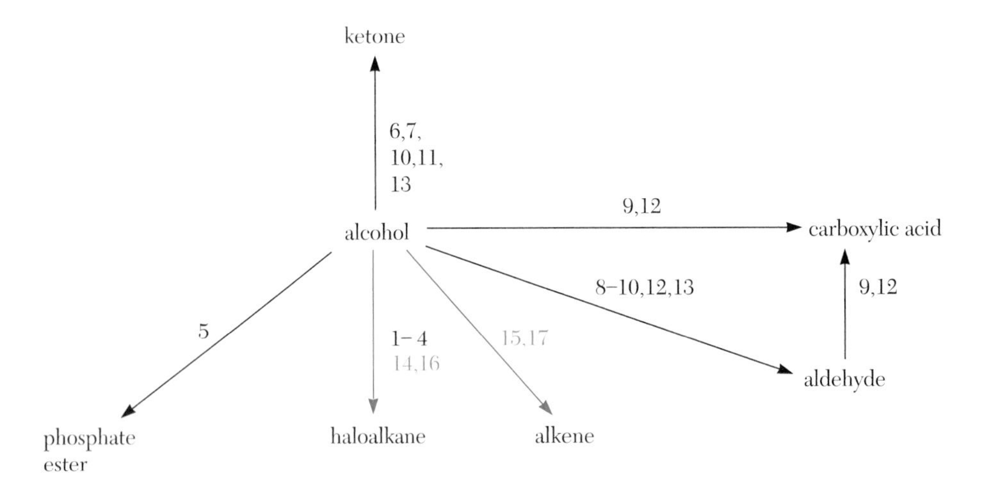

Additional Problems

7.12 Calculate ΔH for each of the following reactions:

a. $CH_4 + Br_2 \longrightarrow CH_3\ddot{B}r\!: + H\ddot{B}r\!:$

b. $C_2H_6 + Cl_2 \longrightarrow C_2H_5\ddot{C}l\!: + H\ddot{C}l\!:$

c. $H_2 + I_2 \longrightarrow 2\,H\ddot{I}\!:$

d. $(CH_3)_3C\ddot{O}H + H\ddot{C}l\!: \longrightarrow (CH_3)_3C\ddot{C}l\!: + H_2\ddot{O}$

7.13 Suppose ethane is heated until the molecules start to fragment. Which bond do you expect to break first? What fragments will form? Explain your answers.

7.14 The oxygen-chlorine bond of HOCl can break in different ways. Write equations for these processes and show any formal charges associated with the fragments.

7.15 Consider all possible migrations that might occur to the electron-deficient carbon of the carbocation shown at the top of page 177. Use the curved-arrow formalism to show these migrations, and draw the structures of the rearranged carbocations. Which of these would you expect to be the major component of an equilibrium mixture of all of these carbocations?

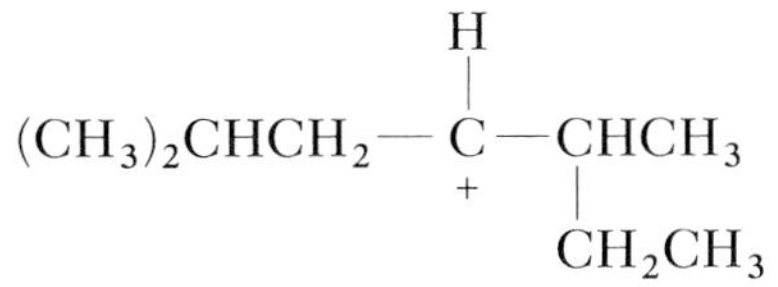

$$(CH_3)_2CHCH_2-\overset{\displaystyle H}{\underset{+}{C}}-\underset{\displaystyle CH_2CH_3}{CHCH_3}$$

7.16 Give the structure of the major organic product formed in each of the following reactions:
a. 1-butanol treated with potassium iodide in phosphoric acid
b. 2-methyl-2-butanol treated with aqueous sulfuric acid
c. 2,3-dimethyl-2-butanol treated with aqueous sulfuric acid
d. 3-methyl-3-hexanol treated with zinc chloride in hydrochloric acid
e. 4-ethyl-1-hexanol treated with hydrochloric acid
f. 4-ethyl-1-hexanol treated with sodium bromide in sulfuric acid

7.17 Give the structure and the IUPAC name of the major product formed when each of the following alcohols is treated with hydrogen bromide:
a. 2,3-dimethyl-1-pentanol b. 2-methyl-2-butanol c. 2,4-dimethyl-3-hexanol
d. 2,2,6,6,-tetramethyl-3-heptanol e. 4-ethyl-1-hexanol f. 3-methyl-2-butanol

7.18 Primary carbocations are generally less stable than other types of carbocations. However, both methoxymethyl bromide (CH_3OCH_2Br) and allyl bromide ($H_2C{=}CH{-}CH_2Br$) readily lose bromide ion to form rather stable cations. Suggest a reason for the unusual stability of these cations.

7.19 The treatment of 2,2-dimethyl-1-propanol (neopentyl alcohol) with sulfuric acid results in the formation of two alkenes. Give their structures, and write a mechanism for the formation of each using the curved-arrow formalism. Predict which will be formed in the greater amount.

7.20 Consider the reaction of 1-butanol with a strong acid.
a. If the initially formed oxonium ion undergoes heterolysis of the carbon-oxygen bond, what carbocation would result?
b. To which carbocation would it rearrange?
c. Which bromoalkane of formula C_4H_9Br would you expect to be formed if HBr were the acid, assuming the reactions proceeded according to the steps alluded to in parts a and b?
d. The actual product from 1-butanol reaction with HBr is 1-bromobutane. What does this result tell us about the mechanism of the reaction? What is the actual mechanism by which the product forms?
e. When the acid used is sulfuric acid, 2-butene is the major product. Explain how it forms.

7.21 On treatment of butane-1,4-diol ($HOCH_2CH_2CH_2CH_2OH$) with sulfuric acid, a compound of formula C_4H_8O is formed. This compound does not react with sodium metal. Give its structure, and write a mechanism for its formation.

7.22 If *tert*-butyl alcohol is treated with sulfuric acid dissolved in ^{18}O labeled water (i.e., $^{18}OH_2$), the ^{18}O becomes incorporated into the *tert*-butyl alcohol. Write reactions to show how this could occur.

7.23 The structures shown below all represent tertiary carbocations of formula $C_{10}H_{21}{}^+$. However, they are of different relative stabilities. Arrange them in order of increasing stability, and give an explanation for the order you assigned.

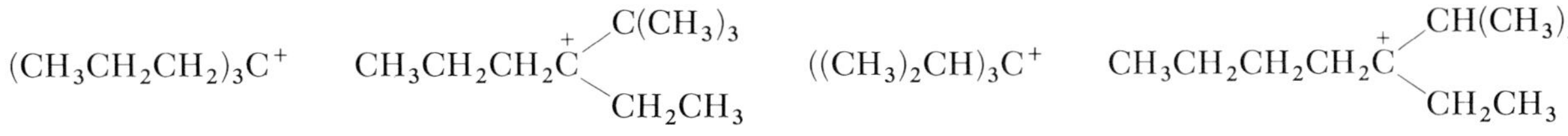

$$(CH_3CH_2CH_2)_3C^+ \qquad CH_3CH_2CH_2\overset{+}{C}\begin{smallmatrix} C(CH_3)_3 \\ CH_2CH_3 \end{smallmatrix} \qquad ((CH_3)_2CH)_3C^+ \qquad CH_3CH_2CH_2CH_2\overset{+}{C}\begin{smallmatrix} CH(CH_3)_2 \\ CH_2CH_3 \end{smallmatrix}$$

7.24 Treatment of 1-butanethiol ($CH_3CH_2CH_2CH_2SH$) with sulfuric acid and sodium bromide yields 1-bromobutane. Write a mechanism for this reaction. Would you expect this reaction to proceed faster or more slowly than the corresponding reaction of 1-butanol? Explain your answer.

CHAPTER 8 Stereochemical Principles

8.1 Introduction

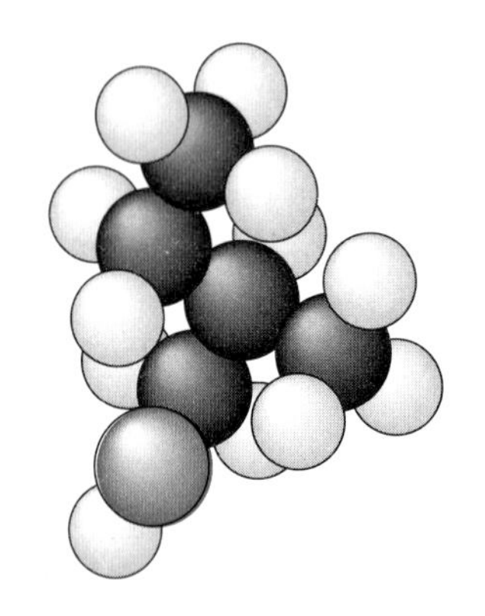

Stereochemistry is the study of the three-dimensional shapes of molecules. In general, we find that the spatial arrangement of atoms in a molecule is of fundamental importance in determining its chemical and physical properties. Accordingly, most studies of organic compounds and their reactions involve stereochemistry at some level. X-ray diffraction techniques can determine the exact three-dimensional structure of a molecule, as long as a sample is available in good crystalline form. However, it is also possible to make less direct inferences about structures.

As early as the nineteenth century, chemists had concluded that when four groups are attached to a carbon atom, the bonding geometry is tetrahedral. They reached this conclusion long before X-ray diffraction techniques had been developed and long before there were any theories for predicting molecular geometry. We can appreciate the thought processes involved by looking at as simple a molecule as ethanol. If the geometry about carbon were either a square planar array or a pyramidal array, *two* isomers of C_2H_5OH could exist, as shown in Figure 8.1. However, only *one* alcohol with the formula C_2H_5OH has ever been isolated. This finding is consistent with a tetrahedral geometry about carbon, as shown in Figure 8.2.

PROBLEM 8.1 Using molecular models, verify that there can be only one alcohol isomer of formula C_2H_5OH if carbon forms four bonds with tetrahedral geometry. To do this, make *two* models of ethanol. Superimpose them (as much as is physically possible) to verify that they are identical. Now physically dismantle one of these models in order to *exchange* two of its groups (e.g., hydroxyl and methyl) in their positions about the central carbon atom. Again superimpose the two models to verify their congruence. Make any other exchanges you find possible with one of the models, retaining the C_2H_5OH formula, to verify further that all changes result in regeneration of the original structure.

In general, we can often infer geometry on the basis of **isomer number** (the number of isomers that are experimentally obtainable for a given formula). Conversely, we can always deduce the isomer number exactly from knowledge of bonding geometry.

We need to know the geometry of bonding about carbon atoms in order to understand fully the mechanisms of organic reactions. Mechanisms provide models that describe the way nuclei and electrons are shifted in the course of

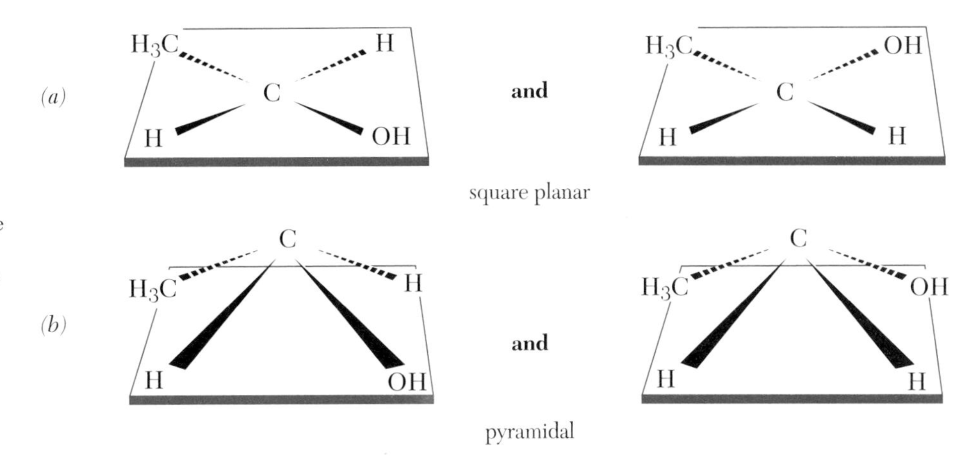

Figure 8.1 Hypothetical bonding geometries about carbon. (*a*) A square planar arrangement of groups about carbon presents two possible structures for an alcohol of formula C_2H_6O. One has the methyl and hydroxyl groups along the same side of a square and the other has the methyl and hydroxyl groups across the square from each other. (*b*) A pyramidal geometry about carbon presents the same possibilities as does the square planar arrangement.

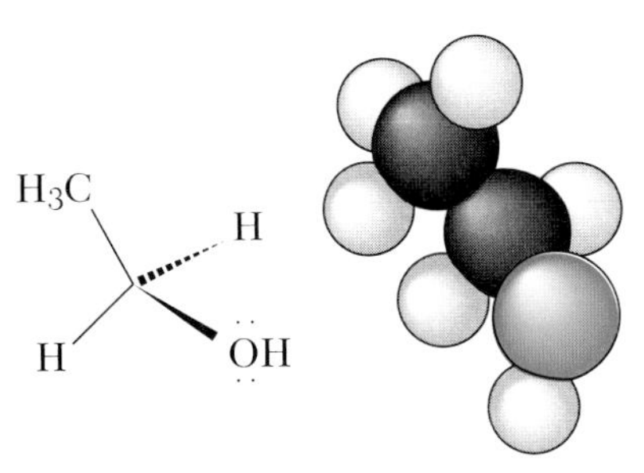

Figure 8.2 Tetrahedral geometry about carbon in ethanol. Only one type of ethanol has ever been observed, leading to the deduction of tetrahedral geometry about carbon.

a reaction. If we understand the mechanism of a reaction, we understand in principle how to control its course.

Many reaction mechanisms require very specific geometrical relationships among the reactants. Moreover, molecules must at times adopt specific shapes for reactions to be possible. Such requirements are of particular importance for molecules in biological processes. Reactions occurring in biological organisms require more than the presence of the proper functional groups. The location of these groups within the molecule and the specific shape of the molecule are usually critical as well.

We have already been concerned with some aspects of stereochemistry in earlier chapters, for example, we considered the relationship between bonding geometry and hybridization. In this chapter we will take a new and more detailed look at this topic.

8.2 Isomer Number in Three- and Four-Carbon Alcohols

THREE-CARBON ALCOHOLS

Consider alcohols of the formula C_3H_7OH. Two structures can be written, those of 1-propanol (**8.1**) and 2-propanol (**8.2**). These two alcohols are **regioisomers** (or positional isomers). Interconversion of these isomers requires the breaking of existing bonds and the making of new bonds. No rotation about single bonds can transform one into the other.

$$CH_3CH_2CH_2\ddot{O}H \qquad CH_3CH(\ddot{O}H)CH_3$$

1-propanol **8.1**   2-propanol **8.2**

FOUR-CARBON ALCOHOLS

Consider alcohols of the general formula C_4H_9OH. Even more isomers are possible with this formula than with C_3H_7OH. Of the five possible isomeric alcohols of this formula, three are shown in Figure 8.3.

The remaining two isomers are secondary alcohols that differ from each other in a subtle way. Both can be described by the name *2-butanol*, but they

Figure 8.3 Three isomeric alcohols of the formula C_4H_9OH. These three differ in their fundamental carbon skeleton and the position at which the hydroxyl group is attached.

$CH_3CH_2CH_2CH_2\ddot{O}H$	$(CH_3)_2CHCH_2\ddot{O}H$	$(CH_3)_3C\ddot{O}H$
1-butanol	2-methyl-1-propanol	2-methyl-2-propanol

Figure 8.4 Two forms of 2-butanol. These two structures are nonsuperimposable mirror images.

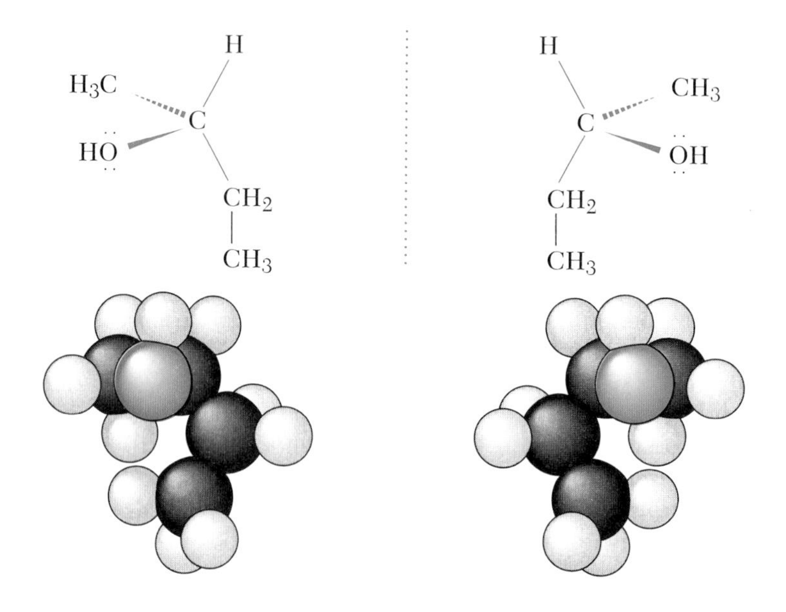

differ in that they are *nonsuperimposable mirror images*. Diagrams of these two structures are shown in Figure 8.4 along with their molecular models. The placement of the structures in Figure 8.4 emphasizes their mirror-image relationship.

Notice that the two forms of 2-butanol shown in Figure 8.4 are *not* simply different conformations of a single molecule. Rotations about single bonds *cannot* interconvert the two mirror-image structures. In fact, the two forms can be isolated from each other and stored without interconverting. It is simple to verify that we are indeed dealing with isomeric structures by attempting to superimpose models of the two molecules, as shown in Figure 8.5.

PROBLEM 8.2 Construct molecular models of the two structures shown in Figure 8.4. Verify that they are *not* superimposable, as has been illustrated in Figure 8.5.

Physically dismantle one of the two models you have constructed in order to exchange the positions of any *two* groups about the carbinol carbon atom. Is the resulting model superimposable on the unchanged model? Exchange a different combination of any two substituents of the carbinol carbon atom in the same model. Are the models *now* superimposable? Continue switching different combinations of two substituents of the carbinol carbon atom and checking for superimposability of the two models. After how many exchanges are the models superimposable? When are they nonsuperimposable?

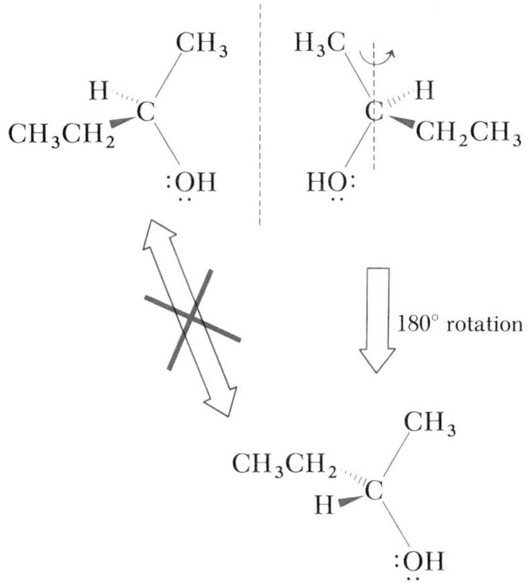

Figure 8.5 An attempt to superimpose two mirror-image structures of 2-butanol. Rotating the molecule on the right 180° about a vertical axis allows the methyl group, the central carbon atom, and the hydroxyl group to be superimposed with the corresponding sites on the molecule on the left. However, the remaining hydrogen and ethyl groups are not superimposed on their corresponding sites on the molecule on the left. No amount of rotation in space allows all four groups attached to the central carbon to be superimposed on their corresponding members at the same time.

Molecules that are not superimposable on their mirror images are said to be **chiral** (the Greek word *chir* means "hand"). The property of chirality is not limited to molecules. *Any* object that is not superimposable on its mirror image is said to be chiral. The most common example is our hands. The right hand is a nonsuperimposable mirror image of the left hand. Although we can bring a right hand and a left hand together palm-to-palm, we can not superimpose them—they have a "handedness." One consequence of this chirality is that a right hand does not fit properly into a left glove. We will encounter similar phenomena in dealing with chiral molecules. Let us stress here what we mean by superimposable: if two objects are superimposable, we have no way of telling them apart; if the objects are *not* superimposable, for example, a right and a left shoe, we *can* tell them apart.

Look again at the 2-butanol molecules shown in Figure 8.4. Notice that both show the same *sequence* of attachment for the component atoms. The hydroxyl carbon in each 2-butanol structure has the same four unlike groups—a hydrogen, a methyl group, an ethyl group, and the hydroxyl group—attached to it. We say that both molecules exhibit the same *connectivity* (i.e., the same sequence of bonded atoms). However, because of the tetrahedral geometry of carbon bonding, there are two different *spatial* arrangements (**configurations**) for these four groups. Molecules that have the same sequence of atoms but a different configuration are called **stereoisomers.** We find that *any* molecule containing a single atom bound to four different groups in a tetrahedral array is chiral, that is, it has a nonsuperimposable mirror image. We refer to the carbon atom bound to four unlike groups and thus generating this chirality as a **stereogenic carbon atom.** (Such a carbon atom is sometimes referred to as a chiral center, a chiral carbon atom, or an asymmetric center.)

In summary, 2-butanol exists in two stereoisomeric forms. The two forms are nonsuperimposable mirror images of each other. While there is a close structural relationship between these forms, they *are* different. Stereoisomers that are nonsuperimposable mirror images are known as **enantiomers.** Since the two structures are different, we might expect them to have different physical and/or chemical characteristics. We will return to explore these differences later in this chapter.

8.3 Stereogenic Carbon and Racemic Mixtures

A substance can exist in enantiomeric forms whenever its structure is not superimposable on its mirror image. We have seen this situation occur for a molecule in which a tetrahedral carbon atom has four unlike groups attached to it. In general, enantiomeric forms will exist *whenever* a molecule has a single stereogenic carbon atom, as shown in Figure 8.6. We describe such a molecule as **asymmetric** (without symmetry).

If a tetrahedral carbon does not have four unlike groups attached, it is not a stereogenic center. For example, the ethanol molecule does not have a stereogenic carbon atom. If we construct a model of an ethanol molecule and a model of its mirror image, we find that they are completely superimposable. (The exercise you did in Problem 8.1 is illustrated in Figure 8.7 for ethanol.) The molecules are *identical* rather than being enantiomers. This example should alert you to be careful. Every molecule has a mirror image. However, only if the molecule and its mirror image are not identical (cannot be superimposed) are they classed as enantiomers.

A tetrahedral center with two or more identical groups attached is referred to as being **achiral,** that is, it is without chirality. For this reason only a single structure can be written (or isolated) for the formula C_2H_5OH. No separation into enantiomers is possible.

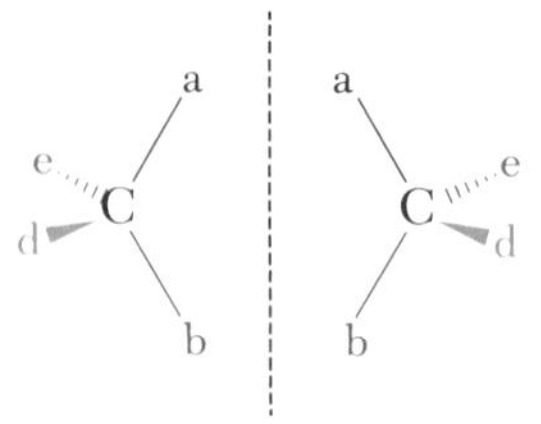

Figure 8.6 A stereogenic carbon center. Enantiomeric forms of a molecule can exist whenever a single stereogenic carbon atom is present. No amount of rotation of the structures in space will allow them to be superimposed.

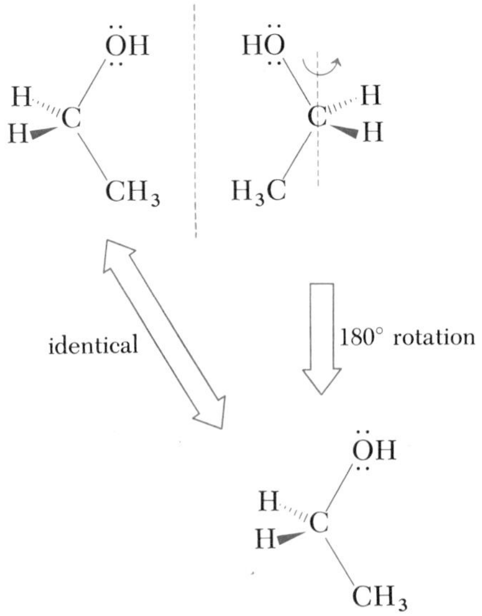

Figure 8.7 Superimposable mirror images of the ethanol molecule. There is no stereogenic center. Each of the (two) tetrahedral carbon atoms has at least two identical groups attached to it.

PROBLEM 8.3 Draw clearly the structures for the pair of enantiomers of each of the following compounds:

a. 3-bromo-1-butanol **b.** 3-methyl-3-hexanol **c.** 1-bromo-2-butanol

Steps to Solving the Problem

Solution to Problem 8.3a

1. First, write out the fundamental structure and locate the stereogenic center. The stereogenic center is the carbon with four unlike groups attached.

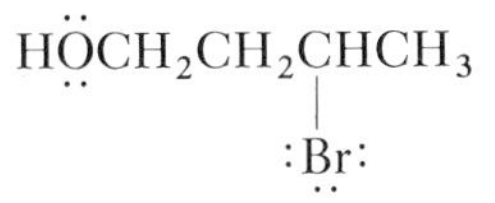

$$HOCH_2CH_2CH(Br)CH_3$$

We see that the stereogenic center is carbon-3 of the chain. It is bonded to a hydrogen atom, a bromine atom, a methyl group, and a hydroxyethyl group.

2. We must now construct *one* enantiomer, so we set up a tetrahedral carbon atom, as shown below on the left, and then place the four groups about it, as shown on the right.

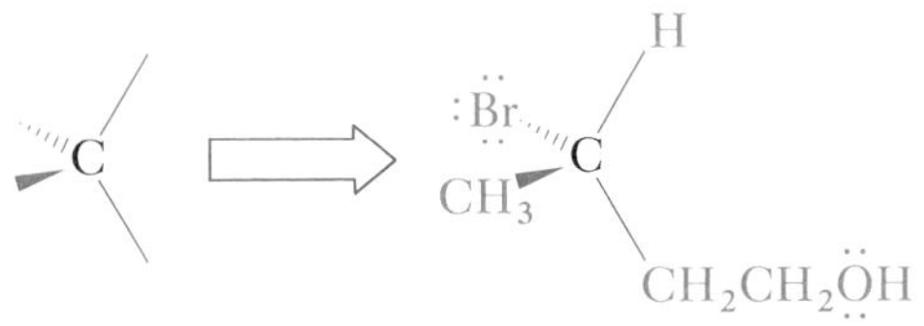

H, :Br:, CH_3, C, CH_2CH_2OH

This structure represents *one* of the enantiomers for the compound.

3. To construct the other enantiomer, we now envision a reflecting plane on one side of the structure already drawn and create its mirror image:

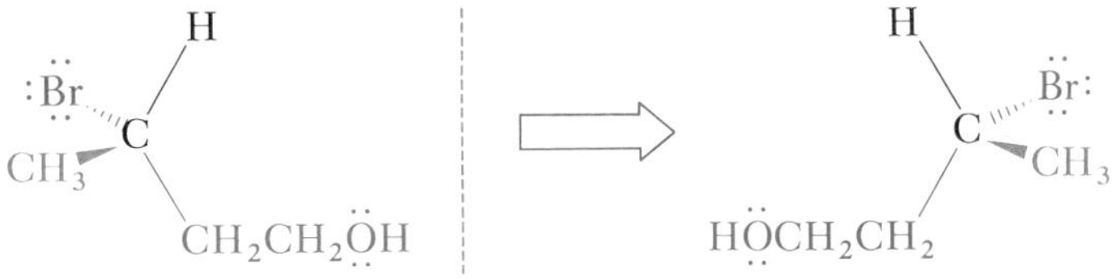

H, :Br:, CH_3, C, CH_2CH_2OH → H, Br:, C, CH_3, $HOCH_2CH_2$

8.4 Naturally Occurring Chiral Molecules

Most organic molecules found in nature are asymmetric. Usually, only one of the two possible enantiomers is actually found in a given biological source. In this section we will describe several examples of chiral molecules from biological sources.

2-Methyl-1-butanol is the simplest chiral alcohol to occur naturally. Only one of its enantiomers, that shown on the right in Figure 8.8, has been isolated from biological sources. The other enantiomer is available only by synthesis in the laboratory.

Fermentation of plant materials has long been used to prepare ethanol. 2-Methyl-1-butanol can be isolated as a by-product of the fermentation. After the ethanol has been removed from the fermentation broth by distillation, there remains a mixture of higher-boiling alcohols. This mixture is commonly known as *fusel oil*. The structure shown on the right side of Figure 8.8 is the form of 2-methyl-1-butanol isolated from fusel oil.

Another primary alcohol that has a single stereogenic center and thus has enantiomeric forms is β-citronellol, which is shown in Figure 8.9. Each of these enantiomers is produced biologically, but in different organisms.

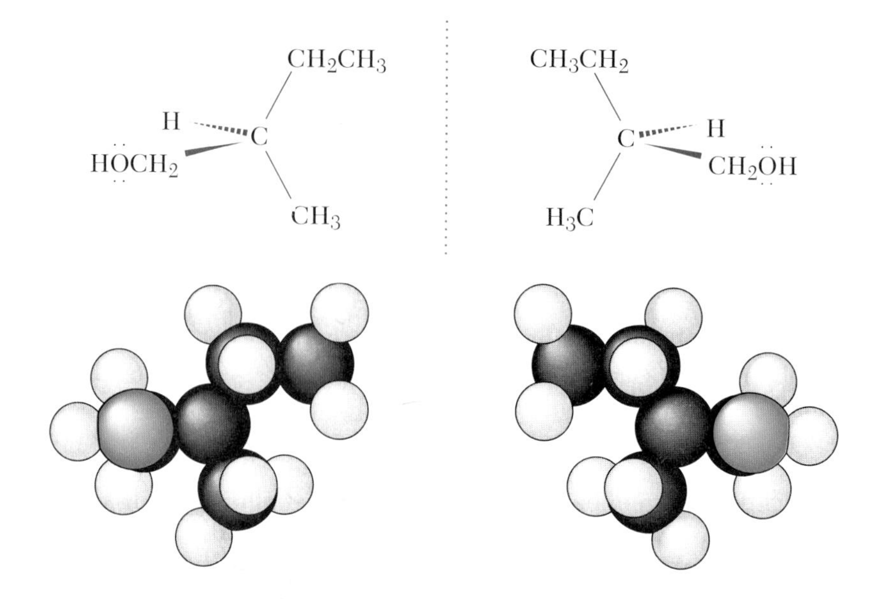

Figure 8.8 Enantiomeric forms of 2-methyl-1-butanol. Only the structure shown on the right has been isolated from biological sources. The structure on the left has been generated in laboratory preparations.

α-Terpineol is a relatively simple, naturally occurring tertiary alcohol with a single stereogenic center. One difference between α-terpineol and the previously described chiral molecules is that the stereogenic center here is part of a ring. The four attached groups are —H, —$C(CH_3)_2OH$, and the two alkyl groups that join to form the ring. Examination of the structure in Figure 8.10

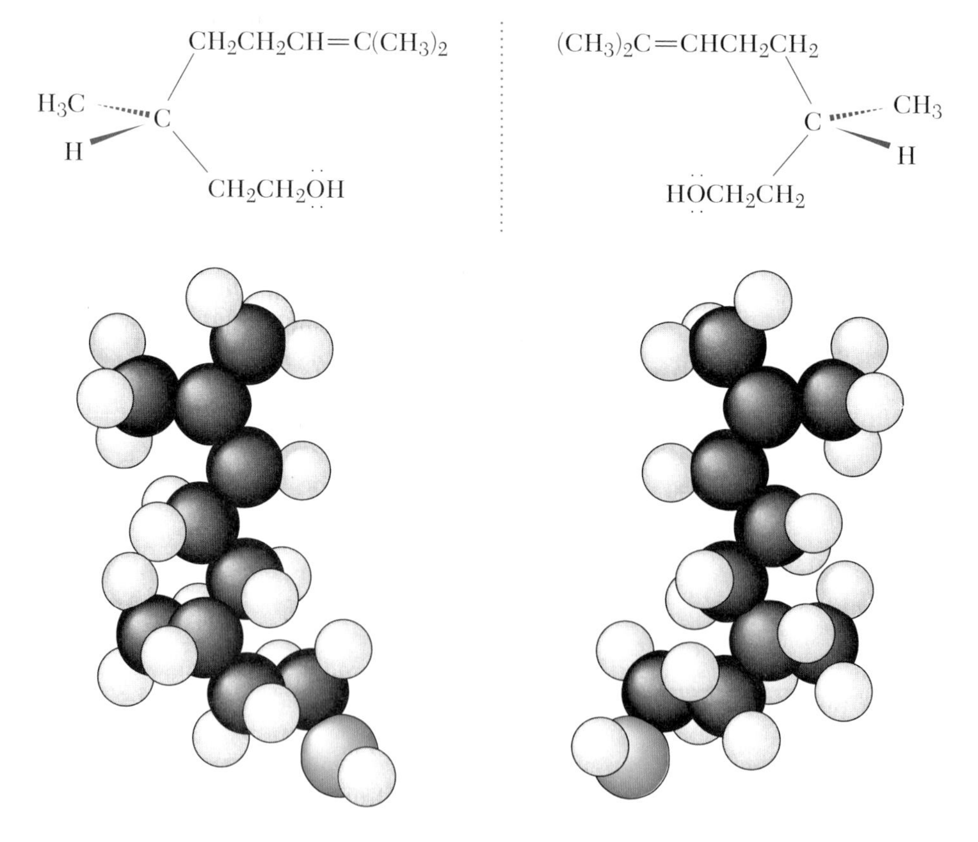

Figure 8.9 Enantiomeric forms of β-citronellol. The structure shown on the left occurs naturally in the geranium plant. The structure on the right is obtained from oils isolated from plants native to Sri Lanka and Java. These materials are used in perfumes.

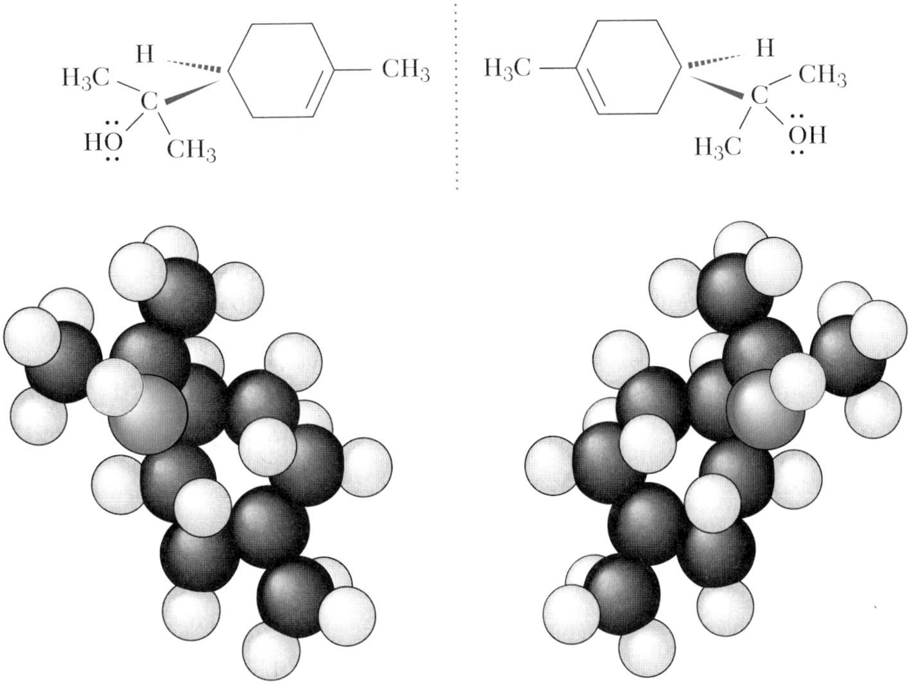

Figure 8.10 Enantiomers of α-terpineol. Each enantiomer may be isolated in pure form from plants. The structure shown on the left is isolated from longleaf pine oil, while that shown on the right is a constituent of petitgrain oil. Both substances are used in perfumes.

shows that the sequences of atoms encountered going in opposite directions around the ring from the stereogenic center are *not* identical. Thus the two alkyl groups are not identical.

Another source of α-terpineol is cajeput oil. The material isolated from this source is a mixture of equal amounts of the two enantiomers. Such a mixture is known as a **racemic mixture.** We are unable to separate the two components of a racemic mixture without the use of some special technique. We will discuss this problem further in the next section, and techniques that can be used to separate enantiomers will be covered in a later section of this chapter.

The phenomenon of chirality is found over the entire range of organic molecules, particularly those of biological origin. For example, alanine (**8.3**), the simplest chiral amino acid, is almost always encountered as the single enantiomer shown below. Similarly, the carbohydrate glyceraldehyde (**8.4**) contains a single stereogenic carbon atom. Derivatives of it are produced in living organisms only with the chirality shown.

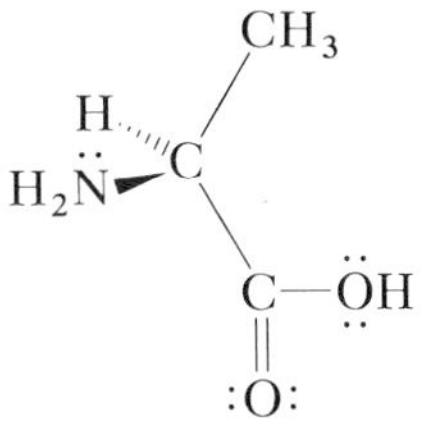

alanine
8.3

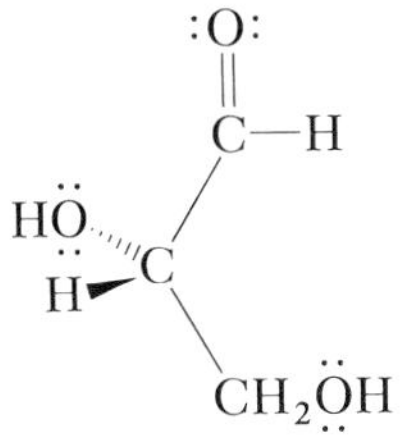

glyceraldehyde
8.4

We will have much more to say about these and related compounds in Chapters 24 and 26.

8.5 Experimental Observation of Enantiomers

We have seen that nonsuperimposable mirror images of a given item *are* different forms of that item, albeit closely related forms. Different forms of molecules are different isomers, and as we noted previously, we anticipate that different properties will be associated with isomeric structures. But what differences in properties distinguish enantiomeric molecules? Let's consider some chemical and physical characteristics of the enantiomeric forms of 2-methyl-1-butanol.

When we analyze each enantiomer for percentage composition and molecular weight, we get identical results: 68.13% C, 13.72% H, 18.15% O, and a molecular weight of 88 g/mole. If we measure the solubility of each enantiomer in water, methanol, or ethanol, we again find them to be identical. Moreover, these enantiomers exhibit the same melting temperature, boiling temperature, and index of refraction. In fact, we find them to be identical in *all* their common physical properties. While we could easily distinguish 2-methyl-1-butanol from other compounds of the formula $C_5H_{12}O$ on the basis of these physical properties, we cannot distinguish between the members of the enantiomeric pair. This situation is not unique to 2-methyl-1-butanol—we find that the members of all enantiomeric pairs exhibit exactly the same common physical properties.

When we look at the *chemical* properties of two enantiomers, we find that they react in the same way with a large variety of common reagents. For example, their acidities are the same, and their rates of reaction with phosphorus trichloride are the same. For that matter, the rates of reaction of the two enantiomers of 2-methyl-1-butanol are the same with *any* of the reagents for which we have discussed reactions with alcohols.

Consider another reaction, the oxidation of each enantiomer of 2-methyl-1-butanol with chromic anhydride in sulfuric acid, as shown in Figure 8.11. In these reactions we *do* get a different product from each enantiomer. However, the products are themselves a pair of enantiomers.

Our earlier question has still not been answered. Although enantiomers *are* different molecules, all the examples of their behavior that we have con-

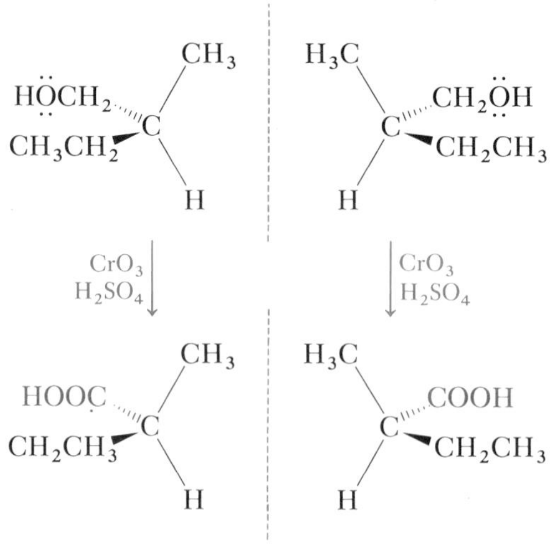

Figure 8.11 Oxidation of enantiomers of 2-methyl-1-butanol. The oxidation of the two enantiomers of 2-methyl-1-butanol leads to two different products. These two products, however, constitute an enantiomeric pair for 2-methylbutanoic acid. These two products have corresponding properties just as the enantiomeric forms of 2-methyl-1-butanol do.

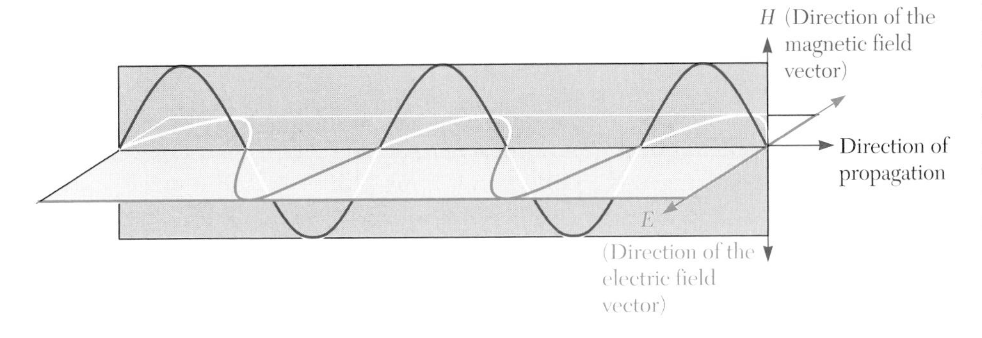

Figure 8.12 Component vectors of electromagnetic radiation. Light is composed of magnetic and electric component vectors with directions perpendicular to each other and to the direction of propagation of the ray of light.

sidered so far show them to behave identically. Even so, there *are* important ways in which they differ. Having considered the ways in which enantiomers are alike, we will now turn our attention to the ways in which they differ.

The principal *physical* difference between enantiomers is the way in which each interacts with **plane-polarized light.** Each enantiomer of a pair rotates the plane of plane polarized light to an equal amount in opposite directions. We say that such molecules are **optically active.** To help in understanding this property, we will review some of the characteristics of light.

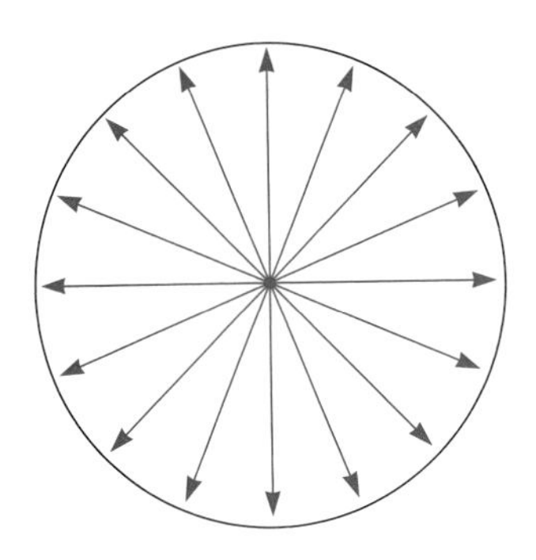

Figure 8.13 End-on view of the electric vectors of ordinary monochromatic light. A beam of light consists of many separate rays, each with an electric vector component. The electric vectors of these individual rays are not all oriented in the same direction. In fact, there is an equal distribution of the electric vectors over the full circle of arc about the direction of propagation. We refer to such light as *random* light. Magnetic vectors are perpendicular to electric vectors but have the same type of distributions as electric vectors.

Light is an example of **electromagnetic radiation,** indicating that it has both electric and magnetic characteristics. Light can be thought of as a wave in which the magnetic field and electric field components are perpendicular to each other and to the direction of propagation, as illustrated in Figure 8.12.

Consider a beam of light from a monochromatic source (that is, the light emitted has only one wavelength). It has an electric component that is randomly distributed in all directions perpendicular to the direction of propagation (and a magnetic component with a similar random distribution). Figure 8.13 represents an end-on view of the electric vectors of this light.

If a beam of light passes through a **polarizer,** only light that has an electric vector in a particular direction is transmitted. A typical polarizer is a prism constructed from crystallized calcium carbonate; light with one direction of electric vector is transmitted and the rest is reflected (this type of prism is called a *Nicol prism,* after its inventor, William Nicol). A Polaroid lens can also act as a polarizer. The effect of a polarizer is represented graphically in Figure 8.14.

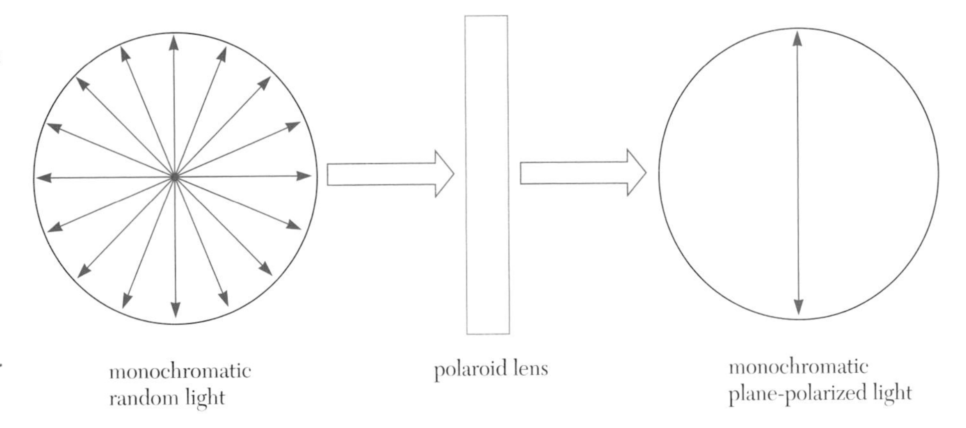

Figure 8.14 Random light passing through a Polaroid lens. When a beam of random monochromatic light consisting of many rays passes through a polarizer, only that portion with the electric vector in a particular direction is transmitted. The direction of the electric vector of the transmitted light is determined by the direction of polarization of the polarizer. The transmitted light, in which the electric vector is in only one direction, is known as plane-polarized light.

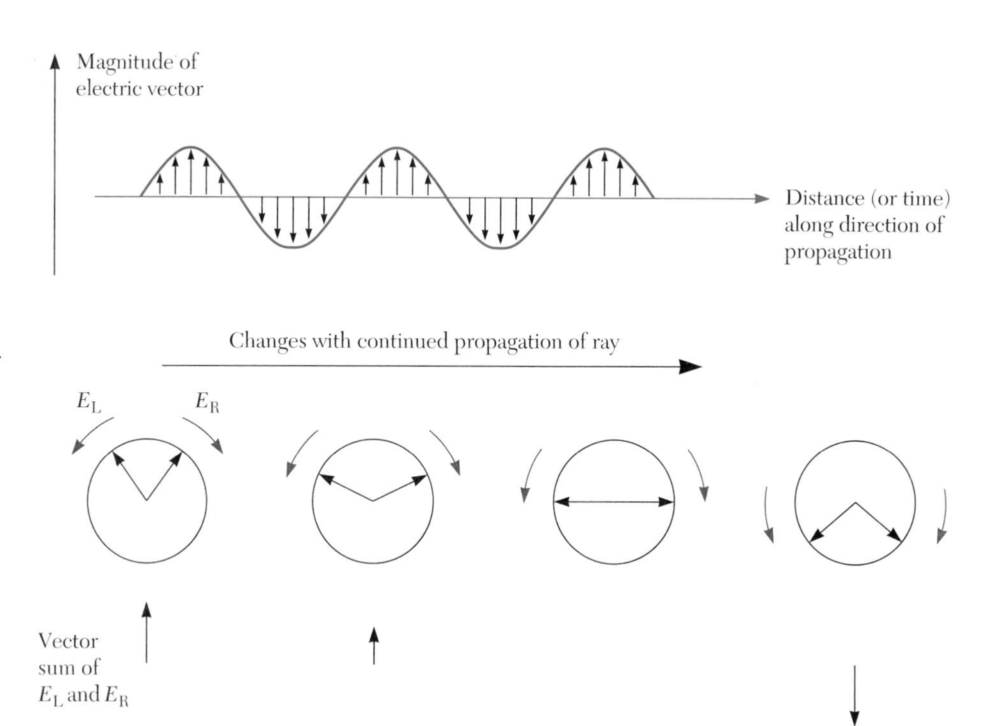

Figure 8.15 Variation in electric vector of plane-polarized light with propagation. Only the *magnitude* of the electric vector changes as the ray is propagated. It increases and decreases along the original direction and alternates between being positive and being negative.

Figure 8.16 Variation of circularly polarized light components with propagation of a ray. Plane-polarized light is the vector sum of the two components of circularly polarized light. The electric vectors of left and right circularly polarized light are represented here as E_L and E_R. The variation of these components with propagation of the ray of light is shown at the top of the figure. The components rotate about the axis of propagation in opposite directions at the same rate, producing a variation in the *magnitude* of the vector sum (the electric vector of plane-polarized light) but not its plane of polarization. Unless acted upon by some other force, the plane of polarization will always be along the same axis. Here, that axis is vertical. Although the electric vector passes through zero magnitude into the opposite direction, the plane of polarization remains along the vertical axis.

Plane-polarized light has some interesting characteristics. As it is propagated (passes through space), the *magnitude* of the electric vector varies. However, its *direction of polarization* does not change. The variation of its magnitude is sinusoidal with time (or distance), as shown in Figure 8.15. This variation in magnitude without change in direction occurs because plane-polarized light consists of two components of **circularly polarized light.** These components vary by rotating about the direction of propagation of the ray of light, as shown in Figure 8.16.

The direction of polarization of plane-polarized light can be determined by experiment. If we allow the plane-polarized light to impinge on a *second* polarizer, it will pass through the second polarizer only if its direction of polarization is aligned with that polarizer. This can be demonstrated by viewing a light source through two sheets of Polaroid. (Two Polaroid sunglass lenses will suffice.) As the lenses are rotated relative to each other, we find one extreme position at which no light is transmitted. Rotating the lenses 90° relative to each other from this point, we find that light is transmitted with maximum brightness. We know the direction of polarization of plane-polarized light from the analyzing (second) polaroid lens. When light is transmitted at maximum brightness, the direction of polarization of the light is aligned with that of the analyzing polaroid lens.

If we place various substances between the polarizing and analyzing Polaroid lenses, we can then see if those substances have any effect on the *direction* of polarization of the plane-polarized light. A great many substances have *no* effect on the direction of polarization of plane-polarized light. However, certain materials—chiral substances—cause a significant and interesting effect. For example, if we place a sample of 2-methyl-1-butanol isolated from fusel oil

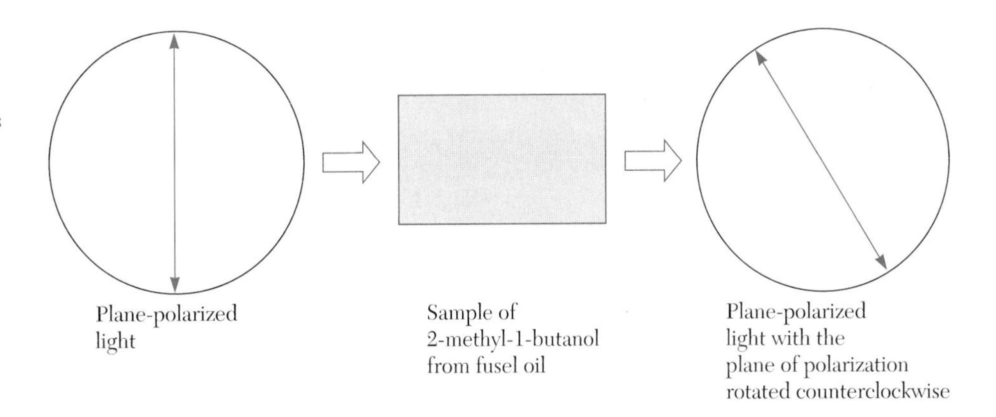

Figure 8.17 Rotation of the plane of plane-polarized light when it passes through a sample of 2-methyl-1-butanol from fusel oil. Although the light passes through the sample, it does not pass through unaffected. The direction of the plane of polarization is rotated counterclockwise from its orientation when it entered the sample.

between the Polaroid lenses, we observe a *change in the direction of polarization*. The axis of the plane-polarized light exiting the sample is rotated counterclockwise from its orientation when it entered the sample. We infer that a rotation in the plane of plane-polarized light is produced by the sample (see Figure 8.17).

We can think of this phenomenon as involving the different interactions of right and left circularly polarized light with the chiral sample, causing a shift in the resultant vector. In essence, the light itself is *chiral*, consisting of right and left circularly polarized components. Just as a right hand fits differently into a right glove than into a left glove, right and left circularly polarized light interact differently with a chiral molecule. Only chiral substances rotate the plane of plane-polarized light. Materials that are not chiral, and even racemic mixtures of chiral compounds, give no rotation. Another important observation is that the *members of an enantiomeric pair rotate the plane of polarization by equal amounts but in opposite directions*. The magnitude and direction of rotation for a given material is as fundamental a property as its melting temperature or boiling temperature.

Pasteur was the first (in 1848) to isolate *both* enantiomers of a single substance. He noticed that a compound with which he was working, sodium ammonium tartrate (**8.5**), formed different types of crystals. He also saw that one type of crystal was a nonsuperimposable mirror image of the other type of crystal. Pasteur patiently separated the two types of crystals using tweezers. The two types of crystals had identical properties in most regards. However, they rotated the plane of plane-polarized light *equal amounts in opposite directions*. Pasteur had achieved the first **resolution** (separation into enantiomers) of a racemic mixture. Fortunately, we now have less tedious and more general methods (which we will discuss later) for performing resolutions.

$$Na^+ \quad {}^-O_2C-\underset{\substack{|\\ :\ddot{O}H}}{CH}-\underset{\substack{|\\ :\ddot{O}H}}{CH}-CO_2^- \quad NH_4^+$$

sodium
ammonium
tartrate
8.5

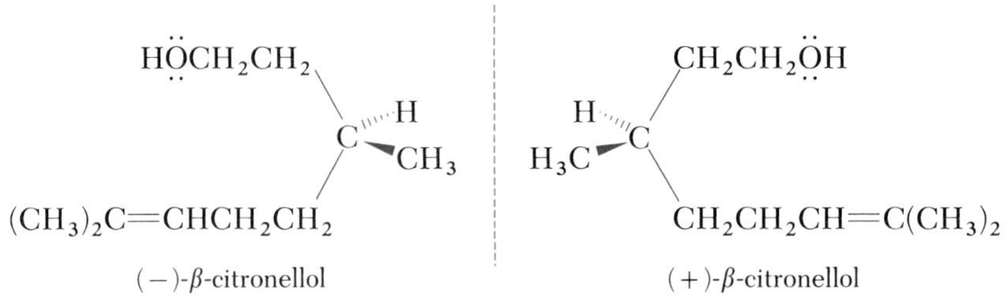

Figure 8.18 Enantiomers of *β*-citronellol with their rotations. The structure on the left rotates plane-polarized light in a counterclockwise direction, and that on the right rotates plane-polarized light in a clockwise direction. The notations (*d*) and (*l*) are sometimes used instead of (+) and (−).

$HOCH_2CH_2$ — C(H)(CH_3) — $(CH_3)_2C{=}CHCH_2CH_2$

(−)-*β*-citronellol

CH_2CH_2OH — C(H)(H_3C) — $CH_2CH_2CH{=}C(CH_3)_2$

(+)-*β*-citronellol

Materials that rotate the plane of plane-polarized light in a clockwise direction are called **dextrorotatory** or (+)-rotating. Materials that rotate the plane of plane-polarized light counterclockwise are referred to as **levorotatory** or (−)-rotating. One way of differentiating the two enantiomers of a chiral compound is by measuring the direction in which they rotate plane-polarized light. The enantiomers of *β*-citronellol and their rotations are shown in Figure 8.18.

The magnitude of the observed rotation depends on the number of molecules with which the light interacts on passing through the sample, and this is turn depends on the length of the tube, l, and the concentration, c, of the solution. In practice, we convert the measured rotation to what is known as a **specific rotation** using the equation:

$$\text{specific rotation of a solution of a pure substance} = [\alpha]_D^t = \frac{\alpha}{l \times c}$$

In the above equation, α refers to the experimentally measured rotation, c is the concentration of the sample in g/mL, and l is the length of the tube in decimeters. The superscript t refers to the temperature at which the measurement is made. The subscript D indicates the wavelength of light used; the most common light source is a sodium vapor light that emits light (the sodium D line) of wavelength 598 nm. When different samples are compared, it is important that the operating temperature and wavelength be the same. Workers in different laboratories may make measurements with different polarimeters or use different concentrations, but all should arrive at the same specific rotation by dividing their measured rotations by the product of l and c.

For the two *β*-citronellol enantiomers, the specific rotations using the D line at 20 °C in ethanol solution are +5.3° and −5.3°. If a different wavelength of light were used, different values for the specific rotation would be observed. (In fact, opposite *directions* of rotation could be found with different wavelengths. The standard notations (+) and (−) refer to the direction of rotation using the D line.)

At times we measure the specific rotation using a sample of a pure liquid rather than a solution. We then calculate the specific rotation using the formula:

$$\text{specific rotation of a pure liquid substance} = [\alpha]_D^t = \frac{\alpha}{l \times d}$$

Here, d refers to the density of the sample.

Table 8.1 Observed Specific Rotations of Some Naturally Occurring Chiral Molecules

Compound	Source	[α] at 20 °C, D line
2-methyl-1-butanol	fusel oil	−5.8°
β-citronellol	geranium	−5.3°
β-citronellol	citronella oil	+5.3°
α-terpineol	petitgrain oil	+100°
α-terpineol	longleaf pine oil	−100°
solanone	tobacco	+13.6°
alanine	biological peptides	+2.8°
lactic acid	blood	+2.6°
lactic acid	sour milk	−2.6°

The specific rotations for several naturally occurring chiral molecules are given in Table 8.1.

PROBLEM 8.4

Calculate the specific rotation using the data given for each of the following samples:

a. A rotation of −7.87° is observed for a 2.00 *M* solution of leucine ($(CH_3)_2CHCH_2CH(NH_2)COOH$) in 5.0 *N* hydrochloric acid using a cell 20.0 cm in length.

b. A rotation of −30.9° is observed for a 2.00 *M* solution of cholesterol (molecular weight 386.66) in chloroform using a cell 1.00 dm in length.

c. A rotation of +14.8° is observed for a liquid sample of pure 2-octanol in a cell 2.00 dm in length. The density of 2-octanol is 0.838 g/mL.

Steps to Solving the Problem

Solution to Problem 8.4a

1. Use the appropriate formula:

$$\text{specific rotation of a solution of a pure substance} = [\alpha]_D^t = \frac{\alpha}{l \times c}$$

2. Substitute the observed values with the appropriate units:

The cell length is 20.0 cm = *2.00 dm*.

The concentration is 2.00 *M* = 2(131.18 g)/1000 mL = *0.262 g/mL*.

The observed rotation is *−7.87°*.

3. Then calculate the specific rotation:

$$[\alpha] = (-7.87)/2(0.262) = -15.0^\circ$$

The rotation produced by a racemic mixture is zero. Any clockwise rotation produced by molecules of one enantiomer is exactly offset by the counterclockwise rotation produced by the other enantiomer. If a sample of one enantiomer is contaminated with even a small amount of the other enantiomer, its observed rotation is decreased. Once we have measured the optical rotation of a pure enantiomer, we can find the **optical purity** of any sample of that material. The optical purity is a measure of the excess of one enantiomer over the other in a sample of the substance. It is calculated using the equation shown below, where $[\alpha]$ is the specific rotation of the pure enantiomer and $[\alpha']$ is the specific rotation of the sample in question.

$$\text{optical purity (as a percentage)} = 100([\alpha']/[\alpha])$$

PROBLEM 8.5 Remembering that a racemic mixture has zero rotation and 0% optical purity for each enantiomer, calculate the optical purity of each of the following:

a. β-citronellol that exhibits a specific rotation of $-1.4°$
b. lactic acid that exhibits a specific rotation of $+0.4°$
c. 2-methyl-1-butanol that exhibits a specific rotation of $-5.2°$

Steps to Solving the Problem

Solution to Problem 8.5a

1. Look up the specific rotation of a pure enantiomer of β-citronellol. The specific rotation of pure levorotatory β-citronellol is $-5.3°$.
2. Calculate the optical purity of the sample in question using the appropriate formula:

$$\% \text{ optical purity} = 100(-1.4°/-5.3°) = 26.4\%$$

This tells us that the sample is 73.6% *racemic* (100% − 26.4%). Overall there is an excess of levorotatory enantiomer; specifically, 37% is dextrorotatory and 63% is levorotatory. The optical activity of a *portion* (37%) of the levorotatory enantiomer is compensated by the presence of an equal amount of the dextrorotatory enantiomer (37%).

In summary, handed molecules show an important difference in their interaction with plane-polarized light. Plane-polarized light is really a chiral probe for looking at chiral molecules. Analogies can help us understand this difference. For example, *screws* are chiral; they come in two varieties—right-handed screws (which screw in clockwise) and left-handed screws (which screw in counterclockwise). If we are foolish enough to use a hammer (the use of which is an achiral probe) to drive a screw into a board, we would find no difference between the two types of screw. However, if we use a screwdriver (the use of which is a chiral probe), we would need to turn it in opposite directions to drive the two different types of screw into the board. Extending our analogy, we can also anticipate that two enantiomers will behave differently toward another molecule that is already chiral. This behavior is observed, and indeed there are significant *chemical* differences between enantiomers, which we will consider in Section 8.10.

8.6 Absolute Configurations

Suppose that, like Pasteur, we separate a racemic mixture into its (+) and (−) rotating components. We label two bottles "+" and "−" and put the appropriate sample into each bottle. We diagram the two possible molecular structures of the enantiomers and label them I and II. We know that bottle labeled "+" contains only molecules of one type, corresponding to either structure I or structure II. But which sample is structure I and which is structure II? The question is a very important one if we wish to know which type of molecule we are working with when using a particular (+) or (−) rotating sample.

How is it possible to determine which structure (I or II) produces dextrorotatory behavior and which produces levorotatory behavior? Until 1951 there was no good answer to this type of question. Chemists were only able to group molecules that were inferred to have the same **relative configuration** because of the ways in which they had been prepared. By the *configuration* of a molecule we mean the spatial arrangement of the atoms that makes it different from any other stereoisomer. In analogy, if we placed a ring on a finger of someone's hand, we might say that the hand has the same relative configuration before and after having the ring placed on it.

Continuing our hand analogy, suppose we were to put the ring on someone's hand in the dark. Unless we examined the hand by touch, we wouldn't know if it had been the left hand or the right hand. That is, we wouldn't know the **absolute configuration** of the hand. This was the situation in which chemists found themselves until 1951. They had no way to determine the absolute configuration of any given enantiomer. However, they could relate configurations of different molecules by taking note of the way in which they had been prepared.

Consider now the concept of relative configuration. Look at the reaction of 2-methyl-1-butanol with an oxidizing agent (CrO_3/H_2SO_4) to produce 2-methylbutanoic acid; this reaction was previously shown in Figure 8.11 and appears again in Figure 8.19. We see that the $-CH_2OH$ group has been converted to the $-COOH$ function. No bonds to the stereogenic carbon atom have been affected, consequently this oxidation does not alter the steric relationship of the four groups about the stereogenic center. *The reactant and the product accordingly have the same relative configurations;* they have similar substituents situated similarly in space.

Experimentally, we find that if we begin with (−)-2-methyl-1-butanol, it is oxidized to (+)-2-methylbutanoic acid. We can thus *infer* that (−)-2-methyl-1-butanol and (+)-2-methylbutanoic acid must have the same relative configuration about their stereogenic centers. Although one compound is dextrorotatory and one levorotatory, we nevertheless must conclude that they have the same *relative* configuration. *In general, if no bonds to a stereogenic center are broken, then we can always correlate the relative configurations of the reactant and product.*

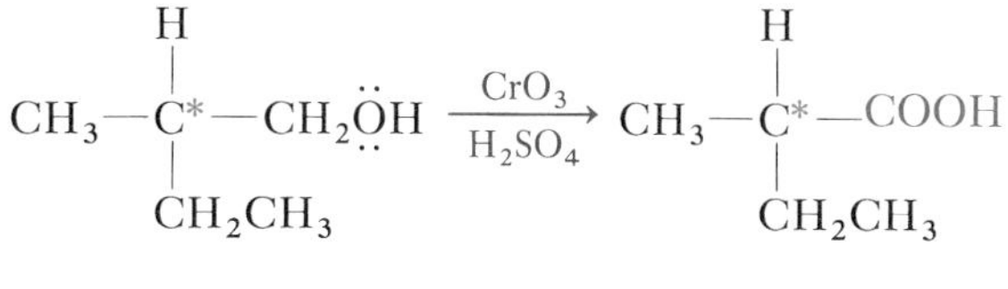

$$CH_3-\overset{\displaystyle H}{\underset{\displaystyle CH_2CH_3}{\overset{|}{\underset{|}{C^*}}}}-CH_2\ddot{\underset{\cdot\cdot}{O}}H \xrightarrow[H_2SO_4]{CrO_3} CH_3-\overset{\displaystyle H}{\underset{\displaystyle CH_2CH_3}{\overset{|}{\underset{|}{C^*}}}}-COOH$$

Figure 8.19 Oxidation of 2-methyl-1-butanol. The stereogenic carbon atom is indicated by the asterisk (*). No bonds are broken to the stereogenic center, therefore the product must have the same *relative configuration* about the stereogenic center as the starting material.

In spite of this knowledge, the problem of assigning *absolute configurations* remains. We do not know which of the structures shown in Figure 8.11 actually correspond to the (+) and (−) enantiomers.

X-Ray diffraction studies provide the means of associating an absolute configuration with a given sample. The first application of this technique to a study of enantiomers was made in 1951. In X-ray diffraction, a crystal of the sample to be studied is irradiated with X-rays, and a photographic film or other detector surrounding the sample records the diffraction pattern produced by the scattered X-rays. Using some rather complex mathematical calculations, it is possible to work backwards from the diffraction pattern to the actual three-dimensional structure of the sample molecule. This technique gives the absolute configuration of the sample. Once we know the absolute configuration of *one* compound, we can infer the absolute configuration of all substances of the same relative configuration. Through this approach it can be shown that (−)-2-methyl-1-butanol and (+)-2-methylbutanoic acid have the structures shown on the left side of Figure 8.11.

8.7 Representations of Optical Isomers

We can always see the detailed stereochemical nature of molecules by using molecular models. However, molecular models are not always convenient for the communication of information. Conventions have been developed to represent stereochemical features simply in two-dimensional drawings. By following these conventions we can deal with stereochemistry without having great artistic skills for drawing three-dimensional molecules.

In Chapter 2 we introduced several structural representations of this type. One approach is to use *wedge* structures. A solid wedge indicates a bond directed toward the viewer from the plane of the paper, while a broken wedge represents a bond directed away from the viewer, behind the plane of the paper. Bonds shown by simple solid lines are understood to lie in the plane of the paper. Figure 8.20 shows wedge representations of several views of one enantiomer of 2-butanol, along with molecular models of each view.

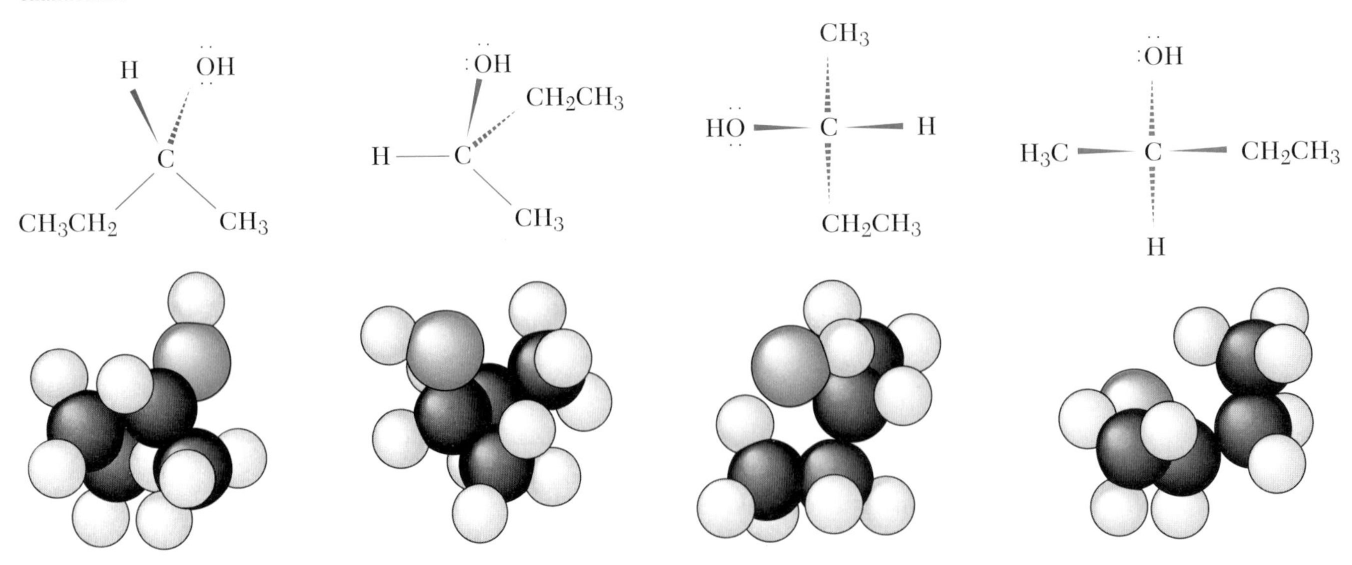

Figure 8.20 Wedge representation and the corresponding molecular models of one enantiomer of 2-butanol. Each structure represents a different view of the same enantiomer.

Fischer projections (also discussed in Chapter 2) provide another means of indicating absolute configuration, as shown in Figure 8.21.

The Fischer projection method and the wedge structure method are slight variations of the same approach to represent stereochemistry. A third two-dimensional representation of molecular geometry is the Newman projection. This method was also introduced in Chapter 2.

Let us examine the enantiomers of 2-butanol using Newman projections. If we sight along the C—H bond at the stereogenic center with the C toward the foreground and the H toward the background, we get different representations for each enantiomer, as shown in Figure 8.22.

We now introduce a useful idea: if we exchange *any* pair of groups at a stereogenic center, we *invert* its absolute configuration. Inspection of Figure 8.22 shows how the inversion works. The two structures differ *only* in having their methyl and hydroxyl groups switched. Thus one switch inverts the configuration. Further illustration is provided by Figure 8.23.

It follows of course that a *second* exchange takes us back to the original stereoisomer. These facts are useful when we must decide whether two different representations depict enantiomers or simply different views of the same molecule (see Problem 8.6).

Figure 8.21 Equivalent wedge and Fischer projections of one enantiomer of 2-butanol. The stereogenic carbon is not shown in a Fischer projection—it is understood to be at the center of the cross. The horizontal bonds are understood to come up from the plane of the paper and the vertical bonds to go behind the plane of the paper.

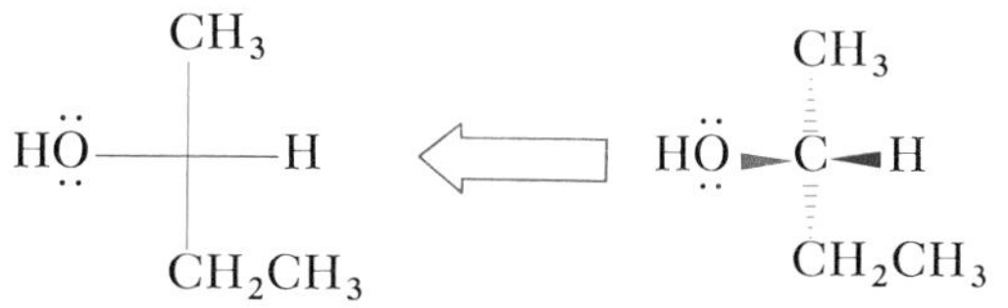

Figure 8.22 Newman projections showing absolute configurations of the enantiomers of 2-butanol. Each enantiomer is viewed along the carbon-hydrogen bond at the stereogenic carbon.

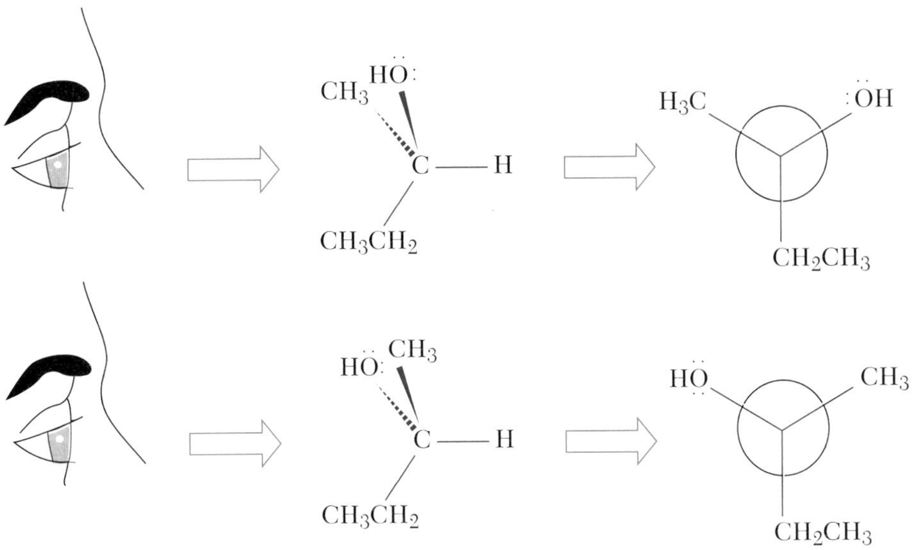

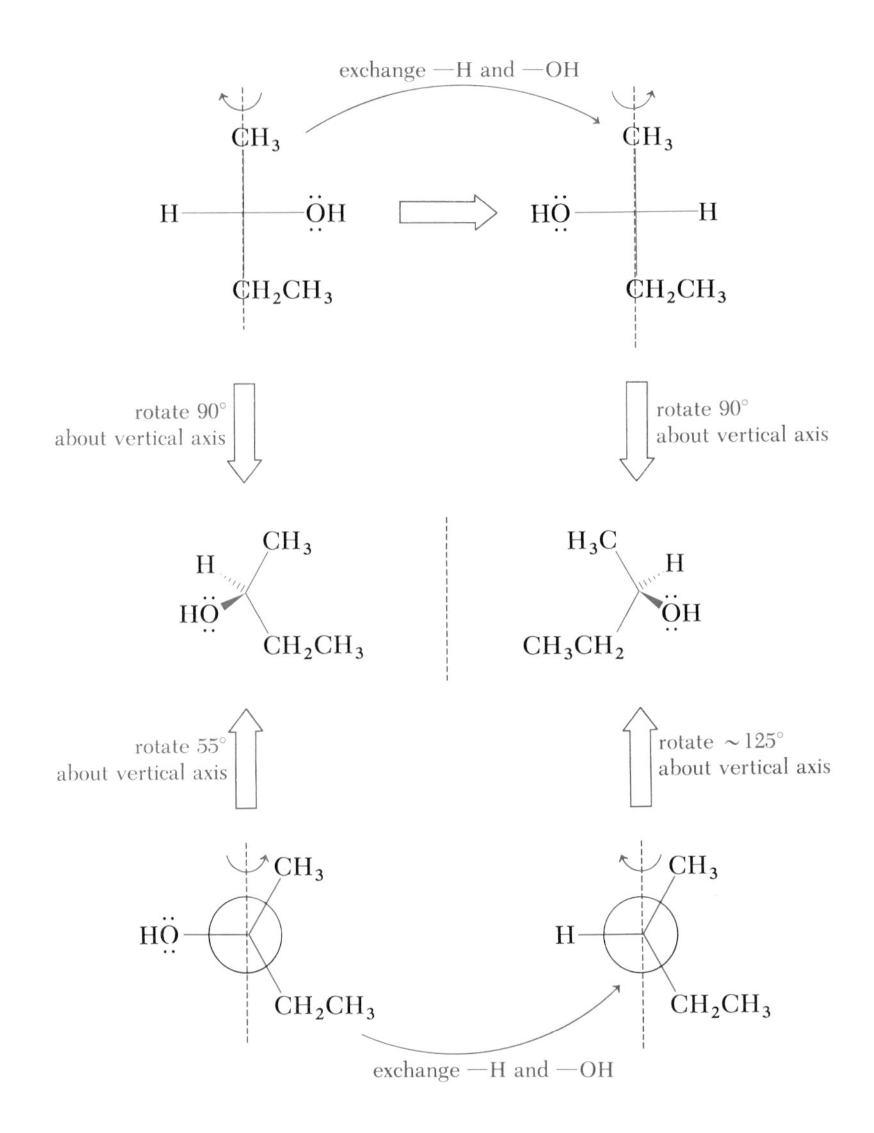

Figure 8.23 Exchange of two groups at a stereogenic center. If *any* two groups are exchanged at a stereogenic center, the absolute configuration at that center is inverted. All the structures shown on the right are enantiomers of those shown on the left.

PROBLEM 8.6 Tell whether each of the structural pairs shown below represents enantiomers or identical structures.

a.

CH_3 / H—C—Br: / CH_2CH_3 and CH_2CH_3 / :Br—C—H / CH_3

b.

CH_3, H, $CH_2{=}CH$, :I: and H / :I—C—$CH{=}CH_2$ / CH_3

c. $CH_2{=}CH$–C(:ÖH)(H)–CH_2CH_3 and $CH_2{=}CH$–C(H)(ÖH)(CH_2CH_3)

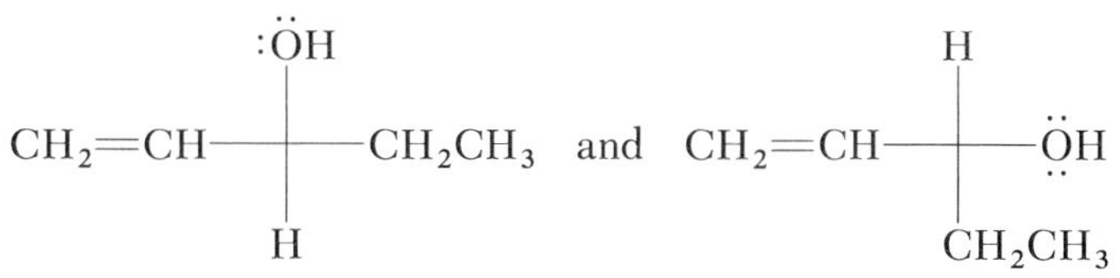

d. CH_3, $(CH_3)_2CH$, :Br:, H (wedge-dash structure) and CH_3–C(:Br:)(H)–$CH(CH_3)_2$

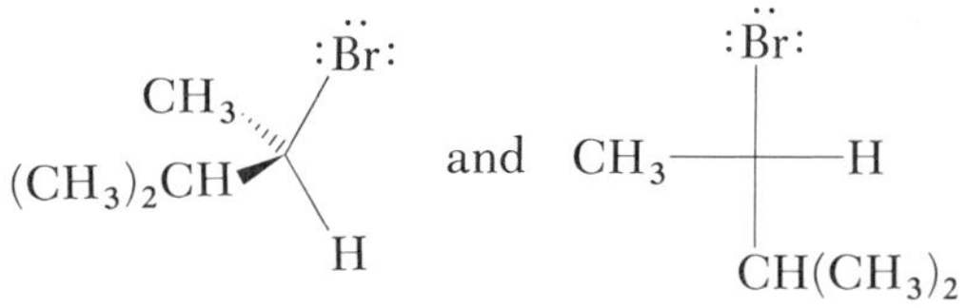

Steps to Solving the Problem

Solution to Problem 8.6a

1. We must look at the process of converting one structure into the other, so we switch groups on one structure until it matches the alternative structure. If an *even* number of switches are required, the two structures have the same configuration. If an *odd* number of switches are required, the two structures are of opposite configuration.
2. Consider the structure shown on the left. If we switch *any* two groups, we invert its configuration. Suppose we switch the H and the Br in this structure:

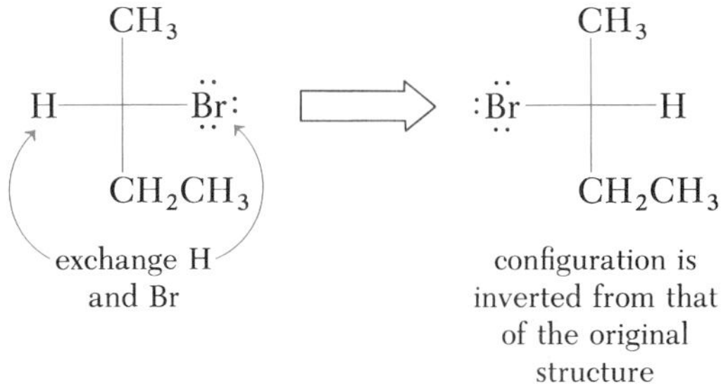

CH_3 / H — Br: / CH_2CH_3 ⇨ CH_3 / :Br — H / CH_2CH_3

exchange H and Br

configuration is inverted from that of the original structure

3. Continue switching two groups at a time *until* we generate the structure given on the right in the problem. If we now switch the ethyl and methyl groups, we arrive at the alternative structure given in the problem.

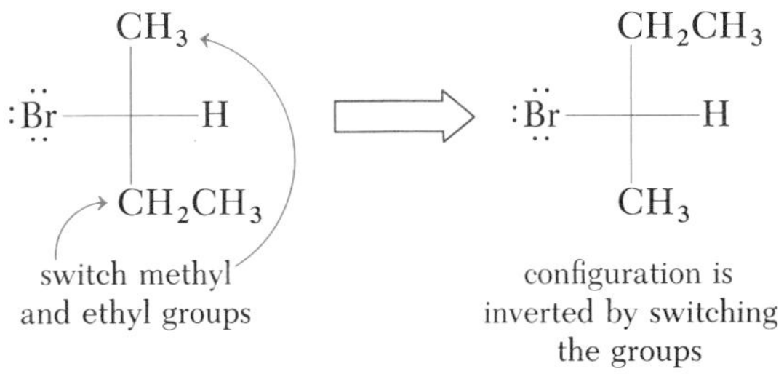

CH_3 / :Br — H / CH_2CH_3 ⇨ CH_2CH_3 / :Br — H / CH_3

switch methyl and ethyl groups

configuration is inverted by switching the groups

4. How many switches were required for this interconversion? *Two* switches were required to arrive at the desired structure, so the two structures have the *same* absolute configuration. The two structures shown are therefore different views of the same enantiomer.

Figure 8.24 Wedge and Fischer projection representations of one particular isomer of 2,3-butanediol. Both stereogenic centers in the Fischer projection are shown as crosses.

Figure 8.25 Wedge and Fischer projection representations of two isomers of 2,3-butanediol that are nonsuperimposable mirror images (enantiomers).

Figure 8.26 Interconversion of Newman and Fischer projections. The Fischer projection is a representation of an eclipsed conformation. Therefore, we first rotate the groups of the original Newman projection by 60° to get an eclipsed conformation. Then, we imagine the eclipsed Newman projection to be rotated backwards through 90°. The wedge structure (middle, right) depicts the view we now have of the molecule. The Fischer projection is a stylized representation of the wedge projection. At the bottom of the figure the same rotations are shown using space-filling models.

The Fischer projection method is particularly useful for depicting the geometry about several stereogenic centers in the same molecule. For example, the configuration of one particular isomer of 2,3-butanediol can be represented quite simply, as shown in Figure 8.24.

The configurations of two other isomer of 2,3-butanediol are represented by distinctly different Fischer projections, as shown in Figure 8.25.

These examples introduce us to the fact that more than two stereoisomers need to be considered when more than one stereogenic center is present. We will have much more to say about this later in the chapter.

The ability to interconvert Fischer, wedge, and Newman projections quickly and accurately is a useful skill. Consider the Newman projection shown in Figure 8.26, which depicts a staggered conformation of one particular stereoisomer of a molecule with two chiral centers. In order to convert this New-

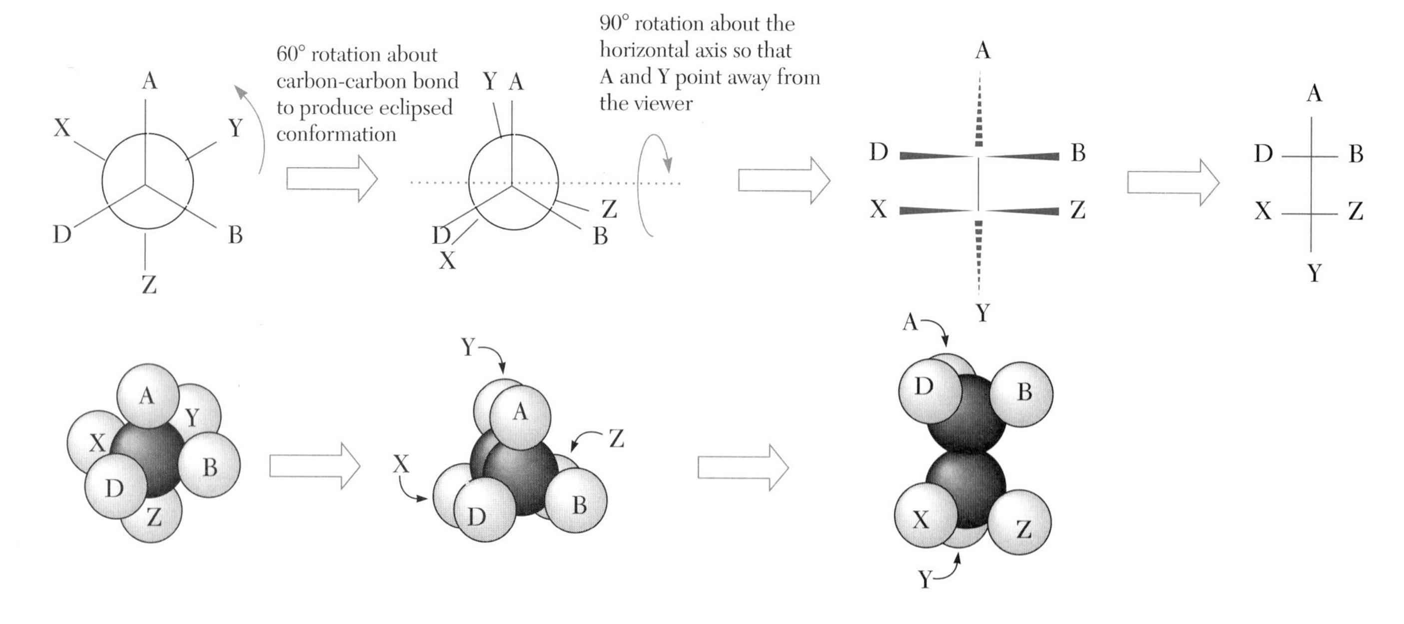

man projection to a Fischer projection, we must first rotate the groups so as to produce an *eclipsed* conformation.

We *then* imagine this eclipsed conformation to be rotated by 90° about a horizontal axis in the plane of the paper. In Figure 8.26 we see that this will leave the groups A and Y directed away from the viewer, and the other groups directed toward the viewer. We can then draw the Fischer projection directly, as shown.

PROBLEM 8.7 For each of the following Newman projections, provide a correct Fischer projection showing the configuration at each stereogenic center.

a. Newman projection: front carbon CH_3 (top), H, $\ddot{H\!O}$; rear carbon $:\ddot{Br}:$, CH_2CH_3, CH_3 (bottom) ⟹ Fischer projection: CH_3 (top), CH_3 (bottom)

b. Newman projection: front carbon H (top), $\ddot{O}H$, $H\ddot{O}$; rear carbon CH_3CH_2, CH_3, H (bottom) ⟹ Fischer projection: H (top), H (bottom)

c. Newman projection: front carbon H (top), $CH{=}CH_2$, H_3C; rear carbon H, $:\ddot{Cl}:$, $:\ddot{Cl}:$ (bottom) ⟹ Fischer projection: $:\ddot{Cl}:$ (top), $:\ddot{Cl}:$ (bottom)

To convert a Fischer projection into a Newman projection, these steps are reversed.

PROBLEM 8.8 For each of the following Fischer projections, provide a correct Newman projection (staggered conformation) showing the configuration at each stereogenic center.

a. Fischer projection: H (top); $CH_2{=}CH$ — C — $:\ddot{Cl}:$; H — C — $:\ddot{Br}:$; CH_3 (bottom) ⟹ Newman projection: $:\ddot{Cl}:$, H

b.

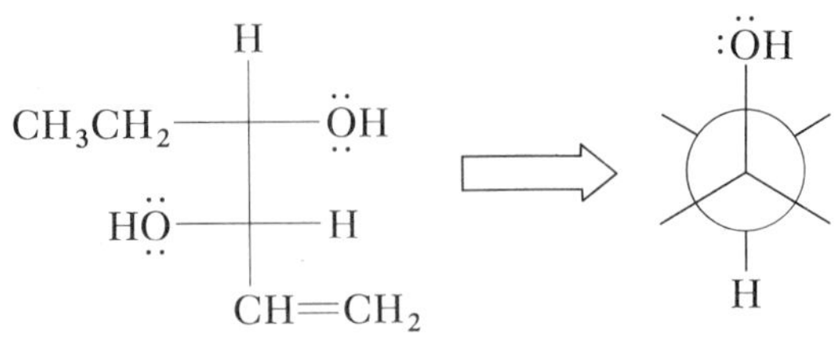

H

CH_3CH_2 — $\ddot{O}H$

$H\ddot{O}$ — H

$CH{=}CH_2$

⇨

:ÖH

H

c.

:ÖH

H — $CH(CH_3)_2$

H_3C — Br:

H

⇨

:ÖH

:Br:

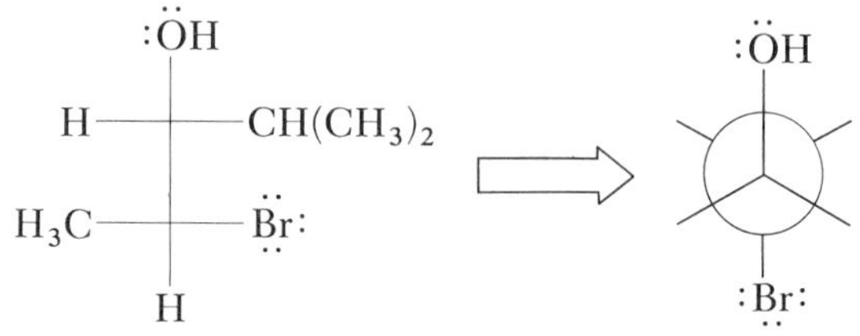

PROBLEM 8.9 For each of the structures shown in Problems 8.7 and 8.8, construct a stereochemically correct molecular model.

8.8 Nomenclature of Chiral Molecules

We have seen that we need to consider stereoisomeric structures when working with substances containing one or more stereogenic centers. An addition to the basic IUPAC name is necessary so that different stereoisomers can be given different names. This addition is known as a *stereochemical descriptor*. It is a letter (*R* or S) or combination of these letters that conveys to an informed reader knowledge of the absolute configuration about each stereogenic center.

The problem of naming chiral molecules can be likened to the problem of naming hands, gloves, or shoes as right or left. We all learn the rules for naming such objects at an early age and can quickly tell whether an object is left or is right. But suppose we had to describe the right/left naming system to someone who had no knowledge of it. We would need to formulate a set of rules that, when followed, lead to the correct right or left designation. Any such rules would need to contain the proviso that the item be looked at in a certain way. For example, we might specify that a hand be viewed "palm up" in order to determine right from left.

If we look at a *right hand* "palm up," our eyes move in a *clockwise* direction on passing from the tip of the smallest finger across the other fingertips to the thumb; they move *counterclockwise* if we are viewing a *left hand*. (We hope that the popularity of digital watches has not eliminated the concepts of clockwise and counterclockwise.) Thus we have a systematic procedure for assigning right or left to hands. Remember the need for viewing a hand in a particular way. If we forget the rule and look at a right hand "palm down," our eyes would travel counterclockwise in going from the small finger to the thumb, and we would get the wrong answer.

We use a similar method to assign stereochemical descriptors to molecules. We view the molecule in a certain manner and see if our eyes travel clockwise or counterclockwise on passing from one group to another. As in the above analogy, we must always be careful to view the molecule in a specified way.

The system we use is known as the **Cahn-Ingold-Prelog system.** It allows a unique designation to be given to each stereoisomer. The method involves the application of a series of purely arbitrary, human-made rules to obtain these designations. Thus the notation system bears no relationship to the direction or magnitude of rotation of the plane of plane-polarized light. It only provides a means for us to transmit information regarding absolute configurations about stereogenic centers. We can convey information without drawing the structures, as long as the sender and receiver of the information follow the same rules.

Determining the notation for the absolute configuration about a stereogenic center requires several steps. The first step involves the identification of the four unlike groups about the stereogenic center. Once we have identified these groups, we assign them *priorities* (1–4) following our arbitrary set of rules. We then view the stereogenic center such that the group of lowest priority points directly away from us. For example, we can use a Newman projection with the group of lowest priority (priority 4) pointing away from the viewer. We describe the stereogenic center as *R* if the remaining groups (1–3) have a *clockwise* sequence in the Newman projection, and we describe it as S if groups 1–3 have a *counterclockwise* sequence in the Newman projection (see Figure 8.27).

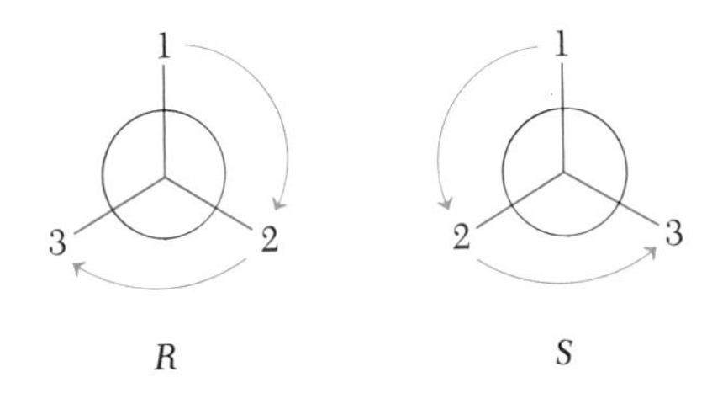

Figure 8.27 Assignment of configuration as *R* or S. The views shown represent the standard method for viewing a stereogenic center for the assignment of absolute configuration. The group of lowest priority (4) is directly behind the stereogenic center. The remaining groups have either a *clockwise* or *counterclockwise* sequence. If they are ordered in a *clockwise* direction, the stereogenic center is designated as *R*. If they are ordered in a *counterclockwise* direction, the stereogenic center is designated as S. *R* and S are derived from the Latin words for right (*rectus*) and left (*sinister*).

Priorities are assigned by noting the *atomic number* of the atoms bound directly to the stereogenic center. A sequence of priorities is established by assigning a higher priority to atoms with higher atomic numbers. Thus a bromine atom (atomic number 35) has a higher priority than an oxygen atom (atomic number 8). An oxygen atom in turn has a higher priority than a carbon atom (atomic number 6). Hydrogen (atomic number 1) has the lowest priority of any of the atoms. Isotopes are assigned priorities by atomic weight. Thus deuterium (^2H) has a higher priority than hydrogen (^1H).

When the stereogenic center is an atom other than carbon, it is possible for one of the attached groups to be an electron pair. A *pseudo atomic number* of zero is assigned to an electron pair.

Complications can arise. Often each of two (or more) groups about a stereogenic center are attached by the same type of atom. For example, in 2-butanol the stereogenic center is the second carbon atom of the chain. Attached to this atom are a methyl group and an ethyl group in addition to the hydroxyl and the hydrogen. Both of these alkyl groups begin with a carbon atom attached to the stereogenic center. Which group is assigned the higher priority? We differentiate them by looking at the *next* atoms in the groups, going away from the stereogenic center. For the methyl group, the atoms attached to the initial carbon are all hydrogens. With an ethyl group, one of these atoms is another carbon. The ethyl group is thus assigned a higher priority than the methyl group. The method of differentiation often referred to as "the point of first difference" is illustrated in Figure 8.28.

Sometimes we must look at atoms quite distant from the stereogenic center. For example, when we consider the stereogenic center in 5-dodecanol, we assign priorities to the two alkyl groups using the procedure indicated in Figure 8.29.

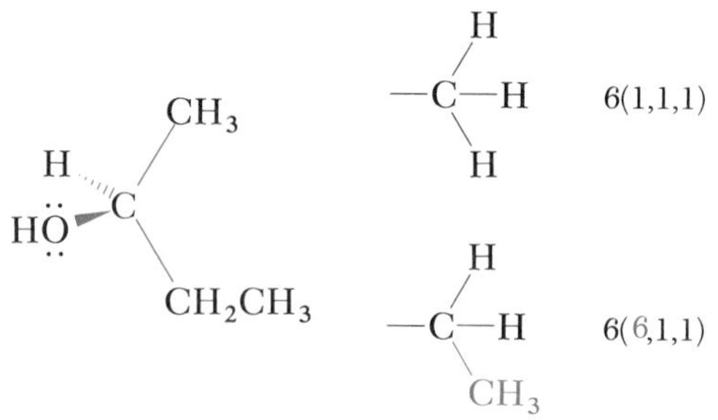

Figure 8.28 Assigning priorities to methyl and ethyl groups. The sets of numbers listed after the alkyl structures indicate the atomic numbers of the atoms connected to the stereogenic center. The first number is 6 for both groups. The numbers in parentheses indicate the subsequent atoms attached to the initial atom. For the methyl group, three hydrogens are indicated by (1,1,1). A carbon and two hydrogens (6,1,1) are attached to the ethyl group. The point of first difference determines the priority—here the second carbon atom(6) of the ethyl group gives that group the higher priority.

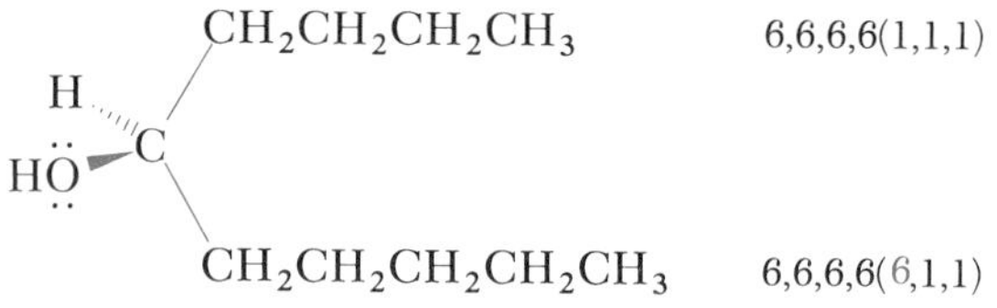

Figure 8.29 Assignment of priorities to *n*-butyl and *n*-pentyl groups. The two groups have the same designation through the first four carbons. The first point of difference occurs with atoms attached to the fourth carbon. The *n*-pentyl group is assigned the higher priority.

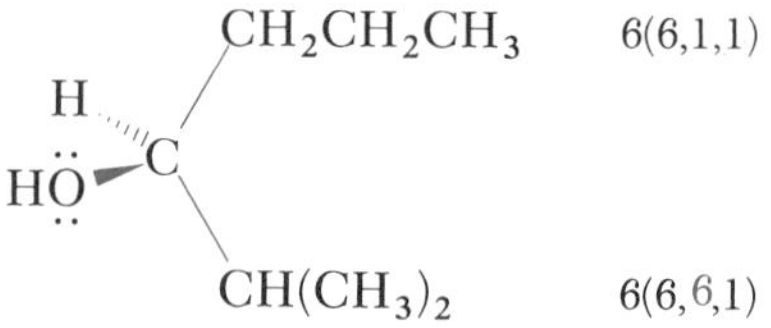

Figure 8.30 Assigning priorities to *n*-propyl and isopropyl groups. For each group, the first atom connected to the stereogenic center is carbon. *One* carbon and *two* hydrogen atoms are connected to the first carbon of the *n*-propyl group (6(6,1,1)). However, the first carbon of the isopropyl group is attached to two carbons and one hydrogen (6(6,6,1)). We assign a higher priority to the group with the greater number of the higher atomic number atoms attached at the point of first difference. Thus the (6(6,6,1)) (isopropyl) group is assigned a higher priority than the (6(6,1,1)) (*n*-propyl) group.

We also need to consider groups that are branched. In 2-methyl-3-hexanol, for example, a branched alkyl group (isopropyl) is present at the stereogenic center. Our approach to assigning priorities is shown in Figure 8.30.

For the purpose of assigning configuration designations, a carbon atom that is involved in a double bond is treated as having multiple groups attached. For example, a C=Y group is treated as being CY_2. Consider, for example, the assignment priorities to the 1-penten-3-ol isomer shown in Figure 8.31.

Several multiply bonded groups are listed in Table 8.2 with their number sets for determining their relative priorities. From this table and our previous examples, we can establish the following relative priorities:

$$-CH=\ddot{O} > -CH_2\ddot{O}H > -C\equiv N: > -CH=\ddot{N}H > -C\equiv CH > -CH=CH_2 > -CH_2CH_3$$

A final point needs to be considered when assigning priorities to groups containing multiple bonds. Consider for example the group $-CH=CH_2$. Fol-

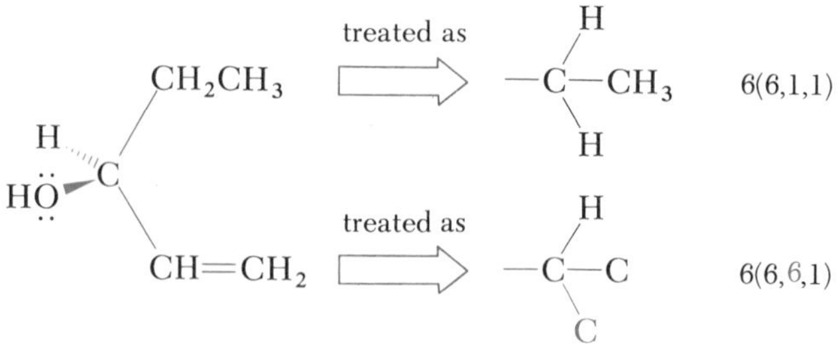

Figure 8.31 Assigning priorities to the groups about the stereogenic center of 1-penten-3-ol. The unsaturated two-carbon group has a higher priority than the saturated two-carbon group. We consider the unsaturated group as having *two* carbon atoms attached to the one linked immediately to the stereogenic center. The overall priorities assigned are thus: 1. —OH; 2. $-CH=CH_2$; 3. $-CH_2CH_3$; 4. —H.

Table 8.2 Analysis of Unsaturated Linkages for the Assignment of Cahn-Ingold-Prelog Priorities

Linkage	Number Set for the First Carbon Atom of the Group
$-CH{=}CH_2$	6(6,6,1)
$-C{\equiv}CH$	6(6,6,6)
$-C{\equiv}N:$	6(7,7,7)
$-CH{=}\ddot{\underset{..}{O}}$	6(8,8,1)
$-CH{=}\ddot{N}H$	6(7,7,1)

lowing the guidelines above (see Figure 8.31) this group is treated as:

$$\begin{array}{c} C \\ | \\ -C-H \\ | \\ C \end{array}$$

How do we proceed when there is also present a group such as an isopropyl group, $-CH(CH_3)_2$, that actually has two carbon atoms and a hydrogen bonded to carbon? In such instances, the multiply bonded group is assigned the higher priority, that is,

$$-CH{=}CH_2 > -CH(CH_3)_2$$

and similarly

$$-C{\equiv}CH > -C(CH_3)_3$$

We can use these rules to assign relative priorities to each of the groups about a stereogenic center. Consider now the application of these rules to the assignment of stereochemical descriptors.

The structure of one enantiomer of 2-methyl-3-hexanol is shown in Figure 8.32. The hydroxyl group is clearly of highest priority, and the hydrogen of lowest priority. The remaining two groups are an *n*-propyl and an isopropyl group. Applying the rules described earlier, we find the isopropyl group to be of higher priority than the *n*-propyl group.

Once priorities are assigned, we view the molecule with the group of lowest priority (hydrogen) pointing directly away from us, as shown in Figure 8.32.

If we count 1, 2, 3 from the group of priority 1, past the group of priority 2, to the group of priority 3, we are counting in a *counterclockwise* direction. We therefore refer to this molecule as having an S absolute configuration and name it (S)-2-methyl-3-hexanol.

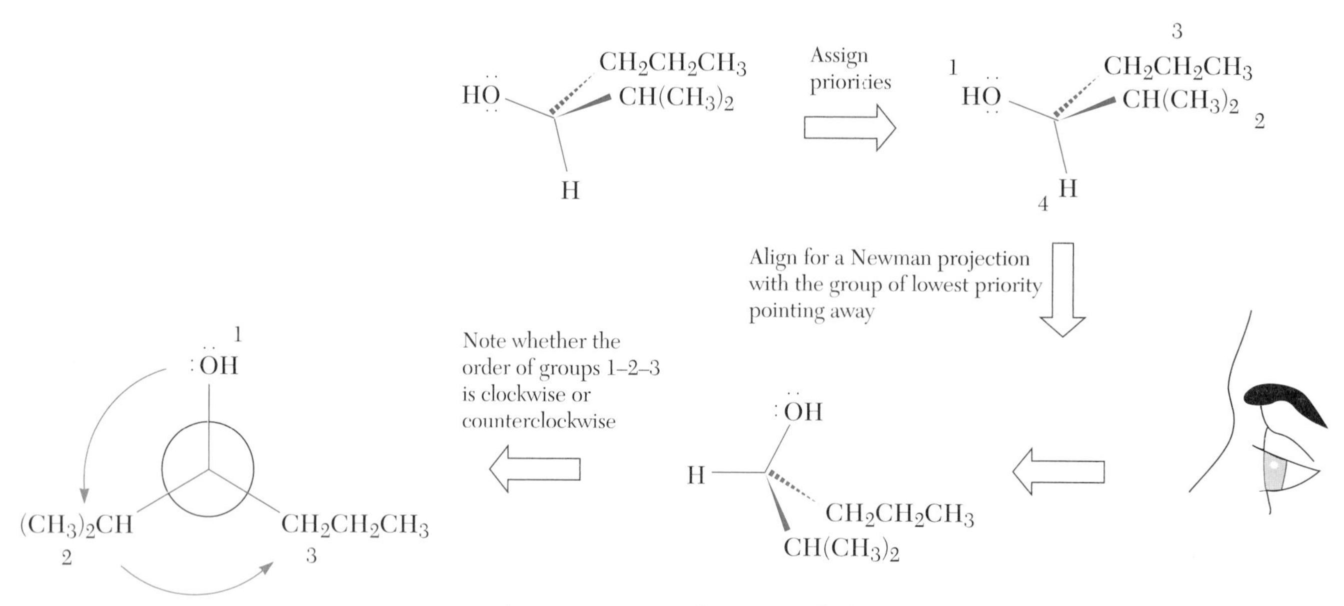

Figure 8.32 Assignment of absolute configuration for one enantiomer of 2-methyl-3-hexanol. The designation for the structure shown is S. The compound is named (S)-2-methyl-3-hexanol.

The enantiomer of (S)-2-methyl-3-hexanol is shown in Figure 8.33. When we view it at the stereogenic center with the hydrogen pointing directly away from us, we get a different Newman projection. This view is clearly different from that of its enantiomer. Looking from higher to lower priority groups, we count in a *clockwise* direction. We therefore refer to this molecule as having an *R* absolute configuration and name it (*R*)-2-methyl-3-hexanol.

The overall procedure for noting the absolute configuration of a stereogenic center in a given structure is summarized as:

1. Draw a proper three-dimensional representation of the molecule.

Figure 8.33 Comparison of the enantiomers of 2-methyl-3-hexanol. The Newman projections for the two enantiomers show opposite handedness in the orientations of groups.

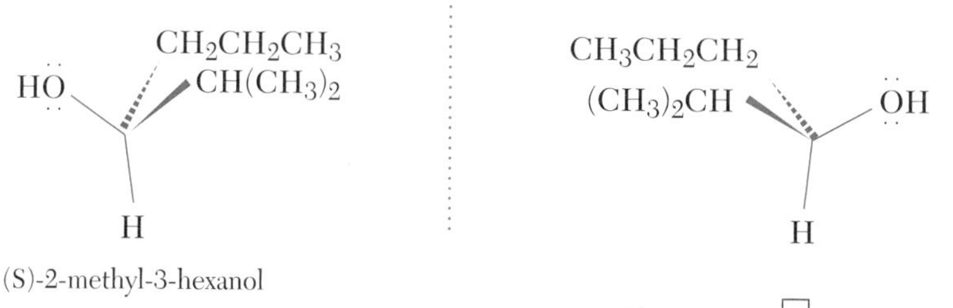

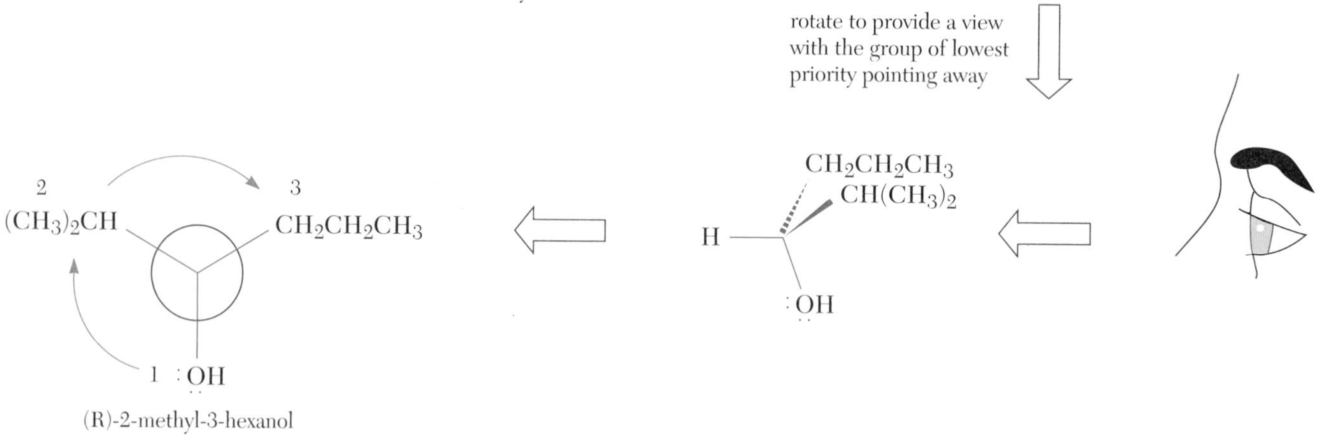

(S)-2-methyl-3-hexanol

rotate to provide a view with the group of lowest priority pointing away

(R)-2-methyl-3-hexanol

2. Assign priorities for the four groups attached to the stereogenic center according to the Cahn-Ingold-Prelog rules.
3. Orient the drawing to view it along the bond between the stereogenic center and the group of lowest priority. The group of lowest priority now points directly away from the viewer.
4. Note whether the order of groups 1–2–3 is clockwise or counterclockwise.
5. If it is clockwise, the stereogenic center is *R*. If it is counterclockwise, the stereogenic center is S.

PROBLEM 8.10 Give the proper designation (*R* or S) for the stereogenic center in each of the following molecules:

a. 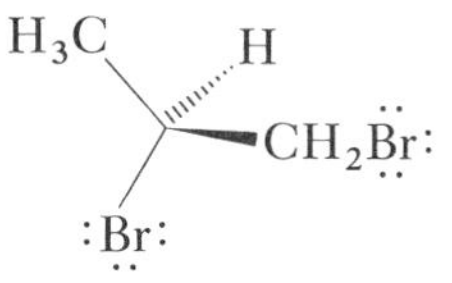 H_3C, H, CH_2Br, :Br:

b. 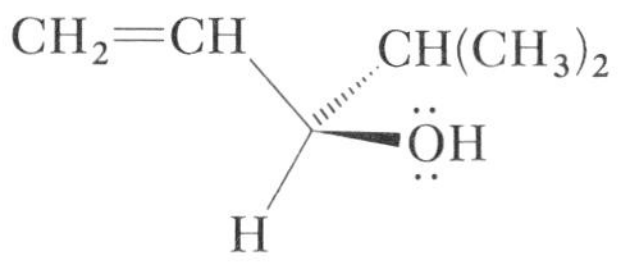 $CH_2{=}CH$, $CH(CH_3)_2$, OH, H

c. 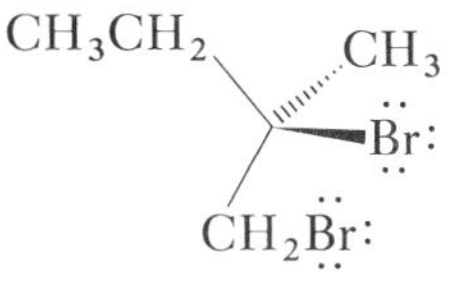 CH_3CH_2, CH_3, Br, CH_2Br

d. 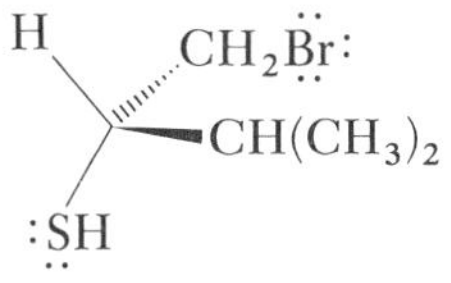 H, CH_2Br, $CH(CH_3)_2$, :SH

e. 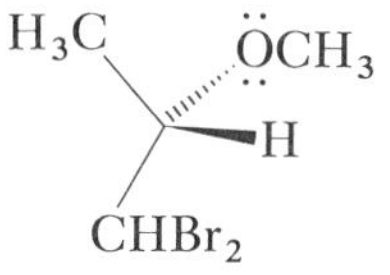 H_3C, OCH_3, H, $CHBr_2$

Steps to Solving the Problem

Solution to Problem 8.10a

1. Assign priorities to the groups attached to the stereogenic center. Since —Br is the highest atomic number atom attached, we assign it priority 1. The methyl group would be described as 6(1,1,1) and the bromomethyl group as 6(35,1,1). Thus the bromomethyl group is assigned priority 2 and the methyl group priority 3. The hydrogen is the lowest priority group attached to the stereogenic center.
2. As the molecule is shown, the group of lowest priority is directed away from the viewer. Thus we can directly see the proper view for determining the absolute configuration designation. Looking along the carbon-hydrogen bond, we see the Newman projection given below.

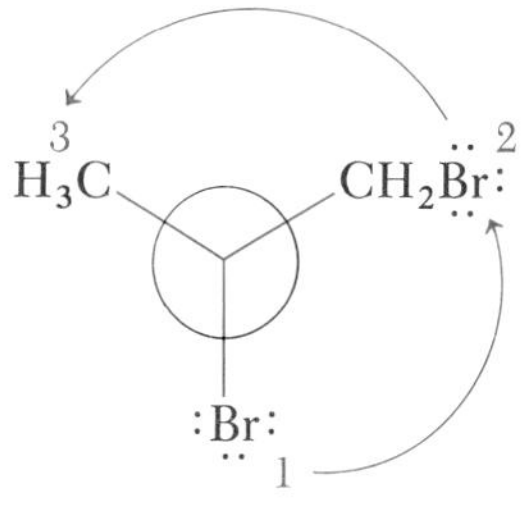

3 H_3C 2 CH_2Br :Br: 1

The direction 1–2–3 is counterclockwise, so we describe the stereogenic center as S.

Solution to Problem 8.10b

1. Again, start by assigning priorities to the groups attached at the stereogenic center. The hydroxyl group is priority 1, and hydrogen is priority 4. Of the two carbon functions attached at the stereogenic center, the $-CH{=}CH_2$ group is assigned a higher priority (2) than the isopropyl group (3).
2. We must now set up the molecule to view it from the standard direction, since the view given of the molecule is not the proper one for assigning the absolute configuration. To view the molecule properly, we could either rotate it in space until the hydrogen points away from us, or we could switch groups until a proper view is obtained. Let's consider using the second approach. If we make two switches, we will return to the original configuration:

$CH_2{=}CH$ $CH(CH_3)_2$ $\ddot{O}H$ H switch ⟹ $CH_2{=}CH$ H $\ddot{O}H$ $CH(CH_3)_2$ switch

inverted configuration

⇓

1 $H\ddot{O}$ H 2 $CH{=}CH_2$ 3 $CH(CH_3)_2$

original configuration

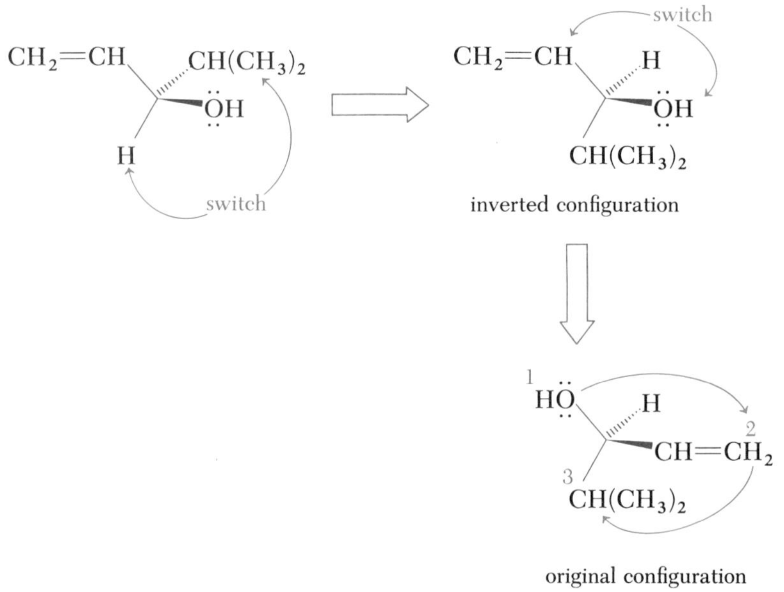

After two switches we return to the original configuration with a proper view for assigning the configuration designation.
3. We now need to consider the sequence of the groups about the stereogenic center. The direction for the sequence 1–2–3 is clockwise, so the designation for the stereogenic center should be *R*.

For molecules with more than one stereogenic center, the absolute configuration about *each* center must be determined. For example, consider the 2,3-butanediol isomer that was shown in Figure 8.24.

We need to look at each of the stereogenic centers in turn. We will arbitrarily choose to look first at the upper center of the molecule as shown in Figure 8.34.

We now need to consider the other stereogenic center in the molecule. The steps are summarized in Figure 8.35.

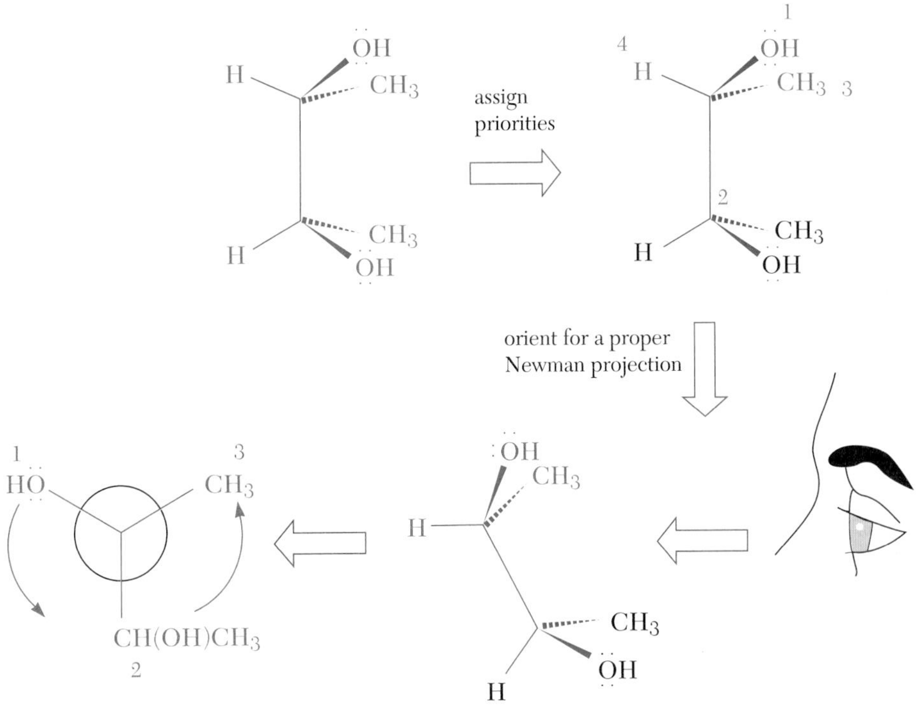

Figure 8.34 Absolute configuration of stereogenic centers in a particular stereoisomer of 2,3-butanediol. One stereogenic center is chosen arbitrarily as a starting point. Looking at the upper carbon atom (as drawn) we assign priorities and then orient the molecule for the proper viewing with a Newman projection. The group of priority 2 is the whole group at the bottom. For this particular stereogenic center we find the absolute configuration to be S.

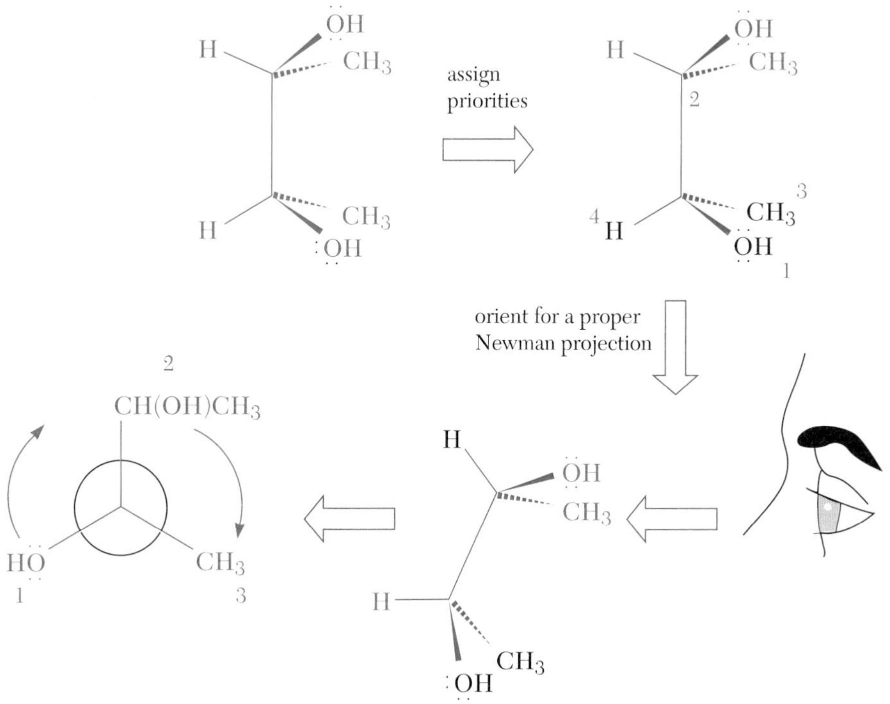

Figure 8.35 Absolute configuration of stereogenic centers in a particular stereoisomer of 2,3-butanediol (continued). We apply to the lower carbon atom the same procedure as was used with the upper carbon atom. We see a clockwise orientation of the groups about this stereogenic center. We thus designate it as *R*. The complete name of the molecule is then (2*S*,3*R*)-2,3-butanediol.

PROBLEM 8.11 The stereoisomer of 2,3-butanediol considered in Figures 8.34 and 8.35 could also be named as (2*R*,3*S*)-2,3-butanediol. Verify that both names describe the same material.

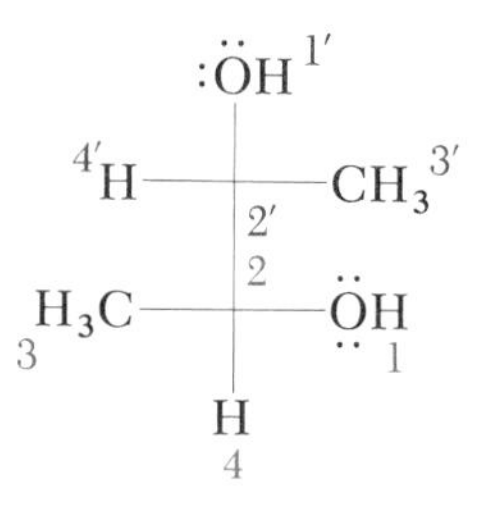

Figure 8.36 Fischer projection for one of the stereoisomers of 2,3-butanediol. The numbers 1,2,3,4 and 1′,2′,3′,4′ indicate the priorities for the lower and upper stereogenic centers, respectively. First look at the lower stereogenic center. Group 4 is in the vertical (down) position, so is behind the plane of the paper. Since we see a clockwise direction for the other three groups 1–2–3, we easily see that the lower stereogenic center has an *R* absolute configuration. However an assignment for the upper stereogenic center is not so straightforward, since the group of lowest priority (4′) is *not* pointing away from us.

It is not always necessary to use Newman projections to determine the absolute configurations of stereogenic centers. In fact, molecules containing several stereogenic centers often prove difficult to handle using Newman projections. Fischer projection or wedge projection drawings are often used in such cases. To assign *R* or S, we need to view the molecule with the group of lowest priority pointed away from us, for example, on one of the vertical positions of a Fischer projection. If the projection drawing indeed shows the group of lowest priority pointed away, our task in assigning *R* or S is relatively simple. But what should we do if the projection drawing does *not* show the group of lowest priority pointing away? There are in fact various ways to proceed. One is to identify the groups' priorities 1–2–3–4 in the normal way. If we count 1–2–3 in a clockwise direction and the group 4 is pointed *away* from us, the configuration is *R*, while if we count 1–2–3 in a clockwise direction and the group of lowest priority points *toward* us, the configuration is S.

Consider, for example, the Fischer projection in Figure 8.36. Look at the upper of the two stereogenic centers. The way the structure is drawn, the group of lowest priority is shown in a *horizontal* position, that is, pointing *toward* the viewer (keep this in mind when making a determination of *R* and S). We see that we count in a counterclockwise direction when going from group 1' to 2' then 3'. Thus this stereocenter has the *R* absolute configuration. Here (and in general), we must remember that the relationship between the *R* or S assignment and the clockwise or counterclockwise direction of counting 1–2–3 depends on whether group 4 points toward the viewer or away from the viewer. These rules are summarized in Table 8.3.

Since both stereogenic centers of the molecule in Figure 8.36 are *R*, the full name of the compound is (2*R*,3*R*)-2,3-butanediol.

Table 8.3 Relationship between (*R*)- and (*S*)-configuration and clockwise or counterclockwise arrangement of groups.

The relationship depends on the orientation of the group of lowest priority—whether it points toward the viewer or away from the viewer.

Position of group 4	1–2–3 Direction	Configuration
Away from viewer	Clockwise	*R*
Away from viewer	Counterclockwise	S
Toward viewer	Clockwise	S
Toward viewer	Counterclockwise	*R*

PROBLEM 8.12 Determine the (R,S)-configuration for each of the stereogenic centers in the naturally occurring carbohydrate ribose. The structure is shown below as a Fischer projection.

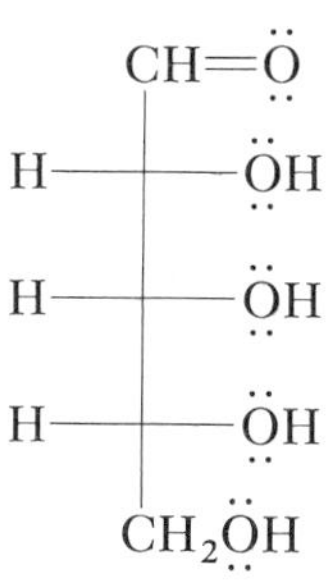

PROBLEM 8.13 Draw all possible valid Fischer projections for (R)-2-butanol. How many are there? Now flip each diagram by 180° (i.e., so that the top and bottom groups interchange and the two side groups interchange). Are the flipped projections still R?

Now rotate your original drawings (a) clockwise through 90° and (b) counter-clockwise through 90°. Do these new diagrams still represent (R)-2-butanol? Explain why or why not. What general conclusions can you make about the validity of flipping a Fischer projection through 90° and 180° to get a different view of the original stereoisomer?

8.9 Determining the Potential for Optical Activity

We would often like to be able to look at the structure of a molecule and quickly tell if it would or would not be optically active. We know that the ultimate criterion for a molecule to be optically active is for its structure to be nonsuperimposable on its mirror image. Unfortunately, it is not always easy for us to make this determination, particularly when we are presented with a two-dimensional representation of a structure. However, there are useful shortcuts that we can take.

The presence of a *single* stereogenic center signals that the molecule is not superimposable on its mirror image. It is therefore capable of optical activity. If more than one stereogenic center is present, the molecule may or may not be optically active. In general, molecules containing n stereogenic centers can have up to 2^n stereoisomers. For *most* compounds with n stereogenic centers, we do find the full 2^n stereoisomers, and each stereoisomer is optically active. However, for some such compounds, there may actually be fewer stereoisomers, and some of these may not be chiral.

Consider again the isomers of 2,3-butanediol. As we have seen, there are two stereogenic centers in this structure, so we calculate that there are a maximum of four stereoisomers. Actually, only three stereoisomers of 2,3-butanediol exist. The stereoisomer in Figures 8.34–8.35 is one that is optically inactive. This compound has one stereogenic carbon atom of (R)-configuration and one of (S)-configuration, and because identical groups are attached to the two carbon atoms, any clockwise rotation of plane-polarized light induced by one stereogenic center is cancelled by the other. There also exist a pair of enantiomers of 2,3-butanediol: (2R,3R)-2,3-butanediol and (2S,3S)-2,3-butanediol. Both of these isomers are optically active. In contrast, 2,3-pentanediol

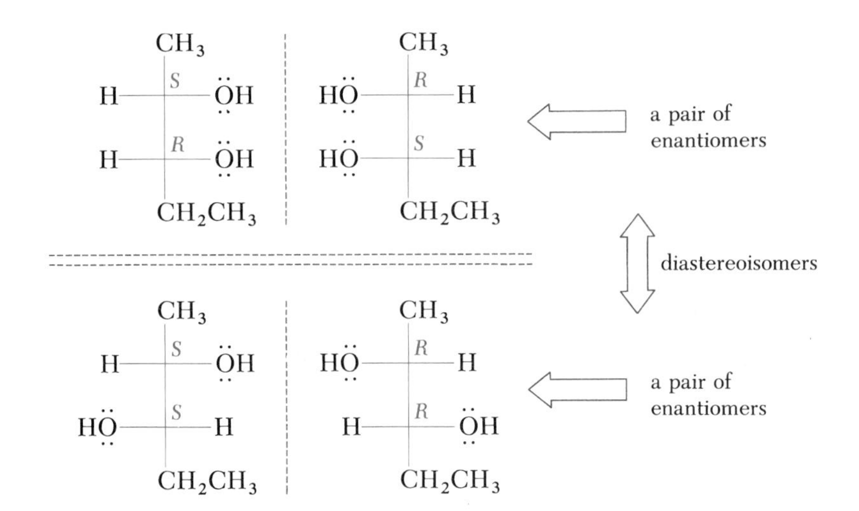

Figure 8.37 Stereoisomers of 2,3-pentanediol. The full $2^n(n = 2)$ stereoisomers are found. The upper two structures depict an enantiomeric pair, as do the lower pair. The upper pair are **diastereoisomers** of the lower pair. The stereoisomers containing one carbon atom of (R)- and one of (S)-configuration *are* optically active in this case. This is because the groups attached to the (R)-carbon are not exactly the same as those attached to the (S)-carbon.

has the full complement of four stereoisomers predicted by the 2^n formula and all are optically active. The two pairs of enantiomers constituting these stereoisomers are shown in Figure 8.37. All four of these structures are optically active. These structures illustrate the term **diastereoisomer** (also known as *diastereomer*). *Diastereoisomers are defined as stereoisomers that are not enantiomers.*

Symmetry properties can be used to recognize the potential for optical activity. When properly used, recognition of symmetry factors can greatly simplify looking for chirality in a molecule. For example, the presence of an internal **plane of symmetry** indicates that a molecule will be superimposable on its mirror image, and thereby optically inactive. The molecules illustrated in Figure 8.38 each have more than one stereogenic center, but they also have an internal plane of symmetry. None are optically active. We refer to such compounds as ***meso*-compounds.**

Figure 8.38 Examples of *meso*-compounds. Each compound shown has more than one stereogenic center. Each compound also has an internal plane of symmetry.

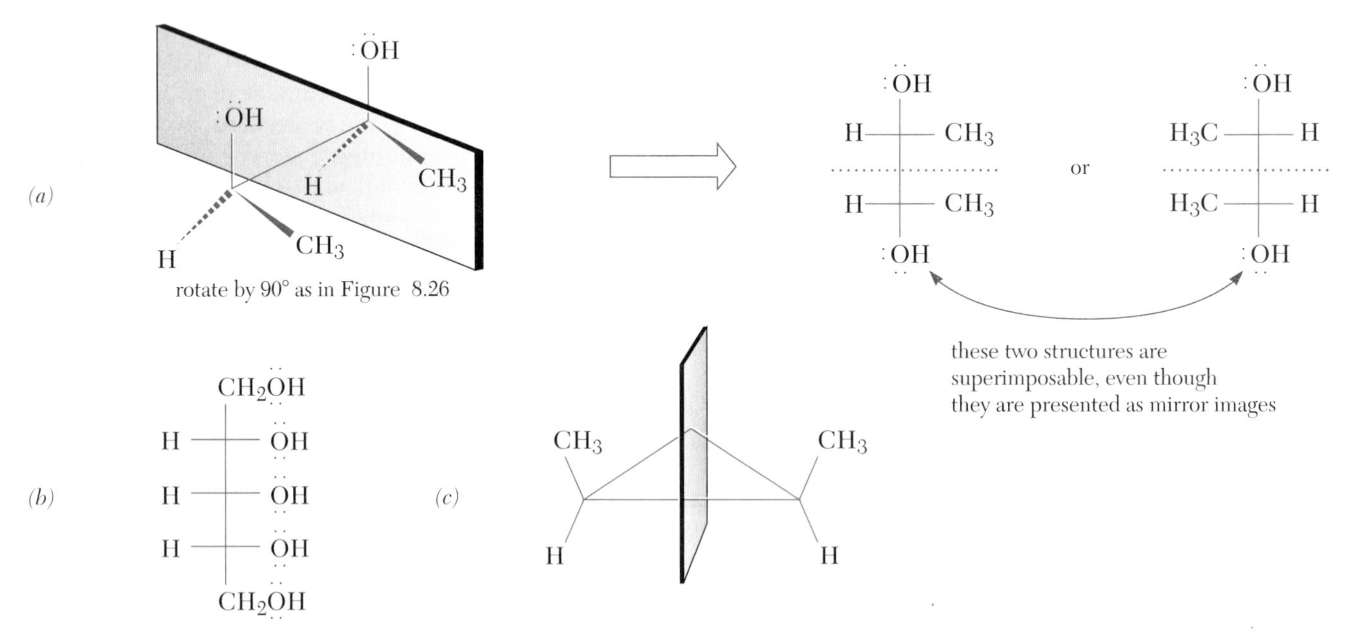

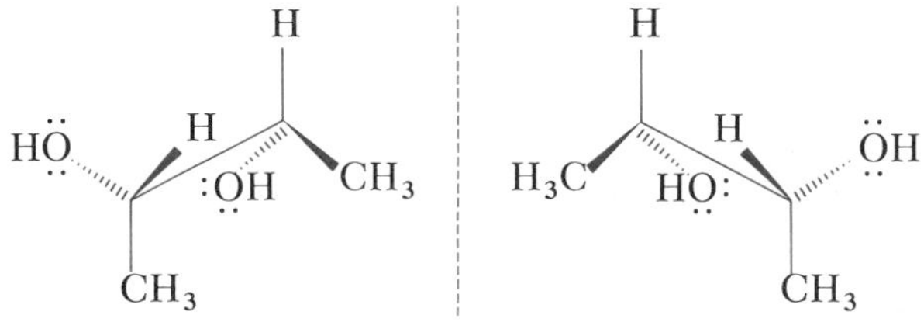

Figure 8.39 Conformational enantiomers of *meso*-2,3-butanediol. The two structures shown are mirror images that are not superimposable. However, equal amounts of the two are present in a sample of *meso*-2,3-butanediol.

Recognition of a plane of symmetry precludes the need to check for the superimposability of mirror images. However, caution should be exercised. Failure to observe an internal plane of symmetry may not mean that one does not exist—we may simply have overlooked it, or we may not be able to sée a plane of symmetry for the particular conformation we chose to view. For example, if we had chosen the conformation of *meso*-2,3-butanediol shown in Figure 8.39, we would not find a plane of symmetry. The conformation shown would be optically active, because it is not superimposable on its mirror image However, no sample of *meso*-2,3-butanediol that we encounter is ever optically active. In a collection of molecules of *meso*-2,3-butanediol there are equal numbers of each of the **conformational enantiomers.** The result is zero net optical rotation. If we find a plane of symmetry in *any* conformation of a molecule, it indicates that the molecule is optically inactive.

PROBLEM 8.14 For each of the following pairs of structures, tell which are ordinary enantiomers and which are conformational enantiomers.

a.

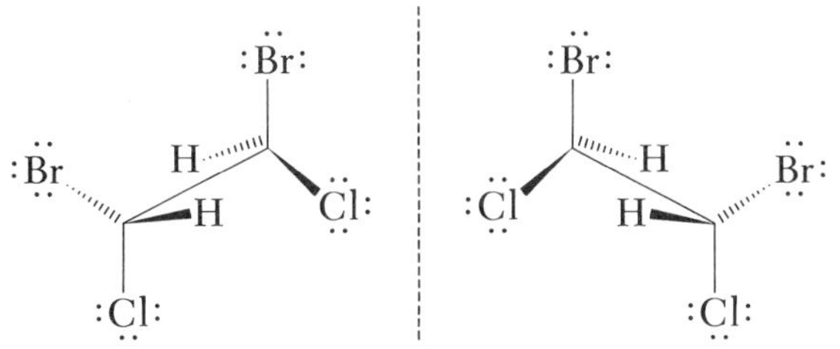

b.

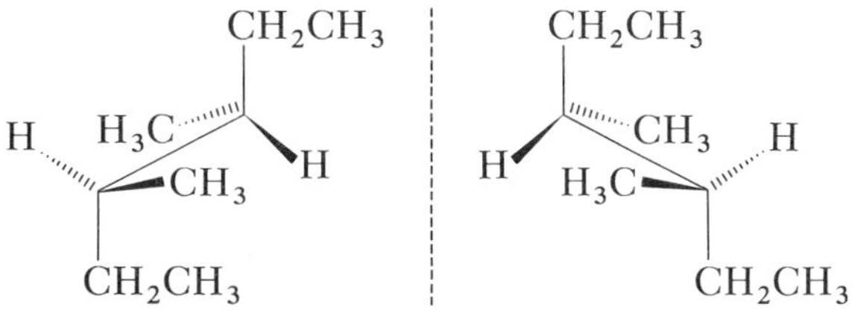

c.

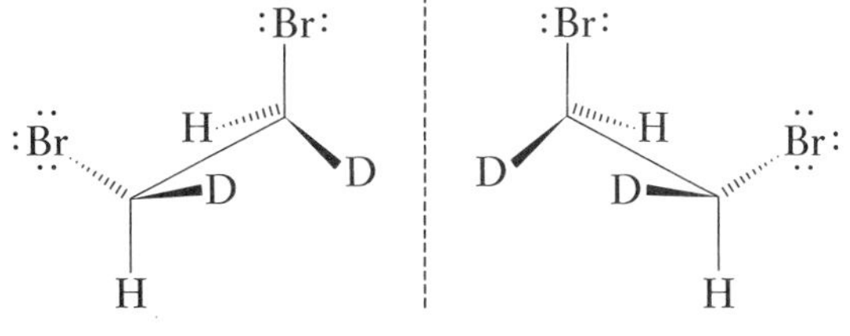

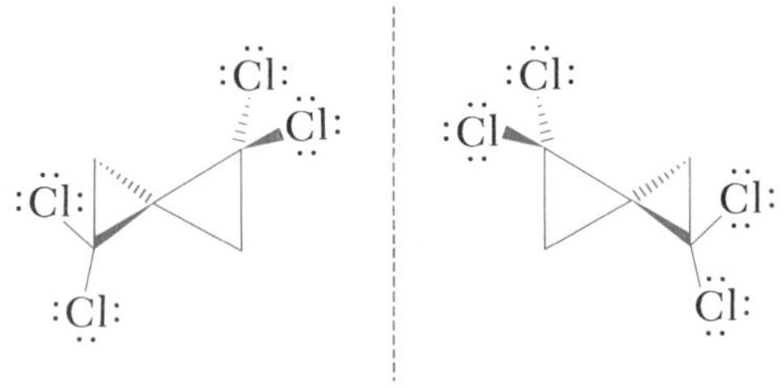

Figure 8.40 Molecules with molecular chirality. Although no stereogenic center is present, there is a handedness to each molecule that results in the nonsuperimposability of the mirror images.

As we have seen, the presence of a single stereogenic atomic center signals that a molecule is chiral. However, the absence of such a center does not necessarily eliminate the possibility of chirality. The *ultimate* criterion for chirality is nonsuperimposability on the mirror image. A molecule may possess a **molecular chirality** without having a stereogenic atomic center. An important structural type giving rise to an inherent chirality is the helix. Screws are chiral because they are helical, like a spiral staircase. On the molecular level, helical molecules are chiral, as we can see in helical double-stranded DNA. Chirality caused by a helical structure is seen in smaller molecules as well. A pair of enantiomers of this type (without a stereogenic atomic center) is illustrated in Figure 8.40.

8.10 Diastereoisomers and Resolution

In addition to physical differences between enantiomers, there are also chemical differences. However, these chemical differences are seen only in reactions with other chiral substances. An analogy with hands is again useful. The major difference between hands appears when they interact with other chiral objects, such as gloves. A right hand fits better into a right glove than into a left glove. In terms of molecules, the fit of one molecule with another is of great importance in determining how (and even *if*) reaction can occur. In Figure 8.41 we show in a rough way how only one enantiomer can fit with a specified template. The alternate enantiomer does not fit with the template.

This type of distinction between enantiomers is frequently found in biological systems. Two enantiomers may be supplied to an organism, but only one is used by it. The other enantiomer is ignored by the chiral biological reagents and is usually excreted unchanged.

Such differences appear in nonbiological systems as well. Consider a generalized reaction of both the dextrorotatory and levorotatory forms of an alcohol

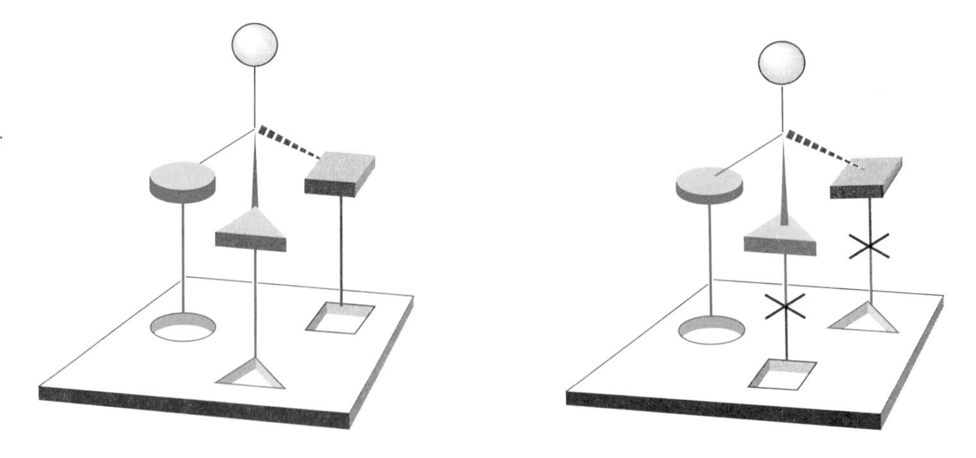

Figure 8.41 Fit of enantiomers with an ordered template. Only one of the models is able to match groups with the template. The other enantiomer cannot match groups with the template no matter how we rotate it or orient it in space.

Figure 8.42 Addition of a (+)-reagent to each of an enantiomeric pair of alcohols. The two reactions in general do *not* proceed at the same rate or produce the same yield. Moreover, while each reactant has one stereogenic center, there are two stereogenic centers in each product. These products are *not* enantiomers; they are diastereoisomers. The enantiomer of the product (+)-alcohol:(+)-reagent would be (−)-alcohol:(−)-reagent, but this species does not form in this reaction since no (−)-reagent is present.

$$(+)\text{-alcohol} + (+)\text{-reagent} \longrightarrow ((+)\text{-alcohol}:(+)\text{-reagent})$$

$$(-)\text{-alcohol} + (+)\text{-reagent} \longrightarrow ((-)\text{-alcohol}:(+)\text{-reagent})$$

with only the dextrorotatory form of a chiral reagent, as shown in Figure 8.42. The fit between the (+)-reagent and the alcohol is different with each of the enantiomers of the alcohol. This difference in fit leads to a rate difference for the two reactions.

Consider further the reaction pair shown in Figure 8.42. Each of the products contains two stereogenic centers. One stereogenic center is derived from the initial alcohol and one from the initial reagent. The two products are *diastereoisomers*, not enantiomers. One portion of each product may be thought of as being a mirror image of the corresponding portion of the other product. However, the entire molecules are not mirror images of each other—they are diastereoisomeric.

Again we can construct analogies using common chiral items to help us understand the molecular concept. We are interested in what happens when we combine two separately chiral entities into one structure. We once again call upon our hands to illustrate the concept. If we use our right hand to clasp the right hand of another person, we get a different combination (right-right) than if we use our right hand to clasp the other person's left hand (right-left). Furthermore, the two handclasps are *not* mirror images. They differ from each other in a way other than the way mirror images differ. (The mirror image of a right-right handclasp is a left-left handclasp.)

Except for the rotation of the plane of plane-polarized light and reactions with other chiral molecules, one enantiomer of a compound exhibits the same chemical and physical properties as the other. Diastereoisomers exhibit significantly different chemical and physical properties. An actual formation of diastereoisomers from a racemic alcohol is shown in Figure 8.43.

Diastereoisomeric relationships are possible whenever more than one stereogenic center is present in a molecule. Consider again the stereoisomers of 2,3-butanediol shown in Figure 8.44.

Each of the (+) and (−) rotating pure enantiomers (*A* and *B* in Figure 8.44) exhibits a melting temperature of 20 °C. A racemic mixture of these two enantiomers melts at 7.6 °C. Structure *C* has a melting temperature of 34.4 °C.

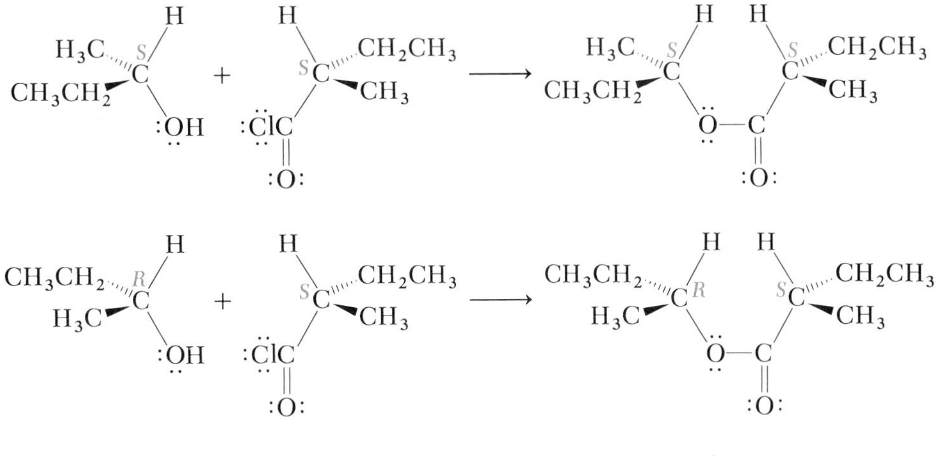

Figure 8.43 Formation of diastereoisomers from an enantiomeric pair of alcohols. The reaction shown here is that of an alcohol with an organic acid chloride to form an ester (similar to the formation of a phosphate ester as discussed in Chapter 6). Both the alcohol and the acid chloride contain stereogenic centers. The products each contain two stereogenic centers. Only one of these stereogenic centers is the same in the two products, which are therefore diastereoisomers rather than enantiomers.

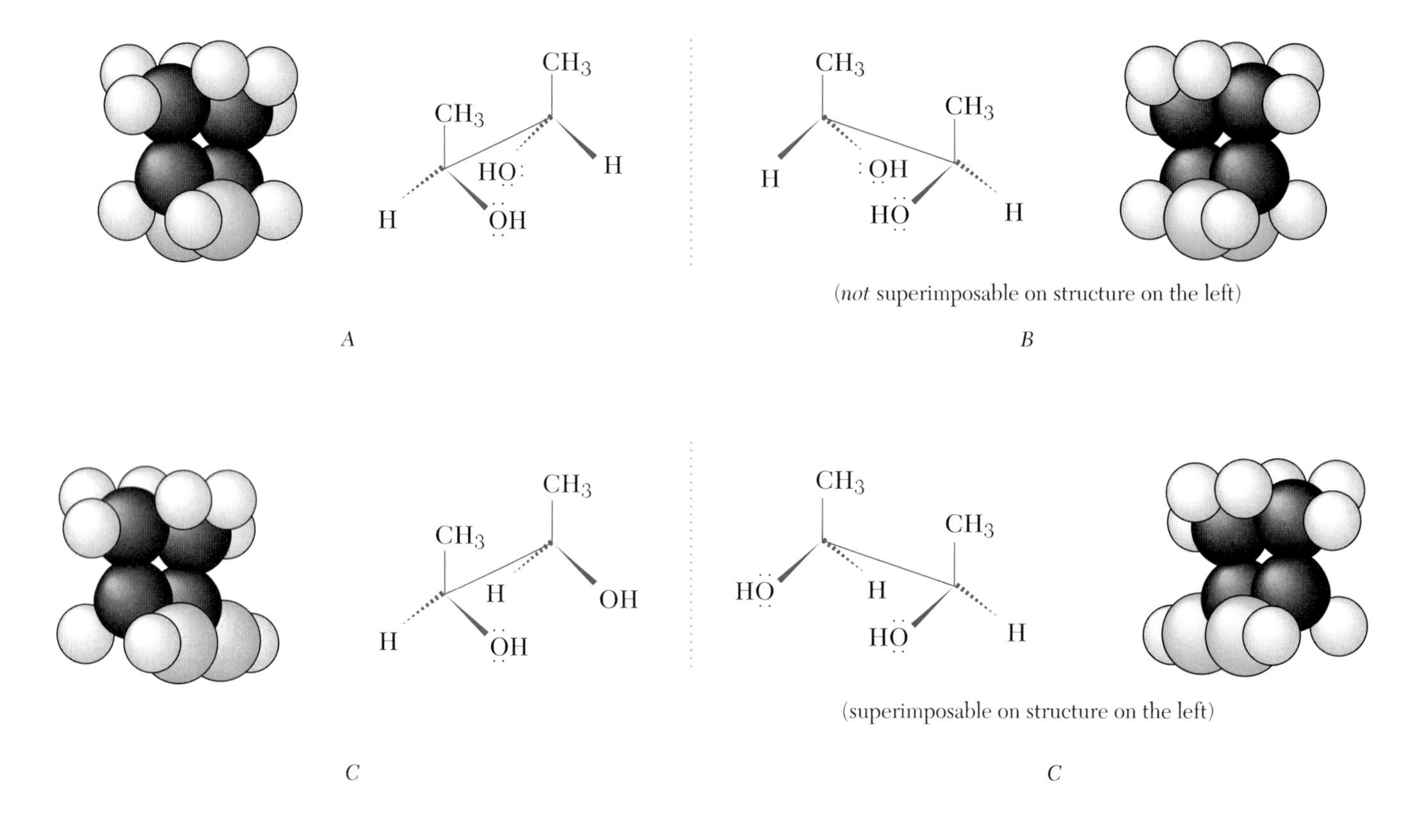

Figure 8.44 Stereoisomers of 2,3-butanediol. Structures *A* and *B* represent a pair of enantiomers. Structure *C* contains the same groups bound to each of the two stereogenic centers as do *A* and *B* (they all have the same connectivity), but it is not a mirror image of either. It represents a different structure, and it is a diastereoisomer of *A* and *B*. Structure *C* is superimposable on its mirror image (shown) and is therefore *not* optically active (also see earlier discussion).

The different properties of diastereoisomers turn out to be useful for the separation of enantiomers. If we perform a reaction on a racemic mixture with a suitable chiral reagent, diastereoisomers will be formed. For example, diastereoisomers are formed in the reaction of racemic 2-butanol with a single enantiomer of 2-methylbutanoyl chloride, as shown in Figure 8.43.

Once the diastereoisomers have been formed, we can use their different chemical and physical properties to separate them. Sometimes a solvent can be found in which one diastereoisomer is more highly soluble than the other. The less soluble diastereoisomer can then be isolated by precipitation and filtration.

We can also use other methods that are often more efficient than fractional crystallization for separating diastereoisomers. For example, we can often separate diastereoisomers by ordinary chromatographic procedures. Diastereoisomers in general have different interactions with even achiral materials. Suppose we dissolve a pair of diastereoisomers in some solvent. We then allow the solution to drip through a column of an insoluble solid such as alumina (Al_2O_3). The diastereoisomers interact differently with the alumina, one adsorbing to it more strongly than the other. The one that binds less strongly exits the column more quickly (using less solvent) than the one that bonds more strongly. The earliest volume of solvent coming through the column will contain one diastereoisomer. The other diastereoisomer will be in some later volume of solvent.

Once the diastereoisomers have been separated, a reversal of the formation reaction can be used to obtain the pure (+) and (−) rotating forms of the alcohol. (For the system shown in Figure 8.43, we would cleave the alcohol and acid portions of the ester using aqueous base. This reaction will be discussed

SPECIAL TOPIC

Biochemical Resolutions

Resolutions may be performed directly on racemic mixtures without the preliminary isolation of diastereoisomers. However, the enantiomers still need to interact with a chiral reagent. The catalysts for biological reactions (enzymes) are always chiral. Thus, we can at times use them to provide us with pure enantiomers directly from racemic mixtures.

An example of this technique is the selective oxidation of only one enantiomer of racemic *cis*-3-(2′-hydroxyethyl) cyclopentanol [we will refer to the two enantiomers as (±)A]. The enzyme catalyzing the oxidation is horse liver alcohol dehydrogenase (HLADH), with NAD^+ as the biological oxidizing agent. (We discussed NAD^+ as an oxidizing agent in the "Biological Oxidations" section in Chapter 5. We will consider it in more structural and chemical detail in Chapter 28.)

Both the NAD^+ and the enzyme are chiral species. The NAD^+ molecule in biological systems is a single stereoisomer containing eight stereogenic centers. The enzyme is made up of amino acids, each of which (except for achiral glycine) is present in only one stereoisomeric form. The chiral catalyst and oxidizing agent interact preferentially with *one* of the enantiomeric forms of the substrate (A). That form of the subtrate is oxidized much more rapidly than its enantiomer, as illustrated below.

NAD^+ + [(±)A] $\xrightarrow{\text{HLADH}}$ unreacted (+)A + B + NADH + H^+ + other products derived from B

The (−)A reacts rapidly and is converted to B and other related materials. The (+)A species, however, remains untouched and can be isolated as a pure enantiomer from the reaction mixture. In one sense this reaction is not a true resolution, as one of the original enantiomers is destroyed. The procedure is often called a *kinetic* resolution—one enantiomer reacts faster than the other.

in later chapters.) The separation of enantiomers by these approaches is again a resolution, but with more efficient techniques than Pasteur used.

An analogy of this resolution procedure with hands and gloves is again useful. A pile (racemic mixture) of unsorted gloves must be resolved into right and left forms. Each glove is fitted onto the right hand of a volunteer. Volunteers encountering an awkward fit put their gloves in box A, while those encountering a normal fit put them in box B. *Voilà*, the gloves are separated (resolved) into right and left forms. The separation is efficient. It is based on the different characteristics (the fit) when a chiral reagent (a right hand) interacts with each of a pair of enantiomers (a pair of gloves).

The optically active reagents used in resolutions often have biological origins, such as plants.

Summary

- The tetrahedral nature of bonding about carbon leads to the phenomenon of chirality in organic molecules. When four different groups are attached to a tetrahedrally bonded carbon atom, we say that the carbon atom is stereogenic.
- When a single stereogenic (chiral) carbon atom is present in a molecule, that molecule will exist in two enantiomeric forms, which are nonsuperimposable mirror images.
- Enantiomers exhibit identical physical and chemical properties, except for: (1) their interaction with plane-polarized light and (2) their interaction with other chiral molecules.
- Enantiomers will rotate the plane of polarization of plane-polarized light in equal amounts but in opposite directions.
- Because they fit differently with other chiral molecules, enantiomers will react with them at different rates.
- When more than one stereogenic center is present in a molecule, there may exist as many as 2^n optical isomers, where n is the number of stereogenic centers.
- Fewer stereoisomers than 2^n will exist if there is the possibility of particular symmetry in the structure. Stereoisomers exist as enantiomeric pairs and/or as *meso*-compounds, with the *meso*-compounds being optically inactive.
- Enantiomeric pairs and their diastereoisomeric *meso*-compounds have the same connectivity.
- Diastereoisomers exhibit different physical and chemical properties and may be differentiated by ordinary chemical and physical means.
- We have several methods of making two-dimensional representations of three-dimensional stereogenic centers. We can use these methods to deduce systematic designations for the absolute configuration about any given stereogenic center.

Terms to Remember

stereochemistry
isomer number
regioisomers
chiral
configuration
stereoisomer
stereogenic carbon atom
enantiomers
asymmetric
achiral
racemic mixture
plane-polarized light
optically active
electromagnetic radiation
polarizer
circularly polarized light
resolution
dextrorotatory
levorotatory
specific rotation
optical purity
relative configuration
absolute configuration
Cahn-Ingold-Prelog system
diastereoisomers
plane of symmetry
meso-compound
conformational enantiomers
molecular chirality

Additional Problems

8.15 Draw the structure of each of the following compounds, indicating any stereogenic centers that are present:
a. 2-bromobutane b. 2-methylcyclohexanol c. 3,4,6-octanetriol
d. 2,4-dibromopentane e. 2,3-dimethylbutane f. 1,2-cyclopentanediol
g. 1,3-cyclohexanediol h. 2,4-dibromo-3-ethylpentane

8.16 For each of the compounds listed in Problem 8.15, give the number of theoretically possible stereoisomers.

8.17 For each of the compounds listed in Problem 8.15, draw a clear stereochemical wedge structure for each of the stereoisomers.

8.18 For each of the structures in Problem 8.17, give the correct *R*,*S* designation for each stereogenic center.

8.19 Tell whether each of the compounds in Problem 8.18 is a *meso*-compound.

8.20 Draw a clear stereochemical wedge structure for each of the following:
a. (*R*)-2-hexanol b. (*S*)-2-methyl-3-hexanol
c. (3*R*,5*R*,6*S*)-5-bromo-3,5,6-trimethylnonane d. (*S*)-3-chloro-2-methylpentane
e. (3*S*,4*R*)-3,4-dibromohexane f. (1*S*,3*R*)-1,3-dimethylcyclopentane
g. (3*S*,4*R*,5*S*)-3,4,5-octanetriol h. (1*R*,2*R*,5*S*)-2-chloro-5-methylcyclohexanol
i. (*S*)-3-methyl-3-hexanol j. (3*R*,4*R*)-3,4-dichloro-2-methylhexane

8.21 For each of the compounds listed in Problem 8.20, draw a correct Fischer projection showing each of the stereogenic centers.

8.22 A sample of (+)-*β*-citronellol was found to exhibit a specific rotation of +4.00° under standard conditions. Calculate the optical purity of the sample.

8.23 A pure sample of detrorotatory *α*-pinene exhibits a rotation of +51.14°. What is the optical purity of a sample of *α*-pinene that exhibits a rotation of +10.5° under the same conditions?

8.24 Decide whether each of the following is true or false. Give an explanation for each answer.
a. All chiral compounds have diastereoisomers.
b. All molecules with stereogenic carbon atoms are chiral.
c. All (*R*)-configuration molecules are dextrorotatory.
d. Chemical reaction of an (*R*)-configuration molecule will always produce another (*R*)-configuration molecule, provided that no bonds to the stereogenic center are broken.

8.25 How many stereogenic carbon atoms are present in each of the following molecules?

a. CH_3, H (cyclobutane ring)
b. CH_3, H (cyclobutene ring)
c. CH_3 CH_3, H_3C, $\ddot{O}H$, CH_3CH_2, :O:
d. :O:, H_3C, CH_3, CH_3

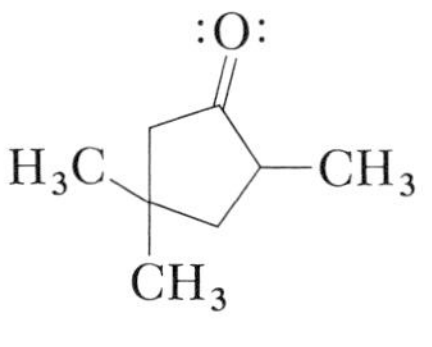

e. cholesterol (structure **6.2**)

8.26 Identify the stereogenic center in each of the following molecules as either *R* or *S*:

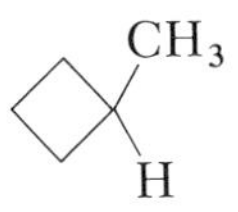

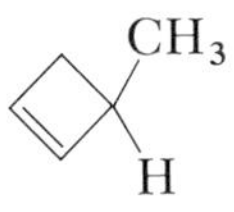

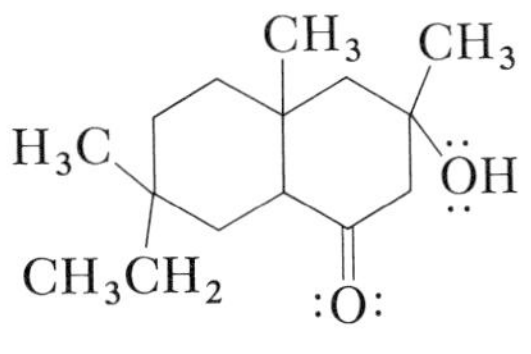

a. Fischer projection: top H; left CH_3CH_2; right CH_3; bottom $CH{=}CH_2$

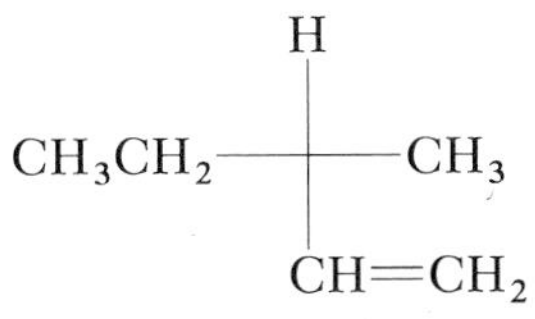

b. Fischer projection: top CH_3; left H; right $CH{=}CH_2$; bottom CH_2CH_3

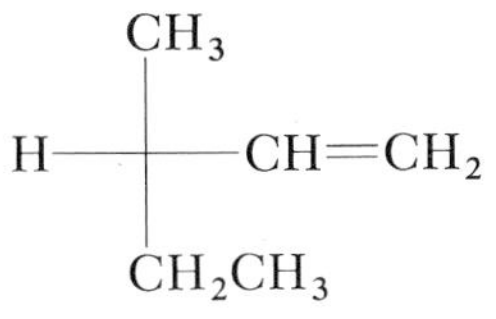

c. (Fischer projection: top $CH{=}CH_2$; left H_3C; right CH_2NH_2; bottom $C{\equiv}N$:)

d. (Fischer projection: top :Br:; left CH_3CH_2; right CH_3; bottom CH_2OH)

8.27 Identify as *R* or *S* the stereogenic center(s) in each of the following compounds:

a. (Newman projection: front $C{\equiv}N$:, H, H; back CH_2OH, CH_3, H)

b. (Newman projection: front CH_2CH_3, H, $CH(CH_3)_2$; back Br:, CH_3, H)

c. (Newman projection: front $C{\equiv}N$:, H_3C, H; back $CH{=}O$, $CH{=}CH_2$, H)

8.28 Identify as *R* or *S* the stereogenic center(s) in each of the following compounds:

a. :OH, H, H, $CH{=}CH_2$, I, Br:

b. :Br:, :Br, H, CH_3, Br:, $CH(CH_3)_2$

c. $CH_2CH_2CH(CH_3)_2$, H, H, OH, $CH_2CH_2CHCl_2$, $CH{=}O$

8.29 For each of the following, complete the Fischer projection on the right so that it represents the same stereoisomer as the Newman projection on the left.

a. (Newman projection: front :Cl:, H, CH_2CH_3; back H, :Br:, H_3C) ⟹ (Fischer projection: top :Cl:; bottom :Br:)

b. (Newman projection: front CH_3, H, Cl:; back Br:, CH_3, H) ⟹ (Fischer projection: top :Cl:; bottom :Br:)

8.30 For each of the Fischer projections shown on the right, complete the Newman projection on the left so that it represents the same stereoisomer.

a. (Newman projection: front CH_2CH_3; back CH_3) ⟸ (Fischer projection: top CH_2CH_3; H—C—$C{\equiv}N$:; HO—C—H; bottom CH_3)

b. (Newman projection: front CH_3; back :Br:) ⟸ (Fischer projection: top CH_3; H—C—Br:; H—C—Br:; bottom $CH{=}CH_2$)

8.31 When (*R*)-3-chloro-2-methyl-1-propanol is treated with phosphorus tribromide, a compound of formula C_4H_8BrCl is produced. Give the complete structure of this compound, showing its stereochemistry. Give the name of the compound, indicating the configuration of any stereogenic center.

8.32 A chiral compound of formula $C_6H_{13}OBr$ is converted to an achiral compound of formula $C_6H_{12}Br_2$ when treated with phosphorus tribromide. Deduce the structure of the organic starting material and product in this reaction.

8.33 How many stereoisomers are possible for each of the following?
a. $HOCH_2CH(OH)CH(OH)CH(OH)CH_3$ b. 2,3-dibromopentane c. 2,3-dibromobutane

8.34 Draw a wedge structure illustrating the stereochemistry of each of the compounds in Problem 8.33.

8.35 A solution of a sample is examined in the polarimeter. An apparent rotation of +5.0° is measured. What further experiment would you need to do to determine whether the sample had rotated the plane of plane-polarized light by +5.0°, +365°, or −355°?

8.36 A certain dextrorotatory stereoisomer has a specific rotation of +14.6° when pure. Calculate the percentages of dextrorotatory and levorotatory forms present in a sample that has a measured rotation of +9.4°.

8.37 Identify the pairs of structures shown below as enantiomers, identical, or diastereoisomers.

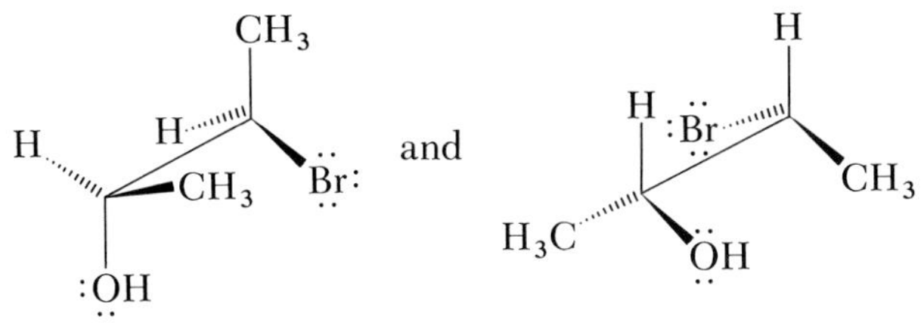

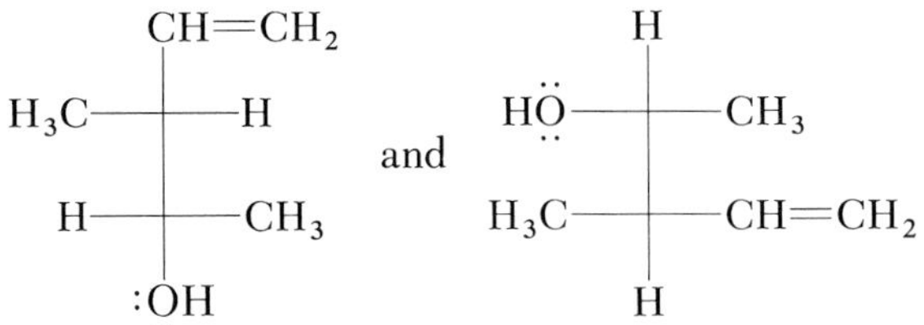

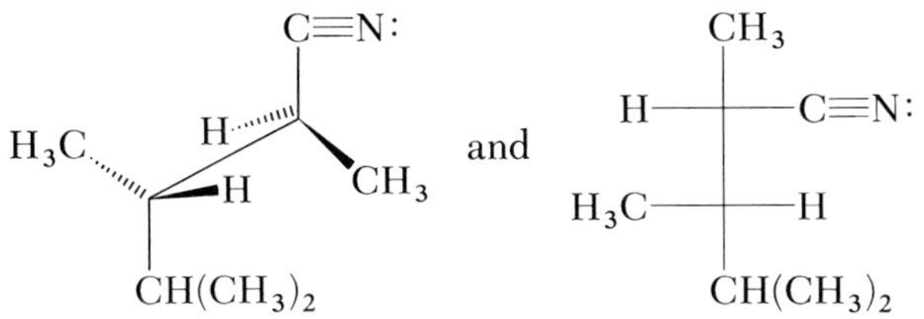

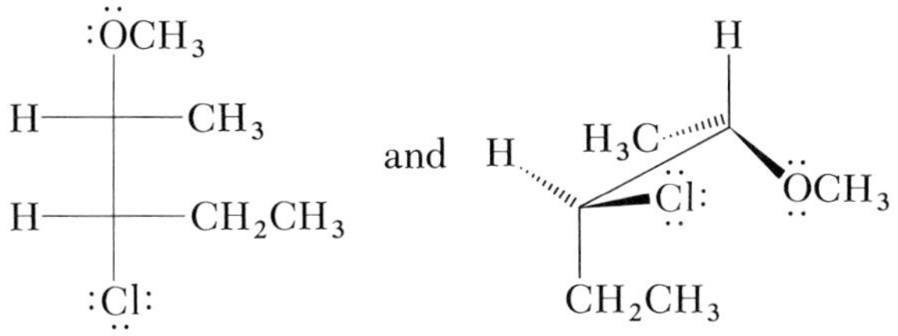

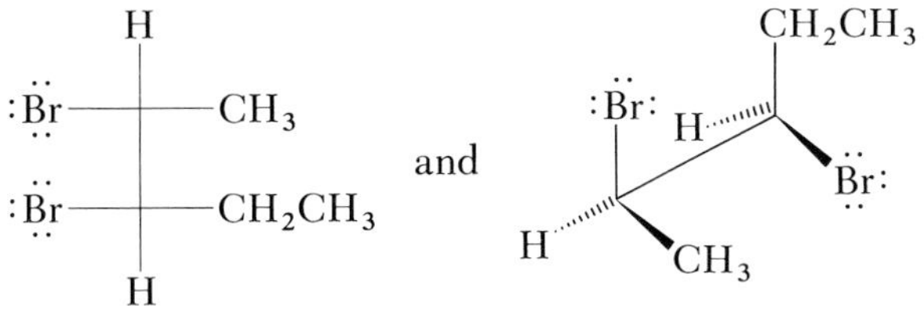

8.38 How many *meso*-structures can exist for the following general formula?

$$HOCH_2CH(OH)CH(OH)CH(OH)CH(OH)CH_2OH$$

Draw the structure for each *meso*-compound.

8.39 For the general formula given in Problem 8.38, draw wedge structures for those molecules that are optically active.

8.40 A variety of compounds containing phosphorus as a stereogenic center can be isolated and stored as pure enantiomers. For each of the following structures, give the Cahn-Ingold-Prelog designation of their chirality.

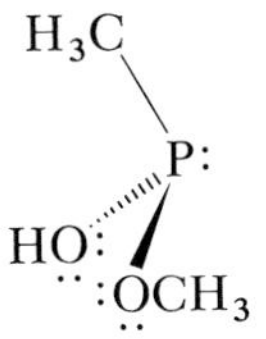

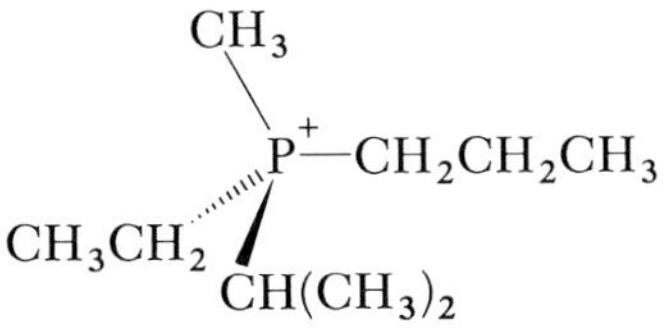

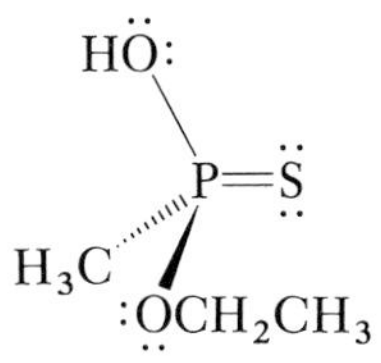

8.41 How many stereogenic centers are present in the structure shown below?

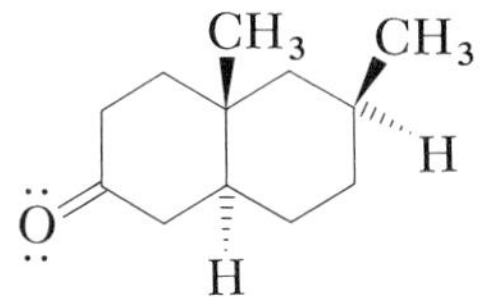

For each of these stereogenic centers, give the *R*,*S* designation.

8.42 The compound (*R*)-1-chloro-2-methylbutane is levorotatory. On treatment with chlorine under appropriate conditions it is converted to dextrorotatory 1,4-dichloro-2-methylbutane. Is the product *R* or *S*, or is there insufficient data to decide? Explain your answer.

8.43 Provide a complete IUPAC name and stereochemical designation for the following compound:

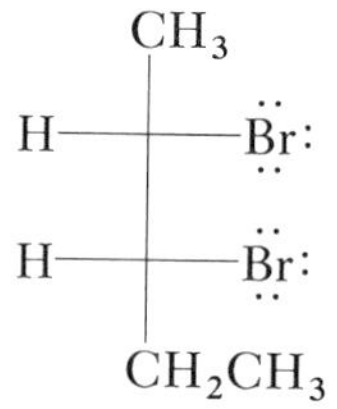

8.44 Compare each of the following structures with the structure shown in Problem 8.43. Indicate whether each depicts an enantiomer of that structure, a diastereoisomer of that structure, or simply a different view of that structure.

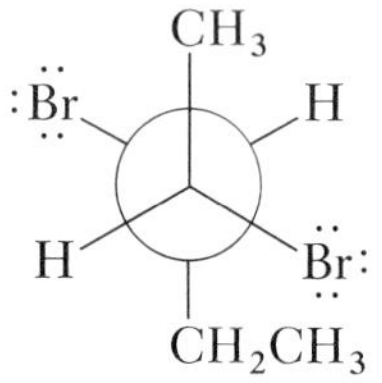

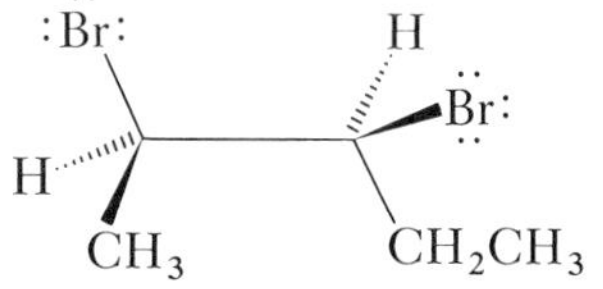

8.45 Which of the following objects are chiral?
a. a baseball bat b. a golf club c. a six-sided (cubic) die (with spots)

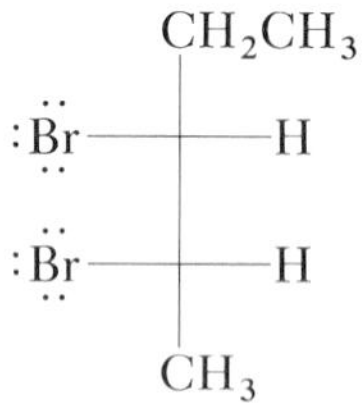

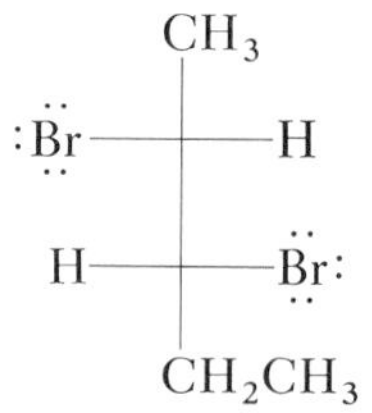

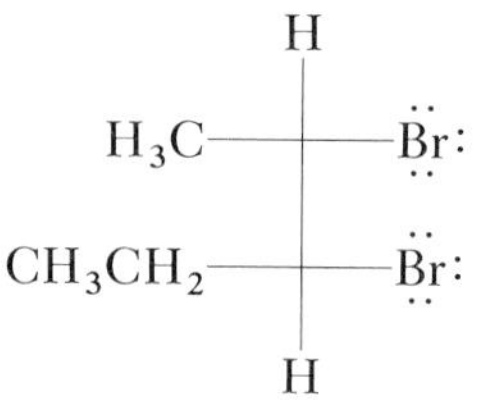

8.46 Draw Newman projections depicting the *R* enantiomer of each of the following:
a. 1-bromo-1-chloroethane b. 1-bromo-1-methoxypropane

8.47 From each of the following pairs, choose the group with the higher Cahn-Ingold-Prelog priority.
a. —N=O or —N(OH)CH_3 b. —P(O)$(OH)_2$ or —$P(OH)_3$
c. —C≡C—H or —C(CH_3)$_2$—C(CH_3)$_2$—H
d. 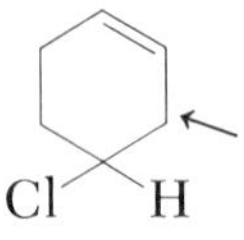 (cyclohexene ring with Cl and H; arrow to indicated carbon) or (cyclohexene ring with Cl and H; arrow to indicated carbon)

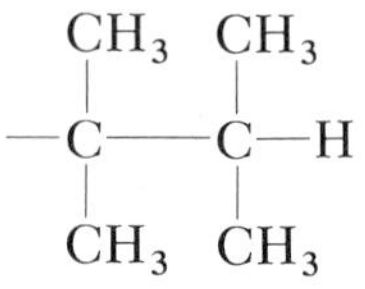

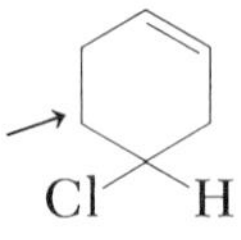

Carbon-Carbon Doubly Bonded Systems I. Structure, Nomenclature, and Preparation

9.1 Introduction

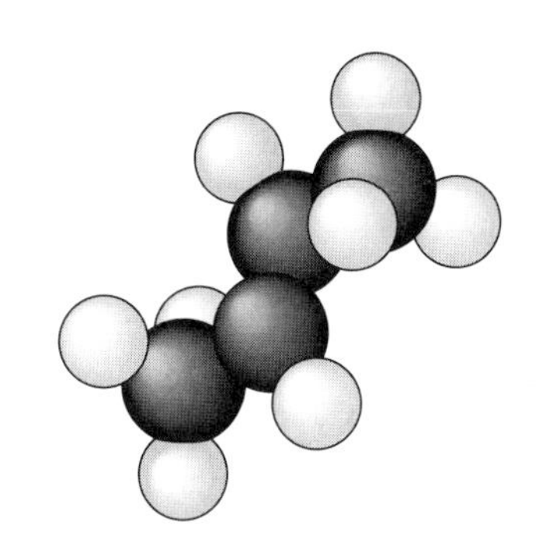

We briefly mentioned substances containing the carbon-carbon double bond in earlier chapters. The carbon-carbon double bond constitutes the **alkene** functional group. Substances that contain the carbon-carbon double bond as their only functional group are referred to as either alkenes or *olefins* (an older term).

A large number of naturally occurring substances contain the alkene functional group. These compounds range from components of petroleum to substances of importance in animals and plants. The simplest alkene, ethene (**9.1**), is not only a major industrial chemical but is also a plant hormone. In this latter role it helps to ripen fruit.

ethene
(also known as ethylene)
9.1

Substances with two, three, four, . . . double bonds are called dienes, trienes, tetraenes, ... Many such substances play major roles in living organisms. We will discuss some of them later in this chapter.

The alkene functional group has a rich and interesting chemistry. In this chapter and the next we will begin to explore the structural and chemical properties associated with the carbon-carbon double bond. In doing so we will forge ahead into some new areas. At the same time, however, we will see that the principles we learned in earlier chapters will guide us. We will even encounter some of the same reaction intermediates that we first saw in the reactions of alcohols.

9.2 Structure and Geometry Associated with the Alkene Group

PLANAR TRIGONAL GEOMETRY

Each carbon atom of an alkene group is *tricoordinated*, that is, it is bonded to three other atoms. Use of the VSEPR model suggests a planar trigonal geometry about such carbon atoms. This prediction is generally in good agreement with experimental observations. Even so, small deviations from the ideal bond angles of 120° are commonly observed. Several examples are shown in Figure 9.1.

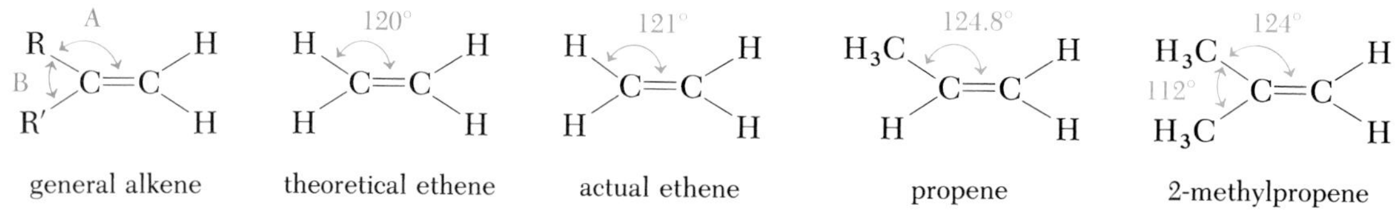

general alkene (angles A, B) | theoretical ethene (120°) | actual ethene (121°) | propene (124.8°) | 2-methylpropene (124°, 112°)

Figure 9.1 Bond angles in alkenes. Small deviations from the theoretical 120° bond angle are common. For the general alkene, angle A is increased over 120° while angle B is decreased.

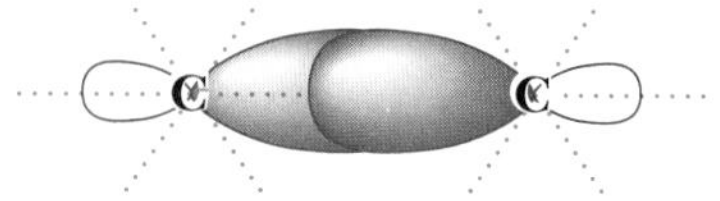

σ bond formed by the overlap of sp^2 hybrids

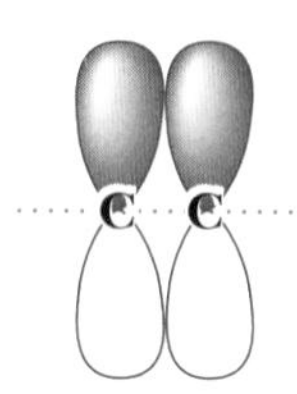

π bond formed by the overlap of unhybridized p orbitals

Figure 9.2 The carbon-carbon double bond. The σ bond involves an end-on interaction of a pair of sp^2 hybrid orbitals. The π bond involves a side-to-side interaction of two carbon $2p$ orbitals.

HYBRIDIZATION

Earlier we applied the hybridization model to a tricoordinated carbon atom. From the bonding geometry of alkenes, we infer that each carbon atom of the double bond uses three sp^2 hybrid orbitals to form three σ bonds to the atoms attached to it. All of these bonds lie in a plane with angles of 120° between them. For each carbon atom of the double bond, one of the three available p orbitals is not hybridized. Thus, two p orbitals lie side-by-side in a plane perpendicular to the plane containing the six atoms bonded by the sp^2 orbitals. A π bond results from the side-to-side interaction of these two p orbitals.

The carbon-carbon σ bond component of the double bond is the result of an *end-on* sp^2-sp^2 overlap. The carbon-carbon π bond is formed by a *side-to-side* overlap of the unhybridized p orbitals. The π bond has electron density above and below the plane containing the atoms of the alkene unit. These bonding interactions are schematically presented in Figure 9.2, and an overall bonding diagram is shown in Figure 9.3.

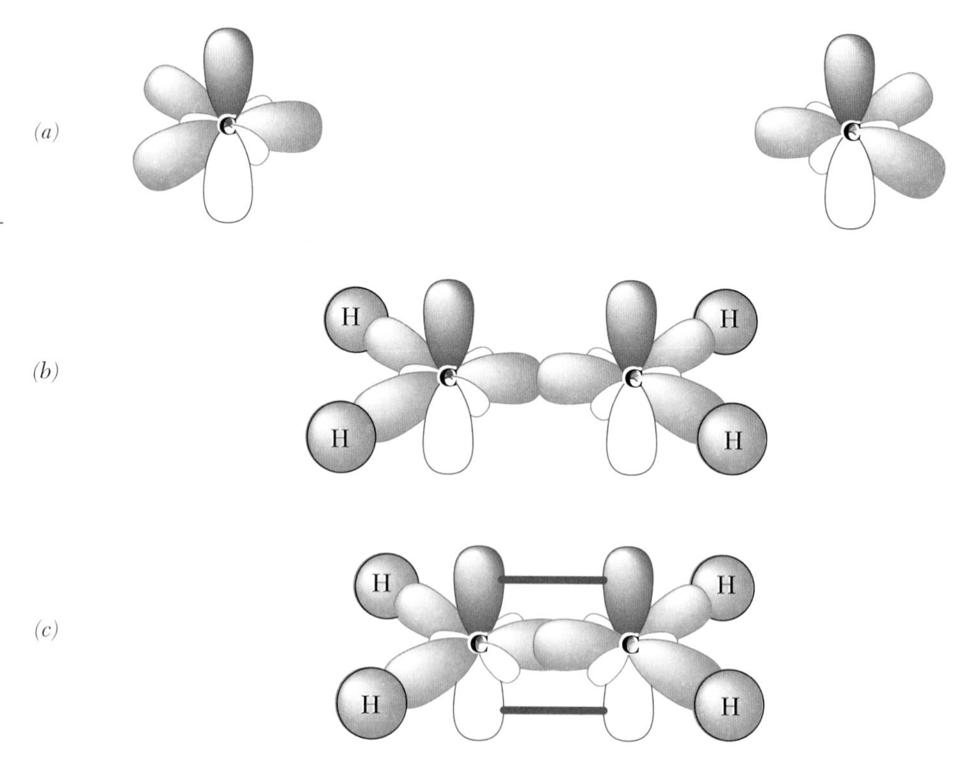

Figure 9.3 Schematic diagram showing the formation of a carbon-carbon double bond. (*a*) Two sp^2 hybridized carbons with parallel p orbitals. (*b*) Formation of the carbon-carbon σ bond by end-on overlap of two sp^2 hybrids (bonds are also shown to the associated hydrogen atoms). (*c*) Formation of the π bond by side-to-side overlap of the unhybridized p orbitals.

Table 9.1 Carbon-Hydrogen Bond Energies and Distances

Compound	Hybrid Used by Carbon	C—H Bond Distance (angstrom)	Homolytic C—H Bond Dissociation Energy (kcal/mole)
$H_3C—CH_3$	sp^3	1.112	98
$H_2C{=}CH_2$	sp^2	1.103	104
$HC{\equiv}CH$	sp	1.079	121

Not surprisingly, a double bond is stronger than a single bond. However, it is important to realize that a double bond is not *twice* as strong as a single bond—π bonding is appreciably weaker than σ bonding. Indeed, it is the relative weakness and the spatial disposition of the π bond that lead to much of the important chemistry of the alkene functional group. In terms of bond energies, we find that only 60–65 kcal/mole must be expended to break the π bond of a double bond, compared with about 160–170 kcal/mole to break both bonds of the double bond. We can infer that about 100–110 kcal/mole is needed to break the σ bond of a double bond. Thus the σ bond is 40–50 kcal/mole stronger than the π bond.

We also find that the carbon-carbon double bond distance is shorter than the carbon-carbon single bond distance. The carbon-carbon (single) bond of ethane is 1.53 angstrom, whereas the double bond of ethene is only 1.34 angstrom. A subtle point relating to both bond energies and bond distances is that σ bonds formed from sp^2 hybrids are somewhat stronger (and shorter) than corresponding bonds formed by sp^3 hybrids. This strength can be correlated with the greater degree of s character of the electrons in the bond formed with sp^2 hybrid orbitals. Electrons in an orbital with greater s character are more tightly held to the nucleus. Thus, bonds formed from hybrids with greater s character are more difficult to break. If we compare the various types of hybrids, we find that sp^3 hybrids have 25%, sp^2 hybrids $33\frac{1}{3}\%$, and sp hybrids 50% s character. A comparison of the carbon-hydrogen bond lengths and bond dissociation energies for ethane, ethene, and ethyne are given in Table 9.1. The correlation between the different types of hybridization and bond length and strength are clearly seen.

The carbon-hydrogen bonds are both shorter and stronger in alkenes and alkynes than they are in alkanes. We rationalize this difference in terms of the greater degree of s character in the carbon orbitals used in forming the σ bonds in the unsaturated molecules. The greater degree of s character in the hybridization correlates with the bonds being both shorter and stronger.

We will later find that we can associate different types of hybridization with significant differences in the chemistry of apparently similar molecules. We will need to consider this phenomenon in several different contexts as we meet new classes of compounds and reactions.

CONFORMATIONAL RIGIDITY

A molecule such as ethane moves through a spectrum of conformations as rotation about its carbon-carbon bond occurs. In Chapters 1 and 8 we used

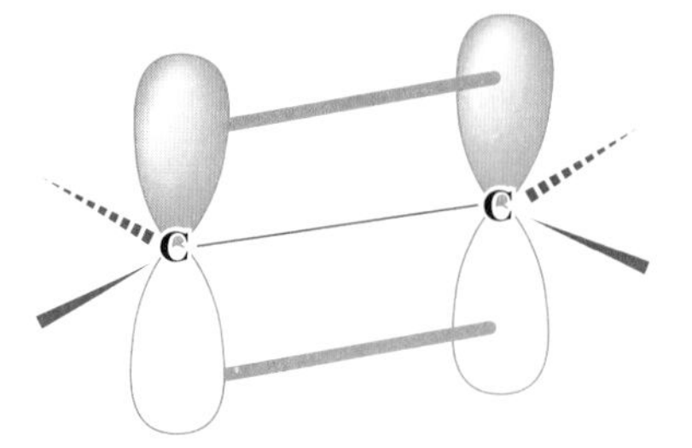

parallel orbitals, clean overlap

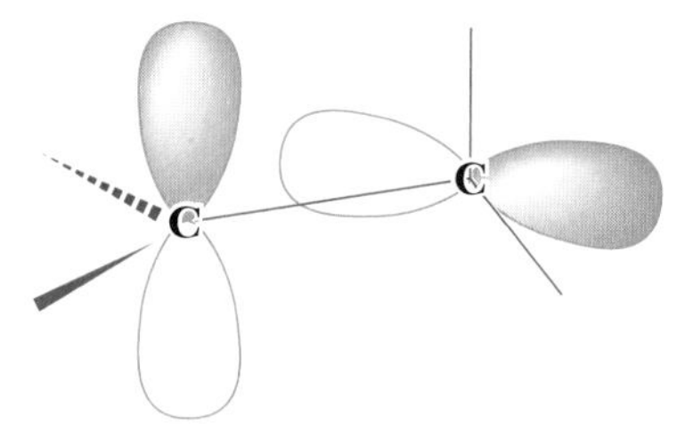

orthogonal orbitals, no overlap

Figure 9.4 Rotation about a π bond. Rotation about a double bond weakens the bond since it destroys p orbital overlap. After 90° of rotation the p orbitals are in perpendicular planes and cannot overlap. The π bond is then completely broken.

various projection drawings (such as sawhorse and Newman) to depict the different conformations. We say that there is *free rotation* about carbon-carbon single bonds.

A very important feature of the double bond is that there is *no* free rotation about it. This rigidity is associated with the different symmetry properties of the bonding orbitals of σ bonds and π bonds. Let us consider these differences in symmetry. The electron density associated with a single (σ) bond has cylindrical symmetry with respect to the internuclear axis. The σ bond therefore remains intact when rotation occurs. We find that molecules containing only single bonds are generally able to rotate freely into various conformational forms, unless some other type of barrier is imposed by the molecular structure.

Now, consider what happens when a double bond is present. We remember that a double bond is a combination of one σ bond and one π bond. If we consider rotation about the internuclear axis, we again find that the σ bond remains intact. At no stage of rotation is the end-to-end σ interaction of the carbon atom sp^2 hybrid orbitals disrupted. However, the π bond is progressively weakened as rotation occurs. In fact, it is completely destroyed after 90° of rotation (see Figure 9.4). After a 90° rotation, the two p orbitals would be in mutually perpendicular planes. The p orbitals so oriented are said to be **orthogonal.** Orthogonal orbitals do not interact with each other.

This model predicts some significant features for alkenes. One is a rigid structure about the carbon-carbon double bond. Indeed, we find that while the conformational forms of butane shown in Figure 9.5 do constantly interconvert under ambient conditions, the corresponding structures of 2-butene (also see Figure 9.5) do not. These structures of 2-butene are in fact not those of conformers but of true isomers. The two isomers of 2-butene can be isolated from one another and do not readily interconvert.

These isomers of 2-butene, like other isomers, have different chemical and physical properties. Any naming system for alkenes must be capable of assigning unique names to the two isomers. We will now address this issue in the general context of alkene nomenclature.

9.3 Nomenclature of Alkenes

BASIC PRINCIPLES

The IUPAC approach to naming simple alkenes requires that we first locate the longest continuous carbon chain *containing the carbon-carbon double bond.* This chain provides the root name for the compound. We number the chain

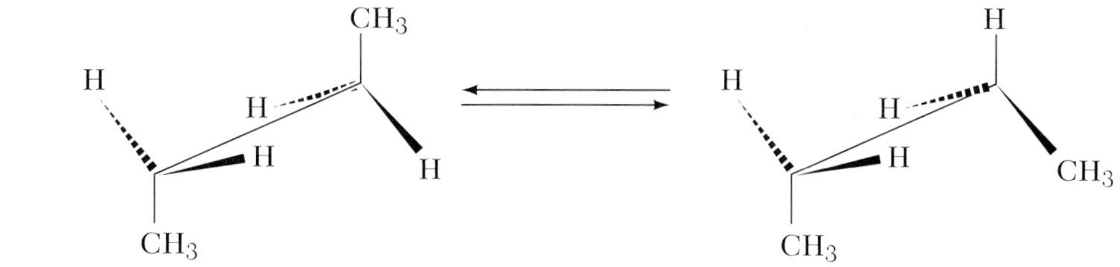

These conformations of butane are interconvertible due to free rotation about the central carbon–carbon bond.

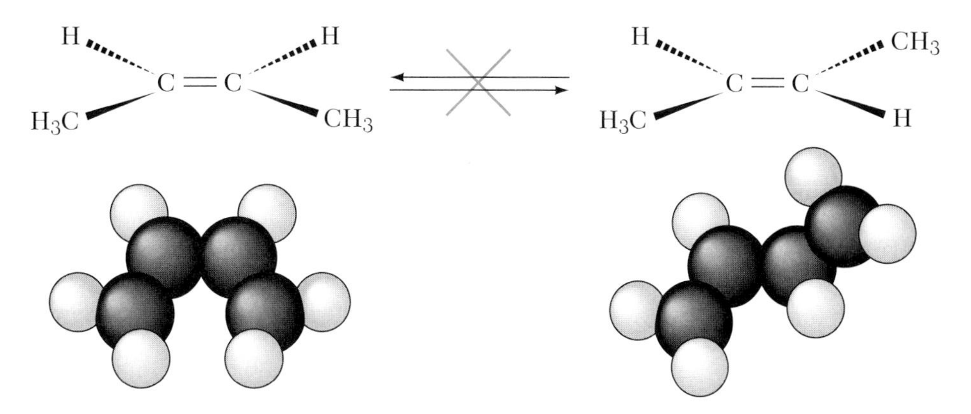

Figure 9.5 Structures of butane and 2-butene. While butane is able to undergo free rotation about the central carbon-carbon bond, 2-butene is not. There are two isomers of 2-butene, whose nomenclature is described in Section 9.3.

beginning at the end that provides the smaller number for the first carbon atom of the double bond. This number is used as a prefix to specify the position of the double bond along the chain. To indicate that the compound is an alkene, we replace the *-ane* ending of the root alkane name with the *-ene* ending. We list substituents as usual in alphabetical order with numerical designation of their positions along the chain. Cycloalkenes are named in an analogous manner, assigning one sp^2 carbon the number -1- and the other the number -2-. Six examples are shown in Figure 9.6.

Figure 9.6 Nomenclature for simple alkenes and cycloalkenes.

$CH_3CH_2CH{=}CH_2$ — 1-butene

$CH_3CH_2CH{=}C(CH_3)_2$ — 2-methyl-2-pentene

$(CH_3CH_2)_2C{=}C(CH_2CH_3)_2$ — 3,4-diethyl-3-hexene

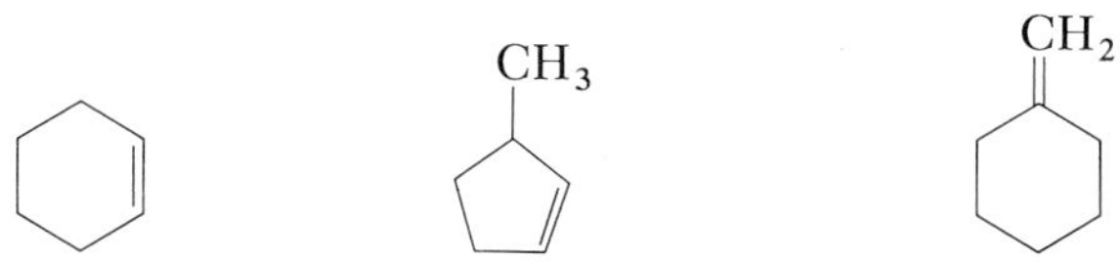

cyclohexene

CH_3 — 3-methyl-1-cyclopentene

CH_2 — methylenecyclohexene

PROBLEM 9.1 Provide IUPAC names for each of the following structures.

a. 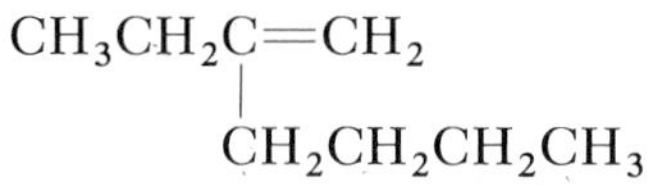 $CH_3CH_2C{=}CH_2$ with $CH_2CH_2CH_2CH_3$ on C-2

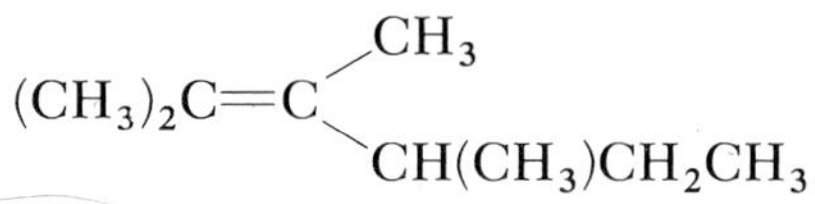

b. $(CH_3)_2C{=}C(CH_3)CH(CH_3)CH_2CH_3$

c. $(CH_3CH_2)_2C{=}C(CH_2CH_2CH_2CH_2CH_3)CH(CH_3)CH_2CH_3$

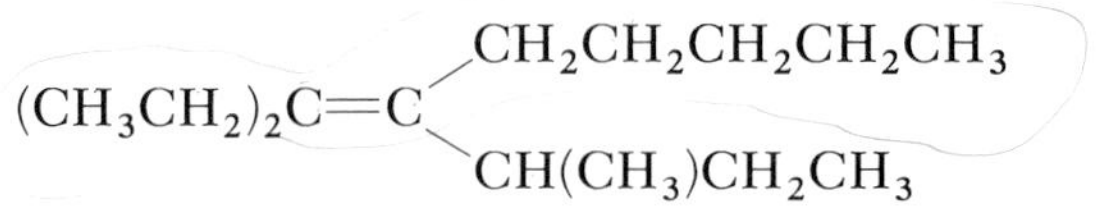

d. 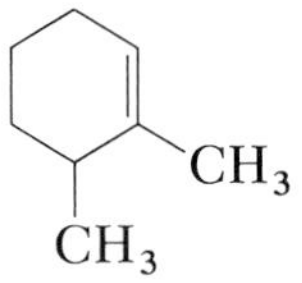 (cyclohexene ring bearing two CH_3 groups)

e. 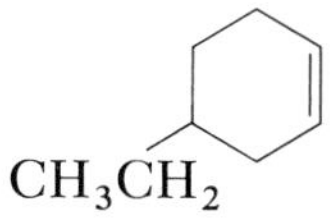 (cyclohexene ring bearing CH_3CH_2)

Steps to Solving the Problem

Solution to Problem 9.1a

1. We look for the longest continuous chain that contains the double bond. We find it to be a chain of six carbons, so we name the compound as a *hexene*. There *is* a chain of seven carbons present; however, it does not contain the double bond.
2. We locate the position of the double bond. The double bond is located between carbons 1 and 2 of the chain, so we name it as a *1-hexene*.
3. We look for any alkyl substituents and note their positions on the chain. We find an ethyl substituent at the 2 position. The IUPAC name of the compound is *2-ethyl-1-hexene*.

PRIORITIES IN NOMENCLATURE

Consider substance **9.2**, illustrated below.

$$:\ddot{Br}CH_2CH{=}CH_2$$

9.2

This compound contains both a double bond and a bromine atom. Should we name it *1-bromo-2-propene* or *3-bromo-1-propene*?

The IUPAC rules provide a system of priorities for functional groups to enable us to choose a standard name for such compounds. A partial listing of functional group priorities for nomenclature is given in Table 9.2.

We see that the alkene functional group has a higher nomenclature priority than does a halogen atom. The double bond of compound **9.2** takes precedence in numbering the carbon chain and the suffix for the root name. We give the double bond the lower of the possible numbers and name the compound *3-bromo-1-propene*.

In contrast, consider structure **9.3.** Table 9.1 shows that a hydroxyl group has a higher nomenclature priority than does an alkene group. This time we

Table 9.2 Partial List of Functional Group Nomenclature Priorities

	Functional Group	Name Ending
Increasing Priority ↑	$-CO_2H$	-oic acid
	$-C(H)=\ddot{O}$	-al
	$-C(-)=\ddot{O}$	-one
	$-\ddot{O}H$	-ol
	$-\ddot{N}R_2$	-amine
	$>C=C<$	-ene
	$-C\equiv C-$	-yne
	$-R, -X, -NO_2$	used only as prefixes

must number the carbon chain so as to attach the lower possible number to the carbon bearing the hydroxyl group. The IUPAC name is *3-buten-1-ol.*

$$H_2C=CHCH_2CH_2\ddot{O}H$$

3-buten-1-ol
(*not* 1-buten-4-ol or
4-hydroxy-1-butene)
9.3

PROBLEM 9.2 Name each of the following compounds by the IUPAC method.

a. 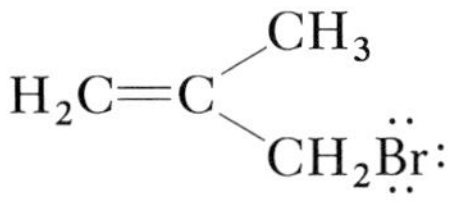 $H_2C=C(CH_3)CH_2\ddot{Br}:$

b. $H_2C=CHCH_2CH_2\ddot{Br}:$

c. 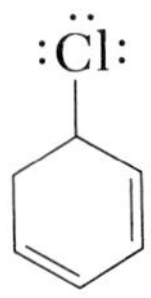 $:\ddot{Cl}:$ attached to a cyclohexadiene ring

d. $(CH_3)_2C=CHCH(Br)CH_2\ddot{O}H$

e. 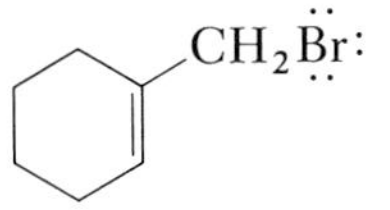 cyclohexene ring bearing $CH_2\ddot{Br}:$

f. 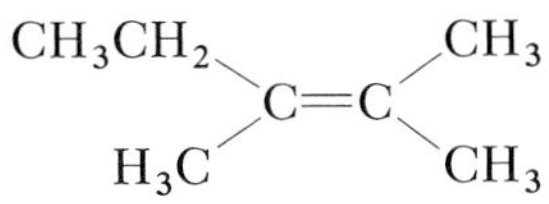 $(CH_3CH_2)(H_3C)C=C(CH_3)(CH_3)$

Steps to Solving the Problem

Solution to Problem 9.2a

1. We first find the longest chain containing the group of highest nomenclature priority (the double bond). It is a three-carbon chain, so we name the compound as a substituted propene. Actually two *different* three-carbon chains are present. We choose the one containing the greater number of substituents:

$H_2C{=}C(CH_3)CH_2{-}\ddot{B}r{:}$ rather than $H_2C{=}C(CH_3)CH_2{-}\ddot{B}r{:}$

two substituents — one substituent

2. We note the location of the double bond and begin the numbering from the end of the chain that provides the smaller number. We note that the double bond is at the 1-position.
3. Looking for substituents, we see that there is a bromine at the 3-position and a methyl group at the 2-position. Using an alphabetical ordering of the substituents, we name the compound *3-bromo-2-methyl-1-propene*.

NAMING GEOMETRIC ISOMERS

The ***cis/trans* notation** is commonly used to specify the distribution of substituents about a carbon-carbon double bond. For example, the two 2-butene isomers in Figure 9.5 are known as *cis*-2-butene (**9.4**) and *trans*-2-butene (**9.5**). These isomers are **geometric isomers,** a category of stereoisomers. Because these compounds are stereoisomers but *not* enantiomers, it follows that they are *diastereoisomers* (Chapter 8).

$(H)(H_3C)C{=}C(H)(CH_3)$ — $(H)(H_3C)C{=}C(CH_3)(H)$

cis-2-butene
9.4

trans-2-butene
9.5

The two methyl groups of the *cis*-2-butene molecule are on the *same* side of the double bond, while the methyl groups of *trans*-2-butene are on *opposite* sides. In general, the term *cis* is used when two similar groups are on the same side of the double bond, and *trans* is used when they are on opposite sides. The groups could be hydrogen atoms, alkyl groups, and so forth, or the alkyl groups of the parent chain itself.

PROBLEM 9.3 Draw the structures for *cis*-1,2-dibromoethene and *trans*-1,2-dibromoethene. Which compound do you expect to have the higher boiling temperature? (*Hint*: Compare their dipole moments and the resulting intermolecular attractions.)

When more than one double bond is present, we must indicate the position and geometry about *each* double bond. Two examples are illustrated below, *trans,trans*-2,4-heptadiene (**9.6**), and *trans,cis*-2,4-heptadiene (**9.7**).

CH_3CH_2, H / C=C / H, H / C=C / H, CH_3

trans,trans-2,4-heptadiene
9.6

H, CH_3 / C=C / CH_3CH_2, H / C=C / H, H

trans,cis-2,4-heptadiene
9.7

PROBLEM 9.4 There are two other geometric isomers (besides **9.6** and **9.7**) for the general category of compounds called 2,4-heptadiene. Draw their structures and name them.

Unfortunately, the *cis/trans* notation system might not always provide an unambiguous name for a compound. Consider, for example, the following compound (**9.8**):

H_3C, $CH_2CH_2CH_3$ / C=C / $(CH_3)_2CH$, CH_2CH_3

9.8

We see that the methyl group is *cis* relative to a propyl group, but *trans* relative to an ethyl group. The IUPAC rules recommend the use of ***E/Z* descriptors** to avoid any ambiguity in such cases. With this approach the recommended protocol for describing molecules is related to that used for describing the absolute configuration about chiral centers.

The pairs of groups attached at each end of the double bond are assigned priorities according to the Cahn-Ingold-Prelog rules (see Chapter 8). Using these rules, the isopropyl group at the left end is assigned a higher priority than the methyl group on the same carbon. Similarly, the propyl group at the right end is assigned a higher priority than the ethyl group on the same carbon. When the groups of higher priority at each end are on opposite sides of the double bond (as they are here), that is, in a *trans* relationship, the descriptor *E* is used (*E* comes from the German word *entgegen*, meaning "opposite"). If

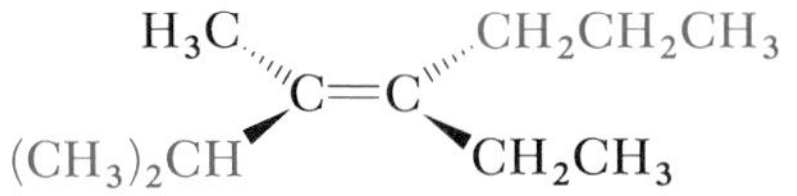

Figure 9.7 Demonstration of the use of *E*/*Z* notation for the geometry about carbon-carbon double bonds. When the groups of higher priority at each end of the double bond are on *opposite* sides of the double bond, the descriptor *E* is used; when they are on the *same* side of that double bond, the notation Z is used. The groups of higher priority are shown in blue.

H_3C, $(CH_3)_2CH$ / $C{=}C$ / $CH_2CH_2CH_3$, CH_2CH_3

(*E*)-4-ethyl-2,3-dimethyl-3-heptene
9.8

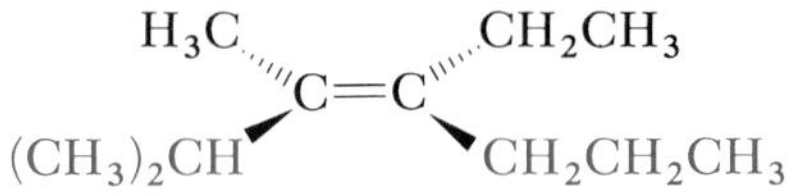

H_3C, $(CH_3)_2CH$ / $C{=}C$ / CH_2CH_3, $CH_2CH_2CH_3$

(Z)-4-ethyl-2,3-dimethyl-3-heptene
9.9

the groups of higher priority at each end are on the same side of the double bond (i.e., are in a *cis* relationship), the descriptor Z is used (Z comes from the German word *zusammen*, meaning "together"). The naming of **9.8** and its geometric isomer **9.9** is shown in Figure 9.7.

PROBLEM 9.5 Use the *E*/*Z* notation system to provide an unambiguous name for each of the following compounds.

a. 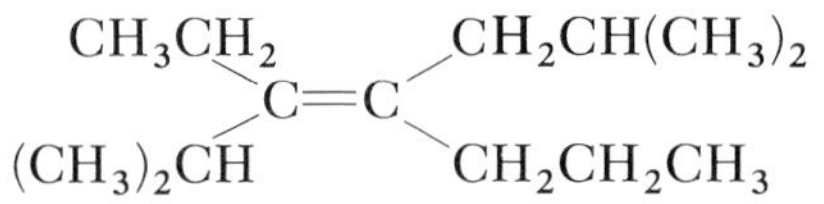 CH_3CH_2, $(CH_3)_2CH$ / $C{=}C$ / $CH_2CH(CH_3)_2$, $CH_2CH_2CH_3$

b. 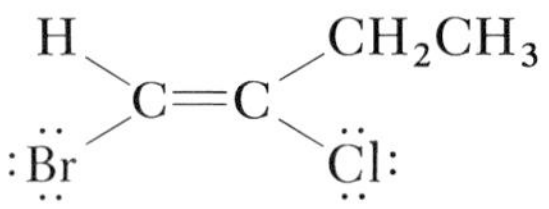 H, :Br: / $C{=}C$ / CH_2CH_3, :Cl:

c.

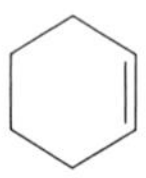

d. 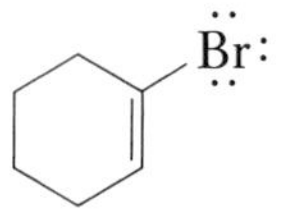 :Br:

e. 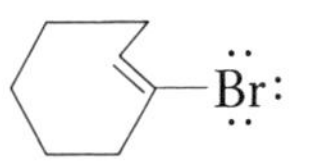 —Br:

Steps to Solving the Problem

Solution to Problem 9.5a

1. Determine the relative priorities of the groups at each end of the double bond. The carbon on the left side has bound to it an ethyl and an isopropyl group. The isopropyl group has the higher priority according to the Cahn-Ingold-Prelog rules. Attached to the carbon on the right are an isobutyl and a propyl group. The isobutyl has the higher priority according to the same rules.
2. What is the relationship of the groups of higher priority at each end of the double bond? The isobutyl and isopropyl groups are attached to opposite faces of the double bond, so we name the compound (*E*)-3-ethyl-2,6-dimethyl-4-propyl-3-heptene.

PROBLEM 9.6 Draw structures for each of the following:

a. (*E*)-2-bromo-2-pentene b. (Z)-3-methyl-1,3,5-hexatriene
c. (2Z,4Z)-hexadiene

PROBLEM 9.7 Draw the structures for all of the Z alkenes of formula C_8H_{16}.

At times we can use either the *cis*/*trans* system or the *E*/*Z* system to name a compound without ambiguity. However, it is not necessarily true that all *E* compounds are *trans* or that all Z compounds are *cis*. For example, we could name molecule **9.10** unambiguously as either (Z)-2-iodo-2-butene or as *trans*-

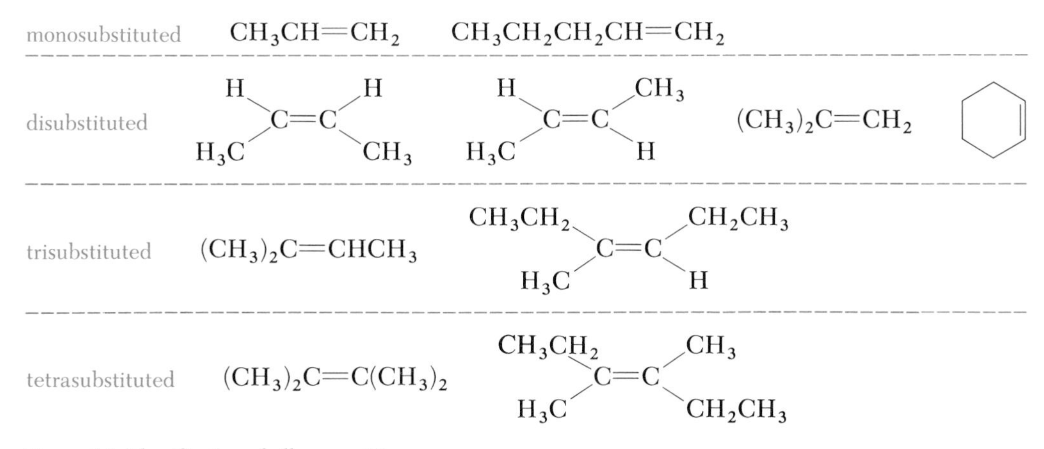

Figure 9.8 Classification of alkenes. We classify alkenes as mono-, di-, tri-, or tetrasubstituted according to the number of alkyl groups attached to the carbon atoms of the double bond.

2-iodo-2-butene. Each system uses a different basis for the descriptor, and each describes the molecule correctly according to its rules.

9.10

DEGREE OF SUBSTITUTION ABOUT A DOUBLE BOND

We often refer to double bonds as being *monosubstituted*, *disubstituted*, and so forth. This classification system is based on the number of alkyl groups attached to the carbon atoms of the double bond. Several examples are shown in Figure 9.8.

PROBLEM 9.8 Provide IUPAC names for each of the alkenes in Figure 9.8.

PROBLEM 9.9 Provide structures and unambiguous names for all of the disubstituted alkenes of formula C_5H_{10}.

9.4 Natural Products Containing Double Bonds

Many important natural products contain one or more carbon-carbon double bonds. Of particular interest are those that contain repeating five-carbon structural units known as **isoprene units.** Isoprene itself is the diene 2-methyl-1,3-butadiene (**9.11**).

$$H_2C{=}CH{-}\underset{}{\overset{CH_3}{\overset{|}{C}}}{=}CH_2$$

2-methyl-1,3-butadiene
(isoprene)
9.11

The *skeleton* of isoprene is found as a repeating unit in the structure of a great many natural compounds, hence the term *isoprene unit*. These natural

Figure 9.9 Isoprene units in geraniol. We can envision the carbon skeleton of geraniol as being composed of two fragments (isoprene units) joined as shown. The isoprene units in the geraniol molecule are outlined on the structure to the right.

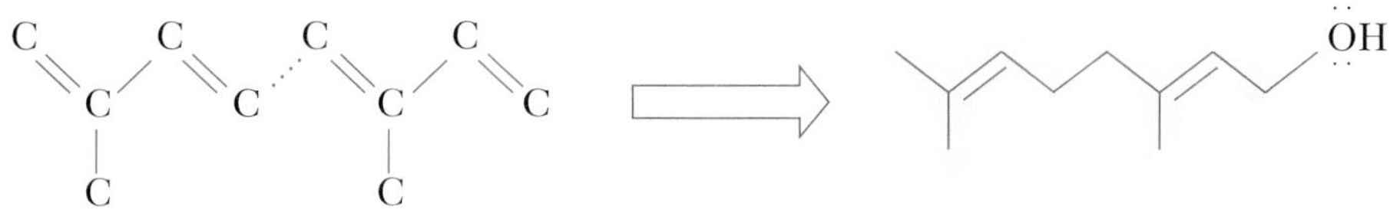

compounds do not contain carbon-carbon double bonds in the positions where they occur in isoprene—instead, the carbon *skeleton* is present. For example, consider the molecule geraniol (**9.12**), a compound found in the oil of the geranium plant.

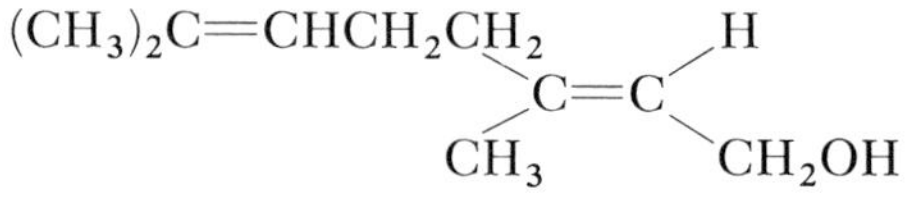

$$(CH_3)_2C{=}CHCH_2CH_2(CH_3)C{=}C(H)CH_2OH$$

geraniol
9.12

We can envision the carbon skeleton of geraniol as arising from the union of two isoprene units, as shown in Figure 9.9.

The structures of several other familiar substances composed of isoprene units are shown in Figure 9.10. Hydrocarbons formally derived from two isoprene units are known as **monoterpenes.**

Figure 9.10 Several compounds composed of joined isoprene units. The common names shown are in standard use. We can derive IUPAC names for these and related compounds, but such names are quite unwieldly for general use. The classification of terpenoids as a function of the number of isoprene units each contains is shown in Table 9.3. The isoprene units are outlined in α-farnesene and β-carotene.

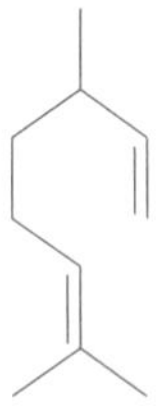

myrcene (found in bayberry, contains two isoprene units)

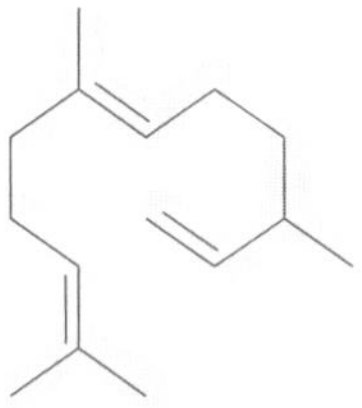

α-farnesene (isolated from oil of citronella, contains three isoprene units)

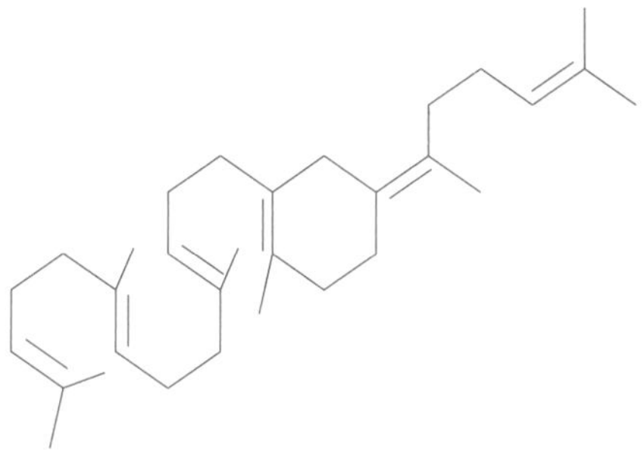

squalene (present in large quantities in shark oil —up to 40%, also present in yeast, wheat germ, and olive oil, contains six isoprene units and is the biological precursor of steroids)

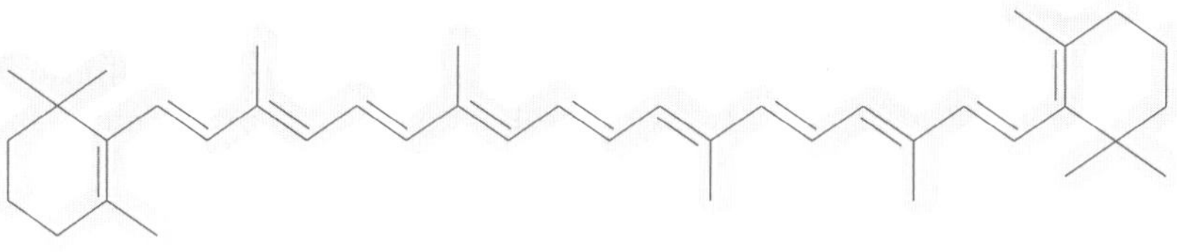

β-carotene (found in carrots and other plants, contains eight isoprene units)

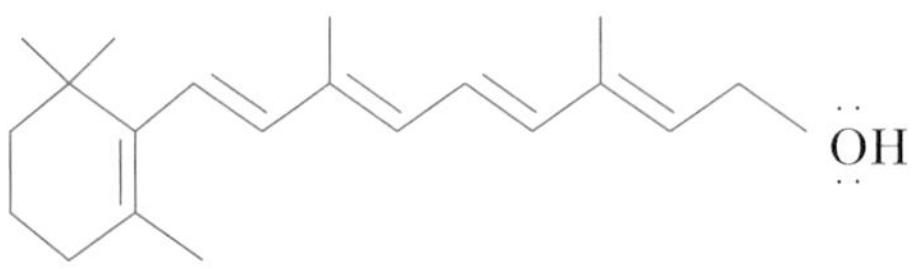

Vitamin A (retinol)
Carotene is broken down in the body into two molecules of retinol, each of which contains four isoprene units. Vitamin A, being derived from a diterpene, is known as a **terpenoid.**

SPECIAL TOPIC

Rubber

Raw rubber must be *vulcanized* before use to give it desirable properties. The process of vulcanization was invented in 1839 by Charles Goodyear and involves heating crude rubber with sulfur. Vulcanization forms crosslinks between polymer chains, and these crosslinks enable the rubber to resist distortion. The gross structure of vulcanized rubber is shown schematically below.

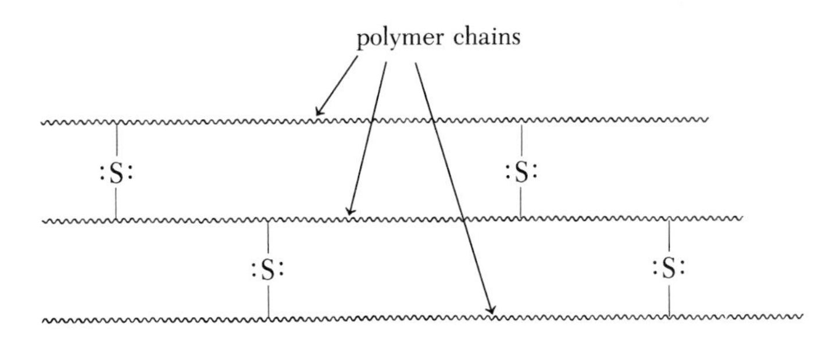

Sulfur atoms provide the crosslinks between individual polymer chains. Vulcanized rubber returns to its original shape when stress is removed. It is said to be an *elastomer*. Elastomers have flexible chains with some crosslinking.

Natural rubber is a compound of high molecular weight, obtained from the milky sap (latex) of the rubber tree. When we heat natural rubber in the absence of air, it yields mainly isoprene. We can think of natural rubber as a **polymer** of isoprene units, as shown in Figure 9.11.

Figure 9.11 The structure of natural rubber. Natural rubber can be represented as a polymer composed of repeating isoprene units.

$$-\!\left[CH_2-C(H_3C)=CH-CH_2-CH_2-C(H_3C)=CH-CH_2-CH_2-C(H_3C)=CH-CH_2-CH_2-C(H_3C)=CH-CH_2\right]\!-$$

or

$$-\!\left[CH_2-C(H_3C)=CH-CH_2\right]_n\!-$$

Polymers are substances containing many repeating units of some fundamental building block. Most natural rubber has a molecular weight in excess of one million. However, variations in molecular weight occur depending on the source of the rubber and the method of processing. A material essentially identical to natural rubber can be synthesized by the reaction of isoprene with a **Ziegler-Natta catalyst.** This catalyst is a mixture of triethylaluminum and titanium tetrachloride that facilitates the polymerization of isoprene and other dienes. (Refer to Chapter 29 for a full discussion of polymers, Ziegler-Natta catalysts, and related topics.)

PROBLEM 9.10 For each of the remaining compounds shown in Figure 9.10, outline the individual isoprene units.

The synthesis of terpenes and terpenoids by living systems does not involve isoprene itself. Rather, synthesis proceeds through isopentenyl pyrophosphate (**9.13**) and dimethylallyl pyrophosphate (**9.14**), which are biosynthesized from acetic acid (see Problem 9.33). These materials contain phosphate ester linkages (see Chapter 6).

$$H_2C{=}C(CH_3){-}CH_2{-}CH_2O{-}P({=}O)(O^-){-}O{-}P({=}O)(O^-){-}O^-$$

isopentenyl pyrophosphate
(trianion form)
9.13

$$(H_3C)_2C{=}CH{-}CH_2O{-}P({=}O)(O^-){-}O{-}P({=}O)(O^-){-}O^-$$

dimethylallyl pyrophosphate
(trianion form)
9.14

The pyrophosphate group in each of these compounds is easily displaced. It is a good leaving group, being the anion of a moderately strong acid. The biosynthesis of terpenes occurs through the displacement of pyrophosphate by another isopentenyl pyrophosphate or dimethylallyl pyrophosphate unit. Larger isoprenoid molecules are produced in a similar fashion. We classify these materials as monoterpenes, diterpenes, and so forth, on the basis of the number of carbon atoms in the molecule. This classification is shown in Table 9.3.

Table 9.3 Classification of Terpenoids

Number of Carbons	Classification
10	monoterpenes
15	sesquiterpenes
20	diterpenes
30	triterpenes
40	tetraterpenes

MOLECULAR ORBITAL ANALYSIS

9.5 Alkene HOMO and LUMO

The molecular orbital picture of the π bond of a simple alkene starts with the side-to-side overlap of carbon $2p$ orbitals, which generates π bonding and π antibonding orbitals as shown in Figure 9.12. The π bonding orbital is the alkene HOMO and the π antibonding orbital is the LUMO.

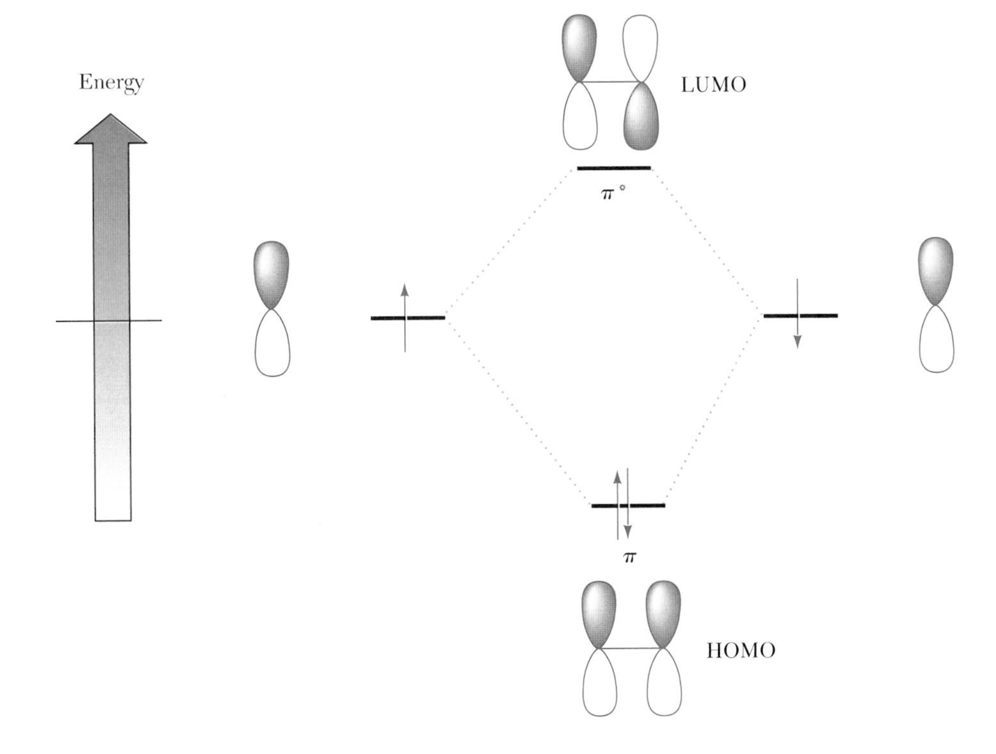

Figure 9.12 The π molecular orbitals associated with an alkene. In the ground state a pair of electrons occupies the π-bonding molecular orbital.

SPECIAL TOPIC

Pheromones Containing Carbon-Carbon Double Bonds

Pheromones are chemicals that organisms use to communicate with one another. The purpose of the chemical communication might be the attraction of a mate, sending a signal for alarm, providing defense, or marking the location of food (trail pheromone). For example, geraniol (**9.12**) is a trail pheromone used by the honeybee. Some species even use chemicals to help their members to gather for an event such as migration.

Pheromones can be effective in extremely small quantities. For example, a male moth responds to 10^{-12} mg of sex attractant present in a female. For this reason, pheromone research may lead to more effective and environmentally acceptable methods of insect control. Small amounts of sex-attracting pheromones can be placed in traps to lure insects. Alternatively, tiny amounts of pheromone distributed over large areas of land confuse male insects as to the location of females. Breeding is then severely curtailed.

Pheromones occur in miniscule amounts in organisms. In one study it was necessary to collect a half-million virgin moths to extract just 12 mg of their sex attractant. For widespread use, it is therefore necessary for organic chemists to elucidate the structures of pheromones and synthesize them in the laboratory. Fortunately, many pheromones have reasonably simple structures. Many contain carbon-carbon double bonds. Some are terpenes. The structures of several pheromones are shown below.

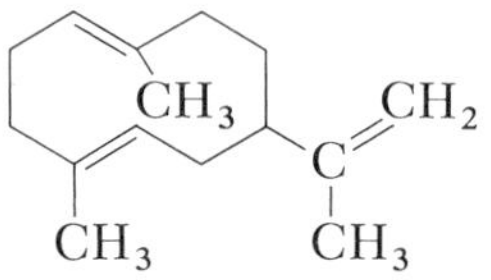

CH_3 CH_2 C CH_3 CH_3

The alarm pheromone for several species of aphids. Other aphids stay away when they detect this substance. Squashing the body of even one aphid releases enough of this chemical to alert other aphids.

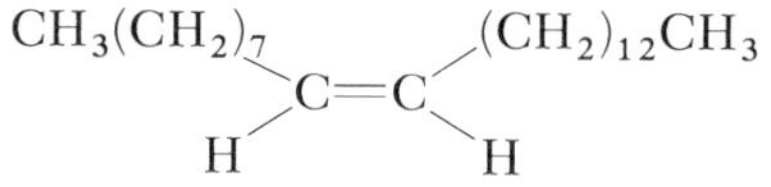

$CH_3(CH_2)_7$ $(CH_2)_{12}CH_3$ C=C H H

muscalure (the sex attractant of the common housefly)

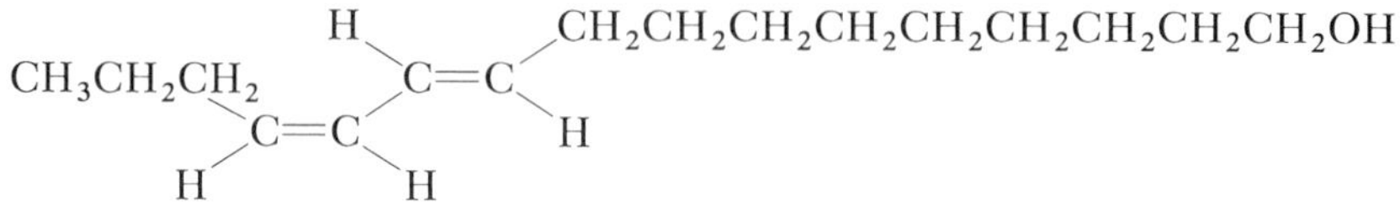

H $CH_2CH_2CH_2CH_2CH_2CH_2CH_2CH_2CH_2OH$ $CH_3CH_2CH_2$ C=C C=C H H H

sex attractant of the silkworm moth

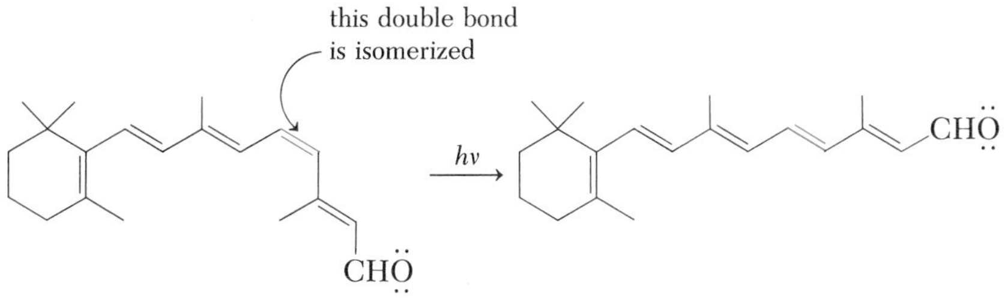

Figure 9.13 Geometric isomerization in the process of vision. The light-induced isomerization of 11-*cis*-retinal to 11-*trans*-retinal is important in the process of vision. The rod cells of the eye contain a red pigment, rhodopsin, that is a complex of a protein, opsin, and the aldehyde 11-*cis*-retinal. Light induces a *cis* to *trans* isomerization of the double bond shown. This isomerization causes a nerve impulse to be sent to the brain. The 11-*trans*-retinal so produced is recycled back to the *cis* isomer in the presence of more light and the enzyme retinal isomerase.

this double bond is isomerized

CHO

11-*cis*-retinal $\xrightarrow{h\nu}$ 11-*trans*-retinal

Light can cause the promotion of an electron from the π to the π^* level, as shown in Equation 9.1.

Eqn. 9.1
$$\pi \xrightarrow{h\nu} \pi^*$$

An alkene molecule that has been excited in this way has one electron in a π molecular orbital and one in a π^* molecular orbital. No net π bonding exists. The alkyl groups can now rotate about the carbon-carbon bond, and interconversions of *cis* and *trans* isomers can occur. This process is important for a variety of systems. For example, the chemistry of vision depends on this process.

In the rods of the eyes, retinal combines with a protein called opsin to produce rhodopsin. Of the five carbon-carbon double bonds in retinal, one is converted from a *cis* form to the *trans* form by the absorption of light, as illustrated in Figure 9.13.

This isomerization causes a nerve impulse to be sent to the brain, initiating the sensation of vision. The *cis* compound is constantly regenerated from the *trans* isomer through the action of proteins (enzymes). The regeneration process takes time—that is why a very bright light produces temporary blindness. Compare the structures of retinal and vitamin A (Figure 9.10). The vitamin A that we eat is oxidized in the body to retinal. Lack of vitamin A in the diet can lead to total blindness since there is no other route to form the required retinal.

PROBLEM 9.11 What nonenzymatic laboratory procedure could you use to convert vitamin A to 11-*trans*-retinal?

Variations in the energy of the HOMO and LUMO of different alkenes provide insights into the operation of **substituent effects,** that is, electronic effects that substituents exert on the systems to which they are attached. The energy differences between HOMO and LUMO can be calculated using the methods of wave mechanics or can be determined experimentally. A useful experimental procedure for investigating occupied orbitals involves measuring the amount of energy that must be supplied to an electron to free it from its orbital. The higher the energy of the orbital, the smaller the amount of energy that is needed to free an electron from it, as illustrated in Figure 9.14.

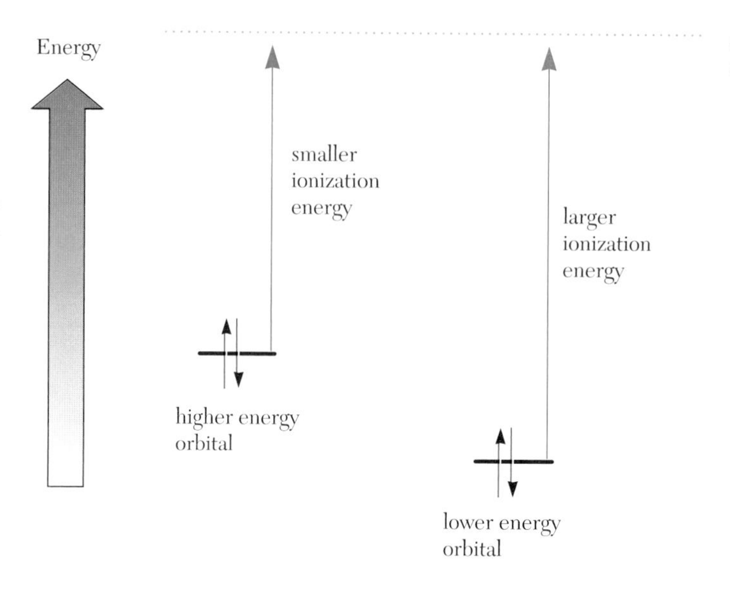

Figure 9.14. Ionization energy for electrons in orbitals. The energy required to remove an electron from its parent orbital completely out of the molecule is a measure of the orbital energy. Electrons in higher-energy orbitals are more easily removed than those in lower-energy orbitals. These energies are necessarily higher than those required for excitation to an empty orbital.

We refer to the energy needed to free an electron from the HOMO of a molecule as the first ionization energy or **ionization potential** of the molecule. The ionization potentials of alkenes provide an excellent probe of the HOMO energy. The ionization potentials of some simple alkenes are compared in Table 9.4.

Increasing the number of methyl groups about the double bond lowers the ionization potential as a direct result of the higher HOMO energy. From this observation we infer that the methyl groups are able to donate electron density into the region of the double bond. The donation of electron density helps to stabilize the positive charge that develops as the electron is ejected.

This situation might remind us of the role of alkyl groups in stabilizing carbocations and radicals. The effects we learn about in dealing with one type of organic system generally apply to related systems as well, so we can often

Table 9.4 Ionization Potentials of Several Alkenes

Compound	Ionization Energy (eV)
$H_2C{=}CH_2$	10.52
$H_2C{=}CHCH_3$	9.73
$H_2C{=}C(CH_3)_2$	9.23
$CH_3CH{=}CHCH_3$ (*cis* and *trans*)	9.13
$CH_3CH{=}C(CH_3)_2$	8.68
$(CH_3)_2C{=}C(CH_3)_2$	8.30

1 eV = 1 electron volt = 23.06 kcal/mole = 96.48 kJ/mole

make useful generalizations. Here our generalization is that methyl (and other alkyl) groups function as electron-donating substituents toward electron-deficient centers.

We also expect that an alkene with a higher-energy HOMO should be a more effective electron-pair donor than an alkene with a lower-energy HOMO, that is, the one with the higher-energy HOMO will react more quickly. We frequently observe this type of behavior, and we will meet some examples in the next chapter.

PROBLEM 9.12

Which compound of each pair do you predict to have the higher ionization potential?

a. propane or propene **b.** 1-pentene or 2-pentene

c. 2-methyl-1-pentene or 2-trifluoromethyl-1-pentene

9.6 Synthesis of Alkenes

In Chapter 7 we saw one important synthetic route to alkenes, the dehydration of alcohols (Reactions 15 and 17). Recall the mechanistic steps of these reactions. Protonation of the alcohol occurs first. Water is then lost, and a carbocation forms. The carbocation then gives up a proton from an adjacent carbon atom to some base in the solution.

A second important method of alkene synthesis is **dehydrohalogenation,** the loss of the elements of a hydrogen halide from a haloalkane. The reaction occurs by treatment of the haloalkane with a base. This reaction bears a superficial resemblence to the dehydration of alcohols, as shown in Figure 9.15.

However, major mechanistic differences exist between the two reactions. Most alkenes undergoing dehydrohalogenation do so by the so-called **E2 mechanism.** E stands for *elimination* (the H and X are eliminated). The 2 indicates that the reaction is a *bimolecular* process (two reactants come together in the rate-determining step). We will focus our attention on the detailed aspects of this and related mechanisms in Chapter 12. We will have much to say then about the use of kinetic data in studying organic reaction mechanisms. For the present, simply note that the E2 mechanism is a one-step reaction in which all bond-breaking and bond-formation occur in concert. Such a reaction is known as a **concerted reaction.** The curved-arrow formalism for the E2 reaction is shown in Figure 9.16.

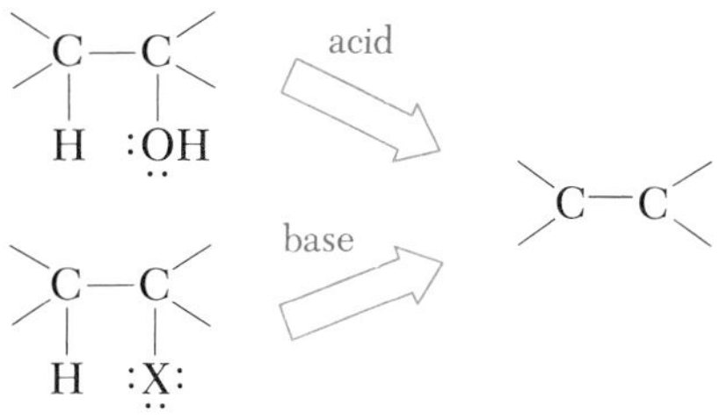

Figure 9.15 Formal relationship between dehydration and dehydrohalogenation.

C—C (H, :OH) —acid→ C=C

C—C (H, :X:) —base→ C=C

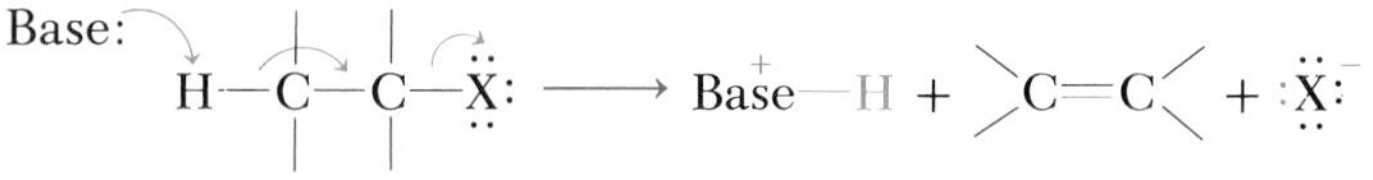

$$\text{Base:} \quad H-\underset{|}{\overset{|}{C}}-\underset{|}{\overset{|}{C}}-\ddot{\underset{..}{X}}: \longrightarrow \overset{+}{\text{Base}}-H + \; >C=C< \; + :\ddot{\underset{..}{X}}:^-$$

Figure 9.16 Curved-arrow depiction of the E2 reaction. The base provides a pair of electrons that bind a proton from the haloalkane. At the same time, the pair of electrons from the carbon-hydrogen bond moves into the region between the two carbon atoms, producing the π bond. The halogen simultaneously departs with the pair of electrons from the carbon-halogen bond. Part of the driving force for this reaction is the solvation of the displaced halide ion. The reaction occurs in a single mechanistic step. Further discussion of this reaction and a molecular orbital analysis of it are presented in Chapter 12.

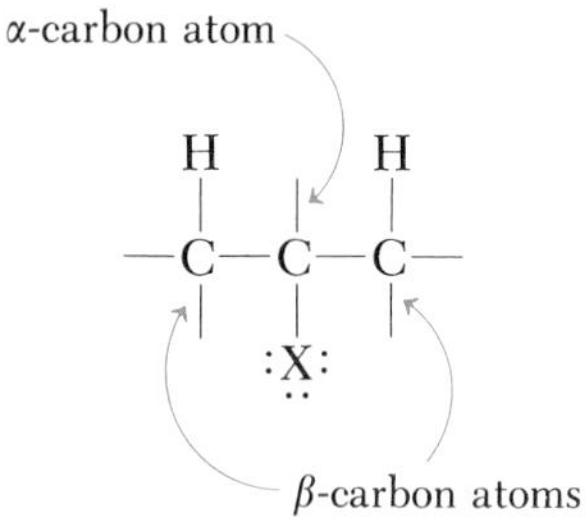

α-carbon atom

β-carbon atoms

Figure 9.17 Terminology of haloalkane sites. Haloalkanes must have at least one hydrogen attached to a β-carbon atom in order for E2 elimination to be possible. The carbon bearing the halogen is referred to as the α-carbon, and carbons adjacent to it are referred to as β-carbons.

A minimum requirement for the E2 reaction is a hydrogen atom bound to the carbon atom adjacent to that bearing the halogen, as shown in Figure 9.17. This site is referred to as the β-carbon atom.

Several examples of the formation of alkenes by the dehydrohalogenation route are given in Equations 9.2–9.7. In most of these examples, the base is an alkoxide ion, that is, the conjugate base of an alcohol. Remember that alcohols have pK_a values >15 and thus are weak acids. Therefore alkoxide ions are relatively strong bases. You should also recall that alkoxides can be prepared from alcohols by the action of sodium or potassium metal.

Eqn. 9.2

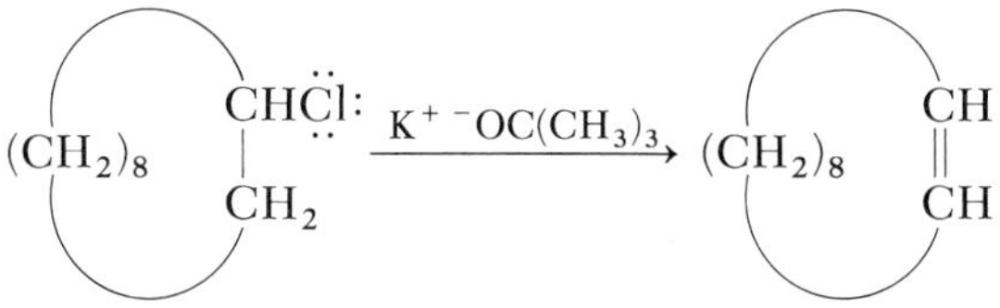

$$(CH_2)_8\text{CHCl–CH}_2 \text{ (ring)} \xrightarrow{K^+ \, ^-OC(CH_3)_3} (CH_2)_8\text{CH=CH (ring)}$$

chlorocyclodecane — 97% cyclodecene

Eqn. 9.3

$$CH_3CH_2CH_2CH_2CH_2CH_2CH_2Br: \xrightarrow{Li_2CO_3} CH_3CH_2CH_2CH_2CH_2CH=CH_2$$

1-bromoheptane — 51% 1-heptene

Eqn. 9.4

$$(CH_3)_2CHI: \xrightarrow{K^+ \, ^-OCH_2CH_3} CH_3CH=CH_2$$

2-iodopropane — 94% propene

Eqn. 9.5

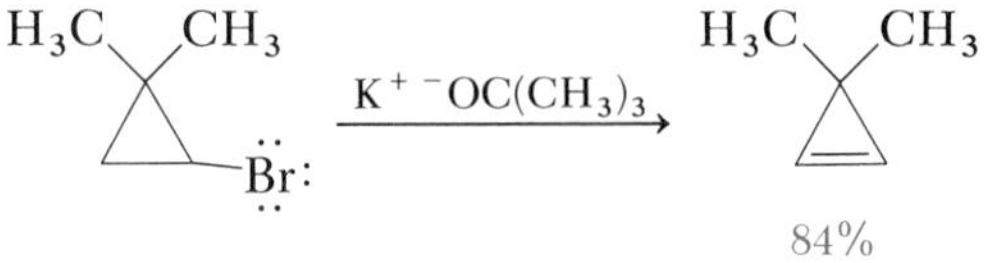

$$\text{(H}_3\text{C)(CH}_3\text{)C-cyclopropyl-Br} \xrightarrow{K^+ \, ^-OC(CH_3)_3} \text{(H}_3\text{C)(CH}_3\text{)C-cyclopropene}$$

2,2-dimethyl-1-bromocyclopropane — 84% 3,3-dimethylcyclopropene

Eqn. 9.6

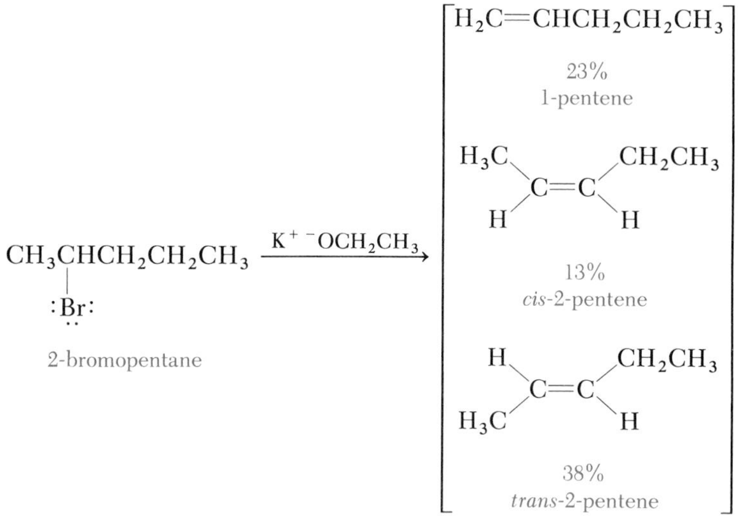

$$CH_3CH(Br)CH_2CH_2CH_3 \xrightarrow{K^{+}\ {}^{-}OCH_2CH_3} \left[H_2C{=}CHCH_2CH_2CH_3 \;+\; cis\text{-}CH_3CH{=}CHCH_2CH_3 \;+\; trans\text{-}CH_3CH{=}CHCH_2CH_3 \right]$$

2-bromopentane → 23% 1-pentene; 13% *cis*-2-pentene; 38% *trans*-2-pentene

Eqn. 9.7

$$\text{bromocyclohexane} \xrightarrow[\text{18-crown-6}]{K^{+}\ {}^{-}OCH_2CH_3} \text{cyclohexene}$$

bromocyclohexane → 83% cyclohexene

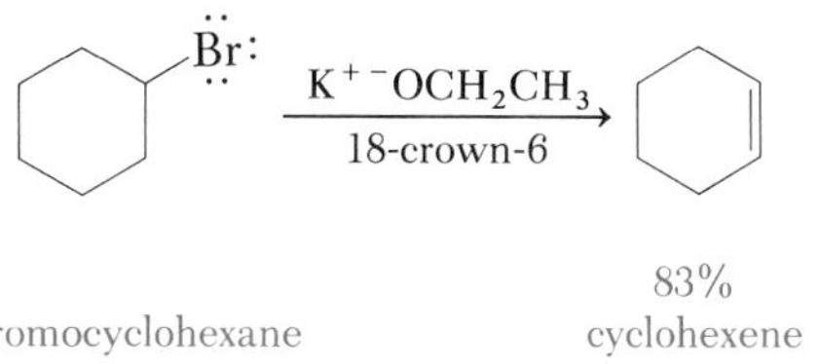

In Equations 9.2–9.5 a single alkene is formed in the dehydrohalogenation reaction. In each case there is only one way in which the elimination can occur. However, in Equation 9.6 we find that a mixture of three isomeric pentenes is obtained (1-pentene, *cis*-2-pentene, and *trans*-2-pentene). The mixture arises because there is *more* than one way for H and Br to be eliminated from 2-bromopentane, as shown in Figure 9.18.

When internal nonsymmetrical haloalkanes undergo E2 elimination using unhindered bases, formation of the more highly substituted alkene products is favored. (*Hindered* bases often result in a reversal of the orientation; see Chapter 12.) For example, as illustrated in Equation 9.6, the dehydrohalogenation of 2-bromopentane with ethoxide ion produces only 23% 1-butene, while

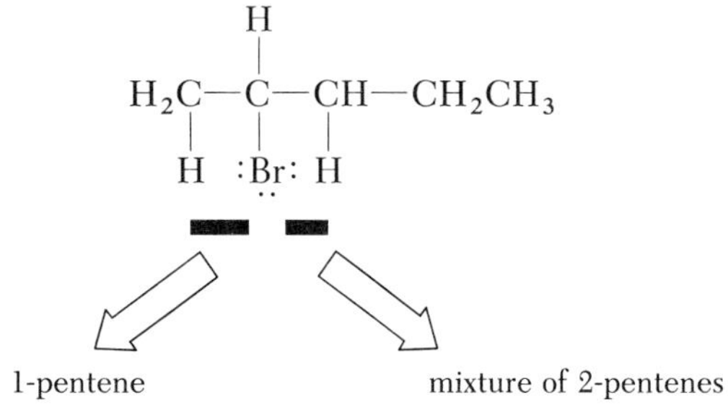

$$H_2C(H)-C(H)(Br)-CH(H)-CH_2CH_3$$

1-pentene ← → mixture of 2-pentenes

Figure 9.18 Formation of pentenes from 2-bromopentane. In general, the dehydrohalogenation reaction yields a single alkene product in only two types of systems. Only terminal alkene is formed if the halogen is attached to a terminal carbon atom. Also, a single alkene product is obtained for certain symmetric haloalkanes for which all modes of dehydrohalogenation yield the same product.

the 2-pentenes constitute 51% of the yield. This result is important and revealing, and we will return to consider it in various contexts in the next several chapters. For the moment we will simply note that for most (but not all) purposes, the formation of mixtures of products is a nuisance that we wish to avoid.

The last example (Equation 9.7) is a simple elimination that is facilitated by the ionophore 18-crown-6 (**9.15**). This material is a polyether that binds the potassium ion, leaving the ethoxide ion as a more reactive naked anion. (See the special topic "Supramolecular Chemistry" in Chapter 3. There is a further discussion of crown ethers in Chapter 14.) The trivial name for this material derives from its three-dimensional shape (a crown with six points) and the presence of eighteen atoms in the ring, six of which are oxygen atoms. A molecular model of 18-crown-6 was shown in Chapter 3.

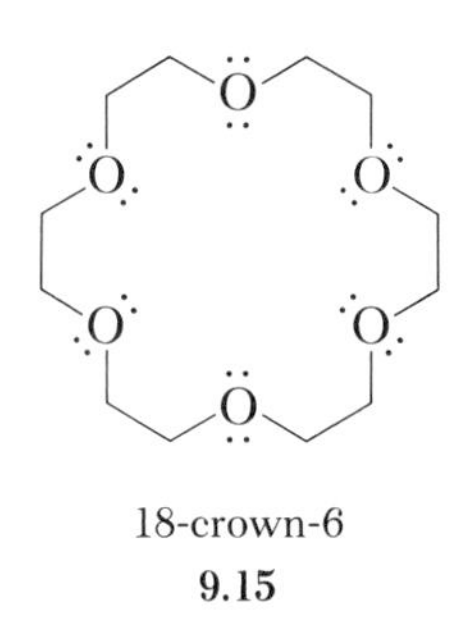

18-crown-6
9.15

Dehydrohalogenation of haloalkanes is but one of the methods for the synthesis of alkenes. However, it has limitations for the preparation of specific alkenes in high yield. These limitations and our attempts to overcome them will be discussed in Chapter 12.

PROBLEM 9.13 Consider the dehydration of 1-butanol upon reaction with strong acid. A mixture of three alkenes is obtained from this reaction. Draw the structures of the alkenes and name them. Suggest a mechanism for the formation of each alkene.

PROBLEM 9.14 When 1-bromopentane is treated with strong base to cause dehydrohalogenation, only a single alkene product is obtained (1-pentene). Explain why this observation suggests that a carbocation intermediate is not involved in this reaction.

PROBLEM 9.15 Given 1-pentanol as your starting material, what series of reactions could you use to prepare 1-pentene uncontaminated by other alkene products?

PROBLEM 9.16 Give the structure of a bromoalkane with the formula C_4H_9Br that is not primary and yet will yield a single product, C_4H_8, upon dehydrohalogenation.

Summary

- Each carbon atom of an alkene double bond is sp^2 hybridized, resulting in a trigonal planar array of bonds about each carbon atom. The two carbon atoms of the double bond and the four attached atoms all lie in the same plane.
- The π bond of an alkene results from side-to-side overlap of the p orbitals that are left unhybridized.
- We name simple alkenes by finding the longest continuous sequence of carbon atoms containing the double bond and the greatest number of substituents, and then naming any alkyl or halo substituents.
- Under normal conditions, free rotation about the double bond is impossible since there is insufficient energy to break the π bond. This rigidity makes possible the existence of geometric isomers.
- We may name geometric isomers by either the *cis/trans* system or the *E/Z* system.
- In naming compounds with multiple functional groups, group priorities (Table 9.1) tell which group takes precedence in the numbering of the carbon chain.
- Many natural products contain carbon-carbon double bonds. The terpenes, whose structures are composed of fragments known as isoprene units, make up one class of such compounds.
- Two important preparative methods for generating a carbon-carbon double bond are dehydration of an alcohol using an acid and dehydrohalogenation of an alkyl halide using a base. While dehydration involves the intermediate formation of a carbocation, dehydrohalogenation usually does not.
- The principal mechanism by which dehydrohalogenation occurs is E2, a one-step reaction in which bond breaking and bond formation occur simultaneously.
- The molecular orbital view of a double bond provides insight into many of the details of alkene behavior.
- The energy of the HOMO provides information about the effects of substituent groups (electron donating or releasing) attached to the double bond.
- The ionization energy (potential) of the molecule is a good experimental measure of the HOMO energy.
- With increasing alkyl substitution about a double bond, there is a steady decrease in ionization potential, suggesting an electron-donating ability for the alkyl groups that is consistent with our earlier findings.
- Light can promote a π bonding electron into a π antibonding orbital. The π bond order is thus reduced to zero, and rotation about the carbon-carbon linkage can occur. This process is important in vision and a variety of other systems.

Terms to Remember

alkene	isoprene unit	substituent effects
orthogonal	monoterpenes	ionization potential
cis/trans notation	terpenoid	dehydrohalogenation
geometric isomers	polymer	E2 mechanism
E/Z descriptors	Ziegler-Natta catalyst	concerted reaction

Reactions of Synthetic Utility

18. $\mathrm{H{-}\overset{|}{\underset{|}{C}}{-}\overset{|}{\underset{|}{C}}{-}X \xrightarrow{\text{base}} {>}C{=}C{<}}$ **9.6**

Halide is 1° or symmetrical in nature; the base is generally an alkoxide or other strong base.

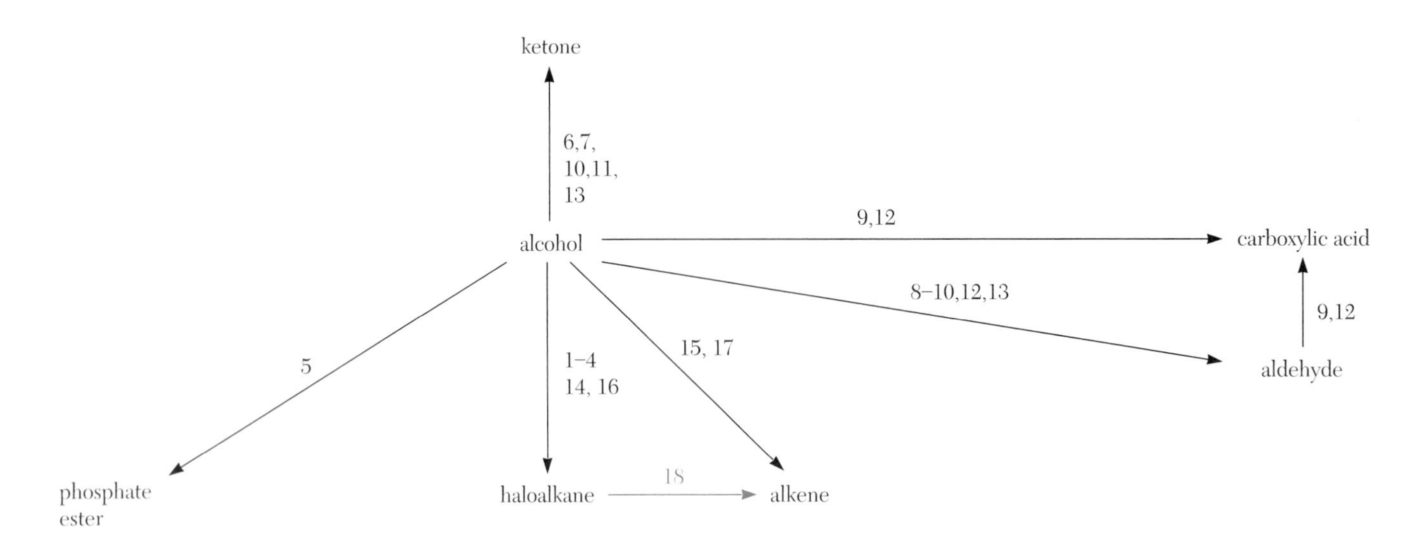

Additional Problems

9.17 Provide IUPAC names for the molecules represented below. Be sure to specify any stereochemical descriptors (*R*,*S*,*E*,*Z*) that are needed to distinguish the given structures from any stereoisomeric forms.

a.
$CH_3CH_2CH_2$ $CH(CH_3)_2$
C=C
H CH_3

b.
H_3C H
C=C
H CH_2CH_3

c.
CH_3 H_3C H
$(CH_3)_2C$=C C=C
CH_2CH_2 CH_3

d.
H
CH_3

e.
$CH{=}CH_2$
H_3C— —CH_2CH_3
H

f.
H
H C
C CH_3
H_3C— —$CH(CH_3)_2$
H

g.
$(CH_3)_2CH$ $CH_2CH_2CH_3$
C=C
$CH_3CH_2CH_2$ CH_3

9.18 Draw structures for each of the following:

a. (*Z*)-4-methyl-2-pentene
b. (*E*)-(*S*)-4-chloro-3-methyl-2-pentene
c. (*Z*,*Z*)-2,4-hexadiene
d. (*Z*)-2-methyl-2-buten-1-ol
e. (*E*)-3,7-dimethyl-2,6-octadien-1-ol
f. (*Z*)-4-(2-methylpropyl)-1,4-hexadiene

9.19 Examine the structure of squalene in Figure 9.10. Which of the double bonds in the molecules must be specified as *E* or *Z* in writing an IUPAC name for it? Make these assignments and tell why it is not necessary to specify *E* or *Z* for all of the double bonds in this molecule.

9.20 Name a bromoalkane that will yield 4-ethyl-1-hexene and no other alkenes on treatment with potassium *tert*-butoxide in *tert*-butyl alcohol.

9.21 Provide the structure and name for each of the following:
a. all disubstituted alkenes of formula C_6H_{12}
b. all noncyclic trisubstituted alkenes of formula C_7H_{14}

9.22 Tell which compound of each of the following pairs you would expect to have the larger dipole moment. Explain each answer.
a. *cis*-2-butene or *trans*-2-butene
b. *cis*-1,2-dichloropropene or *trans*-1,2-dichloropropene
c. (Z)-2,3-dichloro-2-butene or (*E*)-2,3-dichloro-2-butene

9.23 *cis*-1-Chloropropene has a larger dipole moment than *cis*-1-bromopropene, yet it has a lower boiling temperature. Offer an explanation for this behavior.

9.24 Outline the isoprene units present in each of the following:

a. 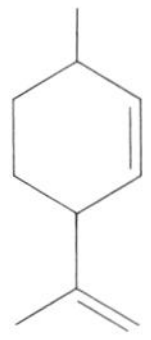 limonene

b. 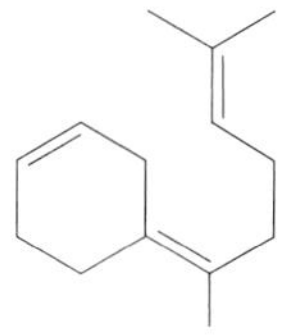 zingiberene

c. 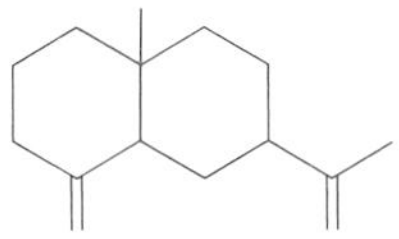 *β*-selinene

d. 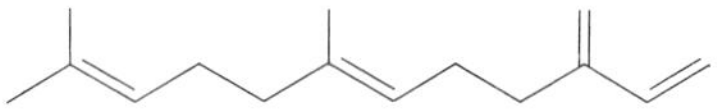 *trans*-*β*-farnesene

9.25 Consider the treatment of 1,3-dichloro-3-methylpentane with potassium *tert*-butoxide in *tert*-butyl alcohol. Draw the structures of all anticipated products and predict the relative amount of each that would be formed.

9.26 Name each of the following compounds, making use if necessary of the nomenclature priorities given earlier.

a. $(CH_3CH_2)_2C{=}CH_2$

b. 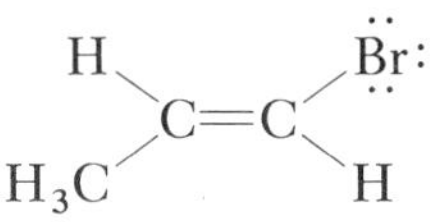 $\mathrm{H(H_3C)C{=}C(H)\ddot{B}r\!:}$ (H and H_3C on one carbon; Br and H on the other)

c. $CH_3CH_2CHCH_2\ddot{O}H$ with $CH{=}CH_2$ on C-3

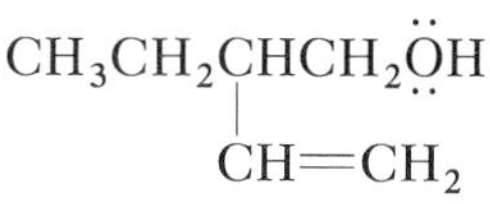

9.27 The compounds shown below have been identified as pheromones. Provide complete IUPAC names with appropriate stereochemical descriptors for each. (*Hint:* The *n*-alkane $C_{12}H_{26}$ is known as dodecane.)

a. 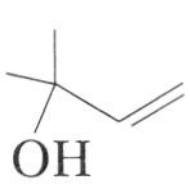 OH

bark beetle pheromone

b. 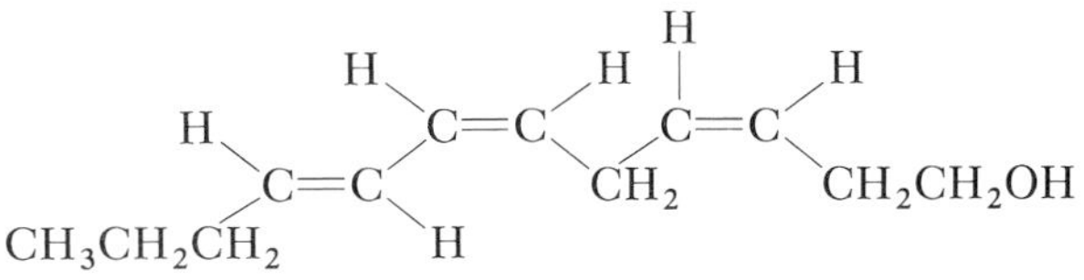 $CH_3CH_2CH_2(H)C{=}C(H)\text{–}C(H){=}C(H)\text{–}CH_2\text{–}C(H){=}C(H)CH_2CH_2OH$

trail pheromone of termites

9.28 Using the curved-arrow formalism, show how each of the following reactions occurs:
a. 1-bromopentane with KOH in ethanol to yield 1-pentene
b. *tert*-butyl chloride with KOH in ethanol to yield 2-methylpropene

9.29 A student plans to prepare 1-hexene by dehydration of 1-hexanol. What problems do you see in accomplishing this synthesis? Devise a better synthetic route to 1-hexene from 1-hexanol.

9.30 Considering isomers of the formula $C_6H_{13}Br$, provide names for any compounds that:
a. cannot undergo an elimination reaction to form an alkene when treated with base
b. will yield a single alkene product as a result of E2 dehydrohalogenation

***9.31** The ionization potential of acrylonitrile, $H_2C{=}CH{-}C{\equiv}N{:}$, is larger than that of ethylene. In both cases ionization involves the ejection of an electron from the carbon-carbon π-bonding molecular orbital. What can we infer about the electron-donating or electron-withdrawing effect of a $-C{\equiv}N{:}$ group from this information?

***9.32** Many reactions of alkenes involve the transfer of electron density from the carbon-carbon π bond to another molecule. Which type of alkene (mono-, di-, tri-, or tetrasubstituted) is expected to react more quickly on the basis of HOMO/LUMO interactions? Explain your answer.

9.33 Consider the following curved-arrow depiction of a key step in the biosynthesis of geranyl pyrophosphate.

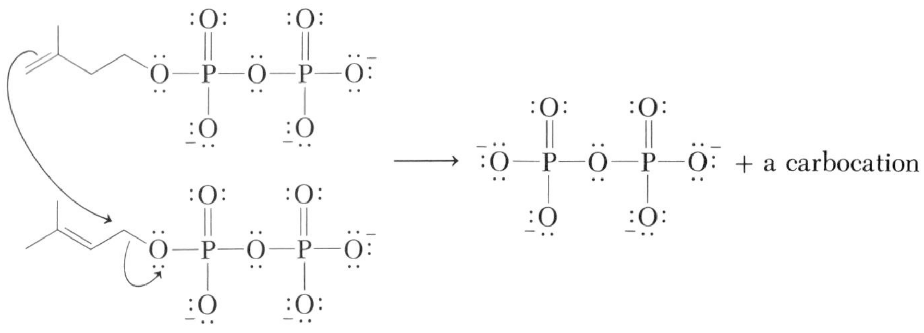

Draw a structure of the carbocation produced in this reaction. Show with the curved-arrow formalism how this carbocation could be converted into geranyl pyrophosphate. (Geranyl pyrophosphate is the pyrophosphate ester of geraniol.)

Carbon-Carbon Doubly Bonded Systems II. Reactions of Alkenes

10.1 Introduction

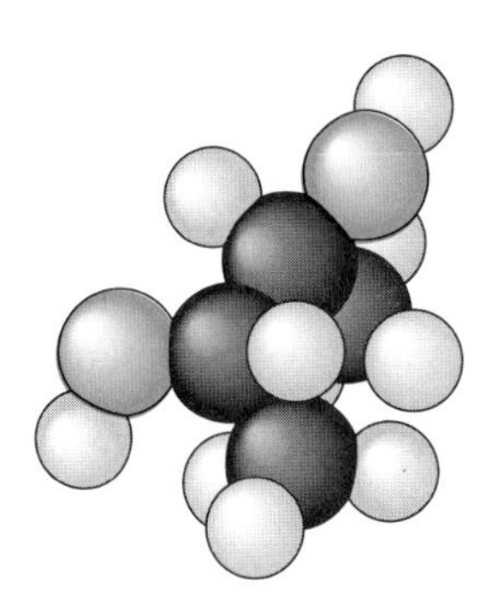

In this chapter we will be concerned with reactions at the carbon-carbon double bond. We will focus on two main categories of reactions: **addition reactions** and **oxidative cleavage reactions.**

In an addition reaction, two reactant molecules combine to give a single product molecule. For alkenes, there are many addition reactions of the general type shown in Figure 10.1. In the first step of the reaction of Y—Z with the alkene, it is the *alkene* that supplies the electrons for new bond formation to Y or Z. Conversely, the molecule Y—Z seeks electron-rich reagents. We call the molecule Y—Z an **electrophile** and this reaction type **electrophilic addition.**

These addition reactions involve breaking the weaker π bond of the double bond and forming two new σ bonds, one to Y and one to Z. Many addition reactions are of great synthetic importance—the products are either of direct utility, or they are converted by subsequent reactions into useful materials.

Oxidative cleavage reactions involve breaking both the π and σ bonds of the carbon-carbon double bond. Carbon-oxygen double bonds are formed in their place, as shown in Figure 10.2.

Further oxidation of these products may occur, depending on the conditions used and on the nature of the reagents used to effect the cleavage.

We will now explore the scope of these two types of reactions and relate them to topics and principles covered in earlier chapters.

10.2 Addition Reactions: Stereochemical Aspects

Consider the addition of the two groups Y and Z to a carbon-carbon double bond. First, we will look at an important stereochemical question: do Y and Z add to the *same* face of the double bond, or to *opposite* faces of the double bond, or do we find a mixture of the two types of products?

Two new stereochemical terms will prove helpful in our discussion: ***syn* addition** is the addition of two groups to the *same* face of the double bond; and ***anti* addition** is the addition of the two groups to *opposite* faces of the double bond. The two modes of addition are illustrated in Figure 10.3.

To investigate the stereochemistry of addition reactions we must use an alkene that gives *different* products depending on the mode of addition. It is important to realize that many simple alkenes give the same product regardless of whether *syn* or *anti* addition occurs. Consider, for example, the reaction shown in Equation 10.1.

Eqn. 10.1

$$CH_2BrCH{=}CH_2 + Br_2 \xrightarrow[CCl_4]{} CH_2BrCHBrCH_2Br$$

3-bromopropene → 1,2,3-tribromopropane (98% yield)

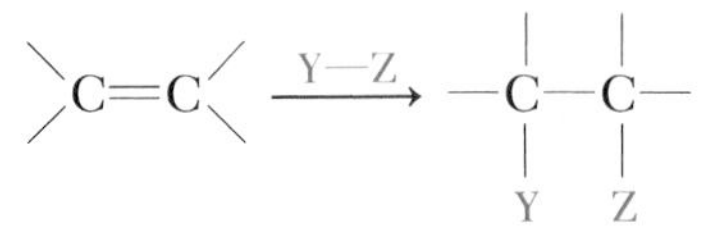

$$>C{=}C< \xrightarrow{Y-Z} -\underset{Y}{\overset{|}{C}}-\underset{Z}{\overset{|}{C}}-$$

Figure 10.1 An addition reaction at the carbon-carbon double bond. Y and Z represent two atoms or groups that add across the carbon-carbon double bond. It is possible for Y and Z to be identical.

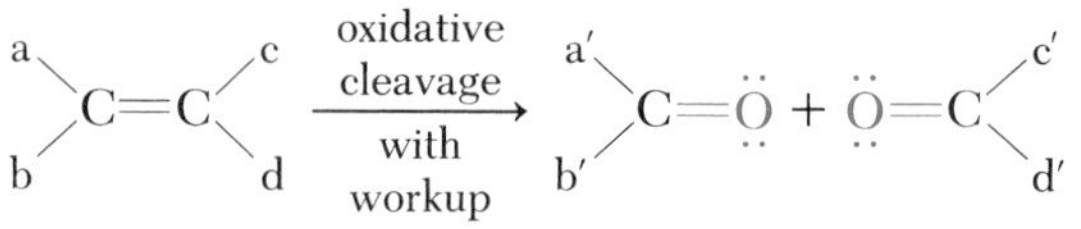

$$\text{(a)(b)}C{=}C\text{(c)(d)} \xrightarrow[\text{with workup}]{\text{oxidative cleavage}} \text{(a}'\text{)(b}'\text{)}C{=}\ddot{O} + \ddot{O}{=}C\text{(c}'\text{)(d}'\text{)}$$

Figure 10.2 Oxidative cleavage reactions of carbon-carbon double bonds. Both the π bond and the σ bond of the double bond are broken. The products contain the carbon-oxygen double bond. The substituents a, b, c, and d may be modified (to a′, b′, c′, and d′) in the course of the reaction and workup (see section 10.13).

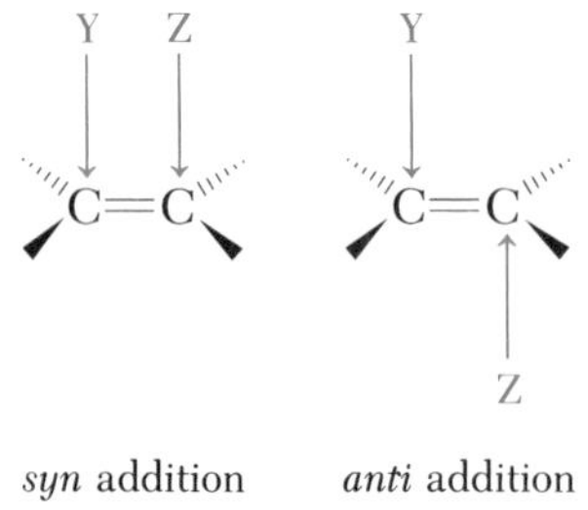

syn addition — *anti* addition

Figure 10.3 Stereochemistry of addition to carbon-carbon double bonds. In *syn* addition, both groups add to the same face of the double bond. In *anti* addition, the groups add to opposite faces of the double bond.

In this case the different modes of addition simply result in the initial formation of different conformations of the same product. While *syn* addition leads initially to an eclipsed conformation, *anti* addition leads initially to a staggered conformation of the product. These conformations can then readily interconvert by rotation about single bonds. While we can see clearly that bromine atoms have added to each end of the double bond, we can tell nothing about the stereochemistry of the reaction.

However, *disubstituted* alkenes are useful for deducing the stereochemistry of addition reactions. Cyclic alkenes are particularly useful for this purpose. Consider the same type of addition reaction as shown in Equation 10.1, with cyclohexene as the alkene. If the two bromine atoms add in a *syn* manner, the product is *cis*-1,2-dibromocyclohexane. (Refer to Chapter 4 for an introductory discussion of *cis/trans* isomerism in cyclic compounds.) If the bromine atoms add in an *anti* manner, the product is *trans*-1,2-dibromocyclohexane. These two possibilities are shown in Figure 10.4. Only *trans*-1,2-dibromocyclohexane is formed in this reaction, so we infer that the two bromine atoms add in an *anti* manner. Similar results with other alkenes lead to the *general* conclusion that two bromine atoms add in an *anti* manner to double bonds.

Our ability to determine the stereochemistry of addition of bromine to cyclohexene depends on the existence of two distinct isomers of 1,2-dibromocyclohexane, each having unique properties. For example, the *cis* isomer has a melting temperature of 10 °C, whereas the *trans* isomer has a melting temperature of −4 °C. (Notice also that the *trans* compound is resolvable into (+) and (−) enantiomers, while the *cis* compound is not—it is *meso*.)

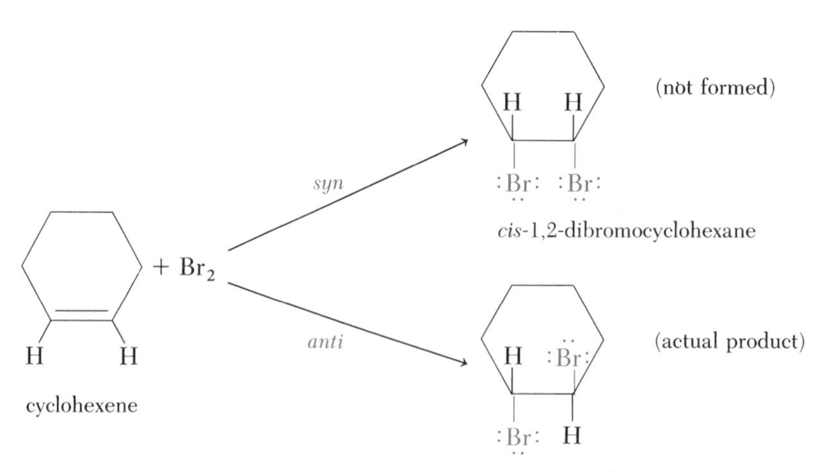

Figure 10.4 Possible routes of bromine addition to cyclohexene. The *syn* addition would produce *cis*-1,2-dibromocyclohexane, whereas *anti* addition would produce *trans*-1,2-dibromocyclohexane. Experimentally, we find that only the *trans* isomer is actually formed.

PROBLEM 10.1

At times we cannot immediately distinguish between *syn* and *anti* addition even by working with cyclic compounds. Explain why a study of the reaction of cyclohexene with hydrogen to give cyclohexane could not distinguish whether the hydrogen addition occurred through a *syn* or an *anti* route. Suggest a structure for an alkene that would allow us to distinguish between *syn* and *anti* addition of hydrogen.

Some open-chain alkenes can give different products following *syn* and *anti* addition. In these alkenes both carbon atoms of the double bond are **prochiral.** A prochiral carbon atom is one that is not itself stereogenic, but becomes stereogenic upon a single reaction. The concept of prochirality with a trisubstituted (sp^2) carbon atom (as in an alkene) is illustrated in Figure 10.5.

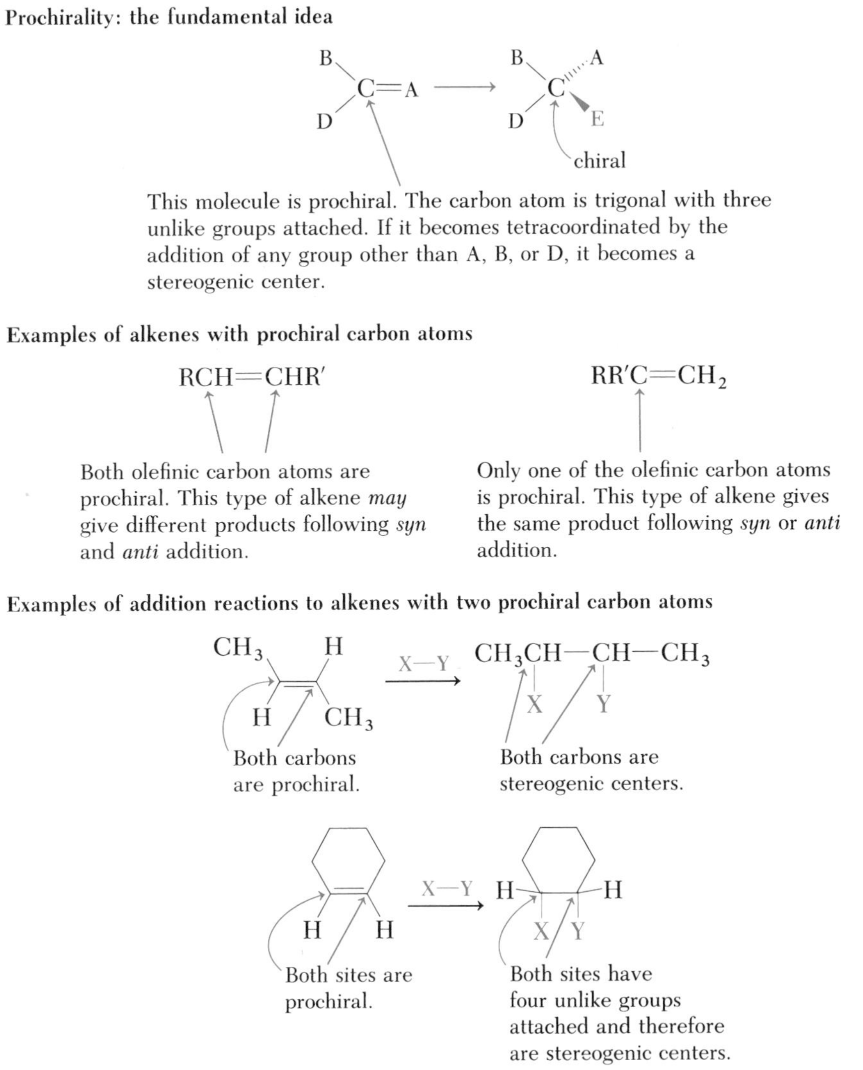

Figure 10.5 Prochirality in alkenes. The fundamental requirement for a trigonal carbon to be prochiral is shown at the top. Shown directly beneath it are two alkenes. The alkene on the left is disubstituted, and both olefinic carbons are prochiral. This alkene gives different products following *syn* or *anti* addition, as will be shown directly below. The alkene on the right has only one prochiral carbon and does not give different products following *syn* or *anti* addition. In *trans*-2-butene and cyclohexene (at the bottom), both olefinic carbons are prochiral, and as shown above, different products are formed via *syn* and *anti* addition.

Prochirality: the fundamental idea

B, D C=A ⟶ B, D, A, E C

chiral

This molecule is prochiral. The carbon atom is trigonal with three unlike groups attached. If it becomes tetracoordinated by the addition of any group other than A, B, or D, it becomes a stereogenic center.

Examples of alkenes with prochiral carbon atoms

RCH=CHR′

Both olefinic carbon atoms are prochiral. This type of alkene *may* give different products following *syn* and *anti* addition.

$RR'C=CH_2$

Only one of the olefinic carbon atoms is prochiral. This type of alkene gives the same product following *syn* or *anti* addition.

Examples of addition reactions to alkenes with two prochiral carbon atoms

CH_3, H, H, CH_3 $\xrightarrow{X-Y}$ $CH_3CH-CH-CH_3$ (X, Y)

Both carbons are prochiral.

Both carbons are stereogenic centers.

H, H $\xrightarrow{X-Y}$ H, H, X, Y

Both sites are prochiral.

Both sites have four unlike groups attached and therefore are stereogenic centers.

In this context consider now the products that would be obtained by bromine addition to *cis*-2-butene and *trans*-2-butene. We can quickly deduce that the product is 2,3-dibromobutane. However, since there are two stereogenic centers in 2,3-dibromobutane, there are potentially four (2^2) stereoisomers. In fact, only *three* stereoisomers of 2,3-dibromobutane actually exist. One of these stereoisomers is a *meso* structure, diastereoisomeric with regard to the other two structures, which constitute a pair of enantiomers.

We need to know which of these stereoisomers will actually be formed in the bromination of each of the 2-butenes. Will there be just the *meso* product, just the pair of enantiomers, or a mixture of all three stereoisomers? Do the two alkenes give the same product(s) or different ones? We can use stereochemical drawings to predict the outcome or *syn* and *anti* addition in order to answer our questions.

Figure 10.6 shows the result we would observe with *syn* addition of bromine to *cis*-2-butene. For completeness we show *two* possible ways in which this addition could occur. Bromine could add from the top face or from the bottom face. These two modes of *syn* addition are equally likely. We predict that *syn* addition will result in the formation of *meso*-2,3-dibromobutane. Experimentally, however, we do *not* find that *meso*-2,3-dibromobutane is formed in this reaction. We therefore infer that bromine does *not* add in a *syn* manner to the alkene.

Consider now the *anti* addition of bromine to *cis*-2-butene, as shown in Figure 10.7. Two modes of addition are possible. One leads to (2*R*,3*R*)- and one to (2*S*,3*S*)-2,3-dibromobutane.

We see that *syn* and *anti* addition of bromine to *cis*-2-butene would lead to *different* products. Experimentally, we observe *only* the products of *anti* addition as shown in Figure 10.7. Just as in the reaction with cyclohexene we infer that bromine adds to the double bonds of *cis*- and *trans*-2-butene with *anti* stereochemistry. *Bromine adds to alkenes in an* anti *fashion.*

In the next sections we will consider in more detail the additions of bromine, hydrogen, and other reagents to the olefinic linkage. We will find that in some cases addition occurs exclusively with *syn* stereochemistry, in others the ster-

Figure 10.6 The *syn* addition of bromine to *cis*-2-butene. The predicted product is *meso*-2,3-dibromobutane regardless of whether the two bromine atoms add to the top or bottom face. In fact, we do not observe *meso*-2,3-dibromobutane as a product of this reaction, and thus we conclude that the mode of addition is not *syn*.

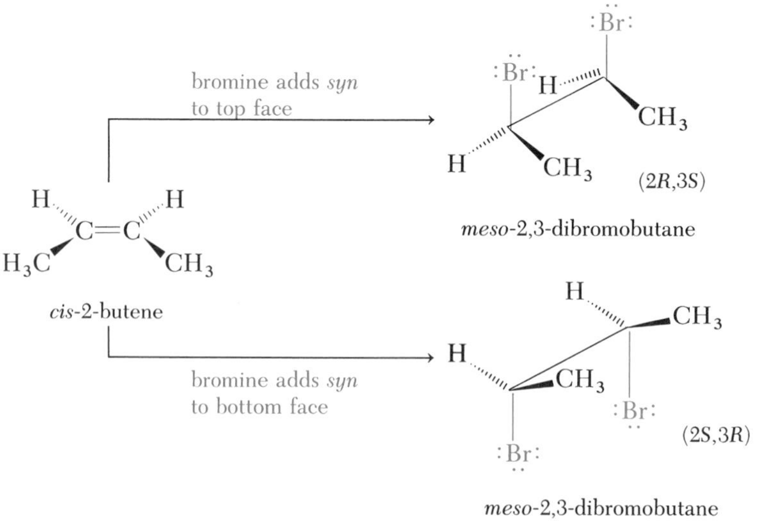

Figure 10.7 The *anti* addition of bromine to *cis*-2-butene. The predicted products are the pair of enantiomers shown, which are also the experimentally observed products in this reaction.

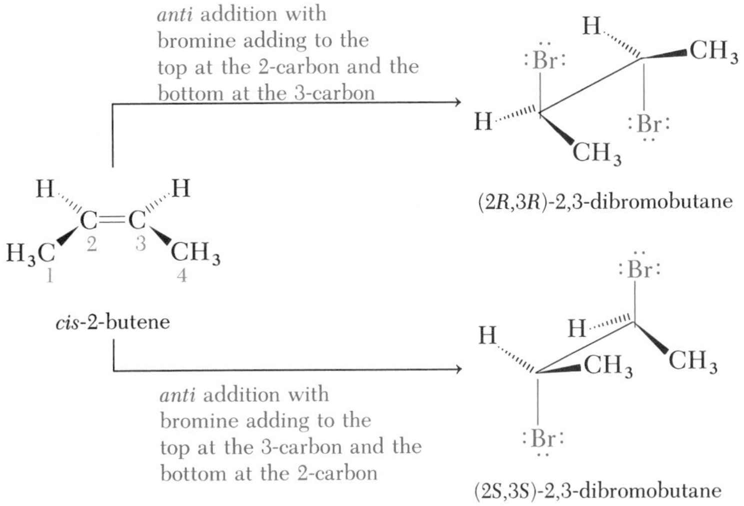

anti addition with bromine adding to the top at the 2-carbon and the bottom at the 3-carbon

cis-2-butene

(2*R*,3*R*)-2,3-dibromobutane

anti addition with bromine adding to the top at the 3-carbon and the bottom at the 2-carbon

(2*S*,3*S*)-2,3-dibromobutane

eochemistry will be exclusively *anti*, and for some there will be no preference. Throughout our discussion we will be using the stereochemical principles described here. It is extremely important that you practice using stereochemical drawings of the type shown in Figures 10.6 and 10.7 to predict the possible products of *syn* and *anti* addition.

PROBLEM 10.2 Use drawings of the wedge type to deduce the expected products from the *syn* and *anti* addition of bromine to:
a. *trans*-2-butene **b.** *trans*-2-pentene **c.** *cis*-2-pentene

Many reactions occur exclusively or predominantly with *syn* or *anti* addition. Three important terms in this context are:

stereoselective reaction—a reaction that yields predominantly one stereoisomer (or an enantiomeric pair) of several possible diastereoisomers

stereospecific reaction—a reaction that yields only one stereoisomer (or an enantiomeric pair) of product from a particular stereoisomer of starting material, while the opposite stereoisomer of starting material yields the opposite stereoisomer (or enantiomeric pair) of product

nonstereospecific reaction—a reaction in which all of the possible stereoisomeric products are formed

The addition of bromine to an alkene is an example of a stereospecific reaction.

10.3 Addition of Hydrogen

The addition of two hydrogen atoms across a carbon-carbon double bond (Figure 10.1, Y = Z = H) is referred to as **hydrogenation** of the double bond. This reaction is also a reduction, since the number of carbon-hydrogen bonds to each of the olefinic carbons is increased.

In addition to being important for synthetic purposes, the hydrogenation reaction provides valuable insights into stereochemistry, and it can be used to probe the relative stabilities of different alkenes. Hydrogenation involves treating an alkene with molecular hydrogen (H_2) in the presence of a *catalyst*. A catalyst provides a route between reactants and products that has a lower energy of activation than is otherwise available. Catalysts do *not* change the position of equilibrium but simply allow the reaction system to reach equilibrium more rapidly. Catalysts for the hydrogenation of alkenes are grouped into two categories, **heterogenous catalysts** and **homogeneous catalysts.**

HYDROGENATION WITH HETEROGENEOUS CATALYSTS

Stereochemistry and Mechanism Heterogeneous catalysts are insoluble in the reaction medium. They are usually composed of finely divided metals with large surface areas that provide sites for the reaction to occur. Both alkene and hydrogen molecules interact with the metal surface, and as a result both the alkene π bond and the bond of the hydrogen molecule are partially broken.

The catalyst facilitates the bond breaking necessary if new bond formation is to occur. Both reactants are activated for the formation of the new carbon-hydrogen bonds. These activated species are able to combine to generate the product.

The equilibrium position for hydrogen addition across an alkene π bond lies far to the side of the product alkane. The catalyst facilitates reaching this equilibrium position. In simple additions to alkenes the two hydrogens are usually added to the same face of the alkene (there *are* some exceptions).

A schematic representation of the reaction is shown in Figure 10.8. The *syn* nature of the addition is a predicted consequence of adding the two hydrogens from the catalyst surface to the activated alkene.

PROBLEM 10.3 The *syn* addition of hydrogen to *cis*-3,4-dimethyl-3-hexene produces a single *meso* compound. However, *syn* addition of hydrogen to *trans*-3,4-dimethyl-3-hexene produces a racemic mixture of an enantiomeric pair. Give the structure and complete name of each of these products.

Practical Details Several metals are commonly used as hydrogenation catalysts. Platinum, palladium, rhodium, and ruthenium are the most common choices. With palladium and ruthenium, the active catalyst is normally prepared by dispersing the metal on the surface of finely divided charcoal. Platinum is commonly used in the form of its oxide, PtO_2, sometimes called Adam's catalyst. Platinum oxide is a brown powder that undergoes a rapid reduction in the presence of hydrogen to form finely divided platinum metal. This material, which is black in color, is the actual hydrogenation catalyst.

Consider now how the hydrogenation reaction is performed. We dissolve the alkene in a suitable solvent (often ethanol) in the presence of the catalyst. The reaction vessel is attached to a reservoir of hydrogen gas and the reaction mixture is stirred vigorously or shaken. It is important to agitate the heterogeneous reaction mixture to allow all reactants to come into contact. As the reaction proceeds, hydrogen gas is absorbed. A gas manometer measures how much hydrogen gas reacts with the alkene. From the temperature and pressure

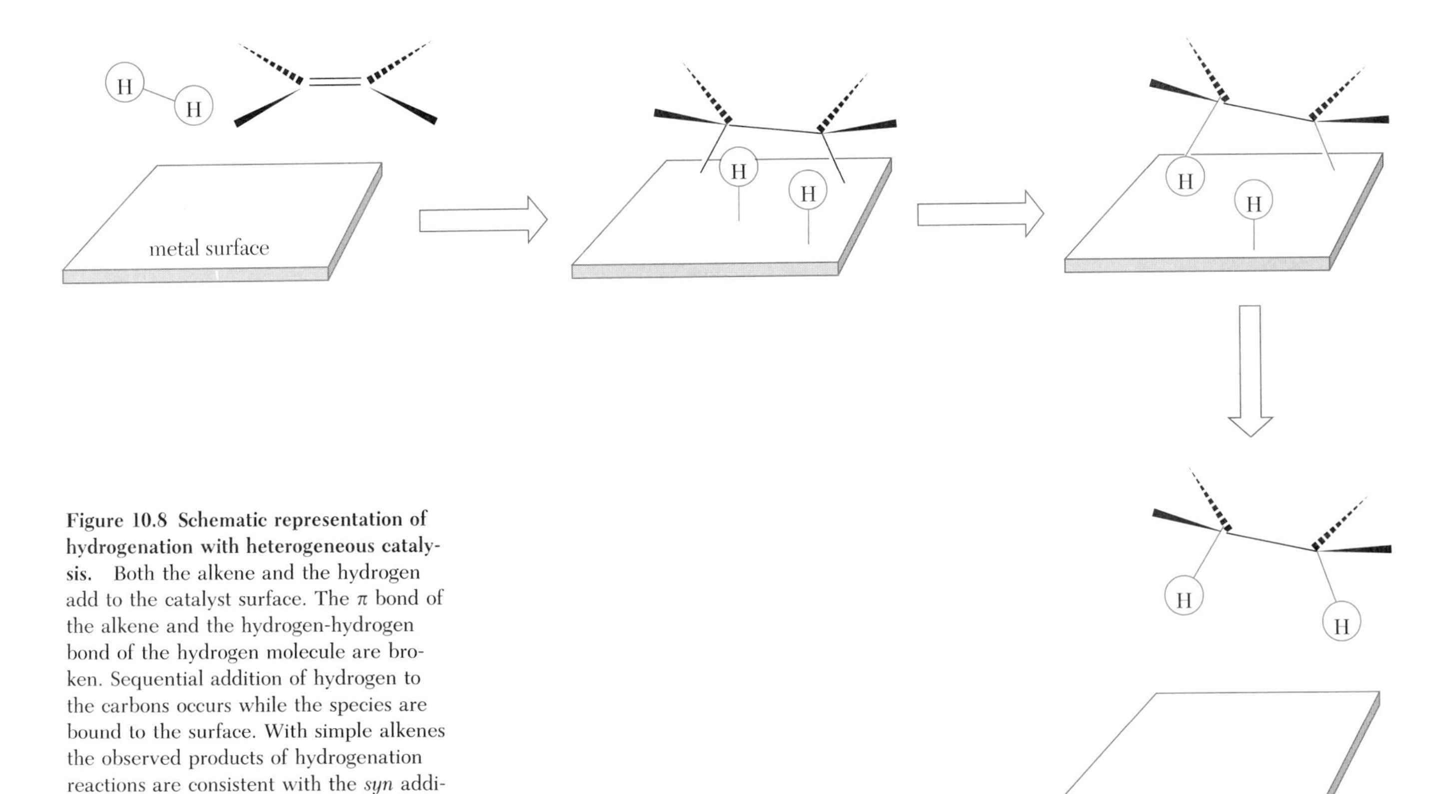

Figure 10.8 Schematic representation of hydrogenation with heterogeneous catalysis. Both the alkene and the hydrogen add to the catalyst surface. The π bond of the alkene and the hydrogen-hydrogen bond of the hydrogen molecule are broken. Sequential addition of hydrogen to the carbons occurs while the species are bound to the surface. With simple alkenes the observed products of hydrogenation reactions are consistent with the *syn* addition of two hydrogen atoms.

of the system and the change in the volume of the gas in the manometer, we can calculate the number of moles of hydrogen consumed.

For many hydrogenations a hydrogen pressure of one atmosphere is adequate for facile reaction. Higher pressures (and special apparatus) are sometimes required.

A practical advantage of heterogeneous catalysts is the ease of isolation of the product. Once the reaction is complete, we can simply remove the catalyst by filtration and then evaporate the solvent to isolate the product.

There are several disadvantages as well to the heterogeneous catalysis system. The reaction is relatively slow, a common problem with heterogeneous reactions in general. Further, many catalysts are easily *poisoned*, that is, the catalytic activity of the metal is destroyed by trace contaminants, commonly sulfur or sulfur-containing compounds. Metal sulfides are readily formed and do not support hydrogenation. Ordinary rubber stoppers contain sufficient amounts of sulfur to poison most heterogeneous catalysts. Another difficulty is that the rate of reduction depends on the degree of substitution about the double bond. Trisubstituted alkenes generally require elevated temperatures and pressures higher than several atmospheres for reduction to be accomplished. It is extremely difficult to reduce tetrasubstituted alkenes. Reactions other than simple addition, such as cleavage of certain types of bonds may also occur.

Finely divided nickel (Raney nickel) can also be used for hydrogenations. This catalyst is prepared by treating a nickel-aluminum alloy with aqueous base that dissolves the aluminum and leaves behind the finely divided nickel. After repeated washings with alcohol, the nickel is in a finely divided state with hydrogen adsorbed on its surface. Higher temperatures and pressures are usually required for Raney nickel reductions, and numerous side reactions can occur. Nevertheless, nickel has the distinct advantage for industrial use of being much less expensive than the other heterogeneous catalysts.

HOMOGENEOUS CATALYSTS FOR HYDROGENATION

In the 1970s catalysts began to be developed for hydrogenation under homogeneous conditions. These catalysts, which are complexes of transition metals, are soluble in the reaction medium. They have a number of appealing characteristics, including an increased rate of reaction, a decrease in the possibility of poisoning, and fewer side reactions. Furthermore, the reduction of carbon-carbon double bonds in the presence of a variety of other functional groups is possible.

The most common homogeneous catalysts are complexes of rhodium(I) or ruthenium(II). The most widely used catalyst, $[(C_6H_5)_3P]_3RhCl$ (the group C_6H_5— is the phenyl group, sometimes abbreviated as Ph or as ϕ), is known as the *Wilkinson catalyst* for its inventor, Professor Geoffrey Wilkinson. This catalyst has no effect on several groups that are reduced when other heterogeneous hydrogenation catalysts are used. Among the groups unaffected by the Wilkinson catalyst are the nitro group (—NO_2), the cyano group (—CN), and the aldehyde function (—CHO). The Wilkinson catalyst can be used to reduce carbon-carbon double bonds in the presence of these groups without having undesirable side reactions occur.

An important ruthenium(II) homogeneous catalyst is $([C_6H_5]_3P)_3RuClH$. This catalyst brings about the selective reduction of carbon-carbon double bonds at the end of a chain [terminal double bonds]. Internal carbon-carbon double bonds are unaffected by this catalyst. An example is shown in Equation 10.2.

Eqn. 10.2

$$CH_2CH{=}CH_2\text{-cyclohexene} \xrightarrow[H_2]{([C_6H_5]_3P)_3RuClH} CH_2CH_2CH_3\text{-cyclohexene}$$

3-(3-propenyl)-1-cyclohexene

84% yield
3-propyl-1-cyclohexene

The internal olefinic linkage is left untouched while the terminal olefinic linkage is reduced.

THERMOCHEMISTRY OF HYDROGENATION REACTIONS

Chemical reactions are generally accompanied by energy changes. The heat evolved (an exothermic reaction) or absorbed (an endothermic reaction) is generally expressed in terms of ΔH. ΔH for a reaction is the difference in enthalpy between reactants and products. (If necessary, you should review the introductory discussion of thermodynamic functions in Chapter 7.) We can measure the change in enthalpy for a reaction by performing it in a calorimeter. The heat evolved (or absorbed) is transferred to a surrounding reservoir of water, and the change in the temperature of the water is used to compute the amount of heat evolved (or taken up) by the reaction.

In general terms, ΔH reflects the relative strengths of the bonds broken and formed in the course of a reaction. Consider a simple reaction in which one weak bond is broken and one strong bond is formed. The energy difference between the strengths of the weak bond broken and the strong bond formed determines the extent to which the reaction is exothermic.

In the hydrogenation of alkenes, several bonds are broken and formed. Specifically, the π bond of the alkene is broken along with the hydrogen-hydrogen bond of the hydrogen molecule, and two carbon-hydrogen σ bonds are formed. The combined strengths of the π bond of the alkene and the hydrogen-hydrogen bond are less than that of the two carbon-hydrogen bonds formed. Thus, the overall reaction is exothermic. The heat evolved when hydrogen reacts with an alkene is known as the **heat of hydrogenation.**

We can calculate the energy of the alkene π bond knowing the heat of hydrogenation of the alkene and the strengths of the other bonds broken and formed. Consider the hydrogenation of 1-pentene as shown in Equation 10.3. The reaction is exothermic to the extent of approximately 30 kcal/mole.

Eqn. 10.3

$$\underset{\text{1-pentene}}{CH_3CH_2CH_2CH{=}CH_2} + H_2 \xrightarrow{\text{catalyst}} \underset{\text{pentane}}{CH_3CH_2CH_2CH_2CH_3} \qquad \Delta H^\circ = -30 \text{ kcal/mole}$$

The bond energy of the hydrogen molecule is 104 kcal/mole and the energy of each of the carbon-hydrogen bonds formed is 99 kcal/mole. Given these energies and the measured heat of hydrogenation, we can calculate the energy of the π bond to be approximately 64 kcal/mole. The energetics of reactants, products, and intermediate species are shown in Figure 10.9.

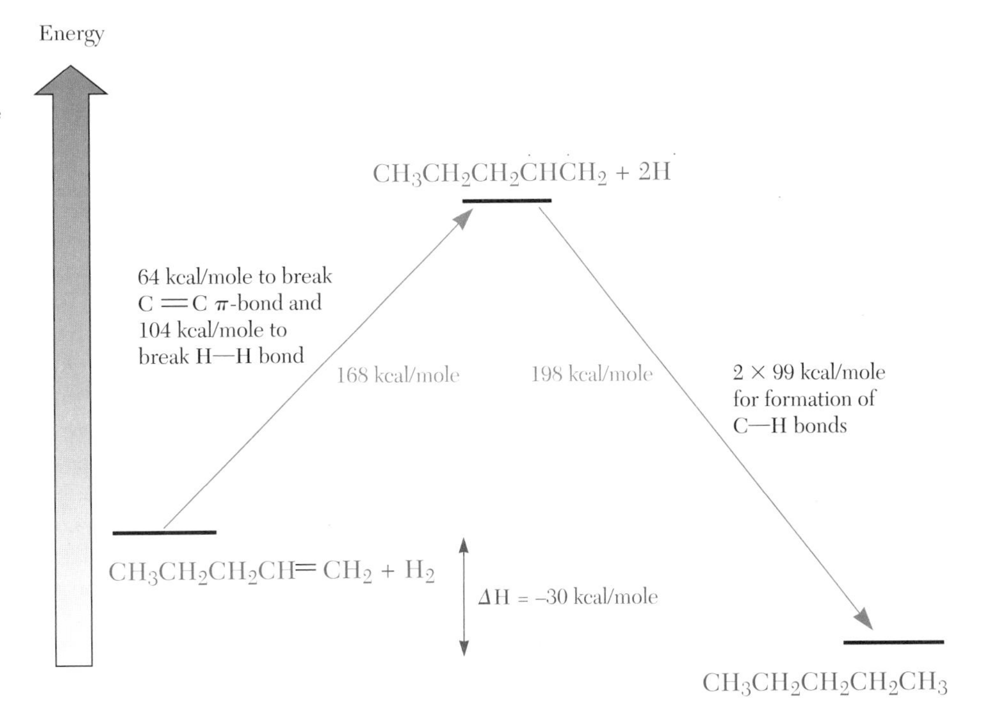

Figure 10.9 Heat of hydrogenation of 1-pentene. The overall reaction is exothermic to the extent of approximately 30 kcal/mole, which reflects the difference in the strength of the bonds that are formed and the bonds that are broken in the reaction. This difference is illustrated graphically here.

Figure 10.10 Heats of hydrogenation of *cis*-2-butene and *trans*-2-butene. The heat of hydrogenation of *cis*-2-butene is more exothermic than that of *trans*-2-butene by 1.0 kcal/mole. Since both reactions give the same product, the difference must be attributed to an energy difference in the starting materials. We infer that *cis*-2-butene is 1.0 kcal/mole higher in energy than *trans*-2-butene. An equivalent conclusion is that *cis*-2-butene is 1.0 kcal/mole less stable than *trans*-2-butene.

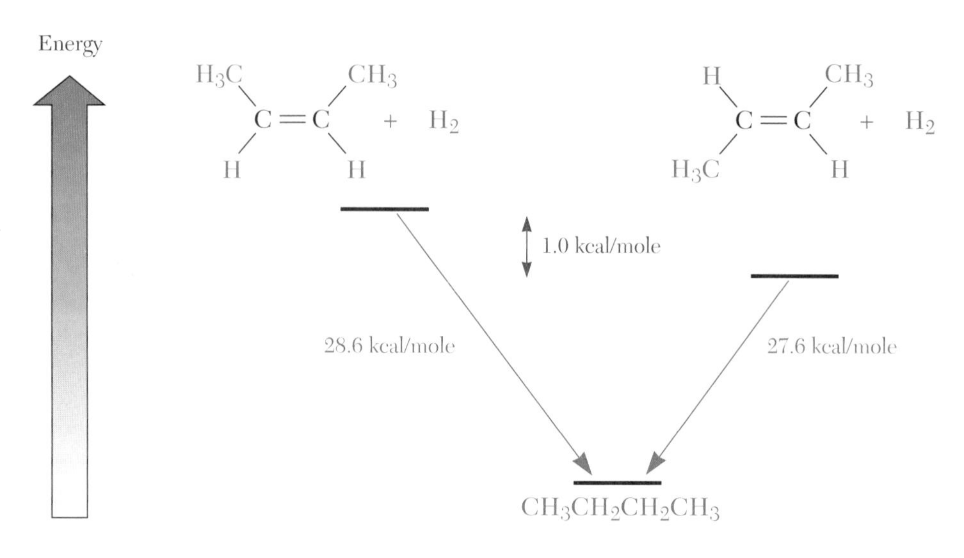

PROBLEM 10.4 Would you expect to measure different heats of hydrogenation for 1-pentene depending on whether a heterogeneous catalyst or a homogeneous catalyst is used? Explain your answer.

Heats of hydrogenation are particularly useful for comparing the strengths of π bonds in isomeric alkenes of the same fundamental skeleton. For isomeric alkenes, differences in heats of hydrogenation can be attributed to differences in the strengths of the alkene π bonds and strain in the structure.

Let's consider an example. Upon hydrogenation, *cis*-2-butene liberates a greater amount of energy than does *trans*-2-butene. Since both reactants give the same product (butane), we infer that *cis*-2-butene is of higher energy than *trans*-2-butene. Being of higher energy, *cis*-2-butene is less stable than *trans*-2-butene, as shown in Figure 10.10.

The difference in energy between the two 2-butenes is attributed to **steric repulsion** that occurs in *cis*-2-butene but not in *trans*-2-butene. The two methyl groups in *cis*-2-butene are closer to each other than they are in *trans*-2-butene, resulting in a van der Waals repulsion (see Chapter 4).

You should recall that if two groups approach within a distance smaller than the sum of their individual van der Waals radii, there is a destabilizing interaction between them. In *cis*-2-butene the distance between the methyl groups is approximately 3.0 angstrom, as shown in Figure 10.11. This distance is significantly less than the sum of the van der Waals radii for two methyl groups ($\sim$4.0 angstrom). We associate a repulsion of $\sim$1.0 kcal/mole with this interaction, based on the heats of hydrogenation for the 2-butenes.

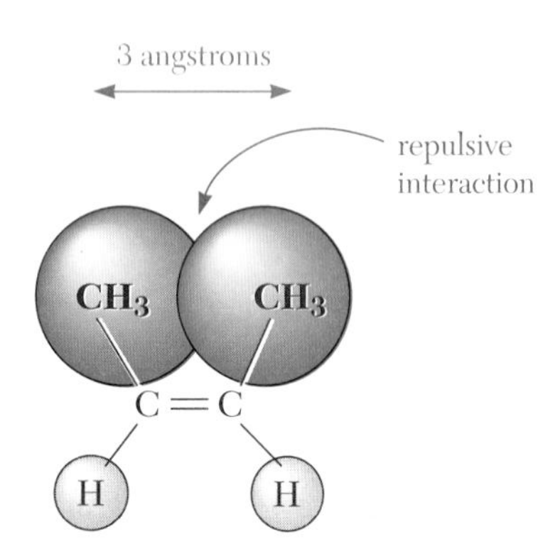

Figure 10.11 van der Waals repulsion in *cis*-2-butene. The two methyl groups are closer together than the sum of their van der Waals radii (4 angstrom). The result is a destabilization. We infer the magnitude of this destabilization to be $\sim$1.0 kcal/mole on the basis of heats of hydrogenation of *cis*-2-butene and *trans*-2-butene.

In general we find that most *trans* alkenes are more stable than the isomeric *cis* alkenes owing to what appear to be destabilizing steric repulsions in the latter isomers.

PROBLEM 10.5 The heat of hydrogenation of 1-butene (30.0 kcal/mole) is larger than that of either *cis*-2-butene or *trans*-2-butene. Similarly, the heat of hydrogenation of 1-pentene is larger than that of either *cis*-2-pentene or *trans*-2-pentene. What do these observations suggest about the relative stabilities of monosubstituted alkenes and disubstituted alkenes?

PROBLEM 10.6 The difference between the heat of hydrogenation of 1-butene and that of *trans*-2-butene is 2.4 kcal/mole. Their heats of combustion (the heat liberated when they react completely with oxygen to generate carbon dioxide and water) *also* differ by this amount. Is this a coincidence, or is it to be expected? Explain your answer.

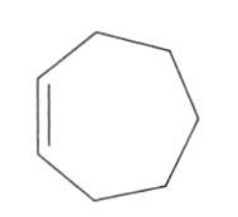

cis-cycloheptene

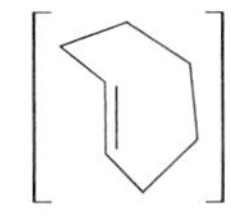

trans-cycloheptene (not isolable)

Figure 10.12 Possible isomers of cycloheptene. Only the *cis* isomer is isolable. The *trans* isomer is too unstable to be isolated but has been inferred as a reaction intermediate. Because only the *cis* isomer is isolable, we usually drop the *cis* label and simply name the compound "cycloheptene."

One effect that reverses the normal order of *cis/trans* stabilities occurs when the double bond is in a small ring (less than ten carbon atoms). For these types of compounds the *cis* isomer is more stable than the *trans*. In fact, for rings of less than eight carbon atoms, the *trans* isomers are so unstable that they cannot be isolated (see Figure 10.12).

COMPOUND CAPSULE

trans-cyclooctene

The smallest *trans* cycloalkene that has been isolated is *trans*-cyclooctene. This compound was first isolated in the 1950s. The presence of a *trans* carbon-carbon double bond in rings smaller than eight members is a source of such great strain (try making a model) that it is impossible to isolate compounds containing them. However, *trans* carbon-carbon double bonds in smaller rings are implicated as *intermediates* in some reactions. Even in *trans*-cyclooctene, the carbon-carbon double bond is twisted, with a torsional angle of 136°. The twisted nature of *trans*-cyclooctene renders it disymmetric, and it has been resolved into its enantiomers. The isolated enantiomers have very high specific rotations ($[\alpha]_{290} = \pm 411°$). Although larger *trans* cycloalkenes also exist in enantiomeric forms, they racemize rapidly on heating because they undergo a conformational twist that converts one enantiomer into its mirror image. This twisting requires the passage of one of the bound olefinic hydrogen atoms through the interior of the ring. The larger the ring, the more easily this twisting occurs. Optically pure *trans*-cyclooctene does not racemize, even when heated above 60 °C for many days, while *trans*-cyclononene retains optical purity only at temperatures below 0 °C.

A different type of strain comes into play with these ring compounds. Because of the constraints of the ring, the p orbitals making up the π bond in the *trans* alkene are twisted and cannot overlap efficiently. You can appreciate this type of strain by trying to make a molecular model of *trans*-cycloheptene.

PROBLEM 10.7 The heats of hydrogenation of *cis*-cyclooctene and *trans*-cyclooctene differ by almost 10.0 kcal/mole. Which has the more exothermic heat of hydrogenation? Explain your answer.

SPECIAL TOPIC

Hydrogenation of Oils

We often find the term "partially hydrogenated vegetable oils" on the contents labels of processed foods. This term refers to the addition of hydrogen across olefinic linkages in lipid compounds (oils) isolated from the vegetable sources.

Oils from vegetables (or animal sources) are esters of carboxylic acids bearing long hydrocarbon chains. Illustrated below is an ester of linoleic acid, a common vegetable oil that contains two *cis* alkene linkages.

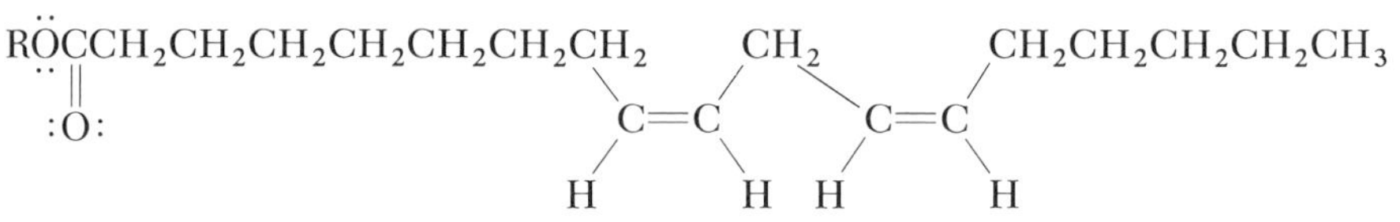

$$\mathrm{R\ddot{O}CCH_2CH_2CH_2CH_2CH_2CH_2CH_2 \qquad CH_2 \qquad CH_2CH_2CH_2CH_2CH_3}$$
$$\mathrm{:\!O\!: \qquad C{=}C \qquad C{=}C}$$
$$\mathrm{H \qquad H \quad H \qquad H}$$

Oils from vegetable sources are commonly *polyunsaturated*, that is, they contain several olefinic linkages in most of the carboxylic acid chains. These types of oils have dietary characteristics that are quite desirable in the proper amount and are not available from other sources. Unfortunately, the polyunsaturated oils exist as liquids, a form that is less convenient than solids. Reduction of *some* of the olefinic linkages causes these oils to take on physical characteristics more amenable to packaging and use. They become *plastic*, deformable solids, for example, margerine.

If all of the olefinic linkages are reduced to saturate the carboxylic acid chain completely, the materials become solids at ordinary temperatures and their dietary properties are much less desirable than those of unsaturated oils. *Partial* hydrogenation of the vegetable oils is performed, generally using nickel catalysts, to give desirable physical characteristics to the oils without converting them into nutritionally less desirable completely saturated fats.

There are difficulties in the process of partial hydrogenation, however. When the polyunsaturated oil interacts with the catalyst and the π bond is activated, isomerization to the thermodynamically more favored *trans* form can occur. These *trans* olefinic linkages give a different shape to the molecule and can cause physical and nutritional difficulties.

10.4 Addition of Halogens

EXPERIMENTAL OBSERVATIONS

Fluorine, chlorine, and bromine all add readily to carbon-carbon double bonds. However, fluorine is so highly reactive that the reaction is of little practical value. Iodine is the least reactive of the halogens in this type of process.

We will use the reaction involving bromine as our example. The reaction is visually revealing and can be used as a test for the presence of the carbon-carbon double bond. (Carbon-carbon triple bonds are also reactive.) Normally we use a solution of bromine in carbon tetrachloride to test for a carbon-carbon double bond. The red solution is added to the sample to be tested. If the sample contains a carbon-carbon double bond, the red color disappears completely as the bromine is consumed. The addition product, a dibromoalkane, is colorless.

PROBLEM 10.8

Using bond dissociation energies (Table 7.1) and assuming the π bond energy of ethylene to be 64 kcal/mole, calculate ΔH° of reaction for the addition of each of the following to ethylene:

a. F_2 **b.** Cl_2 **c.** Br_2 **d.** I_2

Assuming that reactivities follow the same order as the ΔH° values, which halogen is expected to be the most and which the least reactive?

Steps to Solving the Problem

Solution to Problem 10.8a

1. We calculate ΔH° for the reaction by looking at the energies of the bonds that are broken and the energies of the bonds that are formed.
2. Two bonds are broken in the reaction, the alkene π bond ($\sim$64 kcal/mole) and the fluorine-fluorine bond (38 kcal/mole) (data from Table 7.1). The energy required for bond breaking in the reaction is thus 102 kcal/mole.
3. We now calculate the energy released by the formation of new bonds. Two carbon-fluorine bonds (106 kcal/mole each, Table 7.1) are formed. The total energy release is therefore 212 kcal/mole.
4. We can now calculate ΔH° for the reaction. The difference between the bond breaking and bond making is

$$(102 - 212)\ \text{kcal/mole} = -110\ \text{kcal/mole}$$

ΔH° is *negative*, so the reaction is overall exothermic.

In an earlier section we contrasted the stereochemistry of bromine and hydrogen addition to a carbon-carbon double bond. Bromine adds in an *anti* manner, whereas hydrogen adds mainly in a *syn* manner. The stereoselectivity of a reaction depends on its mechanism. We proposed that hydrogenation using a heterogeneous catalyst occurs through a transfer of two hydrogen atoms from the surface of the catalyst to the same face of the alkene. This mechanism is consistent with the observed preference for *syn* addition.

What kind of mechanism can we invoke to account for the observed *anti* mode of addition? To develop a reasonable mechanistic description for any reaction, we need to gather and organize various types of experimental observations. We can obtain relevant experimental data by performing the reaction

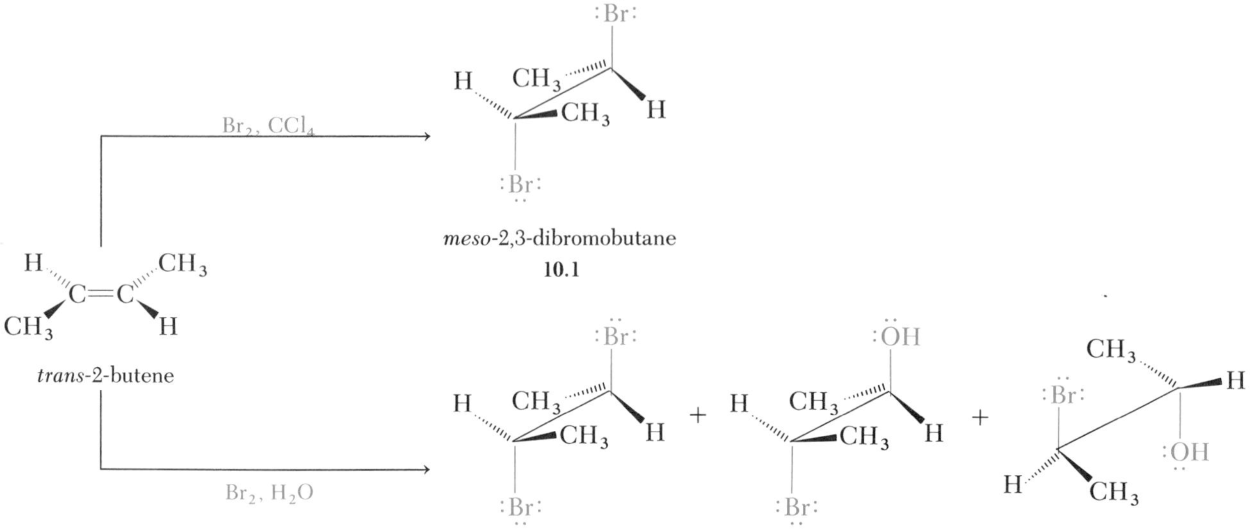

trans-2-butene

Br_2, CCl_4

meso-2,3-dibromobutane
10.1

Br_2, H_2O

meso-2,3-dibromobutane
10.1

(2*R*,3*S*)-3-bromo-2-butanol
10.2

(2*S*,3*R*)-3-bromo-2-butanol
10.3

Figure 10.13 Reaction of *trans*-2-butene with bromine. When the reaction is performed in carbon tetrachloride solution, only one product is formed, *meso*-2,3-dibromobutane (**10.1**). When the reaction is performed in aqueous solution, *meso*-2,3-dibromobutane is formed again along with two additional products. These products are (2*R*,3*S*)-3-bromo-2-butanol (**10.2**) and (2*S*,3*R*)-3-bromo-2-butanol (**10.3**), and they constitute a racemic mixture.

in a solvent other than carbon tetrachloride. If we use bromine in aqueous solution, we find that additional products form. Consider the reaction of bromine with *trans*-2-butene in both carbon tetrachloride and aqueous solution. The products formed are shown in Figure 10.13.

Two of the products formed in the reaction of bromine with *trans*-2-butene in aqueous solution (**10.2** and **10.3**) are known as **bromohydrins.** Bromohydrins have hydroxyl and bromine substituents on adjacent carbon atoms. The formation of these two bromohydrins in this reaction corresponds to the *anti* addition of —Br and —OH to the alkene. Obviously the —OH group comes from the water. But just how does this addition occur?

Another revealing observation is that if we add some sodium chloride to the reaction mixture, we obtain two other *additional* products, a racemic mixture of (2*R*,3*S*)-2-bromo-3-chlorobutane and (2*S*,3*R*)-2-bromo-3-chlorobutane, as shown in Figure 10.14.

Let's take stock of the experimental observations we have made so far. First, we recognize that when bromine and an alkene are mixed, *anti* addition of the two groups always occurs. However, the two added groups vary depending on the reaction conditions. At least one bromine atom is always added,

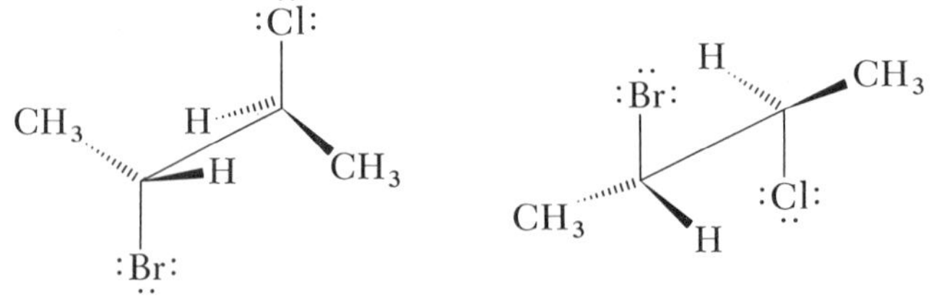

Figure 10.14 Products formed upon reaction of bromine with *trans*-2-butene in aqueous solution containing sodium chloride. A racemic mixture of (2*R*,3*S*)-2-bromo-3-chlorobutane (**10.4**) and (2*S*,3*R*)-2-bromo-3-chlorobutane (**10.5**) is formed in the reaction along with the three products shown in Figure 10.13 (**10.1**, **10.2**, and **10.3**).

(2*R*,3*S*)-2-bromo-3-chlorobutane
10.4

(2*S*,3*R*)-2-bromo-3-chlorobutane
10.5

but the other added group varies. With carbon tetrachloride as the solvent, two bromine atoms are added. If water is used as the solvent, a hydroxyl group is added along with the bromine atom. If another anion, such as chloride ion, is present in the aqueous solution, *it* adds to the alkene along with a bromine atom.

MECHANISM FOR BROMINATION OF ALKENES

We can deduce a mechanism for the bromination of alkenes that is fully compatible with the experimental results just described. We consider the reaction as occurring in two steps.

MECHANISM OF REACTION

Step 1 The π electrons of the alkene perform a nucleophilic attack on molecular bromine. A bromide ion departs as a leaving group. We say that the bromine molecule is acting as an electrophile, that is, a *lover of electrons*, as described at the beginning of this chapter.

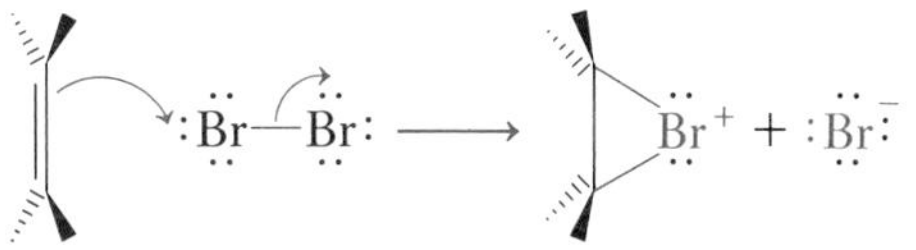

:Br—Br: ⟶ Br$^+$ + :Br:$^-$

The intermediate species generated in this reaction is known as a *bromonium ion.* We write it with two bonds to a positively charged bromine. This structure might seem strange—normally we do not think of bromine with either a positive charge or two bonds. We need to consider the valence bond description of this intermediate.

We can think of the bromonium ion structure using resonance-contributing forms of classical valence bond structures. These resonance forms are shown below. The blending of these forms indicates that there is a partial bond between each carbon and the bromine and that the positive charge is delocalized over three atoms.

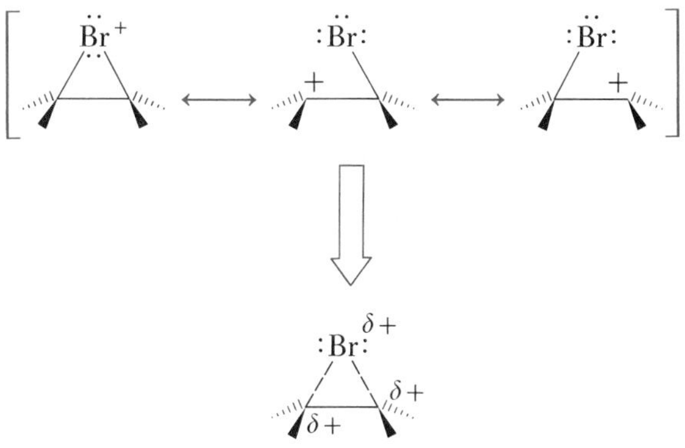

Br$^+$ ⟷ :Br: + ⟷ :Br: +

:Br: $\delta+$ $\delta+$ $\delta+$

Step 2 The bromonium ion is attacked by a *nucleophile* to give the observed product. When the reaction is performed in carbon tetrachloride solution, the only nucleophile present is the bromide ion produced in Step 1. However, in aqueous solution water can serve as the nucleophile, as we will discuss in detail below. Chloride ion can also serve as a nucleophile when it is present. We infer from the observed *anti* stereochemistry of the reaction that the incoming nucleophile must attack the bromonium ion from the face opposite that already bonded to the first bromine atom. This nucleophilic attack can occur at either carbon atom.

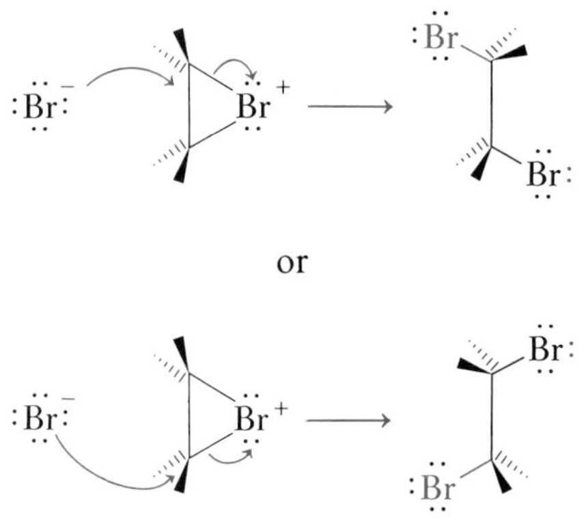

:Br:⁻ + bromonium ion (Br⁺) ⟶ anti-dibromide

or

:Br:⁻ + bromonium ion (Br⁺) ⟶ anti-dibromide

MOLECULAR ORBITAL ANALYSIS

It is possible to consider the formation of a bromonium ion in terms of the frontier molecular orbital model. We consider the interaction of the alkene HOMO and the bromine LUMO. The alkene HOMO is the filled π-bonding molecular orbital. The LUMO for the bromine molecule is its σ^* (antibonding) molecular orbital. They interact as shown in Figure 10.15 to generate the bromonium ion and a bromide anion.

We need to consider the attack of the nucleophile on the bromonium ion and the accompanying stereochemistry of the process. In valence bond terms, bromide ion adds to an electron-deficient carbon, a carbocation, albeit an unusual carbocation. Two of the contributing resonance forms for the bromonium ion contain carbocation sites. The bromide ion is equally likely to combine with either of these two sites. The *anti* stereochemistry can be rationalized by assuming that approach at one face of the electron-deficient carbon is blocked by the bromine already there. We infer that the incoming bromide ion prefers to approach from the opposite face, as illustrated in Figure 10.16.

When we find stereospecificity in a reaction, however, the most satisfying rationalization is usually found in an analysis of the orbital interactions of that reaction. Such an analysis for the addition of bromide ion to a bromonium ion is presented below.

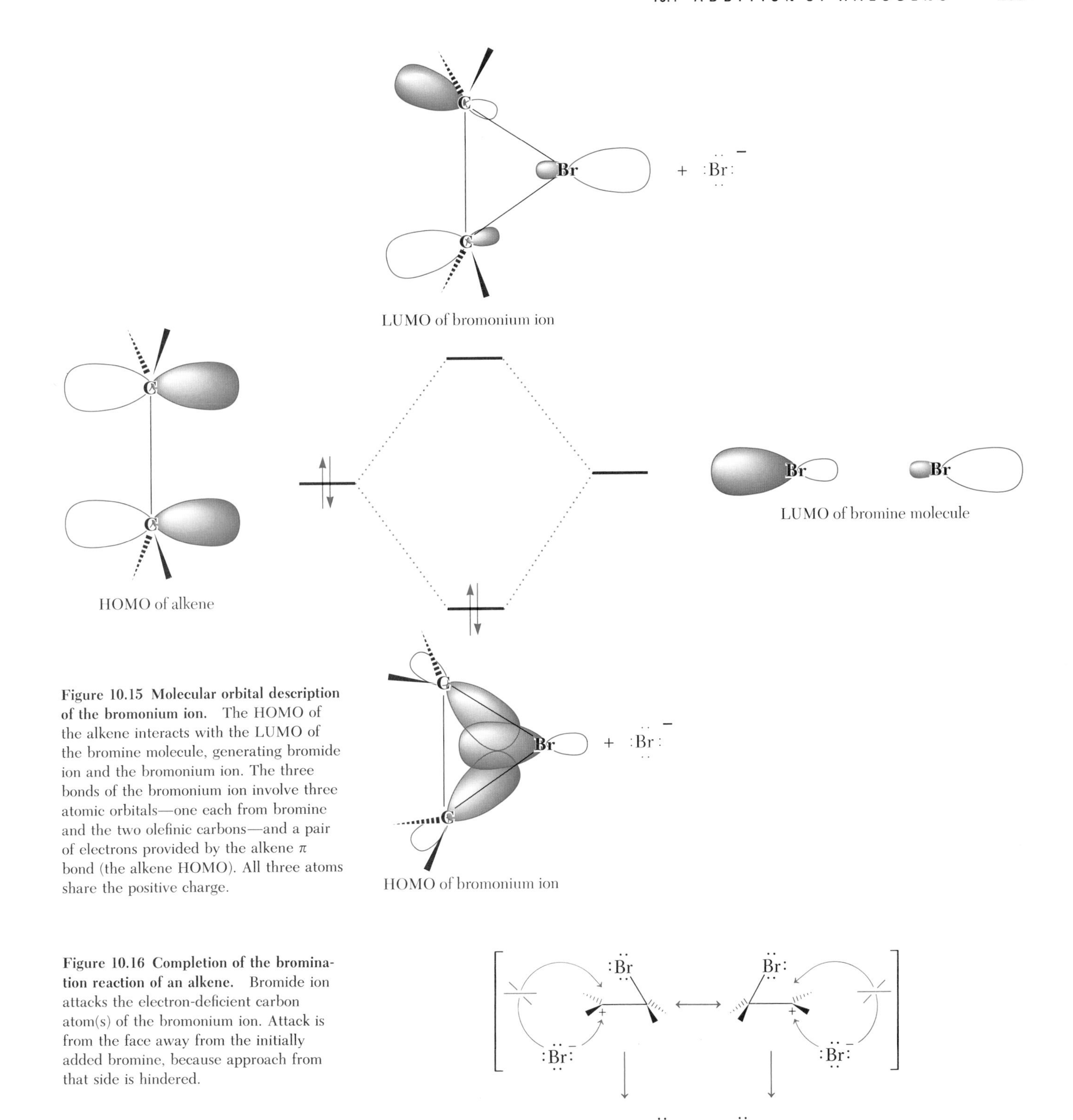

Figure 10.15 Molecular orbital description of the bromonium ion. The HOMO of the alkene interacts with the LUMO of the bromine molecule, generating bromide ion and the bromonium ion. The three bonds of the bromonium ion involve three atomic orbitals—one each from bromine and the two olefinic carbons—and a pair of electrons provided by the alkene π bond (the alkene HOMO). All three atoms share the positive charge.

Figure 10.16 Completion of the bromination reaction of an alkene. Bromide ion attacks the electron-deficient carbon atom(s) of the bromonium ion. Attack is from the face away from the initially added bromine, because approach from that side is hindered.

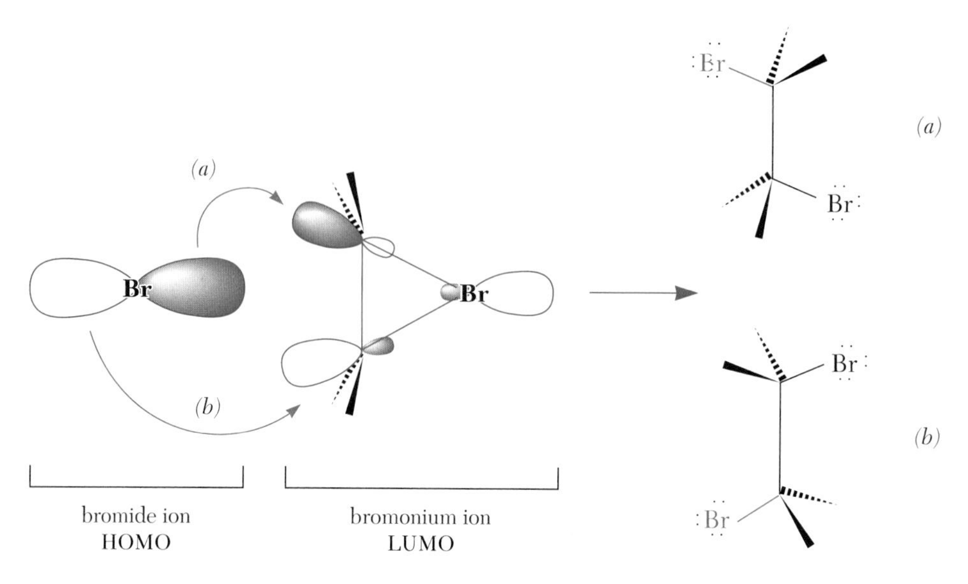

Figure 10.17 Molecular orbital view of completion of the addition of bromine to an alkene. The bromide ion attacks the bridged bromonium ion on the face opposite that of the initial bromine addition. Attack is from the back where the large lobes of the LUMO are available for overlap and new bond formation. Attack at each of the two carbon sites is indicated by approaches (*a*) and (*b*).

MOLECULAR ORBITAL ANALYSIS

Using the frontier molecular orbital approximation, we focus on the interaction of the HOMO of the attacking bromide ion and the LUMO of the bromonium ion, as illustrated in Figure 10.17. We would expect the bromide ion to attack the back of the bromonium ion because the larger lobes of the LUMO protrude to the back.

PROBLEM 10.9 Consider the attack of bromide ion on the two available carbons of the bromonium ion formed from *cis*-2-hexene. Use stereochemical drawings to show the stereoisomers formed. Name the products with their stereochemical descriptors.

When water is used as the solvent, it can compete with bromide ion as the nucleophile attacking the bromonium ion. Bromide ion is a better nucleophile than water. However, since water is the solvent, there are many more water molecules than bromide ions. Under these circumstances water can compete very effectively because of the statistical advantage.

Consider the reaction in which water acts as a nucleophile on the bromonium ion from *trans*-2-butene. Actually *two* bromonium ions are formed by the reaction of bromine with *trans*-2-butene; this pair of enantiomers is shown in Figure 10.18. The two bromonium ions are formed in equal amounts. Association of bromine with one face of the alkene is just as likely as association with the other face, leading ultimately to the formation of a pair of enantiomeric bromohydrins.

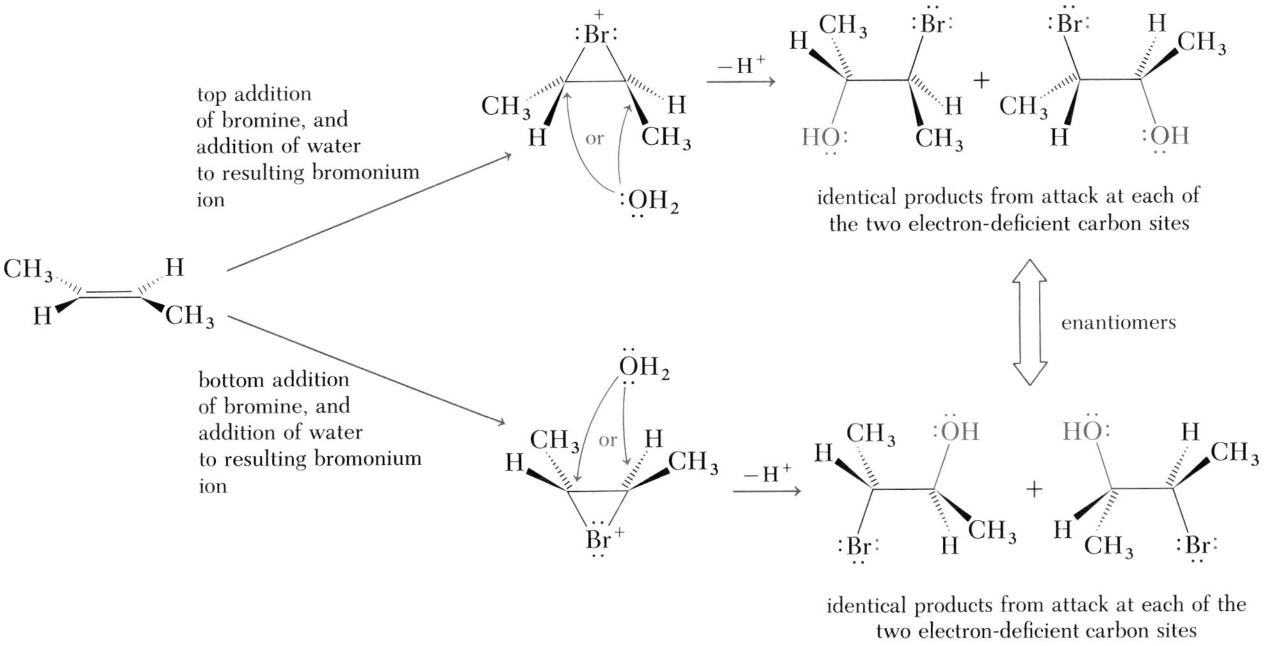

Figure 10.18 **Bromohydrin formation with *trans*-2-butene.** Addition of bromine is equally likely at the two faces of the alkene. Thus a racemic mixture of two enantiomeric bromonium ions is generated. Each of these bromonium ions leads to one of an enantiomeric pair of bromohydrins.

top addition of bromine, and addition of water to resulting bromonium ion

bottom addition of bromine, and addition of water to resulting bromonium ion

identical products from attack at each of the two electron-deficient carbon sites

enantiomers

identical products from attack at each of the two electron-deficient carbon sites

UNSYMMETRICAL ALKENES

Consider the formation of a bromohydrin from an unsymmetrical alkene such as 2-methyl-2-butene. We can imagine that two isomeric bromohydrins, (**10.6** and **10.7**) could possibly be formed. Experimentally, however, only one (**10.7**) can be isolated in an appreciable yield, as shown in Figure 10.19.

We refer to this type of selectivity as **regioselectivity.** We can rationalize the regioselectivity in the addition reaction by considering the intermediate bromonium ion. Recall the three resonance structures for the bromonium ion

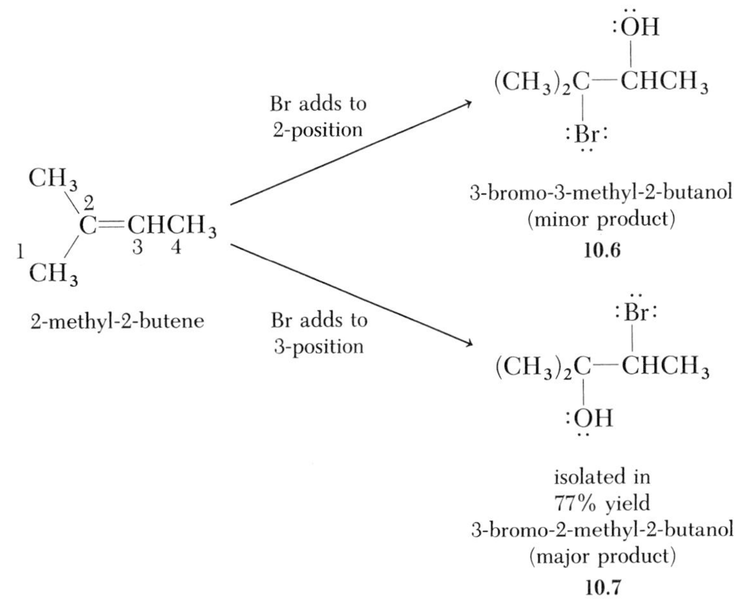

Figure 10.19 **Bromohydrin formation with 2-methyl-2-butene.** An unsymmetrical alkene can generate different bromohydrins, depending on the olefinic carbons to which the Br— and HO— attach. Experimentally, we find that one mode of addition is preferred to the other. The HO— becomes attached to the carbon that bears more alkyl groups.

2-methyl-2-butene

Br adds to 2-position

$(CH_3)_2C(Br)-CH(OH)CH_3$

3-bromo-3-methyl-2-butanol (minor product) **10.6**

Br adds to 3-position

$(CH_3)_2C(OH)-CH(Br)CH_3$

isolated in 77% yield 3-bromo-2-methyl-2-butanol (major product) **10.7**

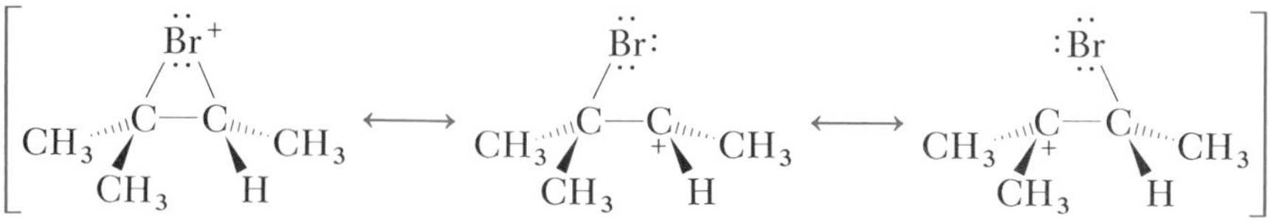

Figure 10.20 Contributing resonance structures for the bromonium ion from 2-methyl-2-butene. The acyclic structure on the far right is a tertiary carbocation, while the one in the center is a secondary carbocation. The structure on the far right, being a more stable resonance form, contributes more to the true structure of the bromonium ion than does the center structure. Thus the true structure has more tertiary carbocation character than it does secondary carbocation character, and the incoming water molecule reacts preferentially at the more highly substituted site, which is the more electrophilic site.

that were shown earlier. With a symmetrical alkene, the two acyclic structures would be energetically equivalent. With an unsymmetrical alkene this is not the case, however, and there is an uneven charge distribution. This uneven charge distribution results in regioselectivity for the overall addition process. The contributing resonance structures of the bromonium ion are shown in Figure 10.20.

It is interesting to note that the degree of stereoselectivity diminishes as the relative importance of the acyclic resonance structure to the right in Figure 10.20 increases. If the contributing structure on the far right were so dominant that the bromonium ion actually existed as the open carbocation, there would be no stereoselectivity in the reaction. We sometimes find this lack of stereoselectivity with reactions in which a particularly stable open-chain carbocation can be formed.

ALKENE REACTION WITH HALOGENS IN ALCOHOL SOLUTION

The addition of halogens to alkenes in alcohol solution (rather than water or carbon tetrachloride) leads to β-haloethers. An example is shown in Equation 10.4.

Eqn. 10.4

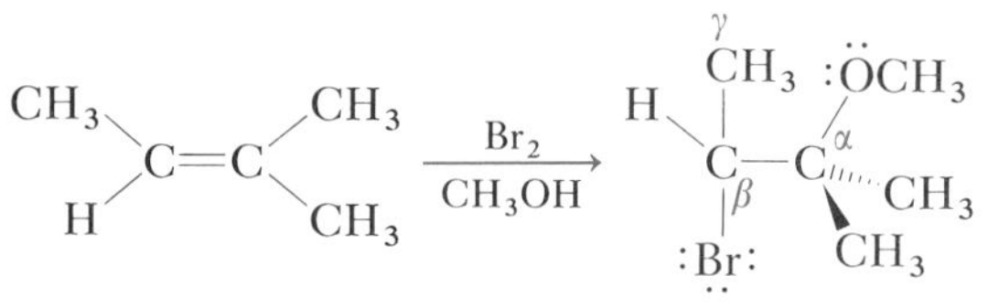

$$\text{2-methyl-2-butene} \xrightarrow[CH_3OH]{Br_2} \text{3-bromo-2-methoxy-2-methylbutane (76\% yield)}$$

2-methyl-2-butene

76% yield
3-bromo-2-methoxy-2-methylbutane

We refer to the product in this reaction as a *β-halo ether*. The carbon attached to the ether oxygen is the *α-position*, and the next carbon along the chain is the *β-position*, as indicated on the product in Equation 10.4.

PROBLEM 10.10 Write a complete mechanism for the formation of a β-bromoether by the reaction of an alkene with bromine in methanol solution.

10.5 Addition of Hydrogen Halides

Hydrogen halides (HX) react with alkenes to produce haloalkanes. These reactions, like those discussed earlier, are electrophilic addition reactions. An electrophilic HX molecule adds to the carbon-carbon double bond, as is shown in Equation 10.5 for 1-butene.

Eqn. 10.5

$$\underset{\text{1-butene}}{CH_3CH_2CH{=}CH_2} \xrightarrow[\text{acetic acid}]{HBr} \underset{\substack{\text{63\% yield} \\ \text{2-bromobutane}}}{CH_3CH_2CH(Br)CH_3}$$

The mechanism of this reaction involves two steps.

MECHANISM OF REACTION

Step 1 The hydrogen halide transfers a proton to the alkene to form a carbocation.

$$H_2C{=}CH_2 + H{-}\ddot{Cl}: \longrightarrow H_2\overset{+}{C}{-}CH_2(H) + :\ddot{Cl}:^-$$

Step 2 The halide ion combines with the carbocation to give the product.

$$H_2\overset{+}{C}{-}CH_3 + :\ddot{Cl}:^- \longrightarrow CH_2(:\ddot{Cl}:){-}CH_3$$

The ease with which hydrogen halides add to alkenes follows the order of their acidity. Hydrogen iodide, the most acidic of the hydrogen halides, is the most reactive, and hydrogen fluoride, the least acidic, is the least reactive:

$$\text{Reactivity for alkene addition:} \quad H\ddot{I}: > H\ddot{Br}: > H\ddot{Cl}: > H\ddot{F}:$$

The addition of hydrogen and a halogen to alkenes can also be brought about by using a halide salt and a strong acid such as phosphoric acid. The mechanism is the same as shown above for HCl addition, except that the phosphoric acid causes the initial protonation of the alkene. One useful preparation that uses this technique is shown in Equation 10.6.

Eqn. 10.6

$$\text{cyclohexene} \xrightarrow[H_3PO_4]{KI} \text{iodocyclohexane (85\% yield)}$$

Because the addition of hydrogen halides to alkenes proceeds through an *open* carbocation, we anticipate stereochemical consequences different from those found in the bromination of alkenes. Consider an open carbocation of the type we have already discussed. With a p orbital at the electron-deficient

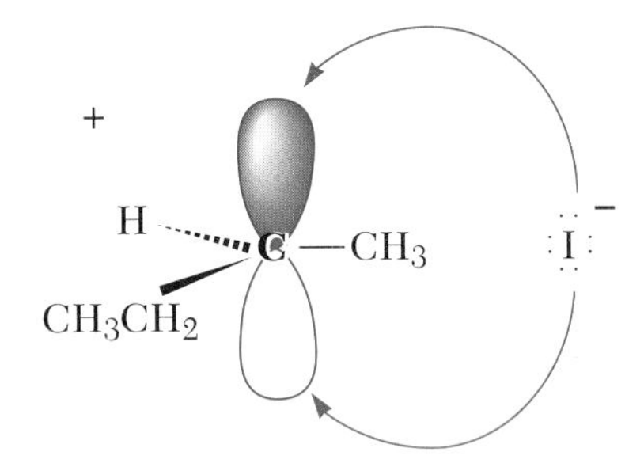

Figure 10.21 Routes for I^- addition to the 2-butyl cation. The two lobes of the empty *p* orbital are equally capable of participating in binding to the incoming anion. A racemic product is generated.

carbon, attachment of the incoming anion should occur equally well from the top or the bottom, as illustrated in Figure 10.21. The product of this addition would be *racemic* 2-iodobutane.

While we would not expect to find any stereochemical preference with a truly *open* carbocation, experiments often do indicate a preference. Often there is a preference for *anti* addition, and occasionally for *syn* addition. The stereochemical outcome depends largely on the structure of the alkene. Since there is a preference in many cases, we infer that the carbocation is not completely free and open. The two-step mechanism we presented earlier for hydrogen halide addition is, in fact, somewhat simplified. Nevertheless, this simplified mechanism suffices for most purposes and we will use it throughout our discussion.

ADDITION TO UNSYMMETRICAL ALKENES

With unsymmetrical alkenes, initial protonation primarily yields the more highly substituted of the possible carbocations. The protonation of 1-methylcyclopentene is shown in Figure 10.22 as an example.

Selectivity in the reaction of 1-methylcyclopentene with potassium iodide and phosphoric acid is shown in Equation 10.7.

Eqn. 10.7

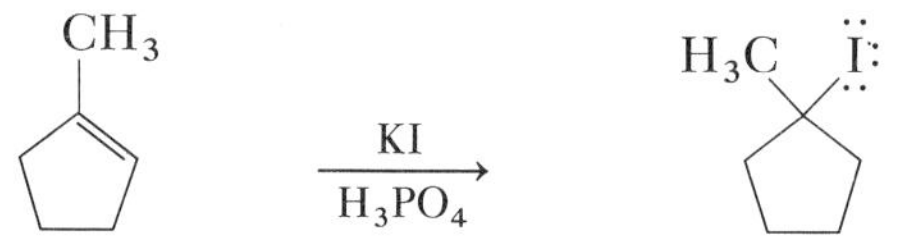

CH_3 (1-methylcyclopentene) $\xrightarrow[H_3PO_4]{KI}$ H_3C $\ddot{I}$: (1-iodo-1-methylcyclopentane)

1-methylcyclopentene

80% yield
1-iodo-1-methylcyclopentane

This reaction is regioselective. One of the two possible positional isomers is favored over the other. A Russian chemist, Vladimir Markovnikov, had as early as 1869 recognized the regioselectivity of addition reactions at double bonds. Long before any mechanistic details of the reaction were known, he recognized the pattern of behavior and developed a rule for predicting the major product of such reactions. We can paraphrase *Markovnikov's Rule* as follows: When an acid, HX, adds to a double bond, the hydrogen becomes attached to the carbon atom that already has more hydrogen atoms attached to it.

Today, we say that reactions that give products in accord with Markovnikov's Rule proceed with **Markovnikov orientation.** Reactions that do *not* follow Markovnikov's Rule are said to proceed with **anti-Markovnikov orientation.** An example of a reaction proceeding with anti-Markovnikov orientation is shown in Equation 10.8.

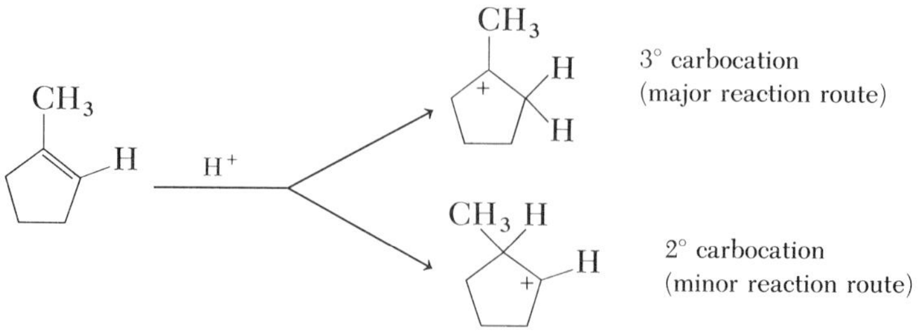

Figure 10.22 Carbocation formation from an unsymmetrical alkene. The proton is added to the less highly substituted of the olefinic carbon atoms, generating the more highly substituted of the possible carbocations.

CH_3, H $\xrightarrow{H^+}$

CH_3, H, H, + — 3° carbocation (major reaction route)

CH_3 H, H, + — 2° carbocation (minor reaction route)

Eqn. 10.8

$$CF_3CH{=}CH_2 + H\ddot{B}r\!: \longrightarrow CF_3CH_2CH_2\ddot{B}r\!:$$

3,3,3-trifluoropropene — 1-bromo-3,3,3-trifluoropropane, 97% yield

Although this reaction proceeds contrary to Markovnikov's Rule, it does *not* violate mechanistic principles. It *does* proceed through the more stable of the possible carbocations. The trifluoromethyl group is strongly electron withdrawing and destabilizes a positive charge at the adjacent carbon atom, as shown in Figure 10.23.

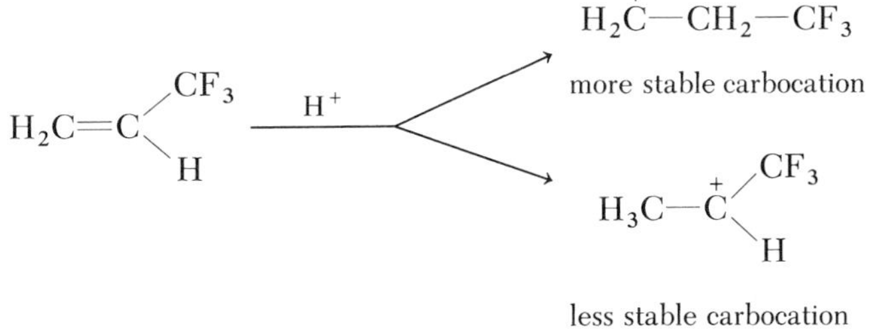

$$H_2C{=}C(CF_3)H \xrightarrow{H^+} \begin{cases} H_2\overset{+}{C}{-}CH_2{-}CF_3 & \text{more stable carbocation} \\ H_3C{-}\overset{+}{C}(CF_3)H & \text{less stable carbocation} \end{cases}$$

Figure 10.23 Protonation of 3,3,3-trifluoropropene. Protonation occurs at the internal olefinic carbon to give a primary carbocation. Protonation at the external olefinic carbon to form the more highly substituted carbocation is disfavored because of the presence of the adjacent trifluoromethyl group, a strongly electron-withdrawing group. In this case the secondary carbocation is less stable than the primary carbocation.

In Section 10.12 we will take up another important example of an addition reaction of alkenes that proceeds with anti-Markovnikov orientation.

REARRANGEMENTS ACCOMPANYING ADDITION

In our earlier discussion of carbocations we saw that they sometimes rearrange to give more stable carbocations. Since the addition of hydrogen halides to alkenes proceeds through a carbocation, we might anticipate that this type of rearrangement could occur in these reactions. We do indeed see skeletal rearrangements in this type of reaction, and they provide good confirmation that the reaction proceeds via a carbocation intermediate.

For example, hydrogen chloride in acetic acid reacts with 3,3-dimethyl-1-butene to give 2-chloro-2,3-dimethylbutane as the major product. We explain this product formation in terms of a carbocation rearrangement, as shown in Figure 10.24.

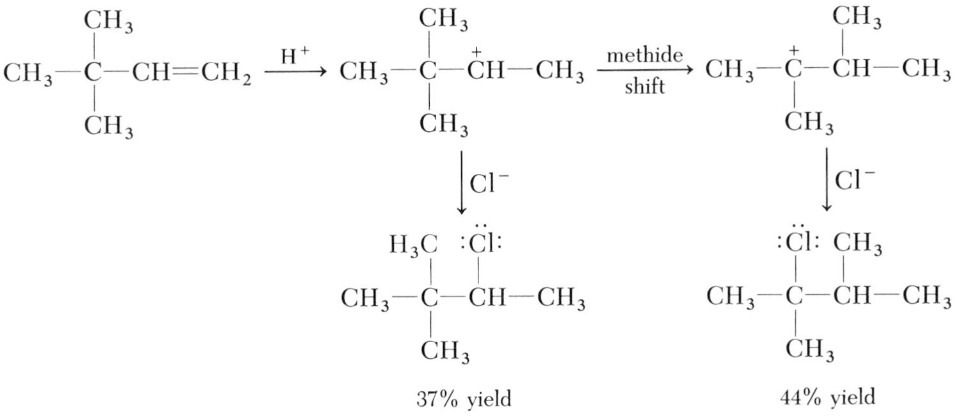

$$(CH_3)_3C{-}CH{=}CH_2 \xrightarrow{H^+} (CH_3)_3C{-}\overset{+}{C}H{-}CH_3 \xrightarrow{\text{methide shift}} (CH_3)_2\overset{+}{C}{-}CH(CH_3){-}CH_3$$

$$(CH_3)_3C{-}\overset{+}{C}H{-}CH_3 \xrightarrow{Cl^-} (CH_3)_3C{-}CH(\ddot{C}l\!:){-}CH_3 \quad \text{37\% yield}$$

$$(CH_3)_2\overset{+}{C}{-}CH(CH_3){-}CH_3 \xrightarrow{Cl^-} (CH_3)_2C(\ddot{C}l\!:){-}CH(CH_3){-}CH_3 \quad \text{44\% yield}$$

Figure 10.24 Reaction of 3,3-dimethyl-1-butene with hydrogen chloride in acetic acid at 25°. Initial protonation of the double bond gives a 2° carbocation. A methide shift produces a more stable 3° carbocation. Chloride ion addition to the 2° carbocation gives the relatively minor haloalkane product (37%). Chloride ion addition to the rearranged carbocation gives the relatively major haloalkane product (44%). The remainder of the product arises from attack of the acetic acid solvent on the carbocations.

REACTION PROGRESS DIAGRAMS AND THE HAMMOND POSTULATE

Reaction progress diagrams are often useful for the graphical display of mechanistic steps. In a reaction progress diagram we show progress of the reaction from reactant to product along the horizontal axis. The potential energy (vertical axis) associated with a given species (reactant, product, or intermediate) is represented by the height of the curve. The first step of the addition of HX to 2-methylpropene is shown in Figure 10.25 along with its reaction progress diagram. We compare the addition of the proton at the two possible sites.

We see in Figure 10.25 that the potential energy of the tertiary carbocation is lower than that of the less stable primary carbocation. However, the starting material for each carbocation is the same, and therefore the formation of each carbocation begins at the same energy level.

To proceed from reactants to carbocations, the reactants must possess sufficient energy to reach the **transition state,** the point of *highest* potential energy as the reaction proceeds from reactants to products. (A *transition state* occurs at a point of relative *maximum* energy on a reaction progress diagram; an *intermediate* occurs at a point of relative *minimum* energy.) The difference between the maximum potential energy of the transition state and the potential energy of the reactants is the **activation energy** (E_{act}), which we have discussed briefly in earlier chapters. The magnitude of E_{act} governs how fast the reaction will occur. Reaction occurs only if the colliding reactants can change enough of their kinetic energy into potential energy to reach the required maximum

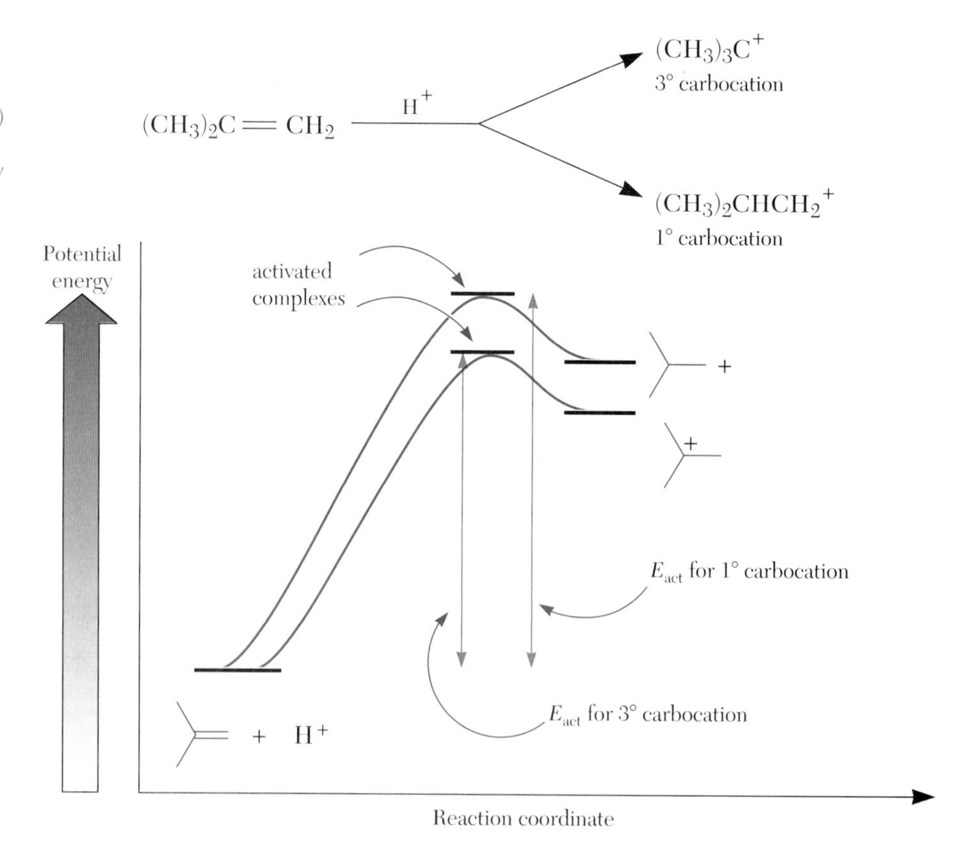

Figure 10.25 Reaction progress diagram for competing protonations of 2-methylpropene. The tertiary carbocation is formed more readily (virtually exclusively) because the activation energy for its formation is lower than the activation energy for formation of the primary carbocation.

value. For the reaction to occur, the molecules must collide with sufficient energy (and with the proper relative orientation).

If the required E_{act} is high, relatively few colliding molecules will have sufficient energy for reaction to occur. Most collisions will not lead to product, and the rate of reaction will be slow. For *competing* reactions like these protonations, the process with the lower E_{act} will proceed more rapidly.

There is an inverse exponential relationship between the **rate constant** for the reaction and the activation energy. The rate constant of a reaction is a proportionality constant relating the rate of product formation (e.g., in moles/liter·second) to the concentrations of the reactants. For a given reaction, the rate constant varies with temperature. The relationship of the rate constant and the activation energy is known as the Arrhenius equation:

$$k = Ae^{-E_{act}/RT}$$

where k is the rate constant of the reaction, R is the gas constant, T is the Kelvin temperature, and A is a proportionality constant. Small changes in E_{act} can produce large changes in reaction rate.

PROBLEM 10.11

At 25 °C, how much faster is a reaction with $E_{act} = 0.25$ kcal/mole than one with $E_{act} = 0.30$ kcal/mole? ($R = 1.987$ kcal/mole K) Assume A is the same for both reactions.

At the potential energy maximum (the transition state), the specific arrangement of the atoms of the reacting species is known as the **activated complex.** The activated complex is a species whose structure lies somewhere between those of reactants and products. Some bonds of the reactants are partially broken and some new bonds of the product are partially formed in the activated complex. Beyond the transition state, potential energy is converted back to kinetic energy until the potential energy level of the products is reached.

For a multistep reaction (as for HX addition to an alkene) we need to show a reaction progress diagram for all of the steps. In HX addition to an alkene, the first step is slower than the second, indicating that the activation energy for the first step is greater than for the second step. The overall reaction progress diagram for the addition of hydrogen chloride to 2-methylpropene is shown in Figure 10.26.

Activation energies are in effect *energy barriers* that reactants must overcome in proceeding to products. The higher the activation energy, the slower the reaction. It may seem intuitively reasonable that the more stable of the two carbocations will be formed more readily. However, there is no *fundamental* relationship between thermodynamics, which tells us about the overall energy changes in a reaction, and kinetics, which describes how fast a reaction will occur (see the following section) and depends on the energies of the transition states or activated complexes.

When a proton reacts with an alkene to form a carbocation, the thermodynamically more stable carbocation *is* formed faster. In fact, it is usually found that the more stable of the possible carbocations forms more rapidly by any

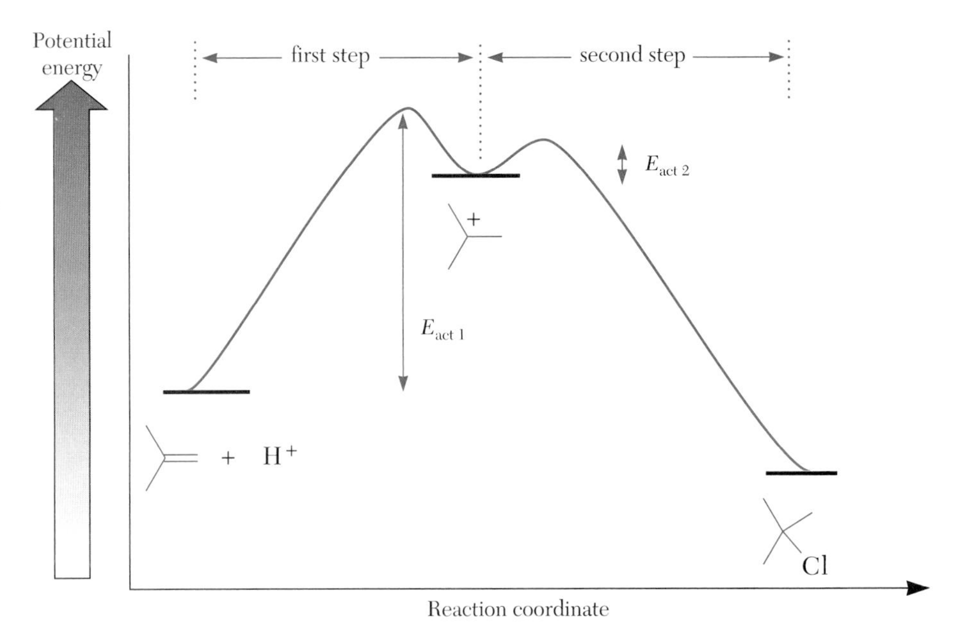

Figure 10.26 Overall reaction progress diagram for the addition of hydrogen chloride to 2-methylpropene. The activation energy for the first step (E_{act1}) is higher than the activation energy for the second step (E_{act2}). The overall reaction has two activated complexes (two transition states), and there is *one* intermediate species formed in the reaction (the *tert*-butyl carbocation). Intermediates occur at potential energy minima on the reaction progress diagram, and activated complexes occur at potential energy maxima.

process we use to generate them. We will encounter this generalization many times.

Let us again consider the carbocations illustrated in Figure 10.25. The formation of each of the possible carbocations requires a separate activated complex. Consider the structures for these two activated complexes, which are shown in Figure 10.27. In each of the activated complexes, positive charge has developed to some extent on one of the carbon atoms. We expect the favored activated complex to be the one with the more stable positive charge. A positive charge on carbon is stabilized by alkyl groups. We therefore can predict that the favored activated complex will be the one leading to the tertiary carbocation.

We need to examine activated complexes more closely. We have said that positive charge is partially developed on carbon and that some of the bonds of the products are partially formed and some of the bonds of the reactants are

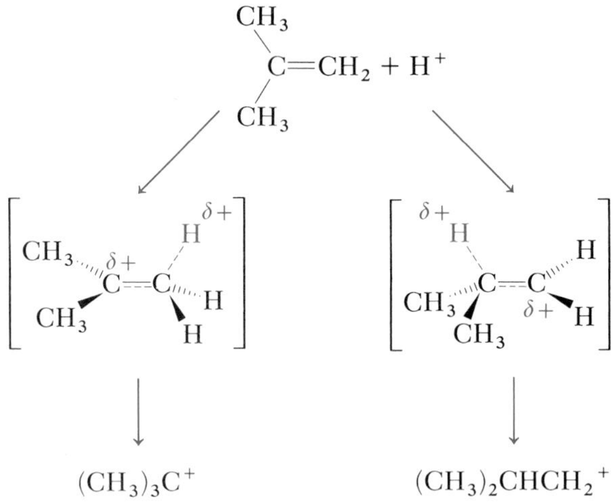

$(CH_3)_2C{=}CH_2 + H^+$

$[(CH_3)_2C^{\delta+}{=}CH_2 \cdots H^{\delta+}]$ → $(CH_3)_3C^+$

$[H^{\delta+} \cdots (CH_3)_2C{=}C^{\delta+}H_2]$ → $(CH_3)_2CHCH_2^+$

Figure 10.27 Activated complexes for the formation of carbocations from 2-methylpropene. The activated complexes for the two possible carbocations are shown in the brackets. Dashed lines represent partially formed or partially broken bonds.

SPECIAL TOPIC

Kinetics and Thermodynamics

Consider a stone placed on the surface of thick oil in a drum. *Thermodynamics* tells us that the stone, being denser than the oil, will be more stable at the bottom of the drum than at the top, that is, the stone has a natural tendency to sink to the bottom of the drum. Thermodynamics cannot tell us, however, how *fast* the stone will sink.

In principle, we *might* be able to calculate the rate of fall of the stone if we knew enough about the oil and the stone and had a satisfactory mathematical model to make meaningful calculations. If we didn't have enough information or a suitable mathematical model, we would need to resort to experimental means to measure the rate of fall.

In general, thermodynamics can only compare energy content between some initial and some final state. If the energy content in the final state is less than the energy content in the initial state, then the final state is more stable and there will be a natural tendency to attain this final state. Thermodynamics, however, says nothing about the rate of conversion between the two states. In the example of the stone and the thick oil, the rate of fall would be rather slow. In some other medium (e.g., water or air) the rate of fall would be more rapid. The overall energy change, however, would be the same in any medium, because the stone falls the same distance.

In chemical reactions ΔG (the free energy change, see Chapter 7) tells us the thermodynamic driving force for a reaction. Reactions with a negative ΔG have a natural tendency to proceed from reactants to products. We say that such reactions have a thermodynamic driving force. While reactions with a large driving force often occur rapidly, this is by no means always true. For example, most of the biological molecules of our bodies react at negligible rates with oxygen of the air (fortunately), even though there is a large driving force (large negative ΔG) for their oxidation. Similarly, soot does not change into diamonds at any perceptible rate, in spite of the fact that carbon in the form of diamond is more stable than it is in soot. (Fortunately, neither do diamonds change into graphite, an even more stable form of carbon, at any perceptible rate.) Species that endure for significant periods of time in spite of inherent thermodynamic instability are referred to as being *metastable* or *kinetically stable*. The unqualified use of the term *stable* can cause ambiguities. If is often necessary to spell out exactly what we mean when we say that something is stable or unstable.

Theory, if sufficiently advanced, could in principle predict the rate of any given reaction, just as it could in principle be used to calculate the rate of fall of a stone in a drum of oil. However, calculations of rate from first principles are not yet possible for the majority of chemical reactions. Nevertheless, by measuring and comparing the rates of many different reactions, chemists have been able to develop some useful correlations. We will look at some of these correlations as we proceed.

partially broken. It is often important to know the *extent* to which charge has been developed and the degree to which bonds have been broken and formed in the activated complex. In other words, we would like to know to what extent the activated complex resembles the reactants or the products.

An insightful analysis of the factors involved in the activation process was developed by Professor George Hammond in 1955. This analysis is generally referred to as the **Hammond postulate.** This postulate tells us that the activated complex for a reaction step that is exothermic tends to resemble the reactants more closely (structurally). Moreover, the activated complex for a reaction step that is endothermic more closely resembles the product (structurally). We say that an exothermic reaction step has an *early transition state* and an endothermic reaction step has a *late transition state*. We can illustrate these concepts with one further look at the reaction progress diagram for the addition of HX to 2-methylpropene (Figure 10.28).

When an alkene reacts with a hydrogen halide, the first step is the formation of a carbocation. This step is endothermic. According to the Hammond postulate, it will have a late transition state. The activated complex will resemble the eventual carbocation intermediate in that significant positive charge will have developed on carbon. In the reaction of 2-methylpropene with a hydrogen halide, two carbocations could, in principle, form (as shown in Figure 10.28). The selectivity of a reaction is measured by the extent to which one product is formed compared to the other—this in turn depends on the difference in the activation energies of the two processes. If the difference is large, there is high selectivity. If the difference is small, there is little selectivity. For the reaction between 2-methylpropene and a hydrogen halide, we expect high selectivity because the competing reactions have late (carbocationlike) transition states. The two activated complexes differ significantly in energy because one closely

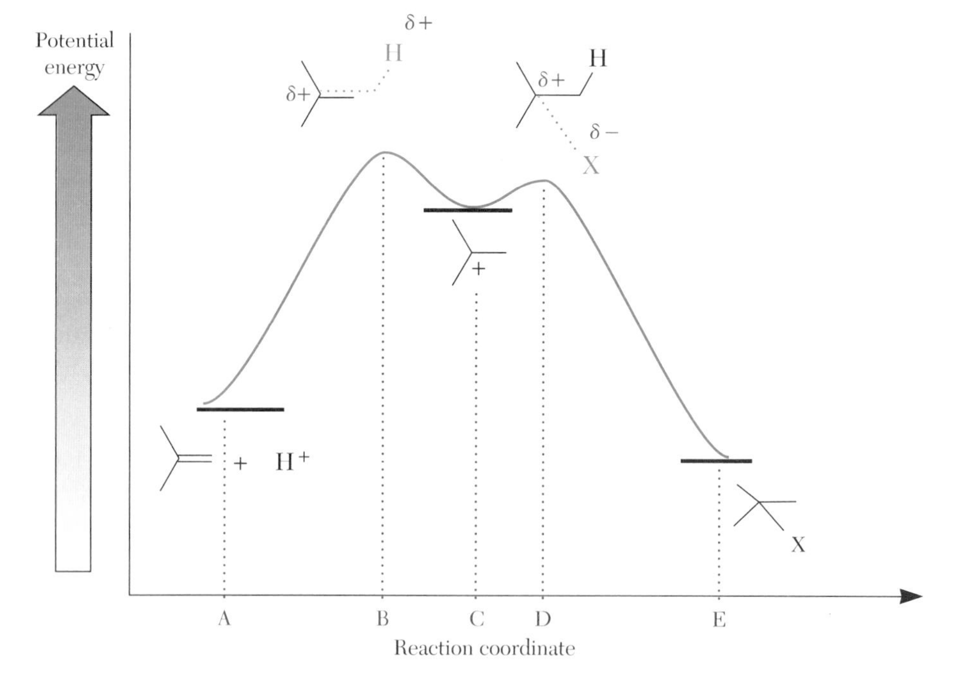

Figure 10.28 Structures of activated complexes in the addition of HX to 2-methylpropene. The first step is endothermic. The activated complex (B) is structurally more similar to the carbocation intermediate (C) than it is to the starting material (A). That is, at the transition state, the hydrogen ion (H^+) is almost completely bound to carbon and considerable positive charge has developed on the tertiary carbon atom. Along the reaction coordinate we show B being closer to C than to A; it is a late transition state. In the second step the activated complex (D) involves only the beginning of new bond formation between the carbocation (C) and the anion. The activated complex (D) is structurally more similar to C than it is to the product (E); it is an early transition state.

resembles a tertiary carbocation and the other resembles a primary carbocation. Whatever stabilizes the product (a carbocation) also stabilizes the transition state for that product.

If the transition state were *earlier*, charge would not be as fully developed on carbon. Then the transition state would be *less* cationlike and there would be a smaller difference between the energies of the two activated complexes. The selectivity of the process would be diminished, and the eventual formation of the more stable carbocation product would be less dominant.

10.6 Addition of Sulfuric Acid

Cold, concentrated sulfuric acid (H_2SO_4) reacts with alkenes; H and HSO_4 are added across the double bond, producing an alkyl hydrogen sulfate. Experimentally, we observe the alkene "dissolving" in the acid (it is really the reaction product that dissolves).

If the alkene is gaseous, we can allow it to react by bubbling it into the acid. If the alkene is a liquid, we can simply mix the two liquids to cause reaction to occur. The reaction system is shown in Figure 10.29.

The products of the reaction of alkenes with sulfuric acid are *esters* of sulfuric acid. We earlier discussed esters of several inorganic and organic acids. As esters, these products can undergo several useful reactions. For example, on heating, the alkyl hydrogen sulfates are converted back into the parent alkenes, and if the ester is diluted with water and heated, hydrolysis occurs and an alcohol is formed. Both of these reactions are shown in Figure 10.29.

These two reactions of alkyl hydrogen sulfates are quite important. First, reaction with sulfuric acid to form the alkyl hydrogen sulfate followed by thermal decomposition is a good purification method for alkenes. This approach allows alkenes to be isolated efficiently from mixtures with alkanes. In addition, the hydrolysis of alkyl hydrogen sulfates is quite suitable for the industrial manufacture of alcohols. All of the ingredients are readily available—the alkenes from petroleum cracking, and the sulfuric acid from oxidation of sulfur. (Sulfuric acid has been the "number 1" industrial chemical for many years.)

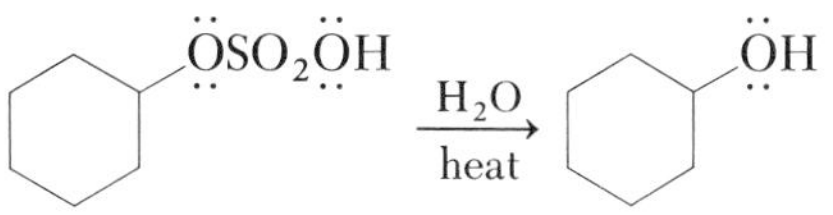

Figure 10.29 Formation and reactions of an alkyl hydrogen sulfate.

Formation of an alkyl hydrogen sulfate

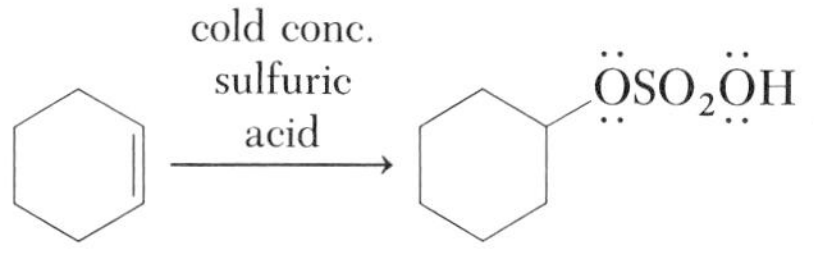

cold conc. sulfuric acid

$\ddot{O}SO_2\ddot{O}H$

Thermal decomposition of an alkyl hydrogen sulfate

$\ddot{O}SO_2\ddot{O}H$

heat

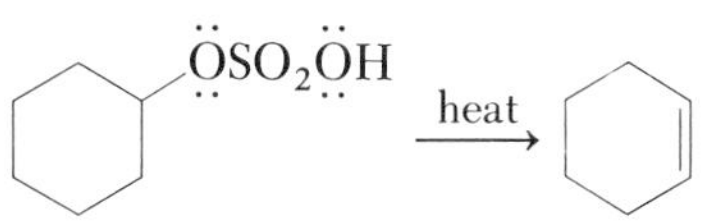

Hydrolysis of an alkyl hydrogen sulfate

$\ddot{O}SO_2\ddot{O}H$

H_2O

heat

$\ddot{O}H$

PROBLEM 10.12 1-Propanol can be dehydrated to propene by treatment with hot sulfuric acid. Treatment of the propene with cold, concentrated sulfuric acid yields compound A of formula $C_3H_8SO_4$. When A is treated with water, compound B, which is an isomer of 1-propanol, is formed. Give structures for A and B and explain these results.

PROBLEM 10.13 Explain why it is *not* possible to manufacture isobutyl alcohol by the method of treating an alkene with cold, concentrated sulfuric acid followed by hydrolysis of the product.

PROBLEM 10.14 You have performed a synthesis of hexane by the catalytic hydrogenation of 1-hexene. You suspect that there are traces of 1-hexene remaining in the product. Experimentally, how would you proceed to remove the traces of the alkene from the product alkane?

10.7 Hydration of a Double Bond Using Water and a Strong Acid

Hydration of a double bond refers to the addition of the elements of water (H and OH) across the olefinic carbons to produce an alcohol. It is a very important synthetic reaction. This section and the two following will describe the most common methods that have been devised to accomplish hydration.

Water itself will not react with alkenes. However, it *will* react in the presence of strong acids, and this route provides the most direct method for the hydration of alkenes. Reaction begins with protonation of the alkene to produce a carbocation. The water present then acts as a nucleophile, adding to the carbocation to form an oxonium ion. Final loss of a proton from the oxygen yields the alcohol. Examples of this synthetic method are shown in Equations 10.9 and 10.10.

Eqn. 10.9

$$CH_3CH_2CH_2CH{=}CH_2 \underset{}{\overset{H_3PO_4}{\rightleftharpoons}} CH_3CH_2CH_2\overset{+}{C}HCH_3 \overset{OH_2}{\rightleftharpoons} CH_3CH_2CH_2CH(\overset{+}{O}H_2)CH_3 \overset{-H^+}{\rightleftharpoons} CH_3CH_2CH_2CH(OH)CH_3$$

1-pentene

80% yield
2-pentanol

Eqn. 10.10

$$\text{methylenecyclobutane} \xrightarrow{H_2SO_4,\ H_2O} \text{1-methylcyclobutanol (}CH_3\text{, :OH)}$$

methylenecyclobutane

66% yield
1-methylcyclobutanol

Since a carbocation intermediate is involved in this reaction, we must remember several points:

1. If an unsymmetrical alkene is used, protonation will occur to yield the more stable of the possible carbocations. In general, we expect Markovnikov's Rule to be followed in the addition of water.
2. Rearrangements of the carbon skeleton are possible prior to reaction with water.
3. The reaction is not stereospecific, because water can attack the carbocation intermediate from the top or the bottom.

This method of hydration of an alkene involves the use of strong acid, and it is useful only for molecules that have no other sensitive functional groups. For molecules that *do* have acid-sensitive groups, milder methods of hydration must be used, as we will discuss in the next sections.

10.8 Hydration by Means of Oxymercuration/Demercuration

ALCOHOL SYNTHESIS

Many reactions of alkenes are initiated by the addition of a proton to the double bond to form a carbocation. The carbocation then goes on to react with some nucleophile present in solution. Certain metal ions may be used (instead of the proton) as the electrophile in the initial step of such reactions. Mercuric ion (Hg^{2+}) is a particularly important example of such a metal ion. If we treat an alkene with a solution of mercuric acetate [$Hg(OAc)_2$], an intermediate organomercury compound is formed, as shown in Figure 10.30. We refer to this reaction as **oxymercuration.**

The addition is regiospecific. Mercury adds to the less substituted carbon of the alkene, and the hydroxyl group becomes attached to the more highly substituted carbon. We do not usually isolate this intermediate but instead reduce it in situ (in the same pot) to an alcohol by adding sodium borohydride to the reaction mixture. Since the reduction results in the loss of mercury from the organic species, we call the reaction **demercuration.** This step is also illustrated in Figure 10.30.

Figure 10.30 Oxymercuration/demercuration of 1-pentene.

Oxymercuration

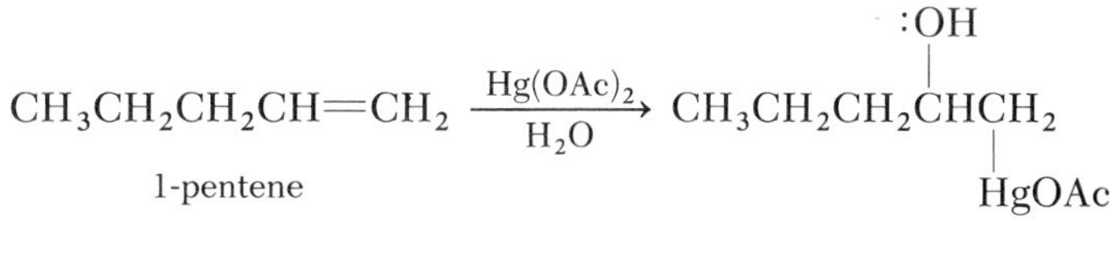

$$\underset{\text{1-pentene}}{CH_3CH_2CH_2CH{=}CH_2} \xrightarrow[H_2O]{Hg(OAc)_2} CH_3CH_2CH_2\underset{\ddot{O}H}{C}HCH_2HgOAc$$

Demercuration

$$CH_3CH_2CH_2CH(\ddot{O}H)CH_2HgOAc \xrightarrow{NaBH_4} \underset{\text{96\% yield, 2-pentanol}}{CH_3CH_2CH_2CH(\ddot{O}H)CH_3} + Hg$$

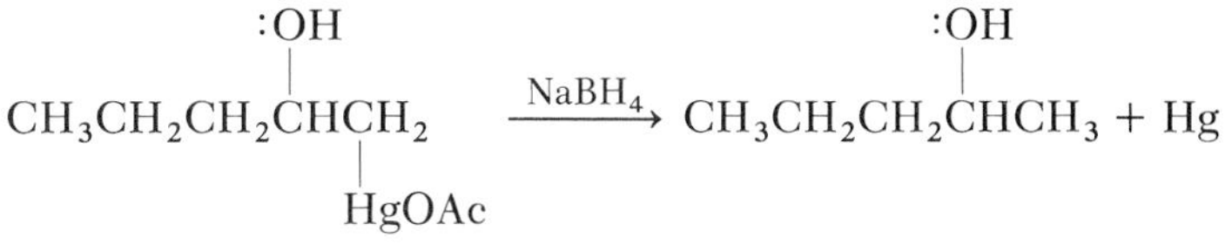

96% yield
2-pentanol

The overall result of oxymercuration/demercuration is to add the elements of water across the double bond with a Markovnikov orientation. The mild conditions make this a particularly attractive laboratory preparation of alcohols from alkenes. It is usually a high yield reaction, but unfortunately the *overall* hydration is not stereospecific. The oxymercuration step *is* stereospecific (*anti*), but the demercuration step is not. The demercuration step is believed to proceed via a free radical mechanism and the overall result is a mixture of *syn* and *anti* addition products with Markonikov regiospecificity.

MECHANISM

The oxymercuration process proceeds in three steps that lead to an intermediate organomercury compound.

MECHANISM OF REACTION

Step 1 The π bond electrons of the alkene interact with the mercury of the mercuric acetate.

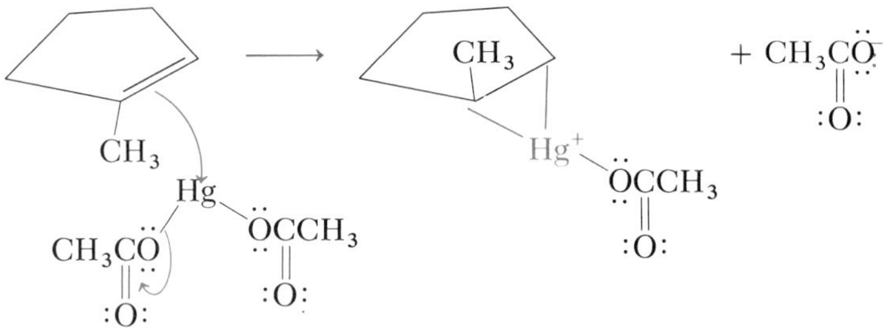

CH_3 Hg CH_3CO $OCCH_3$ O → CH_3 Hg^+ $OCCH_3$ O + CH_3CO^- O

Unlike the species generated by proton attack, the species produced in this initial attack by mercury does *not* have a formal σ bond between carbon and the electrophile but rather consists of a three-membered ring akin to a bridged bromonium ion. The mercury is associated with one face of the original π bond, and the methyl group is forced to the opposite side of the ring.

Step 2 Water attacks the intermediate species from the face opposite the attached mercury *at the more highly substituted carbon atom* (again in a manner akin to water attack on a bridged bromonium ion). This step is a stereospecific *anti* addition overall and is also regiospecific (has Markovnikov orientation).

H H O CH_3 Hg^+ $OCCH_3$ O CH_3CO^- O → H H O^+ CH_3 Hg—$OCCH_3$ O CH_3CO^- O

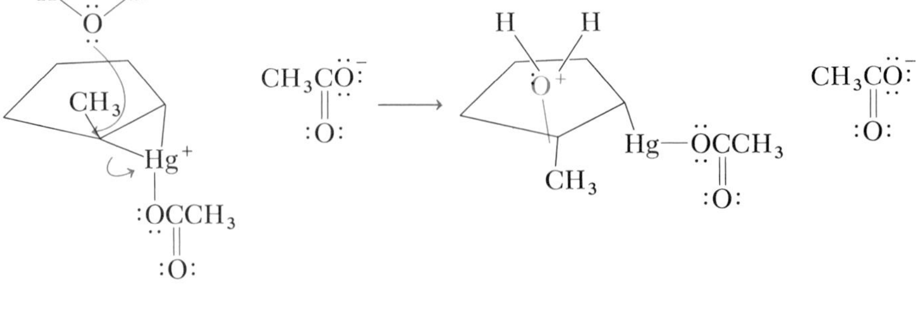

Step 3 A base present in the reaction system (acetate ion) removes a hydrogen ion from the intermediate oxonium ion to give the organomercury species.

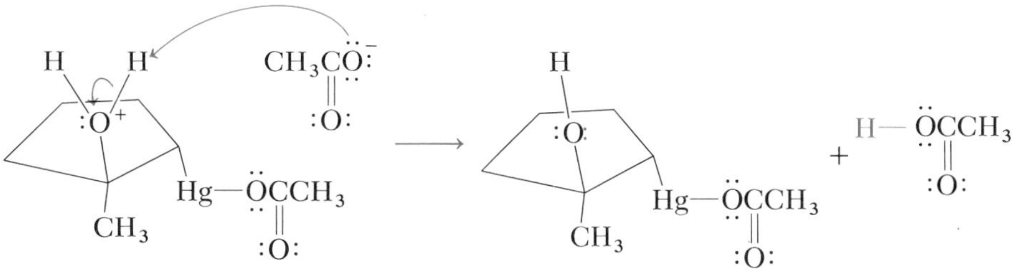

The demercuration process is *not* stereospecific; it proceeds through a free radical species of the type shown in Figure 10.31.

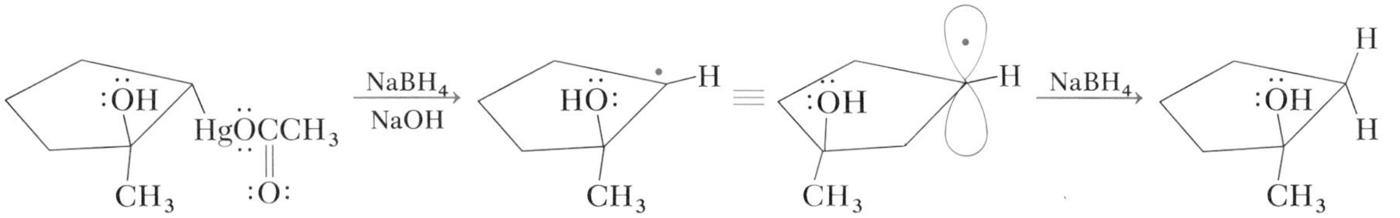

Figure 10.31 Free radical species in the demercuration step of oxymercuration/demercuration. Two ways of illustrating the free radical are shown in the center. The structure on the left simply shows an unpaired electron at the carbon originally bound to mercury. The structure on the right shows the *p* orbital bearing the unpaired electron. Attachment of a hydrogen atom can occur from either the top or the bottom, so this step is nonstereospecific.

10.9 Hydration by Means of Hydroboration/Oxidation

Consider the problem of converting 1-butene to 1-butanol. Hydration of the double bond with anti-Markovnikov orientation is required. None of the hydration methods we have discussed is suitable for this conversion because they all add the elements of water with Markovnikov stereochemistry and would produce 2-butanol from 1-butene.

Fortunately, there is a method for adding the elements of water across a double bond with anti-Markovnikov orientation. The conversion is performed by means of a two-step procedure known as **hydroboration/oxidation.** In addition to being regiospecific (anti-Markovnikov), the reaction is also stereospecific. The elements of water are added to the double bond in a *syn* manner.

The reagent used for hydroboration reactions is borane, BH_3, in the form of a complex with either dimethyl sulfide (**10.8**) or tetrahydrofuran (THF) (**10.9**).

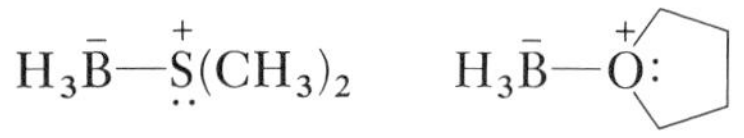

$$H_3\bar{B}-\overset{+}{S}(CH_3)_2 \qquad H_3\bar{B}-\overset{+}{O}\text{(THF)}$$

10.8 **10.9**

Borane itself is not sufficiently stable to be isolated and stored. When prepared in an uncomplexed form, it is present as the dimer, B_2H_6, a spontaneously flammable gas known as diborane. Diborane can be used for hydroboration, although it is difficult to handle. The complexed forms are much easier to use and store, and they behave chemically as we would expect BH_3 to behave. For simplicity, we will refer to borane reagents here simply as *borane* or BH_3, recognizing that a complexed form or diborane is actually used.

Equation 10.11 shows the overall hydroboration/oxidation procedure applied to 1-pentene.

Eqn. 10.11

$$CH_3CH_2CH_2CH{=}CH_2 \xrightarrow[2.\ H_2O_2/^-OH]{1.\ BH_3} CH_3CH_2CH_2CH_2CH_2\ddot{\underset{..}{O}}H$$

1-pentene — 85% yield 1-pentanol

In fact, only one-third mole of borane is required for every mole of 1-pentene to be converted. Each of the three boron-hydrogen bonds of borane reacts sequentially with a molecule of the alkene (pentene), giving tri-1-pentylborane (**10.10**), as shown in Equation 10.12.

Eqn. 10.12

$$3\ \text{(1-pentene)} + BH_3 \longrightarrow (CH_3CH_2CH_2CH_2CH_2)_3B \xrightarrow[^-OH]{H_2O_2} 3\ \text{(1-pentanol)} + B(OH)_3$$

tri-1-pentylborane
10.10

Since tri-1-pentylborane (**10.10**) contains no further boron-hydrogen bonds, it is incapable of any further alkene addition reactions. In general, hydroboration of an alkene results in the formation of a trialkylborane.

Trialkylboranes are important species for organic synthesis because they undergo a variety of most useful reactions. Among these reactions is oxidation to alcohols. The oxidation is conveniently effected by an aqueous alkaline solution of hydrogen peroxide. All carbon-boron bonds are replaced by carbon-hydroxyl bonds in this process. In the reaction shown in Equation 10.12, three carbon-boron bonds are broken and hydroxyl groups become attached to each of the carbons involved.

MECHANISM, REGIOSELECTIVITY, AND STEREOCHEMISTRY

Each stage of the hydroboration occurs with anti-Markovnikov orientation. That is, in the first stage of the reaction shown in Equation 10.16, only mono-1-pentylborane (**10.11**) is formed. No mono-2-pentylborane (**10.12**) is formed.

$$CH_3CH_2CH_2CH_2CH_2{-}BH_2 \qquad CH_3CH_2CH_2\underset{\displaystyle BH_2}{\underset{|}{C}H}{-}CH_3$$

(formed) **10.11** — (not formed) **10.12**

The two subsequent additions to alkene also occur with anti-Markovnikov orientation to give tri-1-pentylborane (**10.10**).

To account for this regioselectivity we need to consider the nature of boranes and the activated complex for their addition to alkenes. Borane and alkylboranes contain an electron-deficient boron atom—boron has less than a noble gas complement of electrons. These boron species are therefore *electrophiles*. By contrast, an alkene is electron rich in the region of the double bond. As reaction begins, electron density is transferred from the alkene π bond toward boron and a carbon-boron bond begins to form, exactly as in the mechanisms described earlier for bromination, protonation, and mercuration of alkenes. However, unlike these reactions, hydroboration does *not* proceed through a cationic intermediate.

As the boron-carbon bond is being formed, an electron-rich hydrogen attached to boron simultaneously begins to bond with the other (more electrophilic) carbon of the olefinic linkage. We have previously considered the differing natures of the carbon atoms of an unsymmetrical olefinic linkage. In borane the hydrogen is relatively electron rich compared to the electron-deficient boron. It acts as a *hydride* reagent. Boron binds to the more nucleophilic (less highly substituted) of the carbon atoms of the olefinic linkage, and hydrogen binds to the more highly substituted of the carbon atoms of the olefinic linkage. The result is *syn* addition of H and B across the double bond.

We can look at the stereochemistry of the process by considering the reaction involving 1-methylcyclopentene (see Equation 10.13). The *syn* nature of the reaction is shown by the formation of the *trans* borane (**10.13**) as an intermediate and *trans*-2-methylcyclopentanol as the product. (*Note:* The product here is named *trans* even though a *syn* addition occurred.) The stereochemical result of the first step is *syn addition;* the result of the second step is *retention.*

Eqn. 10.13

CH_3 $\xrightarrow{BH_3}$ CH_3, H, H, BH_2 $\xrightarrow[HO^-,\ H_2O]{H_2O_2}$ CH_3, H, H, :ÖH

1-methylcyclopentene

10.13

85% yield
trans-2-methylcyclopentanol

PROBLEM 10.15

Predict the major products to be expected on application of the hydroboration/oxidation procedure to each of the following:

a. 2-methyl-1-butene
b. 2-methyl-2-butene
c. 1,2-dimethylcyclopentene
d. (Z)-3-methyl-2-pentene

Steps to Solving the Problem

Solution to Problem 10.15a

1. What are the atoms that add to each of the carbons of the olefinic linkage? The reaction occurs in a regiospecific manner with anti-Markovnikov orientation. With 2-methyl-1-butene, the more highly substituted of the olefinic carbons is the 2-position. The boron adds to the 1-position.

2. What is involved in the formation of the final product? In the second step the boron is replaced by a hydroxyl group without rearrangement. The product has the hydroxyl group at the 1-position and is 2-methyl-1-butanol, as shown below.

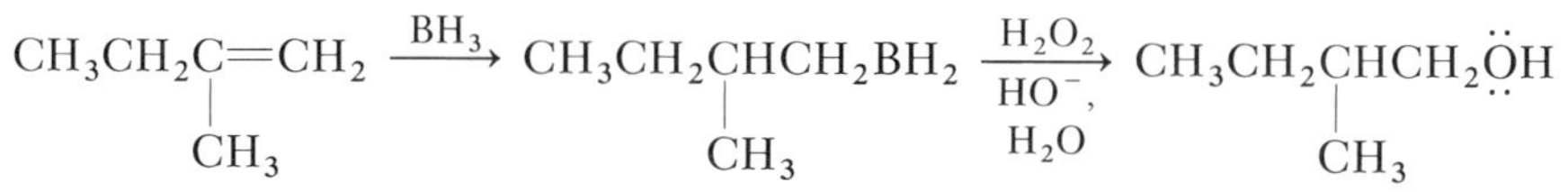

$$CH_3CH_2\underset{\displaystyle CH_3}{\underset{|}{C}}{=}CH_2 \xrightarrow{BH_3} CH_3CH_2\underset{\displaystyle CH_3}{\underset{|}{C}}HCH_2BH_2 \xrightarrow[HO^-,\ H_2O]{H_2O_2} CH_3CH_2\underset{\displaystyle CH_3}{\underset{|}{C}}HCH_2\ddot{O}H$$

The *syn* stereoselectivity suggests that addition of a borane to a double bond is a *concerted* process, that is, it occurs in a single step. As the double bond breaks, bonds to boron and to hydrogen begin to form. We usually view this reaction as occurring by means of a four-center activated complex, as shown in Figure 10.32.

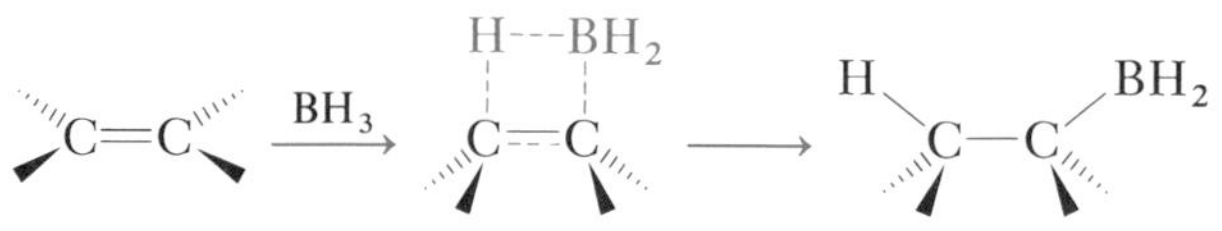

Figure 10.32 Addition of borane to an alkene. The *syn* addition is presumed to occur by means of a concerted process involving a cyclic four-centered activated complex. The reaction occurs *without* rearrangement of the carbon skeleton, suggesting the absence of a carbocation.

$$\text{C=C} \xrightarrow{BH_3} \begin{matrix}\text{H---BH}_2\\ \vdots \quad \vdots\\ \text{C---C}\end{matrix} \longrightarrow \begin{matrix}\text{H} \quad\quad \text{BH}_2\\ \text{C—C}\end{matrix}$$

MOLECULAR ORBITAL ANALYSIS

The *syn* nature of hydroboration is in accord with molecular orbital views of the alkene and the borane. Figure 10.33 shows the available orbitals of the two reagents that can interact in a concerted manner.

The oxidation of the intermediate trialkylborane proceeds via several steps. Initially, hydrogen peroxide and hydroxide ion react to form the hydroperoxide ion. The hydroperoxide ion then adds to the electron-deficient boron of the trialkylborane. Migration of an alkyl group from boron to oxygen then occurs

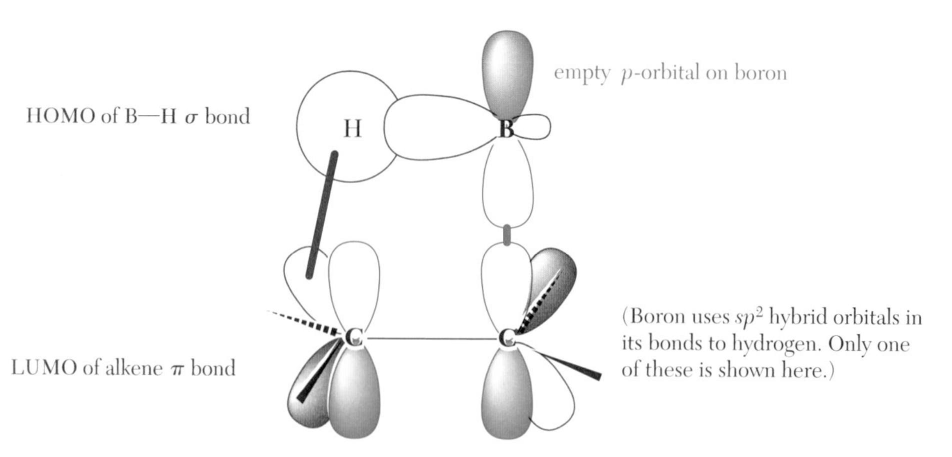

Figure 10.33 Molecular orbitals interacting in hydroboration reaction. Unlike other addition reactions we have considered for alkenes, hydroboration involves an atom (boron) that has an empty p orbital able to interact with the alkene. As the B—H and π bonds are being broken, two new bonds can be formed simultaneously (indicated by the broad lines).

with displacement of hydroxide ion. When this process has occurred with all three of the alkyl groups attached to boron, the result is a trialkyl borate ester. Finally, the trialkyl borate ester is hydrolyzed under the aqueous basic conditions of the reaction to form borate ion and three equivalents of the alcohol.

MECHANISM OF REACTION

Step 1 Hydroxide ion and hydrogen peroxide react as base and acid to form hydroperoxide ion and water.

$$HO^- + H{-}O{-}O{-}H \longrightarrow H{-}O{-}H + {}^-O{-}O{-}H$$

Step 2 The hydroperoxide ion undergoes nucleophilic addition to the empty *p* orbital on the borane.

$$R_2B(R) + {}^-O{-}O{-}H \longrightarrow R_2\overset{-}{B}(R){-}O{-}O{-}H$$

Step 3 An alkyl group migrates from boron to oxygen, displacing hydroxide ion from the peroxide linkage.

$$R_2\overset{-}{B}(R){-}O{-}O{-}H \longrightarrow R_2B{-}O{-}R + {}^-OH$$

Step 4 The process of Step 3 is repeated with each of the remaining alkyl groups attached to boron.

$$R_2B{-}O{-}R + 2\,{}^-O{-}O{-}H \longrightarrow \longrightarrow B(OR)_3 + 2\,{}^-OH$$

Step 5 The three B-OR linkages are cleaved by hydroxide ion attack on boron. The initially formed products of this cleavage are alkoxide ions, RO^-, and boric acid, $B(OH)_3$. Further acid-base reactions convert the alkoxide ions to alcohol molecules and the boric acid to borate ion.

$$B(OR)_3 + 3\,OH^- \longrightarrow B(OH)_3 + 3\,RO^-$$

$$RO^- + H_2O + B(OH)_3 \longrightarrow ROH + B(OH)_4^-$$

Of particular importance in this sequence is Step 3, the migration of the alkyl group from boron to oxygen. If the alkyl group has a stereogenic carbon bound to boron, we find that migration occurs with *retention* of configuration at that carbon. In effect, the carbon slides along the boron-oxygen bond to displace the hydroxyl group and becomes bound to oxygen. We see the result of this migration in the reaction shown in Equation 10.13. The hydroxyl group becomes bound to carbon on the side of the carbon where the boron was originally attached. Thus *syn* addition of boron and hydrogen, followed by retention in the replacement of boron by oxygen, results in overall *syn* addition of H and OH.

10.10 Other Uses of Hydroboration

ISOMERIZATION OF ALKYLBORANES

The hydroboration reaction is reversible. A significant consequence of this reversibility can be observed with the hydroboration of an internal alkene. The alkylborane so produced can regenerate the original alkene or form an isomeric alkene, as shown in Figure 10.34.

If the hydroboration reaction mixture is heated, addition-elimination reactions occur continuously. The most thermodynamically stable alkylborane predominates in the equilibrium mixture so produced. As noted previously, the boron atom attaches preferentially to the less highly substituted carbon atom of the alkene linkage. Ultimately, the boron becomes attached to (and stays with) the terminal position of the carbon chain, which is the least highly substituted of any carbon of the chain. Upon oxidation of the trialkylborane we obtain a primary alcohol. An example of this reaction system is shown in Equation 10.14.

Eqn. 10.14

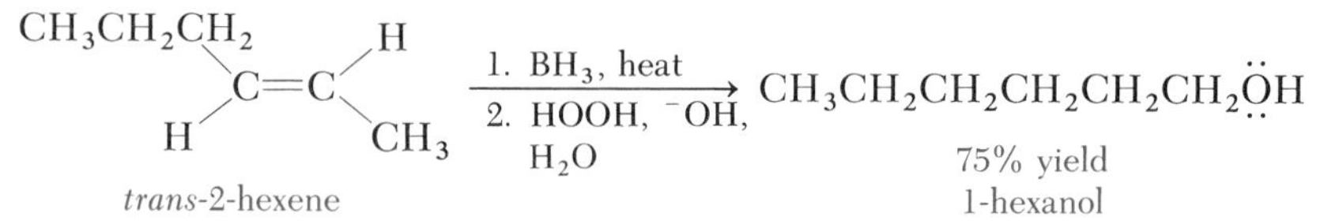

$$\underset{trans\text{-2-hexene}}{(CH_3CH_2CH_2)(H)C{=}C(H)(CH_3)} \xrightarrow[\text{2. HOOH, }^-\text{OH, } H_2O]{\text{1. BH}_3\text{, heat}} \underset{\substack{75\%\text{ yield} \\ \text{1-hexanol}}}{CH_3CH_2CH_2CH_2CH_2CH_2\ddot{O}H}$$

In summary, isomerization of the initially formed trialkylborane occurs upon heating. At equilibrium, the terminal trialkylborane predominates. Upon oxidation we then isolate the primary alcohol. If we want the reaction to occur *without* isomerization, we perform the hydroboration reaction at lower temperature.

HYDROBORATION/HALOGENATION

Upon treatment of a trialkylborane with a halogen (chlorine, bromine, or iodine) in the presence of methoxide ion, boron is replaced by halogen. The overall result of hydroboration/halogenation of an alkene is the addition of the elements of hydrogen halide to the original alkene with anti-Markovnikov orientation. Accordingly, haloalkanes that cannot be prepared by the direct ionic addition

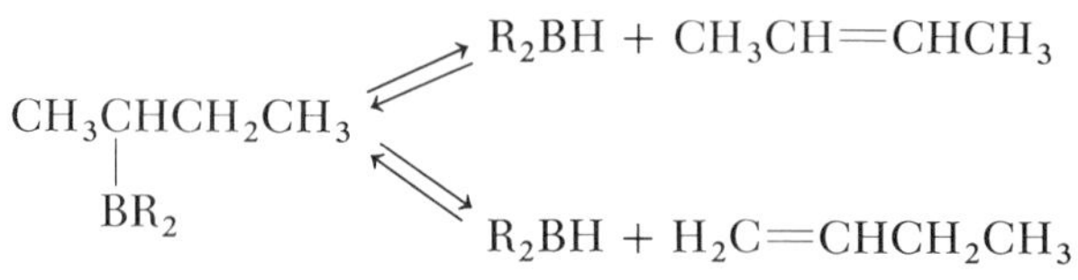

$$CH_3\underset{|\atop BR_2}{C}HCH_2CH_3 \rightleftharpoons R_2BH + CH_3CH{=}CHCH_3$$

$$CH_3\underset{|\atop BR_2}{C}HCH_2CH_3 \rightleftharpoons R_2BH + H_2C{=}CHCH_2CH_3$$

Figure 10.34 Reversibility of hydroboration. The alkylborane can eliminate R_2BH, either regenerating the original alkene or forming an isomer of it.

Figure 10.35 Specific hydrogen isotope incorporation with hydroboration/reduction. Reduction of an alkene linkage can be performed to incorporate one hydrogen and one deuterium regiospecifically.

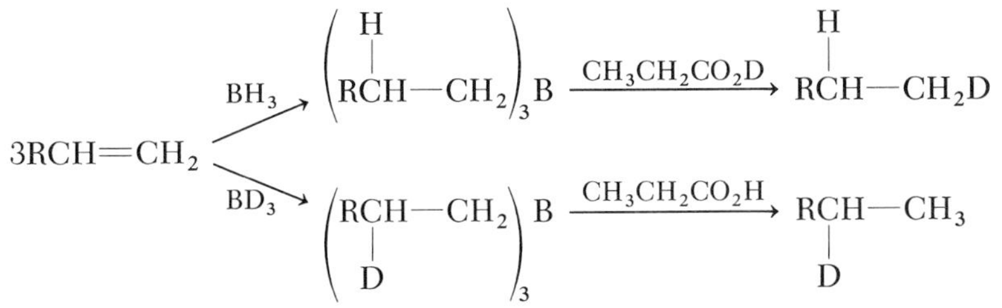

$$3RCH{=}CH_2 \xrightarrow{BH_3} (RCH(H){-}CH_2)_3B \xrightarrow{CH_3CH_2CO_2D} RCH(H){-}CH_2D$$

$$3RCH{=}CH_2 \xrightarrow{BD_3} (RCH(D){-}CH_2)_3B \xrightarrow{CH_3CH_2CO_2H} RCH(D){-}CH_3$$

of HX to an alkene can be prepared by the hydroboration/halogenation method. An example of this reaction is shown in Equation 10.15.

Eqn. 10.15

$$CH_3CH_2CH_2CH_2CH{=}CH_2 \xrightarrow[2.\ Br_2,\ NaOCH_3]{1.\ BH_3} CH_3CH_2CH_2CH_2CH_2CH_2\ddot{Br}:$$

1-hexene → 93% yield 1-bromohexane

REDUCTION OF ALKYLBORANES

The reduction of trialkylboranes occurs upon treatment with a carboxylic acid. The acidic hydrogen of the carboxylic acid replaces the boron on carbon. An example of this reaction is shown in Equation 10.16.

Eqn. 10.16

$$CH_3CH_2CH_2CH_2CH{=}CH_2 \xrightarrow[2.\ CH_3CH_2CO_2H]{1.\ BH_3} CH_3CH_2CH_2CH_2CH_2CH_3$$

1-hexene → 91% yield hexane

This method accomplishes the same overall result as does catalytic hydrogenation. However, it has an advantage in that it allows a single hydrogen isotope (deuterium or tritium) to be introduced at either of the two olefinic carbon atoms. If an isotopically labeled borane reagent is used, the hydrogen isotope is introduced at the more highly substituted carbon of the olefinic linkage. To introduce the hydrogen isotope at the less highly substituted carbon of the olefinic linkage, labeled acid is used in the second step. These procedures are summarized in Figure 10.35.

PROBLEM 10.16 Specify the two-step sequence of reactions needed to convert methylpropene into each of the following:

a. $(CH_3)_2CDCH_3$ **b.** $(CH_3)_2CHCH_2D$

10.11 Hydroxylation

Hydroxylation is the name given to the addition of two hydroxyl groups across a double bond. The product of hydroxylation is a *1,2-diol,* also called a *vicinal diol,* or a *glycol.*

SYN ADDITION

We can accomplish hydroxylation by several means, with either *syn* or *anti* stereoselectivity. The stereoselectivity depends on the reagent system used for the reaction. Products of *syn* hydroxylation are formed through the use of either dilute alkaline solutions of permanganate salts or osmium tetroxide with bisulfite workup. Examples of these procedures are shown in Equations 10.17 and 10.18.

Eqn. 10.17

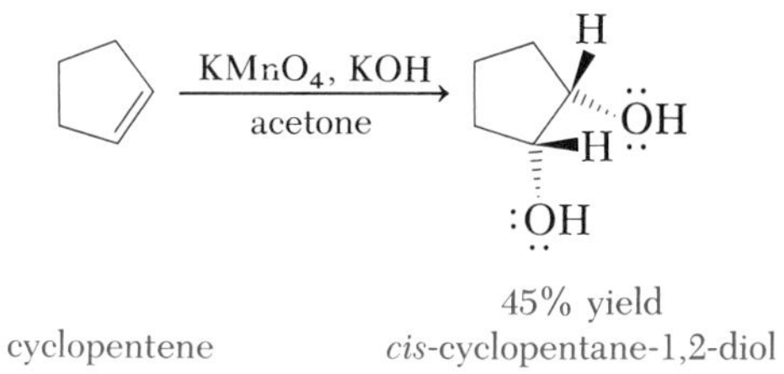

cyclopentene $\xrightarrow[\text{acetone}]{KMnO_4,\ KOH}$ *cis*-cyclopentane-1,2-diol (45% yield)

Eqn. 10.18

cyclohexene $\xrightarrow[\text{2. } H_2O,\ NaHSO_3]{\text{1. } OsO_4}$ *cis*-cyclohexane-1,2-diol (75% yield)

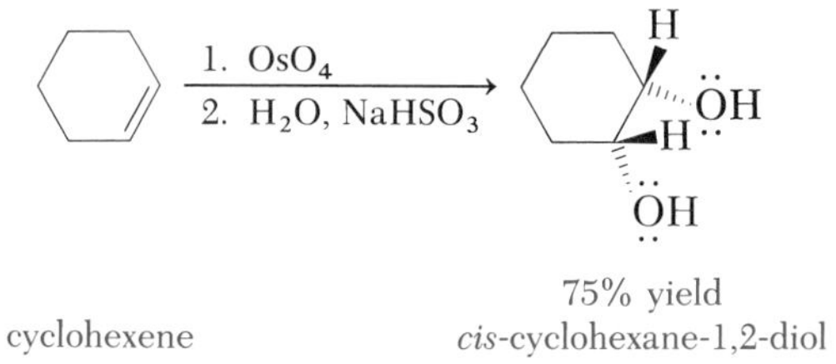

Reactions using osmium tetroxide usually produce higher yields of the vicinal diol than those using permanganate. However, osmium tetroxide is quite expensive and highly toxic.

The reaction using permanganate is visually revealing. The purple color of the permanganate solution disappears as the reaction proceeds, and a brown precipitate of manganese dioxide forms. We can use this reaction as a rapid test for the presence of carbon-carbon double bonds in unknown substances. When used in this manner, this reaction is known as the *Baeyer Test*.

The initial reaction of either permanganate or osmium tetroxide with an alkene produces a cyclic ester as a reaction intermediate. The intermediates in the reaction of cyclohexene with each reagent are shown in Figure 10.36.

Under the reaction conditions the permanganate ester decomposes to form the 1,2-diol product. The corresponding osmate esters, which form as black precipitates, are more stable and are usually treated with water to form the 1,2-diol product. Sodium bisulfite reduces the initially formed Os(VI) to form easily removed osmium by-products.

OsO_4 ; H_2O, $NaHSO_3$; MnO_4^- ; H_2O

Figure 10.36 Cyclic ester intermediates in hydroxylation of alkenes using either permanganate or osmium tetroxide.

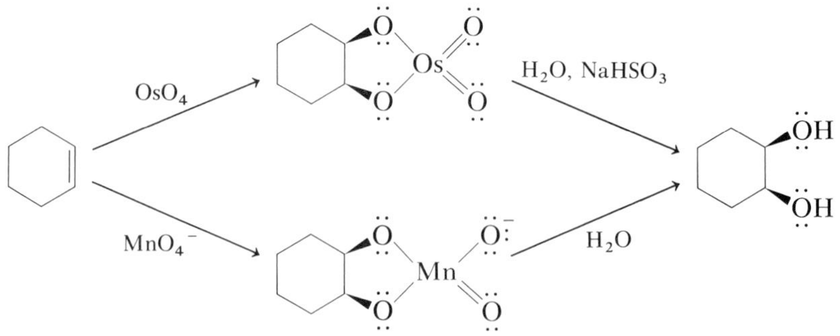

PROBLEM 10.17 Write the structure, paying particular attention to stereochemistry where pertinent, for the diols produced by treatment of each of the following alkenes with osmium tetroxide followed by workup with aqueous sodium bisulfite.
a. cyclooctene **b.** *cis*-2-butene **c.** *trans*-2-butene

ANTI ADDITION

We can achieve *anti* hydroxylation of alkenes by treating them with hydrogen peroxide in formic acid. The hydrogen peroxide first reacts with the formic acid to form peroxyformic acid (**10.14**).

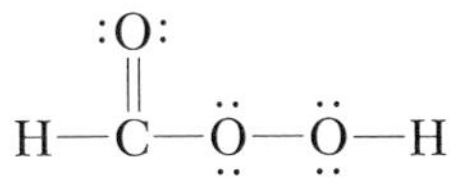

$$\mathrm{H{-}C({=}O){-}O{-}O{-}H}$$

10.14

The peroxyformic acid then reacts with the alkene to produce a protonated epoxide, as shown in Figure 10.37.

A protonated epoxide is highly strained and is susceptible to attack by nucleophiles. Water, which is present as the solvent, attacks the protonated epoxide from the side of the ring opposite to the oxygen. This attack is entirely analogous to the reaction of a bromonium ion with a nucleophile to give overall *anti* addition. Upon loss of a proton, the *trans*-1,2-diol is formed, as shown in Figure 10.38.

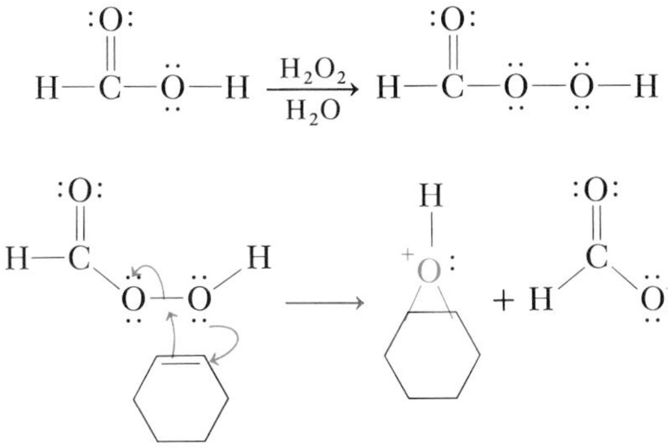

Figure 10.37 Formation of a protonated epoxide intermediate in the reaction of cyclohexene with peroxyformic acid.

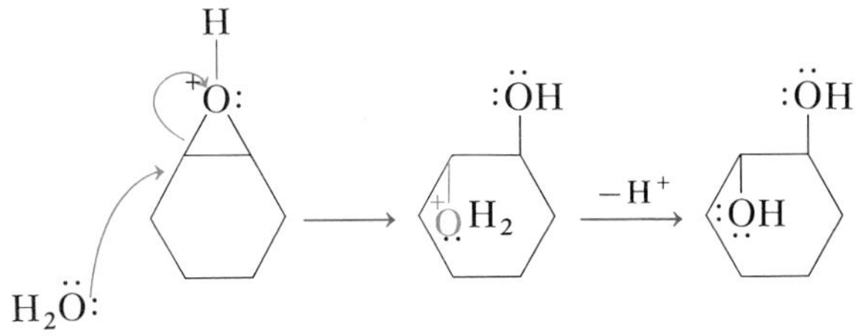

$$\mathrm{H{-}C({=}O){-}O{-}H} \xrightarrow[H_2O]{H_2O_2} \mathrm{H{-}C({=}O){-}O{-}O{-}H}$$

H—C(=O)—O—O—H + cyclohexene ⟶ protonated epoxide (H—O⁺) + H—C(=O)—O⁻

Figure 10.38 Completion of the hydroxylation of cyclohexene using formic acid and hydrogen peroxide. The reaction produces a racemic mixture of 1,2-cyclohexanediol.

H_2O: + protonated epoxide ⟶ :OH / $^{+}OH_2$ cyclohexane $\xrightarrow{-H^+}$:OH / :OH cyclohexane

PROBLEM 10.18 Figure 10.38 shows the formation of one enantiomer of cyclohexane-1,2-diol. Use the curved-arrow formalism to show the formation of the other enantiomer.

PROBLEM 10.19 What is the stereochemical relationship of the product of permanganate hydroxylation of cyclohexene to that formed using peroxyformic acid?

The chemistry of the epoxides will be discussed in detail later. At that time we will reconsider in more detail the *anti* hydroxylation reaction.

10.12 Addition Reactions Involving Free Radicals

Anti-Markovnikov orientation in the addition of HBr (but not other hydrogen halides) to alkenes involves free radicals. Initially, this reaction was discovered quite by accident when free radicals generated from impurities in the reaction system initiated the first examples of this type of reaction. We can *cause* the anti-Markovnikov addition to occur by the specific addition of *free radical initiators*. Free radical initiators are substances that readily form free radicals under mild conditions such as gentle heating or irradiation with light. Many peroxides serve as free radical initiators. Two examples of anti-Markovnikov addition are shown in Equations 10.19 and 10.20.

Eqn. 10.19

$$H_3C{-}C({=}\ddot{O}{:}){-}\ddot{O}{-}CH_2(CH_2)_8CH{=}CH_2 \xrightarrow[\text{(C}_6\text{H}_5\text{CO)}_2\text{ benzoyl peroxide (initiator)}]{\text{HBr, heat}} H_3C{-}C({=}\ddot{O}{:}){-}\ddot{O}{-}CH_2(CH_2)_9CH_2\ddot{B}r{:}$$

11-(1-undecenyl) acetate → 82% yield, 11-bromoundecyl acetate

Eqn. 10.20

$$CH_3CH{=}CH_2 \xrightarrow[(C_6H_5CO)_2]{\text{HBr heat}} CH_3CH_2CH_2\ddot{B}r{:}$$

propene → 98.5% yield, 1-bromopropane

The accidental discovery of conditions favoring anti-Markovnikov orientation occurred due to the use of ether solvents in polar HBr addition reactions with alkenes. Upon standing in contact with oxygen of the air, ethers (Chapter 14) accumulate peroxides. Peroxides are compounds that contain the oxygen-oxygen linkage. The peroxide shown in Equations 10.19 and 10.20 is benzoyl peroxide, a commonly used material for the generation of free radicals. We have already seen some other examples of peroxides, for example, hydrogen

Figure 10.39 Homolytic cleavage of the oxygen-oxygen bond of a peroxide. The products are two alkoxy radicals.

$$R{-}\ddot{\underset{..}{O}}{-}\ddot{\underset{..}{O}}{-}R \longrightarrow R{-}\dot{\underset{..}{O}}: + :\dot{\underset{..}{O}}{-}R$$

peroxide and peroxyformic acid. The oxygen-oxygen bond of peroxides is quite weak and is easily broken homolytically, as shown in Figure 10.39.

The resultant alkoxy radicals initiate the sequence of reactions shown below, which lead to anti-Markovnikov addition of HBr to the alkene.

MECHANISM OF REACTION

Step 1 The peroxide bond undergoes homolytic cleavage to form two alkoxy radicals.

$$R{-}\ddot{\underset{..}{O}}{-}\ddot{\underset{..}{O}}{-}R \longrightarrow R{-}\dot{\underset{..}{O}}: + :\dot{\underset{..}{O}}{-}R$$

Step 2 An alkoxy radical abstracts a hydrogen atom from a hydrogen bromide molecule.

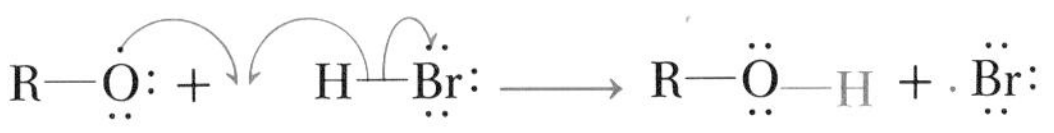

$$R{-}\dot{\underset{..}{O}}: + H{-}\ddot{\underset{..}{Br}}: \longrightarrow R{-}\ddot{\underset{..}{O}}{-}H + \cdot\ddot{\underset{..}{Br}}:$$

Step 3 The bromine atom formed in the previous step adds to one of the olefinic carbon atoms of the alkene.

$$:\dot{\underset{..}{Br}}: + H_2C{=}CHR \longrightarrow H_2C(\ddot{\underset{..}{Br}}:){-}\dot{C}HR$$

Step 4 The alkyl radical abstracts a hydrogen atom from a molecule of hydrogen bromide.

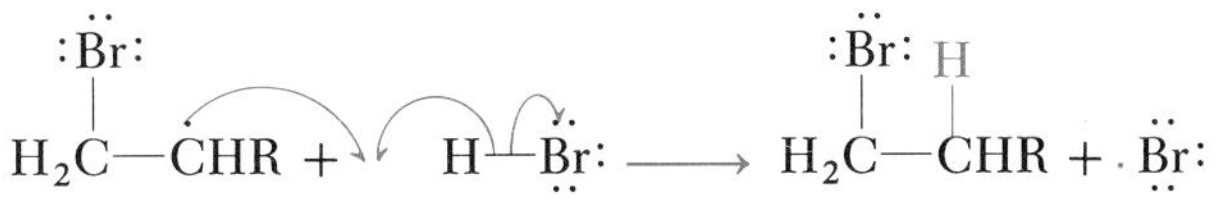

$$H_2C(\ddot{\underset{..}{Br}}:){-}\dot{C}HR + H{-}\ddot{\underset{..}{Br}}: \longrightarrow H_2C(\ddot{\underset{..}{Br}}:){-}CH(H)R + \cdot\ddot{\underset{..}{Br}}:$$

This sequence of reactions is an example of a chain reaction. The bromine atom produced in the last step can react with another molecule of alkene. The first two reactions of the sequence are *chain-initiation steps*—they are the reactions that produce the free radicals necessary to start the reactions that actually form products. The third and fourth steps are *chain-propagation steps.* Each propagation step involves the reaction of a free radical with a nonradical species to produce a new free radical. These steps follow each other in a repetitive, self-sustaining manner, until all starting materials are used up or the chain process is interrupted.

$$:\ddot{Br}\cdot + :\ddot{Br}\cdot \longrightarrow Br_2$$

$$:\ddot{Br}\cdot + R\dot{C}H{-}CH_2\ddot{Br}: \longrightarrow RCHBr{-}CH_2\ddot{Br}:$$

Figure 10.40 Two chain-termination steps in the anti-Markovnikov addition of HBr to alkenes.

Occasionally two of the chain-propagating free radicals collide and combine to give a nonradical species. Such a reaction is a *chain-termination step.* Two chain-termination steps are shown in Figure 10.40.

PROBLEM 10.20 Chain-termination steps other than those shown above are possible for the free radical addition of HBr to alkenes. Give three other chain-termination steps possible in this reaction.

If we want to have anti-Markovnikov addition of HBr to an alkene, we must arrange for a source of free radicals to be present. The free radical chain reaction can then compete with the more usual ionic reaction that leads to Markovnikov orientation. Under free radical conditions we find that the free radical reaction proceeds much more rapidly than the ionic reaction. (The ionic reaction still *does* occur—the free radical reaction is simply faster.)

The anti-Markovnikov orientation is the result of preferential formation of the more stable of the two possible free radicals that can be formed in the initial addition of a bromine atom to the alkene. As with carbocations, the greater alkyl substitution about the electron-deficient radical site gives the more stable species. Tertiary free radicals are more stable than secondary free radicals, which in turn are more stable than primary free radicals. An example is shown in Figure 10.41.

PROBLEM 10.21 Give the structure of the major product upon reaction of 1-methylcyclohexene with HBr under each of the following conditions:

a. in acetic acid
b. in diethyl ether with added benzoyl peroxide

10.13 Oxidative Cleavage of Alkenes

Some oxidizing agents are sufficiently powerful to cleave both the π and σ bonds of a double bond. The products of these reactions are compounds containing a carbon-oxygen double bond, that is, aldehydes, ketones, carboxylic acids, or even carbon dioxide. In each case the carbon atoms of the original olefinic linkage are no longer joined to one another—a complete splitting of the carbon-carbon linkage has occurred.

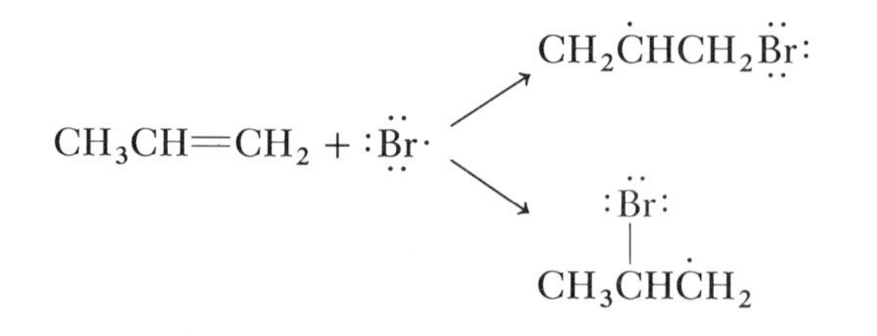

Figure 10.41 Addition of a bromine atom with an alkene. The more stable of the possible free radicals is formed preferentially.

THE USE OF PERMANGANATE

In an earlier section we considered the reaction of cold, aqueous alkaline permanganate with alkenes. Reaction leads to the formation of a 1,2-diol. If we use a *hot* solution of permanganate, the diol is further oxidized. The nature of the product(s) from this further oxidation depend on the substitution about the original olefinic linkage. In summary, we find the following:

- If two alkyl groups are attached to a carbon atom of the olefinic linkage, that carbon atom is oxidized to a ketone function.
- If an olefinic carbon atom has only one alkyl group attached to it, that carbon atom is initially oxidized to an aldehyde. This aldehyde is then *further* oxidized to a carboxylic acid.
- If an olefinic carbon atom has only hydrogen attached to it, the initial product formed from it is formaldehyde, which is further oxidized to formic acid, which in turn is oxidized to carbon dioxide.

These products of reaction are illustrated in Figure 10.42.

Figure 10.42 Products of alkene oxidation upon heating with aqueous alkaline permanganate.

$KMnO_4$, KOH, H_2O, heat → ketone + ketone

$KMnO_4$, KOH, H_2O, heat → ketone + aldehyde

aldehyde → 1. $KMnO_4$, KOH, H_2O, heat 2. aq. acid → carboxylic acid

$KMnO_4$, KOH, H_2O, heat → ketone + formaldehyde

formaldehyde → 1. $KMnO_4$, KOH, H_2O, heat 2. aq. acid → formic acid

formic acid → $KMnO_4$, KOH, H_2O, heat → carbonic acid (unstable) → $-H_2O$ → O=C=O

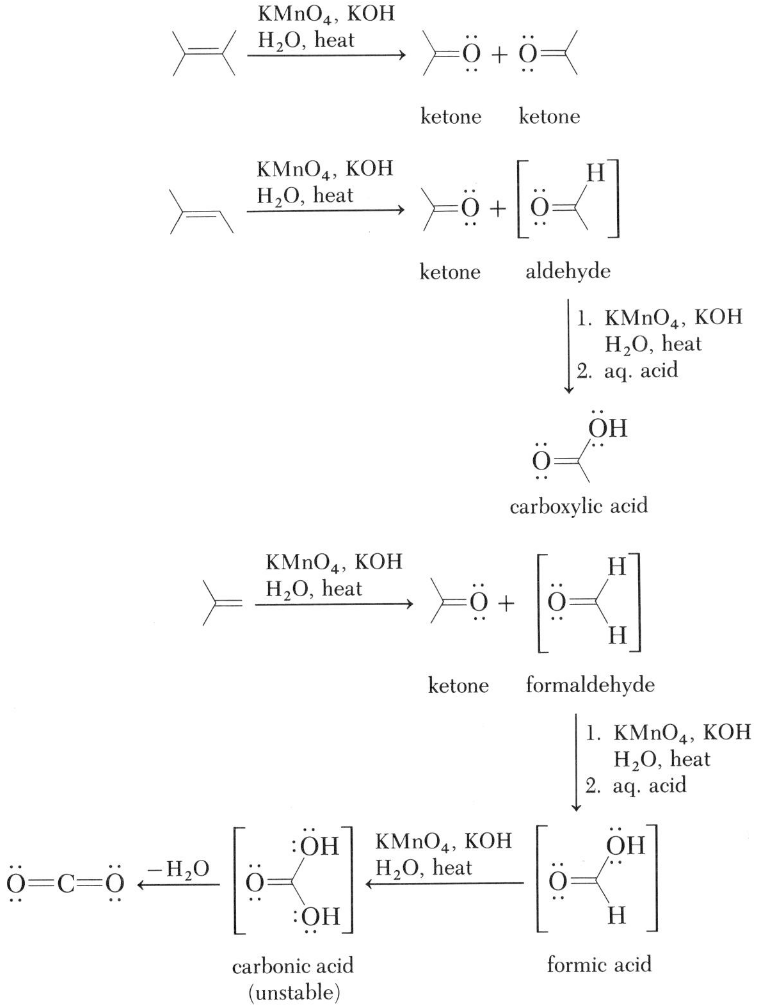

Cyclic compounds containing a double bond in the ring behave analogously, except that the cleavage produces one difunctional molecule. An example is shown in Equation 10.21.

Eqn. 10.21

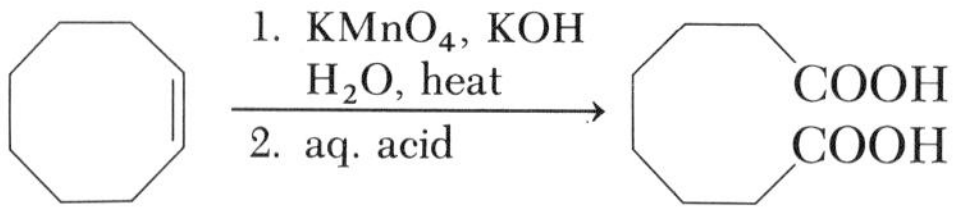

$$\text{cyclooctene} \xrightarrow[\text{2. aq. acid}]{\text{1. } KMnO_4,\ KOH,\ H_2O,\ \text{heat}} \text{subaric acid (cyclic, COOH, COOH)}$$

cyclooctene

69% yield
subaric acid

THE USE OF OZONE

Carbon-carbon double bonds can also be cleaved by using ozone (O_3). The reaction is known as **ozonolysis.** Ozone is a highly reactive allotrope of oxygen that must be generated at the time it is used (you cannot get a bottle of ozone at your local chemical supply house). Ozone is readily generated from ordinary oxygen in electrical discharges. It is the source of the distinctive odor associated with electrical sparks. In the laboratory we generate ozone by passing a stream of oxygen through a silent electrical discharge and then into the reaction vessel. The reaction system is usually cooled to $-78\,°C$ (the temperature of dry ice). The ozone content of the oxygen stream is low, never amounting to more than a few percent. However, this low concentration is quite sufficient for ozonolysis.

The reaction of alkenes with ozone proceeds in stages. The terminal oxygen atoms of the ozone molecule initially add across the π bond of the alkene to give an unstable intermediate known as a *molozonide.* This intermediate then undergoes a rapid rearrangement with cleavage of the remaining σ bond to give an *ozonide,* as illustrated in Figure 10.43.

Workup of an ozonlysis reaction is effected by adding an appropriate reducing or oxidizing agent. When an ozonide is treated with a *reducing* agent (for example, with zinc or nickel metal and an acid or with dimethyl sulfide), it is cleaved. An example of ozonolysis with such a *reductive* workup is shown in Equation 10.22.

Eqn. 10.22

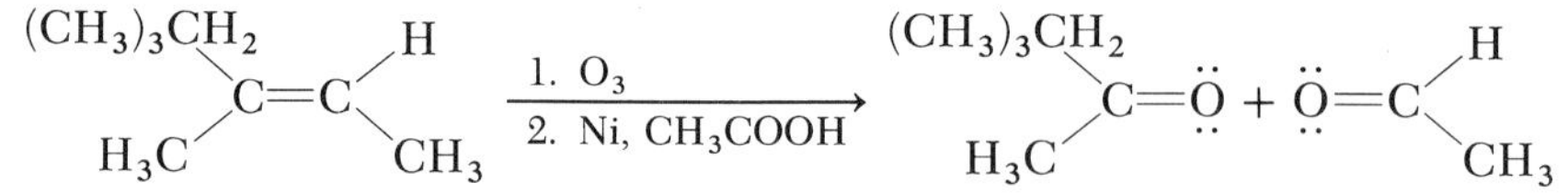

$$(CH_3)_3CH_2(H_3C)C{=}C(H)CH_3 \xrightarrow[\text{2. Ni, } CH_3COOH]{\text{1. } O_3} (CH_3)_3CH_2(H_3C)C{=}O + O{=}C(H)CH_3$$

(*E*)-3,5,5-trimethyl-
2-hexene

75% yield
4,4-dimethyl-2-pentanone

ethanal

Figure 10.43 Formation of an ozonide from an alkene by reaction with ozone.

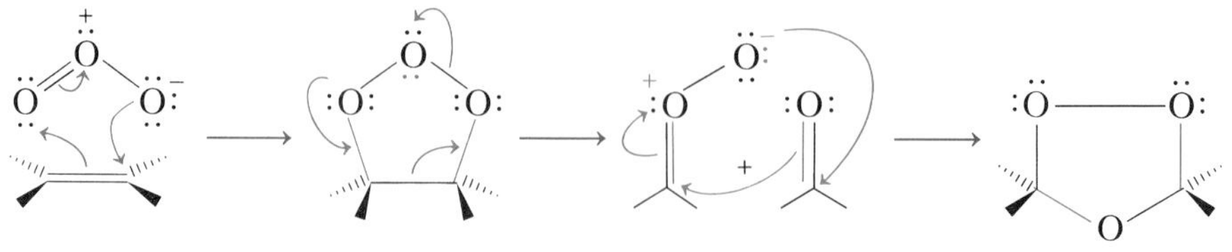

a molozonide

an ozonide

Under reductive workup conditions, hydrogen atoms initially attached to an olefinic carbon remain unchanged, and any aldehydes that are formed remain as aldehydes. This is *not* the case when workup is carried out under *oxidative* conditions. For example, when hydrogen peroxide is used to decompose the ozonide, any aldehydes formed initially are *further* oxidized by the hydrogen peroxide to carboxylic acids. The final observed products are then similar to those observed when permanganate is used as the cleavage reagent. An example of ozonolysis with oxidative workup is shown in Equation 10.23.

Eqn. 10.23

$$\text{cyclohexene} \xrightarrow[\text{2. } H_2O_2,\ H_2O]{\text{1. } O_3} \text{HOOC(CH}_2)_4\text{COOH}$$

cyclohexene — adipic acid, 85% yield

An exception to the similarity in products given by permanganate cleavage and by ozonolysis with oxidative workup occurs with terminal alkenes. On ozonolysis with oxidative workup, the terminal carbon of a terminal alkene is oxidized to formic acid. When cleavage of the terminal alkene is performed with permanganate, the terminal carbon atom is further oxidized to carbon dioxide.

PROBLEM 10.22 Give the structure of the compound that will yield the given set of products following ozonolysis and workup with zinc and acetic acid.

a. $CH_3CH\ddot{O}$ and $H_2C\ddot{O}$
b. cyclobutanone and $CH_3CH\ddot{O}$
c. propanone and $CH_3CH_2CH\ddot{O}$

PROBLEM 10.23 When either (*E*)- or (*Z*)-2,11-dimethyl-2,6,10-dodecatriene is ozonized and worked-up under oxidative conditions, two products are obtained in a 1:1 molar ratio. Give the structures of these two products. (Note: The prefix *dodeca*- signifies 12 carbon atoms.)

STRUCTURAL ANALYSIS BY OXIDATIVE CLEAVAGE

The oxidative cleavage of alkenes is a useful chemical method of organic structural analysis. We often have difficulty in assigning full structures to newly prepared large molecules or molecules isolated from natural sources. Our task is simplified if we can break these molecules into smaller units in a systematic manner. The oxidative cleavage reactions we have discussed in this chapter are useful for this purpose.

If we are able to identify the fragment molecules of alkene oxidative cleavage reactions, we can piece the units together to reconstruct the original structure. Several examples of the reconstruction of original structures from ozonolysis fragments are illustrated in Figure 10.44.

Figure 10.44 Reconstruction of starting material structures in alkene ozonolysis. We identify the oxidized carbon atoms (carbonyl or carboxylate carbon atoms) as the olefinic carbon atoms in the starting alkene; that is, oxidized carbon atoms were originally bound to each other by a double bond.

(a) Ozonolysis with reductive workup

$CH_3CH_2C(CH_3)=O$ + $O=$cyclohexane (products) — must have come from → $CH_3CH_2C(CH_3)=$cyclohexylidene

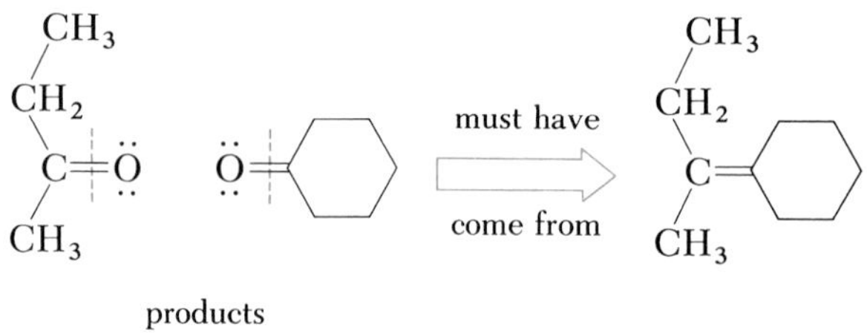

(b) Ozonolysis with oxidative workup

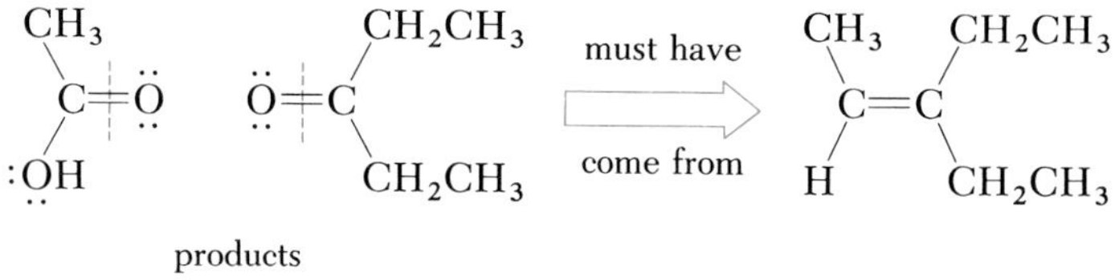

$CH_3C(OH)=O$ + $O=C(CH_2CH_3)_2$ (products) — must have come from → $CH_3CH=C(CH_2CH_3)_2$

(c) Ozonolysis of a cyclic alkene with reductive workup

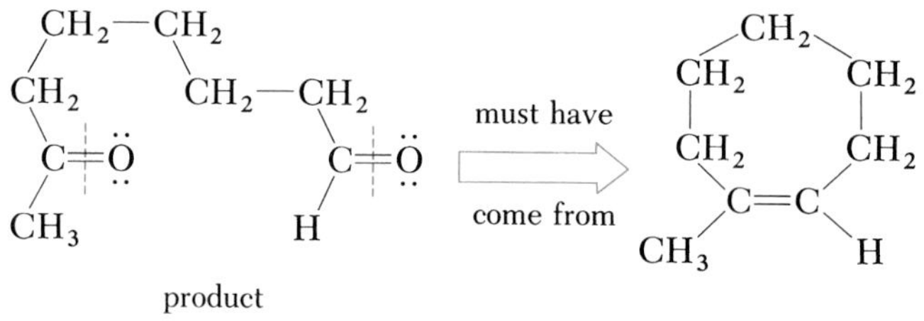

$CH_3C(=O)CH_2CH_2CH_2CH_2CH_2CH=O$ (product) — must have come from → 1-methylcyclooctene ($CH_3C=CH$ in a ring of CH_2 groups)

PROBLEM 10.24 Predict the products of ozonolysis and reductive workup for each of the following alkenes:

a. $(CH_3)_2C{=}C(CH_3)_2$

b. 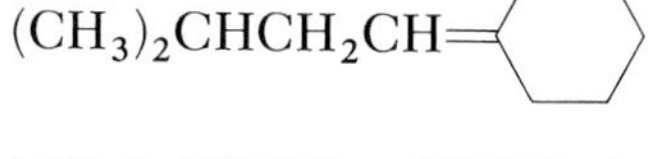 $(CH_3)_2CHCH_2CH{=}$cyclohexylidene

c. $(CH_3)_2CHCH{=}CHCH_2CH{=}C(CH_3)_2$

PROBLEM 10.25 Reconstruct the original alkene structures for each of the following sets of products of ozonolysis with reductive workup:

a. cyclopentanone ($=\ddot{O}$) + $HC(=O)CH_2CH_2CH_3$

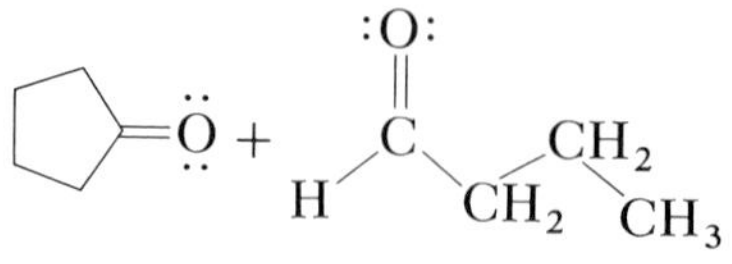

b. 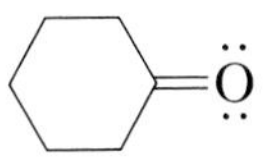 (cyclohexanone structure)

c. 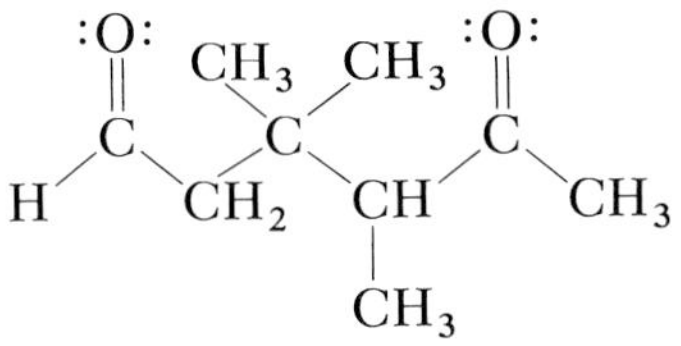 $H-C(=O)-CH_2-C(CH_3)_2-CH(CH_3)-C(=O)-CH_3$

d. 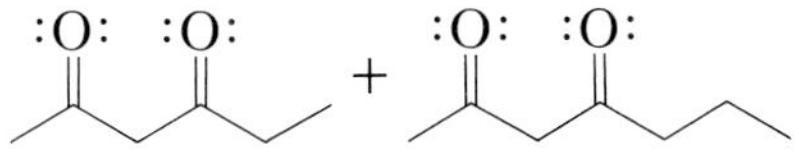 :O: :O: + :O: :O: from a C_{13}-compound; give all possibilities

e. 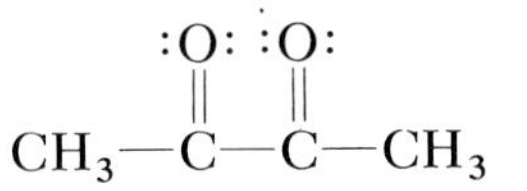 $CH_3-C(=O)-C(=O)-CH_3$ from: (i) C_6H_{12}, (ii) $C_{12}H_{18}$

10.14 Degree of Unsaturation

A common problem in organic chemistry is to assign a structure to a reaction product or to some material isolated from a plant or animal. Usually the first step in assigning a structure is to determine the molecular formula (we considered this type of determination earlier). The formula itself often reveals useful structural information.

For example, all open-chain alkanes have the general formula C_nH_{2n+2}, where n is an integer. On the other hand, both open-chain alkenes and monocyclic alkanes have the general formula C_nH_{2n}. Each ring or double bond in a molecule reduces the number of hydrogen atoms present by two, compared to the open-chain alkane with the same number of carbon atoms. A triple bond reduces the number of hydrogen atoms by four from that expected for the open-chain alkane. These general rules are illustrated in Figure 10.45 for compounds containing three carbon atoms.

Let's see how we can apply this analysis to deduce organic structures. Suppose we find that an unknown compound has a formula of $C_{12}H_{22}$. Since an open-chain alkane with 12 carbon atoms would have 26 hydrogen atoms ($2n + 2$, where $n = 12$), we quickly deduce the possible structural features of

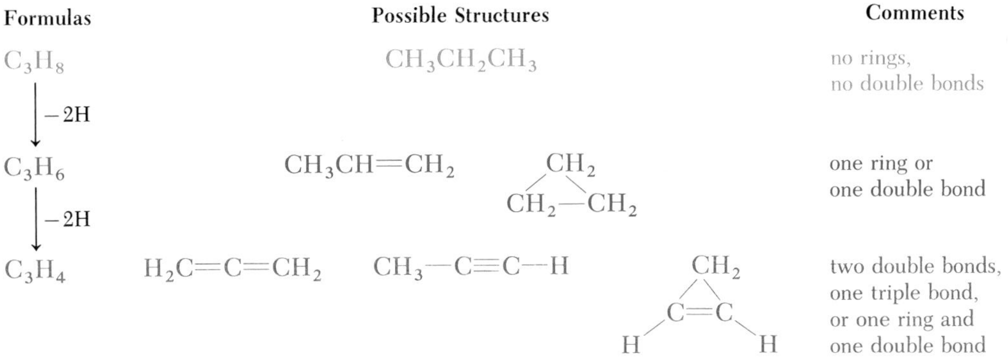

Figure 10.45 Analysis of rings and multiple bonds in three-carbon compounds based on the molecular formula.

Formulas	Possible Structures	Comments
C_3H_8	$CH_3CH_2CH_3$	no rings, no double bonds
↓ −2H		
C_3H_6	$CH_3CH{=}CH_2$; cyclopropane (CH_2 ring: CH_2, CH_2—CH_2)	one ring or one double bond
↓ −2H		
C_3H_4	$H_2C{=}C{=}CH_2$; $CH_3-C\equiv C-H$; cyclopropene (CH_2, H—C=C—H)	two double bonds, one triple bond, or one ring and one double bond

the compound. It must contain one of the following: one triple bond, two double bonds, two rings, or one ring and one double bond. We say that this compound has two *degrees of unsaturation*. From the molecular formula, we know the possible structural features of the molecule.

How do we then distinguish a double bond from a ring? The answer to this question is usually straightforward, since double bonds undergo addition reactions whereas alkane rings do not. For example, suppose our compound of formula $C_{12}H_{22}$ did not decolorize solutions of bromine or potassium permanganate nor react with hydrogen in the presence of a catalyst. We could safely deduce that it contained two rings rather than any multiple bonds.

If we measure the number of moles of bromine or hydrogen that add to a compound we can deduce the number of multiple bonds present. For example, suppose our $C_{12}H_{22}$ compound reacted with only one mole of hydrogen to give a compound of formula $C_{12}H_{24}$. We would then deduce that it contained one double bond and one ring.

When atoms other than carbon and hydrogen are present, some modifications in our deductive procedure are required:

- Oxygen atoms are ignored. That is, C_5H_8O is treated exactly like C_5H_8. Two degrees of unsaturation are present.
- For each halogen atom that is present we increase the number of hydrogen atoms by one before performing our analysis. For example, $C_6H_3Br_3$ is treated exactly like C_6H_6. Four degrees of unsaturation are present in each.
- If nitrogen is present, we *subtract* one hydrogen from the number of hydrogens present before performing our analysis. For example, a compound of formula C_5H_5N is treated as being equivalent to C_5H_4. Four degrees of unsaturation are present in each.

PROBLEM 10.26 Calculate the degree of unsaturation for each of the following:

a. C_8H_{14} b. C_6H_9Br c. C_5H_7N
d. C_6H_5OBr e. $C_{10}H_8BrN$ f. $C_8H_6Br_2$

PROBLEM 10.27 What are the possibilities for multiple bonds in a molecule of formula $C_{10}H_{16}$ if on catalytic hydrogenation it yields a compound of formula $C_{10}H_{20}$?

PROBLEM 10.28 One mole of a substance of formula C_5H_8 absorbs two moles of hydrogen on catalytic hydrogenation to yield methylbutane. Suggest a structure for the original compound.

10.15 Protection of Alkenes through Halogen Addition

The design and use of *protecting groups* is an important theme in synthetic organic chemistry. The need for a protecting group often arises when we intend to perform a synthetic operation on just one of several functional groups in a molecule. A problem arises if the reagent we intend to use on one functional group is known to react with another functional group that is also present. One solution to our problem is to mask temporarily the functional group we wish to remain unchanged. We then perform the desired reaction on the functional group we wish to change, and finally we remove the mask from the group that we had protected.

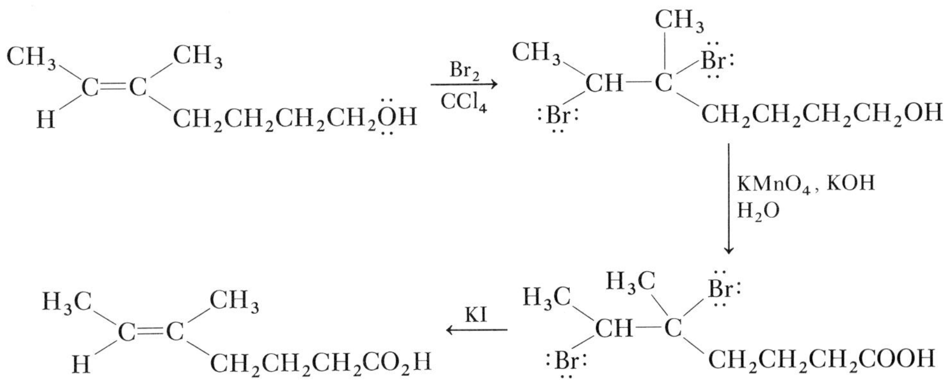

Figure 10.46 Use of halogenation for protection of a double bond. We wish to oxidize the primary alcohol of the starting material to a carboxyl group using potassium permanganate. To do so, we must first mask the double bond. Once the double bond has been saturated by halogenation, it is no longer susceptible to attack by the oxidizing agent. After the oxidation of the alcohol has been performed, the olefinic linkage is regenerated.

Since the olefinic linkage is reactive with a variety of reagents, we often need to protect it from these reagents when we perform transformations on other parts of the molecule. One way of protecting an olefinic linkage is by adding bromine to it in tetrachloromethane solution. When the olefinic linkage is protected as the dibromide, we can perform the desired functional group change in another part of the molecule. Finally, we regenerate the olefinic linkage by treating the dibromide with either zinc (in an alcohol or acetic acid solvent) or with iodide ion. An example of this procedure is shown in Figure 10.46.

Using either of the reagents (zinc or iodide), we regenerate the olefinic linkage with the same geometry it had prior to halogenation. The dehalogenation process proceeds with *anti* stereochemistry, as does the halogen addition reaction. The dehydrohalogenation reaction occurs in a single step, as is illustrated in Figure 10.47.

Figure 10.47 Dehalogenation of a vicinal dibromide with iodide ion.

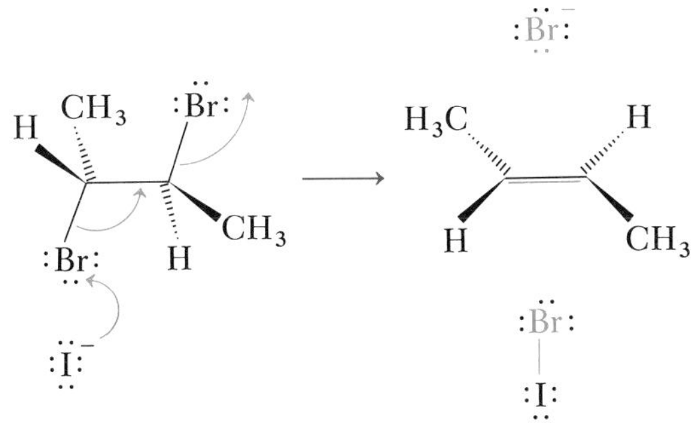

Summary

- The carbon-carbon double bond of an alkene undergoes a variety of addition reactions that leave each of the olefinic carbons tetracoordinated.
- The alkene linkage is a site of *unsaturation*. Addition reactions cause it to become *saturated*.

- Addition reactions of alkenes have both regiochemical and stereochemical consequences.
- Additions can be stereochemically *syn* or *anti*. We determine the stereochemistry of a given addition reaction through the examination of the products formed from suitably substituted alkenes.
- Additions may be regiochemically Markovnikov or anti-Markovnikov. We again can find the course of a given reaction by looking at the products formed from suitably substituted alkenes.
- The major addition reactions of alkenes can be summarized as follows:
  - □ Hydrogenation (or reduction)—the addition of the elements of a hydrogen molecule across the double bond, usually by *syn* addition.
  - □ Halogenation—the addition of the elements of a halogen molecule across the double bonds; bromine always adds *anti*.
  - □ Halohydrin formation—the addition of the elements of HO—X across the double bond; stereochemistry is mixed; HO— adds to the carbon atom yielding the most stable carbocation.
  - □ Hydration—the addition of the elements of water across the double bond; Markovnikov addition regiochemistry.
  - □ β-Haloether formation—the addition of the elements of X—OR across the double bond; like halohydrin formation.
  - □ Hydrohalogenation—the addition of the elements of a hydrogen halide across the double bond; Markovnikov regiochemistry unless adding in the presence of radicals—then anti-Markovnikov.
  - □ Hydroxylation—the addition of the elements of hydrogen peroxide (HO—OH) across the double bond; *syn* or *anti* addition depends on the reagents used.
- Several routes are available for the accomplishment of most of these addition reactions. Each route has particular characteristics with regard to stereochemistry and regiochemistry. By choosing one route rather than another, we can control the outcome of the synthetic procedure.
- Another type of reaction of the carbon-carbon double bond is oxidative cleavage. In this type of reaction both the π and the σ bond of the double bond are broken. Each of the original olefinic carbon atoms (originally bound to each other) is doubly bound to an oxygen in the product(s). These reactions are of use not only for synthesis of new materials, but also for purposes of structural analysis.

Terms to Remember

addition reactions
oxidative cleavage reactions
electrophile
electrophilic addition
syn addition
anti addition
prochiral
hydrogenation
stereoselective reaction
stereospecific reaction
nonstereospecific reaction
heterogeneous catalysis
homogeneous catalysis
heat of hydrogenation
steric repulsion
bromohydrin
regioselectivity
Markovnikov orientation
anti-Markovnikov orientation
reaction progress diagram
transition state
activation energy
rate constant
activated complex
Hammond postulate
hydration
oxymercuration/demercuration
hydroboration/oxidation
hydroxylation
ozonolysis

Reactions of Synthetic Utility

19. $$>C{=}C< + H_2 \xrightarrow{\text{catalyst}} -\overset{|}{\underset{H}{C}}-\overset{|}{\underset{H}{C}}-$$ 10.3

20. $$>C{=}C< + HX \xrightarrow{\text{polar solvent}} -\overset{|}{\underset{H}{C}}-\overset{|}{\underset{X}{C}}-$$ 10.5

X = F, Cl, Br, I; Markovnikov orientation

21. $\rangle C{=}C\langle + HBr \xrightarrow{\text{peroxides}} -\underset{H}{\overset{|}{C}}-\underset{Br}{\overset{|}{C}}-$ 10.12

anti-Markovnikov orientation

22. $\rangle C{=}C\langle + X_2 \xrightarrow{CCl_4} -\underset{X}{\overset{|}{C}}-\overset{X}{C}-$ 10.4

X = Br, Cl; *anti* addition

23. $\rangle C{=}C\langle + X_2 \xrightarrow{H_2O} -\underset{X}{C}-\overset{OH}{C}-$ 10.4

X = Br, Cl; X goes to less highly substituted carbon; *anti* addition

24. $\rangle C{=}C\langle + X_2 \xrightarrow{ROH} -\underset{X}{C}-\overset{OR}{C}-$ 10.4

X = Br, Cl; X goes to less highly substituted carbon; *anti* addition

25. $-\underset{X}{C}-\overset{X}{C}- \xrightarrow{Zn,\ CH_3COOH} \rangle C{=}C\langle$ 10.15

X = Br, Cl

26. $\rangle C{=}C\langle \xrightarrow{KMnO_4,\ KOH} -\overset{HO}{C}-\overset{OH}{C}-$ 10.11

syn addition

27. $\rangle C{=}C\langle \xrightarrow[\text{heat}]{KMnO_4,\ KOH} \rangle C{=}O + O{=}C\langle$ 10.13

28. $\rangle C{=}C\langle \xrightarrow[2.\ NaHSO_3]{1.\ OsO_4} -\overset{HO}{C}-\overset{OH}{C}-$ 10.11

syn addition

29. $\rangle C{=}C\langle \xrightarrow[H_2O_2,\ H_2O]{HCOOH} -\underset{OH}{C}-\overset{OH}{C}-$ 10.11

anti addition

30. $\rangle C{=}C\langle \xrightarrow[2.\ H_2O_2,\ KOH]{1.\ BH_3} -\underset{H}{C}-\underset{OH}{C}-$ 10.9

anti-Markovnikov orientation; *syn* addition

31. $\rangle C{=}C\langle \xrightarrow[2.\ X_2,\ NaOCH_3\ HOCH_3]{1.\ BH_3} -\underset{H}{C}-\underset{X}{C}-$

X = Cl, Br; anti-Markovnikov orientation 10.10

32. $\rangle C{=}C\langle \xrightarrow[2.\ CH_3COOH]{1.\ BH_3} -\underset{H}{C}-\underset{H}{C}-$ 10.10

33. $\rangle C{=}C\langle \xrightarrow{H_2O,\ acid} -\overset{H}{C}-\underset{OH}{C}-$ 10.6

Markovnikov orientation; rearrangement possible

34. $\rangle C{=}C\langle \xrightarrow[H_2O\quad 2.\ NaBH_4/^-OH]{1.\ Hg(O_2CCH_3)_2,} -\underset{H}{C}-\underset{OH}{C}-$ 10.9

Markovnikov orientation

35. $\underset{H}{\rangle} C{=}C \underset{H}{\langle} \xrightarrow[2.\ Zn,\ CH_3COOH]{1.\ O_3}$

$\underset{H}{\rangle} C{=}O + O{=}C \underset{H}{\langle}$

10.13

36. $\underset{H}{\rangle} C{=}C \underset{H}{\langle} \xrightarrow[2.\ H_2O_2]{1.\ O_3} \underset{HO}{\rangle} C{=}O + O{=}C \underset{OH}{\langle}$

10.13

The reactions map below is the last that will be included in the text. Students are advised to make their own for future chapters.

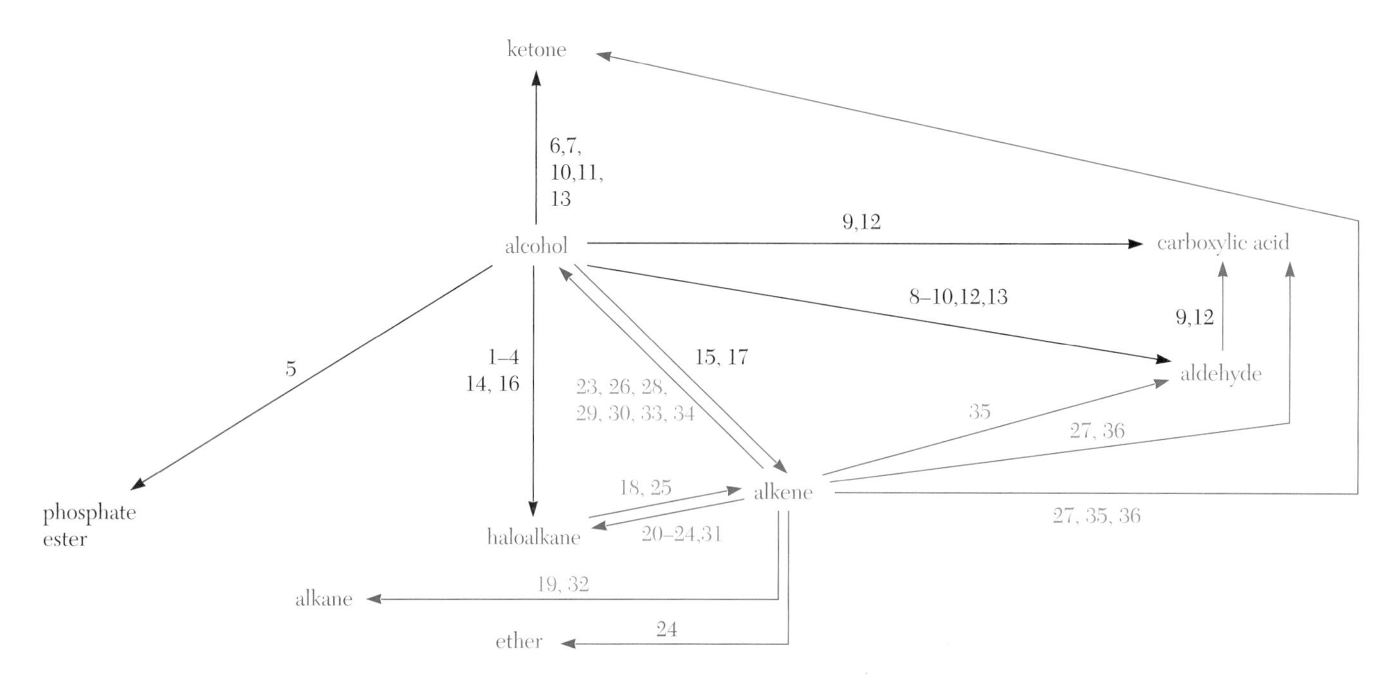

Additional Problems

10.29 How many isomers of the formula C_5H_{10} can you find? Show structures and provide complete IUPAC names for each. (*Hint:* All structures have either one double bond or one ring.)

10.30 Give structures for the organic products of each of the following reactions. Make sure that any stereochemical features are clearly shown.

a. 2-methyl-2-butene + bromine in carbon tetrachloride
b. 2-methylpropene + hydrogen/platinum
c. 2-methylpropene + hydrogen iodide
d. (Z)-2-pentene + mercuric acetate in water, followed by treatment with sodium borohydride
e. (*E*)-3-methyl-2-pentene + borane-THF complex, followed by alkaline hydrogen peroxide
f. 3-ethyl-2-pentene treated with ozone and worked-up with zinc and acetic acid
g. 3-ethyl-2-pentene + hydrogen bromide with benzoyl peroxide
h. 3-ethyl-2-pentene + cold, aqueous alkaline potassium permanganate
i. cyclopentene treated with mercuric acetate in water, followed by treatment with sodium borohydride
j. cyclohexene treated with osmium tetroxide, followed by treatment with sodium bisulfite in water
k. 1-methylcyclopentene + hydrogen iodide
l. (Z)-2-pentene + bromine in carbon tetrachloride
m. 1,3-cyclohexadiene + hot aqueous potassium permanganate (acid workup)
n. 1,3-cyclohexadiene treated with ozone and worked-up with zinc and acetic acid

10.31 What reagent or combination of reagents should be used for each of the following conversions:

a. cyclopentene into *trans*-cyclopentane-1,2-diol
b. *trans*-2-butene into *meso*-2,3-butanediol

c. *cis*-2-butene into *meso*-2,3-butanediol
d. cyclobutene into $HO_2C—CH_2—CH_2—CO_2H$
e. cyclobutene into $OHC—CH_2—CH_2—CHO$
f. cyclobutene into *cis*-cyclobutane-1,2-diol
g. 1-ethylcyclopentene into 1-ethylcyclopentanol
h. 1-ethylcyclopentene into 2-ethylcyclopentanol
i. 1-bromohexane into 1-hexene
j. 2,3-dimethyl-2-butene into acetone $[(CH_3)_2C{=}O]$

10.32 Which alkene, 2,3-dimethyl-2-butene or *trans*-2-butene, is expected to have the smaller activation energy for reaction with an acid (H^+) to form a carbocation? Explain your answer.

10.33 Which alkene, (E)-2-pentene or (Z)-2-pentene, is expected to have the smaller (less exothermic) heat of hydrogenation? Explain your answer.

10.34 Which alkene will give a mixture of (3S,4R)-3,4-heptanediol and its enantiomer on treatment with osmium tetroxide followed by workup with aqueous sodium bisulfite?

10.35 Give the IUPAC name for the major product(s) obtained when (R)-3-methyl-1-pentene is treated with hydrogen bromide in the presence of benzoyl peroxide.

10.36 Show Fischer projections for the product(s) obtained by treating (E)-2-pentene with D_2 in the presence of a heterogeneous catalyst.

10.37 Show synthetic reactions that will bring about each of the following conversions. More than one step is required in most cases.
a. 2-bromopropane to 1,2-dibromopropane
b. bromocyclohexane to cyclohexanol
c. 1-butanol to 2-butanol
d. 1-butanol to 2-bromobutane
e. bromocyclopentane to $HO_2C—(CH_2)_3—CO_2H$
f. cyclohexene to cyclohexanone
g. 1-methylcyclohexene to 2-methylcyclohexanone
h. 1-bromopentane to 2-iodopentane
i. 3-bromopentane to 1-pentanol
j. 2-propanol to 1,2-propanediol
k. 1-butene to $CH_3CH_2CH_2CO_2H$
l. 1-butanol to $CH_3CH_2CO_2H$

10.38 When 2-chloropropene reacts with hydrogen iodide, the product is 2-chloro-2-iodopropane. Show a resonance structure for the intermediate carbocation in which every atom has a complete octet of electrons. Suggest a reason why the reaction occurs with the observed regiochemistry, that is, explain why 2-chloro-1-iodopropane is not formed.

10.39 Substance A of formula C_6H_{12} yields equimolar quantities of the two products shown below upon treatment with ozone and workup with zinc and acetic acid. What is the structure of A?

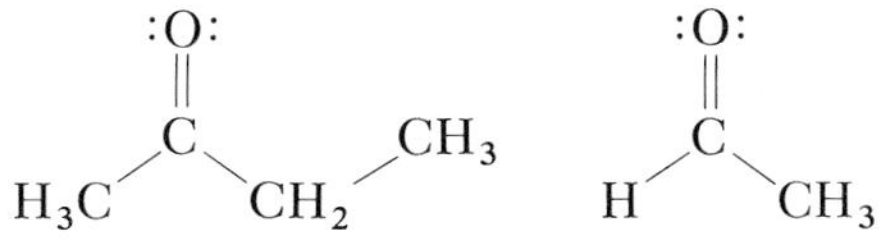

$$H_3C—C({=}\ddot{O}{:})—CH_2—CH_3 \qquad H—C({=}\ddot{O}{:})—CH_3$$

10.40 Name a bromoalkane that will yield 4-ethyl-1-hexene and no other alkenes upon treatment with a strong base.

10.41 When 2-methylpropene is treated with BrCl, 1-bromo-2-chloro-2-methylpropane is obtained. Which halogen, Br or Cl, must add first to the alkene? How do you know? Rationalize your conclusion and show a complete mechanism for the reaction.

10.42 Assuming the strength of the π bond of ethylene is 65 kcal/mole, calculate $\Delta H°$ for the reaction of ethylene with I—Br, given that the bond dissociation energy for the I—Br bond is 43 kcal/mole. Considering the information in Problem 10.41, what product would you expect from the reaction of 2-methylpropene with I—Br? (*Hint:* You will need to refer to Table 9.1.)

10.43 Alcohols can add to bromonium ions to form β-bromoethers. In light of this, deduce the structure of a six-membered cyclic compound, $C_7H_{13}OBr$, that is produced when (*E*)-5-hepten-1-ol reacts with bromine in carbon tetrachloride solution.

10.44 Use reasoning similar to that needed in Problem 10.43 to deduce the structures of the cyclic products formed in each of the following reactions.

a. (*E*)-5-hepten-1-ol is treated with hydrogen bromide to give a product that does not contain bromine.
b. 4-buten-1-ol is treated with bromine.
c. $H_2C{=}CH{-}CH_2{-}CH_2{-}CO_2H$ is treated with sulfuric acid.

10.45 Alkene B, of formula C_5H_{10}, reacts with hydrogen bromide to yield C. On treatment with base, C yields mainly D, an isomer of B. When D is ozonized and the ozonide is decomposed under oxidative conditions, a mixture of acetone and acetic acid is obtained. There are two possible structures for B consistent with these data. What are those two structures and the structures of C and D?

10.46 Alcohol E, of formula $C_5H_{12}O$, can be oxidized to ketone F. Dehydration of the alcohol yields an alkene G that on oxidation with hot aqueous permanganate yields a mixture of ketone H and carboxylic acid I. Suggest structures for compounds E–I.

10.47 One mole of substance J of formula $C_{11}H_{20}$ reacts with two moles of hydrogen under catalytic conditions. On oxidation of J with hot aqueous permanganate, a mixture of butanone [$CH_3C(O)CH_2CH_3$], acetone [$(CH_3)_2C{=}O$], and succinic acid ($HO_2C{-}CH_2{-}CH_2{-}CO_2H$) is obtained. What is the structure of J?

10.48 Addition of a proton to an alkene generates a carbocation. Although the carbocation usually undergoes an *addition* reaction with a nucleophile, it sometimes acts as a Brønsted acid to donate a proton. When it does donate a proton to a Brønsted base, an alkene is formed. That is, the initial protonation is reversible. Use this fact to rationalize the observation that *cis*-2-butene is partially isomerized to *trans*-2-butene on treatment with acid. If the process is allowed to continue until equilibrium is obtained, which alkene will dominate the equilibrium mixture? Explain your prediction. Show a reaction progress diagram for the isomerization. Use the thermochemical data given in this chapter to calculate the value of $\Delta H°$ for the conversion of *cis*-2-butene to *trans*-2-butene (be careful about the sign of $\Delta H°$).

10.49 An alkene of formula C_6H_{10} yields the same product when treated with HBr in the presence or absence of benzoyl peroxide. Suggest a structure for the alkene.

10.50 A unknown substance of formula $C_{10}H_{12}$ is known to contain double bonds. What is the maximum number of double bonds that could be present in this compound? When 6.6 grams of the compound is treated with an excess of bromine in carbon tetrachloride, approximately 22.5 grams of a bromine-containing organic compound is isolable from the reaction mixture. On this basis, how many double bonds would you say are present in the compound?

10.51 Substance K of formula $C_{15}H_{26}$ is treated with ozone and worked-up under reductive conditions. A mixture of acetone, 2-butanone, and biacetyl ($CH_3COCOCH_3$) is obtained from the reaction mixture. The number of moles of biacetyl is found to be twice that of each of the other products. Suggest a structure for K that is consistent with these observations.

10.52 Alkoxy radicals (RO·) react with carbon tetrabromide to form ROBr and $\cdot CBr_3$. Write a complete mechanism for the production of 1,1,1,3-tetrabromononane from 1-octene and carbon tetrabromide upon heating with an organic peroxide (RO—OR). Explain why this reaction has the observed regiospecificity with the tribromomethyl group at the end of the chain.

10.53 Alkenes sometimes react with carbocations. Suggest a mechanism by which a mixture of 2,4,4-trimethyl-1-pentene and 2,4,4-trimethyl-2-pentene arises when 2-methylpropene is heated with 60% sulfuric acid.

10.54 In light of your answer to Problem 10.53, suggest a likely structure for a cyclic product, $C_{10}H_{18}$, that is produced when 3,7-dimethyl-2,6-octadiene is heated with sulfuric acid.

10.55 Write free radical chain mechanisms to account for each of the following:

a. the formation of 1,1,1-trichlorooctane by heating 1-heptene with chloroform in the presence of benzoyl peroxide.

b. the formation of 2-decanone [$CH_3CO(CH_2)_7CH_3$] by the heating of 1-octene with acetaldehyde [CH_3CHO] in the presence of benzoyl peroxide.

10.56 Explain each of the following observations:

a. 1-Butene and the 2-butenes react with HCl at different rates.

b. The reaction of 1-pentene with bromine in aqueous sodium chloride solution provides a chlorine-containing product, but no chlorine-containing product results from the reaction of 1-pentene with bromine in carbon tetrachloride.

c. Hydrogen cyanide (HCN) does not react with alkenes in the presence of a radical initiator, although HBr does react.

CHAPTER 11 Carbon-Halogen and Carbon-Metal Bonds: Two Extremes of Polarity

11.1 Introduction

The electronegativity of a carbon atom is intermediate between the two extremes of the halogens (high electronegativity) and the metals (low electronegativity). As a result, carbon forms polar bonds both to metals and to halogens. The carbon atom can be either the negative or the positive end of the bond dipole, as shown in Figure 11.1.

The polarities of these bonds make possible a wide range of useful reactions. In general terms, the carbon atom of a carbon-halogen bond is **electrophilic** (electron deficient) and is susceptible to attack by nucleophiles (electron-rich species). By contrast, the carbon atom of a carbon-metal bond is electron rich; it can function as a nucleophile (and as a base) under the appropriate circumstances.

$$\overset{\delta+}{C}-\overset{\delta-}{\ddot{\underset{..}{X}}}: \qquad \overset{\delta-}{C}-\overset{\delta+}{\text{metal}}$$

Figure 11.1 Polarities of carbon-halogen and carbon-metal bonds. In bonding to halogens, carbon is the positive end of the bond dipole. However, in bonding to metals, carbon is the negative end of the bond dipole.

Haloalkanes constitute a particularly useful class of organic compounds. The halogen atom of a haloalkane is attached to an sp^3 hybridized carbon atom. For the present we will focus our attention on only this type of halogen-containing organic compound. Compounds containing a halogen attached to an sp^2 or sp hybridized carbon often have very different reactivities compared with the haloalkanes.

We refer to compounds containing a carbon-metal bond as *organometallic compounds*, or simply as **organometallics.** They also are useful reagents. However, we often need to use special handling techniques because of their high reactivity with moisture and/or air. Many must be made in situ. Some are available commercially in special bottles that contain a solution of the organometallic and are sealed from the air by a rubber septum. A dry, nitrogen-flushed syringe is used to withdraw a portion of the solution. This portion is then injected into a suitable reaction vessel, again through a rubber septum.

11.2 Preparation of Haloalkanes

We have previously surveyed several approaches for the preparation of haloalkanes from alcohols and from alkenes. Let us review these methods and reexamine some in more detail.

HYDROGEN HALIDES WITH ALCOHOLS

In Chapter 7 we considered the preparation of haloalkanes by the reaction of alcohols with hydrogen halides. Reaction occurs by different mechanisms, depending on the nature of the alcohol. In each case, the alcohol is initially protonated by the acid. The protonated hydroxyl group is then replaced by a halide ion. If the alcohol is methanol or a primary alcohol, replacement occurs through a direct displacement reaction as shown in Equation 11.1.

$$CH_3(CH_2)_{10}CH_2-\ddot{O}H \xrightarrow{H-Br} CH_3(CH_2)_{10}CH_2-\overset{+}{O}H_2 \;\; :\ddot{Br}:^- \longrightarrow CH_3(CH_2)_{10}CH_2Br + \ddot{O}H_2$$

1-dodecanol

88% yield
1-bromododecane

Eqn. 11.1

If the alcohol is *not* methanol or a primary alcohol, a carbocation is presumed to form by loss of water from the initially formed oxonium ion. The carbocation then combines with a halide ion to give the haloalkane product as shown in Equation 11.2.

H^+

$:\ddot{Cl}:^-$

$+ H_2\ddot{O}$

Eqn. 11.2

Combination of a carbocation with chloride ion can occur equally well at each of its faces, leading to a racemic product if the original hydroxyl is at a stereogenic carbon atom. As usual, we must be alert to the possibility of rearrangements occurring in reactions that involve carbocation mechanisms. Indeed, rearrangements are quite common in reactions of many secondary alcohols with hydrogen halides.

HYDROGEN HALIDES WITH ALKENES

Alkenes are also convenient precursors for haloalkanes (see Chapter 10). In good ion-solvating media, hydrogen halides add with a high degree of regiospecificity across the olefinic linkage. The halogen attaches preferentially at the more highly substituted of the olefinic carbons (Markovnikov addition). If we use hydrogen bromide under free radical reaction conditions the reaction remains regioselective. However, it produces the opposite orientation (anti-Markovnikov)—the bromine attaches at the less highly substituted of the olefinic carbons. Examples of these reactions are shown in Equations 11.3 and 11.4.

Eqn. 11.3

$$CH_3CH_2CH_2CH{=}CH_2 \xrightarrow[\text{acetic acid}]{HBr} CH_3CH_2CH_2\underset{}{C}H(\ddot{B}r\colon)CH_3$$

1-pentene — 84% yield 2-bromopentane

Eqn. 11.4

$$CH_3CH_2CH_2CH{=}CH_2 \xrightarrow[C_6H_5\overset{\|}{C}O{-}O\overset{\|}{C}C_6H_5]{HBr} CH_3CH_2CH_2CH_2CH_2\ddot{B}r\colon$$

1-pentene — (benzoyl peroxide) — 96% yield 1-bromopentane

ALCOHOLS WITH INORGANIC ACID HALIDES

Phosphorus Halides Alcohols can react with phosphorus halides to give haloalkanes (Chapter 6). The hydroxyl group is replaced by the halide. An example is shown in Equation 11.5.

Eqn. 11.5

$$CH_3CH_2CH_2CH_2CH_2\ddot{O}H \xrightarrow{PI_3} CH_3CH_2CH_2CH_2CH_2\ddot{I}\colon + \colon P(OH)_3$$

1-pentanol — 90% yield 1-iodopentane

By working with chiral alcohols, we find that this type of reaction proceeds with inversion of configuration. For example, treating (S)-2-octanol with phosphorus trichloride yields (R)-2-chlorooctane, as shown in Equation 11.6.

Eqn. 11.6

$$CH_3(CH_2)_5(H_3C)(H)C{-}\ddot{O}H \xrightarrow{PCl_3} \colon\ddot{C}l{-}C(H)(CH_3)(CH_2)_5CH_3$$

(S)-2-octanol — 94% yield, 99% optical purity (>99% inversion) (R)-2-chlorooctane

We introduced the basic mechanism for this reaction in Chapter 6. We will now reexamine it in light of the observed inversion of configuration at the stereogenic carbon atom.

MECHANISM OF REACTION

Step 1 The alcohol first displaces chloride ion.

$$CH_3(CH_2)_5(H_3C)(H)C{-}\ddot{O}{-}H + \colon PCl_3 \longrightarrow CH_3(CH_2)_5(H_3C)(H)C{-}\overset{+}{\ddot{O}}(H){-}\ddot{P}Cl_2 + \colon\ddot{C}l\colon^-$$

Step 2 Chloride ion makes a nucleophilic attack, displacing Cl_2POH as a leaving group.

$$:\ddot{Cl}:^{-} + CH_3(CH_2)_5CH(CH_3)-\overset{+}{O}(H)-\ddot{P}Cl_2 \longrightarrow :\ddot{Cl}-CH(CH_3)(CH_2)_5CH_3 + H-\ddot{O}-\ddot{P}Cl_2$$

We infer that this chloride ion approaches from the side opposite that of the leaving group since we observe inversion of configuration at the displacement site. Molecular orbital theory provides a rationalization of the observed stereochemistry of the reaction.

MOLECULAR ORBITAL ANALYSIS

Consider the frontier molecular orbitals of the system. The chloride ion acts as a nucleophile, donating a pair of electrons from its HOMO, a full *p* orbital. The protonated ester acts as a Lewis acid, accepting the pair of electrons into an empty orbital (its LUMO). An energy diagram showing the HOMO–LUMO interaction is given in Figure 11.2. The reaction is entirely analogous to the reaction of halide ion with ethyloxonium ion, described in Chapter 5.

The shapes of the interacting orbitals are shown in Figure 11.3. Since the larger lobe of the σ^* LUMO protrudes to the rear, attack from the back allows the most efficient interaction between the orbitals.

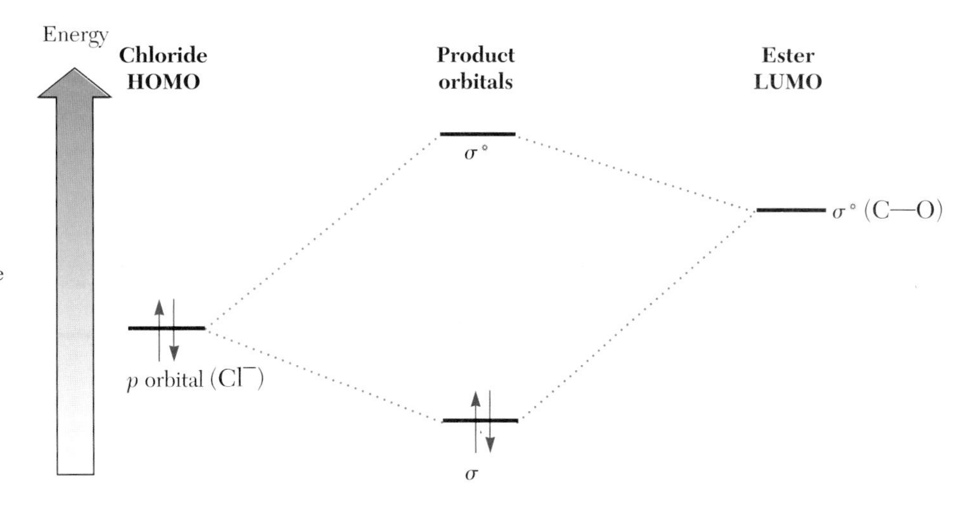

Figure 11.2 Frontier orbital energy diagram for the reaction of chloride ion with the protonated ester intermediate formed from phosphorus trichloride and alcohol. The starting orbitals are shown at each side of the diagram. The product orbitals are shown at the center. The filled *p* orbital of the chloride ion interacts with the empty σ^* orbital of the protonated ester to generate a new σ/σ^* orbital pair for the product haloalkane.

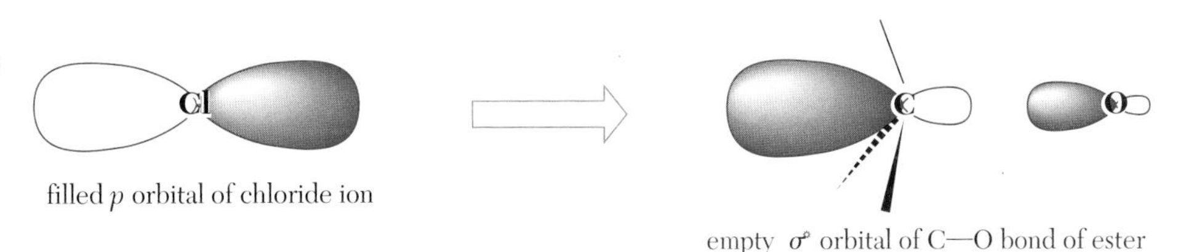

Figure 11.3 Interacting orbitals in the chloride attack on the intermediate species in the reaction of phosphorus trichloride with alcohols. The chloride approaches from the back to interact with the large lobe of the empty σ^* orbital.

Thionyl Chloride with Alcohols Thionyl chloride can also be used to convert alcohols to alkyl halides. Examples of this type of conversion are shown in Equations 11.7 and 11.8.

Eqn. 11.7

$$CH_3CH_2CH_2CH_2CH_2CH_2CH_2CH_2\ddot{O}H \xrightarrow[\text{heat, no solvent}]{SOCl_2} CH_3CH_2CH_2CH_2CH_2CH_2CH_2CH_2\ddot{Cl}:$$

1-octanol

80% yield
1-chlorooctane

Eqn. 11.8

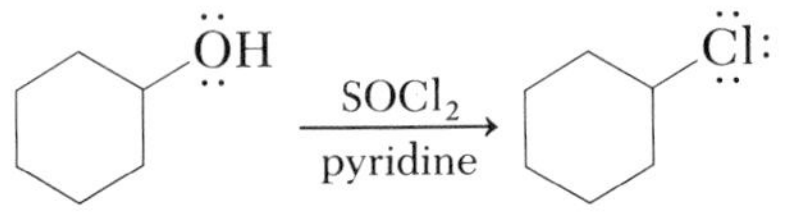

cyclohexanol $\xrightarrow[\text{pyridine}]{SOCl_2}$ chlorocyclohexane

95% yield

When the hydroxyl group of the alcohol is at a secondary stereogenic carbon atom, we observe different stereochemical results depending on the reaction conditions used. The reaction proceeds with *retention of configuration* at the hydroxyl carbon in ether solvents such as dioxane. An example is the formation of (*R*)-2-chlorobutane from (*R*)-2-butanol, as shown in Equation 11.9.

Eqn. 11.9

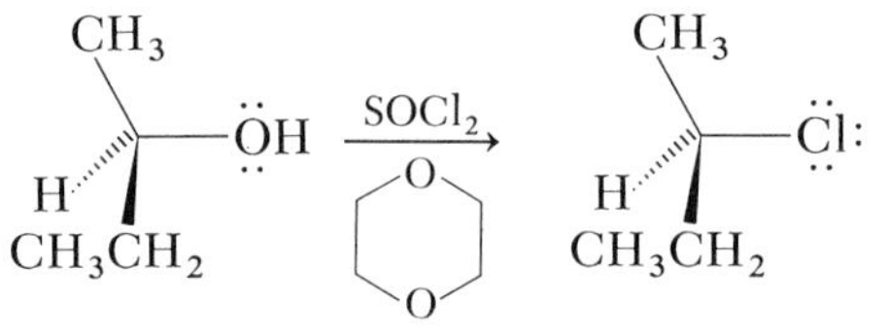

(*R*)-2-butanol $\xrightarrow[\text{(dioxane) 62 °C}]{SOCl_2}$ (*R*)-2-chlorobutane

50% yield
96.5% optical purity
(>98% retention)

The mechanism of this reaction is thought to proceed as shown below.

MECHANISM OF REACTION

Step 1 The alcohol reacts with thionyl chloride to generate a chlorosulfite ester and hydrogen chloride.

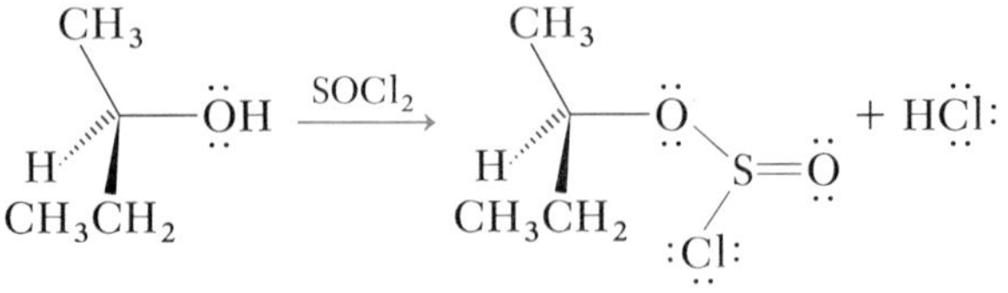

$$CH_3CH(OH)CH_2CH_3 \xrightarrow{SOCl_2} CH_3CH(O\text{–}S(=O)Cl)CH_2CH_3 + H\ddot{Cl}:$$

(a chlorosulfite ester)

Step 2 On heating, the dioxane solvent attacks the chlorosulfite ester to form a further intermediate. An *inversion* of configuration about the stereogenic site occurs in this step.

Step 3 A chloride ion performs a nucleophilic displacement of dioxane. This reaction involves a second inversion about the stereogenic site—the two inversions result in a net *retention* of configuration at the stereogenic site.

The use of other types of solvents leads to chloroalkanes of inverted configuration compared to the starting alcohol. Although pyridine is often used as the solvent, hexamethyl phosphoric triamide (HMPT) (**11.1**) results in better yields of product of higher optical purity. Unfortunately HMPT is carcinogenic, so its use is limited to laboratories with strictly controlled handling facilities.

$$O{=}P[N(CH_3)_2]_3$$

hexamethyl phosphoric triamide (HMPT)
11.1

One example of the use of this solvent is in the reaction of menthol with thionyl chloride, as shown in Equation 11.10.

Eqn. 11.10

$\xrightarrow[\text{HMPT}]{SOCl_2}$

menthol

78% yield
95.8% optical purity
(>97% inversion)
methyl chloride

In HMPT (and pyridine) the overall reaction has one fewer step than in dioxane.

MECHANISM OF REACTION

Step 1 The chlorosulfite ester forms as noted previously.

Step 2 Chloride ion, which is present in significant amount in HMPT (and in pyridine but not in dioxane) from the initial reaction of thionyl chloride and the alcohol, performs a nucleophilic displacement reaction directly on the chlorosulfite ester. The HMPT and pyridine are able to support the existence of free chloride ion, while dioxane cannot.

In HMPT (or pyridine) the chloroalkane forms with only *one* inversion of configuration at the stereogenic carbon atom (the site of displacement), yielding net *inversion*. In dioxane the amount of free chloride ion is negligible. The chloride ion from the initial reaction is present as hydrogen chloride, which does not dissociate to ions in the ether solvent.

TRIPHENYLPHOSPHINE AND TETRAHALOMETHANE

The reagents we have discussed so far for converting alcohols to haloalkanes have all been *acidic*—they were all either acids themselves or acid chloride derivatives of acids. Sometimes the use of such acidic reagents is undesirable due to possible reactions with other functional groups. Fortunately, there is an alternative to these reagents. An alcohol can be converted to a haloalkane under very mild conditions using triphenylphosphine (**11.2**) and tetrahalomethane. An example is shown in Equation 11.11.

Eqn. 11.11

$$(C_6H_5)_3P: + CCl_4 + CH_3CH_2CH_2CH_2OH \longrightarrow (C_6H_5)_3P{=}O + HCCl_3 + CH_3CH_2CH_2CH_2Cl$$

triphenylphosphine **11.2**; 1-butanol; triphenylphosphine oxide **11.3**; 99% yield 1-chlorobutane

The by-products of this reaction are a haloform, CHX_3 (chloroform in this example), and triphenylphosphine oxide (**11.3**).

With tetrabromomethane, the reaction leads cleanly to a bromoalkane, as shown in Equation 11.12.

Eqn. 11.12

$$[C_6H_5]_3P: + CBr_4 + \text{1-methyl-4-(1-methyl-2-hydroxyethyl)cyclohexene} \longrightarrow [C_6H_5]_3P{=}O + HCBr_3 + \text{1-methyl-4-(1-methyl-2-bromoethyl)cyclohexene}$$

1-methyl-4-(1-methyl-2-hydroxyethyl)cyclohexene

93% yield
1-methyl-4-(1-methyl-2-bromoethyl)cyclohexene

When the hydroxyl group is at a secondary stereogenic center, the reaction proceeds with inversion of configuration, as shown in Equation 11.13.

Eqn. 11.13

$$CH_3(CH_2)_5CH(CH_3)OH \xrightarrow[65\,°C,\ 4\ hr]{CCl_4,\ Ph_3P} Cl{-}CH(CH_3)(CH_2)_5CH_3$$

50% yield
100% optical purity
(100% inversion)

Numerous mechanistic studies have been performed on this reaction, which is understood to involve the steps shown below.

MECHANISM OF REACTION

Step 1 Triphenylphosphine performs a nucleophilic attack on *chlorine*, displacing the trichloromethyl anion.

$$(C_6H_5)_3P: + :\ddot{Cl}{-}CCl_3 \longrightarrow (C_6H_5)_3\overset{+}{P}{-}\ddot{Cl}: + {}^{-}:CCl_3$$

Step 2 The chlorophosphonium ion formed in Step 1 combines with the alcohol, bonding oxygen to phosphorus.

$$(C_6H_5)_3\overset{+}{P}-\ddot{\underset{..}{Cl}}: + R-\ddot{\underset{..}{O}}-H \longrightarrow (C_6H_5)_3P(\ddot{\underset{..}{Cl}}:)(\overset{+}{\underset{..}{O}}(H)-R)$$

Step 3 The trichloromethyl anion, acting as a base, removes a proton from the oxygen atom of the oxonium ion.

$$(C_6H_5)_3P(\ddot{\underset{..}{Cl}}:)(\overset{+}{\underset{..}{O}}(H)-R) + \bar{:}CCl_3 \longrightarrow (C_6H_5)_3P(\ddot{\underset{..}{Cl}}:)(\ddot{\underset{..}{O}}-R) + H-CCl_3$$

Step 4 The neutral pentacoordinated phosphorus species produced in Step 3 undergoes dissociation to yield a chloride ion and a phosphonium ion in which one of the ligands is an alkoxy group.

$$(C_6H_5)_3P(\ddot{\underset{..}{Cl}}:)(\ddot{\underset{..}{O}}-R) \longrightarrow (C_6H_5)_3\overset{+}{P}-\ddot{\underset{..}{O}}-R + :\ddot{\underset{..}{Cl}}:^-$$

Step 5. Chloride ion performs a nucleophilic displacement reaction on the phosphonium ion at the carbon bound to oxygen to generate the products.

$$(C_6H_5)_3\overset{+}{P}-\ddot{\underset{..}{O}}-R + :\ddot{\underset{..}{Cl}}:^- \longrightarrow (C_6H_5)_3P=\ddot{\underset{..}{O}} + R-\ddot{\underset{..}{Cl}}:$$

Overall, the reaction causes *inversion* of configuration at the original stereogenic carbon atom of the alcohol.

We have now introduced numerous methods for the preparation of haloalkanes. They are summarized briefly in the following list.

Summary of Methods for Preparing Haloalkanes

1. *Alcohols with hydrogen halides.* Overall, the halogen from the hydrogen halide replaces the hydroxy group of the alcohol. With most secondary and tertiary alcohols, the reaction proceeds through a carbocation intermediate and the possibility of skeletal rearrangement exists.
2. *Alkenes with hydrogen halides.* The elements of the hydrogen halide add across the carbon atoms of the alkene linkage. Under ionic conditions, the reaction is regiospecific giving Markovnikov orientation. With hydrogen bromide under free radical conditions, anti-Markovnikov orientation results.
3. *Alcohols with phosphorus trihalides.* Halogen from the phosphorus trihalide replaces the hydroxyl group of the alcohol. The reaction results in inversion of the configuration at the carbon atom bearing the hydroxyl group.
4. *Alcohols with thionyl chloride.* Halogen from the thionyl chloride replaces the hydroxyl group of the alcohol. The reaction results in either inversion

or retention of the configuration at the carbon atom bearing the hydroxyl group, depending on the reaction conditions chosen.

5. *Alcohols with triphenylphosphine and tetrahalomethane.* A halogen from the tetrahalomethane replaces the hydroxyl group of the alcohol. The reaction results in inversion of the configuration at the carbon atom bearing the hydroxyl group.

PROBLEM 11.1 Describe how to prepare each of the following haloalkanes from (*R*)-2-hexanol.
a. (*S*)-2-chlorohexane **b.** (*R*)-2-chlorohexane

PROBLEM 11.2 Describe how to prepare each of the following haloalkanes from 1-hexene.
a. 1-bromohexane **b.** (±)-2-chlorohexane

11.3 Properties of Haloalkanes

Haloalkanes are moderately polar molecules. The carbon-halogen bond is a polar covalent linkage. The carbon atom is at the positive (electron-deficient) end of the dipole, and the halogen end is electron rich.

The polarity of haloalkanes is similar to that of alcohols. Although there are some similarities in the physical properties of alcohols and haloalkanes, there are also significant differences. The solubilities of the haloalkanes in water are significantly lower than those for alcohols of corresponding molecular weight. However, their solubility in hydrocarbon solvents is high. The main reason for these differences is the ability of alcohols to participate in hydrogen bonding. For example, alcohols hydrogen bond to water, while haloalkanes do not.

Hydrogen bonding is also responsible for the relatively high boiling temperatures of the alcohols. If we compare haloalkanes with alcohols of similar molecular weight, we find the haloalkanes to have significantly lower boiling temperatures. For example, while methanol (molecular weight 32) is a liquid under ambient conditions, chloromethane (molecular weight 50.5) is a gas. Looking at van der Waals forces only, chloromethane would be expected to have a higher boiling temperature than methanol. However, alcohols hydrogen bond to each other, while haloalkanes do not.

The halogen *does* have an effect on the density of the haloalkanes. All chloro-, bromo-, and iodoalkanes have higher specific gravities than alcohols of corresponding molecular weight. Table 11.1 gives some relevant comparisons between alcohols and haloalkanes.

Many of the *chemical* properties of haloalkanes reflect the polarity of the carbon to halogen bond. An extremely important reaction type is nucleophilic substitution. Nucleophiles attack the carbon of the carbon-halogen bond, and the halogen is displaced as halide ion. Also, in Chapter 9, Section 9.6, we introduced another important type of reaction for haloalkanes—elimination reactions, in which the elements of a hydrogen halide molecule are removed from the haloalkane by a suitable base, and an alkene forms. The nucleophilic substitution reactions and elimination reactions that haloalkanes undergo are of very great importance, and the whole of the next chapter (Chapter 12) will be devoted to an in-depth discussion.

Table 11.1 Physical Data for Alcohols and Haloalkanes
All boiling temperatures are given in °C.

Alkyl Group	Alkyl Halide				Alcohol		
	X	Molecular Weight	Boiling Temperature	Specific Gravity	Molecular Weight	Boiling Temperature	Specific Gravity
Methyl	Cl	50.5	−24.2	0.916	32	64.7	0.792
	Br	95	4	1.732			
	I	142	42.2	2.282			
Ethyl	Cl	64.5	12.2	0.92	46	78.5	0.789
	Br	109	38	1.43			
	I	156	72.2	1.933			
n-Propyl	Cl	78.5	46	0.892			
	Br	123	71	1.353	60	97.2	0.804
	I	170	102	1.947			
n-Butyl	Cl	92.5	78	0.891	74	117.7	0.810
	Br	137	102	1.274			
	I	184	130	1.617			
Isobutyl	Cl	92.5	69	0.881	74	107.9	0.802
	Br	137	90	1.260			
	I	184	120	1.602			
tert-Butyl	Cl	92.5	51	0.851			
	Br	137	73	1.202	74	82.5	0.789
	I	184	99	1.544			
sec-Butyl	Cl	92.5	68	0.871	74	99.5	0.808
	Br	137	91	1.255			
	I	184	120	1.592			

11.4 Nomenclature of Haloalkanes

The longest continuous chain of carbon atoms bearing the halogen provides the root hydrocarbon name for simple haloalkanes. We indicate the position of the halogen by the number of the carbon atom to which it is attached. The chain is numbered from the end closest to the halogen substituent. Several examples are illustrated in Figure 11.4.

Figure 11.4 Nomenclature of haloalkanes. The longest continuous chain bearing the halogen provides the parent name for the compound.

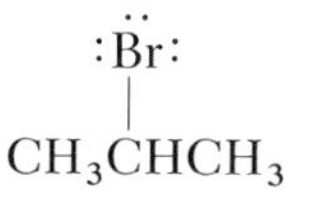

$CH_3CH(Br)CH_3$
2-bromopropane
(isopropyl bromide)

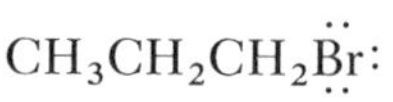

$CH_3CH_2CH_2Br$
1-bromopropane
(*n*-propyl bromide)

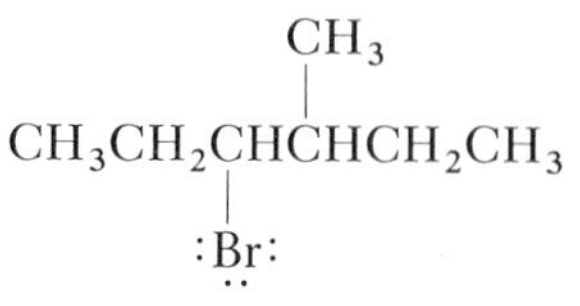

$CH_3CH_2CH(Br)CH(CH_3)CH_2CH_3$
3-bromo-4-methylhexane
(*not* 3-methyl-4-bromohexane)

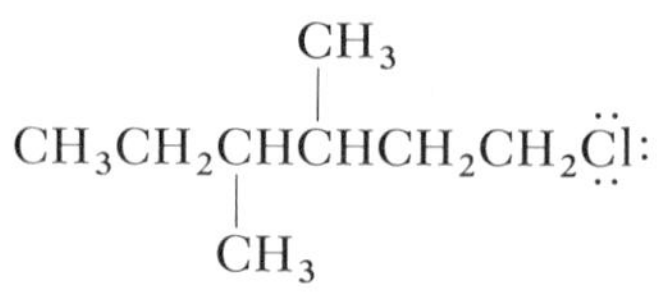

$CH_3CH_2CH(CH_3)CH(CH_3)CH_2CH_2Cl$
1-chloro-3,4-dimethylhexane

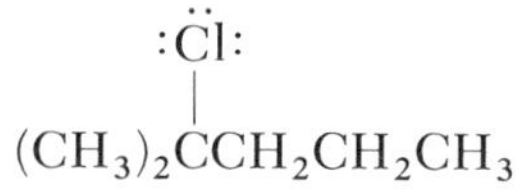

$(CH_3)_2C(Cl)CH_2CH_2CH_3$
2-chloro-2-methylpentane

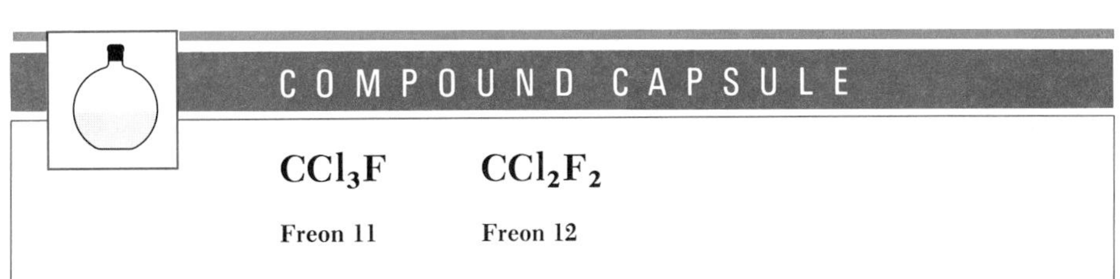

CCl_3F — Freon 11

CCl_2F_2 — Freon 12

The Freons are gaseous chlorofluoroalkanes. They were developed approximately fifty years ago as refrigerants to replace toxic materials such as ammonia and sulfur dioxide that had been used previously. More recently Freons have been widely used as propellants in aerosol cans. The Freons are extremely stable substances. Once they escape from a spray can, they are not broken down under ordinary circumstances and therefore persist in the environment.

Being gaseous, they diffuse slowly upward into the stratosphere, which lies 8–30 miles above the surface of the earth. Therein lies an environmental concern. In the middle of the stratosphere is a layer of ozone that helps shield the earth below from the harmful effects of solar ultraviolet radiation. (Ozone is a good absorber of ultraviolet light.) When Freons reach the stratosphere, they can undergo light-induced homolytic cleavage of a carbon-chlorine bond:

$$CF_2Cl_2 \xrightarrow{h\nu} \dot{C}F_2\ddot{\underset{..}{Cl}}: + :\ddot{\underset{..}{Cl}}\cdot$$

The chlorine atoms produced in this reaction are highly reactive. They can react efficiently with the ozone molecules present in the stratosphere, destroying them in the process. It is predicted that over a period of time the ozone layer could become severely depleted. Concern has been expressed about "holes" in the ozone layer over the earth's poles. Environmental groups have called for the banning of all Freon-based aerosol sprays to reduce this problem. (For further discussion see the Special Topic "A free radical chain reaction of environmental concern" in Chapter 13).

For more complex molecules containing more than one functional group, the longest continuous chain containing the functional group of higher nomenclature priority provides the root name. Where possible, when more than one functional group is on the root chain, we number the chain so as to give a lower number to the group of higher nomenclature priority (see Chapter 9). Several more examples of nomenclature are shown in Figure 11.5.

Figure 11.5 Nomenclature of haloalkanes (continued). The relative nomenclature priorities of the individual functional groups must be considered when naming complex molecules. Halides have a lower nomenclature priority than do alkene linkages, which in turn are of lower nomenclature priority than alcohols.

$CH_3CH_2CH(\ddot{O}H)CH_2\ddot{Br}:$ — 1-bromo-2-butanol

$(CH_3)_2C{=}C(CH_2CH_2\ddot{Br}:)(CH_2CH_2CH_3)$ — 3-(2-bromoethyl)-2-methyl-2-hexene

$H_2C{=}C(CH_3)CH(:\ddot{Cl}:)CH(:\ddot{O}H)CH_3$ — 3-chloro-4-methyl-4-penten-2-ol

Haloalkanes are classified as primary, secondary, or tertiary according to the nature of the carbon atom to which the halogen atom is attached (using exactly the same classification we used earlier for alcohols).

PROBLEM 11.3 Draw structures for each of the following compounds:

a. 4-bromo-2-methyl-2-hexene
b. (Z)-2-bromo-4,4-dimethyl-2-pentene
c. 3-chloro-3-methylcyclohexene
d. 5-chloro-5-methyl-3-heptanol
e. 1-chloromethylcyclohexene

PROBLEM 11.4 Give a complete IUPAC name for each of the following structures:

a. $CH_3CH_2CH_2C(Cl)(CH_2CH_3)CH(CH_3)CH_2CH_3$

b. $CH_3CH_2CH_2CH_2(H)C{=}C(CH_2Br)(CH_3)$

c. $H_2C{=}C(CH_2CH_3)CH(Br)CH_2CH_3$

d. $(CH_3CH_2)_2C(CH_3)CH(I)CH{=}CH_2$

PROBLEM 11.5 For each of the compounds in Problem 11.4, tell whether the halogen is at a primary, secondary, or tertiary site.

11.5 Organometallics

We consider haloalkanes and organometallics in the same chapter for two reasons. First, the haloalkanes are the usual starting materials for the preparation of the wide range of organometallic reagents. Second, there is a special relationship between haloalkanes and organometallics that is of great utility in devising syntheses of complex organic compounds.

Carbon bound to halogen in a haloalkane is *electron deficient*. However, once we convert the carbon-halogen bond to a carbon-metal bond, the carbon becomes *electron rich*. The electronic nature of the involved carbon atom is thus reversed by a single reaction. This process has become a topic of great interest in recent years because it is highly useful in organic syntheses. We commonly use the German term ***umpolung*** (reversal of polarity) to describe the change that occurs. It leads to a profound change in chemistry.

PREPARATION OF ORGANOMETALLICS FROM HALOALKANES: GRIGNARD REAGENTS

Generally, we prepare organometallics by treating an ether solution of the appropriate haloalkane with a metal. The most widely used organometallics, the **Grignard reagents**, are prepared in this way. These materials were originally reported by the French chemist Victor Grignard in 1901 (he won the Nobel Prize in chemistry in 1912). Since that time these reagents have been used in an extremely wide range of chemical conversions.

A Grignard reagent is generally prepared by the reaction of a haloalkane with magnesium metal in an ether solvent, most commonly diethyl ether (**11.4**) or tetrahydrofuran (**11.5**).

$$CH_3CH_2\ddot{\underset{..}{O}}CH_2CH_3$$

diethyl ether

11.4

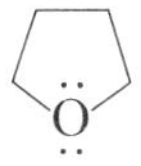

tetrahydrofuran (THF)

11.5

The solvent we use must contain unshared electron pairs to help stabilize the organometallic compound, but it cannot contain any electrophilic sites. (Organometallics react with electrophilic reagents.) The first requirement excludes hydrocarbons, and the second excludes all alcohols, all compounds containing the C=O linkage, and other compounds containing even weakly acidic hydrogens. Ethers, however, serve admirably. An example of the formation of a Grignard reagent is shown in Equation 11.14.

Eqn. 11.14

$$CH_3CH_2\ddot{\underset{..}{Br}}: + Mg \xrightarrow{(CH_3CH_2)_2O} CH_3CH_2Mg\ddot{\underset{..}{Br}}:$$

bromoethane — ethylmagnesium bromide ("ethyl Grignard")

Magnesium with a large surface area (magnesium turnings) is used to prepare Grignard reagents. The haloalkane is added slowly to magnesium that is covered by anhydrous ether. On gentle heating of the reaction mixture, formation of the Grignard reagent begins. The addition of the haloalkane is continued at a rate sufficient to maintain a mildly exothermic process. A crystal of iodine often helps to initiate the reaction. The presence of even a trace of moisture inhibits the Grignard-forming reaction. For this reason we must carefully dry all of the reagents *and* the glassware before starting the reaction. Moreover, we prevent atmospheric moisture and oxygen from disturbing the reaction by using a dry nitrogen atmosphere. The reactions occurring at the surface of the magnesium metal are quite complex. They appear to involve the formation of free radical species as intermediates.

The use of a solvent with unshared valence level electron pairs, such as diethyl ether, also appears to be necessary for the formation of the Grignard reagent. The solvent becomes complexed with the organometallic as it is generated and stabilizes the Grignard reagent. The structure of the Grignard reagent is complex and probably varies with the concentration of the reagent in solution. When we write RMgX as the Grignard structure, we recognize that it represents only a stoichiometric relationship of the reagents used in the formation of the reagent. It is *not* an exact representation of structure. Grignard reagents nevertheless behave much as we would expect an RMgX structure to behave. In this type of structure, R represents a **carbanion,** a species with a negative charge on carbon, and MgX represents a positive counterion. In most cases we imagine that the Grignard reagent behaves as if it were R^-MgX^+, although in actuality its structure is much more complex, and there is considerable covalent character to the C—Mg bond.

The Grignard reagent is strongly basic and strongly nucleophilic. It forms new bonds by bringing a pair of electrons to an electron-deficient center. General and specific examples of this reactivity are shown in Equations 11.15–11.19.

General example of Grignard reagent acting as a base:

$$R^- \; ^+Mg\ddot{\underset{..}{X}}: \xrightarrow{Y-H} R-H + MgXY$$

Specific example 1:

Eqn. 11.15

$$\text{chlorocyclohexane} \xrightarrow[(CH_3CH_2)_2O]{Mg} \text{cyclohexyl-MgCl} \xrightarrow{(CH_3)_2CHOH} \text{cyclohexane}$$

chlorocyclohexane

83% yield
cyclohexane

Specific example 2:

Eqn. 11.16

$$\text{cyclohexyl-}CH_2Br \xrightarrow[(CH_3CH_2)_2O]{Mg} \text{cyclohexyl-}CH_2MgBr \xrightarrow{H_2O} \text{cyclohexyl-}CH_3$$

bromomethylcyclohexane

94% yield
methylcyclohexane

General example of Grignard reagent entering into nucleophilic substitution reaction:

$$R^- \; ^+Mg\ddot{\underset{..}{X}}: \xrightarrow{Y_2} R-\ddot{\underset{..}{Y}}: + MgXY$$

Specific example:

Eqn. 11.17

$$(CH_3)_2CHCH_2CH_2\ddot{\underset{..}{Cl}}: \xrightarrow[(CH_3CH_2)_2O]{Mg} (CH_3)_2CHCH_2CH_2Mg\ddot{\underset{..}{Cl}}: \xrightarrow{I_2} (CH_3)_2CHCH_2CH_2\ddot{\underset{..}{I}}:$$

1-chloro-3-methylbutane

80% yield
1-iodo-3-methylbutane

General example of Grignard reagent entering into nucleophilic addition reaction:

$$R^- \; ^+Mg\ddot{\underset{..}{X}}: \xrightarrow{>C=O} R-\overset{|}{\underset{|}{C}}-\ddot{\underset{..}{O}}:^- \; Mg\ddot{\underset{..}{X}}:^+ \xrightarrow{\text{aq workup}} R-\overset{|}{\underset{|}{C}}-\ddot{\underset{..}{O}}H$$

Specific example 1:

Eqn. 11.18

$$CH_3CH_2\ddot{\underset{..}{Br}}: \xrightarrow[(CH_3CH_2)_2O]{Mg} CH_3CH_2Mg\ddot{\underset{..}{Br}}: \xrightarrow[\text{aq workup}]{(CH_3)_2C=O} CH_3CH_2\overset{:\ddot{O}H}{\overset{|}{C}}(CH_3)_2$$

bromoethane

86% yield
2-methyl-2-butanol

Specific example 2:

Eqn. 11.19

$$CH_3CH_2\ddot{B}r: \xrightarrow[(CH_3CH_2)_2O]{Mg} CH_3CH_2Mg\ddot{B}r: \xrightarrow[\text{aq workup}]{CH_3CHO} CH_3CH_2CH(\ddot{O}H)CH_3$$

bromoethane — 73% yield 2-butanol

Grignard reagents act as very strong bases, abstracting protons from even weak acids, as shown in Equations 11.15 and 11.16. The strong basicity of Grignard reagents stems from the fact that they behave as a source of $R:^-$ ions. These ions are the conjugate bases of alkanes, RH. Alkanes are among the weakest of all acids (see Table 11.2), and conversely their conjugate bases are among the strongest of all bases.

Table 11.2 pK_a Values of Some Weak and Strong Acids
For each acid, the proton considered is underlined.

Acid	pK_a
$(CH_3)_2\underline{CH_2}$	51
$CH_3\underline{CH_3}$	50
$\underline{CH_4}$	48
$\ddot{N}\underline{H_3}$	38
$CH_3CH_2\ddot{O}\underline{H}$	16
$\underline{H_2}\ddot{O}$	15.74
$CH_3\ddot{O}\underline{H}$	15.2
$N\underline{H_4}^+$	9.24
$\underline{H_3}\ddot{O}^+$	−1.74

Grignard reagents act as *nucleophiles* in their attack on halogen molecules (Equation 11.17) and in their addition to a carbonyl group (Equations 11.18 and 11.19). We will explore the latter type of reaction in more detail later in this chapter (in the section "Organometallics as Nucleophiles") and again in our discussion of carbonyl chemistry.

In summary, the electron-rich carbon center in the Grignard reagent is a site of high reactivity. Grignard reagents are, in fact, far more basic and nucleophilic than the conjugate bases of many solvents. Since Grignard reagents will react with these solvents (e.g., water, alcohols, ammonia), they can not be used in Grignard-forming reactions.

ALKYLLITHIUM REAGENTS

Other organometallics can be prepared by the direct reaction of haloalkane with an electropositive metal. After the Grignard reagents, alkyllithium reagents are the most commonly used organometallics. A general method for the preparation of alkyllithium reagents is illustrated in Equation 11.20.

Eqn. 11.20

$$R\ddot{X}: + 2\,Li\cdot \xrightarrow[\text{or hexane}]{(CH_3CH_2)_2O} RLi + LiX$$

$$CH_3CH_2CH_2CH_2\ddot{B}r: + 2\,Li\cdot \xrightarrow{(CH_3CH_2)_2O} CH_3CH_2CH_2CH_2Li + LiBr$$

1-bromobutane — butyllithium

An inert atmosphere of argon is preferable to nitrogen for the preparation of alkyllithium reagents from lithium metal and haloalkanes, because lithium metal reacts with elemental nitrogen at a significant rate. Alkyllithium reagents (unlike Grignards) do not require the stabilizing influence of an ether solvent. Hydrocarbon solvents can be used instead of ethers. Alkyllithium reagents exist in hydrocarbon solution as tetramers (four associated units), hexamers (six associated units), or even higher associated species.

Like the Grignard reagents, the alkyllithium reagents react as carbanion sources, R^-Li^+. Also, like the Grignard reagents, they react violently with even mildly acidic substances (e.g., water) to form hydrocarbons, as shown in Equation 11.21.

Eqn. 11.21

$$CH_3CH_2CH_2CH_2Li + H_2\ddot{O} \longrightarrow CH_3CH_2CH_2CH_3 + LiOH$$

butyllithium — 100% yield butane

Compared to the Grignard reagents, however, the alkyllithium reagents are significantly more reactive. The combination of two factors, the extremely exothermic nature of the hydrolysis reaction and the volatility of the hydrocarbon product and solvent, make this a reagent system that must be handled with extreme care.

Alkyllithium reagents, like Grignard reagents, can react as nucleophiles, as illustrated in Equation 11.22. (Compare with Equations 11.18 and 11.19 and see later section, "Organometallics as Nucleophiles," for a detailed discussion.)

Eqn. 11.22

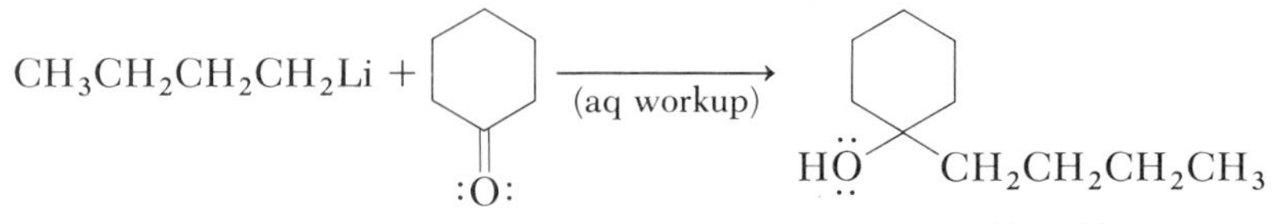

$$CH_3CH_2CH_2CH_2Li + \text{cyclohexanone} \xrightarrow{\text{(aq workup)}} \text{1-butylcyclohexanol (HO, } CH_2CH_2CH_2CH_3)$$

butyllithium — cyclohexanone — 89% yield 1-butylcyclohexanol

OTHER ORGANOMETALLICS

Beside the Grignard reagents and the alkyllithium reagents, many other types of organometallics can be prepared. Some are prepared from the Grignard reagents or the alkyllithium reagent by means of a metal exchange reaction. We will meet some of these reagents and their special uses later in this chapter and elsewhere in the text. Basically, all these reagents can behave as a source of R^-, a carbanion. However, their reactivities vary depending on the metal species and the solvent used.

PROPERTIES OF ORGANOMETALLICS

Each of the polar functional groups we have previously examined involved carbon attached to a more electronegative atom, so in these cases carbon is the electron-deficient partner in the polar bond. In an organometallic, where the metal atom is significantly more electropositive than the carbon atom, the linkage is extremely polar (but nevertheless *still covalent*). The carbon atom is the negative end of the dipole, as shown in Figure 11.6.

The polarity of the carbon-metal bond results in a special type of chemistry. The carbon center acts as a basic/nucleophilic site, serving as an electron-pair donor to electron-deficient sites.

ORGANOMETALLICS AS BRØNSTED BASES

Organometallics act as a source of R^- and are therefore powerful bases (see Table 11.2), although their basicity does vary with the ionic nature of the carbon-

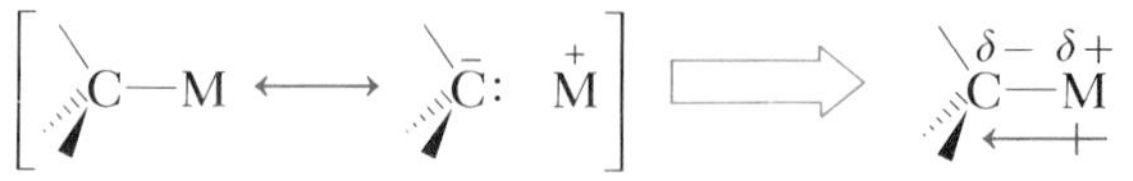

$$\left[\text{C—M} \longleftrightarrow \ddot{\text{C}}^{-}\!: \ \overset{+}{\text{M}} \right] \Longrightarrow \overset{\delta-}{\text{C}}\text{—}\overset{\delta+}{\text{M}}$$

Figure 11.6 Polarity in a carbon-metal bond. We can describe carbon-metal bonds as having a significant ionic character, as shown by the resonance-contributing forms on the left.

$$CH_3MgBr: + CH_3CH_2OH \rightleftharpoons CH_4 + CH_3CH_2OMgBr:$$

stronger base	stronger acid $pK_a = 16$	weaker acid $pK_a = 48$	weaker base

Figure 11.7 Grignard reagent acting as a Brønsted base. As indicated by the pK_a values listed in Table 11.2, methane is a much weaker acid than is ethanol. Therefore, the conjugate base of methane is a much stronger base than the conjugate base of ethanol. The equilibrium lies extremely far to the right in this reaction. In fact, for all practical purposes, the reverse arrow is inoperative.

metal bond. Most organometallics abstract protons readily from many types of organic and inorganic substances. An example of such a reaction is shown in Figure 11.7.

PROBLEM 11.6 Why would liquid ammonia be a poor choice as a solvent in which to prepare a Grignard reagent?

PROBLEM 11.7 Consider an attempt to prepare propylsodium (along with ethanol as the by-product) by adding sodium ethoxide to propane. Comment on the feasibility of this reaction.

SYNTHETIC UTILITY OF ORGANOMETALLICS AS BASES

As we have noted, organometallics abstract protons from even very weak acids. We can take advantage of this reactivity in several synthetically useful reactions. One simple illustration was given in Equation 11.16. This reaction type involves a reduction of the haloalkane (and oxidation of the magnesium), as shown in Figure 11.8.

$$CH_3{-}I: \xrightarrow[2.\ H_2O]{1.\ Mg,\ (CH_3CH_2)_2O} CH_4$$

Figure 11.8 Reduction of a haloalkane. Using the standard oxidation numbers of +1 for hydrogen and −1 for iodide, we calculate an oxidation number or −2 for carbon in iodomethane. In methane the oxidation number for carbon is −4. The reaction shown is therefore a *reduction*.

A general strategy for converting an alcohol to the corresponding alkane is shown in Figure 11.9. The alcohol and the haloalkane intermediate both have the polarity normally associated with bonds between carbon and more electronegative atoms. Once this polarity is reversed (*umpolung*) in the organometallic RMgBr, the carbon becomes carbanionic and can easily pick up a proton to yield the alkane.

We can use this reaction type for the synthesis of alkanes with isotopes of hydrogen located at specific sites. For example, by using deuterium oxide (D_2O) with a Grignard reagent, we can introduce a single deuterium atom ($^2H = D$) where the halogen was originally located, as shown in Equation 11.23.

Eqn. 11.23
$$CH_3CH_2CH_2CH_2Cl: \xrightarrow[2.\ D_2O]{1.\ Mg,\ (CH_3CH_2)_2O} CH_3CH_2CH_2CH_2D$$

95% yield

For purposes of radioisotope labeling, we can use tritiated water (water in which some percentage of the ordinary protons have been replaced by tritons, $^3H = T$). Radioisotope labeling is often used to explore what happens to a

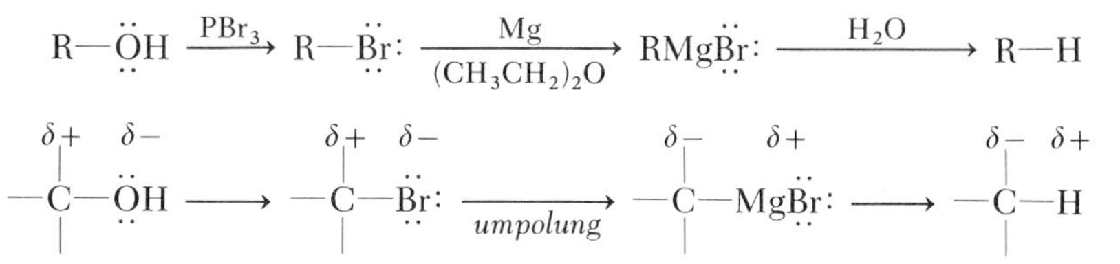

$$R{-}OH \xrightarrow{PBr_3} R{-}Br: \xrightarrow[(CH_3CH_2)_2O]{Mg} RMgBr: \xrightarrow{H_2O} R{-}H$$

$$\overset{\delta+}{-C}{-}\overset{\delta-}{OH} \longrightarrow \overset{\delta+}{-C}{-}\overset{\delta-}{Br}: \xrightarrow[umpolung]{} \overset{\delta-}{-C}{-}\overset{\delta+}{MgBr}: \longrightarrow \overset{\delta-}{-C}{-}\overset{\delta+}{H}$$

Figure 11.9 Overall reduction of an alcohol to an alkane. Alcohols can be converted to haloalkanes using a variety of reagents. When we use the haloalkane for the formation of an organometallic reagent, the polarity of the bond to carbon is reversed and the carbon can be protonated.

specific hydrogen atom in the course of a chemical reaction or a biological pathway.

PROBLEM 11.8 For each of the following specifically labeled compounds, give the haloalkane that would be used in its synthesis through an organometallic intermediate.

a. $(CH_3)_2CHCH_2CH_2D$

b. 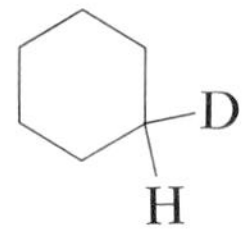 (cyclohexane ring with a carbon bearing D and H)

c. $CH_3CH_2CH_2CH_2CHTCH_3$

PROBLEM 11.9 Give the reagents and the reaction conditions for the synthesis of each of the following specifically labeled compounds from the indicated starting materials. (*Note:* Several steps are involved in each synthesis. You should show the reagents and reaction conditions for each step.)

a. 4-deuterio-2-methylpentane ($(CH_3)_2CHCH_2CHDCH_3$) from 4-methyl-1-pentene

b. 5-deuterio-2-methylpentane ($(CH_3)_2CHCH_2CH_2CH_2D$) from 4-methyl-1-pentene

c. 5-deuterio-2-methylpentane from 2-bromo-4-methylpentane

d. 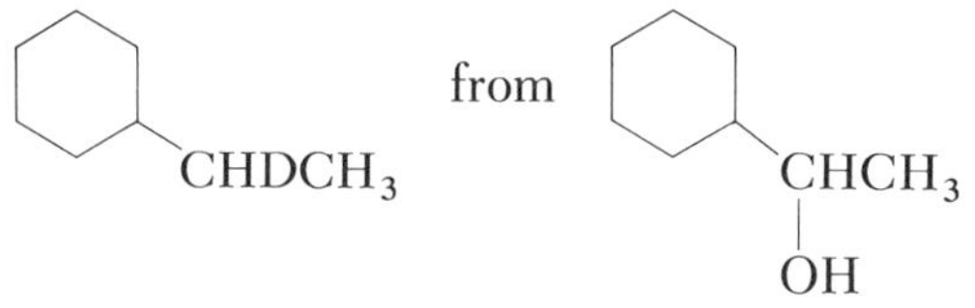 $C_6H_{11}CHDCH_3$ (cyclohexyl–CHDCH$_3$) from $C_6H_{11}CH(OH)CH_3$ (cyclohexyl–CHCH$_3$ with OH)

Steps to Solving the Problem

Solution to Problem 11.9a

1. To devise multistep syntheses of this type, it is a good practice to begin with the ultimate product (the **target molecule**) and work back to the available starting material. In this way we concentrate our thinking on one reaction at a time, specifically, a single reaction that will produce the desired material from some other compound. We then concern ourselves with the preparation of that intermediate species from some other compound, and so on, until we arrive back at the starting material.
2. We need to devise a preparation of the target material in a *single step* from *something else*. In this problem, the target molecule is 4-deuterio-2-methylpentane. What reaction will give us this compound in a *single step* from some other compound? As shown below cleavage of the Grignard reagent with deuterium oxide is effective:

$$(CH_3)_2CHCH_2\underset{\underset{MgBr}{|}}{C}HCH_3 \xrightarrow{D_2O} (CH_3)_2CHCH_2\underset{\underset{D}{|}}{C}HCH_3$$

(There are numerous *other* ways of preparing the target material in one step from other substances. We must eventually look beyond the immediate reaction to see where other approaches will lead us.)

3. We must now consider the formation of the Grignard reagent. It is prepared by the reaction of the bromoalkane with magnesium in ether.

$$(CH_3)_2CHCH_2\underset{\underset{:\ddot{Br}:}{|}}{C}HCH_3 \xrightarrow[(CH_3CH_2)_2O]{Mg} (CH_3)_2CHCH_2\underset{\underset{Mg\ddot{Br}:}{|}}{C}HCH_3$$

4. Continuing to work back to our starting material, we consider the formation of the bromoalkane. There are several methods available to us for forming bromoalkanes. We might contemplate forming this one directly by the ionic addition of hydrogen bromide to the starting alkene, as shown below.

$$(CH_3)_2CHCH_2CH{=}CH_2 \xrightarrow{HBr} (CH_3)_2CHCH_2\underset{\underset{:\ddot{Br}:}{|}}{C}HCH_3$$

However, this approach could possibly result in rearrangement of the carbon skeleton due to the formation of an intermediate carbocation:

$$(CH_3)_2CHCH_2CH{=}CH_2 \xrightarrow{H^+} (CH_3)_2CHCH_2\overset{+}{C}HCH_3 \xrightarrow{\sim H^-} (CH_3)_2CH\overset{+}{C}HCH_2CH_3$$

$$(CH_3)_2CH\overset{+}{C}HCH_2CH_3 \xrightarrow{\sim H^-} (CH_3)_2\overset{+}{C}CH_2CH_2CH_3$$

A better approach is to form the bromoalkane from the alcohol by treatment with phosphorus tribromide. We can form the alcohol from the starting alkene without rearrangement by using the oxymercuration/demercuration route.

$$(CH_3)_2CHCH_2CH{=}CH_2 \xrightarrow[\text{2. } NaBH_4]{\text{1. } Hg(OAc)_2,\ H_2O} (CH_3)_2CHCH_2\underset{\underset{:\ddot{O}H}{|}}{C}HCH_3$$

$$(CH_3)_2CHCH_2\underset{\underset{:\ddot{O}H}{|}}{C}HCH_3 \xrightarrow{PBr_3} (CH_3)_2CHCH_2\underset{\underset{:\ddot{Br}:}{|}}{C}HCH_3$$

5. Overall, the synthetic route can be summarized as:

$$(CH_3)_2CHCH_2CH{=}CH_2 \xrightarrow[\text{2. } NaBH_4]{\text{1. } Hg(OAc)_2,\ H_2O} (CH_3)_2CHCH_2\underset{\underset{:\ddot{O}H}{|}}{C}HCH_3$$

$$(CH_3)_2CHCH_2\underset{\underset{:\ddot{O}H}{|}}{C}HCH_3 \xrightarrow{PBr_3} (CH_3)_2CHCH_2\underset{\underset{:\ddot{Br}:}{|}}{C}HCH_3$$

$$(CH_3)_2CHCH_2\underset{\underset{:\ddot{Br}:}{|}}{C}HCH_3 \xrightarrow[\text{2. } D_2O]{\text{1. Mg, ether}} (CH_3)_2CHCH_2\underset{\underset{D}{|}}{C}HCH_3$$

(Can you derive a *different* route to the product, by using hydroboration/reduction of the alkene?)

ORGANOMETALLICS AS NUCLEOPHILES

Many important reactions are based on the ability of organometallics to act as nucleophiles. These reactions are of two types—nucleophilic substitution and **nucleophilic addition.** Earlier we gave some introductory examples (see Equations 11.17–11.19). We will now discuss these reactions in some detail.

Nucleophilic Addition Reactions Organometallic compounds perform nucleophilic addition on several organic functional groups. We will limit the present discussion to the reaction of organometallics with simple carbonyl compounds, that is, aldehydes and ketones. Aldehydes and ketones both contain the carbonyl group, which contains a carbon atom doubly bonded to the more electronegative oxygen atom. As such, the carbon is electron deficient and susceptible to attack by electron-rich reagents. The reaction of a carbonyl group with an organometallic is summarized in Figure 11.10.

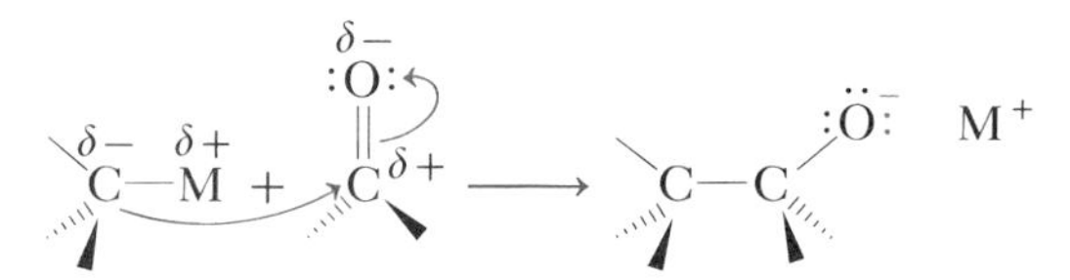

Figure 11.10 General reaction of an organometallic with a carbonyl group. The electron-rich carbon of the organometallic donates a pair of electrons to the electron-deficient carbon of the carbonyl group and a pair of electrons is displaced onto the oxygen atom.

MOLECULAR ORBITAL ANALYSIS

It is helpful to look at the molecular orbitals involved in this type of reaction and in other nucleophilic addition reactions at the carbonyl group. The attacking nucleophile brings to the reaction a pair of electrons in its HOMO. The lowest-energy empty orbital (the LUMO) associated with the carbonyl compound is the π^* orbital of the carbonyl group. The largest lobe of this π^* orbital (which provides the most efficient overlap,) is on the carbon and has the orientation shown in Figure 11.11.

In the addition reaction, the (filled) π molecular orbital of the carbonyl group is transformed into an unshared electron pair on the oxygen; as the carbonyl carbon becomes bonded to the nucleophile, it changes hybridization from sp^2 to sp^3. The cation from the organometallic remains associated with the new alkoxide site.

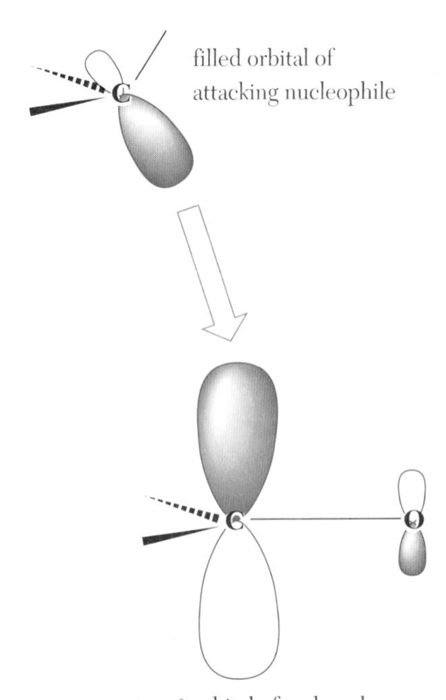

Figure 11.11 Molecular orbitals involved in addition of a nucleophile to a carbonyl group. The nucleophile is an electron-pair donor and the carbonyl group is an electron-pair acceptor. The orientation of approach that provides the most efficient reaction is shown; the nucleophile orbital approaches nearly perpendicular to the plane of the atoms of and around the carbonyl group.

The carbonyl compound is added directly (and slowly) into the reaction flask containing the Grignard reagent. This results in a rapid exothermic reaction that produces an alkoxide salt. We met alkoxides earlier—they are the conjugate bases of alcohols and are thus readily converted to alcohols by the addition of a proton source.

The addition of a Grignard reagent (or other suitable organometallic) to a carbonyl compound is an example of a *carbon-carbon bond-forming reaction.* It is a useful route to alcohols of relatively complex structure. The type of alcohol produced depends on the carbonyl compound used. If formaldehyde is used as the carbonyl compound, a *primary alcohol* is produced. An example of this type of synthesis is shown in Equation 11.24.

Eqn. 11.24

$$H_2C{=}\ddot{O}: + C_6H_{11}CH_2CH_2Mg\ddot{Br}: \xrightarrow[\text{workup}]{\text{aq acid}} C_6H_{11}CH_2CH_2CH_2\ddot{O}H$$

methanal — 2-cyclohexylethylmagnesium bromide — 79% yield 3-cyclohexyl-1-propanol

The Grignard reagent needed for the reaction shown in Equation 11.24 is prepared by the standard method, reaction of the haloalkane (2-cyclohexyl-1-bromoethane) with magnesium in diethyl ether solution. Formaldehyde (methanal) is usually added in the form of its trimer, trioxane (**11.6**), or the polymer, paraformaldehyde (**11.7**).

$$(-CH_2\ddot{O}-CH_2\ddot{O}-CH_2\ddot{O}-)_n$$

trioxane **11.6** — paraformaldehyde **11.7**

Grignard reagents react with other aldehydes to generate *secondary alcohols*. An example is shown in Equation 11.25.

Eqn. 11.25

$$CH_3CH_2\ddot{Br}: + Mg \xrightarrow[\text{ether}]{\text{diethyl}} CH_3CH_2Mg\ddot{Br}: \xrightarrow[\text{2. aq acid workup}]{\text{1. }(CH_3)_2CHCHO} (CH_3)_2CHCH(\ddot{O}H)CH_2CH_3$$

bromoethane — 68% yield 2-methyl-3-pentanol

Ketones react with Grignard reagents to produce *tertiary alcohols*, as shown in Equation 11.26.

Eqn. 11.26

$$CH_3CH_2CH_2CH_2\ddot{Br}: \xrightarrow[\text{diethyl ether}]{Mg} CH_3CH_2CH_2CH_2Mg\ddot{Br}: \xrightarrow[\text{2. aq acid workup}]{\text{1. }(CH_3CH_2)_2C{=}O\ \text{(3-pentanone)}} (CH_3CH_2)_2C(\ddot{O}H)CH_2CH_2CH_2CH_3$$

1-bromobutane — 67% yield 3-ethyl-3-heptanol

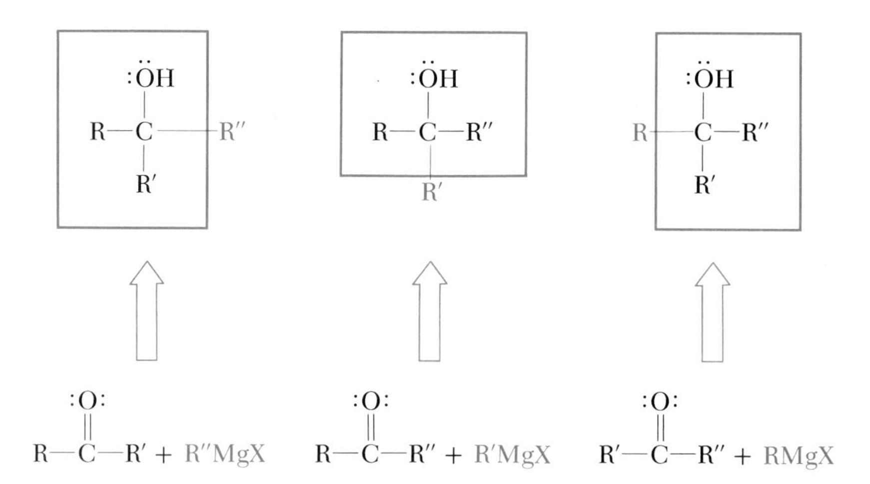

Figure 11.12 Possible routes to alcohols using Grignard reagents. As shown, three alternative routes can, in principle, be used to prepare an alcohol from a carbonyl compound and a Grignard reagent. However, unless the alcohol is tertiary, one or more of the attached R groups will be a hydrogen atom, and this limits the number of viable approaches as there are no hydrogen Grignard reagents, HMgX (they cannot be prepared by the reaction of HX and magnesium or by any other method). Thus only two of the three routes are viable for the preparation of secondary alcohols, and only one is viable for the preparation of primary alcohols.

Thus, we can synthesize the full spectrum of primary, secondary, and tertiary alcohols by using Grignard reagents and the appropriate carbonyl compound. Often, *several* approaches can be compared for the Grignard synthesis of alcohols. The carbinol carbon of the alcohol necessarily is derived from the original carbonyl carbon. However, the alkyl groups attached to the carbinol carbon may be derived *either* from the Grignard reagent or the carbonyl compound. We can see all the possible routes to an alcohol target molecule by considering its structure, as shown in Figure 11.12.

PROBLEM 11.10 Give the structure of the carbonyl compound that would be used for the synthesis of each of the following alcohols from the indicated Grignard reagents.

a. 3-methyl-3-pentanol from methylmagnesium iodide
b. 1-hexanol from 1-pentylmagnesium bromide
c. 2-methyl-3-hexanol from 1-propylmagnesium iodide
d. 1-methylcyclohexanol from methylmagnesium iodide

Steps to Solving the Problem

Solution to Problem 11.10a

1. First, we must draw the structure of the target alcohol, 3-methyl-3-pentanol.

$$CH_3CH_2-\underset{\underset{\displaystyle CH_3}{|}}{\overset{\overset{\displaystyle :\ddot{O}H}{|}}{C}}-CH_2CH_3$$

2. We analyze the possible sources of the component atoms of the target material. The methyl group at the carbinol carbon comes from our Grignard reagent. The remainder of the target structure then must be derived from the carbonyl component of the reaction:

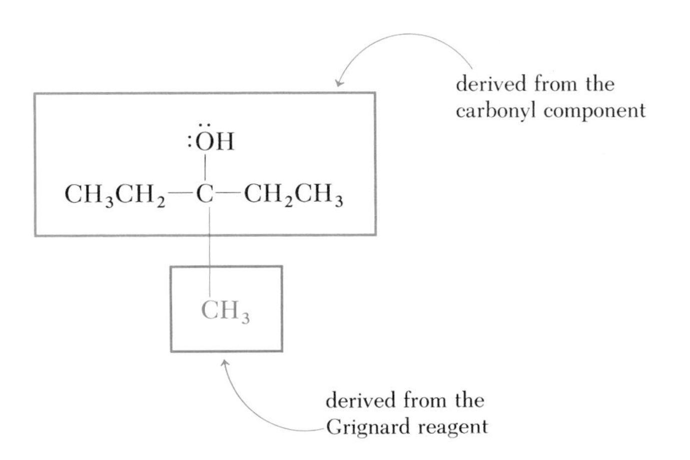

3. The carbonyl component of the synthesis must then be 3-pentanone:

$$CH_3CH_2-\overset{\overset{\large :O:}{\|}}{C}-CH_2CH_3$$

PROBLEM 11.11 For each of the following alcohols, give *all* of the possible combinations of Grignard reagent and carbonyl compound that could be used for its synthesis.

a. 5-ethyl-5-decanol **b.** 3-methyl-2-pentanol
c. 2,3-dimethyl-1-butanol **d.** 3-ethyl-3-pentanol

PROBLEM 11.12 For each of the following alcohols, devise a synthesis that involves a Grignard reagent in at least one of the steps. You should use formaldehyde and alcohols of three carbons or fewer as the source of all of the carbon atoms in the product, along with any inorganic reagents you find necessary for the syntheses.

a. 3-pentanol **b.** 2,3-dimethyl-2-butanol **c.** 2-methyl-3-pentanol

Steps to Solving the Problem

Solution to Problem 11.12a

1. Again, we need to consider the structure of the target molecule to decide on the possible Grignard reagent and carbonyl compound to be used in the synthesis. The components of the target molecule can be outlined as shown below:

$$CH_3CH_2-\boxed{\overset{\overset{\large :\ddot{O}H}{|}}{CH}-CH_2CH_3}$$

2. What is the carbonyl component in this procedure? The portion of the target molecule derived from the carbonyl component has been outlined. We see that the carbonyl component of the reaction is propanal and the Grignard component is ethylmagnesium halide.

3. We can now write the final reaction in the overall synthesis:

$$CH_3CH_2MgBr + CH_3CH_2\overset{\overset{O}{\|}}{C}H \xrightarrow[\text{aq acid workup}]{} CH_3CH_2\overset{\overset{OH}{|}}{C}HCH_2CH_3$$

4. Working our way back to the available starting materials, we must now derive the two reactants of the above reaction from alcohols of three carbons or less. It is helpful to write these conversions in reverse order to understand the thinking involved in completing this problem. These conversions are:

$$CH_3CH_2MgBr \xleftarrow[(CH_3CH_2)_2O]{Mg} CH_3CH_2Br \xleftarrow{PBr_3} CH_3CH_2OH$$

and

$$CH_3CH_2\overset{\overset{O}{\|}}{C}H \xleftarrow[\text{pyridine}]{CrO_3} CH_3CH_2CH_2OH$$

We thus have a complete synthesis of 3-pentanol from alcohols of three carbons or less using a Grignard reaction as the final step.

Although alkyllithium reagents also undergo nucleophilic addition reactions with carbonyl compounds (an example is given in Equation 11.22), Grignard reagents are usually preferred because they are easier to prepare and handle.

Alkyllithium reagents do, however, have a special utility for one type of nucleophilic addition reaction. This involves carboxylic acids. Both Grignard reagents and alkyllithium reagents are powerful bases and will remove the acidic proton from a carboxylic acid, as shown in general in Equations 11.27 and 11.28, to produce carboxylate anions, RCO_2^-.

Eqn. 11.27

$$R{-}Li + R'{-}\overset{\overset{O}{\|}}{C}{-}O{-}H \longrightarrow R{-}H + R'{-}\overset{\overset{O}{\|}}{C}{-}O^- \; Li^+$$

Eqn. 11.28

$$R{-}MgX + R'{-}\overset{\overset{O}{\|}}{C}{-}O{-}H \longrightarrow R{-}H + R'{-}\overset{\overset{O}{\|}}{C}{-}O^- \; MgX^+$$

While the Grignard reagent is nucleophilic toward aldehydes and ketones, it is insufficiently nucleophilic to add to the carbonyl group of a carboxylate anion. The presence of the negative charge on the carboxylate anion inhibits attack by the electron-rich Grignard reagent, as shown in Equation 11.29.

Eqn. 11.29

$$R{-}MgX + R'{-}\overset{\overset{O}{\|}}{C}{-}O^- \; MgX^+ \not\longrightarrow R'{-}\underset{\underset{R}{|}}{\overset{\overset{O^- \; MgX^+}{|}}{C}}{-}O^- \; MgX^+$$

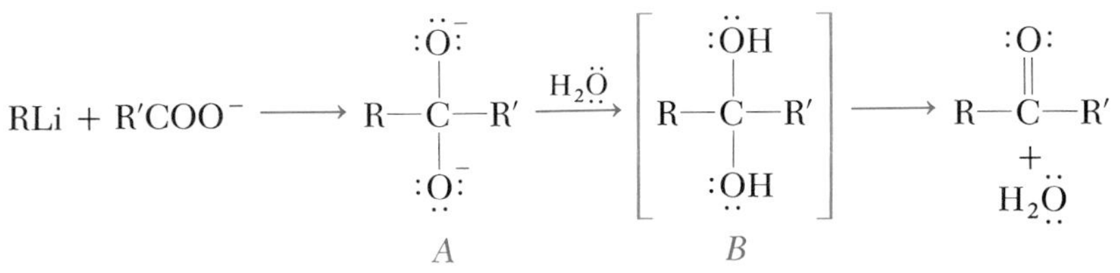

$$RLi + R'COO^- \longrightarrow R{-}\underset{:\ddot{O}:^-}{\overset{:\ddot{O}:^-}{C}}{-}R' \xrightarrow{H_2\ddot{O}} \left[R{-}\underset{:\ddot{O}H}{\overset{:\ddot{O}H}{C}}{-}R' \right] \longrightarrow R{-}\overset{:O:}{\overset{\|}{C}}{-}R' + H_2\ddot{O}$$

A B

Figure 11.13 Reaction of a alkyllithium reagent with a carboxylate anion. The intermediate dianion *A* is produced directly by the nucleophilic addition reaction and is incapable of undergoing any further addition reaction at carbon. Upon the addition of water to the reaction, the negatively charged oxygen sites are protonated to give the hydrated ketone structure *B*, which spontaneously loses a molecule of water to generate the ketone. The nature of this last reaction will be considered in our discussion of carbonyl chemistry in Chapter 19.

However, alkyllithium reagents *are* sufficiently nucleophilic to undergo addition to carboxylate anions. This reactivity can be used to good advantage in the synthesis of ketones from carboxylic acids. An example is shown in Equation 11.30.

Eqn. 11.30

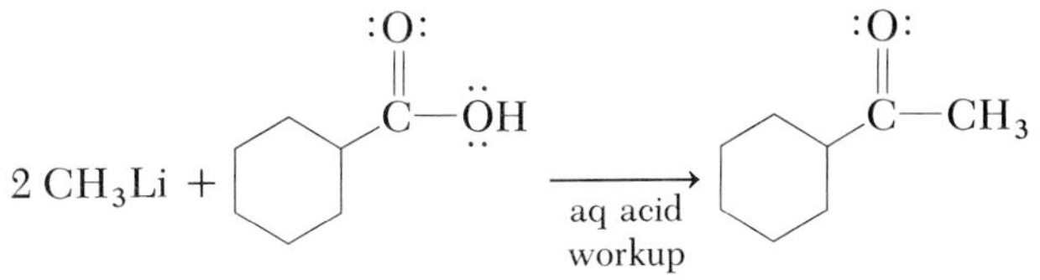

$$2\,CH_3Li + C_6H_{11}{-}\overset{:O:}{\overset{\|}{C}}{-}\ddot{O}H \xrightarrow[\text{workup}]{\text{aq acid}} C_6H_{11}{-}\overset{:O:}{\overset{\|}{C}}{-}CH_3$$

cyclohexane carboxylic acid → 93% yield methyl cyclohexyl ketone

Two equivalents of the alkyllithium reagent are required for this conversion. The first equivalent removes the acidic proton from the carboxylic acid, producing a carboxylate ion. The second equivalent then performs a nucleophilic addition reaction on the carboxylate anion, forming dianion *A* of Figure 11.13. When an aqueous acid is then added in the workup of the reaction, *A* is diprotonated to give intermediate *B*, which is unstable and loses water to form the ketone product.

PROBLEM 11.13 Give the alkyllithium reagent and the carboxylic acid that could be used for the synthesis of each of the following. If more than one combination of reagents is possible, give all possibilities.

a. $CH_3CH_2\underset{CH_3}{\underset{|}{C}H}\overset{:O:}{\overset{\|}{C}}CH_3$

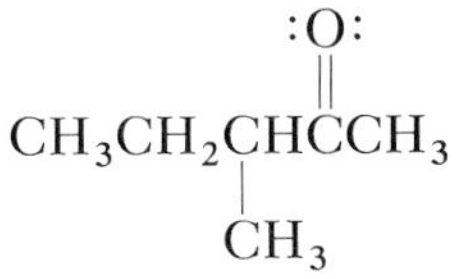

b. $C_6H_{11}{-}CH_2\overset{:O:}{\overset{\|}{C}}CH_3$ (cyclohexyl)

c. $(CH_3)_2CH\overset{:O:}{\overset{\|}{C}}CH(CH_3)_2$

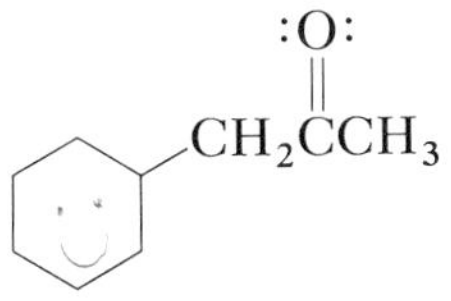

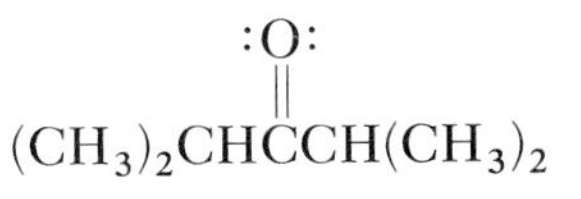

Substitution Reactions Many organometallics react with haloalkanes, causing the halogen to be replaced by an alkyl group from the organometallic. As such, these are *substitution* reactions. Various kinds of mechanisms are involved, and various kinds of organometallics can be used. One approach involves the formation of an alkylsodium reagent as the reactive organometallic. This species can react with haloalkanes to form a new carbon-carbon bond, as illustrated in Equation 11.31.

Eqn. 11.31

$$R\ddot{\underset{\cdot\cdot}{Br}}: + 2\,Na\cdot \longrightarrow RNa \xrightarrow{RBr} R{-}R$$

This reaction, known as the Wurtz reaction, is an old reaction of severely limited synthetic utility. Along with the formation of a variety of side products under even the best of conditions, it is virtually useless for the preparation of compounds where the two alkyl groups to be connected are not identical. That is, an attempted Wurtz reaction involving 1-bromobutane and 2-bromopropane in the hope of forming 2-methylhexane would not be fruitful. Some of the target material would be formed, but considerable amounts of other products would also be formed. The reaction is of some utility for the formation of small rings (by intramolecular reaction) where the organometallic site and the replaced halide site are in close proximity. An example of its use for such a reaction is shown in Equation 11.32.

Eqn. 11.32

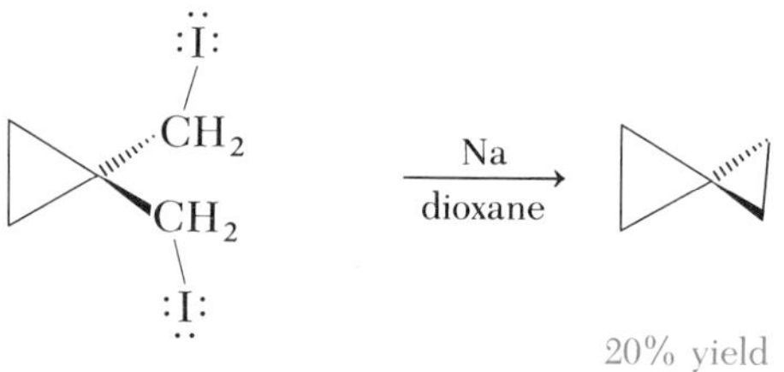

:I: — CH_2 / CH_2 — :I: (on cyclopropane) $\xrightarrow[\text{dioxane}]{Na}$ spiropentane

1,1-di(iodomethyl)cyclopropane — 20% yield spiropentane

A more modern and much more efficient alternative to the Wurtz reaction for the formation of carbon-carbon bonds is found in the use of lithium dialkylcuprate reagents. These reagents (also known as **Corey-House reagents**) are formed by the reaction of alkyllithium reagents with a cuprous halide at low temperature, generally with diethyl ether as the solvent. Their formation is illustrated in Figure 11.14.

Lithium dialkylcuprates react with haloalkanes to replace the halide with the alkyl group of the organometallic. An example of such a reaction is shown in Equation 11.33.

$$2\,RLi + CuX \xrightarrow{(CH_3CH_2)_2O} R_2CuLi + LiX$$

$$2\,CH_3Li + CuI \xrightarrow{(CH_3CH_2)_2O} (CH_3)_2CuLi + LiI$$

lithium dimethylcuprate

Figure 11.14 Formation of lithium dialkylcuprate reagents. Two equivalents of the alkyllithium reagent, formed in ether solution from the corresponding haloalkane, are treated with one equivalent of cuprous halide to form the lithium dialkylcuprate reagent. The R group for the reaction can be methyl, primary, secondary, or tertiary; that is, the starting organic halide may be CH_3X, RCH_2X, R_2CHX, or R_3CX.

Eqn. 11.33

$$CH_3CH_2CH_2CH_2\ddot{\underset{..}{I}}: + (CH_3)_2CuLi \longrightarrow CH_3CH_2CH_2CH_2CH_3$$

1-iodobutane — 98% yield pentane

There are limitations to the use of this method for forming carbon-carbon bonds. The reaction usually works most efficiently if the haloalkane on which the substitution reaction is performed is a halomethane or a primary haloalkane. With regard to the organometallic, the reactions proceed better with methyl or primary alkyl groups than with secondary, and tertiary alkyl groups require special reaction conditions. However, tertiary alkyl groups can be used successfully for the formation of carbon-carbon bonds.

An interesting aspect of the lithium dialkylcuprate reaction with haloalkanes is that it can proceed in the presence of carbonyl groups in the haloalkane. The Corey-House reagent does not react with carbonyl groups under these conditions. An example of this selectivity for substitution (as opposed to addition to a carbonyl carbon) is shown in Equation 11.34.

Eqn. 11.34

$$(CH_3)_2C(Br)—C(=O)—CH(CH_3)_2 + (CH_3)_2CuLi \longrightarrow (CH_3)_3C—C(=O)—CH(CH_3)_2$$

2-bromo-2,4-dimethyl-3-pentanone — 90% yield 2,2,4-trimethyl-3-pentanone

PROBLEM 11.14 Give the haloalkane that would be used in reaction with lithium di-1-butylcuprate to generate each of the following materials:

a. 2-methyloctane **b.** 2,4-dimethyldecane **c.** 1-cyclohexylbutane

Other organometallics can also effect substitution reactions. In special cases Grignard reagents will undergo substitution reactions with haloalkanes. Fortunately, this is not a common means of reaction for ordinary haloalkanes and their derived Grignard reagents. If it were, haloalkanes (R—X) would immediately form symmetrical alkanes (R—R) upon treatment with magnesium. Grignard reagents do perform substitution reactions with certain activated organic halides. Two types of activated organic halides are allylic halides and benzylic halides. Allylic halides have a halogen atom attached to a carbon atom adjacent to an alkene carbon-carbon double bond. Benzylic halides have a halogen atom attached to a carbon atom adjacent to a benzene ring. The simplest allylic and benzylic bromides are allyl bromide (**11.8**) and benzyl bromide (**11.9**).

$$CH_2{=}CH—CH_2\ddot{\underset{..}{Br}}: \qquad C_6H_5—CH_2\ddot{\underset{..}{Br}}:$$

allyl bromide **11.8** — benzyl bromide **11.9**

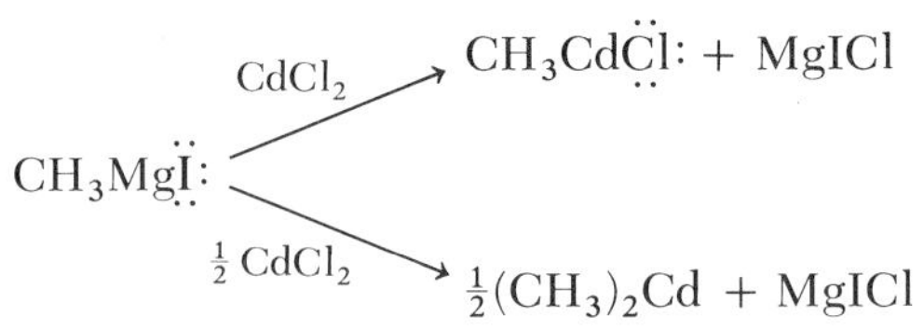

Figure 11.15 Formation of organocadmium reagents from Grignard reagents. Different organometallic species are formed, depending on the relative amounts of Grignard reagent and cadmium chloride. These two species will have slightly different reactivities with organic substrates. However, neither is reactive with carbonyl compounds in the manner that Grignard reagents are. Organocadmium compounds are especially useful for converting carboxylic acid halides to ketones (see Chapter 19).

$$CH_3MgI \xrightarrow{CdCl_2} CH_3CdCl + MgICl$$

$$CH_3MgI \xrightarrow{\frac{1}{2}CdCl_2} \tfrac{1}{2}(CH_3)_2Cd + MgICl$$

If an activated organic halide is added to a Grignard reagent, we can often isolate the product of alkyl coupling in good yield. An example is shown in Equation 11.35.

$$\underset{\text{allyl bromide}}{CH_2{=}CH{-}CH_2Br} + CH_3CH_2CH_2CH_2CH_2MgBr \longrightarrow \underset{\substack{\text{89\% yield} \\ \text{1-octene}}}{CH_2{=}CHCH_2CH_2CH_2CH_2CH_2CH_3} \qquad \text{Eqn. 11.35}$$

Ordinary haloalkanes do not undergo this type of coupling reaction readily. The Grignard reagent survives the conditions of preparation to be used in other reactions.

Reduced-Reactivity Organometallics The lithium dialkylcuprate reagent is one example of a less reactive organometallic that can be prepared from a more reactive organometallic. Some other useful organometallics are also available. Organocadmium reagents represent a further example of this type of reduced-reactivity organometallic.

An organocadmium reagent is usually prepared by the addition of anhydrous cadmium chloride to an ether solution of a freshly prepared Grignard reagent. The type of organocadmium reagent formed depends on the relative amounts of Grignard reagent and cadmium chloride used, as shown in Figure 11.15.

The rules that govern whether one organometallic can be converted into another by metal exchange are similar to other rules of equilibria we have met before. For example, in acid-base equilibria, formation of the weaker acid and base is favored. Similarly, with organometallics the less reactive species is favored at equilibrium. Thus we are able to convert a Grignard reagent to the (less reactive) organocadmium reagent, but we can not convert it to the (more reactive) organolithium reagent.

Summary

- Several methods are available for the preparation of simple haloalkanes, including the addition of hydrogen halides to carbon-carbon double bonds and replacement reactions for the hydroxyl group of alcohols.
- Various reaction conditions allow alcohols to be converted to haloalkanes with either inversion or retention of the configuration about the original carbinol carbon.

- A variety of organometallics can be prepared by reaction of the electropositive metal with a haloalkane. Of particularly great interest in this category are the Grignard reagents (RMgX) and the alkyllithium reagents (RLi).
- Both Grignard and alkyllithium reagents are extremely powerful bases and nucleophiles, reacting as though they consisted of a carbanion with an associated metal cation (R^-M^+).
- The reactivity of an organometallic is opposite to that found with the parent haloalkane. With a haloalkane, the carbon bearing the halogen is electron deficient and subject to attack by electron-rich reagents. The reversal of the polarity of the carbon bearing the halogen by its conversion to an organometallic is referred to as *umpolung*. This reversal of polarity is a characteristic of haloalkanes that is useful for organic synthesis.
- Grignard reagents and alkyllithium reagents both abstract protons from even weakly acidic sources.
- Both types of reagents undergo nucleophilic addition at the carbonyl carbon to form alcohols upon reaction workup.
- Alkyllithium reagents are more reactive than Grignard reagents. Alkyllithium reagents perform nucleophilic attack on carboxylate anions, leading ultimately to ketones upon workup, while Grignard reagents are unreactive with carboxylate anions.
- We can prepare a variety of other organometallics of reduced reactivity from the Grignard reagents and alkyllithium reagents. Of particular interest are the lithium dialkylcuprates, which are useful for performing substitution reactions on haloalkanes. A new carbon-carbon bond is formed in the process.

Terms to Remember

electrophilic	Grignard reagent	nucleophilic addition
organometallic	carbanion	Corey-House reagent
umpolung	target molecule	

Reactions of Synthetic Utility

37. $R{-}OH + (C_6H_5)_3P + CX_4 \longrightarrow R{-}X$ — 11.2

 X = Br, Cl; inversion at stereogenic carbon

38. $R{-}X \xrightarrow[\text{ether}]{Mg} \xrightarrow{H{-}Y} R{-}H$ — 11.5

 H—Y is at least weakly acidic

39. $R{-}X \xrightarrow[\text{ether}]{Mg} \xrightarrow{Y_2} R{-}Y$ — 11.5

 Y—I, Br, Cl

40. $R{-}X \xrightarrow[\text{ether}]{Mg} \xrightarrow{>C{=}O} R{-}\overset{|}{\underset{|}{C}}{-}OH$ — 11.5

 $>$=O is aldehyde or ketone; aqueous acid workup

41. $R{-}X \xrightarrow[\text{ether}]{Mg} \xrightarrow{O_2} R{-}OH$ — 11.5

42. $R{-}X \xrightarrow{Li} \xrightarrow{H{-}Y} R{-}H$ — 11.5

 H—Y is at least weakly acidic

43. $R{-}X \xrightarrow{Li} \xrightarrow{>C{=}O} R{-}\overset{|}{\underset{|}{C}}{-}OH$ — 11.5

 $>$=O is an aldehyde or ketone; aqueous workup

44. $R{-}X \xrightarrow{Li} \xrightarrow{R'COOH} R'{-}\overset{O}{\overset{||}{C}}{-}R$ — 11.5

 aqueous workup; two molar amounts of RLi intermediate are required

45. $R{-}X \xrightarrow{Li} \xrightarrow{CuX} \xrightarrow{R'Y} R{-}R'$ — 11.5

 $R' = 1°$, allylic, benzylic; $R = 1° > 2° \gg 3°$; X and Y = I, Br, Cl

Additional Problems

11.15 Draw structures for the following compounds:
- a. 3-chloro-2-methyl-1-butene
- b. (*E*)-1-bromo-2-ethyl-1-pentene
- c. (*S*)-1-chloro-2-propanol
- d. all secondary haloalkanes of formula C_4H_9Cl
- e. all tertiary, chiral haloalkanes of formula $C_7H_{15}Cl$
- f. (*R*)-2-chloro-2-methyl-1-butanol

11.16 Give the organic products for each of the following reactions.
- a. 2-hexanone treated with ethylmagnesium bromide and worked-up with aqueous acid
- b. 2-hexanone treated with methyllithium and worked-up with aqueous acid
- c. 1-butene treated sequentially with (i) hydrogen bromide in the presence of peroxides, (ii) magnesium in ether solution, (iii) formaldehyde, and worked-up with aqueous acid
- d. ethanol treated with 1-butyllithium
- e. cyclopentylmagnesium bromide upon treatment with 2-ethylbutanal [$CH_3CH_2CH(CH_3)CHO$] and worked-up with aqueous acid
- f. 1-butene treated sequentially with (i) hydrogen chloride, (ii) lithium in ether solution, and (iii) deuterium oxide
- g. acetic acid upon treatment with two equivalent amounts of ethylmagnesium bromide followed by workup with aqueous acid
- h. acetic acid treated with two equivalent amounts of ethyllithium followed by workup with aqueous acid
- i. 1-bromobutane treated with lithium diethylcuprate
- j. 2-bromobutane treated sequentially with (i) lithium in ether solution, (ii) cuprous iodide, and (iii) ethyl bromide
- k. 1-methylcyclopentanol treated sequentially with (i) hydrobromic acid, (ii) magnesium in ether, (iii) deuterium oxide
- l. 1-bromo-3-chlorocyclobutane treated with sodium in ether
- m. *cis*-2-methylcyclohexanol treated with thionyl chloride in pyridine solution
- n. *cis*-2-methylcyclohexanol treated with thionyl chloride in dioxane

11.17 Give the reagents and reaction conditions required to accomplish each of the following conversions.
- a. 1-bromobutane to 1-pentanol
- b. 1-pentanol to 2-hexanone
- c. 1-hexanol to 1-heptanol
- d. cyclohexene to deuteriocyclohexane ($C_6H_{11}D$)
- e. cyclopentene to 3,7-nonanedione
- f. 1-bromobutane to pentane
- g. ethyl bromide to diethylcadmium

11.18 When carbon dioxide is bubbled through a solution of 1-butylmagnesium bromide in ether and the reaction is worked-up with aqueous acid, a compound of formula $C_5H_{10}O_2$ is obtained. This same substance is also prepared by refluxing 1-pentanol with hot aqueous permanganate followed by workup with aqueous acid. Give the structure of the compound. Explain how it is formed in the reaction of the Grignard reagent with carbon dioxide. Show a curved-arrow mechanism.

11.19 A bromoalkane is treated with magnesium in ether followed by the addition of water. 2,3-Dimethylbutane is produced in this reaction. Give all possible structures for the bromoalkane.

11.20 Another bromoalkane is treated with magnesium in ether followed by the addition of water. In this reaction 2,2-dimethylpropane is produced. Give all possible structures for the bromoalkane.

11.21 Bromoalkane *A* of formula C_3H_7Br is treated with magnesium in ether followed by the addition of ketone *B*, of formula $C_7H_{14}O$. After workup with aqueous acid, product *C* of formula $C_{10}H_{22}O$ is isolated. Heating *C* with sulfuric acid yields *D*, of formula $C_{10}H_{20}$. On ozonolysis of *D* followed by workup with zinc and acetic acid, 2-propanone and 2,4-dimethyl-3-pentanone are isolated. Suggest structures for compounds *A–D*. (*Hint:* In solving this type of problem, start at the point where the greatest structural information is given—in this case it happens to be at the end of the reaction scheme. Start with these given compounds and work stepwise back to the beginning.)

11.22 When allyl bromide is refluxed with magnesium metal in ether solvent, a compound of formula C_6H_{10} is formed. Explain this result.

11.23 Provide structures for the compounds *E–H* in the reaction sequence shown below.

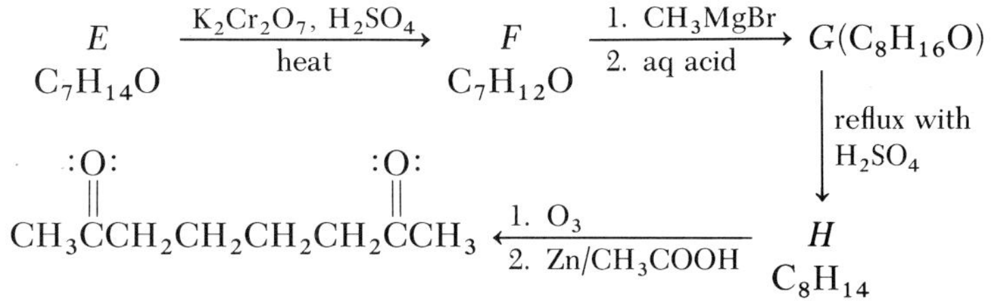

$$\underset{C_7H_{14}O}{E} \xrightarrow[\text{heat}]{K_2Cr_2O_7,\ H_2SO_4} \underset{C_7H_{12}O}{F} \xrightarrow[\text{2. aq acid}]{\text{1. }CH_3MgBr} G(C_8H_{16}O) \xrightarrow{\text{reflux with } H_2SO_4} \underset{C_8H_{14}}{H} \xrightarrow[\text{2. Zn/}CH_3COOH]{\text{1. }O_3} CH_3\overset{\overset{:O:}{\|}}{C}CH_2CH_2CH_2CH_2\overset{\overset{:O:}{\|}}{C}CH_3$$

11.24 Give a reaction sequence (reagents and reaction conditions) to accomplish each of the following preparations:
a. 2,7-octanediol from cyclohexene
b. 2-methyl-2-pentanol from alcohols containing three carbons or less

11.25 Show all steps in the preparation of each of the following compounds. Start with alcohols of five carbons or fewer and any other reagents deemed necessary.

a. 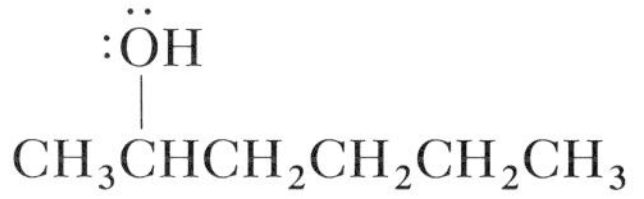 $CH_3\overset{\overset{:\ddot{O}H}{|}}{C}HCH_2CH_2CH_2CH_3$

b. cyclopentyl–$CH_2\ddot{O}H$

c. $CH_3CH_2\overset{\overset{:\ddot{O}H}{|}}{C}HCH_2CH(CH_3)_2$

d. 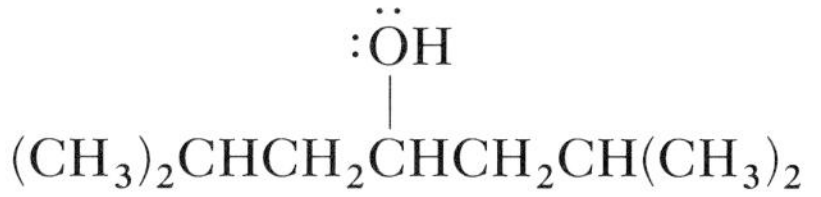 $(CH_3)_2CHCH_2\overset{\overset{:\ddot{O}H}{|}}{C}HCH_2CH(CH_3)_2$

e. 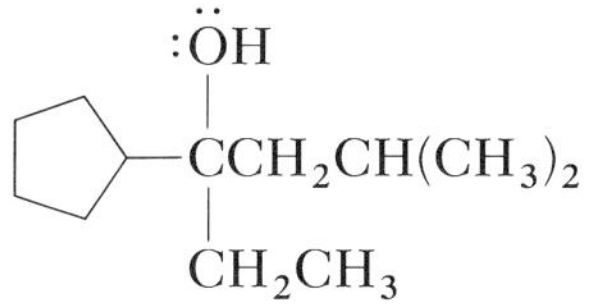 cyclopentyl–$\overset{\overset{:\ddot{O}H}{|}}{\underset{\underset{CH_2CH_3}{|}}{C}}CH_2CH(CH_3)_2$

f. $(CH_3CH_2)_2CHCH_3$

g. 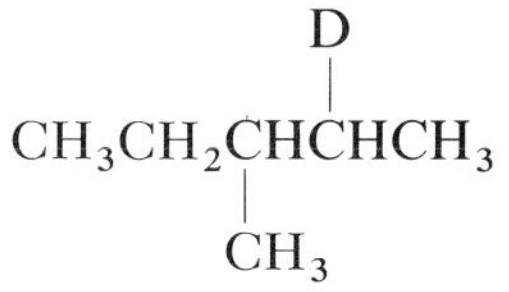 $CH_3CH_2\underset{\underset{CH_3}{|}}{C}H\overset{\overset{D}{|}}{C}HCH_3$

h. $CH_3CH_2\overset{\overset{CH_2D}{|}}{C}HCH_2CH_3$

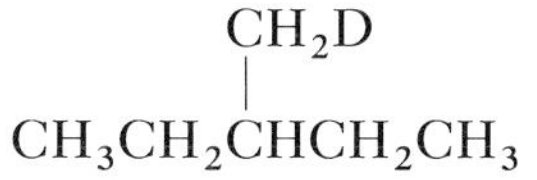

i. 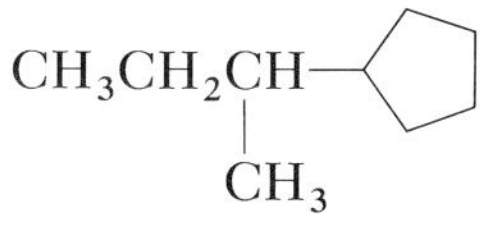 $CH_3CH_2\underset{\underset{CH_3}{|}}{C}H$–cyclopentyl

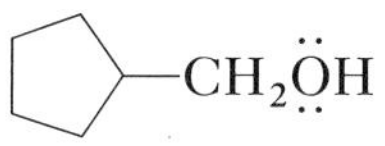

j. $CH_3CH_2CH_2CH_2CH_2CH_2CH_2CH_3$

k. $(CH_3)_2CHCH_2CH_2CH_3$

l. 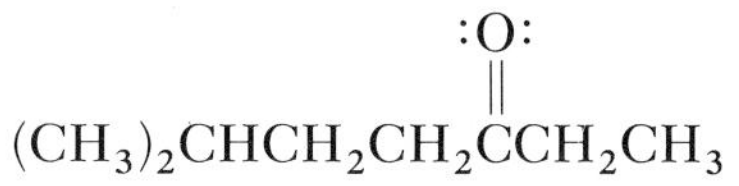 $(CH_3)_2CHCH_2CH_2\overset{\overset{:O:}{\|}}{C}CH_2CH_3$

m. 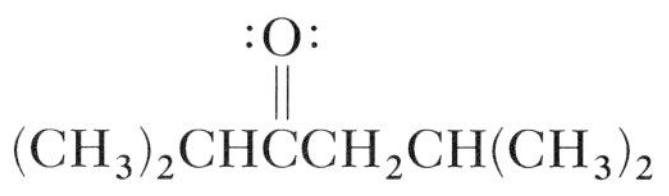 $(CH_3)_2CH\overset{\overset{:O:}{\|}}{C}CH_2CH(CH_3)_2$

Substitution and Elimination Reactions of Haloalkanes

12.1 Introduction

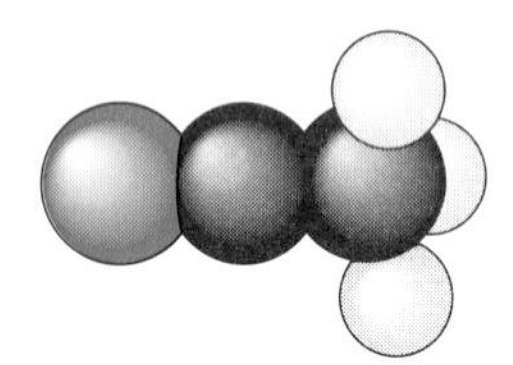

The previous chapter introduced a few aspects of the chemistry of haloalkanes, also known as alkyl halides. It emphasized methods of preparation and the *umpolung* that accompanies their conversion to organometallics. In this chapter we continue to explore the chemistry of this versatile and important group of compounds. In particular we will examine in some detail two common and important reaction types—*nucleophilic substitution* reactions and *elimination* reactions.

When a haloalkane undergoes a nucleophilic substitution reaction, the halogen is displaced as a halide ion and its place is taken by the nucleophile. This type of reaction can be used to introduce many functional groups into organic molecules. One example will suffice for the present: when treated with cyanide ion (CN^-), many haloalkanes (RX) yield **nitriles** (RCN). In such reactions, the nucleophile (cyanide ion) displaces the halogen X as X^- from the organic substrate.

Elimination reactions of haloalkanes may occur when they are treated with suitable bases. In these reactions, a hydrogen atom and a halogen atom are eliminated from a pair of adjacent carbon atoms, and a carbon-carbon double bond is introduced (see the discussion in Chapter 9).

Both elimination and substitution reactions make it possible for chemists to synthesize a great variety of substances from haloalkanes. You will recall that haloalkanes are readily prepared from alcohols, so you can begin to appreciate that the sequence of conversions

$$\text{alcohol} \longrightarrow \text{haloalkane} \longrightarrow \text{other organic substances}$$

is very common in synthetic work.

12.2 Nucleophilic Substitution Reactions—General Concepts

THE NATURE OF NUCLEOPHILIC SUBSTITUTION REACTIONS

We first encountered nucleophilic substitution reactions while discussing the reactions of alcohols. We will begin by reviewing some aspects of these reactions that are relevant for the discussion of haloalkanes in this chapter. The first point to stress is that alcohols themselves are not reactive toward nucleophiles. The —OH group is *not* easily displaced as a hydroxide ion. In an acidic medium, however, an alcohol is protonated, resulting in a significant change in the alcohol molecule's chemistry. The protonated alcohol (or oxonium ion) contains an $—^+OH_2$ group that is readily lost as a water molecule. Recall from the earlier alcohol chapters that there are two modes of reactivity for the oxonium ion. The oxonium ion may react *directly* with a nucleophile in the reaction mixture, as illustrated in Figure 12.1. Alternatively, the oxonium ion

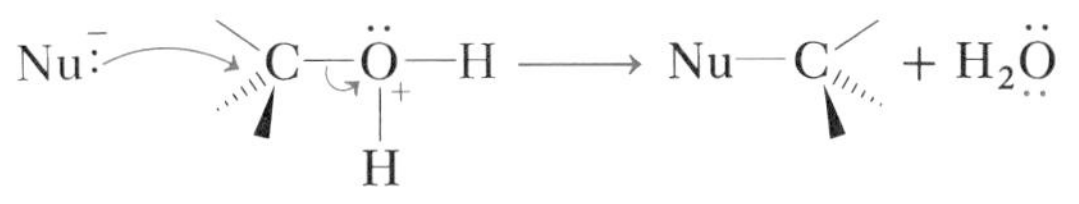

$$Nu^{-} + \rangle C-\ddot{O}^{+}(H)-H \longrightarrow Nu-C\langle + H_2\ddot{O}$$

Figure 12.1 Direct reaction of an oxonium ion with a nucleophile.

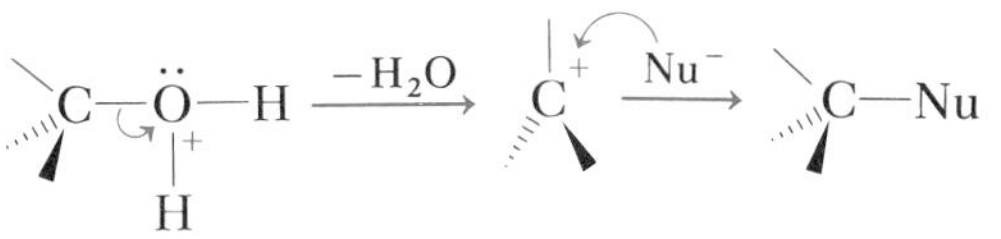

$$\rangle C-\ddot{O}^{+}(H)-H \xrightarrow{-H_2O} \rangle C^{+} \xrightarrow{Nu^{-}} \rangle C-Nu$$

Figure 12.2 Decomposition of an oxonium ion to a carbocation prior to reaction with a nucleophile.

may spontaneously lose a molecule of water to form a further intermediate—a carbocation—that then reacts with a nucleophile in solution. This mode of reactivity is summarized in Figure 12.2.

In either case, the overall reaction is nucleophilic substitution in which the nucleophile substitutes for the leaving group (water). Many species other than oxonium ions react with nucleophiles via the two pathways just illustrated. In each case, a suitable leaving group must be present. Among the most important examples of substances possessing good leaving groups are the haloalkanes. We will now consider their reactions in some detail.

HALOALKANES AS SUBSTRATES FOR NUCLEOPHILIC SUBSTITUTION

Halogen atoms are more electronegative than carbon atoms. As a result, the electron density of a carbon-halogen bond is not distributed evenly along the length of the bond. Rather, the halogen end is electron rich and the carbon end is electron deficient. The carbon atom is an **electrophilic site** (electron-loving), and as such, it is subject to attack by (electron-rich) nucleophiles.

When substitution reactions are carried out on alcohols, the hydroxyl group must be protonated so that substitution can occur, since hydroxide ion is not a good leaving group. A much better leaving group, water, is generated by protonation. Earlier, we introduced a useful inverse correlation between leaving group ability and basicity. Here we recognize that water is a *weaker* base and a *better* leaving group than is hydroxide ion. In general, weak bases are better leaving groups than are strong bases.

Chloride, bromide, and iodide ions are all weak bases (each is the conjugate base of a strong acid). We can therefore predict that all could serve as good leaving groups in nucleophilic substitution reactions. In fact we do find that chloro-, bromo-, and iodoalkanes are effective substrates for nucleophilic substitution reactions. On the other hand, fluoride ion is a strong base (its conjugate acid, HF, is weak). Not surprisingly, fluoroalkanes are not useful substrates for nucleophilic substitution reactions.

In summary the relative abilities of the halides to serve as leaving groups in nucleophilic substitution reactions are:

$$I^{-} > Br^{-} > Cl^{-} > F^{-}$$

This order is the *reverse* of the order of their basicities (base strengths).

THE NUCLEOPHILE: NUCLEOPHILICITY

Both ions and molecules can function as nucleophiles provided they have an electron pair capable of forming a new bond to an electrophilic site. The term

$$\begin{array}{c}\text{rate of formation} \\ \text{of product}\end{array} = \frac{d[\text{product}]}{dt} = \frac{\text{change in } [\text{product}]}{\text{period of time}} = k[\text{A}]^a[\text{B}]^b$$

Figure 12.3 General form of a rate law. The concentrations of the reactants (A and B) are indicated by [A] and [B]. The exponents a and b are determined by experimental measurement of the effect of changing the concentrations of reactants on the observable rate of formation of product. In the rate law expression, k (the **rate constant**) is a proportionality constant relating the observed rate to the concentrations. The rate constant is a characteristic of a given reaction under a specific set of conditions (temperature, solvent, pressure, and so forth). The rate constant, unlike the *rate* itself, does not vary with concentration of the reactants but is uniquely characteristic of the reaction under the given conditions.

nucleophilicity refers to the relative strength or reactivity of a nucleophile. Nucleophilicities are measured by comparing the rates at which different nucleophiles react with a given substrate. Later in the chapter we will compare nucleophilicities and contrast them with basicities.

AN INTRODUCTION TO KINETICS

Kinetics is the branch of chemistry dealing with the rates of reactions. In a typical kinetics experiment, a chemist measures the rate of a reaction by monitoring the rate at which the concentrations of the reactants decrease and/or the rate at which the concentration of the products increase. Experimental studies of kinetics have played a most important role in providing insights into the natures and mechanisms of many types of reactions, including nucleophilic substitution reactions. One important avenue of investigation in kinetics experiments is to examine how reaction rates depend on the concentrations of each of the reactants.

For all reactions, a relationship known as a **rate law** can be derived from experimental measurements. A rate law expresses the dependence of the reaction rate on the concentrations of the reactants. The general form of a rate law for a reaction involving two reactants A and B is shown in Figure 12.3.

In general, we determine the rate law for a given reaction by performing kinetic experiments. Specifically, we vary the concentration of each of the reactants in turn and look at the effect of these variations on the rate of reaction. For example, if we triple the concentration of one reagent (say A) and find that the reaction rate triples, the rate must be directly proportional to the concentration of that reagent. We would say that the reaction is *first order with respect to* A, since the exponent a has the value of unity. If, on the other hand, the rate remains the same when we change the concentration, we see that the rate is *independent* of the concentration of that reagent and we would omit its concentration term from the rate law, or, equivalently, raise it to the zeroth power.

The exponent of a concentration term in the rate law is called the **reaction order** with regard to that reagent. The sum of all exponents of concentration terms in the rate law is the reaction order for the entire reaction. For example, if the experimentally determined rate expression is

$$\text{rate} = k[\text{A}][\text{B}]$$

then the reaction is first order with regard to each reagent and second order overall. If the experimentally determined rate expression is

$$\text{rate} = k[\text{A}]^2[\text{B}]$$

the rate is third order overall. It is first order with regard to B and second order with regard to A.

Consider Equation 12.1, which shows a reaction between two reactants A and B to produce a product (or products) Z.

Eqn. 12.1 $$\mathrm{A} + \mathrm{B} \longrightarrow \mathrm{Z}$$

Suppose that this conversion occurs in a single step by means of collision of A and B. The rate of formation of Z depends on how often one molecule of A and one molecule of B actually collide with each other in the reaction mixture. The more frequent these collisions, the more rapidly Z is generated. Not *every* collision can be expected to result in reaction, but the more collisions that occur, the more reactions there will be. The rate of reaction will be proportional to the concentrations of both A and B. If we increase these concentrations, the probability of collision (and hence reaction) will increase proportionally.

Many reactions involve more than one mechanistic step. How do the concentrations of reactants affect the rates of these reactions? We find that the concentrations of reagents that are consumed *during the slow step* of the reaction appear in the rate law with positive integral exponents. We can think of the slow step of a reaction as the *bottleneck* in the process of forming product. It is the **rate-determining step** of the reaction. Only the frequency and the effectiveness of collisions between molecules actually involved in the rate-determining step can affect the overall reaction rate. Reagents that are consumed *before or after the slow step* have their concentrations raised to the zeroth power in the rate law. That is, their concentrations are omitted or indicated by unity. The observable rate of reaction is independent of their concentrations.

PROBLEM 12.1 For the reaction shown in Equation 12.1, the experimental rate expression is found to be

$$\text{rate} = k[\mathrm{A}]\,[\mathrm{B}]$$

It is found that the initial rate of formation of Z is 2.4×10^{-5} M/sec when the initial concentrations of A and B are each 1 M.

a. Calculate the value of the rate constant k for this reaction.
b. What is the rate of formation of Z when 25% of A has been consumed?
c. What is the rate of formation of Z when 50% of A has been consumed?
d. If we raise the temperature of the reaction by 10 C°, we find the initial rate of reaction to be 4.8×10^{-5} M/sec using initial concentrations of A and B of 1 M. What is the rate constant at this higher temperature?

Steps to Solving the Problem

Solution to Problem 12.1a and b

1. Consider the given rate expression

$$\text{rate} = k[\mathrm{A}]\,[\mathrm{B}]$$

and the values of the quantities in that expression:

$$[\mathrm{A}] = [\mathrm{B}] = 1\ M, \qquad \text{rate} = 2.4 \times 10^{-5}\ M/\text{sec}$$

2. We can then calculate the value of k under the reaction conditions used:

$$k = (2.4 \times 10^{-5}\ M/\text{sec})/(1\ M^2)$$
$$= 2.4 \times 10^{-5}\ M^{-1}\ \text{sec}^{-1}$$

3. We can now calculate the rate of formation of Z when 25% of A has been consumed. Remember, for each molecule of A that is consumed, one molecule of B is also consumed. The concentrations of both A and B are reduced by 25%. Thus,

$$\text{rate} = (2.4 \times 10^{-5}\ M^{-1}\ \text{sec}^{-1})/(0.75\ M)^2$$
$$= 1.35 \times 10^{-5}\ M/\text{sec}$$

12.3 Observation of Nucleophilic Substitution Reactions of Haloalkanes

A study of the kinetics of nucleophilic substitution reactions of haloalkanes reveals two different types of rate laws, that is, two ways in which the rate varies with changes in reagent concentration. In some cases we find that the rate of the reaction is *proportional* to the concentration of the nucleophile, while in others it is completely *independent* of the concentration of the nucleophile. In both types of reactions we observe that the reaction rate changes in proportion to the concentration of haloalkane. These observations suggest that there are (at least) two different mechanisms by which nucleophilic substitution can occur. The observed rate dependencies are shown in Table 12.1 with their common designations as $\mathbf{S_N1}$ and $\mathbf{S_N2}$.

12.4 Bimolecular Nucleophilic Substitution (S_N2) Reactions of Haloalkanes

Bimolecular nucleophilic substitution reactions (S_N2 stands for substitution (S), nucleophilic (N), bimolecular (2)) are conceptually the simpler of the two reaction types (S_N1 and S_N2) that we will now consider in some detail. In an S_N2 reaction, the rate of product formation is found to be directly proportional to the concentration of both the nucleophile and the haloalkane reagent. This observation is consistent with a mechanism in which both nucleophile and substrate are involved in the rate-determining step of the reaction. The rate-determining step is therefore *bimolecular;* it involves a collision of two species. Increasing the concentration of *either* species increases the number of collisions in the rate-determining step, and the observed reaction rate increases.

THE HALOALKANE

The ease with which S_N2 reactions occur is highly dependent on the structure of the alkyl group to which the halogen is attached. Specifically, the greater

Table 12.1 Rate Dependencies for Nucleophilic Substitution Reactions of Haloalkanes

rate = k[RX]	S_N1 (first-order kinetics)
rate = k[RX] [Nu:]	S_N2 (second-order kinetics)

Table 12.2 Relative Rates of S_N2 Reaction of Bromoalkanes with Ethoxide Ion in Ethanol

$$CH_3CH_2\ddot{O}:^- + R-\ddot{Br}: \longrightarrow CH_3CH_2\ddot{O}-R + :\ddot{Br}:^-$$

Effect of α-branching		Effect of β-branching	
Bromoalkane	Relative Rate	Bromoalkane	Relative Rate
$CH_3\ddot{Br}:$	1600	$CH_3CH_2\ddot{Br}:$	100
$CH_3CH_2\ddot{Br}:$	100	$CH_3CH_2CH_2\ddot{Br}:$	28.4
$(CH_3)_2CH\ddot{Br}:$	1	$(CH_3)_2CHCH_2\ddot{Br}:$	3.06
$(CH_3)_3C\ddot{Br}:$	~0	$(CH_3)_3CCH_2\ddot{Br}:$	0.00043

the degree of branching at the electrophilic site (the α-carbon, the one to which the halogen is attached) or the adjacent site (the β-carbon), the slower the rate of an S_N2 reaction. Highly branched haloalkanes usually react only very slowly with a nucleophile by the S_N2 mechanism. (However, they may react via the S_N1 mechanism, in which case the rate of reaction could be quite rapid. We will discuss this possibility later.) Table 12.2 shows the effects of branching at the α- and β-positions on the rate of an S_N2 reaction.

The tendency to undergo S_N2 reaction drops markedly as the substrate changes from a methyl to a primary to a secondary to a tertiary haloalkane. That is, α-branching drastically decreases the rate of the S_N2 reaction.

Although all the entries in the right-hand column of Table 12.2 are primary bromoalkanes, it is clear that β-branching is important. With increased β-branching, there is a continuous drop in reaction rate.

THE NUCLEOPHILE

A wide variety of nucleophiles take part in S_N2 reactions. We will consider here five types that are of mechanistic importance and synthetic utility.

Nucleophilic Substitution by Hydroxide Ion or Water Haloalkanes may be converted into alcohols by treatment with hydroxide ion or water. Substitution of hydroxide for a halogen often proceeds cleanly when the haloalkane is methyl or primary and there is no β-branching of the carbon skeleton. However, heating some haloalkanes (particularly secondary and tertiary haloalkanes) with aqueous hydroxide ion results in the formation of large amounts of elimination side products (alkenes). To avoid this, milder conditions have been developed to favor substitution over elimination (see Chapter 9). Solutions of water in hexamethylphosphoric triamide (HMPT, **11.1**) can be used to obtain high yields of primary alcohols from primary haloalkanes and moderate yields of secondary alcohols from secondary haloalkanes. Examples are shown in Equations 12.2 and 12.3.

Eqn. 12.2

$$CH_3CH_2CH_2CH_2CH_2CH_2CH_2CH_2\ddot{\underset{..}{I}}: \xrightarrow[100\,°C]{H_2O,\ HMPT} CH_3CH_2CH_2CH_2CH_2CH_2CH_2CH_2\ddot{\underset{..}{O}}H$$

1-iodooctane

95% yield
1-octanol

Eqn. 12.3

$$CH_3CH_2CH_2CH_2CH_2CH_2\underset{:\underset{..}{I}:}{\underset{|}{C}}HCH_3 \xrightarrow[100\,°C]{H_2O,\ HMPT} CH_3CH_2CH_2CH_2CH_2CH_2\underset{:\underset{..}{O}H}{\underset{|}{C}}HCH_3$$

2-iodooctane

75% yield
2-octanol

In these reactions, nucleophilic attack by water first produces a protonated alcohol (an oxonium ion) which then loses a proton to form the observed product.

Nucleophilic Substitution by Alkoxide Ion Alkoxide ions are the conjugate bases of alcohols. We form alkoxide ions by treating an alcohol with a strong base or an electropositive metal. The alkoxide ions thus generated are, like hydroxide ion, not only strong bases but also potent nucleophiles.

The use of alkoxide ions to effect nucleophilic substitution reactions on haloalkanes, again like the use of hydroxide ion, suffers from competing elimination side reactions (in which the alkoxide acts as a base). Halomethanes and primary haloalkanes without β-branching are the best substrates for alkoxide ion substitution because the competing elimination reactions are least important for them. Although secondary and other branched primary haloalkanes *do* give substitution reactions, competing elimination reactions are more likely to occur. Similarly, tertiary haloalkanes yield mainly alkenes on reaction with alkoxide ions—elimination dominates over substitution. These competing elimination reactions will be discussed in detail later in the chapter.

The products of the alkoxide substitution reaction of haloalkanes are **ethers.** The reaction, known as the **Williamson ether synthesis,** is one of several major methods for the synthesis of ethers. Two examples of ether syntheses using this approach are shown in Equations 12.4 and 12.5. (We will discuss the synthetic aspects of the Williamson ether synthesis in detail in Chapter 14.)

Eqn. 12.4

$$\text{(dihydropyranyl)}CH_2\ddot{\underset{..}{O}}H \xrightarrow{NaH} \text{(dihydropyranyl)}CH_2\ddot{\underset{..}{O}}:^- \xrightarrow{CH_3I} \text{(dihydropyranyl)}CH_2\ddot{\underset{..}{O}}CH_3$$

6-hydroxymethyl-
5,6-dihydropyran

91% yield
6-methoxymethyl-
5,6-dihydropyran

Eqn. 12.5

$$CH_3(CH_2)_5CH_2\ddot{\underset{..}{O}}H \xrightarrow{NaH} CH_3(CH_2)_5CH_2\ddot{\underset{..}{O}}:^- \xrightarrow{CH_3I} CH_3(CH_2)_5CH_2\ddot{\underset{..}{O}}CH_3$$

1-heptanol

40% yield
1-heptyl methyl ether

PROBLEM 12.2 In Equations 12.4 and 12.5 the strong base hydride ion, H^-, in the form of its sodium salt, sodium hydride, is used to convert the alcohol to its alkoxide ion. Hydrides are frequently used for this purpose. What is the conjugate acid of hydride ion?

When the Williamson ether synthesis is applied to a chiral haloalkane (stereogenic at the carbon atom bearing the halogen), there is an *inversion* of configuration. An example using optically active 1-chloro-1-phenylethane is shown in Equation 12.6.

Eqn. 12.6

$$(H_3C)(H)(C_6H_5)C-\ddot{\underset{..}{Cl}}: \xrightarrow[HOCH_2CH_3]{NaOCH_2CH_3} CH_3CH_2\ddot{\underset{..}{O}}-C(H)(CH_3)(C_6H_5)$$

(*R*)-1-chloro-1-phenylethane

43% yield
92.5% optical purity
(95% inversion)
(*S*)-1-ethoxy-1-phenylethane

Inversion of configuration about the electrophilic carbon atom is a phenomenon observed with all S_N2 reactions. Such observations lead to a presumption regarding the nature of the reaction: for successful reaction, the nucleophile must approach the electrophilic carbon site from the *back side* (the side opposite the leaving group). A final point is that, although the reaction shown in Equation 12.6 proceeds with virtually complete inversion of configuration, the yield is only moderate because a significant amount of the starting haloalkane is consumed in a competing elimination reaction.

PROBLEM 12.3 Give a preparation for each of the following compounds using the Williamson ether synthesis.

a. $(CH_3)_2CHCH_2\ddot{\underset{..}{O}}CH_2CH_2CH_3$ b. $CH_3CH_2\ddot{\underset{..}{O}}CH_2C(CH_3)_3$

c. $(CH_3)_2CHCH(CH_3)CH_2\ddot{\underset{..}{O}}CH_2C(CH_3)_3$

Nucleophilic Substitution by Halide Ion We find that iodoalkanes are often preferable to other haloalkanes in preparative reactions. For example, iodoalkanes usually form Grignard reagents more readily than the corresponding chloro- and bromoalkanes. However, haloalkanes are usually prepared from alcohols, and in general it is simpler to convert alcohols to chloro- or bromoalkanes than to iodoalkanes. Fortunately, it is a relatively simple matter to convert a chloro- or bromoalkane to an iodoalkane using an S_N2 reaction with iodide ion as the nucleophile.

The S_N2 reaction of iodide ion with a haloalkane is sometimes known as the **Finkelstein reaction.** It is one of the simplest organic reactions to perform. Sodium iodide is dissolved in acetone (2-propanone) or 2-butanone, and the chloro- or bromoalkane is added to it, usually at room temperature. We can monitor the progress of the reaction by observing the formation of a precipitate of sodium chloride (or sodium bromide). When the precipitation is complete, the organic product can be isolated by removal of the inorganic precipitate, followed by evaporation of the solvent. Two examples are shown in Equations. 12.7 and 12.8.

Eqn. 12.7

$$\text{BrCH}_2\text{C(CH}_2\text{Br)}_2\text{CH}_2\text{Br} \xrightarrow[\text{2-butanone}]{\text{NaI}} \text{ICH}_2\text{C(CH}_2\text{I)}_2\text{CH}_2\text{I} + \text{NaBr}\downarrow$$

1,3-dibromo-2,2-dibromomethylpropane → 89% yield 1,3-diiodo-2,2-diiodomethylpropane

Eqn. 12.8

$$\text{C}_6\text{H}_5\text{C(=O)OCH}_2\text{CH}_2\text{Cl} \xrightarrow[\text{2-butanone}]{\text{NaI}} \text{C}_6\text{H}_5\text{C(=O)OCH}_2\text{CH}_2\text{I} + \text{NaCl}\downarrow$$

2-chloroethyl benzoate → 81% yield 2-iodoethyl benzoate

As is typical with S_N2 reactions, primary haloalkanes react more rapidly than secondary haloalkanes, which in turn react more rapidly than tertiary haloalkanes. The reaction is an equilibrium that is forced to the iodoalkane side by the precipitation of the by-product sodium chloride (or sodium bromide). Good conversions are obtained because the reactant sodium iodide is soluble in the reaction medium but the by-product salts (NaBr or NaCl) are not.

Nucleophilic Substitution by Cyanide Ion The formation of new carbon-carbon bonds is of great importance in organic synthesis. The substitution of halide by cyanide forms a new carbon-carbon bond, increasing by one the number of carbon atoms in a molecule. An example of this substitution reaction is shown in Equation 12.9.

Eqn. 12.9

$$\text{CH}_3\text{CH}_2\text{CH}_2\text{CH}_2\text{Br} \xrightarrow[\text{dimethyl sulfoxide}]{\text{NaCN}} \text{CH}_3\text{CH}_2\text{CH}_2\text{CH}_2\text{C}\equiv\text{N}$$

1-bromobutane → 92% yield 1-cyanobutane

The product in this reaction, an alkyl cyanide, is also known as a *nitrile*. The preparation of a nitrile from a haloalkane is a useful reaction in multistep syntheses. As we will see in later chapters, nitriles serve as precursors for a host of other functional groups.

Dimethyl sulfoxide (DMSO, **12.1**), the solvent used for the reaction of Equation 12.9, is a most effective solvent for many S_N2 reactions in which the nucleophile is anionic.

$$(H_3C)_2\ddot{S}^{+}-\ddot{\underset{..}{O}}:^{-}$$

12.1

Such reactions often occur at a much faster rate in DMSO than in solvents such as water and alcohols. The reason is presumed to be that anions are well solvated (and are therefore stabilized and rendered less reactive) in water and in other protic solvents, but are poorly solvated in DMSO. As a solvent, DMSO is able to solvate cations well because it can associate with the positive ion by using its electron rich oxygen atom. However, it is not so effective in solvating anions. First, the electron-deficient sulfur atom is buried within the molecule, making it relatively inaccessible for interaction with anions. Secondly, DMSO cannot act as a hydrogen bond donor toward anions, as it contains no hydrogen atoms bound to electronegative atoms. DMSO is an example of a **polar aprotic solvent**—one that is polar, but is not able to donate a hydrogen atom in hydrogen bonding. Such solvents are the preferred choice for S_N2 reactions in which the nucleophile is an anion—they leave the anion relatively unsolvated ("naked") and free for reaction. (The anions of salts dissolved in solvents containing ionophores such as crown ethers are also relatively naked—see the Special Topic "Supramolecular Effects" in Chapter 3.)

SPECIAL TOPIC

Dimethyl Sulfoxide

Although the toxicity of DMSO itself is rather low (LD_{50} oral ~4 g/Kg; i.e., the lethal dose to 50% of test subjects is approximately 4g per Kg of body weight), it is rapidly absorbed through intact skin. Many materials dissolved in DMSO are carried with it through the skin and into the bloodstream. Included among these materials are cyanide salts and a variety of other toxic agents. Thus, a DMSO solution of sodium cyanide is a powerful contact poison.

Dimethyl sulfoxide has potential for beneficial health use as well. Aside from reported direct therapeutic effects, many of which have been seriously disputed, DMSO might prove to be an agent suitable for "needle-less injections." For example, DMSO is known to enhance the uptake of insulin across intact tissue membranes.

PROBLEM 12.4 Draw a Lewis structure for the DMSO molecule, in which there are no formal charges. (It is necessary to have sulfur exceed an octet).

PROBLEM 12.5 Consider a nucleophilic substitution reaction in which the (*R*) stereoisomer of $CH_3CH_2OCH_2CH(Cl)CH_2CH_3$ reacts with sodium cyanide in DMSO so that cyanide replaces chloride. The product is the (*R*) stereoisomer of $CH_3CH_2OCH_2CH(CN)CH_2CH_3$. Is this product consistent with the occurrence of an S_N2 reaction?

Nucleophilic Substitution by Ammonia So far, almost all of the nucleophiles we have discussed have been anionic, that is, negatively charged. However, neutral molecules can also behave as nucleophiles. We have already seen that water plays this role in some reactions. Ammonia, NH_3, is also a good nucleophile that can bring about substitution reactions on haloalkanes. The organic products of the reaction of ammonia with haloalkanes are **amines.** An example is shown in Equation 12.10.

Eqn. 12.10

$$\underset{\text{1-bromoheptane}}{CH_3CH_2CH_2CH_2CH_2CH_2CH_2\ddot{\underset{..}{Br}}:} \xrightarrow[CH_3OH]{NH_3} \underset{\substack{\text{47\% yield} \\ \text{1-heptylamine}}}{CH_3CH_2CH_2CH_2CH_2CH_2CH_2\ddot{N}H_2}$$

Reaction proceeds by way of an initially formed **alkylammonium ion,** as shown in Figure 12.4.

There is a complication to the ammonia substitution reaction. Notice that the product amine has an unshared electron pair on nitrogen. This unshared electron pair makes the amine product, like ammonia itself, a potential nucleophile. In fact, with an alkyl group attached to the nitrogen, the amine is an even *more* potent nucleophile than is ammonia. Thus, if the concentration of the amine product is allowed to increase relative to that of the ammonia, further reaction can occur, as illustrated in Figure 12.5. If we wish to isolate the primary amine product in good yield, it is often useful to employ an *excess* of ammonia. In Chapter 20 we will also consider other procedures that we can use for the preparation of primary amines in good yields, free of secondary and tertiary amines.

$$H_3N: + R-\ddot{\underset{..}{X}}: \longrightarrow \underset{\substack{\text{protonated amine} \\ \text{(an alkylammonium ion)}}}{H_3\overset{+}{N}-R} + :\ddot{\underset{..}{X}}:^- \quad \text{followed by} \quad H_2\overset{+}{\underset{H}{N}}-R + :NH_3 \rightleftharpoons \underset{\substack{\text{a primary} \\ \text{amine}}}{H_2\ddot{N}-R} + H-\overset{+}{N}H_3$$

Figure 12.4 Formation of an amine by reaction of ammonia with a haloalkane. The initial reaction of amine and haloalkane produces a protonated amine (an alkylammonium ion). Then, an equilibrium involving proton exchange with another molecule of ammonia generates the unprotonated amine product and an ammonium halide as the by-product. In order to have complete conversion of the haloalkane into amine, at least an extra equivalent of ammonia is required.

$$R{-}\ddot{N}H_2 + R{-}\ddot{X}: \longrightarrow R_2\overset{+}{N}H_2 + :\ddot{X}:^- \quad \text{followed by} \quad R_2\overset{+}{N}H{-}H + R\ddot{N}H_2 \longrightarrow R_2\ddot{N}H + R\overset{+}{N}H_3$$

a primary amine; a secondary amine

Figure 12.5 Continued reaction of a primary amine with a haloalkane. A primary amine is a stronger nucleophile than ammonia. Thus, as the concentration of the primary amine increases in the reaction mixture, continuing reaction becomes more likely, leading to the formation of secondary amine side product.

MECHANISM OF THE S_N2 REACTION

In our discussions of specific S_N2 reactions we have noted several points that tell us about the mechanism of the process:

- The reactions are first order in both the haloalkane and the nucleophile, that is, second order overall. We infer that one molecule of haloalkane and one molecule (or ion) of nucleophile are involved in the rate-determining step of the reaction.
- Reaction rates vary with substitution about the electrophilic carbon. Halomethanes react more rapidly than primary haloalkanes, which in turn react more rapidly than secondary haloalkanes. Tertiary haloalkanes react very slowly, if at all, in S_N2 processes. In general, the ease of approach of the nucleophile to the back side of the electrophilic carbon is of dominant importance for S_N2 reactions.
- The reactions proceed with inversion of configuration about the electrophilic carbon.

SPECIAL TOPIC

Alkylation of Nucleic Acids

Nucleophilic substitution reactions in which a nitrogen bearing an unshared electron pair replaces a halide on electrophilic carbon are common. Amines in biological systems undergo these reactions, as do ammonia or other amines in ordinary laboratory reactions. This reaction is a type of **alkylation** (addition of an alkyl group to an electronegative atom), and the haloalkanes are known as *alkylating agents*.

Reaction can occur between a haloalkane and an amino nitrogen that serves as a functional group of a nucleic acid. Such reactions can have far-reaching consequences for subsequent biological processes of the nucleic acid. For example, suppose a guanine residue of a nucleic acid is alkylated by an iodoalkane. Once the guanine residue has been alkylated, its ability to participate in hydrogen bonding is changed (see "Hydrogen Bonding in Biological Systems" in Chapter 3). As a result, the normal chemical recognition of the guanine residue is changed and a misreading of the genetic information can result. Such alkylations of nucleic acid residues in an organism can lead to mutagenesis and carcinogenesis. Accordingly, haloalkanes and other alkylating agents should always be handled with extreme care.

In light of these data, we understand that the mechanism of the S_N2 reaction is completely analogous to the mechanism for the reactions of methyl alcohol and primary alcohols with hydrogen halides.

MECHANISM OF REACTION

Mechanism of the S_N2 Reaction of Haloalkanes

A nucleophile approaches the substrate from the side opposite that of the departing halide ion. This approach is referred to as *backside attack*. As the nucleophile donates an electron pair to the electrophilic carbon, the carbon-halogen bond begins to break. The overall reaction occurs with inversion of configuration about the electrophilic carbon atom.

$$\text{Nu:}^- \; \text{C—X:} \longrightarrow \left[\overset{\delta-}{\text{Nu}}\text{---C---}\overset{\delta-}{\text{X}} \right] \longrightarrow \text{Nu—C} + \text{:X:}^-$$

an activated complex,
not an intermediate

The reaction progress diagram for the S_N2 reaction (Figure 12.6) has a single energy maximum as is the case for all one-step reactions. Increasing substitution about the electrophilic carbon results in **steric crowding** in the activated complex, as shown in Figure 12.7.

Steric crowding, as we discussed earlier, results when atoms approach closer than the sum of their van der Waals radii. Energy input is required to

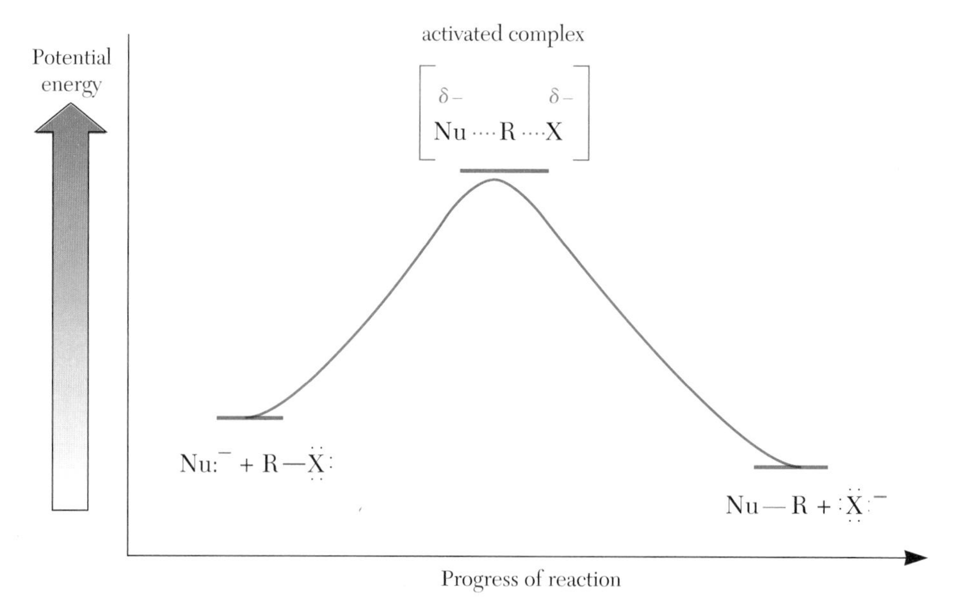

Figure 12.6 Reaction progress diagram for an S_N2 reaction. The incoming nucleophile may be neutral or (as shown here) negatively charged. If it is neutral, the attacking atom will bear a positive charge in the product.

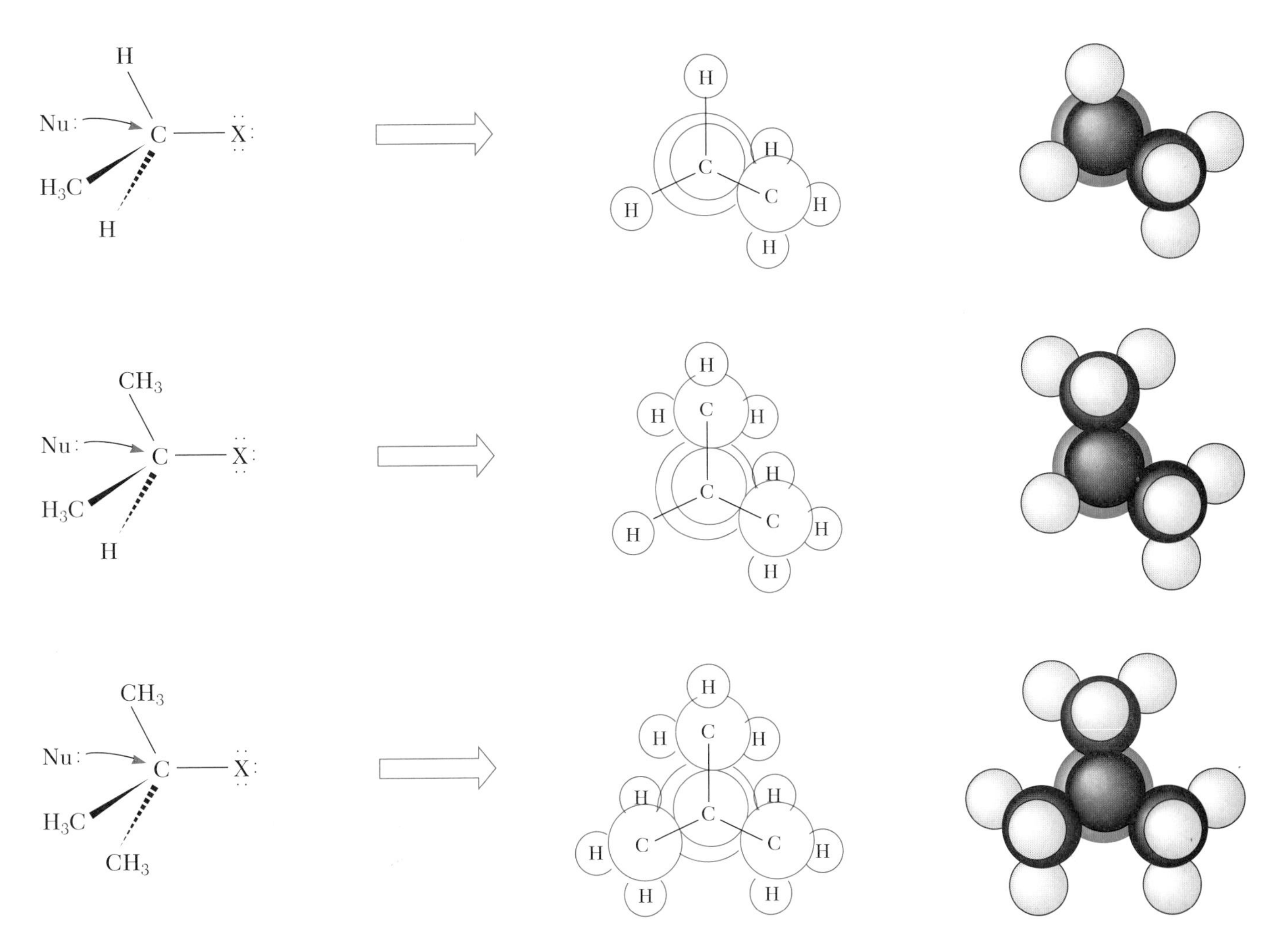

Figure 12.7 Steric effects in S_N2 reactions. The backside approach of a nucleophile to primary, secondary, and tertiary haloalkanes is depicted. The illustrations on the right show the view from the attacking nucleophile (sighting down the back side of the C—X bond). With increasing substitution about the carbon atom of the C—X bond, there is increased crowding in the transition state.

overcome these repulsions. Reactions in which steric crowding is a major factor occur more slowly than those where steric crowding is minimal.

SOLVENT EFFECTS IN S_N2 REACTIONS

The effect of solvent on an S_N2 reaction of a haloalkane depends on the nature of the nucleophile being used. For reactions in which an anionic nucleophile attacks the haloalkane, *decreasing* the polarity of the reaction medium slightly *speeds* the reaction. In the activated complex of such an S_N2 reaction, negative charge is dispersed over two atoms (see Figure 12.5), and so the activated complex is less polar than the reactants. A less polar solvent thus favors the activated complex over the reactants, and the reaction is speeded.

However, for reactions involving neutral nucleophiles, *increasing* the polarity of the reaction medium *speeds* the reaction. In this type of reaction, the activated complex is more polar than the reactants. The charge development is supported by a polar solvent that can provide external stabilization.

Another important point was introduced earlier. Polar *aprotic* solvents (such as DMSO) speed the reaction of anionic nucleophiles in S_N2 reactions (compared with polar *protic* solvents such as ethanol). For example, in aqueous ethanol, treatment of 1-chlorobutane with sodium cyanide *at reflux for ninety hours* gives the nitrile in 85% yield. When DMSO is used as the solvent, the same product is obtained in 93% yield in *fifteen minutes*.

MOLECULAR ORBITAL ANALYSIS

The interacting orbitals of a nucleophile and a substrate participating in an S_N2 reaction are shown in Figure 12.8. Backside attack correlates with the major lobe of the substrate σ^* protruding to the rear.

12.5 Unimolecular Nucleophilic Substitution Reactions (S_N1) of Haloalkanes

The rate of unimolecular nucleophilic substitution reactions is directly proportional to the concentration of the substrate only—it is *independent* of the concentration of the nucleophile. Nucleophilic substitution reactions showing this concentration dependence are classified as S_N1 reactions (substitution (S), nucleophilic (N), unimolecular (1)).

It may seem intuitively strange that the concentration of a nucleophile could have no effect on the rate of product formation in a nucleophilic substitution reaction. However, this independence simply means that the nucleophile

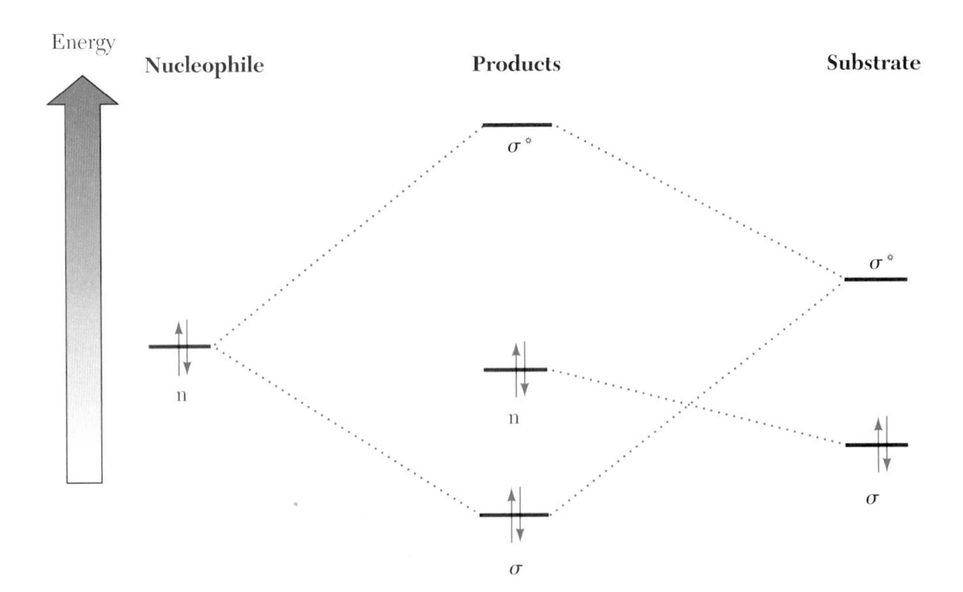

Figure 12.8 Molecular orbitals involved in the S_N2 reaction. The orbital approach is shown at the top of the diagram. An energy correlation diagram for the orbital interaction is shown at the bottom.

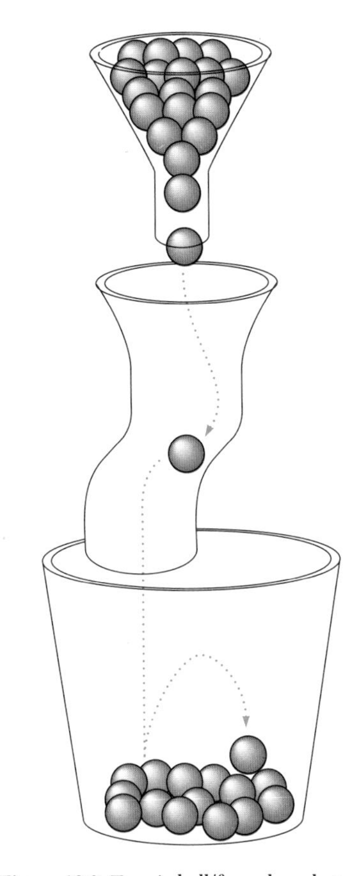

Figure 12.9 Tennis ball/funnel analogy of an S_N1 reaction. Once the dropping of the tennis balls has begun, the rate at which they enter the bucket is the same as the rate at which they drop from the top funnel. The second funnel serves only to guide the balls into the bucket—it doesn't change the *rate* of balls entering the bucket as long as its neck is sufficiently wide.

is involved in the reaction *after* the rate-determining step has occurred. A simple analogy can help us understand this phenomenon.

Imagine a collection of tennis balls falling through a funnel with a neck of a size such that only a single ball can pass at a time (see Figure 12.9). Upon passing through the neck of the funnel, the balls fall into another funnel with a much wider neck, and then drop through the wide-neck funnel into a bucket. If we place a large number of tennis balls into the upper funnel, they will drop from it slowly due to its narrow neck. However, every time a ball enters the lower funnel it exits without any delay. The rate of balls entering the bucket is independent of the second funnel, as long as its neck is sufficiently wide not to hinder their passage.

In our analogy, the balls in the upper funnel represent the haloalkane. The upper funnel represents a reaction of the haloalkane. The reaction (passage through the first funnel) generates an intermediate from the haloalkane (the dropping tennis ball) that can participate in a further reaction (guidance by the second funnel). The first process occurs rather slowly; it is the rate-determining step for the overall reaction (transfer of the tennis balls). The second funnel represents the reaction of the intermediate with the nucleophile. Every time an intermediate species is generated, the second step occurs very rapidly. The second step does not slow the overall reaction but simply directs the intermediate to a product of a specific structure (balls in the bucket).

The S_N1 reaction occurs in (at least) two steps. *Whenever two reagents react with first-order kinetics, more than one step must be involved.* One reagent is involved in the rate-determining step, and the other reagent is involved before or after the rate-determining step. Let's consider some important aspects of nucleophilic substitution reactions showing first-order kinetics.

THE HALOALKANE

The order of reactivity of haloalkanes in S_N1 reactions is the reverse of their reactivity in S_N2 reactions. Tertiary haloalkanes undergo S_N1 reactions much more rapidly than do secondary haloalkanes; secondary haloalkanes in turn react in S_N1 processes more readily than do primary haloalkanes. Halomethanes are not known to undergo S_N1 reactions. In contrast, allylic and benzylic halides react extremely rapidly in S_N1 reactions. (We met allyl bromide and benzyl bromide in Chapter 11, structures **11.8** and **11.9**. In general, *allylic* halides have an alkene linkage attached to the electrophilic carbon, and *benzylic* halides have a phenyl group, Ph, attached to the electrophilic carbon. *Vinylic* halides are those in which the halogen is attached to an *olefinic* carbon. Vinylic halides are generally unreactive in nucleophilic substitution reactions.) In summary

Relative rates: allylic (>C=C—C(X)—) ≈ benzylic (Ph—C—X) $> 3° > 2° > 1° \gg CH_3$, vinylic (>C=C< X)

THE NUCLEOPHILE

In principle, any Lewis base has the potential to serve as a nucleophile for the S_N1 reaction. In practice, the difficulty with many Lewis bases is not to get them to participate in S_N1 reactions but to prevent them from performing other side reactions (eliminations). For example, consider the reaction of 2-methyl-2-bromopropane with water to form 2-methyl-2-propanol.

When 2-methyl-2-bromopropane is allowed to stand in aqueous ethanol for an extended period of time, it reacts completely to form two products, as shown in Equation 12.11.

Eqn. 12.11

$$(CH_3)_3C—\ddot{\underset{..}{Br}}: \xrightarrow[\text{57 hours}]{\text{80/20 water/ethanol}} (CH_3)_3C—\ddot{\underset{..}{O}}H + (CH_3)_2C{=}CH_2$$

2-bromo-2-methylpropane → 87% yield 2-methyl-2-propanol (nucleophilic substitution product) + 13% yield 2-methylpropene (elimination product)

If we try to speed the formation of the alcohol by adding sodium hydroxide to the reaction system, we actually isolate *less* alcohol, as shown in Equation 12.12.

Eqn. 12.12

$$(CH_3)_3C—\ddot{\underset{..}{Br}}: \xrightarrow[\text{10\% NaOH, 24 hours}]{\text{80/20 water/ethanol}} (CH_3)_3C—\ddot{\underset{..}{O}}H + (CH_3)_2C{=}CH_2$$

74% yield + 26% yield

Hydroxide ion is not only a more potent nucleophile than the water molecule—it is also a more potent base. When we use hydroxide ion in a nucleophilic substitution reaction with a tertiary haloalkane, we increase the formation of an alkene side product. This side reaction is again an elimination reaction. In general, with tertiary haloalkanes that undergo S_N1 reactions, increasing the basicity of the nucleophile increases the extent of the elimination side reaction.

SOLVENT EFFECTS IN S_N1 REACTIONS

It is found that S_N1 reactions of haloalkanes proceed faster in more polar solvents than they do in less polar solvents (recall that a measure of the polarity of a solvent is given by its dielectric constant; see Table 3.2.) This result suggests that either a highly polar intermediate or actual ions are involved in the reaction.

STEREOCHEMISTRY OF S_N1 REACTIONS

In Equation 12.6 we considered the reaction of an optically active, substituted benzyl halide with ethoxide ion in an S_N2 reaction. The reaction proceeded with virtually complete inversion of configuration at the electrophilic center. Benzyl halides also undergo S_N1 reactions with great facility, even more rapidly than do tertiary haloalkanes. Consider the same optically active, substituted benzylic chloride as used in Equation 12.6 in reaction with water under S_N1

reaction conditions. In this reaction we find first-order kinetics for the formation of the corresponding alcohol and the alkene side product. The reaction is shown in Equation 12.13.

Eqn. 12.13

$$\text{(R)-PhCH(CH}_3\text{)–}\ddot{\text{Cl}}\text{:} \xrightarrow{H_2O} \text{H}\ddot{\text{O}}\text{–CH(CH}_3\text{)Ph (S)} + PhCH{=}CH_2$$

(R)-1-chloro-1-phenylethane

87% yield
18% optical purity
(59% inversion,
41% retention)
(S)-1-phenylethanol

styrene

This stereochemical result is quite different from the result of the second-order reaction in Equation 12.6. Here we find mostly *racemization* occurring. Although there is net inversion in the reaction, there is a tremendous loss of optical activity. We say that the reaction proceeds with 82% racemization. It is clearly *nonstereospecific*. This result is common in S_N1 reactions, regardless of the nucleophile. *In S_N1 reactions where the electrophilic carbon site is stereogenic, there is a loss of optical activity.*

REARRANGEMENTS IN S_N1 REACTIONS

Although primary haloalkanes generally exhibit second-order kinetics in nucleophilic substitution reactions, we *can* induce them to undergo reactions that are zeroth order in nucleophile (that is, S_N1 reactions). For example, some primary haloalkanes form alcohols by S_N1 reaction when treated with aqueous silver nitrate. However, the product alcohol is often of *rearranged* structure compared to the starting haloalkane. An example is shown in Equation 12.14.

Eqn. 12.14

$$(CH_3)_3C{-}CH_2{-}\ddot{\underset{..}{I}}{:} \xrightarrow[H_2O]{AgNO_3} (CH_3)_2\underset{:\ddot{O}H}{C}{-}CH_2{-}CH_3 + (CH_3)_2C{=}CHCH_2$$

1-iodo-2,2-dimethylpropane

97% yield
2-methyl-2-butanol

2-methyl-2-butene

The rearrangement that occurs is of the type we have seen before with carbocations. This and similar observations strongly suggest that carbocations are involved as intermediates in S_N1 reactions.

MECHANISM OF THE S_N1 REACTION

We have noted several points about S_N1 reactions from which we can infer their mechanism:

- The reaction rate depends on the concentration of the haloalkane but is independent of the concentration of the nucleophile.

- The greater the alkyl substitution about the electrophilic center, the more rapidly the reaction proceeds.
- Benzylic and allylic halides proceed even more rapidly in S_N1 reactions than do tertiary haloalkanes.
- Increasing the basicity of the nucleophile leads to increasing amounts of elimination reaction in competition with substitution.
- Increasing the polarity of the reaction medium increases the rate of the S_N1 reaction.
- Reactions proceed principally with racemization about the electrophilic center. There is often some small net inversion of configuration.
- Skeletal rearrangements reminiscent of those of carbocations occur when some haloalkanes are induced to undergo S_N1 reactions.

In light of these data we can infer a mechanism for S_N1 reactions.

MECHANISM OF REACTION

Step 1 The haloalkane undergoes a slow dissociation (the rate-determining step) to a carbocation and a halide ion.

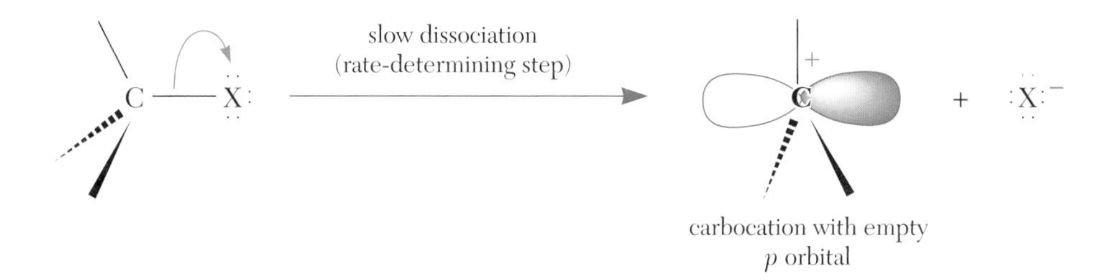

Step 2 The carbocation reacts rapidly with a nucleophile to generate the product, with racemization about the electrophilic carbon site.

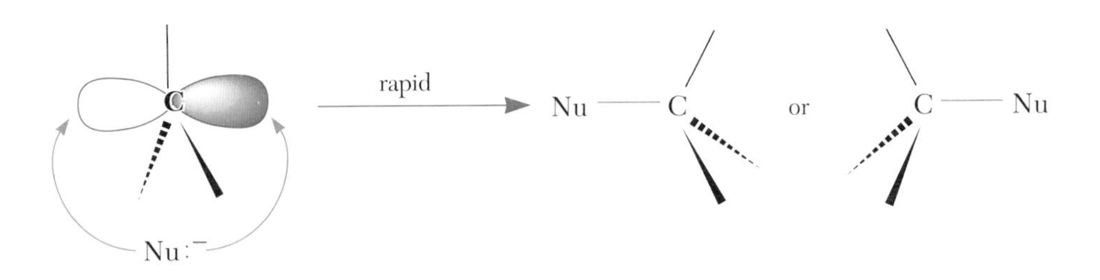

We can understand all of the data regarding S_N1 reactions in terms of this mechanism. The observed rate of the reaction depends only on the concentration of the haloalkane because the nucleophile is not involved until *after* the slow step of the reaction has occurred. First-order kinetics in a substitution reaction implies that an intermediate is involved. We understand the intermediate to be a carbocation on the basis of relative reactivities of different haloalkanes, solvent effects, and the stereochemistry of the reaction. Tertiary haloalkanes give rise to the more stable tertiary carbocations and thus react more rapidly than other haloalkanes. Polar solvents stabilize carbocation intermediates and thus speed the reactions. The stereochemistry of the reaction involves a high degree of racemization at the electrophilic site.

We might anticipate reactions involving carbocations formed at initially stereogenic centers to proceed with *complete* racemization. In the example shown in Equation 12.13 (and quite often in other reactions), there is some small amount of net inversion that results from the leaving group (the halide) partially blocking the side it left in the early stage of the reaction. If the halide ion is still close to the side from which it departed, an incoming nucleophile will be more likely to add to the opposite side. Complete racemization occurs when the carbocation survives long enough to be completely free of the leaving group. (Also notice that if the carbocation captures the leaving group, the starting material is regenerated.)

ENERGETICS IN THE S_N1 REACTION

Consider a reaction progress diagram for an S_N1 reaction (Figure 12.10). The activation energy for the formation of the carbocation depends on the structure of the carbocation. The less stable the carbocation, the higher the activation energy for its formation.

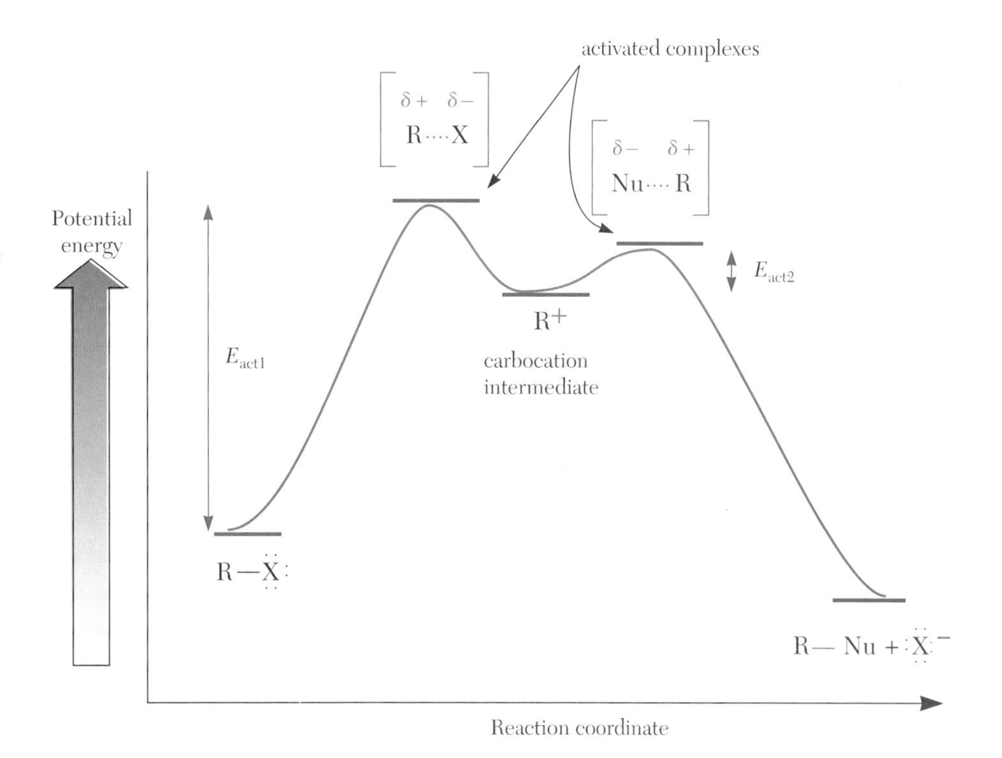

Figure 12.10 Reaction progress diagram for an S_N1 reaction. An activated complex is involved in each step. The formation of the first activated complex is a relatively high-energy process (E_{act1}) and thus is the slow step of the reaction. The second step has a low activation energy (E_{act2}) and therefore is relatively rapid. The first activated complex occurs late (is formed in an endothermic process) and, according to Hammond's postulate, is structurally similar to the carbocation.

Let us consider competition between S_N1 and S_N2 processes. Theoretically, we can construct at least two reaction progress diagrams for any nucleophilic substitution reaction—one for S_N1 reaction and the other for S_N2 reaction. Figure 12.11 shows two such reaction progress diagrams for the reaction of iodomethane with hydroxide ion in water.

We now compare competing S_N1 and S_N2 processes for a similar reaction—the reaction of 2-bromo-2-methylpropane with aqueous hydroxide ion. The reaction progress diagrams are shown in Figure 12.12.

Consider again the reactions of 1-chloro-1-phenylethane we mentioned earlier (Equations 12.6 and 12.13). You might wonder why one proceeded via an S_N1 mechanism and the other an S_N2. The reason is that water (the reactant in the S_N1 reaction in Equation 12.13) is a poorer nucleophile than is methoxide ion (the reactant in the S_N2 reaction in Equation 12.6). The effect of the low nucleophilicity of water on the rate of an S_N1 reaction is insignificant, since it does not become involved until *after* the rate-determining step. However, it does significantly affect S_N2 reactions, slowing them so much that the alternative S_N1 route becomes competitive or (as here) dominant.

The examples chosen here are relatively clear-cut in terms of the actual mechanism involved because the activation energies for the competing S_N1 and S_N2 routes are very different. This is not always the case, however, particularly with *secondary* haloalkanes. Furthermore, the detailed mechanism of a particular nucleophilic substitution reaction can be complicated by such factors as stability of the intermediate carbocations, the nature of solvation, and nucleophile potency. In the *limiting cases*, where the reactions are clearly S_N1 or S_N2, the reactions are often of synthetic utility. In intermediate cases it is often difficult to prepare pure substitution products in high yields because of the formation of product mixtures from intermediate carbocations that undergo rearrangement.

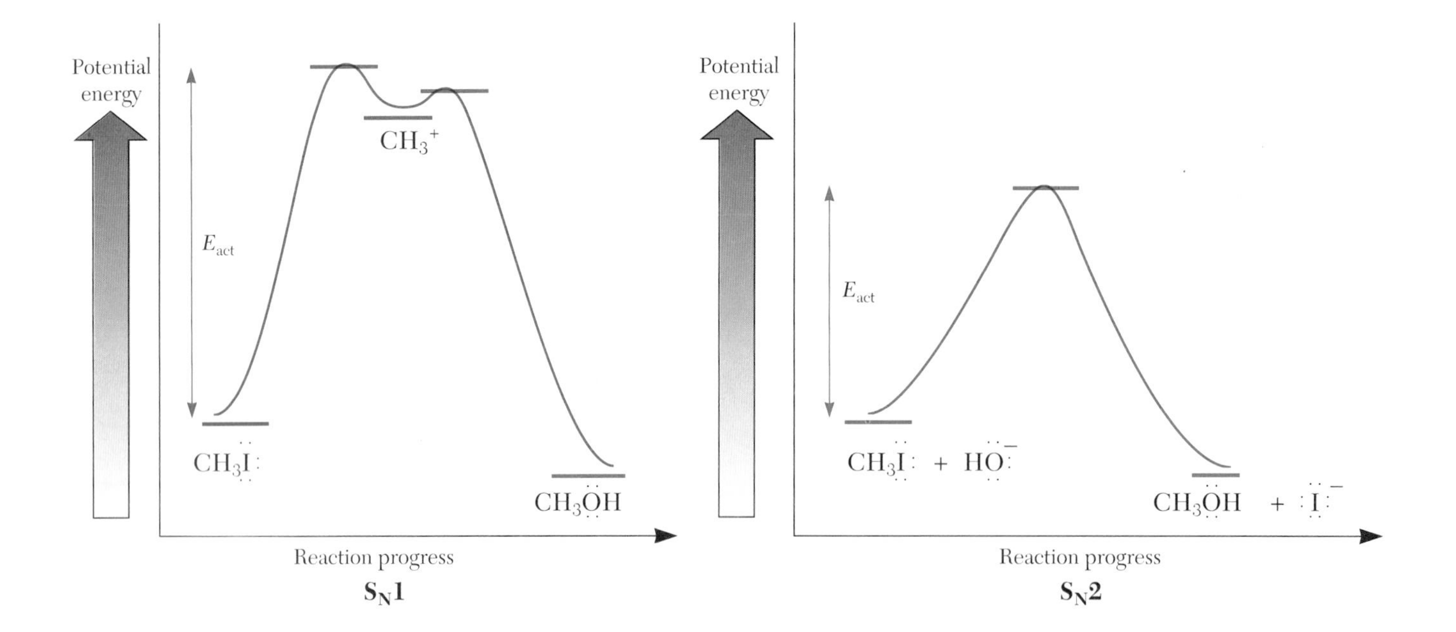

Figure 12.11 S_N1 and S_N2 reaction progress diagrams for the reaction of iodomethane with hydroxide ion in water. For S_N1 reaction, formation of a very high energy (unstable) carbocation is required. This process has a very high activation energy. For S_N2 reaction, no ionic intermediate is formed. Because the activation energy is lower than for the S_N1 process, substitution occurs via the S_N2 mechanism.

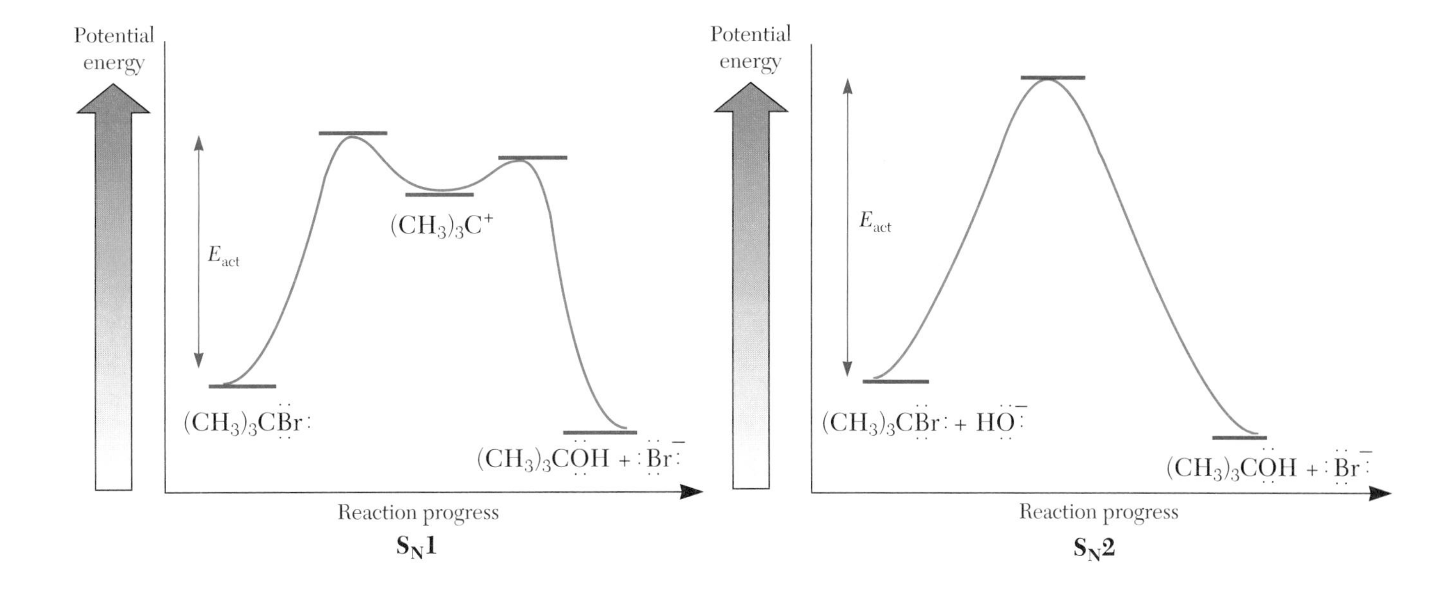

Figure 12.12 Reaction progress diagrams for S_N1 and S_N2 reaction of 2-bromo-2-methylpropane with aqueous hydroxide ion. Because of steric crowding, the activation energy for the S_N2 reaction is greatly increased relative to that for the iodomethane reaction (Figure 12.11). Moreover, the activation energy for the rate-determining step of the S_N1 reaction is greatly decreased relative to the S_N1 reaction of iodomethane owing to the stabilization of the tertiary carbocation. In fact, for 2-bromo-2-methylpropane, the activation energy of its S_N1 reaction is less than that of its S_N2 route. The 2-bromo-2-methylpropane thus reacts via the S_N1 route.

SUMMARY OF S_N1 REACTIONS

If we understand the following characteristics of S_N1 reactions, we can properly plan reaction systems and understand their results.

- In general, the mechanism of an S_N1 reaction of a haloalkane involves two steps. The first step is slow dissociation of the haloalkane to a carbocation and a halide ion. This step is followed by a rapid combination of the carbocation with an available nucleophile.
- Only haloalkanes that can form relatively stable carbocations tend to undergo the S_N1 reaction.
- The intended nucleophile should not be a powerful base, because strong bases tend to promote elimination as a side reaction.
- Polar solvents facilitate the S_N1 reaction by stabilizing the polar activated complexes and the ionic intermediates.
- Skeletal rearrangements can occur if the intermediate carbocation can undergo hydride or alkide shifts to generate a more stable carbocation.
- Optically active haloalkanes that are stereogenic about the electrophilic site give substitution products with a high level of racemization.

12.6 More about Nucleophiles

Earlier in this chapter we mentioned that some nucleophiles were better (more reactive) than others. In this section we will look a little more deeply at the question of what makes a reactive (or a weak) nucleophile.

CHARGE AND NUCLEOPHILICITY

To serve as a nucleophile, a reagent needs an unshared electron pair that can be used to form a new bond. Although many nucleophiles are anions, a nucleophile can also be a neutral species. However, for a given atom serving as

Table 12.3 Comparative Nucleophilicities of Anions and Related Neutral Species. The structures shown on the left are anionic. The related structures on the right can also be nucleophiles, but they are neutral and are less nucleophilic. They give slower reactions with a particular electrophilic reagent (haloalkane) if the reaction proceeds via a bimolecular mechanism.

← Increasing Nucleophilicity		
HO^-	>	H_2O
HS^-	>	H_2S
H_2N^-	>	H_3N
H_2P^-	>	H_3P
CH_3O^-	>	CH_3OH
$N{\equiv}C^-$	>	$HC{\equiv}N$
Cl^-	>	HCl

Table 12.4 Variation of Nucleophilicity Across a Periodic Row

← Increasing Nucleophilicity						
CH_3^-	>	NH_2^-	>	OH^-	>	F^-
		NH_3	>	OH_2	>	HF
		PH_2^-	>	SH^-	>	Cl^-
		PH_3	>	SH_2	>	HCl

the reactive site in a nucleophile, increasing negative charge *does* make it a better nucleophile. Several examples are shown in Table 12.3.

We find another systematic variation among nucleophiles that have the same charge and whose reactive sites are different elements of the same periodic row. Several examples are shown in Table 12.4.

The variations shown in these two sets of nucleophiles are in the same direction as the variation of their basicities. There are other variations of nucleophilicity that are *not* in the same direction as changes in basicity. However, we must use caution in making general statements about these variations since they are solvent dependent (different orders of nucleophilicity are found in different solvents). An example of such variations is found among the halide ions. In a solvent such as water, their nucleophilicities vary in the opposite direction from their basicities, as shown in Table 12.5.

NUCLEOPHILICITY VERSUS BASICITY

It would seem reasonable that basic character (basicity) and nucleophilic character (nucleophilicity) should be related, since both involve electron-pair donation to an electrophilic site. Relative base strengths and nucleophilicities often *do* parallel one another for a given series of compounds. However, there are also important exceptions (like those in Table 12.5) in which the order of

Table 12.5 Variation of Nucleophilicities and Basicities

Increasing Nucleophilicity →			
F^-	Cl^-	Br^-	I^-
HO^-	HS^-	HSe^-	HTe^-
H_2N^-	H_2P^-	H_2As^-	H_2Sb^-
← Increasing basicity			

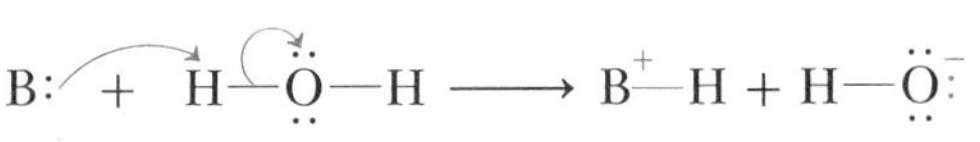

$$B\colon + H{-}\ddot{O}{-}H \longrightarrow {}^{+}B{-}H + H{-}\ddot{O}\colon^{-}$$

$$K_b = [{}^{+}B{-}H][{}^{-}O{-}H]/[B\colon]$$

$$B^{+}{-}H + H_2\ddot{O} \longrightarrow B\colon + H_2\overset{+}{O}{-}H$$

$$K_a = [B\colon][H_3O^+]/[{}^{+}B{-}H]$$

$$(K_a)(K_b) = K_w = [H_3O^+][HO^-] = 10^{-14}$$

Figure 12.13 Basicity of B: and acidity of its conjugate acid, $^{+}B{-}H$. The basicity of B: is assessed by the position of the equilibrium when it reacts with water. K_b is a measure of the basicity of B:, as is $pK_b(-\log K_b)$. Alternatively, we can assess the basicity of B: by looking at the acidity of its conjugate acid, $^{+}B{-}H$. The acidity of $^{+}B{-}H$ is measured by looking at the position of the equilibrium when $^{+}B{-}H$ reacts with water. The K_a (or $pK_a = -\log K_a$) is a measure of the acidity of $^{+}B{-}H$. For a base–conjugate acid pair, K_b and K_a measured in water are related. The product of the two values, $(K_a)(K_b)$, is the autoprotolysis constant of water, $K_w(10^{-14})$. The stronger the base, the weaker its conjugate acid.

reactivity for a particular group of Lewis bases when they act as Brønsted bases is the exact reverse of their order when they act as nucleophiles. It is important that we understand these differences. First, we must stress that there are important differences in the ways we measure and quantify these properties.

BASES: BASICITY MEASURED IN TERMS OF AN EQUILIBRIUM CONSTANT

Consider the reaction of a base, B:, as shown in Figure 12.13. It reacts by accepting a proton from the acid, water.

Typically, acid-base reactions come to equilibrium extremely rapidly. The strength of the base is measured in terms of the position of equilibrium. A large K_b indicates a strong base, and a small K_b indicates a weak base. A stronger base is one that on reaction with an acid, HA, produces a greater equilibrium concentration of A^- than does some weaker base. Since K_b is related to $\Delta G°$ ($\Delta G° = -RT \ln K$), our definition of basicity is a *thermodynamic* one.

PROBLEM 12.6 Refer back to Table 11.2. Give the conjugate base of each acid listed there. List these bases in order of increasing basicity.

NUCLEOPHILES: NUCLEOPHILICITY MEASURED IN TERMS OF REACTION RATE

You will recall from our earlier discussion that nucleophilicities are measured in terms of the *rates* at which nucleophiles react with a given substrate. Nucleophilic substitution reactions do not generally come to equilibrium as quickly as do acid-base reactions. In light of this, a *kinetic* rather than a thermodynamic criterion is used to compare nucleophilicities. The relative rates of reactions of nucleophiles serve as a convenient yardstick of reactivity and are more useful than equilibrium constants in predicting what will happen in a laboratory experiment.

Why do basicity and nucleophilicity sometimes correlate inversely? One very important factor is **solvation.** Solvents play a major role in reactions beyond that of a passive medium in which the reagents happen to be dissolved. For example, in a protic solvent like water, halide ions are rather strongly solvated. This solvation stabilizes the anion and is the major driving force for the dissolution of the salt in the first place. However, while solvation stabilizes ions, it also makes them less reactive. They react more slowly because they must shed the associated solvent molecules in order to react.

The degree of solvation is particularly important in influencing patterns of reactivity. For example, fluoride ion is more strongly solvated in water than are the other halide ions because of its small size and high charge density. This solvation diminishes the rate at which it reacts so much that it is a poor nucleophile compared to the other halides. However, in a polar aprotic solvent such as DMSO, fluoride ion is a powerful nucleophile. Recall that DMSO is able to solvate cations well but not anions. DMSO leaves an anion relatively naked and accordingly more reactive.

12.7 Elimination Reactions

In our earlier discussion of the substitution reactions of haloalkanes, we saw that there are competing reactions that generate alkenes. Even with primary haloalkanes under conditions producing good yields of substitution products, some alkene product is usually formed as the result of an elimination reaction; with highly branched haloalkanes, alkenes are the dominant products. Elimination reactions occur when the Lewis base we use with the substrate acts as a Brønsted base rather than as a nucleophile.

BEHAVIOR AS A BASE AND A NUCLEOPHILE IN THE SAME REACTION SYSTEM

Given the proper reaction conditions, Lewis bases can behave as either nucleophiles or Brønsted bases. At times we can control the reaction conditions such that the Lewis base being used behaves only as a nucleophile or only as a Brønsted base. At other times we are not so capable (or fortunate)—with some haloalkane substrates in certain solvents, our Lewis base may act in one collision as a nucleophile and in another as a Brønsted base. When the Lewis base acts as a nucleophile, the product is one of substitution. When the Lewis base acts as a Brønsted base, the product is one of elimination and we obtain an alkene. In some cases the activation energies for the two modes of action are comparable, and a mixture of products results. Elimination reactions are important competitors with substitution reactions. When the elements of hydrogen halide are removed from adjacent carbon atoms in these elimination reactions, the reaction is described as a **dehydrohalogenation.**

Let us begin by considering some experimental results. Reactions of three bromoalkanes with ethoxide ion in ethanol are shown in Equations 12.15–12.17.

Eqn. 12.15

$$CH_3CH_2CH_2\ddot{\underset{..}{Br}}: \xrightarrow[HOCH_2CH_3]{NaOCH_2CH_3} CH_3CH_2CH_2\ddot{\underset{..}{O}}CH_2CH_3 + CH_3CH{=}CH_2$$

1-bromopropane; 91% yield ethyl propyl ether; 9% yield propene

Eqn. 12.16

$$(CH_3)_2CH\ddot{\underset{..}{Br}}: \xrightarrow[HOCH_2CH_3]{NaOCH_2CH_3} (CH_3)_2CH\ddot{\underset{..}{O}}CH_2CH_3 + CH_3CH{=}CH_2$$

2-bromopropane; 25% yield ethyl isopropyl ether; 75% yield propene

Eqn. 12.17

$$(CH_3)_3C\ddot{\underset{..}{Br}}: \xrightarrow[HOCH_2CH_3]{NaOCH_2CH_3} (CH_3)_3C\ddot{\underset{..}{O}}CH_2CH_3 + (CH_3)_2C{=}CH_2$$

2-bromo-2-methylpropane; 0% yield ethyl *tert*-butyl ether; 100% yield 2-methylpropene

With a primary haloalkane (Equation 12.15), nearly 10% of the product is the result of an elimination reaction. With the secondary haloalkane (Equation 12.16), elimination is the dominant process, and *only* elimination (no substitution) occurs with the tertiary haloalkane (Equation 12.17).

If we are trying to perform a substitution reaction on a haloalkane, the competing dehydrohalogenation reaction presents a serious problem. However, if we understand the mechanistic characteristics of the elimination reaction, we should be able to minimize the difficulty. Moreover, we can use elimination reactions constructively to synthesize desired alkenes.

TWO MECHANISMS FOR ELIMINATION

Elimination reactions of haloalkanes occur by means of (at least) two different mechanisms. These mechanisms are differentiated on the same basis as we differentiated substitution mechanisms, that is, their molecularity.

In some cases the rate of the elimination reaction is found to be directly proportional to the concentration of both the haloalkane and the base. These reactions are second order overall and have the following rate law expression:

$$\text{rate} = k[\text{RX}][\text{B:}] \qquad (\text{B: represents a base})$$

Such reactions are referred to as **E2** (elimination (E), bimolecular (2)) processes. The E2 process is the most common mechanism of elimination for simple haloalkanes (primary, secondary, and tertiary). We met this reaction briefly in our earlier discussion of alkenes (Chapter 9).

Some dehydrohalogenation reactions of haloalkanes show a rate that depends only on the concentration of the haloalkane:

$$\text{rate} = k[\text{RX}]$$

We refer to such processes as **E1** (elimination (E), unimolecular (1)) reactions. E1 is the usual mechanism of elimination when a tertiary haloalkane is used with a weak base. (With strong bases the E2 mechanism is more common, even for tertiary haloalkanes.)

THE E2 MECHANISM

The rate of an E2 reaction depends on the concentrations of both the base and the substrate. Thus we expect that changing the *nature* of either of the reagents would affect the rate of elimination significantly. We will consider various aspects of the E2 process.

Effect of the Leaving Group The rate of an E2 reaction varies with the nature of the leaving group. The order of E2 reactivity for haloalkanes is:

$$\text{RI} > \text{RBr} > \text{RCl}$$

Not surprisingly, the compound with the weaker carbon-halogen bond reacts more rapidly. (Also remember the correlation between the weaker base and the preferred leaving group; I^- is a weaker base than the other halide ions (X^-) and is a better leaving group).

Effect of Alkyl Group Structure In general, the rates of E2 reaction increase with increasing substitution about the electrophilic carbon, that is,

$$3^\circ \text{ RX} > 2^\circ \text{ RX} > 1^\circ \text{ RX}$$

This order is the *opposite* of the order for S_N2 reactivities. Increasing substitution about the electrophilic carbon (α-branching) speeds the elimination reaction. We explain this phenomenon in terms of the developing π bond being stabilized by attached alkyl groups. (Recall from Chapter 11 that more highly substituted π bonds are more stable than less highly substituted ones.)

Concerted Nature of the E2 Reaction There are kinetic similarities between the S_N2 and E2 reactions. Fundamentally, the S_N2 reaction involves both nucleophile and haloalkane in the rate-determining step. It is a concerted reaction in the sense that both bond breaking and new bond making at the electrophilic carbon occur in the same step.

The E2 reaction of a haloalkane is also a concerted process. Both the base and the haloalkane are consumed in its only step, which therefore must be the rate-determining step. Thus it is necessary for both the carbon-hydrogen and the carbon-halogen bonds to begin to break in concert. At the same time, new bond formation is occurring. Both the bond between the base and the hydrogen removed from the substrate and the π bond are beginning to form.

Consider the reaction of an alkoxide ion with a primary haloalkane in this context. With regard to substitution, this reaction constitutes a reasonably good method for the synthesis of ethers via S_N2 reaction. However, elimination also occurs to a certain extent in this reaction system. In addition to being a good nucleophile, alkoxide ion is a good Brønsted base. If the alkoxide ion approaches a hydrogen on a carbon adjacent to the electrophilic carbon (a β-hydrogen), it can use an electron pair to begin bonding to that hydrogen. The competing routes of reaction are illustrated in Figure 12.14.

MECHANISM OF REACTION

The curved-arrow formalism can be used to illustrate the mechanism of the E2 reaction:

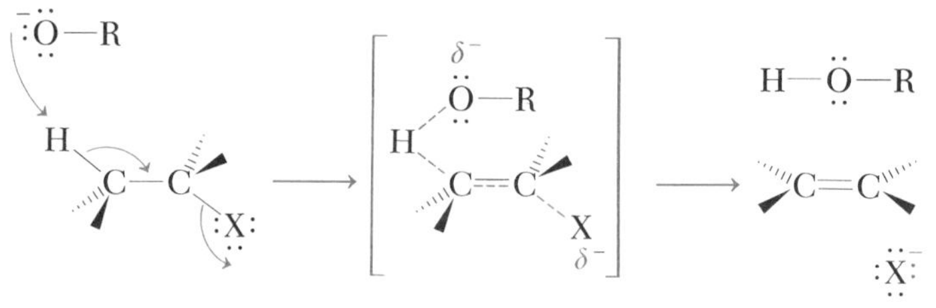

activated complex

Stereochemical Consequences of the Concerted E2 Mechanism A feature of concerted reactions is that bond breaking is facilitated by the simultaneous bond-forming process. The energy release associated with partial formation of

Figure 12.14 Competing routes of substitution and elimination in the reaction of an alkoxide ion with a primary haloalkane. In route *A* the alkoxide ion acts as a nucleophile, attacking the electrophilic carbon. In route *B* the alkoxide ion acts as a Brønsted base, attacking the *β*-hydrogen atom.

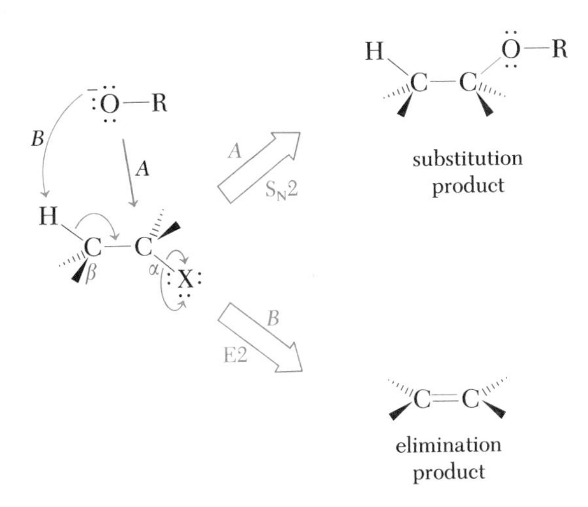

a new bond offsets to some extent the energy required to break an old bond. In the E2 reaction, hydrogen-oxygen σ bond and carbon-carbon π bond formation occur simultaneously with carbon-hydrogen and carbon-halogen bond breaking. This concerted nature of the reaction has an important stereochemical consequence.

For π bond formation to occur, the sp^3 hybridized carbon atoms must undergo a change in hybridization to $sp^2 + p$. The pair of atomic p orbital components on adjacent carbon atoms in this rehybridization should be parallel in order that a π bond can form between them. A nonparallel relationship between these orbitals is inefficient for π bond formation. Figure 12.15 shows several arrangements that illustrate this stereochemical requirement. Unless the p orbital components from the two bonds being broken are parallel in the E2 process, simultaneous π bond formation can not occur. If no new π bond

Figure 12.15 Orientation of *p* orbital components for *π* bond formation in a dehydrohalogenation reaction. (a) Notice the parallel arrangement of the *p* orbital components during the departure of the hydrogen and halide from the haloalkane. Here the *p* orbital components are in a suitable position to interact for *π* bond formation as they are being generated. Bond making supports bond breaking. (b) The *p* orbital components are not parallel but are almost perpendicular. Since they are essentially orthogonal, they are unable to interact for *π* bond generation.

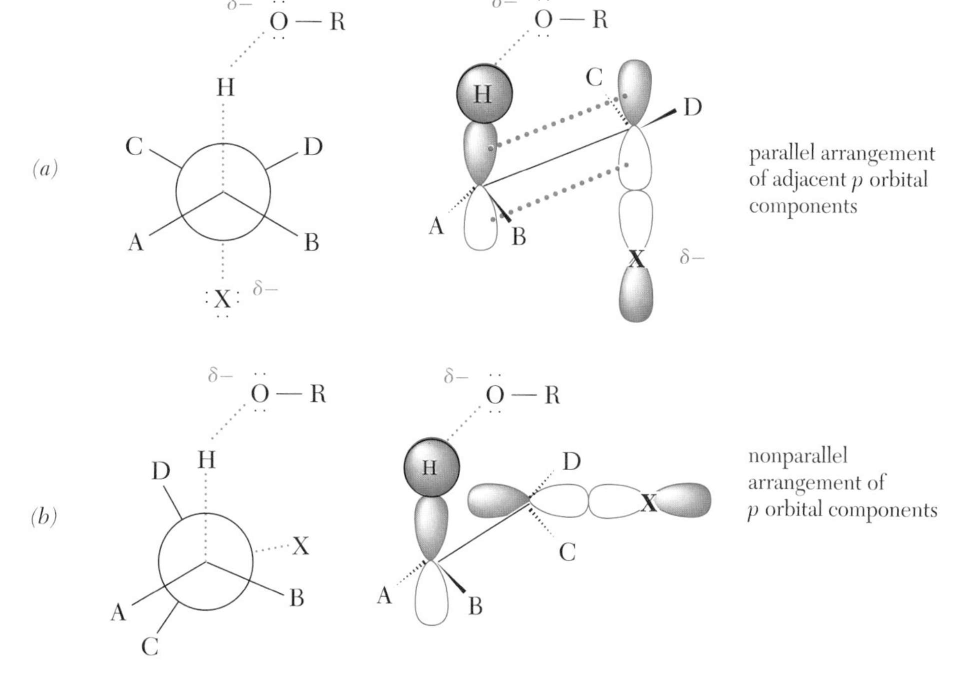

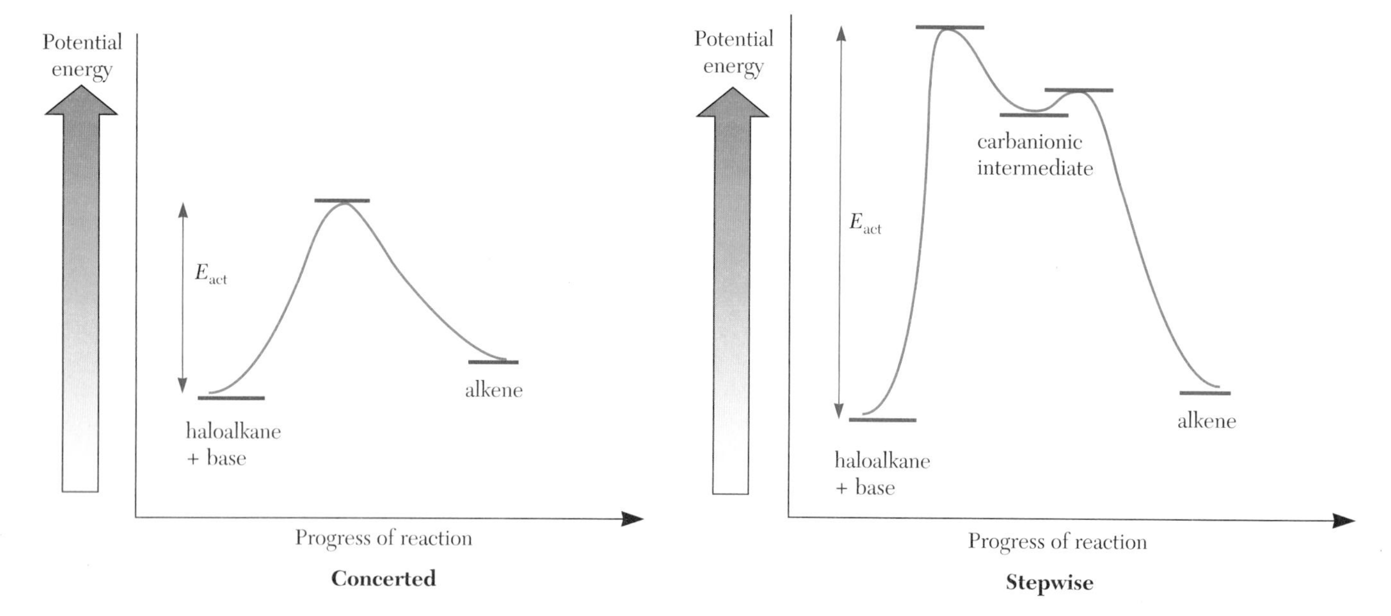

Figure 12.16 Reaction progress diagrams for concerted and stepwise elimination. When bond formation accompanies bond breaking, the activation energy is lower. If the base first removes a proton to form a carbanionic intermediate but there is no π bond formation, the activation energy is much higher.

formation accompanies bond breaking, the activation energy is increased greatly.

A relatively low activation energy for reaction is bought at the expense of a requirement for a particular conformation of the molecule. Only conformations that allow a parallel arrangement of the orbitals of the bonds being broken can take part in the concerted elimination process. A very high activation energy would be involved if the base removed a hydrogen in a first step to generate a carbanion intermediate, followed by loss of the halide ion in a second step. Reaction progress diagrams comparing these two routes are shown in Figure 12.16.

In the first conformation shown in Figure 12.15, the developing p orbitals are parallel, and they can interact productively for the creation of a new π bond. (In the second conformation, the developing p orbitals are nearly perpendicular; they have little or no interaction with each other.) We describe the bonds to the eliminated groups in the productive conformation as having a **dihedral angle** of 180°. A dihedral angle is defined by *four* points rather than the three we normally consider defining an angle. A dihedral angle thus is the angle between two intersecting *planes* rather than two intersecting lines. For our present purposes, the dihedral angle refers to the angle made by a pair of bonds on adjacent atoms when viewed along the bond that joins those two atoms. This angle is best viewed in a Newman projection, as shown in Figure 12.17.

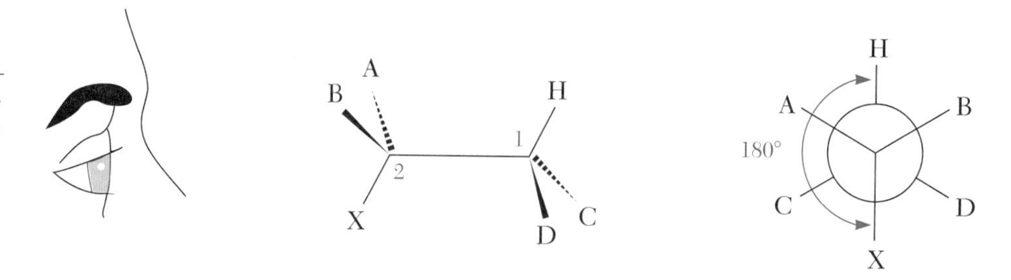

Figure 12.17 The concept of dihedral angle. The four points defining the dihedral angle of interest are: H–carbon 1–carbon 2–X. When viewed along the central bond (carbon 2–carbon 1) we see the dihedral angle as illustrated on the right. In this case the dihedral angle is 180°.

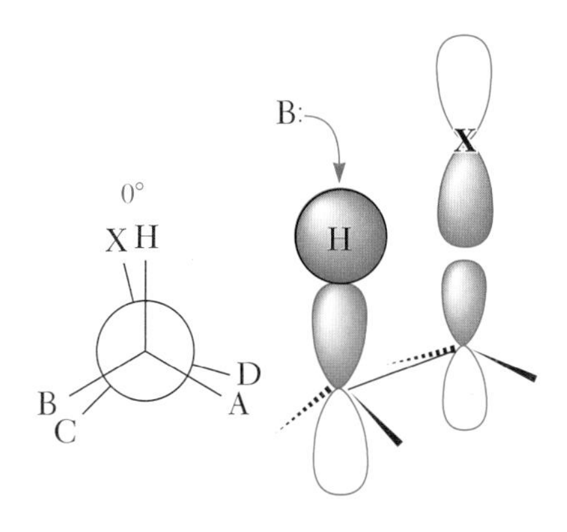

Figure 12.18 E2 reaction occurring with a dihedral angle of 0° between the groups being eliminated. With a dihedral angle of 0°, the developing *p* orbitals are parallel and in position to interact, providing π bond formation as the other two bonds are breaking.

The E2 reaction is favorable energetically when there is a dihedral angle of 180° between the eliminated groups. A conformation with a dihedral angle of 0° between these groups is also favorable for E2 reaction. As shown in Figure 12.18, a dihedral angle of 0° allows interaction of the developing *p* orbitals for π bond formation as both H and X are eliminated.

The conformation with the dihedral angle of 180° between the eliminated groups is referred to as having an ***anti*-periplanar** arrangement of the *p* orbitals. The conformation having a dihedral angle of 0° with the eliminated groups is said to have a ***syn*-periplanar** arrangement of the *p* orbitals. Most E2 reactions proceed through an *anti*-periplanar arrangement, that is, through an *anti* conformation (see Chapters 2 and 8). Some E2 reactions do proceed through a *syn*-periplanar arrangement (involving an eclipsed conformation), although these reactions are much less common (see Chapter 13) and generally occur when an *anti*-periplanar arrangement is not possible.

The requirement for a parallel arrangement of the developing *p* orbitals in the E2 reaction of haloalkanes is quite strict. Elimination simply does not occur if the molecule is incapable of having a conformation that places the departing groups in the proper geometry. Elimination via the E2 route is a *stereospecific process.*

PROBLEM 12.7 In Figure 12.17, what is the dihedral angle between each of the following pairs of groups in the Newman projection:

a. C—B **b.** H—B **c.** X—C

PROBLEM 12.8 In Figure 12.18, what is the dihedral angle between each of the following pairs of groups in the Newman projection:

a. H—C **b.** D—A **c.** B—D

PROBLEM 12.9 Consider the dehydrohalogenation via an E2 mechanism with an *anti*-periplanar arrangement of departing groups for the molecule (2*R*,3*R*)-2-bromo-3-methylpentane.

a. Do you expect the (*E*) or the (Z) isomer of 3-methyl-2-pentene to be the major product?

Which isomer of alkene would you obtain from each of the following:

b. (2S,3S)-2-bromo-3-methylpentane

c. (2*R*,3S)-2-bromo-3-methylpentane

Steps to Solving the Problem

Solution to Problem 12.9a

1. Draw a sawhorse structure of the original compound, illustrating the proper stereochemistry at each stereogenic atom.

CH_3CH_2
CH_3
CH_3
H
:Br: H

2. To consider the stereochemistry for formation of a 2-pentene from this compound, view the molecule along the carbon 2–carbon 3 bond (C-2–C-3) using a Newman projection.

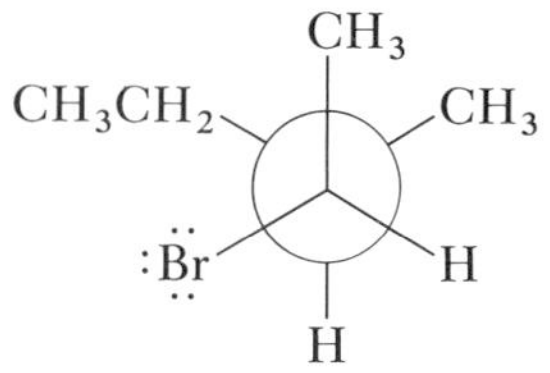

3. The particular conformation we have chosen is *not* suitable for *anti*-periplanar E2 reaction. We must rotate the molecule about the C-2–C-3 bond until we have the proper conformation—one in which the H and Br atoms are *anti* to one another:

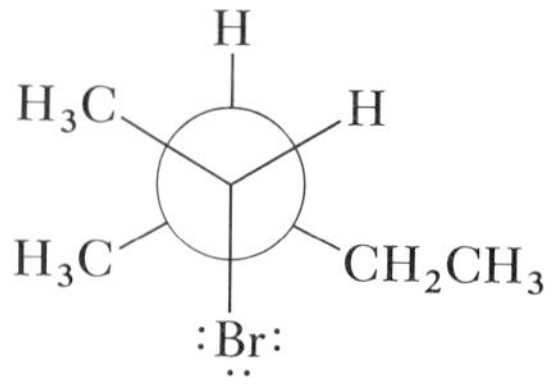

4. We now envision the E2 reaction occurring, with H and Br departing from opposite sides and a flattening of the remainder of the molecule.

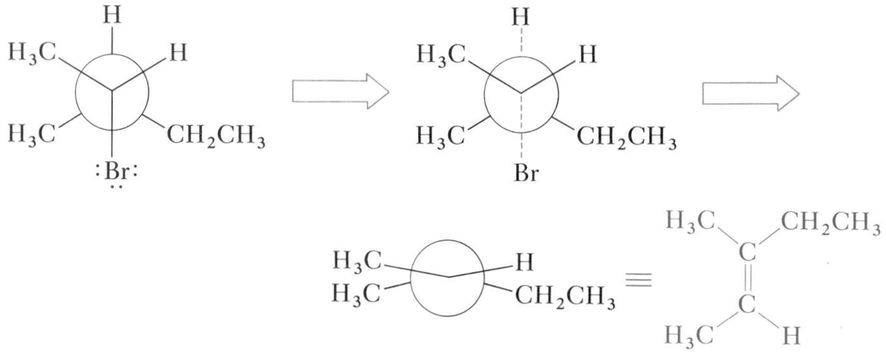

5. We now have the structure of the alkene product, which we see to be (*E*)-3-methyl-2-pentene.

Distribution of Alkene Products Consider the E2 reaction of 2-bromopentane when it is treated with potassium ethoxide as the base. (For the moment we will ignore any substitution that occurs in the reaction.) Three alkene products are formed, as shown in Equation 12.18.

Eqn. 12.18

$$\underset{\text{2-bromopentane}}{CH_3\overset{:\ddot{Br}:}{\overset{|}{C}}HCH_2CH_2CH_3} \xrightarrow{KOCH_2CH_3} \left[\begin{array}{c} \text{trans-}CH_3CH{=}CHCH_2CH_3 \ (H_3C, H \text{ on one C}; H, CH_2CH_3 \text{ on the other}) \\ \textit{trans}\text{-2-pentene (38\%)} \\ \text{cis-}CH_3CH{=}CHCH_2CH_3 \\ \textit{cis}\text{-2-pentene (14\%)} \\ H_2C{=}CHCH_2CH_2CH_3 \\ \text{1-pentene (23\%)} \end{array}\right]$$

There are several features about this reaction that merit analysis. First, a hydrogen atom can be removed as a proton from C-1 or from C-3. Removal of a hydrogen atom from C-1 leads to 1-pentene, while removal from C-3 leads to either *cis*- or to *trans*-2-pentene. From the product distribution, we can infer that most of the product derives from removal of a hydrogen atom from C-3 (the net yield of *cis*- and *trans*-2-pentene is 52%, more than double that of 1-pentene (only 23%)). Why is there this regioselectivity? Also we see that much more *trans*-2-pentene than *cis*-2-pentene is formed. Can we rationalize this difference?

Let us first consider the question of removal of a hydrogen atom from C-3 and from C-1. Looking at the starting 2-bromopentane, we can certainly see why *both* 1-pentene and 2-pentene products would be formed. There are hydrogens on both the 1-carbon and the 3-carbon, and both hydrogens can easily attain either an *anti*- or *syn*-periplanar arrangement with the bromine atom on the 2-carbon. In fact, *three* hydrogen atoms at the 1-carbon and *two* at the 3-carbon are available for elimination. Based solely on statistical arguments, we would predict 1-pentene to be the major product (3 : 2 compared to the 2-pentenes). However, less than half of the alkene actually formed is 1-pentene. Obviously, factors other than statistical considerations are important.

Earlier (in Chapter 9) we inferred that internal alkenes are thermodynamically more stable than terminal alkenes since terminal alkenes have higher heats of hydrogenation than do internal alkenes (reflecting the greater stability of the latter). Carbon-carbon π bonds are stabilized by alkyl substituents in a manner similar to the stabilization of carbocations.

The observed major product (*trans*-2-pentene) is the thermodynamically more favored of the three possible alkene products. However, since the reaction is *irreversible* under the conditions used, thermodynamics does not determine which product is formed. Instead, the product that is formed *faster* is the one we isolate as the major product. We say that the reaction is subject to *kinetic control* rather than *thermodynamic control*. We conclude that the activated complex leading to the more stable product is also lower in energy than those activated complexes leading to the less stable products—this is another example of the useful Hammond postulate. The postulate applies in this case since the factors that govern the stability of a fully formed π system also govern the relative stabilities of the developing π bonds. The activated complex occurs late and resembles the product alkene. The activated complexes leading to 1-pentene

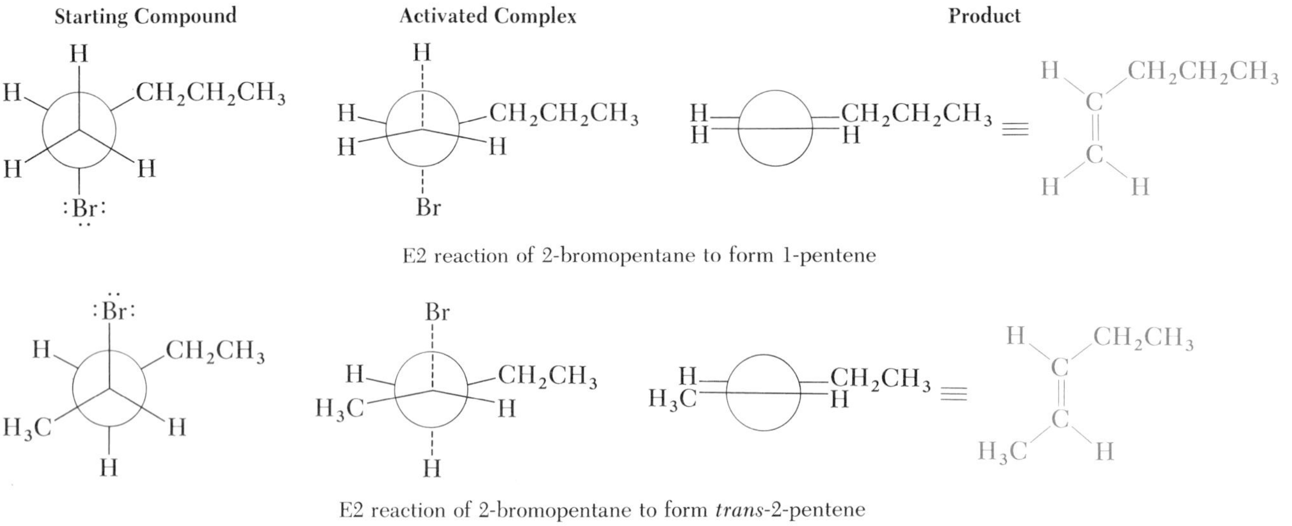

Starting Compound | Activated Complex | Product

E2 reaction of 2-bromopentane to form 1-pentene

E2 reaction of 2-bromopentane to form *trans*-2-pentene

Figure 12.19 Structures of starting compound, activated complex, and product in competing E2 reactions of 2-bromopentane. The activated complexes each resemble their respective product alkene. The stabilization of the alkene is thus reflected in the respective stabilities of the activated complexes. Because the internal alkene has a greater thermodynamic stability than the terminal alkene, the activated complex leading to the internal alkene is also relatively more stable.

and to *trans*-2-pentene are shown in Figure 12.19 and the associated reaction progress diagrams in Figure 12.20.

Elimination reactions in which the thermodynamically more stable alkene is the dominant product (as in the reaction we just discussed) are commonly referred to as having **Zaitzev orientation.** In the nineteenth century the Russian chemist Alexander Zaitzev recognized the general pattern of product formation in this type of elimination reaction and formulated an empirical rule predicting the dominant product to be the more highly substituted alkene.

The preference for Zaitzev orientation does not hold for all haloalkanes and all bases in E2 reactions. Some reactions give a major alkene product that is not the most stable alkene. This type of reaction is said to follow **Hofmann orientation.** The nineteenth-century German chemist August Hofmann investigated elimination reactions in which the dominant alkene is the one in which fewer alkyl groups are attached to the olefinic linkage, that is, the less stable alkene. In E2 reactions of haloalkanes, Hofmann orientation is commonly found when particularly bulky bases are used.

An example of the effect of changing the size of the base is found in the dehydrohalogenation of 2-bromopentane using potassium *tert*-butoxide. The yield of 1-pentene is increased from 23% when ethoxide ion is used as the base (Equation 12.18) to 59% when *tert*-butoxide ion is used.

The preference for Hofmann orientation in the *tert*-butoxide reaction can be rationalized in terms of *steric accessibility*. Steric accessibility is greatest for methyl hydrogens and least for tertiary hydrogens. If Zaitzev orientation is to dominate, the *least* sterically accessible hydrogen must be removed. With small bases, this is not a problem, so Zaitzev orientation is commonly observed. However, with bulky bases, such as *tert*-butoxide, the problem of accessibility is magnified. Steric constraints become a dominant consideration and Hofmann orientation results.

A second question to consider in looking at the alkene product distribution is the relative amounts of *cis*- and *trans*-2-pentene (Equation 12.18). On a statistical basis, we would expect equal amount of the two products to be formed. There is one hydrogen on the 3-carbon that can be removed to form

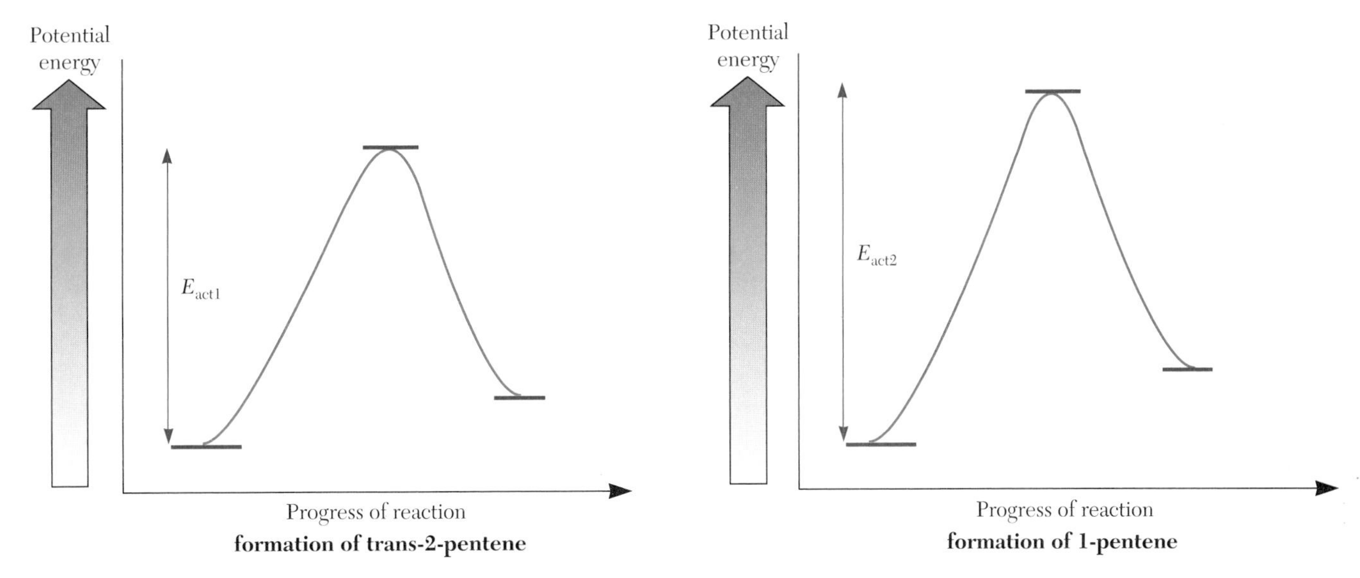

Figure 12.20 Reaction progress diagrams for the E2 reactions of 2-bromopentane to form *trans*-2-pentene and 1-pentene. The activated complex in each reaction reflects the substituent stabilization present in the product. Since the stabilization of the internal alkene is greater than that of the terminal alkene, the activated complex leading to the internal alkene is lower in energy than that leading to the terminal alkene, that is, E_{act1} is less than E_{act2}. The more stable product also forms more rapidly; its path of formation has the lower activation energy.

trans- and one that can be removed to form *cis*-2-pentene. However, the amount of *trans*-2-pentene formed is much greater than the amount of *cis*-2-pentene. We can understand this product distribution by again looking at the activation energies associated with reaching the activated complexes for each product.

We know from heats of hydrogenation (Chapter 9) that *trans*-2-pentene is thermodynamically more stable than *cis*-2-pentene. This stability is reflected in greater stability of the activated complex leading to the *trans*-2-pentene in an E2 reaction. The activated complexes are compared in Figure 12.21, and the reaction progress diagrams are shown in Figure 12.22.

Figure 12.21 Reactant, activated complexes, and products in the formation of *cis*- and *trans*-2-pentene by an E2 reaction of 2-bromopentane. The steric crowding in *cis*-2-pentene raises its energy relative to *trans*-2-pentene and is reflected in the activated complex leading to it. As a result, formation of *trans*-2-pentene is faster.

Starting Compound **Activated Complex** **Product**

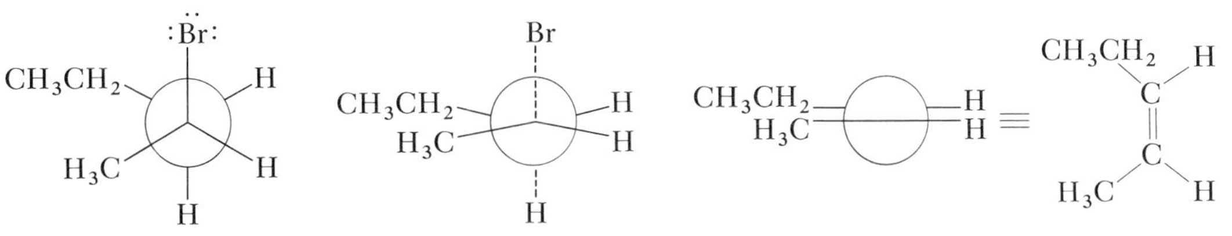

E2 reaction of 2-bromopentane to form *cis*-2-pentene

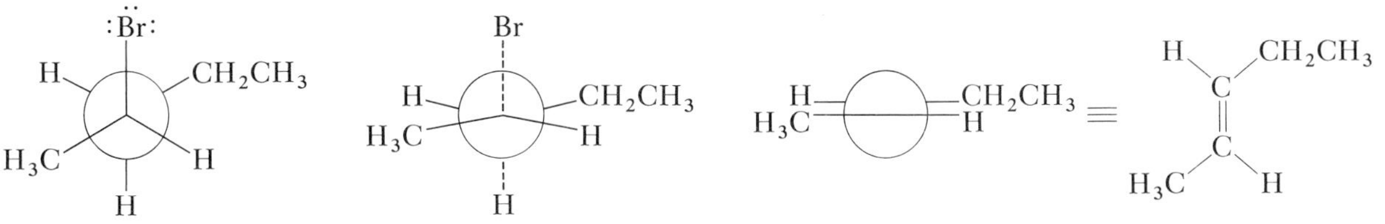

E2 reaction of 2-bromopentane to form *trans*-2-pentene

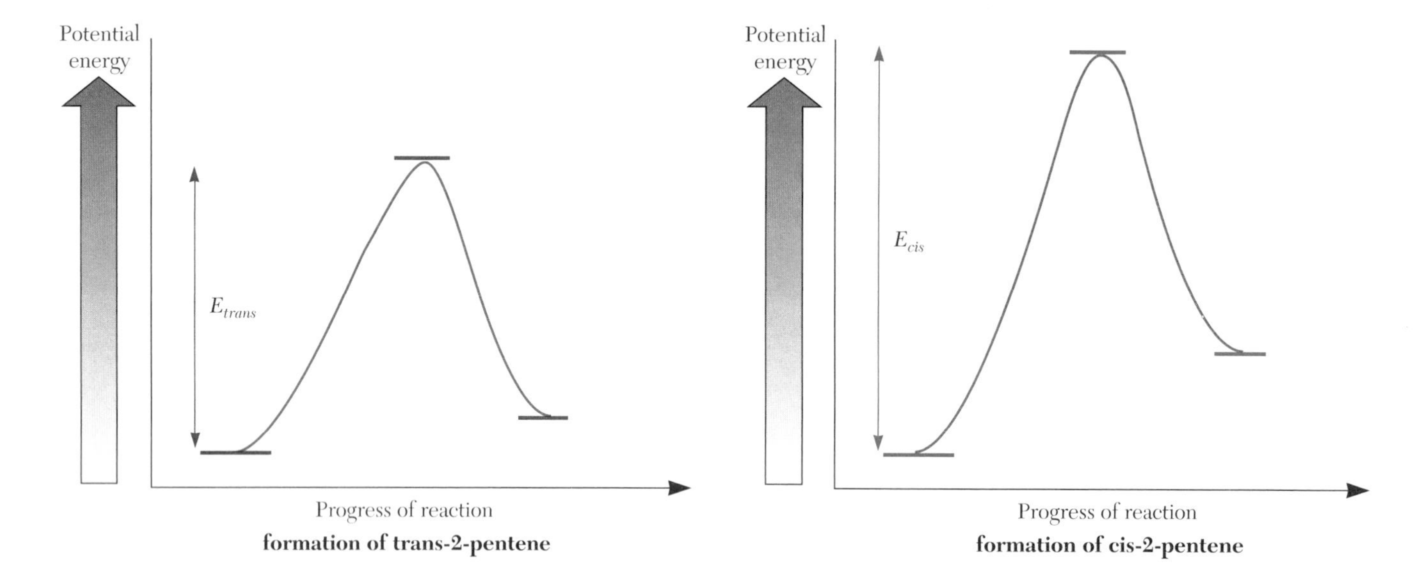

Figure 12.22 Reaction progress diagrams for the formation of *cis*- and *trans*-2-pentene by E2 reaction of 2-bromopentane. The higher energy of the *cis*-2-pentene product is reflected in the energy of the activated complex leading to it. The higher activation energy for the formation of the *cis*- compared to the *trans*-2-pentene product leads to formation of a greater amount of the *trans*-2-pentene.

In the absence of special interactions, the formation of *trans* alkenes is favored over the related *cis* alkenes in E2 reactions.

E1 REACTIONS OF HALOALKANES

Unimolecular elimination (E1) reactions of haloalkanes occur principally with tertiary haloalkanes in the presence of weak bases. For example, water (and ethanol) serve as weak bases that accomplish the E1 reaction on *tert*-butyl chloride shown in Equation 12.19.

Eqn. 12.19

$$(CH_3)_3C\ddot{\underset{..}{C}}l\colon \xrightarrow[\text{room temp}]{\text{80\% water, 20\% ethanol}} (CH_3)_2C{=}CH_2 + (CH_3)_3C\ddot{\underset{..}{O}}H$$

2-chloro-2-methylpropane	36% yield E1 product 2-methylpropene	64% yield S_N1 product 2-methyl-2-propanol

In this type of reaction, known as **solvolysis,** the solvent itself plays the role of nucleophile/base. We normally encounter E1 reactions in solvolysis reactions of tertiary haloalkanes. The reaction shown in Equation 12.19 illustrates not only the facility with which tertiary haloalkanes undergo E1 reaction but also that E1 reactions are in competition with S_N1 reactions.

Both E1 and S_N1 reactions proceed through carbocation intermediates. Skeletal rearrangements are observed in alkene formation as well as in first-order substitutions. The first step in each type of reaction is the dissociation of the haloalkane into a carbocation and a halide ion. Once the carbocation has been generated (the rate-determining step), it can either lose a proton to form an alkene (E1) or add a nucleophile (S_N1). This competition is illustrated in Figure 12.23.

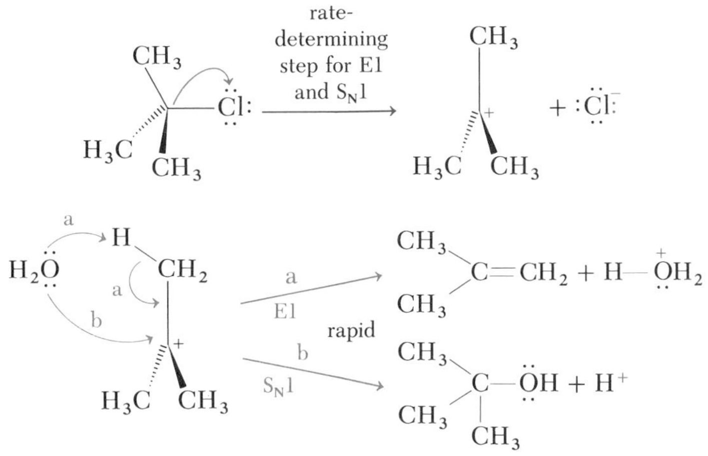

Figure 12.23 Competition between E1 and S_N1 reactions. The S_N1 reaction forms an intermediate oxonium ion that gives up the proton (to a solvent molecule), yielding the alcohol product.

When alkenes are formed by an E1 mechanism, Zaitzev orientation generally results. That is, the more highly substituted of the possible alkenes is formed preferentially. The rationale for this result again is based on the activation energies for the competing processes. With a carbocation, loss of a hydrogen from a β-carbon site is more favorable from the β-carbon bearing the fewest hydrogens. The additional stabilization by alkyl substituents of the developing π bond favors the generation of the more highly substituted alkene. This type of reaction is of only limited utility for the synthesis of alkenes.

PROBLEM 12.10 When 2-bromo-2-methylpropane is solvolyzed in aqueous ethanol a mixture of the following three products is formed:

a. $C_6H_{14}O$ b. $C_4H_{10}O$ c. C_4H_8

Give the structure for each of these products and tell how each is formed.

12.8 The Competition between Elimination and Substitution

Nucleophilic substitution and elimination reactions of haloalkanes are usually competing processes. The E1 and S_N1 reactions even involve the same intermediate, a carbocation. When performing a particular substitution (or elimination) reaction for the synthesis of a target compound, we must carefully consider the possibility of side product formation.

THE NUCLEOPHILE/BASE

Elimination processes become favored over substitution as the basicity of the nucleophile/base increases. For example, the use of hydroxide ion with a given primary or secondary haloalkane generally results in a mixture of substitution and elimination products. If we change the nucleophile/base to a stronger base such as alkoxide ion, we find an increased amount of elimination product.

If an alkene is the target molecule (elimination is desired rather than substitution), *tert*-butoxide ion is often the base of choice. Being a tertiary alcohol, *tert*-butyl alcohol is a weaker acid than primary or secondary alcohols, and therefore its conjugate base is a stronger base than alkoxide ions derived from most primary and secondary alcohols. It is also a highly hindered and therefore poor nucleophile.

We use a more potent nucleophile that is a weaker base in order to increase the relative amount of substitution reaction. The *rate* of the reaction is retarded, but a weaker base has a preference for substitution rather than elimination. The result is that little difficulty is encountered in causing only substitution to occur in reactions using weak Brønsted bases. For example, halide ion exchange reactions occur with virtually no elimination, an observation consistent with the low basicity of halide ions.

THE NATURE OF THE SUBSTRATE

The carbon skeleton of the haloalkane substrate also has an effect on the competition between substitution and elimination. For second-order reactions, the degree of elimination increases with increasing alkyl substitution at the electrophilic carbon; that is, secondary haloalkanes undergo a greater degree of elimination than do primary haloalkanes with the same nucleophile and solvent.

Similarly, increasing the branching at the β-carbon leads to increased elimination over substitution. For a substitution reaction, the greater the branching at the β-position, the greater the steric crowding of the incoming nucleophile. This crowding increases the activation energy for substitution and therefore reduces its rate relative to elimination, since the hydrogen atoms available for attack by base are still relatively unhindered.

12.9 α-Eliminations

The elimination reactions we have considered thus far are the most commonly encountered types. These reactions involve the elimination of the elements of a hydrogen halide between adjacent carbon atoms. We commonly refer to these reactions as *β-eliminations*. There is another category of reactions known as *α-eliminations* wherein both atoms are removed from the same carbon atom. With most haloalkane substrates the α-elimination reactions are unimportant because the β-eliminations are so facile and occur much more rapidly. The α-elimination reactions have a high activation energy and occur only when ordinary β-elimination routes are precluded. A major example is illustrated in Figure 12.24.

Because the chlorine atoms are strongly electron withdrawing (highly electronegative), the hydrogen atom of chloroform is actually moderately acidic. Upon treatment with strong base, chloroform loses a proton to give the trichloromethyl anion. Subsequently, this anion loses a chloride ion to give a neutral divalent carbon species known as a **carbene.** In this reaction *dichlorocarbene*

$$Cl_3C{-}H + :\ddot{\underset{..}{O}}C(CH_3)_3^- \longrightarrow Cl_3C:^- + H{-}\ddot{\underset{..}{O}}C(CH_3)_3$$

$$Cl_2C(:\ddot{\underset{..}{Cl}}:):^- \longrightarrow Cl_2C: + :\ddot{\underset{..}{Cl}}:^-$$

Figure 12.24 α-elimination reaction of chloroform. Chloroform is unable to undergo a β-elimination reaction. The only reaction route available to it upon treatment with strong base is removal of the lone hydrogen to generate the trichloromethyl anion. In the absence of any proton source, the trichloromethyl anion undergoes decomposition to a chloride ion and dichlorocarbene.

is formed. The elements of hydrogen chloride have been removed from a single carbon atom.

Carbenes are highly reactive species that can undergo a variety of reactions. One reaction of particular interest is addition to alkenes. Two examples of dichlorocarbene addition to alkenes are shown in Equations 12.20 and 12.21.

Eqn. 12.20 $$CHCl_3 + \text{cyclohexene} \xrightarrow{KOC(CH_3)_3} \text{7,7-dichloronorcarane}$$

cyclohexene

59% yield
7,7-dichloronorcarane

Eqn. 12.21 $$CHCl_3 + (CH_3)_2C{=}CH_2 \xrightarrow{KOC(CH_3)_3} \text{1,1-dichloro-2,2-dimethylcyclopropane}$$

2-methylpropene

65% yield
1,1-dichloro-
2,2-dimethylcyclopropane

The products of these addition reactions are dichlorocyclopropanes. Other routes leading to the formation of cyclopropanes will be studied in Chapter 13.

Summary

- Haloalkanes can undergo two contrasting types of reactions when challenged with Lewis bases.
- One reaction involves *substitution:* the Lewis base replaces the halide, which leaves the molecule. The Lewis base is referred to as a nucleophile when it acts in this manner.
- Nucleophilic substitution reactions occur by two general mechanisms known as S_N1 and S_N2.
- One nucleophilic substitution reaction involves the direct displacement of halide ion by *backside* attack of the nucleophile at the electrophilic carbon. This type of reaction exhibits second-order kinetics and is referred to as an S_N2 reaction. It is of dominant importance for methyl and primary haloalkanes, and is also significant for secondary haloalkanes. It is generally not important for tertiary haloalkanes. Overall, the S_N2 reaction involves inversion of configuration at the electrophilic carbon.
- Alternatively, the haloalkane can undergo an initial dissociation to a carbocation and a halide ion. The carbocation can then combine with a nucleophile to give the substitution product. The first step of this reaction is the rate-determining step. The second step occurs rapidly after the carbocation has been generated. This reaction often involves nearly complete racemization about the electrophilic carbon. It is of particular significance for tertiary haloalkanes but also occurs with secondary haloalkanes. It is relatively unimportant for methyl and primary haloalkanes.
- *Elimination* is the second fundamental type of reaction between haloalkanes and Lewis bases. The elements of a hydrogen halide are eliminated between adjacent carbon atoms. This type of reaction can also occur via two general mechanisms known as E1 and E2.
- With a bimolecular elimination reaction (E2) both the base and the substrate are involved in a single step. The hydrogen and halide ion lost from the substrate must have either an *anti*-periplanar or a *syn*-periplanar arrangement for the reaction to occur. Intermediate conformations do not allow π bond formation to occur when bond breaking is also occurring. With ordinary bases, regioselectivity is observed in

the E2 reaction. The more highly substituted of the possible alkenes is formed preferentially. This arrangement is known as Zaitzev orientation. With bulky bases, the less highly substituted of the possible alkenes is formed preferentially (Hofmann orientation).

- Elimination can also occur by a unimolecular (E1) mechanism that involves initial dissociation of the haloalkane to a carbocation and a halide ion, as in the S_N1 reaction. A hydrogen is then lost from a β-carbon of the carbocation to form the alkene. This mechanism occurs principally with tertiary haloalkanes upon treatment with weak bases.
- Substitution and elimination reactions are always in competition when a haloalkane is treated with a Lewis base. We can often favor one route or the other by the judicious choice of nucleophile/base and solvent.

Terms to Remember

nitrile	Williamson ether synthesis	E2
electrophilic site	Finkelstein reaction	E1
kinetics	polar aprotic solvent	dihedral angle
rate law	amine	*anti*-periplanar
rate constant	alkylammonium ion	*syn*-periplanar
reaction order	alkylation	Zaitzev orientation
rate-determining step	steric crowding	Hofmann orientation
S_N1	solvation	solvolysis
S_N2	dehydrohalogenation	carbene
ether		

Reactions of Synthetic Utility

46. $-\overset{|}{\underset{|}{C}}-X + HO^- \longrightarrow -\overset{|}{\underset{|}{C}}-OH$ 12.4

There is increasing competition from elimination side reactions as the haloalkane goes from primary to secondary to tertiary.

47. $-\overset{|}{\underset{|}{C}}-X + H_2O \longrightarrow -\overset{|}{\underset{|}{C}}-OH$ 12.4

3°

48. $-\overset{|}{\underset{|}{C}}-X + R'O^- \longrightarrow -\overset{|}{\underset{|}{C}}-OR'$ 12.4

There is increasing competition from elimination side reactions as the haloalkane goes from primary to secondary to tertiary.

49. $-\overset{|}{\underset{|}{C}}-X + HOR' \longrightarrow -\overset{|}{\underset{|}{C}}-OR'$ 12.4

3°

50. $-\overset{|}{\underset{|}{C}}-X + NaI \longrightarrow -\overset{|}{\underset{|}{C}}-I$ 12.4

X = Cl, Br
1° > 2° > 3°

51. $-\overset{|}{\underset{|}{C}}-X + NaCN \longrightarrow -\overset{|}{\underset{|}{C}}-CN$ 12.4

52. $-\overset{|}{\underset{|}{C}}-X + NH_3 \longrightarrow -\overset{|}{\underset{|}{C}}-NH_2$ 12.4

$1° > 2°$

53. $R_2\underset{X}{\underset{|}{C}}-\underset{H}{\underset{|}{C}}R_2 + \text{base} \longrightarrow R_2C{=}CR_2$ 12.7

$3° > 2° > 1°$ haloalkane; favored by alkyl branching at electrophilic and adjacent carbons

54. $X_3CH + KOC(CH_3)_3 + R_2C{=}CR_2 \longrightarrow$ (cyclopropane with two X on one carbon) 12.9

X = Br, Cl

Additional Problems

12.11 For each of the following, choose the reaction that would proceed more rapidly and give an explanation for your choice:

a. iodomethane or bromomethane with aqueous potassium hydroxide
b. iodomethane or iodoethane with aqueous potassium hydroxide
c. methanol or bromomethane with sodium iodide dissolved in acetone
d. 2-bromopropane or 1-bromopropane with sodium iodide dissolved in acetone
e. 2-bromo-2-methylbutane or 2-bromo-3-methylbutane with ethanol
f. aqueous potassium bromide or aqueous hydrogen bromide with butanol
g. bromocyclohexane or chlorocyclohexane with aqueous acetone
h. 2-chloro-3,3-dimethylbutane or 2-chloro-3-methylbutane with potassium *tert*-butoxide
i. 1:1 by volume aqueous ethanol or 1:4 by volume aqueous ethanol with 2-chloro-2-methylpropane
j. water or hydrogen sulfide with 1-bromopentane
k. 1-chloropentane or 1-chloro-2,2-dimethylpropane with potassium ethoxide in ethanol
l. sodium cyanide in water or sodium cyanide in DMSO with methyl iodide

12.12 Rank each of the following sets of bases in order of decreasing base strength:

a. $H\ddot{O}:^-$, $H\ddot{S}:^-$, $H\ddot{Se}:^-$ b. $H\ddot{O}:^-$, $CH_3CH_2\ddot{O}:^-$, $(CH_3)_3C\ddot{O}:^-$ c. $H_2\ddot{N}^-$, $H_3\ddot{N}$, $H\ddot{O}:^-$

12.13 Consider the addition of (a) NH_3 and (b) NH_2^- to a solution of 1-bromo-2-methylpropane. It is observed that a much greater ratio of substitution to elimination occurs when ammonia is used rather than amide ion. Name the substitution and elimination products, and deduce whether ammonia or amide ion has the larger basicity/nucleophilicity ratio.

12.14 Under which of the following sets of conditions will the ratio E2/E1 be greater:

a. 2-chloro-2-methylpropane with 0.1 *M* aqueous sodium hydroxide
b. 2-chloro-2-methylpropane with 0.1 *M* aqueous ammonia

Explain your choice.

12.15 Predict the major product or products for each of the following reactions, and indicate the mechanisms by which they are formed. If no reaction is expected, so indicate.

a. 2-chloro-2-methylbutane with sodium methoxide in methanol

b. iodomethane with potassium *tert*-butoxide in *tert*-butyl alcohol
c. 2-chloro-2-methylbutane with methanol
d. 2-bromobutane with potassium ethoxide in ethanol
e. 1-bromo-3-chloropropane with one equivalent of potassium cyanide in acetone
f. (*R*)-2-bromobutane with sodium iodide in acetone
g. 1-propanol with potassium iodide in acetone
h. (*R*)-3-bromo-3-methylhexane with water
i. 2-methyl-2-butene with chloroform and potassium *tert*-butoxide
j. 1-bromo-2-ethylcyclopentane with potassium ethoxide in ethanol
k. *trans*-1-bromo-3-methylcyclopentane with sodium iodide in acetone

12.16 2,2,3-Trimethylpentan-1-ol reacts with concentrated aqueous hydrogen bromide to give a bromoalkane of formula $C_8H_{17}Br$. The product has a different carbon skeleton from the starting alcohol. Give a structure for the product, and write a mechanism for its formation.

12.17 When 2-chloro-3-methylbutane is solvolyzed in methanol, one of the observed products is an ether whose carbon skeleton is rearranged from that of the starting alcohol. Give a structure for this material and explain its formation.

12.18 Alkene *A* reacts with hydrogen bromide in the absence of peroxides to yield compound *B*, which contains 53.0% bromine. On treatment of *B* with potassium ethoxide in ethanol, *C*, an isomer of *A*, is formed. When *C* is ozonized and the workup is performed under oxidative conditions, acetone and acetic acid are obtained. Give structures for compounds *A* to *C*.

12.19 Compound *D* is an alkene of formula C_5H_{10}. Under conditions of catalytic hydrogenation it is converted to 2-methylbutane. Compound *D* gives an alkyl halide, *E*, on treatment with hydrogen iodide. Compound *E* is converted to alcohol *F* upon reaction with hydroxide ion. Alcohol *F* is oxidized to ketone *G* by treatment with aqueous potassium dichromate. Suggest structures for compounds *D* through *G*.

12.20 Methoxymethyl chloride, (CH_3OCH_2Cl), a powerful alkylating agent and a suspected carcinogen, reacts rapidly with nucleophiles, but the reaction follows first-order kinetics in spite of the substrate being a primary haloalkane. Draw the structure (and any viable resonance structures) of the carbocation that would be formed from this substrate, and explain why this material undergoes a first-order reaction.

12.21 Give the structure of the major alkene formed in each of the following dehydrohalogenations:
a. (3*S*,4*R*)-4-bromo-2,3,4-trimethylhexane on treatment with potassium *tert*-butoxide
b. treatment of *meso*-2,3-dibromobutane with potassium *tert*-butoxide to remove a single equivalent of hydrogen bromide

12.22 A haloalkane, RX, undergoes reaction with a base, $B:^-$, in solvent BH. There is a competition between the E2 and E1 mechanistic pathways for the elimination reaction of the haloalkane. The rate constants for the two pathways are:

E1	$1.2 \times 10^{-4}\ \text{sec}^{-1}$
E2	$2.0 \times 10^{-4}\ \text{L mol}^{-1}\ \text{sec}^{-1}$

Calculate the rates of both E1 and E2 reactions when:
a. the concentration of the haloalkane is 0.01 *M* and the concentration of the base is 0.40 *M*
b. the concentration of the haloalkane is 0.01 *M* and the concentration of the base is 2.0 *M*
Based on your calculation, do you expect a high or low base concentration to favor the E2 route of elimination in the general situation where E1 and E2 routes are in competition?

12.23 For a particular reaction

$$A + 2B \longrightarrow C$$

(the reaction occurs in more than one step) the rate equation has the form

$$\text{rate} = k[\text{A}][\text{B}]$$

If an initial rate of $6.0 \times 10^{-5}\ M\ \text{sec}^{-1}$ is observed on mixing 1 M solutions of each A and B, what would the rate be after:

a. 20% of A is consumed b. 40% of A is consumed

12.24 The thiocyanate ion, SCN^-, is an ambident nucleophile (it can act as a nucleophile using either of two atoms). Write two contributing resonance structures for this ion, and predict the two products of the reaction of sodium thiocyanate with ethyl bromide in acetone solution.

12.25 When *cis*-1-bromo-2-butene is treated with ethanol, three compounds of the formula $C_6H_{12}O$ can be isolated. Give the structures of these three compounds and explain their formation.

12.26 Suggest structures for the haloalkanes that satisfy the requirements given below.

a. a haloalkane that yields 4-ethyl-1-hexene as the only alkene when treated with potassium *tert*-butoxide

b. a haloalkane that contains six carbon atoms and gives a mixture of three alkenes on treatment with sodium ethoxide

c. a haloalkane of formula C_4H_9Cl that yields three isomeric alkenes on treatment with sodium ethoxide

12.27 Substance *H*, of formula $C_{10}H_{19}Br$, gives a mixture of two isomers, *I* and *J*, upon treatment with base. Compound *I* is the dominant product when the base is ethoxide ion, but *J* is dominant when *tert*-butoxide ion is used. Both *I* and *J* are converted to *K*, of formula $C_{10}H_{22}$, on treatment with an excess of hydrogen in the presence of a platinum catalyst. Compound *I*, on treatment with hot, alkaline permanganate solution, followed by acidification, yields a mixture of acetone and succinic acid ($HO_2C—CH_2—CH_2—CO_2H$), in a molar ratio of two parts acetone to one part succinic acid. Suggest structures for compounds *H* through *K*.

12.28 Substance *L*, of formula $C_7H_{13}Br$, is known to contain two methyl groups and gives no reaction with bromine in carbon tetrachloride solution. When treated with base, *L* yields *M*, of formula C_7H_{12}, as the only organic product. Compound *M* does not produce *L* when treated with hydrogen bromide in the absence of peroxides. Treatment of *M* with hot, alkaline permanganate solution followed by acidification yields *N*, of formula $C_7H_{12}O_3$. Provide structures for compounds *L* through *N*.

12.29 Propose methods for each of the following syntheses. More than one step is necessary in each synthesis.

a. cyanocyclohexane from cyclohexanol

b. $CH_3CH_2CH_2CH_2C{\equiv}N{:}$ from *trans*-2-butene

c. 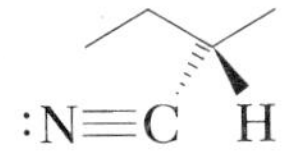

from (S)-2-chlorobutane

d. cyclohexyl methyl ether from any alcohol and any haloalkane

e. 1,1-dichloro-2,2,3,3-tetramethylcyclopropane from 2-bromo-2,3-dimethylbutane

12.30 Explain why a solution of (*R*)-2-iodobutane loses optical activity upon standing in a solution of sodium iodide in acetone.

12.31 Although 2-bromo-2-methylpropane solvolyzes in water to give *tert*-butyl alcohol and 2-methylpropene ten times more rapidly than does 2-chloro-2-methylpropane, the ratio of elimination to substitution products is the same for these two alkyl halides. Explain why.

12.32 An undergraduate organic student, Oscar, is having problems. He is instructed by his mentor to use the alkene shown below as a starting material for a particular conversion. However, Oscar carelessly spills sulfuric acid into his sample of the alkene. He makes a valiant effort to recover the alkene by neutralizing the acid, extracting his product into ether, distilling off the ether using a warm water bath, and distilling the recovered material. Oscar does recover a small amount of the alkene, but most of the recovered material is a mixture of two isomers of the original alkene. Oscar's friend, Felix, working in his usual meticulous manner, is able to purify the two other isomers from Oscar's minor disaster. Suggest structures for the two isomers formed from the original alkene, and give a mechanistic interpretation for their formation.

CH_3

CH_2

12.33 Sulfides are useful nucleophiles for preparing cyclic substances. For example, when 1,3-dibromopropane is treated with sodium sulfide, the following structure (known as thietane) is formed:

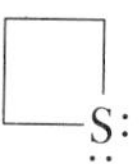

Suggest a mechanism for the formation of thietane in this reaction.

12.34 Loss of chloride ion from 3-chloro-2-methylpentane yields a carbocation that can lose a proton to give a mixture of three alkenes. Give the structures of these three alkenes, and tell which will form more rapidly. Draw a reaction progress diagram consistent with the Hammond postulate to illustrate the competing processes.

12.35 Compound *O*, of formula C_4H_8, reacts with hydrogen chloride to give compound *P*. When treated with potassium *tert*-butoxide, *P* gives back *O* as the only organic product. Compound *O*, on treatment with hydrogen in the presence of platinum oxide, yields *Q*, of formula C_4H_{10}, which does not decolorize bromine in carbon tetrachloride solution. Suggest structures for compounds *O* through *Q*.

12.36 For the following set of compounds, predict the order of their rate of reaction with sodium iodide in acetone solution (list them in increasing order):

2-bromobutane	2-chloro-3-methylbutane
1-chlorobutane	2-bromo-2-methylpropane
1-bromobutane	

12.37 For the compounds listed in Problem 12.36, indicate the order of their rate of reactivity with 80% aqueous ethanol (list them in increasing order).

12.38 Draw reaction progress diagrams for the two possible routes of substitution (S_N1 and S_N2) with 2-bromopropane in a 0.1 *M* solution of sodium hydroxide in 80% aqueous ethanol.

12.39 Consider the *meso*-3,4-dibromo-2,2,5,5-tetramethylhexane and racemic 3,4-dibromo-2,2,5,5-tetramethylhexane. Suppose that each compound is treated with an amount of sodium ethoxide such that one equivalent of hydrogen bromide is removed from each. Draw the structure of the alkene formed from each substrate. Which substrate would you expect to react more rapidly in this elimination reaction? Explain your answer.

12.40 On careful treatment with ammonia, 1,5-dibromopentane yields a compound of formula $C_5H_{11}N$. Give the structure of this product and explain how it is formed.

12.41 On treatment with excess base, dihalides can be induced to undergo double dehydrohalogenation reactions. For example, 1,1-dibromobutane can be treated with amide ion to form 1-butyne, as shown below.

$$CH_3CH_2CH_2CHBr_2 \xrightarrow{NaNH_2} CH_3CH_2C{\equiv}CH$$

However, on prolonged treatment of 1,1-dibromocyclohexane with sodium amide, only one equivalent of hydrogen bromide can be removed. That is, the product is 1-bromocyclohexene. Explain this result.

Alkanes and Cycloalkanes II. Reaction Mechanisms and Conformational Analysis

13.1 Introduction

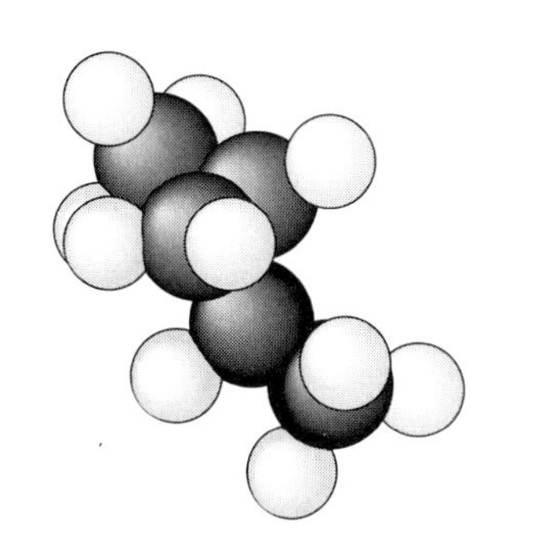

In Chapter 4 we began to study the structures of alkanes and several types of cycloalkanes. This chapter covers additional aspects of their chemistry and relates it to topics that were introduced after Chapter 4.

Some synthetic routes to alkanes and cycloalkanes will be introduced. We will analyze the mechanistic aspects of the reactions of halogens with alkanes and cycloalkanes so that we can understand the distribution of products in such reactions. We will also explore in more detail the conformational forms that alkanes and cycloalkanes can adopt, giving special attention to cyclohexane and its derivatives. The cyclohexane ring is a common component of natural and synthetic compounds, and knowledge about its conformation and dynamic nature is crucial for a satisfactory understanding of their properties. Finally, we will examine reactions in which a change in ring size occurs as a result of a carbocation rearrangement.

13.2 Bicyclic Alkanes

In Chapter 4 we met some cycloalkanes that contain more than one ring; in addition to the types of cycloalkanes noted in Chapter 4, there is an additional category—cycloalkanes that have more than one ring and that share more than one atom between the rings. For some of these complex structures, it may not be immediately obvious how many rings are actually present. We define the number of rings in a molecule as being equal to the minimum number of cuts required to produce an open-chain compound. Two examples are shown in Figure 13.1.

While open-chain compounds are generally capable of undergoing relatively free rotation about single bonds, cyclic compounds have much greater restrictions built into them. Bicyclic, tricyclic, and polycyclic compounds often are completely rigid with regard to the bonds of their rings. Often little or no rotation about ring single bonds is possible.

For our present purposes we will limit our attention to bicyclic molecules sharing two or more atoms. Many naturally occurring molecules fall into this category.

The procedure for assigning a systematic name to a bicyclic compound is outlined in Figure 13.2. The first step is to count the number of carbon atoms making up the rings of the two-ring system. This number provides the root name for the bicyclic compound. We then identify *bridgehead atoms*, that is, the atoms that are common to both rings. Finally, we count the number of atoms in each of the *bridges* joining the bridgehead positions. The complete name is given by preceding the root name with the word bicyclo and a square bracket containing the numbers of atoms in each bridge, listed in decreasing numerical order.

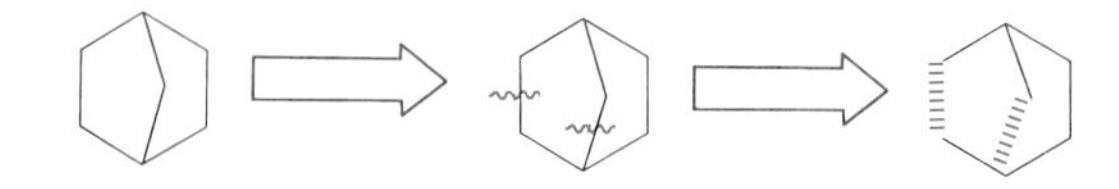

two cuts

two rings originally present; the original compound is a **bicyclic** compound

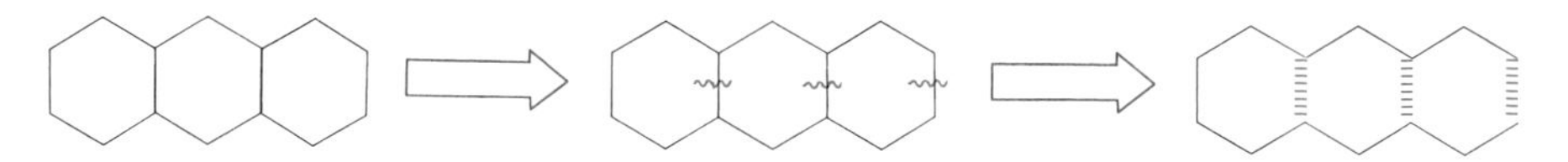

three cuts

three rings originally present; the original compound is a **tricyclic** compound

Figure 13.1 Polycyclic alkanes. The number of rings in a molecule is defined by the number of cuts required to generate an open-chain structure. A *bicyclic* and a *tricyclic* structure are shown.

Different types of drawings can be used to depict bicyclic molecules. For example, Figure 13.3 shows three alternative representations of the bicyclo[2.2.1]heptane molecule. You should be able to recognize that these structures represent the same molecule. One way to do this is to assign a systematic name to each of the structures. Structures with the same (correct) name represent the same compound.

In order to specify substituent positions in a bicyclic molecule, we start numbering at a bridgehead position and proceed along the longest bridge present to the other bridgehead. We then continue numbering along the next longest bridge until we return to the original bridgehead. Finally, any remaining atoms are numbered along the shortest bridge present. Figure 13.4 shows some other examples of bicyclic compounds with their systematic names.

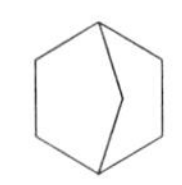

Count the number of carbon atoms in the fundamental structure. In this case, seven carbon atoms are present in the ring structure, so we name it as a *bicycloheptane*.

(*a*)

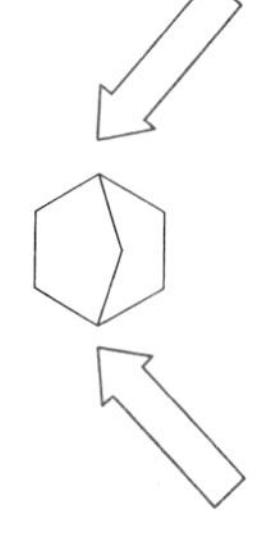

Locate the bridgehead carbon atoms. The bridgehead carbons (indicated by arrows) are common to both rings.

(*b*)

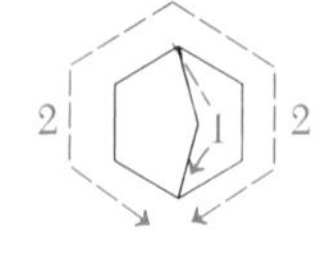

Count the number of carbons in each bridge. The bridges are indicated by the dashed lines, and the number of carbon atoms in each bridge is indicated. The systematic name is thus *bicyclo[2.2.1]heptane*.

(*c*)

Figure 13.2 Deriving the systematic name for a bicyclic compound.

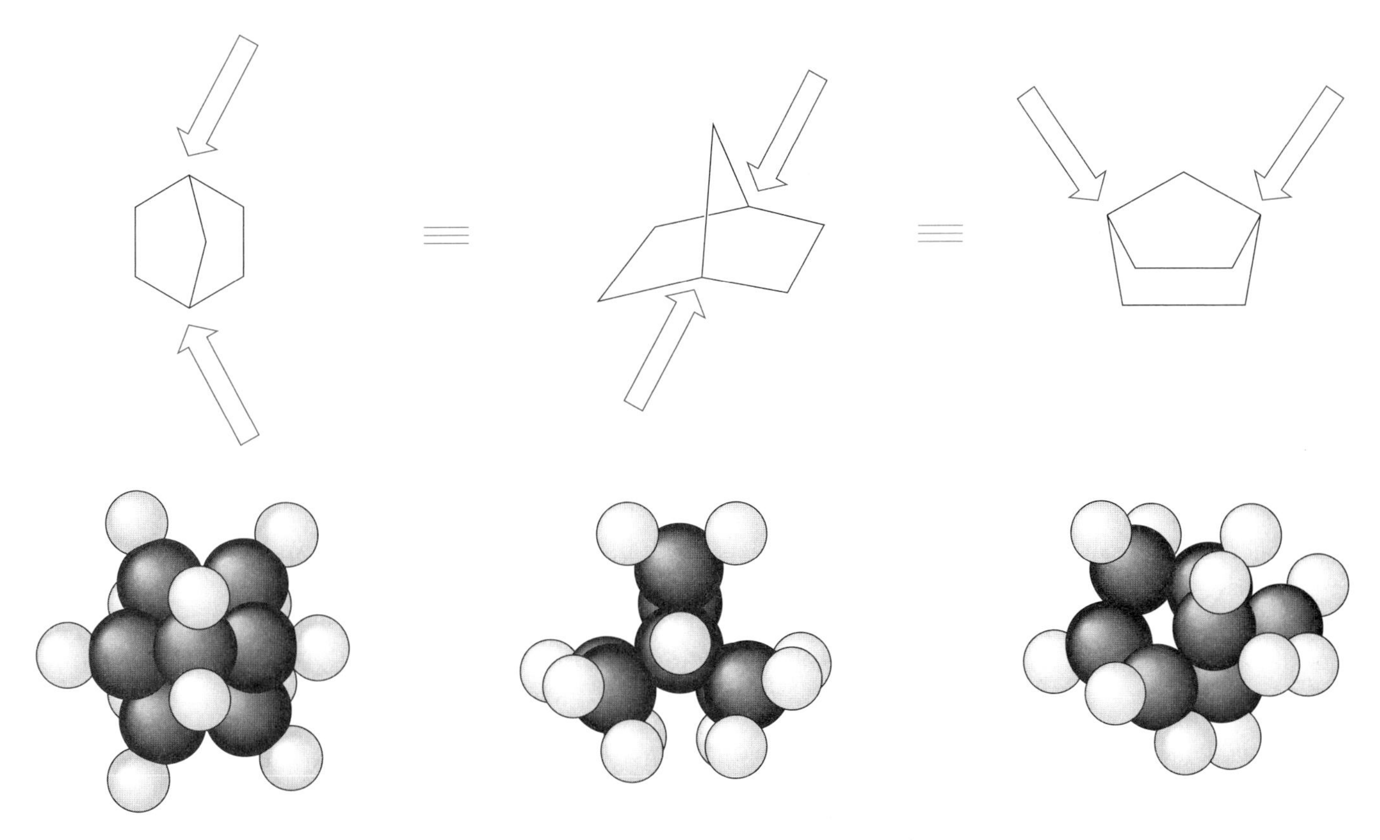

Figure 13.3 Alternative representations of bicyclo[2.2.1]heptane. Bridgehead carbons are indicated by arrows for easy identification. We can think of these representations as top, side, and end views of the molecule.

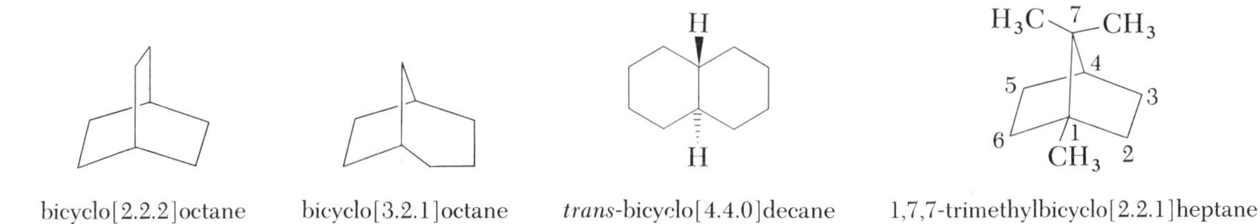

Figure 13.4 Bicyclic molecules with their systematic names.

PROBLEM 13.1 Draw structures and provide the systematic names of two different bicyclic molecules of formula C_6H_{10}.

PROBLEM 13.2 Give systematic names for each of the following molecules:

a. H_3C

b. $\ddot{\text{Cl}}$: $\ddot{\text{Cl}}$:

c. 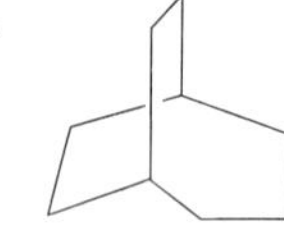 d. 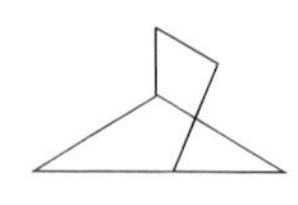

PROBLEM 13.3 Give a systematic name to the bicyclic product obtained upon treating cyclopentene with chloroform and potassium *tert*-butoxide.

13.3 Synthesis of Alkanes and Cycloalkanes

There are several reactions that provide useful syntheses of alkanes from compounds containing other functional groups. Many of these reactions can be used to prepare cycloalkanes. Among the more important methods are:

1. Catalytic reduction (addition of hydrogen) of an alkene or cycloalkene, as described in Chapter 10 (Reaction 19).
2. Reaction of an organocuprate with a haloalkane (Corey-House reaction), as described in Chapter 11 (Reaction 45).
3. Conversion of a haloalkane to an organometallic, followed by treatment with a hydroxylic solvent such as water, as described in Chapter 11 (Reaction 38).
4. Reduction of a haloalkane by one of the following methods:
   - □ Treatment of a bromo- or iodoalkane with lithium aluminum hydride ($LiAlH_4$), as illustrated in Equation 13.1. Primary haloalkanes react more rapidly than do secondary haloalkanes, and iodoalkanes react more rapidly than do bromoalkanes.

Eqn. 13.1

$$\underset{\text{1-bromooctane}}{CH_3(CH_2)_6CH_2\ddot{\underset{..}{Br}}:} \xrightarrow[\text{ether solvent}]{LiAlH_4 \atop 60^\circ} \underset{\text{96\% yield} \atop \text{octane}}{CH_3(CH_2)_6CH_3}$$

Lithium aluminum hydride must be handled with care. It is a powdery material that is highly reactive with moisture or any weakly acidic material. It reacts to supply a hydrogen atom with an electron pair (i.e., a hydride ion) to electrophilic sites. Upon contact with water or other acidic compounds, hydrogen is liberated and may ignite. It is used in ether solvents.

   - □ Treatment of a primary or secondary haloalkane with sodium borohydride ($NaBH_4$), as illustrated in Equation 13.2. This reaction is also more efficient with bromo- and iodoalkanes than with chloroalkanes, but with any haloalkane the reaction proceeds more slowly than it does with lithium aluminum hydride.

Eqn. 13.2

$$\underset{\text{1-chlorooctane}}{CH_3(CH_2)_6CH_2\ddot{\underset{..}{Cl}}:} \xrightarrow[DMSO]{NaBH_4} \underset{\text{42\% yield} \atop \text{octane}}{CH_3(CH_2)_6CH_3}$$

Sodium borohydride is significantly less reactive than is lithium aluminum hydride. It is commonly used in solvents such as simple alcohols, and it can also be used in DMSO.

□ Reaction of a haloalkane with an electropositive metal (such as zinc or tin) in the presence of an acid, as shown in Equation 13.3.

Eqn. 13.3

$$CH_3(CH_2)_{14}CH_2\ddot{\underset{..}{I}}: \xrightarrow[\text{acetic acid}]{\text{Zn, HCl}} CH_3(CH_2)_{14}CH_3$$

1-iodohexadecane — 85% yield hexadecane

□ Reaction of a bromo- or iodoalkane with a trialkyltin hydride (R_3SnH) in the presence of a peroxide. Chloroalkanes are less reactive than bromo- or iodoalkanes. Thus, bromine or iodine atoms can be replaced selectively by hydrogen, as shown in Equation 13.4.

Eqn. 13.4

$$\text{7-bromo-7-chloronorcarane} \xrightarrow[\text{benzoyl peroxide, heat}]{(CH_3CH_2CH_2CH_2)_3SnH} \text{7-chloronorcarane}$$

7-bromo-7-chloronorcarane — 97% yield 7-chloronorcarane

These reductions of haloalkanes to alkanes provide a convenient route for the overall conversion of *alcohols* to *alkanes*, that is, R—OH to R—X to R—H.

PROBLEM 13.4 Beginning with 1-pentanol as your only organic starting material, give syntheses for each of the following materials:

a. pentane **b.** 1-deuteriopentane **c.** 2-deuteriopentane
d. decane **e.** 4-methylnonane

13.4 Reactions of Alkanes with Halogens (Revisited)

In Chapter 4 we presented a brief introduction to the substitution reaction in which a halogen atom replaces a hydrogen atom in an alkane. An example is shown in Equation 13.5.

Eqn. 13.5

$$\text{cyclohexane} \xrightarrow[h\nu]{Br_2} \text{bromocyclohexane}$$

cyclohexane — 90% yield bromocyclohexane

All halogens except iodine react in this way. The order of reactivity is

$$F_2 > Cl_2 > Br_2$$

The reaction of fluorine with alkanes is generally not of practical utility because of the high reactivity of fluorine. In this chapter we will consider in greater detail the mechanism and synthetic applications of the halogen substitution reaction.

MECHANISM OF THE SUBSTITUTION REACTION

The halogen substitution reaction involves free radicals as intermediates in a chain reaction in which two or more steps are continuously repeated. Chain reactions are common when free radical intermediates are involved.

MECHANISM OF REACTION

Step 1 The first reaction constitutes the **chain-initiation step** for the process. In this step a reactive free radical is produced by homolysis of the bromine molecule. This step begins the entire series of reactions.

$$:\ddot{Br}-\ddot{Br}: \xrightarrow[h\nu]{\text{heat or}} 2\ :\ddot{Br}\cdot$$

Steps 2 and 3 The second and third reactions are the **chain-propagation steps,** reactions that consume one free radical and generate a new one.

$$:\ddot{Br}\cdot + H-R \longrightarrow H-\ddot{Br}: + R\cdot$$

$$R\cdot + :\ddot{Br}-\ddot{Br}: \longrightarrow R-\ddot{Br}: + :\ddot{Br}\cdot$$

The sum of Steps 2 and 3 is the net observed reaction:

$$R-H + Br_2 \longrightarrow R\ddot{Br}: + H-\ddot{Br}:$$

Steps 4, 5, and 6 The chain propagation steps are repeated continuously until interrupted by one of the **chain-termination steps.** These reactions remove free radicals from the reaction system.

$$R\cdot + :\ddot{Br}: \longrightarrow R-\ddot{Br}:$$

$$R\cdot + R\cdot \longrightarrow R-R$$

$$:\ddot{Br}\cdot + \cdot\ddot{Br}: \longrightarrow :\ddot{Br}-\ddot{Br}:$$

PROBLEM 13.5

a. Use bond energies (Table 7.1) to compare the exothermicities of the net observed reaction in the free radical fluorination, chlorination, and bromination of methane to produce, respectively, fluoromethane, chloromethane, and bromomethane.
b. Calculate the heats of reaction for Steps 2 and 3 for the bromination of methane.

DISTRIBUTION OF PRODUCTS

Suppose we use butane as our alkane substrate in a free radical chlorination reaction. Substituting a chlorine for a hydrogen atom can lead to two different products, because there are two different types of hydrogen present in butane.

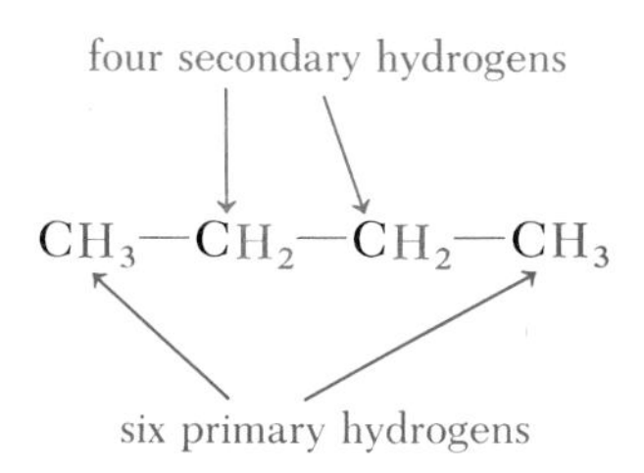

Figure 13.5 Types of hydrogen in butane. A butane molecule contains four secondary and six primary hydrogens.

Six of the ten hydrogens are primary, while the remaining four are secondary, as shown in Figure 13.5. Reaction with chlorine thus leads to either 1-chlorobutane or 2-chlorobutane, depending on the site of reaction (see Figure 13.6).

If the primary and secondary hydrogens of butane were to react with chlorine at the same rate, a statistical distribution of the two products would result. That is, three moles of 1-chlorobutane would be formed for every two moles of 2-chlorobutane, since a chlorine atom is 1.5 times as likely to collide with butane at a primary hydrogen site as at a secondary hydrogen site. However, by experiment we find that the relative yields of the two products are reversed: there are approximately three moles of 2-chlorobutane formed for every two moles of 1-chlorobutane formed. This result implies that secondary hydrogens must be *more reactive* than primary hydrogens in this type of reaction. This conclusion is confirmed by studies of other alkanes in reaction with halogens. Furthermore, if a molecule contains a tertiary hydrogen atom, that hydrogen is even more reactive than is a secondary hydrogen. Let's analyze the relative yields of the several monochlorination products of a molecule containing primary, secondary, and tertiary hydrogens (see Equation 13.6.)

Eqn. 13.6

$$(CH_3CH_2)_3CH \xrightarrow[\text{heat}]{Cl_2}$$

3-ethylpentane

	Relative Yields
$(CH_3CH_2)_3C\ddot{\underset{..}{Cl}}:$ 3-chloro-3-ethylpentane	1
$(CH_3CH_2)_2CHCHCH_3$ (with :Cl: on the CH) 2-chloro-3-ethylpentane	4.6
$(CH_3CH_2)_2CHCH_2CH_2\ddot{\underset{..}{Cl}}:$ 1-chloro-3-ethylpentane	1.8

(+ other products)

If the reaction shown in Equation 13.6 were to proceed simply according to statistics, the relative yields of 3° : 2° : 1° substituted products would be 1 : 6 : 9 (3-ethylpentane contains one 3°, six 2°, and nine 1° hydrogen atoms). Why is there more substitution of tertiary hydrogen and less substitution of primary

$$CH_3—CH_2—CH_2—CH_3 \xrightarrow{\text{substitution of primary hydrogen}} CH_3—CH_2—CH_2—CH_2—\ddot{\underset{..}{Cl}}:$$

1-chlorobutane

$$CH_3—CH_2—CH_2—CH_3 \xrightarrow{\text{substitution of secondary hydrogen}} CH_3—\underset{:\underset{..}{Cl}:}{CH}—CH_2—CH_3$$

2-chlorobutane

Figure 13.6 Possible products of chlorine substitution reaction on butane. Two monochlorinated products are formed upon free radical chlorination of butane. Replacement of any of the primary hydrogens by chlorine leads to 1-chlorobutane, while replacement of any of the secondary hydrogens leads to 2-chlorobutane (2-chlorobutane is formed as a racemic mixture of *R* and *S* enantiomers; C-2 is a stereogenic carbon atom).

SPECIAL TOPIC

A Free Radical Chain Reaction of Environmental Concern

The "Compound Capsule" of Chapter 11 introduced the Freons, which are used as propellants in aerosol cans and can rise into the stratosphere. There are concerns that this process could result in the destruction of the earth's protective ozone layer, which absorbs much of the high-energy ultraviolet radiation from the sun.

The source of ozone in the ozone layer is normal dioxygen, O_2, that has itself drifted up from the earth's atmosphere. Ultraviolet light causes some of these molecules to undergo a homolytic cleavage to oxygen atoms:

$$O_2 + h\nu \longrightarrow 2\,O^{\cdot}$$

Ozone is formed when some of these oxygen atoms react with dioxygen molecules:

$$O_2 + O^{\cdot} \longrightarrow O_3$$

The destruction of the ozone layer by Freons involves a free radical chain reaction. Ultraviolet light initiates the process by causing the homolysis of a carbon-chlorine bond of a Freon, for example,

$$CF_2Cl_2 + h\nu \longrightarrow CF_2Cl^{\cdot} + Cl^{\cdot}$$

The highly reactive chlorine radicals that are produced then react with ozone:

$$Cl^{\cdot} + O_3 \longrightarrow ClO^{\cdot} + O_2$$

The real problem is that chlorine atoms are regenerated from $ClO\cdot$ radicals through reaction with oxygen atoms (which are always present in the stratosphere, as described above):

$$ClO^{\cdot} + O^{\cdot} \longrightarrow Cl^{\cdot} + O_2$$

Thus an initial cleavage of a single Freon molecule can precipitate a chain reaction in which there is a cycle of destruction: a chlorine atom is produced and destroys an ozone molecule; this reaction produces $ClO\cdot$, which in turn reacts further to regenerate a chlorine atom. The cycle will repeat until some chain-terminating step takes place. Thus many ozone molecules can be destroyed as the result of each cleavage of a Freon molecule.

hydrogen than predicted on a statistical basis? We will now examine this question in some detail.

As we saw in Chapter 12, the rate of an entire reaction is determined by the rate of the slowest step of that reaction. We should therefore examine the slowest of the chain-propagation steps to look for clues leading to an answer to the question posed above. Simple calculations based on bond energies show that the least exothermic of the chain-propagation steps is the abstraction of a hydrogen atom by a chlorine atom (Step 2).

Many types of experimental observations confirm that this step is also the rate-determining step. Let us analyze the chlorination of butane (Figure 13.6) with this in mind. For the butane molecule there are two *competing* hydrogen abstractions. The chlorine atom can abstract either a primary hydrogen atom from one of the terminal carbon atoms or a secondary hydrogen atom from one of the interior carbon atoms. Bond energies (Table 13.1) indicate that abstraction of a secondary hydrogen atom is more favorable by 3.5 kcal/mole.

Table 13.1 C—H Bond Dissociation Energies

Bond	Bond dissociation energy (kcal/mole)
CH_3—H	104.0
RCH_2—H	98.0
R_2CH—H	94.5
R_3C—H	91.1

The Hammond postulate thus suggests that the rate of abstraction of secondary hydrogen atoms should be faster than the rate of abstraction of primary hydrogen atoms. To quantify this difference, we must take into account that the observed ratio of the two overall products of free radical chlorination of butane (1-chlorobutane and 2-chlorobutane) actually depends on *two* factors. We have already discussed the *statistical* factor—the greater the number of hydrogen atoms of a particular type, the more likely it is that such a hydrogen will be abstracted. The second factor is the *relative reactivity* (i.e., the relative rate of abstraction) for each type of hydrogen. In Equation 13.7 we see how these two factors combine to reflect the observed ratio of products.

Eqn. 13.7

$$\frac{\text{observed number of moles of } 2^\circ \text{ product}}{\text{observed number of moles of } 1^\circ \text{ product}} = \frac{\text{number of } 2^\circ \text{ H}}{\text{number of } 1^\circ \text{ H}} \times \frac{\text{reactivity of } 2^\circ \text{ H}}{\text{reactivity of } 1^\circ \text{ H}}$$

When butane undergoes free radical chlorination, the observed product ratio is approximately 3 parts 2-chlorobutane to 2 parts 1-chlorobutane. Since the ratio of primary to secondary hydrogens in the reactant is 3 : 2, substituting this value in Equation 13.7 indicates that for this compound the secondary hydrogens are 2.25 times as reactive as the primary hydrogens toward chlorine atoms (see Figure 13.7). This result is in keeping with the Hammond postulate.

Type of Hydrogen	*Statistical Ratio*		*Relative Yield of Haloalkane*
1°	1	⟶	1
2°	0.67	⟶ (factor of 2.25)	1.5

Figure 13.7 Relative yields of 1-chlorobutane and 2-chlorobutane in chlorination of butane. The ratio of primary to secondary hydrogens in butane is 1:0.67. However, free radical chlorination leads to a ratio of 1:1.5 for the products derived from substitution of primary and secondary hydrogens. It follows that the secondary hydrogens are 2.25 times as reactive as primary hydrogens with regard to abstraction by chlorine atoms.

PROBLEM 13.6 From the product distribution for the chlorination of 3-ethylpentane (Equation 13.6), calculate the relative reactivities of primary, secondary, and tertiary hydrogens of alkanes in this type of reaction.

PROBLEM 13.7 The relative yields of the monobromination products in the reaction of 3-ethylpentane with bromine are shown below. Using this data, calculate the

relative reactivities of primary, secondary, and tertiary hydrogens of alkanes in reaction with bromine atoms.

		Relative Yields
$(CH_3CH_2)_3CH \xrightarrow[\text{heat}]{Br_2}$	$(CH_3CH_2)_3C\ddot{B}r:$	1
	$(CH_3CH_2)_2CHCHCH_3$ (with $:\ddot{B}r:$ on the second CH)	0.32
	$(CH_3CH_2)_2CHCH_2CH_2\ddot{B}r:$	0.006

Bromine atoms are much less reactive than chlorine atoms toward hydrogen abstraction and also *more* discriminating among the types of hydrogen atoms abstracted (see Problem 13.7). Bromine thus offers *selectivity* in its reaction.

This selectivity provides another illustration of the Hammond postulate. Consider again the competing hydrogen abstractions in the rate-determining step of the halogenation of butane. Either a primary or a secondary hydrogen can be abstracted. Both types of abstraction are endothermic with bromine but exothermic with chlorine. This difference can be attributed to the developing hydrogen-bromine bond being weaker than a developing hydrogen-chlorine bond. To appreciate the consequences, we must look carefully at the activated complex for the rate-determining step.

Because the abstraction of a hydrogen by bromine is endothermic, we can infer that bromine abstraction will have a later (more product-like) activated complex than will chlorine abstraction. The degree to which the activated complex is early or late in this reaction determines its carbon-radical character. With bromination, the activated complex occurs late. Thus, it has more carbon-radical character than the transition state for chlorination. The activated complexes for the competing types of hydrogen abstraction differ more in their energies when bromine is used since they are closer to radicals of different stabilities than when chlorine is used (in which case both are more similar to the starting alkane). These differences are illustrated in Figure 13.8.

POLYHALOGENATION

Free radical halogenations not only can provide mixtures of monosubstituted products but also frequently yield products containing more than one halogen atom.

Consider as an example the chlorination of methane. Shortly after initiating the reaction, chloromethane begins to accumulate, and as it accumulates, it begins to compete with the remaining unreacted methane for the available chlorine atoms.

Consider the reaction when 50% of the methane has been converted to chloromethane. Chlorine atoms then have an equal probability of colliding with a methane molecule or with a chloromethane molecule. It is therefore quite likely that a chlorine atom will abstract a hydrogen from chloromethane (to form $\cdot CH_2Cl$), and this will ultimately lead to CH_2Cl_2. Therefore, we expect a sizable quantity of methylene chloride (dichloromethane) and even chloroform

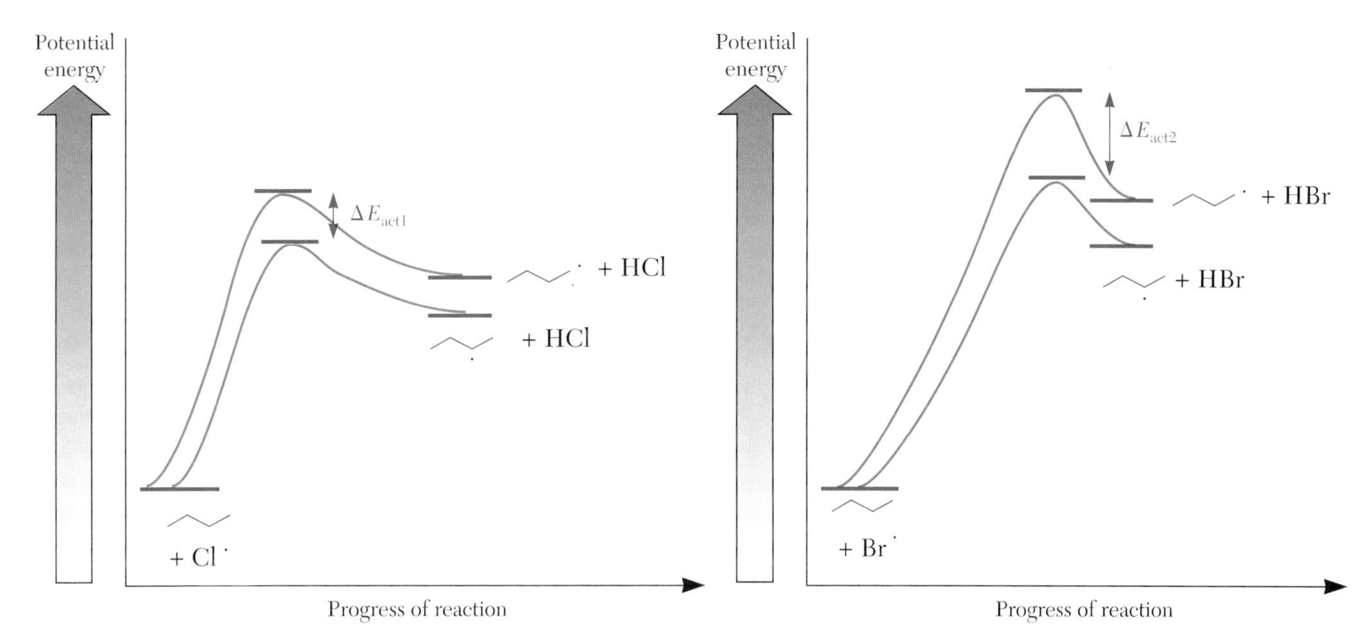

Figure 13.8 Competing abstractions of secondary and primary hydrogens from butane in free radical reactions with bromine and chlorine. The difference in activation energies is significantly greater in the bromination reaction (ΔE_{act2}) than in the chlorination reaction (ΔE_{act1}). Correspondingly, we find that the ratio of major (2°) substitution product to minor (1°) substitution product is greater with bromination than with chlorination. The Hammond postulate helps us to rationalize this result. The endothermic bromination reaction has a later activated complex and more radical character. The difference in stabilities of 1° and 2° radicals is reflected more in the bromination activated complexes than in the chlorination activated complexes. *Differences in rates of reaction depend on differences in the activation energies of the reactions being compared.*

($CHCl_3$) and carbon tetrachloride (CCl_4) to be formed if we start with equal numbers of moles of chlorine and methane. For more complex molecules, the formation of many multisubstituted products is possible, and this seriously limits the synthetic utility of the reaction.

PROBLEM 13.8

For each of the alkanes listed below, give the structure of each of the possible dichlorination products. Consider enantiomeric pairs as one product, but consider diastereoisomers as different compounds.

a. butane **b.** pentane **c.** 2-methylbutane
d. 2,2-dimethylpropane **e.** cyclopentane

Steps to Solving the Problem

Solution to Problem 13.8a

1. Look first at one substitution, then at the second. For the butane molecule there are two different types of hydrogen atoms. Thus, we can have two different monosubstitution products, 1-chlorobutane and 2-chlorobutane, as shown below.

$$:\ddot{\underset{\cdot\cdot}{Cl}}CH_2-CH_2-CH_2-CH_3 \qquad CH_3-\underset{}{\overset{:\ddot{Cl}:}{\overset{|}{C}H}}-CH_2-CH_3$$

1-chlorobutane 2-chlorobutane

2. Consider 1-chlorobutane first. For 1-chlorobutane there are four different types of hydrogen atoms (indicated by the arrows shown with the structure below) and thus there are four different sites for the second chlorine substitution. The resulting structures of these chlorine substitutions are shown on the right. Structures 2 and 3 exist as enantiomeric pairs.

$:\ddot{C}lCH_2—CH_2—CH_2—CH_3$ (arrows 1, 2, 3, 4) ⟹

$Cl_2CH—CH_2—CH_2—CH_3$ 1

$:\ddot{C}lCH_2—CH(:\ddot{C}l:)—CH_2—CH_3$ 2

$:\ddot{C}lCH_2—CH_2—CH(:\ddot{C}l:)—CH_3$ 3

$:\ddot{C}lCH_2—CH_2—CH_2—CH_2\ddot{C}l:$ 4

3. Now consider the further chlorination of 2-chlorobutane. There are four carbon atoms with hydrogen atoms available for substitution by chlorine atoms. Substitution at positions 1 or 4 of 2-chlorobutane leads to products also formed in the chlorination of 1-chlorobutane (specifically, compounds 2 and 3). Substitution of the hydrogen atom at position 2 yields a new product, 2,2-dichlorobutane (5). Substitution of a hydrogen atom at position 3 can yield different products, depending on which enantiomer of 2-chlorobutane is reacting, and which hydrogen atom is replaced. There are *two* 2,3-dichlorobutane products possible—one is a racemic mixture of the (2*R*,3*R*) and (2*S*,3*S*) enantiomers (6), and the other is the *meso* compound (7).

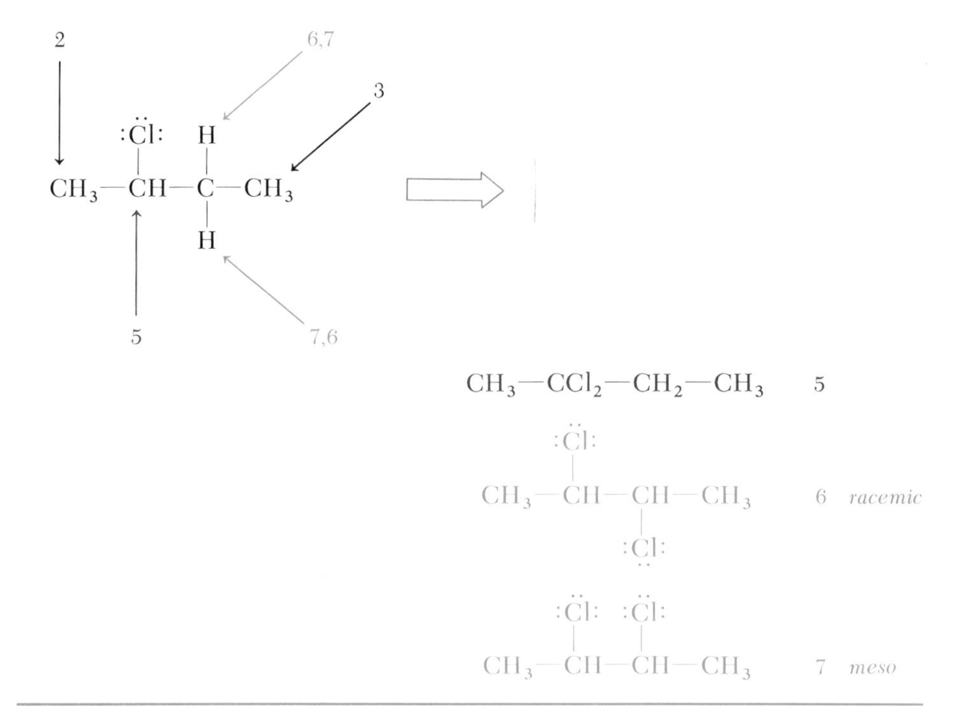

SYNTHETIC UTILITY

Since they often yield a mixture of products, free radical halogenations are of only limited synthetic utility. However, they do provide viable preparative routes for certain types of compounds.

One example is the halogenation of molecules that have only one type of carbon-hydrogen bond. For the monohalogenation of substances such as methane, ethane, 2,2-dimethylpropane, and the unsubstituted cycloalkanes, we only need to prevent multiple halogenation from occurring, and we can accomplish this by using a large excess of the hydrocarbon compared to the halogen. In this way a chlorine atom is *always* more likely to collide with a hydrocarbon molecule than with a molecule that has already undergone a halogen substitution reaction. The monohalogenation product is generally of sufficiently high boiling temperature compared to the alkane that we can isolate it with ease. If **perhalogenation** (substitution of *all* of the hydrogens in a molecule by halogen) is our goal, we use an excess of the halogen and a long reaction time.

For the introduction of a single halogen at a specific site in a complex molecule, the usefulness of free radical halogenation with molecular halogen is very limited. One exception to this limitation is the replacement of a tertiary hydrogen by a bromine. The high degree of selectivity of bromination (see Problem 13.7) allows us to accomplish this substitution efficiently.

PROBLEM 13.9 In the free radical chlorination of propane, three products of formula C_6H_{14} are formed in small quantity. Give their structures and explain their formation.

OTHER HALOGENATION REACTIONS

Other halogenating agents besides the halogen molecules themselves can be used to achieve substitution of halogen for hydrogen in alkanes. The most common of these is **sulfuryl chloride,** SO_2Cl_2. Sulfuryl chloride is the *bis* acid chloride of sulfuric acid (*both* acidic hydroxyl groups of sulfuric acid are replaced by halogen atoms). Used with a free radical initiator, sulfuryl chloride promotes chlorine substitution for hydrogen more rapidly than does chlorine itself. Moreover, it involves a liquid rather than a gaseous reagent. Its use is troubled by the same difficulties found with molecular chlorine. Specifically, multiple products are formed and the reaction is unselective. An example of the use of sulfuryl chloride is shown in Equation 13.8.

Eqn. 13.8

$$(CH_3)_2CHCH(CH_3)_2 + SO_2Cl_2 \xrightarrow[\text{benzoyl peroxide}]{\text{heat}} (CH_3)_2CHCH(CH_3)CH_2\ddot{\underset{..}{Cl}}: + (CH_3)_2CHC(CH_3)_2(:\ddot{\underset{..}{Cl}}:)$$

2,3-dimethylhexane

Products: $(CH_3)_2CHCHCH_2Cl$ with CH_3 on the second CH — 63% yield, 1-chloro-2,3-dimethylbutane; $(CH_3)_2CHC(CH_3)_2$ with :Cl: on the quaternary carbon — 37% yield, 2-chloro-2,3-dimethylbutane

PROBLEM 13.10 Compare the product distribution illustrated above for the reaction of 2,3-dimethylbutane and sulfuryl chloride with the product distribution that would be obtained using molecular chlorine. Which reagent exhibits the greater degree of selectivity?

PROBLEM 13.11 Write a mechanism for the formation of chloromethane from methane and sulfuryl chloride. (*Hint:* You need first to determine the chain-initiation step.)

13.5 Cyclopropane Formation and Reactions

Of the cycloalkanes, cyclopropane is a special case. The cyclopropane ring is highly strained, leading to chemical reactions unlike those of other cycloalkanes. In the next sections we will focus on cyclopropane and its derivatives. First, we will describe methods of synthesis and then explore the unusual reactivity of these interesting compounds. We will then look at larger ring systems in greater detail.

FORMATION OF THE CYCLOPROPANE RING

A convenient method for preparing cyclopropanes is the reaction of alkenes with divalent carbon species (i.e., compounds containing a carbon atom that is involved in only two bonds). This reaction was briefly described in the previous chapter. Divalent carbon species, sometimes called carbenes, are highly reactive and must be generated in situ.

The simplest carbene is methylene, $:CH_2$. Free methylene is most commonly produced by the decomposition (thermolysis or photolysis) of **diazomethane** (CH_2N_2), which is a highly toxic and explosive compound. We must generate diazomethane itself in situ and handle it with great care. In the reaction scheme shown in Figure 13.9, it is generated by the reaction of base on N-nitroso-N-methyltoluenesulfonamide. Also shown is the reaction of methylene (from decomposition of diazomethane) with 2-methylpropene.

Figure 13.9 Formation and reaction of methylene. Methylene is prepared by the decomposition of diazomethane. Diazomethane must be prepared in situ. One method involves treating N-nitroso-N-methyltoluenesulfonamide with base. Once formed, diazomethane can undergo several types of reactions. With 2-methylpropene, the major route of reaction is addition to the olefinic linkage. Minor products result from its insertion into carbon-hydrogen and carbon-carbon bonds.

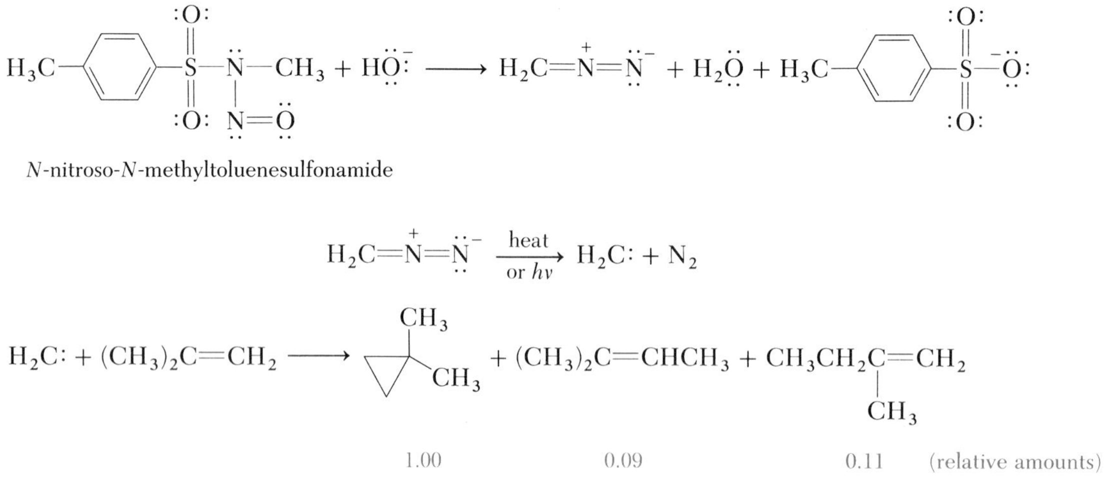

$$H_3C{-}C_6H_4{-}SO_2{-}N(N{=}O){-}CH_3 + HO^- \longrightarrow H_2C{=}\overset{+}{N}{=}N^- + H_2O + H_3C{-}C_6H_4{-}SO_2{-}O^-$$

N-nitroso-N-methyltoluenesulfonamide

$$H_2C{=}\overset{+}{N}{=}N^- \xrightarrow[\text{or } h\nu]{\text{heat}} H_2C: + N_2$$

$$H_2C: + (CH_3)_2C{=}CH_2 \longrightarrow \text{1,1-dimethylcyclopropane} + (CH_3)_2C{=}CHCH_3 + CH_3CH_2C(CH_3){=}CH_2$$

1.00 0.09 0.11 (relative amounts)

PROBLEM 13.12 Diazomethane was represented in Figure 13.9 by a structure having two double bonds and opposite charges on adjacent nitrogen atoms. Show a further resonance structure in which every atom has a complete octet of electrons. Indicate formal charges in your structure.

Difficulties in performing reactions with diazomethane and the complex nature of the products obtained have spurred the search for other methods of generating cyclopropanes. One method that achieves a cyclopropane synthesis while avoiding the difficulties of methylene generation is the **Simmons-Smith reaction.** In the Simmons-Smith reaction, diiodomethane is treated with a zinc-copper alloy to give an organometallic species. The structure of this organometallic is complex, but it is usually shown in simplified form as in **13.1.**

$$:\ddot{\underset{..}{I}}-CH_2-Zn\ddot{\underset{..}{I}}:$$

(prepared from CH_2I_2 + Zn)

13.1

This reagent undergoes reaction with alkenes to give cyclopropanes as the only product. Examples are shown in Equations 13.9 and 13.10. The reaction is completely stereospecific—the geometry of the original alkene is maintained in the cyclopropane product. As shown in Equation 13.9, the reaction of *cis*-2-butene produces only *cis*-1,2-dimethylcyclopropane.

Eqn. 13.9

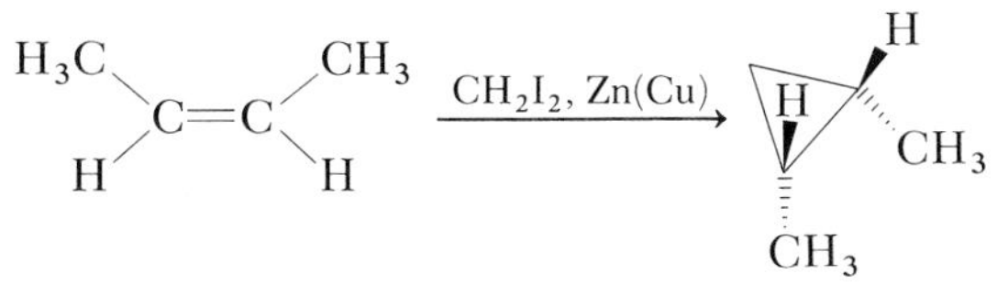

$H_3C(H)C=C(H)CH_3$ $\xrightarrow{CH_2I_2,\ Zn(Cu)}$ cyclopropane with H, CH_3, H, CH_3

cis-2-butene

50% yield
cis-1,2-dimethylcyclopropane

Eqn. 13.10

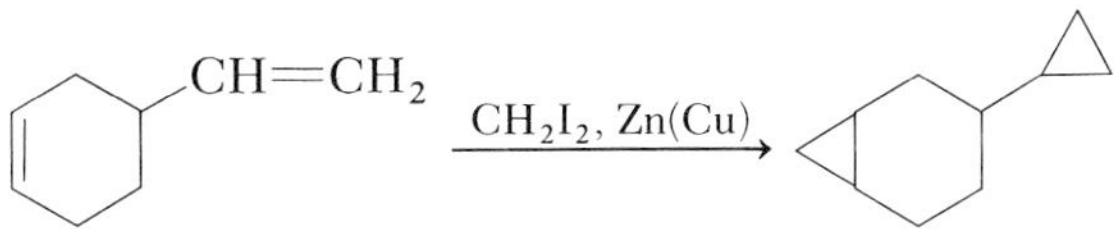

cyclohexene–$CH{=}CH_2$ $\xrightarrow{CH_2I_2,\ Zn(Cu)}$

4-vinylcyclohexene

67% yield
3-cyclopropylnorcarane

No free methylene ($:CH_2$ species) is generated in the Simmons-Smith reaction. However, the organometallic reacts to give the same product as would have been formed by $:CH_2$ itself. For this reason we say that the organmetallic is a *carbenoid* or a *carbene-equivalent*.

Other divalent carbon species can be prepared and allowed to react with alkenes to form cyclopropanes. The most common of these is dichlorocarbene, which we met in Chapter 12. We will now look at the mechanism of its production from chloroform and its reaction with cyclohexene.

MECHANISM OF REACTION

Overall:

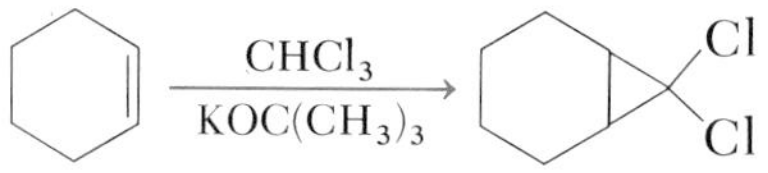

$$\text{cyclohexene} \xrightarrow[KOC(CH_3)_3]{CHCl_3} \text{7,7-dichlorobicyclo[4.1.0]heptane}$$

Step 1 Acid/base reaction of chloroform and *tert*-butoxide ion:

$$HCCl_3 + {}^{-}\!:\ddot{O}C(CH_3)_3 \longrightarrow {}^{-}\!:CCl_3 + H\ddot{O}C(CH_3)_3$$

Step 2 Loss of chloride ion from the trichloromethyl anion:

$$^{-}\!:CCl_3 \longrightarrow :\ddot{Cl}:^{-} + :CCl_2$$

Step 3 Addition of dichlorocarbene to the alkene:

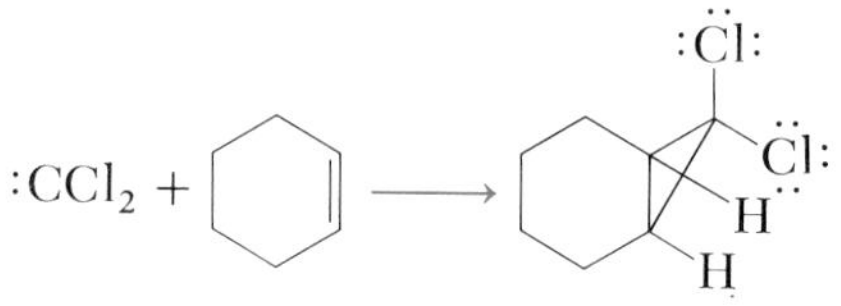

$$:CCl_2 + \text{cyclohexene} \longrightarrow \text{bicyclic product with } :\ddot{Cl}:, :\ddot{Cl}:, H, H$$

CLEAVAGE REACTIONS OF THE CYCLOPROPANE RING

Cyclopropane and its derivatives undergo a number of reactions that are not typical of alkanes or of other cycloalkanes. These special reactions are a direct result of the nature of the ring carbon-carbon bonds in cyclopropanes. For example, 1,1-diethylcyclopropane reacts with hydrogen gas in the presence of a platinum catalyst to form 3,3-dimethylpentane, as shown in Equation 13.11.

Eqn. 13.11

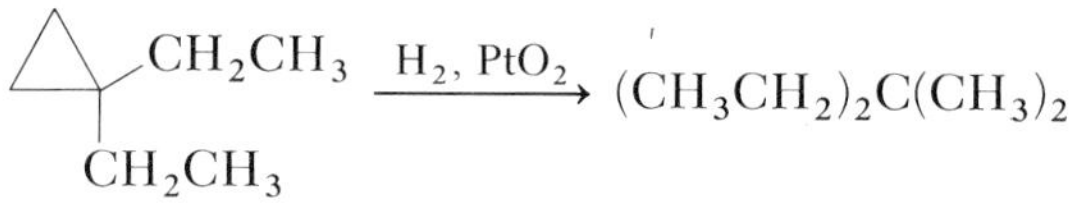

$$\text{cyclopropane}(CH_2CH_3)(CH_2CH_3) \xrightarrow{H_2,\ PtO_2} (CH_3CH_2)_2C(CH_3)_2$$

1,1-diethylcyclopropane — 80% yield 3,3-dimethylpentane

Carbon-carbon bonds that are *not* part of a cyclopropane ring are not broken under these conditions, and of the ring bonds, it is the least substituted bond that is broken. Cyclopropane rings can be cleaved selectively in the presence of other rings under these conditions. An example is shown in Equation 13.12.

Eqn. 13.12

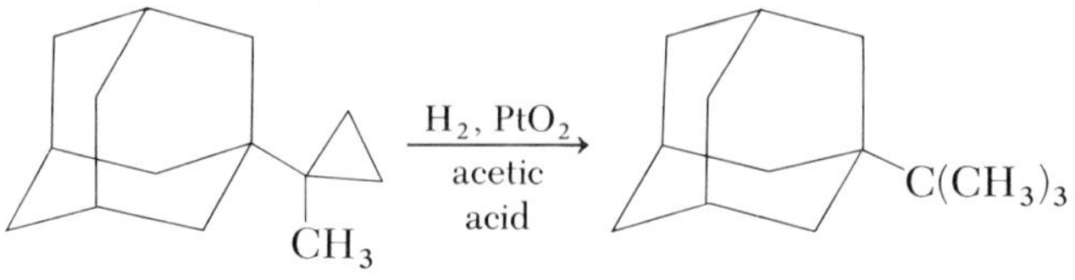

$$\text{adamantyl–cyclopropane}(CH_3) \xrightarrow[\text{acetic acid}]{H_2,\ PtO_2} \text{adamantyl–}C(CH_3)_3$$

1-(1-adamantyl)-1-methylcyclopropane — 96% yield 1-*tert*-butyladamantane

The cyclopropane ring is also unique among rings in its reaction with halogens. Cyclopropanes undergo *addition reactions* with halogens, while other cycloalkanes (and alkanes) undergo only free radical substitution reactions. An example of this type of reaction is shown in Equation 13.13.

Eqn. 13.13

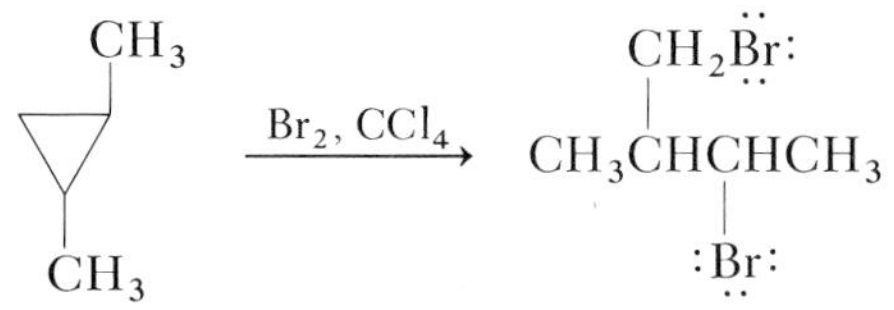

$$\text{trans-1,2-dimethylcyclopropane} \xrightarrow{Br_2,\ CCl_4} CH_3CH(CH_2Br)CH(Br)CH_3$$

trans-1,2-dimethylcyclopropane — 84% yield 1,3-dibromo-2-methylbutane

Likewise, hydrogen halides add to cyclopropane and its derivatives, as shown in Equation 13.14.

Eqn. 13.14

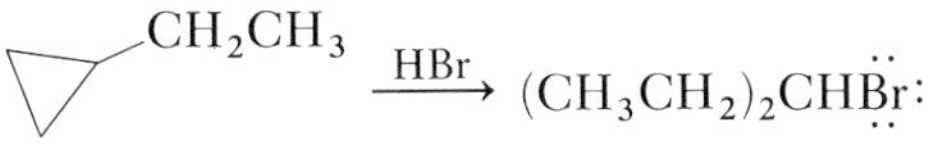

$$\text{ethylcyclopropane} \xrightarrow{HBr} (CH_3CH_2)_2CHBr$$

ethylcyclopropane — 79% yield 3-bromopentane

13.6 Comparison of Cyclopropane, Cyclobutane, and Cyclopentane

Cyclopropane suffers not only from angle strain but also from torsional strain. The molecule is forced into a rigid triangular structure in which hydrogen atoms on adjacent carbon atoms are essentially eclipsed, as shown in Figure 13.10. Approximately 6 kcal/mole of strain in cyclopropane can be attributed to this feature.

Unlike cyclopropane, cyclobutane is able to undergo some bending away from a rigidly planar structure. In the gas phase the cyclobutane ring is somewhat puckered, as shown in Figure 13.11. The ring puckering relieves the considerable torsional strain (at the expense of angle strain) that would be present in a planar structure. There would be eight hydrogen-hydrogen eclipsing interactions in a planar structure. The geometry of some substituted cyclobutanes, however, is planar or close to planar.

In general, we find that as the size of the ring increases, deviations from planarity decrease the amount of torsional strain.

If we view the cyclobutane molecule in a Newman projection along one of the ring bonds, we can see the limits to rotation, as illustrated in Figure 13.12.

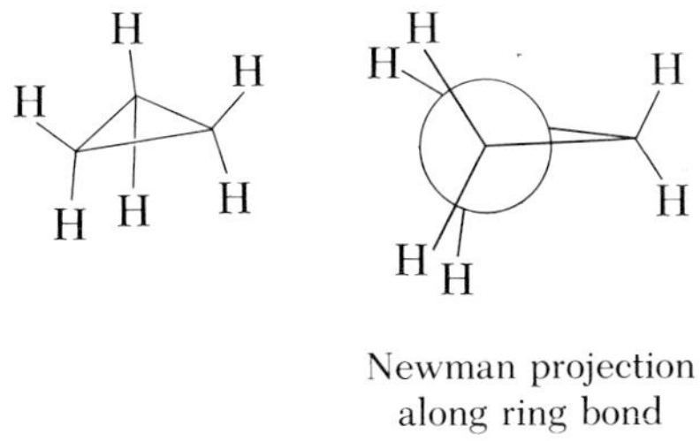

Newman projection along ring bond

Figure 13.10 Eclipsing in cyclopropane. Torsional strain is present along with angle strain.

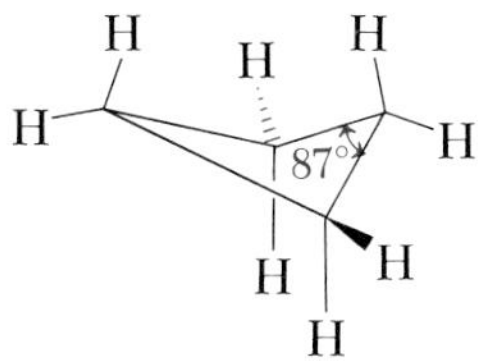

87°

Figure 13.11 Puckered ring of cyclobutane. The puckering of the ring overcomes the torsional strain that would be present if the ring were planar.

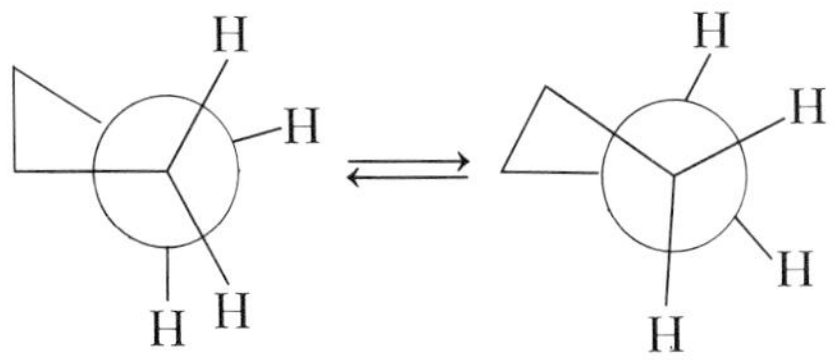

Figure 13.12 Newman projections of cyclobutane. The limit to rotation about a ring carbon-carbon bond of cyclobutane is rather small. For the interconversion of the (limiting) structures shown, each ring bond must undergo a rotation of approximately 70°. Rotation about a ring bond can proceed no further in either direction, or else the remaining bonds will be stretched to breaking.

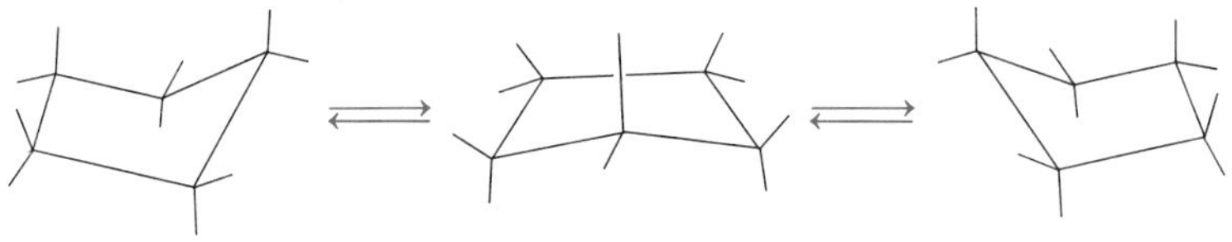

Figure 13.13 Puckered conformations of cyclopentane. An equilibrium of different puckered forms exists in cyclopentane.

The stereochemistry of cyclopentane is rather interesting. If the molecule were planar, the internal bond angles of cyclopentane would be very close to tetrahedral. We can compute the interior angles of any regular polygon using the formula

$$a = [180 - (360/n)]$$

where n is the number of sides to the polygon. We thus see that a regular pentagon has interior angles of 108°, very close to the tetrahedral angle of 109°28′. Clearly, there would be little angle strain in planar cyclopentane. However, planar cyclopentane would possess considerable torsional strain because there would be ten hydrogen-hydrogen eclipsing interactions. Cyclopentane, like cyclobutane, bends from a planar structure to avoid the torsional strain.

One of the puckered forms of cyclopentane has four of the five carbon atoms in the ring occupying approximately the same plane. However, the fifth carbon atom is twisted slightly out of that plane. Moreover, the ring bonds undergo rapid (albeit small) rotation, moving the molecule between different puckered forms (see Figure 13.13). The energy barrier for this interconversion is measured as 5.2 kcal/mole.

13.7 Cyclohexane Rings

CHAIR CONFORMATIONS: EQUATORIAL AND AXIAL BONDS

The cyclohexane ring (and other six-membered rings) occupy a special place among cyclic structures. Six-membered rings are the most important and common of all ring systems. Among the important groups of compounds containing six-membered rings are hormones, many plant products, and sugars. Heat of combustion data shows that a cyclohexane ring is unstrained. This lack of strain accounts in part for its common occurrence.

There are several shapes that a cyclohexane ring can assume; some important ones are shown in Figure 13.14. The most important of these conformations is the **chair conformation,** in which all forms of strain are at a minimum. Compare the chair and boat conformations, shown together in Figure 13.15. Models are shown along with conventionally drawn structures. Although both conformations are free of angle strain, the **boat conformation** suffers from hydrogen-hydrogen eclipsing interactions while the chair does not.

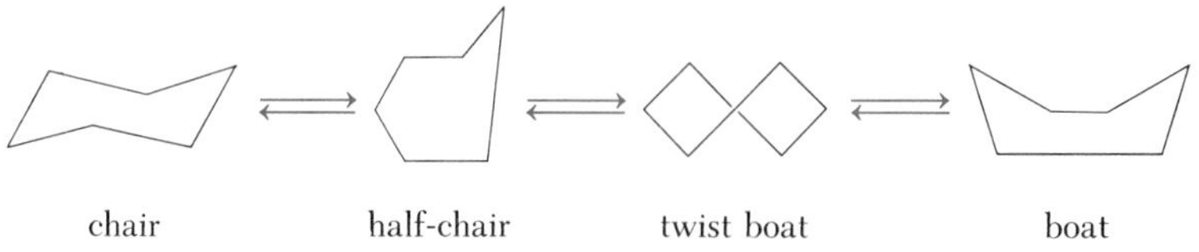

Figure 13.14 Various conformations of cyclohexane.

chair half-chair twist boat boat

Figure 13.15 Views of chair and boat conformations of cyclohexane. Sighting along the ring bonds produces Newman projections for each conformation. With the chair conformation we clearly see that all carbon-hydrogen bonds on adjacent carbon atoms are staggered (we get the same view no matter which ring bonds we choose). With the boat conformation we see eclipsing of four pairs of carbon-hydrogen bonds as well as the carbon-methylene bonds. The boat conformation is 7.1 kcal/mole less stable than the chair conformation.

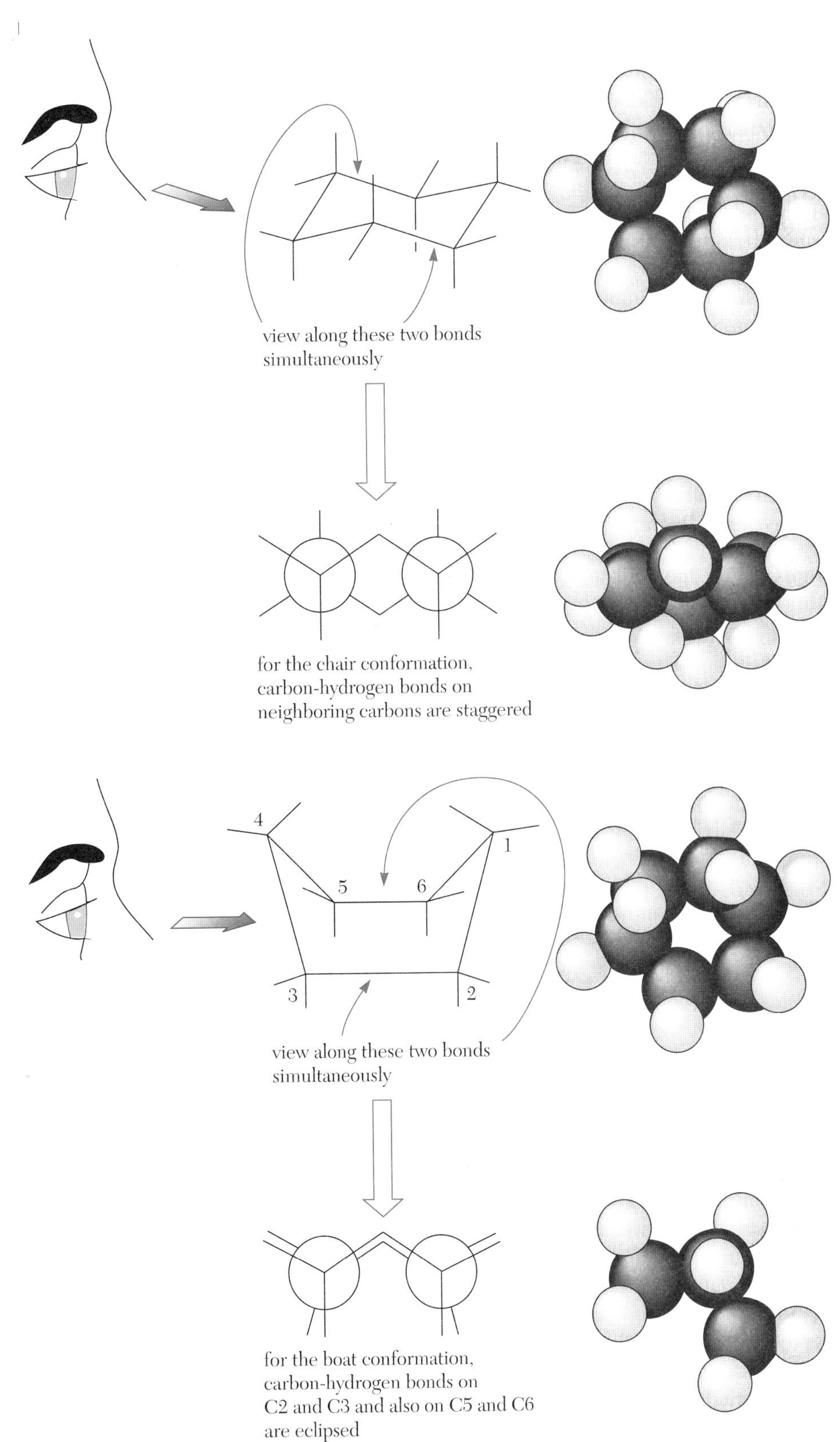
view along these two bonds simultaneously
for the chair conformation, carbon-hydrogen bonds on neighboring carbons are staggered
4
1
5
6
3
2
view along these two bonds simultaneously
for the boat conformation, carbon-hydrogen bonds on C2 and C3 and also on C5 and C6 are eclipsed

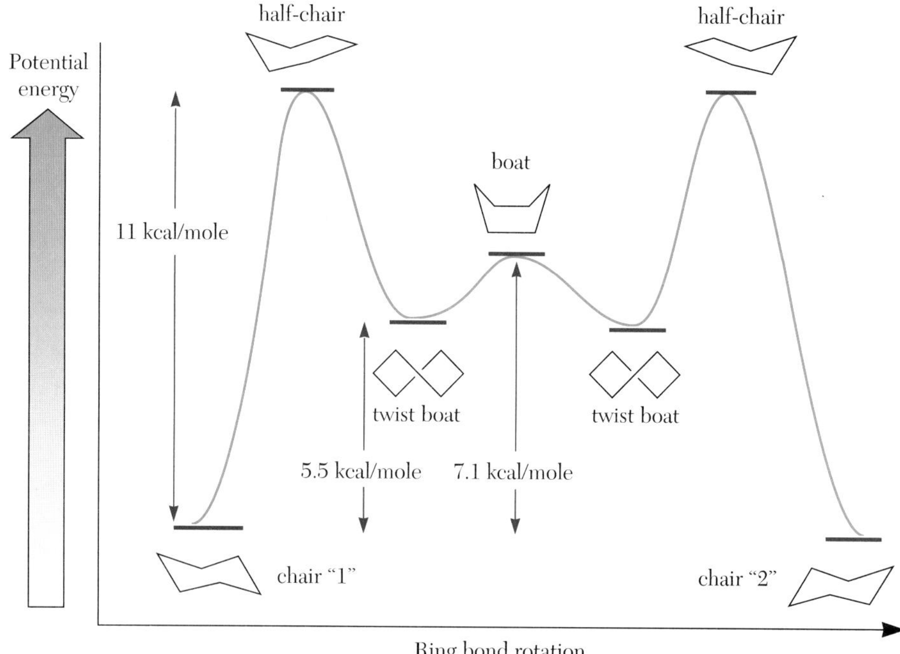

Figure 13.16 Energies of conformations of cyclohexane. The conformations of cyclohexane are interconverted by partial rotation about the ring bonds. The chair form is the most stable form. Note that upon rotation, one chair conformation is converted into a different chair conformation.

The relative energies of the several conformations of cyclohexane are shown in Figure 13.16. In the following discussion we will concentrate on the chair conformation, which is the conformation most commonly adopted by cyclohexane and its derivatives. However, we will also need to discuss the boat conformation when we consider bicyclic molecules with six-membered rings.

Chair structures have several subtle but extremely important nuances that are best seen with molecular models. Models of the chair and boat conformations were shown in Figure 13.15. We strongly suggest that you work through this section with a molecular model in hand. A measure of the significance of this area of organic chemistry is that Professor Derek Barton (formerly of Imperial College, London; presently at Texas A & M University) and Otto Hassell (University of Oslo, Norway) were awarded the Nobel Prize in 1969 for their insights into the conformational analysis of cyclohexane derivatives.

Although models are invaluable, you must also learn to *draw* the chair conformation properly. Figure 13.17 illustrates some important features of a properly drawn structure.

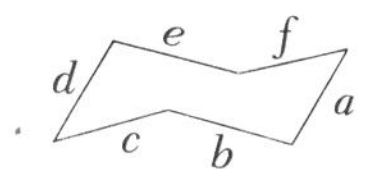

Bonds *e* and *b* are parallel and slanted slightly down. Bonds *a* and *d* are parallel, as are bonds *c* and *f*.

Figure 13.17 Chair conformation of cyclohexane. An accurately drawn chair conformation for cyclohexane should have three sets of parallel ring bonds. When viewing such a drawing, we recognize (by convention) that a lower bond (such as *b*) is in front (closer to the viewer) and that an upper bond (such as *e*) is in back (further from the viewer).

A very important feature of the chair conformation of cyclohexane is that two different types of carbon-hydrogen bonds are present: **axial** and **equatorial.** The six equatorial carbon-hydrogen bonds of cyclohexane are emphasized in the structure shown in Figure 13.18. These equatorial bonds are directed out from the sides of the ring, alternating slightly up and down with dihedral angles of 60° relative to adjacent equatorial bonds.

The remaining six carbon-hydrogen bonds of cyclohexane are directed up and down from the top and bottom of the ring. Three of these (on alternate carbons) are directed upward from the plane, and the remaining three are directed downward. These bonds, referred to as axial bonds, are shown in Figure 13.19.

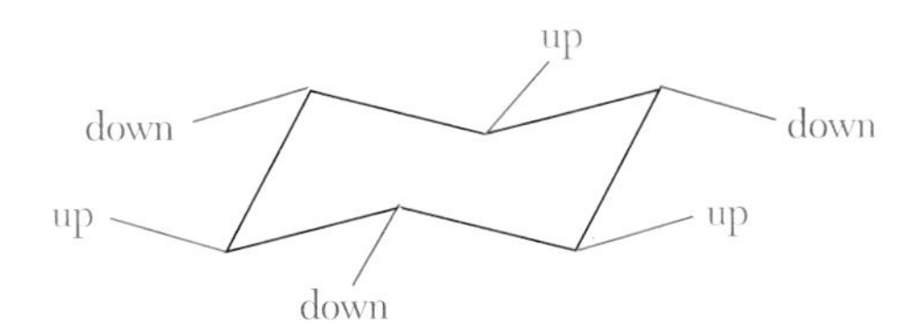

Equatorial bonds are directed out from the side of the ring. They alternate slightly up, down, up, down, up, down about the ring.

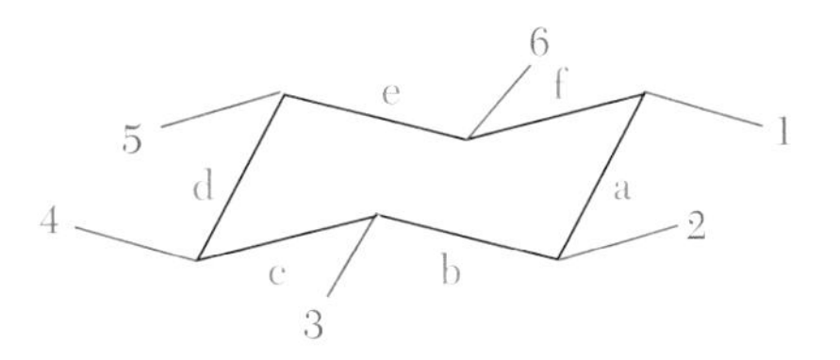

In a properly drawn structure, equatorial bonds are shown parallel to ring bonds. For example, C—H bond 1 is parallel to ring bonds *e* and *b*.

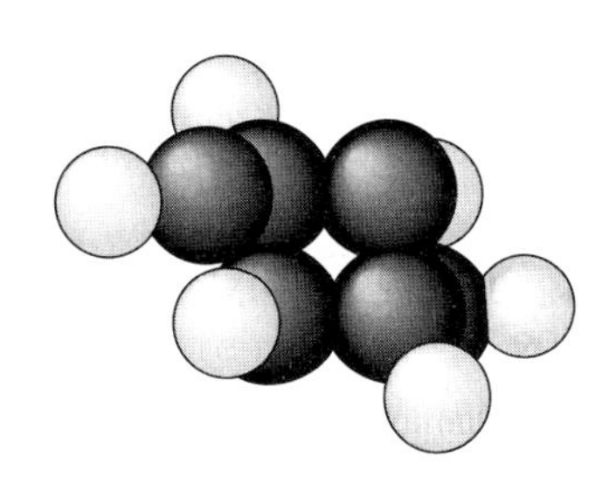

Figure 13.18 The six equatorial carbon-hydrogen bonds of cyclohexane. Beside the drawings is shown a model of cyclohexane emphasizing the equatorial bonds (the axial bonds have been deleted). Notice that bonds 6, 2, and 1 all point to the right, while bonds 5, 4, and 3 all point to the left.

In general, substituents on a cyclohexane ring are referred to as being in an *axial* or an *equatorial position*, depending on the type of bond attaching them to the ring.

Some bonds in a chair conformation point up and some point down. This difference is most notable upon comparing axial bonds but is also true for equatorial bonds. *Both* axial and equatorial bonds alternate in pointing up and down on adjacent carbon atoms around the ring. These orientations are important for recognizing *cis*/*trans* relationships. For example, a 1,2-dichlorocyclohexane in which both chlorine atoms are adjacent and equatorial is the *trans* isomer, since one equatorial carbon-chlorine bond points up and the other points down. In another form of the same isomer (another conformation), both chlorines occupy adjacent axial positions (see Figure 13.20). These *diequatorial* and *diaxial* structures are actually different conformational forms of *trans*-1,2-dichlorocyclohexane, and they are in equilibrium with each other (we will consider this equilibrium in more detail in the next section). If we consider *cis*-1,2-dichlorocyclohexane, we recognize that one of the chlorines must be equatorial and the other axial, as shown in Figure 13.21.

Figure 13.19 Axial bonds in the chair conformation of cyclohexane. The structure on the left shows the arrangement of the six axial bonds (the equatorial bonds are not shown for reasons of clarity). On the right is shown the chair cyclohexane structure with the full set of axial and equatorial bonds. Note that on any carbon atom there is one axial and one equatorial bond. Furthermore, notice that if the axial bond points down, the equatorial bond points up, and vice versa.

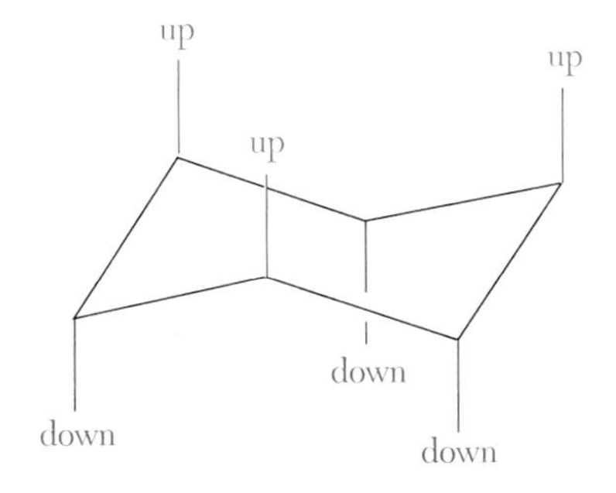

The six axial carbon-hydrogen bonds of cyclohexane are shown. Like equatorial bonds, they alternate up and down on adjacent carbon atoms.

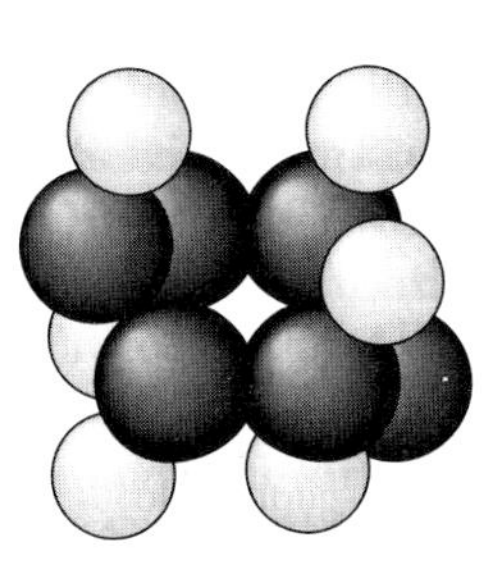

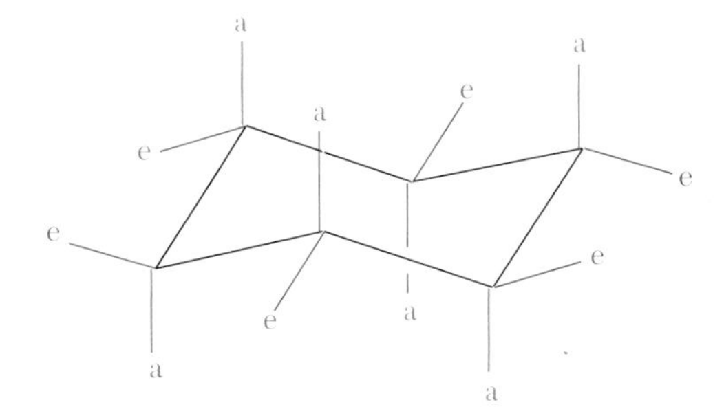

Figure 13.20 Conformations of *trans*-1,2-dichlorocyclohexane. A chair conformation of *trans*-1,2-dichlorocyclohexane must have either both chlorines axial or both chlorines equatorial.

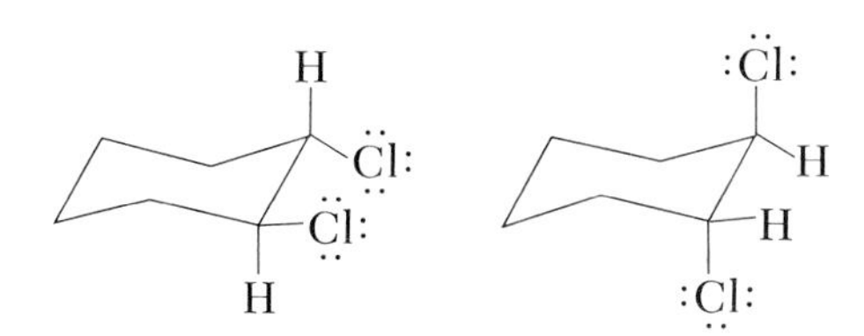

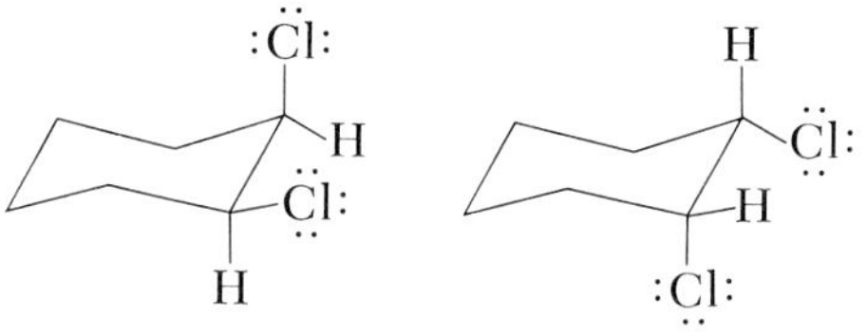

Figure 13.21 Chair conformations of *cis*-1,2-dichlorocyclohexane. In the chair conformation of *cis*-1,2-dichlorocyclohexane, one chlorine must be axial and one must be equatorial.

PROBLEM 13.13 Classify as *cis* or *trans* the dibromocyclohexanes in which:

a. The two bromines are in a 1,3-relationship and both occupy equatorial positions
b. The two bromines are in a 1,4-relationship and one is axial while the other is equatorial

TWO CHAIR FORMS IN DYNAMIC EQUILIBRIUM

Because of the geometric constraints of the ring system, only partial rotation is possible about the ring bonds of cyclohexane. The maximum rotation about a ring carbon-carbon bond is only 120°. If each ring bond undergoes a rotation of 120° simultaneously, one chair form is converted into another chair form, as illustrated in Figure 13.22. One way to visualize this conversion is to think of one corner rotating upward as the opposite corner rotates downward. Note that in the process of ring bond rotation, *each* original axial bond becomes equatorial and *each* original equatorial bond becomes axial. Models are of *substantial* help in visualizing these changes.

PROBLEM 13.14 Using Newman projections of each of the chair conformations of cyclohexane shown in Figure 13.25, confirm that the total rotation about a ring bond is 120°.

The rotations about cyclohexane ring bonds occur very rapidly under normal laboratory conditions. Since there is only a low energy barrier for the rotation (see Figure 13.16), the two chair forms interconvert readily and are in dynamic equilibrium. Moreover, since the two forms are of equal energy, they are present in equal amounts at equilibrium. Each hydrogen has an equal probability of being found in an axial or an equatorial position at any given time.

For substituted cyclohexanes, the two possible chair conformations are generally not of equal energy. The simplest cases to consider are monosubstituted cyclohexanes. The chair conformation in which the substituent is in an equatorial position is more stable and therefore more abundant (see Figure 13.23).

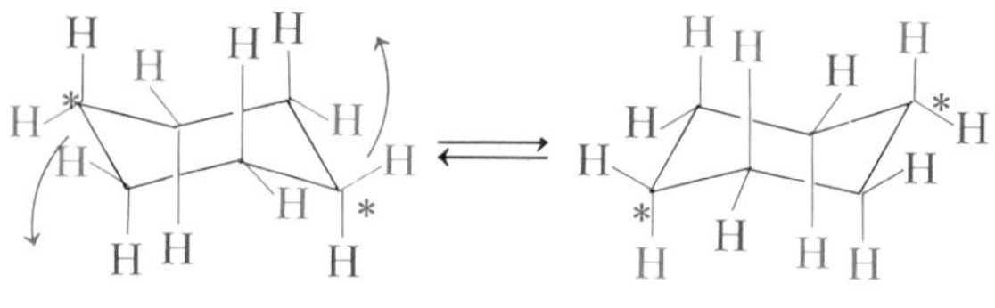

Figure 13.22 Interconversion of chair conformations of cyclohexane. Consider the starred carbon atoms being rotated in the directions indicated. Each of the equatorial and axial positions is interconverted in the process.

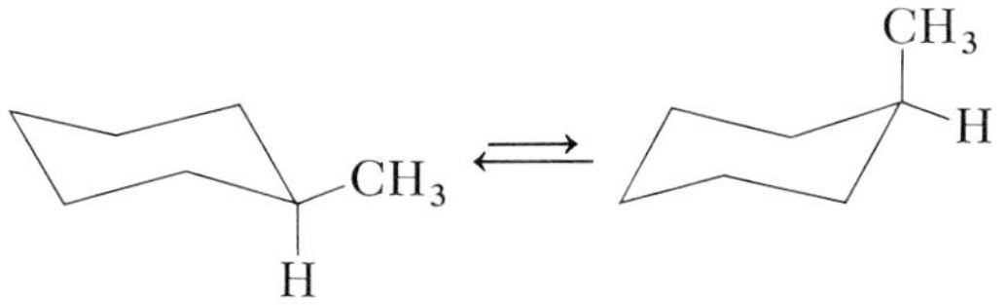

Figure 13.23 Conformations of methylcyclohexane. The conformation with the methyl group in an equatorial position is the more stable one by 1.8 kcal/mole. At room temperature 95% of methylcyclohexane molecules exist with the methyl group in an equatorial position.

conformation with equatorial methyl; 95% at equilibrium

conformation with axial methyl; 5% at equilibrium

2.3 angstrom

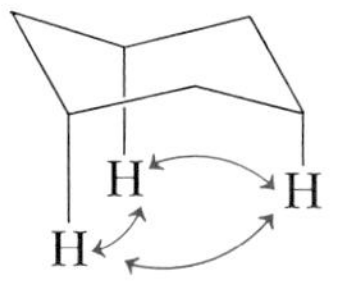

Figure 13.24 Axial hydrogens of cyclohexane. The axial hydrogens of cyclohexane are too far apart to produce any steric strain among them.

The difference in energy between the two conformations results from steric strain. To appreciate its source, we need to examine closely the spatial relationship among the axial substituents. If we view an unsubstituted cyclohexane molecule, we see three axial hydrogens pointing down and another three pointing up. The three axial hydrogens lying on the same side of the ring are too far apart to produce any steric strain (Figure 13.24).

However, when an axial hydrogen is replaced by an axial methyl group, there is steric strain. The distance between the axial methyl group and the axial hydrogens is less than the sum of their van der Waals radii. This steric interaction is called a **1,3-methyl/hydrogen diaxial interaction.** The conformation in which the methyl group is in an equatorial position suffers no such steric strain since the methyl group points away from the rest of the molecule. (Figure 13.25).

The strain resulting from a 1,3-methyl/hydrogen diaxial interaction is the same strain we associate with a gauche-butane interaction. The identical magnitude of the interaction is not a coincidence. The steric strain embodied in a 1,3-methyl/hydrogen diaxial interaction can be viewed using a Newman projection as a gauche-butane interaction between a methyl and a methylene group, as shown in Figure 13.26.

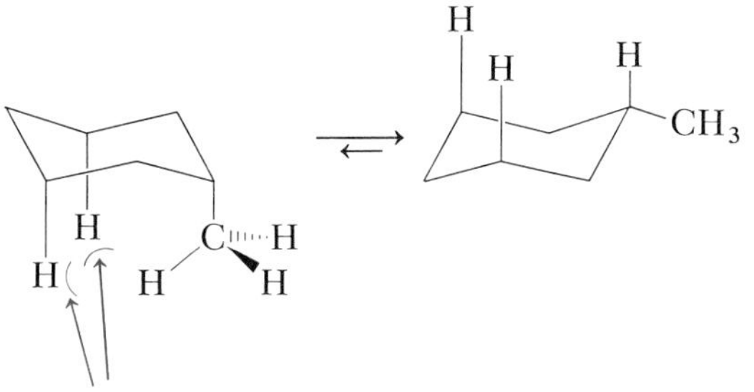

Figure 13.25 1,3-Methyl/hydrogen diaxial interaction. Axial methylcyclohexane suffers from two 1,3-methyl/hydrogen diaxial interactions. Each interaction destabilizes the structure by 0.9 kcal/mole, for a total destabilization of 1.8 kcal/mole.

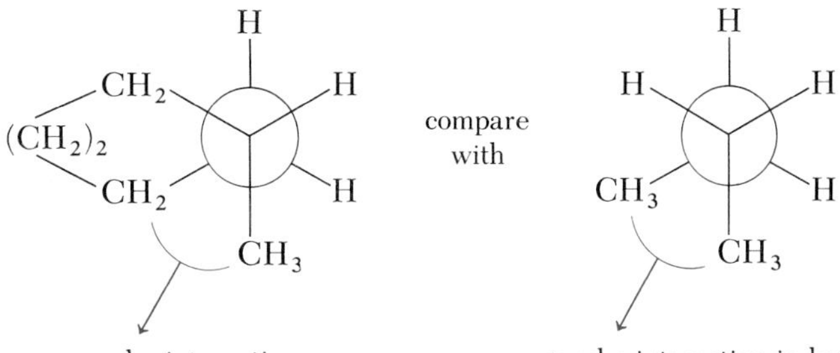

1,3-methyl/hydrogen diaxial interactions

methyl group causes no steric strain

Figure 13.26 Gauche interaction in axial methylcyclohexane. The interaction involves the methyl group and a methylene (CH_2) of the ring. There are two of these interactions in an axial methylcyclohexane molecule. A view of the gauche conformation of butane is also shown for comparison.

compare with

gauche interaction

gauche interaction in butane

Table 13.2 Steric Strain Associated with 1,3-Diaxial Interactions

Substituent	CH_3	C_2H_5	$CH(CH_3)_2$	$C(CH_3)_3$	OH	Cl, Br
Strain due to one H—Y interaction (kcal/mole)	0.90	0.96	1.10	2.70	.50	0.24

PROBLEM 13.15 One of the gauche-butane–type interactions of axial methylcyclohexane was shown in Figure 13.26. Draw Newman projections of the molecule (labeling all carbon atoms in all views) to show both such interactions.

Describing the repulsion as a 1,3-methyl/hydrogen diaxial interaction or as a gauche-butane interaction are equivalent ways of describing the same phenomenon.

The amount of steric strain associated with an axial substituent depends on the bulk of the substituent. The magnitudes of the strain caused by some common substituents are shown in Table 13.2.

PROBLEM 13.16 Notice in Table 13.2 that there is only a small jump in the magnitude of a 1,3-diaxial interaction on going from ethyl to isopropyl, but the value more than doubles on going from isopropyl to *tert*-butyl. Suggest an explanation for this observation. (Use molecular models if necessary.)

When the substituent is very large, such as a *tert*-butyl group, there is a large destabilization of the conformation with the group in an axial position. As a result, the axial conformation is present only in trace amounts in the equilibrium mixture. Nevertheless, the two structures are still rapidly interconverting, as is illustrated in Figure 13.27. At any given moment, a snapshot of the mixture would show 999+ molecules of the structure *e* for every molecule of structure *a*.

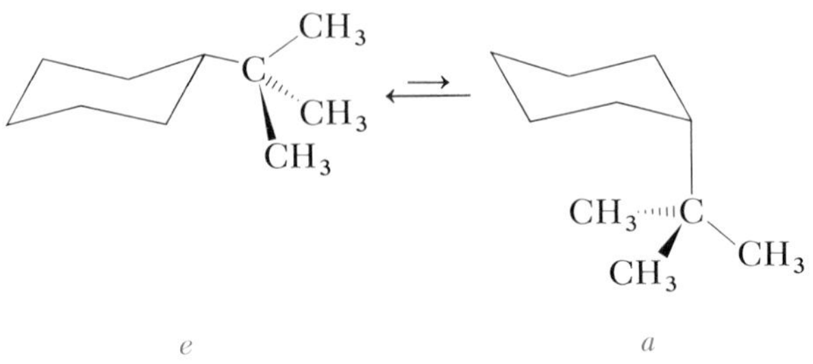

CH_3 C CH_3 CH_3 ⟷ CH_3 C CH_3 CH_3

e *a*

Figure 13.27 Conformations of *tert*-butylcyclohexane. The *tert*-butyl group is responsible for a large steric strain when present in an axial position. The result is that only one chair conformation needs to be considered, the conformation on the left. Similarly, other cyclohexane derivatives containing a *tert*-butyl group tend to adopt a conformation in which the *tert*-butyl group is equatorial.

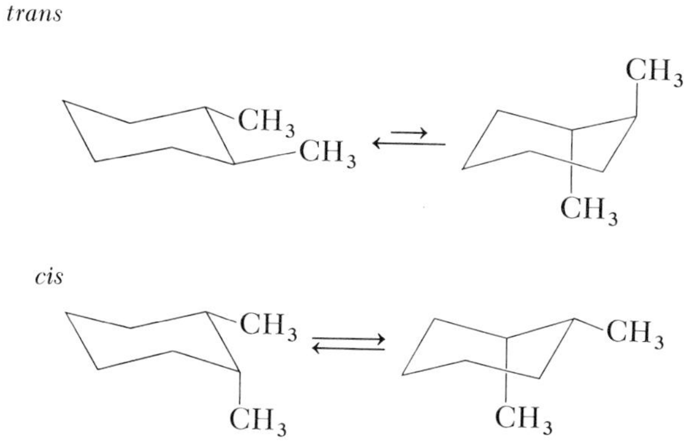

Figure 13.28 Chair conformations of *trans*- and *cis*-1,2-dimethylcyclohexanes. For the *trans* isomer, the chair with both methyl groups equatorial is significantly more stable than the chair with both methyl groups axial. Almost all (>99%) of the *trans*-1,2-dimethylcyclohexane molecules exist in the diequatorial form. For the *cis* isomer, one methyl group must be axial regardless of the chair adopted, and the amounts of the two conformers are equal.

trans

CH_3 CH_3 ⇌ CH_3 CH_3

cis

CH_3 CH_3 ⇌ CH_3 CH_3

PROBLEM 13.17 Are the chlorine atoms equatorial or axial in the more important chair conformation of

a. *cis*-1-chloro-4-*tert*-butylcyclohexane
b. *trans*-1-chloro-2-*tert*-butylcyclohexane

In summary, the chair conformation for monosubstituted cyclohexanes is more stable with the substituent in an equatorial position than in an axial position. For disubstituted or polysubstituted cyclohexanes, this analysis is not so simple. Consider *trans*-1,2-dimethylcyclohexane and *cis*-1,2-dimethylcyclohexane.

For the *trans* isomer, the two conformations shown in Figure 13.28 are possible. The conformation with both methyl groups in equatorial positions is far more stable than that with both methyl groups in axial positions. However, with the *cis* isomer, each of the two possible conformations necessarily involves one methyl group in an axial position; locating one substituent in an axial position cannot be avoided, regardless of the chair conformation adopted.

PROBLEM 13.18 The diequatorial form of *trans*-1,2-dimethylcyclohexane contains no axial methyl group, yet it suffers from 0.9 kcal/mole of strain. Similarly, *cis*-1,2-dimethylcyclohexane suffers from 2.7 kcal/mole strain, although it contains only one axial methyl group. Explain why.

PROBLEM 13.19 Estimate the difference in the heats of combustion of *cis*- and *trans*-1,2-dimethylcyclohexane.

Although there is a general preference for substituents to assume equatorial positions, at times the location of a substituent in an axial position is favored by other interactions. Hydrogen bonding is one important interaction that produces this result. An example is illustrated in Figure 13.29.

Figure 13.29 Conformations of *cis*-1,3-cyclohexanediol. The diaxial form is favored over the diequatorial form due to a favorable hydrogen-bonding interaction in the diaxial conformation. The stabilization of intramolecular hydrogen bonding is absent in the diequatorial conformation.

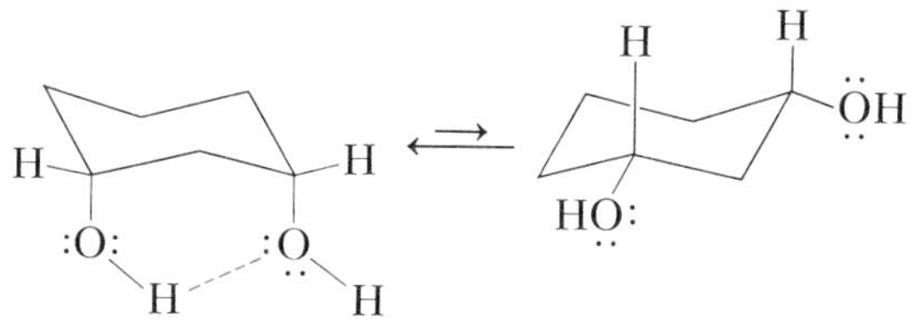

Figure 13.30 Interconversion of chair and boat forms of cyclohexane. A chair conformation is changed into a boat by twisting only one corner.

twist corner up

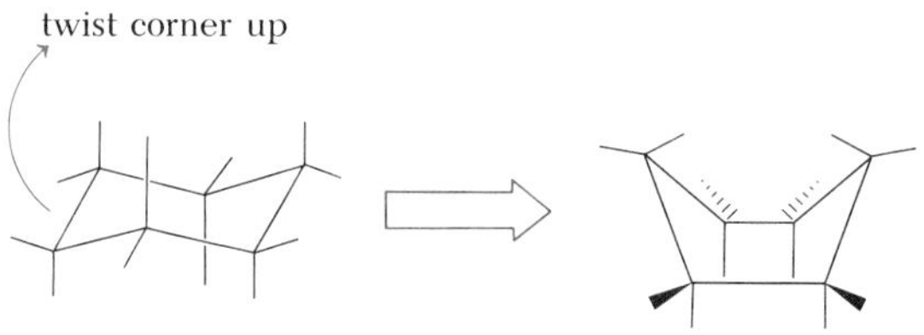

13.8 A Closer Look at Other Cyclohexane Conformations

There are three rotational forms of cyclohexane in which the bond angles are all tetrahedral: the chair, the boat, and the twist boat. We discussed the chair form in detail in the preceding section, so we will now examine the boat and twist boat forms. As illustrated in Figure 13.30, we can generate the boat conformation from the chair conformation by twisting only one corner of the chair.

The boat form of cyclohexane is important for bicyclic compounds in which the 1- and 4-positions are joined by a bridge. We have already seen several examples of this type of compound. Two more examples in Figure 13.31 emphasize the boat geometry.

Compounds of this type, which are locked into a boat geometry, are useful for a variety of mechanistic determinations. We will discuss two such applications here.

Consider the geometry of elimination reactions proceeding via an E2 mechanism (Chapter 12). There is much evidence to indicate that the elimination is successful if the eliminated groups are *anti* in the starting material. Bicyclics provide a test for the possibility of *syn* elimination. A bicyclic compound that is held in a boat conformation can be used to lock groups to be eliminated in a *syn* relationship.

Consider using *cis*-2-bromo-3-deuteriobicyclo[2.2.2]octane in an elimination reaction. We isolate only a single alkene product in this reaction. The product indicates that the elements of DBr were eliminated, but not those of HBr (see Figure 13.32). This and similar experiments indicate that *syn* elimination occurs in such systems where *anti* elimination is impossible.

A second mechanistic point that the boat geometry of bicyclics illustrates is the requirement for a planar array of groups about a carbocation center. Normally, tertiary haloalkanes undergo S_N1 reaction very rapidly. On this basis

Figure 13.31 Two bicyclic compounds that incorporate a boat cyclohexane structure. The bonds external to the ring are all to hydrogen.

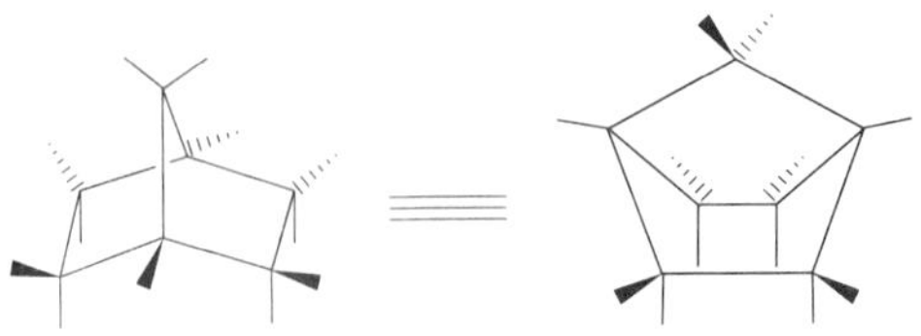

bicyclo[2.2.1]heptane

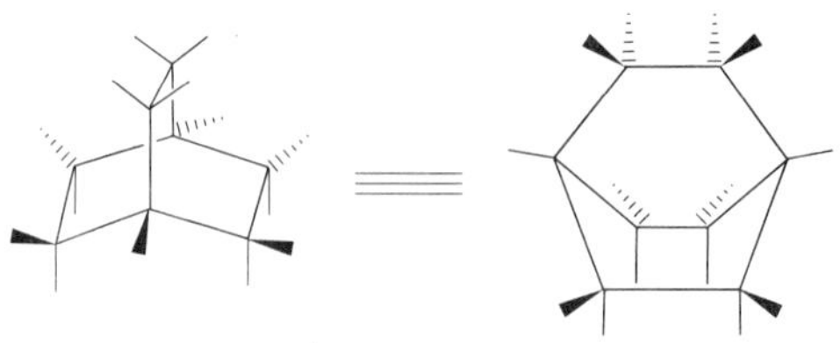

bicyclo[2.2.2]octane

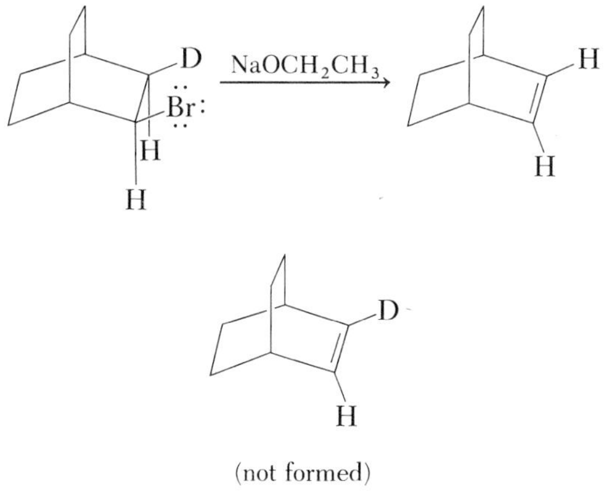

Figure 13.32 A test case for *syn* elimination. Only DBr is eliminated from the bicyclic with sodium ethoxide. The D and Br are in a *syn* periplanar arrangement, whereas H and Br have a dihedral angle of 120°.

$NaOCH_2CH_3$

(not formed)

we would expect 1-bromobicyclo[2.2.1]heptane to undergo ethanol solvolysis rapidly. (The competing S_N2 reaction is clearly prohibited because the nucleophile cannot approach from the side opposite that of bromine attachment.)

However, S_N1 reaction proceeds at a negligible rate with this material. We infer that product does not form because a carbocation is not generated. A carbocation at the bridgehead position would require the bicyclic to become flattened and would involve the introduction of considerable angle strain. This situation is illustrated in Figure 13.33. Use of a model helps in visualizing these structural relationships.

PROBLEM 13.20 In 1924, Julius Bredt deduced from experimental observations that unless at least one ring in a bicyclic is relatively large, carbon-carbon double bonds cannot be generated at the bridgehead position (**Bredt's rule**). That is, compounds of the type illustrated below cannot be formed.

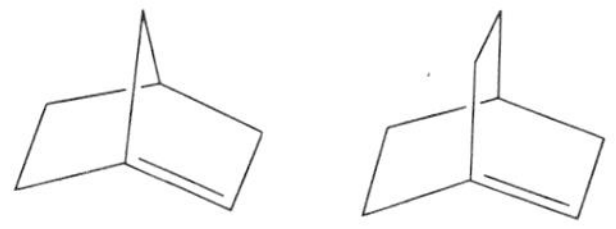

Rationalize Bredt's rule in terms of bond generation (use orbital concepts).

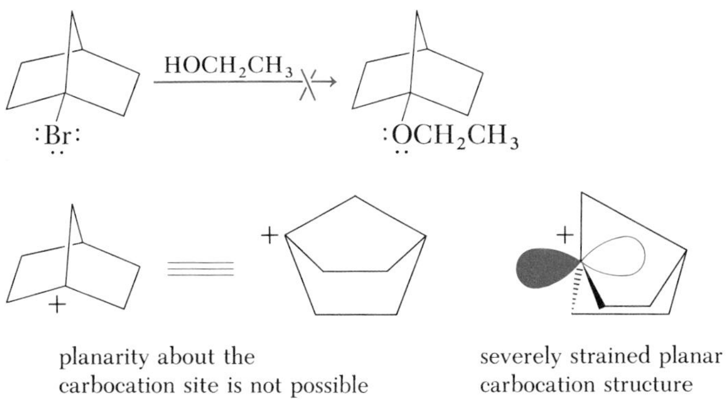

Figure 13.33 Carbocation generation at a bridgehead position. A carbocation cannot achieve planarity at a bridgehead position. Thus, it will form only rarely, even though this site is tertiary.

$HOCH_2CH_3$

:Br:

$:OCH_2CH_3$

planarity about the carbocation site is not possible

severely strained planar carbocation structure

The **twist boat** (or simply *twist*) conformation is a structure that is an intermediate when one chair conformation rotates into the alternate chair conformation. The conformations existing at the relative energy maxima between chair and twist boat forms are **half-chair** forms. The relationships among these forms have been shown in Figures 13.14 and 13.16.

It is estimated that for cyclohexane and most simple substituted cyclohexanes, the twist boat is 5.5 kcal/mole higher in energy than the chair conformation. Thus, the twist boat is present only in very small concentrations at equilibrium. However, it becomes much more important (even dominant) if the chair forms are raised in energy by the presence of bulky groups in a *cis*-1,2-relationship, as, for example, in *cis*-1,2-di-*tert*-butylcyclohexane (**13.2**). In either chair form, one bulky *tert*-butyl group would necessarily be in an axial position, making the structure of very high energy. This orientation is avoided in the twist conformation.

13.2

A molecule that is *locked* into a twist conformation has also been synthesized. Bridging both the 1,4- and the 2,5-positions of cyclohexane gives a completely rigid molecule known as *twistane* (**13.3**), in which a cyclohexane ring is maintained in a twist geometry.

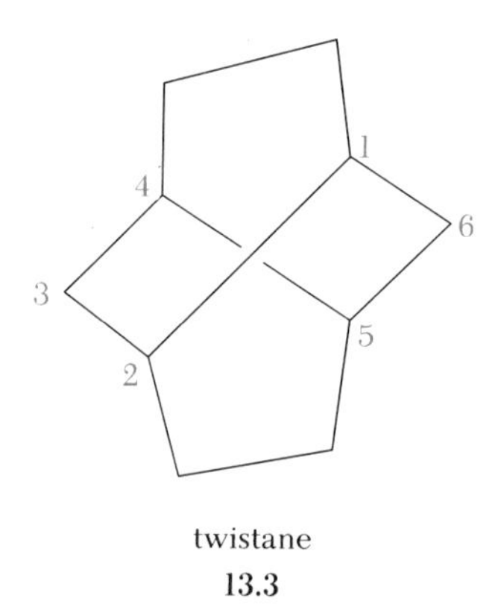

twistane
13.3

The synthesis of substances with unusual geometries, such as twistane, is a fascinating area of research in organic chemistry. The fruits of such research are an improved understanding of structure and of the ways in which structure affects properties. Highly strained compounds and compounds in unusual conformations often have different properties from similar compounds of normal conformation.

13.9 Rings Larger than Six Carbons

As was indicated by the combustion data summarized earlier, moderate-size rings of more than six carbon atoms are slightly less stable than cyclohexane, indicating that there is some strain (usually from nonbonded repulsion between hydrogen atoms) in these molecules. The saturated six-membered ring is unique in that it is the only small or medium-size ring system that is free of all three types of strain, (bond angle strain, torsional strain, and steric strain).

The shapes of seven-, eight-, and nine-membered rings are illustrated in Figure 13.34. The differentiation of axial and equatorial positions is also unique to the six-membered rings. With the larger rings, this distinction is blurred, although the *cis/trans* differentiation still exists.

Figure 13.34 Conformations of seven-, eight-, and nine-membered rings.

cycloheptane cyclooctane cyclononane

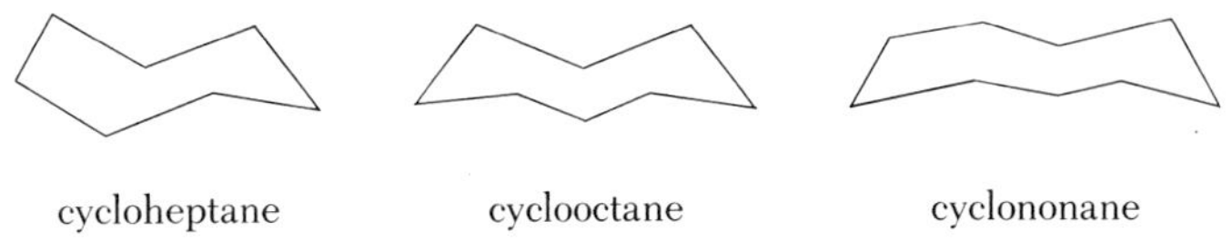

13.10 Ring Expansions and Contractions

In some reactions of cyclic systems, the product contains a ring of a different size than the starting material did. We say that *ring expansion* or *ring contraction* occurs in these systems. Two examples are shown in Figure 13.35. While these changes in ring size might initially seem puzzling, they do have a rational explanation. Both examples involve carbocation rearrangements of a type we met earlier.

Consider the first ring expansion reaction in Figure 13.35. Protonation of the alcohol followed by the loss of water leads to a tertiary carbocation. However, even though the carbocation is tertiary, there is strain associated with the cyclobutane ring. This strain can be relieved by a carbocation rearrangement. One of the bonds adjacent to the carbocation site shifts (with its bonding electron pair) to bind to the positively charged carbon atom. This shift generates a five-membered ring with significantly less strain.

Figure 13.35 Ring expansion and ring contraction reactions. In a ring expansion, the product contains a larger ring than the reactant. In a ring contraction, the converse is true.

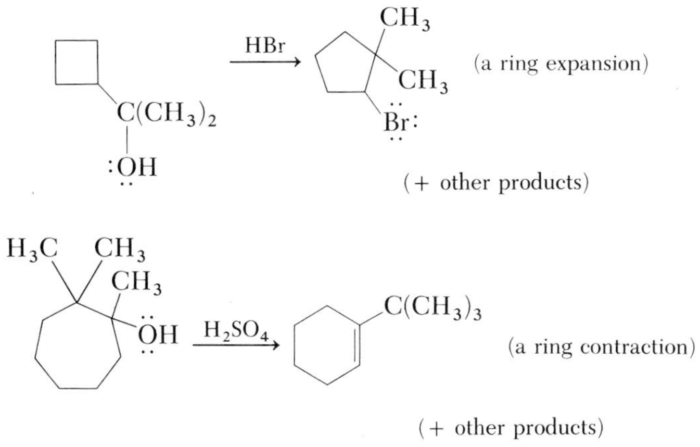

$C(CH_3)_2$:OH $\xrightarrow{HBr}$ CH_3 CH_3 Br: (a ring expansion)

(+ other products)

H_3C CH_3 CH_3 OH $\xrightarrow{H_2SO_4}$ $C(CH_3)_3$ (a ring contraction)

(+ other products)

MECHANISM OF REACTION

Overall:

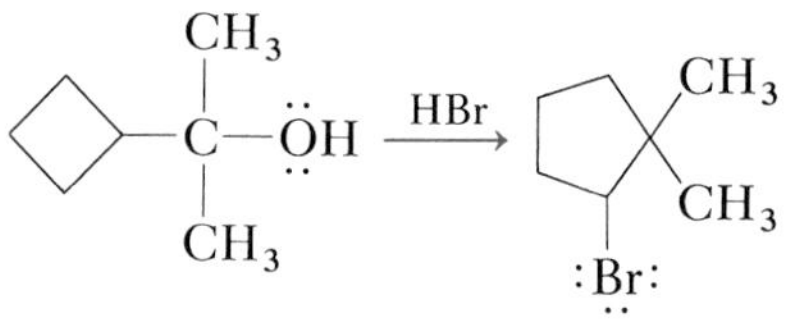

CH_3 C $\ddot{O}H$ CH_3 $\xrightarrow{HBr}$ CH_3 CH_3 :Br:

Steps 1 and 2 Formation of a carbocation by protonation of the alcohol and loss of water

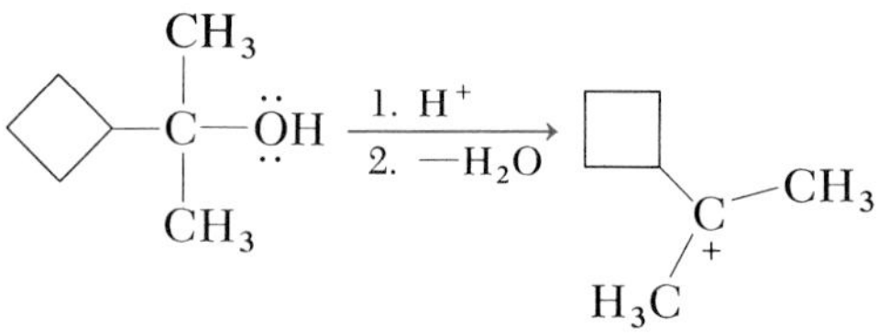

CH_3 C $\ddot{O}H$ CH_3 $\xrightarrow[2.\ -H_2O]{1.\ H^+}$ C CH_3 + H_3C

Step 3 Rearrangement of the carbocation by alkide migration

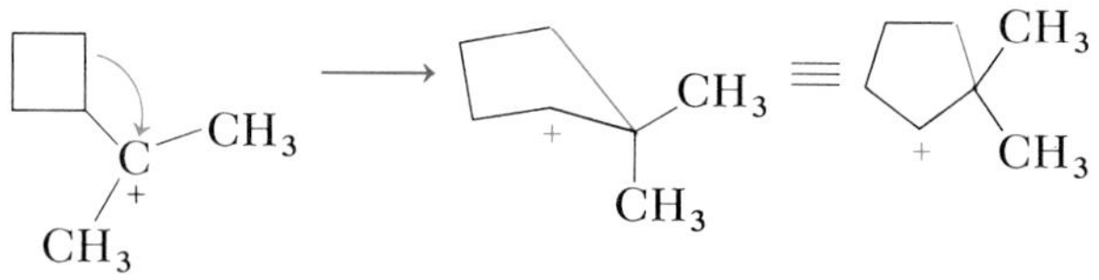

C CH_3 + CH_3 $\longrightarrow$ + CH_3 CH_3 $\equiv$ CH_3 + CH_3

Step 4 Combination of the carbocation with a bromide ion

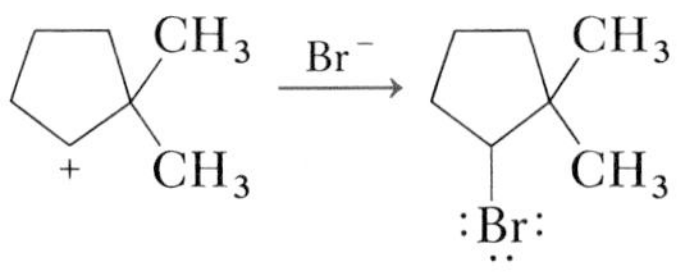

CH_3 + CH_3 $\xrightarrow{Br^-}$ CH_3 CH_3 :Br:

Even though the rearrangement in the above reaction leads to a secondary carbocation from a tertiary carbocation, it is a favorable process. The relief of ring strain on going from a four- to a five-membered ring is considerable—it is more than enough stabilization to compensate for changing from a tertiary to a secondary carbocation.

The conversion of 1,2,2-trimethyl-1-cycloheptanol to a six-membered ring product (Figure 13.35) is similar.

MECHANISM OF REACTION

Overall:

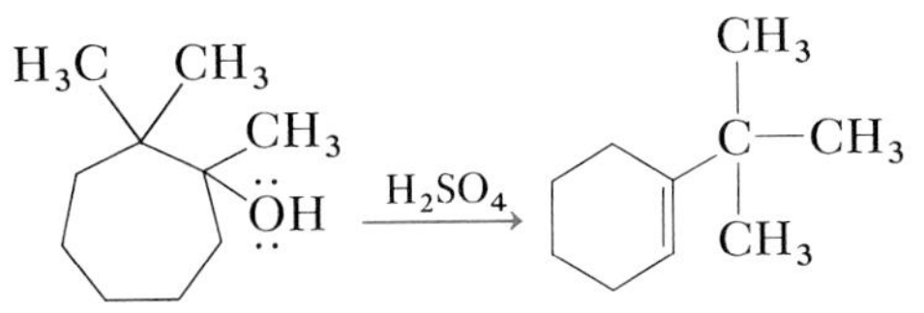

Steps 1 and 2 Formation of the carbocation by protonation of the alcohol and loss of water

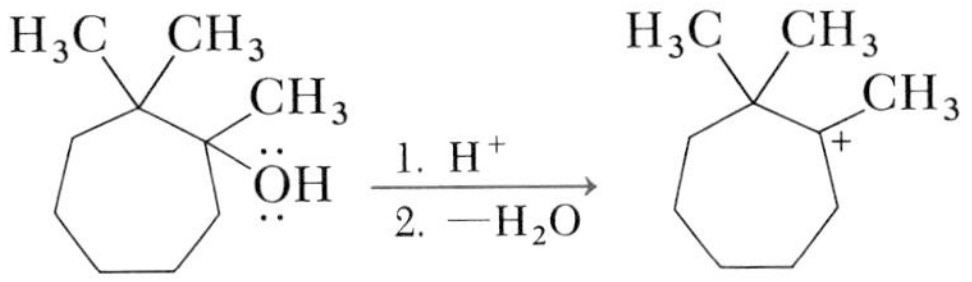

Step 3 Rearrangement of the carbocation by alkide migration. This rearrangement relieves the strain of the seven-membered ring.

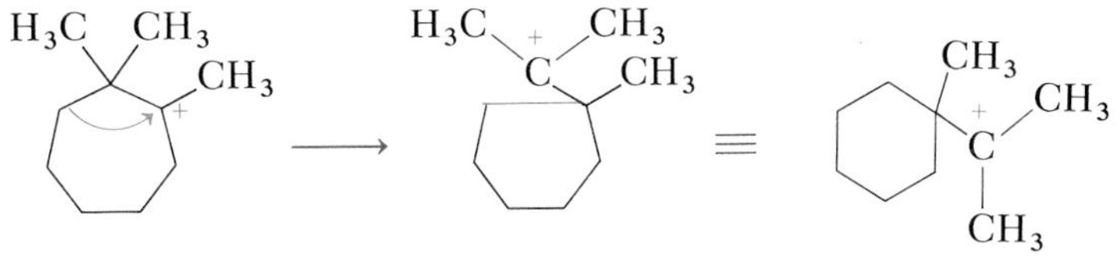

Step 4 Further rearrangement by methide migration

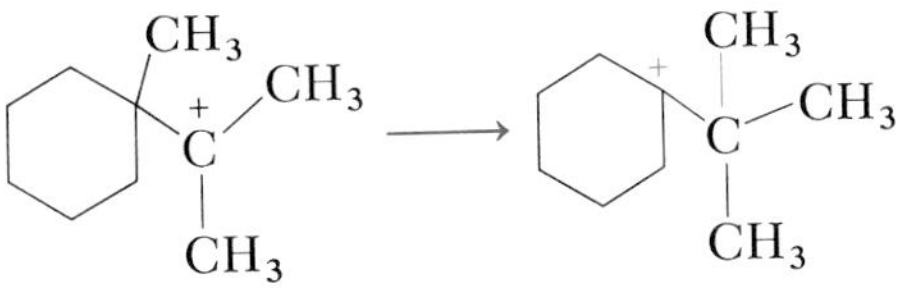

Step 5 Loss of a proton to a base present in the reaction system to generate the alkene product

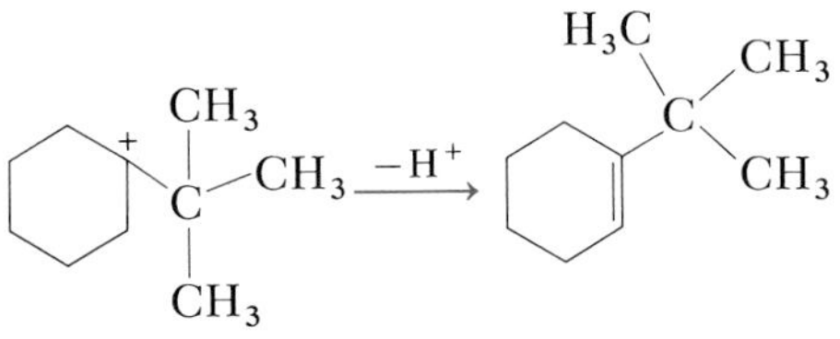

The driving force for the ring contraction is again a relief of strain. The six-membered ring is less strained than the seven-membered ring.

Summary

- Cyclic molecules adopt conformations that result in minimal strain.
- Minimization of strain at times involves a compromise between angle strain and torsional strain. For example, cyclobutane puckers out of a planar geometry to relieve torsional strain, although puckering does increase the angle strain slightly.
- For simple cyclohexane derivatives, the most important conformation is the chair conformation.
- Chair conformations contain two types of linkages to the ring. These linkages are axial and equatorial with respect to a horizontal plane through the ring.
- The orientations of both axial and equatorial bonds alternate up and down going around the cyclohexane ring.
- Two chair forms of simple cyclohexane derivatives can always exist and are in rapid equilibrium.
- The conversion of one chair to another results in all equatorial substituents becoming axial and all axial substituents becoming equatorial.
- Substituents generally create less strain in equatorial positions than in axial positions. In axial positions they normally cause steric strain because they are located close to axially oriented groups across the ring. Repulsions between these groups are known as 1,3-diaxial interactions.
- It is sometimes necessary to consider cyclohexane conformations other than the chair.
- Most notable of the nonchair cyclohexane conformations is the boat conformation; it is often found in bicyclic compounds containing a bridged six-membered ring.
- Alkanes and cycloalkanes react with halogens under thermal or photochemical conditions through free radical chain mechanisms.
- In many free radical halogenations, mixtures of products are formed. The product distribution depends both on statistical factors (the relative number of hydrogen atoms of different types) and on reactivity factors (how reactive primary, secondary, and tertiary hydrogens are toward abstraction by a halogen atom).

Terms to Remember

bicyclic
tricyclic
chain-initiation step
chain-propagation step
chain-termination step
sulfuryl chloride
diazomethane
Simmons-Smith reaction
chair conformation
boat conformation
axial
equatorial
1,3-methyl/hydrogen diaxial interaction
Bredt's rule
twist boat

Reactions of Synthetic Utility

55. $R{-}X \xrightarrow[\text{DMSO}]{\text{NaBH}_4} R{-}H$ — 13.3

$X = Cl, Br, I;\ R = 1^\circ, 2^\circ$

56. $R{-}X \xrightarrow[\text{ether}]{\text{LiAlH}_4} R{-}H$ — 13.3

$X = Cl, Br, I;\ R = 1^\circ, 2^\circ, 3^\circ$

57. $R{-}H \xrightarrow{X_2,\ h\nu \text{ or heat}_4} R{-}X$ — 13.4

$X = F >> Cl > Br;\ R = 3^\circ > 2^\circ > 1^\circ > CH_4$

58. $C{=}C \xrightarrow{CH_2I_2,\ Zn(Cu)}$ [cyclopropane] (stereospecific) — 13.5

59. $C{=}C \xrightarrow[\text{base}]{CHCl_3}$ [1,1-dichlorocyclopropane] Cl Cl (stereospecific) — 13.5

60. $R-X \xrightarrow[\text{acid}]{\text{Zn (or Sn)}} R-H$ 13.3

61. $R-X \xrightarrow[\text{benzoyl peroxide, heat}]{(C_4H_9)_3SnH} R-H$ 13.3

$X = Br, I$

Additional Problems

13.21 Draw all possible structures for:

a. a substance of formula C_5H_8 that yields a product of formula $C_5H_8Br_4$ on treatment with Br_2/CCl_4

b. a substance of formula C_5H_{10} that yields five dibromination products

13.22 Give systematic names for each of the following compounds:

a. 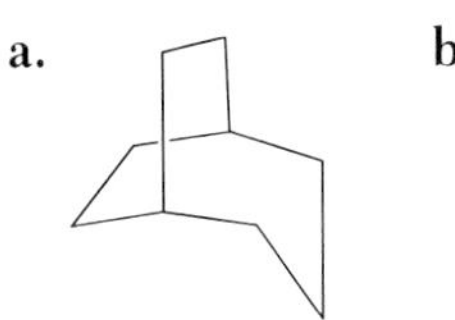

b. 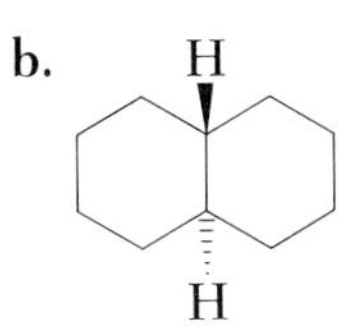

c. 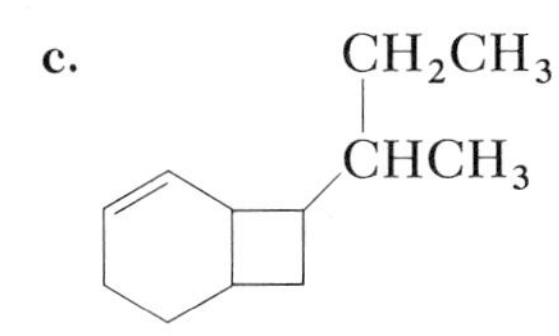

d. 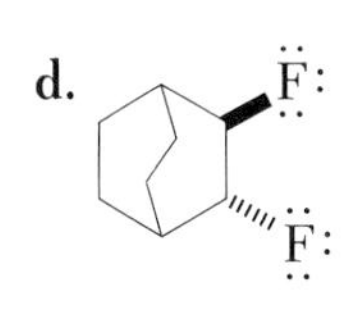

13.23 Give the structure with a proper conformational representation for each of the following:

a. 1,7,7-trimethylbicyclo[2.2.1]heptane (camphane)

b. the *cis* and *trans* isomers of bicyclo[3.3.0]octane

c. the *cis* and *trans* isomers of bicyclo[4.4.0]decane (decalin)

13.24 Draw and name the most strained isomer for each of the following formulas. (*Hint*: None of the required isomers contains double bonds.)

a. C_5H_8 b. C_5H_{10}

13.25 Under extreme conditions, cyclobutanes can be hydrogenated. Heating ethylcyclobutane and hydrogen (1 atmosphere pressure) at 250°C in the presence of palladium on carbon results in the formation of two alkanes. Give their structures.

13.26 Although cyclobutane is puckered, some related four-membered ring structures are planar. It is observed that the dipole moment of *trans*-1,3-dibromocyclobutane is 1.10 Debyes. Is this value more consistent with a puckered or a planar structure? Explain your answer.

13.27 Treatment of methylcyclopropane with HBr yields two isomers, of which one is dominant. Give structures for the two isomeric products and suggest why one is dominant.

13.28 Draw structures for each of the following:

a. 9,9-dibromobicyclo[6.1.0]nonane

b. *cis*-1,2-dimethylcyclohexane in a chair conformation

c. *trans*-1,3-dimethylcyclohexane in a chair conformation

d. *trans*-1,4-dimethylcyclohexane in a chair conformation

e. *cis*-1-*tert*-butyl-4-methylcyclohexane in its more stable chair conformation

f. *trans*-1-*tert*-butyl-3-methylcyclohexane in its more stable chair conformation

g. a substance of formula $C_4H_8Cl_2$, which yields just two isomers of formula $C_4H_7Cl_3$ (not including stereoisomers) on free radical chlorination

h. a substance of formula $C_7H_{13}OBr$ obtained by treating 1-methylcyclopentene with bromine in methanol

13.29 Consider the following general reaction:

$$C_3H_8 + X_2 \longrightarrow CH_3CH_2CH_2\ddot{\underset{..}{X}}: + CH_3\underset{\underset{:\ddot{X}:}{|}}{C}HCH_3$$

Calculate the relative reactivity of X· atoms with primary and secondary hydrogens if 95% of the product by weight is $CH_3CH(X)CH_3$ and 5% by weight is $CH_3CH_2CH_2X$.

13.30 A chemist allows hexane to react with chlorine in the presence of light. She isolates 1.0 g of 1-chlorohexane, plus two other chlorohexane isomers. What are the IUPAC names for these products? How many grams of each are expected to be formed? (Assume that the relative reactivities of primary and secondary hydrogens with chlorine atoms are 1.0 and 2.25, respectively.)

13.31 Name any optically inactive substances produced in the monochlorination (using chlorine and light) of the following compounds.
a. (*R*)-2-chlorobutane b. (2*R*,3*R*)-2-chloro-3-methylpentane

13.32 When (−)-1-chloro-2-methylpentane is treated with chlorine and light, 1,5-dichloro-2-methylpentane is obtained along with other products. Is the 1,5-dichloro-2-methylpentane
a. *R* b. *S* c. racemic d. insufficient information to decide
Explain your choice.

13.33 Which reagent or combination of reagents would you use to accomplish the following conversions in a single step?
a. deuterioethane from bromoethane
b. *cis*-1,2-cyclohexanediol from cyclohexene
c. *tert*-butyl bromide from 2-methylpropane
d. (cyclopentane with COOH, COOH) (*cis*) from bicyclo[2.2.1]-2-heptene

13.34 The following synthetic conversions require more than one step. Suggest a way to accomplish each conversion.
a. 2-deuterio-2-methylpropane from *tert*-butyl alcohol
b. 1,3-cyclohexadiene from cyclohexene
c. 1,1-dichloro-2-ethylcyclopropane from 1-chlorobutane
d. bicyclo[4.1.0]heptane from cyclohexanol
e. cyclohexene from cyclohexane
f. methylcyclohexane from cyclohexane
g. 1-bromo-2,3-dimethylpropane from *tert*-butyl chloride
h. $H-C(=O)-(CH_2)_3-C(=O)-H$ from cyclopentane

13.35 Which haloalkane should be used to prepare a lithium dialkyl cuprate that will yield:
a. 2,3,6-trimethylheptane on treatment with 1-bromo-3-methylbutane
b. 2,2,5-trimethylheptane on treatment with 1-bromo-3,3-dimethylbutane

13.36 How many equatorial methyl groups do you expect in the more stable chair conformation of each of the following:

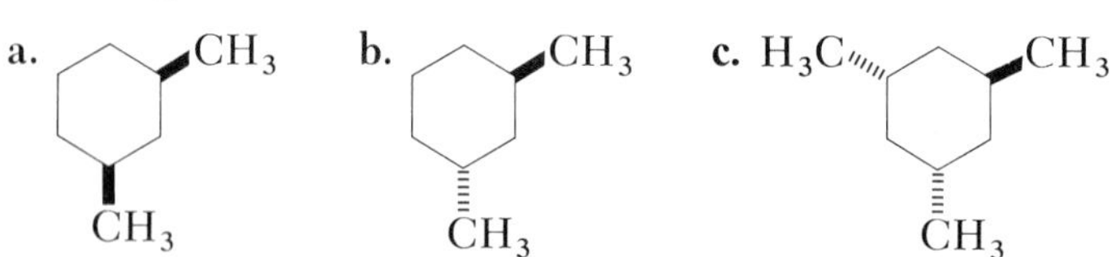

13.37 a. Consider *cis*- and *trans*-1,2-dimethylcyclohexane and *cis*- and *trans*-1,4-dimethylcyclohexane. Do any of these molecules have stereogenic carbon atoms? Do you expect any of these substances to be resolvable, at least in principle? Explain your answer.

b. Make a model of a chair conformation of *cis*-1,2-dimethylcyclohexane. Label it A. Without disturbing A, make another model that is a mirror image of A. Label it B. What is the relationship between A and B—are they superimposable? Now take model A, and manipulate it so that it undergoes a conformational flip into *another* chair form, C. What is the relationship between models B and C—superimposable or not? Based on your observations, do you expect *cis*-1,2-dimethylcyclohexane to be resolvable in practice? Explain your answer.

c. Repeat the model building and analysis for the chair forms of *trans*-1,2-dimethylcyclohexane. Do you expect it to be resolvable? Explain your answer.

d. Are *cis*- and *trans*-1,3-dimethylcyclohexane resolvable in principle?

13.38 Is *cis*-1,2-dimethylcyclopropane more or less stable than *trans*-1,2-dimethylcyclopropane? Explain.

13.39 Using data given in this chapter and Chapter 4, estimate which molecule should have the higher heat of combustion, bicyclo[3.1.0]hexane or bicyclo[2.2.0]hexane. Estimate the magnitude of the difference in their heats of combustion.

13.40 Draw structures for the products of each of the following reactions, indicating any relevant stereochemical details:

a. cyclopropane with deuterium (D_2) and a Raney nickel hydrogenation catalyst

b. cyclohexene with bromine monochloride (BrCl) (show the more stable chair conformation)

c. 1-methylcyclohexene treated with BD_3 and worked-up with D_2O_2/NaOD (show the more stable chair conformation)

d. cyclobutylmethanol with sulfuric acid, giving a product of formula C_5H_8 that does not contain a four-membered ring

13.41 *trans*-4-Bromocyclohexanol can be prepared by the addition of HBr to cyclohexane-1,4-oxide (structure shown below). Suggest a mechanism for the conversion.

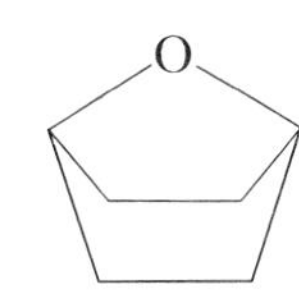

13.42 Estimate the energy difference between the two chair conformations of *trans*-1,4-dimethylcyclohexane.

13.43 The more stable chair conformations of both *trans*-1,4-dimethylcyclohexane and *trans*-1,2-dimethylcyclohexane have both methyl groups in equatorial positions. However, in one case the more stable chair conformation is 3.6 kcal/mole more stable than the less stable chair, while in the other case the two chairs differ by only 2.7 kcal/mole. Draw the chair structures and use them to explain this difference in relative stabilities.

13.44 A 1,3-methyl/methyl diaxial interaction has been estimated to be approximately 3.7 kcal/mole destabilizing. This is significantly more than the 0.9 kcal/mole associated with a 1,3-hydrogen/methyl diaxial interaction. Use this value to calculate the energy difference between the two chair conformations of *cis*-1,3-dimethylcyclohexane.

13.45 Use the value given in the previous problem to estimate the relative stabilities of the two chair conformations of *trans*-1,1,3,5-tetramethylcyclohexane.

13.46 There are four possible diastereoisomeric forms of 3,4-dichloro-*tert*-butylcyclohexane. Draw chair conformations for each of these forms.

13.47 The molecules *cis*- and *trans*-4-bromo-*tert*-butylcyclohexane undergo halogen exchange reactions when treated with iodide ion. What products will be obtained if each of the isomers is stirred with sodium iodide in acetone? Which isomer do you expect to react faster in the initial stages of the reaction? Why?

13.48 A graduate student has been working on some synthetic sequences beginning with 1-methylcyclohexene. However, he has lost his laboratory notebook and cannot remember the conditions he used for the thionyl chloride reaction of the following sequence. Specifically, did he or did he not use hexamethylphosphoric triamide (HMPT) along with the thionyl chloride?

$$\text{1-methylcyclohexene} \xrightarrow{\text{hydroboration/oxidation}} [C_7H_{14}O] \xrightarrow{SOCl_2} [C_7H_{13}Cl] \xrightarrow{KOCH_2CH_3,\ HOCH_2CH_3} \text{3-methylcyclohexene}$$

(*only* alkene product)

Fortunately, it is possible to deduce what the conditions must have been. Was HMPT used as the solvent? Explain.

13.49 Show a complete mechanism for the reaction in which the alkene shown below reacts with sulfuric acid and water and is converted into a derivative of cyclohexanol of formula $C_8H_{16}O$.

CH_3 / $CH{=}CH_2$ (on cyclopentane carbon)

13.50 There is a much smaller difference in energy between a tertiary and a secondary radical than there is between a tertiary and a secondary carbocation. One of the following statements is true. Applying the Hammond postulate, which do you favor?

a. Secondary radicals rearrange to tertiary radicals so much more rapidly than secondary carbocations rearrange to tertiary carbocations that skeletal rearrangements are very common in reactions involving radical intermediates.

b. Secondary radicals rearrange at such a slow rate that skeletal rearrangements are not observed in reactions involving radicals. Rather, the initially formed radical reacts before rearranging.

13.51 One of the substances present in oil of turpentine is α-pinene, which has structure *A* shown below. Modify the structure *A'* (by adding methyl groups and noting the position of the double bond) so that it represents the structure of the α-pinene molecule.

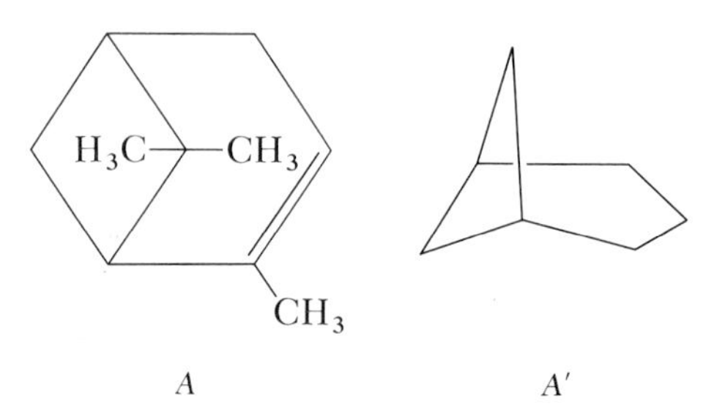

When *A* is treated with HI it is converted to *B*, of formula $C_{10}H_{17}I$, which is a bicyclo[2.2.1]heptane derivative. When compound *B* reacts with an alkoxide base, it yields *C*, an isomer of *A*. Compound *C*, on heating with hot aqueous potassium permanganate solution, produces the compound shown below. Draw structures for compounds *B* and *C*, and give a mechanism for the conversion of *A* to *B* upon the action of HI.

COOH, CH_3, CH_3, COOH, CH_3 (substituted cyclopentane)

CHAPTER 14 Ethers and Epoxides

14.1 Introduction

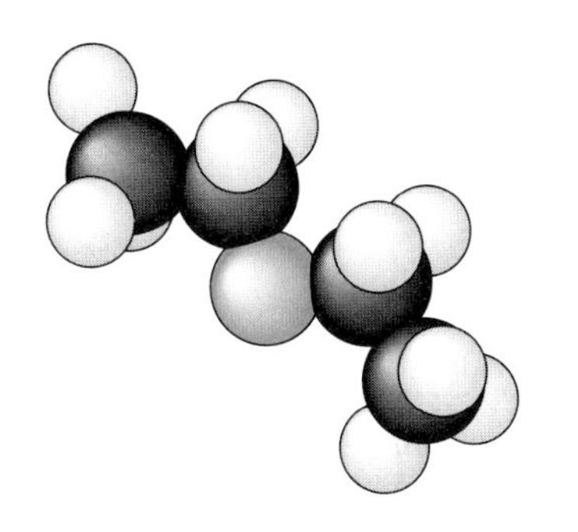

On a structural basis, first one, then both hydrogen atoms of water are replaced by alkyl groups in progressing to alcohols, R—OH, and then to ethers, R—O—R′. Ethers thus resemble water less than do the alcohols. Because ether molecules contain no hydrogen attached to oxygen, ethers do not show any of the characteristic properties of weak acids that we saw for alcohols. The lack of the hydroxyl hydrogen also eliminates the possibility of hydrogen bonding among ether molecules. As a result, ethers exhibit substantially lower boiling temperatures than do alcohols of similar molecular weight.

Ethers can, however, behave as bases or nucleophiles under the appropriate circumstances, because an oxygen atom with unshared electron pairs is still present. For the most part, however, ethers are rather inert to chemical transformations. In this respect they are similar to the alkanes and cycloalkanes we met in Chapter 13. For this reason ethers are useful as solvents for performing a wide range of chemical reactions.

Diethyl ether, $CH_3CH_2OCH_2CH_3$, is better known than other ethers. It is often referred to simply as *ether*. An early (1842) application of diethyl ether was as a general anesthetic in surgical procedures. Diethyl ether, along with other ethers such as methyl propyl ether, ethyl vinyl ether, and divinyl ether, produces unconsciousness by depressing activity of the central nervous system.

14.2 Ether Nomenclature

The nomenclature of ethers is straightforward, at least for the simple dialkyl ethers. Two methods are recognized as acceptable by the IUPAC, the *radicofunctional* method and the *substitutive* method. There are special names and variations for cyclic ethers and some more complex structures.

Simple dialkyl ethers can be named using either the radicofunctional method or the substitutive method. In the radicofunctional method we first name each of the alkyl groups present and then add the term *ether*. Several examples are shown in Figure 14.1.

For more complex structures, the substitutive method is usually simpler to use. In the substitutive method, the ether linkage is noted as an *alkoxy* substituent of the parent molecule. It is the method of choice when an awkward name would result from the radicofunctional method. Two examples are given in Figure 14.2.

PROBLEM 14.1 Provide names for the first three compounds in Figure 14.1 using the substitutive method of nomenclature.

Figure 14.1 Examples of the radicofunctional method of nomenclature for simple ethers.

$CH_3CH_2OCH_2CH_3$
diethyl ether

$(CH_3)_2CHCH_2OCH_2CH_2CH_3$
isobutyl propyl ether
(2-methylpropyl propyl ether)

$(CH_3)_2C{=}CHCH_2CH_2OCH_2CH_2CH_2CH_3$
butyl 4-methyl-3-pentenyl ether

$:ClCH_2CH_2OCH_2CH_2Cl:$
bis(2-chloroethyl) ether

Figure 14.2 Substitutive nomenclature of more complex ethers. We name the ether by specifying an alkoxy substituent on a parent structure.

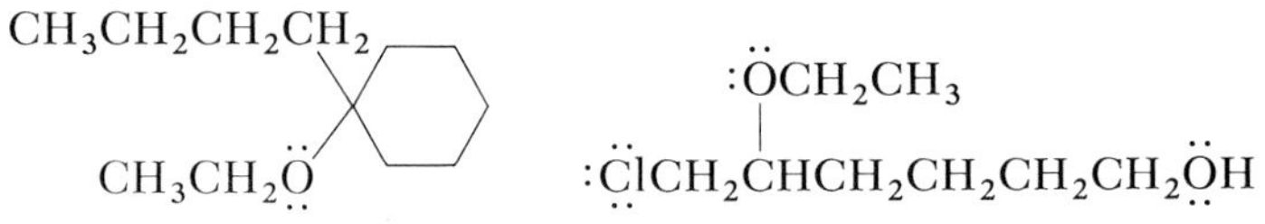

$CH_3CH_2CH_2CH_2$, CH_3CH_2O
1-butyl-1-ethoxycyclohexane

$:OCH_2CH_3$
$:ClCH_2CHCH_2CH_2CH_2CH_2OH$
6-chloro-5-ethoxy-1-hexanol

Special names are used for ring systems in which the ether oxygen is part of the ring. Examples of some of the more common oxygen-containing ring systems are shown in Figure 14.3.

Cyclic ethers, and indeed *any* cyclic compound bearing a noncarbon atom (a **heteroatom**) in the ring, are called **heterocyclic** compounds (or heterocycles). In naming heterocycles, we assign the heteroatom the 1-position. The location of substituents is then specified in the usual way. Two examples are shown in Figure 14.4.

Figure 14.3 Common ethers in which the oxygen atom is part of a ring.

furan

tetrahydrofuran
(oxolane)

pyran

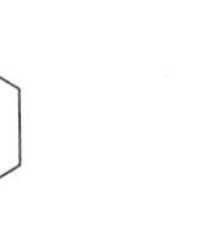
tetrahydropyran
(oxane)

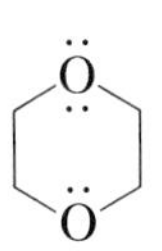
1,4-dioxane

oxetane

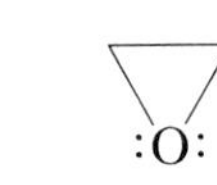
ethylene oxide
(oxirane)

Figure 14.4 Nomenclature of cyclic ethers. In numbering the atoms of a cyclic ether, the ring oxygen is assigned the 1-position.

H_3C, CH_3
trans-2,5-dimethyl-1,4-dioxane

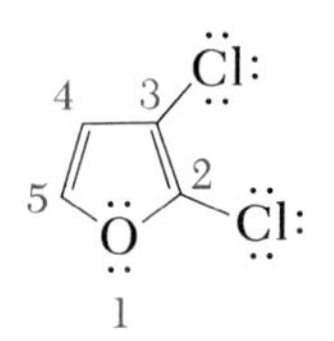

2,3-dichlorofuran

Figure 14.5 Nomenclature of epoxides. Both the systematic IUPAC names and the alkene oxide names are shown.

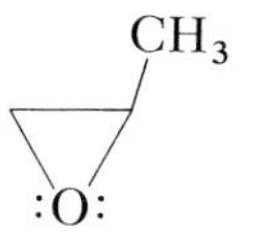

CH_3 epoxide	H_3C / CH_3 epoxide	$CH_2CH_2CH_2Cl$ epoxide
2-methyloxirane (propylene oxide)	*trans*-2,3-dimethyloxirane (*trans*-2-butene oxide)	2-(3-chloropropyl)oxirane (5-chloro-1-pentene oxide)

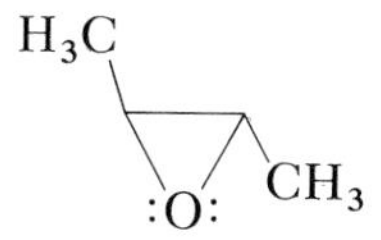

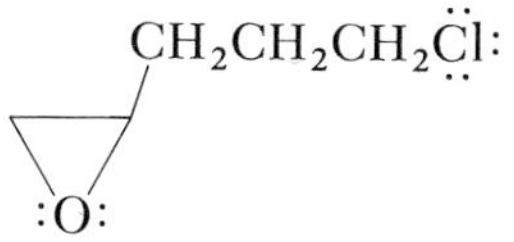

PROBLEM 14.2 1,4-Dioxane, like cyclohexane, adopts a chair conformation. Draw the more stable chair conformation for *cis*- and *trans*-2,5-dimethyl-1,4-dioxane.

Three-membered rings containing oxygen are also common and important materials. Like cyclopropane and other three-membered ring compounds, three-membered cyclic ethers suffer from angle strain. Thus their activity is qualitatively different from the other ethers.

Compounds of this type, generically known as **epoxides,** are named as **oxiranes** using the IUPAC method. More commonly they are named as derivatives of the alkenes from which they can be derived chemically. In this type of nomenclature, the name of the alkene is followed by the word *oxide*. Several examples of the nomenclature of epoxides are given in Figure 14.5. The chemistry of these compounds will be given special attention later in this chapter.

PROBLEM 14.3 Give IUPAC names for each of the following epoxides:

a. 2-methyl-1-butene oxide
b. *cis*-1-chloro-1-butene oxide

PROBLEM 14.4 Draw structures for each of the following:

a. *sec*-butyl isobutyl ether
b. *cis*-3-hexene oxide
c. (Z)-3-ethyl-2-hexene oxide

14.3 Properties of Ethers

PHYSICAL PROPERTIES

Ethers are structurally related to alcohols and to water but lack a hydrogen atom bound to the oxygen. Thus ethers cannot act as hydrogen donors in hydrogen bonding with other molecules. While water and alcohols exist as hydrogen-bonded agglomerates, ethers do not, so ethers have lower boiling temperatures than alcohols of similar molecular weight. Several comparisons are given in Table 14.1.

Similarly, the melting temperatures of ethers are generally (but not always) lower than those of alcohols of similar molecular weight. Melting temperatures (as discussed in Chapter 3) depend on factors other than just the strength of

Table 14.1 Boiling Temperatures of Ethers Compared with Those of Isomeric 1-Alcohols

Ether	Ether Boiling Temperature (°C)	Alcohol Boiling Temperature (°C)	Alcohol
$CH_3\ddot{O}CH_3$	−24.9	78.3	$CH_3CH_2\ddot{O}H$
$CH_3CH_2\ddot{O}CH_2CH_3$	34.6	117.7	$CH_3CH_2CH_2CH_2\ddot{O}H$
$CH_3\ddot{O}CH_2CH_2CH_2CH_3$	70.3	138.0	$CH_3CH_2CH_2CH_2CH_2\ddot{O}H$
$(CH_3CH_2CH_2CH_2)_2\ddot{O}$	141	194.0	$CH_3(CH_2)_6CH_2\ddot{O}H$

intermolecular associations. The fit of the molecules in a lattice is also quite important.

ETHERS AS SOLVENTS

The presence of an ether linkage in a molecule provides two means of interaction with solutes. First, the unshared electron pairs constitute a Lewis base site. Ethers can provide solvation and stabilization to solutes containing a Lewis acid site. We have already seen an example of this role in our earlier discussion of Grignard reagents. Ethers are useful solvents for the preparation of Grignard reagents since they provide stabilizing interactions with the metal site (a Lewis acid) of the organometallic.

A second solubilizing characteristic arises from the polarity of the carbon-oxygen bonds. The polarities of the two carbon-oxygen bonds of an ether do *not* cancel because of the tetrahedral bonding geometry about the sp^3 hybridized oxygen atom. The resulting molecular polarity gives ethers a means of interacting with polar solutes. Ethers are not, however, strongly basic or polar. In general, ethers are more like hydrocarbons than like alcohols in their abilities to act as solvents.

ETHERS AS SOLUTES

Some striking contrasts in solubilities are seen when cyclic ethers are compared with their open-chain analogues. For example, while diethyl ether is soluble in water only to an extent of approximately 8%, tetrahydrofuran (THF) is completely miscible with water, as is 1,4-dioxane. The explanation for these contrasting behaviors appears to lie in the relatively greater conformational rigidity of the cyclic ethers. This rigidity allows efficient hydrogen bonding to water, as is illustrated in Figure 14.6.

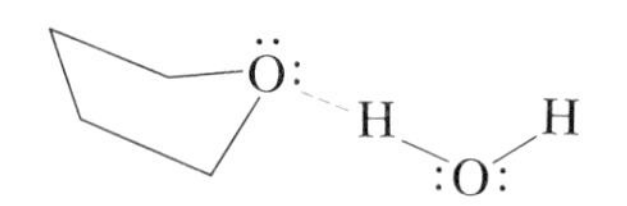

Figure 14.6 Hydrogen bonding between tetrahydrofuran and water. The degree of hydrogen bonding is greater for most cyclic ethers than for their open-chain counterparts. Thus there are significant differences in water solubilities for cyclic ethers and comparable open-chain ethers.

With an open-chain compound such as diethyl ether, there is much greater conformational freedom than with a cyclic structure. A contributing reason for the difference in water solubilities may be that as the compound continuously alters its conformation, the ethyl groups sweep out an approximately spherical *exclusion zone* about the oxygen atom that prevents efficient hydrogen bonding to water. The region around the oxygen of the more rigid tetrahydrofuran molecule would be expected to be more accessible to water molecules.

PROBLEM 14.5 Based on the type of reasoning used to rationalize the relatively high water solubility of THF compared to diethyl ether, which of the following do you expect to be the more potent nucleophile? Explain your answer.

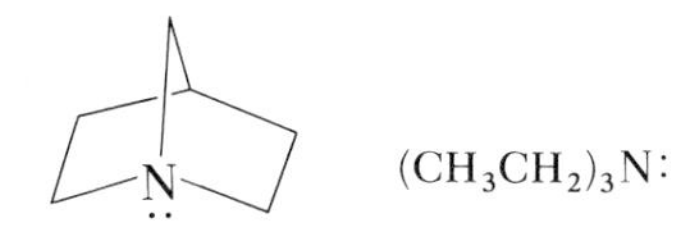

$(CH_3CH_2)_3N:$

Most ethers (there are a few special exceptions) are soluble in concentrated aqueous solutions of mineral acid. In fact, almost all organic compounds containing oxygen are sufficiently basic (due to the unshared electron pairs on oxygen) to dissolve in concentrated sulfuric acid. Most ethers are also fairly soluble in hydrocarbons.

REACTIVITY

Ethers are relatively unreactive compounds compared to other organic compounds containing carbon-oxygen bonds. Since they have no good leaving group, they are inert to nucleophiles in the absence of acid. They are not susceptible to reduction because they are saturated in the same sense as alkanes are saturated and they are also inert to most common oxidizing agents.

Like hydrocarbons, ethers do undergo combustion (burning) on heating with oxygen. In fact, the high volatility of simple ethers (such as diethyl ether) makes their use a severe fire hazard—ethers form explosive mixtures with air.

The principal way that dialkyl ethers react is through the unshared electron pairs on the oxygen. These electron pairs can bind to a proton or another Lewis acid, as shown in Figure 14.7.

Once addition to the ether oxygen has occurred, further reaction is possible. For example, a protonated ether contains a good leaving group (an alcohol molecule), and attack by a suitable nucleophile is possible. An example is shown in Equation 14.1.

Eq. 14.1

$$CH_3CH_2-\ddot{\underset{..}{O}}-CH(CH_3)_2 \xrightarrow[H_2O]{HI} CH_3CH_2\ddot{\underset{..}{I}}: + H\ddot{\underset{..}{O}}CH(CH_3)_2$$

ethyl isopropyl ether — 31% yield iodoethane — 2-propanol

Figure 14.7 Reactivity of ethers as Lewis bases. The examples show addition of (*a*) a proton and (*b*) an aprotic Lewis acid.

$$(a)\quad (CH_3CH_2)_2\ddot{\underset{..}{O}} + H^+ \longrightarrow (CH_3CH_2)\overset{+}{\underset{..}{O}}-H$$

$$(b)\quad (CH_3CH_2)_2\ddot{\underset{..}{O}} + BF_3 \longrightarrow (CH_3CH_2)_2\overset{+}{\underset{..}{O}}-\overset{-}{B}F_3$$

MECHANISM OF REACTION

Overall:

$$CH_3CH_2\ddot{O}CH(CH_3)_2 \xrightarrow[H_2O]{HI} CH_3CH_2\ddot{I}: + H\ddot{O}CH(CH_3)_2$$

(Note: if excess HI is used, $(CH_3)_2CH\ddot{O}H$ is further converted to $(CH_3)_2CH\ddot{I}:$).

Step 1 Protonation of the ether to form an oxonium ion.

$$CH_3CH_2-\ddot{O}-CH(CH_3)_2 + H^+ \longrightarrow CH_3CH_2-\overset{+}{\dot{O}}(H)-CH(CH_3)_2$$

Step 2 Nucleophilic attack by iodide ion.

$$:\ddot{I}:^- + CH_3CH_2-\overset{+}{\dot{O}}(H)-CH(CH_3)_2 \longrightarrow :\ddot{I}-CH_2CH_3 + :\ddot{O}(H)-CH(CH_3)_2$$

14.4 The Synthesis of Ethers

THE WILLIAMSON SYNTHESIS

The Williamson synthesis of ethers was briefly introduced in Chapter 12. It consists of a nucleophilic substitution reaction of an alkoxide ion on a haloalkane, and as such is a classic example of the S_N2 process. An example is shown in Equation 14.2. The purpose of the sodium hydride is to convert the alcohol to its corresponding alkoxide salt. The alkoxide then performs a nucleophilic attack on methyl iodide to form the observed product.

Eqn. 14.2

$$\text{cis-2-methylcyclohexanol (ring-}CH_3\text{, ring-}\ddot{O}H) \xrightarrow[CH_3I]{NaH} \text{cis-1-methoxy-2-methylcyclohexane (ring-}CH_3\text{, ring-}\ddot{O}CH_3)$$

100% yield

cis-2-methylcyclohexanol *cis*-1-methoxy-2-methylcyclohexane

PROBLEM 14.6 Use the curved-arrow formalism to show the mechanism for the reaction in Equation 14.2.

This type of reaction works rather well when the substrate is a halomethane or a primary haloalkane. However, with secondary and particularly with tertiary haloalkanes, the rate of the substitution reaction leading to an ether product decreases and dehydrohalogenation (E2 reaction) to form alkenes competes with the desired nucleophilic substitution reaction (the alkoxide reagent tends to act as a base rather than as a nucleophile).

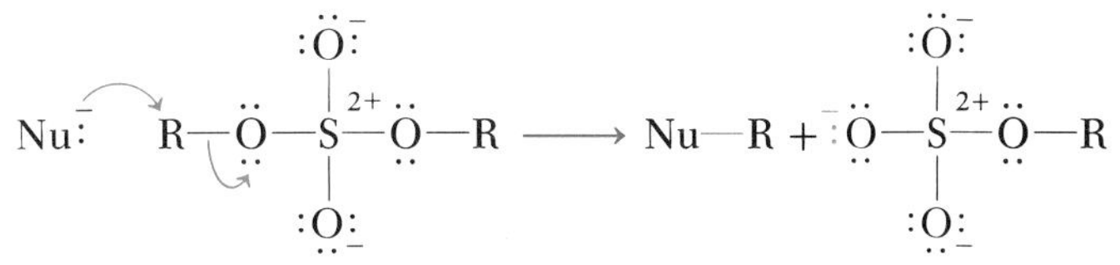

Figure 14.8 Nucleophilic substitution reaction on a sulfate diester.

$$Nu^{-} + R{-}O{-}S^{2+}(O^{-})_2{-}O{-}R \longrightarrow Nu{-}R + {}^{-}O{-}S^{2+}(O^{-})_2{-}O{-}R$$

a good leaving group
(the conjugate base of HO_3SOR)

Esters of sulfuric acid (*sulfate esters*, see Chapter 6) may be used instead of haloalkanes in the Williamson synthesis. These reagents also provide a good leaving group (see Figure 14.8).

Dimethyl sulfate, the simplest dialkyl sulfate, is commercially available (it can be manufactured cheaply from methanol and sulfuric acid). It is a convenient reagent for the preparation of methyl ethers. However, it is corrosive, and like other alkylating agents, it is a carcinogen. Examples of the use of diethyl sulfate and dimethyl sulfate are shown in Equations 14.3 and 14.4, respectively.

Eqn. 14.3

$$(CH_3CH_2O)_2SO_2 + CH_2{=}CHCH_2OH \xrightarrow[DMSO]{KOH} CH_2{=}CHCH_2OCH_2CH_3$$

allyl alcohol — 70% yield, 3-ethoxypropene

Eqn. 14.4

$$(CH_3O)_2SO_2 + HOCH_2C{\equiv}CCH_2OH \xrightarrow[H_2O]{NaOH} CH_3OCH_2C{\equiv}CCH_2OCH_3$$

2-butyne-1,4-diol — 88% yield, 1,4-dimethoxy-2-butyne

RETROSYNTHETIC ANALYSIS APPLIED TO THE WILLIAMSON SYNTHESIS

Organic chemists generally reason backwards from the target molecule to suitable starting materials when planning a synthesis. We refer to this procedure as **retrosynthetic analysis.** In recent years chemists have formalized the process and incorporated standard symbols and procedures so that they can communicate their ideas more easily. The symbol used to indicate a retrosynthetic step (or a **disconnection**) is an open arrow written from product to possible precursors, as illustrated in Figure 14.9.

To illustrate the use of retrosynthetic analysis in planning a synthesis, consider the preparation of *tert*-butyl methyl ether by the Williamson approach. We need to consider two possible combinations of haloalkane and alkoxide ion for the preparation of a nonsymmetric ether. The general problem is illustrated in Figure 14.10.

The two possible combinations of reactants for the preparation of *tert*-butyl methyl ether are shown in Figure 14.11.

We can now compare the routes leading to the target compound. We need to determine whether the routes are comparable or if one route is superior.

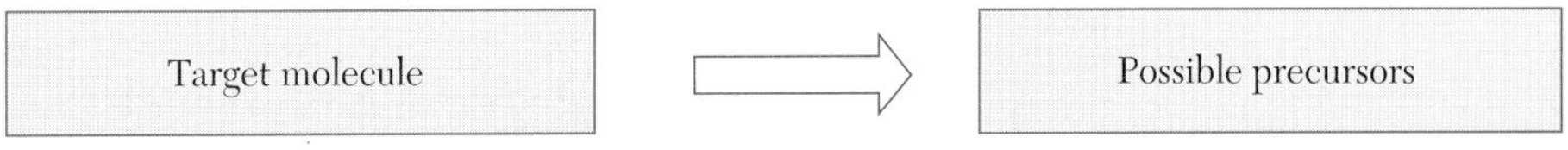

Target molecule ⇨ Possible precursors

Figure 14.9 The process of retrosynthetic analysis. In presenting a retrosynthetic analysis, we write open arrows pointing from the target molecule to possible precursors.

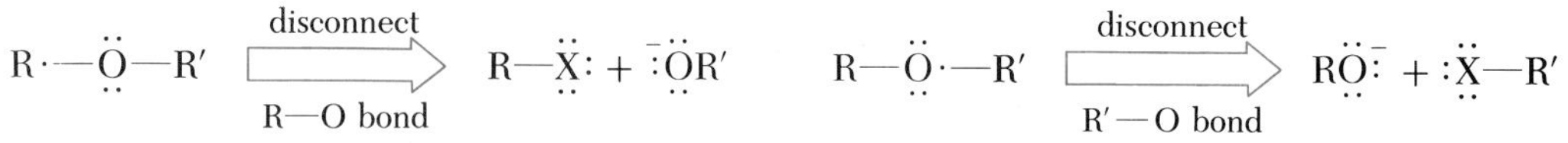

$$R\cdot\!-\!\ddot{O}\!-\!R' \xrightarrow[\text{R—O bond}]{\text{disconnect}} R\!-\!\ddot{X}\!: + \,^{-}\!:\!\ddot{O}R' \qquad R\!-\!\ddot{O}\cdot\!-\!R' \xrightarrow[\text{R}'\text{—O bond}]{\text{disconnect}} R\ddot{O}\!:^{-} + :\!\ddot{X}\!-\!R'$$

Figure 14.10 Retrosynthetic analysis of a Williamson ether synthesis. Two possible combinations of alkoxide ion and haloalkane exist for the synthesis. We deduce a possible combination by disconnecting a carbon-oxygen bond in the product. The bond that is disconnected is the one that must be formed in the synthesis.

Figure 14.11 Retrosynthetic analysis of the Williamson approach to *tert*-butyl methyl ether.

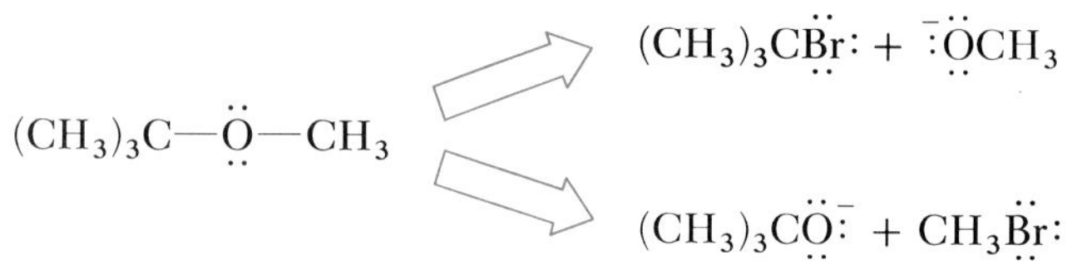

$$(CH_3)_3C\!-\!\ddot{O}\!-\!CH_3 \Rightarrow (CH_3)_3C\ddot{Br}\!: + \,^{-}\!:\!\ddot{O}CH_3$$

$$(CH_3)_3C\!-\!\ddot{O}\!-\!CH_3 \Rightarrow (CH_3)_3C\ddot{O}\!:^{-} + CH_3\ddot{Br}\!:$$

Here we see that one approach is definitely superior. If we allow *tert*-butyl bromide to react with methoxide ion, we expect the major product to be 2-methylpropene by an E_2 reaction, because we know that tertiary haloalkanes in reaction with strong bases yield primarily elimination products. The method of choice is therefore the reaction of *tert*-butoxide with bromomethane (no competing elimination reaction is possible).

PROBLEM 14.7 Use the retrosynthetic analysis approach to evaluate possible routes for the Williamson synthesis of each of the compounds listed below. In each case decide whether one of the routes is superior to the other route.

a. methyl propyl ether
b. cyclopentyl ethyl ether

ALKOXYMERCURATION/DEMERCURATION

An alternative ether synthesis involves the addition of the elements of an alcohol across a carbon-carbon double bond. Two examples are shown in Equations 14.5 and 14.6.

Eqn. 14.5

$$(CH_3)_2C\!=\!CH_2 \xrightarrow[\text{2. } NaBH_4,\ NaOH]{\text{1. } Hg(OAc)_2,\ CH_3OH} (CH_3)_3C\!-\!\ddot{O}CH_3$$

2-methylpropene → 100% yield methyl *tert*-butyl ether

Eqn. 14.6

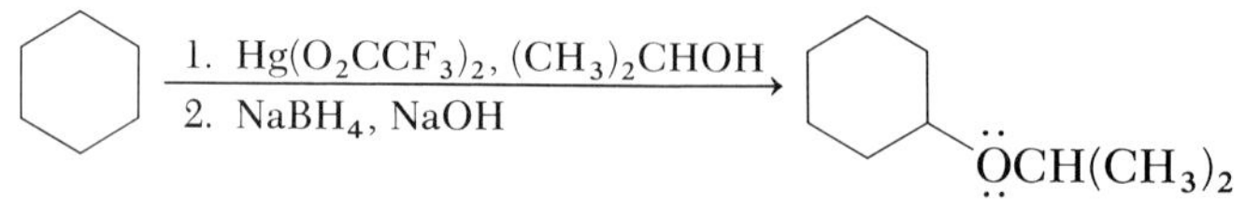

$$\text{cyclohexene} \xrightarrow[\text{2. } NaBH_4,\ NaOH]{\text{1. } Hg(O_2CCF_3)_2,\ (CH_3)_2CHOH} \text{cyclohexyl}\!-\!\ddot{O}CH(CH_3)_2$$

cyclohexene → 98% yield cyclohexyl isopropyl ether

We refer to this overall procedure as **alkoxymercuration/demercuration.**

MECHANISM OF REACTION

Overall:

R–CH=CH$_2$ $\xrightarrow[\text{Hg(OAc)}_2]{\text{R'OH}}$ R–CH(OR')–CH$_2$–HgOAc $\xrightarrow{\text{NaBH}_4}$ R–CH(OR')–CH$_3$

Step 1 The electron-rich alkene interacts with the mercuric ion of mercuric acetate.

R–CH=CH$_2$ + Hg(OAc)$_2$ ⟶ (mercurinium ion, Hg^+–OAc) + OAc$^-$

Step 2 The nucleophilic oxygen atom of the alcohol attacks the (now) electrophilic carbon of the alkene. The oxygen adds at the more electrophilic of the two alkene carbon atoms (the alkene carbon bearing the greater number of substituents).

(mercurinium ion, Hg^+–:OAc) + HÖ–R' ⟶ R–CH($\overset{+}{\text{O}}$(H)R')–CH$_2$–Hg–ÖAc

Step 3 Acetate ion removes a proton from the oxonium ion to give an intermediate organomercury compound.

R–CH($\overset{+}{\text{O}}$(H)R')–CH$_2$–HgÖAc + $^-$:ÖAc ⟶ R–CH(ÖR')–CH$_2$–HgÖAc + H–ÖAc

Step 4 In a following reaction, sodium borohydride reduces the organomercury compound to mercury metal and the ether.

R–CH(ÖR')–CH$_2$–Hg–OAc + NaBH$_4$ ⟶ R–CH(ÖR')–CH$_3$ + Hg + HOAc

This preparative method is completely analogous to the oxymercuration/demercuration procedure we discussed earlier for the synthesis of alcohols

(Chapter 10). The significant difference between the two reactions is that an alcohol rather than water attacks the mercury complex of the alkene. In some cases the trifluoroacetate salt, $Hg(O_2CCF_3)_2$, is used in place of mercuric acetate.

Alkoxymercuration/demercuration allows the synthesis of dialkyl ethers that are difficult or impossible to prepare using the Williamson approach, for example, di-*sec*-alkyl ethers or *sec*-alkyl *tert*-alkyl ethers. Of particular significance is the application of the method in the preparation of tertiary alkyl ethers, as shown in Equation 14.5.

PROBLEM 14.8 Give the method for the preparation of ethyl isopropyl ether using:

a. the Williamson approach
b. the alkoxymercuration/demercuration approach

PROBLEM 14.9 What problem would make the Williamson approach entirely unsuitable for the synthesis of di-*tert*-butyl ether?

PROBLEM 14.10 Do a retrosynthetic analysis of the synthesis of cyclohexyl isopropyl ether, using the alkoxymercuration/demercuration approach to determine an alternative route to the one shown in Equation 14.6.

PROBLEM 14.11 Which approach, Williamson or alkoxymercuration/demercuration, would be the method of choice for the synthesis of each of the ethers shown below?

a. $CH_3CH_2CH_2CH_2\ddot{O}CH_2CH_2CH_2CH_3$

b. (cyclohexyl)$\ddot{O}CH_2CH_2CH_3$

c. $(CH_3)_3C—\ddot{O}—$(cyclopentyl)

PREPARATION OF ETHERS FROM ALCOHOLS

In several earlier chapters we saw that a protonated alcohol is subject to nucleophilic substitution reactions. In these reactions a water molecule is displaced as a good leaving group. If the attacking nucleophile is a second (unprotonated) alcohol, an ether is formed. This reaction is generally of synthetic value only for primary alcohols.

MECHANISM OF REACTION

Overall:

$$2R\ddot{O}H \xrightarrow{H^+} R\ddot{O}R + H_2O$$

Step 1 An alcohol molecule is protonated.

$$R{-}\ddot{\underset{..}{O}}{-}H + H^+ \longrightarrow R{-}\overset{+}{\ddot{O}}H_2$$

Step 2 An unprotonated alcohol molecule makes a nucleophilic attack on the protonated alcohol molecule.

$$R{-}\ddot{\underset{..}{O}}{-}H + R{-}\overset{+}{\ddot{O}}H_2 \longrightarrow R_2\overset{+}{\ddot{O}}{-}H + H_2\ddot{\underset{..}{O}}$$

Step 3 A base present in the reaction system accepts a proton from the dialkyl oxonium ion to generate the free dialkyl ether. The base involved in the third step can be any proton acceptor in the reaction medium.

$$R_2\overset{+}{\ddot{O}}{-}H + {:}B \rightleftharpoons R{-}\ddot{\underset{..}{O}}{-}R + H{-}B^+$$

This procedure can be useful for the preparation of cyclic ethers as shown in Equation 14.7 for the preparation of tetrahydropyran.

Eqn. 14.7

$$H\ddot{\underset{..}{O}}CH_2CH_2CH_2CH_2CH_2\ddot{\underset{..}{O}}H \xrightarrow{H_2SO_4} \text{tetrahydropyran}$$

pentane-1,5-diol — 76% yield tetrahydropyran

PROBLEM 14.12 On treatment with phosphoric acid, 2-methyl-2,5-hexanediol is converted into a compound of formula $C_7H_{14}O$. Suggest a structure for the product, and show a full mechanism for its formation, including all intermediates and indicating electron shifts using the curved-arrow formalism.

PROBLEM 14.13 On treatment with acid, 1,2,4-butanetriol forms a compound of formula $C_4H_8O_2$. Suggest a structure for this compound.

PROBLEM 14.14 Why is the treatment of secondary alcohols (ROH) with acid generally not useful for the preparation of ethers (ROR)?

The dehydrative coupling of alcohols is usually unsatisfactory for the preparation of unsymmetrical ethers (R—O—R′) because a mixture of products results, as illustrated in Figure 14.12.

An exception to this difficulty exists if one of the alcohols is tertiary and can lose water rapidly to form a particularly stable carbocation and the other

Figure 14.12 Multiplicity of products in the dehydrative coupling of a mixture of alcohols.

$$R-\ddot{\underset{..}{O}}-H + R'-\ddot{\underset{..}{O}}-H \xrightarrow{\text{acid}} R-\ddot{\underset{..}{O}}-R + R'-\ddot{\underset{..}{O}}-R + R'-\ddot{\underset{..}{O}}-R'$$

alcohol is primary or secondary. For example, *tert*-butyl alcohol and isopropyl alcohol react under mildly acidic conditions to give a good yield of *tert*-butyl isopropyl ether, as shown in Equation 14.8.

Eqn. 14.8

$$\underset{\textit{tert}\text{-butyl alcohol}}{(CH_3)_3C\ddot{\underset{..}{O}}H} + \underset{\text{2-propanol}}{(CH_3)_2CH\ddot{\underset{..}{O}}H} \xrightarrow[H_2O]{H_2SO_4} \underset{\substack{\text{82\% yield} \\ \textit{tert}\text{-butyl isopropyl ether}}}{(CH_3)_3C-\ddot{\underset{..}{O}}-CH(CH_3)_2}$$

This reaction is performed by slowly adding *tert*-butyl alcohol from a dropping funnel to a mixture of isopropyl alcohol in an aqueous solution of sulfuric acid. The *tert*-butyl alcohol adds a proton quickly and then loses water to form the *tert*-butyl cation. A molecule of isopropyl alcohol then attacks the *tert*-butyl cation, leading to the formation of the ether product.

A variation of this procedure involves generating the carbocation by the protonation of an alkene. For example, by bubbling 2-methylpropene gas through an acidic solution of an alcohol, we can obtain an ether bearing a *tert*-butyl group.

MECHANISM OF REACTION

Overall:

$$(CH_3)_2C{=}CH_2 \xrightarrow[H_2SO_4]{ROH} R\ddot{\underset{..}{O}}C(CH_3)_3$$

Step 1 Protonation of 2-methylpropene occurs to form the *tert*-butyl cation.

$$(CH_3)_2C{=}CH_2 \xrightarrow{H_2SO_4} (CH_3)_3C^+$$

Step 2 An alcohol performs a nucleophilic attack on the carbocation.

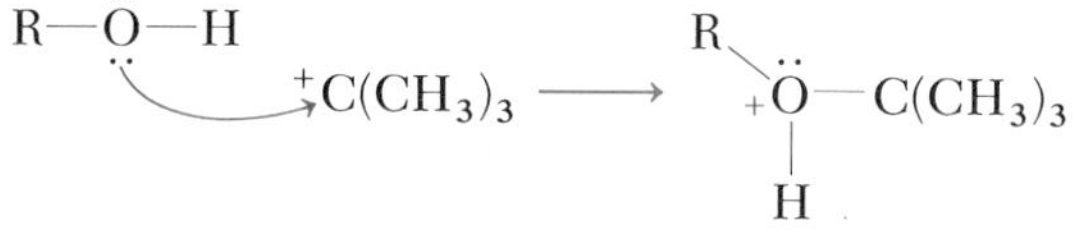

$$R-\ddot{\underset{..}{O}}-H \quad {}^+C(CH_3)_3 \longrightarrow R-\overset{+}{\ddot{O}}(H)-C(CH_3)_3$$

Step 3 The oxonium ion loses a proton to a base in the solution to generate the observed ether product.

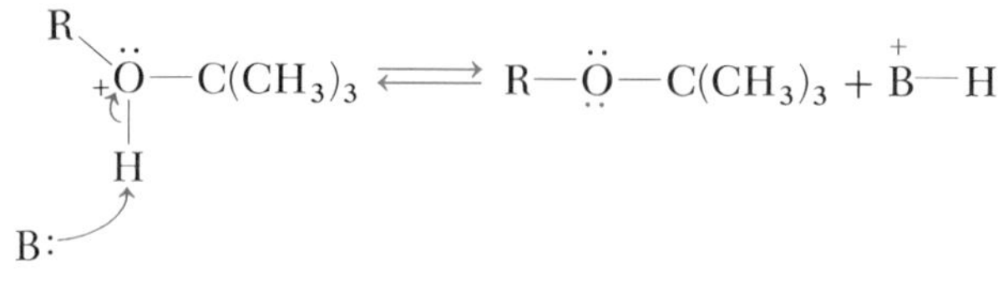

$$R-\overset{+}{\ddot{O}}(H)-C(CH_3)_3 + B: \rightleftharpoons R-\ddot{\underset{..}{O}}-C(CH_3)_3 + \overset{+}{B}-H$$

14.5 The Cleavage of Ethers

Simple dialkyl ethers are cleaved by concentrated HI, as described earlier in the chapter (see Equation 14.1 and accompanying discussion). If an excess of HI is used, both alkyl groups of the ethers are converted into alkyl iodide products (ROR′ + HI[excess] → RI + R′I). This reaction can be useful for structure determination of an unknown ether. The alkyl iodide products are separated and analyzed, and from their identities we can reconstruct the structure of the ether.

PROBLEM 14.15

Deduce the structure of the starting compound in each of the following cleavage reactions.

a. A compound of formula $C_6H_{14}O_2$ on treatment with an excess of HI yields a mixture of iodomethane, 1,2-diiodoethane, and 2-iodopropane.
b. A compound of formula $C_4H_{10}O_2$ on treatment with hot HI yields a mixture of iodomethane and 1,2-diiodoethane in a 2:1 molar ratio.
c. A compound of formula C_4H_8O on treatment with excess KI in phosphoric acid yields 1,4-diiodobutane.
d. A compound of formula $C_4H_8O_2$ on treatment with hot HI yields 1,2-diiodoethane as the only product.

Steps to Solving the Problem

Solution to Problem 14.15a

1. Draw the structures of the products. They are:

$$CH_3{-}\ddot{\underset{..}{I}}: \qquad :\ddot{\underset{..}{I}}{-}CH_2CH_2{-}\ddot{\underset{..}{I}}: \qquad :\ddot{\underset{..}{I}}{-}CH(CH_3)_2$$

2. Determine the source of each carbon atom in each product. Each carbon-iodine bond of the products can be traced to a carbon-oxygen bond in the starting compound. The alkyl groups of the two monoiodo-products could not originally have been joined to each other (if they were, there would be no way to account for the 1,2-diiodoethane product). The methyl and isopropyl groups must originally have been joined through the $-CH_2CH_2-$ unit of the 1,2-diiodoethane. That is, the original structure was:

$$CH_3\ddot{\underset{..}{O}}CH_2CH_2\ddot{\underset{..}{O}}CH(CH_3)_2$$

Certain types of ethers undergo cleavage reactions much more readily than others. One important class of these easily cleaved ethers consists of *vinyl ethers*, also known as **enol ethers.** Enol ethers contain an alkoxy group attached directly to an olefinic carbon. The hydrolysis of these compounds proceeds by means of protonation of the alkene double bond.

MECHANISM OF REACTION

Overall:

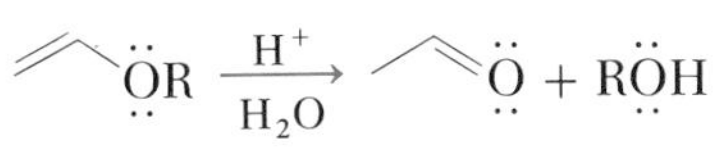

$$CH_2{=}CH{-}\ddot{\underset{..}{O}}R \xrightarrow[H_2O]{H^+} CH_3CH{=}\ddot{\underset{..}{O}} + R\ddot{\underset{..}{O}}H$$

Step 1 Protonation of the enol ether at the β-carbon

$$\mathrm{H_2C{=}CH{-}\ddot{O}R} \xrightarrow{H^+} \left[\mathrm{H_3C{-}\overset{+}{C}H{-}\ddot{O}R} \longleftrightarrow \mathrm{H_3C{-}CH{=}\overset{+}{O}R}\right]$$

Step 2 Attack of water on the carbocation

$$\mathrm{H_3C{-}\overset{+}{C}H{-}\ddot{O}R} \underset{}{\overset{H_2O}{\rightleftharpoons}} \mathrm{H_3C{-}CH(\overset{+}{O}H_2){-}\ddot{O}R}$$

Step 3 Loss of a proton to a Lewis base in the solution

$$\mathrm{CH_3{-}CH(\overset{+}{O}H_2){-}\ddot{O}R} \overset{-H^+}{\rightleftharpoons} \mathrm{CH_3{-}CH(\ddot{O}H){-}\ddot{O}R}$$

Step 4 Protonation of the ether oxygen

$$\mathrm{CH_3{-}CH(\ddot{O}H){-}\ddot{O}R} \overset{H^+}{\rightleftharpoons} \mathrm{CH_3{-}CH(\ddot{O}H){-}\overset{+}{O}(H)R}$$

Step 5 Dissociation of the oxonium ion

$$\mathrm{CH_3{-}CH(\ddot{O}H){-}\overset{+}{O}(H)R} \rightleftharpoons \mathrm{R\ddot{O}H} + \left[\mathrm{CH_3{-}\overset{+}{C}H{-}\ddot{O}H} \longleftrightarrow \mathrm{CH_3{-}CH{=}\overset{+}{O}H}\right]$$

Step 6 Loss of a proton to a Lewis base in the reaction system

$$\mathrm{CH_3{-}CH{=}\overset{+}{O}H} \xrightarrow{-H^+} \mathrm{CH_3{-}CH{=}\ddot{O}}$$

PROBLEM 14.16 Explain why the initial protonation of the enol ether in the preceding mechanism occurs at the β-carbon atom rather than at the α-carbon atom (i.e., the carbon bonded to oxygen) or at the oxygen atom.

At no point in the hydrolysis of an enol ether is a potent nucleophile required. Enol ethers undergo hydrolysis in dilute aqueous acid with water playing the role of the nucleophile. Water attacks the resonance-stabilized carbocation formed in the initial protonation.

Ethers containing a *tert*-butyl group bonded to oxygen also undergo cleavage readily in aqueous sulfuric acid. After protonation, the breaking of the bond between oxygen and the carbon atom of the *tert*-butyl group yields a relatively stable *tert*-butyl carbocation. Some of the *tert*-butyl carbocations lose a proton to form 2-methylpropene, a gas that bubbles out of the reaction mixture and forces the equilibrium toward the cleavage products.

MECHANISM OF REACTION

Overall:

$$R-\ddot{O}-C(CH_3)_3 \xrightarrow{\text{aq. } H_2SO_4} R\ddot{O}H + (CH_3)_2C{=}CH_2$$

Step 1 Protonation of the ether.

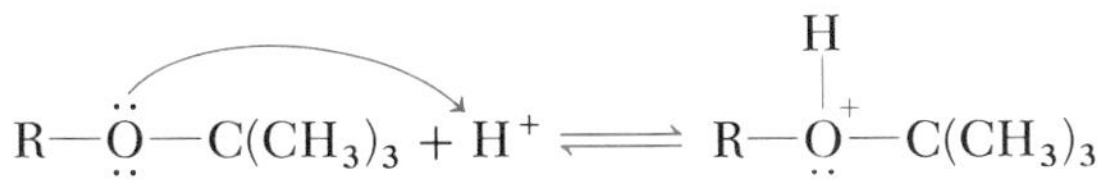

$$R-\ddot{O}-C(CH_3)_3 + H^+ \rightleftharpoons R-\overset{H}{\underset{..}{O^+}}-C(CH_3)_3$$

Step 2 Cleavage of C—O bond and formation of a *tert*-butyl carbocation.

$$R-\overset{H}{\underset{..}{O^+}}-C(CH_3)_3 \rightleftharpoons R-\ddot{O}-H + {}^+C(CH_3)_3$$

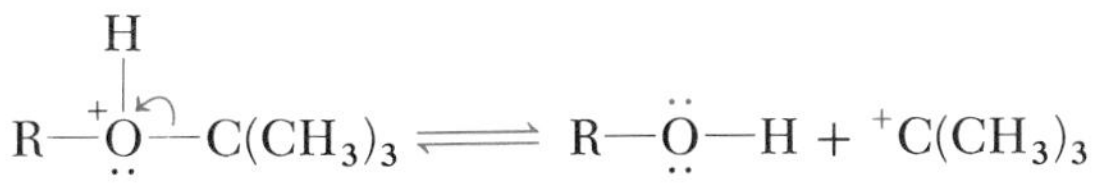

Step 3 A base removes a proton from the *tert*-butyl carbocation to form 2-methylpropene.

$$(CH_3)_2\overset{+}{C}-CH_2-H \;\; :B \rightleftharpoons (CH_3)_2C{=}CH_2 + H-B^+$$

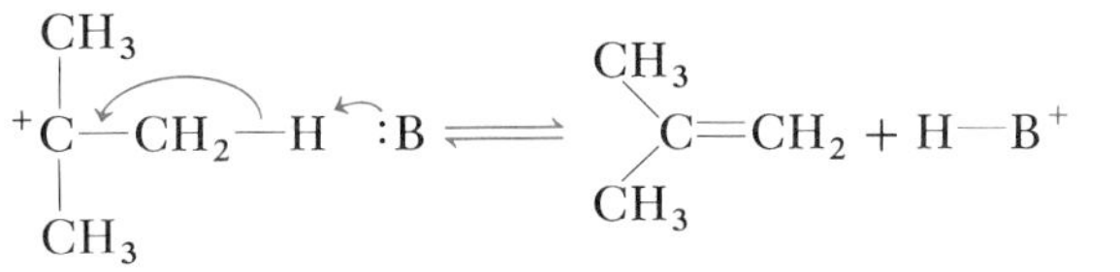

(gas; bubbles out of solution)

The base in step 3 can be any one of a number of species in solution, for example, water, or another molecule of the ether starting material.

14.6 Use of the Ether Functional Group to Protect Alcohols

The generally inert character of the ether linkage is exploited by using it as a **protecting group** for alcohols. (See Chapter 10 for an earlier discussion of protecting groups.) Consider a synthetic problem in which protection of an alcohol function is required. Suppose we need to convert 5-bromo-1-pentanol to 2-methylheptane-2,7-diol, as shown in Figure 14.13.

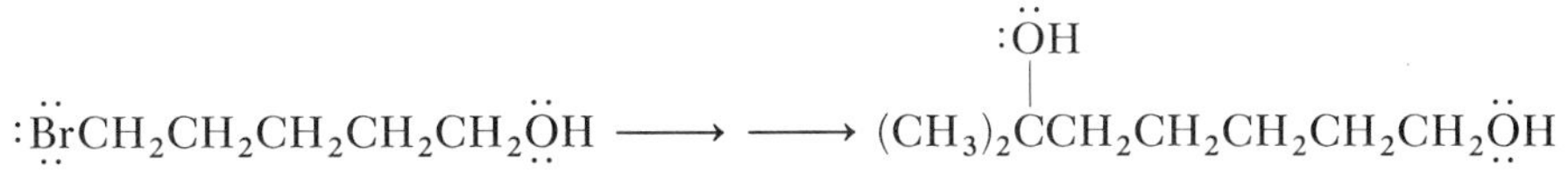

$$:\ddot{Br}CH_2CH_2CH_2CH_2CH_2\ddot{O}H \longrightarrow \longrightarrow (CH_3)_2\overset{:\ddot{O}H}{C}CH_2CH_2CH_2CH_2CH_2\ddot{O}H$$

Figure 14.13 A synthetic problem—conversion of 5-bromo-1-pentanol to 2-methylheptane-2,7-diol.

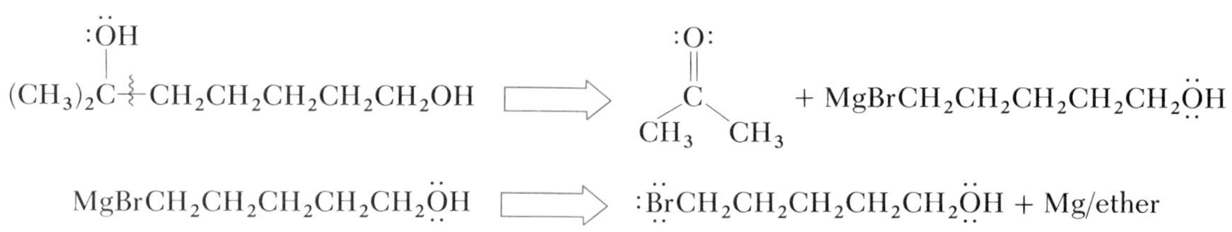

$$(CH_3)_2C(\ddot{O}H)\text{-}CH_2CH_2CH_2CH_2CH_2OH \Longrightarrow (CH_3)_2C{=}\ddot{O}: + MgBrCH_2CH_2CH_2CH_2CH_2\ddot{O}H$$

$$MgBrCH_2CH_2CH_2CH_2CH_2\ddot{O}H \Longrightarrow :\ddot{Br}CH_2CH_2CH_2CH_2CH_2\ddot{O}H + Mg/ether$$

Figure 14.14 Retrosynthetic analysis of the preparation of 2-methylheptane-2,7-diol.

Using the retrosynthetic analysis shown in Figure 14.14, we see that we need to form a new carbon-carbon bond. An appealing strategy for accomplishing this is to generate the Grignard reagent and allow it to react with acetone, followed by workup with dilute aqueous acid. (The general strategy for preparing alcohols from Grignards and carbonyl compounds was introduced in Chapter 11; you may wish to review this material.) However, the presence of the hydroxyl group in the starting material is a problem. Hydroxyl groups react immediately with Grignard reagents to form an alkoxide ion and protonate the nucleophilic carbon of the Grignard reagent. Thus we cannot hope to maintain a Grignard function sufficiently long to react with an added carbonyl compound when the molecule contains a hydroxyl group.

Fortunately, we can get around this problem by temporarily masking the hydroxyl function with a protecting group. We can do this quite conveniently by converting it to an ether. Of course, no matter what we use as a protecting function, we must be able to remove it under relatively mild conditions once its purpose has been fulfilled, and we no longer need it.

A common procedure for accomplishing our goal is to convert the alcohol to a *tert*-butyl ether using one of the procedures mentioned earlier. After the desired manipulations with the Grignard reagent have been performed, the *tert*-butyl group can be cleaved with aqueous acid to regenerate the hydroxyl group. The full sequence of reactions needed to accomplish the conversion of Figure 14.13 is shown in Figure 14.15.

A very useful alternative to masking hydroxyl groups as *tert*-butyl ethers involves converting them to **silyl ethers.** Silyl ethers, which contain the carbon-oxygen-silicon linkage, are generally less reactive than ordinary ethers to both acid and base. They can be cleaved using highly selective reaction conditions that have virtually no effect on other portions of the molecule.

There are several methods for the preparation of silyl ethers. Two examples of their preparation under neutral conditions are shown in Equations 14.9 and 14.10.

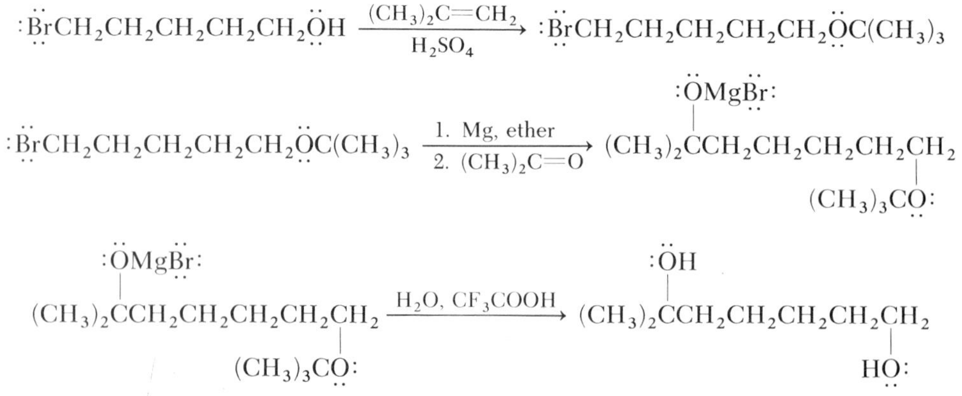

Figure 14.15 Synthesis of 2-methylheptane-2,7-diol from 5-bromo-1-pentanol. The hydroxyl group is temporarily masked as a *tert*-butyl ether so that the manipulations with the Grignard reagent may be performed.

$$:\ddot{Br}CH_2CH_2CH_2CH_2CH_2\ddot{O}H \xrightarrow[H_2SO_4]{(CH_3)_2C{=}CH_2} :\ddot{Br}CH_2CH_2CH_2CH_2CH_2\ddot{O}C(CH_3)_3$$

$$:\ddot{Br}CH_2CH_2CH_2CH_2CH_2\ddot{O}C(CH_3)_3 \xrightarrow[2.\ (CH_3)_2C{=}O]{1.\ Mg,\ ether} (CH_3)_2C(\ddot{O}Mg\ddot{Br}:)CH_2CH_2CH_2CH_2CH_2\ddot{O}C(CH_3)_3$$

$$(CH_3)_2C(\ddot{O}Mg\ddot{Br}:)CH_2CH_2CH_2CH_2CH_2\ddot{O}C(CH_3)_3 \xrightarrow{H_2O,\ CF_3COOH} (CH_3)_2C(\ddot{O}H)CH_2CH_2CH_2CH_2CH_2\ddot{O}H$$

Eqn. 14.9

2-cyclohexen-1-ol $\xrightarrow[\text{pyridine}]{(CH_3)_3SiCl}$ 3-trimethylsiloxycyclohexene (75% yield)

Eqn. 14.10

cyclohexanol $\xrightarrow[\text{pyridine}]{(CH_3)_2Si(C(CH_3)_3)Cl}$ *tert*-butyldimethylsilyl cyclohexyl ether (90% yield)

Both the trimethylsilyl and the *tert*-butyldimethylsilyl protecting groups can be removed by reaction with fluoride ion. However, the use of the bulkier *tert*-butyldimethylsilyl group is often preferred because it is more stable to other reaction conditions. Two methods for the removal of these groups are shown in Equations 14.11 and 14.12.

Eqn. 14.11

$C_6H_{11}O{-}Si(CH_3)_2{-}C(CH_3)_3 \xrightarrow[\text{THF}]{(C_4H_9)_4N^+F^-} C_6H_{11}OH$ (99% yield)

Eqn. 14.12

tert-butyldimethylsilyl benzyl ether $C_6H_5CH_2{-}O{-}Si(CH_3)_2{-}C(CH_3)_3 \xrightarrow[\text{KF (dihydrate)}]{(C_4H_9)_4N^+Cl^-} C_6H_5CH_2OH$ benzyl alcohol (95% yield)

Fluoride ion cleaves silyl ethers quickly and selectively. In polar aprotic solvents, where fluoride is not highly solvated, it serves as a good nucleophile. Attack of fluoride ion is selective for silicon under these conditions because of the high thermodynamic driving force for the formation of the silicon-fluorine bond. Formation of the fluorine-silicon bond releases 128 kcal/mole, compared with 102 kcal/mole that would be released by the formation of a carbon-fluorine bond. (The oxygen-silicon bond that is broken requires only 89 kcal/mole.)

14.7 Epoxides

Cyclic ethers in which the oxygen atom is part of a three-membered ring are referred to as *epoxides*. These compounds are much more reactive than ordinary ethers, largely due to strain in the three-membered ring. Opening the ring relieves this strain. In this regard, epoxide chemistry resembles the chemistry of cyclopropane and its derivatives. However, because of the presence of an oxygen atom in the ring, epoxides are able to react with a much wider range of reagents than are cyclopropanes. Many reagents cause epoxides to undergo ring-opening reactions. In fact, epoxides find wide use in organic chemisty because of their special reactivity, which allows them to be converted into a range of useful compounds.

PREPARATION OF EPOXIDES

Several methods are available for the preparation of epoxides. Most of these methods use alkenes as precursors, either directly or indirectly. One common method involves a facile intramolecular nucleophilic substitution reaction of **halohydrins.** Halohydrins (Chapter 10) are formed by the reaction of alkenes with halogens in aqueous solution, as illustrated in Equation 14.13.

Eqn. 14.13

$$(CH_3)_2C{=}CHCH_3 \xrightarrow{Br_2,\ H_2O} (CH_3)_2C(\ddot{O}H){-}CH(\ddot{Br}:)CH_3$$

2-methyl-2-butene → 76% yield, 3-bromo-2-methyl-2-butanol

Halohydrins are alcohols so they are in equilibrium with their conjugate bases (alkoxide ions) when placed in basic solution. The alkoxide oxygen atom of the conjugate base of a halohydrin is in perfect position to effect a rapid intramolecular nucleophilic substitution reaction in which the alkoxide oxygen atom displaces bromide ion and forms an epoxide with inversion of configuration. An example is shown in Equation 14.14.

Eqn. 14.14

$$(CH_3)_2C(\ddot{O}H){-}CH(\ddot{Br}:)CH_3 \xrightarrow[H_2O]{KOH} (CH_3)_2C(\ddot{O}:^-){-}CH(\ddot{Br}:)CH_3 \longrightarrow (H_3C)_2C\overset{:O:}{\frown}CH{-}CH_3$$

3-bromo-2-methyl-2-butanol → 47% yield, 2,2,3-trimethyloxirane

An important stereochemical point is involved here. *The geometry of the original alkene is maintained in the product epoxide.* This point is not evident in the reaction shown in Equation 14.14, but it becomes clear in reactions involving cyclic alkenes and certain open-chain alkenes. For example, only *meso*-2,3-dimethyloxirane (*cis*-2-butene oxide) is formed in a reaction that starts with *cis*-2-butene (see Figure 14.16). The corresponding reaction sequence that starts with *trans*-2-butene yields racemic 2,3-dimethyloxirane.

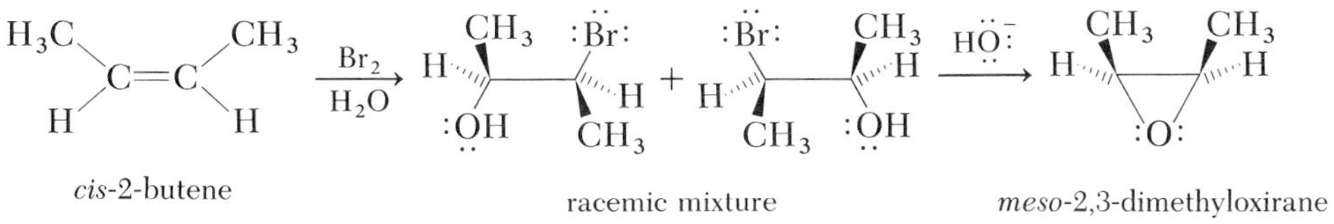

Figure 14.16 **Epoxide formation from *cis*-2-butene.** Only *meso*-2,3-dimethyloxirane is formed when *cis*-2-butene is converted to the bromohydrin and the bromohydrin is then treated with base. The geometry of the original alkene is maintained throughout the reaction sequence.

PROBLEM 14.17 Write out the complete mechanism for the epoxidation of *trans*-2-butene through the use of bromine/water followed by treatment with base.

Another commonly used method for the preparation of epoxides involves the reaction of alkenes with peroxides. While a variety of peroxides and conditions can be used, we will consider only two of the most important methods here.

For the direct preparation of epoxides from alkenes in aqueous solution, hydrogen peroxide and a carboxylic acid are used. Hydrogen peroxide is commercially available as an aqueous solution. Acetic acid is quite commonly used as the carboxylic acid. The initial reaction involves the transfer of oxygen from hydrogen peroxide to acetic acid to form **peroxyacetic acid.** This species, generated in situ, then oxidizes the alkene to the epoxide. Alternatively, commercially available peroxyacetic acid can be used directly; however, it is a powerful oxidizing agent and may react violently with some organic substances. The formation of the peroxyacetic acid and the oxygen transfer to the alkene are illustrated in Figure 14.17. The reaction is stereospecific. The geometry originally present in the alkene is maintained in the product epoxide.

Other carboxylic acids can be used in this reaction. Like acetic acid, they undergo initial oxidation to the peroxy stage prior to their reaction with the alkene. Acetic acid is commonly used because it is so readily available and convenient for use, compared with higher molecular weight carboxylic acids.

One difficulty is sometimes encountered in using this approach for the direct preparation of epoxides from alkenes. If the alkene to be epoxidized is

Figure 14.17 **Reaction of an alkene with peroxyacetic acid.**

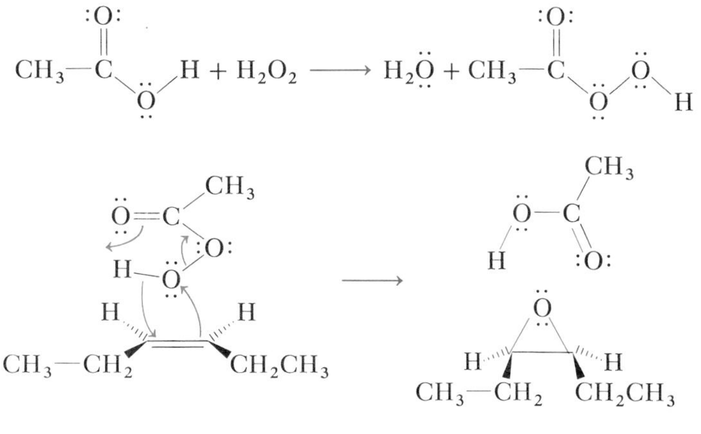

SPECIAL TOPIC

An Epoxide Insect Hormone

Hormones play important roles in insects as well as in other complex organisms. (A hormone can be thought of as a *chemical messenger* whose chemical interactions signal other processes to begin, stop, or change rate.) One set of hormones in insects controls their development from the larval stage to maturity. Tiny quantities of a hormone known as **juvenile hormone** have been isolated from insects. This hormone must be present to prevent the insect from maturing too rapidly. Conversely, an excess of juvenile hormone prevents the insect from developing into an adult. The structure of juvenile hormone, shown below, is that of an isoprenoid (see Chapter 9) containing an epoxide ring.

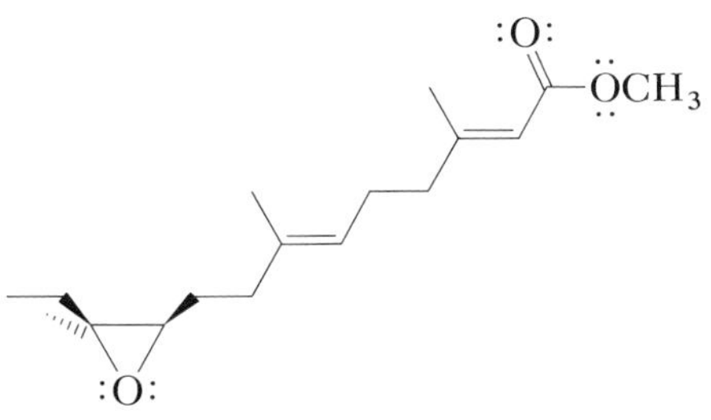

:O: $\ddot{O}CH_3$

:O:

insect juvenile hormone

Since hormones are active in such minute quantities, it has sometimes been speculated that they could be used in relatively small (and arguably safe) amounts to control insect pests. This would, of course, require their synthesis at the laboratory bench. Several syntheses of juvenile hormone have been reported. The final step in these routes is the epoxidation of a triene precursor using *meta*-chloroperoxybenzoic acid to give a 40% yield of the juvenile hormone. Some epoxidation of the "wrong" double bonds occurs, and this is in part responsible for the moderate yield.

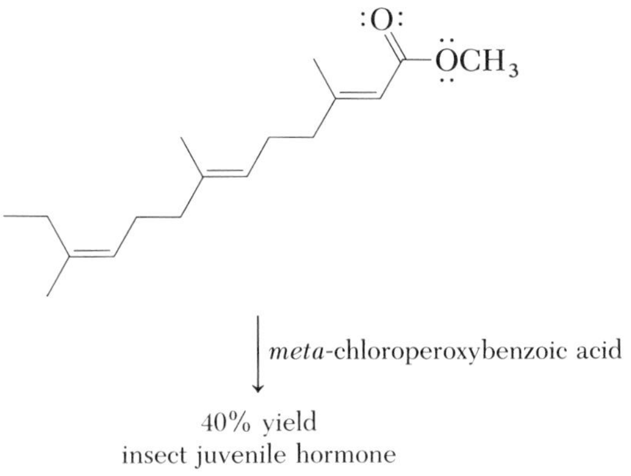

:O: $\ddot{O}CH_3$

meta-chloroperoxybenzoic acid

40% yield
insect juvenile hormone

(continued)

(continued from previous page)

Juvenile hormone itself is not suitable as a biological pest control agent because it is not specific to one insect species. Other hormones may be more species-specific. Investigation of these hormones is an area of intense research interest.

insufficiently soluble in the aqueous reaction system, reaction will be extremely slow. We can then use an alternative method employing a peroxy carboxylic acid that is soluble in organic solvents. ***meta*-Chloroperoxybenzoic acid** is most commonly used, with methylene chloride as the solvent. *meta*-Chloroperoxybenzoic acid is a reasonably stable substance that is commercially available and can be stored for extended periods of time without decomposition. The reaction of *meta*-chloroperoxybenzoic acid proceeds in a manner entirely analogous to that shown before for peroxyacetic acid. The oxygen transfer process is illustrated in Figure 14.18.

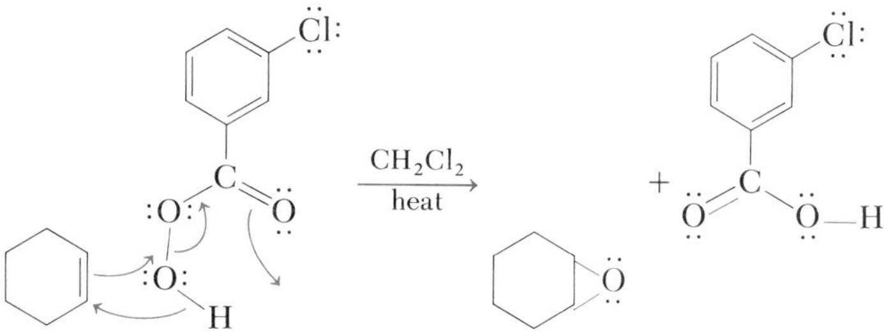

Figure 14.18 Epoxidation of cyclohexene with *meta*-chloroperoxybenzoic acid.

$$\xrightarrow[\text{heat}]{CH_2Cl_2}$$

PROBLEM 14.18 Label all stereocenters in insect juvenile hormone as *R*, *S*, *E*, or *Z*.

PROBLEM 14.19 Outline the "isoprene units" in the structure of insect juvenile hormone.

PROBLEM 14.20 Suggest how to prepare 2-methyl-2-ethyloxirane in one step from:
a. an alkene **b.** a halohydrin

OPENING OF EPOXIDE RINGS

We mentioned earlier that carboxylic acids other than acetic acid could be used with hydrogen peroxide to synthesize epoxides directly from alkenes. Suppose we were to use the readily available **formic acid** (HCO_2H) to generate in situ **peroxyformic acid** as the epoxidizing agent. The reaction would, in fact, generate the epoxide in a manner entirely analogous to the reactions we have already seen. The reaction using formic acid is summarized in Figure 14.19.

However, we do not actually isolate the epoxide under these reaction conditions. The epoxide continues to react, forming a **vicinal diol** as shown in

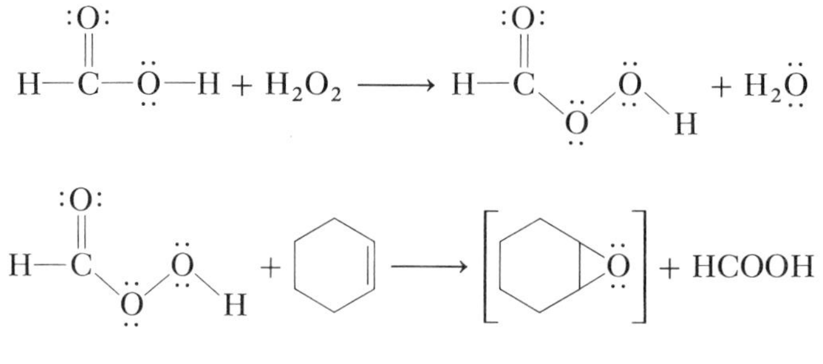

Figure 14.19 Reaction of peroxyformic acid with an alkene.

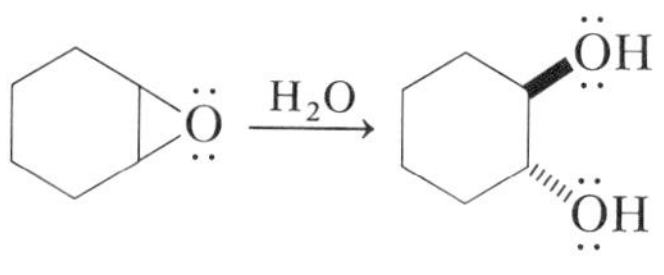

$$H{-}C({=}O){-}O{-}H + H_2O_2 \longrightarrow H{-}C({=}O){-}O{-}O{-}H + H_2O$$

$$H{-}C({=}O){-}O{-}O{-}H + \text{cyclohexene} \longrightarrow [\text{cyclohexene oxide}] + HCOOH$$

$$\text{cyclohexene oxide} \xrightarrow{H_2O} \text{trans-1,2-cyclohexanediol (racemic)}$$

racemic

Figure 14.20 Continuation of reaction of cyclohexene oxide in peroxyformic acid reaction.

Figure 14.20. Overall, this reaction amounts to **hydroxylation** of the parent alkene (see Chapter 10). Two hydroxyl groups with an *anti* stereochemistry have been added to the alkene skeleton.

How and why does this reaction occur? Why should this reaction occur when we use peroxyformic acid but not when we use peroxyacetic acid? The answer lies in the relative acidity of the two parent acids. Acetic acid is a weak acid of $pK_a = 4.7$. Formic acid is also a weak acid, but it is stronger than acetic acid, with a $pK_a = 3.7$. Formic acid is an order of magnitude stronger than is acetic acid, and its greater acidity is sufficient to allow the ring-opening process to occur rapidly in aqueous solution.

With acetic acid or other weaker acids, the equilibrium between free and protonated epoxide lies rather far to the free epoxide side, and the concentration of the protonated epoxide is sufficiently low that reaction with water is slow. However, when we use acids stronger than acetic acid, the equilibrium lies significantly farther toward the protonated epoxide side and the reaction with water then proceeds at a measurable rate (see Figure 14.21).

The opening of the epoxide ring in the presence of acid catalysis is a general phenomenon. If we use epoxides isolated from preparative experiments and place them in aqueous acid solution, we obtain the same diols as are formed in the reaction with formic acid and hydrogen peroxide. The stereochemistry of the diols indicates the mechanism by which ring opening occurs. Water attacks the protonated epoxide from the *backside* of the carbon-oxygen bond that is being broken. Moreover, with a symmetric epoxide, attack occurs with equal probability at each of the two possible sites. With cyclohexene oxide, water attack produces the racemic *trans*-1,2-cyclohexanediol rather than the *meso* (*cis*) isomer (see Figure 14.22). The process is entirely analogous to

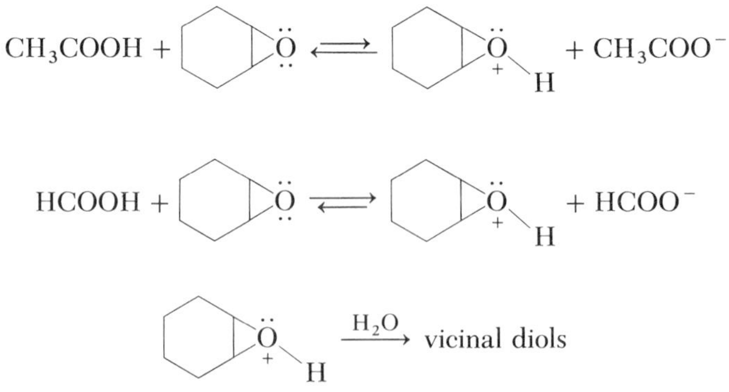

$$CH_3COOH + \text{epoxide} \rightleftharpoons \text{protonated epoxide} + CH_3COO^-$$

$$HCOOH + \text{epoxide} \rightleftharpoons \text{protonated epoxide} + HCOO^-$$

$$\text{protonated epoxide} \xrightarrow{H_2O} \text{vicinal diols}$$

Figure 14.21 Relative degrees of protonation of peroxides. Formic acid, being stronger, pushes the protonation equilibrium farther to the right than does the weaker acetic acid. Since it is the protonated epoxide form that reacts with water to generate the vicinal diols, formic acid facilitates this ring opening much more than does acetic acid. The attack of water on the protonated epoxide occurs too fast in formic acid solution for us to isolate the epoxide.

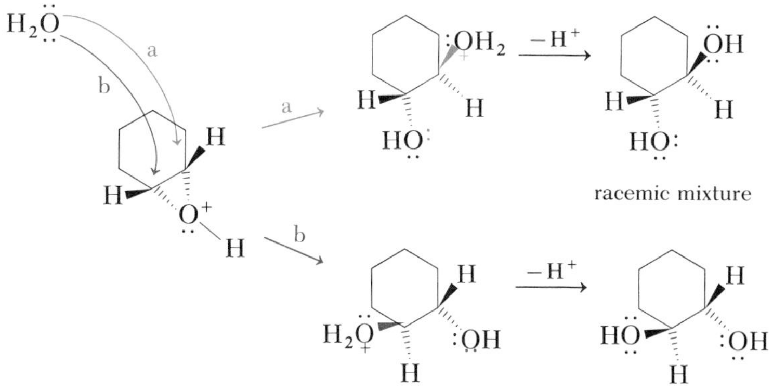

Figure 14.22 Water attack on a protonated epoxide. Water attacks from the backside of the carbon-oxygen bond of the protonated epoxide. This attack is completely analogous to nucleophilic displacements on protonated alcohols or ethers. The incoming nucleophile (water) interacts with the large back lobe of the empty σ^* orbital of the carbon-oxygen linkage. With a symmetric epoxide, attack at each of the possible carbon sites has an equal probability of occurring. Note the similarity to the reactions of bromonium ions discussed in Chapter 10.

racemic mixture

the reaction of cyclohexene with bromine (Chapter 10); however, we can isolate the cyclic intermediate, that is, the epoxide, whereas we cannot isolate a bromonium ion.

We see that this route provides vicinal diols corresponding to overall *anti* hydroxylation of the original alkene, in contrast to the methods of hydroxylation discussed in Chapter 10 (using permanganate or osmium tetroxide), which gave *syn* hydroxylation. The two types of procedures nicely complement each other. We can produce all possible stereoisomeric diols from a single alkene by judicious choice of the hydroxylation reagents.

Protonated epoxides react with many nucleophiles other than water. For example, in the presence of bromide ion they open to produce bromohydrins. An example of this reaction is shown in Equation 14.15.

Eqn. 14.15

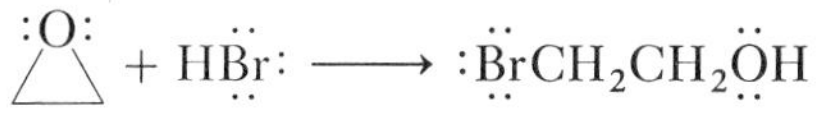

$$\text{oxirane} + HBr \longrightarrow BrCH_2CH_2OH$$

oxirane — 90% yield 2-bromoethanol

Some nucleophiles also open epoxide rings under neutral or basic conditions, in marked contrast to the behavior of open-chain ethers or other cyclic ethers. Nucleophiles attack these species only under strongly acidic conditions. Three examples of nucleophilic attack on epoxides under basic conditions are shown in Equations 14.16–14.18.

Eqn. 14.16

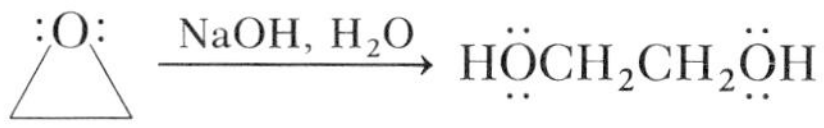

$$\text{oxirane} \xrightarrow{NaOH,\ H_2O} HOCH_2CH_2OH$$

oxirane — 90% yield ethylene glycol

Eqn. 14.17

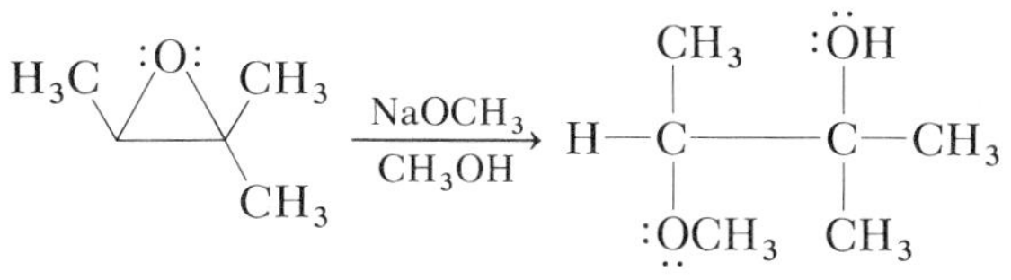

$$\text{2,2,3-trimethyloxirane} \xrightarrow[CH_3OH]{NaOCH_3} H\text{—}C(CH_3)(OCH_3)\text{—}C(OH)(CH_3)\text{—}CH_3$$

2,2,3-trimethyloxirane — 53% yield 3-methoxy-2-methyl-2-butanol

Eqn. 14.18

$$\text{oxirane} \xrightarrow[\text{workup with aq acid}]{CH_3(CH_2)_5MgBr,\ \text{ether, heat}} CH_3(CH_2)_5CH_2CH_2\ddot{O}H$$

oxirane

71% yield
1-octanol

We find that under neutral or basic conditions nucleophilic attack on unsymmetrical epoxides (as in Equation 14.17) occurs preferentially at the least sterically hindered carbon of the ring. This preference is consistent with the S_N2 nature of the reaction. The reaction illustrated in Equation 14.18 is another useful Grignard synthesis of primary alcohols; overall, *two* carbon atoms are added to the skeleton of the original haloalkane.

We also find the nucleophile attacks from the backside of the ring carbon-oxygen bonds. Thus, inversion of configuration occurs at the carbon atom undergoing attack, as is illustrated in Equation 14.19, where ammonia is the nucleophile.

Eqn. 14.19

$$\xrightarrow{\text{aq } NH_3}$$

each stereogenic carbon atom has an (*S*)-configuration

70% yield

The reaction under acidic conditions, in which the attack proceeds through a protonated epoxide, is less clear-cut. Attack usually occurs at the carbon atom of the ring that can best stabilize a positive charge, in a manner equivalent to the attack of water or alcohol on a bridged bromonium ion. While the attack formally occurs at the more highly substituted carbon atom, it is not a simple S_N2 process. In the protonated oxirane, the bond to the more highly substituted carbon atom is greatly weakened compared with the bond from oxygen to the less highly substituted carbon atom. Equation 14.20 shows a reaction under acidic conditions that proceeds with a different regiochemistry than the equivalent reaction under basic conditions (Equation 14.17).

Eqn. 14.20

$$\xrightarrow{CH_3OH,\ H_2SO_4} H_3C{-}CH(\ddot{O}H){-}C(CH_3)(\ddot{O}CH_3){-}CH_3$$

2,2,3-trimethyloxirane

76% yield
3-methoxy-3-methyl-2-butanol

The direction of attack of a nucleophile on a protonated epoxide is consistent with the idea that the positive charge is not confined to the oxygen atom but is spread over the entire ring. In this regard, the reaction is very similar to that of bromonium ions we met earlier. With bromonium ions, attack also tends to occur on the ring carbon that can best stabilize a positive charge.

SPECIAL TOPIC

Epoxides and Cancer

Epoxides are highly reactive as substrates for nucleophilic attack. The bases of RNA and DNA contain nucleophilic nitrogen sites, so it is not surprising that they can undergo reaction with epoxides. In Chapter 12 we described how haloalkanes, which are also highly reactive substrates for nucleophiles, are able to alter DNA molecules. The normal functioning of the DNA is compromised as a result of such reactions, and the consequence is a series of chemical events that may lead to cancer. Some (but not all) simple epoxides have been shown to cause cancer in laboratory animals (presumably some epoxides are unable to penetrate cells in sufficient concentration to cause deleterious effects on DNA). Three epoxides that have been demonstrated to be carcinogenic are shown below.

:O: $CH_2{=}CH$:O: :O: :O:

2-phenyloxirane (styrene oxide) 2-ethenyloxirane 1,3-butadiene dioxide

The relation between structure and the ability to damage DNA is a topic of active research. It is possible in some cases for epoxides to be synthesized in the body. This synthesis occurs in liver cells, which contain enzymes causing the epoxidation of benzene derivatives. It is believed that this reaction renders some benzene derivatives carcinogenic.

Epoxides are, of course, able to modify the DNA of cancer cells as well as of healthy cells. Some epoxides have been investigated and show promise for use as chemotherapeutic agents. These epoxides damage both healthy and cancerous cells but can be effective if the cancerous tissue is more vulnerable than the healthy tissue.

PROBLEM 14.21 Predict the result of treating propylene oxide with lithium aluminum hydride, followed by workup with aqueous acid. (*Hint:* The products of lithium aluminum hydride reductions can often be deduced by assuming that the reagent serves as a source of $H\!:^-$.)

PROBLEM 14.22 In separate experiments (*R*)-propylene oxide is allowed to react with aqueous hydroxide and with aqueous acid. Compare these reactions. Do you expect the products to be identical, enantiomers, or diastereoisomers? Explain your answer.

PROBLEM 14.23 Predict the product obtained by treating cyclohexene oxide with hydrogen cyanide.

14.8 Crown Ethers

The term **crown ether** applies to a group of substances containing a ring composed of several carbon atoms and several oxygen atoms that is able to adopt a crownlike conformation. This type of compound was first synthesized about twenty years ago. We discussed some aspects of this type of compound in Chapter 3 (in the section titled "Supramolecular Effects"). Many of these substances exhibit remarkable properties.

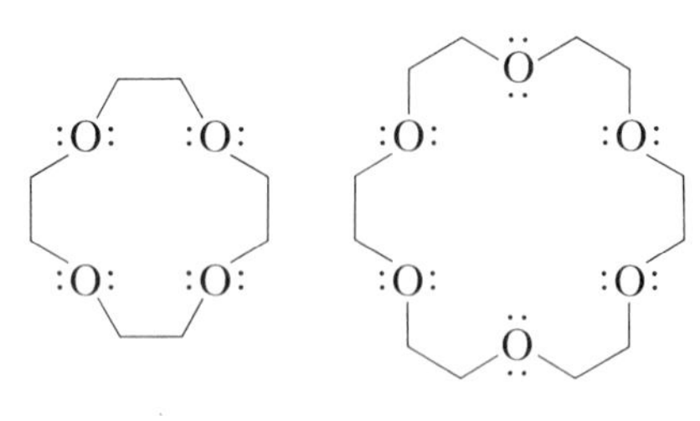

Figure 14.23 Examples of crown ethers. Each name is of the form *x*-crown-*y*, where *x* specifies the size of the ring, and *y* specifies the number of oxygen atoms in the ring. In both examples the oxygen atoms are separated from each other by $-CH_2CH_2-$ linkages.

Since the systematic names for these compounds are quite complex, chemists have developed an alternative naming system, which is in common use. Two examples are shown in Figure 14.23.

The remarkable properties of crown ethers stem from their ability to bind cations within their crown-shaped cavities. Consider, for example, the potassium ion. Potassium salts are generally very soluble in water, in large part because water molecules are able to solvate and stabilize the potassium ion and its accompanying anion. In water the potassium ion binds to the oxygen of several water molecules, as shown schematically in Figure 14.24.

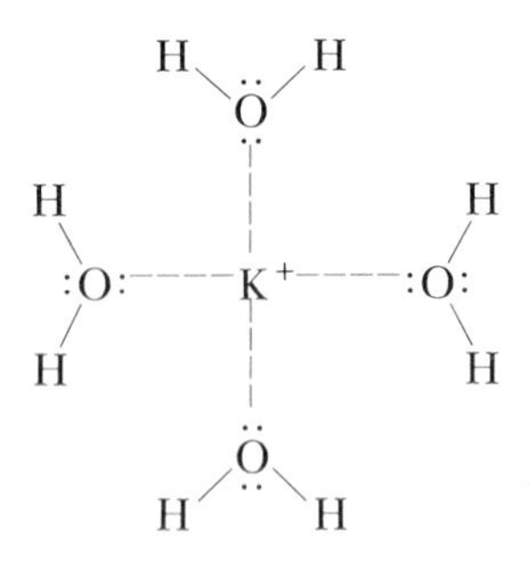

Figure 14.24 Schematic diagram of the solvation of potassium ions in water.

In contrast, potassium salts are generally quite insoluble in relatively nonpolar organic solvents such as ethers. In most organic solvents, no stabilization of the potassium ion (or its counterion) occurs, precluding the separation of the ions and the dissolution of the salt. However, potassium salts can be forced to dissolve in many such solvents by adding 18-crown-6 to the medium. The cavity of 18-crown-6 is of just the proper size to accommodate a potassium ion, which is stabilized by interaction with the six surrounding oxygen sites (see Figure 14.25). The special characteristic of these crown ethers is that they provide sites that are *already organized* for interaction with the cation. Providing these sites is an entropy effect. No reorganization of the solvent is required to enable these interactions.

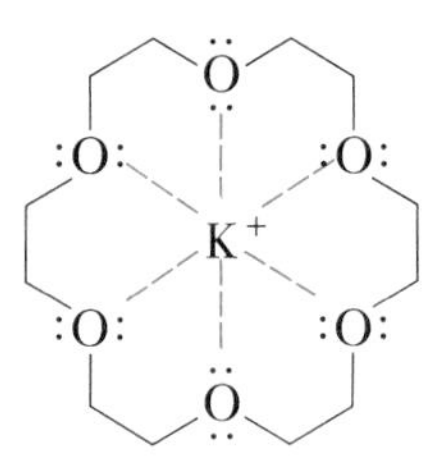

Figure 14.25 Potassium ion held in the cavity of 18-crown-6. A potassium ion is of the proper size to fit into the cavity of 18-crown-6. The relationship between the potassium ion and the crown ether is known as a host-guest relationship and is an example of a supramolecular interaction (Chapter 3).

In effect, the environment that the crown ether provides for the potassium ion is rather like that provided in an aqueous solution.

The outer periphery of a crown ether is quite hydrocarbonlike. Thus crown ethers dissolve easily in typical nonpolar organic solvents, even when they contain a guest cation in the cavity. As a result, the positive ion is carried into organic solution, along with the accompanying anion. For example, potassium permanganate gives a purple solution when it is added to a solution of benzene or methylene chloride containing 18-crown-6. No dissolution at all occurs in the absence of the crown ether.

These organic solutions of inorganic salts have several special characteristics. They include the following:

- Reactions (e.g., permanganate oxidations) that normally need to be performed under two-phase heterogeneous conditions (since the organic compound is of only limited solubility in aqueous media) can be performed under homogeneous conditions in an organic solvent.
- The counterion of a cation held in the crown has unusually great reactivity in a nonpolar organic solvent. The anion is unsolvated (a *naked anion*) and is similar to anions dissolved in polar aprotic solvents such as DMSO (Chapter 12).

The function of certain antibiotics appears to be related to their ability to accommodate a guest cation. The guest cation, concealed in the cavity of the antibiotic, is transported through the cell walls of the bacterium, producing a disruption of the proper balance of ion concentrations inside and outside of the cell. For example, nonactin (**14.1**) is able to smuggle sodium ions through bacterial cell walls. The resulting disruption of ion concentrations produces an osmotic pressure that eventually causes rupture of the cell.

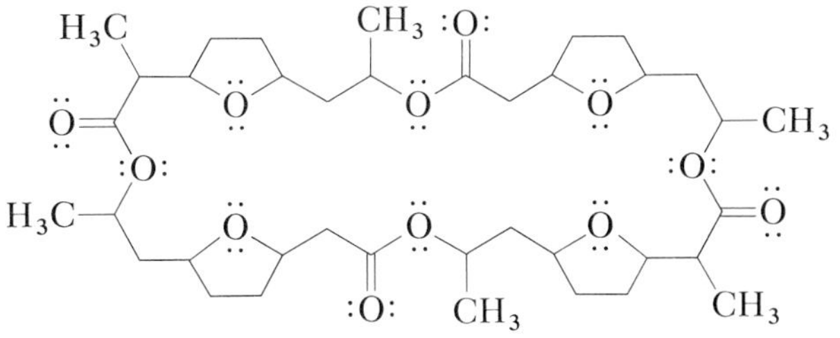

nonactin, a polyether antibiotic

14.1

Summary

- Ethers are relatively unreactive molecules.
- Ethers can be cleaved upon treatment with strongly acidic reagents. Ordinary dialkyl ethers require the presence of a potent nucleophile for cleavage under acidic conditions.
- Tertiary and enol ethers undergo cleavage with considerable ease compared to other alkyl ethers. With tertiary ethers, protonation of the ether oxygen and heterolysis of the carbon-oxygen bond generates a relatively stable tertiary carbocation.
- Enol ethers undergo cleavage after protonation at carbon.
- Dialkyl ethers are relatively insensitive to basic conditions and reagents.
- One method for the preparation of ethers is the Williamson synthesis, which involves the S_N2 attack of an alkoxide ion on a haloalkane. The substrate should be a halomethane or a primary haloalkane, as secondary and tertiary halides undergo elimination under the conditions of the reaction.
- An alternative synthetic route to ethers is alkoxymercuration/demercuration.
- Preparation and hydrolysis of *tert*-butyl ethers is an effective protecting-group strategy.
- Epoxides are much more reactive than other ethers because of the strain in the three-membered ring. In particular, epoxides undergo ring-opening reactions when challenged with a variety of nucleophiles.
- In general, epoxides are attacked by nucleophiles at the least-substituted carbon atom of the ring when neutral or basic conditions are used.
- Under acidic conditions, nucleophiles usually attack epoxides at the most-substituted carbon atom of the ring.
- Ring-opening reactions of epoxides are of widespread synthetic importance. They provide entry to a great variety of products, depending on the nucleophile used.
- Epoxides can be prepared by the direct oxidation of alkenes using peroxy acids.
- An alternative route for the preparation of epoxides is via the treatment of halohydrins with base. The two methods result in epoxides of opposite stereochemistry.
- Each of the routes for epoxide synthesis involves an alkene as the starting point for epoxide formation and maintains the original stereochemistry of the alkene in the epoxide.
- Crown ethers are large ring compounds containing several carbon and oxygen atoms. They adopt crownlike conformations into which guest cations of appropriate size can fit.

■ Crown ethers are useful for causing inorganic salts to dissolve in relatively nonpolar organic solvents. For example, potassium permanganate dissolves in benzene containing 18-crown-6 to give *purple benzene*, a useful oxidizing agent.

Terms to Remember

heteroatom
heterocyclic
epoxide
oxirane
retrosynthetic analysis
disconnection
alkoxymercuration/demercuration
enol ether
protecting group
silyl ether
halohydrin
peroxyacetic acid
meta-chloroperoxybenzoic acid
juvenile hormone
formic acid
peroxyformic acid
vicinal diol
hydroxylation
crown ether

Reactions of Synthetic Utility

62. $2\,R{-}OH \xrightarrow{H_2SO_4} R{-}O{-}R$ — 14.4

63. $R'{-}O{-}R \xrightarrow[NaX]{H_2SO_4} R{-}X + R'{-}X$ — 14.5
$X = I > Br$

64. Halohydrin (X, OH) $\xrightarrow{HO^-}$ epoxide — 14.7
X=Cl, Br, I

65. Alkene $\xrightarrow[CH_3COOH]{H_2O_2}$ epoxide — 14.7

66. Alkene $\xrightarrow[\text{methylene chloride}]{\textit{meta}\text{-chloroperoxybenzoic acid}}$ epoxide — 14.7

67. Alkene $\xrightarrow[HCOOH]{H_2O_2}$ diol (OH, OH) — 14.7
anti-stereochemistry

68. Epoxide $\xrightarrow[\text{aq base}]{\text{aq acid or}}$ diol (OH, OH) — 14.7
anti-stereochemistry

69. Epoxide (R) $\xrightarrow[\text{ether}]{R'MgX}$ R′, R, OH — 14.7
anti-stereochemistry
(other organometallics may also be used)

70. Epoxide (R) $\xrightarrow[\text{ether}]{LiAlH_4}$ H, R, OH — 14.7
anti-stereochemistry

71. $R{-}OH \xrightarrow{R'_3SiCl,\ \text{base}} R{-}OSiR'_3$ — 14.6

72. $R{-}OSiR'_3 \xrightarrow{(C_4H_9)_4N^+F^-,\ H_2O} R{-}OH$ — 14.6

Additional Problems

14.24 Draw structures for each of the following:
a. isopentyl methyl ether
b. 3-isopropoxy-1-propanol
c. allyl vinyl ether
d. (Z)-1-methoxy-2-butene
e. *sec*-butyl methyl ether

14.25 Provide systematic names for each of the following:

a. 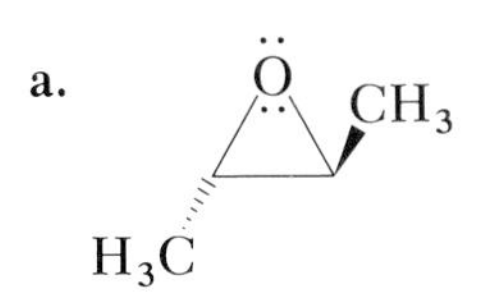

b. $(CH_3)_2CHOCH_2CH_2CH_3$

c. (cyclopropyl)$-O-CH_2CH_3$

d. $CH_2{=}CHOC(CH_3)_3$

e. O CH3
O CH3

f. (cyclobutyl)$-O-$(cyclobutyl)

g. $(CH_3)_2CHCH_2CH_2OCH_2CH{=}CH_2$

14.26 Starting with any alcohols of your choice, outline syntheses for the following:
a. *tert*-butyl methyl ether (two ways)
b. diisopropyl ether (using alkoxymercuration/demercuration)
c. *sec*-butyl isobutyl ether (using a Williamson approach)
d. hexyl isopropyl ether (two ways)
e. *tert*-butyl cyclohexyl ether

14.27 The reaction of (*R*)-*sec*-butyl methyl ether with HBr yields bromomethane and (*R*)-*sec*-butyl alcohol. Use the curved-arrow formalism to show the mechanistic steps in this reaction.

14.28 Which products would be expected in the following reactions? If no reaction occurs, so specify.
a. diisopropyl ether with sulfuric acid and sodium iodide
b. *sec*-butyl ethyl ether with sodium
c. butyl ethyl ether refluxed with concentrated aqueous sodium hydroxide solution
d. 1-methylcyclohexene with formic acid/hydrogen peroxide
e. *cis*-3-hexene treated first with chlorine in water, then with aqueous hydroxide, and finally with aqueous acid
f. cyclopentene oxide with anhydrous HCl

14.29 Which of the 2-butenes should be used to prepare a racemic mixture of 2,3-butanediol by epoxidation followed by workup using aqueous potassium hydroxide followed by aqueous acid?

14.30 Give the major product formed in each of the following reactions.
a. ethylene oxide treated with methylmagnesium bromide and worked-up with aqueous acid
b. 2,2-dimethyloxirane treated with sodium methoxide followed by workup with aqueous acid
c. oxetane treated with hot, concentrated HI
d. *tert*-butyl chloride treated with potassium ethoxide
e. 5-bromo-1-pentanol treated with potassium ethoxide in ethanol

14.31 Cyclopentene reacts with chlorine in water to yield compound *A*, of formula C_5H_9ClO. Treatment of *A* with cool, dilute aqueous sodium hydroxide solution yields *B*, of formula C_5H_8O. When *B* is heated with aqueous sodium hydroxide, followed by workup with acid, *C*, of formula $C_5H_{10}O_2$, is formed. Show structures for the compounds *A*–*C*, indicating the proper stereochemistry where relevant. Use the curved-arrow formalism to show the mechanism of each of the reactions involved.

14.32 An ether, on treatment with sulfuric acid and sodium iodide, yields a single iodoalkane that contains 74.7% iodine by weight and that undergoes hydrolysis to give a secondary alcohol. Suggest a structure for the ether.

14.33 Treatment of 2-methyl-4-penten-1-ol with mercuric acetate followed by sodium borohydride yields a compound of formula $C_6H_{12}O$. Suggest a structure for this compound and explain its formation.

14.34 The annual industrial production of ethylene oxide amounts to millions of tons. Some ethylene oxide is used as a fumigant, but the epoxide is principally used as a starting material to prepare a variety of other chemicals. Deduce the structures of the following compounds, which are made from ethylene oxide.

a. an anti-freeze of formula $C_2H_6O_2$, made by treating ethylene oxide with water
b. "cellosolve," of formula $C_4H_{10}O_2$, a high-boiling solvent for lacquers and paints, made by treating ethylene oxide with ethanol
c. ethanolamine, of formula C_2H_7NO, used in making plastics, obtained by treating ethylene oxide with ammonia
d. diethanolamine, of formula $C_4H_{11}NO_2$, also used in making plastics, obtained by treating ethanolamine with ethylene oxide
e. acrylonitrile, of formula C_3H_3N, which is used in the manufacture of orlon and is formed by treating ethylene oxide with hydrogen cyanide followed by dehydration

14.35 Under certain conditions treatment of ethylene oxide with acid yields a product of formula $C_4H_8O_2$. This product is unreactive with sodium metal and does not decolorize an aqueous solution of potassium permanganate. The first two steps of the mechanism for its formation are: (i) protonation of the ethylene oxide molecule and (ii) nucleophilic attack of an unprotonated ethylene oxide molecule on a protonated ethylene oxide molecule. Suggest a structure for the final product and provide the remaining mechanistic steps.

14.36 Under appropriate conditions, treatment of ethylene oxide with aqueous sodium hydroxide followed by workup with aqueous acid yields a substance of formula $C_4H_{10}O_3$. Suggest a structure for this product, and provide a mechanism for its formation.

14.37 Using stereochemical drawings, predict the outcome of a reaction of *trans*-2,3-dimethyloxirane with aqueous sodium hydroxide.

14.38 Suggest a series of synthetic steps that will bring about each of the following conversions.

a. cyclohexene to methoxycyclohexane
b. cyclohexene to *trans*-2-methoxy-1-cyclohexanol
c. 1-butanol and isobutyl alcohol to isobutyl butyl ether
d. 3-bromo-1-butanol to 3-deuterio-1-butanol
e. bromocyclohexane to *cis*-1,2-cyclohexanediol
f. bromocyclohexane to *trans*-1,2-cyclohexanediol

14.39 Suggest a structure for a substance of formula $C_6H_{14}O_2$ that yields iodoethane and 1,2-diiodoethane in a 2:1 ratio on treatment with excess sodium iodide in sulfuric acid.

14.40 The substance shown below is isomerized when it is treated with aqueous potassium hydroxide. The product contains a six-membered ring. Give the structure of the product and suggest a mechanism for its formation.

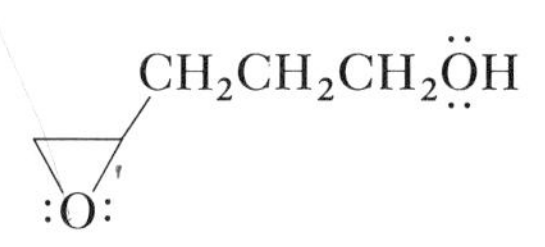

14.41 Give the best set of reagents for each of the following conversions.

a. 2-methylpropene to *tert*-butyl isobutyl ether
b. cyclohexanol to *trans*-2-methylcyclohexanol
c. cyclopentane to *trans*-1,2-cyclopentanediol
d. 2-propanol to 1-isopropoxy-2-propanol

14.42 Dihydropyran is sometimes used to protect primary alcohols. The reaction between dihydropyran and the alcohol (ROH) takes place in the presence of an acid catalyst to produce an ether linkage. An example of this reaction is

$$\text{dihydropyran} + C_2H_5OH \xrightarrow{H^+} C_7H_{14}O_2$$

dihydropyran

Give the structure of the protected alcohol and give a mechanism for its formation.

14.43 The cleavage of a silyl ether (R—O—SiR′$_3$) is accomplished by treatment with $(C_4H_9)_4NF$ in the presence of a small amount of water. One product is the alcohol, R—OH. What is the other product in this reaction?

14.44 Give the more stable chair conformation for *cis*-2,6-dimethyl-1,4-dioxane.

15 CHAPTER Alkadienes and Alkynes

15.1 Introduction

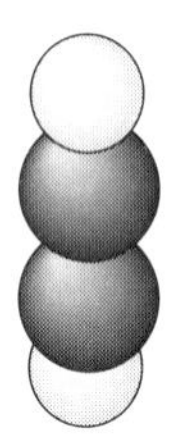

In this chapter we turn our attention to substances that contain two carbon-carbon double bonds (dienes) and substances that contain one (or more) carbon-carbon triple bonds (alkynes). The chemistry of dienes provides useful insights into many important phenomena. Of particular importance is the observation that the relative position of the two carbon-carbon double bonds in an alkadiene is central in determining its properties. We will learn why their position is so important and will explore the consequences of this structural feature.

Alkynes exhibit reactions that are counterparts to many of the addition reactions we studied earlier for alkenes, and alkynes also have some special properties that are uniquely theirs, making them very different from alkenes. The hybridization model is useful for analyzing the chemical characteristics of alkynes. We will therefore reexamine this model and consider its relationship to structure and chemical properties.

15.2 Nomenclature

The nomenclature for molecules containing two or more carbon-carbon double bonds is usually straightforward. It is an extension of the system used for simple alkenes. Several examples are shown in Figure 15.1. Notice that for some molecules, the geometry about each double bond must be specified to give an unambiguous description.

At times it is awkward to provide a parent name for a unit that contains both of the carbon-carbon double bonds. In such cases (e.g., **15.1**), one of the double bonds can be named as part of a substituent.

1-methyl-2-[(Z)-1-propenyl]cyclohexene
15.1

When we use this type of nomenclature, one of the carbons in the olefinic linkage of the parent structure must be assigned as position 1. Numbering then progresses across the double bond, that is, the second olefinic carbon atom is position 2.

For molecules containing carbon-carbon triple bonds, we again use a simple nomenclature system akin to that used for alkenes. The longest continuous carbon chain containing the carbon-carbon triple bond provides the parent

$CH_2{=}CH{-}CH{=}CH_2$
1,3-butadiene

$CH_2{=}C{=}CH{-}CH_3$
1,2-butadiene

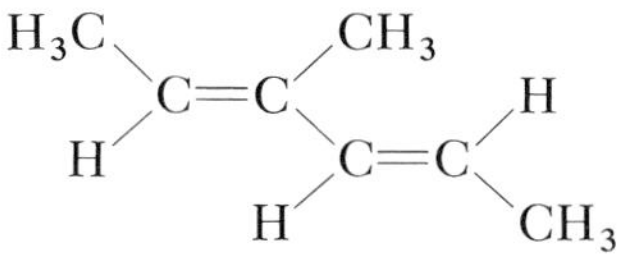

H_3C, CH_3, $C{=}C$, H, H, $C{=}C$, H, CH_3
(2*E*,4*E*)-3-methyl-2,4-hexadiene

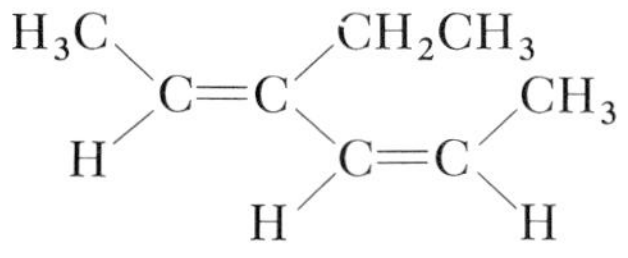

H_3C, CH_2CH_3, $C{=}C$, CH_3, H, $C{=}C$, H, H
(2*E*,4*Z*)-3-ethyl-2,4-hexadiene

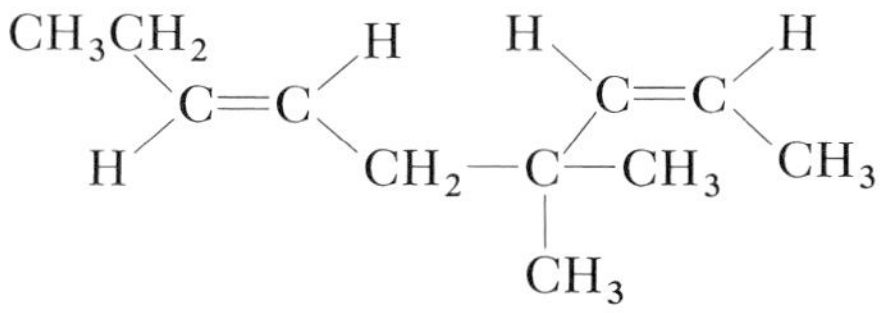

CH_3CH_2, H, H, H, $C{=}C$, $C{=}C$, H, $CH_2{-}C{-}CH_3$, CH_3, CH_3
(2*Z*,6*E*)-4,4-dimethyl-2,6-nonadiene

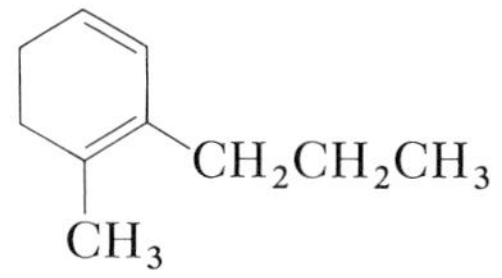

$CH_2CH_2CH_3$, CH_3
1-methyl-2-propyl-1,3-cyclohexadiene

Figure 15.1 Nomenclature of some dienes. The use of *E*/*Z* descriptors avoids the ambiguities introduced by the *cis* and *trans* prefixes.

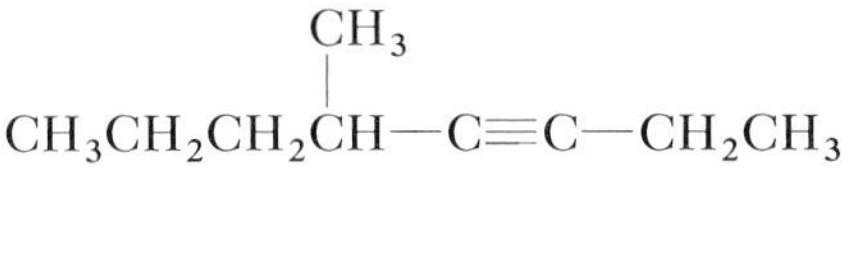

$CH_3CH_2CH_2CH(CH_3){-}C{\equiv}C{-}CH_2CH_3$
5-methyl-3-octyne

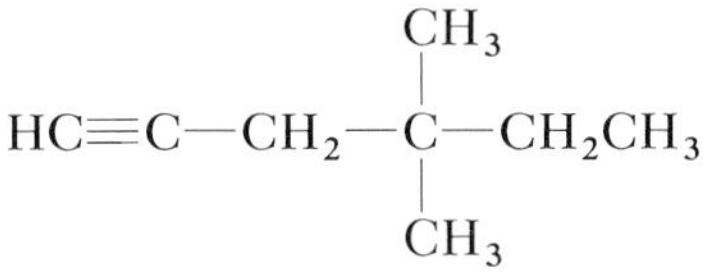

$HC{\equiv}C{-}CH_2{-}C(CH_3)_2{-}CH_2CH_3$
4,4-dimethyl-1-hexyne

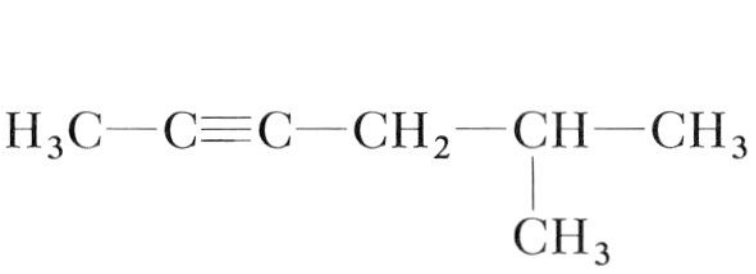

$H_3C{-}C{\equiv}C{-}CH_2{-}CH(CH_3){-}CH_3$
5-methyl-2-hexyne

Figure 15.2 Nomenclature of alkynes.

name, and then we add the suffix *yne* to it. Several examples of alkyne nomenclature are shown in Figure 15.2.

Sometimes alternative names are used for simple alkynes. These names result from considering the alkyne to be a derivative of the simplest alkyne, acetylene (ethyne). Several examples are shown in Figure 15.3. The method is awkward for more complex alkynes.

$CH_3CH_2{-}C{\equiv}C{-}CH_2CH_3$
diethylacetylene

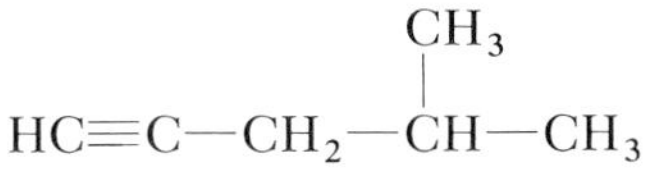

$HC{\equiv}C{-}CH_2{-}CH(CH_3){-}CH_3$
isobutylacetylene

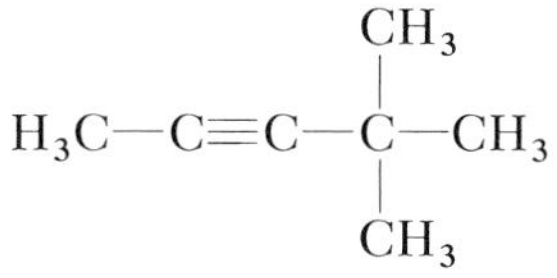

$H_3C{-}C{\equiv}C{-}C(CH_3)_2{-}CH_3$
t-butylmethylacetylene

Figure 15.3 Naming alkynes as derivatives of acetylene.

15.3 Bonding and Structure in Dienes and Alkynes

CONJUGATED DOUBLE BONDS

Conjugated dienes have double bonds separated by only one single bond. Several examples of conjugated dienes are shown in Figure 15.4.

Unless the molecule is twisted about the intervening single bond, the double bonds of conjugated dienes interact with each other. This interaction is important for their chemistry. The effect of conjugation can be rationalized using

(Z)-1,3-pentadiene

1-ethenylcyclohexene
(1-vinylcyclohexene)

(E)-2-methyl-2,4-hexadiene

1,3-cyclohexadiene

Figure 15.4 Examples of conjugated dienes. The two double bonds of conjugated dienes are separated by one single bond. A further point of nomenclature is illustrated here: the substituent ($-CH=CH_2$) can be named as a *vinyl* group.

a model of mutual overlap of the adjacent p orbitals involved in the π bonds of the diene. This interaction is shown schematically in Figure 15.5.

In the next chapter we will discuss how we consider the interaction of these p orbitals as leading to the formation of π molecular orbitals. For the present, we need simply to recognize that the π electrons of a conjugated diene are not localized between a pair of adjacent carbons as they are with a simple alkene. Instead, π electron density is delocalized over the entire diene unit.

Consider the Lewis electron structure for the simplest conjugated diene, 1,3-butadiene. The structure

$$H_2C=CH-CH=CH_2$$

focuses our attention on π bonds between C1 and C2 and between C3 and C4. This representation is artificially simplistic because it implicitly ignores p orbital interaction between C2 and C3. In fact, there is evidence that all three of the carbon-carbon bonds of 1,3-butadiene have some double-bond character. The carbon-carbon bond lengths of 1,3-butadiene are of interest here. As Table 15.1 shows, all of the carbon-carbon bonds of 1,3-butadiene are shorter than the carbon-carbon single bond of ethane.

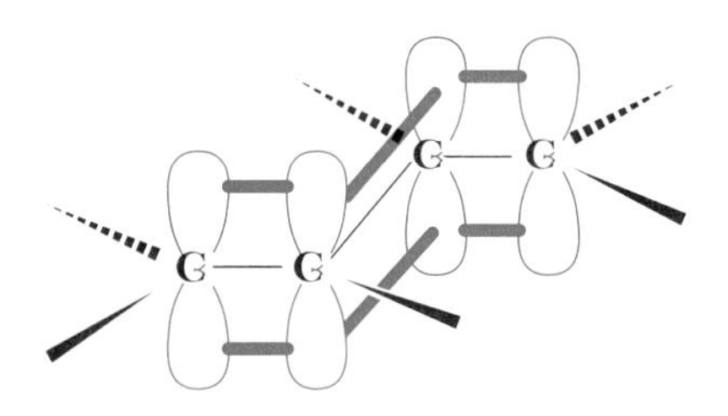

Figure 15.5 Orbital interaction for conjugation in a diene. Neighboring p orbitals of conjugated dienes are in position to interact and produce a π system extending over the entire diene unit.

The short C2–C3 linkage can be rationalized at least partly in terms of the hybridization of the orbitals involved in its σ bond. We use the model of two sp^3 hybrid orbitals to describe the carbon-carbon bond in ethane, but for the C2–C3 bond of 1,3-butadiene we must use two sp^2 hybrids. The greater the s character of a hybrid orbital, the closer the electrons in it are held to the nucleus. The increased s character of the hybrids used to form the C2–C3 σ bond in 1,3-butadiene should result in a stronger and shorter bond. Also, if there is π-bond character associated with the C2–C3 bond, that too will result in a shortened bond.

Thermochemical measurements indicate conjugated dienes to be more stable than nonconjugated dienes. Some experimental data on these relative stabilities are shown in Table 15.2. (You might want to review the section

Table 15.1 Carbon-Carbon Bond Lengths in Ethane and 1,3-Butadiene

Molecule	Bond Length
H_3C-CH_3	1.53 angstrom
$H_2C=CH-CH=CH_2$	C1–C2 (C3–C4) 1.34 angstrom C2–C3 1.46 angstrom

SPECIAL TOPIC

Polyacetylene

Electron delocalization over the four carbon atoms of conjugated doubly bonded systems has an interesting practical application. Polymerization of acetylene produces a material known as *polyacetylene*. Under the proper conditions, this material is a conductor of electricity—a very unusual characteristic for an organic molecule. Polyacetylene is a high molecular weight conjugated polyene containing many repeating units of the structure:

$$(-CH{=}CH-CH{=}CH-)_n$$

Thin films of polyacetylene can be used as electrodes in batteries. Because organic materials are much lighter than metal conductors, lighter and potentially cheaper batteries can be made.

"Thermochemistry of Hydrogenation Reactions" in Chapter 10.) For example, the heat of hydrogenation of the nonconjugated diene 1,5-hexadiene is twice that of 1-hexene. However, the heat of hydrogenation of 1,3-butadiene is less than twice that of 1-butene by about 3.9 kcal/mole. (See the first two entries in Table 15.2. We might have expected the heat of hydrogenation of 1,3-butadiene to be 2 × 30.2 kcal/mole, i.e., 60.4 kcal/mole, but this value is 3.9 kcal/mole higher than the experimental value.) We associate this difference with the improved stability of the conjugated diene.

ISOLATED DOUBLE BONDS

If double bonds are separated by one or more sp^3 hybridized carbon atoms, they are referred to as isolated double bonds. There is little or no interaction between the individual π systems. Each double bond behaves like an ordinary alkene double bond. A typical example of a molecule with isolated double bonds is 1,5-hexadiene (the last compound listed in Table 15.2).

Table 15.2 Observed Heats of Hydrogenation of Alkenes and Dienes

Compound	Heat of Hydrogenation (kcal/mole)
$CH_3CH_2CH{=}CH_2$	30.2
$CH_2{=}CH-CH{=}CH_2$	56.5
$CH_3CH_2CH_2CH_2CH{=}CH_2$	30.0
$CH_2{=}CHCH_2CH_2CH{=}CH_2$	60.0

CUMULATED DOUBLE BONDS

The simplest structure containing two consecutive double bonds along a carbon chain is 1,2-propadiene (**15.2**), also known as allene.

$$H_2C{=}C{=}CH_2$$

1,2-propadiene (allene)
15.2

Other substances containing two consecutive double bonds are often referred to as *allenes*. That is, we think of them as derivatives of allene. If a molecule contains more than two consecutive double bonds, we refer to it as a **cumulene.** Allenes and cumulenes contain *cumulated* double bonds. The simplest cumulene, 1,2,3-butatriene (**15.3**), is shown below.

$$H_2C{=}C{=}C{=}CH_2$$

1,2,3-butatriene
15.3

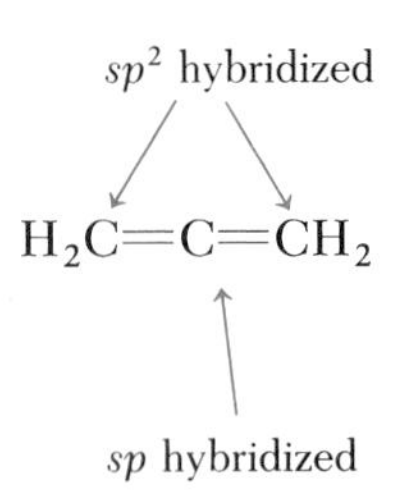

Figure 15.6 Hybridization in allene. The central carbon atom of allene is involved in two π bonds, each requiring a p orbital to interact with p orbitals of the terminal carbon atoms. Thus only one p orbital on the central carbon atom can be used to form hybrid orbitals for the formation of σ bonds. The hybridization of the central carbon atom must therefore be sp.

The two double bonds of an allene are physically closer than those of a conjugated diene. We might naively expect them to interact more strongly than the double bonds of a conjugated diene. However, the special geometry of the p orbitals of an allene prevents their interaction. This geometry results from the types of orbitals available to the central carbon atom. Since this carbon atom forms four bonds to only *two* other atoms, it is sp-hybridized (see Figure 15.6).

An sp hybridized carbon atom has two remaining unhybridized p orbitals. These two p orbitals are used by the central carbon atom to form two π bonds. Since the unhybridized p orbitals are perpendicular to each other (see Chapter 1), it follows that the two π bonds are also perpendicular to each other. It is simply not possible for an allene to have a continuous coplanar arrangement of p orbitals as occurs in conjugated dienes. For this reason, the two π bonds do not interact. The geometries of the π bonds in conjugated dienes and allenes are contrasted in Figure 15.7.

It follows that the sets of ligands at the two ends of an allenic system are in perpendicular planes. The geometry of an allene is thus similar in some ways to that associated with a tetracoordinated carbon atom. For example, both the methane molecule and the allene molecule have two sets of hydrogen ligands in perpendicular planes, as illustrated in Figure 15.8.

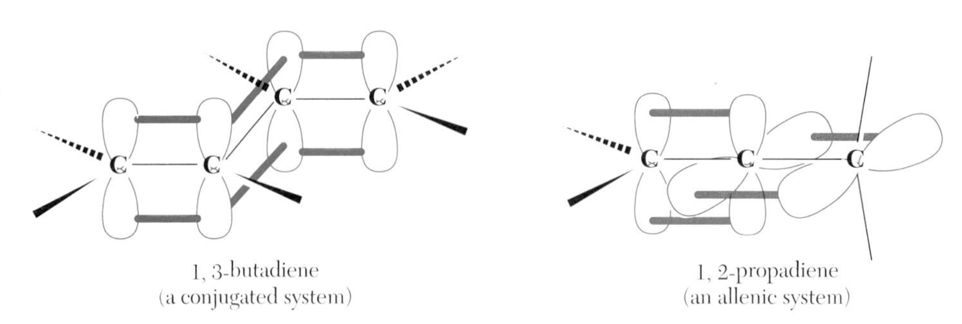

Figure 15.7 Contrasting arrangements of p orbitals in conjugated dienes and allenes. In an allene, the two π systems associated with the two double bonds are in perpendicular planes (orthogonal). A continuous coplanar arrangement of p orbitals cannot exist for allenes in the same way that it can for conjugated dienes.

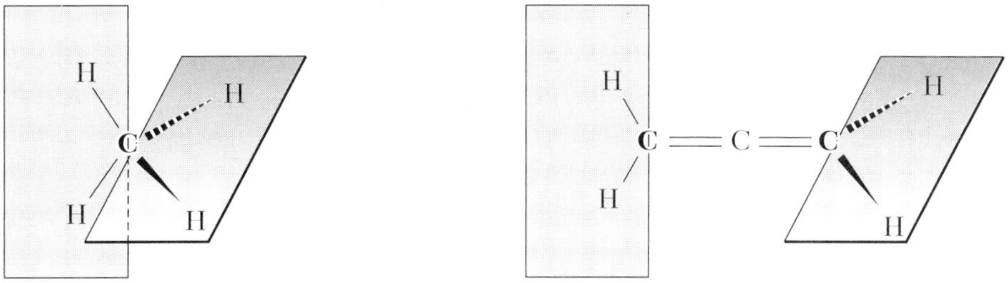

Figure 15.8 Geometry of ligands in methane and allene. The carbon and the two hydrogen atoms at one end of the allene molecule define a plane that is perpendicular to the plane defined by the carbon atom and the two attached hydrogen atoms at the other end. Note the similarity to the geometric arrangement of the atoms in methane.

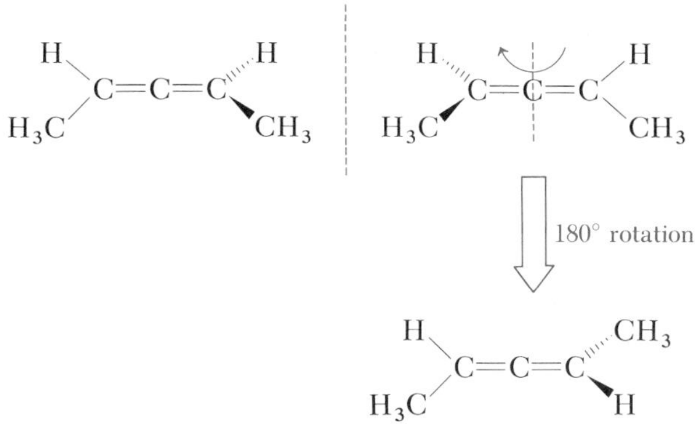

Figure 15.9 Chirality of the 2,3-pentadiene molecule. Even though it contains no stereogenic atom, 2,3-pentadiene is a chiral molecule, and each of its two enantiomers is optically active. The structure shown on the left is *not* superimposable upon its mirror image (shown on the right). The latter structure is shown rotated 180° in space to emphasize the nonsuperimposable nature of the enantiomers. We find this type of chirality in allene derivatives whenever two unlike groups (here methyl and hydrogen) are attached to each of the terminal carbon atoms.

180° rotation

The geometric arrangement of the bonds in allenes has an interesting stereochemical consequence: when the two ends of the allene structure bear unlike pairs of ligands, the molecule is not superimposable upon its mirror image and therefore can exist in enantiomeric forms, as is illustrated for 2,3-pentadiene in Figure 15.9.

This example emphasizes that the fundamental criterion for optical activity is not the presence of a stereogenic atom (none is present in 2,3-pentadiene), but rather the nonsuperimposability of mirror images of the molecule (Chapter 8).

PROBLEM 15.1

Draw the enantiomeric forms for each of the following:

a. 2,3-hexadiene

b. 1,4-dichloro-1,2-butadiene

c. 3-methyl-3,4-heptadiene

Steps to Solving the Problem

Solution to Problem 15.1a

1. Draw the fundamental structure for the molecule.

$$CH_3CH{=}C{=}CHCH_2CH_3$$

2. Showing the geometry about the allenic linkage as in Figure 15.9, construct one enantiomer of the compound.

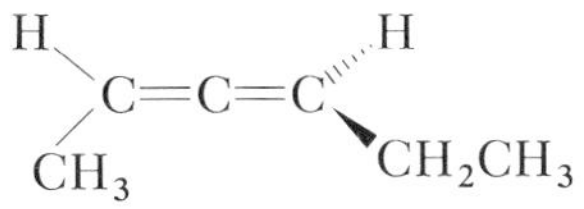

3. Now envision a mirror plane alongside this enantiomer, and construct the other enantiomer.

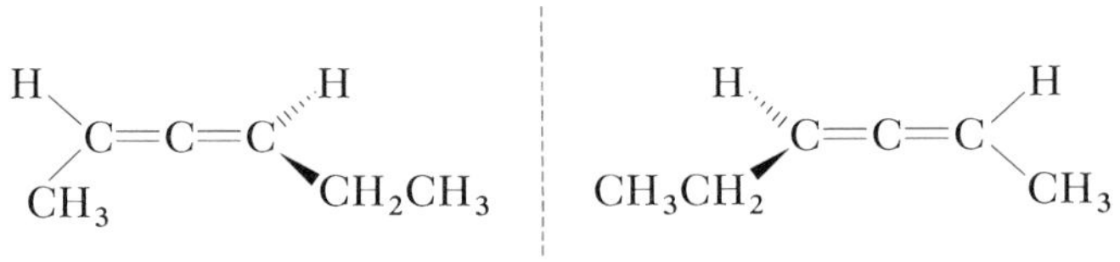

H(CH$_3$)C=C=C(H)CH$_2$CH$_3$ | CH$_3$CH$_2$(H)C=C=C(H)CH$_3$

A further consequence of the allene structure is that it imposes a limit to the ring size in which such a linkage can exist in a stable molecule. The smallest isolable cyclic allene is 1,2-cyclononadiene, shown in Figure 15.10. Attempts to prepare stable allenes with smaller rings have failed. We infer that the lack of stability derives from severe ring strain. However, small allene rings can exist as transient, reactive intermediates.

Figure 15.10 Allene linkages in small rings. Cyclic allenes with rings smaller than nine carbons are too reactive to be isolated. The smallest cyclic allene that is stable enough to be isolated is 1,2-cyclononadiene. The presence of an *sp* hybridized carbon atom requires that the three-carbon allenic unit be linear. Attempting to incorporate such a linear region in a small ring introduces strain on the π bonds, twisting them away from the ideal π-bonding orientation in which the *p* orbitals are parallel. This twisting weakens the π bond and destabilizes the molecule.

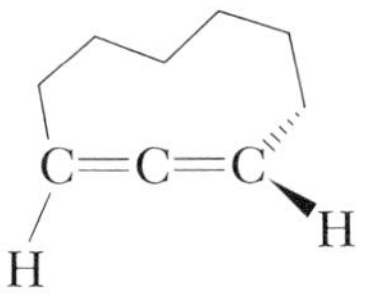

C=C=C (ring), H, H

1,2-cyclononadiene

We can extend these considerations to larger cumulenes. The simplest of these is 1,2,3-butatriene (**15.3**). All of the atoms in this molecule lie in the same plane. When there are three cumulated double bonds, the ligands at the termini lie in the same plane (this is true for any *odd* number of cumulated double bonds). When there are an *even* number of cumulated double bonds, the ligands at one end lie in a plane perpendicular to that defined by the ligands at the opposite end.

PROBLEM 15.2

Draw all isomers defined by the following names:

a. 2,3,4-heptatriene **b.** 2,3,4,5-nonatetraene

c. 2,3,4,6-nonatetraene

BONDING IN ALKYNES

The Carbon-Carbon Triple Bond In an alkyne two *sp* hybridized carbon atoms are bound to each other by one σ and two π bonds. The two π bonds between

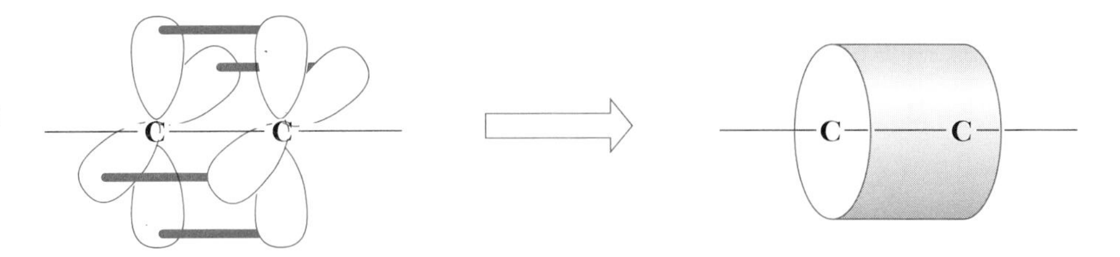

Figure 15.11 Representations of the carbon-carbon triple bond. A triple bond contains two mutually perpendicular π bonds. The net electron density associated with the two π bonds is a complete cylinder about the internuclear axis.

COMPOUND CAPSULE

$$H{-}C{\equiv}C{-}C{\equiv}C{-}C{\equiv}C{-}C{\equiv}C{-}C{\equiv}C{-}C{\equiv}N$$

Cyanodecapentayne

Each of the eleven carbon atoms in cyanodecapentayne is *sp* hybridized. As a result, all thirteen atoms in the molecule lie in a straight line. This remarkable molecule has been identified by Canadian radio astronomers as a component of the cloud surrounding the carbon-emitting star CW Leonis. It is one of the most complex organic compounds thus far discovered in intergalactic space.

the pair of *sp* hybridized carbon atoms combine to produce a complete cylinder of π electron density about the internuclear region (Figure 15.11).

Because the *sp* orbitals of each carbon atom are colinear, the atoms attached to the *sp* carbons, as well as the *sp* carbons themselves, lie in a straight line, as shown in Figure 15.12. This geometrical requirement correlates with the observation that it is not possible to isolate compounds containing a triple bond in a small ring. Cyclic alkynes are stable only when the ring contains nine or more carbons. The strain exhibited by small-ring alkynes is entirely analogous to that of small-ring allenes.

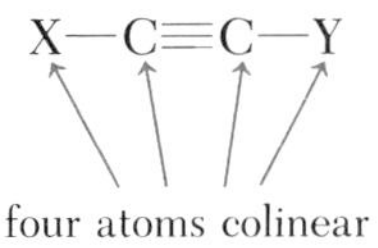

$$X{-}C{\equiv}C{-}Y$$

four atoms colinear

Figure 15.12 Bonding geometry about a carbon-carbon triple bond. An important stereochemical consequence of an unstrained triple bond is that four consecutive atoms lie in a straight line. This geometry results from the *sp* hybridization of the carbon atoms of the triple bond.

Terminal Carbon-Hydrogen Bonds *Terminal* alkynes are those in which the carbon chain ends with the structural unit $-C{\equiv}C{-}H$. Terminal alkynes are unusually acidic relative to other alkynes and to most other hydrocarbons (e.g., alkanes and alkenes). The terminal hydrogen atom is lost as a proton when terminal alkynes are treated with suitable bases. The relative acidity of terminal alkynes is most easily rationalized by considering their conjugate bases (which are, of course, *carbanions*). We can use the hybridization model to predict the strengths of the conjugate bases of terminal alkynes, terminal alkenes, and alkanes. As shown in Figure 15.13, each type of conjugate base has a different type of hybridization.

The unshared electron pair of the acetylide ion is in an *sp* hybrid orbital. This orbital has 50% *s* character. Any electrons in this orbital are therefore closer to the nucleus and bound more strongly to it than are the electrons of other types of carbanions. Carbanions derived from ethane and ethylene hold their unshared electron pairs in sp^3 and sp^2 hybrid orbitals, respectively. These orbitals have less *s* character (25% and 33%, respectively), and electrons in them are held less tightly to the carbon nucleus.

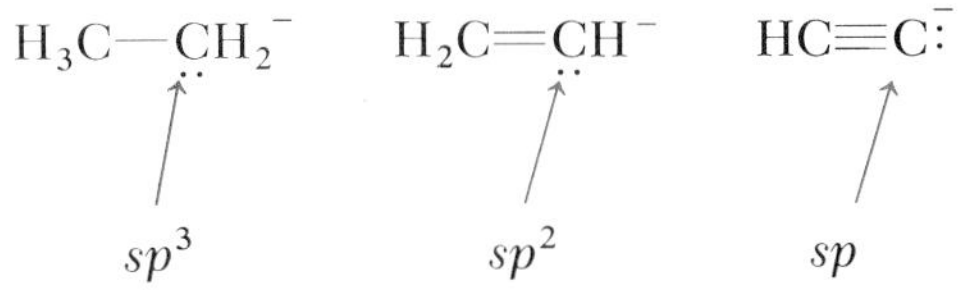

$$H_3C{-}\ddot{C}H_2^- \qquad H_2C{=}\ddot{C}H^- \qquad HC{\equiv}C{:}^-$$

sp^3 $\qquad sp^2$ $\qquad sp$

Figure 15.13 Hybridization in carbanions. The carbon atoms that bear the negative charges in the conjugate bases of alkanes, alkenes, and alkynes have different hybridization.

Table 15.3 Hydrocarbon Acidities

Hydrocarbon	$H—C{\equiv}C—H$ >	$H_2C{=}CH_2$ >	CH_4 >	CH_3CH_3
pK_a	25	44	48	50

An acetylide ion is therefore predicted to be a weaker base than these other carbanions because the free electron pair is less available than those of the other carbanions. The corollary is that the parent acetylene (or terminal alkyne) is predicted to be a stronger acid than (most) other hydrocarbons. Experimental results are generally in accord with such predictions. To illustrate this relationship, the relative order of acidities for several hydrocarbons is listed in Table 15.3 with their approximate pK_a values.

This enhanced acidity of terminal alkynes should be kept in proper perspective. While terminal alkynes are significantly stronger acids than most other hydrocarbons, they are still quite weak acids. They are much less acidic than hydrofluoric acid ($pK_a \sim 3$) or even water ($pK_a \sim 16$), which are both prototypical weak inorganic acids. Nevertheless, the enhanced acidity of the terminal alkynes means that we can form salts of these materials by reaction with strong bases. Amide ions (from ammonia, $pK_a = 38$) or carbanions derived from typical organometallics are sufficiently basic to generate **acetylide salts** from terminal alkynes. Two examples are shown in Equations 15.1 and 15.2.

Eqn. 15.1

$$\underset{\text{stronger acid}}{CH_3CH_2C{\equiv}C{-}H} + \underset{\text{stronger base}}{KNH_2} \rightleftharpoons \underset{\text{weaker base}}{CH_3CH_2C{\equiv}\ddot{C}{:}^{-}\ {}^{+}K} + \underset{\text{weaker acid}}{\ddot{N}H_3}$$

Eqn. 15.2

$$\underset{\text{stronger acid}}{CH_3C{\equiv}C{-}H} + \underset{\text{stronger base}}{CH_3Mg\ddot{Br}{:}} \rightleftharpoons \underset{\text{weaker base}}{CH_3C{\equiv}C{:}^{-}\ {}^{+}Mg\ddot{Br}{:}} + \underset{\text{weaker acid}}{CH_4}$$

These reactions are simply acid-base equilibria. As always, the position of equilibrium favors the weaker acid and weaker base. The substituted acetylide ions are quite useful in a variety of synthetic manipulations that will be discussed in detail later in this chapter.

PROBLEM 15.3 Rank the following in order of decreasing acidity:

$$H_2\ddot{O}, \quad CH_3C{\equiv}CH, \quad \ddot{N}H_3, \quad CH_3C{\equiv}CCH_3$$

CHEMICAL TESTS FOR TERMINAL ALKYNES

The tendency of terminal alkynes to form salts can serve an analytical function. Reactions that use heavy metals such as silver or copper to form salts result in the precipitation of the terminal alkyne salt from solution. Only *terminal* alkynes produce precipitates when treated with an aqueous ammonia solu-

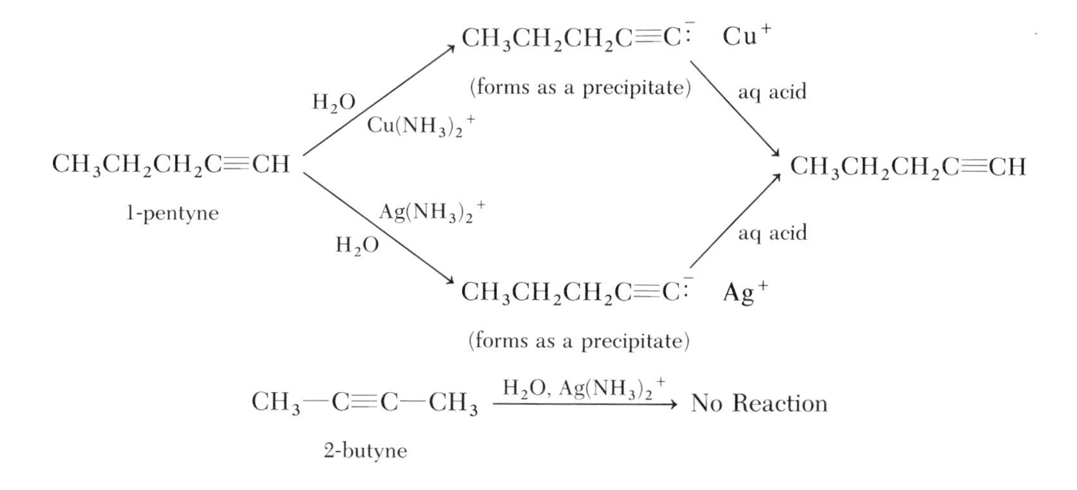

Figure 15.14 Formation of copper and silver acetylides. The salts of terminal alkynes precipitate from the aqueous ammonia solutions containing the metal ions. Internal alkynes do not react under these conditions. The salts can be converted back to their parent alkynes by adding acid.

tion of the Ag(I) or Cu(I) species. We thus have a quick (test-tube) method of testing for the presence of a terminal alkyne linkage in an unknown hydrocarbon sample. The reactions are shown in Figure 15.14.

Heavy-metal acetylides must be handled with care. They are shock-sensitive and detonate violently if they are isolated by filtration and dried. Apparently the dry salts are not pure but contain occluded solvent or other materials. Similarly, acetylene and some other alkynes undergo violent decomposition. Acetylene itself may undergo a violent exothermic reaction if pure or if it is in sufficiently high concentration in the gas phase. Cylinders of acetylene do not contain the pure substance, as do cylinders of nitrogen, oxygen, or propane. Instead, they contain a dispersing medium (sawdust) from which the acetylene escapes when the valve is opened.

15.4 Preparation of Alkynes

SPECIAL METHODS FOR ACETYLENE

On an industrial scale, acetylene can be produced easily (but not cheaply) from inorganic materials. A common procedure uses limestone (calcium carbonate) and coal (carbon) as the starting materials. On heating, limestone loses carbon dioxide to form quicklime (calcium oxide), which reacts with carbon in an electric furnace at 2000 °C, forming calcium carbide. Calcium carbide is a strong base, the carbide ion being protonated by even weak acids such as water. The final step in the manufacture of acetylene by this route is the addition of water to the calcium carbide. The entire route is summarized in Figure 15.15

Figure 15.15 Preparation of acetylene from limestone and coal.

$$\underset{\text{limestone}}{CaCO_3} \xrightarrow{\text{heat}} \underset{\text{quicklime}}{CaO} + CO_2$$

$$2\,CaO + \underset{\text{coke}}{5\,C} \xrightarrow{2000\,^\circ C} \underset{\text{calcium carbide}}{2\,CaC_2} + CO_2$$

$$CaC_2 + 2\,H_2\ddot{\underset{..}{O}} \longrightarrow HC{\equiv}CH + Ca(OH)_2$$

The hydrolysis of calcium carbide is the principal source of acetylene for welding in the Third World.

Other methods are also used for the preparation of acetylene, including the partial oxidation of methane with molecular oxygen and the cracking of petroleum at temperatures of 2000 °C.

ALKYNES FROM DOUBLE DEHYDROHALOGENATION OF DIHALOALKANES

A common laboratory method for the preparation of alkynes is the dehydrohalogenation of dibromoalkanes with a strong base. An example is shown in Equation 15.3.

Eqn. 15.3

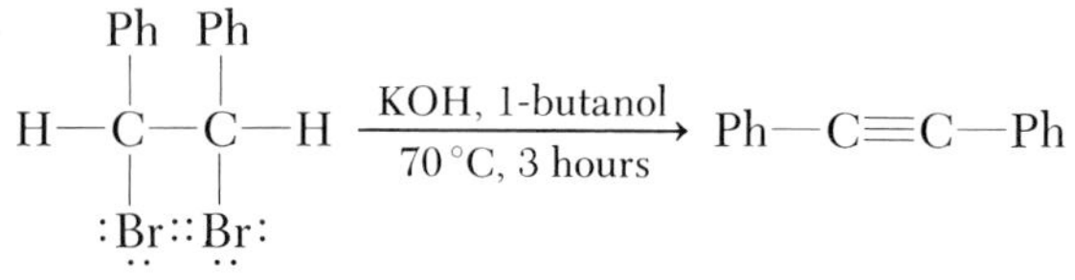

$$\text{H—C(Ph)(Br)—C(Ph)(Br)—H} \xrightarrow[70\,^\circ\text{C, 3 hours}]{\text{KOH, 1-butanol}} \text{Ph—C}\equiv\text{C—Ph}$$

1,2-dibromo-1,2-diphenylethane — 93% yield diphenylacetylene

These double dehydrohalogenations occur by means of two successive eliminations, as shown in Figure 15.16.

The dihalide initially loses a hydrogen atom and a halogen atom to form a vinylic halide, (this reaction is completely analagous to the dehydrogenation of haloalkanes to alkenes, as discussed in Chapter 9). Then the vinylic halide undergoes a second dehydrohalogenation to give the alkyne product. The second dehydrohalogenation step often requires a stronger base than hydroxide. In order to ensure that reaction does not stop at the vinyl halide stage, it is common practice to use sodium amide in liquid ammonia rather than potassium hydroxide to achieve double dehydrohalogenation. An example is shown in Equation 15.4.

Eqn. 15.4

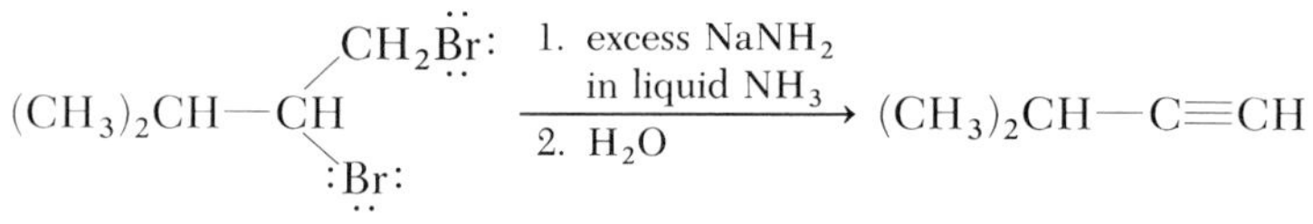

$$(CH_3)_2CH\text{—}CH(Br)CH_2Br \xrightarrow[\text{2. } H_2O]{\text{1. excess } NaNH_2 \text{ in liquid } NH_3} (CH_3)_2CH\text{—}C\equiv CH$$

1,2-dibromo-3-methylbutane — 52% yield 3-methyl-1-butyne

The workup of these reactions merits comments. First, the liquid ammonia solvent is allowed to evaporate. Any terminal alkyne product will at this stage be present as its acetylide salt, $R\text{—}C\equiv C\!:^- \; Na^+$, as the reaction conditions are sufficiently basic to remove a proton from the terminal carbon atom. In

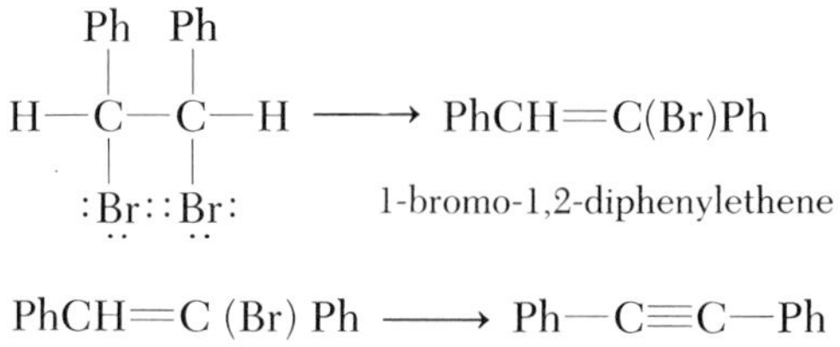

Figure 15.16 Stepwise progress of double dehydrohalogenation. The generation of an alkyne from a dihalide proceeds in two distinct steps. The first step produces a vinylic halide, which is then further dehydrohalogenated to give the alkyne product.

$$\text{H—C(Ph)(Br)—C(Ph)(Br)—H} \longrightarrow \text{PhCH}=\text{C(Br)Ph}$$

1-bromo-1,2-diphenylethene

$$\text{PhCH}=\text{C (Br) Ph} \longrightarrow \text{Ph—C}\equiv\text{C—Ph}$$

order to obtain the free alkyne, we must add a source of protons (water is sufficient) after the ammonia has evaporated. The yield of isolated alkyne is generally in the range 50–85%.

PROBLEM 15.4 Why would water or ethanol not be a good solvent for performing a sodium amide dehydrohalogenation reaction?

PROBLEM 15.5 Dihalides required for the synthesis of alkynes are usually available from the bromination or chlorination of alkenes. Show all steps in the synthesis of propyne from propene.

The dihalides used in the preceding examples were **vicinal dihalides,** in which the two halogen atoms are attached to adjacent carbon atoms. We can also synthesize an alkyne in a double dehydrohalogenation reaction using a **geminal dihalide.** A geminal dihalide is one in which the two halogen atoms are attached to the same carbon atom. An example of an alkyne synthesis using a geminal dihalide is shown in Equation 15.5.

Eqn. 15.5

$$(CH_3)_3C-CH_2-CCl_2-H \xrightarrow[2.\ H_2O]{1.\ \text{excess } NaNH_2 \text{ in liquid } NH_3} (CH_3)_3C-C\equiv C-H$$

1,1-dichloro-3-3,-dimethylbutane — 60% yield 3,3-dimethyl-1-butyne

PROBLEM 15.6 Two different alkynes can result from the double dehydrohalogenation of some geminal dihalides. Which two alkynes would be expected on double dehydrohalogenation of 3,3-dibromo-5,5-dimethylhexane?

We generally prepare vicinal dihalides from alkenes, and we can obtain geminal dihalides from carbonyl compounds. An example of the synthesis of a geminal dihalide from a ketone is shown in Equation 15.6.

Eqn. 15.6

$$CH_3CH_2COCH_2CH_3 \xrightarrow{PCl_5} CH_3CH_2CCl_2CH_2CH_3$$

3-pentanone — 81% yield 3,3-dichloropentane

PROBLEM 15.7 Outline the best synthesis of 2-pentyne from an aldehyde or a ketone.

COMPOUND CAPSULE

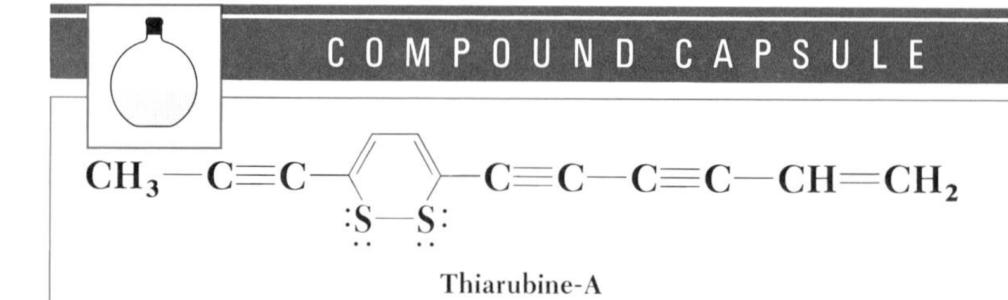

Thiarubine-A

Thiarubine-A is a powerful antibiotic that has recently been discovered as a component of the leaves of the Aspila bush. The discovery of this structurally interesting compound followed observations that sick chimpanzees in the wild seek out and swallow the leaves.

ELABORATION OF TERMINAL ALKYNES

An important method for the synthesis of internal alkynes is their preparation from terminal alkynes. The terminal alkyne is first treated with a strong base (often sodium amide) to generate an acetylide salt. Acetylide ions are potent nucleophiles that readily perform S_N2 reactions on methyl or primary haloalkanes that are unbranched at the β-position. An example is shown in Equation 15.7.

Eqn. 15.7

$$\underset{\text{acetylene}}{HC{\equiv}CH} \xrightarrow[\text{2. } CH_3CH_2CH_2CH_2Br]{\text{1. } NaNH_2} \underset{\substack{\text{75\% yield} \\ \text{1-hexyne}}}{HC{\equiv}CCH_2CH_2CH_2CH_3}$$

An important point to keep in mind is that an acetylide ion is able to behave as a strong base or as a potent nucleophile. We learned earlier (Chapter 12) that many secondary and most tertiary haloalkanes readily undergo dehydrohalogenation when treated with strong bases. Indeed, we find that acetylide ions dehydrohalogenate secondary and tertiary haloalkanes to alkenes. These types of haloalkanes should not be used if our attention is to effect nucleophilic substitution.

PROBLEM 15.8 Predict the major product that forms when *tert*-butyl bromide is allowed to react with sodium acetylide.

PROBLEM 15.9 Describe the synthetic procedures needed to prepare 2-hexyne from each of the following:

a. propyne **b.** acetylene **c.** acetone

PROBLEM 15.10 Acetylide ions behave as nucleophiles toward classes of compounds other than haloalkanes. Predict the product of formula $C_6H_{10}O$ obtained by treating 1-butyne with sodium amide followed by ethylene oxide, followed by workup with aqueous acid. Show a complete mechanism for the formation of the product using the curved-arrow formalism.

15.5 Preparation of Conjugated Dienes

DIENES BY DOUBLE DEHYDROHALOGENATION OF ALKYL DIHALIDES

Conjugated dienes (as well as alkynes) can be prepared by double dehydrohalogenation of dihaloalkanes. Three examples are shown in Equations 15.8–15.10.

Eqn. 15.8

$$CH_3-C(CH_3)(Br)-C(CH_3)(Br)-Ph \xrightarrow[\text{aq } Na_2CO_3]{\text{heat}} H_2C{=}C(CH_3)-C(Ph){=}CH_2$$

2,3-dibromo-2-methyl-3-phenylbutane — 2-methyl-3-phenyl-1,3-butadiene, 51% yield

Eqn. 15.9

$$\text{2,3-di}(CH_2Cl)\text{bicyclo[2.2.1]heptane} \xrightarrow[HOCH_2CH_2OH]{\text{KOH, heat}} \text{2,3-di}(=CH_2)\text{bicyclo[2.2.1]heptane}$$

2,3-di(chloromethyl)bicyclo[2.2.1]heptone — 2,3-dimethylenebicyclo[2.2.1]heptane, 40% yield

Eqn. 15.10

$$\text{1-Cl-2-}(CH_2Cl)\text{cyclohexane} \xrightarrow[HOCH_2CH_2OH]{\text{KOH, heat}} \text{3-}(=CH_2)\text{cyclohexene}$$

1-chloro-2-chloromethylcyclohexane — 3-methylenecyclohexene, 40% yield

These examples demonstrate that 1,2-, 1,3-, or 1,4-dihalides can be used to synthesize conjugated dienes. However, several different modes of dehydrohalogenation can occur with some dihalides, leading, in principle, to mixtures of alkynes, conjugated dienes, and allenes. We must keep these multiple routes in mind when planning synthetic strategies for conjugated dienes.

PROBLEM 15.11 Double dehydrohalogenation of 1,2-dibromocyclohexane could, in principle, lead to an alkyne, an allene, or a conjugated diene. However, only one of these products is actually obtained. Tell which one is obtained, and offer an explanation for this result.

PROBLEM 15.12 Each of the following dihalides can yield three possible products when subjected to double dehydrohalogenation. What are the possible products from each of the dihaloalkanes?

a. 2,3-dibromobutane **b.** 2,2-dibromobutane

Steps to Solving the Problem

Solution to Problem 15.12a We need to work out all of the possible ways in which H and Br can be eliminated from adjacent carbon atoms. The best approach is to set up the following diagrams to show all the possible arrangements:

$$H{-}\overset{\boxed{H}}{\underset{H}{C}}{-}\overset{\boxed{Br}}{\underset{H}{C}}{-}\overset{H}{\underset{\boxed{Br}}{C}}{-}\overset{H}{\underset{\boxed{H}}{C}}{-}H \longrightarrow H_2C{=}CH{-}CH{=}CH_2$$

1,3-butadiene

$$H{-}\overset{H}{\underset{H}{C}}{-}\overset{\boxed{Br}}{\underset{H}{C}}{-}\overset{\boxed{H}}{\underset{\boxed{Br}}{C}}{-}\overset{H}{\underset{\boxed{H}}{C}}{-}H \longrightarrow CH_3{-}CH{=}C{=}CH_2$$

1,2-butadiene

$$H{-}\overset{H}{\underset{H}{C}}{-}\overset{\boxed{Br}}{\underset{\boxed{H}}{C}}{-}\overset{\boxed{H}}{\underset{\boxed{Br}}{C}}{-}\overset{H}{\underset{H}{C}}{-}H \longrightarrow CH_3{-}C{\equiv}C{-}CH_3$$

2-butyne

DIENES BY DOUBLE DEHYDRATION OF DIOLS

Another important route for the preparation of conjugated dienes is the double dehydration of 1,2-, 1,3-, or 1,4-diols. The use of 1,2-diols is particularly convenient because they are easily prepared from alkenes (Chapter 10). An example of a diene synthesis from a 1,2-diol is shown in Equation 15.11.

Eqn. 15.11

$$H_3C{-}\overset{CH_3}{\underset{H\ddot{O}:}{C}}{-}\overset{CH_3}{\underset{:\ddot{O}H}{C}}{-}CH_3 \xrightarrow{48\%\ HBr} H_2C{=}\underset{CH_3}{C}{-}\underset{CH_3}{C}{=}CH_2$$

2,3-dimethylbutane-2,3-diol

70% yield
2,3-dimethyl-1,3-butadiene

An important alternative to the hydroxylation of alkenes for the preparation of 1,2-diols is the reductive dimerization of aldehydes or ketones. Reductive dimerization occurs when a carbonyl compound is allowed to react with an amalgam of an active metal (aluminum or magnesium). In some cases titanium tetrachloride facilitates the reaction. Examples are shown in Equations 15.12 and 15.13.

Eqn. 15.12

$$(CH_3CH_2)_2C{=}\ddot{O} \xrightarrow[CH_2Cl_2]{Al\,(Hg)\ reflux} (CH_3CH_2)_2\underset{H\ddot{O}:}{C}{-}\underset{:\ddot{O}H}{C}(CH_2CH_3)_2$$

3-pentanone

55% yield
3,4-diethylhexane-3,4-diol

Eqn. 15.13

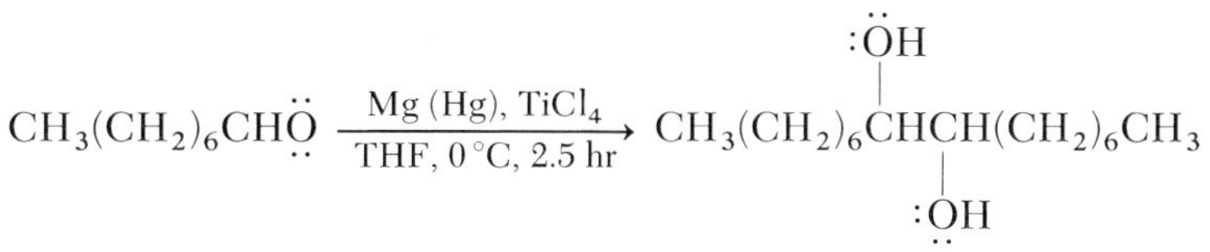

$$CH_3(CH_2)_6CH\ddot{\underset{\cdot\cdot}{O}} \xrightarrow[\text{THF, 0 °C, 2.5 hr}]{\text{Mg (Hg), TiCl}_4} CH_3(CH_2)_6CH(\ddot{O}H)CH(\ddot{O}H)(CH_2)_6CH_3$$

octanal — 80% yield hexadecane-8,9-diol

PROBLEM 15.13 When 3,4-dimethylhexane-3,4-diol is heated with sulfuric acid, a conjugated diene is isolated in 84% yield. Suggest a structure for this diene.

PROBLEM 15.14 On treatment with acid, 2-methylpentane-2,4-diol yields three isomeric conjugated dienes. Give their structures.

PROBLEM 15.15 Which ketone would you use as a starting material to prepare 2,3-dimethylbutane-2,3-diol for further use in the diene synthesis shown in Equation 15.11?

PROBLEM 15.16 Reductive dimerization of the ketone shown below leads to a mixture of a *meso*-diol and a racemic diol. Draw Fischer projections for each of these diols. Would you expect them to be formed in equal amounts in this reaction? Explain why or why not. What diene would be formed in the double dehydration of the mixture of diols?

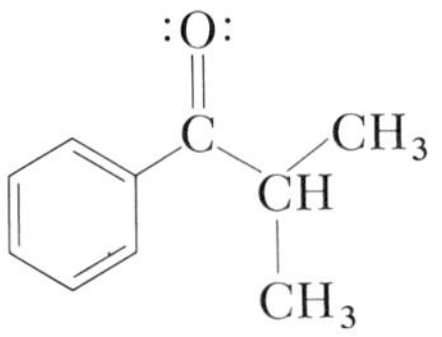

$$C_6H_5-C(=\ddot{O}:)-CH(CH_3)CH_3$$

DIENES BY ELABORATION OF ALKENES

If one double bond is already present in a molecule, we can often introduce a second double bond, conjugated with the first, by means of a two-step procedure. The first step in the procedure is **allylic bromination,** in which we introduce a bromine atom into an allylic position of the alkene. *N*-bromosuccinimide (**15.4**) is commonly used to accomplish this conversion.

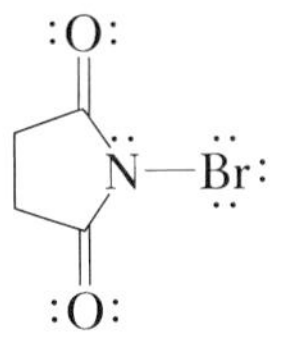

N-bromosuccinimide
(NBS)
15.4

An example of allylic bromination using NBS is shown in Equation 15.14.

Eqn. 15.14

NBS + cyclohexene $\xrightarrow[\text{heat or light, with peroxides}]{CCl_4}$ succinimide + 3-bromocyclohexene

cyclohexene succinimide 67% yield 3-bromocyclohexene

An allylic bromide, once prepared, can be dehydrohalogenated to obtain a conjugated diene, as illustrated in Equation 15.15.

Eqn. 15.15

3-bromocyclohexene $\xrightarrow[\text{(quinoline)}]{\text{heat}}$ 1,3-cyclohexadiene

90% yield 1,3-cyclohexadiene

The quinoline used in Equation 15.15 is an organic base. It removes a proton in the dehydrohalogenation reaction.

Allylic bromination is a free radical reaction. The reaction begins with the production of a low concentration of molecular bromine. The bromine forms by the reaction of NBS with traces of HBr that are always present in NBS. Under the reaction conditions (peroxides, heat or light), bromine undergoes homolysis to form bromine atoms. The bromine atoms subsequently abstract a hydrogen atom from the allylic position of the alkene, producing a resonance-stabilized free radical.

Bromine atoms abstract allylic hydrogen atoms preferentially to ordinary aliphatic hydrogens. A comparison of bond energies is instructive. The bond dissociation energy for an allylic carbon-hydrogen bond is ~86–88 kcal/mole, while that of an ordinary tertiary carbon-hydrogen bond is ~91 kcal/mole. Thus, removal of an allylic hydrogen gives a more stable radical than removal of an ordinary aliphatic hydrogen (1°, 2°, or 3°). The improved stability of an allylic radical correlates with our ability to draw two resonance structures (see mechanism below). The Hammond postulate predicts that the allylic radical will also form faster than an ordinary aliphatic radical in this type of reaction, and this prediction is confirmed by experimental observations.

Once the allylic radical forms, it reacts with traces of molecular bromine in the reaction mixture to give the product allylic bromide and another bromine atom. The bromine atom then initiates another cycle of the chain reaction.

MECHANISM OF REACTION

Overall:

cyclohexene $\xrightarrow[h\nu\text{ peroxides}]{\text{NBS}}$ 3-bromocyclohexene

Step 1 Hydrogen bromide reacts with NBS to give succinimide and bromine.

:O: N—Br: + HBr: ⟶ :O: N—H + Br_2

Step 2 Homolysis of the bromine molecule occurs.

$$Br_2 \xrightarrow{h\nu} 2\,Br\cdot$$

Step 3 An allylic hydrogen atom is abstracted by the bromine atom. HBr is regenerated in this step.

:Br· + ⟶ [⟷] + H Br:

H

Step 4 The allylic radical abstracts a bromine atom from a bromine molecule.

+ :Br—Br: ⟶ + ·Br:

:Br:

PROBLEM 15.17 The fact that a low concentration of bromine is generated in NBS reactions is of great significance in achieving allylic substitution. What would be the difficulty involved in trying to bring about allylic bromination of cyclohexene by mixing cyclohexene directly with bromine from a bottle and shining light on the mixture?

PROBLEM 15.18 When 1-hexene is treated with NBS under conditions conducive to allylic bromination, we can isolate by distillation three different allylic bromides, all of formula $C_6H_{11}Br$. Explain this result. Which product do you expect to be formed in the greater amount? Why does cyclohexene yield only a single allylic bromide when treated similarly?

PROBLEM 15.19 Propose a synthesis of 1-hexen-4-yne starting from propene.

15.6 Addition Reactions of Alkynes and Conjugated Dienes

Many of the reagents that add to alkene double bonds also add to alkyne triple bonds and to dienes. However, in addition to many similarities, there are also some important differences in these reactions. These differences provide significant new insights into the natures of alkynes and conjugated dienes. We will first consider additions to triple bonds and then move on to consider addition to conjugated dienes.

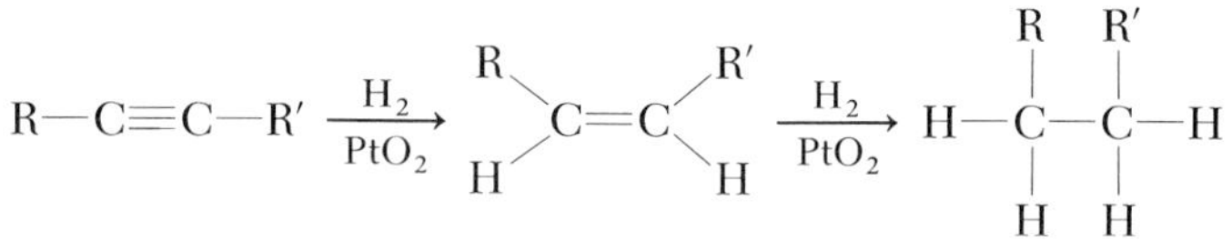

$$R{-}C{\equiv}C{-}R' \xrightarrow[PtO_2]{H_2} \underset{H\quad\quad H}{\overset{R\quad\quad R'}{C{=}C}} \xrightarrow[PtO_2]{H_2} H{-}\underset{H}{\overset{R}{C}}{-}\underset{H}{\overset{R'}{C}}{-}H$$

Figure 15.17 Addition of hydrogen to an alkyne in the presence of a typical hydrogenation catalyst. The reaction proceeds in two steps. The initially formed alkene is reduced further to the alkane.

ADDITIONS TO THE ALKYNE TRIPLE BOND

Addition of Hydrogen There are two main experimental approaches for adding two hydrogen atoms to a triple bond. One is catalytic hydrogenation, in which the two hydrogens add in a *syn* manner, and the other uses lithium in liquid ammonia, in which case the two hydrogen atoms add *anti*.

There are several aspects of the catalytic hydrogenation procedure that we need to consider. The alkene that forms upon addition of two hydrogens to an alkyne is itself susceptible to further hydrogenation under the conditions of the reaction. In practice, it is difficult to prevent the hydrogenation reaction from continuing all the way to an alkane, as illustrated in Figure 15.17.

The most convenient way to stop hydrogenation at the alkene stage is to use a modified catalyst. Several such catalysts are available. The most common ones are $Pd/BaSO_4$ (palladium dispersed on barium sulfate) and **Lindlar's catalyst** ($Pd/CaCO_3{-}PbO$). Although alkynes add hydrogen in the presence of these catalysts, alkenes do not. Thus we can isolate an alkene after adding hydrogen to the alkyne in a *syn* manner. An example is shown in Equation 15.16.

Eqn. 15.16

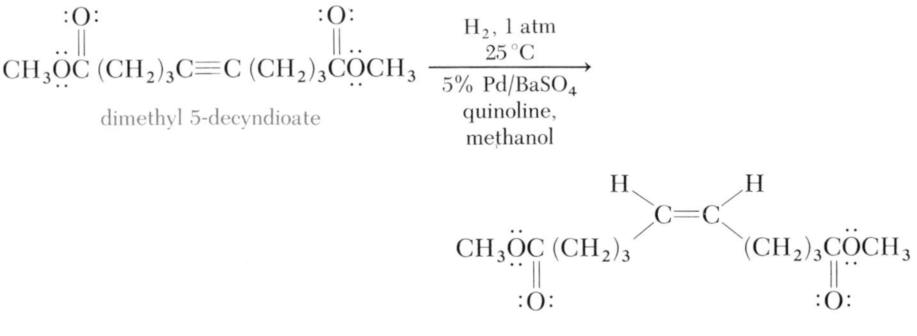

$$CH_3O\overset{O}{\overset{\|}{C}}(CH_2)_3C{\equiv}C(CH_2)_3\overset{O}{\overset{\|}{C}}OCH_3 \xrightarrow[\text{5\% } Pd/BaSO_4,\ \text{quinoline, methanol}]{H_2,\ 1\ \text{atm},\ 25\,^\circ C} \underset{CH_3O\underset{O}{\underset{\|}{C}}(CH_2)_3\quad\quad (CH_2)_3\underset{O}{\underset{\|}{C}}OCH_3}{\overset{H\quad\quad H}{C{=}C}}$$

dimethyl 5-decyndioate

97% yield
dimethyl *cis*-5-decendioate

The second method for adding two hydrogen atoms to a triple bond involves placing the alkyne in liquid ammonia and then adding lithium or sodium metal. The reaction is referred to as a **dissolving metal reduction.** An example is shown in Equation 15.17. This reaction is quite *different* from the reaction of a terminal alkyne (a weak acid) with a strong base such as sodium amide ($NaNH_2$). In this reduction the alkyne reacts with sodium *metal*.

Eqn. 15.17

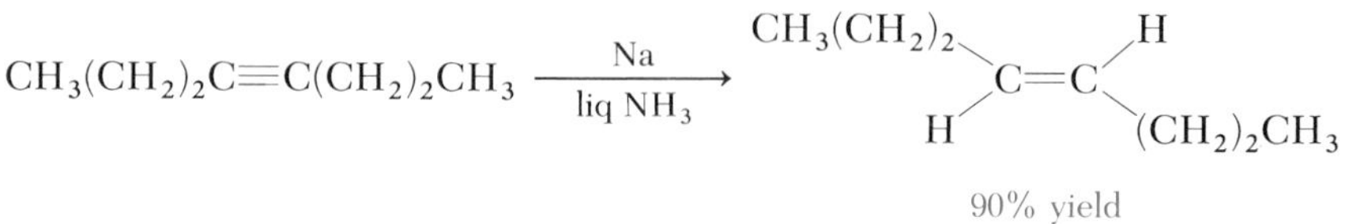

$$CH_3(CH_2)_2C{\equiv}C(CH_2)_2CH_3 \xrightarrow[\text{liq } NH_3]{Na} \underset{H\quad\quad (CH_2)_2CH_3}{\overset{CH_3(CH_2)_2\quad\quad H}{C{=}C}}$$

4-octyne

90% yield
(*E*)-4-octene

Because alkenes are unaffected by electropositive metals in liquid ammonia, the reaction stops at this stage. The reduction occurs in several steps.

MECHANISM OF REACTION

Overall:

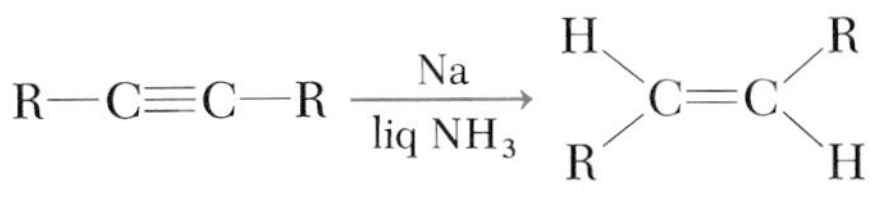

$$R{-}C{\equiv}C{-}R \xrightarrow[\text{liq } NH_3]{Na} \underset{R}{\overset{H}{\;}}C{=}C\underset{H}{\overset{R}{\;}}$$

Step 1 A sodium atom transfers an electron to the alkyne. A radical anion is formed.

$$R{-}C{\equiv}C{-}R + Na^{\cdot} \longrightarrow R{-}\dot{C}{=}\ddot{C}^{-}{-}R + Na^{+}$$

Step 2 The radical anion is a strong base. It removes a proton from the liquid ammonia solvent, forming a vinyl radical with a preferred *trans* geometry.

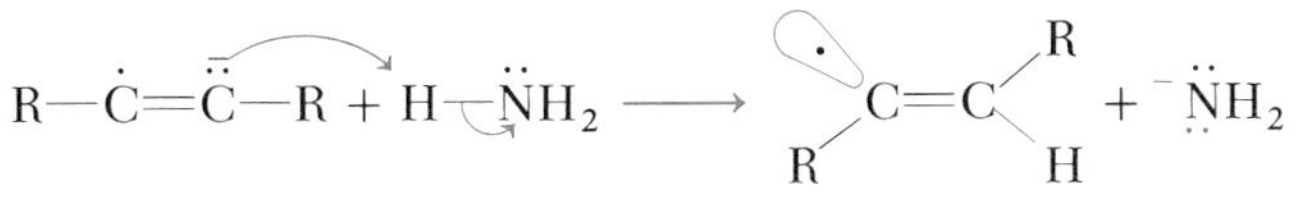

$$R{-}\dot{C}{=}\ddot{C}^{-}{-}R + H{-}\ddot{N}H_2 \longrightarrow \underset{R}{\overset{\cdot}{\;}}C{=}C\underset{H}{\overset{R}{\;}} + {}^{-}\ddot{N}H_2$$

Step 3 The vinyl radical picks up an electron from another sodium atom. The vinyl radical is converted to a vinyl anion.

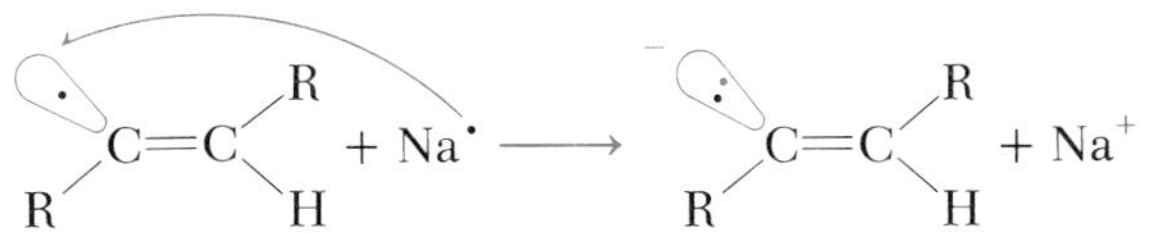

$$\underset{R}{\overset{\cdot}{\;}}C{=}C\underset{H}{\overset{R}{\;}} + Na^{\cdot} \longrightarrow \underset{R}{\overset{:^{-}}{\;}}C{=}C\underset{H}{\overset{R}{\;}} + Na^{+}$$

Step 4 The vinyl anion is a strong base. It picks up a proton from the liquid ammonia solvent.

$$\underset{R}{\overset{:^{-}}{\;}}C{=}C\underset{H}{\overset{R}{\;}} + H{-}\ddot{N}H_2 \longrightarrow \underset{R}{\overset{H}{\;}}C{=}C\underset{H}{\overset{R}{\;}} + {}^{-}\ddot{N}H_2$$

$$\underset{R}{\overset{\cdot}{\;}}C{=}C\underset{H}{\overset{R}{\;}} \rightleftarrows \underset{R}{\overset{\cdot}{\;}}C{=}C\underset{R}{\overset{H}{\;}}$$

more stable less stable

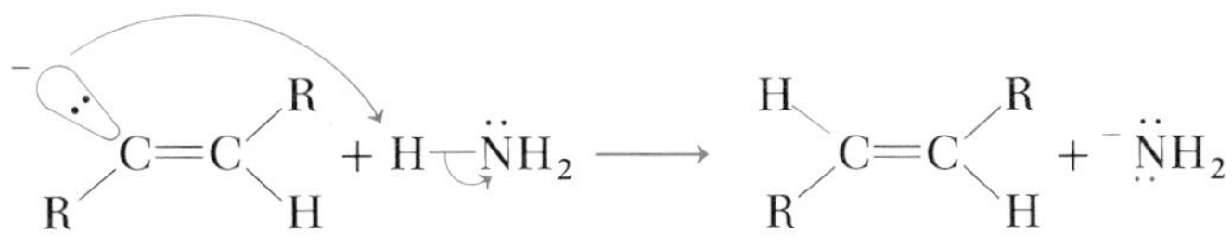

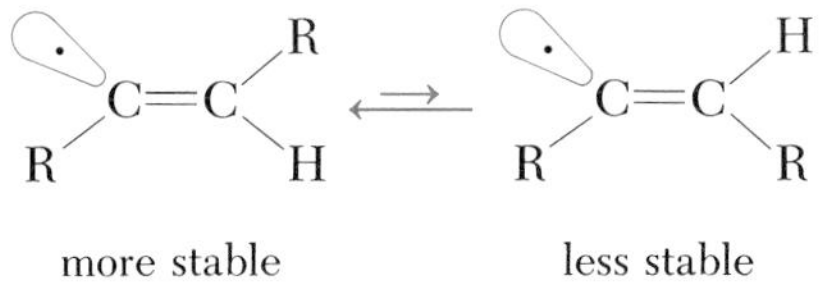

Figure 15.18 Relative stabilities of vinyl radicals. The second step of the sodium/liquid ammonia reduction reaction produces a vinyl radical. Of the two possible geometries, the (*E*) form, with the two alkyl groups *trans* to each other, is more stable than the (Z) form in which the two alkyl groups are *cis* to each other. This preferred stereochemistry is reflected in the final alkene product.

The stereospecificity of the reaction arises because the alkenyl radical produced in the second step is more stable with the alkyl groups *trans* than with them *cis* (relative to each other). These configurations are illustrated in Figure 15.18.

Halogen Addition to Alkynes Alkynes react readily with chlorine or bromine. If the alkyne and halogen are present in equimolar quantities, the product is a 1,2-dihaloalkene. An example is shown in Equation 15.18.

Eqn. 15.18

$$CH_3CH_2{-}C{\equiv}C{-}CH_2CH_3 \xrightarrow[Br_2]{\text{1 equivalent}} (\ddot{Br})(CH_3CH_2)C{=}C(CH_2CH_3)(\ddot{Br})$$

3-hexyne → 90% yield (*E*)-3,4-dibromo-3-hexene

Addition of a second molecule of halogen can occur (to give a tetrahaloalkane) but does not proceed as readily as the first addition step. We can usually stop the reaction at the dihaloalkene stage by limiting the amount of halogen used.

PROBLEM 15.20 Consider the successive addition of first bromine (one equivalent) and then chlorine (one equivalent) to 3-hexyne. Assuming that both halogen additions occur with 100% *anti* stereospecificity, provide complete names (including *R*/*S* descriptors) for all possible products.

Hydration of Alkynes Water itself does not react with alkynes. However, we can add the elements of water (H and OH) across the triple bond by indirect methods. These methods are similar (but not exactly the same) as those used to effect the hydration of a double bond.

Table 15.4 compares the reagents used to hydrate double and triple bonds using oxymercuration/demercuration and hydroboration/oxidation procedures.

Table 15.4 Conditions Used to Add the Elements of Water to Double and Triple Bonds.

	Oxymercuration/ Demercuration	**Hydroboration/ Oxidation**
Conditions for alkenes	1. $Hg(OAc)_2$, $H_2\ddot{O}$ 2. $NaBH_4$	1. BH_3, THF 2. H_2O_2, $H\ddot{O}^-$
Conditions for alkynes	$HgSO_4$, H_2SO_4, $H_2\ddot{O}$	Internal: 1. BH_3, THF 2. H_2O_2, $H\ddot{O}^-$ Terminal: 1. R_2BH* 2. H_2O_2, $H\ddot{O}^-$
Stereochemistry for alkenes and alkynes	Markovnikov	anti-Markovnikov

* The R in R_2BH is a bulky alkyl group, usually the 1,2-dimethylpropyl (disiamyl) group.

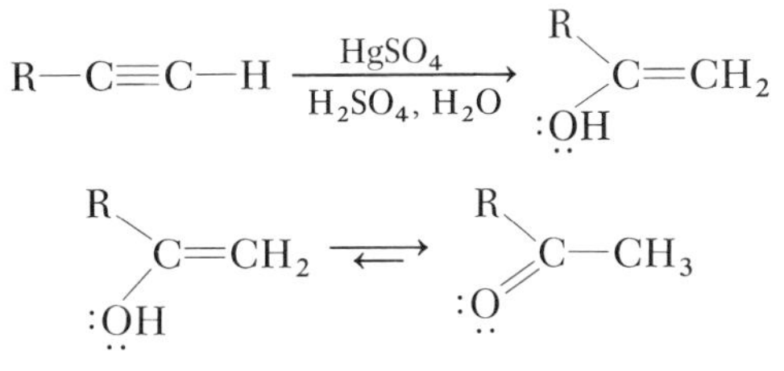

Figure 15.19 Formation of a carbonyl compound by hydration of a terminal alkyne. The initially formed enol is in equilibrium with the carbonyl compound actually isolated as the product of the reaction.

$$R{-}C{\equiv}C{-}H \xrightarrow[H_2SO_4,\ H_2O]{HgSO_4} R(\ddot{O}H)C{=}CH_2$$

$$R(\ddot{O}H)C{=}CH_2 \rightleftharpoons R(\ddot{O}{=})C{-}CH_3$$

Consider the addition of the elements of water to a terminal alkyne using the oxymercuration method specified in Table 15.4. We expect the final product to be an **enol,** that is, a substance containing a double bond (*en-*) and a hydroxyl group (*-ol*). However, an important characteristic of enols is that they exist in equilibrium with carbonyl compounds (aldehydes or ketones). In most cases the position of the equilibrium strongly favors the carbonyl compound, as illustrated in Figure 15.19. Isomerism in which the isomers differ only by the location of a double bond and a hydrogen is known as **tautomerism.**

Thus, when we hydrate an alkyne, we obtain an equilibrium mixture of an enol and a substance containing a carbonyl group. Usually the fraction of enol in this equilibrium mixture is extremely small, so that the major product we actually obtain upon hydration of an alkyne is a carbonyl compound. The mechanism by which an enol is converted into an isomeric carbonyl compound involves acid/base chemistry.

MECHANISM OF REACTION

Overall:

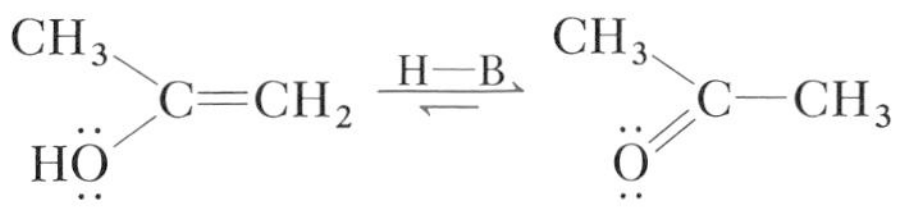

$$CH_3(H\ddot{O})C{=}CH_2 \xrightleftharpoons{H{-}B} CH_3(\ddot{O}{=})C{-}CH_3$$

Step 1 Protonation of the enol

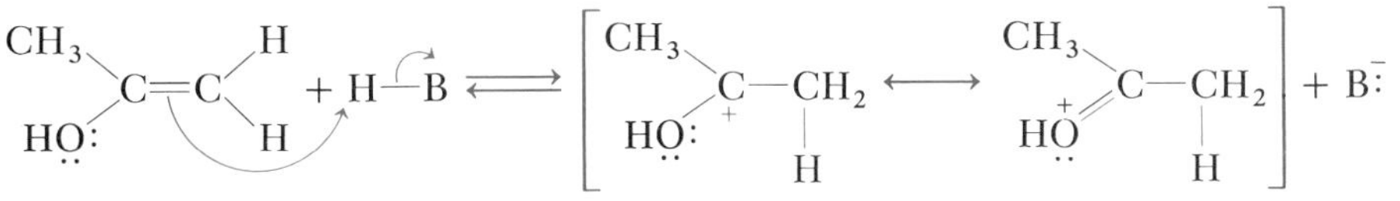

$$CH_3(H\ddot{O}{:})C{=}CH_2 + H{-}B \rightleftharpoons \left[CH_3(H\ddot{O}{:})\overset{+}{C}{-}CH_2{-}H \longleftrightarrow CH_3(H\overset{+}{O}{=})C{-}CH_2{-}H \right] + B{:}^-$$

The acid H—B could be a trace of any acidic material, or could be another molecule of enol.

Step 2 Loss of a proton

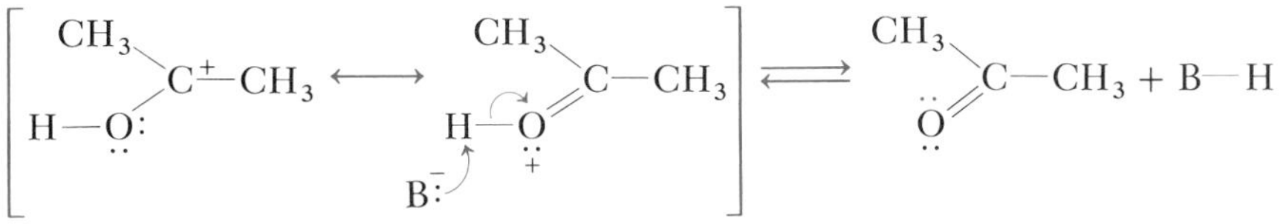

$$\left[CH_3(H{-}\ddot{O}{:})\overset{+}{C}{-}CH_3 \longleftrightarrow CH_3(H{-}\overset{+}{\ddot{O}}{=})C{-}CH_3 \right] \rightleftharpoons CH_3(\ddot{O}{=})C{-}CH_3 + B{-}H$$

At equilibrium, the carbonyl compound is favored over the enol. This correlates with its greater stability. The net strength of the bonds of the carbonyl compound exceeds that of the isomeric enol.

PROBLEM 15.21 Propose a mechanism for the conversion of an enol to a carbonyl compound initiated by the removal of a proton by a base.

Because of the enol/carbonyl tautomerism just discussed, the hydration of alkynes is an efficient method for preparing carbonyl compounds. An example is shown in Equation 15.19.

Eqn. 15.19

$$\underset{\text{1-hexyne}}{HC{\equiv}CCH_2CH_2CH_2CH_3} \xrightarrow[\substack{H_2SO_4 \\ H_2O}]{HgSO_4} H_2C{=}\overset{:\ddot{O}H}{\overset{|}{C}}HCH_2CH_2CH_2CH_3 \rightleftarrows \underset{\substack{\text{80\% yield} \\ \text{2-hexanone}}}{CH_3\overset{:O:}{\overset{\|}{C}}CH_2CH_2CH_2CH_3}$$

This reaction works particularly well with terminal alkynes. It is regiospecific: H adds to the terminal carbon atom and OH to the internal carbon atom of the triple bond. The resulting enol tautomerizes to a ketone. We see that the addition of H and OH to either a double bond or to a triple bond by way of oxymercuration/demercuration occurs with Markovnikov orientation. The hydration of internal alkynes is of little synthetic value (mixtures result) unless we use symmetrical internal alkynes. An example in which a ketone is synthesized in good yield from a symmetrical alkyne is shown in Equation 15.20.

Eqn. 15.20

$$\underset{\text{3-hexyne}}{CH_3CH_2{-}C{\equiv}C{-}CH_2CH_3} \xrightarrow[H_2SO_4]{H_2O,\ HgSO_4} \underset{\substack{\text{85\% yield} \\ \text{3-hexanone}}}{CH_3CH_2{-}\overset{\ddot{O}:}{\overset{\|}{C}}{-}CH_2CH_2CH_3}$$

PROBLEM 15.22 Explain the difficulties associated with using 6-methyl-3-heptyne to synthesize 2-methyl-4-heptanone by hydration with water, mercuric sulfate, and sulfuric acid.

As we mentioned, in the presence of mercuric ion and sulfuric acid, the elements of water add to a triple bond with Markovnikov orientation. In Chapter 10 we saw that the elements of water can be added across a double bond with overall anti-Markovnikov regiospecificity by using hydroboration followed by oxidation. Can we achieve something similar for triple bonds?

Terminal alkynes do react with boranes in a regiospecific (and stereospecific *syn*) manner. A boron atom becomes attached to the terminal carbon atom and a hydrogen atom to the internal carbon atom. (This reaction is entirely analogous to the reaction with alkenes). However, the product of the reaction contains a double bond, and a second addition of the boron reagent can occur, leading to a geminal diborane. On treatment with base and hydrogen peroxide, the geminal diborane yields a primary alcohol. An example is shown in Equation 15.21.

Eqn. 15.21

$$\underset{\text{1-butyne}}{CH_3CH_2{-}C{\equiv}CH} + 2\,BH_3 \longrightarrow [CH_3CH_2CH_2CH(BH_2)_2]$$

$$[CH_3CH_2CH_2CH(BH_2)_2] \xrightarrow[\text{2. } H_2O_2]{\text{1. KOH, 25°, 4 hr}} \underset{\substack{\text{73\% yield} \\ \text{1-butanol}}}{CH_3CH_2CH_2CH_2\ddot{O}H}$$

The addition of the second equivalent of boron reagent can be prevented by working with modified, sterically congested boranes of the type R_2BH. One of the most common reagents of this type is di(1,2-dimethylpropyl)borane (disiamylborane), which is prepared by treating 2-methyl-2-butene with borane. Use of this reagent provides us with a route to aldehydes from terminal alkynes. An example is shown in Equation 15.22.

Eqn. 15.22

$$\underset{\text{3-methyl-1-butyne}}{(CH_3)_2CHC{\equiv}CH} + HB[CH(CH_3)CH(CH_3)_2]_2 \longrightarrow (CH_3)_2CHCH{=}CH{-}B[CH(CH_3)CH(CH_3)_2]_2$$

$$(CH_3)_2CHCH{=}CH{-}B[CH(CH_3)CH(CH_3)_2]_2 \xrightarrow[KOH]{H_2O_2} \underset{\substack{\text{70\% yield} \\ \text{3-methylbutanal}}}{(CH_3)_2CHCH_2CH\ddot{O}}$$

Addition of Hydrogen Halides to Alkynes Hydrogen halides, HX, react readily with alkynes. H and X add to the triple bond with Markovnikov orientation—the same orientation that is seen in the addition of HX to double bonds. An example of this type of addition reaction is shown in Equation 15.23.

Eqn. 15.23

$$CH_3CH_2{-}C{\equiv}CH \xrightarrow{H^+} CH_3CH_2{-}\overset{+}{C}{=}CH(H) \quad [\gg CH_3CH_2{-}C{=}\overset{+}{C}H(H)]$$

$$CH_3CH_2{-}\overset{+}{C}{=}CH_2 + :\ddot{Cl}:^- \longrightarrow CH_3CH_2{-}C(:\ddot{Cl}:){=}CH_2$$

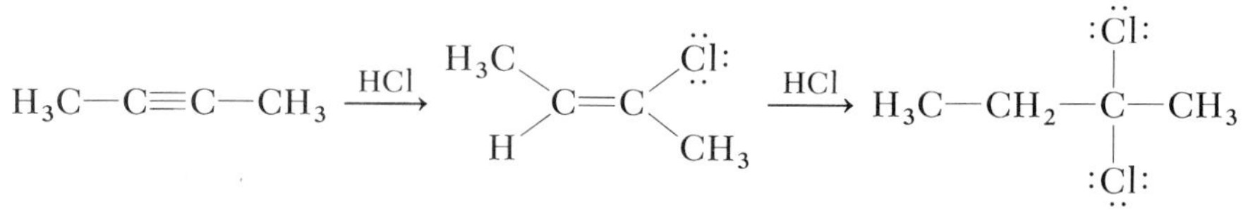

Figure 15.20 Hydrogen halide addition to an alkyne. The first step usually (but not always) proceeds with *anti* stereochemistry. The second step is regiospecific, placing the second chlorine on the same carbon that received the first.

$$H_3C{-}C{\equiv}C{-}CH_3 \xrightarrow{HCl} \underset{H}{\overset{H_3C}{}}\!C{=}C\!\overset{:\ddot{Cl}:}{\underset{CH_3}{}} \xrightarrow{HCl} H_3C{-}CH_2{-}\overset{:\ddot{Cl}:}{\underset{:\ddot{Cl}:}{C}}{-}CH_3$$

Figure 15.21 Two possible carbocations resulting from the addition of a proton to (Z)-2-chloro-2-butene. The carbocation on the right is more stable, and forms in preference to the one on the left. Its further reaction with chloride ion leads to the observed product of the reaction shown in Figure 15.20.

$$\overset{CH_3}{\underset{H}{{}^{+}C}}{-}C\overset{:\ddot{Cl}:\;H}{\underset{CH_3}{}} \quad \text{versus} \quad \overset{CH_3}{\underset{H\;H}{C}}{-}\overset{+}{C}\overset{:\ddot{Cl}:}{\underset{CH_3}{}}$$

The order of reactivity of the hydrogen halides correlates with their relative acidities—hydrogen iodide is most reactive and hydrogen fluoride is least reactive.

PROBLEM 15.23 Give the structure and the name of the product when one equivalent of hydrogen chloride is added to 2-butyne.

Although we can halt the hydrohalogenation of alkynes at the vinyl halide stage, further addition of HX occurs easily. When further addition does occur, it is regiospecific. The addition of the second molecule of hydrogen halide places the incoming halide at the same carbon that received the first one; that is, a geminal dihalide is formed, as illustrated in Figure 15.20.

The regiospecificity can be understood by comparing the two possible carbocations that could form when the vinylic halide is protonated. The two possible carbocations are shown in Figure 15.21. The right-hand structure is more stable than the one on the left. We can associate this stability with a second resonance structure that can be drawn for the right-hand ion; in this structure (shown on the right side of Figure 15.22), every atom (except hydrogen) has a complete octet of electrons.

This example illustrates the general need to consider additional resonance structures for the product or intermediates of a reaction. *Resonance structures in which every atom (except hydrogen) has a complete octet of electrons are usually more significant than structures that do not fulfill this condition.* In addition, the existence of such a resonance structure is usually a good indication that the molecule or ion is more stable than related species that do *not* have electron delocalization. Note that the observed regiochemistry is contrary to what would be expected if we considered only the electronegativity of the halogen. The electron-withdrawing effect of a halogen atom would *destabilize* the cation shown on the right in Figure 15.21 (relative to the cation on the left). However, the effect of resonance is in the direction opposite that of the electronegativity, and it overwhelms the electronegativity effect.

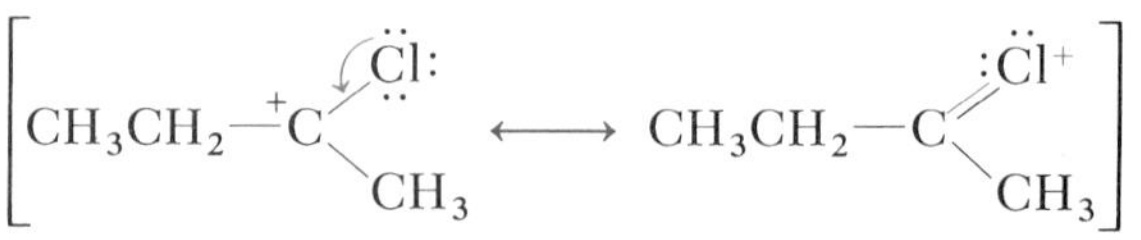

Figure 15.22 Resonance structures of the favored cation in HCl addition to a vinylic chloride. Of the two cations shown in Figure 15.21, only one has an additional resonance structure in which every atom except hydrogen has a complete octet of electrons.

$$\left[CH_3CH_2{-}\overset{+}{C}\overset{:\ddot{Cl}:}{\underset{CH_3}{}} \longleftrightarrow CH_3CH_2{-}C\overset{=\,:\ddot{Cl}^{+}}{\underset{CH_3}{}} \right]$$

$$H_2C{=}CH{-}CH{=}CH_2 + Br_2 \longrightarrow :\ddot{B}rCH_2{-}CHBr{-}CH{=}CH_2 + :\ddot{B}rCH_2{-}CH{=}CH{-}CH_2\ddot{B}r:$$

1,2-addition 1,4-addition

mixed product obtained
3,4-dibromo-1-butene 1,4-dibromo-2-butene

Figure 15.23 Bromine addition to 1,3-butadiene. Addition of one equivalent of bromine to 1,3-butadiene yields a mixture of products. The 1,2-addition product corresponds to simple addition of two bromine atoms across one of the double bonds. The 1,4-addition product arises from addition of bromine atoms to the ends of the conjugated diene system and the establishment of a double bond between C2 and C3.

ADDITION TO CONJUGATED DIENES

The same reagents that add to simple alkenes also add to dienes. If the diene is not conjugated, each double bond behaves as we would expect a simple alkene double bond to behave. However, with conjugated dienes there are some special features that we need to consider carefully. First, let us examine some experimental results.

Consider the addition of one equivalent of bromine in carbon tetrachloride to 1,3-butadiene. From a simple extrapolation of alkene chemistry, we expect two bromine atoms to add to one of the double bonds. There are two double bonds, but addition of bromine to either of these bonds would produce the same product, 3,4-dibromo-1-butene. This compound is observed as a product of the reaction; however, we *also* observe *cis* and *trans* isomers of an initially surprising product, 1,4-dibromo-2-butene (see Figure 15.23).

The relative amounts of 1,2- and 1,4-addition products are strongly dependent on experimental conditions. In general, 1,2-addition dominates at lower temperatures, and 1,4-addition dominates at higher temperatures. The results we have just seen for bromine addition are general. All additions to conjugated dienes give some 1,2- and some 1,4-addition products. We need to consider, first of all, why two types of products are obtained. Then we need to determine why the relative amounts of the two product types are so dependent on reaction conditions.

Why We Get Two Products We will use the addition of HBr to 1,3-butadiene to develop our fundamental ideas about this type of addition. We noted earlier that the addition of hydrogen halides to simple alkenes (Chapter 10) usually proceeds by initial formation of a carbocation. Regioselectivity in the addition of the proton to a double bond is a result of the preferential formation of the more stable of the possible carbocations (Markovnikov orientation).

Extrapolating this concept to 1,3-butadiene, we expect HBr to react by first protonating a terminal carbon atom. The carbocation produced in this process is not only secondary—it is also *allylic*. The allylic nature of the carbocation affords it special stabilization, which we can see by writing an additional resonance structure, as shown in Figure 15.24.

Figure 15.24 Protonation of 1,3-butadiene. The protonation of a terminal carbon atom rather than an internal one is favored. Protonation of the terminal site leads to a more stable carbocation, one that is secondary and allylic (resonance stabilized). The carbocation shown at the top is not allylic and therefore is less stable than the one shown at the bottom.

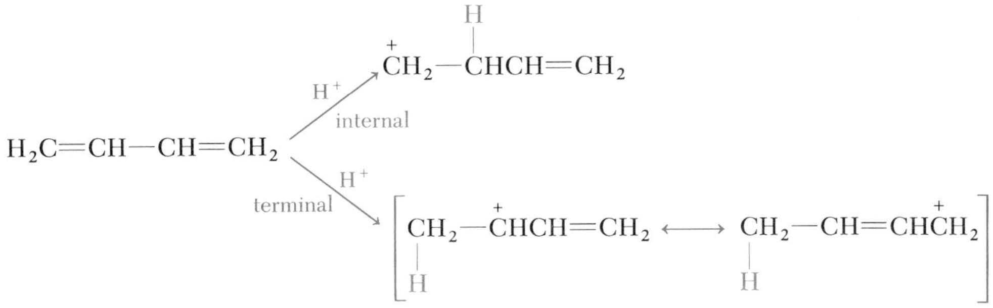

$$H_2C{=}CH{-}CH{=}CH_2 \xrightarrow[\text{internal}]{H^+} \overset{+}{C}H_2{-}\underset{}{C}H(H)CH{=}CH_2$$

$$H_2C{=}CH{-}CH{=}CH_2 \xrightarrow[\text{terminal}]{H^+} \left[CH_2(H){-}\overset{+}{C}HCH{=}CH_2 \longleftrightarrow CH_2(H){-}CH{=}CH\overset{+}{C}H_2 \right]$$

$$H_2C{=}CH{-}CH{=}CH_2 \xrightarrow{H^+} [H_3C{-}\overset{+}{C}H{-}CH{=}CH_2 \longleftrightarrow H_3C{-}CH{=}CH{-}\overset{+}{C}H_2]$$

$$H_3C{-}\overset{+}{C}H{-}CH{=}CH_2 \longleftrightarrow H_3C{-}CH{=}CH{-}\overset{+}{C}H_2 \xrightarrow{Br^-} \left[\begin{array}{c} H_3C{-}CHBr{-}CH{=}CH_2 \\ \text{1,2-addition product} \\ + \\ H_3C{-}CH{=}CH{-}CH_2\ddot{B}r{:} \\ (\textit{cis-} \text{ and } \textit{trans-}) \\ \text{1,4-addition products} \end{array}\right]$$

Figure 15.25 Addition of HBr to 1,3-butadiene.

Because the allylic carbocation has a real structure that is intermediate between the two resonance forms, there are two possible sites for bromide addition: bromide ion can add to either of the positive sites in the resonance structures. These possibilities are shown in Figure 15.25 for HBr addition to 1,3-butadiene.

Kinetic versus Thermodynamic Control in 1,2- and 1,4-Addition These two types of addition (1,2- and 1,4-) are in competition. The relative yields of each product vary with the reaction temperature. Experimental results for the HBr addition to 1,3-butadiene at several temperatures are summarized in Table 15.5. As we increase the temperature of the reaction, the amount of 1,4-addition product increases. At lower temperatures, 1,2-addition predominates.

This reaction system provides us with an interesting example of competing reaction processes. Before we delve into the underlying principles that influence this competition, let's consider another experimental result. Suppose 3-bromo-1-butene (the 1,2-addition product) is allowed to react with small amounts of aprotic Lewis acids (e.g., $FeCl_3$) at a higher temperature. Although some of the 3-bromo-1-butene remains unchanged, significant isomerization to the 1-bromo-2-butenes (the 1,4-addition products) occurs. Similarly, if a pure sample of 1-bromo-2-butene is treated with $FeCl_3$ at the same high temperature, some of it is converted to 3-bromo-1-butene. Furthermore, the ratio of 1,2-addition product to 1,4-addition product is the same regardless of which isomer is used as the starting material. This interconversion of products does not occur at lower temperatures.

At the higher temperatures an equilibrium mixture of the three isomeric forms exists. The internal (disubstituted) alkenes resulting from 1,4-addition are thermodynamically more stable and dominate when equilibrium is reached at higher temperature. In fact, the mixture of isomers is in accord (or nearly

Table 15.5 Product Distribution in HBr Addition to 1,3-Butadiene

Temperature (°C)	1,2-Addition Product	1,4-Addition Product
−78	90%	10%
−12	75%	25%
0	62%	38%
21	44%	56%

so) with their thermodynamic stabilities—this is always true of equilibria. *The relative amounts of substances present in an equilibrium reflect their relative thermodynamic stabilities.*

Now we must ask why we observe the preferential formation of the thermodynamically *less* stable isomer at lower temperatures. Because equilibration of the isomers does not occur readily at low temperatures, we infer that the less stable isomer is formed *faster* than the more stable isomer. *At low temperatures, the rates of formation of the products (not their stabilities) determine their distribution.* We say that the reaction under these conditions is subject to **kinetic control.** At higher temperatures where we obtain an equilibrium mixture of products, we say the reaction is subject to **thermodynamic control.**

In earlier discussions we often mentioned that a thermodynamically more stable product is usually formed more rapidly than a less stable product. Observations of this type led to the formulation of the Hammond postulate. We rationalized the Hammond postulate by supposing that the factors that tend to stabilize a product also tend to stabilize the activated complex leading to that product. In general, the activated complex leading to a more stable product is more stable (lower energy) than that leading to a less stable product. However, we now have a clear exception: at lower temperatures the major product (1,2-addition) is *not* the more stable product (1,4-addition). To understand what is happening in 1,2- versus 1,4-addition, we need to focus carefully on the structures of the starting material and the product in the final step of the reaction (the conversion of the allylic cation to the 1,2- or 1,4-addition product).

The resonance structures for the intermediate allylic carbocation are shown again in Figure 15.26. Notice that the carbocation has two sites where positive charge can be distributed. One of these sites is internal (**15.5**), and the other is terminal (**15.6**). Bromide ion can add to either site, resulting in 1,2- (from **15.5**) or 1,4-addition (from **15.6**). However, the two resonance structures are not equivalent. One is a more significant contributor to the actual structure than is the other. The true structure of the allylic carbocation is more nearly like the more stable resonance structure. Understanding which resonance structure is the more stable one will help us to understand the nature of the 1,2- versus 1,4-addition competition.

It is difficult to decide which resonance structure is of lower energy. We need to consider two effects. First, we need to consider which location is better for the double bond. Second, we need to consider which location is better for the positive charge. Structure **15.5** is favored by the location of the positive charge (a secondary site). However, structure **15.6** is favored by the location of the double bond (internal). Which of these two effects is more important? To answer this question we need to look at both factors quantitatively.

Data from other systems allows us to answer the question just raised. Secondary carbocations are more stable than primary carbocations by approximately 20–25 kcal/mole (84–105 kJ/mole). However, an internal (disubstituted) alkene is more stable than a terminal (monosubstituted) alkene by only 1.9–2.8 kcal/mole (8–12 kJ/mole). The location of the charge is clearly more

$$[H_3C-\overset{+}{C}H-CH{=}CH_2 \longleftrightarrow H_3C-CH{=}CH-\overset{+}{C}H_2]$$

15.5 **15.6**

Figure 15.26 Resonance structures for the allylic carbocation formed upon protonation of 1,3-butadiene.

important for carbocation stabilization than is the location of the double bond. Being more stable, structure **15.5** contributes more to the resonance hybrid than does **15.6**. The positive charge of the allylic carbocation is accordingly concentrated mainly on the internal position, and the double-bond character is principally at the terminal position.

We see that the allylic carbocation intermediate resembles the 1,2-product more than it does the 1,4-product. A greater degree of structural reorganization (changes of bond angles and lengths, and carbon hybridizations) is required for generation of the 1,4-product than for generation of the 1,2-product. In general, a greater change in structure is associated with a higher activation energy for a reaction.

We can now compare the activation energies that control the conversion of the allylic carbocation to each of the possible products. The activation energy for the formation of the 1,2-addition product is lower than that for the formation of the 1,4-addition product. Bromide addition at the internal position occurs faster simply because the positive charge is most highly concentrated at that site. The reaction progress diagram illustrating the competition is shown in Figure 15.27.

At low temperatures, the 1,2-addition product is dominant because collisions between allylic cations and bromide ions are rarely energetic enough to overcome the higher activation energy leading to the 1,4-addition product. At higher temperatures, the molecules are more energetic. Their collisions more frequently provide the energy needed to overcome the activation energy for forming the 1,4-addition product. In the equilibrium case, the 1,4-addition product dominates. At the higher temperatures we say the reaction is under *thermodynamic control*. When a reaction is under thermodynamic control, the product distribution depends on the difference in the stabilities of the products.

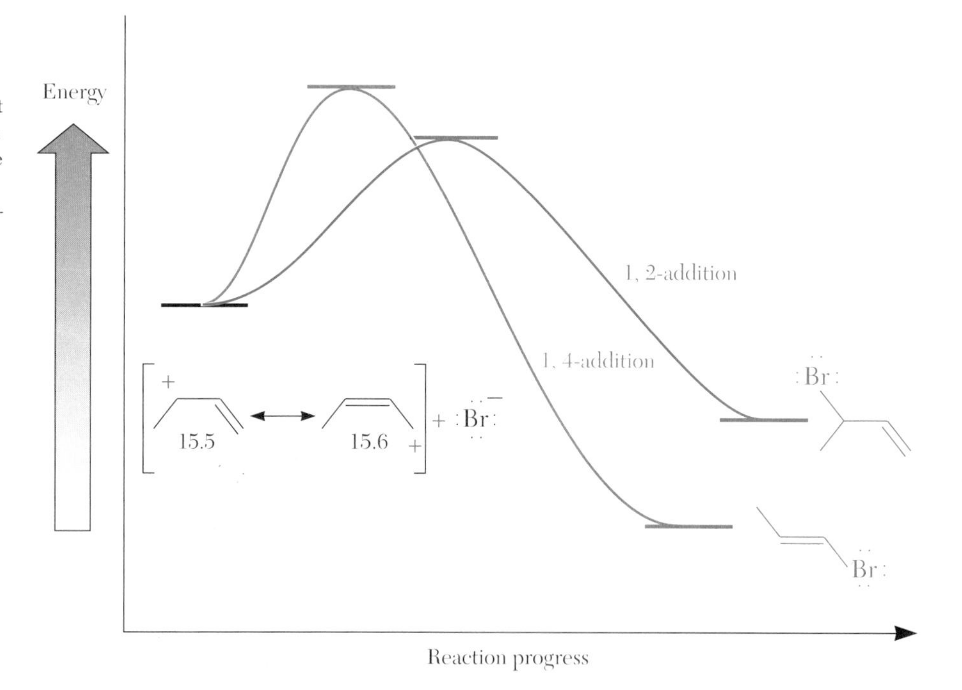

Figure 15.27 Kinetic versus thermodynamic control in the reaction of HBr with 1,3-butadiene. The 1,4-addition product is thermodynamically more stable. Thus, it is the dominant product if equilibrium can be established (at high temperatures). The activation energy for formation of the 1,2-addition product is lower than that for formation of the 1,4-addition product. Thus, it is formed faster, and it is the dominant product if equilibrium is not established (at lower temperatures).

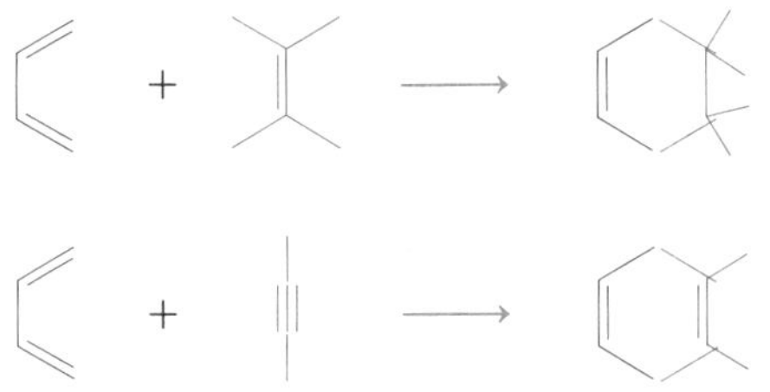

diene component | dienophile component | six-membered ring product

Figure 15.28 Summary of the Diels-Alder reaction. The Diels-Alder reaction involves the addition of a conjugated diene and a **dienophile.** The dienophile is either an alkene or an alkyne. For reaction to occur readily, the dienophile generally requires electron-withdrawing substituents attached to the double or triple bond.

We need to consider one final point. The activation energy leading to 1,2-addition product is *always* less than that leading to the 1,4-addition product. If the 1,2-addition product forms faster at lower temperatures, should it not form faster at higher temperatures as well? The answer is a decided *yes*! However, we must realize that both 1,2- and 1,4-addition products can dissociate back to the allylic carbocation and bromide ion. Indeed, it is this reversibility that allows equilibration and thermodynamic control to occur. The 1,2-addition product not only forms faster, it dissociates faster as well. Its activation energy for dissociation is less than that for the more stable 1,4-addition product. Although the 1,4-addition product forms more slowly, it dissociates more slowly as well (i.e., it tends to stay together once formed), and the product ratio (eventually) reflects the relative stabilities of the two products.

15.7 The Diels-Alder Reaction

One extremely useful reaction of conjugated dienes leads to the formation of a six-membered ring. This reaction is named after its discoverers, Otto Diels and Kurt Alder of the University of Kiel (Germany). For this work they were awarded the Nobel Prize in 1950. Generalized examples of the Diels-Alder reaction are shown in Figure 15.28.

The Diels-Alder reaction is a concerted reaction. It occurs in a single step via a single activated complex. Most evidence argues against the involvement of any discrete intermediates such as radicals or ions. It is convenient to use the curved-arrow formalism to represent the electron-shifts occurring in the Diels-Alder reaction (see Figure 15.29).

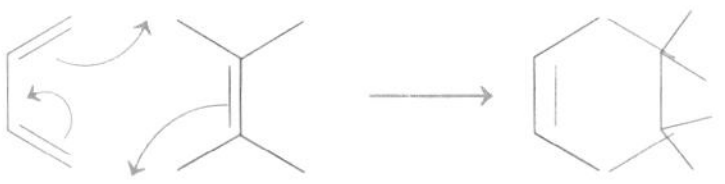

Figure 15.29 Curved-arrow depiction of the Diels-Alder reaction. The direction of the electron-shifts (as given by the arrows) is arbitrary. Shown here clockwise, they could just as well be shown counterclockwise.

Overall, two new σ bonds form between the ends of the original diene and dienophile components, along with a new π bond between the central atoms of the diene. None of the original three π bonds remain in the product.

There are several aspects of the Diels-Alder reaction that are important for its synthetic utility. We will consider these in turn.

REQUIREMENTS FOR THE DIENE COMPONENT

The diene component of a Diels-Alder reaction must be a *conjugated* diene. Allenes and dienes containing isolated double bonds cannot serve as the diene component in the Diels-Alder reaction. Moreover, the diene component must be able to adopt a *cisoid* conformation. The distinction between *cisoid* and *transoid* conformations is shown in Figure 15.30.

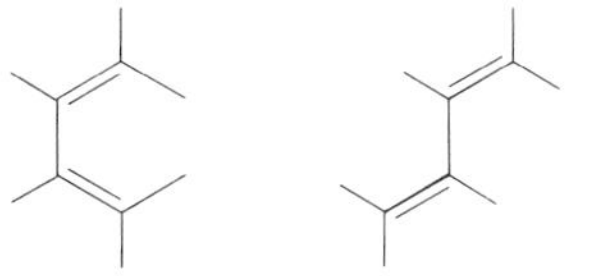

cisoid conformation | *transoid* conformation

Figure 15.30 The *cisoid* and *transoid* conformations of a diene. A diene must be capable of existing in a *cisoid* conformation in order to act as the diene component in a Diels-Alder reaction.

For open-chain dienes such as 1,3-butadiene, free rotation about the central carbon-carbon single bond allows them to adopt either a *cisoid* or *transoid* conformation. However, this ability can be compromised if large substituents are present. For example, (Z,Z)-2,4-hexadiene is unreactive in the Diels-Alder

Figure 15.31 Conformations of (Z,Z)-2,4-hexadiene. The *cisoid* conformation is destabilized because the terminal methyl groups are forced into positions closer than the sum of their van der Waals radii. The molecule is essentially unreactive in the Diels-Alder reaction, although other geometric isomers of 2,4-hexadiene (*E*,*Z*) and (*E*,*E*) are normally reactive.

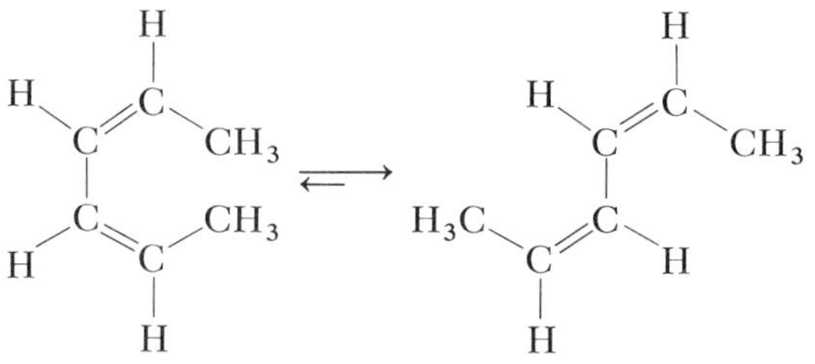

cisoid ⇌ *transoid*

Figure 15.32 Conformationally rigid dienes. Cyclic dienes are conformationally more rigid than are open-chain dienes. Only those that can adopt a *cisoid* structure are reactive toward dienophiles.

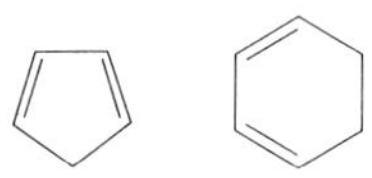

Dienes that are locked into a *cisoid*-type structure undergo the Diels-Alder reaction relatively rapidly because they are always in the *cisoid* form.

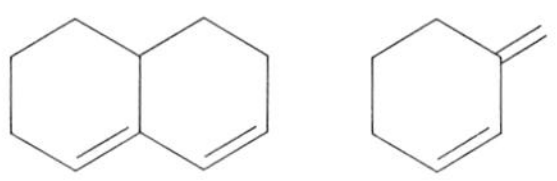

Dienes that are locked into a *transoid*-type structure do not undergo the Diels-Alder reaction.

Figure 15.33 Resonance structures for propenal. The resonance structure on the right is less significant than that shown on the left. However, it does contribute to the overall resonance hybrid. The result is that the true structure of propenal is somewhat electron deficient in the region of the double bond.

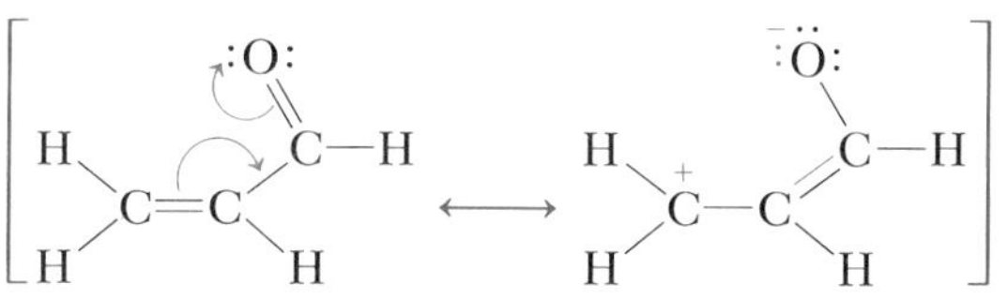

reaction presumably because its *cisoid* conformation is relatively unstable as a result of steric strain. As Figure 15.31 shows, the methyl groups are crowded together in the transition state, thus raising its energy.

Cyclic conjugated dienes are usually rigidly *cisoid* or *transoid*. Only those dienes containing *cisoid* linkages can undergo the Diels-Alder reaction. Several examples are shown in Figure 15.32.

REQUIREMENTS FOR THE DIENOPHILE

The dienophile is usually an alkene, although certain alkynes and other substances with double or triple bonds also react. However, not all alkenes serve well as dienophiles. For example, ethylene, the simplest alkene, does not react as a dienophile under ordinary laboratory conditions. It does react with 1,3-butadiene under forcing conditions (at 200 °C in the gas phase), and likewise other simple alkenes react only with difficulty.

Some types of substituted alkenes are highly reactive as dienophiles. In particular, those with an electron-withdrawing group attached to an olefinic carbon exhibit enhanced reactivity as dienophiles. The electron-withdrawing group can be an element of high electronegativity (e.g., —F), or a group that is electron withdrawing through a resonance effect (e.g., —C≡N or —C=O). This type of resonance effect is illustrated in Figure 15.33 for propenal.

PROBLEM 15.24 Give the product of the Diels-Alder reaction of $H_2C{=}CH{-}C{\equiv}N$: with 1,3-butadiene.

PROBLEM 15.25 Write a contributing resonance structure that helps to explain the reactivity of acrylonitrile ($H_2C{=}CH{-}C{\equiv}N{:}$) in Diels-Alder reactions.

Steps to Solving the Problem

Solution to Problem 15.24

1. To which atoms of the starting material will new bonds be formed? The end carbon atoms of the diene linkage form new σ bonds with the olefinic carbons of the dienophile.
2. What bonds will be broken in the starting material? All three of the original π bonds are removed, and a new π bond is formed between the central carbon atoms of the original diene.
3. Write the resulting structure. The product of the reaction between acrylonitrile and 1,3-butadiene is shown below.

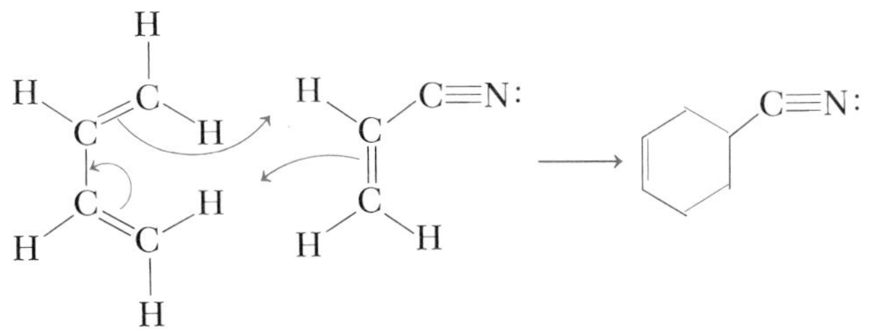

Later we will look in detail at several functional groups that are particularly good at activating alkenes so that they can serve as dienophiles. These include the functional groups of carboxylic acids and carboxylate esters and carbonyl groups. Electron-withdrawing groups in allylic positions also enhance an alkene's ability to act as a dienophile. For example, allyl alcohol (2-propen-1-ol, **15.7**) and allyl chloride (3-chloro-1-propene, **15.8**) are good dienophiles.

$CH_2{=}CHCH_2\ddot{O}H$ allyl alcohol **15.7**

$CH_2{=}CHCH_2\ddot{C}l{:}$ allyl chloride **15.8**

STEREOCHEMICAL RELATIONSHIPS IN THE DIELS-ALDER REACTION

An important aspect of the Diels-Alder reaction is its stereospecificity. The reaction between (*E*,*E*)-2,4-hexadiene and allyl chloride demonstrates several points of stereochemical importance. The reaction is shown in Equation 15.24.

Eqn. 15.24

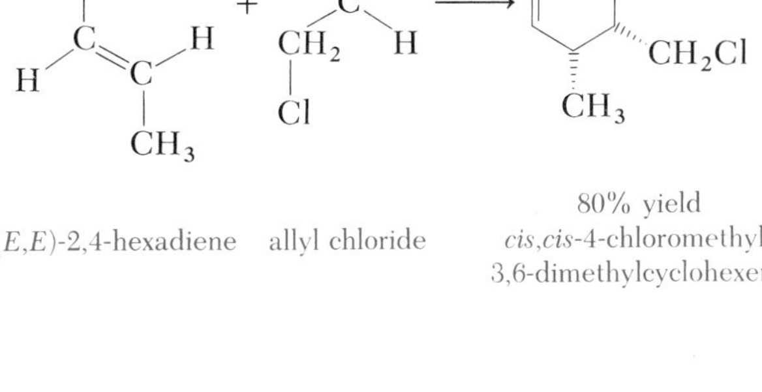

(*E*,*E*)-2,4-hexadiene + allyl chloride → 80% yield *cis*,*cis*-4-chloromethyl-3,6-dimethylcyclohexene

The product retains the stereochemistry of the original diene. If we use an isomeric diene, we see a corresponding result, as shown in Equation 15.25.

Eqn. 15.25

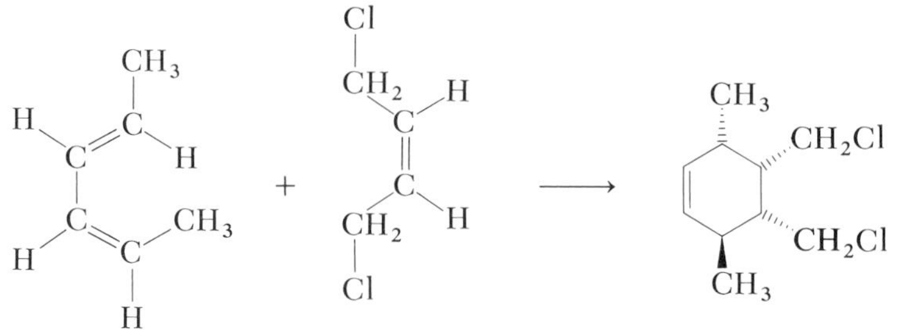

(*E*,*Z*)-2,4-hexadiene (*E*)-1,4-dichloro-2-butene

80% yield
trans,*cis*,*cis*-4,5-di(chloromethyl)-3,6-dimethylcyclohexene

Notice that the product retains the stereochemistry of both the alkene and diene starting materials. As shown in Equation 15.25, the chloromethyl groups are *cis* relative to each other in both the starting alkene and the product.

A third stereochemical detail relates to a specific relationship maintained between the diene and the dienophile. Consider again the reaction shown in Equation 15.24. We can imagine two possible products conforming to the stereochemical restrictions we have just mentioned, as shown in Figure 15.34.

Through the investigation of the stereochemical course of many Diels-Alder reactions, the preferred geometry of approach and reaction has been elucidated. The diene (in a *cisoid* conformation) and the dienophile sit in parallel planes, one above the other; the terminal carbons of one component are directly above the terminal carbons of the other. In this way the orbital lobes of the two molecules can interact most efficiently for the generation of new σ bonds. The geometry of approach is illustrated in Figure 15.35.

If the dienophile bears substituents, there are two possible geometries of approach to the activated complex. In one of these approaches, the ***endo* approach**, the substituent of the dieneophile component is tucked *under* the diene component. In the other possible approach, the ***exo* approach,** the substituent is pointed away from the diene. The activated complexes for these two types of approach and the products resulting from them are illustrated in Figure 15.36.

Figure 15.34 Possible stereoisomeric products of a Diels-Alder addition of allyl chloride and (*E*,*E*)-2,4-hexadiene. Only one of these products is formed in any measurable amount. The reaction is highly stereospecific.

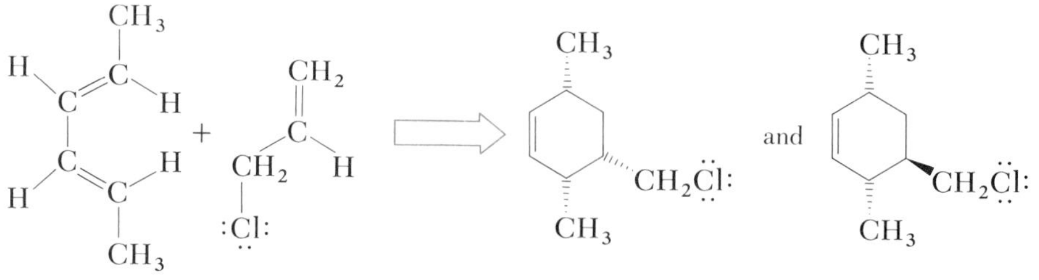

and

actual product

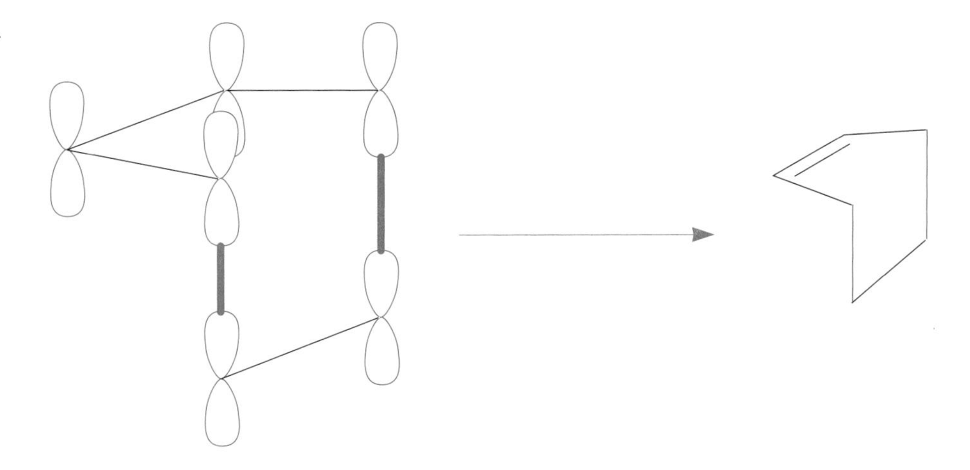

Figure 15.35 Approach of diene and dienophile in the Diels-Alder reaction.

The actual product distribution indicates that the *endo* approach is favored. We infer that this preference is due to energy-lowering interactions between the nonbonding and/or *p* orbitals of the dienophile substituent and the molecular orbital system of the diene. We say that the Diels-Alder reaction proceeds with ***endo* selectivity**; that is, formation of product via the *endo* approach is much more significant than via the *exo* approach.

Figure 15.36 Possible geometries of approach for the Diels-Alder reaction of allyl chloride and (*E*,*E*)-2,4-hexadiene. There is a general preference for the reaction pathway involving the *endo* approach. This preference is understood to result from a stabilizing interaction between the molecular orbitals of the substituent groups and those of the diene (see Chapter 30).

THE USE OF CYCLIC DIENES AND/OR DIENOPHILES

If the reactants in a Diels-Alder reaction are cyclic, the product will be a polycyclic molecule. When a cyclic diene reacts with an open-chain dienophile (alkene), the product is a bicyclic molecule.

The reaction of cyclopentadiene with methyl acrylate is shown in Equation 15.26. The *endo* product is favored over the *exo* product by a large factor and

***Endo* approach** The substituent of the dienophile is tucked under the diene.

***Exo* approach** The substituent of the dienophile is pointed away from the diene.

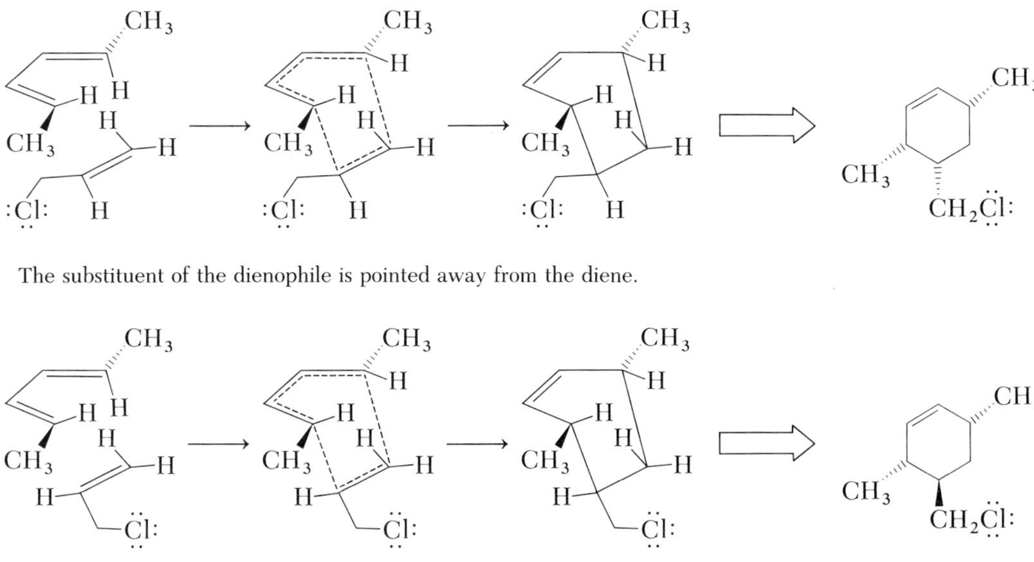

is essentially the only Diels-Alder product formed. When drawing the structure of the *endo* product, we place the original alkene substituent *anti* to the one-carbon bridge.

Eqn. 15.26

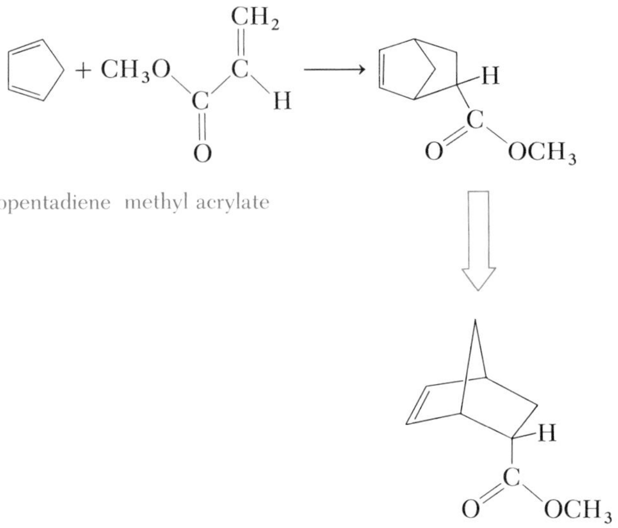

cyclopentadiene + methyl acrylate (CH_3O–C(=O)–CH=CH_2) ⟶ bicyclic product (–H, C(=O)OCH_3)

90% yield
(*endo* isomer)
endo-2-carbomethoxybicyclo[2.2.1]hept-5-ene

A more complex example of the Diels-Alder reaction is shown in Figure 15.37. In this reaction cyclopentadiene dimerizes via a Diels-Alder reaction, with one molecule of cyclopentadiene playing the role of diene and the other playing the role of dienophile. This reaction occurs quite readily—cyclopentadiene dimerizes rapidly at room temperature. The reaction can be reversed by heating the dimer. Whenever cyclopentadiene is needed in an organic reaction, the dimer must be heated first to produce the monomer—this reaction is called a *retro-Diels-Alder reaction.*

Figure 15.37 Dimerization of cyclopentadiene by means of a Diels-Alder reaction.

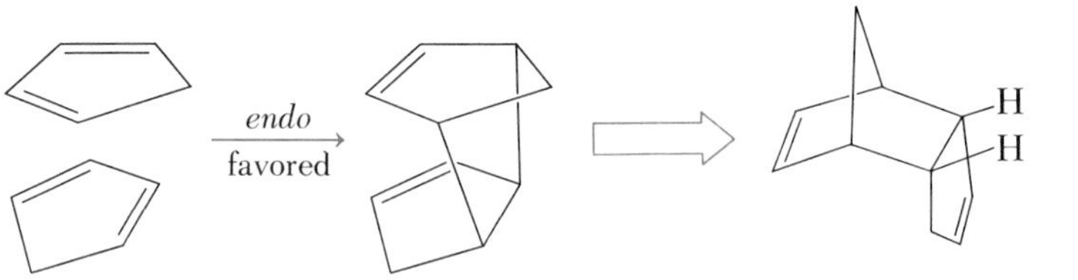

endo favored (H, H)

Addition occurs with the *endo* orientation shown above, rather than the *exo* orientation shown below.

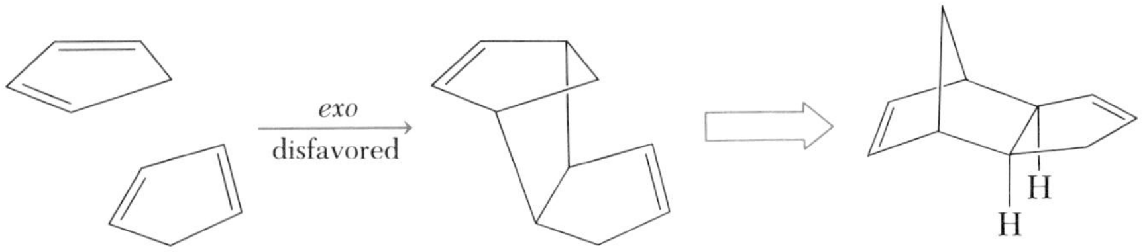

exo disfavored (H, H)

SPECIAL TOPIC

Aldrin and Dieldrin

The reaction of bicyclo[2.2.1]hepta-2,5-diene with hexachlorocyclopentadiene proceeds via the Diels-Alder reaction to produce the compound whose structure is shown below. In this reaction the hexachlorocyclopentadiene serves as the diene and the bicyclic (unconjugated) diene as the dienophile. The product, a tetracyclic compound commonly known as *Aldrin*, is a potent insecticide and was used extensively for that purpose.

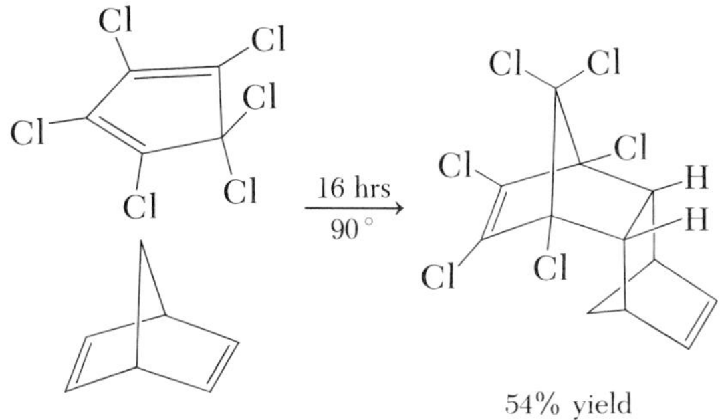

16 hrs, 90°

54% yield
Aldrin

Of similar utility (and ultimate fate) is the epoxidation product of Aldrin, *dieldrin*, whose structure is shown below.

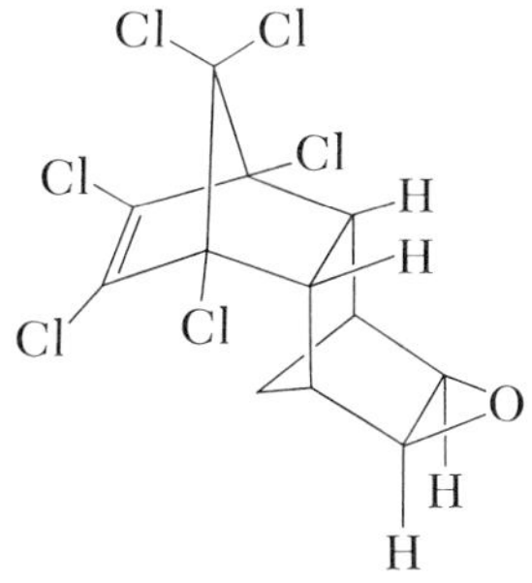

Dieldrin

Both of these compounds are damaging to the liver and kidneys in mammals. As a result, their use in agriculture in the United States has been discontinued.

PROBLEM 15.26 In the Diels-Alder reaction that forms Aldrin from hexachlorocyclopentadiene and bicyclo[2.2.1]hepta-2,5-diene, a product of another Diels-Alder reaction is also formed. This material, known as *isodrin*, is an isomer of Aldrin. Propose a structure for isodrin and draw the activated complex leading to it.

PROBLEM 15.27 Which diene and dienophile should be combined to prepare each of the following compounds?

a. 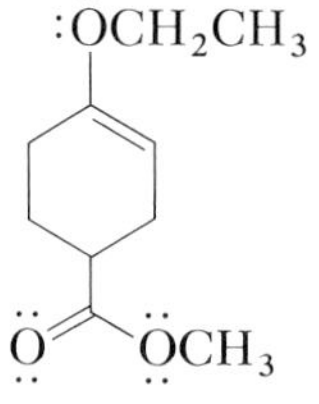 $:\ddot{O}CH_2CH_3$ ... $\ddot{O}$ $\ddot{O}CH_3$

b. 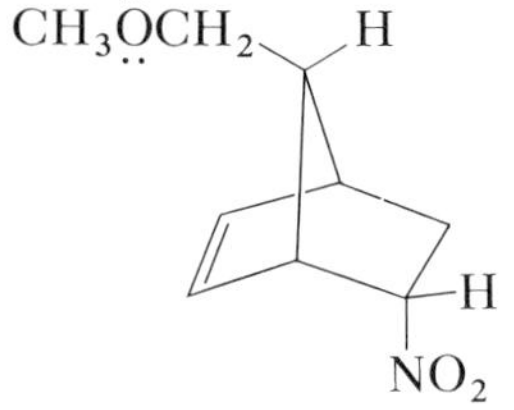 $CH_3\ddot{O}CH_2$ H ... H NO_2

PROBLEM 15.28 Give the structure of substance A, which reacts with 2,3-dimethyl-1,3-cyclohexadiene in a Diels-Alder reaction to give the product as shown below.

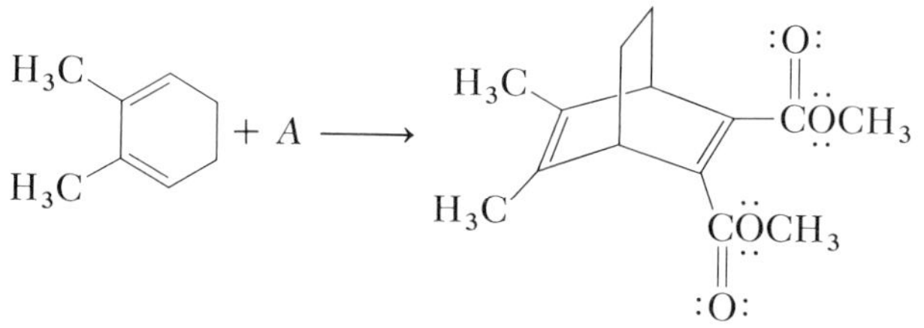

H_3C, H_3C + A ⟶ H_3C, H_3C, $:O:$, $\ddot{C}OCH_3$, $\ddot{C}OCH_3$, $:O:$

15.8 Ozonolysis and Other Oxidations of Alkynes and Dienes

The ozonolysis of dienes is a simple extension of the chemistry of ordinary alkenes—ozone attacks each of the individual π bonds. The cleavage is completed with reductive or oxidative workup. The primary difference between dienes and simple alkenes in this process is the generation of more fragment products with the dienes. Several examples are shown in Figure 15.38.

Figure 15.38 Examples of the ozonolysis of dienes.

1,3-cyclohexadiene $\xrightarrow[2.\ H_2O_2,\ H_2O]{1.\ O_3}$ HOOC—COOH + $HOOCCH_2CH_2COOH$

oxalic acid, succinic acid

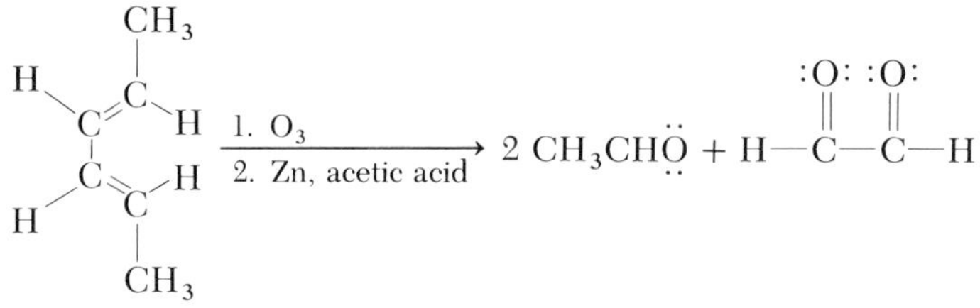

(E,E)-2,4-hexadiene $\xrightarrow[2.\ Zn,\ acetic\ acid]{1.\ O_3}$ 2 $CH_3CH\ddot{O}$ + H—C(=$\ddot{O}$)—C(=$\ddot{O}$)—H

ethanal, glyoxal

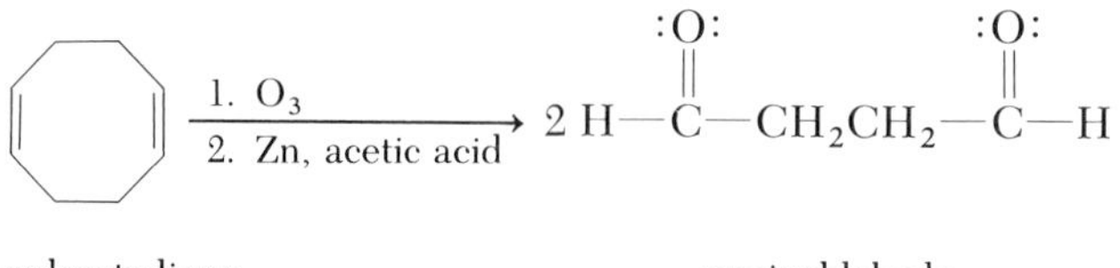

1,5-cyclooctadiene $\xrightarrow[2.\ Zn,\ acetic\ acid]{1.\ O_3}$ 2 H—C(=$\ddot{O}$)—CH_2CH_2—C(=$\ddot{O}$)—H

succinaldehyde

PROBLEM 15.29 A Diels-Alder reaction uses the same compound as both diene and dienophile. The product is a diene that, on ozonolysis and appropriate workup, yields carbon dioxide and the tricarboxylic acid shown below. Give the structure of the compound that serves as both diene and dienophile, the nature of the Diels-Alder reaction, and the nature of the ozonolysis.

$$\mathrm{HOOC{-}CH_2{-}CH_2{-}\underset{\displaystyle |\atop \displaystyle COOH}{CH}{-}CH_2{-}COOH}$$

Figure 15.39 Ozonolysis of alkynes. Ozonolysis of an alkyne with aqueous workup generates carboxylic acids. We can use this reaction for a degradative analysis of alkynes.

$$\mathrm{CH_3CH_2CH_2C{\equiv}CCH_2CH_3 \xrightarrow[2.\ H_2O]{1.\ O_3} CH_3CH_2COOH + CH_3CH_2CH_2COOH}$$

The ozonolysis of alkynes proceeds less readily than the corresponding reaction of alkenes. However, it is useful for the cleavage of carbon-carbon triple bonds. Carboxylic acids result from water workup of alkyne ozonolysis, as illustrated in Figure 15.39.

Alkynes are also oxidized by many reagents that oxidize alkenes. Aqueous acidic dichromate or aqueous basic permanganate cleave alkynes to carboxylic acids or their salts, as illustrated in Figure 15.40.

Figure 15.40 Dichromate oxidation of alkynes. Like ozonolysis, acidic dichromate oxidation of alkynes yields carboxylic acids as fragments.

$$\mathrm{CH_3CH_2C{\equiv}CCH_2CH(CH_3)_2 \xrightarrow[H_2SO_4,\ H_2O]{Na_2Cr_2O_7} CH_3CH_2COOH + (CH_3)_2CHCH_2COOH}$$

Summary

- Both alkynes and dienes can be prepared by dehydrohalogenation of the appropriate dihaloalkanes.
- For alkynes, a useful synthetic method is the S_N2 reaction of an acetylide ion with a primary haloalkane. This route enables terminal alkynes to be converted into more complex internal alkynes.
- Conjugated dienes can be prepared from alkenes by first performing an allylic bromination (with *N*-bromosuccinimide), followed by dehydrohalogenation of the product.
- Terminal alkynes have a higher acidity than most other hydrocarbons. This acidity is associated with the hybridization of the acetylenic carbon atoms.
- Terminal alkynes readily form acetylide salts upon treatment with strong base.
- Both alkynes and dienes undergo addition reactions. In many cases these reactions are completely analogous to those undergone by alkenes.
- Hydration of an alkyne leads initially to an enol, which tautomerizes to an isomeric ketone or aldehyde. This route allows a convenient synthesis of these carbonyl compounds from alkynes.
- Conjugated dienes undergo competing 1,2- and 1,4-addition reactions with electrophilic reagents.
- Generally, the 1,2-addition product is formed via a lower energy activated complex than is the 1,4-addition product. However, the 1,4-addition product is more stable than the 1,2-addition product. As a result, the 1,2-addition product is favored at low reaction temperatures and the 1,4-addition product at higher reaction temperatures. This example illustrates competition between kinetic and thermodynamic control within a reaction.
- The Diels-Alder reaction is a very important synthetic reaction of conjugated dienes. In this reaction, a diene reacts with a dienophile (an alkene or an alkyne) to produce a cyclohexene derivative or a 1,4-cyclohexadiene derivative. The reaction is highly stereospecific.

- Dienes and alkynes undergo oxidation and ozonolysis reactions that result in cleavage of carbon-carbon bonds. These reactions are analogous to those of alkenes.

Terms to Remember

conjugated diene	Lindlar's catalyst	thermodynamic control
cumulene	dissolving metal reduction	dienophile
acetylide salt	enol	*endo* approach
vicinal dihalide	tautomerism	*exo* approach
geminal dihalide	kinetic control	*endo* selectivity
allylic bromination		

Reactions of Synthetic Utility

73. $R{-}CHX{-}CHX{-}R' \xrightarrow{\text{base}} R{-}C{\equiv}C{-}R'$ 15.4

74. $R{-}CH_2{-}CX_2{-}R' \xrightarrow{\text{base}} R{-}C{\equiv}C{-}R'$ 15.4

75. 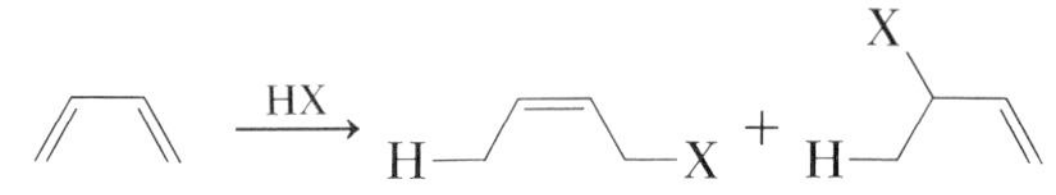 15.6

X = Cl, Br; thermodynamic control; kinetic control

76. 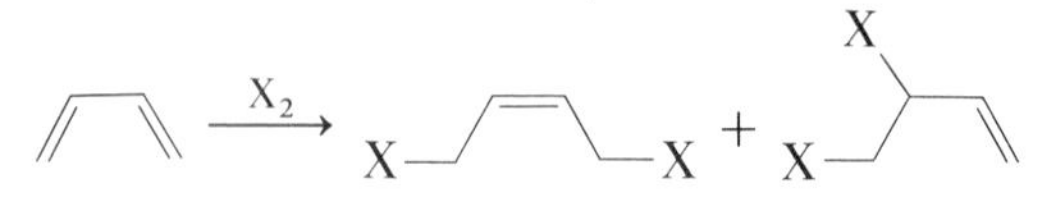 15.6

X = Cl, Br; thermodynamic control; kinetic control

77. 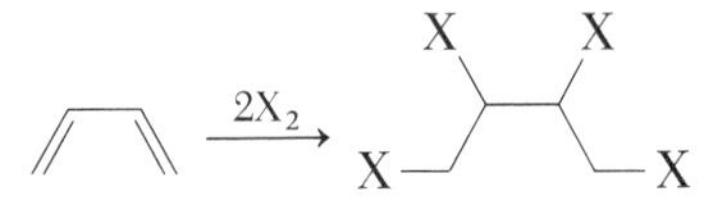 15.6

X = Cl, Br

78. 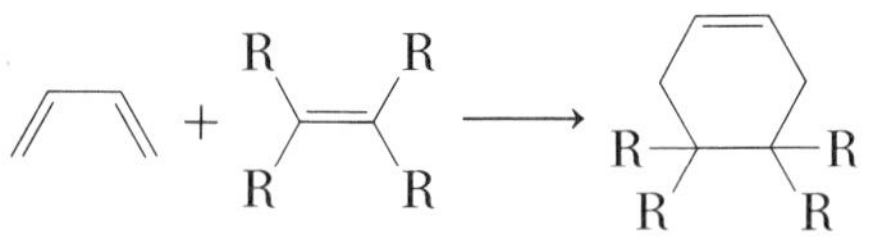 15.7

cisoid

79. $R{-}C{\equiv}C{-}H \xrightarrow{\text{strong base}} R{-}C{\equiv}C{:}^-$ 15.3

80. $R{-}C{\equiv}C{-}H \xrightarrow[\text{2. } R'X]{\text{1. base}} R{-}C{\equiv}C{-}R'$ 15.4

$R' = 1°$

81. $R{-}C{\equiv}C{-}H \xrightarrow[H_2O]{M(NH_3)_2^+} R{-}C{\equiv}C{-}M$ 15.3

M = Ag, Cu

82. $R-C\equiv C-H \xrightarrow[HgSO_4,\ H_2SO_4]{H_2O} R-\overset{\overset{\displaystyle :O:}{\|}}{C}-CH_3$ 15.6

83. $R-C\equiv C-R' \xrightarrow[H_2SO_4]{H_2O,\ HgSO_4} R-\underset{\underset{\displaystyle O}{\|}}{C}-CH_2-R' + R-CH_2-\underset{\underset{\displaystyle O}{\|}}{C}-R'$ 15.6

84. $R-C\equiv C-H \xrightarrow{2\ HX} R-CX_2CH_3$ 15.6

$X = I > Br > Cl > F$

85. $R-C\equiv C-R' \xrightarrow{2\ HX} R-CX_2CH_2-R' + R-CH_2CX_2-R'$ 15.6

$X = I > Br > Cl > F$

86. $R-C\equiv C-H \xrightarrow[2.\ NaOH,\ H_2O_2]{1.\ BH_3} R-CH_2CH_2OH$ 15.6

87. $R-C\equiv C-H \xrightarrow[2.\ NaOH,\ H_2O_2]{1.\ (Sia)_2BH} R-CH_2CHO$ 15.6

sia = 1,2-dimethylpropyl (disiamyl)

88. $R-C\equiv C-R' \xrightarrow[2.\ CH_3COOH]{1.\ BH_3}$ (R)(H)C=C(R')(H) [R and R′ cis; H and H cis] 15.6

89. $R-C\equiv C-R' \xrightarrow{H_2,\ catalyst} RCH_2CH_2R'$ 15.6

catalyst = PtO_2, Pd/C, Ni

90. $R-C\equiv C-R' \xrightarrow{H_2,\ catalyst}$ (R)(H)C=C(R')(H) [R and R′ cis; H and H cis] 15.6

catalyst = $Pd/BaSO_4$, Lindlar's

91. $R-C\equiv C-R' \xrightarrow[liq\ NH_3]{M}$ (R)(H)C=C(H)(R') [R and R′ trans] 15.6

M = Li, Na, K

92. $R-C\equiv C-R' \xrightarrow[2.\ H_2O_2]{1.\ O_3} RCOOH + R'COOH$ 15.8

93. $R-\overset{\overset{\displaystyle O}{\|}}{C}-R' \xrightarrow{PCl_3} R-CCl_2-R'$ 15.4

94. $R-\overset{\overset{\displaystyle O}{\|}}{C}-R' \xrightarrow{Mg(Hg)} R-\underset{\underset{\displaystyle OH}{|}}{\overset{\overset{\displaystyle R'}{|}}{C}}-\underset{\underset{\displaystyle OH}{|}}{\overset{\overset{\displaystyle R'}{|}}{C}}-R$ 15.5

Additional Problems

15.30 Draw structures and provide names for all isomers of formula C_5H_8 that do not contain rings. Classify the compounds as isolated dienes, conjugated dienes, allenes, terminal alkynes, or internal alkynes.

15.31 Show structures for each of the following:

a. (*E*)-3-isopropylhex-2-en-4-yne
b. the carbocation formed by the addition of 1 mole of HBr to 1,4-pentadiene
c. the cationic intermediate formed upon adding 1 mole of HBr to *cis,cis*-2,4-hexadiene
d. the major product obtained by adding 1 mole of Br_2 to *trans*-1,3-hexadiene at relatively high temperature
e. two isomeric products of formula $C_5H_6Br_2$ obtained by adding 1 mole of Br_2 to cyclopentadiene
f. the product of reaction of 3-hexyne with one equivalent of HI
g. the product of reaction of 3-hexyne with Na/liq NH_3
h. the product of reaction of 4-methyl-2-pentyne with ozone followed by water workup
i. an alkyne of formula C_4H_6 that gives a precipitate upon treatment with silver nitrate in aqueous ammonia solution
j. a geminal dichloride of formula $C_7H_{14}Cl_2$ that cannot form an alkyne upon double dehydrohalogenation
k. an aldehyde of formula $C_5H_{10}O$ that cannot exist in a tautomeric enol form
l. a substance of formula $C_4H_6Br_2$ obtained by heating 3,4-dibromo-1-butene at 200 °C
m. the product of a Diels-Alder reaction that occurs when 1,3-butadiene and ethylene are heated together at 200 °C
n. the product of a Diels-Alder reaction between cyclopentadiene and 2,3-dimethyl-2-butene
o. the product obtained by treating 1 mole of cyclohexylacetylene with 2 moles of HBr
p. an alkyne of formula C_8H_{14} that yields a single ketone when treated with water, mercuric sulfate, and sulfuric acid
q. a substance that will react with $H_2C{=}CH{-}CH\ddot{O}$ in a Diels-Alder reaction to yield the product shown below

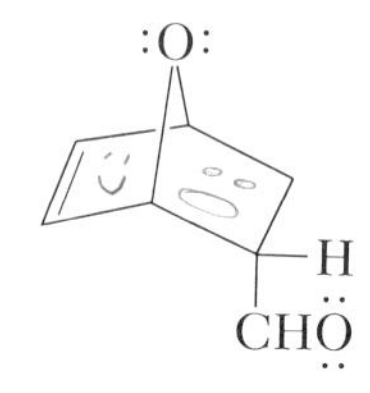

r. the product obtained upon treating the substance shown below with hydrogen in the presence of a PtO_2 catalyst

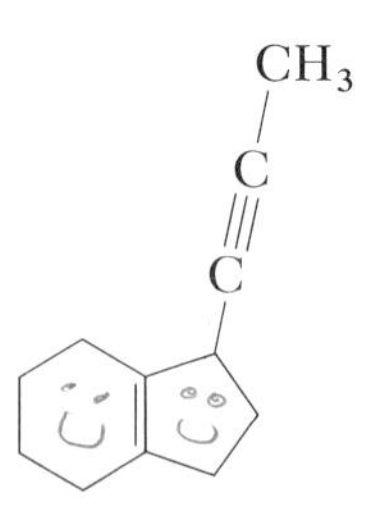

s. the product obtained upon treating the substance shown in part *r* with hydrogen in the presence of a $Pd/BaSO_4$ catalyst
t. the isomeric products of formula C_6H_9Br obtained upon treating 1-methylcyclopentene with *N*-bromosuccinimide in CCl_4 in the presence of peroxides and light

15.32 Consider competing reactions of compound *C* to yield products *A* and *B*. A reaction progress diagram for these competing reactions is shown below. One product dominates at low temperature, and the other dominates at high temperature. Explain this result, telling which product is favored under each of the reaction conditions.

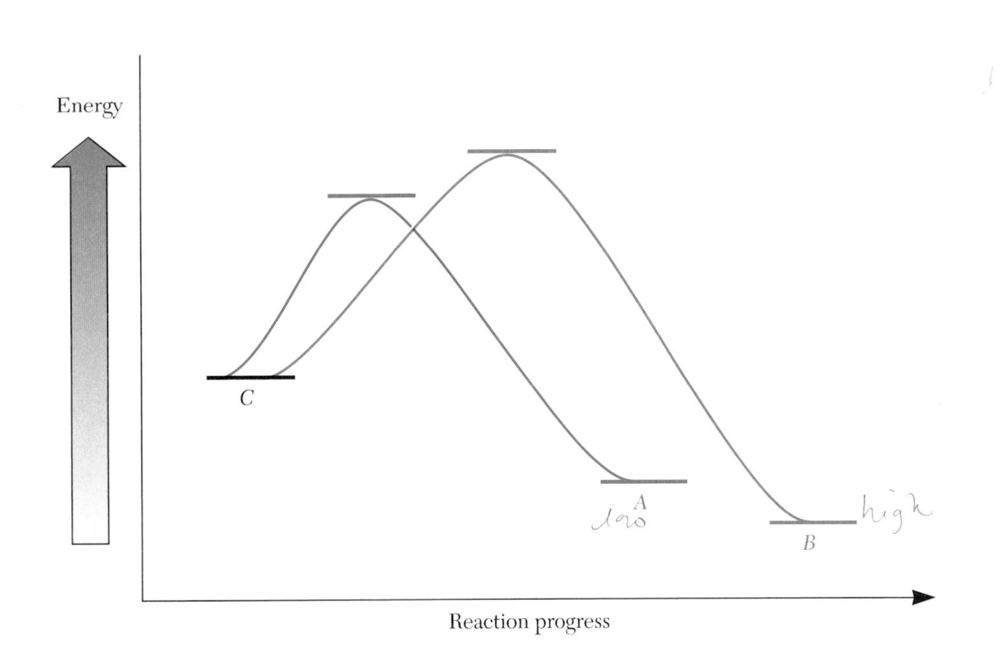

15.33 There are three isomers corresponding to the name 2,4-hexadiene. Name these isomers using the *E*/*Z* notation system. Which of these isomers is expected to be the most reactive and which the least reactive when subjected to Diels-Alder reaction with an appropriate dienophile? Explain your answer.

15.34 Draw resonance structures to help explain why:

a. the carbon-chlorine bond of vinyl chloride ($H_2C{=}CHCl$) is shorter than the carbon-chlorine bond of chloroethane

b. protonation of dihydropyran (shown below) occurs exclusively at C_3

3
2
Ö
1

15.35 Each of the following substances can be prepared in a single step using a suitable diene. Give the reagents and reaction conditions for each of these preparations.

a. 2-bromo-4-methyl-3-hexene

b.

:O:
‖
C—$\ddot{O}CH_2CH_3$

15.36 Each of the following compounds can be prepared from an appropriate alkyne precursor. Show how each can be prepared.

a. 2-pentanone b. $CH_3CH_2CH_2CH_2CH\ddot{\underset{..}{O}}$ c. $CH_3CH_2C{\equiv}CMg\ddot{\underset{..}{Br}}{:}$

15.37 Give the products for each of the following reactions:

a. 3,4-dimethyl-1-pentene treated with *N*-bromosuccinimide followed by heating with ethanolic KOH
b. 1-buten-3-yne treated with silver nitrate in aqueous ammonia
c. propyne treated with two equivalent amounts of HCl
d. 2-methyl-1,3-cyclohexadiene heated with HCl
e. 2,3-dimethyl-1,3-cyclohexadiene treated with bromine at low temperature
f. 1,3-butadiene heated with acrylonitrile ($H_2C{=}CH{-}C{\equiv}N$)
g. cyclopentadiene heated with acrolein ($H_2C{=}CH{-}CHO$)
h. 2-methyl-1,3-butadiene heated with 2-methylacrolein
i. cyclopentadiene heated with cyclopropene
j. cyclononyne treated with aqueous mercuric sulfate and sulfuric acid
k. 1-penten-4-yne treated with hydrogen over Lindlar's catalyst
l. 2,2-dimethyl-3-pentanone treated with PCl_3 followed by reaction with excess $NaNH_2$

15.38 Give the appropriate reagents for each of the following synthetic conversions:

a. 1,3-pentadiene to 1,4-dibromopentane
b. acetylene to *cis*-2-butene
c. acetylene to 3-hexyne
d. 1-butyne to 3-hexanone
e. cyclohexane to 1,3-cyclohexadiene
f. 1-bromopropane to 2-hexyne
g. propyne to pentane
h. propanol to propyne
i. 2-butyne to *meso*-2,3-butanediol
j. cyclohexyl methyl ketone to 2-cyclohexyl-1-bromoethane
k. ethanol to 1-bromobutane (using only inorganic reagents)
l. *cis*-3-hexene to *trans*-3-hexene
m. 3-hexyne to each of the deuterated alkenes shown below

$$\underset{D}{\overset{CH_3CH_2}{}}\!\!>C{=}C<\!\!\underset{D}{\overset{CH_2CH_3}{}} \qquad \underset{D}{\overset{CH_3CH_2}{}}\!\!>C{=}C<\!\!\underset{CH_2CH_3}{\overset{D}{}}$$

n. 1-butyne to *trans*-1-methyl-2-ethylcyclopropane
o. calcium carbide to propyne
p. 1-butyne to butanal ($CH_3CH_2CH_2CH\ddot{\underset{..}{O}}$)

15.39 Show a series of reactions that will result in the synthesis of muscalure (*cis*-9-tricosane), the sex attractant of the housefly, starting with acetylene and any alcohols of your choice. The structure of muscalure is given in Chapter 9.

15.40 The mentor of two graduate students, Oscar and Felix, is interested in studying certain brominated dienes. He instructs Oscar to prepare 3-bromo-1,4-pentadiene, and Felix to prepare 5-bromo-1,3-pentadiene. Oscar decides to treat 1,4-pentadien-3-ol with sodium bromide and sulfuric acid. He obtains a product that his mentor, after hearing of the procedure and looking at some structural elucidation data, hands over to *Felix*, sending Oscar back to the library and laboratory. How did Oscar manage to prepare Felix's compound? Give a mechanism for its formation.

15.41 Suggest structures for compounds *C* and *D* that are consistent with the reaction scheme shown below.

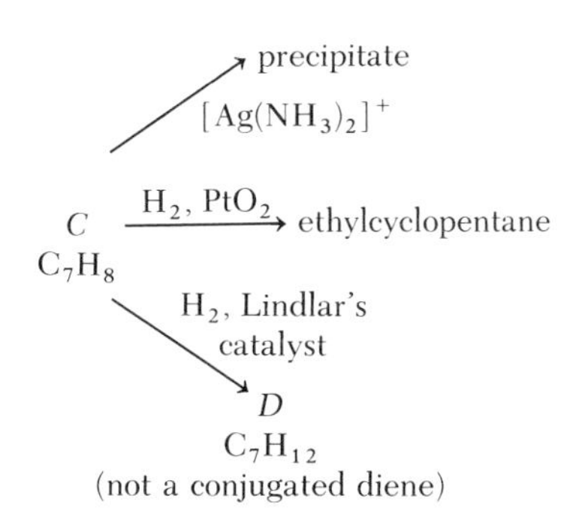

15.42 Conjugated trienes may undergo 1,2-, 1,4-, or 1,6-addition reactions. Deduce the structure of the product obtained upon 1,6-addition of bromine to 1,3,5-hexatriene.

15.43 Substance *E*, of formula C_5H_8O, can be prepared by the reaction of sodium acetylide with acetone, followed by workup with aqueous acid. Compound *E* is reduced by hydrogen in the presence of Lindlar's catalyst to *F*, which on treatment with sulfuric acid yields *G*, of formula C_5H_8. Compound *G*, when ozonized followed by treatment with zinc and water, yields a mixture of the two compounds shown below. Give structures for compounds *E*–*G*.

$$H_2C{=}\ddot{O} \qquad H_3C{-}\overset{\overset{:O:}{\|}}{C}{-}CH\ddot{O}$$

15.44 Substance *H*, of formula $C_{10}H_{19}Br$, gives a mixture of two isomers, *I* and *J*, of formula $C_{10}H_{18}$, on treatment with base. If the base used is KOH in ethanol, the main product is *I*. However, if the base used is potassium *tert*-butoxide in *tert*-butyl alcohol, the main product is *J*. Both *I* and *J* are converted to *K*, of formula $C_{10}H_{22}$, on treatment with an excess of hydrogen in the presence of a catalyst. Compound *I*, on treatment with hot, aqueous permanganate solution followed by acidification, yields a mixture of two compounds, *L* and *M*, whose structures are shown below. The ratio of *L*:*M* produced in this reaction is 2 : 1. Given this information, answer each of the following questions.

a. Suggest structures for the compounds *H*–*K*.

b. What products are expected upon ozonolysis of *J* followed by workup with zinc and water?

c. Compound *M* is formed as the sole product of the reaction of a different alkene, *N*, of formula C_4H_6, with hot, aqueous permanganate solution. Suggest a structure for *N*.

d. Compound *L* is the sole *organic* product obtained by treating yet another alkene, *O*, of formula C_4H_8, with hot, aqueous permanganate solution followed by an acidic workup. Suggest a structure for *O*. Notice that *L* contains three carbon atoms while *O* contains four carbon atoms. What happened to the fourth carbon atom during the permanganate treatment?

$$\underset{L}{H_3C{-}\overset{\overset{:O:}{\|}}{C}{-}CH_3} \qquad \underset{M}{HOOC{-}CH_2CH_2{-}COOH}$$

15.45 When compound *P* is heated with *N*-bromosuccinimide in the presence of peroxide, a product *Q*, of formula C_5H_5BrO, is obtained. When *Q* is treated with a base, compound *R* is isolated. The structures of *P* and *R* are shown below. Give a structure for *Q* and a mechanism for the formation of *R*.

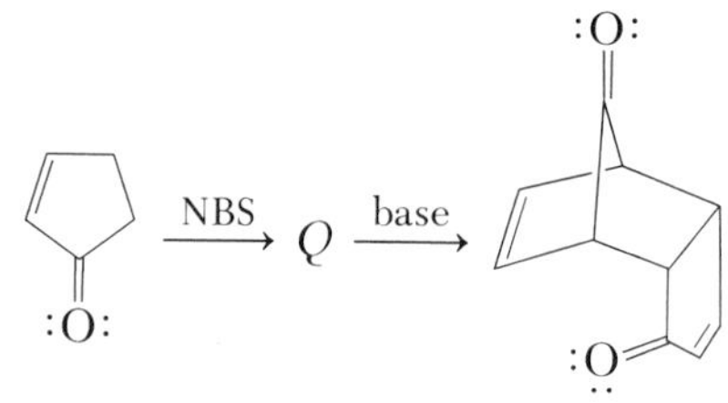

$$P \xrightarrow{\text{NBS}} Q \xrightarrow{\text{base}} R$$

P *R*

15.46 An intramolecular Diels-Alder reaction can occur when molecules containing both a conjugated diene unit and a dienophile unit are heated. Predict the products obtained by means of intramolecular Diels-Alder reaction when each of the following compounds is heated.

a. $H_2C{=}CH{-}CH{=}CH{-}CH_2CH_2CH_2{-}C({=}O){-}CH{=}CH_2$

b. $H_2C{=}CH{-}CH{=}CH{-}CH_2CH_2CH_2{-}CH{=}CH{-}C({=}O){-}OCH_3$

15.47 Once a Diels-Alder reaction has been performed, it is sometimes possible to perform a retro-Diels-Alder reaction on the product to yield not the original diene and dienophile but a new pair of compounds. This procedure can be quite useful for synthetic purposes. For the reactions shown below, give the structure of the Diels-Alder products, *S* and *T*, and the products of retro-Diels-Alder reactions, *U* and *V*.

a. 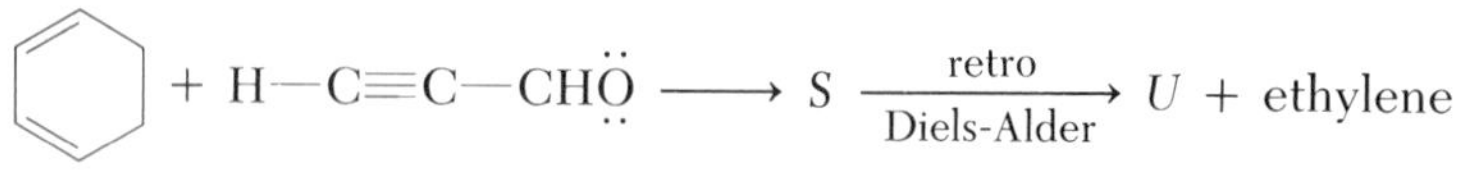 (1,3-cyclohexadiene) $+ H{-}C{\equiv}C{-}CHO \longrightarrow S \xrightarrow[\text{Diels-Alder}]{\text{retro}} U + \text{ethylene}$

b. 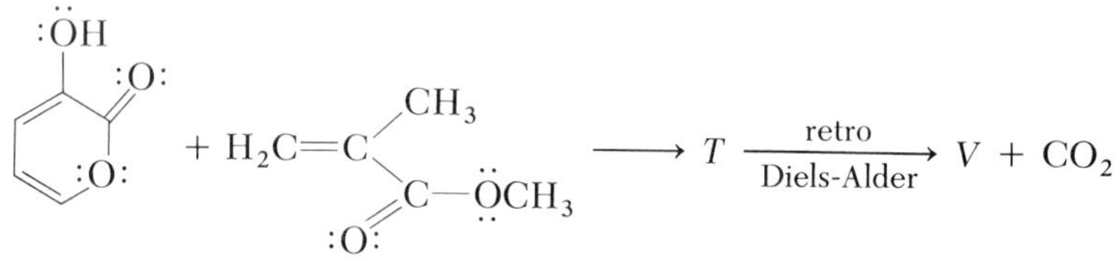 (2-pyranone with OH) $+ H_2C{=}C(CH_3){-}C({=}O){-}OCH_3 \longrightarrow T \xrightarrow[\text{Diels-Alder}]{\text{retro}} V + CO_2$

Molecular Orbital Concepts in Organic Chemistry: Conjugated π Systems and Aromaticity

16.1 Introduction

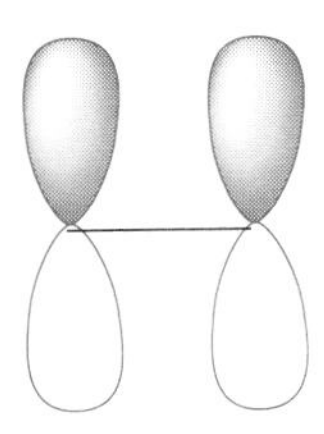

We have now surveyed the structure, synthesis, and reactions of several families of organic compounds. We have frequently used the valence bond theory to rationalize or even to predict various aspects of bonding and chemical behavior. Our explanations have depended largely on the use of simple Lewis structures, resonance-contributing forms, and the hybridization model.

Nevertheless, these methods have their limitations. Sometimes we have found it advantageous to turn to the molecular orbital methods to provide us with an alternative model of bonding. We have seen that molecular orbital theory provides rationalizations and makes predictions that sometimes complement, sometimes add to, and occasionally contradict conclusions made on the basis of the valence bond model. In this chapter we apply the molecular orbital model to conjugated π systems.

16.2 The π Molecular Orbitals of Alkenes

ETHYLENE

We briefly introduced the application of the molecular orbital method to the π system of alkenes in earlier chapters. We begin here by reviewing some fundamental points. Consider ethylene, the simplest alkene. It is convenient and usual to view the carbon-carbon double bond as being composed of a σ bond and a π bond. (Alternative models have been proposed, but they will not be considered here.) The π bond can be considered as arising from a sideways overlap of two p orbitals, as shown in Figure 16.1.

The molecular orbital model of π bonding in ethylene begins with the same pair of parallel carbon p orbitals and considers these orbitals as interacting to produce two new π molecular orbitals. In analyzing their interactions, we need to consider the phases of the lobes, which relate to the signs (+ or −) of the corresponding wave function. Throughout our discussion we will use shaded or open lobes to denote phase (thus avoiding any possible confusion of wave function sign with electronic charge). Two possible types of interaction give rise to the two π molecular orbitals. The two interactions can be described as additive (in phase) and subtractive (out of phase). The additive mode produces a bonding π orbital, and the subtractive mode, a π antibonding orbital, as shown schematically in Figure 16.2.

Since there are only two π electrons in ethylene, both occupy the more stable bonding molecular orbital (the aufbau principle). The π^* molecular orbital is occupied only if the ethylene molecule is excited or if another electron is added to it from an external source to produce a radical anion. The ground state of the ethylene π molecular orbital system is shown in Figure 16.3.

The actual shapes of π molecular orbitals can be represented in a number of different (but ultimately equivalent) ways. Examples are shown in Figure

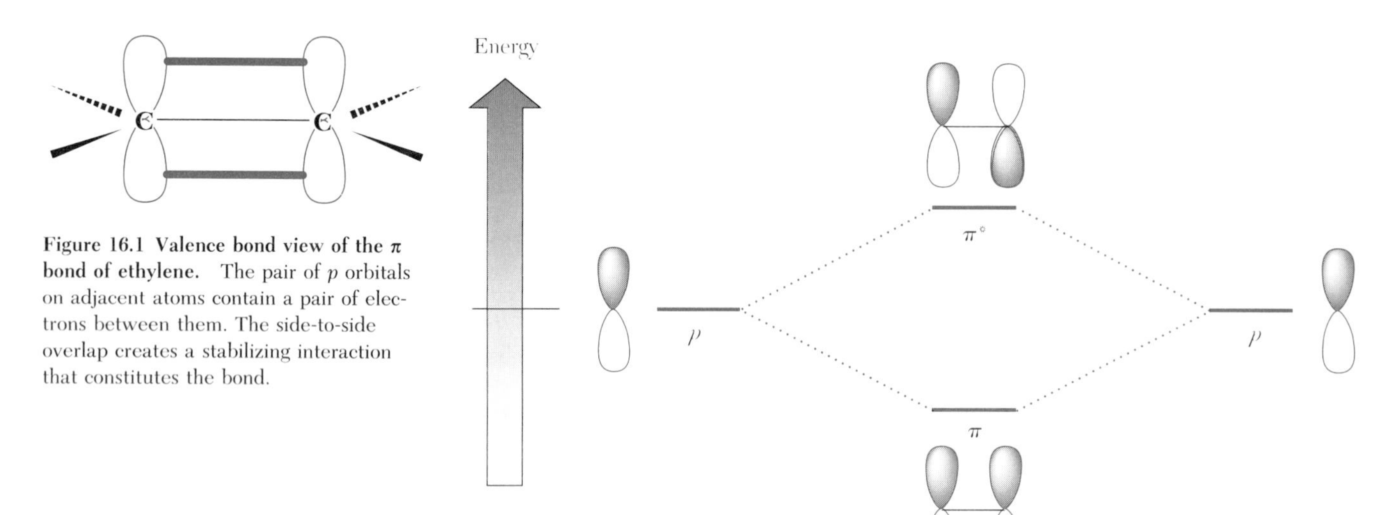

Figure 16.1 Valence bond view of the π bond of ethylene. The pair of p orbitals on adjacent atoms contain a pair of electrons between them. The side-to-side overlap creates a stabilizing interaction that constitutes the bond.

Figure 16.2 Energy diagram for the generation of molecular orbitals from two adjacent and parallel p orbitals. Mixing the wave functions of the atomic orbitals results (via an in-phase overlap) in one molecular orbital that is lower in energy than the starting atomic orbitals. This orbital is a π (bonding) molecular orbital. The other molecular orbital generated in this process (via an out-of-phase overlap) is higher in energy than the starting atomic orbitals. This orbital is the π* (antibonding) molecular orbital. The different phases of the orbital lobes are indicated by shading.

16.4. Some conventions stress the relationship of the molecular orbitals to waves. Others stress the way the initial p orbitals are combined to form the π molecular orbitals, that is, in-phase or out-of-phase. Still others try to show *stylistically* what the final molecular orbital looks like. All three types of representations are shown in Figure 16.4. It is also possible to produce a graphical representation of what a molecular orbital looks like based on a quantitative computerized solution to the appropriate wave equation: these representations are usually more complex than is necessary for the types of considerations we shall be making.

Consider the π bonding molecular orbital of ethylene. An electron in this orbital is delocalized over a region of space above and below the plane occupied by the molecule. The wave function describing this orbital has the same phase at all points above the plane and the same phase at all points below the plane. The plane of the molecule is therefore a **nodal plane.** A nodal plane is a plane in which the wave function is zero, and thus it is devoid of electron probability density. Electrons in this orbital are concentrated between the nuclei but they lie above and below the nodal plane. No π electron density is present along the internuclear axis.

The wave function describing the π* (antibonding orbital) is of a different type. It has a *second* nodal plane that is located midway between the bonded atoms and is perpendicular to the plane containing the two carbon and four hydrogen nuclei (see Figure 16.5). In the π antibonding orbital, electron density is not concentrated in the region between the two atoms as it is in the π bonding orbital. In fact, the electron density actually falls to zero at the nodal plane midway between the two carbon atoms, thus diminishing attractive interactions between an electron in the orbital and the two positively charged

Figure 16.3 The π electrons in the ground state ethylene molecule. According to the molecular orbital model, π bonding is represented by the electron pair in the π (bonding) orbital. The total π bond energy is $2\Delta E$. The transfer of each electron from an atomic p orbital to the π orbital releases ΔE of energy.

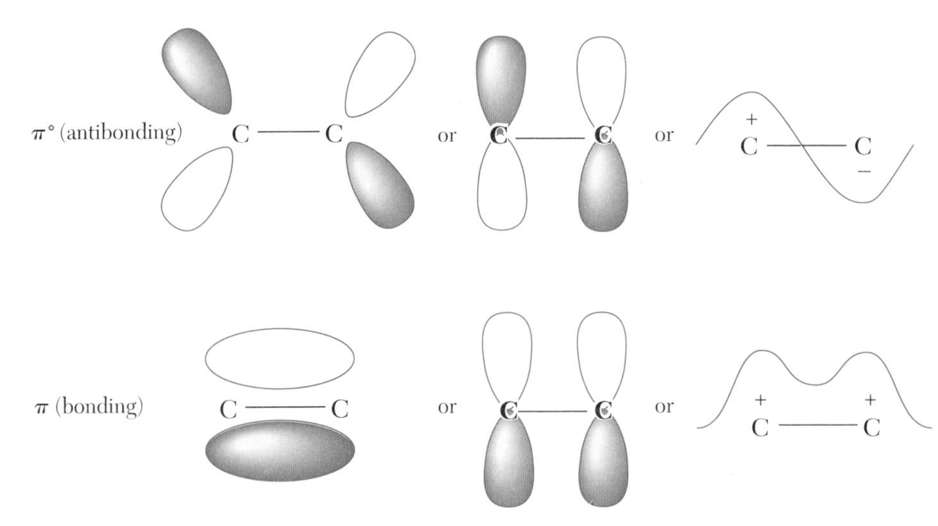

Figure 16.4 Methods used to represent the shapes of the π and π* molecular orbitals of ethylene. The drawings on the left represent the approximate orbital shapes as calculated from wave functions. The center drawings are simplified representations of the atomic *p* orbital shapes that make up each of the molecular orbitals. Both kinds of representations are commonly used and can be regarded as equivalent methods of depicting molecular orbitals. The drawings on the right indicate the variation of the sign of the wave function, Ψ, along the carbon-carbon linkage. The electron probability densities correlate with the *square* of the wave function values.

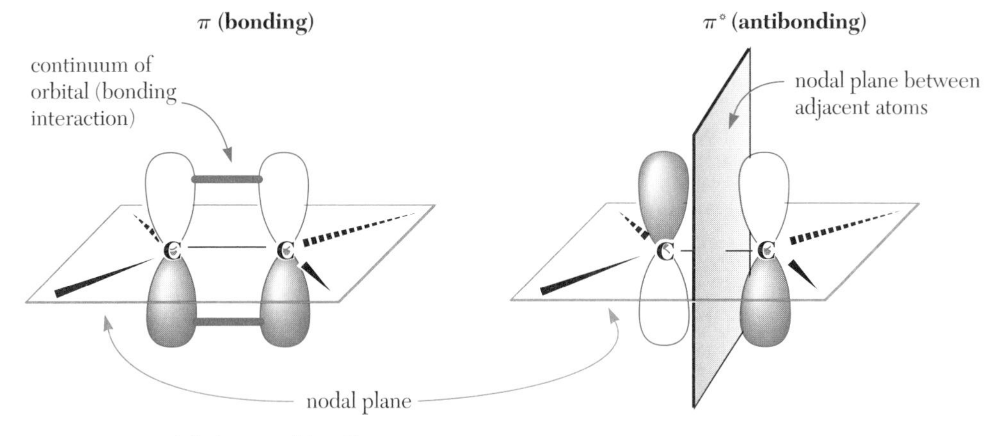

Figure 16.5 Nodal planes and bonding interactions of the ethylene π and π* orbitals.

nuclei. Such interactions are at a maximum when the electron density is concentrated between the nuclei (as it is in a bonding orbital), since this arrangement allows nuclei of both atoms in the bond to exert an attractive influence. In contrast, when an electron is in an antibonding orbital, repulsive interactions (electron-electron and nucleus-nucleus) dominate attractive interactions, so that any electron occupying the antibonding orbital actually results in weakened bonding.

OTHER SIMPLE ALKENES

All simple alkenes have π and π* molecular orbitals that are qualitatively similar to those of ethylene. However there are some quantitative differences. For example, as we mentioned in Chapter 9, alkyl groups raise the energy of the HOMO—the π bonding orbital. A comparison of the ionization energies of propene (224 kcal/mol) and ethylene (242 kcal/mol) illustrates this point. Less energy is needed to remove an electron from the (higher-energy) HOMO of propene than from the (lower-energy) HOMO of ethylene. This difference is reflected in the relative reactivities of the two compounds. For example, when alkenes react with electrophiles, the initial step is the donation of electron density from the alkene π bond to the electrophile. Not surprisingly, the reactivities of alkenes in these reactions usually correlate with their HOMO energies. The higher the alkene HOMO, the easier it is for electrons in the orbital to form a bond to the electrophile.

16.3 Conjugated Dienes

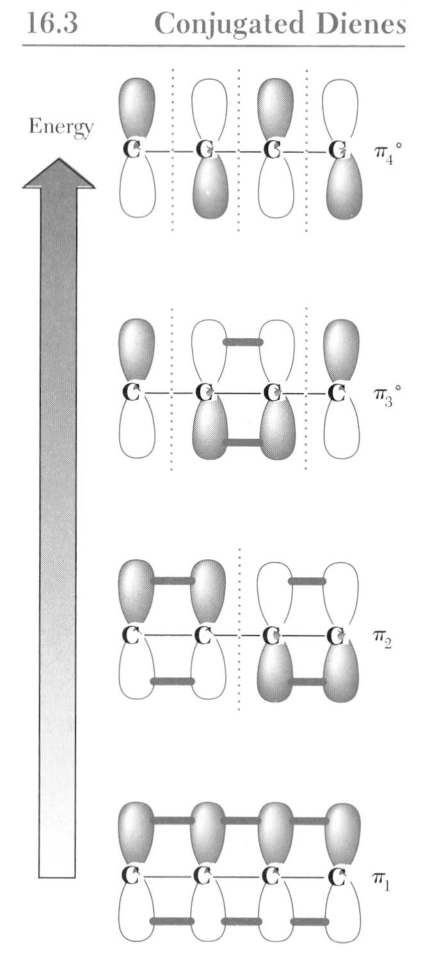

Figure 16.6 The π molecular orbitals of butadiene Vertical nodes (nodal planes) are indicated by the vertical dotted lines. Bonding interactions occur when adjacent lobes are in phase and are indicated by the wide solid lines connecting adjacent lobes. The most stable orbital, labeled π_1, contains no vertical nodes and encompasses three bonding interactions. Antibonding interactions occur when adjacent lobes are out of phase. Thus, orbital π_2 encompasses two bonding interactions and one antibonding interaction. Overall, orbital π_2 is considered a net bonding orbital because bonding interactions outweigh antibonding interactions. On the other hand, orbitals π_3 and π_4 are net antibonding orbitals.

1,3-BUTADIENE

Simple Guidelines for Generating Molecular Orbitals When we considered ethylene and simple alkenes, we had only two p orbitals to use in generating π molecular orbitals. In order to understand the π-electron systems of conjugated dienes and other more complex species on a molecular orbital level, we need to mix a greater number of atomic p orbitals. 1,3-Butadiene illustrates the basic approach that is used for these more complex systems.

The π molecular orbitals of 1,3-butadiene are constructed from *four* parent atomic p orbitals, one from each of the four carbon atoms of the molecule. It is possible to perform detailed wave mechanical calculations to determine the shapes and energies of the molecular orbitals generated from these atomic orbitals. However, organic chemists often use simplified guidelines that rapidly provide a satisfactory pictorial view of the molecular orbitals and their energies. We can summarize these guidelines as follows:

- Interaction of n parallel p orbitals always produces n π molecular orbitals.
- Like p orbitals, each π molecular orbital has a top and a bottom separated by a nodal plane that contains the nuclei. We refer to this plane as the nuclear nodal plane.
- For linear open-chain molecules, the π molecular orbitals *also* contain 0, 1, 2, 3, . . . , (up to $n - 1$) nodal planes along the chain; these nodal planes are at right angles to the nuclear nodal plane, and we will call them *vertical* **nodes.**
- The energies of the orbitals increase with increasing number of vertical nodes. The lowest-energy molecular orbital has no vertical nodes. The highest-energy molecular orbital has $(n - 1)$ vertical nodes.
- Bonding π orbitals have energies that are lower than the energy of an isolated p orbital. Antibonding π^* orbitals have energies that are higher than the energy of an isolated p orbital.
- All molecular orbitals must be **symmetric** or **antisymmetric** with regard to the **symmetry elements** of the molecule as a whole. (Once we have constructed the molecular orbitals of 1,3-butadiene using the first five guidelines, we will discuss the concept of symmetry elements.)

MOLECULAR ORBITALS OF 1,3-BUTADIENE

Following the guidelines just given, we can construct four π molecular orbitals for 1,3-butadiene. They are shown in Figure 16.6. The relative energies of the molecular orbitals and the isolated atomic p orbitals from which they were generated are shown in Figure 16.7.

You might wonder how the placement of the nodes and bonding interactions within each of the molecular orbitals is determined. For example, why did we *not* write the π_3* molecular orbital as shown in Figure 16.8? To answer this

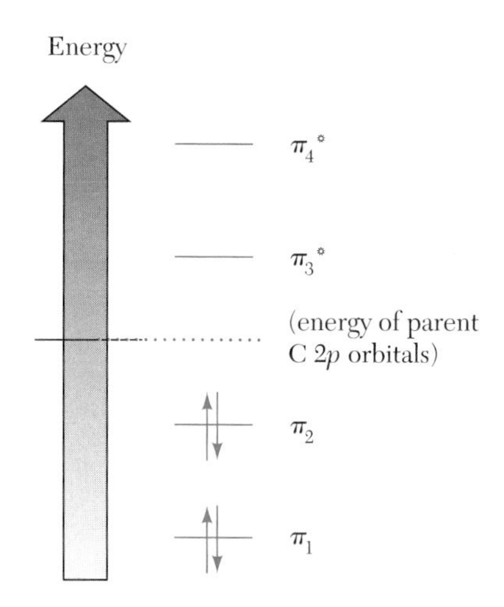

Figure 16.7 Energies of the π molecular orbitals of 1,3-butadiene. Two of the orbitals are bonding and two are antibonding. Bonding orbitals are lower in energy than the p orbitals from which they were generated, while antibonding orbitals are higher in energy. The energy diagram represents the ground state of the 1,3-butadiene molecule—the four π electrons occupy the two π orbitals of lowest energy.

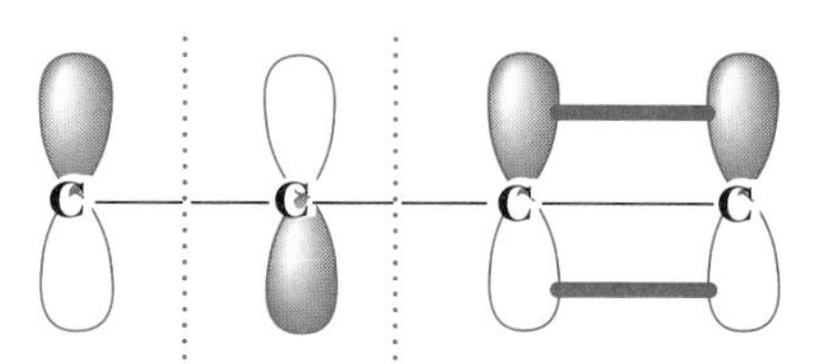

Figure 16.8 *Incorrect* representation of the π_3* of 1,3-butadiene. Although two nodes and one bonding interaction are present, this representation is invalid.

question, we need to consider the last of our guidelines, which relates to symmetry properties.

Symmetry Elements Consider a molecule in which one half is an exact mirror image of the other half. This molecule has a plane of symmetry. The plane of symmetry is a *symmetry element*. For all symmetry elements, some operation related to the element generates a structure that is indistinguishable from the original. In this case, the operation is reflection through the plane. Often it is possible to locate *several* symmetry elements in a molecule. In addition to, or instead of, planes of symmetry, there may be one or more axes of symmetry (rotation of the molecule about an **axis of symmetry** regenerates the original structure). Figure 16.9 depicts two symmetry elements in the *cisoid* conformation of 1,3-butadiene—a plane of symmetry and an axis of symmetry.

Any molecular orbital we derive must have certain symmetry properties; otherwise, it is invalid. To be specific, the orbital must be symmetric or antisymmetric with respect to the symmetry elements of the molecule. If the orbital meets these conditions, it is said to be symmetry correct. To see if an orbital is symmetry correct, we identify the symmetry elements of the molecule and perform the associated symmetry operations on the orbital in question. If a symmetry operation converts the orbital into an identical orbital, the orbital is classified as being symmetric with respect to that particular symmetry element. If the orbital is transformed into one that is like the original in all respects *except* that all the phases are reversed, then the orbital is said to be antisymmetric with respect to that symmetry element.

Consider again the correct π_3* orbital from Figure 16.6 and the incorrect orbital from Figure 16.8. Both are shown again in Figure 16.10, where they will be considered again in relationship to the symmetry elements of the 1,3-butadiene molecule.

Figure 16.9 Two symmetry elements of the 1,3-butadiene molecule in a *cisoid* conformation. We determine the symmetry elements present in a molecule by looking at the location of the atoms and bonds. If we perform a symmetry operation on the molecule (reflection through a plane or rotation about an axis) and end up with the same types of atoms in the same locations, then that operation is a symmetry element of the molecule.

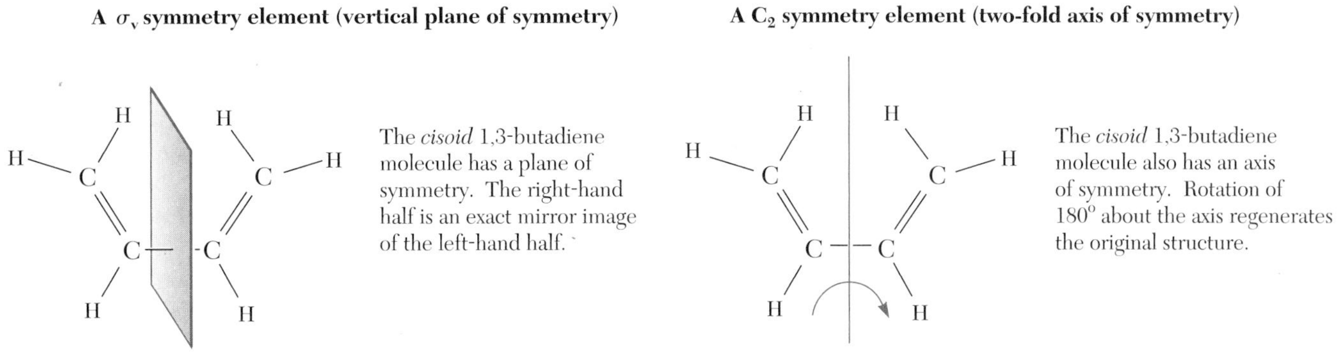

A σ_v symmetry element (vertical plane of symmetry)

The *cisoid* 1,3-butadiene molecule has a plane of symmetry. The right-hand half is an exact mirror image of the left-hand half.

A C_2 symmetry element (two-fold axis of symmetry)

The *cisoid* 1,3-butadiene molecule also has an axis of symmetry. Rotation of 180° about the axis regenerates the original structure.

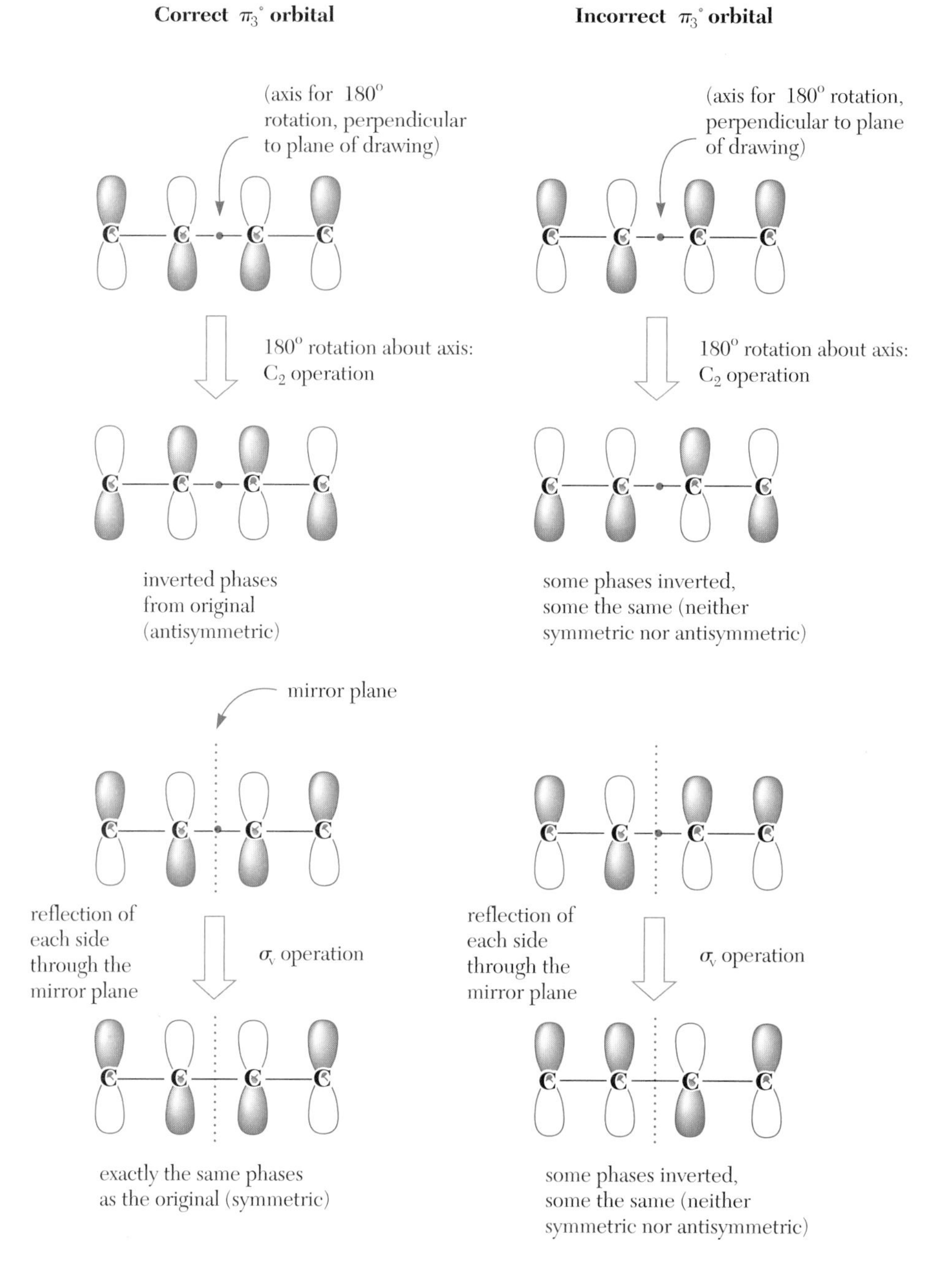

Figure 16.10 Analysis of correct and incorrect π_3* molecular orbitals of 1,3-butadiene with regard to symmetry elements present in the molecule.

With regard to the plane of symmetry, our correct molecular orbital is completely *symmetric*. One half is an exact reflection of the other half. With regard to the axis of symmetry, our correct molecular orbital is *antisymmetric*. That is, after rotation we have an orbital in which *all* of the orbital phases are exactly reversed.

For the incorrect molecular orbital, reflection through the mirror plane of 1,3-butadiene generates an orbital picture in which some of the lobes have the same phase as they had originally while others are reversed in phase. The

SPECIAL TOPIC

Symmetry Correctness of Orbitals

We can rationalize the requirement for correct orbital symmetry by considering the probability of locating an electron at a given position in a molecule. In quantum theory, the *square* of the wave function at a given location gives the probability of finding the electron there. When we take the square of a number, the answer is always positive. Thus, the *square* of a wave function has no phases.

In a symmetric molecule such as 1,3-butadiene, we expect that electrons populate equally those regions of the molecule that are equivalent by symmetry. This requires a symmetry in the square of the wave function. It will be symmetric if the wave function is either symmetric or antisymmetric, but not otherwise.

orbital is thus neither symmetric nor antisymmetric with respect to this element of symmetry. The result is similar when we look at the axis of symmetry. Our incorrect orbital is thus not in accord with our final guideline for constructing molecular orbitals.

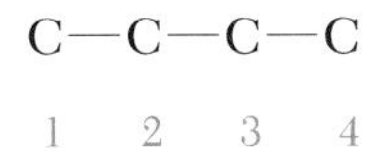

Figure 16.11 Numbering system for carbon atoms in 1,3-butadiene for molecular orbital discussion.

More about Nodes and Energies In the following discussion, we will refer to the orbital representations in Figure 16.6 and the numbering system for the carbon atoms in Figure 16.11.

The four π molecular orbitals of 1,3-butadiene have different numbers of vertical nodes and different energies. The greater the number of nodes, the higher the energy of the orbital. The lowest energy orbital, which has no vertical nodes, is bonding between all pairs of adjacent carbon atoms, that is, between: C1–C2, C2–C3, and C3–C4. If we remove an electron from this orbital, the π bonding between all adjacent pairs of carbon atoms decreases and all of the carbon-carbon bond distances become larger.

In contrast, π_2 is bonding only in the regions C1–C2 and C3–C4. It is *antibonding* in the region C2–C3. An electron in this orbital strengthens the π bonding between C1–C2 and C3–C4, but it actually *weakens* π bonding between C2–C3. If we remove an electron from this orbital, we weaken the C1–C2 and C3–C4 bonding but strengthen the C2–C3 bonding.

The π_2 orbital is the HOMO of the ground state 1,3-butadiene molecule. The remaining π orbitals (π_3* is the LUMO) are unoccupied in the ground state molecule. We will not discuss them in detail at this point. However, they *could* become occupied if excitation energy were applied to the molecule or if an electron were added from an external source.

EXTENDED CONJUGATED π SYSTEMS

It is relatively simple to construct the π molecular orbital pictures for conjugated systems larger than 1,3-butadiene because we use the same guidelines discussed above. Consider the 1,3,5-hexatriene π system.

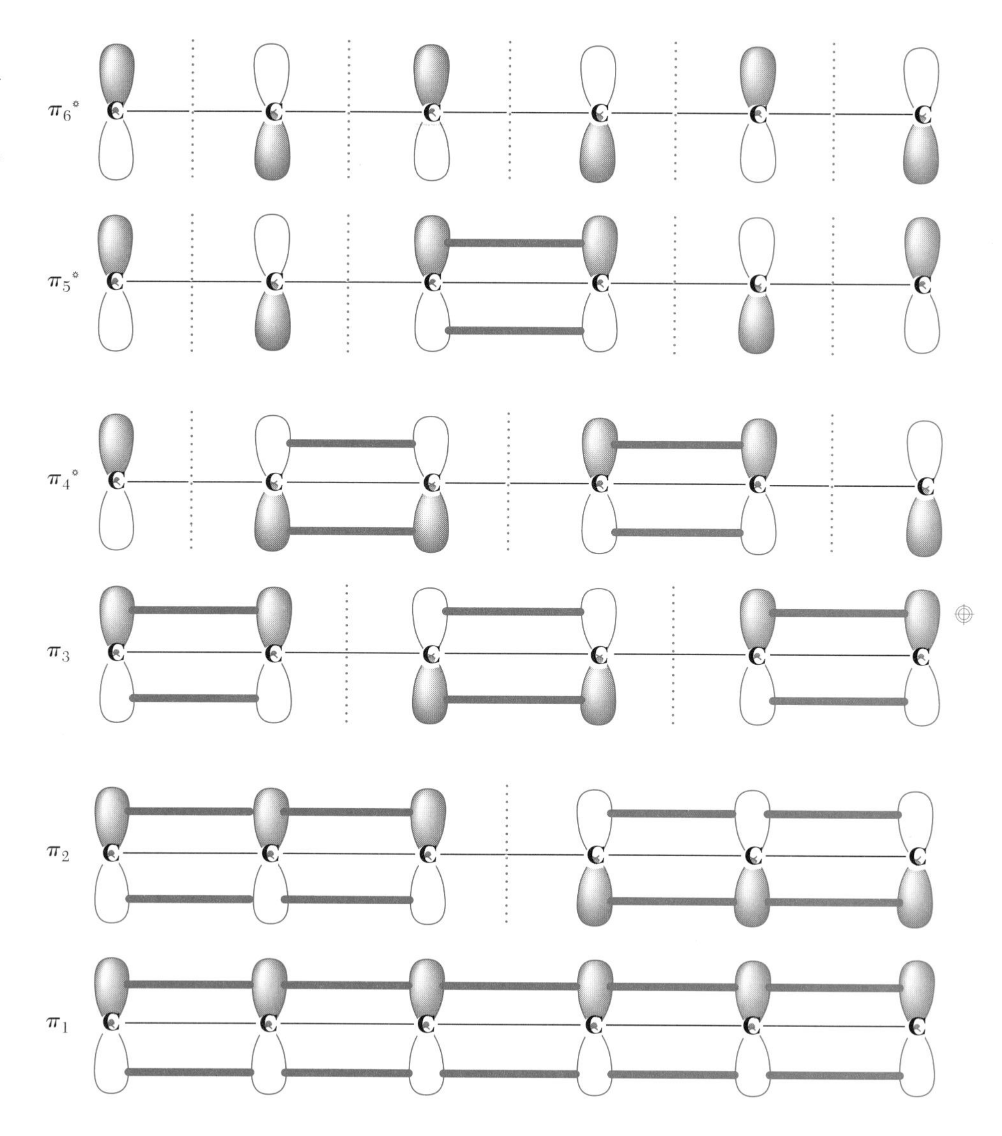

Figure 16.12 The six π molecular orbitals of the 1,3,5-hexatriene molecule The orbitals increase in energy from π_1 through π_6*. Nodes are indicated by the vertical dotted lines, and bonding interactions are indicated by the broad horizontal lines connecting the interacting orbitals.

Because we start with six atomic *p* orbitals, we generate six π molecular orbitals. Of these molecular orbitals, the one with the lowest energy has no vertical nodes, and the one with the highest energy has five vertical nodes. Placing the nodes symmetrically along the chain of carbon atoms (to assure correct symmetry), we generate the six orbitals shown in Figure 16.12.

PROBLEM 16.1 Draw an energy diagram for the π molecular orbital system of 1,3,5-hexatriene, showing the ground state electronic configuration. Your drawing should be similar to Figure 16.7. However, it should show which π orbitals of 1,3,5-hexatriene are actually occupied in the ground state.

PROBLEM 16.2 Draw the orbitals that constitute the HOMO and the LUMO of ground state 1,3,5-hexatriene.

PROBLEM 16.3 Draw the π molecular orbitals for the 1,3,5,7-octatetraene molecule. Indicate all nodes and bonding interactions in each orbital.

PROBLEM 16.4 Construct the π molecular orbital energy diagram for the ground state of the 1,3,5,7-octatetraene molecule. Indicate the HOMO and the LUMO.

16.4 Conjugated Ions and Radicals

We will now consider the delocalization of π electrons in radicals and ions. Allylic systems provide especially simple examples. The **allyl cation,** $H_2C{=}CH{-}CH_2^+$, was introduced earlier (Chapter 12) in the discussion of the relatively high reactivity of allylic halides to S_N1 reaction. We can correlate the facility of this reaction with the special stability of an allylic cation. In this type of reaction, the more stable the carbocation, the faster it forms. According to the valence bond model, the special stability of an allylic cation can be associated with the existence of two resonance structures, as shown in Figure 16.13. Like allylic cations, **allyl radicals** ($H_2C{=}CH{-}\dot{C}H_2$) and anions ($H_2C{=}CH{-}\ddot{C}H_2^-$) also have special stabilities.

PROBLEM 16.5 Draw and show the resonance structures of

a. the most stable cation that can form through the loss of a bromide ion from 2,3-dibromo-1-butene

b. the most stable radical that can form by abstraction of a hydrogen atom from 1-butene

The molecular orbital model gives useful insights into the structure and stability of allylic radicals and ions. In each case, we construct the π orbitals from carbon $2p$ orbitals, one at each of the three carbon atoms. Following the guidelines given in Section 16.3, there are three π molecular orbitals, which are shown in Figure 16.14. These three π molecular orbitals are common to the anion, the radical, and the cation.

Of the three orbitals, π_1 is a bonding orbital, π_2 is a **nonbonding orbital** (no bonding or antibonding interactions between adjacent lobes), and π_3 is an antibonding orbital. To determine which of these orbitals are occupied in the

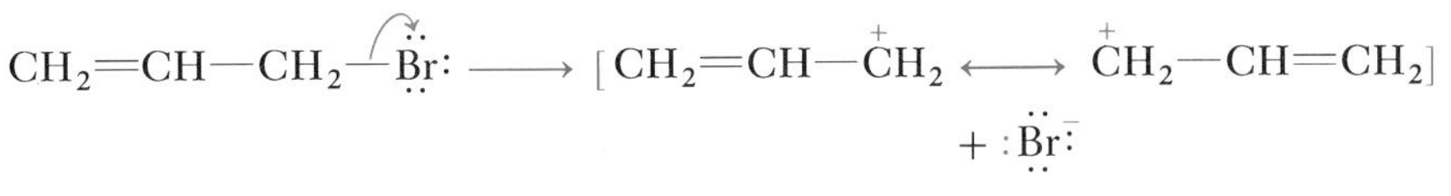

$$CH_2{=}CH{-}CH_2{-}\ddot{B}r{:} \longrightarrow [CH_2{=}CH{-}\overset{+}{C}H_2 \longleftrightarrow \overset{+}{C}H_2{-}CH{=}CH_2] + {:}\ddot{B}r{:}^-$$

resonance-contributing forms for the allyl cation

Figure 16.13 Formation and stabilization of the allyl cation. Although the allyl cation may appear to be a primary carbocation, it is actually highly stabilized. The positive charge is not localized on one carbon but is delocalized partially to a site two carbon atoms away. Delocalization provides stabilization for the charge and thus for the carbocation.

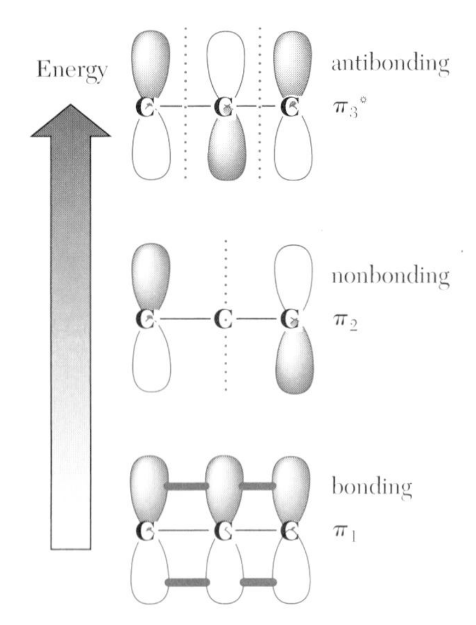

Figure 16.14 The molecular orbitals of an allylic cation, radical, or anion.

$H_2C{=}CH{-}\dot{C}H_2$; $H_2C{=}CH{-}\ddot{C}H_2^-$

three π electrons four π electrons

Figure 16.15 Counting the number of π electrons in the allylic radical and anion.

cation, radical, and anion, we must count π electrons. There are two for the allyl cation, three for the radical, and four for the anion; these π electrons include not just two π electrons from the double bond but also any other electrons that can enter the delocalized π system. Thus, there is one extra electron for the radical and the two extra for the anion, as shown in Figure 16.15.

The distributions of the π electrons for the allylic cation, radical, and anion are shown in Figure 16.16.

Knowing the nodal characteristics of the nonbonding molecular orbital (Figure 16.14), we can predict the location of the positive charge for the allyl cation, the unpaired electron for the allyl radical and the electron pair responsible for the negative charge of the anion. First, consider the cation. To neutralize its positive charge and generate the allyl radical, we need to add an electron, which must enter the orbital π_2. However, since π_2 has a node at the central carbon atom, the added electron cannot contribute to charge density at that position: it can only increase the charge density at the terminal carbon atoms. If follows that the positive charge of the allyl cation (which is neutralized by the added electron in the allyl radical) is located *only* at the terminal carbon atoms, as shown in Figure 16.17. This prediction agrees completely with the one we would make from valence bond considerations and resonance structures. Experimentally, we find that nucleophiles attack allylic cations only at the terminal positions. Our experimental findings thus show that both models have useful predictive capabilities.

Again, we find experimentally that the allyl radical has radical character only at the terminal carbon atoms. Using the molecular orbital model, we say that the unpaired electron of the allyl radical is located in the π_2 molecular orbital. Moreover, we can demonstrate the same conclusion with the valence bond resonance considerations, as illustrated in Figure 16.18.

Figure 16.16 The π electronic configurations for the allyl cation, allyl radical, and allyl anion. The abbreviation SOMO refers to *singly occupied molecular orbital*. We use this term rather than HOMO when the highest occupied orbital contains a single electron.

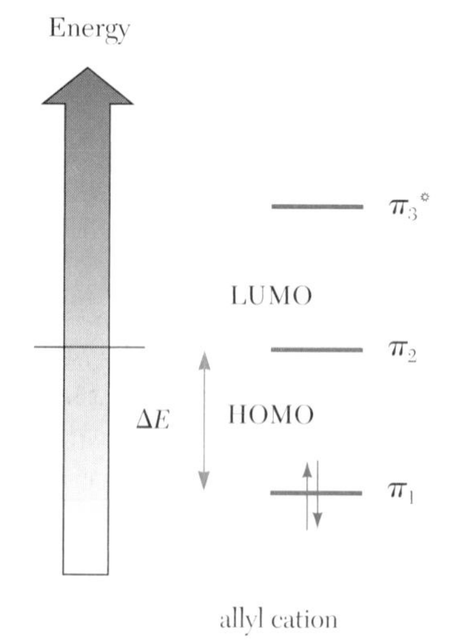

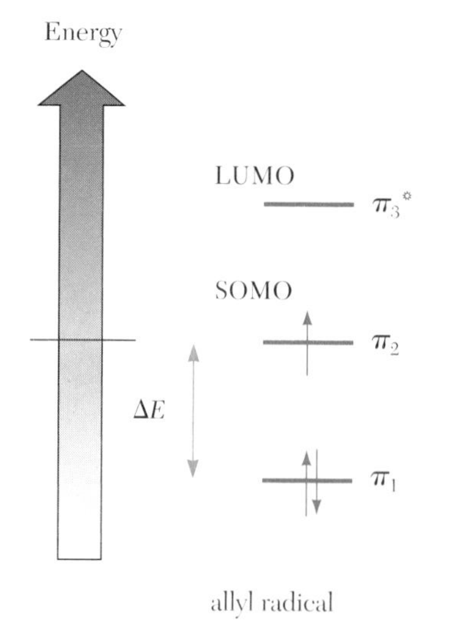

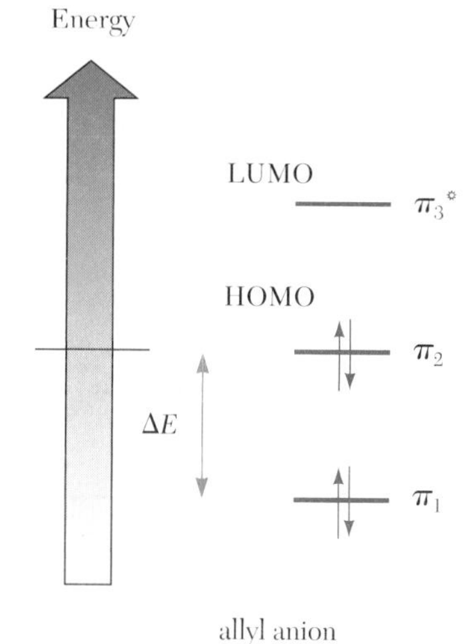

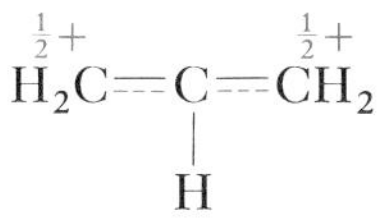

$$\overset{\frac{1}{2}+}{H_2C}\text{=-=}\underset{|}{\overset{}{C}}\text{=-=}\overset{\frac{1}{2}+}{CH_2}$$
H

Figure 16.17 Charge distribution in the allyl cation. The charge is equally distributed between the terminal carbon atoms. The central carbon atom is neutral.

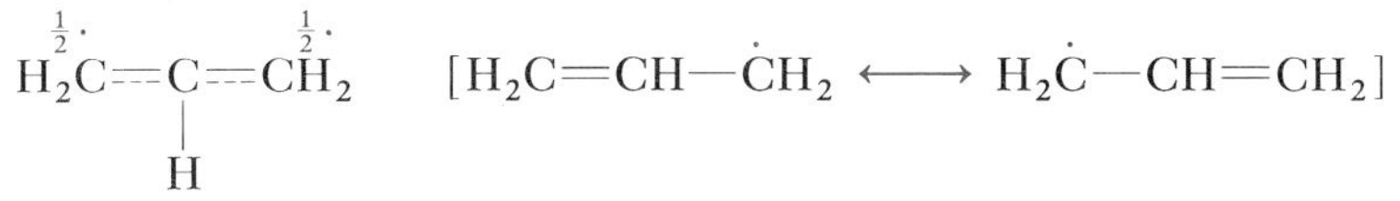

$$\overset{\frac{1}{2}\cdot}{H_2C}\text{=-=}C\text{=-=}\overset{\frac{1}{2}\cdot}{CH_2} \qquad [H_2C{=}CH{-}\dot{C}H_2 \longleftrightarrow H_2\dot{C}{-}CH{=}CH_2]$$
H

Figure 16.18 The allyl radical. The distribution of unpaired electron density predicted by molecular orbital considerations (shown on the left) is equivalent to that predicted by valence bond resonance structures (shown on the right).

Similarly, addition of an electron to an allyl radical can occur only at C1 or C3. The negative charge thus acquired is likewise concentrated on the terminal carbons.

PROBLEM 16.6

When the isotopically substituted propene shown below is treated with *N*-bromosuccinimide under conditions for allylic bromination, two products are formed. Give the structure for each of these two products.

$$H_2{}^{14}C{=}CH{-}CH_3$$

16.5 The Benzene Problem

EXPERIMENTAL OBSERVATIONS

Consider the substance known as **benzene.** Benzene is a naturally occurring compound that can be isolated from petroleum distillates. The molecular formula of benzene, C_6H_6, indicates that it has a total of four degrees of unsaturation (rings or double bonds). Experimental results indicate that the benzene molecule has six carbon atoms joined in a planar ring. The six hydrogen atoms of benzene, one attached to each of the carbons, also lie in that same plane. We thus write a (valence bond) structure for benzene as shown in Figure 16.19.

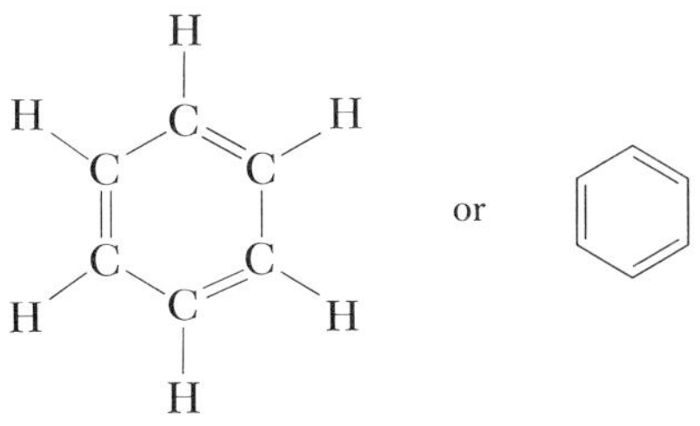

However, if we take this representation too seriously, we quickly run into difficulties in explaining other experimental observations. For example, all the carbon-carbon bond distances are found to be the same. This result is not consistent with alternating double and single bonds as depicted in Figure 16.19, since we would expect double bonds to be shorter than single bonds.

Furthermore, our simple valence bond structure is also at odds with experimental observations of disubstituted benzene derivatives. Consider 1,2-dibromobenzene. The valence bond structure for benzene leads us to think that two isomers of 1,2-dibromobenzene should exist as shown in Figure 16.20. In fact, only one 1,2-dibromobenzene species actually exists.

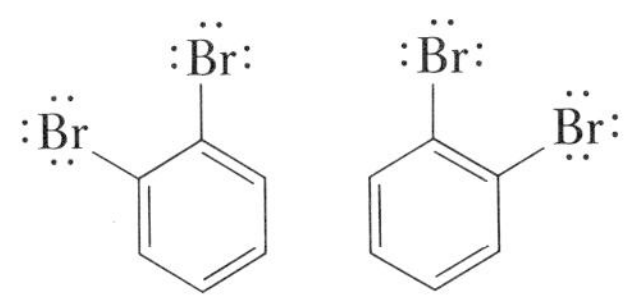

There is a subtle distinction between the two structures shown in Figure 16.20. In the right-hand structure, two bromines are located on a pair of doubly bound carbons. In the left-hand structure, the two bromines are located on a pair of singly bound carbons. In fact, no one has ever been able to isolate two separate 1,2-dibromobenzenes. Only one substance ever has been identified in which bromine atoms are substituted at adjacent positions of a benzene ring.

Lewis structures and valence bond representations offer us an explanation of this dilemma. We write the benzene molecule as a resonance hybrid of two energetically equivalent resonance structures, as shown in Figure 16.21.

H H H C C C C C C H H H or

Figure 16.19 Valence bond representation of benzene. All 12 atoms of the benzene molecule (6 carbons and 6 hydrogens) lie in the same plane. The valence bond representation indicates alternating double and single bonds about the ring. Each of the carbon atoms is sp^2 hybridized.

:Br: :Br: :Br: Br:

Figure 16.20 Two valence bond representations of 1,2-dibromobenzene. Using the valence bond representations for benzene, we anticipate the existence of two isomers of 1,2-disubstituted benzene derivatives. However, only one actually exists.

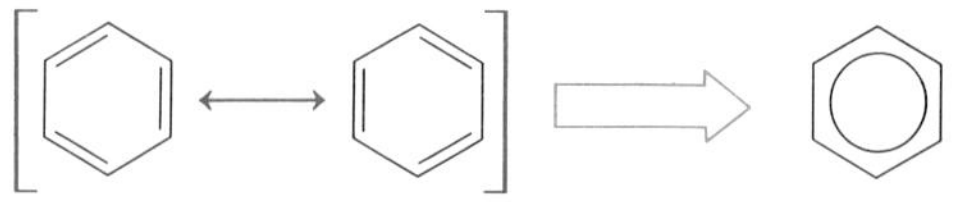

Figure 16.21 Resonance structures of benzene. The two structures on the left represent energetically equivalent resonance hybrid structures of benzene. The structure on the right, with a circle in the hexagon, represents the average of the two structures shown on the left; we often use this representation for benzene.

Thinking of benzene as a resonance hybrid of the structures shown in Figure 16.21, we can see that all of the carbon-carbon linkages of the ring are equivalent. Moreover, we would anticipate that only one 1,2-dibromobenzene would exist, since the two structures represented in Figure 16.20 are only contributing forms for a single molecule.

Chemists often use either one of the classical cyclohexatriene structures or the average structure to represent benzene and its derivatives. When one of the classical structures is used, the reader is expected to understand that it is used only for simplicity. A better description would be to write both structures as a resonance pair.

The valence bond of description of benzene indicates that it is a cyclic conjugated triene. However, the actual properties of benzene are quite different from those of other compounds containing carbon-carbon double bonds. For example, compare benzene with ordinary alkenes and cycloalkenes, and even with conjugated species such as 1,3-butadiene and 1,3,5-hexatriene. All of these molecules undergo addition of bromine quite readily. However, benzene does *not* undergo bromine addition readily. In fact, bromine/carbon tetrachloride and bromine/water reagents have no effect on benzene. Comparable reaction systems are shown in Figure 16.22.

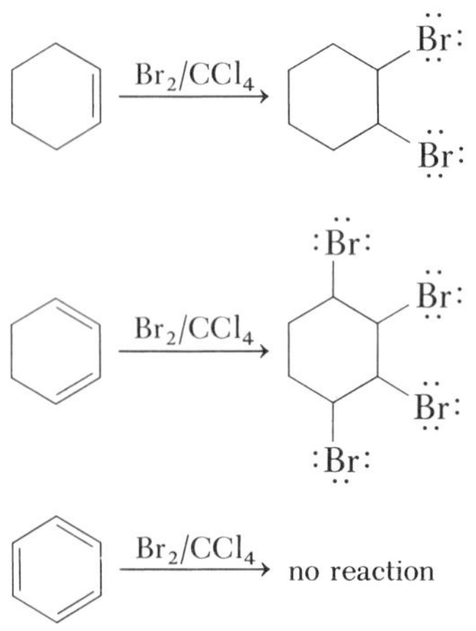

Br_2/CCl_4

Br_2/CCl_4

Br_2/CCl_4 no reaction

Figure 16.22 Reactions with bromine in carbon tetrachloride. Both cyclohexene and 1,3-cyclohexadiene react readily with bromine/carbon tetrachloride to give bromine adducts. Benzene, however, does not react at all under these conditions. The behavior of benzene is quite different from that of other ordinary unsaturated molecules.

Benzene does react with bromine if more forcing reaction conditions and Lewis acid catalysts are used. However, the reaction is a *substitution* reaction—bromine replaces one of the hydrogens attached to the ring to form bromobenzene, C_6H_5Br, as shown in Figure 16.23 (we will discuss this type of reaction and its mechanism in Chapter 18).

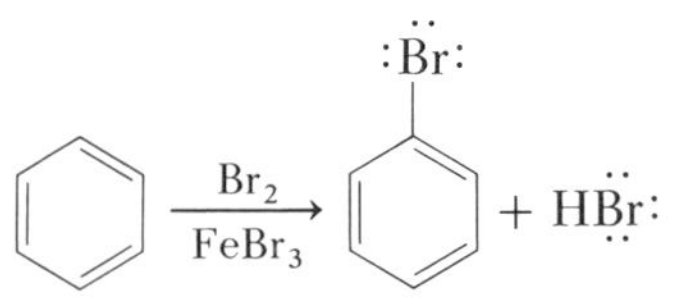

Br_2 / $FeBr_3$ + HBr:

Figure 16.23 Bromine substitution reaction of benzene.

In our earlier discussions we found that addition reactions are common with carbon-carbon double bonds. However, with benzene and its derivatives addition reactions occur only rarely or under forcing conditions. Instead, substitution reactions dominate their chemistry. The system of conjugated double bonds of benzene and its derivatives remains intact in these substitutions. We infer from these observations that there is a special stability associated with the system of three conjugated double bonds in a six-membered ring.

In Chapter 10 we saw that measurement of heats of hydrogenation provided information about the relative stability of unsaturated compounds. We can also learn about the stability of benzene, relative to comparable alkenes, using these thermochemical measurements. There are some experimental difficulties associated with making these measurements for benzene. Hydrogenation is an addition reaction, and benzene is resistant to hydrogenation with the ordinary catalysts commonly used with alkenes. However, at higher temperatures and pressures or with the use of special catalysts (e.g., PtO_2 with a strong acid), benzene does add hydrogen to form cyclohexane, and thermochemical measurements can be made.

The heat of hydrogenation of benzene is striking in comparison to that of ordinary alkenes. It has a remarkably low value, even less than that of 1,3-cyclohexadiene, which has only two double bonds. For ordinary polyenes, the heat of hydrogenation is approximately in proportion to the number of double bonds. Some pertinent values are shown for comparison in Table 16.1.

Table 16.1 Heats of Hydrogenation of Benzene and Structurally Related Alkenes (kcal/mol).
In each case the product is cyclohexane.

Compound	Heat of Hydrogenation (kcal/mole)
Cyclohexene	28.6
1,3-Cyclohexadiene	55.7
Benzene	49.8

Although benzene formally has three double bonds, its heat of hydrogenation is less than that of 1,3-cyclohexadiene, which has only two double bonds. If benzene were a normal polyene, we would anticipate its heat of hydrogenation to be approximately 85 kcal/mol (i.e., 3 × 28.6 kcal/mol).

These measurements confirm the special stability of the π-electron system of benzene, which is quite consistent with the tendency of benzene to undergo substitution reactions rather than addition reactions. In substitution reactions, the integrity of the benzene π system is apparently not disturbed. An addition reaction would convert benzene into a cyclic diene, and its special stability would be lost. In the next sections we will explore the origin of this special stability and consider other cyclic π systems to see if they too have special properties.

MORE ABOUT THE VALENCE BOND VIEW OF BENZENE AND OTHER CYCLIC CONJUGATED POLYENES

The contributing resonance structures in Figure 16.21 describe the benzene molecule using valence bond concepts. The actual benzene molecule is expected to be more stable than would be indicated by either of the resonance structures alone. Thus, valence bond concepts do predict a special stabilization for benzene.

However, when we attempt to make obvious extensions of the valence bond argument, we find serious difficulties. For example, consider the molecule 1,3,5,7-cyclooctatetraene (COT) (**16.1**).

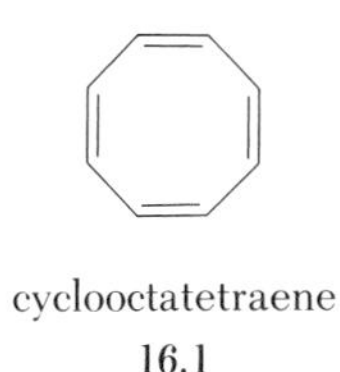

cyclooctatetraene
16.1

In 1911–13, the German chemist Richard Wilstatter and his students first synthesized cyclooctatetraene. (The synthetic route Wilstatter used is quite ingenious and is considered in detail in Chapter 20.) Their intent in the synthesis was to compare the properties of cyclooctatetraene with those of benzene. The fundamental question was whether cyclooctatetraene would, like benzene, resist addition reactions and exhibit a special stability. Would four conjugated bonds in an eight-membered ring behave like three conjugated bonds in a six-membered ring?

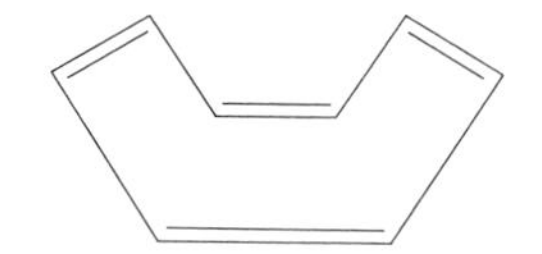

Figure 16.24 Tub conformation of cyclooctatetraene. There is no interaction between adjacent π bonds. Each π bond acts as an isolated alkene linkage.

The answer proved to be a decisive no. Cyclooctatetraene is definitely *not* an eight-carbon analogue of benzene. For example, cyclooctatetraene undergoes halogen addition reactions typical of ordinary alkenes. Similarly, hydrogenation occurs at ordinary temperatures and pressures as it does with simple alkenes. Cyclooctatetraene requires no special reaction conditions or catalyst to add hydrogen and form cyclooctane. Moreover, cyclooctetraene is not a planar molecule, as benzene is. Instead, cyclooctatetraene adopts a *tub* conformation, as shown in Figure 16.24. In this conformation, side-to-side interaction of the π bonds is limited. Thus, cyclooctatetraene does not have a highly delocalized π system. Its carbon-carbon bonds are not all the same length; instead, they alternate double, single, double, . . . about the ring.

Following the usual practice of valence bond theory, we could write two cyclooctatetraene resonance structures that would differ only in the placement of the double bonds. By analogy with benzene, we would then expect all of the carbon-carbon bonds to be equivalent and intermediate between single- and double-bond character. However, since *experiments* show that the carbon-carbon bonds of cyclooctatetraene are not all equivalent, it is inappropriate to consider such resonance structures. There is a fundamental difficulty here. Nothing inherent in the valence bond approach tells us that cyclooctatetraene should be different from benzene, but they are quite different.

Figure 16.25 Valence bond representation of 1,3-cyclobutadiene. Based on the two resonance structures, we would anticipate that all the C—C bonds would be identical and have a bond order of 1.5. Furthermore, there is usually a correlation between stability and number of resonance structures. However, by experiment, we find that cyclobutadiene is very unstable, and that the C—C bond lengths are not identical.

An even greater difficulty arises when we apply valence bond concepts to 1,3-cyclobutadiene. This molecule is the antithesis of benzene. It is so reactive that it can be studied only under conditions in which collisions with other molecules are severely limited. (We can look at the chemical and physical properties of cyclobutadiene when it is isolated in a frozen inert matrix at very low temperature or when it is in a highly rarefied gaseous state.) The behavior of cyclobutadiene is not at all in accord with the characteristics predicted by valence bond structures, which are shown in Figure 16.25.

The valence bond model gives us an incorrect view of the cyclobutadiene molecule. Clearly, we are not able to understand the nature of cyclic conjugated π systems using a valence bond approach. Can a molecular orbital approach do better?

A MOLECULAR ORBITAL APPROACH TO BENZENE AND OTHER CYCLIC POLYENES

We will start by comparing the π orbital energies of open-chain conjugated polyenes with those of their cyclic counterparts. We will assume (initially) that the cyclic species take on a planar conformation that allows the p orbitals maximal side-to-side interaction. In this way we hope to discover why benzene adopts this geometry while cyclooctatetraene does not. Moreover, we hope to discover why benzene has a special stability while cyclooctatetraene and cyclobutadiene do not.

We will also introduce a useful pictorial approach for comparing the energies of the π orbitals of 1,3-butadiene and 1,3-cyclobutadiene. (There are other, mathematically more rigorous methods for comparing energies, but they are deferred until advanced courses.) Imagine that each π orbital of 1,3-butadiene can be transformed into an orbital of 1,3-cyclobutadiene by bringing together the termini of the carbon chain (we will ignore the detailed nature of the σ bonds at these atoms and concentrate on the π orbitals alone).

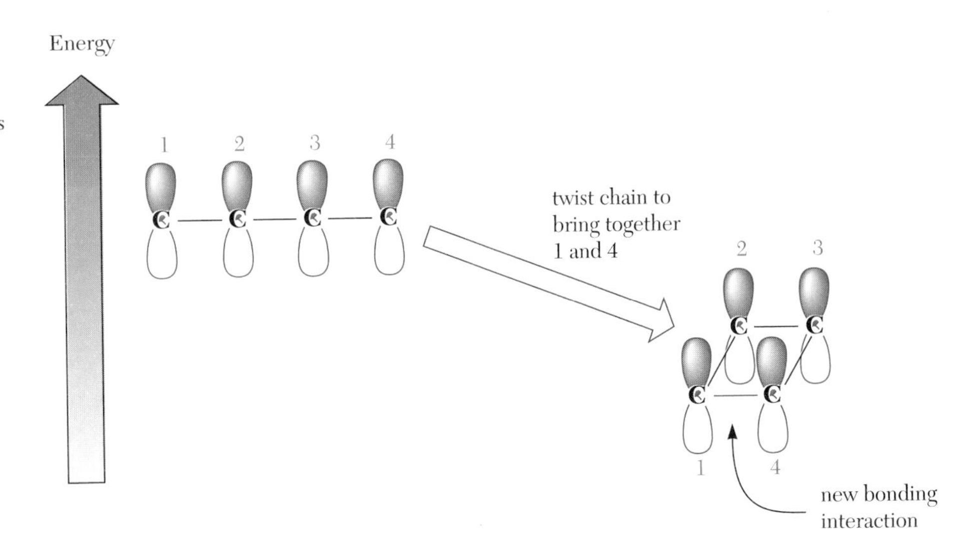

Figure 16.26 Transformation of 1,3-butadiene π_1 orbital into a cyclobutadiene π molecular orbital. If we twist the four-carbon chain to bring the 1- and 4-carbons together, we create a new *bonding* interaction. The 1,3-butadiene molecular orbital contains three bonding interactions, while there are four such interactions in the 1,3-cyclobutadiene molecular orbitals. The 1,3-cyclobutadiene molecular orbital is lower in energy (more stable) than its open-chain counterpart.

Consider first the most stable 1,3-butadiene π molecular orbital (π_1). If we bring the termini together, we generate an additional *bonding* interaction that is expected to stabilize the orbital. This transformation is illustrated in Figure 16.26.

Suppose we perform the same type of transformation with the next π molecular orbital (π_2) of 1,3-butadiene (this orbital is the HOMO of the ground state 1,3-butadiene molecule). This transformation generates a new *antibonding* interaction. The cyclobutadiene molecular orbital is destabilized relative to that of the open-chain species, as illustrated in Figure 16.27.

We can repeat this procedure for the remaining two molecular orbitals of 1,3-butadiene. In each case, we determine whether a new bonding or a new antibonding interaction is generated by the transformation, and thus whether the transformed molecular orbital is stabilized or destabilized relative to the

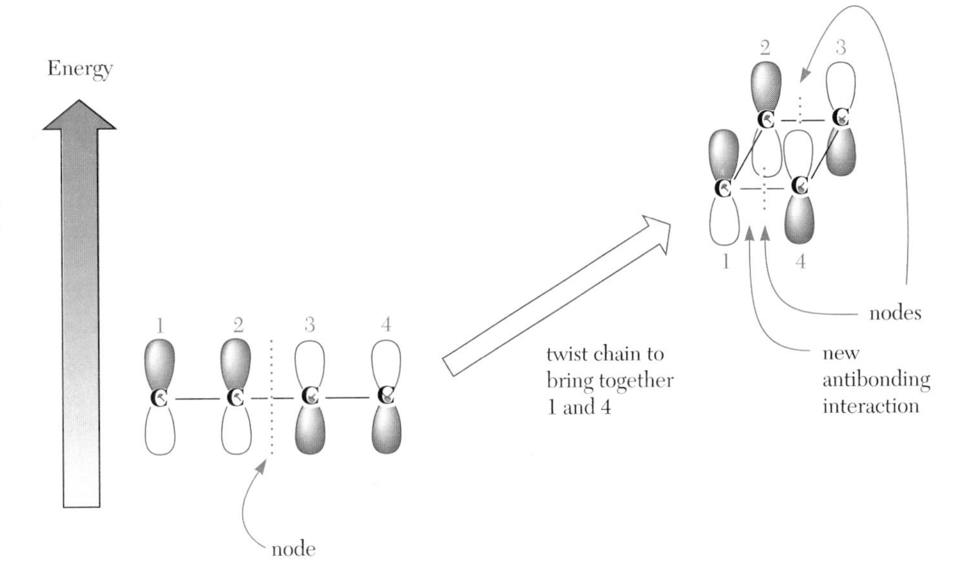

Figure 16.27 Transformation of 1,3-butadiene π_2 molecular orbital into a molecular orbital of cyclobutadiene. Bringing the orbital lobes at the 1- and 4-carbons together generates a new *antibonding* interaction. The molecular orbital of the cyclobutadiene species is thus destabilized relative to the corresponding orbital of the open-chain structure. The cyclic molecular orbital has two nodes, whereas the open-chain molecular orbital has only one node. For the cyclobutadiene molecular orbital there are two bonding and two antibonding interactions. Overall, this is a nonbonding molecular orbital.

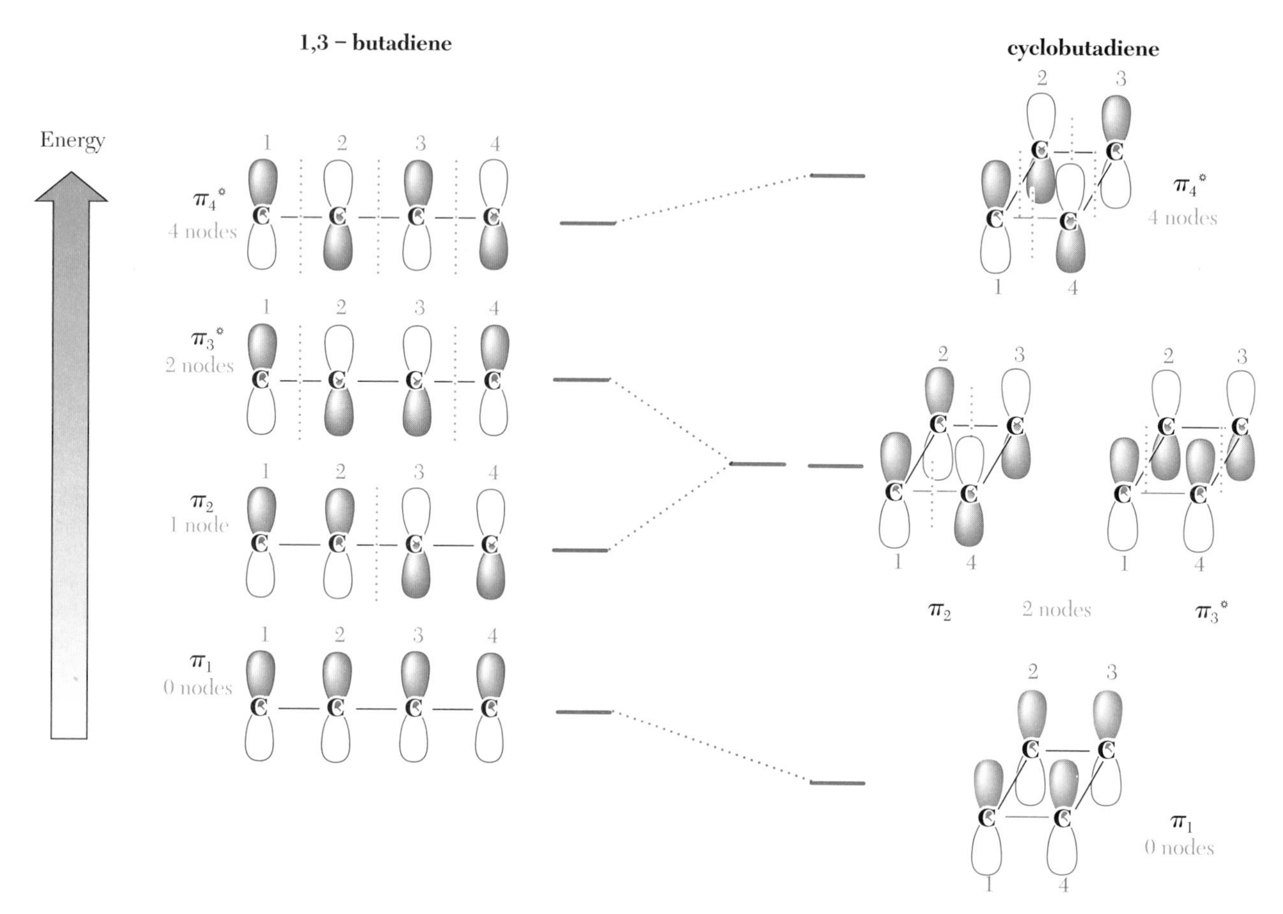

Figure 16.28 Transformation of π molecular orbitals of 1,3-butadiene and cyclobutadiene. New interactions result from bringing together the termini of the open-chain molecular orbitals. Depending on whether these interactions are bonding or antibonding, the resultant cyclobutadiene orbitals are lowered or raised in energy compared to the initial open-chain orbitals. Only one π-bonding molecular orbital and a pair of degenerate nonbonding orbitals are predicted for the cyclobutadiene molecule. This result suggests a reactivity for cyclobutadiene that is very different from that of open-chain 1,3-butadiene.

original orbital of the open-chain species. These transformations are summarized in Figure 16.28.

Quantum mechanical calculations on the molecular orbitals of the cyclobutadiene and 1,3-butadiene molecules confirm the qualitative treatment just given. However, they indicate that the amounts of stabilization and destabilization are not equal. The destabilization of π_2 is *greater* than the stabilization of π_1. Thus cyclobutadiene is predicted to have less π-bonding stabilization than does 1,3-butadiene. This is of course consistent with the lack of stability of 1,3-cyclobutadiene that is found by experiment.

Now let's apply the orbital transformation approach to the 1,3,5-hexatriene/benzene system. The π molecular orbitals of the 1,3,5-hexatriene molecule are shown in Figure 16.12. When we bring together the termini of each molecular orbital and allow them to interact, we generate six new π molecular orbitals that represent the orbitals of benzene. Again, there are stabilizations and destabilizations, depending on the nature of the additional interactions. The end result is shown in Figure 16.29.

PROBLEM 16.7

Using the energy diagram shown in Figure 16.29, add the available π electrons for benzene and show the electronic configuration of the ground state benzene molecule.

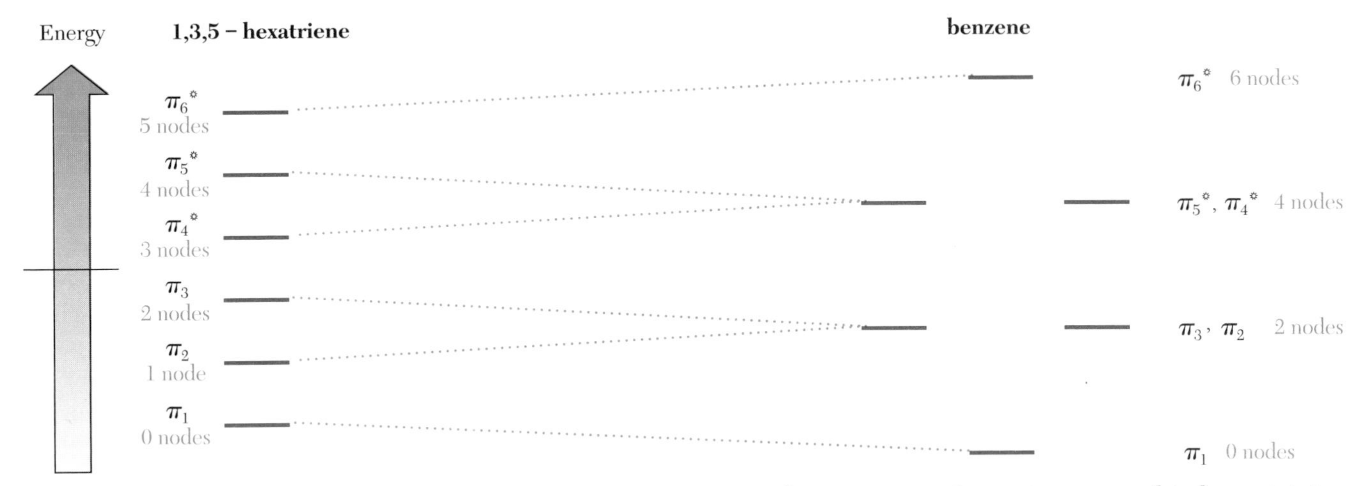

Figure 16.29 Transformation of π molecular orbitals of 1,3,5-hexatriene into benzene molecular orbitals. When the termini of the 1,3,5-hexatriene molecular orbital system are brought together, new interactions result. In some cases these interactions are stabilizing and in others they are destabilizing. The result is a set of molecular orbitals that describe the benzene system.

For the 1,3,5-hexatriene/benzene transformation, two orbitals containing four electrons are stabilized while only one orbital with two electrons is destabilized. Calculations show significant net π stabilization for benzene compared to 1,3,5-hexatriene. This π stabilization rationalizes the observed special stability of benzene and the differences in its observed chemistry compared to that of open-chain polyenes.

The relative π stabilization or destabilization of a cyclic conjugated system and its open-chain counterpart can always be predicted using the orbital transformation method. If equal numbers of electrons are stabilized and destabilized upon going from the open-chain to the cyclic system, then the cyclic system is *less* stable than the open-chain system. However, if more electrons are stabilized than are destabilized in the transformation, then the cyclic system will be *more* stable than the open-chain system.

The orbital transformation method always makes correct predictions about the following properties of the orbitals of the cyclic molecule:

- the number of nodes
- the energy relative to that of its open-chain counterpart
- any degeneracies (orbitals with the same numbers of nodes are degenerate)

Sometimes (as with cyclobutadiene) the method directly gives the proper symmetry-correct orbitals of the cyclic molecule. However, the method sometimes generates an "orbital" that is not symmetry correct when the terminal lobes of the open-chain molecule are brought together. If this happens, the orbital must be adjusted to make it symmetry correct. Therefore, always inspect the orbital you draw following the transformation algorithm. If it is symmetry correct for the cyclic structure, *leave it as is*. If it is not symmetry correct, look for lobes that have a bonding interaction with one neighboring lobe and an antibonding interaction with another. We construct symmetry-correct orbitals by completely eliminating lobes of this type (leaving nodes in their place).

PROBLEM 16.8 Use the transformation algorithm to derive the three occupied π molecular orbitals of benzene from those of 1,3,5-hexatriene.

Consider the same type of transformation for the cylooctatetraene molecule, starting with the π molecular orbitals of 1,3,5,7-octatetraene. Using the orbitals determined in Problem 16.4, we can generate eight π molecular orbitals for the planar cyclooctatetraene species. The orbital energies are shown in Figure 16.30. The π molecular orbital model for planar cyclooctatetraene is quite similar to that for cyclobutadiene. Equal numbers of π electrons are stabilized and destabilized on passing from the open-chain tetraene to the planar cyclic tetraene. In this situation, calculations always show a net destabilization of the cyclic compound compared to the open-chain molecule. In order for the overall cyclic system to be more stable than the open-chain compound, more π electrons must be stabilized than are destabilized.

To summarize, the molecular orbital model makes predictions about the stabilities of *planar* cyclic polyenes. It predicts the π electrons of planar cyclobutadiene and planar cyclooctatetraene to be destabilized relative to their open-chain counterparts, but those of planar benzene to be stabilized relative to those of 1,3,5-hexatriene.

Experiments show that the cyclooctatetraene molecule is *not* planar. It instead adopts the tub-shaped structure shown in Figure 16.24, thereby avoiding the planar geometry that would produce a π destabilization. In the tub conformation, it is not possible for all eight p orbitals to be parallel simultaneously. Cyclooctatetraene has four isolated double bonds and thus avoids the destabilization predicted by the molecular orbital model for a *planar* π-delocalized structure.

Because of its smaller ring, cyclobutadiene cannot twist away from planarity so easily. Cyclobutadiene thus is less able to avoid the destabilizing effect of conjugation and is found to be very reactive. Even so, experiments suggest that the interaction of the p orbitals in cyclobutadiene is limited. For example, the molecule is not square but rectangular, with isolated single and double bonds of unequal lengths.

Figure 16.30 Transformation of 1,3,5,7-octatetraene π molecular orbitals into planar cyclooctatetraene. The method of bringing together the termini of the open-chain system is used.

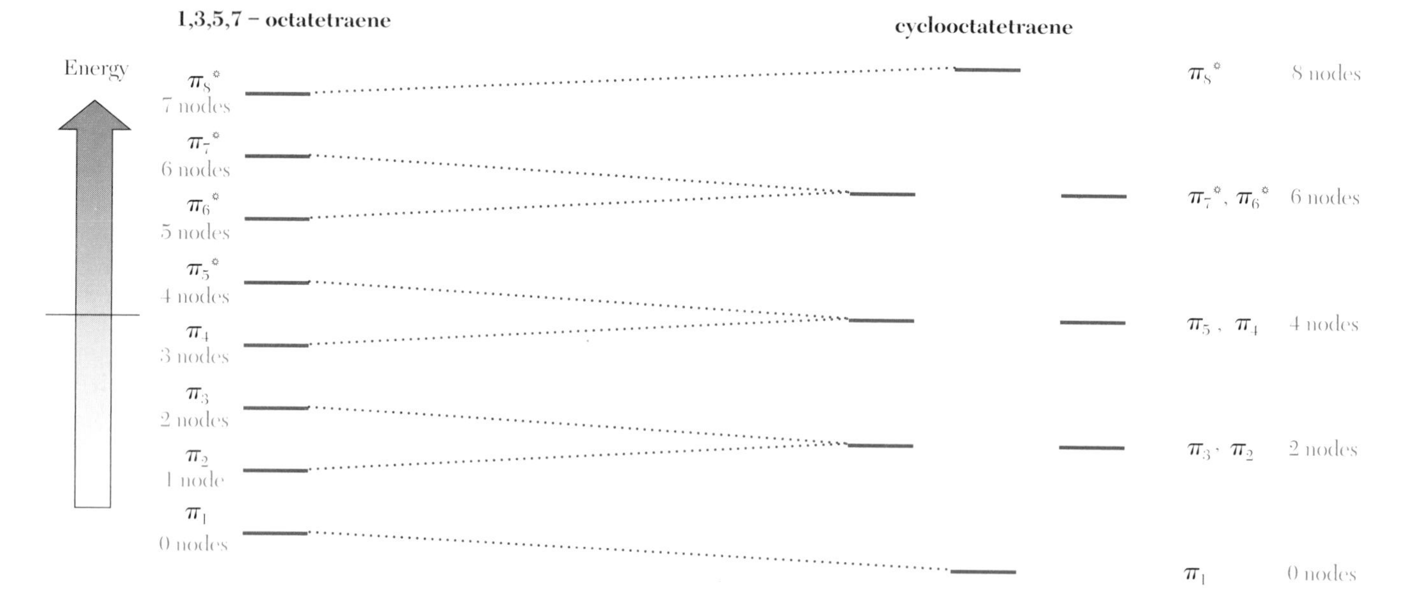

COMPOUND CAPSULE

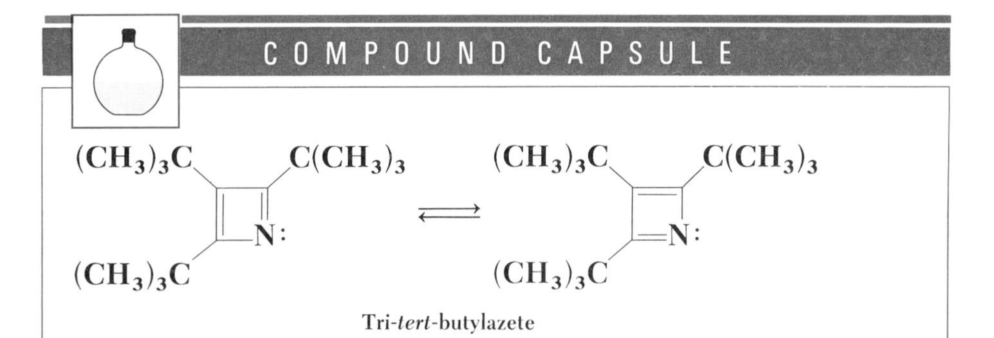

Tri-*tert*-butylazete

Chemists at the Max Planck Institute in Mulheim, Germany, have recently succeeded in preparing tri-*tert*-butylazete, a stable nitrogen analogue of a substituted cyclobutadiene. Like cyclobutadiene, tri-*tert*-butylazete has a cyclic array of four π electrons. The German chemists found that the tri-*tert*-butylazete exists as an equilibrium mixture of two rectangular isomers that have distinct long and short bonds. There is no π electron delocalization like that in benzene. If there were, these two structures would be resonance-contributing forms rather than structures in equilibrium, and we would not find distinct long and short bonds. The tri-*tert*-butylazete molecule might be expected to have a high reactivity like that of cyclobutadiene. For example, even in the absence of other reactants cyclobutadiene reacts with itself to form a dimer. However, it appears that the bulky *tert*-butyl groups prevent two molecules of tri-*tert*-butylazete from approaching one another closely enough for the dimerization to occur. The use of bulky groups to prevent the close approach of molecules is a useful general strategy in preventing dimerization of highly reactive compounds.

PROBLEM 16.9 Perform the orbital transformation on the π molecular orbitals of 1,3,5,7-octatetraene, generating those of planar cyclooctatetraene. Draw the orbital descriptions for the eight π molecular orbitals of the planar cyclooctatetraene molecule, and label each as bonding, nonbonding, or antibonding. (Make sure that all orbitals are symmetry correct.)

16.6 Aromaticity

DEFINITION OF TERMS

Long before the development of molecular orbital theory, chemists recognized that benzene and its derivatives were special—they exhibited unusual types of reactivity and unusual stability. Chemists originally referred to benzene and its derivatives as aromatic because of the characteristic odors of the first examples isolated from plants. As an understanding of the bonding in organic molecules progressed, the word *aromatic* came to describe the special stability of benzene and its derivatives. Today, we still use the old term *aromatic*, but give it a new meaning:

- **aromatic**—characteristic of a fully conjugated, completely planar, cyclic polyene that is *more stable* than its open-chain counterpart.

We also define the term *antiaromatic:*

- **antiaromatic**—characteristic of a fully conjugated completely planar, cyclic polyene that is *less stable* than its open-chain counterpart.

THE HÜCKEL RULE

How can we quickly tell whether a planar, cyclic, conjugated polyene will be aromatic or antiaromatic? Our earlier analysis of three systems indicates a periodicity in aromaticity and antiaromaticity with increasing ring size. The planar four-membered cyclobutadiene ring is antiaromatic. The planar six-membered benzene ring, however, is aromatic. Molecular orbital considerations for the next larger ring size, cyclooctatetraene, indicate it would be antiaromatic if planar. In the 1930s the German physical chemist Erich Hückel expressed this periodicity in terms of a simple formula that is one of several requirements of *special relative stability* (aromaticity). These requirements are summarized below.

Minimum Conditions for Aromatic Character

1. There must be a cyclic π system with an atomic p orbital at each atom of the ring.
2. All atoms of the ring must lie in the same plane, allowing all of the p orbitals to be parallel simultaneously.
3. There must be $(4n + 2)$ π electrons present, where n is zero or an integer.

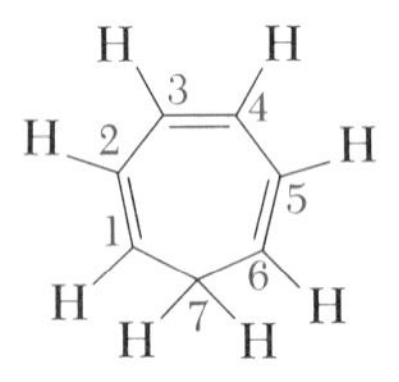

Figure 16.31 Cycloheptatriene. Although the ring system contains six π electrons, it is not aromatic. Carbon atom 7 is sp^3 hybridized and therefore has no free p orbital that can overlap with the p orbitals of carbon atoms 1 and 6.

We will consider several arrays of contiguous p orbitals in this section. It will become apparent that each of the structures may or may not be aromatic, depending solely on the number of electrons contained in the π system. Only if there are $(4n + 2)$ π electrons (where n is zero or a positive integer) can the molecule be aromatic. For example, a system with 18 π electrons could be aromatic, because 18 can be expressed by $(4n + 2)$ with $n = 4$. However, a system with 16 π electrons cannot be aromatic. We must stress that if *any* atom of the ring does not have a free p orbital that can contribute to the π system, that molecule cannot be aromatic, even if it does contain $(4n + 2)$ π electrons. For example, the molecule cycloheptatriene (Figure 16.31) is not aromatic even though, like benzene, it contains 6 π electrons.

Of the three molecules we investigated earlier (cyclobutadiene, benzene, and cyclooctatetraene), only benzene has $(4n + 2)$ π electrons (the other two have $(4n)$ π electrons). Molecules that meet the first two Hückel conditions but have $(4n)$ π electrons are, if planar, less stable than their open-chain counterparts, that is, they are antiaromatic. Given these conditions for aromatic character, we can make a number of predictions about species other than those we have already discussed. For example, we can consider cyclic conjugated polyenes that are larger than any we have discussed thus far. Moreover, we can consider ions that might meet the conditions of aromaticity. What kind of behavior do such species actually exhibit? Let us look at experimental results for both types of species in some detail.

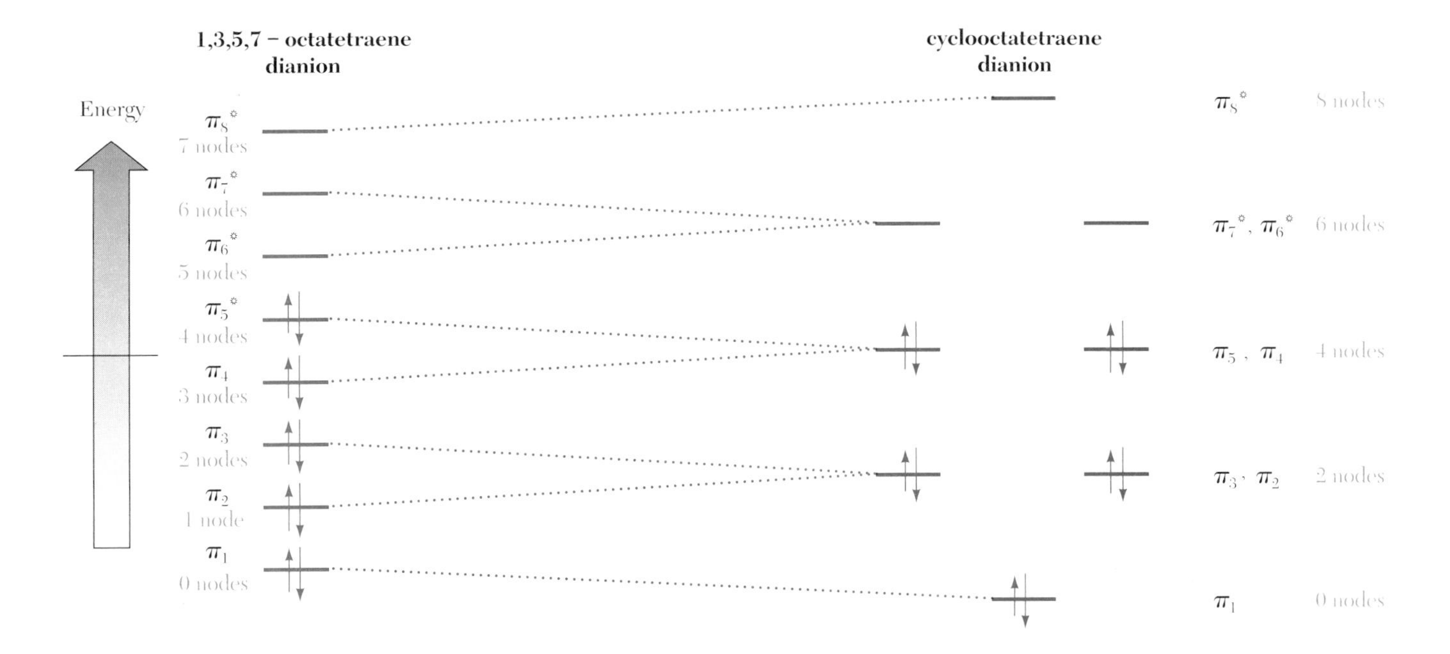

Figure 16.32 The π molecular orbital structure of the 1,3,5,7-octatetraene dianion and the cyclooctatetraene dianion. The molecular orbital structures are the same as shown in Figure 16.30. The fundamental difference is in the number of electrons associated with each species. The neutral species have only 8 π electrons each, while the dianions have 10 π electrons each.

AROMATIC IONS

The Dianion of Cyclooctatetraene Earlier we concluded that a planar cyclooctatetraene molecule was less stable than its open-chain counterpart, 1,3,5,7-octatetraene. Now consider adding another electron pair to the π molecular orbital system of both the open-chain and the cyclic species. Each is now a 10 π electron species, as illustrated in Figure 16.32.

The transformation from the 1,3,5,7-octatetraene dianion to the cyclooctatetraene dianion results in a net π stabilization. Six electrons become located in more stable orbitals, while only four become located in less stable orbitals. Thus, the planar dianion of cyclooctatetraene is more stable than the corresponding open-chain system. On this basis we predict the cyclooctatetraene dianion to be aromatic.

The observed properties of the cyclooctatetraene dianion are consistent with an aromatic structure. It is significantly different from cyclooctatetraene itself. It is also notable that the dianion can be prepared with relative ease. Its formation by the reaction of cyclooctatetraene with potassium metal is shown in Equation 16.1.

$$+ 2\,K \longrightarrow (2-) \quad 2\,K^+$$

The ease of formation of the cyclooctatetraene dianion is an indication of its relative stability. It is quite difficult to prepare dianions of most other hydrocarbons, particularly in the form of stable alkali metal salts. One most significant demonstration of the aromaticity of the cyclooctatetraene dianion is its planar structure (remember that the parent cyclooctatetraene is tub-shaped). Finally, notice that the cyclooctatetraene dianion fits the third criterion for aromatic character (as well as the first two) by having 10 π electrons ($(4n + 2)$ where $n = 2$).

The Monoanion of Cyclopentadiene Cyclopentadiene (**16.2**) is a conjugated diene that is held in a *cisoid* conformation by the remaining methylene group of the ring system. It does not have an unhybridized p orbital at each carbon atom of the ring and thus cannot be an aromatic system, as it is not fully conjugated.

H H
H H
H H

cyclopentadiene
16.2

However, if we remove a proton from the methylene group of cyclopentadiene, we produce the cyclopentadienyl anion, $C_5H_5^-$, in which a p orbital at each atom of the ring is available for participation in a cyclic π system. We can

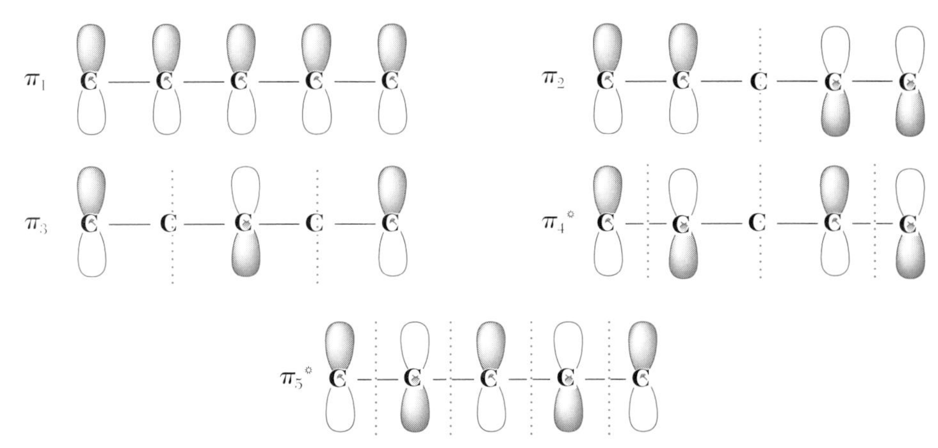

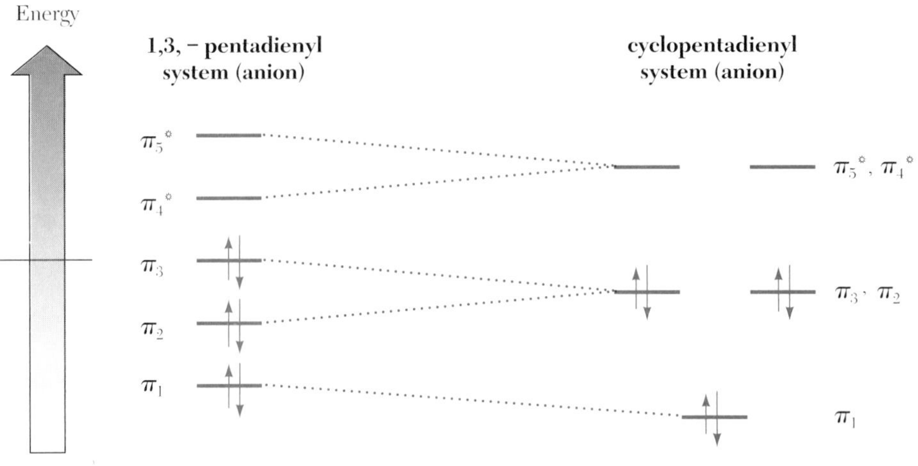

Figure 16.33 Transformation of the π molecular orbitals of the 1,3-pentadienyl system into those of the cyclopentadienyl system. The π molecular orbitals of the 1,3-pentadienyl system, which were generated in accord with the guidelines given earlier in this chapter, are shown at the top. Vertical nodes are indicated by the dotted lines. Note that this system is similar to the allyl system in that an odd number of atoms species are present in the chain and some nodes occur at the atomic centers. Because these are monoanions, six electrons are shown with each set of molecular orbitals.

envision the π molecular orbitals for this cyclic species by transforming the open-chain pentadienyl π molecular orbitals, as shown in Figure 16.33. In the transformation of the pentadienyl anion into the cyclopentadienyl anion, four electrons are stabilized and only two are destabilized. The cyclopentadienyl anion thus represents a more stable π system than does the corresponding open-chain structure, the 1,3-pentadienyl anion. We thus predict the cyclopentadienyl anion to be aromatic.

Experimentally, a special stability is found to be associated with the cyclopentadienyl anion. We can generate the cyclopentadienyl anion by the treatment of cyclopentadiene with a moderately strong base, as shown in Equation 16.2.

Eqn. 16.2

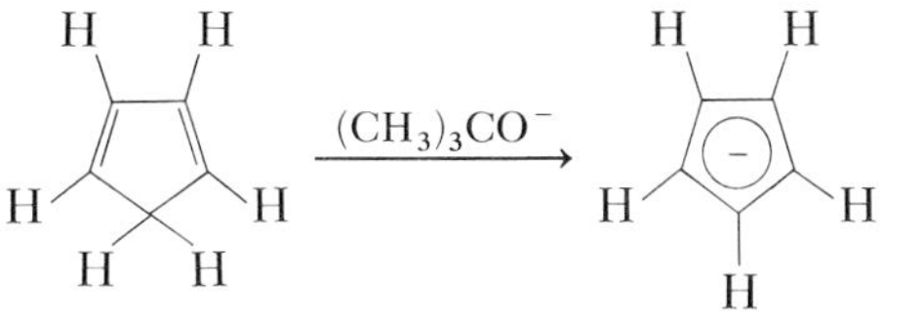

$$C_5H_6 \xrightarrow{(CH_3)_3CO^-} C_5H_5^-$$

We can think of the aromatic ion of Equation 16.2 as a hybrid of the classical resonance structures shown in Figure 16.34.

Cyclopentadiene has a pK_a of 16. It is about as strong an acid as ethanol. Ordinary hydrocarbons are by no means as acidic as cyclopentadiene. Even acetylene has a pK_a of only 25. If we wish to remove a proton from 1,3-pentadiene, the open-chain reference for cyclopentadiene, we need a much stronger base than *tert*-butoxide ion, such as butyllithium. The relatively high acidity of cyclopentadiene correlates with the special stability associated with the conjugate base that is produced upon removal of the proton. Cyclopentadienyl anion exhibits aromatic characteristics, in accord with the predictions of the molecular orbital model. Notice in Figure 16.33 that the cyclopentadienyl anion has six π electrons in its molecular orbitals. In a formal counting of π electrons, each double bond contributes two, and the unshared pair associated with the carbon from which the proton was removed constitutes two more giving an overall total of six π electrons.

Figure 16.34 Resonance-contributing forms for the cyclopentadienyl anion.

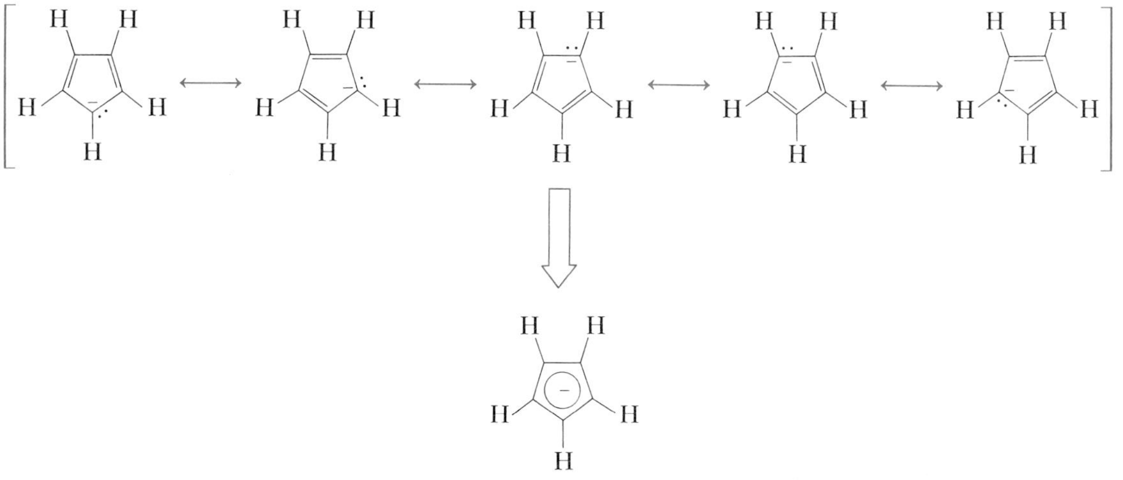

PROBLEM 16.10 Draw the π molecular orbitals of the cyclopentadienyl anion as generated by transformation of the orbitals of the 1,3-pentadienyl system. Show all nodes present in the orbitals.

The Cycloheptatrienyl (Tropylium) Cation Consider a planar ring of seven carbon atoms with a p orbital available at each carbon atom. Using our open-chain/cyclic molecular orbital transformation approach, we can relate this structure to the 1,3,5-cycloheptatrienyl system. The energies of the π molecular orbitals for the cyclic system are shown in Figure 16.35. The molecular orbital approach predicts a special stability for the cycloheptatrienyl cation (also known as the tropylium ion). It has greater stabilization than its open-chain reference system, the 1,3,5-heptatrienyl cation. This prediction can be verified experimentally. Our experience with nucleophilic substitution reactions tells us that carbocations are generally high-energy, reactive species. The cycloheptatrienyl cation, however, is very stable by comparison. We can generate the cycloheptatrienyl cation by dissolving cycloheptatrienyl bromide in a polar medium, as shown in Equation 16.3.

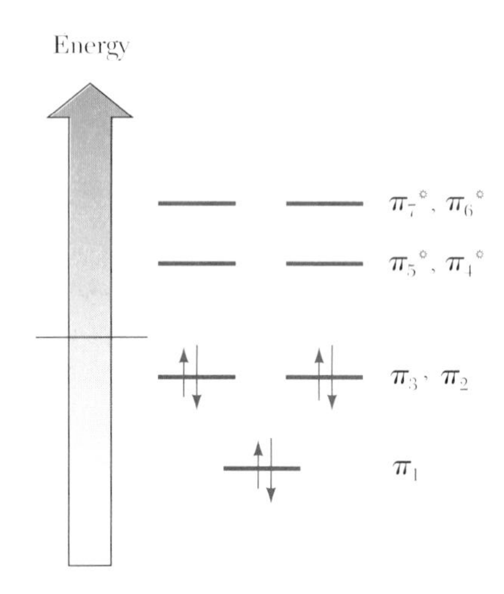

Figure 16.35 The π molecular orbital model for the cycloheptatrienyl cation. The six π electrons are placed in the lowest available orbitals. All of the bonding molecular orbitals are filled, but none of the antibonding orbitals are occupied. The cation provides the maximum π bonding stabilization possible with this system.

Eqn. 16.3 cycloheptatrienyl bromide $\xrightarrow{CH_3OH}$ cycloheptatrienyl cation $+ :\ddot{Br}:^-$

The valence bond model fails to explain why the cycloheptatrienyl *anion* is not also particularly stable, even though we can draw seven resonance structures for it. However, the molecular orbital model correctly predicts the experimental result. The cycloheptatrienyl anion has eight π electrons, a number that cannot be expressed by the Hückel $(4n + 2)$ formula.

PROBLEM 16.11 We can anticipate the formation of four adducts of cycloheptatriene with one equivalent amount of bromine. Draw the structures of these four possible products.

PROBLEM 16.12 Draw the classical valence bond resonance structures that show the delocalization of the positive charge about the ring of the cycloheptatrienyl cation.

PROBLEM 16.13 Draw the π molecular orbitals for the 1,3,5-heptatrienyl cation, and show in an energy diagram which orbitals are occupied by electrons.

PROBLEM 16.14 Using the orbitals drawn in Problem 16.13, perform the transformation to generate the π molecular orbitals for the cycloheptatrienyl system. Draw these orbitals, and verify that the cycloheptatrienyl cation is stabilized relative to the open-chain reference system.

PROBLEM 16.15 Consider the cycloheptatrienyl anion. Draw its molecular orbital energy diagram. Is it stabilized or destabilized relative to the cycloheptatrienyl cation? Is it stabilized or destabilized relative to the 1,3,5-heptatrienyl anion? Explain your answers.

PROBLEM 16.16 Consider the reaction of cycloheptatriene with base. Would you expect a facile reaction between cycloheptatriene and a base to occur with removal of a proton from the cycloheptatriene? Why or why not? Would you expect the open-chain molecule 1,3,5-heptatriene to be more or less acidic than cycloheptatriene? Explain your answer.

Small-Ring Aromatic Ions In general, small rings are strained (Chapter 13). However, the presence of a continuous cyclic π molecular orbital system can enhance the stability of a small-ring compound. For example, although cyclobutadiene is a reactive antiaromatic species, molecular orbital considerations predict the cyclobutadienyl dication to be aromatic. Chemists have synthesized numerous examples of this type of electron-deficient aromatic species, including the tetramethylcyclobutadienyl dication (**16.3**). Similarly, molecular orbital theory predicts the cyclopropenyl cation (**16.4**) to be aromatic. This prediction is also verified by experimental evidence.

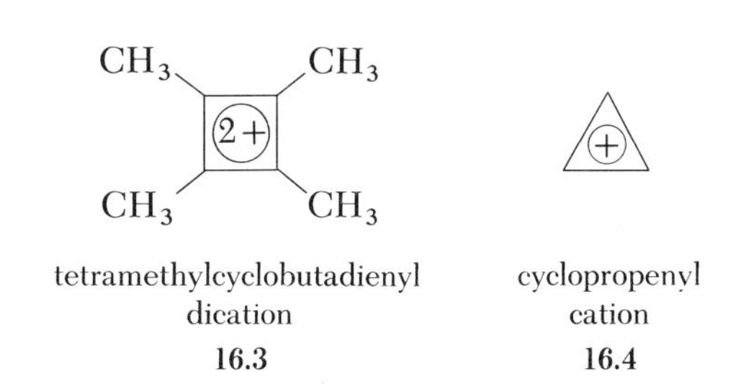

tetramethylcyclobutadienyl dication
16.3

cyclopropenyl cation
16.4

Both of these ions have *two* π electrons. Using the third Hückel criterion for aromatic character, $n = 0$ in the $(4n + 2)$ requirement. We must remember, however, that while these species are aromatic and more stable than their open-chain counterparts, their stabilization is still much less than that of benzene.

PROBLEM 16.17 Consider the π molecular orbitals for the allyl system and transform them to generate the π molecular orbitals of the cyclopropenyl system. Demonstrate that the cyclopropenyl cation should be aromatic.

PROBLEM 16.18 The cyclobutadienyl dication is aromatic, while the neutral cyclobutadiene molecule is antiaromatic. How would you describe the planar cyclobutadienyl dianion? Explain your answer.

NEUTRAL AROMATIC MOLECULES LARGER THAN BENZENE

Using our criteria for aromaticity, we can devise numerous molecules that we would predict to be aromatic. We will consider several of these species and compare them to benzene.

First, consider the molecule 1,3,5,7,9-cyclodecapentaene in which all of the double bonds have the *cis* geometry. This compound (also known as **[10]annulene**) is shown below (**16.5**).

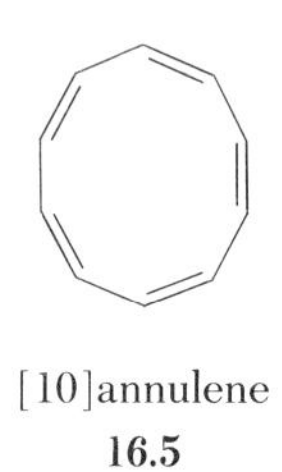

[10]annulene
16.5

The [10]annulene molecule satisfies the third criterion for aromaticity since it possesses ten π electrons in a cyclic conjugated system. For a ten-electron system, $n = 2$ in the expression $(4n + 2)$. We thus expect that [10]annulene would be aromatic, like benzene. In fact, [10]annulene exists as a nonplanar, nonaromatic molecule and is more like cyclooctatetraene than like benzene.

We can understand the distortion of [10]annulene away from planarity by considering factors other than the number of π electrons. If the molecule were to be planar with all ring bonds of equal length, it would resemble a regular decagon. The internal bond angles of a regular decagon are 144° (Chapter 13), much larger than is found with sp^2 hybridized carbons. In a planar [10]annulene molecule, there would be a significant strain on the σ bonds of the ring. This strain would be so large that it would exceed any possible aromatic π stabilization, so the molecule distorts to a nonplanar structure to avoid this angle strain.

Larger neutral rings can exist with aromatic character, but they do not have entirely *cis* geometry. An example is the cyclooctadecaene, [18]annulene (**16.6**), which is shown below. This molecule *does* exhibit aromatic character.

[18]annulene
16.6

The [18]annulene type system, however, is not common in organic molecules. It is difficult to synthesize and is rare as a part of larger organic molecules.

In this respect it is unlike benzene, which is a common structural unit throughout organic chemistry.

PROBLEM 16.19 The ten π electron system shown below does not have the special stability associated with aromatic compounds. Suggest an explanation for its nature.

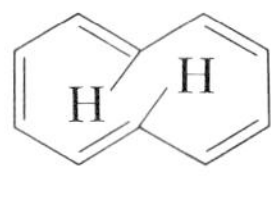

16.7 Benzene as a Special Structural Category

Historically, the chemical phenomenon of aromaticity was first observed with benzene and its simple substituted derivatives. Chemists developed the electronic and structural basis for this behavior only much later. The concept of aromatic character associated with species that are structurally quite different from benzene is of relatively recent vintage.

Benzene and its simple derivatives still enjoy a special place in the classification of organic compounds because of their particular stability, both electronically and structurally, and their ubiquitous nature among organic materials. A major reason for the widespread occurrence of benzene-type structures, aside from the π electronic stabilization, is that its σ structure is free of strain. The ring bond angles in benzene are all 120°, in perfect accord with the sp^2 nature of the ring carbons of benzene. In comparison, the internal bond angles of the cyclopentadienyl anion and the tropylium ion are 108° and 128.5°, respectively (see the discussion in Chapter 13 of internal angles of planar cyclic structures). While these latter species exhibit π electron stabilization, they also have significant angle strain on their σ-bonding system. Their overall stability is thus diminished, a situation that does not occur with benzene and its simple derivatives.

There are also numerous aromatic molecules in which one or more of the ring atoms are an element other than carbon. For example, aromatic six-membered rings with nitrogen atoms in the ring occur naturally and are of extreme importance in biological systems. We have seen several examples of these compounds in our earlier discussions of nucleic acids. Two additional examples are shown in Figure 16.36.

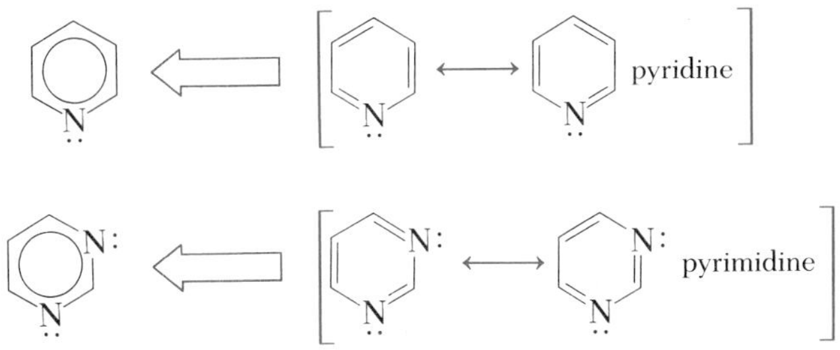

Figure 16.36 Examples of nitrogen containing aromatics. Both pyridine and pyrimidine are aromatic compounds with a π molecular orbital structure completely analogous to that of benzene. In addition to the π molecular orbitals, each nitrogen has an unshared electron pair in a hybrid orbital (sp^2) that is orthogonal (at right angles) to the molecular orbital π-system and thus in the plane of the ring.

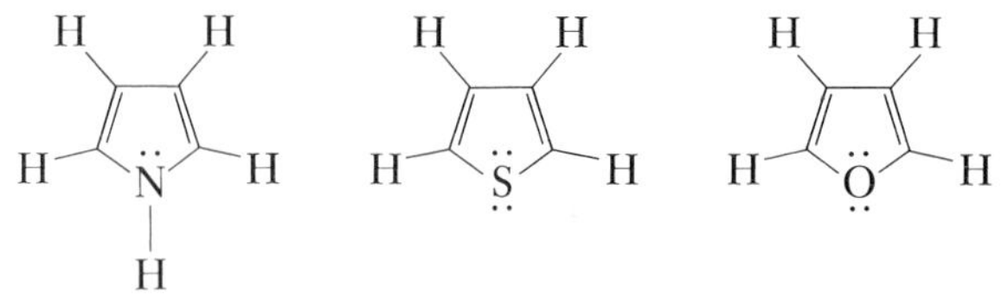

Figure 16.37 Examples of heteroaromatic compounds. Each of the compounds has at least one unshared electron pair associated with the noncarbon atom. An unshared electron pair from each heteroatom makes up part of the six electrons required for the aromatic π system. For thiophene and furan, there is yet an additional unshared electron pair at the noncarbon atom. This additional electron pair is orthogonal to the ring system, occupying a hybridized (sp^2) orbital, and cannot contribute to the cyclic π system.

pyrrole thiophene furan

Other heteroaromatic compounds exist with rings of different sizes. Several examples are shown in Figure 16.37. We will discuss these and other heteroaromatic compounds in more detail in Chapter 28.

PROBLEM 16.20 Rationalize the fact that the unshared electron pair on nitrogen in pyridine is not part of the aromatic sextet of electrons, whereas the unshared electron pair on nitrogen in pyrrole *is* part of the aromatic sextet.

In general, an unshared electron pair can contribute to an aromatic π system if the atom to which it belongs is *not* involved in a double bond (in terms of valence bond structures). If the atom is involved in a double bond, the unshared electron pair cannot contribute to the cyclic π system.

Summary

- The valence bond approach to describing bonding in organic molecules provides inadequate descriptions for certain types of molecules. In particular, it often gives us an incomplete understanding of conjugated π electron systems.
- For conjugated π electron systems, the molecular orbital approach allows a fuller understanding of bonding.
- The molecular orbital approach gives us more versatile descriptions of linear conjugated π systems than does the valence bond model.
- Using a set of simple guidelines, we can quickly construct qualitative π molecular orbitals for linear π systems. Once we have described the π molecular orbitals for a linear polyene or an intermediate, we can introduce the appropriate number of electrons for the species of interest.
- Aromatics represent a class of compounds with particularly interesting characteristics. They have a continuous cyclic π system and exhibit relative electronic stability compared to their open-chain counterparts.
- A continuous cyclic π electron system about a planar array of atoms containing $(4n + 2)$ π electrons provides a system with a special stability.
- Species with $(4n)$ π electrons in a continuous cyclic π system about a planar ring of atoms are destabilized relative to their open-chain counterparts. Such species are referred to as *antiaromatic*.
- Benzene and its derivatives are the most stabilized of the aromatic compounds.
- There are other aromatic compounds in which noncarbon atoms are present in the aromatic ring. Many of these compounds are of great significance in biological processes.

Terms to Remember

nodal plane
node
symmetric
antisymmetric
symmetry elements
axis of symmetry
allyl cation
allyl radical
nonbonding orbital
benzene
aromatic
antiaromatic
[10]annulene

Additional Problems

16.21 Does the energy of an orbital increase or decrease with increasing numbers of nodes? Rationalize your answer in terms of bonding and antibonding interactions between adjacent pairs of atoms.

16.22 How many vertical nodes are present in each of the following orbitals?
a. the π_4 molecular orbital of 1,3,5-hexatriene
b. the π_2 molecular orbital of the 2,4-pentadienyl cation
c. the HOMO of the 2,4-pentadienyl anion
d. the π_2 molecular orbital of the 2,4-pentadienyl anion
e. the LUMO of the 2,4-pentadienyl anion
f. the π_5 molecular orbital of 1,3,5,7-octatetraene

16.23 Sketch the HOMO for each of the following:
a. 1,3-butadiene in its first excited state b. the allyl anion c. the allyl cation

16.24 How many *total* nodes are there in each of the following orbitals?
a. the π_2 molecular orbital of ethylene b. a 2*p* orbital of carbon
c. the π_1 molecular orbital of ethylene d. the 1*s* orbital of hydrogen

16.25 How many π electrons should be included in the molecular orbital energy diagram for each of the following?
a. 1,3,5,7-cyclooctatetraene b. the 2,4-pentadienyl radical
c. cyclopropene d. the cyclopropenyl cation
e. furan f. pyridine

16.26 Compare the stabilities of the HOMOs of the 1,3,5-heptatrienyl cation and the cycloheptatrienyl cation. Which is more stable? Explain your answer. Compare the corresponding anions in the same way.

16.27 How many π electrons are stabilized and how many are destabilized upon transforming each of the following?
a. the 1,3,5-heptatrienyl cation to a tropylium ion
b. the allyl anion to a cyclopropenyl anion
c. the allyl cation to a cyclopropenyl cation

16.28 Arrange reactions *A* through *C* in increasing order of exothermicity.

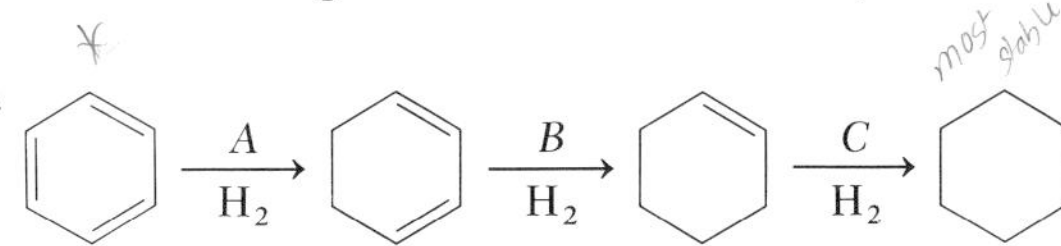

16.29 Which of the following species would be expected to exhibit aromatic characteristics?
a. cyclopropene b. cyclobutene c. 1,3-cyclobutadiene
d. cyclopropenyl anion e. cycloheptatrienyl anion f. bromobenzene

g. 1,3-cyclopentadiene h. 1,4,7-cyclooctatriene

i.

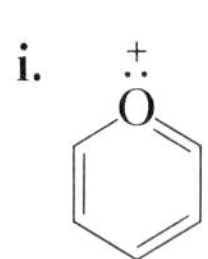

j.

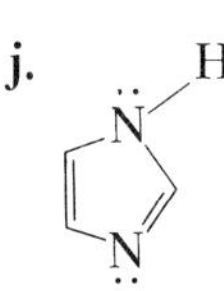

k.

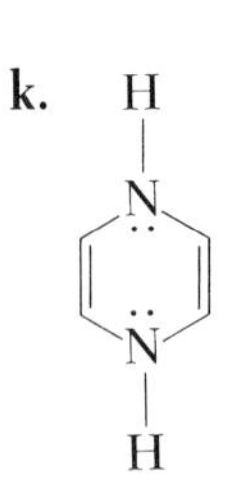

l. +

m.

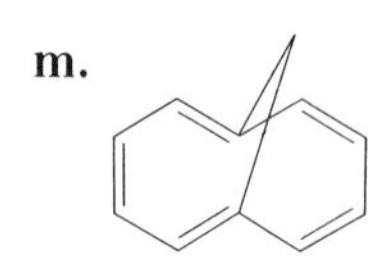

16.30 One of the following reactions requires a significantly lower pH than does the other. Decide which occurs at the lower pH and explain why it does.

H ÖH $\xrightarrow{H^+}$ H + H_2O

H ÖH $\xrightarrow{H^+}$ H + H_2O

16.31 Generally, resonance structures that involve charge separation are considered much less significant than those that do not involve charge separation. However, there are exceptions to this generalization, such as the molecule shown below. Explain why this charge-separated resonance structure is significant.

[C H_3C CH_3 ⟷ C + H_3C CH_3]

16.32 Draw significant charge-separated resonance structures for each of the following molecules. Explain why each is a significant representation of the molecule.

a.

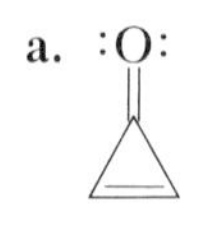

b.

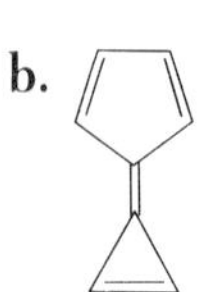

c.

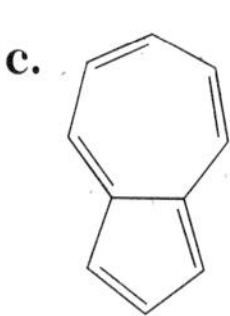

16.33 One of the following molecules has a molecular dipole in which the nitrogen is the negative pole. The other molecule has a molecular dipole in which the nitrogen is the positive pole. Explain this phenomenon using valence bond resonance structures.

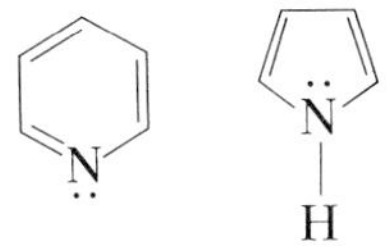

16.34 Antimony pentachloride ($SbCl_5$) is a Lewis acid that reacts with a wide range of halogen compounds according to the equation

$$RCl + SbCl_5 \longrightarrow R^+ + SbCl_6^-$$

Give the structure of organochlorine compounds that would react with $SbCl_5$ to yield aromatic carbocations with:

a. two π electrons **b.** six π electrons

16.35 Would you expect the reaction shown below to be exothermic or endothermic? Explain your answer.

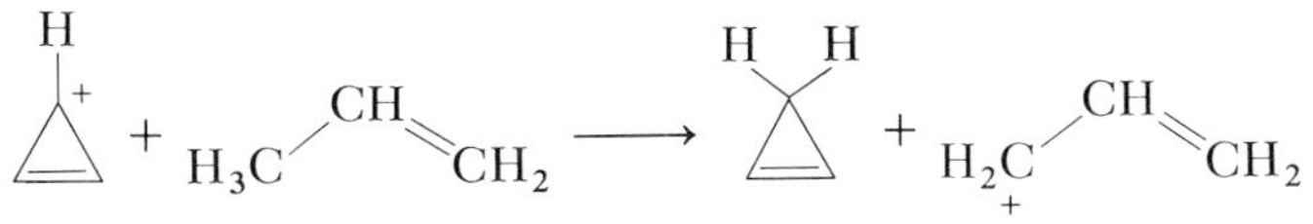

16.36 Which would you expect to be the stronger acid, cyclopropene or cyclopentadiene? Explain your answer.

16.37 Assuming the nitrogen atom to be the basic site, which would you expect to be the stronger base, pyridine or pyrrole? Explain.

16.38 Explain why one mole of molecule *A* (shown below) reacts with just one mole of antimony pentachloride (see Problem 16.34), while one mole of molecule *B* reacts readily with two moles of antimony pentachloride.

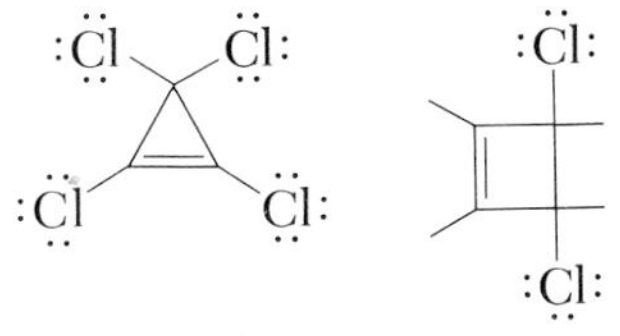

A *B*

16.39 Substance *C* (shown below) reacts with acid to give 2-methylpropene plus an aromatic carbocation. Write a complete mechanism for this reaction of *C* with acid.

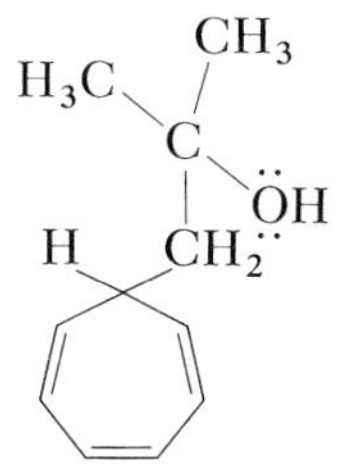

C

16.40 One of the reactions shown below occurs readily while the other reaction does not. Suggest a mechanism for the reaction that occurs readily. Explain why the other reaction does not occur readily.

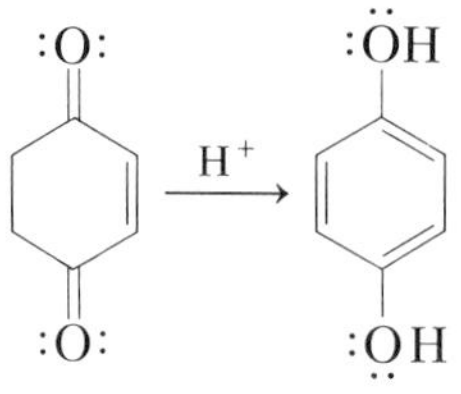

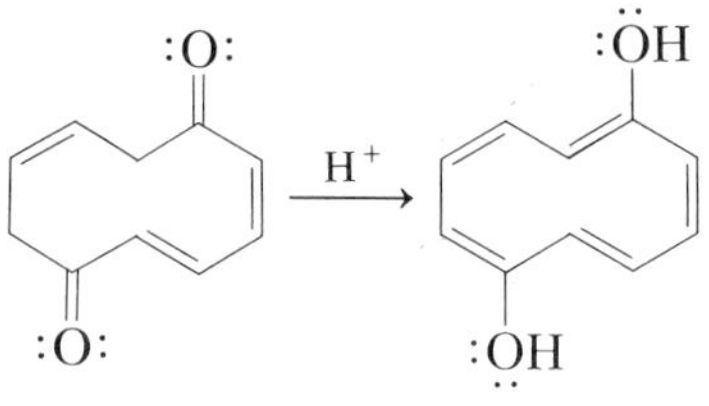

:O: :ÖH

$\xrightarrow{H^+}$

:O: :ÖH

:O: :ÖH

$\xrightarrow{H^+}$

:O: :ÖH

16.41 Which of the following radicals has the greater degree of stabilization? Explain your answer.

$$\dot{C}H_2{-}CH{=}CH{-}CH{=}CH_2 \quad \text{or} \quad H_2C{=}\underset{\dot{C}H_2}{\underset{|}{C}}{-}CH{=}CH_2$$

Physical Methods of Structural Elucidation: Infrared and Nuclear Magnetic Resonance Spectrometry

17.1 Introduction

How do we know the molecular structures of compounds we are studying? We have not yet considered this question, but now we turn our attention to it. We will consider some of the most important methods organic chemists use to determine structures. This area of study is very significant and has seen dramatic changes over the years. Indeed, organic chemists continue to adopt new and better experimental probes of structure, and we can anticipate continuing advances in methodology.

Although chemists usually perform reactions with starting materials of known structure, inevitably they must establish the structures of the reaction products. Even if a known reaction is being repeated, a chemist must establish that the desired product has actually formed and needs to know its purity.

Methods of structural determination are also particularly important in the area of natural-product chemistry. To understand the details of biological processes, we must know the structures of the molecules involved in them. Organic chemists determine the structures of natural products after isolating them from their sources. Natural products often present the greatest challenges for structural elucidation because of their skeletal and stereochemical complexities.

In the early years of organic chemistry, structural elucidation was a formidable task, even for relatively small molecules. The usual strategy involved attempting to relate a new compound to others of previously determined structure by studying reactions of known specificity. At times simple addition or substitution reactions would provide important structural clues. More often, systematic **degradations** played a critical role in structural determinations.

Degradation involves breaking the chemical bonds of molecules to produce smaller fragments, in the hope that the fragments will have simpler structures that are easier to analyze. For example, if we use ozonolysis to cleave molecules containing carbon-carbon double bonds, we can then identify the simpler fragments from their chemical and physical properties. Structural determination at times depends on further degradation of these products. Ultimately, we mentally reconstruct the original structure from the structures of the fragments.

In the past thirty years, chemists have made great advances in developing *physical* methods to complement (and often replace) the older chemical methods of structural determination. These physical methods involve various forms of spectrometry. For example, in infrared spectrometry we observe the change in the amount of light absorbed by a sample as we vary the wavelength of light through the infrared range. In this chapter we consider two techniques, infrared and nuclear magnetic resonance spectrometry, that allow us to reach structural conclusions with even miniscule amounts of sample, much less than is required for most degradation studies. Moreover, these techniques are non-destructive, that is, the sample can be recovered unchanged at the end of the spectrometric measurements.

17.2 Infrared Spectrometry

THE NATURE OF INFRARED RADIATION

In infrared (IR) spectrometry we measure the amount of radiation absorbed by a sample as the wavelength of the radiation is varied through the IR region. The IR region of the electromagnetic spectrum extends from the long-wavelength end of the visible to the short-wavelength end of the microwave (wavelengths of $\sim 0.75\ \mu m$ (7.5×10^{-7} m) to $\sim 50\ \mu m$ (5×10^{-5} m)). For most organic structural determinations, the range 2.5–15.0 μm is paticularly useful.

The **Planck equation** (Equation 17.1) allows the calculation of energy (E) from wavelength (λ).

Eqn. 17.1

$$E = hc/\lambda$$

where h is the Planck constant and c is the speed of light. IR radiation has energy that is in the range $1.3–8.0 \times 10^{20}$ J/photon (7.9–48.9 kJ/mole; 1.9–11.7 kcal/mole).

THE ABSORPTION OF ELECTROMAGNETIC RADIATION BY MOLECULES

When a molecule absorbs electromagnetic radiation (light) it passes from a relatively low initial energy state to a higher-energy final state, called an *excited state*, as illustrated in Figure 17.1.

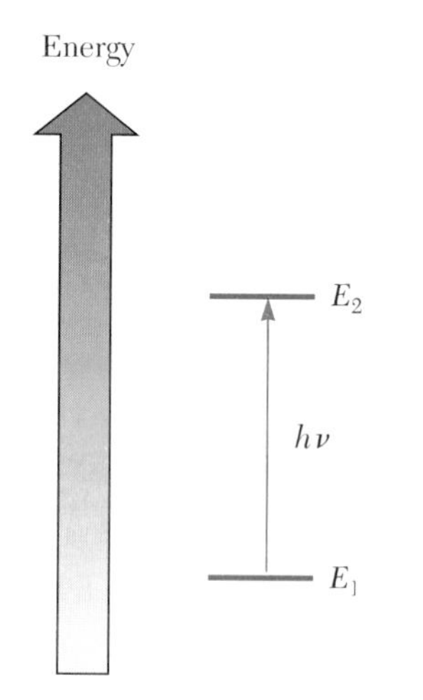

Figure 17.1 Absorption of electromagnetic radiation by a molecule. A molecule in a relatively low energy state (E_1) is energized to a higher energy state (E_2) by the absorption of electromagnetic radiation ($h\nu$). The energy gap between E_1 and E_2 must exactly match the energy of the light ($h\nu$) for the absorption to occur.

The absorption of any type of electromagnetic radiation by a molecule is a **quantized process.** That is, absorption of a photon occurs only if its energy exactly matches the energy difference between the two energy states involved. For example, an electronic transition from a ground state to an excited state of an atom or molecule requires that the photon energy be exactly equal to the energy difference between the two states. Upon absorption of this energy, an electron moves from a lower-energy orbital to a higher-energy orbital. Generally, atoms and molecules require relatively high energy photons (ultraviolet or visible electromagnetic radiation) for electronic excitations.

The energy associated with IR radiation is too small to cause electronic transitions in most molecules. However, IR radiation is in the proper energy range to cause transitions among the **vibrational levels** of a molecule. Absorption of an IR photon can cause a molecule to reach a higher vibrational level. We can think of vibrational levels as different degrees of enhancement of the **vibrational modes** that are always present in a molecule. A vibrational mode is some specific periodic movement of atoms in a molecule. The absorption of IR radiation does not cause a vibration but simply magnifies one already present. For example, the amplitude of a stretching vibration is increased if promotion to a higher vibrational level occurs, as is shown schematically in Figure 17.2.

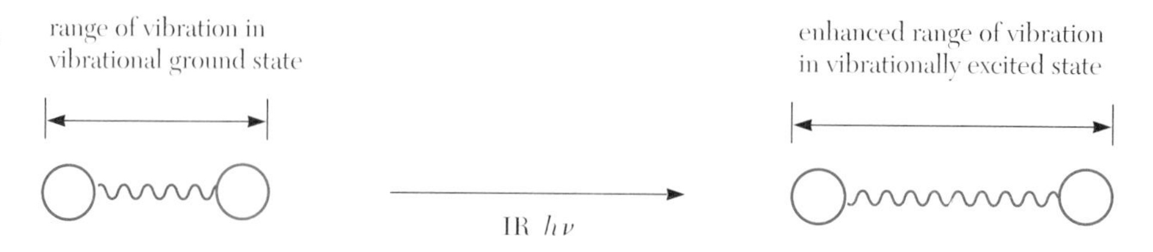

Figure 17.2 A stretching vibration of two atoms in a bond. A stretching vibration is a periodic increase and decrease of bond length. The atoms constantly vibrate, even in the lowest vibrational quantum level and even at absolute zero. Upon absorption of an IR photon of the proper energy, a higher vibrational level is reached and the amplitude of the vibration increases.

AN ANALOGY OF BONDS WITH SPRINGS

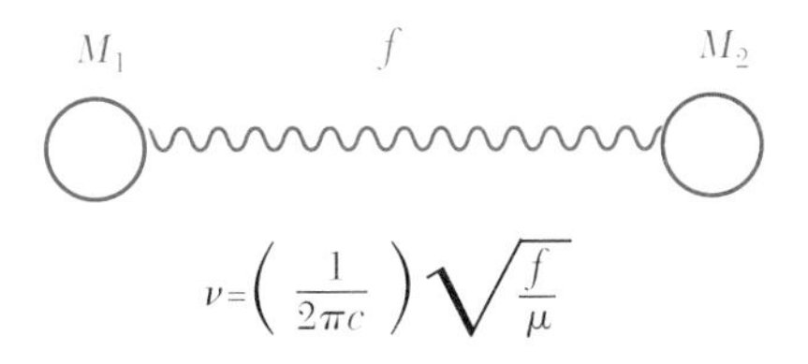

ν = frequency of vibration

μ = reduced mass of system defined by the equation $\frac{1}{\mu} = \frac{1}{M_1} + \frac{1}{M_2}$

f = force constant of the spring

c = velocity of light in a vacuum

M_1, M_2 = masses of the two bodies

Figure 17.3 Hooke's law for springs. The frequency of vibration of a spring depends on the force constant of the spring and the masses of the bodies attached to each end of the spring.

A useful way of thinking about a bond vibration is to make an analogy with a spring connecting two particles of known masses. The **frequency** of vibration (number of vibrations per unit time) *increases* with the strength (stiffness) of a spring and *decreases* as the masses at the ends of the spring increase. These relationships are expressed in Hooke's law, which is shown in Figure 17.3. Different bond strengths are the equivalent of different force constants for springs. Thus, carbon-carbon double bonds, which are stronger than carbon-carbon single bonds, have a larger force constant and a higher vibrational frequency. By using Hooke's law, we can also predict that a carbon-hydrogen stretching vibration will have a higher frequency than a carbon-carbon stretch, due to the lower mass (hydrogen) on one end of the spring (the carbon-hydrogen bond). These predictions are verified by experiment. Similarly, carbon-hydrogen bond stretching is predicted (and found) to have a higher frequency than carbon-deuterium stretching.

The frequency of a vibration is unchanged upon excitation by IR radiation. The bond makes the same number of oscillations each second as it did prior to excitation. The atoms at each end of the bond simply move *farther apart* on each oscillation. They move faster after excitation and therefore traverse a greater distance for a single oscillation.

BENDING VIBRATIONS

Bending as well as stretching vibrations occur in molecules. For example, the *scissoring* motion illustrated in Figure 17.4 is one type of bending vibration that can occur in a three-atom system. The atoms change their respective positions in the direction indicated and then return to their initial positions.

Molecules execute this scissoring vibration with a frequency that depends on the strengths of the bonds and the masses of the attached atoms. There are many other kinds of bending vibrations that molecules undergo. Some are useful in the determination of structure, as we will describe later.

CHARACTERISTIC ABSORPTIONS

In order for IR radiation to be absorbed, *the frequency of the radiation must equal the frequency of some vibration of the molecule.* Thus, if we can determine the frequencies of IR radiation a molecule absorbs, we will know the frequencies of the vibrations it undergoes. The use of IR spectrometry for structural determination depends mainly on empirical correlations of observed absorption frequencies with specific structural units or functional groups.

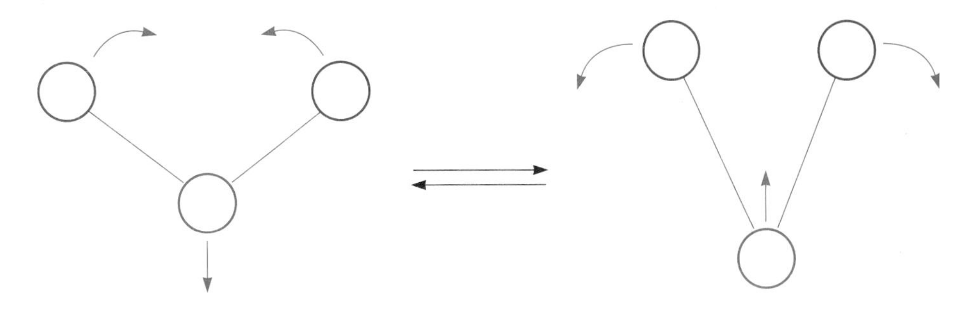

Figure 17.4 Scissoring motion (a bending vibration) in a three-atom system. A bending vibration involves periodic increase and decrease of the bond angle.

Rather than speaking directly of the *energy* of light needed to excite a particular vibration, organic chemists generally refer to the *wavelength* (measured in μm) or the *frequency* of the light. While frequency in simplest terms is the number of vibrations per unit of time (vibrations/sec, sec^{-1}, or Hertz), organic chemists usually replace frequency with a modified unit, *wavenumber*, which is the number of vibrations per centimeter. The units of wavenumber are reciprocal centimeters (1/cm or cm^{-1}).

The empirical correlations between absorbed frequencies and structural units work rather well because the same functional group has very similar vibrational modes in different compounds. For example, the stretching frequency of the carbon-oxygen single bond of ethers is approximately 1100 cm^{-1} in any particular ether under survey.

WHAT AN INFRARED SPECTROMETER MEASURES

An IR **spectrometer** is an instrument that measures the fraction of incident IR radiation that is transmitted by a sample over the range of IR frequencies (wavenumbers) scanned. The output of the spectrometer is a graph (or chart) showing the percent of incident light that is transmitted through the sample as a function of the wavenumber (and wavelength) of the IR light. This chart is known as the **IR spectrum** of the sample. A typical IR spectrum, that of 3,3-dimethyl-1-butene (**17.1**) is shown in Figure 17.5. The peaks in the spectrum (which look like icicles hanging from the top) show the intensity of absorption

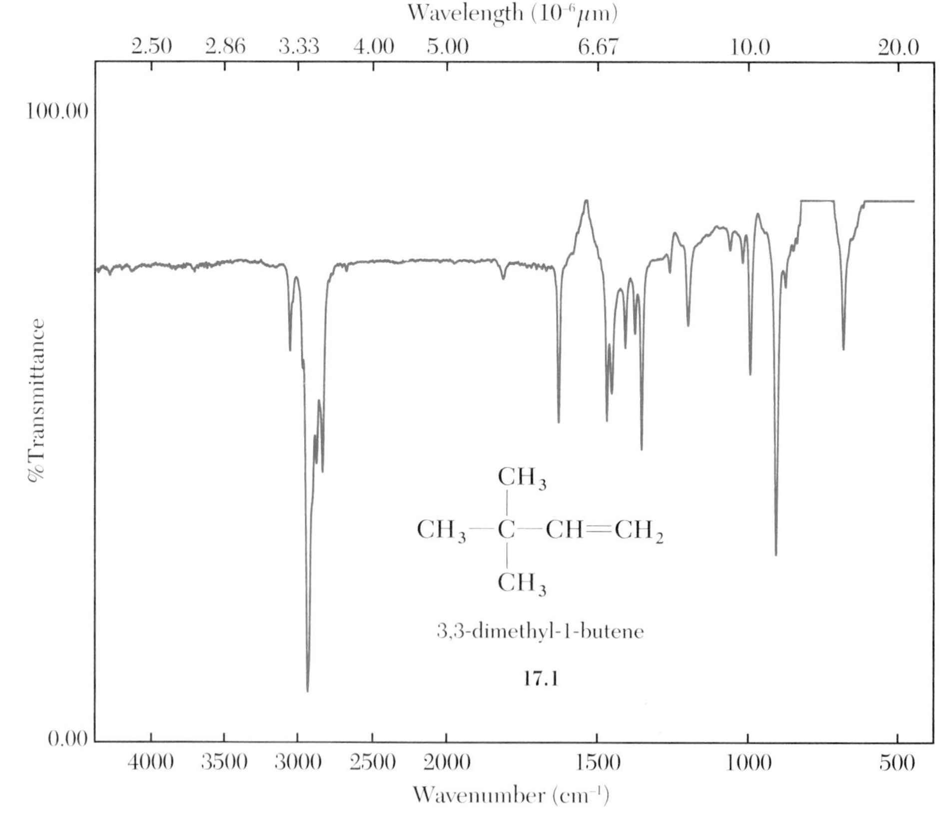

Figure 17.5 The IR spectrum of 3,3-dimethyl-1-butene. The wavelength of IR light impinging on the sample is indicated along the upper edge of the graph. The corresponding frequency is shown along the bottom of the graph as the wavenumber. Wavelength and frequency have an inverse relationship. Energy increases with increasing frequency but decreases with increasing wavelength of light. The percentage of light transmitted is shown on the vertical scale. The closer the absorption curve comes to the bottom of the graph, the stronger the absorption at that wavelength (frequency). The large peak at the left shows that this sample strongly absorbs IR radiation of ~3000 cm^{-1}. Other strong absorptions are also seen at lower frequencies. The peaks in the spectrum correlate with the vibrational modes of 3,3-dimethyl-1-butene; that is, one of the vibrational modes of 3,3-dimethyl-1-butene has a frequency of ~3000 cm^{-1}.

$$H_3C{-}C{\equiv}C{-}CH_3 \rightleftharpoons H_3C{-}C{\equiv}C{-}CH_3$$

2-butyne with triple bond contracted — 2-butyne with triple bond extended

dipole moment = 0 in both contracted and extended forms

Figure 17.6 Symmetrical stretching of the triple bond in 2-butyne. The symmetric stretching of a symmetric alkyne is IR inactive, that is, IR radiation of the frequency corresponding to the stretching of the triple bond is not absorbed. IR inactivity correlates with the absence of a change in dipole moment during vibration. This does not mean that 2-butyne has *no* peaks in its IR spectrum. Any vibration (such as a C—H stretch) that does result in a change in dipole moment is infrared active.

at the various frequencies of IR light and tell us the vibrational frequencies of the sample itself. The detailed spectrum serves as a fingerprint for the sample.

THE IMPORTANCE OF DIPOLE MOMENT

Some of the absorption bands (peaks) in the spectrum of 3,3-dimethyl-1-butene are strong, while others are weak. The intensity of a peak correlates with the efficiency of the absorption of IR radiation at that frequency. Efficient absorption leads to a strong peak, that is, most of the light is absorbed and little is transmitted. Inefficient absorption leads to a weak band—most light is transmitted, little is absorbed.

There is an important correlation between the dipolar properties of a bond that vibrates and the efficiency of IR light in enhancing that vibration. Specifically, IR radiation is efficiently absorbed if its frequency corresponds to the frequency of a vibrational mode that involves a change in dipole moment. If a vibrational mode involves a small (or zero) change in dipole moment, IR radiation matching the frequency of the vibrational mode is absorbed only inefficiently (or not at all). In the extreme case, symmetrical bonds undergoing symmetrical extension and contraction do not absorb IR light at all. Because of their symmetry, there is no change of dipole moment in such systems. Such vibrations are said to be **infrared inactive.** A molecule exhibiting this phenomenon, 2-butyne, is shown in Figure. 17.6.

INFRARED ANALYSIS

Instrumentation In order to measure the IR spectrum of a sample, we must have a spectrometer with several critical components:

1. a source of IR light
2. an agent for dispersing the light according to its wavelength (frequency)
3. a means for directing the light of variable frequency through the sample to be investigated
4. a detector for the light transmitted by the sample
5. a mechanism that compares the amount of light transmitted (or absorbed) with that incident upon the sample
6. a means of displaying the information in an easily used form

A schematic diagram of these components as used in a typical double-beam IR spectrometer is shown in Figure 17.7.

The IR light source is generally a ceramic rod. When this rod is heated by an electric current, it emits IR radiation. Although the radiation is emitted in all directions, narrow slits (collimators) allow only a narrow beam to enter the main region of the spectrometer, where it passes into a monochromator. A monochromator is either a prism or a grating that separates the IR light into

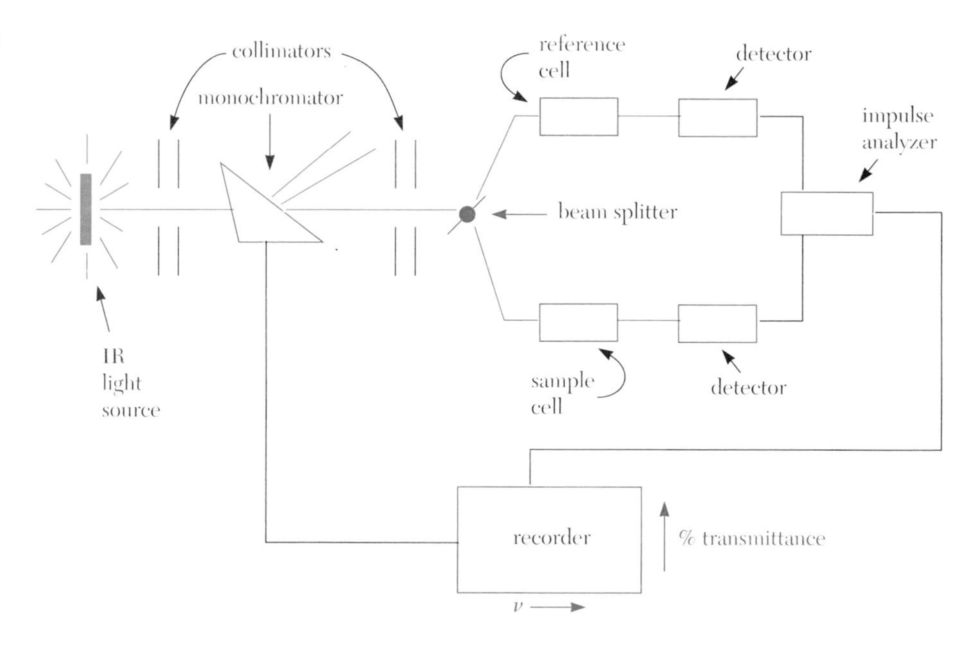

Figure 17.7 Diagram of a double-beam IR spectrometer. A single light source is split into reference and analyzing portions.

a spectrum (i.e., into its individual wavelength components). As the prism or grating rotates, light of continuously varying wavelength passes toward and through the sample.

The resulting beam of **monochromatic light** (light of only one wavelength) strikes the beam splitter, a rapidly rotating mirror. The beam splitter directs one part of the light toward the sample cell and another portion toward the reference cell. The sample to be investigated is held in the sample cell. The reference cell is of the same size and construction as the sample cell but contains only the solvent used to dissolve the sample. (In some cases no solvent is used with the sample, and consequently no reference cell is used.)

The detectors measure the amount of IR light transmitted by the sample and reference cells. For IR light, these detectors are thermocouples linked to a common reference point. The impulse analyzer subtracts the IR signal transmitted through the sample from that transmitted through the reference. This difference is sent to the recorder as an electrical potential (voltage) that produces a chart of wavelength (frequency) versus the transmittance of the sample.

Sample Preparation The physical state of the sample during the measurement of its IR spectrum is critical for proper understanding of that spectrum. Ideally, IR spectra should be measured on isolated molecules of the pure (neat) sample material so that we could observe *only* the simple vibrations of individual sample molecules. We can do this if we have the sample molecules in the gas phase at relatively low density.

While this is an ideal way to measure an IR spectrum, it is not practical for most organic molecules because they are too involatile. Instead, we must study them either in their condensed phases (as pure liquids or solids) or in solution.

It might seem that use of a pure liquid (or solid) would give a good presentation of the IR spectrum. However, there are strong interactions between molecules in the condensed phase, and these interactions obscure the simple vibrational absorption bands of individual molecules, particularly when the molecules contain highly polar bonds. Thus, we produce better (more clearly defined, more highly resolved) IR spectra if we dissolve the material in a suitable solvent.

The choice of an acceptable solvent is limited by several factors. First, the solvent should not react with the sample being studied. Second, it should have minimal absorption in the IR region—if the solvent absorbs all, or a major portion of the IR light, it will obscure the absorptions by the sample. Finally, the solvent must be compatible (i.e., unreactive) with the material from which the cells are constructed.

Cells are generally constructed of finely polished inorganic salt crystals. These salts are transparent to IR radiation (glass cells *cannot* be used because glass is an efficient absorber of IR radiation). Sodium chloride and potassium bromide crystals are most commonly used. To the uninitiated, these cells may look as though they are made of glass. However, since they are made not of glass but of simple inorganic salts, water cannot be used as a solvent. These IR cells dissolve if we add an aqueous solution to them (an embarrassing mistake, since cells are expensive). Even solvents such as methanol, ethanol, and DMSO partially dissolve these cells, so their use must be avoided for measuring IR spectra.

The most common solvents used for measuring IR spectra are carbon tetrachloride, chloroform, and carbon disulfide (CS_2). Carbon tetrachloride is reasonably transparent at frequencies higher than $800\ cm^{-1}$ but absorbs strongly at lower frequencies. In order to observe sample absorbances at frequencies lower than $800\ cm^{-1}$, of which there are a few of significance, we can use carbon disulfide. Carbon disulfide is a flammable, highly volatile, foul-smelling liquid that absorbs only in the region of $\sim 1320\ cm^{-1}$ of the IR spectrum. Elsewhere in the IR region it is transparent. Between these two solvents, we are able to observe sample absorptions in the entire range of the IR spectrum.

A further difficulty arises with compounds that are insoluble in these nonpolar solvents. In such cases we can measure the IR spectrum using a dispersion (rather than a solution) of the sample in an inert transparent material. Commonly, we disperse solid samples in a 100-fold excess of dry potassium bromide powder. The mixture is compressed into a transparent pellet and the IR spectrum of the pellet is measured. Potassium bromide is nominally transparent through the entire IR region; however, it rapidly absorbs moisture from the atmosphere, thus obscuring the region at frequencies greater than $3000\ cm^{-1}$. Alternatively, we can use dispersions (known as mulls) of the sample in mineral oil. Of course, the oil obscures the IR regions in which *it* absorbs (hydrocarbon mineral oils absorb strongly in the regions $2825–2980\ cm^{-1}$ and $1300–1500\ cm^{-1}$).

CHARACTERISTIC ABSORPTIONS OF ORGANIC FUNCTIONAL GROUPS

Examine again the spectrum of 3,3-dimethyl-1-butene shown in Figure 17.5. Like most IR spectra, it shows many peaks corresponding to the enhancement of many modes of vibrations. However, the majority of these peaks do not constitute a useful source of structural information. In fact, much of the raw data (i.e., peak position, shape, intensity) provided by an IR spectrum is not particularly useful to an organic chemist seeking structural information. Only the presence or absence of certain peaks indicates the unambiguous presence

Table 17.1 Characteristic IR Absorption Frequencies (Wavelengths) of Organic Functional Groups

Functional Group		Absorption (cm^{-1})	[μm]	Intensity
Alcohols (and other compounds containing the C—O—H linkage)				
O—H	**(stretch, H-bonded)**	**3200–3600**	**[2.78–3.12]**	**strong, broad**
	(free)	**3500–3700**	**[2.70–2.86]**	**strong, sharp**
C—O	**(stretch)**	**1050–1150**	**[8.69–9.52]**	**strong**
Alkanes (and alkyl groups)				
C—H	**(stretch)**	**2850–2960**	**[3.37–3.50]**	**strong**
—C—H	(bending)	1350–1480	[6.76–7.40]	variable
Alkenes				
=C—H	**(stretch)**	**3010–3100**	**[3.23–3.32]**	**medium**
=C—H	(bending)	675–1000	[10.0–14.8]	strong
C=C	**(stretch)**	**1620–1680**	**[5.95–6.17]**	**variable**
Alkyl Halides				
C—Cl	(stretch)	600–800	[12.5–16.7]	strong
C—Br	(stretch)	500–600	[16.7–20.0]	strong
C—I	(stretch)	500	[20.0]	strong
Alkynes				
C—H	**(stretch)**	**3300**	**[3.03]**	**strong**
—C≡C—	**(stretch)**	**2100–2260**	**[4.43–4.76]**	**variable**
Amines (and other N—H compounds)				
N—H	**(stretch)**	**3300–3500**	**[2.86–3.03]**	**medium**
C—N	**(stretch)**	**1080–1360**	**[7.35–9.26]**	**medium**
N—H	(bending)	1600	[6.25]	medium
Aromatics				
C—H	**(stretch)**	**3000–3100**	**[3.23–3.33]**	**medium**
C—C—H	(bending) and	690–710 730–770	[14.1–14.5] [13.0–13.7]	strong
ortho-disubstituted				
C—C—H	(bending)	735–770	[13.0–13.6]	strong
meta-disubstituted				
C—C—H	(bending) and	680–725 750–810	[13.8–14.7] [12.3–13.3]	strong
para-disubstituted				
C—C—H	(bending)	800–840	[11.9–12.5]	strong
Carbonyl Compounds (compounds containing the C=O group)				
C=O	**(stretch)**	**1670–1820**	**[5.62–6.05]**	**strong**

Table 17.1 (Continued)

Functional Group		Absorption (cm^{-1}) [μm]		Intensity
Ethers (and other C—O compounds)				
C—O	**(stretch)**	**1050–1175**	[8.51–9.52]	**strong**
Nitriles				
C≡N	**(stretch)**	**2210–2260**	[4.43–4.53]	**medium**
Nitro Compounds				
—NO_2	**(stretch)**	**1500–1600**	[6.25–6.67]	**strong**

or absence of important structural units. The topic of following sections will be finding these important pieces of information in IR spectra.

Correlation Tables and Charts Table 17.1 lists the characteristic absorptions of organic molecules by *functional group*. The most important characteristic absorptions are listed in boldface type. Figure 17.8 presents much of the same information but in a different manner. It shows characteristic absorptions as a function of *wavelength* (and *frequency*), along with the functional groups indicated by those absorptions.

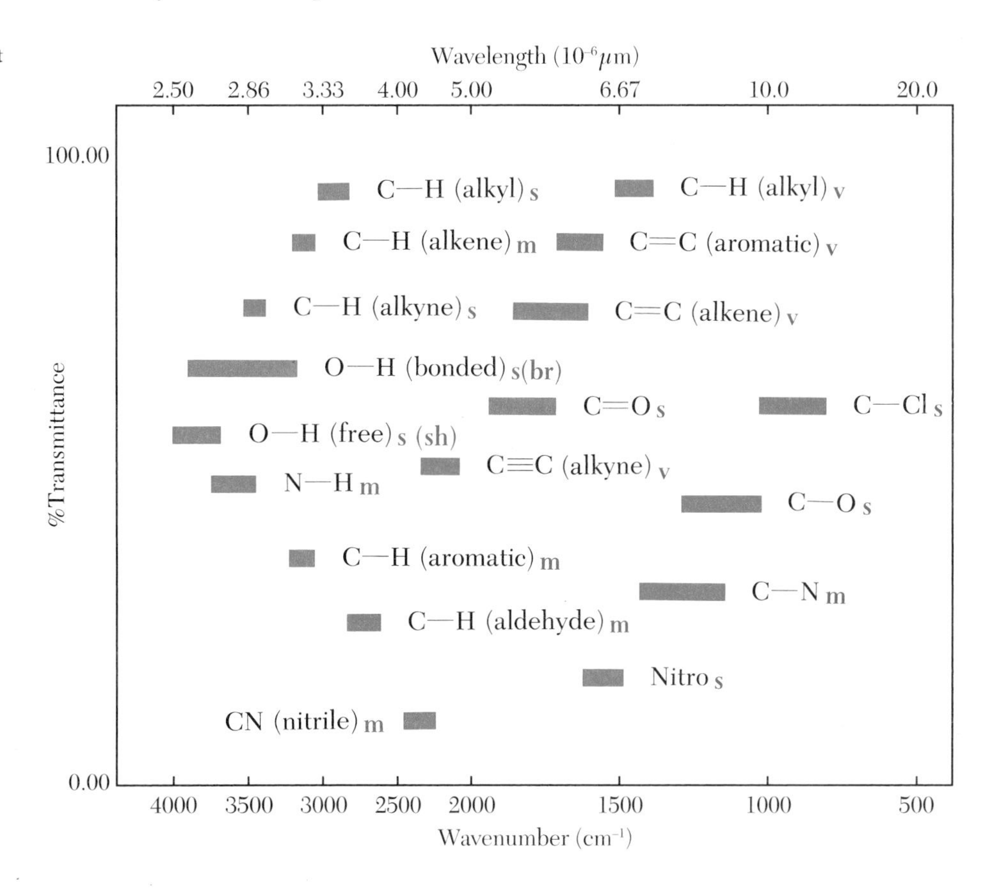

Figure 17.8 Assignment of absorptions at various IR frequencies (wavelengths). s = strong; m = medium; v = variable; sh = sharp; br = broad.

It is important that you quickly commit to memory the characteristic absorptions of the various functional groups and the important regions of the IR spectrum. As you study and interpret IR spectra, you will at first need to use these tables regularly. However, with experience, you will no longer need to refer to them so often.

INTERPRETED SPECTRA OF REPRESENTATIVE COMPOUNDS OF KNOWN STRUCTURE

The following spectra were measured using a 1% solution of the compound in carbon tetrachloride and a cell with a 0.1 mm path and windows (cell walls) of sodium chloride. As we consider these spectra, we will focus only on absorption bands that are particularly revealing in terms of the structure of the sample.

3,3-Dimethyl-1-Butene We will consider first the spectrum of 3,3-dimethyl-1-butene, shown previously in Figure 17.5 and reproduced in Figure 17.9. To begin, let us examine the region near 3000 cm^{-1}. This is the region where peaks associated with the stretching of carbon-hydrogen bonds appear.

Notice that there are two sets of absorptions near 3000 cm^{-1}. Those at higher energy (>3000 cm^{-1}) show the presence of olefinic (sp^2) carbon-hydrogen bonds, and those at lower energy (<3000 cm^{-1}) indicate the presence of alkyl (sp^3) carbon-hydrogen bonds. We can generally distinguish between the two types by their location relative to (i.e., above or below) the 3000 cm^{-1} point in the IR spectrum.

Figure 17.9 IR spectrum of 3,3-dimethyl-1-butene.

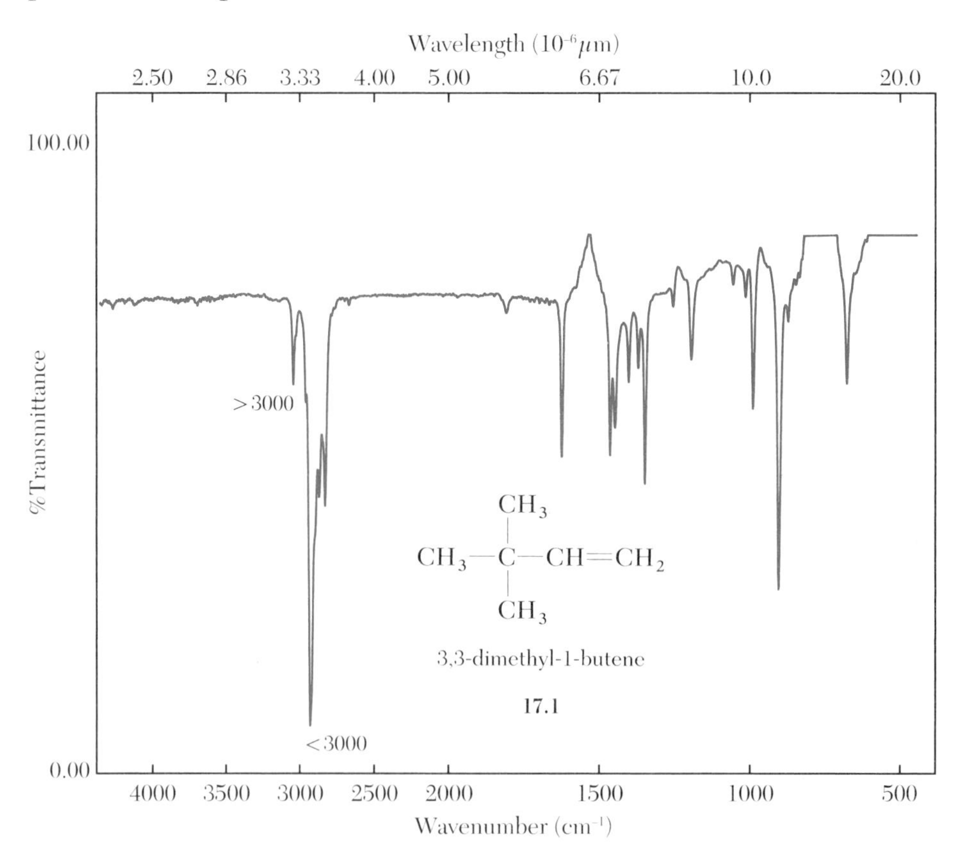

PROBLEM 17.1 According to their IR spectral absorptions, which is the stronger type of bond, sp^2 carbon-hydrogen or sp^3 carbon-hydrogen? Offer an explanation for the different bond strengths.

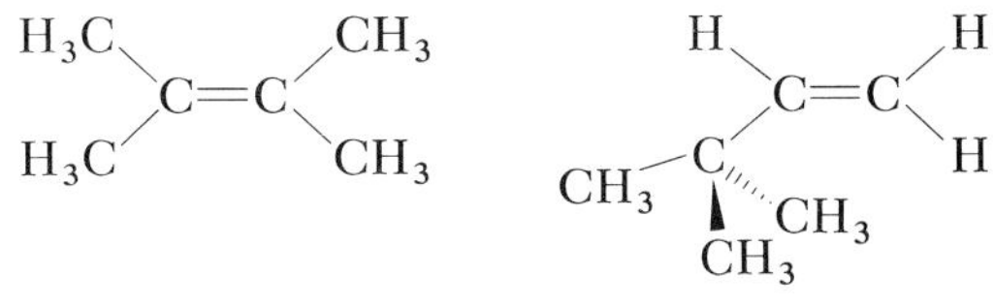

Figure 17.10 Isomeric structures of formula C_6H_{12}. The 2,3-dimethyl-2-butene molecule is completely symmetric about the carbon-carbon double bond. No IR absorption is observed for this bond, as it is IR inactive due to symmetry. However, a relatively strong absorption band is found for the carbon-carbon double bond of 3,3-dimethyl-1-butene. This molecule is not symmetric about the olefinic linkage.

$(H_3C)_2C{=}C(CH_3)_2$ — 2,3-dimethyl-2-butene

$H_2C{=}CH{-}C(CH_3)_3$ — 3,3-dimethyl-1-butene

The relatively strong absorption at 1652 cm^{-1} results from the carbon-carbon double-bond stretching vibration. The strength of the absorption suggests unsymmetrical substitution about the double bond. Recall that efficient absorption of IR radiation (and a strong band in the IR spectrum) requires a large change in the bond dipole moment on vibration, and thus the bond undergoing vibration must be unsymmetrically substituted. For example, the isomeric 2,3-dimethyl-2-butene shows *no* absorption band in the 1600–1700 cm^{-1} region because the double-bond stretching vibration of this compound is inactive due to symmetry (no change in dipole moment occurs during vibration). Figure 17.10 shows the structures of the two compounds, emphasizing their respective symmetries.

Finally, note the presence of alkyl (H—C—H) bending absorptions in the region 1360–1500 cm^{-1}. Bands in this region not only indicate the presence of alkyl groups but sometimes allow us to deduce *which* alkyl groups are present. For example, methyl groups exhibit a peak at 1380 cm^{-1}. This peak is due to the methyl asymmetric bending vibration shown in Figure 17.11. Compounds lacking a methyl group lack this band in their IR spectra. When an isopropyl group is present, this band is split into two components in a rather symmetrical fashion. With a *tert*-butyl group, the band is again split into two components, but not symmetrically. Typical alkyl bands are shown in Figure 17.12.

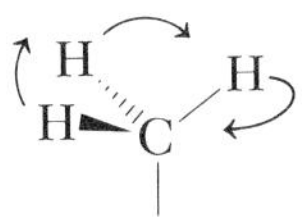

Figure 17.11 Methyl asymmetric bending vibration. This vibration produces an absorption band in the IR spectrum at 1380 cm^{-1}.

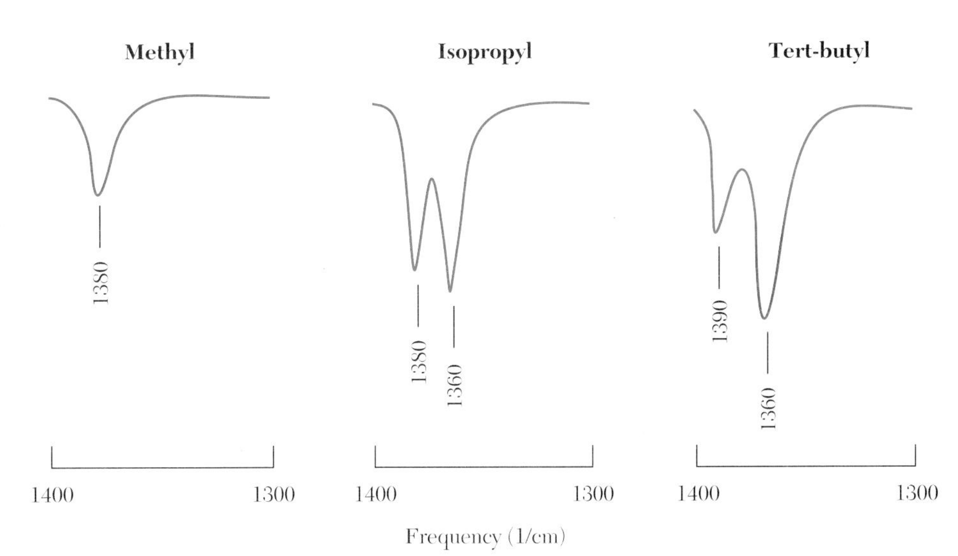

Figure 17.12 Alkyl bending absorptions for methyl, isopropyl, and *tert*-butyl groups.

Cyclohexene The IR spectrum of cyclohexene (**17.2**) is shown in Figure 17.13. Cyclohexene and 3,3-dimethyl-1-butene (the previous sample) might be expected to have similar IR spectra, since both are relatively simple alkenes. In fact, while they have some similarities, they also have striking differences. Again we see two types of carbon-hydrogen stretching absorptions corresponding to olefinic and alkyl carbon-hydrogen bonds, located above and below 3000 cm^{-1}, respectively. The absorption for the carbon-carbon double-bond stretching mode is virtually invisible in this spectrum (at 1625 cm^{-1}). It is significantly weaker than the corresponding band of 3,3-dimethyl-1-butene and becomes visible only in spectra from a more concentrated sample. In general, terminal olefinic linkages give more intense C=C stretching bands than do internal C=C bonds, which have greater symmetry (and smaller resultant dipoles).

Figure 17.13 IR spectrum of cyclohexene.

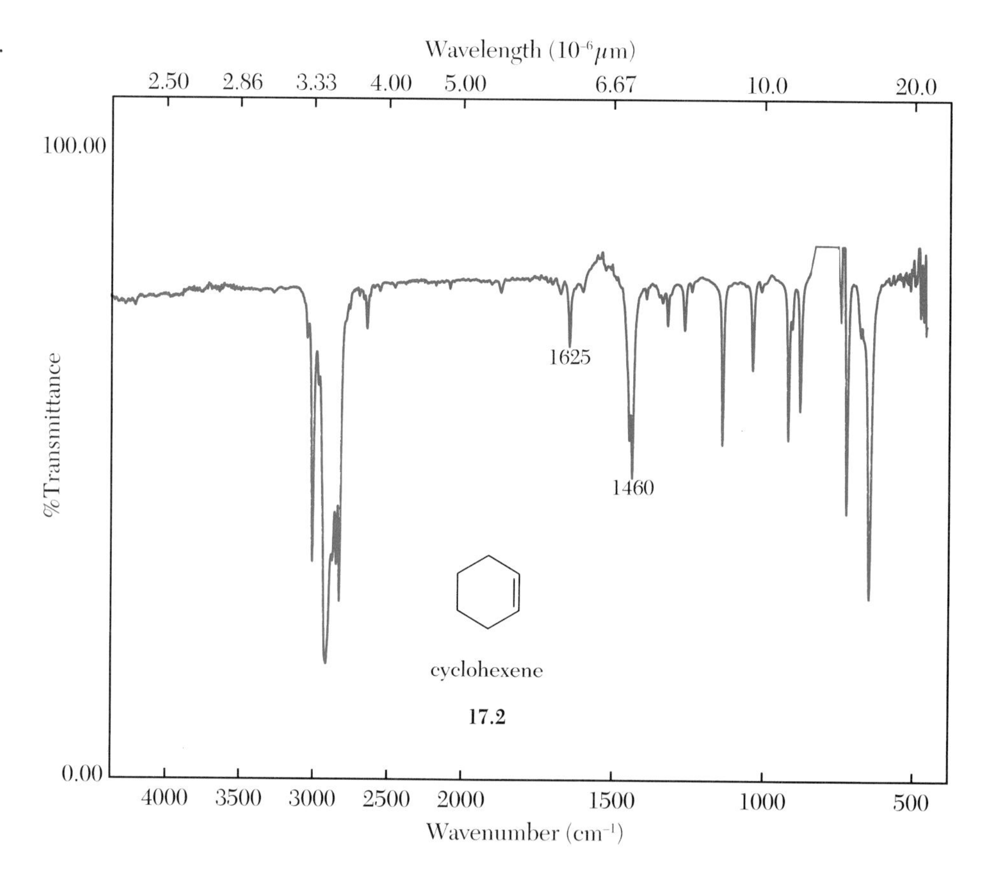

Alkyl bending absorptions are also present in the cyclohexene spectrum but are significantly different from those of 3,3-dimethyl-1-butene. Only methylene (—CH_2—) alkyl bending vibrations are present for cyclohexene, while methyl group bending vibrations are present in the 3,3-dimethyl-1-butene spectrum. Methylene groups in cycloalkanes and cycloalkenes generally give rise to a relatively sharp band at 1460 cm^{-1}.

Differences in IR spectra serve as a kind of fingerprinting technique for compounds. A compound's IR spectrum is as unique to it as fingerprints are to a human, as long as the spectrum is measured under the same conditions each time. In fact, the region of the IR spectrum from ~1250–500 cm^{-1} is known as the *fingerprint region*. Absorptions in this region are the result of a complex combination of rotations and vibrations that are unique to a given molecule. There is little chance that two different compounds will have identical spectra in the fingerprint region, even though they might be quite similar in the functional group region (above 1250 cm^{-1}).

2-Methyl-2-butene The IR spectrum of 2-methyl-2-butene (**17.3**) is shown in Figure 17.14. It provides another example of the IR spectrum of a simple alkene. The absorption in the carbon-hydrogen stretching region is almost (but not quite) completely due to alkyl carbon-hydrogen bonds (<3000 cm^{-1}). This is consistent with the presence of many more alkyl than olefinic carbon-hydrogen bonds. As is common with trisubstituted alkenes, the C=C stretching absorption is very weak. In contrast, the alkyl bending absorptions are strong and sharp, indicating the presence of methyl groups. From the spectrum we can infer that these methyl groups are *not* associated with an isopropyl or *tert*-butyl group. If they were, the peak for alkyl bending would be split (see Figure 17.12).

Figure 17.14 IR spectrum of 2-methyl-2-butene.

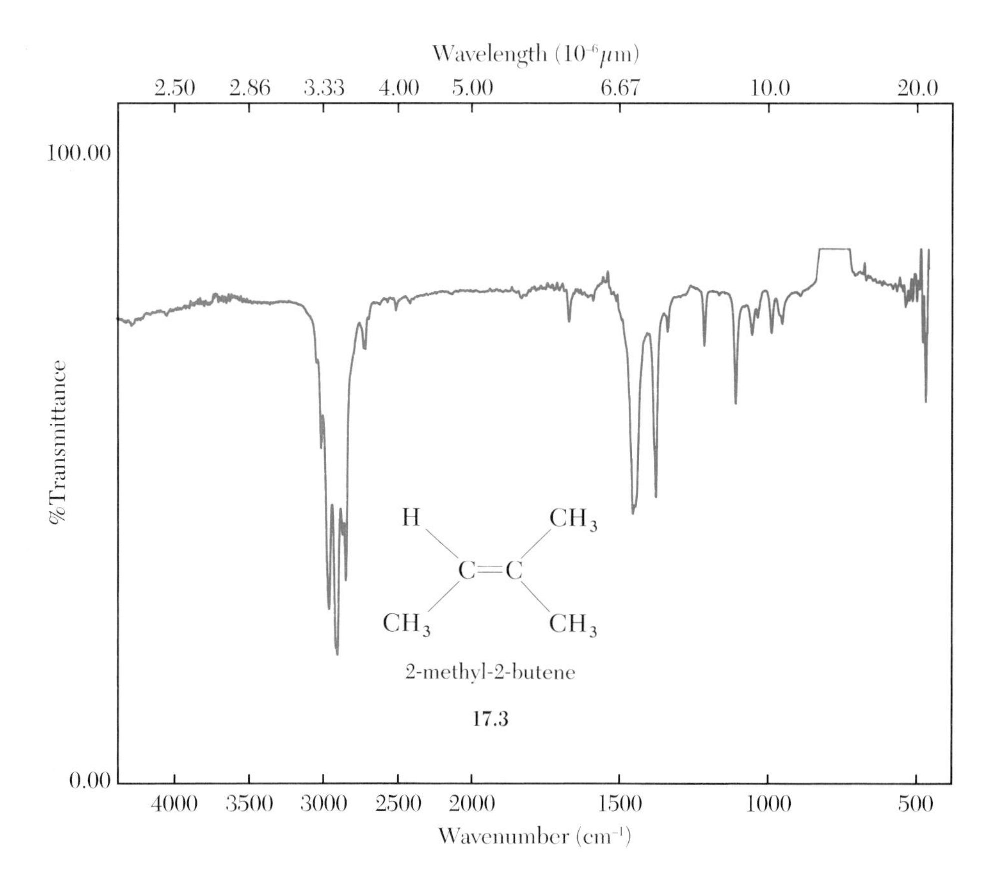

Figure 17.15 IR spectrum of *cis*-1,2-dichloroethene.

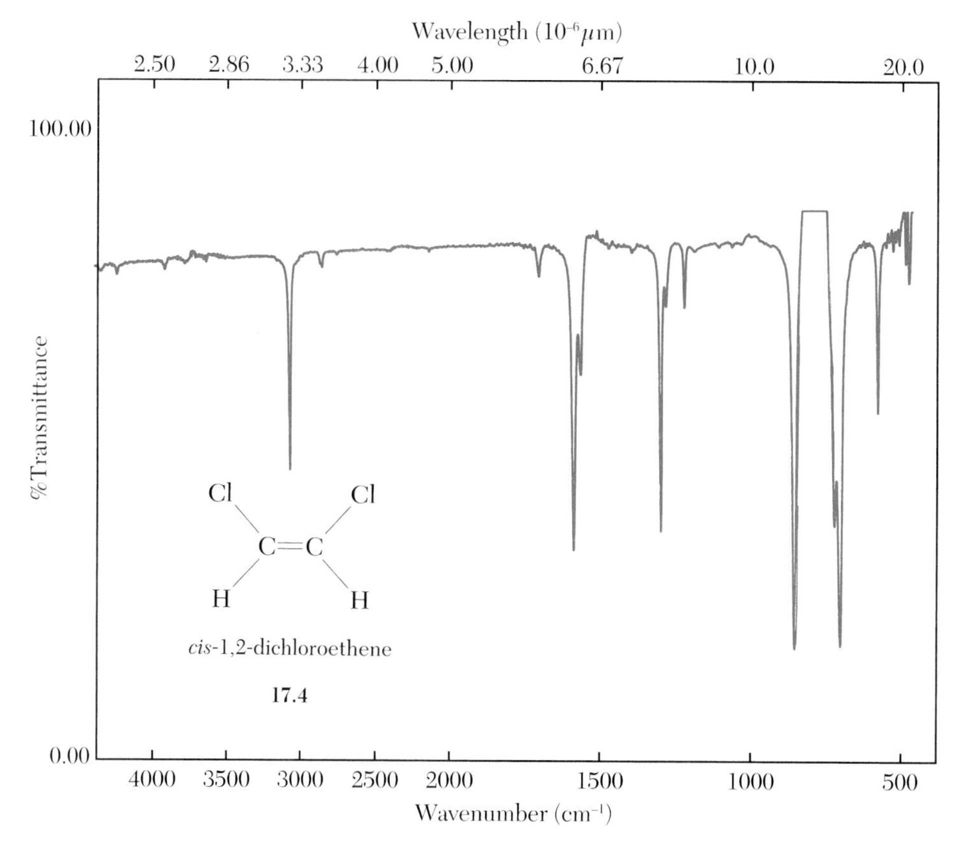

Figure 17.16 IR spectrum of *trans*-1,2-dichloroethene.

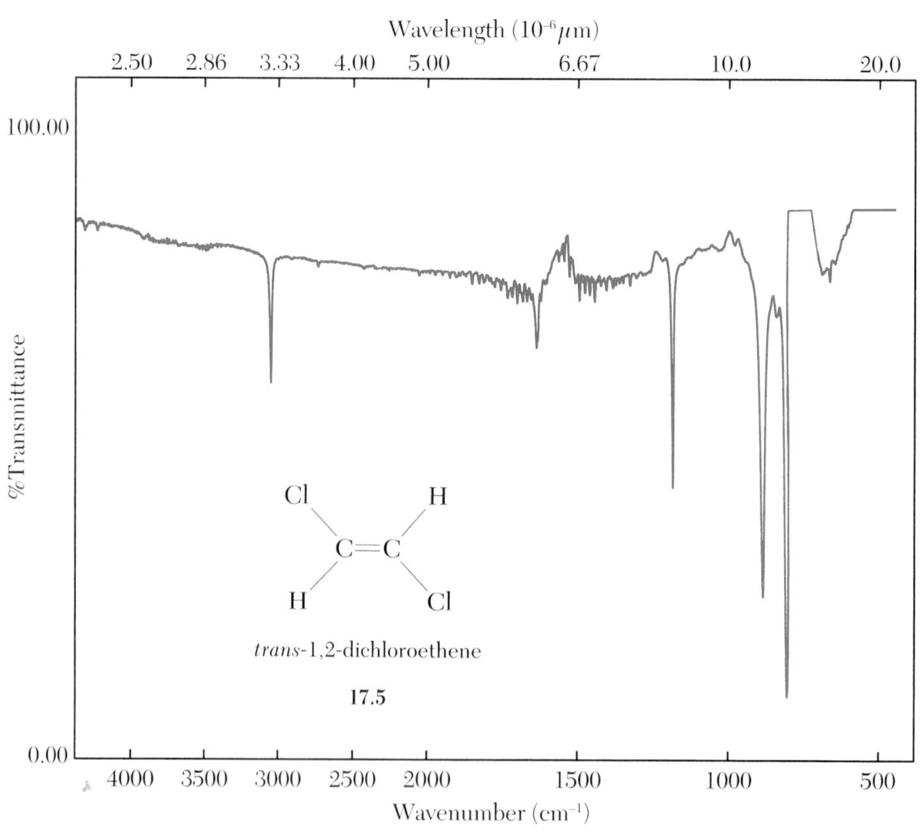

***cis*- and *trans*-1,2-Dichloroethene** The IR spectra for *cis*- (**17.4**) and *trans*-1,2-dichloroethene (**17.5**) are shown in Figures 17.15 and 17.16, respectively. The carbon-hydrogen stretching region of each lacks absorption below 3000 cm^{-1}, consistent with the absence of alkyl carbon-hydrogen bonds. The sharp carbon-hydrogen bands that are present (>3000 cm^{-1}) result from stretching of the olefinic carbon-hydrogen bonds. The C=C stretching band is stronger in the spectrum of the *cis* compound than in the spectrum of the *trans*-isomer as the result of a greater dipole moment change in the stretch of the *cis* isomer.

2-Methoxyethanol The IR spectrum of 2-methoxyethanol (**17.6**) is shown in Figure 17.17.

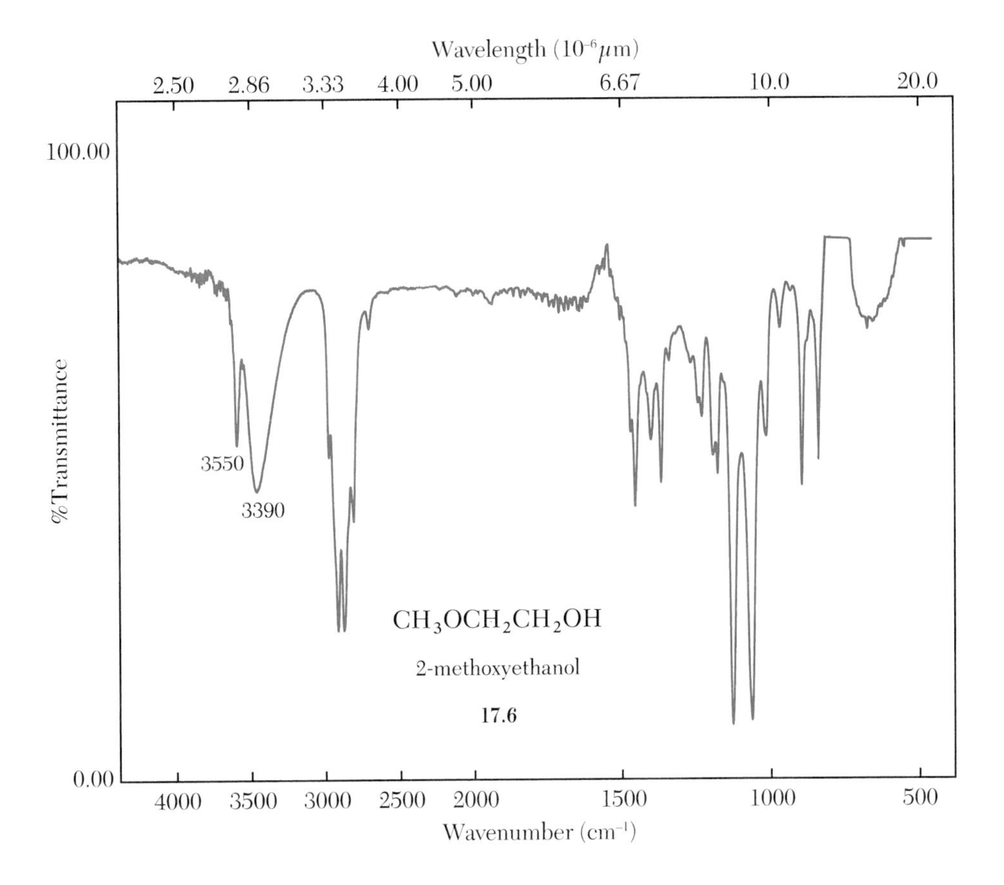

Figure 17.17 IR spectrum of 2-methoxyethanol.

The most striking difference between this sample and the previous ones is that it shows a significant absorption in the 3200–3600 cm^{-1} region. This region was clear in the earlier spectra we studied. Bands in this region are usually the signature of the O—H stretch of a hydroxyl group or the N—H stretch of an amino group. Here the absorption is the result of the hydroxyl group of the 2-methoxyethanol. Careful examination of the absorption shows that it consists of two parts. There is a sharp absorption peak at ~3550 $cm^{-1}$and a broad absorption band at lower frequency (centered at ~3390 cm^{-1}). The two components of the absorption result from the hydroxyl groups of individual sample molecules in two types of environment. Some are hydrogen-bonded to other alcohol molecules, and some are free (not hydrogen-bonded). The free hydroxyl groups account for the relatively sharp absorption band at 3550 cm^{-1}. The hydrogen-bonded hydroxyl groups produce the broad absorption band at 3390 cm^{-1}. The broadness of the latter absorption results from varying degrees of hydrogen bonding among the sample molecules. Slightly different degrees of hydrogen bonding result in slightly different O—H stretching frequencies. The IR absorption band is a composite of all of these slightly different O—H stretches.

When the concentration of the sample in the solution is decreased, the hydrogen-bonded absorption decreases in intensity and at the same time, the intensity of the free absorption band increases. In highly concentrated samples or with the pure material, we see only the absorptions by hydrogen-bonded species.

Although both N—H and O—H stretching vibrations have similar frequencies, we can usually distinguish amines from alcohols with little difficulty. Solubility, pH determination (some amines are basic in aqueous solution, alcohols are not), and elemental analysis (amines contain nitrogen) provide nonspectroscopic data to supplement IR (and other spectroscopic) analyses.

Phenylacetylene The IR spectrum of phenylacetylene (**17.7**) is shown in Figure 17.18.

Figure 17.18 IR spectrum of phenylacetylene.

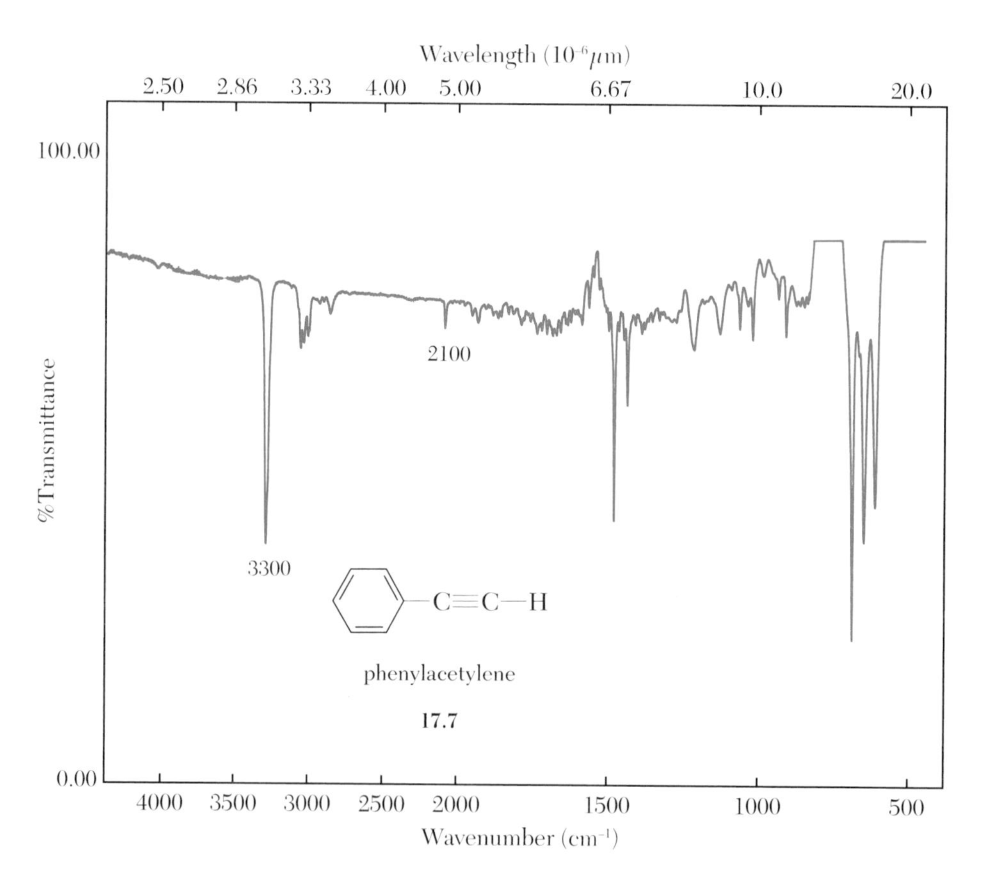

Phenylacetylene exhibits a sharp absorption peak at the relatively high frequency of 3300 cm^{-1}. While this is the region in which we expect to find O—H or N—H absorptions, the sharpness of the band is not typical for either type of bond. The additional presence of a weak absorption peak at 2100 cm^{-1} is consistent with a terminal alkyne. The high-frequency absorption (3300 cm^{-1}) is due to the acetylenic carbon-hydrogen stretch. The weak absorption at 2100 cm^{-1} results from the carbon-carbon triple bond stretching. Symmetric alkynes show no carbon–carbon triple bond stretch in the IR (see earlier discussion), and non-symmetric internal alkynes also show no, or very weak, absorption in the 2100 cm^{-1} region.

Cyclohexanone The IR spectrum of cyclohexanone (**17.8**) is shown in Figure 17.19.

Figure 17.19 IR spectrum of cyclohexanone.

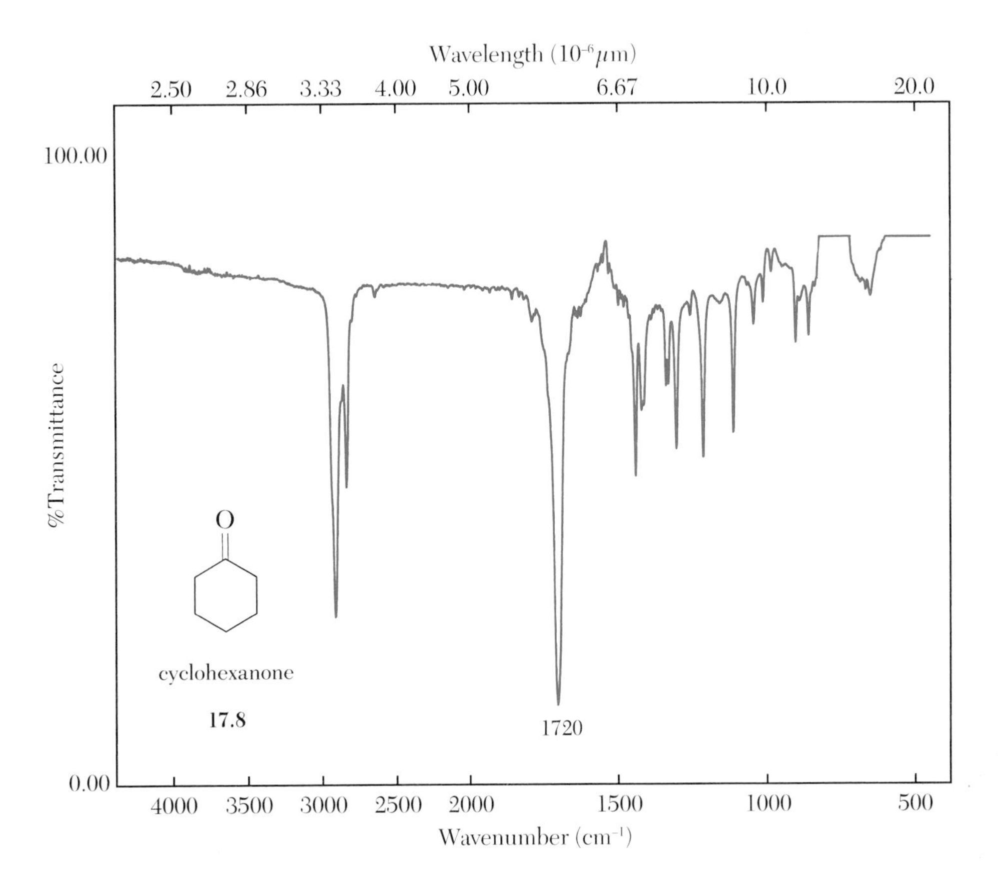

It shows a dominant carbonyl (C═O) stretching absorption at 1720 cm^{-1}. We can easily identify carbonyl groups using IR spectrometry because they give rise to characteristically intense absorptions in the region 1680–1800 cm^{-1}. Other functional groups do not interfere in this region of the IR spectrum. Simple aldehydes and ketones (such as cyclohexanone) always show intense absorptions close to 1720 cm^{-1}. The exact frequency depends on structure. For example angle strain associated with the carbonyl group in small rings raises the frequency of absorption and conjugation of the carbonyl group with an olefinic linkage (C=C—C=O) lowers the frequency of the carbonyl (and the C=C stretching) absorption.

Pentanal The IR spectrum of pentanal (**17.9**) is shown in Figure 17.20.

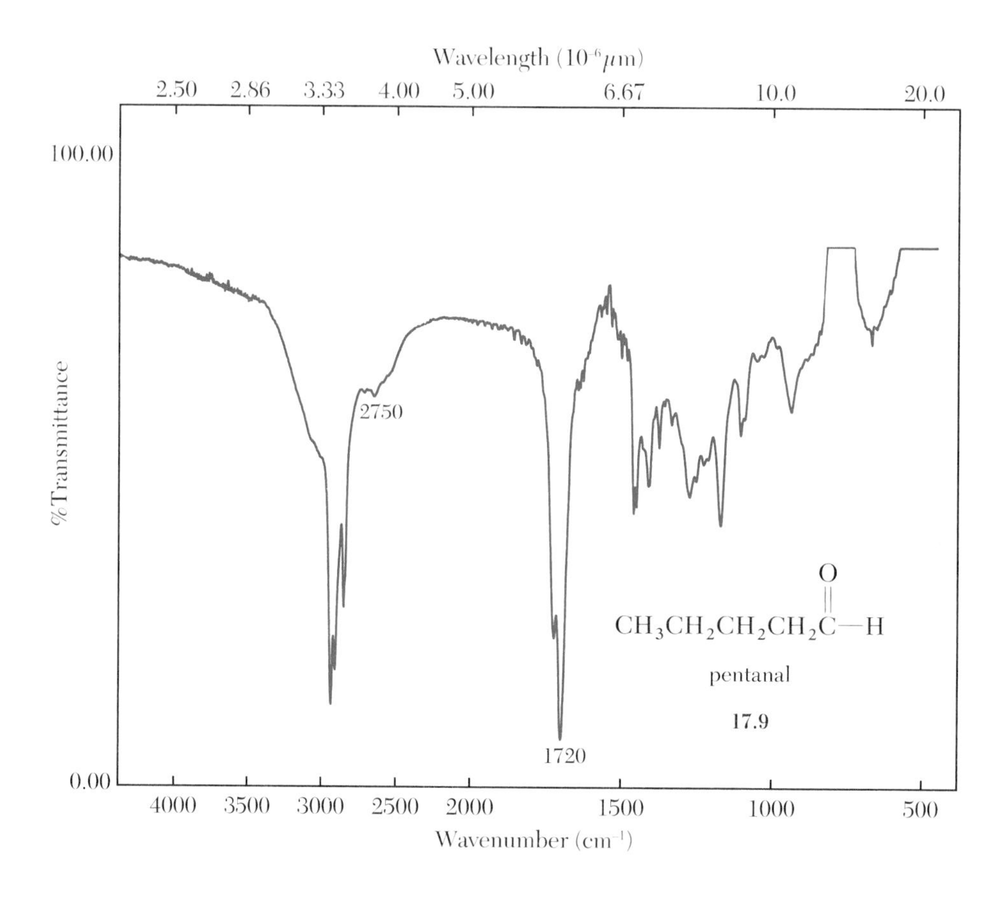

Figure 17.20 **IR spectrum of pentanal.**

Although its intensity is low, the absorption at ~2750 cm^{-1} is important because it is associated with the stretching vibration of the aldehydic (—CHO) carbon-hydrogen bond. This frequency is quite characteristic of aldehydic carbon-hydrogen bonds and is easily spotted since it occurs at significantly lower frequency than other carbon-hydrogen stretchings. Notice also that this spectrum, like the one of cyclohexanone, shows an intense absorption near 1720 cm^{-1} due to carbonyl stretching.

Ethyl Formate The IR spectrum of ethyl formate (**17.10**) is shown in Figure 17.21. There is a major absorption band at ~1740 cm^{-1}. As in the previous

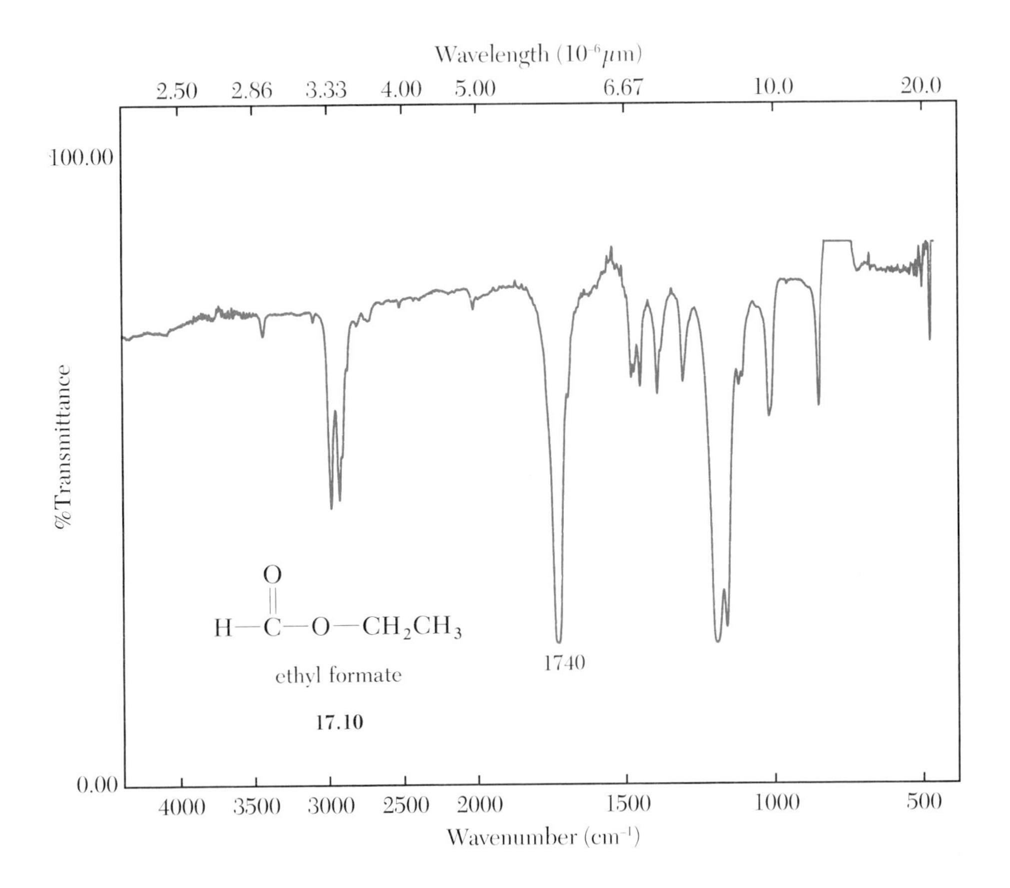

Figure 17.21 IR spectrum of ethyl formate.

two spectra, this absorption results from the stretching vibration of a C=O group. Absorption by the C=O group in ethyl formate occurs at slightly higher frequency than for either cyclohexanone or pentanal because the C=O group in ethyl formate is part of an ester linkage. We also see in this spectrum an intense absorption for the carbon-oxygen single-bond stretching of the ester linkage. This type of absorption commonly occurs in the region 1100–1200 cm^{-1}.

Ethyl Acrylate The IR spectrum of ethyl acrylate (**17.11**) is shown in Figure 17.22. The most notable feature of the spectrum is that both the C=O (1720 cm^{-1}) and C=C (1610 cm^{-1}) groups produce intense absorption bands.

Butanoic Acid The IR spectrum of butanoic acid (**17.12**) is shown in Figure 17.23. The most notable feature of this spectrum is the very broad absorption over the range 2500–3500 cm^{-1}. This type of broad absorption is typical in the IR spectra of carboxylic acids and is associated with the O—H stretching vibration. The unusual broadness is attributable to the great variety of hydrogen-bonding interactions that exist among carboxylic acid molecules (see Chapter 22). Notice that this sample, like the previous four, exhibits a strong C=O

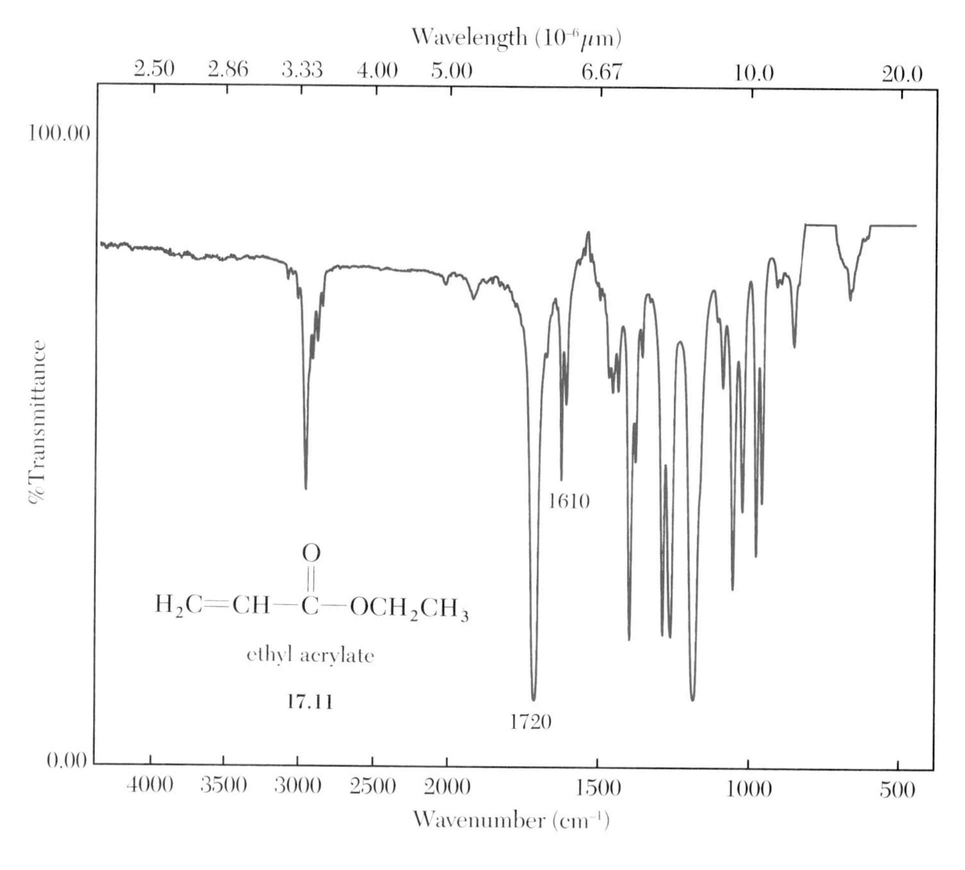

Figure 17.22 IR spectrum of ethyl acrylate.

stretching absorption. The exact position of this absorption in the IR spectra of carboxylic acids varies with concentration and solvent.

PROBLEM 17.2 Predict the major IR absorption bands for each of the following compounds:

a. $H_2C{=}CHCH_2CH(CH_3)_2$

b. cyclohexyl–C(=:O:)–CH_2CH_3

c. CH_3CH_2–(benzene ring, meta)–$C{\equiv}N:$

d. $CH_3CH_2{-}C{\equiv}C{-}CH_2CH_3$

PROBLEM 17.3 Acetone and ethanol are both good solvents for organic compounds. That is, they are capable of dissolving significant amounts of other organic materials. Why, then, would they *not* be suitable solvents for the measurement of IR spectra of organic materials?

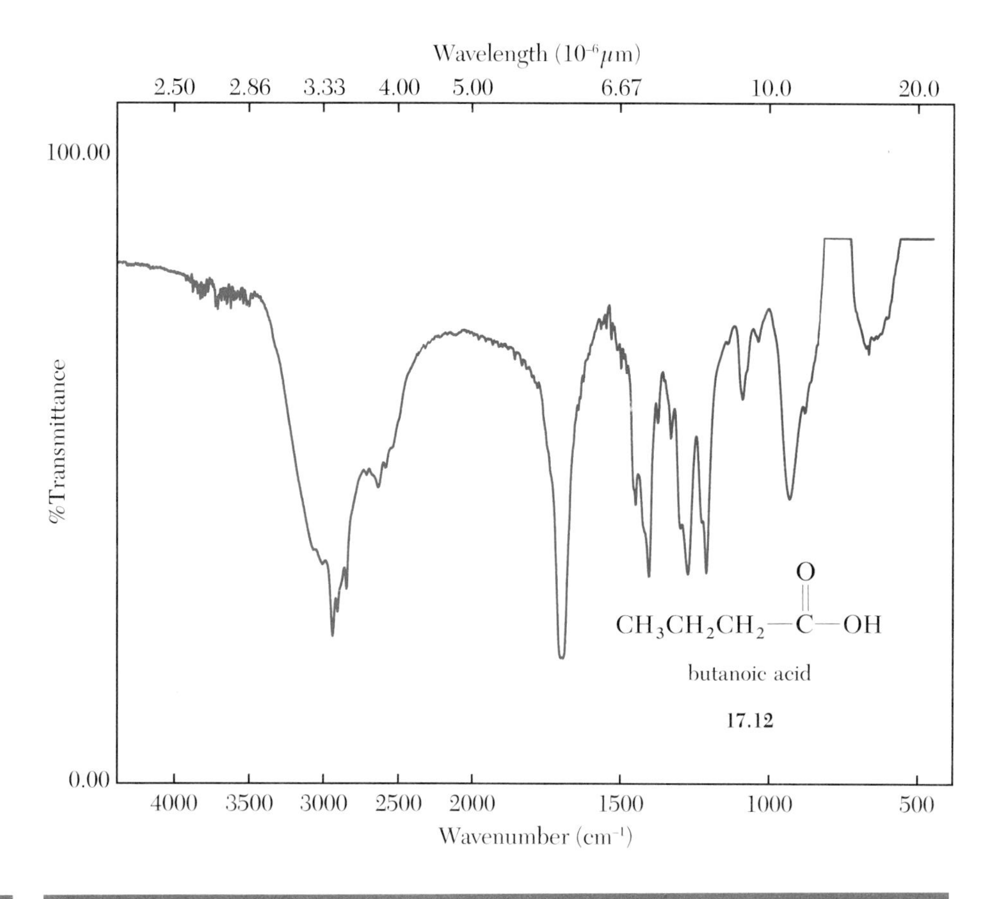

Figure 17.23 IR spectrum of butanoic acid.

PROBLEM 17.4 Alcohols often exhibit a change in their absorption in the hydroxyl region when their concentration in carbon tetrachloride is changed (see the discussion of the 2-methoxyethanol spectrum). On dilution, the intensity of the free hydroxyl absorption usually increases relative to that of the bonded hydroxyl absorption. However, the IR spectrum of *trans*-1,2-dihydroxycyclohexane shows only hydrogen-bonded hydroxyl absorption even under extremely dilute conditions. Rationalize this observation.

STRATEGY FOR INTERPRETING THE IR SPECTRUM OF AN UNKNOWN COMPOUND

The spectra shown in the previous section illustrate many of the important correlations between structure and IR absorption. From the investigation of the IR spectra of many compounds, we can make very good correlations between the positions, shapes, and intensities of IR absorptions and detailed structural features. So far we have examined the IR spectrum of compounds of known structure. How should you proceed when working with an unknown material? It is prudent for beginners to follow a systematic strategy. You should examine different regions of the IR spectrum in turn, looking in each for the presence

Figure 17.24 Flowchart for a systematic analysis of IR spectra. We analyze the IR spectrum in four stages. Each stage is a subsection of the figure. The three symbols used in the flowchart are explained at the beginning of the figure.

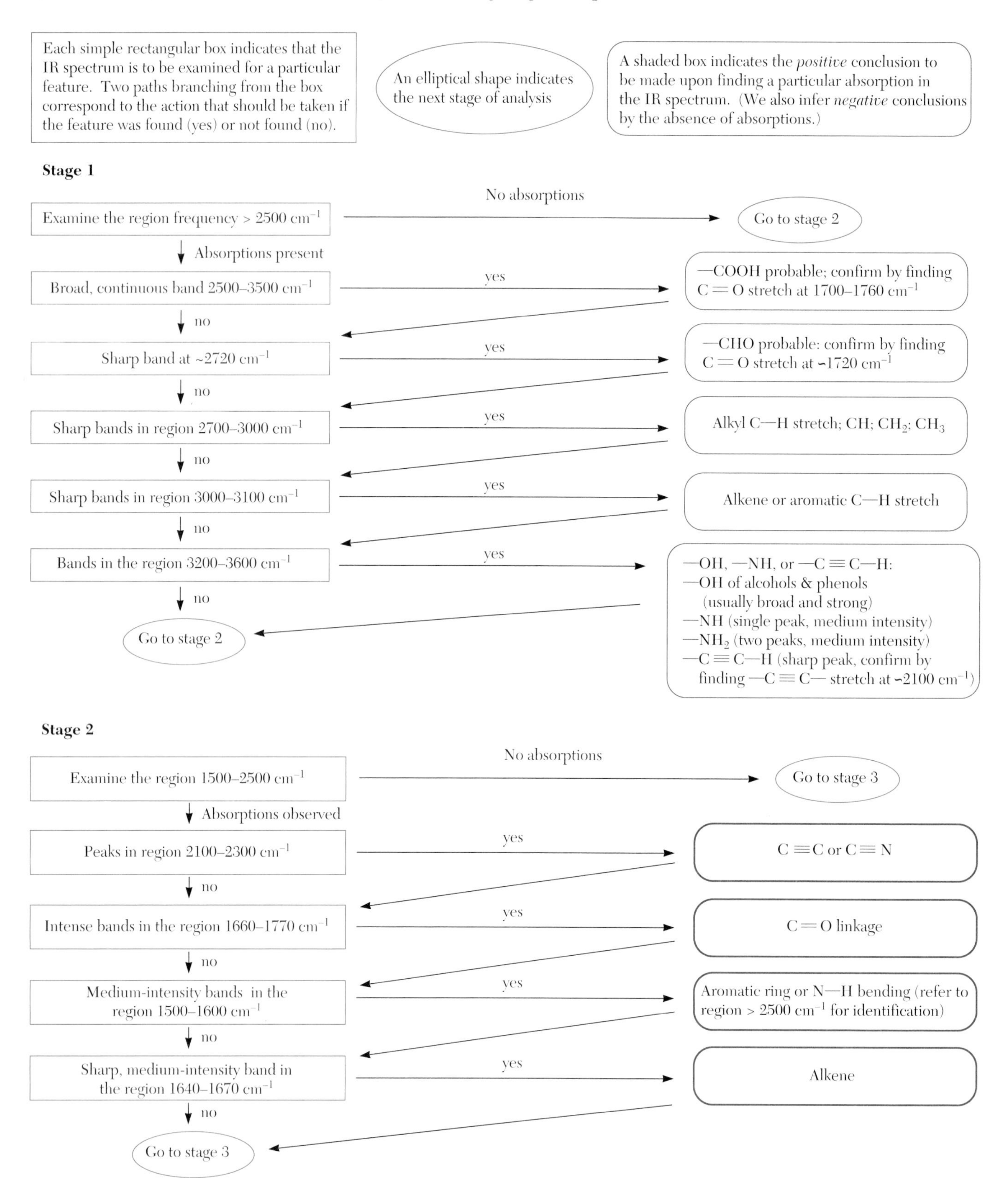

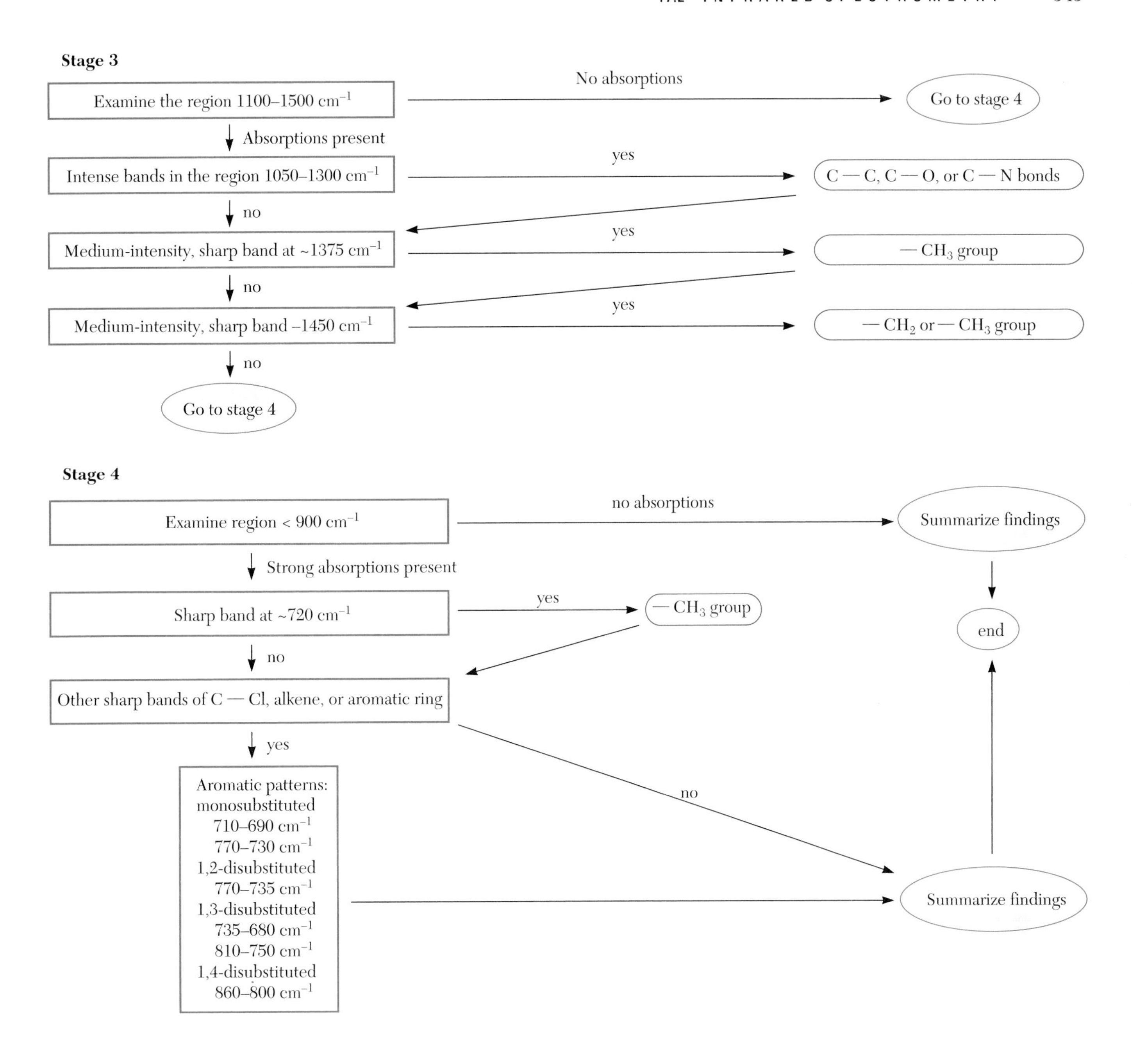

or absence of specific absorptions or features. The flowchart in Figure 17.24 outlines a systematic procedure that you can follow. After gaining experience, you will find that you can progressively lessen your dependence on these charts until you no longer need them.

PROBLEM 17.5 Deduce the structure of the compound of formula C_8H_8O for which the IR spectrum is shown below. The spectrum was measured in CCl_4 solution.

Figure for Problem 17.5

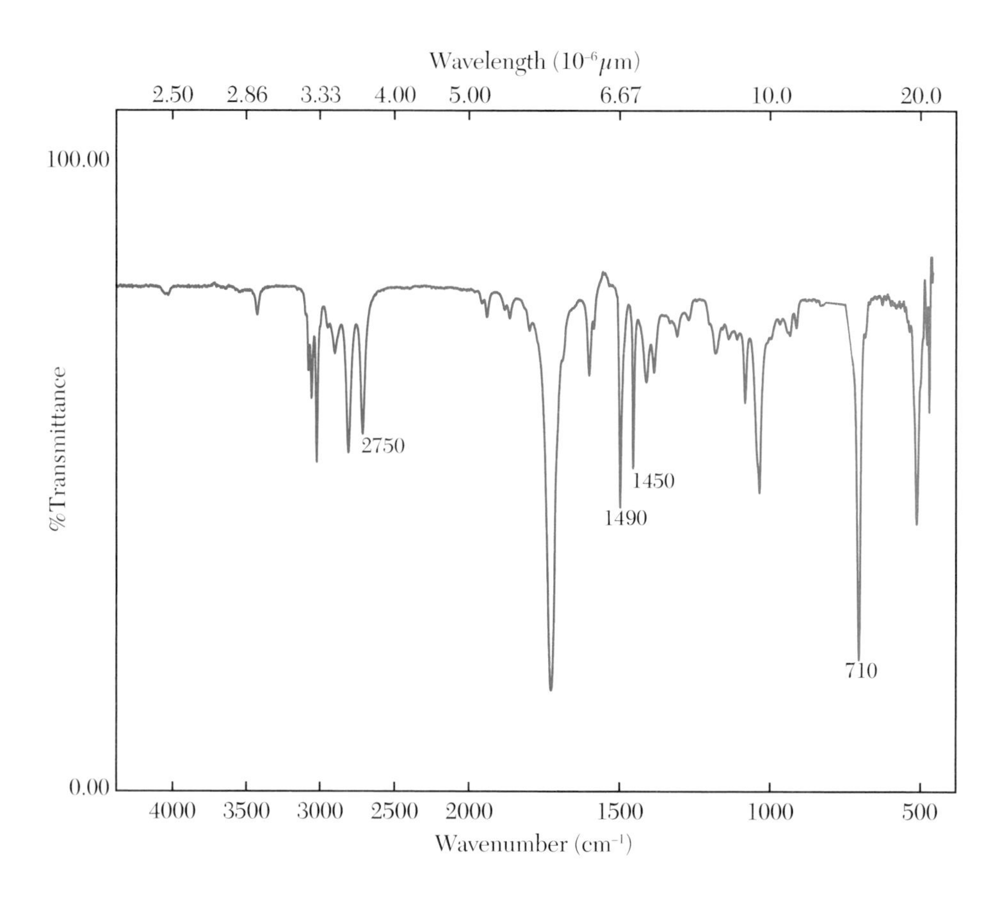

Steps to Solving the Problem

Solution to Problem 17.5

1. We will follow the strategy given in the flowchart (Figure 17.24). There is no broad continuous band in the region 2500–3500 cm^{-1}, so there can be no carboxyl group. This is of course quite consistent with the formula—a compound with a carboxyl group would have a minimum of two oxygen atoms. There is a sharp band at about 2750 cm^{-1}, so we suspect an aldehydic group. There are also other peaks close to 3000 cm^{-1}—some slightly above and some slightly below 3000 cm^{-1}, so we conclude that various types of C—H bonds are present. There is also a weak band at 3400 cm^{-1}, which might suggest a hydroxyl group. However, we already tentatively concluded that we are dealing with an aldehyde, and since the formula indicates that only one oxygen atom is present, we obviously cannot have both —OH and —CHO groups present. We will return to this issue later after we have gathered more information.

2. Move to Stage 2 of the analysis given in the flow chart. We find an intense band near 1720 cm^{-1} that suggests a carbonyl group. This supports our earlier suspicion that the compound is an aldehyde. There is also a sharp band of moderate intensity at $\sim$1490 cm^{-1}, and this indicates a benzene ring. Always keep the molecular formula in mind when analyzing spectra. The formula here is C_8H_8O, so there are five degrees of unsaturation. Since we suspect that the compound is an aldehyde, we can express this formula as C_7H_7—CHO. The C_7H_7 unit must contain four degrees of unsaturation (the carbonyl group accounts for one).
3. Now let's move on to Stage 3. There are no intense bands in the region 1050–1300 cm^{-1}, so it seems that the compound is definitely not an alcohol or ether. Also, importantly, there is no sharp band at $\sim$1375 cm^{-1}, and so we conclude that there is no methyl group present. There is, however, a sharp band of medium intensity at 1450 cm^{-1}, indicating that one methylene group (at the least) is present. We can thus express the formula as C_6H_5—CH_2—CHO, and a reasonable guess would be that the C_6H_5 unit is a phenyl group. This would account for all the remaining degrees of unsaturation, and agree with the conclusion reached above that a benzene ring is present.
4. There is in fact a sharp band at $\sim$710 cm^{-1}, suggesting a monosubstituted benzene ring. Thus the compound appears to be phenylacetaldehyde, $PhCH_2CHO$. As yet, though, we have not explained the weak absorption at 3400 cm^{-1}. In fact, a subtle point is involved here, one that should alert us to be careful in analyzing the spectra of carbonyl compounds. We noted in Chapter 15 that carbonyl compounds exist in tautomeric equilibrium with enols (see Figure 15.19 and related discussion). The —OH group of an enol can be expected to give rise to a peak in the —OH region. Thus we have a rational explanation for the small 3400 cm^{-1} peak—it is caused by the presence of a small amount of the enol form of phenylacetaldehyde.

$$Ph—CH_2—C(=\ddot{O}:)H \rightleftharpoons Ph—CH{=}CH—\ddot{O}H$$

phenylacetaldehyde — enol form

5. Here are some final comments. Chemists never try to derive the entire structure of an unknown compound from infrared spectra alone (even though it is possible to do so for relatively simple compounds). Rather, the infrared spectrum is used along with the NMR spectrum and other data. NMR spectra are especially useful for revealing the presence of certain structural features that are difficult or impossible to be sure about from analysis of an infrared spectrum. For example, in the present case, the NMR spectrum would have given a much clearer indication of the presence of a benzene ring with a —CH_2— group attached than that given by the infrared spectrum.

PROBLEM 17.6 A compound of formula $C_5H_{10}O$ gives the following IR spectrum. The spectrum was measured in CCl_4 solution. Which structure is the most likely?

Figure for Problem 17.6

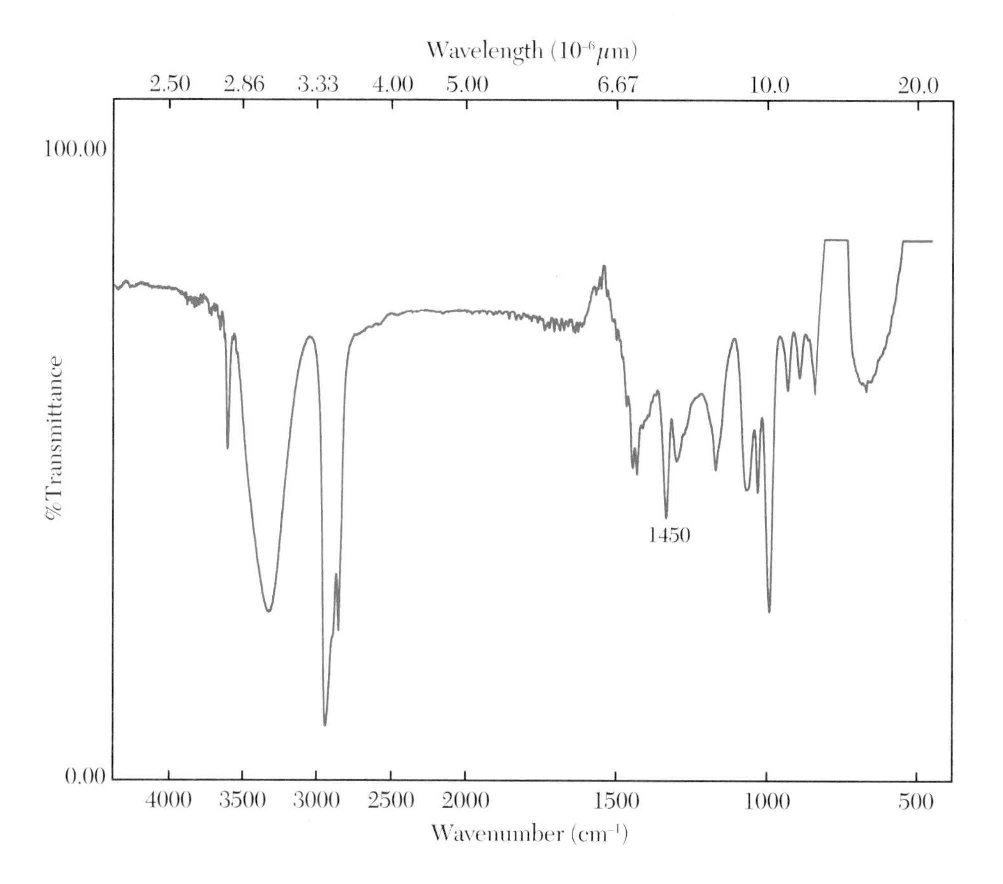

a. $CH_3-\overset{:O:}{\overset{\|}{C}}-CH_2CH_2CH_3$

b. $:\ddot{O}H$ (on a cyclopentane ring)

c. $H-\overset{:O:}{\overset{\|}{C}}-CH_2CH(CH_3)_2$

d. $H_2C{=}CH-\ddot{\underset{..}{O}}-CH(CH_3)_2$

PROBLEM 17.7 Deduce the structure of the compound of formula C_2NCl_3 for which the IR spectrum is shown. The spectrum was measured in CCl_4 solution.

PROBLEM 17.8 A compound of formula C_7H_{14} gives the IR spectrum shown. The spectrum was measured in CCl_4 solution. Which compound do you think it is

a. cycloheptane
b. 1,2-dimethylcyclopentane
c. 3,4-dimethyl-3-pentene
d. 1-heptene?

Figure for Problem 17.7

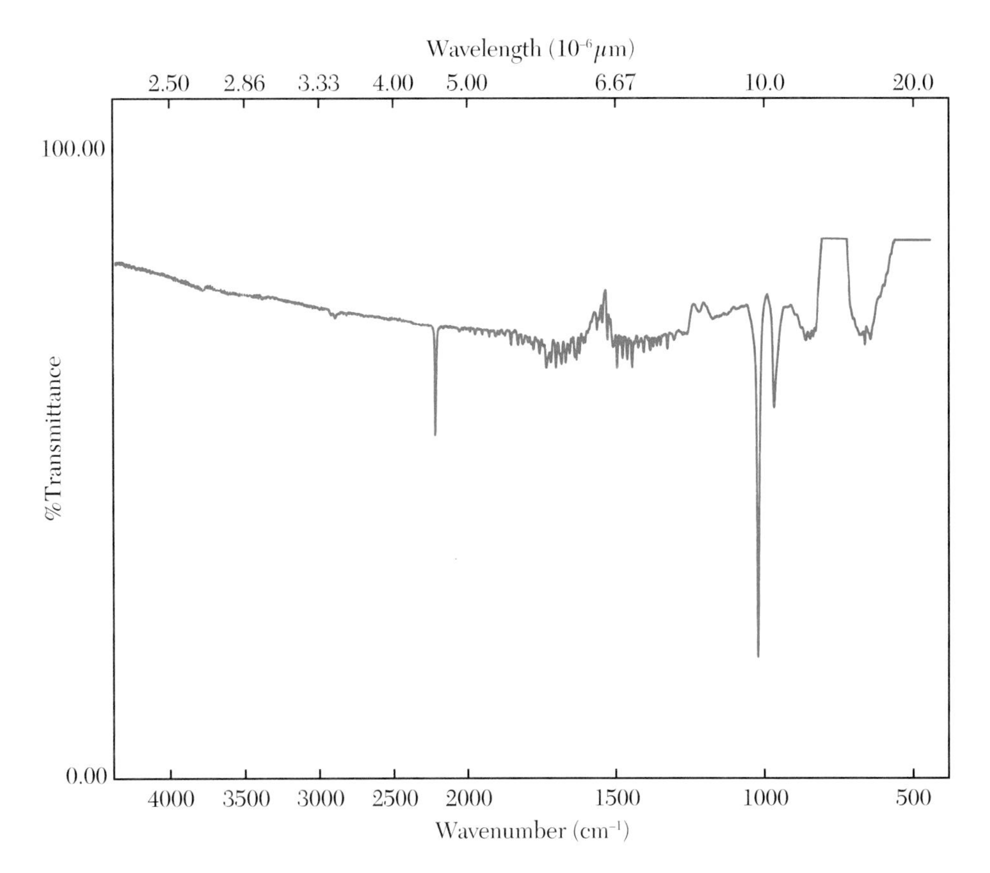

Figure for Problem 17.8

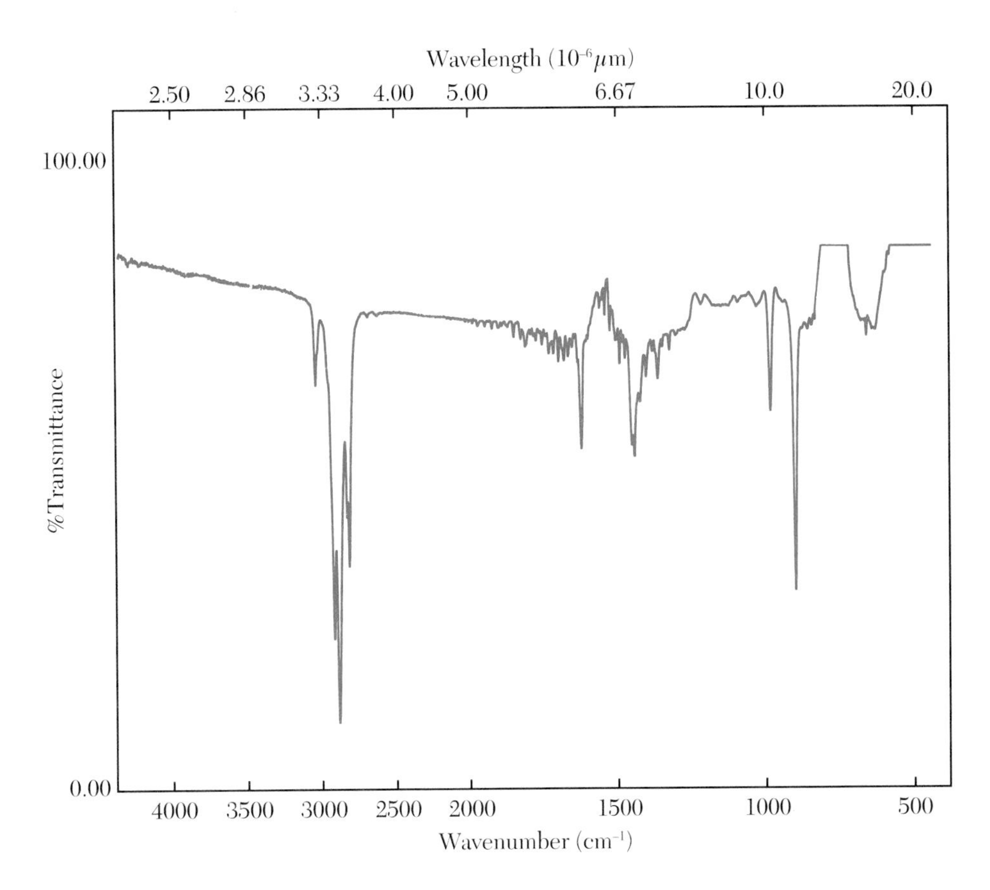

PROBLEM 17.9 Deduce the structure of the compound of formula $C_3H_6O_2$ for which the IR spectrum is shown below. The spectrum was measured in CCl_4 solution.

Figure for Problem 17.9

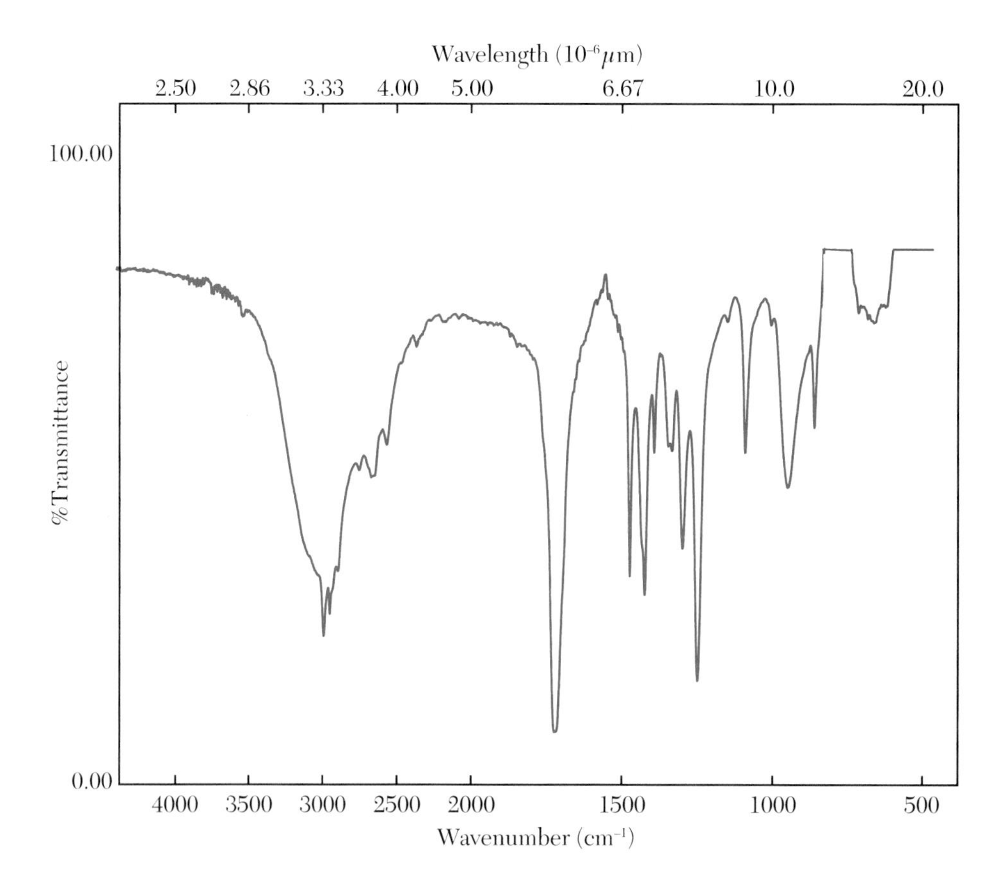

PROBLEM 17.10 A compound of formula C_8H_{12} gives the IR spectrum shown (measured in CCl_4 solution). One mole of the compound reacts with two moles of H_2 in the presence of a platinum catalyst, and when the compound is subjected to ozonolysis, followed by work-up under reductive conditions, a *single* organic product, $C_4H_6O_2$, is obtained. Suggest a structure for the compound.

PROBLEM 17.11 Suggest a possible structure for a compound of formula $C_4H_8O_2$ that gives the IR spectrum shown. The spectrum was measured in CCl_4 solution.

PROBLEM 17.12 Deduce the structure of a compound of formula C_5H_8 for which the IR spectrum is shown. The spectrum was measured in CCl_4 solution. On treatment with excess H_2, in the presence of a catalyst, the compound is converted to 2-methylbutane.

Figure for Problem 17.10

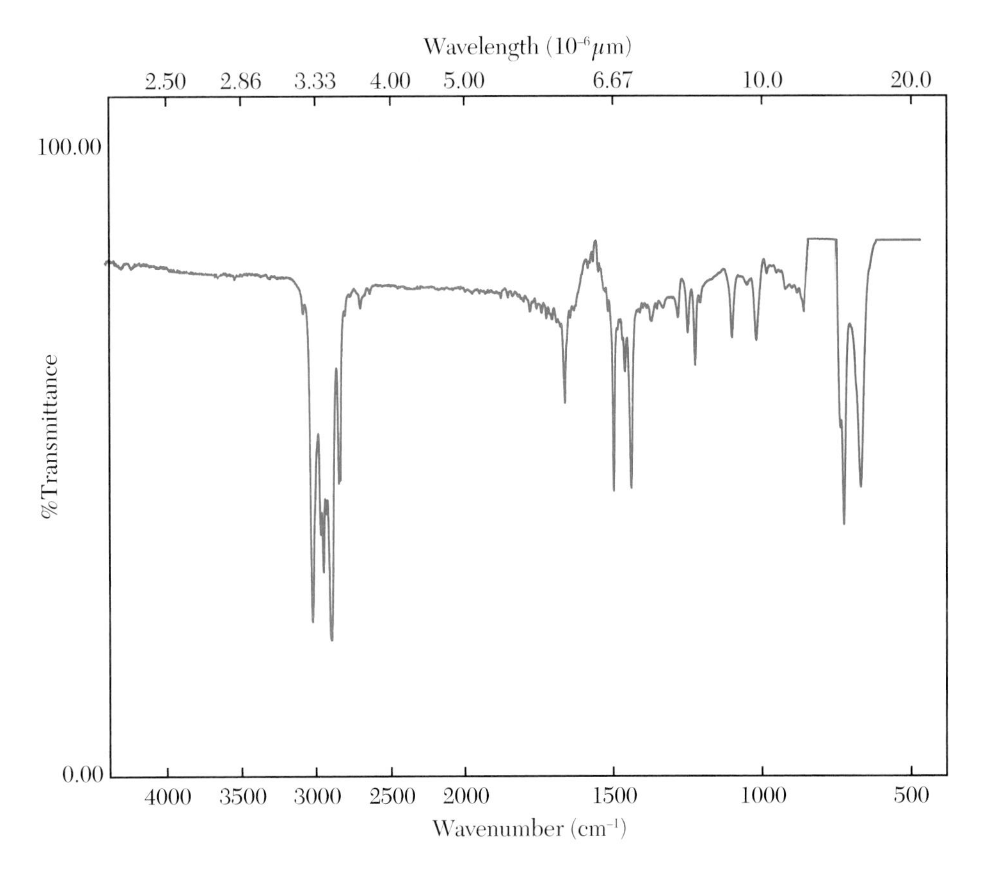

Figure for Problem 17.11

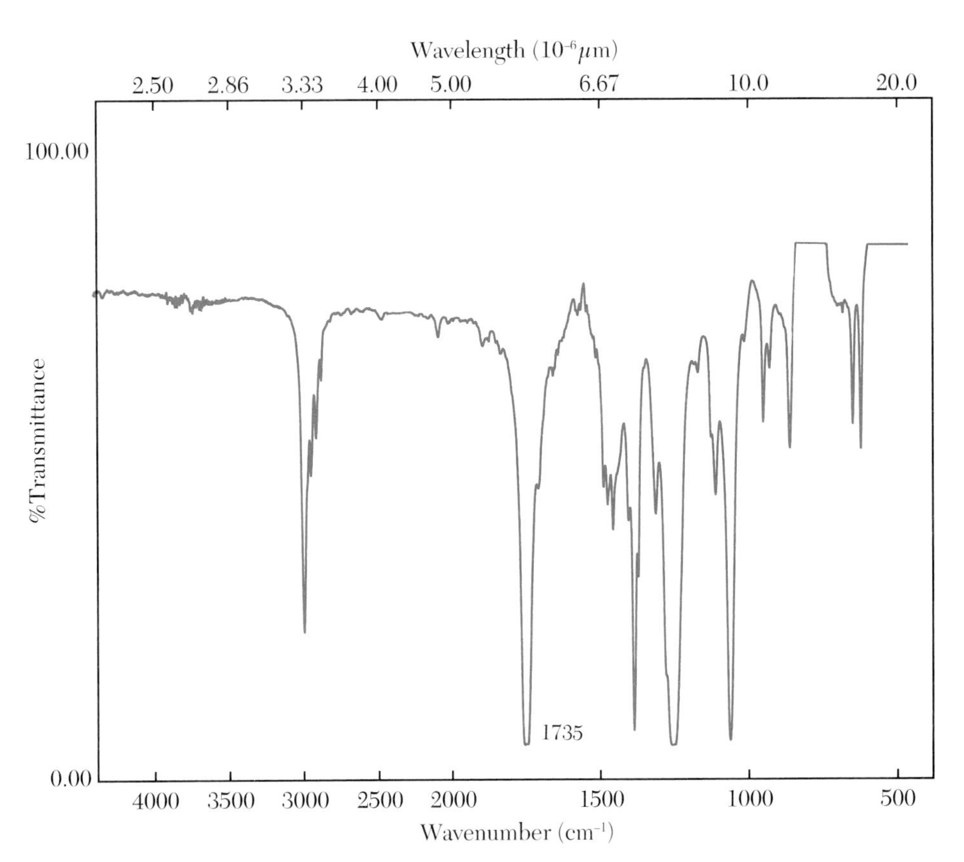

Figure for Problem 17.12

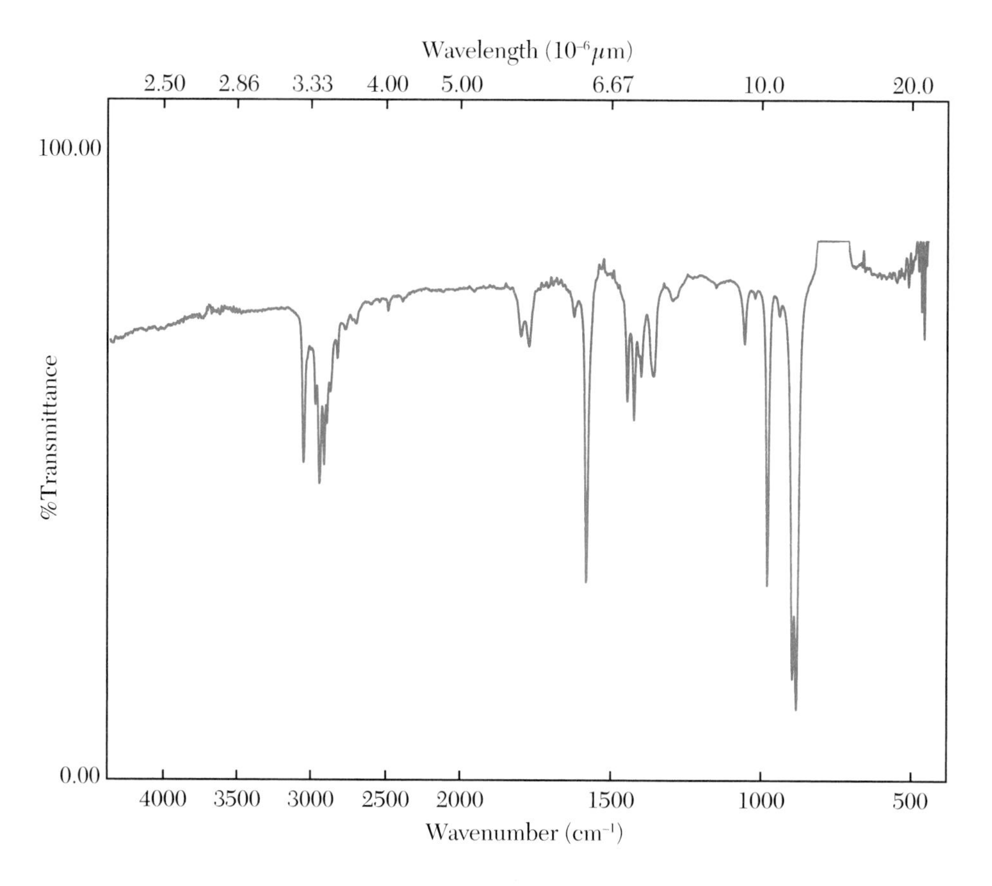

Figure for Problem 17.13

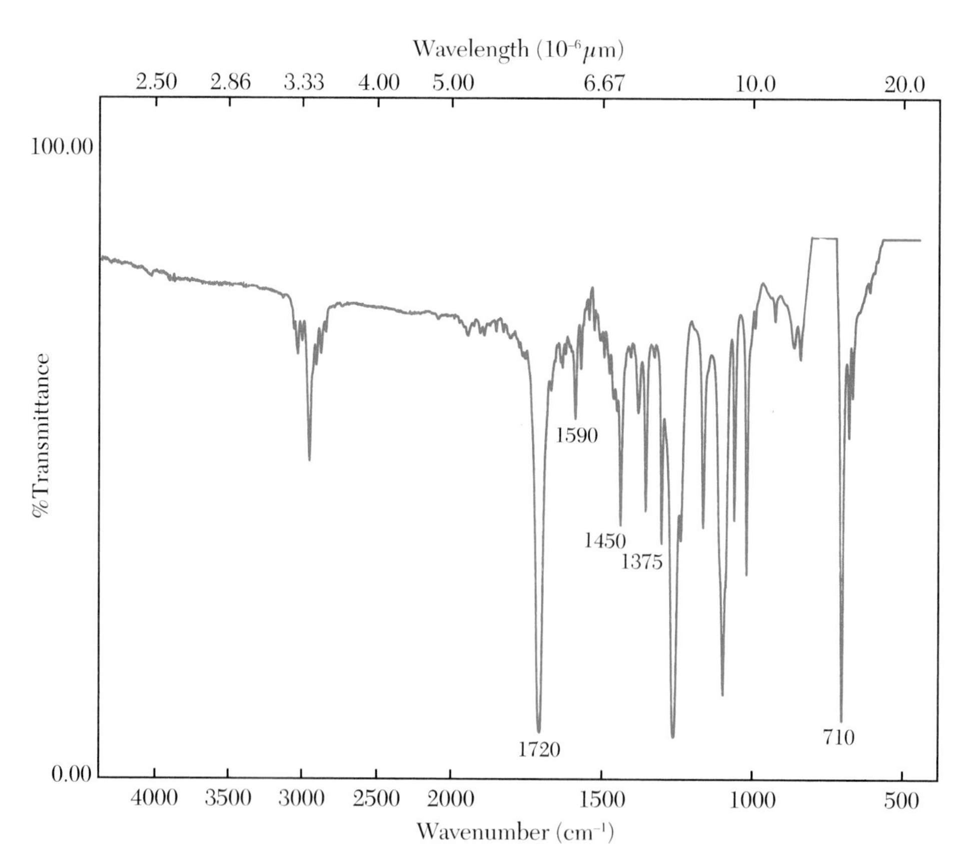

PROBLEM 17.13 A compound of formula $C_9H_{10}O_2$ gives the IR spectrum shown. The spectrum was measured in CCl_4 solution. Which structure do you favor?

a. Ph—Ö—CH_2—CH_2—C(=:O:)—H

b. HÖ—C_6H_4—CH=CH—ÖCH_3

c. HÖ—C(=:O:)—C_6H_4—C_2H_5

d. Ph—C(=:O:)—ÖC_2H_5

PROBLEM 17.14 A compound of formula C_7H_8O gives the IR spectrum shown below. The spectrum was measured in CCl_4 solution. Which of the four compounds do you think it is?

Figure for Problem 17.14

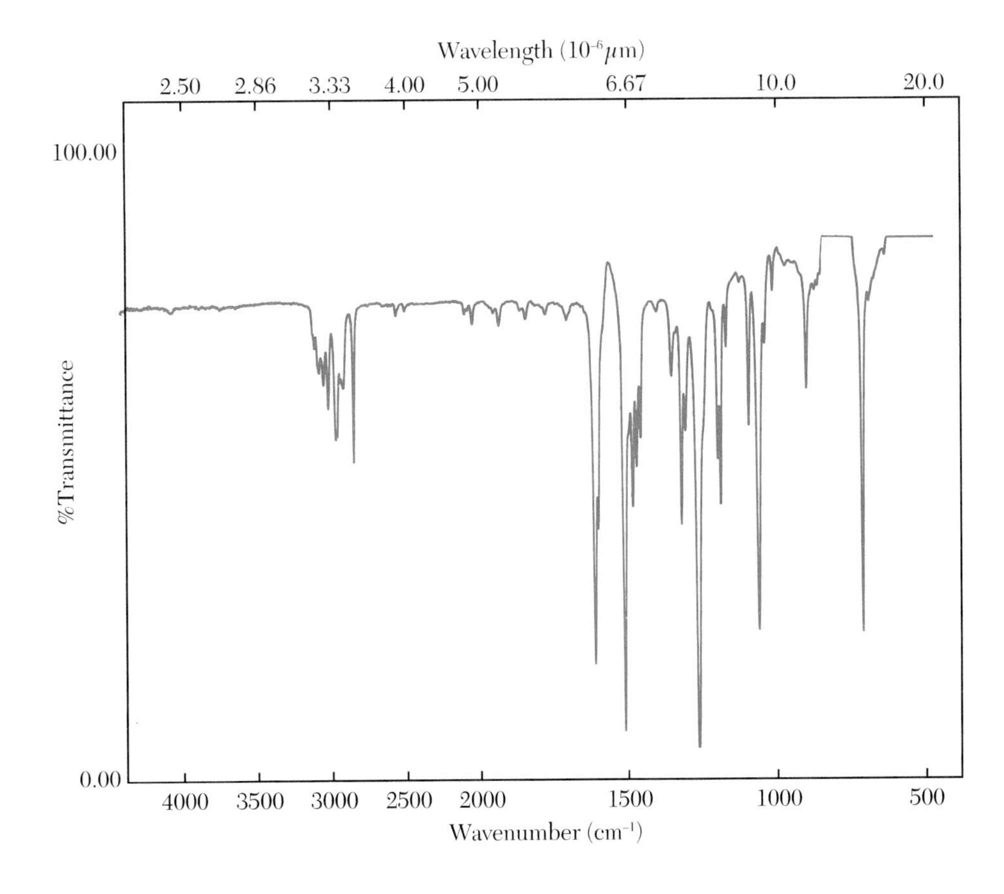

a. H—C≡C—CH_2—Ö—CH_2—C≡C—CH_3

b. H_3C—C_6H_4—ÖH

c. PhÖCH_3

d. $H{-}\underset{\underset{:O:}{\|}}{C}{-}CH{=}CH{-}CH{=}CH{-}\underset{\underset{:O:}{\|}}{C}{-}CH_3$

17.3 Nuclear Magnetic Resonance (NMR) Spectrometry

Nuclear magnetic resonance spectrometry is a very powerful technique for structural elucidation. Our discussion of this topic will begin with some simple NMR spectra so that you can see how spectra are related to structure, then we will embark on a discussion of how the spectra are obtained, and how to interpret them.

The use of NMR spectrometry allows us to probe the environments of atoms in molecules. The value of NMR stems largely from the observation that atomic nuclei in different environments produce signals in different positions of the spectrum. When we perform an NMR analysis of a sample, we can look at atoms of only one element at a time. We most often perform hydrogen NMR spectrometry, in which we look for signals from hydrogen nuclei (protons) in different environments, or carbon NMR spectrometry, where we look for signals from carbon nuclei (^{13}C) in different environments. We will discuss the details and theory of NMR in due course, but first we will show and briefly discuss a few sample spectra.

Figure 17.25 shows the proton NMR spectrum of methyl acetate (**17.13**). Notice that there are two significant peaks in the spectrum. (Ignore the little blips on the baseline. They arise from an instrumental artifact that we will discuss later. Also ignore the peak at the zero position. It is due to a calibrant and is present in all NMR spectra.) The two peaks correspond to the two types of hydrogen in methyl acetate, as illustrated in Figure 17.26. Note that the

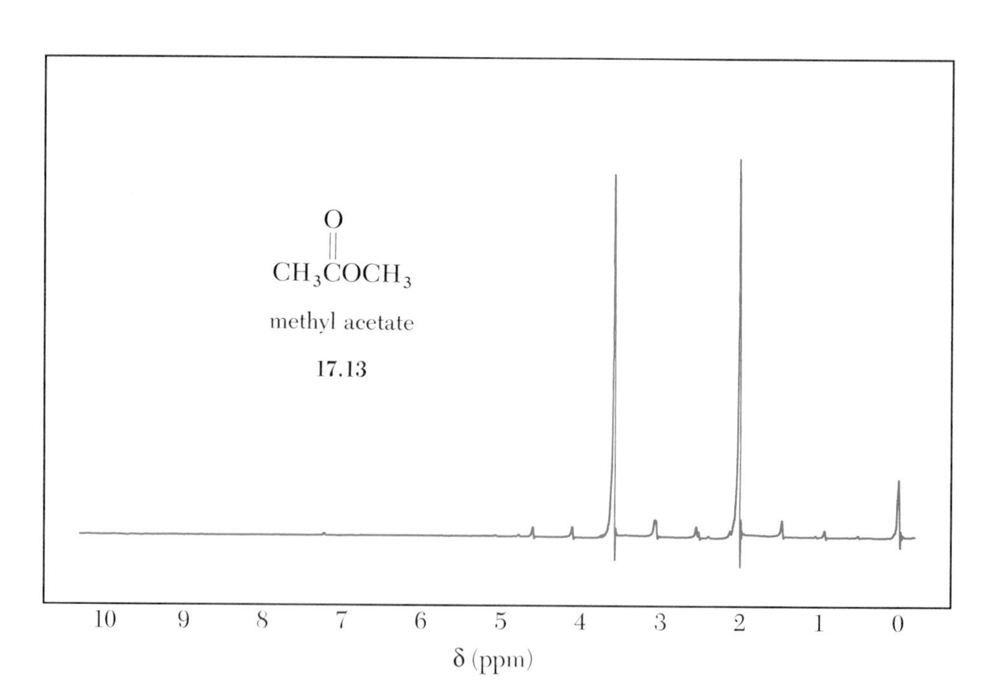

Figure 17.25 The proton NMR spectrum of methyl acetate.

Figure 17.26 Different types of hydrogen atoms in methyl acetate.

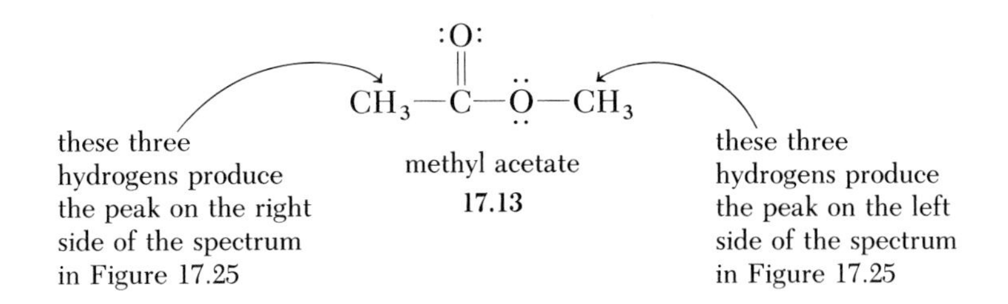

areas of the two peaks in the spectrum have a 1:1 ratio, indicating that equal numbers of each of the two types of hydrogen are present.

The proton NMR spectrum of another ester, *tert*-butyl acetate (**17.14**), is shown in Figure 17.27. Again we see two signals, reflecting the two types of environments for hydrogen nuclei in the molecule. However, the ratio of the peak areas is now 3:1, which accurately reflects the relative numbers of the different types of hydrogen atoms in this molecule. There are nine hydrogens associated with the *tert*-butyl group and three with the methyl group, as shown in Figure 17.28.

Figure 17.27 Proton NMR spectrum of *tert*-butyl acetate.

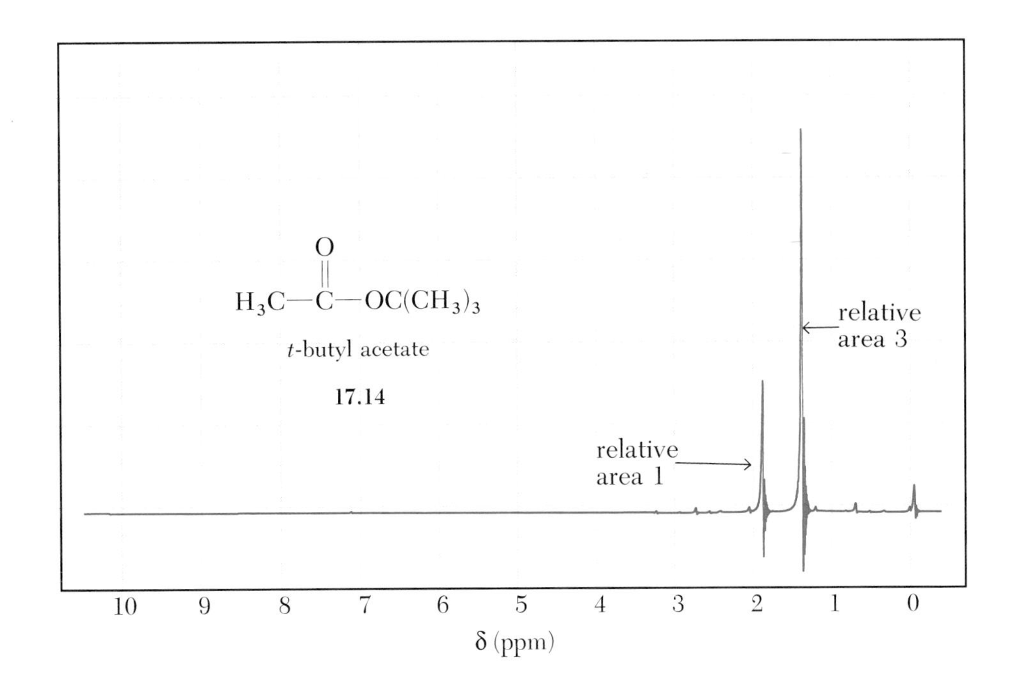

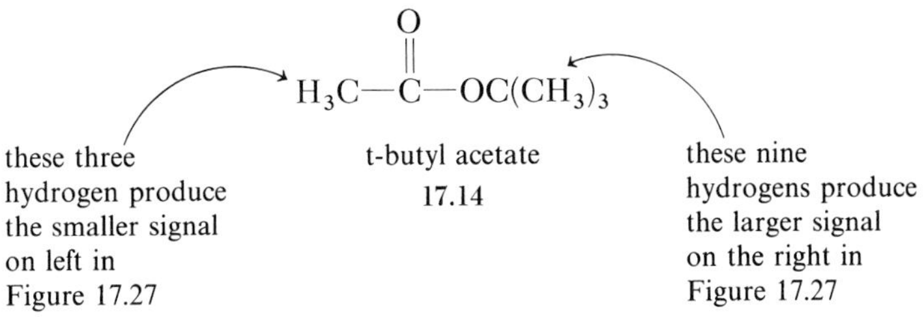

Figure 17.28 Different types of hydrogen in *tert*-butyl acetate. The two types of hydrogen give rise to two distinct signals in the hydrogen NMR spectrum (Figure 17.27).

$$H_3C-\overset{\displaystyle O}{\overset{\|}{C}}-OC(CH_3)_3$$

t-butyl acetate

17.14

these three hydrogen produce the smaller signal on left in Figure 17.27

these nine hydrogens produce the larger signal on the right in Figure 17.27

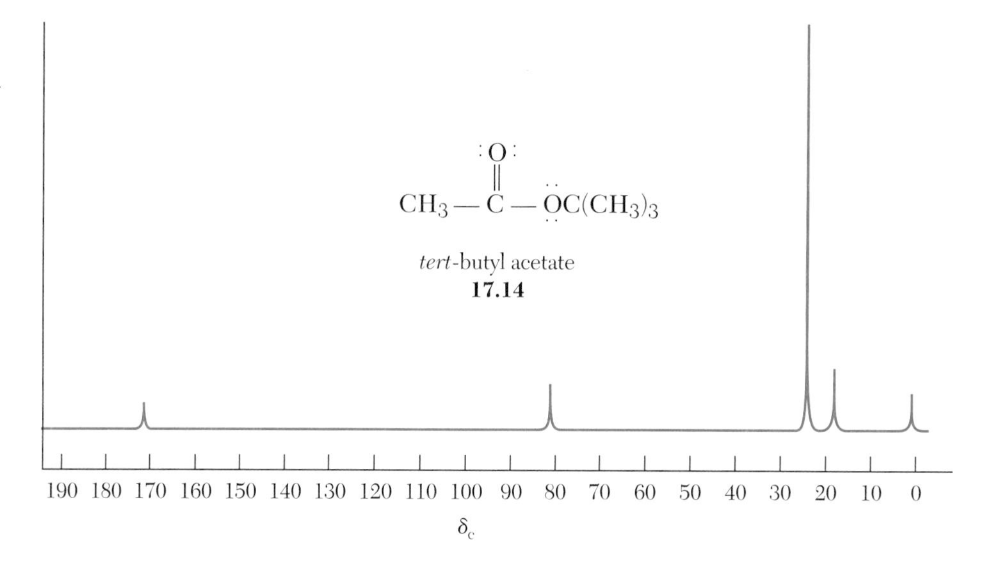

Figure 17.29 Carbon NMR spectrum of *tert*-butyl acetate. The signal at the far right (0) is a reference peak (tetramethylsilane) and is not produced by the *tert*-butyl acetate. (Peak areas are not useful in ^{13}C NMR—see later discussion).

Figure 17.29 shows the carbon NMR spectrum for the same compound. There are four signals corresponding to the four types of carbon atoms in the molecule.

PROBLEM 17.15 How many signals would you expect in the hydrogen and the carbon NMR spectra of each of the following molecules?

a. $CH_3—\ddot{O}—C(CH_3)_3$

b. $CH_3—C{\equiv}C—C(=\!:\!O\!:)—\ddot{O}—CH_3$

c. (ring with two :O: atoms)

d. H_3C–(pyrazine ring with two :N atoms)–CH_3

e. H_3C–(benzene ring)–CH_3, with :Br: on the ring

THEORY OF NMR

To begin our study of NMR theory we need to consider some fundamental characteristics of nuclei. All nuclei consist of protons and (except for the nucleus of a ^{1}H atom) neutrons. All nuclei are positively charged. Certain nuclei have a **nuclear magnetic moment** associated with them. This magnetic moment is a magnetic field (or force) that has its origin in the nucleus. A nucleus with a magnetic moment behaves like a tiny magnet. From classical physics we know that charged particles generate a magnetic moment if they are *spinning*, so we infer that nuclei with a magnetic moment have a mechanical spin. We might anticipate that *all* nuclei would have a magnetic moment, since all nuclei are positively charged. However, the nuclear magnetic moment is a composite of the spin properties of its component protons and neutrons. If the individual *nucleon* (proton and neutron) spins are paired, the nucleus will have no magnetic moment. This pairing is analogous to the pairing of electron spins in atoms.

Only nuclei with a magnetic moment can be detected by NMR spectrometry. The ^1H nucleus, the proton, is the simplest example of such a nucleus. We will use it as our example in the following discussion.

PROTON SPIN

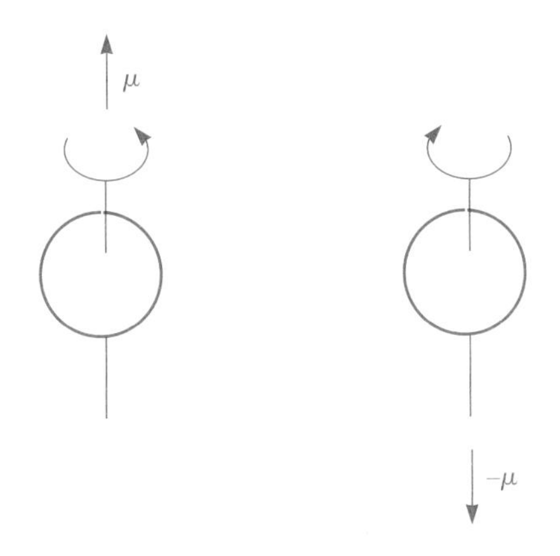

Figure 17.30 Protons with spins in opposite directions. For an isolated proton in space, there is an equal probability that its spin, and resultant magnetic moment, will be in one of the two directions shown.

Suppose we have a hydrogen nucleus, devoid of any associations with electrons or any other nuclei, that is, a "bare" proton. If this proton sits alone in space, there is an equal probability that its nuclear magnetic moment (μ) is in either of two directions, as illustrated in Figure 17.30.

Now consider a large collection of these protons. We expect that half of them will have their magnetic moments in each of the two directions. The two possibilities, shown in Figure 17.30, are energetically equivalent—we say that their energy states are *degenerate*.

Suppose now that we complicate the matter somewhat. Rather than completely removing the protons from any other influences, we apply a magnetic field to the region of space in which they exist. An applied magnetic field has both a magnitude and a direction. Once we apply a magnetic field, the energies of the two types of protons are no longer equal. Those whose nuclear magnetic moments are in the same direction as the applied magnetic field have a lower energy than those of opposite spin, as illustrated in Figure 17.31. The magnitude of the energy gap separating the two spin states, ΔE, is directly proportional to the magnitude of the applied magnetic field.

An analogy is useful here. If we were to take a collection of magnetic compasses to a planet with *no* magnetic field, there would be no preferred

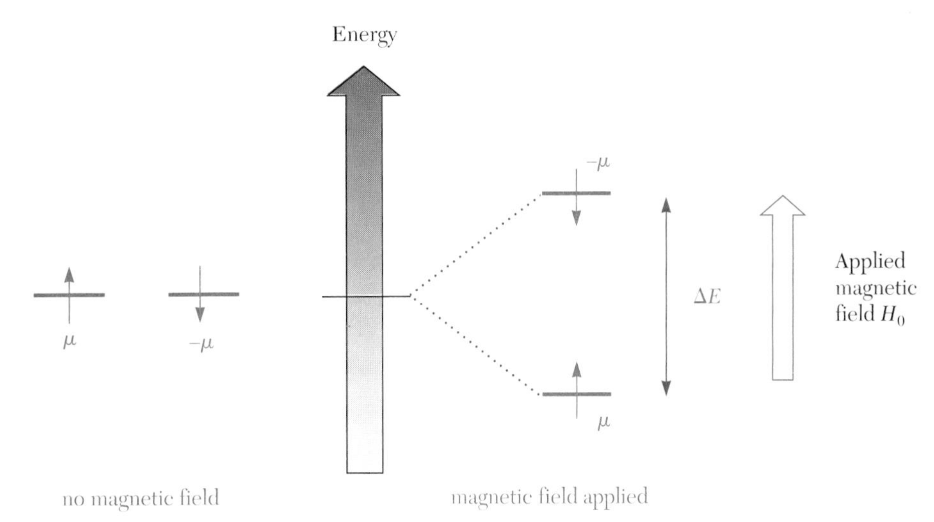

Figure 17.31 Nuclei with a magnetic moment in the absence and presence of an applied magnetic field. The energies of the two types of nuclei are the same in the absence of a magnetic field. When the magnetic field is applied, nuclei with their magnetic moments in the same direction as the applied field become lower in energy than those with their magnetic moments in the opposite direction.

direction in which the compass needles would point. Equal numbers would point more or less north and south. However, on earth, which does have a magnetic field, the compass needles preferentially point north. The earth's magnetic field removes the equivalence (degeneracy) of the various orientations. On earth we must apply energy to force a compass needle to point south. Similarly, on a planet with a *greater* magnetic field than that on earth, we would need to apply even more energy to force a compass needle to point south.

When there is an energy difference between the two spin states of a nucleus, we can excite the nucleus from the lower to higher state by an input of energy. This process is quantized (as are all excitations at the molecular or submolecular level). Excitation requires radiation of a frequency corresponding exactly to ΔE for absorption to occur. Since there is an energy difference between the two spin states, they are no longer equally probable. A greater number of nuclei are in the lower-energy state than are in the higher-energy state. The larger ΔE is, the greater the difference in the populations of the two states. Furthermore, as in the compass analogy, the magnitude of ΔE depends on the strength of the magnetic field applied to the nuclei.

NMR INSTRUMENTATION

There are several ways to perform an NMR analysis. Regardless of the method used, the end product, the NMR spectrum itself, is the same. We will discuss here only one way of causing and measuring the energy absorption of an NMR-active nucleus. This method is not necessarily always the best one, but it is commonly used and conceptually simpler than other methods.

An instrument designed to perform an NMR analysis has several components. In addition to a source of exciting radiation and a detector (components also required for other forms of absorption spectroscopy such as IR spectroscopy), we need a magnetic field. A schematic of these components showing the position of the sample to be studied is shown in Figure 17.32.

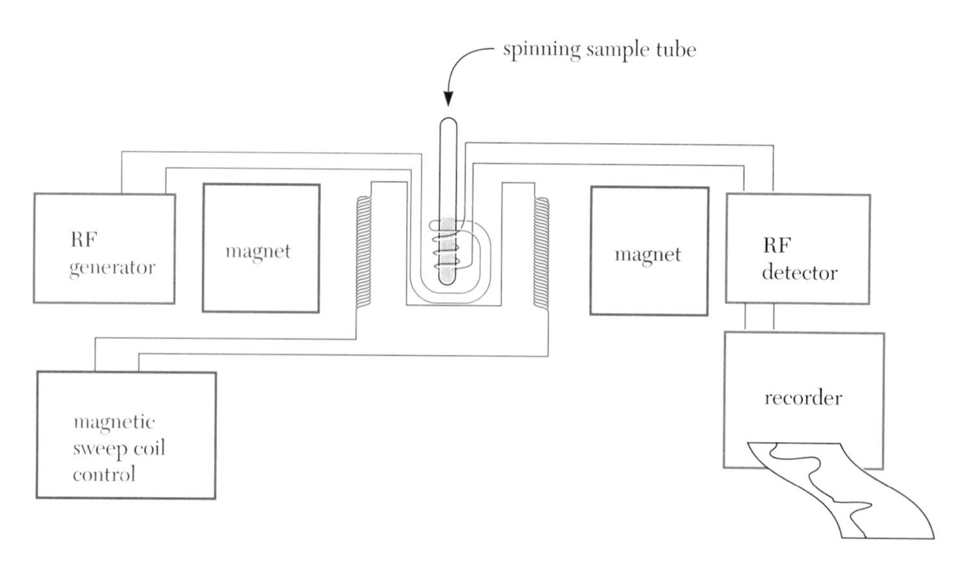

Figure 17.32 Schematic diagram of NMR instrument. The principal components include a sample container, a magnet (two parts—a large magnet with poles on each side of the sample and a fine-control electromagnet system using the magnetic sweep coil control), an energy input system (radio frequency (RF) generator), and a detector of energy not absorbed by the sample (RF detector). The recorder measures the difference between the energy input and the energy detected. The instru ment illustrated measures an NMR spectrum using a *field-sweep* technique. Other methods can also be used to obtain the same NMR spectrum.

Very large magnetic field strengths are required to produce sizable energy differences between the spin states of nuclei. For example, the hydrogen nucleus requires a magnetic field of 14,092 gauss to produce an energy difference corresponding to photons of 60 MHz frequency—a very large magnetic field for a very small energy difference. Electromagnetic radiation of 60 MHz is in the radio frequency (RF) range. (The range for FM radio transmission is 88–108 MHz.) We would like to make ΔE as large as possible in order to increase the sensitivity of the experiment, but there is an experimental difficulty here. Ordinary electromagnets cannot be made indefinitely large—there is a limit to their magnetic field strength beyond which the field is not sustained. For higher field strengths, superconducting magnets operating at liquid helium temperature must be used. NMR instruments use either ordinary electromagnets or superconducting magnets. For simplicity, we will discuss here a system for detecting protons using an ordinary electromagnet producing a field of 14,092 gauss. Many common, commercially available NMR spectrometers are of this type.

As illustrated in Figure 17.32, a magnetic field is applied to the sample in two parts. A large magnet provides a constant field of ~14,092 gauss. A much smaller but variable field is provided by a separate electromagnet (the *magnetic sweep coil control*, see Figure 17.32). These sweep coils can vary the applied magnetic field by about 0.3 gauss, which is approximately 20 **parts per million (ppm)** of the total applied magnetic field strength. The actual applied field (H_0) is therefore the sum of two components, the large, constant field (H_c) and the variable field (H_v). A bare proton will absorb 60 MHz radiation when:

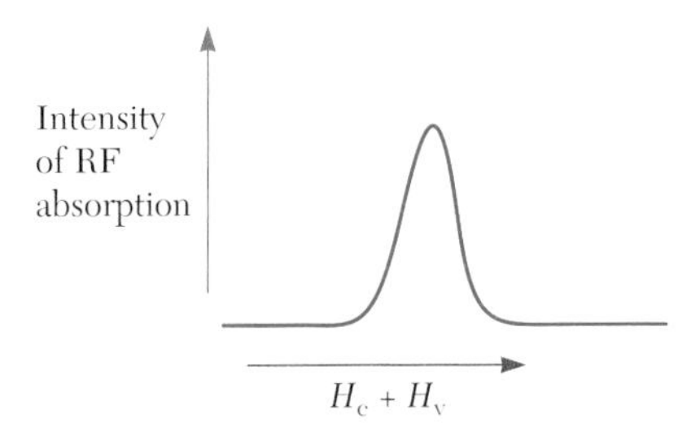

Figure 17.33 Absorption of RF energy by a nucleus as a function of applied magnetic field strength.

$$H_0 = H_c + H_v = 14{,}092 \text{ gauss}$$

The energy that excites the low-energy state proton is applied along a direction perpendicular to both H_0 and the vertical axis of the sample tube. A detector (a radio receiver) senses the electromagnetic radiation that is not absorbed by the sample. The recorder presents the detected energy absorption as a function of ($H_c + H_v$), as shown in Figure 17.33.

THE CHEMICAL SHIFT

The first aspect of NMR spectrometry that makes it useful for structural determination is the **chemical shift** phenomenon. Chemical shift refers to the fact that all protons in real molecules do not absorb energy at exactly the same applied magnetic field strength. When the energy input is constant, different protons in a molecule require different applied magnetic field strengths to absorb that energy. (In NMR spectrometry, we say that the nuclei *come into resonance* when we see a signal for them. This phenomenon has *nothing* to do with the term *resonance* that refers to the delocalization of electrons in a molecule or ion.) These differences are a result of differences in the locations of the individual hydrogen nuclei within the molecule. In other words, *the chemical and electronic environments of individual hydrogen nuclei affect their behavior in the NMR experiment.*

The Diamagnetic Effect When a moving, charged object is placed in a magnetic field, it experiences a force that causes it to alter its path and move in some new direction. When a molecule is placed in a magnetic field, its electrons experience such a force. They are *induced* to move in a particular direction and, in doing so, generate their own magnetic field, H_i (an *induced* field), that is in a direction opposite to the applied field. This phenomenon is known as **diamagnetism.** It causes a nucleus to be partially *shielded* from the applied magnetic field. A nucleus in the midst of a collection of electrons experiences not the applied magnetic field, but the applied magnetic field moderated by the induced field, as shown in Equation 17.2.

Eqn. 17.2

$$\text{actual field experienced by the nucleus} = H_c + H_v - H_i$$

(In Equation 17.2, H_c is the constant field applied by the fixed magnet, H_v is the variable field applied through the sweep coils, and H_i is the field due to the induced circulation of electrons.)

Because of this induced circulation of electrons, a proton in a molecule will not, in general, experience the applied field of 14,092 gauss. In fact, different protons in a molecule will experience different fields, because the induced fields, H_i, about different nuclei will be different. In general, electron distribution and density in an organic molecule are not uniform throughout the molecule. Therefore, nuclei in different environments are shielded to different degrees by the surrounding electrons. A hydrogen nucleus absorbs 60 MHz energy only when it actually experiences a magnetic field of 14,092 gauss. Therefore, if a large H_i decreases the magnetic field experienced by a nucleus, H_v must be increased to compensate for the difference and bring the total actual field back to exactly 14,092 gauss. To obtain an NMR spectrum, we monitor the absorption of incident (60 MHz) radiation as we sweep through a range of H_v values. We then find that different nuclei absorb the incident energy (come into resonance) at different H_v values.

The effect of **shielding** is to increase H_v and shift the recorded peak upfield (to a higher δ value, see next section). Conversely, deshielding moves a peak downfield.

The Reference System In NMR spectrometry, chemical shifts are measured relative to a standard reference signal. When we measure the proton NMR spectrum for a compound, we add to the solution (along with the compound) a small amount of **tetramethylsilane** (TMS), $(CH_3)_4Si$. The signal from the twelve equivalent protons in TMS provides the reference against which all shifts are measured. Chemical shifts are reported as δ values. The δ value associated with a particular type of proton is a measure of how much the NMR signal for that proton is shifted from the reference TMS signal.

We express δ values in parts per million (ppm) of the total applied field. The δ value for the TMS signal is arbitrarily assigned the value of zero. Any peak appearing downfield (to the left) of the TMS signal has a positive δ value, and any upfield (to the right) has a negative δ value. In practice, almost all protons in organic compounds give rise to NMR peaks with positive δ values in the range 0–12 ppm. A tabulation of approximate chemical shifts for protons in different environments is given in Table 17.2.

One of the important trends to notice is that the signal for a proton is shifted to higher δ values, that is, downfield, by the presence of nearby electronegative groups. For example, the signal for the methyl group protons of the halomethanes reflects the electronegativity of the halogen, as shown in Figure 17.34.

Table 17.2 Proton Chemical Shifts (δ) Relative to TMS

Nucleus Environment	Approximate Chemical Shift
H on sp^3 carbon	
1°	0.8–1.0
2°	1.2–1.4
3°	1.4–1.7
allylic	1.6–1.9
benzylic	2.2–2.5
X—C—H	
O—C(O)—	2.0–2.6
R—C(O)—	2.0–2.7
I—	3.0–3.3
Br—	3.3–3.6
Cl—	3.5–3.8
F—	4.0–4.5
RO—	3.3–4.0
HO—	3.3–4.0
RC(O)O—	3.7–4.1
H on sp^2 carbon	
vinylic (olefinic)	4.6–5.9
aromatic	6.0–9.5
—C(O)—H	9.0–10.5
H on *sp* carbon	2.0–3.1
H on heteroatoms*	
R—OH	0.5–6.0
N—H	1.0–5.0
C(O)—OH	10–13
C=C—OH	15–17

* The chemical shifts for protons in these environments vary depending on the solvent and concentration of the sample.

increasing halogen electronegativity →

Compound	$CH_3\ddot{I}$:	$CH_3\ddot{Br}$:	$CH_3\ddot{Cl}$:	$CH_3\ddot{F}$:
δ value	2.1	2.7	3.0	4.3

increasing downfield shift →

Figure 17.34 Effect of electronegativity on the chemical shift of nearby protons. The signal for the protons of halomethanes shifts progressively downfield (to higher δ values) as the electronegativity of the attached halogen increases.

These effects can be rationalized in a fairly simple way. The δ value characteristic of any given nucleus depends on the magnitude of the magnetic field, H_i, associated with nearby electron motion. The greater the nearby electron density, the greater H_i will be, and the more shielded the nucleus will be. Its signal will therefore be relatively far upfield. An electronegative atom,

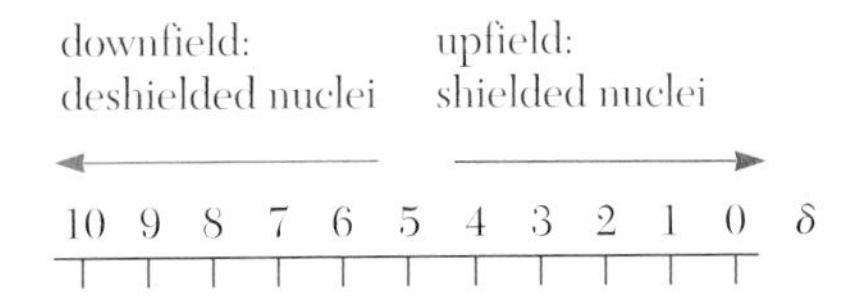

Figure 17.35 Upfield and downfield regions of a proton NMR spectrum.

however, *depletes* a nearby nucleus of its shielding electron density, and thus the signal for the nucleus is shifted in the downfield direction (that is, a smaller H_v is required to bring the actual field back to 14,092 gauss), as shown in Figure 17.35.

Diamagnetic Anisotropy Some chemical shifts run contrary to expectations based on electronegativities. For example, hydrogen atoms attached directly to a benzene ring show a significantly downfield chemical shift even though the benzene ring is not a highly electronegative group. Another unusual shift occurs with the terminal hydrogens of alkynes: the terminal hydrogen of an alkyne comes into resonance significantly *upfield* from an olefinic hydrogen.

Such unusual shifts are the result of **diamagnetic anisotropy** effects. (The term *isotropic* means "the same in all directions." *Anisotropic* means "different in different directions.") When there are π electrons in molecules, the induced magnetic field varies depending on the direction relative to those π electrons. This effect is demonstrated most clearly by hydrogen attached to an aromatic ring. In an aromatic ring there is a continuum of electron density above and below the plane of the ring. When we apply a magnetic field perpendicular to the plane of the aromatic ring, induced electron motion and an associated induced magnetic field result (Figure 17.36.) The lines of force for the magnetic field induced by this particular electron motion (**ring current**) are in different directions at different locations relative to the aromatic ring. On the *outside* of the ring, where the aromatic hydrogens are located, the lines of force are in the same direction as the applied field. As magnetic lines of force must necessarily complete a cycle, it follows that in the interior of the ring and above the plane of the ring they are in a direction opposite that of the applied field.

The hydrogen atoms on the periphery of the aromatic ring are thus in a deshielded region during an NMR analysis. The H_i in this region is in the same

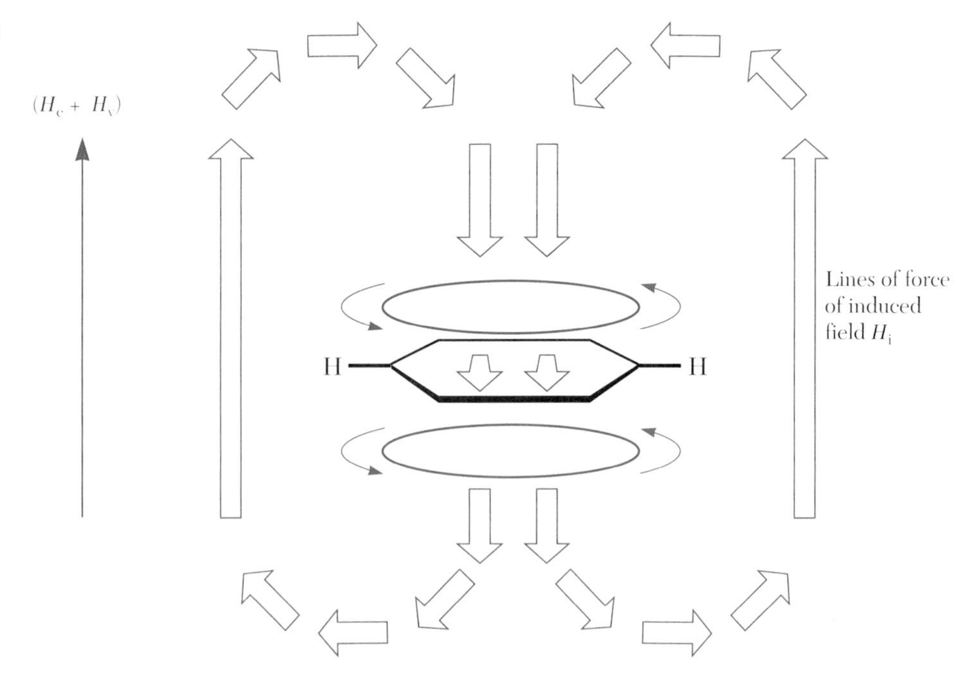

Figure 17.36 Induced magnetic field about an aromatic ring as the result of diamagnetic anisotropy. The π electrons of the aromatic system exist in two rings, one above and one below the ring of atoms and σ bonds. In the presence of an external magnetic field, these electrons circulate in a particular direction around the ring. This motion produces an induced magnetic field H_i with lines of force as shown. The hydrogens attached to the ring are in a deshielded region.

direction as $(H_c + H_v)$. Thus, the signals for those hydrogens occur *downfield* (at a lower H_v) relative to the position in which they would be found in the absence of a ring current effect. Benzene hydrogens absorb at δ 7.27, well below ordinary alkene hydrogens (δ 4.6–5.9).

If we were to place a hydrogen in the interior region of the benzene ring, we would expect it to be shielded, that is, H_i would be in a direction opposed to $(H_c + H_v)$. We do not observe this phenomenon with benzene simply because all of its hydrogen atoms are on the outside of the ring. However, the effect has been observed with other aromatic compounds such as [18]annulene (**17.15**). As noted in Chapter 16, [18]annulene is a monocyclic aromatic hydrocarbon. It contains two types of hydrogen atoms, 12 outside the ring and 6 inside the ring.

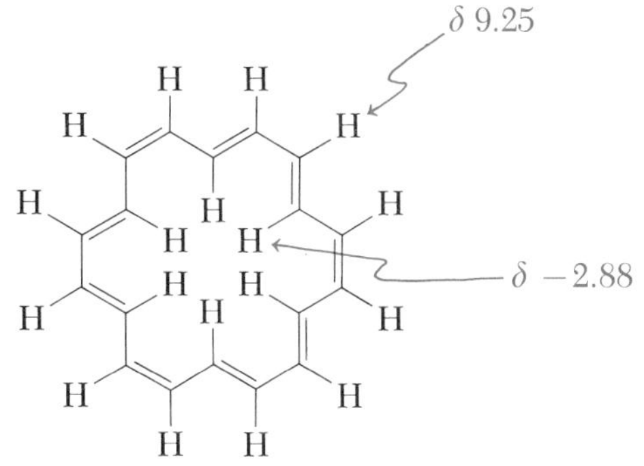

δ 9.25

δ −2.88

[18] annulene
17.15

The 12 exterior hydrogens come into resonance with a chemical shift of δ 9.25, a value within the normal aromatic range. The 6 interior hydrogens come into resonance at δ −2.88, very far upfield. We can understand this unusual chemical shift only if we take into account the ring current effect. (For a further discussion of the effect of diamagnetic anisotropy in benzenoid compounds, see the Compound Capsule "Paracyclophanes" in Chapter 18.)

Alkynes show a diamagnetic anisotropy effect like that of aromatics. Remember that the two π bonds of an alkyne form a cylinder of electron density about the length of the carbon-carbon linkage. If we align the molecule with the applied magnetic field lengthwise along the triple bond, circulation of the π electrons results in the situation illustrated in Figure 17.37. The acetylenic hydrogens lie in a shielded region as a result of the induced magnetic field. At their location, the lines of force for the induced field are opposed to the direction of the applied field. The signal thus occurs at δ 2.38, upfield from the position we might anticipate based only on the molecule's local electron density.

REPRESENTATIVE SPECTRA

We will now consider proton NMR spectra for a few simple organic molecules. These examples will help you get a feeling for the chemical shift phenomenon. The spectra illustrated were measured using a standard 60 MHz instrument as described previously. All spectra were measured in $CDCl_3$ solution with 1%

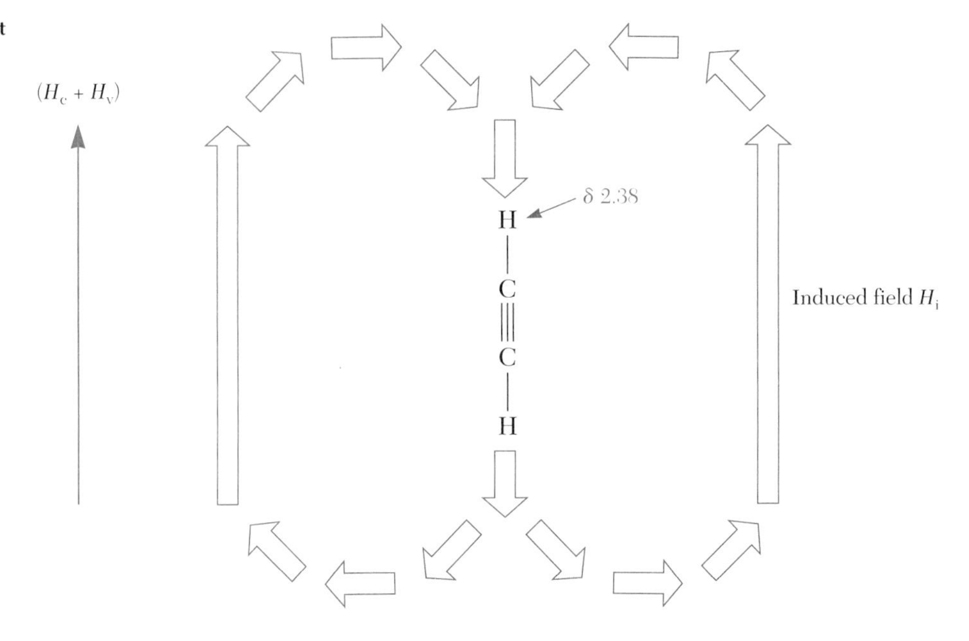

Figure 17.37 Induced magnetic field about a triple bond. The lines of force of H_i place the acetylenic hydrogen in a shielded region.

TMS added. The deuteron of the solvent does not produce a signal in the proton NMR spectrum.

Dibromomethane The proton NMR spectrum of dibromomethane (**17.16**) is shown in Figure 17.38. The single peak for the TMS reference is located at δ 0.00, at the right side of the chart. The signal for the two hydrogens of the dibromomethane is found downfield from the TMS peak. The attached halogens deshield the dibromomethane hydrogens relative to TMS. The small

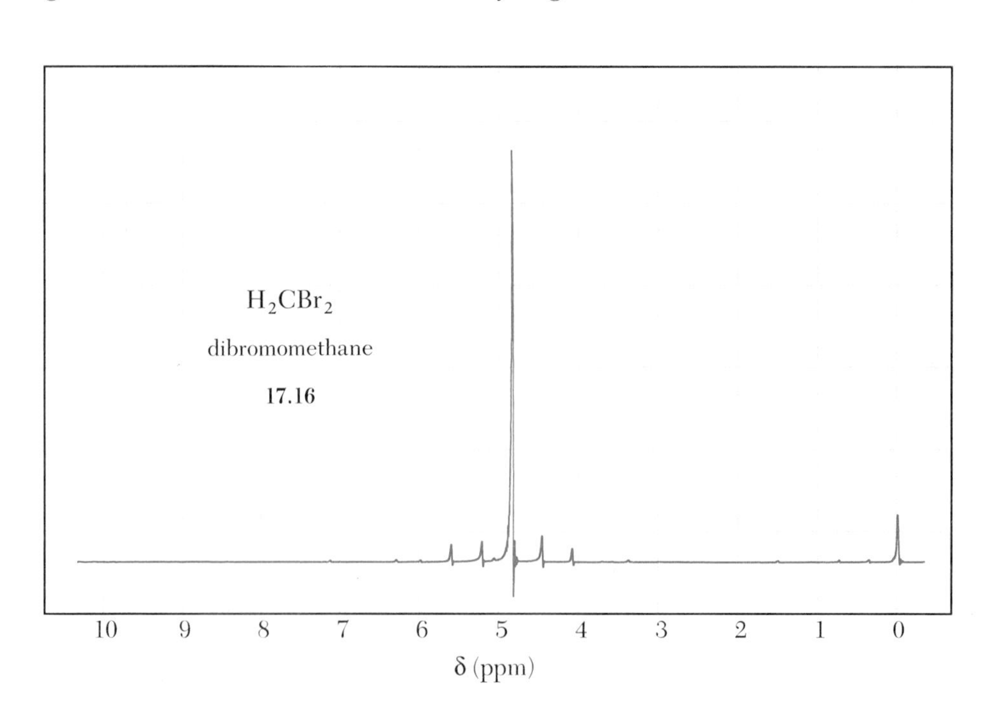

Figure 17.38 The 60-MHz proton NMR spectrum of dibromomethane.

peaks occurring symmetrically about the large single peak are *spinning side bands;* their position varies with the spin-rate of the sample tube and are a generally observed artifact in spectra measured in this way.

***cis-* and *trans*-1,2-Dichloroethene** The 60-MHz proton NMR spectra of *cis*-1,2-dichloroethene (**17.4**) and *trans*-1,2-dichloroethene (**17.5**) are shown in Figures 17.39 and 17.40, respectively. Both of these compounds exhibit proton

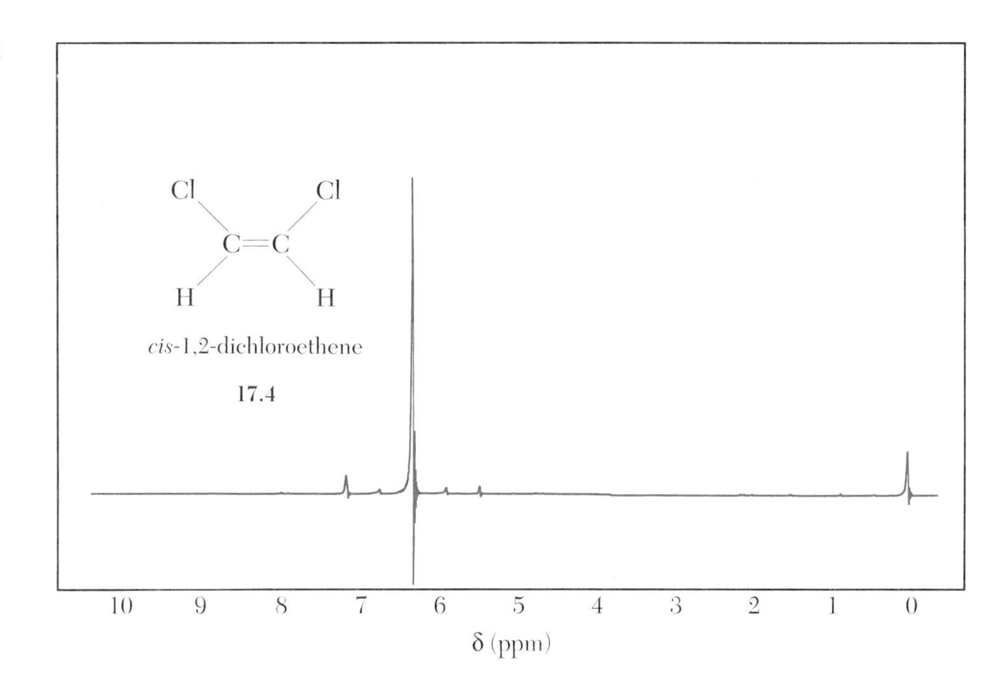

Figure 17.39 The 60-MHz proton NMR spectrum of *cis*-1,2-dichloroethene.

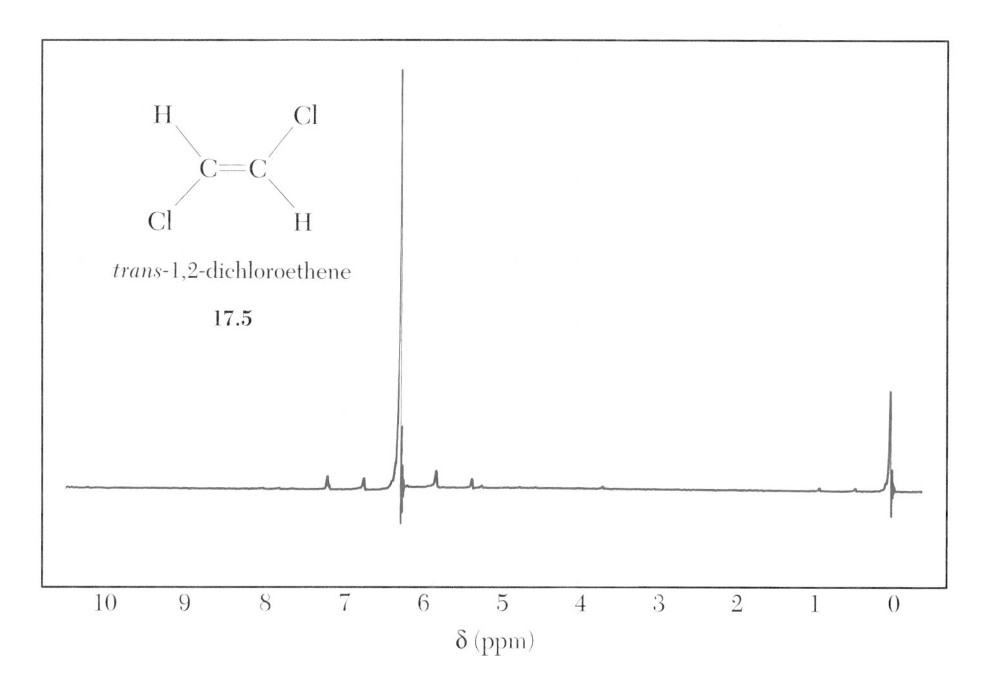

Figure 17.40 The 60-MHz proton NMR spectrum of *trans*-1,2-dichloroethene.

NMR signals that are downfield from that of 1,2-dibromomethane, at δ 6.3. This chemical shift is typical for olefinic hydrogen. We see that the two isomers are indistinguishable by NMR; we would need another piece of data, for example, an IR spectrum, to distinguish between them.

2-Methyl-2-propanol The 60-MHz proton NMR spectrum of 2-methyl-2-propanol (**17.17**) is shown in Figure 17.41. In this spectrum there are two signals

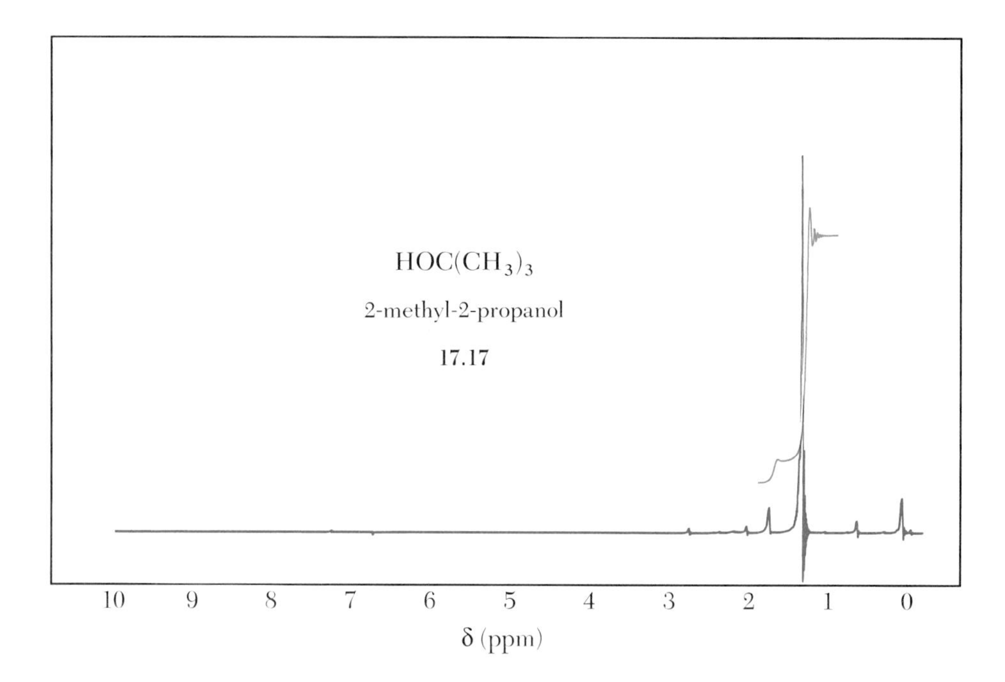

Figure 17.41 The 60-MHz proton NMR spectrum of 2-methyl-2-propanol (*tert*-butyl alcohol).

present other than the TMS reference. The large signal at δ 1.3 is due to the nine equivalent methyl hydrogens. The smaller signal at δ 1.7 is due to the hydroxyl hydrogen.

Notice the trace (in orange) cutting across the NMR spectrum. It provides a measure of the area under each of the signals it crosses. We refer to it as an **integration** of the spectrum, and we can obtain it by choosing the integration mode of operation for the NMR instrument. We find that the relative integration of the hydroxyl and methyl signals is 1 : 9. Again, the integration corresponds to the relative numbers of each type of hydrogen atom present in the compound. Notice, however, that we cannot determine absolute numbers of hydrogens in this way, only their relative amounts.

The integration trace provides the raw data that we use to determine the relative numbers of different types of hydrogens. To calculate these relative numbers, we measure the linear change in the baseline from one end of the signal to the other. An excised section of the 2-methyl-2-propanol spectrum is shown in Figure 17.42 to illustrate this method.

Integration provides a second level of information from the NMR spectrum of a molecule. Not only can we learn something about the nature of the hydrogen atoms present from their chemical shifts, we can also infer the relative number of each type of hydrogen present.

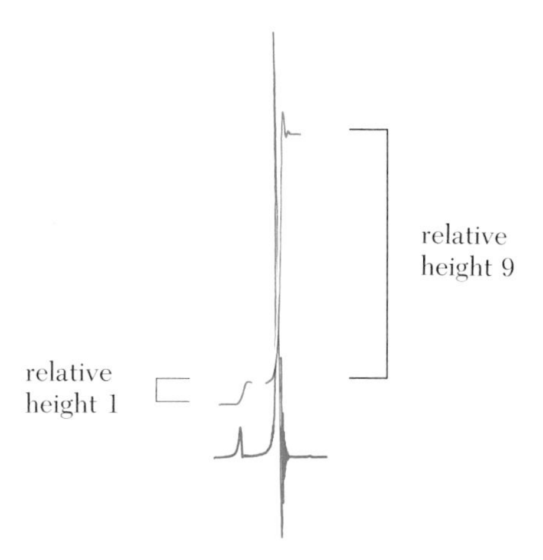

Figure 17.42 Integration of the signals of the 2-methyl-2-propanol spectrum. The vertical change in baseline of the integration curve gives us a measure of the area associated with each of the signals. The area under the normal spectrum curve is directly proportional to the number of nuclei producing the signal.

Dimethoxymethane The 60-MHz proton NMR spectrum of dimethoxymethane (**17.18**) is shown in Figure 17.43. Here we have another molecule with

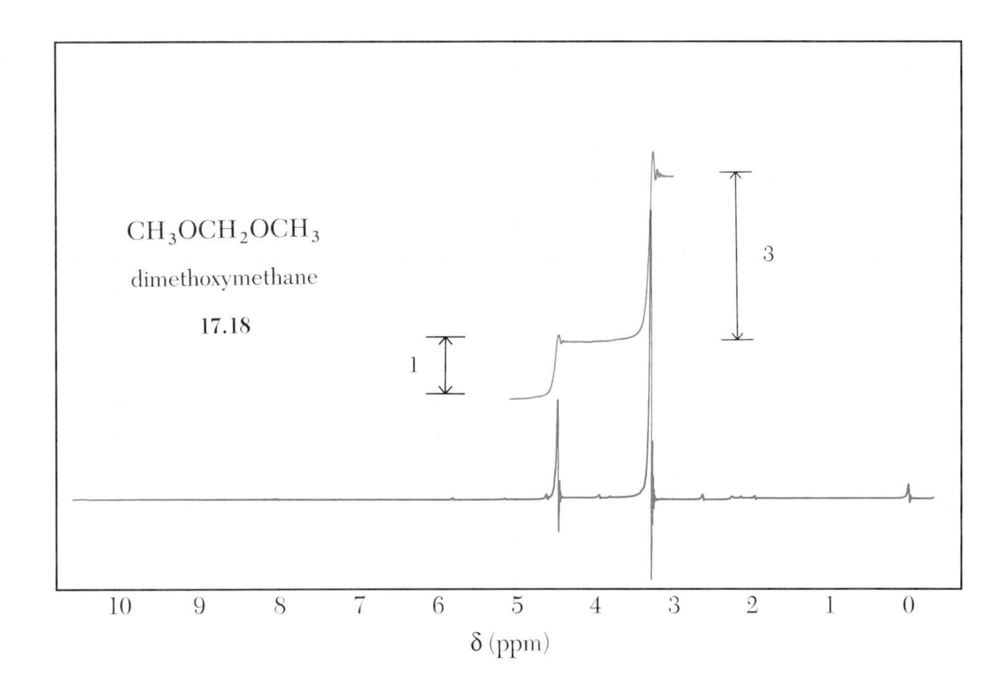

Figure 17.43 The 60-MHz proton NMR spectrum of dimethoxymethane.

two types of hydrogen present. The two methyl groups, each of which is attached to only one oxygen atom, produce a signal that is upfield from that produced by the central methylene group, which is attached to two oxygen atoms. Integration shows the area of the upfield signal to be three times that of the downfield signal, consistent with there being three times as many methyl hydrogens as there are methylene hydrogens.

***p*-Xylene** The 60-MHz proton NMR spectrum of *p*-xylene (**17.19**) is shown in Figure 17.44. Two signals are again present. The downfield signal at δ 7.0 results from the aromatic hydrogens and the upfield signal at δ 2.2 from the

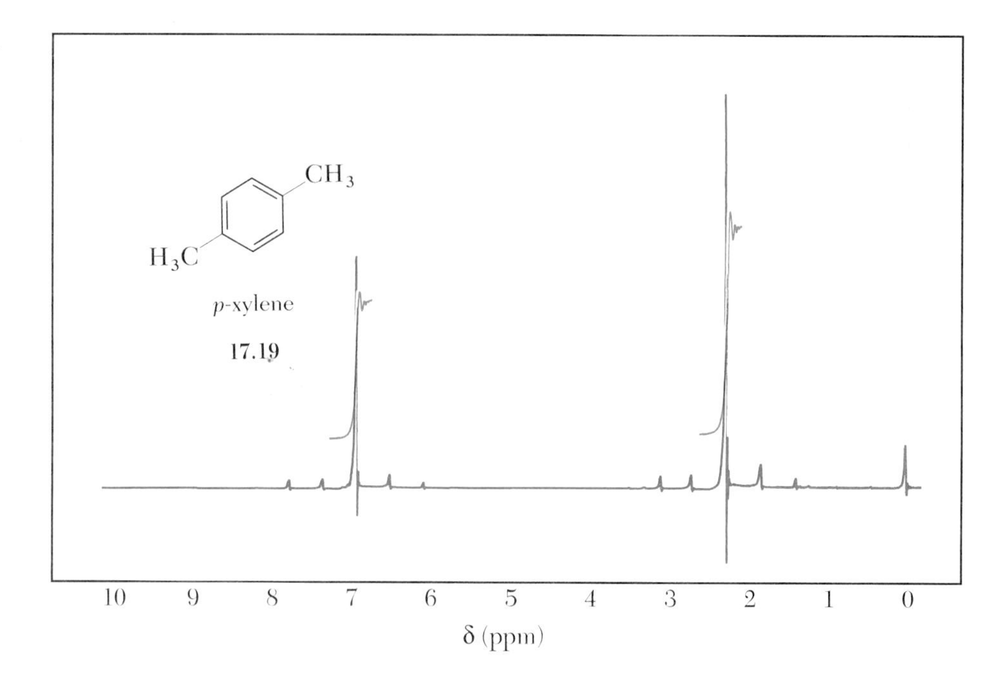

Figure 17.44 The 60-MHz proton NMR spectrum of *p*-xylene.

two methyl groups. The methyl signal occurs relatively far downfield (compared to ordinary methyl groups) because these methyl groups are attached to an aromatic ring. The same ring-current effect that causes a benzene hydrogen signal to be deshielded acts on the attached methyl groups as well. Integration of the two signals indicates the ratio of the two types of hydrogens to be 3 : 2. There are, of course, actually six methyl hydrogens and four aromatic hydrogens in the molecule.

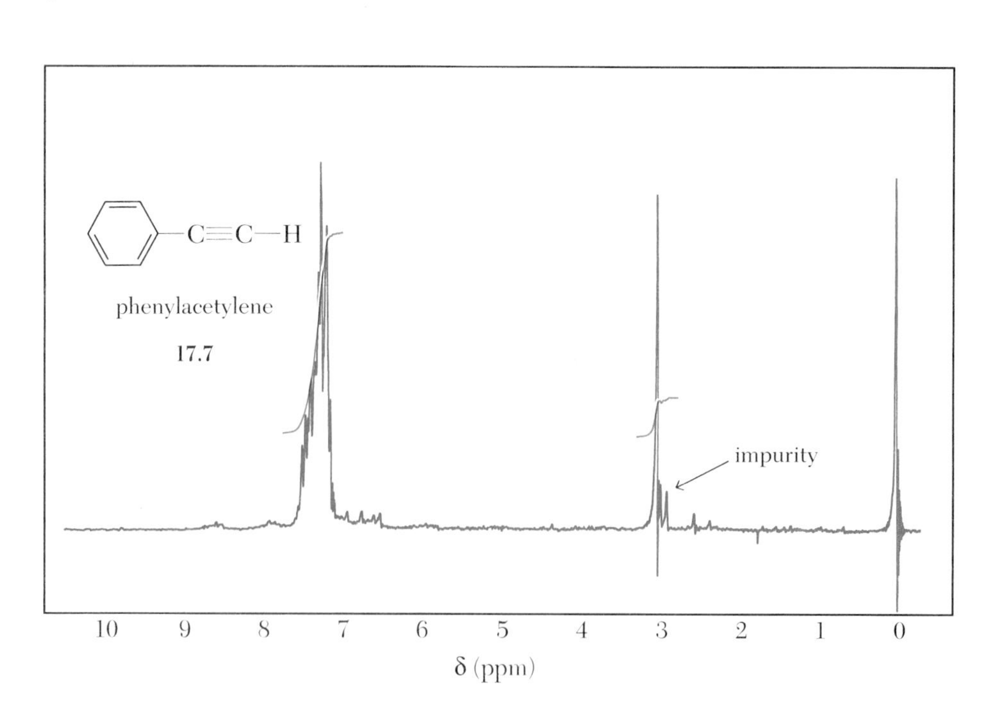

Figure 17.45 The 60-MHz proton NMR spectrum of phenylacetylene.

Phenylacetylene The 60-MHz proton NMR spectrum of phenylacetylene (**17.7**) is shown in Figure 17.45. This spectrum illustrates the shielding of an acetylenic hydrogen atom, which comes into resonance relatively far upfield at δ 3.0. The aromatic hydrogens produce a signal typically far downfield between δ 7.1 and 7.6. However, the aromatic hydrogen signal appears different from those shown in previous spectra—this signal is broad and exhibits fine structure. This fine structure is partly the result of three different types of aromatic hydrogens, located 1,2-, 1,3-, and 1,4- relative to the alkyne linkage, and partly due to a phenomenon known as spin-spin coupling. This will be the focus of our attention in the next section.

PROBLEM 17.16 Sketch the expected proton NMR spectrum for each of the compounds listed below. You should give the approximate chemical shift for each type of hydrogen (see Table 17.2) and the relative integration of each signal in the spectrum.

a. chloromethyl methyl ether
b. 1,2,4,5-tetramethylbenzene
c. 1,4-dihydroxybenzene
d. 1,4-dimethoxybenzene
e. di(2,2-dichloropropyl) ether

THE PHENOMENON OF SPIN-SPIN SPLITTING

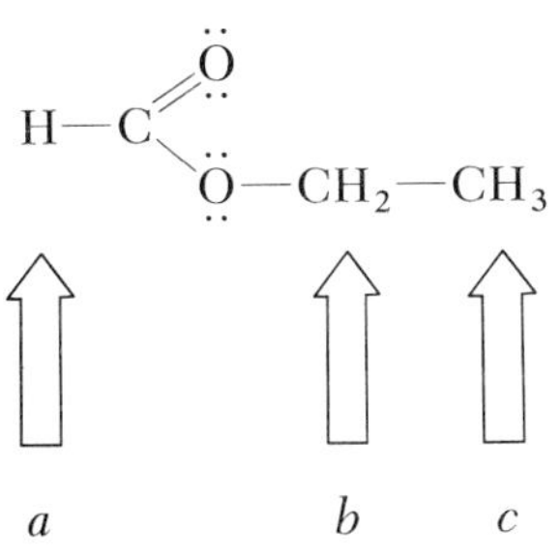

H—C(=Ö:)—Ö—CH_2—CH_3

a b c

ethyl formate
17.20

Figure 17.46 Different types of hydrogen atoms in ethyl formate. Three types of hydrogen atom positions (*a*, *b*, and *c*) are present in the ethyl formate molecule. We expect the three proton NMR signals to have the relative intensities 1 : 2 : 3.

First-Order Coupling Interactions First consider the spectrum of ethyl formate (**17.20**), the structure of which is illustrated in Figure. 17.46. There are three types of hydrogen atoms in ethyl formate. Given our understanding of NMR at this point, we would accordingly predict that its proton NMR spectrum would show three signals.

We expect the signal produced by the hydrogen at *a*, which is attached directly to the carboxyl carbon, to be relatively far downfield. Another signal, resulting from the methyl hydrogens located at *c* would be expected to appear relatively far upfield and to be three times as intense as the one far downfield. Finally, we would expect a signal for the two methylene hydrogens at *b* to have an intermediate chemical shift. In fact, we *do* find three signals, but they are not of the simple nature observed in the previous spectra. The spectrum of ethyl formate is shown in Figure 17.47.

The three signals are in the relative positions we would predict, with the predicted intensities. However, two of these signals are not simple *singlets* (one peak) of the type we saw in previous spectra. The upfield signal, produced by the methyl hydrogens, consists of a closely spaced group of three peaks and the signal at the intermediate chemical shift, produced by the methylene hydrogens, consists of a closely spaced group of four peaks! How can we explain the splitting of these signals into several peaks, while the downfield signal remains a singlet?

We need to consider the nature of the magnetic field that is actually experienced by the methyl hydrogens. We previously expressed (Equation 17.2) the field that is actually felt by a nucleus in terms of the applied field strength ($H_c + H_v$) and the induced magnetic field from electron motion in the molecule (H_i). However, an additional factor influences the magnetic field experienced by the methyl hydrogens in the ethyl formate molecule. This additional factor

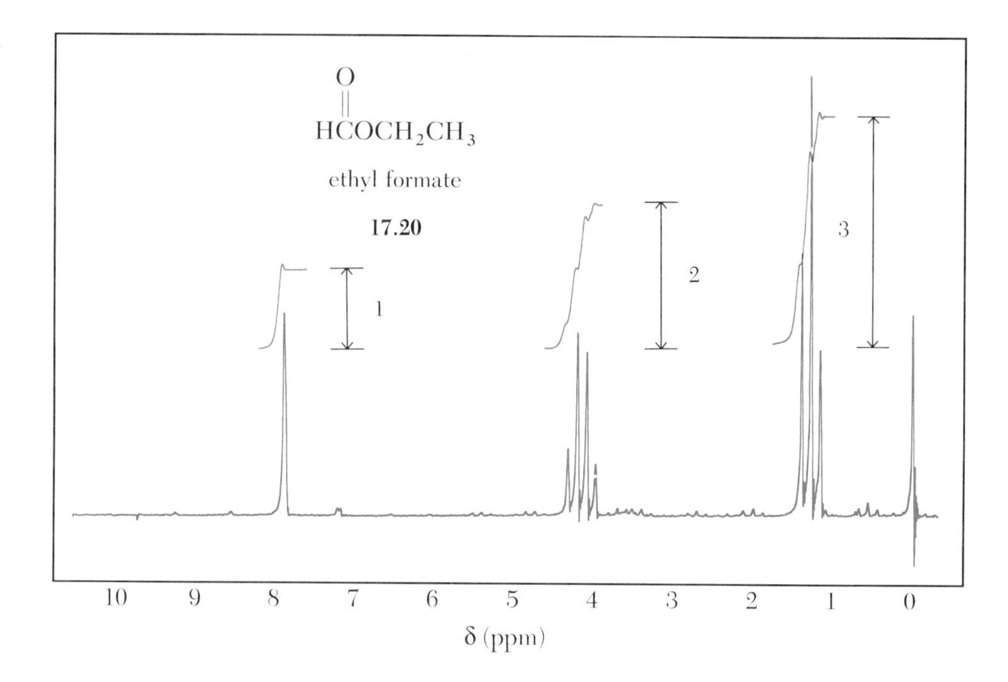

Figure 17.47 The 60-MHz proton NMR spectrum of ethyl formate.

is due to the presence of other nearby "magnets,"—the *hydrogen nuclei* attached to the adjacent carbon atom.

Recall that NMR spectrometry is possible because certain nuclei have a magnetic moment. These nuclei act as small magnets themselves, and thus *they can affect the magnetic field experienced by other nearby nuclei.* This effect is crucial to understanding the origin of the multiple peaks in the spectrum. Suppose that we are observing a particular nucleus A and that there is another nearby nucleus B with a magnetic moment of its own. Nucleus B, because of its magnetic moment, influences the magnetic field that is experienced by A, and vice versa.

In the case of ethyl formate, the methylene ($—CH_2—$) hydrogens (small magnets in their own right) are close enough to the methyl hydrogens to influence their chemical shift. We can understand how their influence causes the splitting of the methyl signal by looking at individual molecules. In the following discussion, H_m represents the magnetic field associated with each of the two methylene group protons.

First, consider a molecule in which the magnetic moments of both of the methylene hydrogens are aligned with the applied magnetic field. The small magnetic field (H_m) from each of these methylene hydrogens will add to the magnetic field experienced by these nearby methyl hydrogens. In this situation (case 1), the magnetic field experienced by the methyl hydrogens is given by Equation 17.3. The methyl hydrogens in this particular molecule are deshielded by the magnetic field of the methylene hydrogens; H_v will be smaller, and the methyl signal will be shifted downfield.

Eqn. 17.3

$$\text{case 1} \quad \text{field for methyl hydrogens} = H_c + H_v - H_i + 2\,H_m$$

Next, consider an ethyl formate molecule in which the two methylene hydrogens have magnetic moments *opposite* to one another, one aligned with the applied magnetic field and one opposed to it. In this situation (case 2), the field experienced by the nearby methyl hydrogens is given by Equation 17.4.

Eqn. 17.4 $$\text{case 2} \quad \text{field for methyl hydrogens} = H_c + H_v - H_i + H_m - H_m$$

In this case, the effects of the two nearby methylene hydrogens will cancel each other.

Finally, consider a molecule of ethyl formate in which the magnetic moments of both methylene hydrogens are opposed to the applied magnetic field (case 3). The field the methyl hydrogens experience is given by Equation 17.5. The methyl hydrogens in this molecule are shielded as a result of the neighboring proton spins.

Eqn. 17.5 $$\text{case 3} \quad \text{field for methyl hydrogens} = H_c + H_v - H_i - 2H_m$$

Methyl hydrogens in this molecule will come into resonance upfield (a larger H_v is required) from case 1 or case 2 molecules.

When we examine a sample of ethyl formate in an NMR experiment, many millions of molecules representing all three of these types are present. Using simple statistical analysis, we can predict that the ratio of case 1 : case 2 : case 3 molecules will be 1 : 2 : 1. Consider why this is so. Let us represent the magnetic moment of each methylene proton as either ↑ (aligned with the applied field) or ↓ (opposed to the applied field). If we select a proton at random there is a 50/50 chance of its magnetic moment being ↑ or ↓. Our three cases can be represented as:

case 1 ↑↑

case 2 ↑↓ or ↓↑

case 3 ↓↓

An analogy with coin tosses is useful—if we toss two coins, the probability of obtaining one head and one tail is twice that of getting either two heads or two tails.

In Figure 17.48 we designate the two methylene hydrogens as A and B and analyze their effects on the shielding or deshielding of adjacent methyl

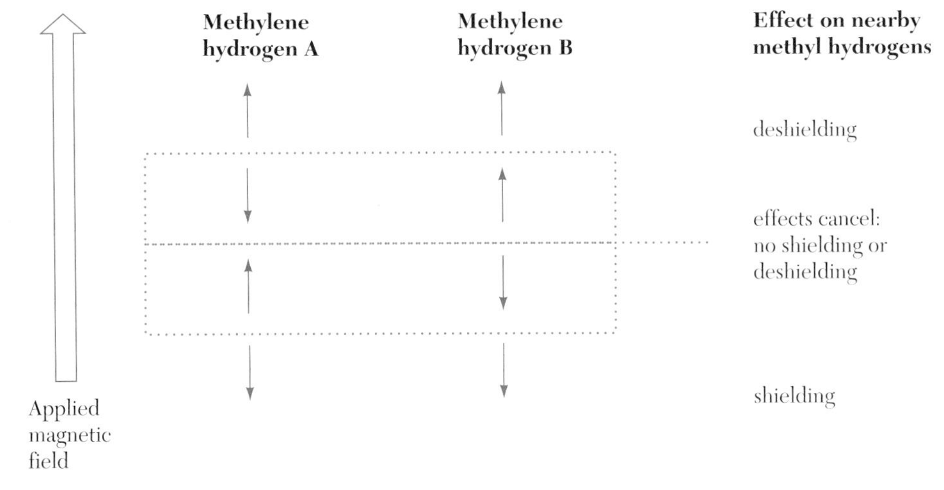

Figure 17.48 Statistical distribution of spin possibilities for the hydrogens of a methylene group. In one fourth of the molecules, the magnetic moments of the two hydrogens are aligned with the applied field and have a deshielding effect on the nearby methyl hydrogens. In another one fourth, the magnetic moments are opposed to the applied field and have a shielding effect on the nearby methyl hydrogens. In the remainder, one nuclear magnetic moment is in each direction, resulting in zero effect on nearby nuclei.

protons. Molecules in which both methylene hydrogen magnetic moments are aligned with the applied field produce the downfield (or deshielded) peak within the methyl signal. Molecules in which both methylene hydrogen magnetic moments are opposed to the applied field produce the upfield (or shielded) peak within the methyl signal. The remainder of the molecules produce the central peak of the methyl signal. Since the statistical probability for mixed magnetic moments (case 2) is twice as great as it is for either case 1 or case 3, the central peak is twice as intense as those on either side of it. The methyl hydrogen resonance in the ethyl formate spectrum is thus a symmetrical triplet. The intensity ratio of the three peaks of the signal is 1:2:1.

The four peaks in the methylene signal arise in an analogous manner. Their chemical shift is influenced by the three nearby methyl hydrogens, whose distributions of nuclear magnetic moments affect the methylene chemical shift in individual molecules. The possible permutations of these three magnetic moments are shown in Figure 17.49.

As we can deduce from Figure 17.49, the signal for the methylene hydrogens in ethyl formate will be split into four peaks due to the nuclear magnetic moments of the nearby methyl hydrogens. The methylene signal is a symmetrical quartet in which the intensity of the individual peaks has a 1:3:3:1 ratio.

Figure 17.49 Statistical distribution of spin possibilities for a methyl group. In one eighth of the molecules all nuclear magnetic moments are aligned with the applied magnetic field. In an equal number of molecules all nuclear magnetic moments are opposed to the applied magnetic field. In three eighths of the molecules the nuclear magnetic moments are partially aligned, and in an equal number they are partially opposed to the applied field.

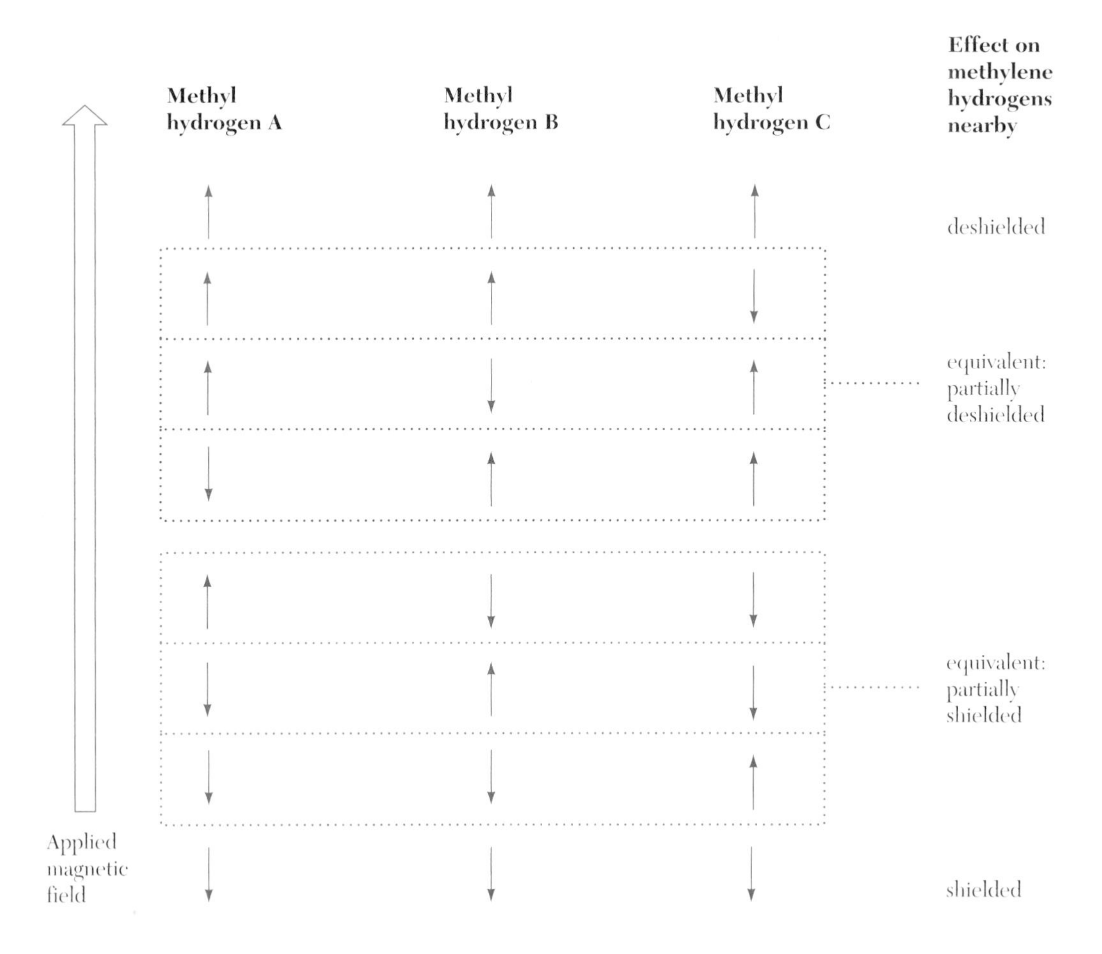

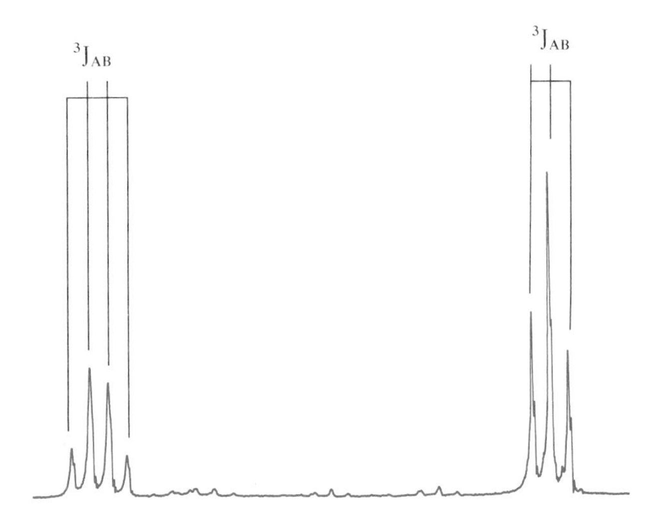

Figure 17.50 Coupling between methylene and methyl hydrogens in the ethyl formate NMR spectrum. Both signals for the coupled hydrogens show splitting, and each signal is split by the same magnitude. The chemical shift difference between the individual peaks of each group is the same, that is, $^3J_{AB} = {}^3J_{BA}$.

This phenomenon is known as **spin-spin splitting** of NMR signals. The presence of a quartet and a triplet with relative intensities of 2:3 as seen in the spectrum of ethyl formate is a characteristic NMR signature of ethyl groups in general. You will develop a recognition for other common splitting patterns with a bit of experience.

There are several important aspects of this spin-spin splitting. First, for nuclei that interact in this way (are *coupled*), we observe splitting in both NMR signals. Furthermore, both signals are split to the same magnitude. We can see this by concentrating on the appropriate sections of the NMR spectrum of ethyl formate, as shown in Figure 17.50. The magnitude of the splitting (the spacing between the peaks) is the same for each set of coupled signals. The coupling is indicated by the symbol $^3J_{AB}$ (or $^3J_{BA}$). The superscript indicates the number of bonds separating the coupled nuclei, *A* and *B*, as illustrated in Figure 17.51. We usually give the magnitude of *J* (the **coupling constant**) in units of Hz, relating to the frequency of the exciting radiation. With 60-MHz NMR (as we are using here), 60 Hz is the equivalent of 1 ppm. The splitting of the signals is quite small. For ethyl formate, the splitting of the methylene and methyl signals is about 7 Hz. In general, the magnitude of the splitting varies from molecule to molecule. Within a molecule, the splitting varies depending on the nuclei that are coupled.

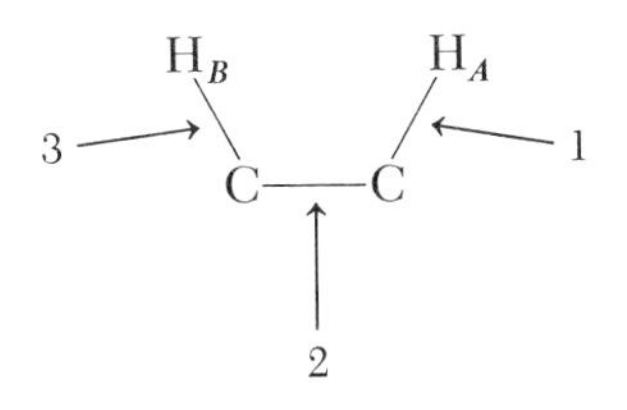

Figure 17.51 Three-bond coupling of H_A and H_B.

A second point regarding spin-spin splitting concerns the distance between the coupled nuclei. In the ethyl formate spectrum, the methylene and methyl hydrogens are coupled, but neither is coupled to the hydrogen bound to the carboxyl carbon. Both the methyl and the methylene hydrogens are too far away from the remaining hydrogen for any magnetic interaction to be seen. There are four intervening bonds between this hydrogen and the methylene hydrogens, and five bonds between it and the methyl hydrogens. As a general rule, we observe coupling when the interacting nuclei are separated by three or fewer bonds. However, we do not observe splittings from interactions of equivalent hydrogens (those with the same chemical shift).

We can make a generalization about the number of peaks in a multiplet and the relative intensities of these peaks. It is not necessary to count the permutations of nuclear magnetic moments (as we did with the ethyl group) to predict the splitting of signals. As a general rule for *first-order coupling*, the NMR signal of a hydrogen will be split into $n + 1$ peaks by its interaction with n *equivalent* nearby hydrogens.

It is also easy to calculate the relative intensities of the individual peaks of a split signal. These relative intensities are given by the coefficients of the terms in the expansion of the binomial expression $(a + b)^n$. Figure 17.52 shows the number and relative intensities of peaks within signals that have been split by nearby equivalent nuclei.

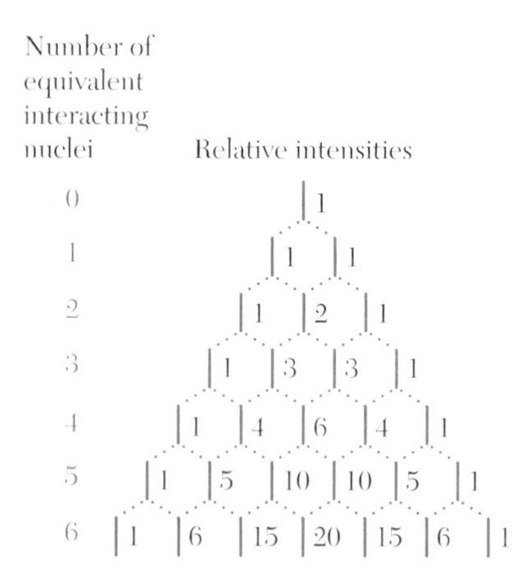

Figure 17.52 Numbers of peaks in an NMR signal and their relative intensities upon interaction with n equivalent nearby nuclei.

Caution must be exercised in the use of this rule. First, the difference in chemical shift ($\Delta\delta$) of the coupled hydrogens should be at least ten times as great as their coupling constant (J). For example, with a coupling constant of 6 Hz, the difference in chemical shift should be at least 60 Hz (1 ppm). If the difference in chemical shift is less, the splitting of the signals is usually not as simple as the $n + 1$ rule would indicate (such couplings are not first-order). Second, we must remember the meaning of the term *nearby*. For these types of interactions, *nearby* means that there are three or fewer intervening bonds between the interacting nuclei.

Now, consider the 60-MHz proton NMR spectrum of 1,3-dibromopropane (**17.21**), shown in Figure 17.53.

$$:\ddot{\underset{..}{Br}}CH_2CH_2CH_2\ddot{\underset{..}{Br}}:$$

1,3-dibromopropane
17.21

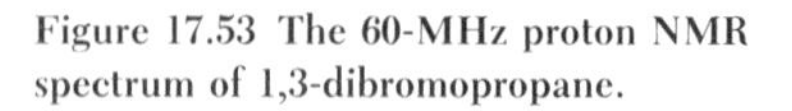

Figure 17.53 The 60-MHz proton NMR spectrum of 1,3-dibromopropane.

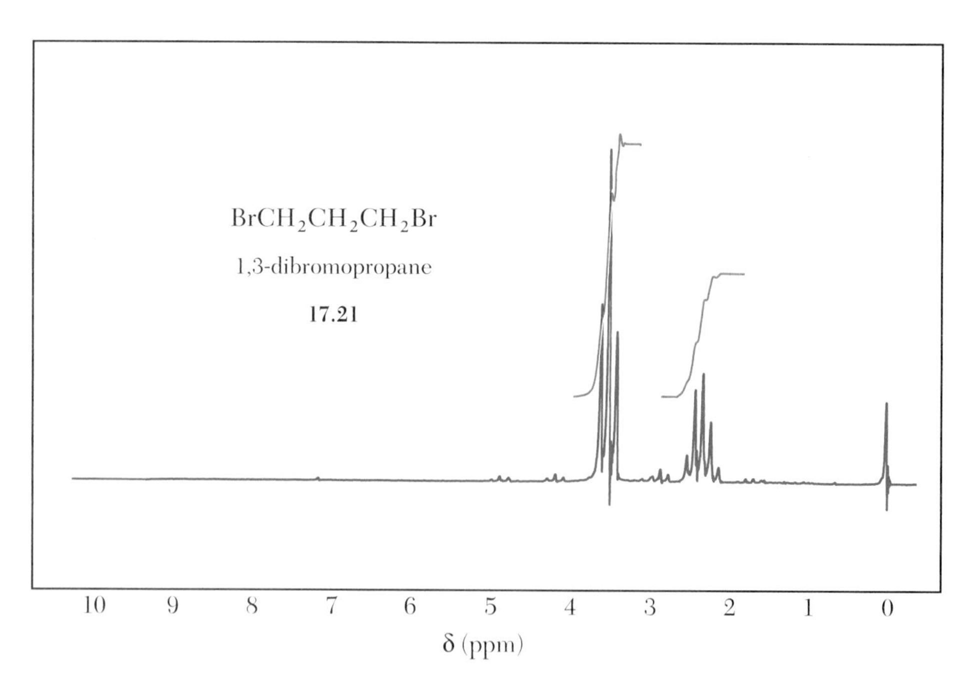

There are two signals, both split into multiplets. Two sets of hydrogens are present in the molecule, and they are spin-coupled with each other. The signal produced by the terminal bromomethylene groups ($—CH_2Br$) occurs as a symmetrical triplet at δ 3.5. This signal is twice as intense as the one at δ 2.3, produced by the central methylene group. The four bromomethylene hydrogens are all *equivalent*—we cannot distinguish between them by any chemical or physical means.

The signal for the bromomethylene hydrogens occurs as a 1 : 2 : 1 triplet as a result of the interaction with the nearby central methylene group. Similarly, the signal for the central methylene group is split into a symmetrical 1 : 4 : 6 : 4 : 1 quintet (five peaks) by interaction with four equivalent hydrogens. The fact that the four equivalent hydrogens with which the central methylene interacts are not all on the same carbon is immaterial.

PROBLEM 17.17 Using the approach of enumerating the permutations of magnetic moments of interacting nuclei (as we did for ethyl formate), rationalize the splitting of the signals in the spectrum of 1,3-dibromopropane.

PROBLEM 17.18 Predict the proton NMR spectrum for each of the compounds listed below. In addition to the approximate chemical shift for each signal, your description should include any signal-splitting that occurs and the total integration and the relative intensities of all peaks.

a. methyl ethyl ether
b. 1-chloro-2,2-dibromoethane
c. 1,4-diethylbenzene
d. 2-propanol
e. isopropyl 2-chloroethyl ether

More Complex Splitting Interactions Consider 1-bromopropane (**17.22**). We can easily predict the relative chemical shifts and total integration for the signals of the proton NMR spectrum of this molecule. They are shown in Figure 17.54.

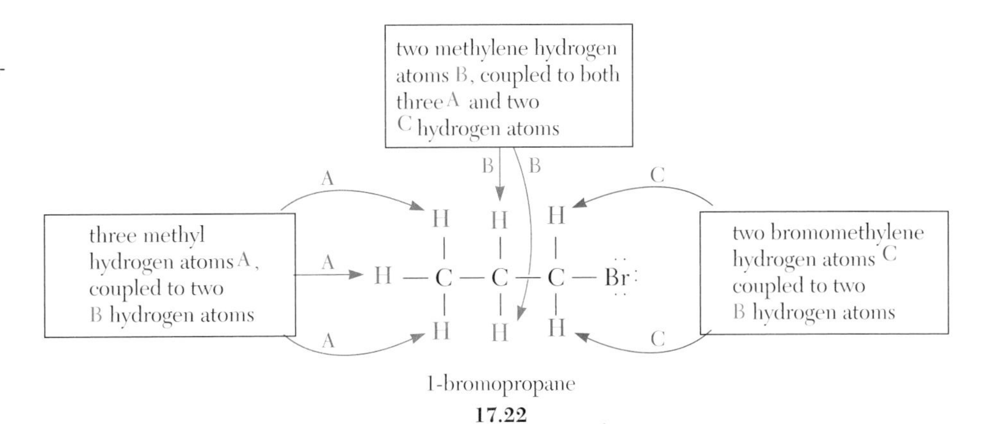

Figure 17.54 Predicted characteristics of the proton NMR spectrum of 1-bromopropane.

Using our $n + 1$ rule, we can easily predict the splittings of the signals of the *A* and *C* hydrogens of 1-bromopropane. Both sets of hydrogens have three-bond interactions with the central methylene hydrogens (*B*). The signals of both the *A* and the *C* hydrogens are expected to appear as *symmetrical triplets* with coupling constants, *J*, in the range 6–10 Hz. Both of these couplings are of the ^3J type. We designate the splitting of *A* hydrogens with the term $^3J_{AB}$, and the splitting of *C* hydrogens with the term $^3J_{BC}$. There is no coupling directly between the *A* and *C* hydrogens because there are four intervening bonds.

But what happens to the signal for the *B* hydrogens? These hydrogens interact with both of the two sets of nearby hydrogens, *A* and *C*. With the *A* hydrogens they have a coupling interaction $^3J_{AB}$, and with the *C* hydrogens, a coupling interaction $^3J_{BC}$. Although both interactions are present at the same time, we can describe the net result most simply by looking at them sequentially. That is, the three methyl *A* hydrogens split the signal of the *B* hydrogen to a symmetrical quartet (four peaks) by interaction $^3J_{AB}$. Then the two *C* hydrogens split *each peak* of this quartet to a triplet by interaction $^3J_{BC}$. These splittings are illustrated in Figure 17.55. (Notice that you would get the same result by splitting *B* first by *C* and then by *A*.)

According to this first-order analysis, the signal for the central methylene hydrogens of 1-bromopropane is predicted to consist of twelve peaks. We do not actually observe twelve separate peaks since there is considerable overlap of the inner peaks. The full complement of peaks will only be seen if the values of $^3J_{AB}$ and $^3J_{BC}$ are sufficiently different that overlap does not occur. Since the two coupling constants for 1-bromopropane are quite similar, fewer distinct peaks are resolved. The 60-MHz proton NMR spectrum for 1-bromopropane is shown in Figure 17.56. As predicted, the upfield (methyl) and downfield (bromomethylene) signals appear as triplets in the 1-bromopropane spectrum. The central methylene signal appears as a broadened and poorly resolved *multiplet* due to the overlapping of individual peaks. We will return to the 1-

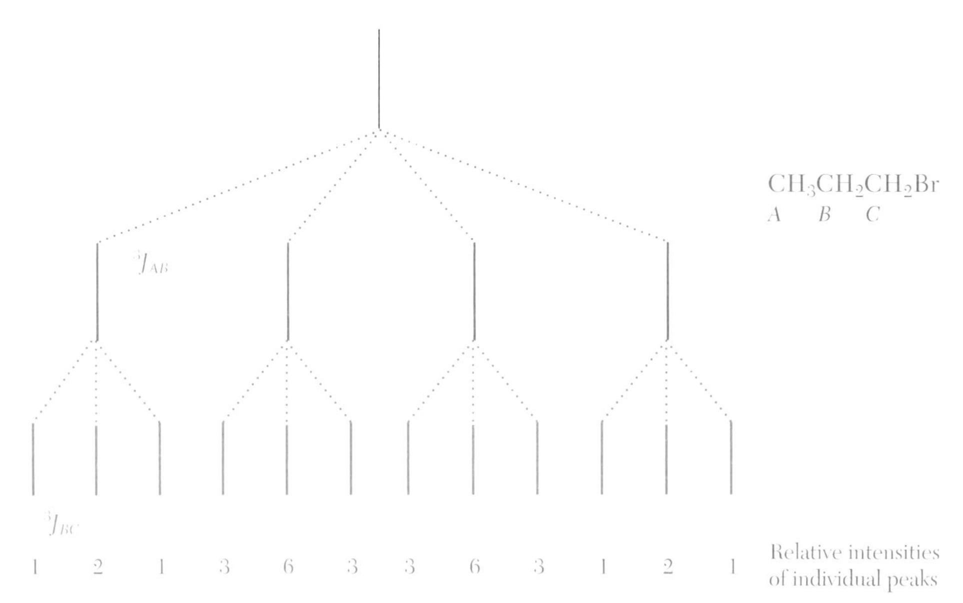

Figure 17.55 Splitting of the proton NMR signal for the central methylene hydrogens of 1-bromopropane. The central methylene hydrogens interact with both the terminal methyl hydrogens and the bromomethylene hydrogens. Considered sequentially, the interaction with the methyl hydrogens splits the signal into a symmetrical quartet. Each peak of the quartet is then further split by interaction with the bromomethylene hydrogens. The relative intensities for each of the total of twelve peaks are shown.

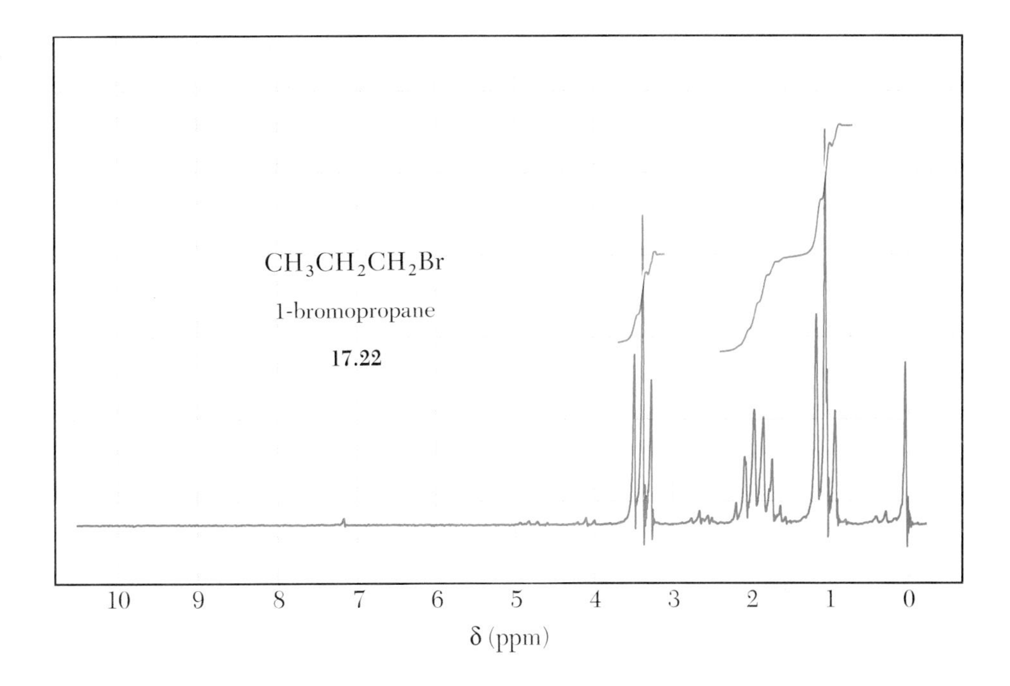

Figure 17.56 The 60-MHz proton NMR spectrum of 1-bromopropane.

bromopropane spectrum in a later section when we study ways of separating the effects of different interactions on a single set of hydrogens.

Consider another relatively simple molecule, 4-bromo-1-butene (**17.23**), in which we see some more complex interactions. Its proton NMR spectrum is shown in Figure 17.57. There are three sets of signals. The two hydrogen atoms bonded to the C4 position appear as a triplet centered at $\sim\delta$ 3.3; it is split to a triplet by interaction with the two equivalent hydrogens at the C3 position.

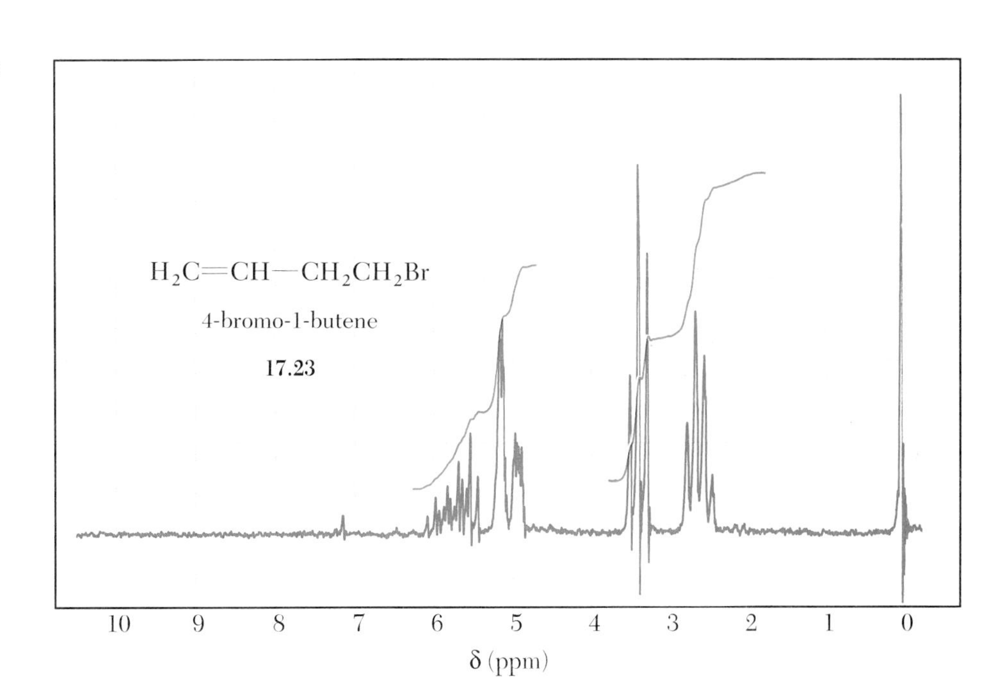

Figure 17.57 The 60-MHz proton NMR spectrum of 4-bromo-1-butene.

Farther downfield is a very complex signal produced by the olefinic hydrogens at C1 and C2. The two hydrogens of the C3 position appear as a multiplet upfield (at $\sim\delta$ 2.6). First order analysis predicts that this signal would be a doublet of triplets (i.e. a total of six peaks) because it is split simultaneously by interaction with one set of two equivalent hydrogens (of $-CH_2Br$) and one of the olefinic hydrogens (from C2). However, the individual peaks overlap and only four distinct peaks can be seen under these conditions.

$$H_2C{=}CH{-}CH_2CH_2{-}\ddot{\underset{..}{Br}}:$$

4-bromo-1-butene

17.23

PROBLEM 17.19 Predict the proton NMR spectrum (chemical shift, integration, and theoretical splitting for each signal) for each of the following compounds:

a. 2-methyl-3-pentanone b. 1-phenyl-2-bromopropane
c. 2-pentanol d. 3-pentanol
e. (Z)-1-chloro-1-butene

Steps to solving the Problem

Solution to Problem 17.19a

1. Draw the structure of 2-methyl-3-pentanone:

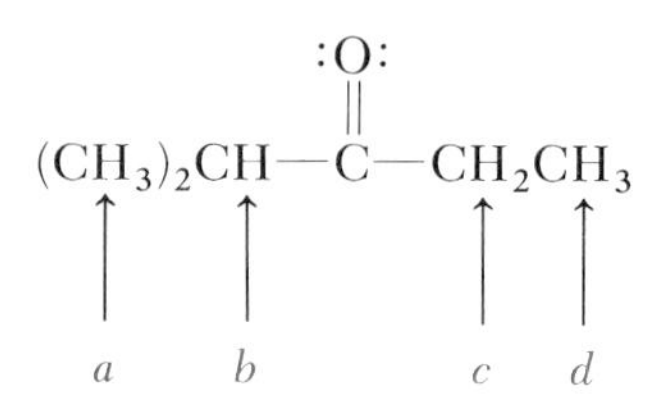

2. Use the structure to find out how many different types of hydrogens are present. There are in fact four sets of hydrogens in the molecule, indicated *a*–*d*. Hydrogens *a* and *b* are part of an isopropyl group, whereas hydrogens *c* and *d* are part of an ethyl group. The ethyl and isopropyl groups are isolated from each other by the carbonyl group, and their hydrogen atoms are not expected to couple with each other.
3. What splittings will these relationships produce in the NMR spectrum? The signals are as follows:

a—six hydrogens, doublet, $\delta \sim 0.9$, J_{ab}

b—one hydrogen, septet, $\delta \sim 2.3$, J_{ba}

c—two hydrogens, quartet, $\delta \sim 2.1$, J_{cd}

d—three hydrogens, triplet, $\delta \sim 0.9$, J_{dc}

DECOUPLING AND EXCHANGE

Suppose that nucleus *A* is spin-coupled to nucleus *B*. The NMR signal for *A* will be split into a doublet because of the coupling. Basically, the splitting occurs because nucleus *A* senses the different spin states of nucleus *B*, as described earlier. In some molecules *B* will have one type of spin, and in others it will have the opposite spin. However, suppose that nucleus *B* can be induced to interconvert between spin states. Further suppose that the interconversion is much more rapid than the time scale of the NMR measurement. Under these conditions, nucleus *A* will not sense two different spin states—but rather an average of the two. An analogy is useful here. Imagine a disk painted half black and half white. These halves correspond to the two possible spin states of *B*. Now imagine that the disk is rapidly rotated. You, the observer, correspond to nucleus *A*. You will sense only the average of the black and white colors—you will see gray. When a nucleus senses only the average of spin states, the effects of coupling are eliminated from its signal in the NMR spectrum. There are several important ways in which this type of decoupling can occur, and we will now consider them in turn.

Exchange Consider the ethanol molecule (**17.24**). The proton NMR spectrum of ethanol measured as a dilute solution in carbon tetrachloride is shown in Figure 17.58.

$$H-\ddot{\underset{..}{O}}-CH_2-CH_3$$

ethanol
17.24

There are two areas of absorption in the spectrum—one near $\delta = 1$ and one in the region between $\delta = 3$ and $\delta = 4$. The band at $\delta \sim 1$ is associated with the hydrogen atoms of the methyl group. The signal is split into a triplet because of spin coupling with the two hydrogen atoms of the neighboring methylene group. The band between $\delta = 3$ and $\delta = 4$ encompasses signals from both the

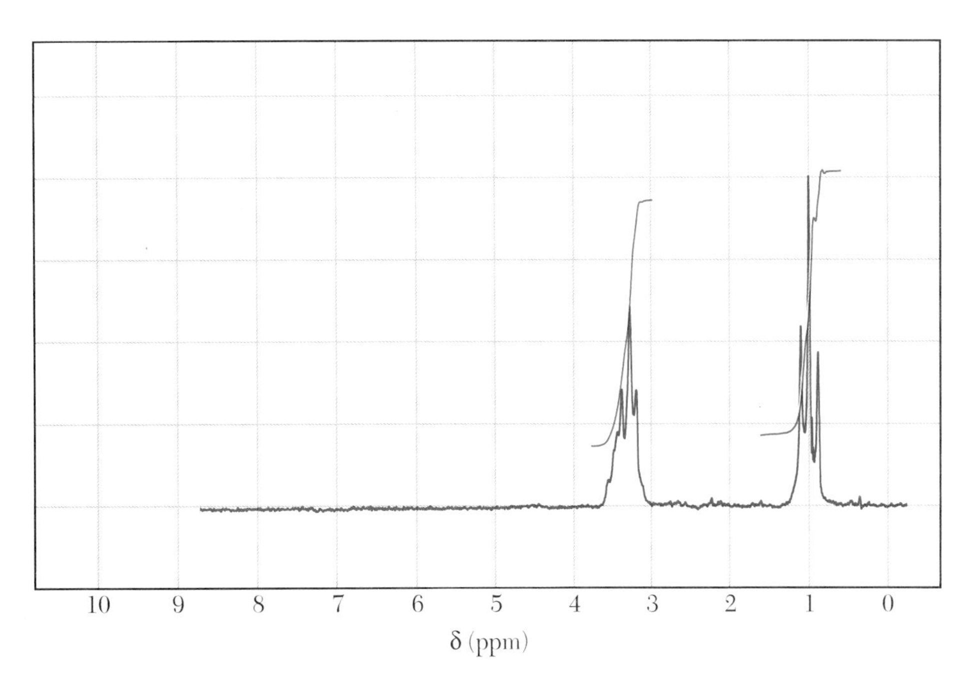

Figure 17.58 The 60-MHz proton NMR spectrum of ethanol measured as a dilute solution in carbon tetrachloride. No TMS has been added to the solution.

hydroxyl group hydrogen atom and the hydrogen atoms of the methylene group (the signals overlap). The complexity of the band is understandable not only because the signals overlap, but also because we can expect each signal to be split by spin-spin coupling. The signal for the hydroxyl proton is expected to be a triplet (because of coupling to the two hydrogen atoms of the neighboring methylene group), and that for the methylene protons themselves is expected to be quite complex (ideally a doublet of quartets) owing to coupling to the hydroxyl hydrogen atom and to the three hydrogen atoms of the methyl group. The appearance of the band is indeed complex, reflecting the various types of spin coupling that are taking place.

Now consider the spectrum of ethanol obtained under different conditions. The spectrum shown in Figure 17.59 is that of pure ethanol containing one drop of concentrated hydrochloric acid. As in the previous spectrum, the three methyl hydrogen atoms come into resonance at $\delta \sim 1.0$ and are split into a triplet by interaction with the two adjacent methylene hydrogens. However, under the new solution conditions, the position of the hydroxyl hydrogen signal shifts significantly downfield and appears as a *singlet;* notice that it is not split by the adjacent methylene hydrogens. Finally, the methylene hydrogens come into resonance at $\delta \sim 3.3$, split into a simple quartet by the three adjacent methyl hydrogens. The observation that the band is not further split suggests that coupling to the hydrogen atom of the hydroxyl group is eliminated.

In summary, this spectrum is much simpler than that obtained in dilute carbon tetrachloride solution (Figure 17.58). In particular, changing the conditions of spectral measurement eliminates any coupling involving the hydroxyl hydrogen.

The rationale for the change in the spectrum is based on the ability of hydroxyl hydrogens to undergo *exchange*. When diluted by carbon tetrachloride,

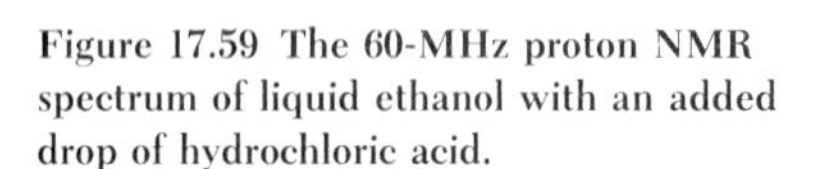

Figure 17.59 The 60-MHz proton NMR spectrum of liquid ethanol with an added drop of hydrochloric acid.

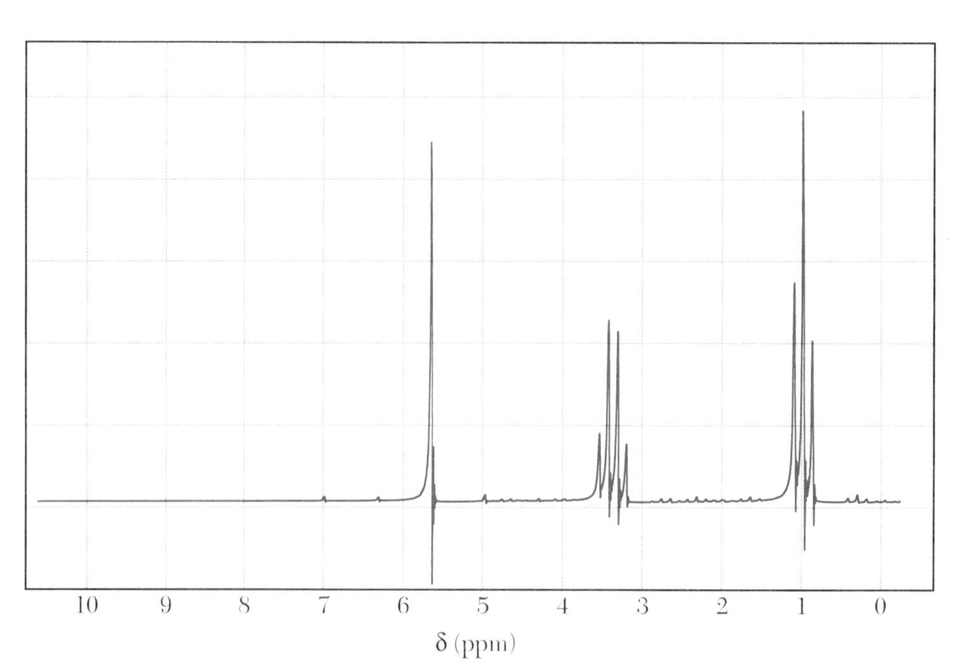

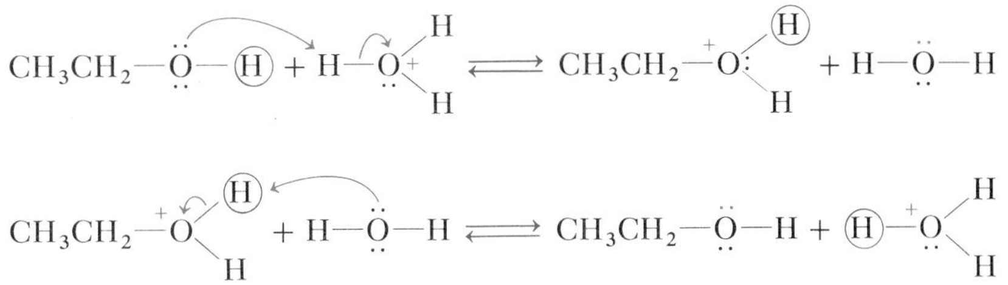

Figure 17.60 Mechanism for the exchange of a hydroxyl hydrogen of an alcohol. Acid-base equilibria are established in which the alcohol acts as a base and another species acts as an acid. The exchange process occurs extremely rapidly, much faster than the time scale of an NMR analysis. Nearby nuclei see the average of all of the spin states of the hydrogen atoms that attach to and detach from the oxygen atom of the ethanol hydroxyl group.

$$CH_3CH_2{-}\ddot{O}{-}H + H{-}\overset{+}{O}H_2 \rightleftharpoons CH_3CH_2{-}\overset{+}{O}H_2 + H{-}\ddot{O}{-}H$$

$$CH_3CH_2{-}\overset{+}{O}H_2 + H{-}\ddot{O}{-}H \rightleftharpoons CH_3CH_2{-}\ddot{O}{-}H + H{-}\overset{+}{O}H_2$$

ethanol molecules only seldom contact each other, and hydrogen bonding among them is at a low level. A hydrogen that is associated with a particular ethanol molecule remains with that molecule for a relatively long period of time. However, with liquid ethanol in the presence of a small amount of hydrochloric acid, exchange of hydroxyl hydrogen among ethanol molecules and the added acid occurs very rapidly. In a collection of hydroxyl hydrogens undergoing exchange, approximately equal numbers have each of the two possible spin states. The rapid exchange of hydroxyl hydrogens constantly changes the spin state of the hydrogen atom associated with a given hydroxyl oxygen atom, and thus the methylene hydrogens are not able to discern a constant spin state for the adjacent hydroxyl hydrogen atom. When exchange is sufficiently rapid, the methylene hydrogens experience only an *average* spin state for the nearby hydroxyl hydrogen, which is equivalent to experiencing *no* spin. As a result, we see only the coupling of the methylene hydrogens with the methyl hydrogens. The chemical shift of the hydroxyl hydrogen also changes upon changing the solvent and altering the conditions for hydrogen exchange. A mechanism for exchange of hydroxyl hydrogens is shown in Figure 17.60.

We can use the exchange phenomenon to discern structural features of some molecules. If a hydrogen that normally participates in coupling interactions undergoes exchange sufficiently rapidly, nearby nuclei will not be able to discern any particular spin associated with that site, which no longer cause splitting of the signals in the NMR spectrum. We very commonly observe this type of exchange decoupling with alcohols; however, we can induce it to occur with some other types of molecules as well. It is often useful to measure the NMR spectrum of a suspected alcohol under two sets of conditions, those facilitating exchange and those hindering exchange.

Deuterium Exchange Suppose we perform an NMR analysis of an alcohol in a special type of solvent—a solvent whose own exchangeable hydrogen atom has been replaced by a deuterium atom. In this case we eliminate not only the coupling of the hydroxyl hydrogen with nearby nuclei but also the *entire hydroxyl hydrogen signal.*

For example, addition of D_2O to the ethanol in carbon tetrachloride solution results in complete disappearance of the hydroxyl hydrogen signal while the triplet and quartet for the ethyl group remain. As a result of exchange, deuterium from the D_2O replaces the exchangeable hydroxyl hydrogen atom of the ethanol. The hydrogen atom from the ethanol ends up in HOD molecules. (Water and its isotopic variants, HOD and D_2O, are lighter than carbon tetrachloride and float on top of the organic solution, away from the region examined in the NMR analysis.)

In summary, when we exchange hydrogen in a sample with deuterium, we remove not only splittings due to the original hydrogen but also remove the signal itself. We can thus identify the signals due to hydrogen atoms in exchangeable locations.

Why does the hydroxyl hydrogen signal disappear? We find the answer in the equilibrium that is established when we add D_2O to the sample. This equilibrium is shown in Equation 17.6.

Eqn. 17.6

$$R{-}\ddot{\underset{\cdot\cdot}{O}}{-}H + D_2\ddot{\underset{\cdot\cdot}{O}} \rightleftharpoons R{-}\ddot{\underset{\cdot\cdot}{O}}{-}D + H\ddot{\underset{\cdot\cdot}{O}}D$$

If D_2O is present in large excess, the equilibrium is driven to the right and most of the ROH molecules become ROD molecules. Deuterium does not exhibit an NMR signal in the region scanned for proton signals. Therefore, the hydroxyl signal disappears. *Only* the hydroxyl signal disappears. Other hydrogen atoms are not exchanged and continue to give signals.

Double-Irradiation Experiments Suppose there is a complex-looking band in a proton NMR spectrum of an unknown compound, and that you suspect that the complexity is caused by the protons under survey participating in spin-spin coupling to several other types of protons. You would like to analyze the complex splitting pattern by selectively eliminating some of the spin-spin coupling interactions. If any of the protons are exchangeable, you can follow the strategy above, but most protons in organic molecules are not exchangeable (in general only those associated with hydroxyl or amino groups can be exchanged). Fortunately, there is another way to achieve spin decoupling—we can use **double-irradiation** experiments. In all the NMR experiments discussed so far the sample was irradiated with radio frequency electromagnetic radiation of one particular frequency (60 MHz). This irradiation causes the nucleus under investigation (let us say nucleus *A*) to absorb energy and change to its higher-energy spin state. Of course, for nucleus *A* to absorb 60 MHz radiation, the applied magnetic field must split the spin states of *A* by just the right amount. This magnetic field will not be appropriate to split the level of some other nucleus *B* so that it too absorbs 60 MHz radiation (that is why we scan the magnetic field to run a spectrum—nuclei in different environments absorb 60 MHz radiation at different applied fields). However nucleus *B* will absorb radio frequency photons of a *different* frequency than 60 MHz. Suppose nuclei *A* and *B* are spin coupled. If we irradiate *B* at this different radiofrequency, while doing the normal NMR scan, nucleus *B* will constantly flip between its two spin states. It follows that any splitting due to spin coupling of nuclei *A* and *B* will be eliminated. Thus we can **decouple** ordinarily interacting nuclei. The constant change of spin states in a double-irradiation experiment is so rapid that the normally coupled nucleus of *A* sees only an average (i.e., zero effect) of the two possible spin states of nucleus *B*.

We previously looked at the proton NMR spectrum of 1-bromopropane (Figure 17.56). In this spectrum the signal for the central methylene group is complex because it is coupled to both the methyl and the bromomethylene hydrogens. Suppose we perform a separate irradiation specifically for the central methylene hydrogens while we perform a normal spectral scan of the entire molecule. The *decoupled* spectrum we obtain is shown in Figure 17.61. Irra-

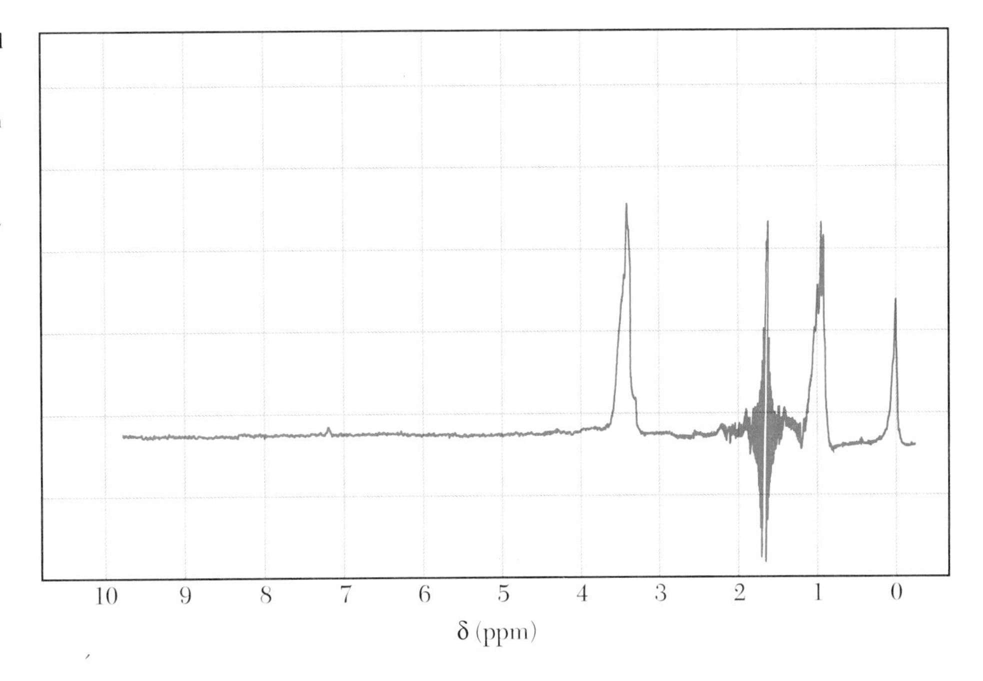

Figure 17.61 The electronically decoupled 60-MHz proton NMR spectrum of 1-bromopropane. The signal for the central methylene group has been irradiated with an extra radio frequency input. The hydrogens of the central methylene group are thus decoupled from the methyl and bromomethylene hydrogens to which they are normally coupled.

diation of the central methylene signal removes the coupling to each of the other signals. Both the methyl and bromomethylene signals become unsplit, that is, they now appear as singlets. At the region of the spectrum where the central methylene signal was originally located, we now see only a *beat pattern* indicating the point of double irradiation. By performing this double irradiation experiment we determine that the signal at δ 1.7 (the methylene hydrogens) is normally coupled to each of the types of hydrogens producing the other signals. In the analysis of the spectra of complex molecules, double irradiation proves to be a useful experimental technique.

REPRESENTATIVE SPECTRA

It is useful to study a variety of NMR spectra with explanations of their characteristics in order to develop a background that can be applied to the determination of structures of unknowns. Here we will make a fairly detailed analysis of the spectra of four compounds.

2-Butanone The proton NMR spectrum of 2-butanone (**17.25**) is shown in Figure 17.62. This spectrum exhibits the classical signature of an ethyl group—an upfield triplet (δ 1.0) and a downfield quartet (δ 2.3). In addition to this triplet and quartet, there is also a singlet at δ 2.0 that integrates to three hydrogens. The fact that this signal is a singlet indicates that there are no hydrogens on nearby carbon atoms. Its chemical shift also indicates that it is attached to a carbonyl carbon. The singlet and the quartet partially overlap in this spectrum—a relatively common occurrence. Experience in studying spectra will allow you to distinguish overlapping signals from single, more complex signals.

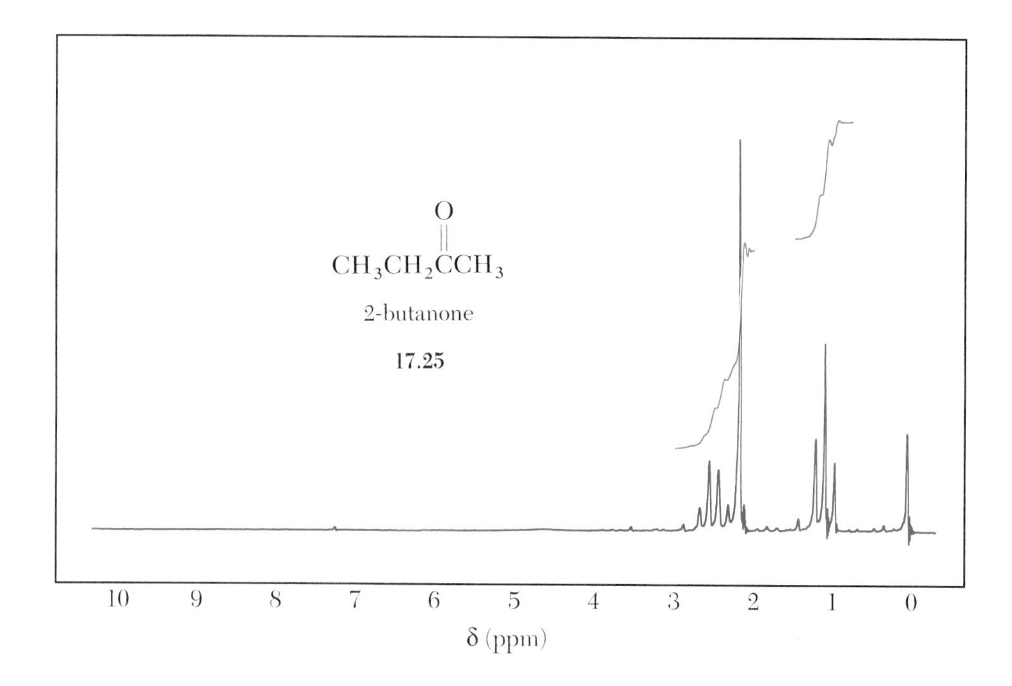

Figure 17.62 The 60-MHz proton NMR spectrum of 2-butanone.

***trans*-Cinnamic Acid** The proton NMR spectrum of *trans*-cinnamic acid (**17.26**) is shown in Figure 17.63. There are four signals in this spectrum. The five aromatic hydrogens produce the broad signal centered at δ 7.3. The difference in the chemical shifts of the three types of aromatic hydrogens (1,2-, 1,3-, and 1,4- relative to the side chain) is small, so their coupling is not first-order, and a complex broad band results.

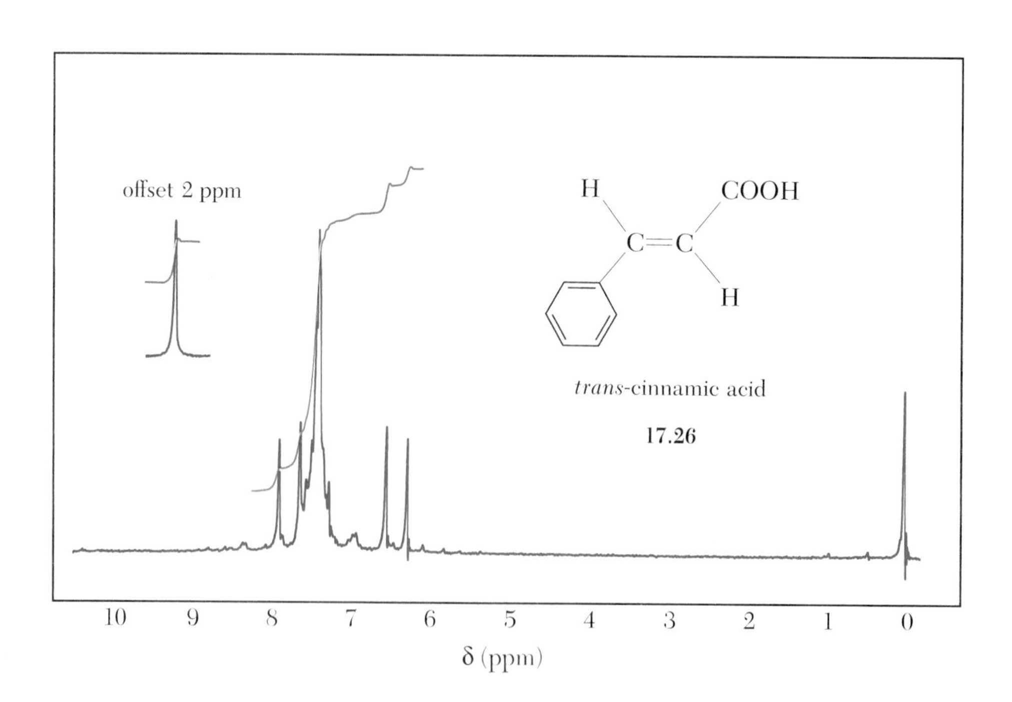

Figure 17.63 The 60-MHz proton NMR spectrum of *trans*-cinnamic acid.

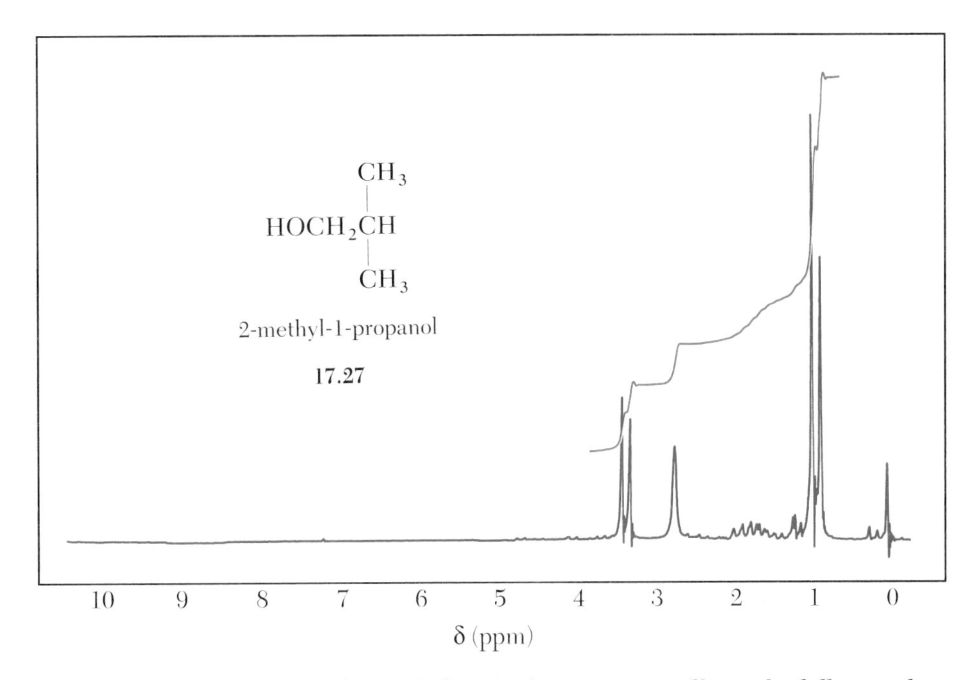

Figure 17.64 The 60-MHz proton NMR spectrum of 2-methyl-1-propanol.

The chemical shifts of two olefinic hydrogens are sufficiently different that coupling between them is first-order. The olefinic hydrogen near the carboxyl group produces the (skewed) doublet centered at δ 6.4. Farther downfield at δ 7.8 and overlapping with the aromatic signal, we find the signal of the other olefinic hydrogen. This peak is also a skewed doublet with the same coupling constant as the signal at δ 6.4. This hydrogen comes into resonance farther downfield than normal for an olefinic hydrogen due to the ring-current effect of the aromatic ring and the electron-withdrawing effect of the carboxyl group.

The final signal in this spectrum is due to the acidic hydrogen of the carboxyl group. It comes into resonance quite far downfield at δ 12.2, a typical location for a highly deshielded hydrogen. In Figure 17.63 the acidic hydrogen is shown in an offset position. The signal was recorded on the chart with a 2.0 ppm offset of the spectrum.

2-Methyl-1-propanol The proton NMR spectrum of 2-methyl-1-propanol (**17.27**) is shown in Figure 17.64. We again find four signals in this spectrum. The pair of equivalent methyl groups produce the doublet found at δ 0.9. The split to a doublet occurs because of interaction with the single adjacent hydrogen. That adjacent hydrogen comes into resonance at δ 1.7. Its signal is split into a multiplet for which only some of the peaks are resolved. Splitting of this single hydrogen results from interaction with two sets of hydrogens, the six equivalent methyl hydrogens and a pair of hydrogens on carbon-1. Theoretically, it consists of a triplet of septets (21 peaks). Under the best of conditions with a 60-MHz spectrum we can see only nine peaks resolved. Signals for the hydroxymethylene and hydroxyl hydrogens occur farther downfield. The hydrogen of the hydroxyl group gives a signal at δ 2.7.

4-Bromotoluene The proton NMR spectrum of 4-bromotoluene (**17.28**) is shown in Figure 17.65. There are only two signals in this spectrum. The first of these is the singlet at δ 2.2, which is produced by the methyl group. It is

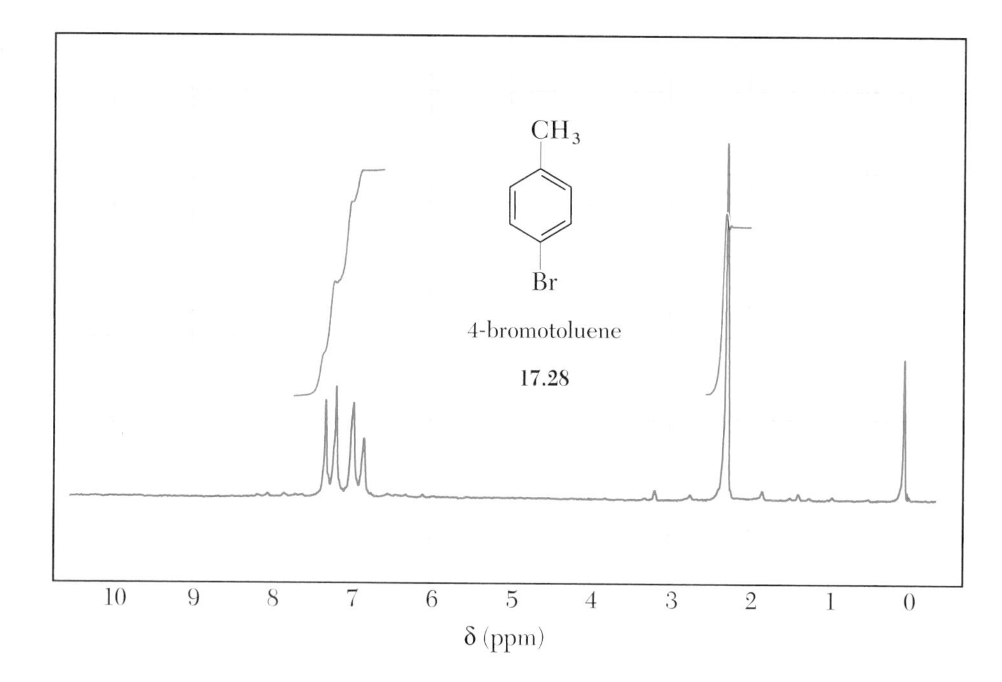

Figure 17.65 The 60-MHz proton NMR spectrum of 4-bromotoluene.

slightly downfield from the ordinary position of a methyl group due to the ring-current effect of the aromatic ring. Since there are no nearby hydrogens with which it can couple, it appears as a singlet.

The aromatic hydrogens come into resonance downfield as a symmetrical set of four peaks. The peaks look something like a symmetrical pair of doublets, a typical pattern for an aromatic ring with 1,4-substitution of two different groups. We refer to it as an *AA′BB′* signal. The appearance of this type of pattern in the aromatic region can give a major clue as to the substitution pattern on an aromatic ring. Other substitution patterns for a pair of unlike substituents produce much more complex splitting patterns.

ANALYSIS OF SPECTRA OF UNKNOWNS

As in IR spectral analysis, it is useful to approach NMR spectra in a systematic manner for structural determination of an unknown. We suggest a three-step approach here. With experience, you will be able more often to abandon the formal procedure and recognize patterns and sets of signals with a quick look. At the beginning, however, it is valuable to follow a standard procedure for each spectrum.

In practice, an organic chemist rarely attempts to decipher an NMR spectrum without having other data available as well. If nothing else, the starting materials and the nature of the reaction are usually known. Other data, such as an IR spectrum or a molecular formula, often assist in interpreting the NMR spectrum. With these additional pieces of information, we can approach the NMR spectrum systematically to determine structural features.

The first step in the interpretation of a proton NMR spectrum is the assignment of signals to particular types of structural components. We look at the chemical shift for each signal, starting at the upfield end of the spectrum and sequentially considering the following regions to make assignments of the types of hydrogens present:

1. δ *0.0.–1.7*. Signals in this region indicate the presence of alkyl hydrogens. The farther downfield the signal, the greater the alkyl substitution about the carbon bearing the hydrogen(s).
2. δ *1.7–1.9*. Signals in this region generally are associated with allylic hydrogens. You should check farther downfield for verification of the presence of olefinic hydrogens, which usually are also present.
3. δ *2.0–2.8*. Several types of hydrogens come into resonance in this region. Once we find signals here, recourse to other stages of the analysis provides us with a differentiation of the possibilities. The first possibility is that benzylic hydrogens are present. The aromatic region of the spectrum should be examined: the absence of aromatic hydrogens excludes this possibility, but their presence may or may not fit with assigning such signals as benzylic hydrogens. A second possibility for signals in this region is an acetylenic terminal hydrogen. Such hydrogens will necessarily appear as singlets. The final possibility is hydrogen on an alkyl carbon that in turn is attached to a carbonyl-type carbon. Splitting patterns and integration of the spectrum, along with other data, may or may not support this possibility.
4. δ *3.0–4.1*. Signals in this region indicate hydrogens attached to a carbon that is also attached to some other electronegative atom, such as oxygen or a halogen.
5. δ *4.6–5.9*. This is the common region for resonances due to olefinic hydrogens. At times the signals may be shifted downfield due to the presence of nearby electronegative atoms or the influence of an aromatic ring current.
6. δ *6.0–9.5*. Aromatic hydrogens come into resonance in this region. The appearance of signals in this region should alert you to look for possible downfield shifts of other signals from their normal regions and for hydrogens in the region of influence of the aromatic ring current.
7. δ *9.0–10.5*. Aldehydic hydrogens produce signals in this region.
8. δ *10–13*. Carboxyl group or enolic hydrogens come into resonance in this region.

Once the presence of individual signals is determined and tentative identifications of their types have been made, we look at the integration of the signals. If we know the molecular formula of the sample, we divide the total integration by the number of hydrogens to obtain the integral per hydrogen. In this way the actual number of hydrogens associated with each signal can be found.

Finally, in the third step we look to the splitting patterns for further information. For each signal, we look at the splitting pattern, if any splitting is present, and match the intensity of the splitting (coupling constant) with that of another signal. Signals that match in their coupling constants are associated with hydrogens attached to adjacent atoms.

Finally, we bring the data together to construct a possible structure for the compound. We can eliminate some possibilities by recourse to other types of data such as a molecular formula or an IR spectrum and others by looking at details of chemical shift data. You should use this approach in the analysis of the spectra in the following set of problems.

PROBLEM 17.20 Deduce the structure of the compound of formula $C_5H_{10}O$ for which the 60-MHz proton NMR spectrum and the IR spectrum are shown below.

Figure for Problem 17.20

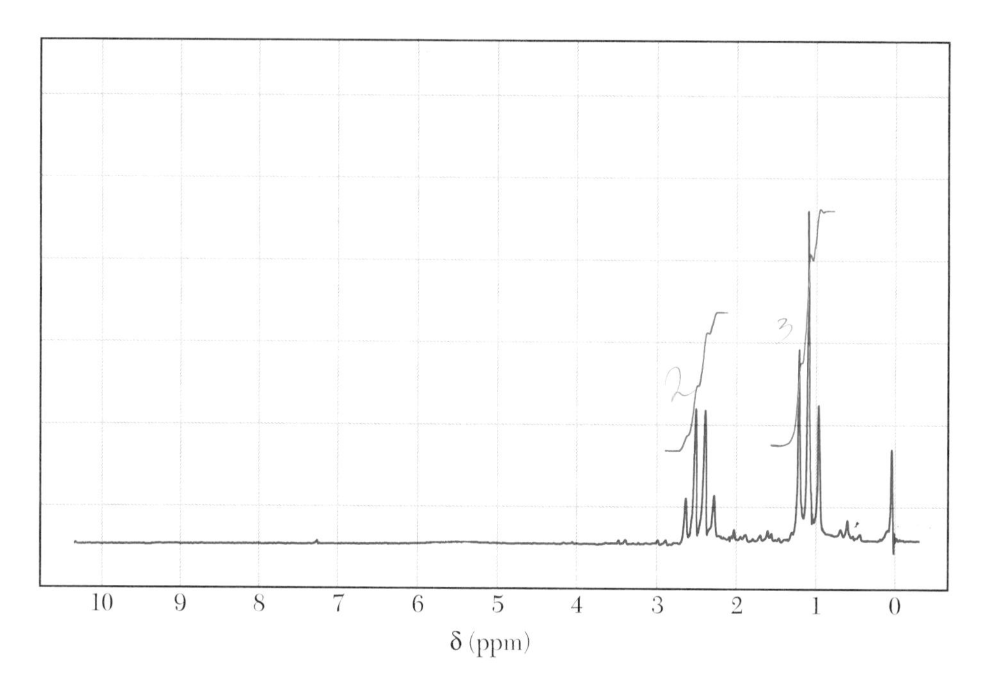

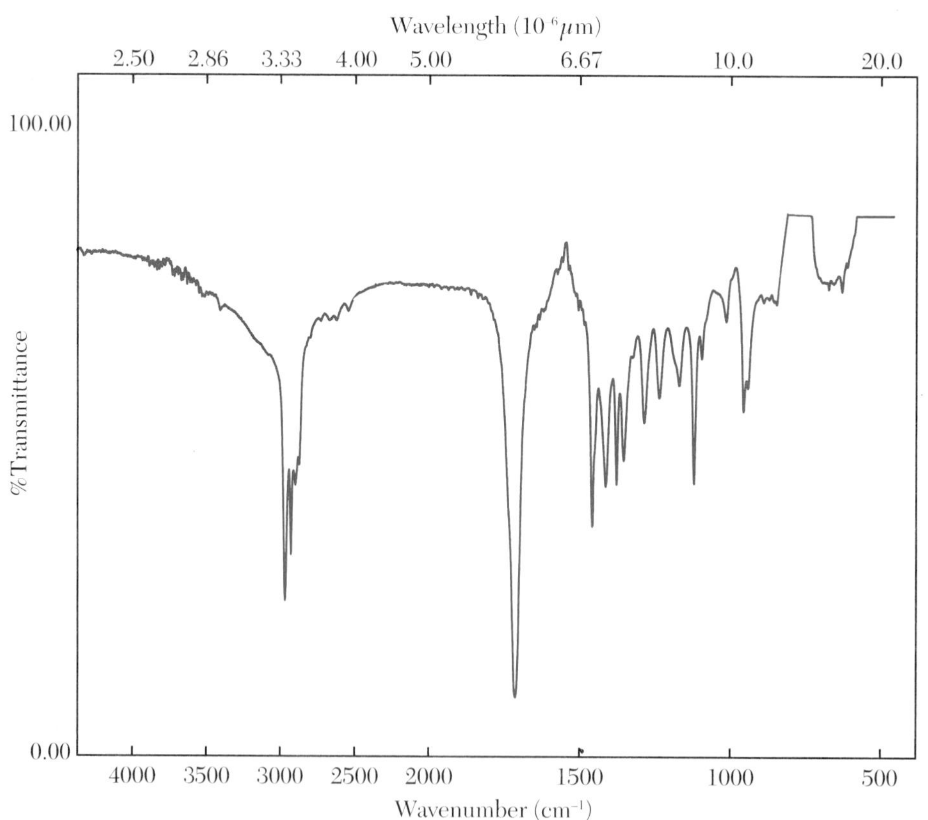

Steps to Solving the Problem

Solution to Problem 17.20

1. Calculate the units of unsaturation from the molecular formula. The formula $C_5H_{10}O$ indicates that there is one degree of unsaturation (one ring or one double bond).
2. Consider the IR spectrum. It exhibits only aliphatic carbon-hydrogen stretching absorptions and an intense absorption at $\sim 1715\ cm^{-1}$ corresponding to a carbonyl group. This group must account for the single unit of unsaturation. There are no absorptions that would be due to hydroxyl or ether groups.
3. Examine the proton NMR spectrum and note the regions (chemical shifts) at which signals are observed. The spectrum exhibits two signals, a triplet centered at $\delta \sim 1.1$ and a quartet centered at $\delta \sim 2.3$.
4. What is the integration of these signals? They integrate to three and two hydrogens, respectively.
5. Consider the spin-spin splitting. The presence of a three-hydrogen triplet and a two-hydrogen quartet indicates the presence of an ethyl group. Since no other signals are present and there are ten hydrogens in the molecule, we conclude that there are two equivalent ethyl groups.
6. Deduce the structure from the NMR data and the given molecular formula. Upon subtracting the elements of two ethyl groups from the molecular formula, we conclude that the remaining portion of the molecule is the carbonyl group we inferred to be present from the IR spectrum. That is, the molecule is 3-pentanone (diethyl ketone), as shown below.

$$CH_3-CH_2-\overset{\overset{\displaystyle :\!O\!:}{\|}}{C}-CH_2-CH_3$$

PROBLEM 17.21 Deduce the structure of the compound of formula $C_7H_6Br_2$ for which the proton NMR and IR spectra are shown.

Figure for Problem 17.21

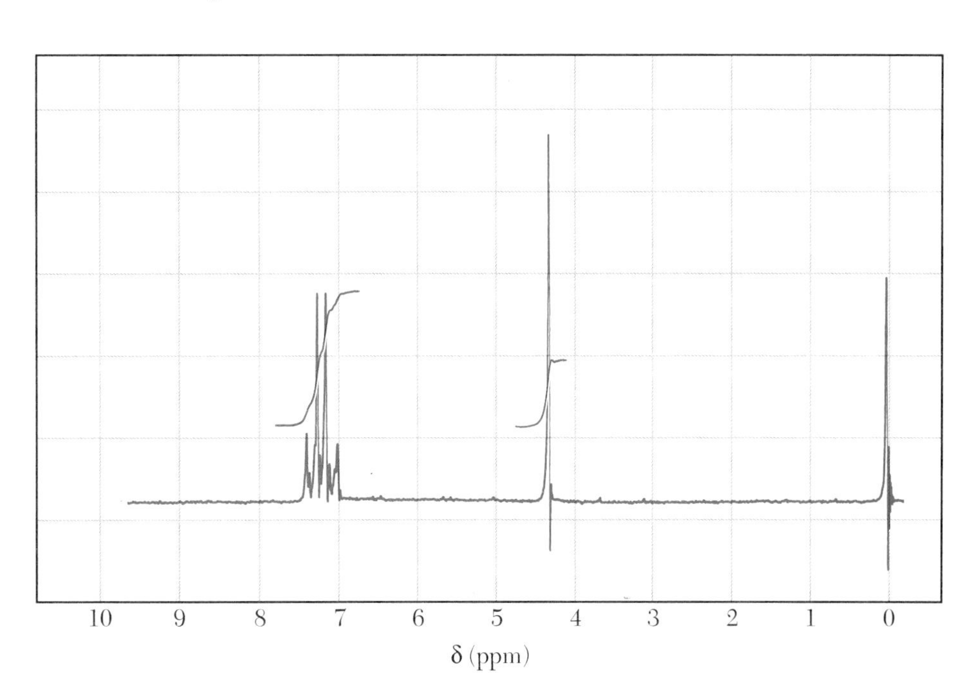

Figure for Problem 17.21 continued

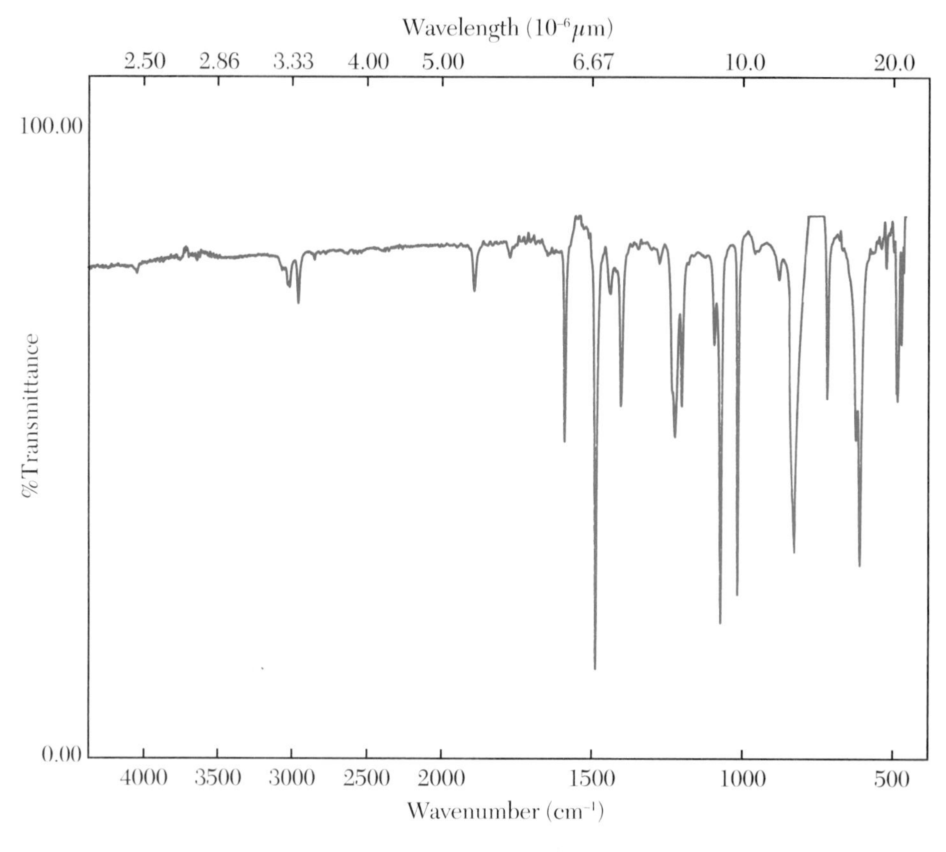

PROBLEM 17.22 Deduce the structure of the compound of formula C_3H_5Br for which the proton NMR and IR spectra are shown. In addition to the structure you deduce, is there any other structure that could possibly be in accord with these spectra?

Figure for Problem 17.22

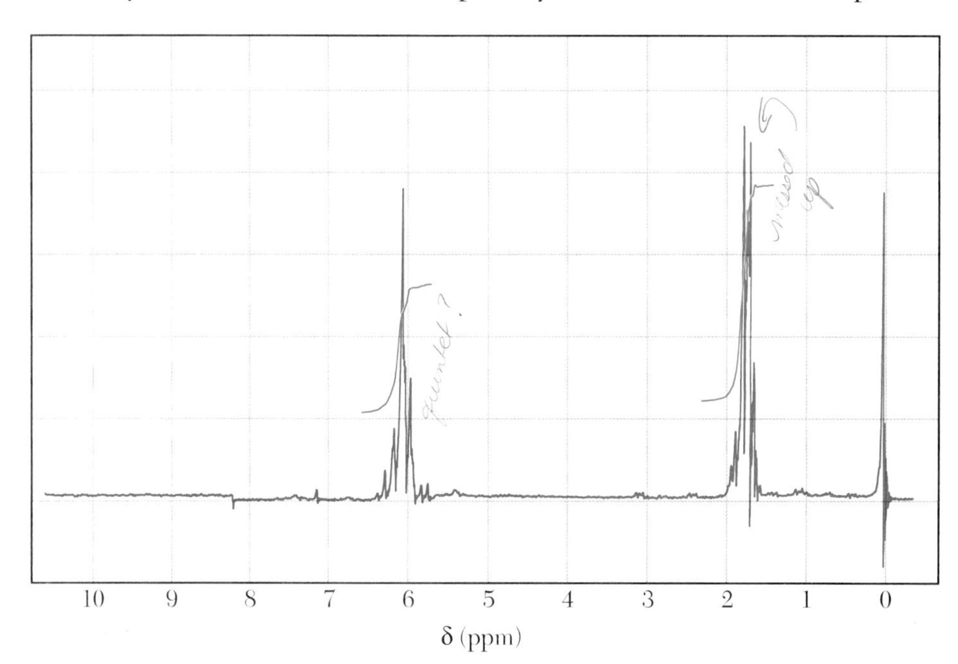

Figure for Problem 17.22 continued

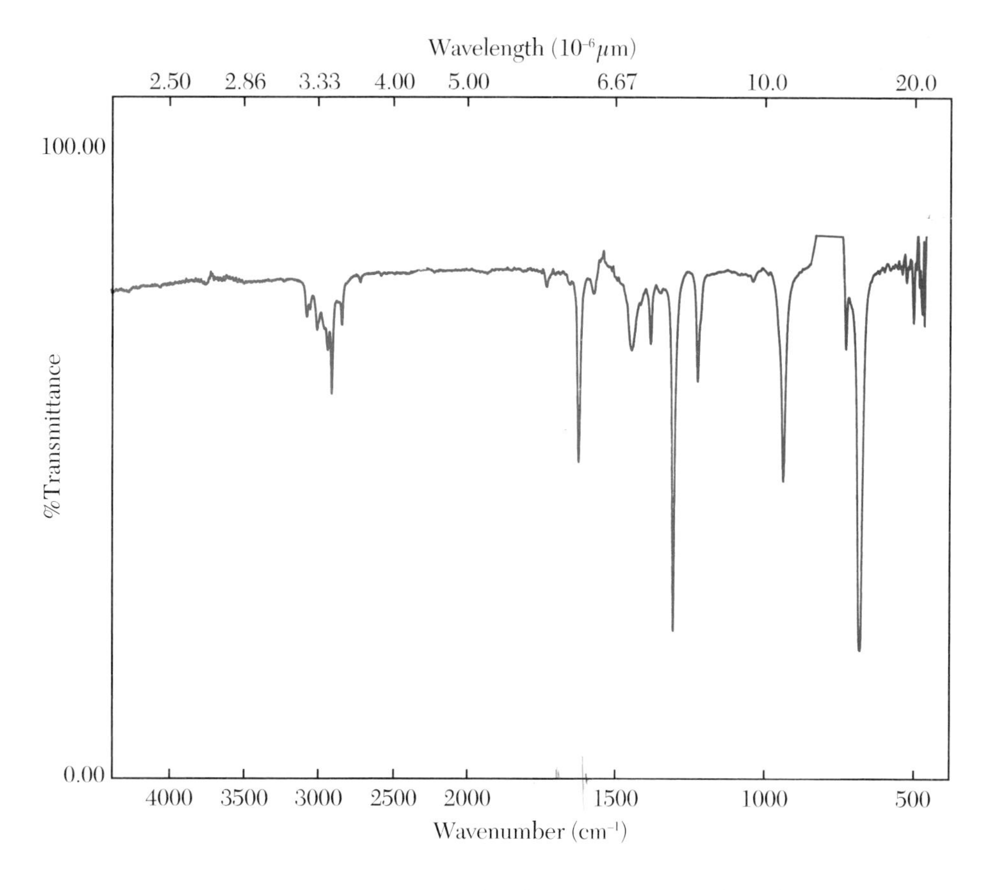

PROBLEM 17.23 Deduce the structure of the compound of formula $C_5H_8O_2$ for which the proton NMR and IR spectra are shown.

Figure for Problem 17.23

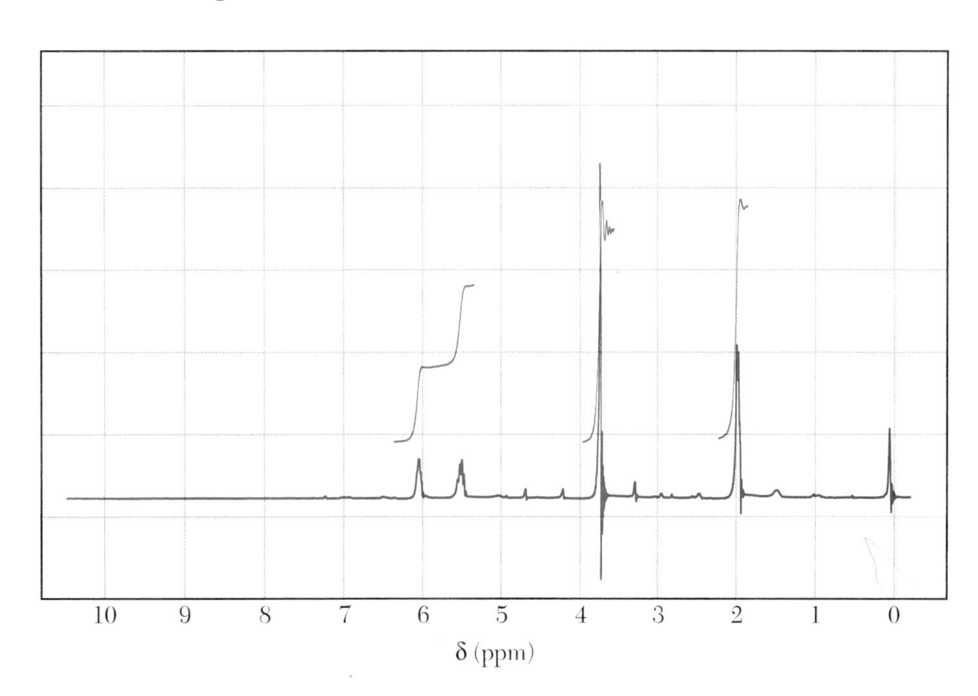

Figure for Problem 17.23 continued

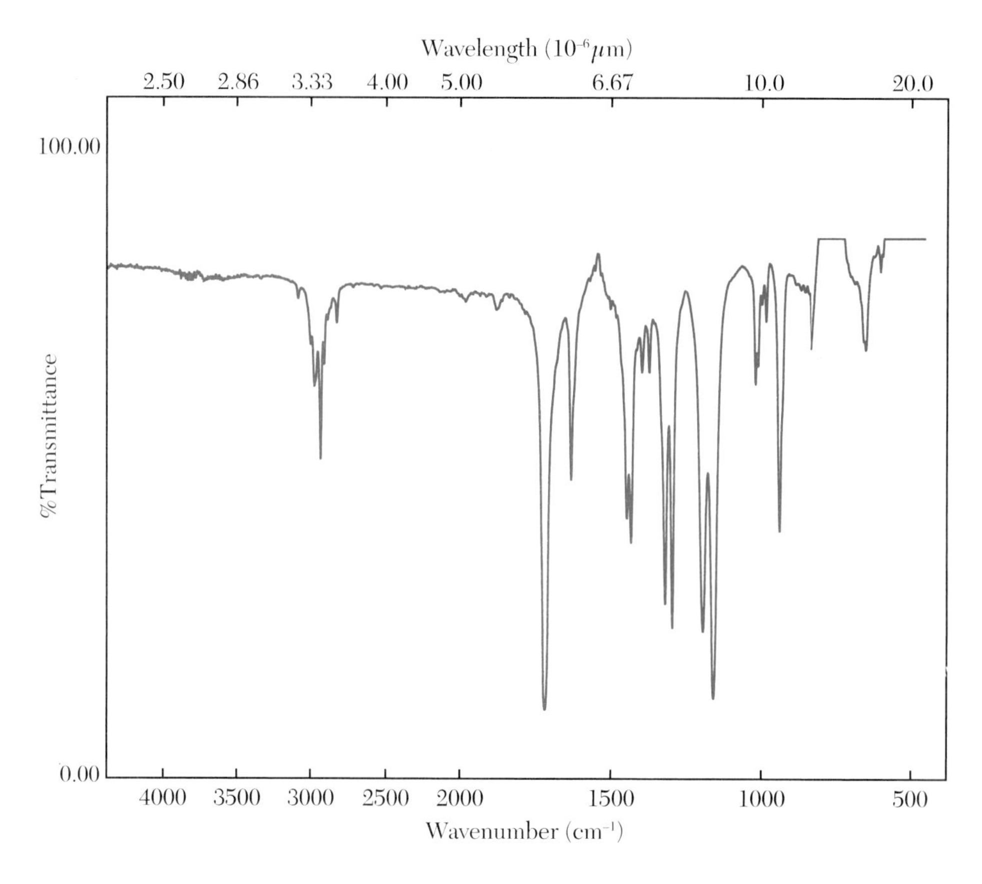

PROBLEM 17.24 Deduce the structure for the compound of formula C_7H_8O for which the proton NMR and IR spectra are shown.

Figure for Problem 17.24

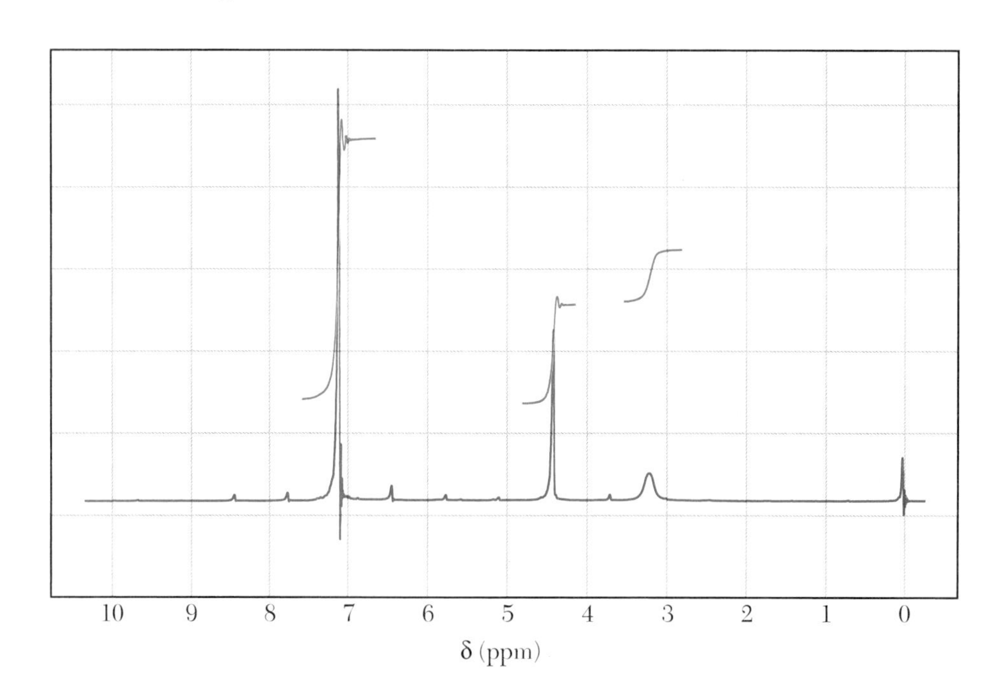

Figure for Problem 17.24 continued

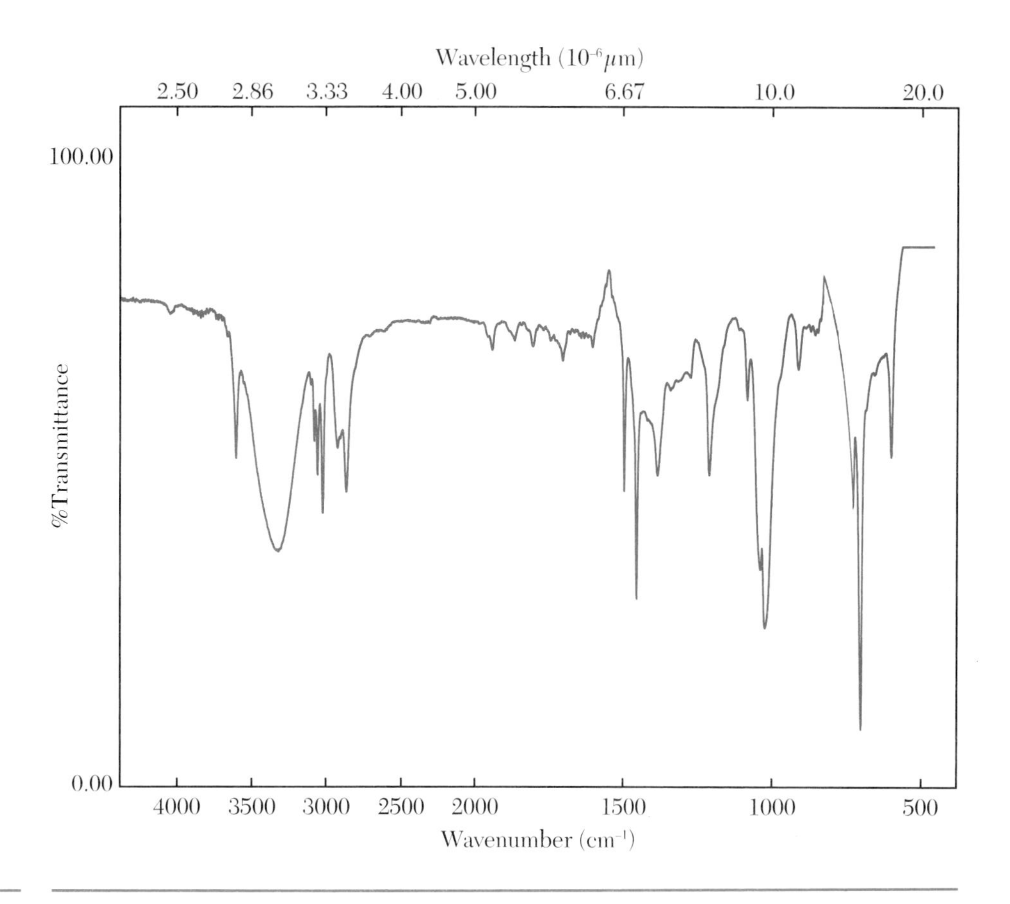

COUPLING OF HYDROGEN TO NUCLEI OTHER THAN HYDROGEN

Any nucleus bearing a single unpaired nucleon is NMR-active. Similarly, any NMR-active nucleus can participitate in spin-spin coupling.

Suppose some NMR-active nucleus other than hydrogen is located near a proton being observed in an NMR analysis. Coupling will occur between the two nuclei, and we will observe splitting of the proton signal. The same splitting rules apply to nuclei with a single unpaired nucleon as applied to proton-proton splitting. The major difference in this **heteronuclear coupling** is that we do not observe the signal for the other nucleus in the proton experiment. NMR-active nuclei other than protons absorb 60-MHz energy only at a very different magnetic field strength; that is, these nuclei have very different chemical shifts from protons at 60 MHz, and they absorb outside the range of the standard NMR analysis. Nonetheless, we see the coupling interaction in the proton spectrum.

When heteronuclear coupling occurs, the splittings are first-order. We observe perfectly symmetrical multiplets with relative intensities as indicated in Figure 17.52. If we were to observe the NMR signals of the nuclei coupled to the proton, we would find these signals to be split in a completely corresponding manner. Performing this experiment requires the use of different field strengths and/or different frequencies of irradiation (we will consider this type of experiment later).

Two spectra are shown here to illustrate the heteronuclear coupling effect. The first is the proton spectrum of 2,2,2-trifluoroethanol (**17.29**), shown in Figure 17.66. We see two signals. The hydroxyl hydrogen atom comes into resonance as a broad singlet at $\delta \sim 3.2$. The signal for the methylene hydrogen atoms, centered at $\delta \sim 3.9$, is a symmetrical quartet. The molecule contains no other hydrogen that could produce the splitting of the methylene hydrogen signal. Splitting of the methylene signal must result from coupling with another nucleus, specifically the fluorine (^{19}F) nucleus. The ^{19}F nucleus has a single unpaired nucleon and produces splitting of the signals of coupled nuclei in the same manner as do protons.

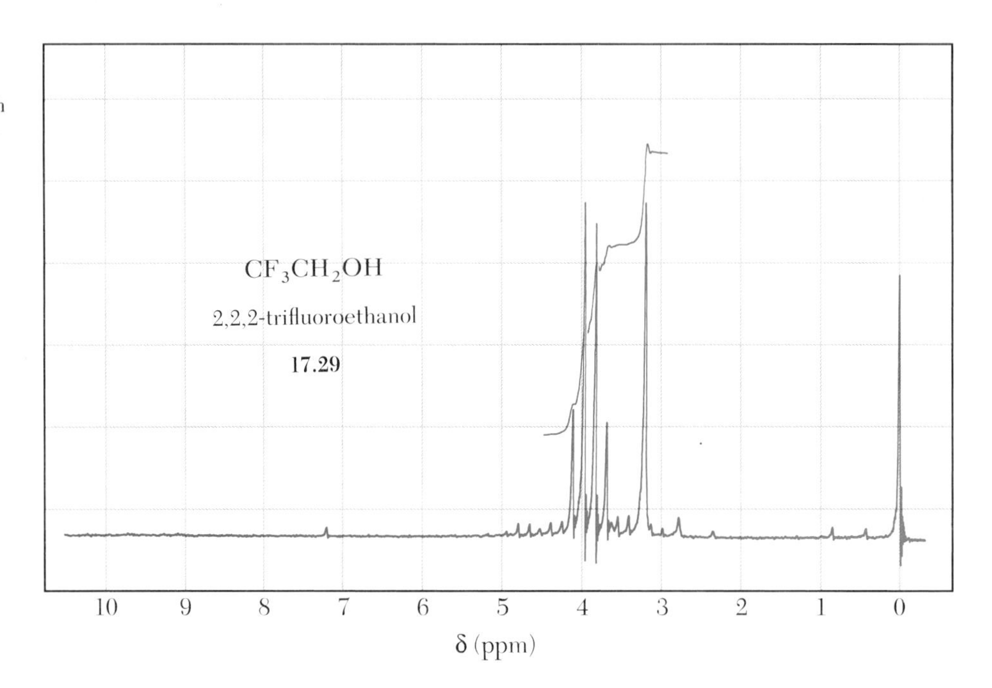

Figure 17.66 The proton NMR spectrum of 2,2,2-trifluoroethanol. Heteronuclear coupling of the methylene hydrogens with the fluorines produces the splitting in the methylene signal.

Another example of heteronuclear coupling is revealed in the spectrum of tetraisopropyl methylenebisphosphonate (**17.30**) which is shown in Figure 17.67. In this spectrum we see a doublet at $\delta \sim 1.4$ produced by the hydrogen atoms of the four equivalent methyl groups. The methyl hydrogen signal appears as a doublet due to interaction with the single methine hydrogen associated with each isopropyl group. However, the methine hydrogen signal is not the classical septet associated with an isopropyl group. Coming into resonance at $\delta \sim 4.8$, it is a more complex multiplet as a result of coupling with phosphorus. Heteronuclear coupling ($^1H-^{31}P$) causes the methine hydrogen signal to appear as a doublet of septets. We do not see all fourteen of the predicted peaks in this signal because of overlap.

The signal for the central methylene group in the compound occurs at $\delta \sim 2.3$. These hydrogens, which are coupled to both of the (equivalent) phosphorus atoms, display a symmetrical triplet with a splitting magnitude of ~ 20 Hz. The magnitude of the splitting is larger than that for the other phosphorus-hydrogen interaction because this interaction is a ^2J coupling. Only two bonds intervene between the phosphorus and hydrogen.

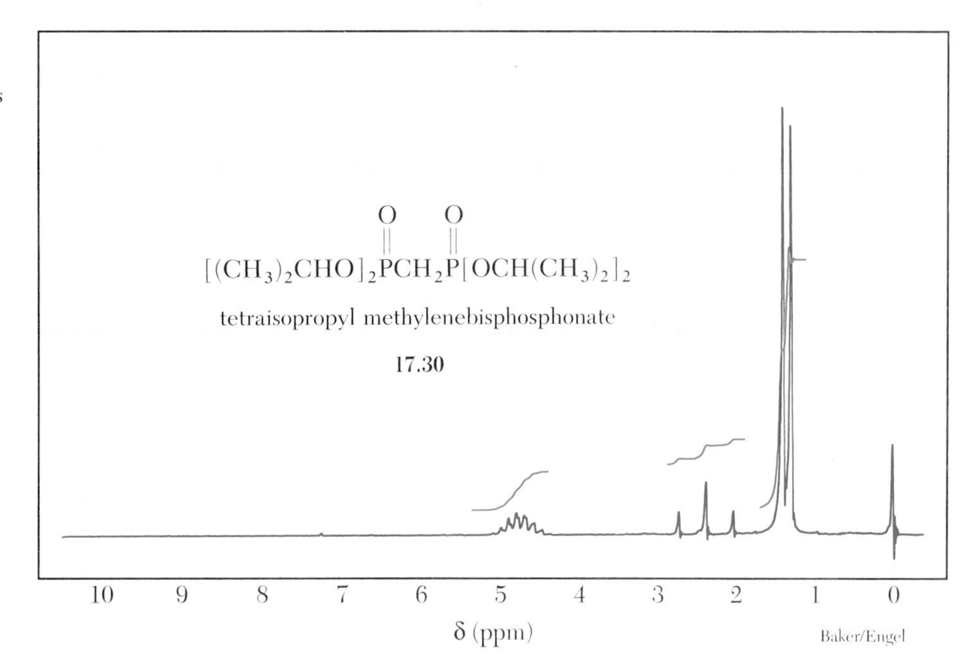

Figure 17.67 The proton NMR spectrum of tetraisopropyl methylenebisphosphonate. Splitting of two of the signals results from interactions with phosphorus.

CARBON NUCLEAR MAGNETIC RESONANCE SPECTROMETRY

By changing the magnetic field strength and/or the irradiating frequency of an NMR analysis, we can observe NMR-active nuclei other than ^{1}H coming into resonance. One of the most important nuclei for NMR structure analysis is ^{13}C. Like ^{1}H, ^{19}F, and ^{31}P, the ^{13}C nucleus has a single unpaired nucleon. However, the natural abundance of ^{13}C is quite low. The major isotope of carbon (^{12}C), which is NMR-inactive, constitutes 98.9% of the naturally occurring element. NMR-active ^{13}C constitutes only 1.1% of naturally occurring carbon. (In contrast, ^{1}H constitutes 99.9844% of naturally occurring hydrogen.)

The low abundance of ^{13}C poses difficulties for the performance of ^{13}C NMR analyses. First, we generally need a larger amount of the compound to offset the lower concentration of the NMR-active nucleus in the sample. This requirement for greater sensitivity has spurred the development of alternative techniques of measuring NMR spectra, including pulsed techniques related to the experiment described in "NMR Imaging." While producing fundamentally the same results for ordinary spectra, these methods allow a variety of other types of analyses to be performed. The details of these alternative methods will be treated in more advanced courses.

A second consequence of the low natural abundance of ^{13}C is that we generally do not observe ^{13}C–^{13}C splitting interactions. The absence of ^{13}C–^{13}C splitting might seem strange at first, but the reason becomes evident when we consider a simple example. In a sample of ethyl bromide, only 1.1% of the molecules have a ^{13}C in the 1-position. Similarly, only 1.1% of the molecules have a ^{13}C at the 2-position. Therefore, only 0.012% (1.1% of 1.1%) of the molecules have ^{13}C at *both* of the carbon positions. Coupling of NMR-active carbons occurs in only ~12/100,000 of the total molecules under observation. The vast majority of ethyl bromide molecules that actually contain ^{13}C do not have *two* ^{13}C nuclei present and therefore show no ^{13}C–^{13}C splitting.

SPECIAL TOPIC

NMR Imaging

Procedures that differentiate nuclei on the basis of chemical shift are referred to as *high-resolution* NMR. These experiments require the use of a highly homogeneous magnetic field directed at a relatively small sample volume. If we wished to use the NMR experiment simply to detect the presence of a particular type of nucleus, such as a proton, we are not bound by the rigorous requirements of high-resolution NMR. One application of *low-resolution* NMR has been developed in recent years in the area of medical diagnostics.

By far the most abundant form of hydrogen in the human organism is in water. We can easily detect the location of water in a large, nonhomogeneous sample (e.g., an intact person) using a low-resolution proton NMR experiment. Using pulsed RF irradiation (rather than continuous irradiation) and computer deconvolution of the energy absorption signals, it is possible to produce a three-dimensional image of the sample showing the location of water within it. Bones and hard tissue give no signal; they show up as dark areas against a background of signals from water molecules.

The water signals by themselves are interesting but not particularly useful. However, we can also determine something about the local environment in which the water exists in different parts of the sample. While it is not possible to detect a chemical shift difference between protons in different local environments, it is possible to measure a difference in their *relaxation times*. The relaxation time for a nucleus is the rate at which a nucleus in the energized state loses energy and reverts to the lower-energy state. A nucleus can absorb RF energy only when it is in the lower-energy state. Those nuclei with rapid relaxation processes will be able to reabsorb RF energy at shorter intervals than those nuclei with inefficient relaxation processes.

The protons of water molecules in the region of certain diseased tissues have longer relaxation times than those in nearby normal regions. Variation of the rate of the RF pulse allows detection of regions with different relaxation rates and thus regions of diseased tissue. An image of the diseased regions can be created on the basis of the relaxation of nuclei in an NMR analysis.

The process of NMR imaging is now commonly referred to as *magnetic resonance imaging* (*MRI*) in order to avoid public fears of anything associated with the term *nuclear*.

Of course, coupling of ^{1}H and ^{13}C occurs and causes splitting of signals. These interactions are generally intense and the splittings generally large. For example, consider the carbon atom at the 1-position of 1-bromopropane. The two hydrogens attached directly to it interact with a relatively large ^{1}J. The two hydrogens at the 2-position also interact with the carbon at the 1-position via a ^{2}J. Finally, the three hydrogens at the 3-position interact with the 1-

carbon via a ^3J. We anticipate that the 1-carbon signal could be split into as many as 36 peaks. With such a large number of splittings, individual ^{13}C signals of even moderately close chemical shifts would overlap so much as to make spectra quite difficult to interpret.

To get around this difficulty we generally measure ^{13}C NMR spectra under conditions that result in the removal of some or all of the ^{13}C–^{1}H couplings. We achieve these conditions experimentally by irradiating the sample simultaneously with two frequencies of irradiation. One source of irradiation is that normally used to scan the ^{13}C resonance, while the second source is one appropriate for the ^{1}H resonances. If the frequency of the second source is in the middle of the proton NMR range, we refer to the technique as **broad-band decoupling.** The result is that we eliminate all ^{13}C–^{1}H spin coupling from the spectrum. All ^{13}C signals appear as single peaks (there are no doublets, triplets, etc.). If the frequency of the second source is 1000–2000 Hz away from the proton region (rather than in the middle of it), we refer to the technique as **off-resonance decoupling.** Spectra obtained in this way show splittings of ^{13}C signals caused by *directly attached* hydrogens only. All other ^{13}C–^{1}H couplings disappear under these conditions.

One difficulty that arises as a result of broad-band decoupling relates to integration of the spectrum. Double irradiation causes the integration to be unreliable, and we thus cannot deduce the number of each type of carbon from the intensity of its signal.

A major advantage of ^{13}C NMR analysis is that the chemical shift differences are relatively large compared to those in the proton spectrum. Table 17.3 summarizes these chemical shifts for the several types of carbon sites common in organic molecules. As on the proton spectrum, we use tetramethylsilane as the reference material. The carbons of TMS are relatively shielded and come into resonance upfield from most other carbon sites. We note chemical shifts in ppm (δ) relative to TMS, with downfield again being noted as positive.

Table 17.3 Approximate ^{13}C Chemical Shifts Relative to TMS at δ 0.0

Type of Carbon	Chemical Shift (δ)
$-CH_3$	0–30
$-CH_2$	15–55
$-CH$ (3°)	20–60
sp (acetylenic)	65–85
sp^2 (vinylic)	100–150
sp^2 (aromatic)	110–160
$-C-Br$	10–65
$-C-Cl$	20–80
$-C-I$	0–40
$-C-O$	40–80
$-C-N$	25–70
$-C{=}O$ (ketone or aldehyde)	190–220
$-C{=}O$ (ester)	160–190
$-C{=}O$ (amide)	160–180
sp (nitrile)	110–130

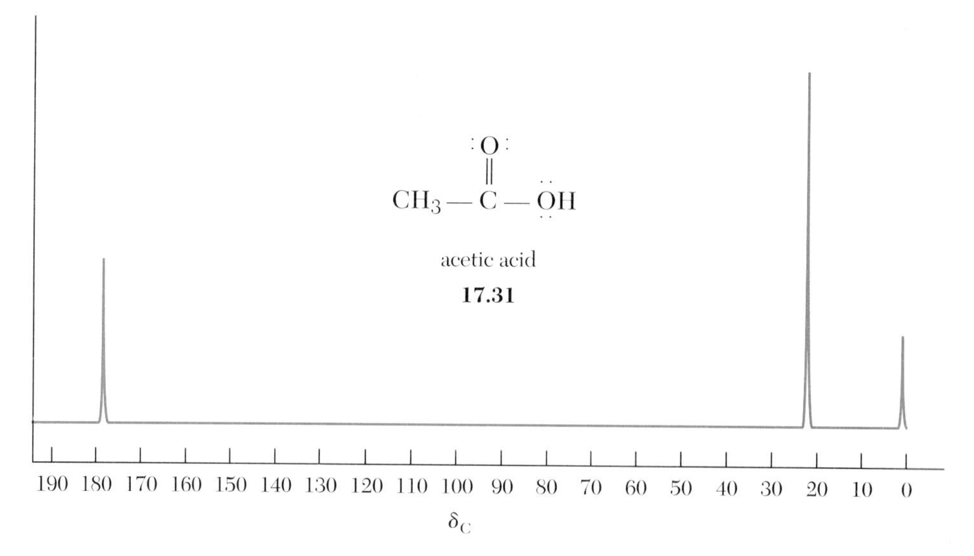

Figure 17.68 The ^{13}C NMR spectrum of acetic acid.

The broad-band decoupled ^{13}C spectra of seven compounds are given here to illustrate the usefulness of this technique for structural differentiation (also see Figure 17.29). The ^{13}C spectrum of acetic acid (**17.31**) is shown in Figure 17.68. The acetic acid molecule contains only two types of carbons. Thus, there are only two signals in its ^{13}C NMR spectrum. The methyl group comes into resonance at $\delta \sim 21$ and the carboxyl carbon at δ 178. Both of these locations are characteristic of the types of carbon atoms involved. Note that both of these signals are singlets. The spectrum was measured under conditions of broad-band decoupling of the proton region. Under these conditions the intensities of the signals are *not* directly proportional to the number of each type of carbon nucleus.

The ^{13}C NMR spectrum of cyclohexanone (**17.32**) is shown in Figure 17.69. There are four signals in this spectrum, representing the four types of carbon sites in the molecule. Farthest downfield, shown in offset at $\delta \sim 211$, is the signal for the carbonyl carbon. The pair of equivalent carbons adjacent to the

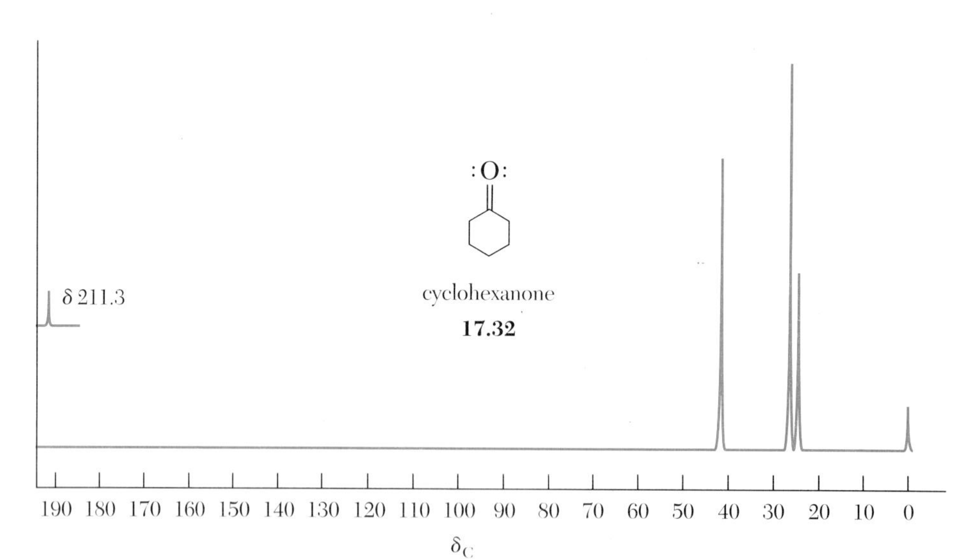

Figure 17.69 The ^{13}C NMR spectrum of cyclohexanone.

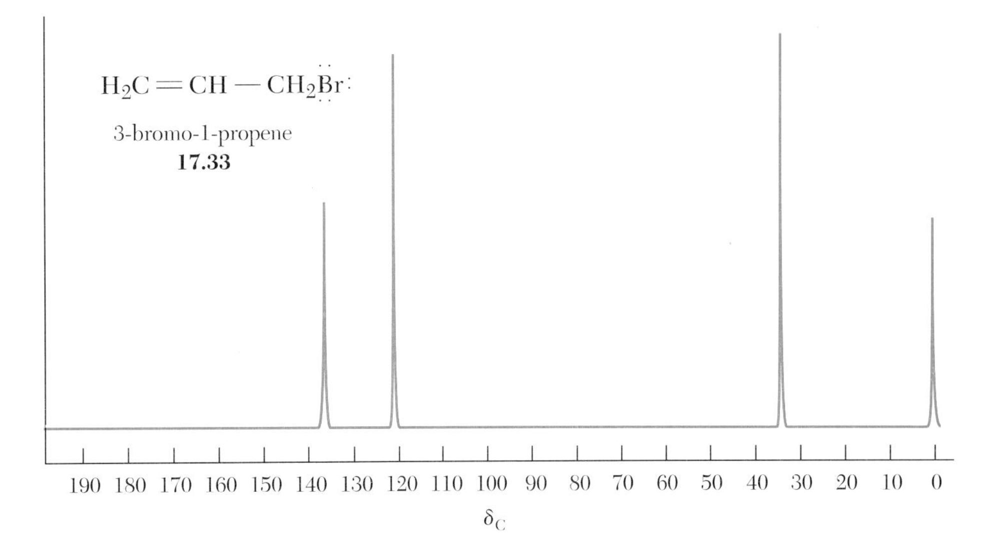

Figure 17.70 The ^{13}C NMR spectrum of 3-bromo-1-propene.

carbonyl group produces the signal at $\delta \sim 42$. The carbons β- and γ-relative to the carbonyl site produce the signals at $\delta \sim 27$ and $\delta \sim 25$, respectively. Again, the relative intensities of the peaks are not proportional to the numbers of carbons producing the signals.

The ^{13}C NMR spectrum for 3-bromo-1-propene (**17.33**) is shown in Figure 17.70. Olefinic carbons come into resonance at chemical shifts significantly different from those in the spectra we have looked at previously. Here, the terminal olefinic carbon produces the signal at $\delta \sim 119$, and the internal olefinic carbon produces the signal at $\delta \sim 135$. The signal for the bromomethylene carbon occurs at $\delta \sim 33$.

The ^{13}C NMR spectrum for 1-hexyne (**17.34**) is shown in Figure 17.71. Signals for the acetylenic carbons occur at distinctive chemical shifts ($\delta \sim 69$ and $\delta \sim 85$). Each of the other carbons produces a signal in the standard alkyl region. The sharp signals and the large chemical shift differences allow ^{13}C

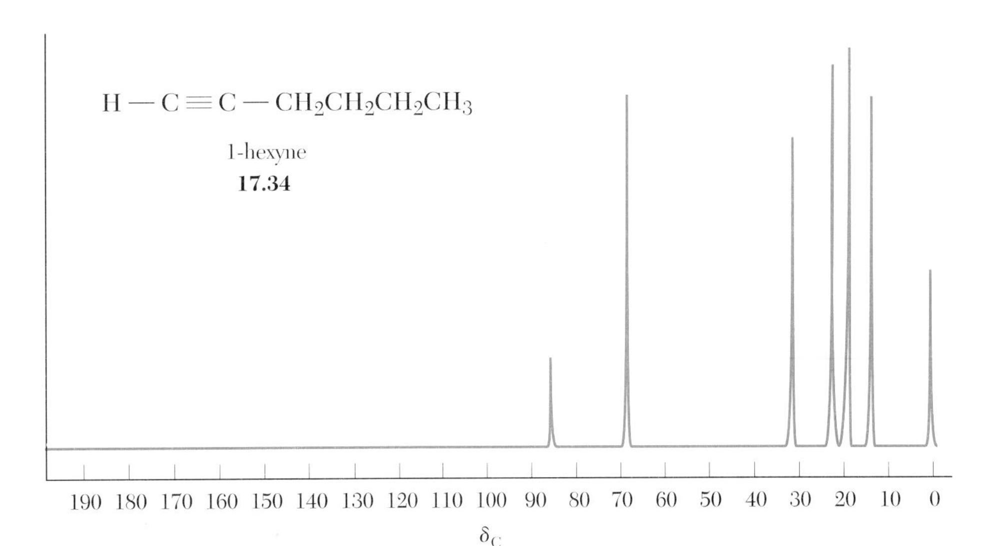

Figure 17.71 The ^{13}C NMR spectrum of 1-hexyne.

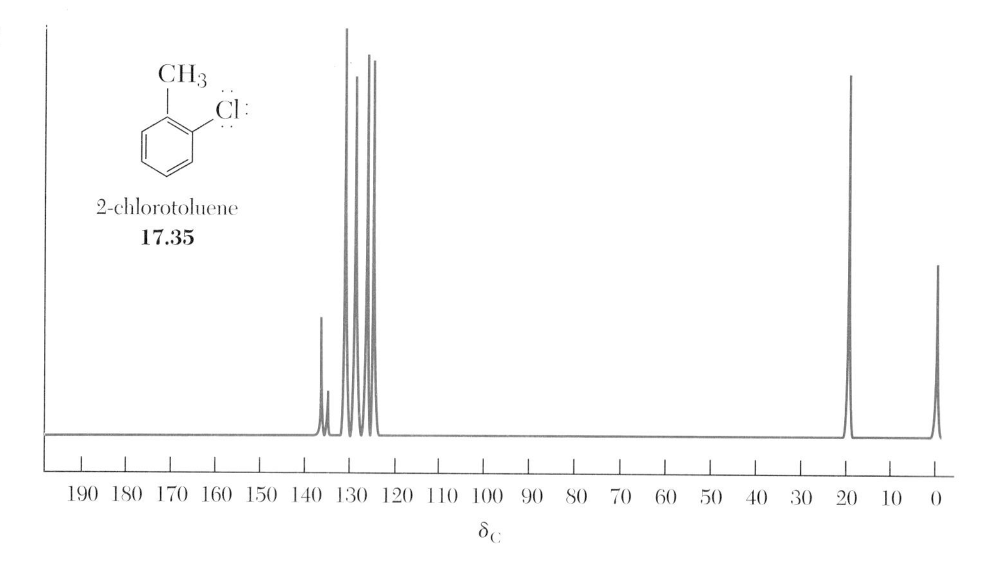

Figure 17.72 The ^{13}C NMR spectrum of 2-chlorotoluene.

NMR spectrometry to discern each carbon atom, even in relatively complex molecules.

The ^{13}C NMR spectrum for 2-chlorotoluene (**17.35**) is shown in Figure 17.72. None of the carbon atoms of 2-chlorotoluene are equivalent. Therefore we expect, and find, six different signals in the aromatic region of the spectrum. We can use this fact to distinguish this molecule from its isomer, 4-chlorotoluene (**17.36**), whose spectrum is shown in Figure 17.73. Only four aromatic carbon signals are present in this spectrum, compared with six for that of its isomer, 2-chlorotoluene. Thus, by using ^{13}C NMR spectra, we can easily distinguish these two compounds.

The ^{13}C NMR spectrum of dimethyl methylphosphonate (**17.37**) is shown in Figure 17.74. Although there are only two different types of carbons present in this molecule, we see three peaks (in addition to that for TMS) as a result of $^{13}C-^{31}P$ splitting interactions. While broad-band decoupling eliminates splitting of the carbon signals by any hydrogens present, it does not

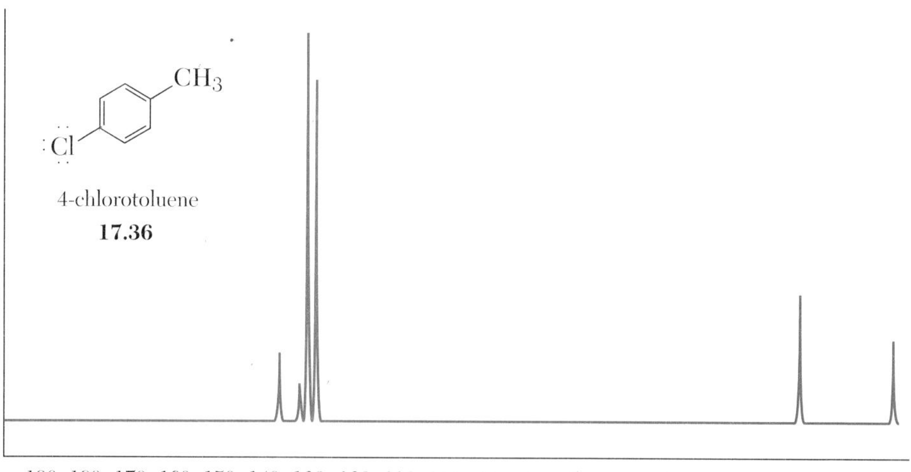

Figure 17.73 The ^{13}C NMR spectrum of 4-chlorotoluene.

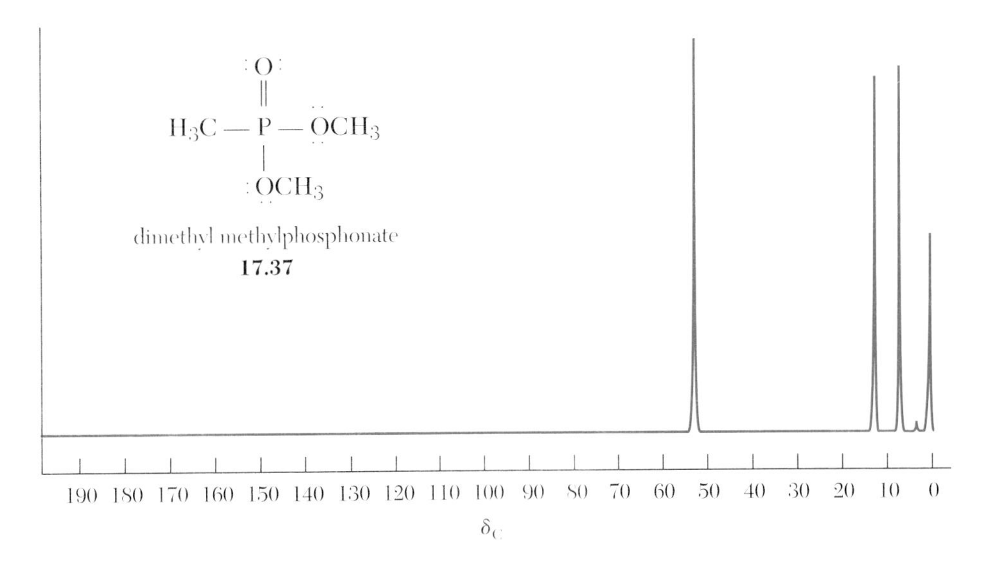

Figure 17.74 The ^{13}C NMR spectrum of dimethyl methylphosphonate.

eliminate couplings to other elements. The two peaks at relatively high field (centered at $\delta \sim 10$) result from the carbon directly bound to phosphorus. The coupling interaction between phosphorus and carbon is quite large here (a ^{1}J interaction). Farther downfield (at $\delta \sim 52$) we find the signal for the two methyl ester carbons. Although there is an interaction between these carbons and the phosphorus, its magnitude is too small to be seen in the spectrum as presented here.

Figure 17.75 shows an example of an off-resonance decoupled ^{13}C NMR spectrum, that of diisopropyl ether (**17.38**). The major difference between an off-resonance decoupled spectrum and a broad-band decoupled spectrum is that the off-resonance decoupled spectrum shows some splitting of the ^{13}C signals. The multiplicity of each signal reflects the number of directly attached protons. (Only *directly* attached protons cause splitting in off-resonance decoupled spectra.) The signal to the left is a doublet. The carbon atom producing the signal has one attached proton. The other signal is a quartet. The carbon

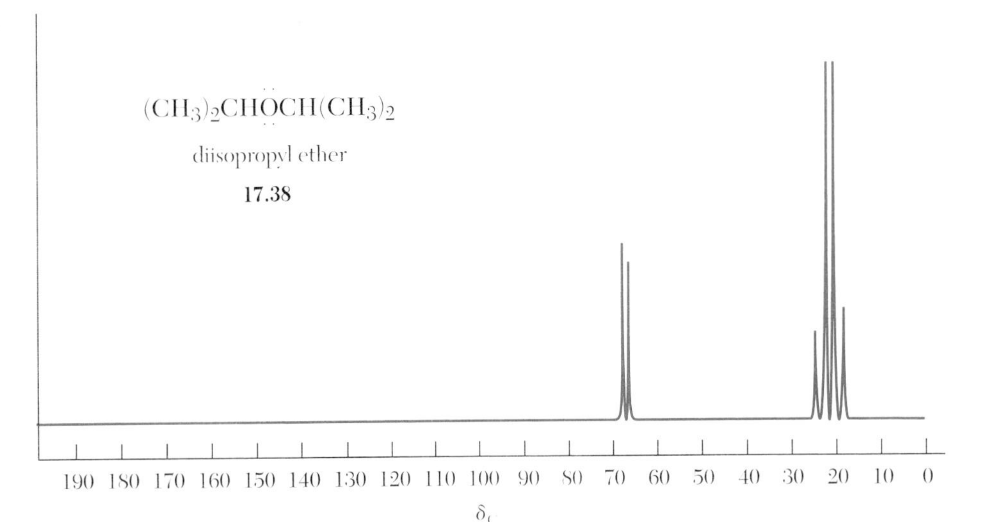

Figure 17.75 ^{13}C off-resonance decoupled NMR spectrum of diisopropyl ether.

atoms producing this signal have three protons attached. Clearly the off-resonance decoupling technique gives us useful information about the number of hydrogen atoms attached to a particular carbon atom.

PROBLEM 17.25

Predict the broad-band decoupled ^{13}C NMR spectrum for each of the following compounds:

a. 2-methyl-1-propanol b. 4-bromotoluene
c. 3-pentanone d. 1-butene

Steps to Solving the Problem

Solution to Problem 17.25a

1. Consider the structure of 2-methyl-1-propanol:

$$(CH_3)_2CHCH_2—\ddot{\underset{\cdot\cdot}{O}}H$$

2-methyl-1-propanol

2. How many different types of carbon atoms are present in 2-methyl-1-propanol? There are three, so we expect three signals in the ^{13}C NMR spectrum.
3. Deduce the approximate chemical shifts for each of the types of carbon atoms. The pair of equivalent methyl groups is expected to come into resonance upfield from each of the other carbons, at $\delta \sim 15$. The carbon in the 2-position, being bound to three other carbons, is predicted to have a further downfield shift, at $\delta \sim 40$. Finally, the carbinol carbon (1-position) is expected at $\delta \sim 60$.

PROBLEM 17.26

For each of the compounds in Problem 17.24, predict the off-resonance decoupled ^{13}C NMR spectrum.

PROBLEM 17.27

Give the structure for the compound of formula $C_6H_3Br_3$ whose ^{13}C NMR spectrum is provided below.

Figure for Problem 17.27

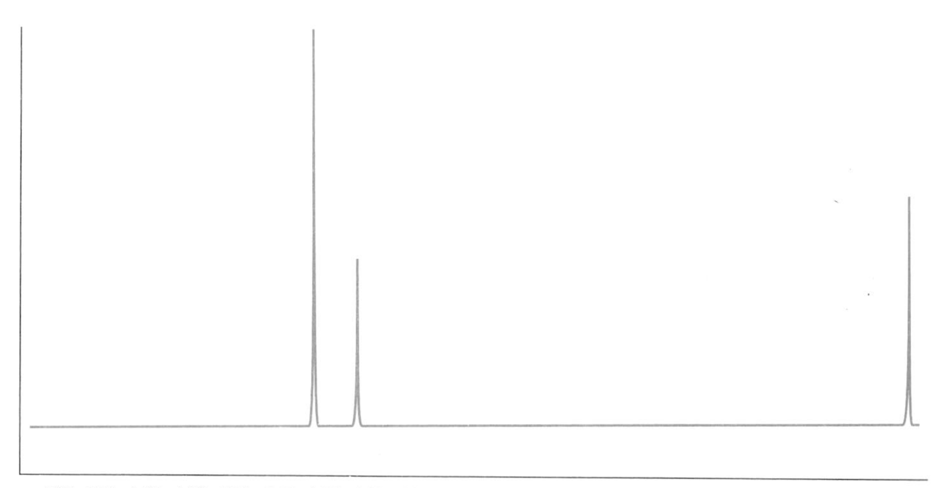

PROBLEM 17.28 Deduce the structure of the compound of formula $C_6H_{14}O$ whose ^{13}C NMR spectrum is shown below.

Figure for Problem 17.28

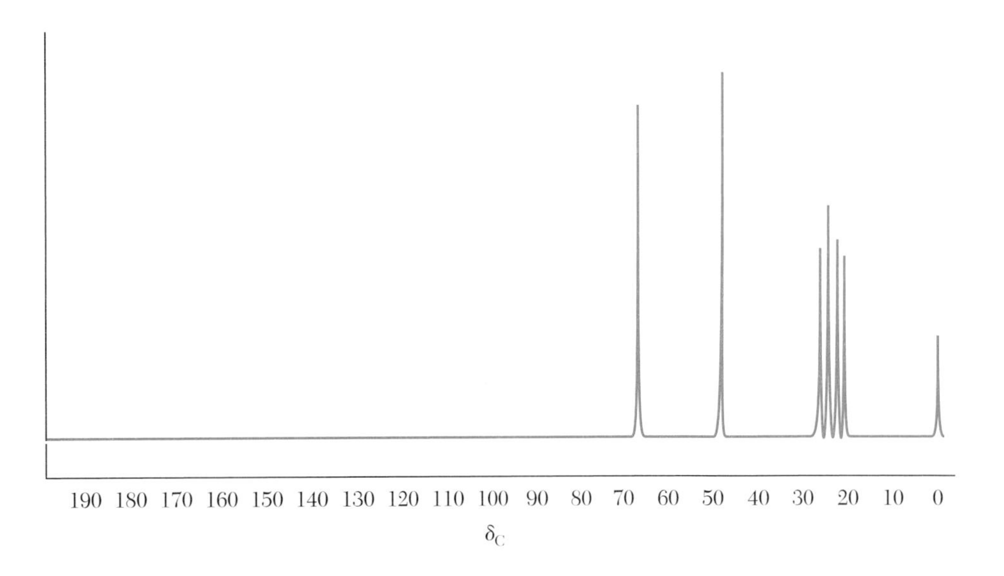

PROBLEM 17.29 Deduce the structure of the compound of formula C_6H_{10} whose ^{13}C NMR is shown below.

Figure for Problem 17.29

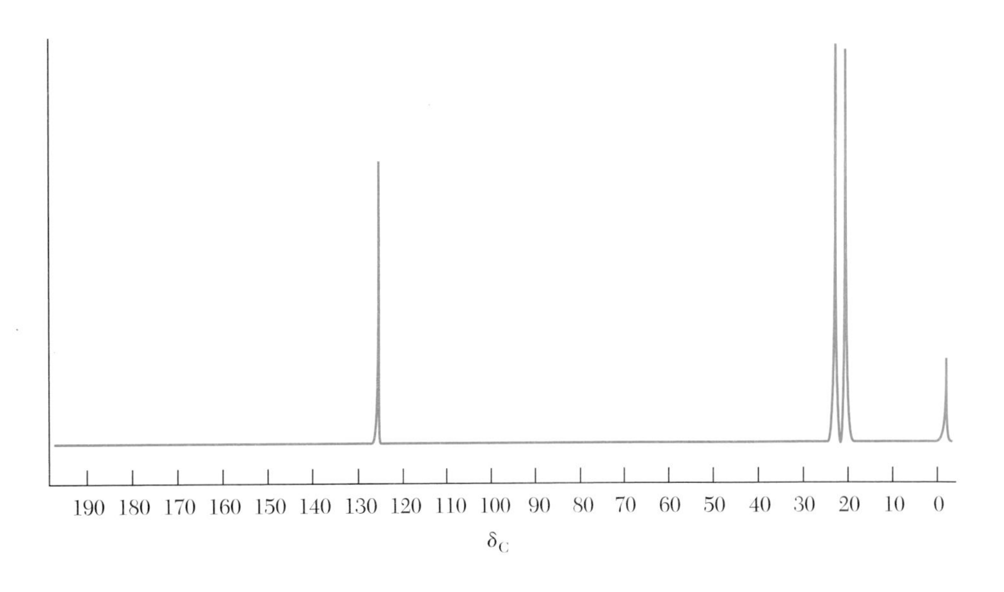

PROBLEM 17.30 Deduce the structure of the compound of formula $C_5H_{10}O$ whose ^{13}C NMR spectrum is shown.

Figure for Problem 17.30

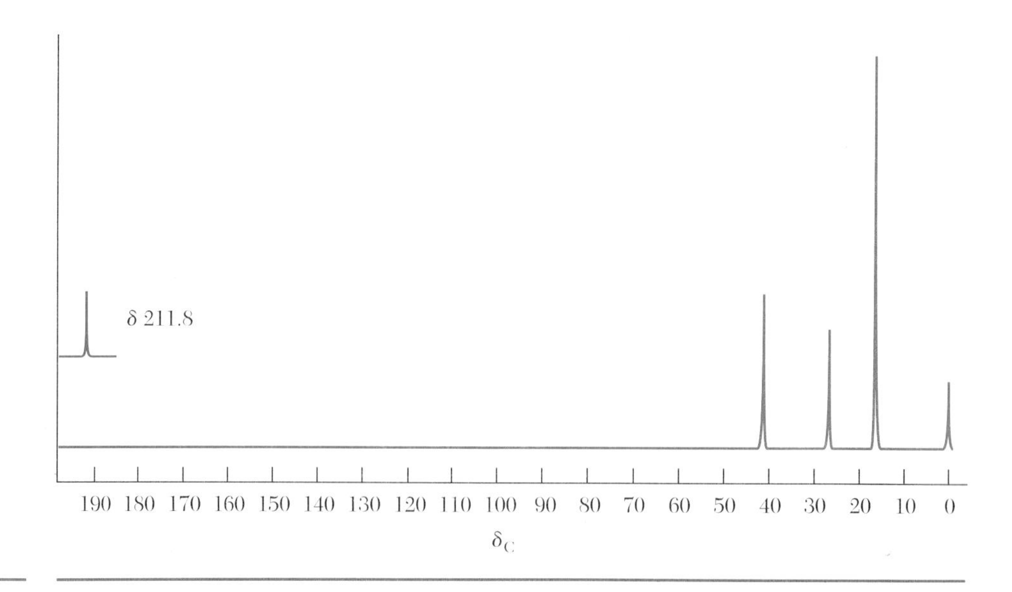

Summary

- Spectrometric methods of analysis have become the primary tools for the determination of structure. The two techniques most commonly used are infrared and nuclear magnetic resonance spectrometry.
- In infrared spectrometry, the sample is exposed to infrared radiation. When a molecule absorbs infrared light, the energy taken up serves to enhance the amplitude of bond vibrations normally present within the molecule.
- The frequencies absorbed are characteristic of the functional groups present in the molecule. For example, compounds containing a carbonyl group (C=O) absorb IR radiation in the region $\sim 1700\ cm^{-1}$.
- Nuclear magnetic resonance spectrometry tells us about the environment of the nuclei of atoms in the sample molecules.
- In the presence of a magnetic field, nuclei that have a net nuclear magnetic moment exist in two possible energy states, one with the nuclear magnetic moment aligned with the applied magnetic field and one with the nuclear magnetic moment opposed to the direction of the applied field.
- It is possible to excite a nucleus from the lower-energy state to the higher-energy state by applying electromagnetic radiation of the proper frequency.
- With typical magnets used in NMR spectrometry, radiofrequency photons have the appropriate energy to bring about the excitation.
- As a result of small differences in their local magnetic environment within a given molecule, different nuclei absorb energy under slightly different conditions. These differences allow us to make deductions regarding the environments of the nuclei within the molecule.
- Proton (^1H) NMR is the most common type of NMR spectrum used by organic chemists.
- In a proton NMR analysis we learn details of the different environments in which hydrogen is present in a molecule. Thus we can make conclusions about the detailed structure of organic molecules.
- Spin-spin splitting of NMR bands results from interactions between nuclei of nearby atoms.
- The degree of band splitting (into doublets, triplets, etc.) provides important structural clues.
- Other NMR-active nuclei are also of interest for NMR experiments. Chief among these is the carbon (^{13}C) nucleus.
- By using ^{13}C NMR we can usually deduce the number of different types of carbon sites present within a molecule as well as the chemical environment of each.
- Used together, infrared and nuclear magnetic resonance spectrometry are extremely powerful analytical methods for the organic chemist.

Terms to Remember

degradation
Planck equation
quantized process
vibrational levels
vibrational mode
frequency
spectrometer
infrared spectrum
infrared inactive
monochromatic light
nuclear magnetic moment
parts per million (ppm)
chemical shift
diamagnetism
shielding
tetramethylsilane (TMS)
diamagnetic anisotropy
ring current
integration
spin-spin splitting
coupling constant
double irradiation
decouple
heteronuclear coupling
broad-band decoupling
off-resonance decoupling

Additional Problems

17.31 Which features in an IR spectrum would most clearly distinguish between each of the following pairs of compounds?

a. cyclohexane and cyclohexene
b. cyclohexanol and cyclohexyl methyl ether
c. butanal and butanone
d. 2-butyne and 1-butyne
e. butanoic acid and 1-butanol
f. benzonitrile ($C_6H_5C{\equiv}N$) and phenylacetylene ($C_6H_5C{\equiv}CH$)

17.32 Suggest structures for each of the compounds described by the following spectral characteristics:

a. a compound of formula $C_5H_{10}O$ whose IR spectrum contains a peak at 1715 cm^{-1} and whose ^1H NMR spectrum consists of a triplet (relative area 3) and a quartet (relative area 2)
b. a compound of formula $C_5H_{10}O$ whose IR spectrum contains a peak at 1715 cm^{-1} and whose ^1H NMR spectrum consists of a singlet (relative area 3), a doublet (relative area 6), and a septet (relative area 1)
c. a compound of formula C_3H_6O whose IR spectrum shows no absorption peaks in the region 1600–1750 cm^{-1} and whose ^1H NMR spectrum consists of a triplet (relative area 2) and a quintet (relative area 1)
d. an alkyne whose ^1H NMR spectrum consists of a quartet and a triplet only
e. an ether whose ^1H NMR spectrum consists of a single peak and whose broad-band decoupled ^{13}C NMR spectrum contains two peaks
f. a compound of formula $C_3H_6O_2$ whose ^1H NMR spectrum consists of two singlets of equal area, one at δ 2.0 and one at δ 4.0
g. a compound of formula $C_2H_3Cl_3$ whose ^1H NMR spectrum consists of a doublet at δ 3.9 (relative area 2) and a triplet at δ 5.9 (relative area 1)
h. a compound of formula $C_3H_5ClO_2$ whose ^1H NMR spectrum consists of a doublet at δ 1.8 (relative area 3), a quartet at δ 4.5 (relative area 1), and a singlet at δ 11.2 (relative area 1)
i. a compound of formula $C_{13}H_{11}Cl$ whose ^1H NMR spectrum consists of two signals, (one is at δ 7.3 and is ten times as intense as the other one, which is located at δ 6.1).

17.33 Predict the major bands (frequency and relative intensity) in the infrared spectrum of each of the following compounds:

a. cyclohexanol
b. 2,3-dimethyl-2-butene
c. 1-bromohexane
d. cyclopentanone
e. 2-nitrotoluene
f. 1-butyne
g. di(1-propyl) ether

17.34 Predict the proton NMR spectrum (approximate chemical shift, integration, and splitting) for each of the following compounds:

a. methoxybenzene
b. *trans*-3-hexene
c. *meso*-2,4-dibrompentane
d. 2-fluoropropane
e. 4-nitrotoluene
f. 1,3-butanediol
g. 1-butyne

17.35 Predict the ^{13}C broad-band decoupled NMR spectrum (chemical shift only) for each of the following compounds:

a. cyclopentanol
b. 2-hexyne
c. 4-nitrotoluene
d. 3-nitrotoluene
e. 1,2-dimethylcyclopentene
f. 3-bromopentane
g. 2-pentanone

17.36 Deduce the structure of the compound of formula $C_8H_{10}O$ that exhibits the following IR and proton NMR spectra.

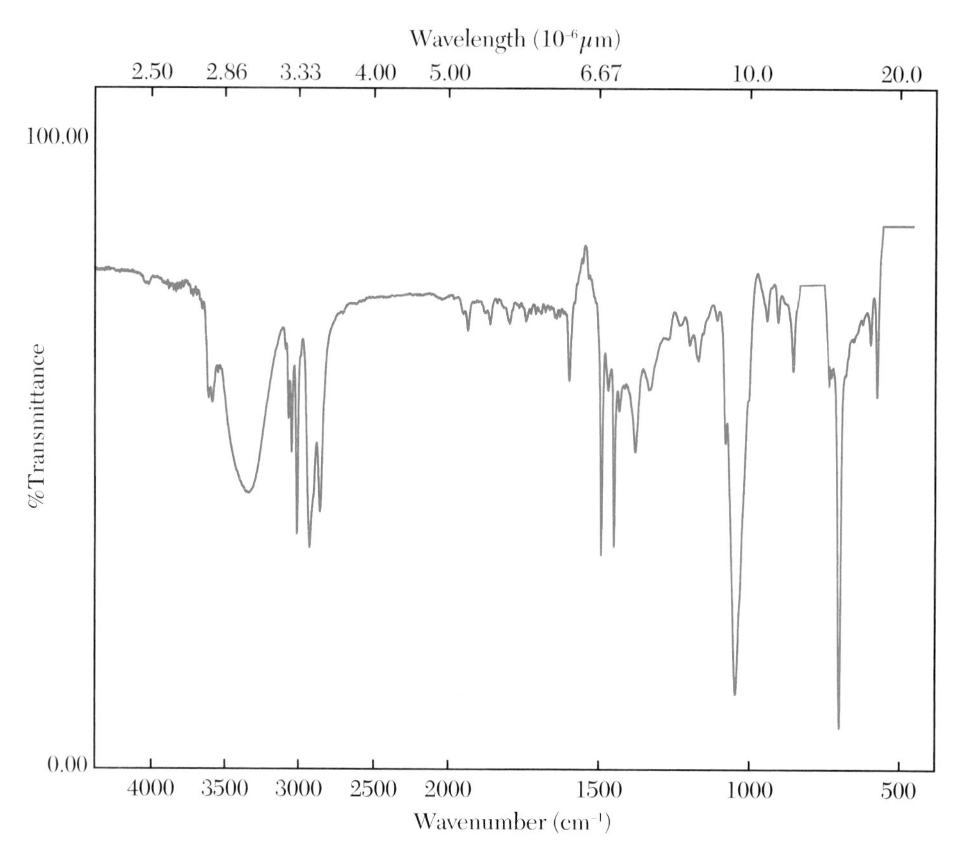

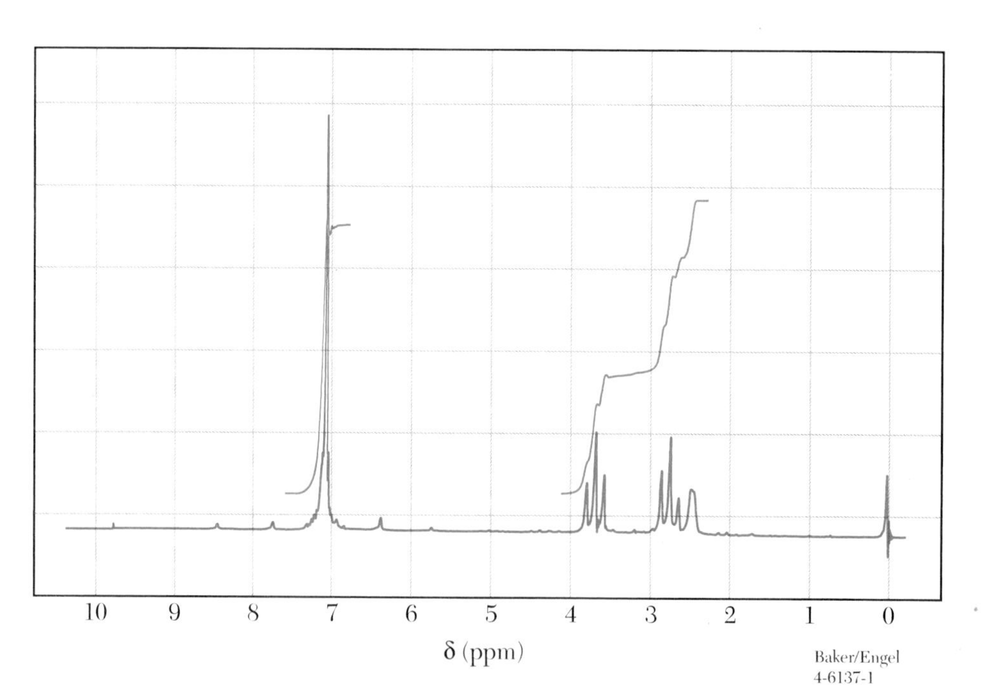

17.37 Deduce the structure of the compound of formula $C_6H_{10}O_3$ that exhibits the following IR and proton NMR spectra.

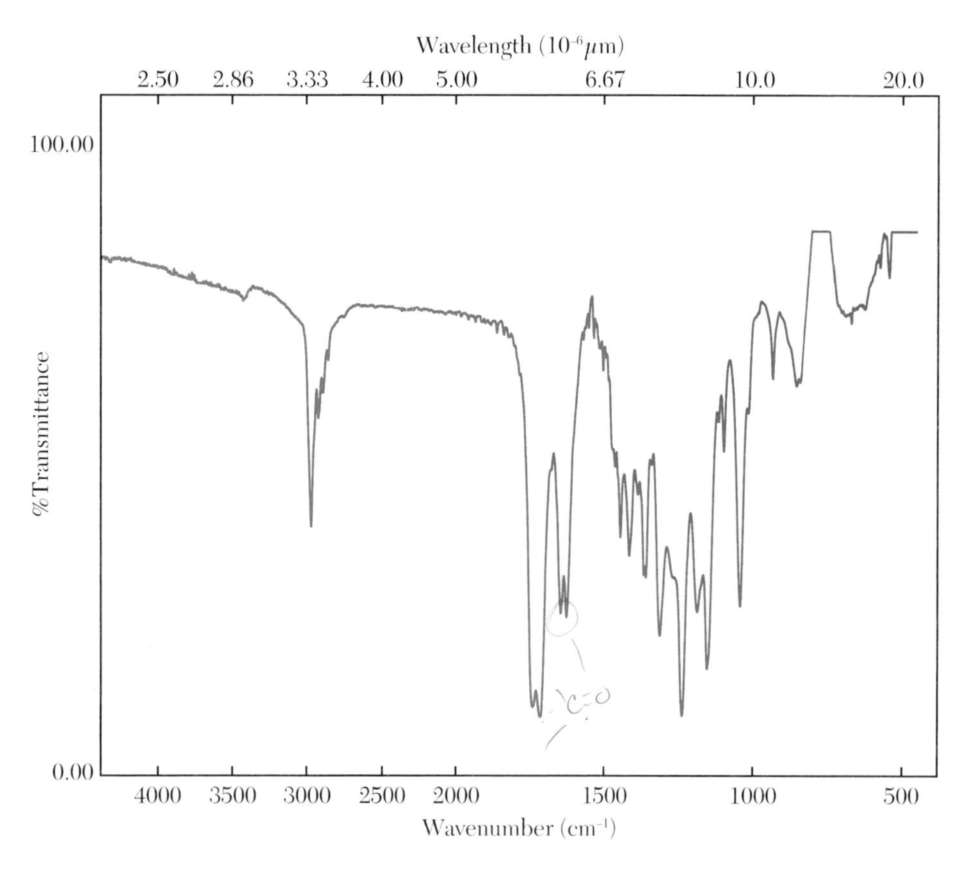

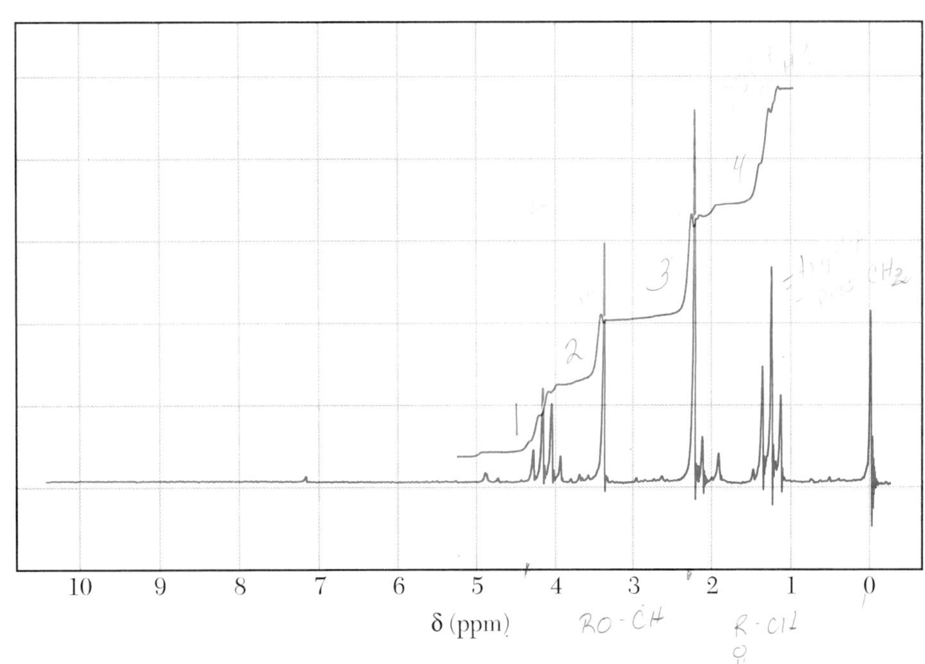

17.38 Deduce the structure of the compound of formula C_5H_8 that exhibits the following IR and proton NMR spectra.

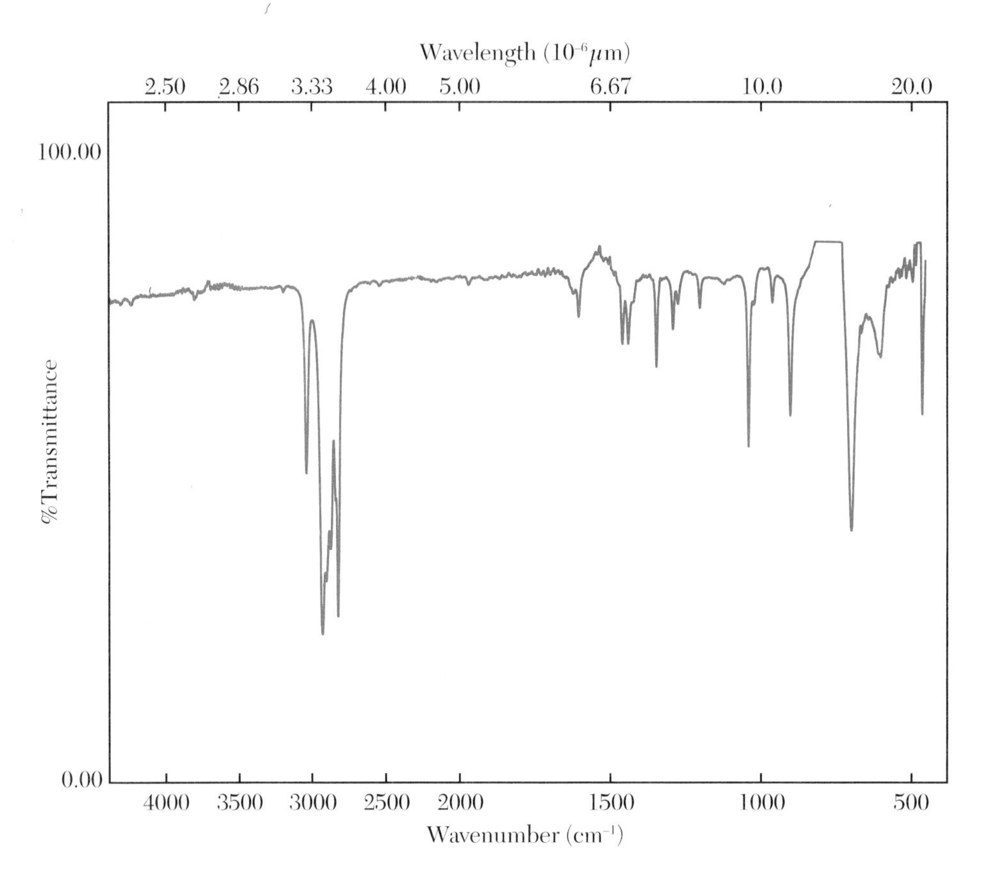

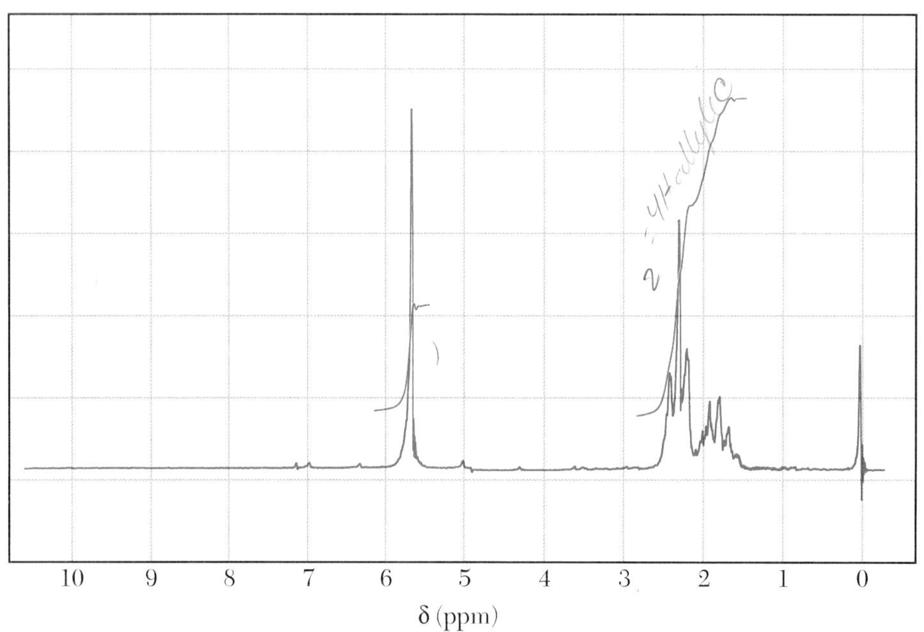

17.39 Deduce the structure of the compound of formula $C_8H_{11}N$ that exhibits the following IR and proton NMR spectra.

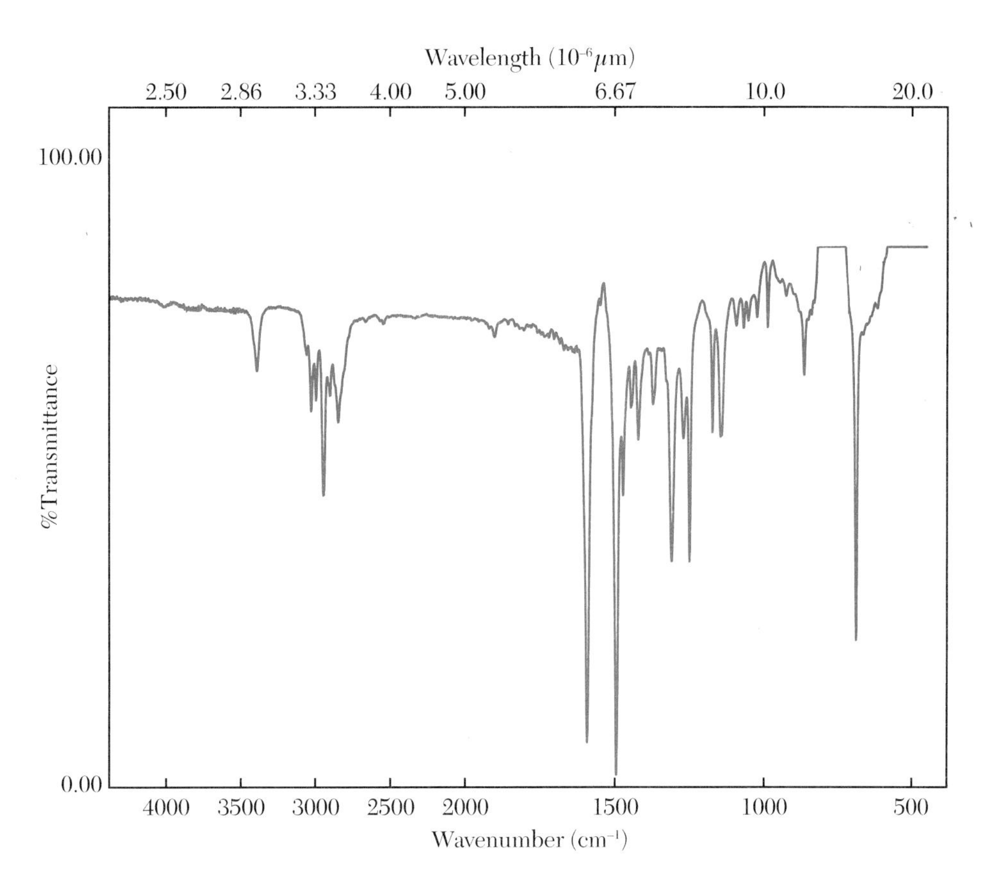

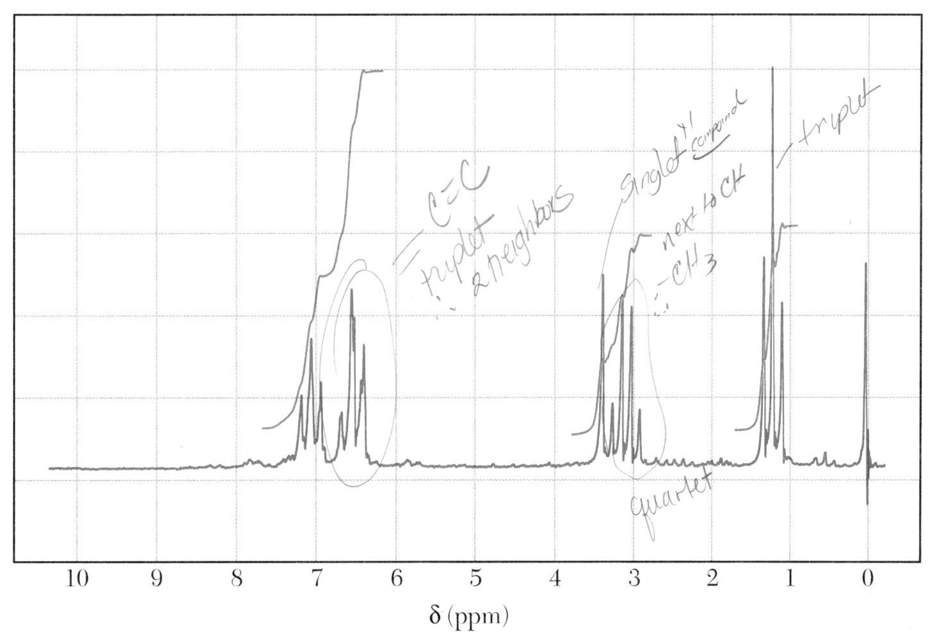

17.40 Deduce the structure of the compound of formula $C_5H_8O_2$ that exhibits the following IR and proton NMR spectra.

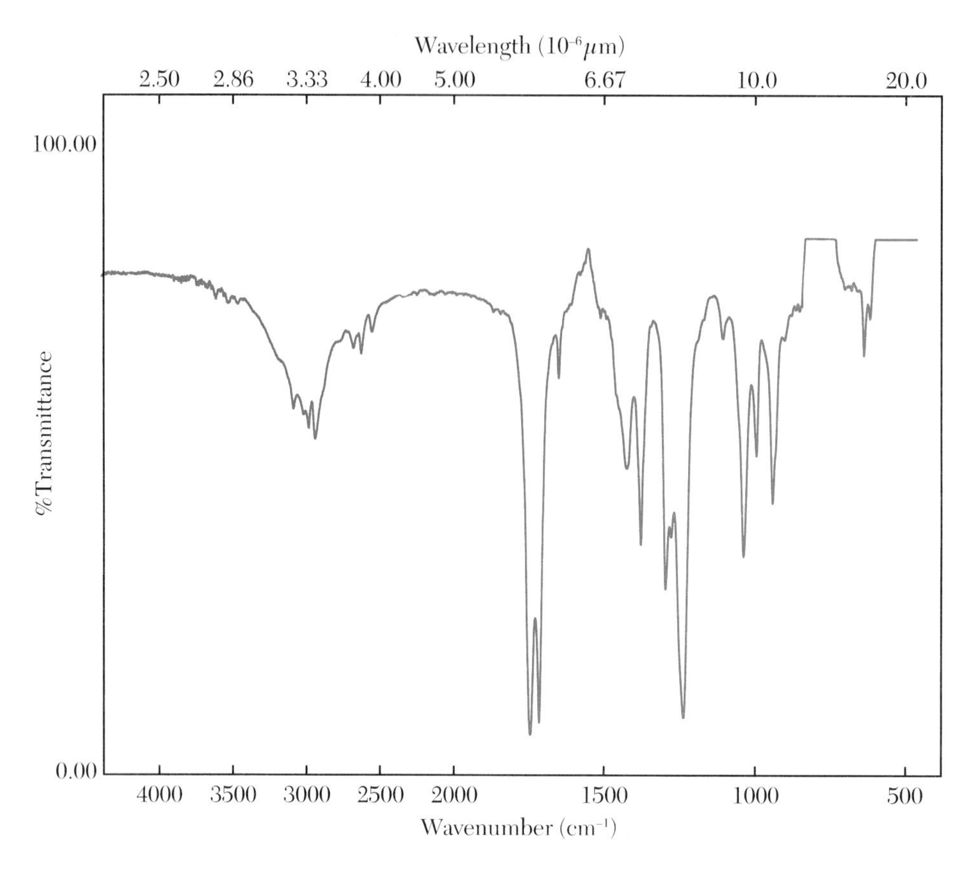

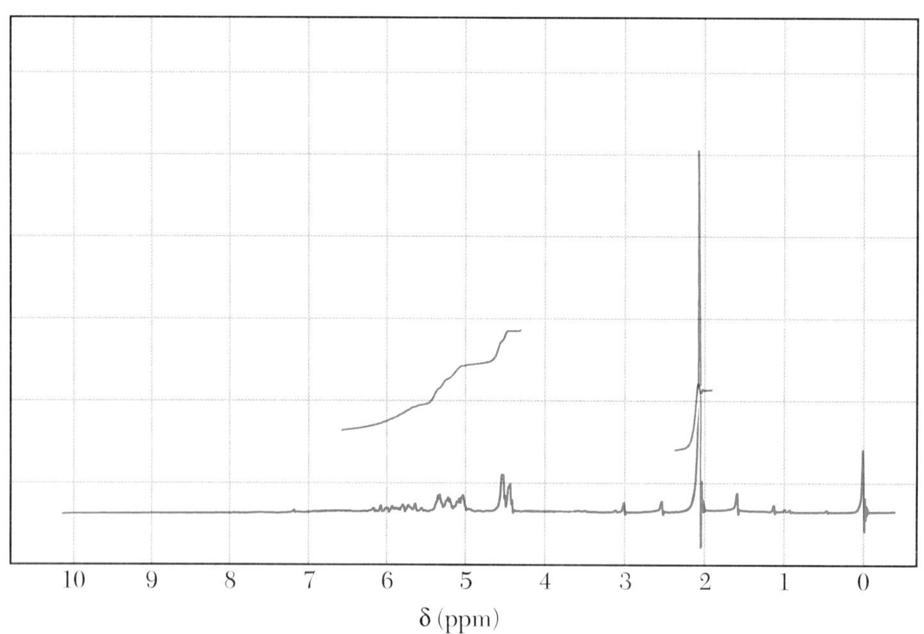

17.41 Deduce the structure of the compound of formula $C_7H_7NO_3$ that exhibits the following IR and proton NMR spectra.

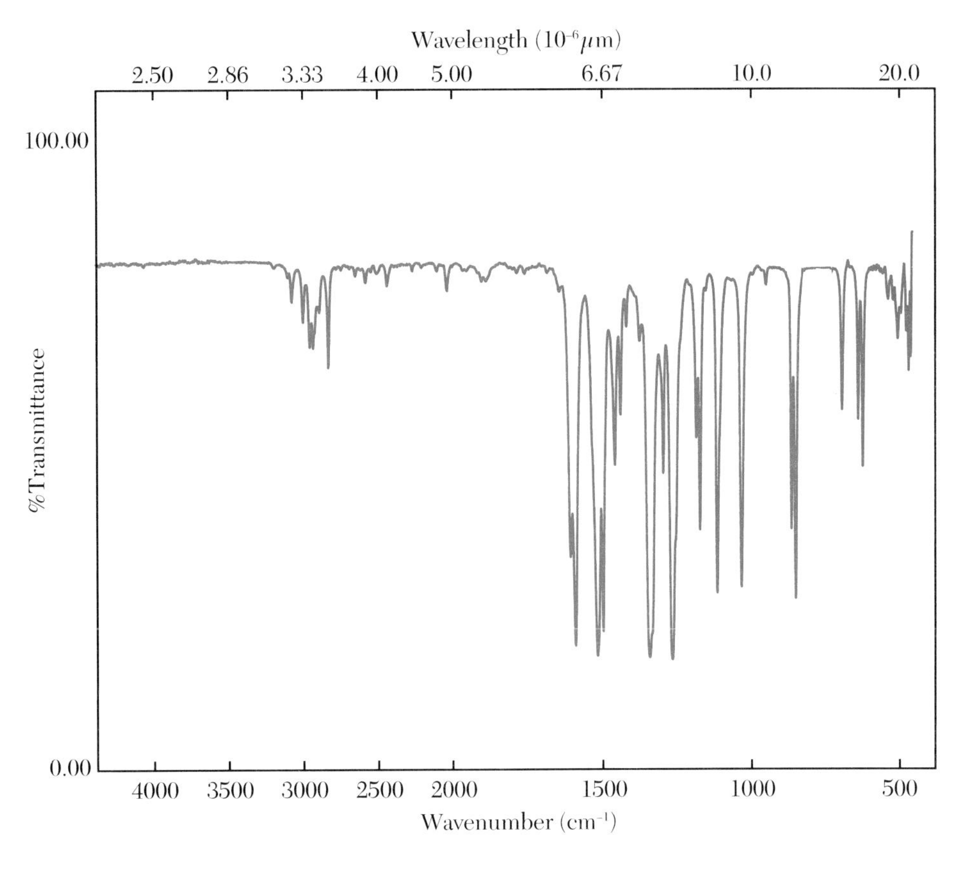

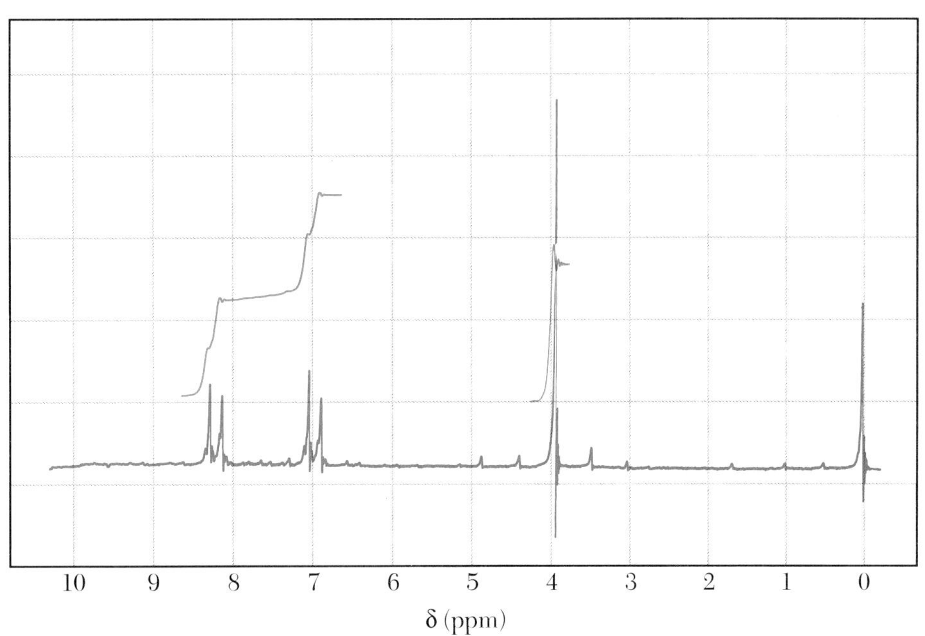

17.42 The following sets of IR and proton NMR spectra are from two isomers of the formula C_9H_{10}. One set of spectra is for α-methylstyrene and the other is for *trans*-β-methylstyrene. Give the correct structure for each set of spectra.

Isomer A:

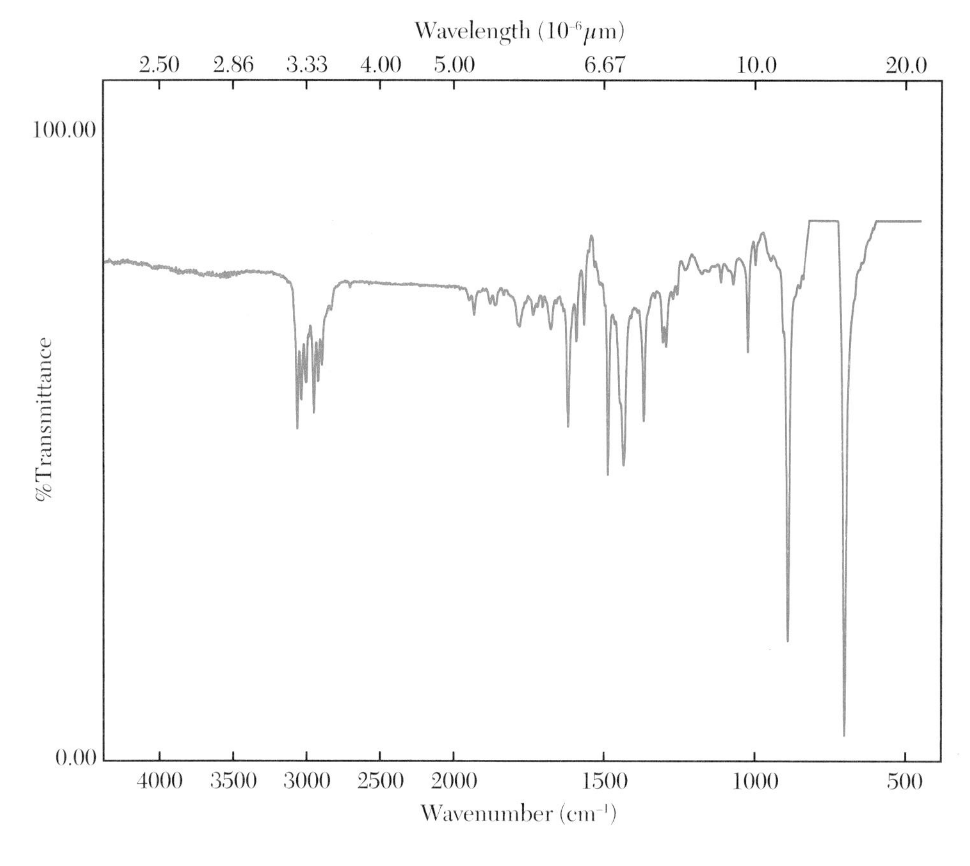

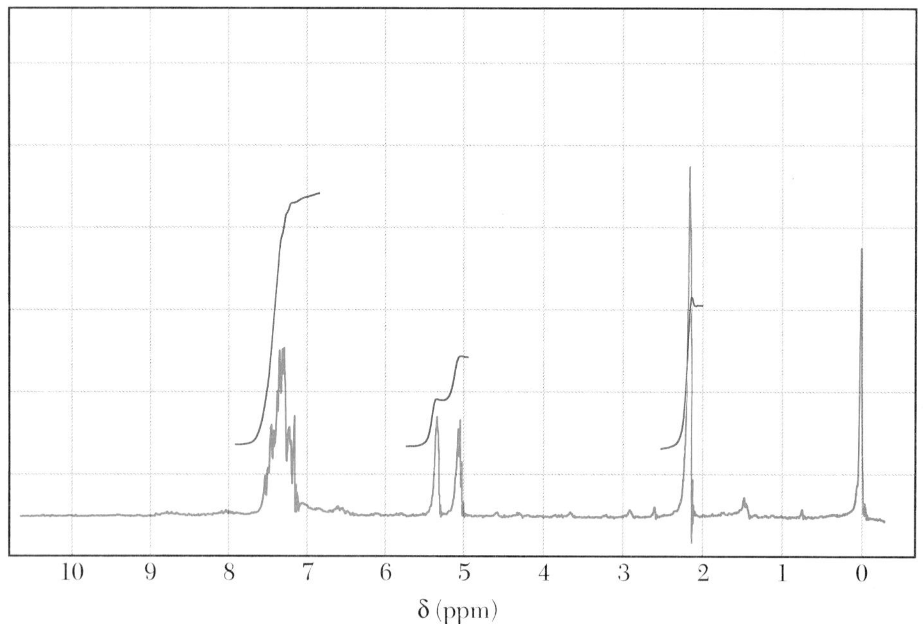

Isomer *B*:

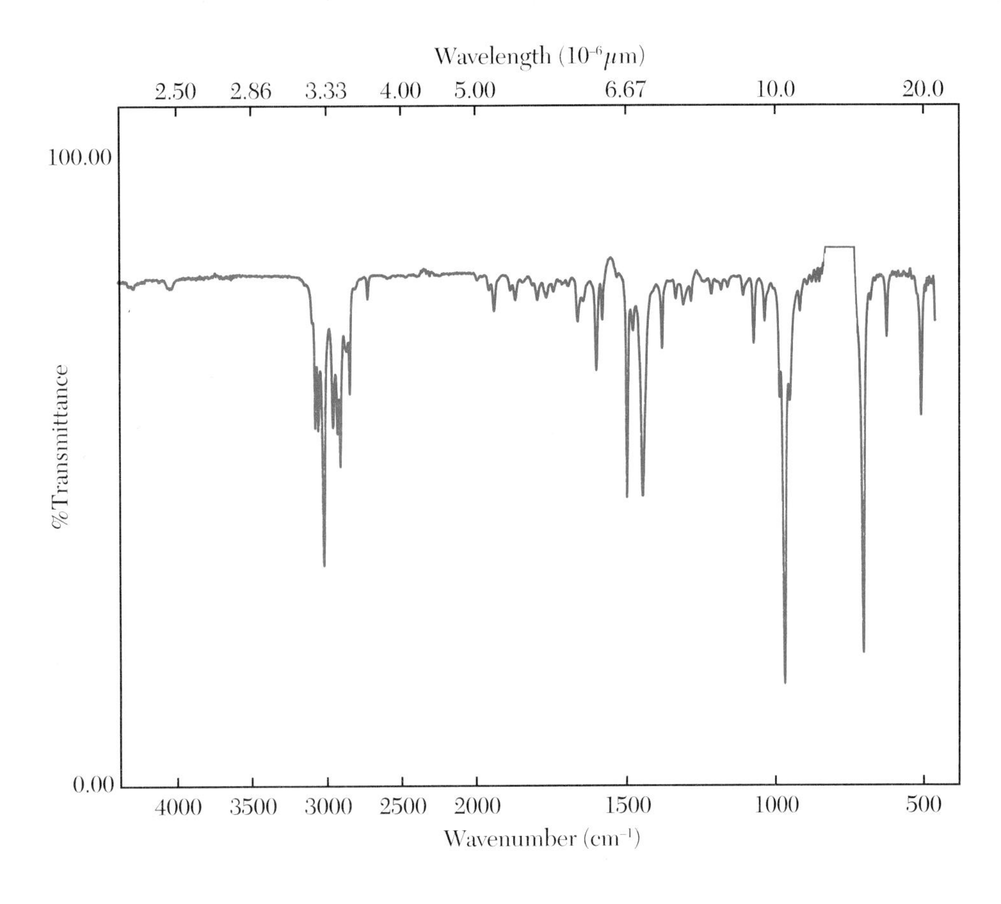
Wavelength (10⁻⁶ μm)
2.50
2.86
3.33
4.00
5.00
6.67
10.0
20.0
100.00
% Transmittance
0.00
4000
3500
3000
2500
2000
1500
1000
500
Wavenumber (cm⁻¹)

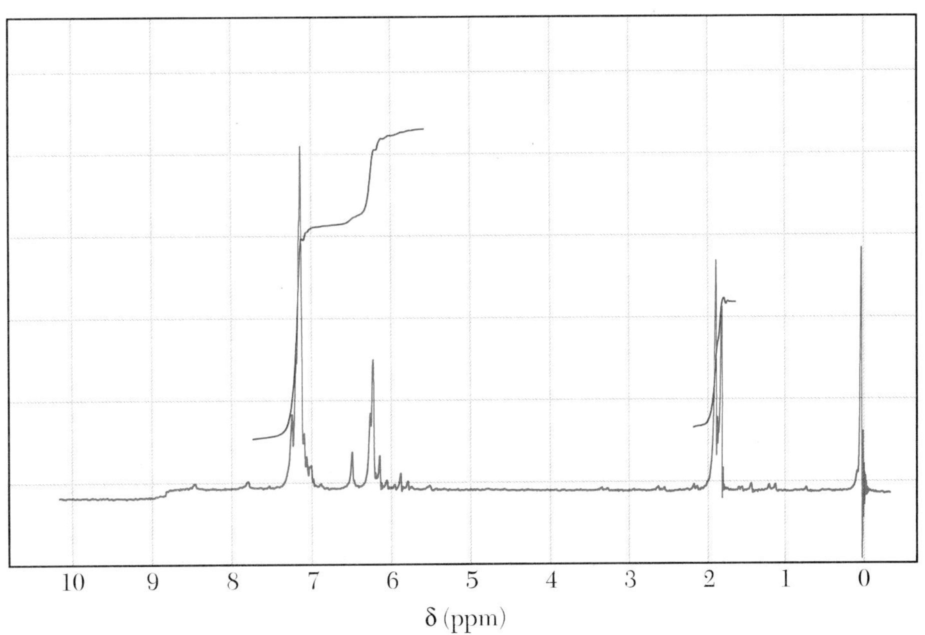
10
9
8
7
6
5
4
3
2
1
0
δ (ppm)

17.43 Deduce the structure of the compound of formula C_3H_7I whose broad-band decoupled ^{13}C NMR is shown below.

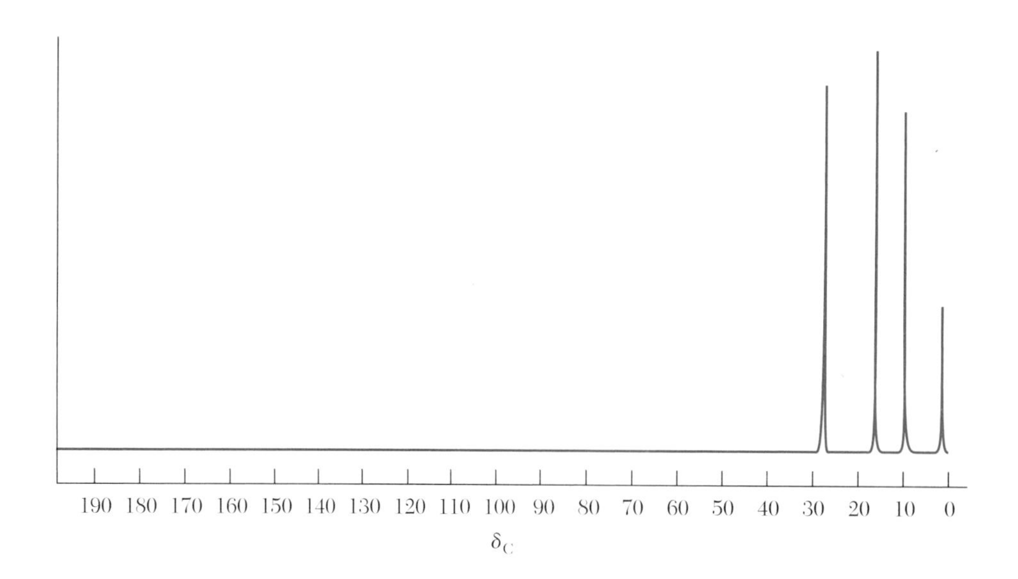

17.44 Deduce the structure of the compound of formula $C_4H_7O_2Br$ that exhibits the broad-band decoupled ^{13}C NMR shown below.

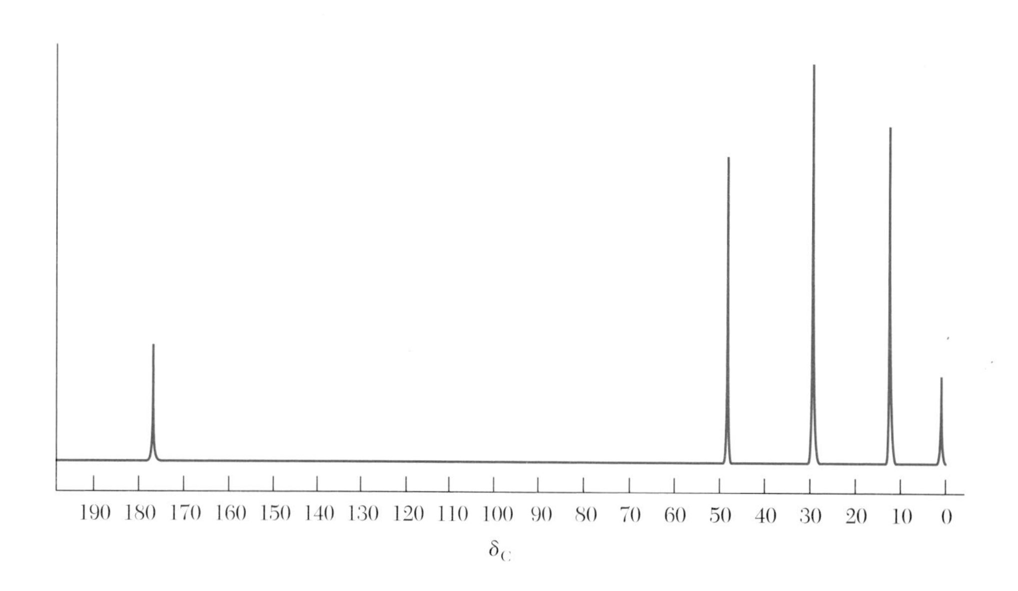

17.45 Deduce the structure of the compound of formula $C_6H_8O_2Cl_2$ that exhibits the following broad band decoupled ^{13}C NMR spectrum shown.

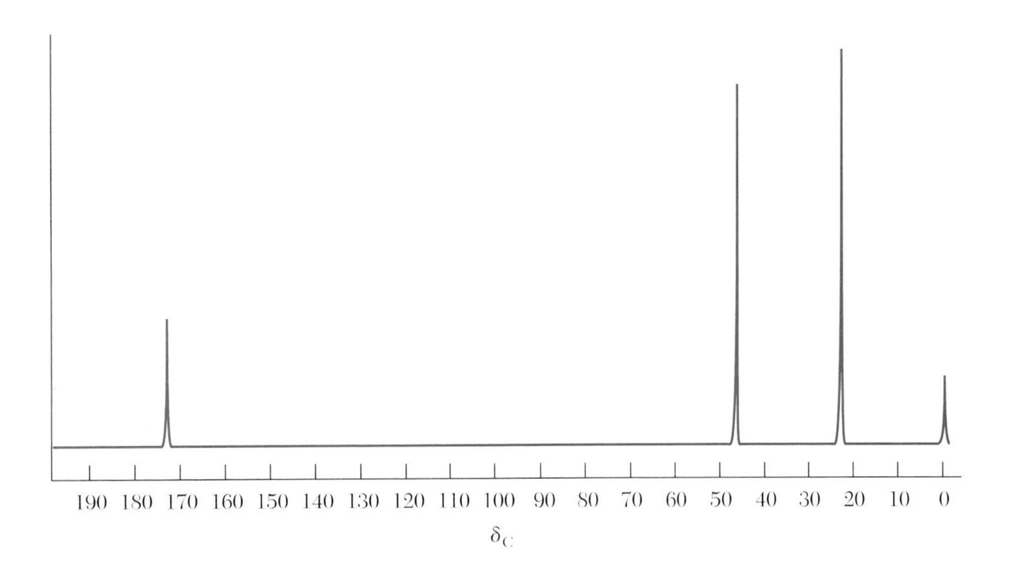

17.46 The three broad-band decoupled ^{13}C NMR spectra shown below are from isomers *C*, *D*, and *E*, which have the formula $C_4H_{10}O$. Spectrum *F* was produced by a compound of formula C_4H_9Br that is the product of the reaction of one of the original isomers (*C*, *D*, or *E*) with phosphorus tribromide. Give the correct structures for each of the compounds *C*–*F*.

Isomer *C*:

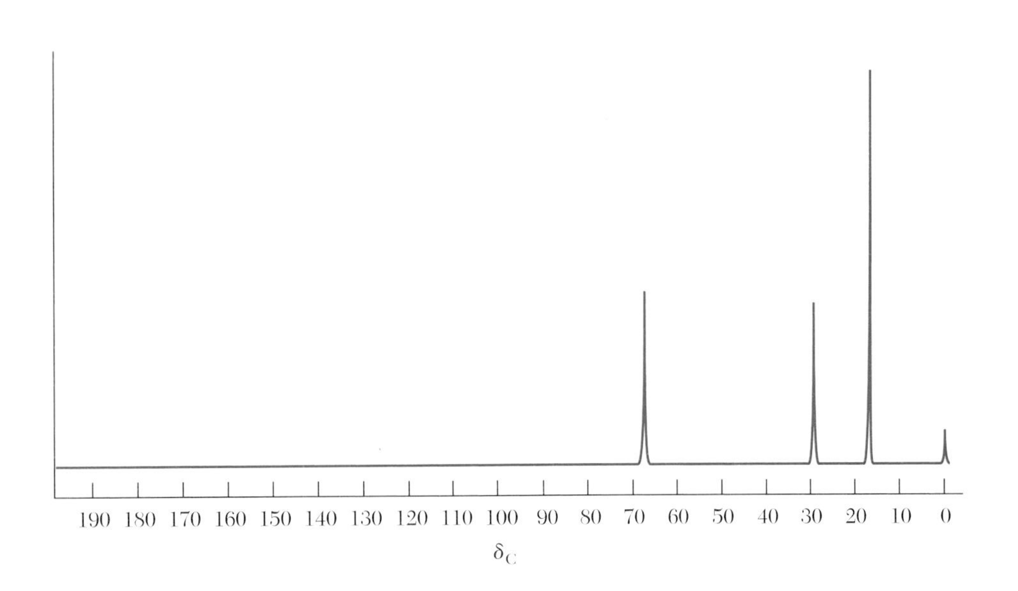

Isomer *D*:

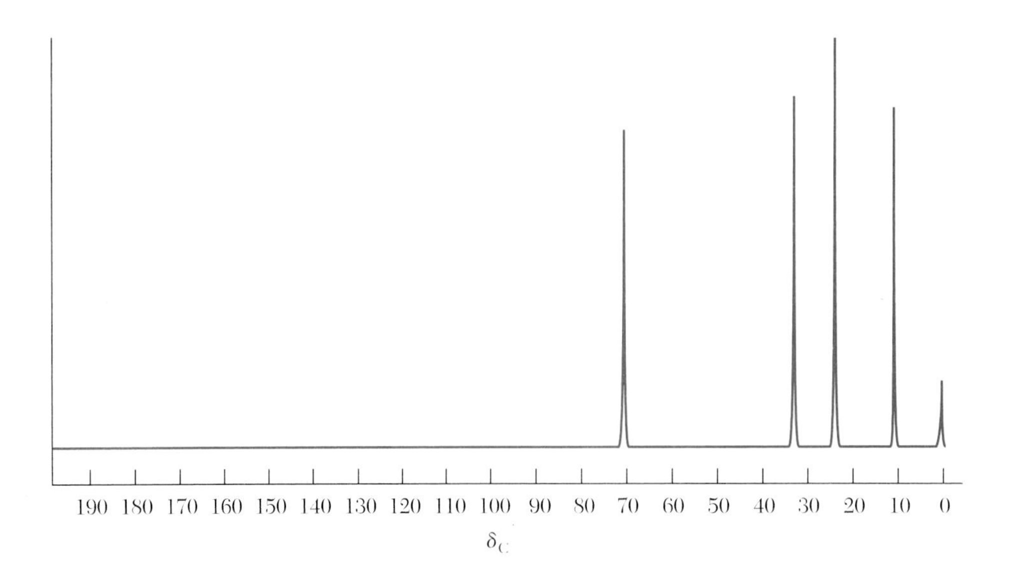

Isomer *E*:

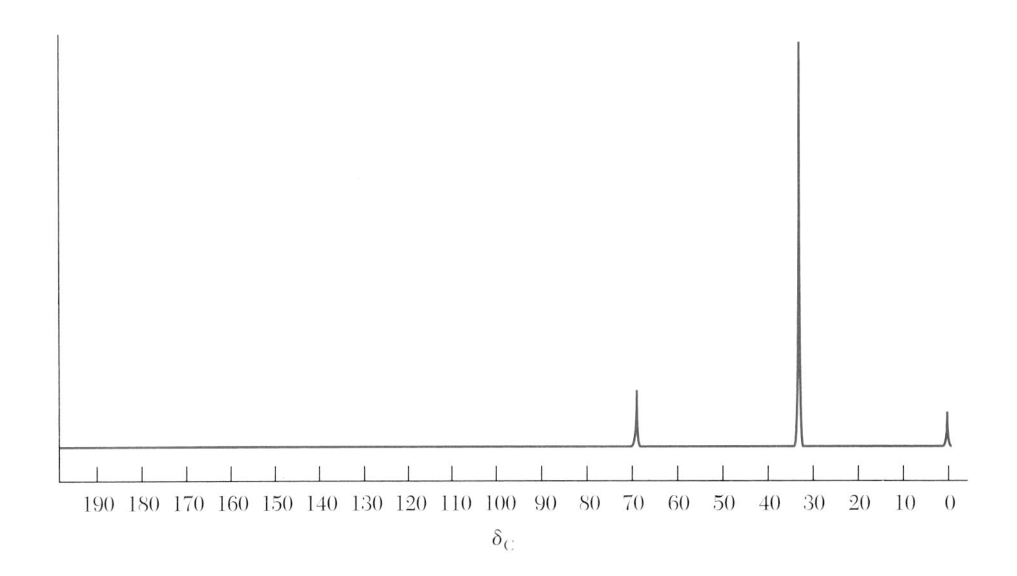

Isomer *F*:

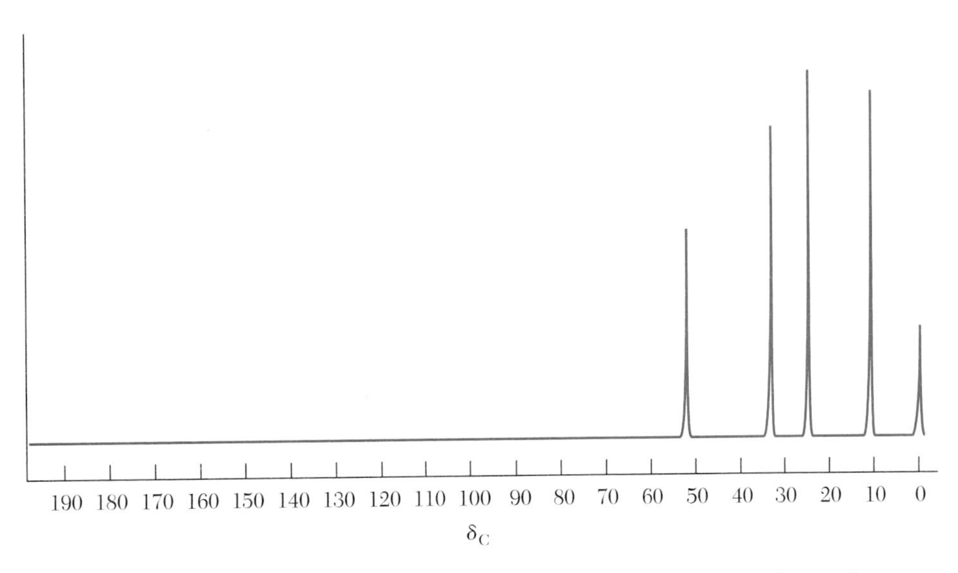

17.47 Compound *G* contains only carbon, hydrogen, and oxygen. On combustion analysis, the percentages of carbon and hydrogen present are found to be:

C	66.63%
H	11.18%

IR Spectrograph for Problem 17.47

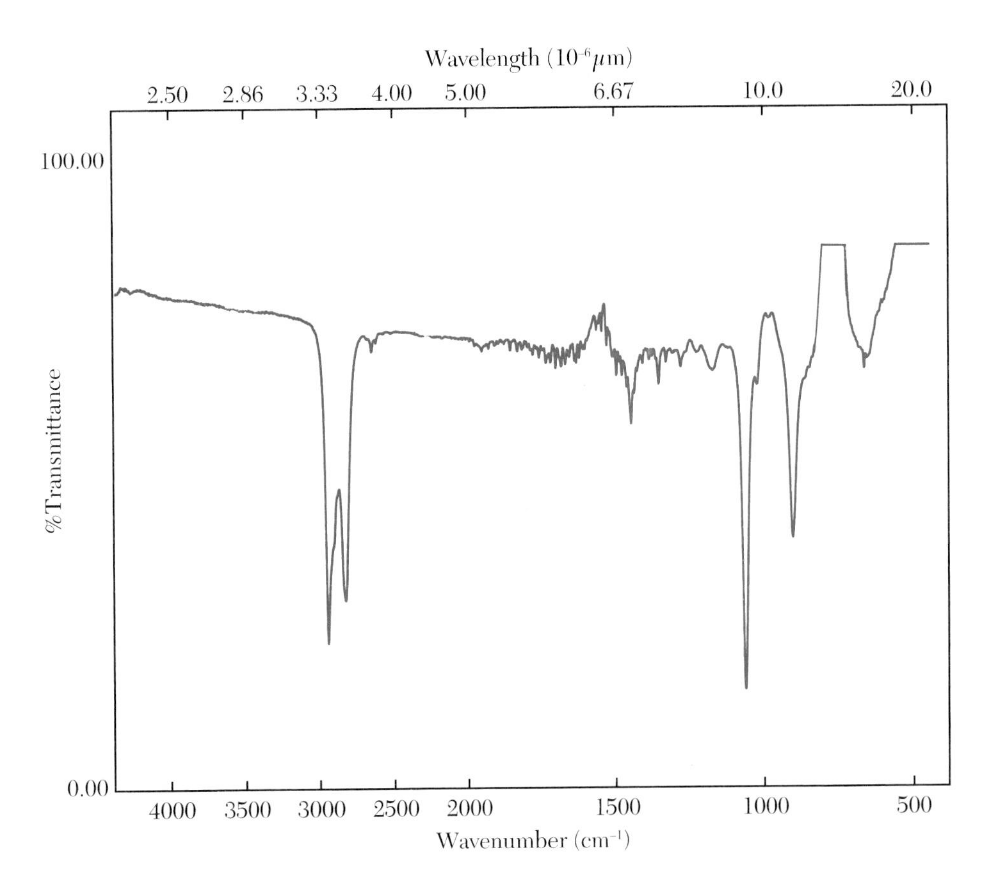

Shown are the IR, proton NMR, and broad-band decoupled ^{13}C NMR spectra for compound *G*. On the basis of these data, give the correct structure for compound *G*.

Proton NMR Spectrograph for Problem 17.47

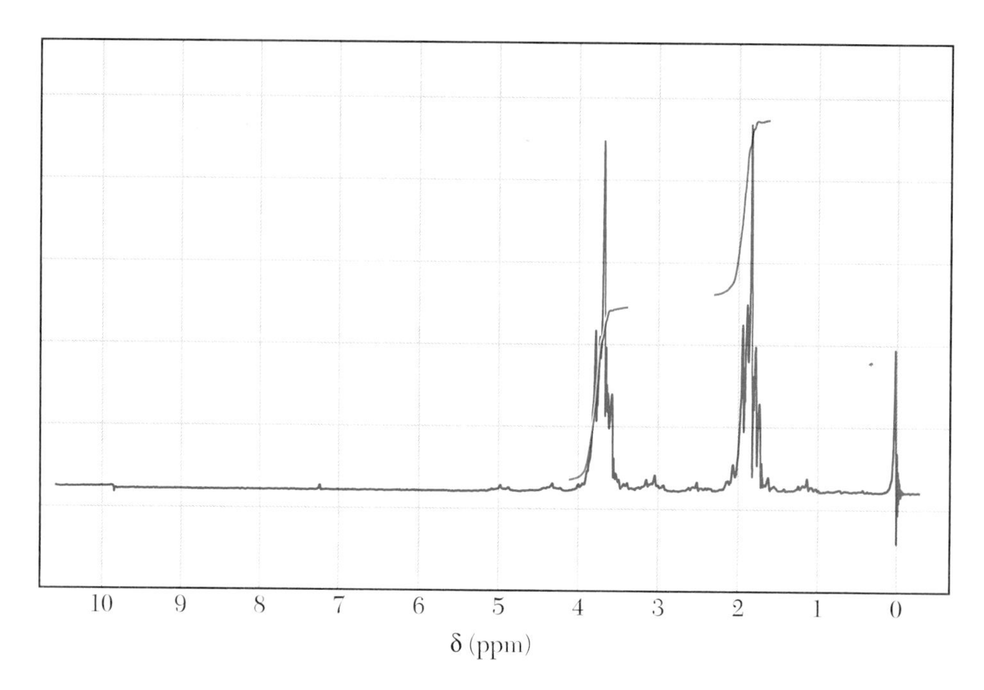

^{13}C NMR Spectrograph for Problem 17.47

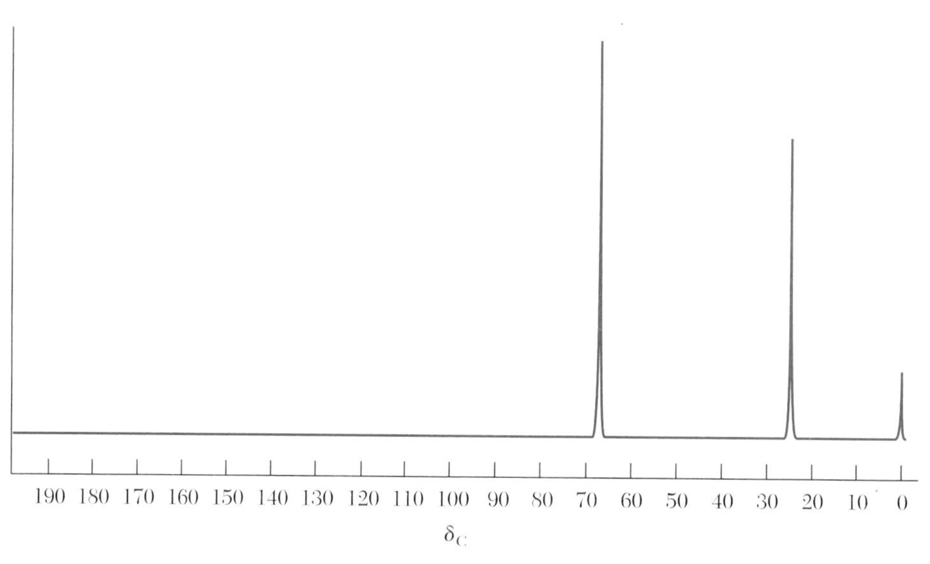

17.48 Explain how you would use IR spectrometry to distinguish each of the pairs of isomeric compounds listed below.

a. 1-hexyne and 2-hexyne
b. cyclohexanone and 1-hexen-3-ol
c. *trans*-3-hexene and cyclohexane

17.49 Explain how you would use proton NMR spectrometry to distinguish each of the pairs of isomeric compounds listed below.

a. ethyl isopropyl ether and 1-pentanol
b. 2-pentanone and 3-pentanone
c. 4-chlorotoluene and 2-chlorotoluene

17.50 Explain how you would use ^{13}C NMR to distinguish each of the pairs of isomeric compounds listed below.
a. 1-bromobutane and 1-bromo-2-methylpropane
b. cyclopentanol and pentanal
c. 1,2-dibromocyclohexane and 1,1-dibromocyclohexane

17.51 For each of the pairs of compounds listed below, explain how you would use one or more of the spectroscopic methods (IR, proton NMR, ^{13}C NMR) to distinguish them. Tell why you chose a particular spectroscopic method (or methods) and what aspect of the spectra of the compounds would allow you to make the differentiation.

a. $CH_3-C(=O)-OCH_2CH_3$ and $CH_3CH_2-C(=O)-OCH_3$

b. (2-bromophenyl)–OCH_3 and (4-bromophenyl)–OCH_3

c. $(CH_3CH_2)(CH_3CH_2)C=CH_2$ and $(H)(H_3C)C=C(CH_3)(H)$

17.52 On the basis of Hooke's law (Figure 17.3), calculate the following ratios of IR absorption frequencies:
a. $\nu(CH)/\nu(CD)$ b. $\nu(^{12}C-H)/\nu(^{13}C-H)$ c. $\nu(C=O)/\nu(C=C)$

17.53 An allylic halide *H* of formula C_5H_9Cl undergoes an S_N1 reaction with water to yield a mixture of two isomeric products, *I* and *J*. The proton NMR spectra of *I* and *J* are shown. Suggest structures for compounds H–*J*.

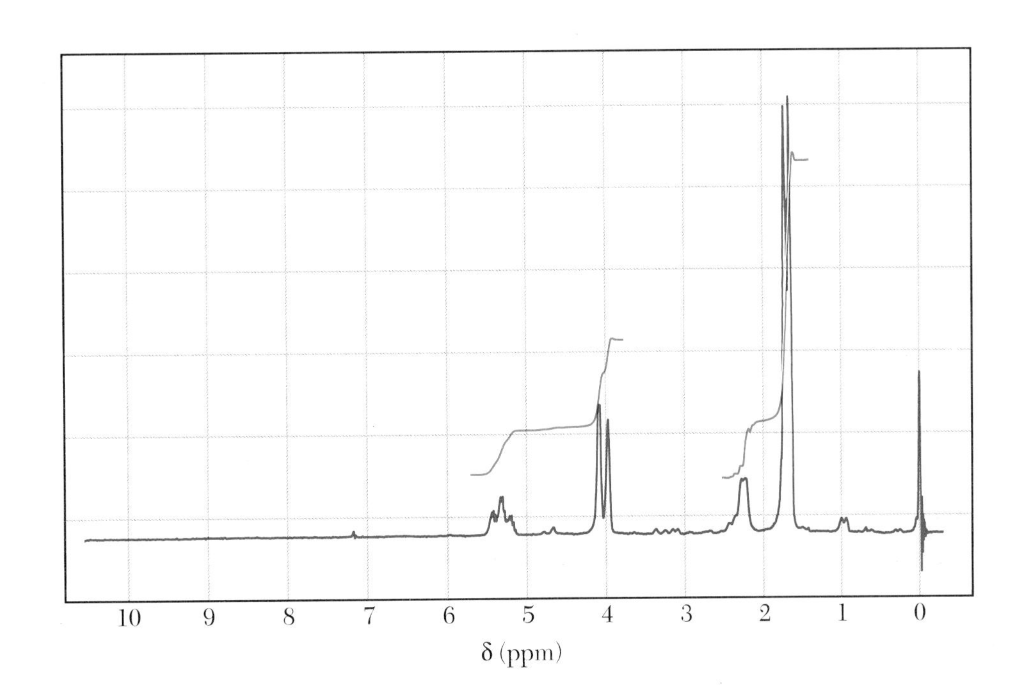

Isomer *J*:

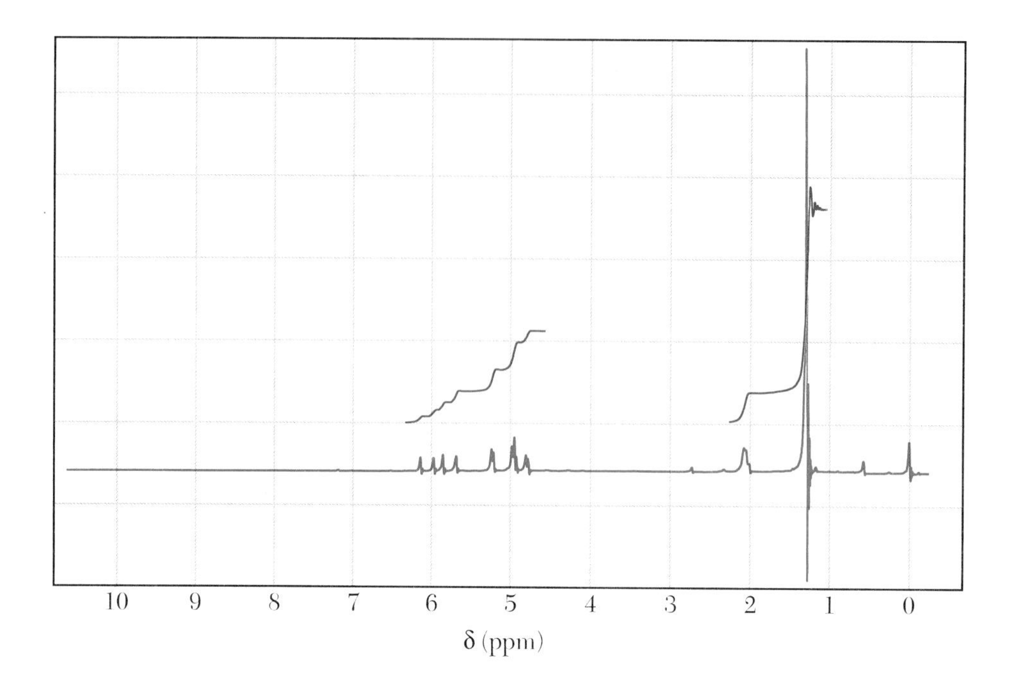

17.54 Both reactions below give the same ion

$$\text{(trans-1,2-dibromocyclopentane)} \xrightarrow[-78\,^\circ\text{C}]{SbF_5} C_5H_8Br^+ \xleftarrow[-120\,^\circ\text{C}]{FSO_3H} \text{(3-bromocyclopentene)}$$

The off-resonance decoupled ^{13}C NMR spectrum of the ion shows three resonances—one at δ 114.6 (doublet), one at δ 31.8 (triplet), and one at δ 18.7 (triplet). The ^{1}H NMR spectrum shows three signals: δ 7.32, 2H, broad; δ 3.14, 4H, broad; and δ 2.50, 2H, broad. Suggest a structure for the ion, and explain its formation from the two precursors. (*Hints:* SbF_5 plays the role of a Lewis acid—review Problem 16.38; and FSO_3H is a strong Brønsted acid.)

Chapter 18: Reactions of Benzene and Its Derivatives

18.1 Introduction

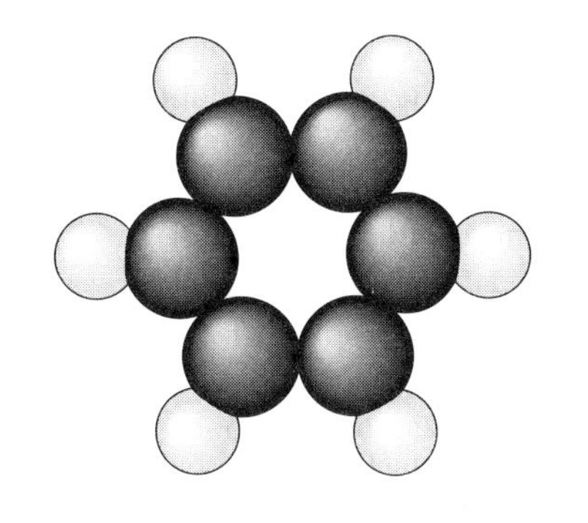

Chapter 16 focused on aromaticity, a special stability associated with fully conjugated planar rings containing a Hückel number ($4n + 2$) of π electrons. Benzene and its derivatives command a central role in the study of aromatic compounds because of their particularly great stabilities and widespread occurrence.

Since we use structures containing carbon-carbon double bonds to depict benzene and its derivatives, we might naively anticipate that these compounds would undergo chemical reactions similar to those of alkenes, that is, we might expect them to undergo addition reactions. However, we find that the most common type of reaction for benzene and its derivatives to undergo is *substitution*, not addition. In a substitution reaction the ring is able to maintain its aromatic stability, which it could not preserve in an addition reaction. These substitution reactions—their mechanisms and synthetic applications—will be the main focus of our attention in this chapter.

18.2 Nomenclature of Benzene Derivatives

Many substituted benzene compounds are named in the same way as other hydrocarbons. That is, the names and positions of any substituents are added to the name of the parent substance, benzene. Some examples are shown in Figure 18.1.

Figure 18.1 Examples of nomenclature for simple derivatives of benzene. When several unlike substituents are present, they are listed in alphabetical order.

:Cl: chlorobenzene

CH_2CH_3 ethylbenzene

NO_2, O_2N, NO_2 1,3,5-trinitrobenzene

:Cl:, :Cl: 1,4-dichlorobenzene

:Br:, :Cl:, :Cl: 2-bromo-1,4-dichlorobenzene

PROBLEM 18.1 Draw structures for and name all isomeric:

a. trinitrobenzenes
b. dichloronitrobenzenes
c. bromochloroethylbenzenes

There are also common names for many derivatives of benzene. Some of these are illustrated in Figure 18.2. You should memorize the names and structures of these monosubstituted benzenes.

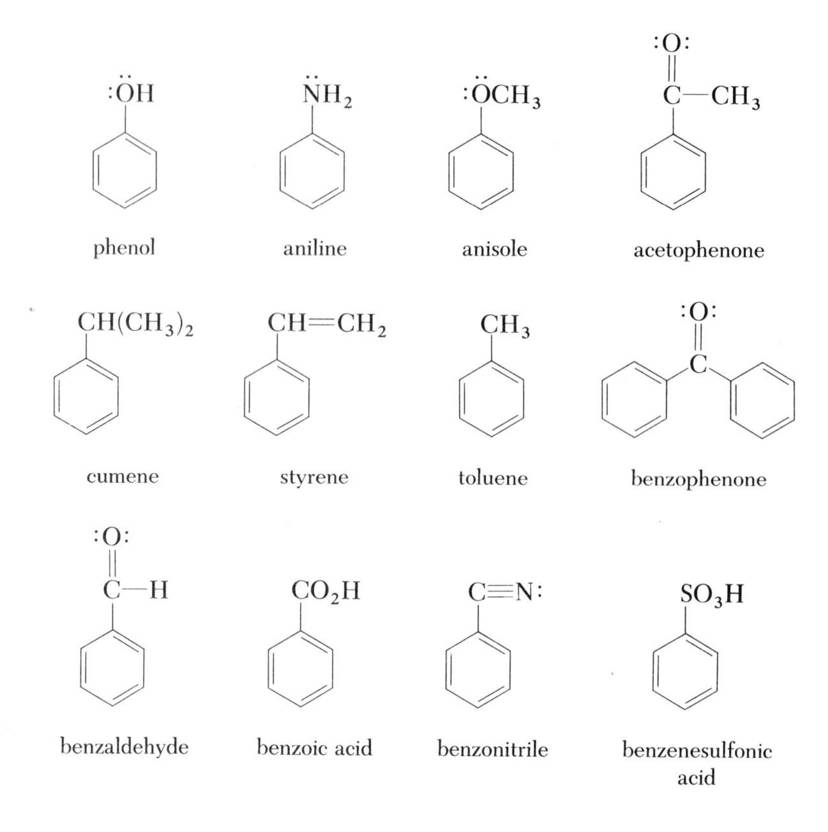

Figure 18.2 Common names of some monosubstituted benzene compounds.

PROBLEM 18.2 Give systematic names for each of the following:
a. anisole b. cumene c. toluene

PROBLEM 18.3 Draw structures for each of the following:
a. 4-bromoacetophenone b. 2,6-divinyltoluene
c. 3,5-dinitrocumene

PROBLEM 18.4 Tell what is wrong with each of the following names, and provide a proper name for each compound:
a. 6-bromotoluene b. 4,5-dichloroanisole

THE TERMS *ORTHO, META,* AND *PARA*

The prefixes *ortho* (*o*), *meta* (*m*), and *para* (*p*) are used to name substituted benzenes when two substituents are respectively 1,2-, 1,3-, or 1,4-relative to each other. Some examples are given in Figure 18.3.

Figure 18.3 Examples of the *ortho*, *meta*, *para* notation system. Dimethylbenzenes are known as *xylenes*, and hydroxytoluenes are known as *cresols*.

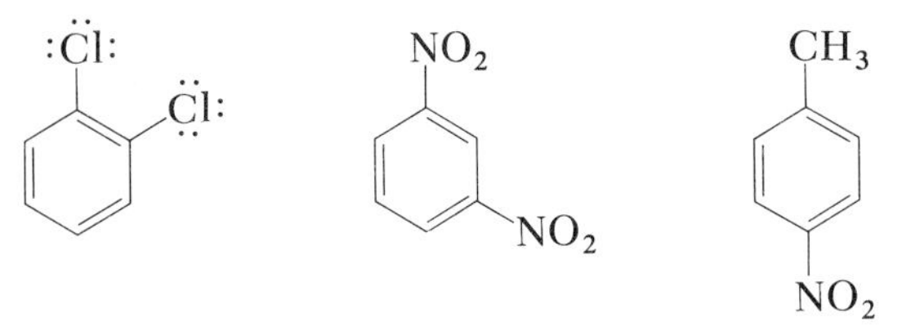

:Cl: :Cl:
o-dichlorobenzene

NO_2 NO_2
m-dinitrobenzene

CH_3 NO_2
p-nitrotoluene

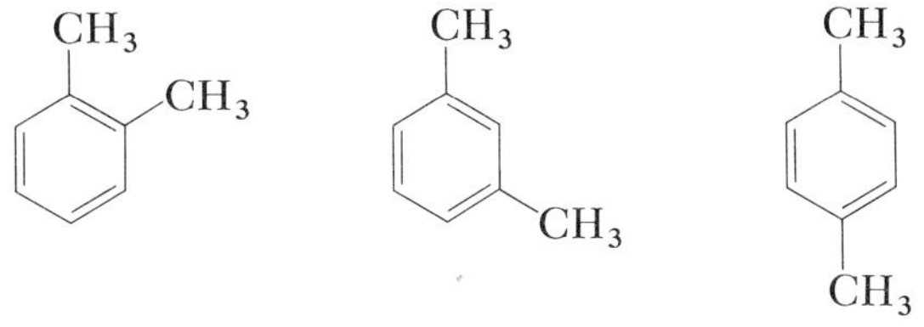

CH_3 CH_3
o-xylene

CH_3 CH_3
m-xylene

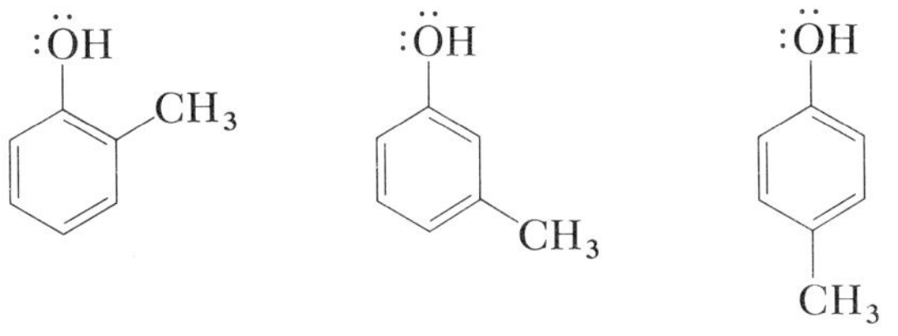

CH_3 CH_3
p-xylene

:ÖH CH_3
o-cresol

:ÖH CH_3
m-cresol

:ÖH CH_3
p-cresol

PROBLEM 18.5

Draw structures for each of the following:

a. *m*-dichlorobenzene b. *o*-chlorotoluene c. *p*-nitroaniline
d. *m*-ethylcumene e. *m*-divinylbenzene

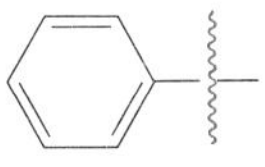

phenyl group

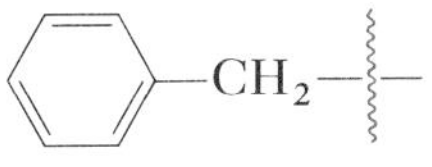

CH_2—
benzyl group

Figure 18.4 Phenyl (Ph or ϕ) and benzyl (Bn) groups.

THE TERMS *PHENYL* AND *BENZYL*

The **phenyl** and **benzyl** groups are shown in Figure 18.4. At times we use an abbreviated notation for these groups: Ph or ϕ for phenyl and Bn for benzyl.

Several examples of nomenclature using these groups are given in Figure 18.5.

$CH_3—CH(Ph)—CH_2—CH(Ph)—CH_3$
2,4-diphenylpentane

$PhCH_2\ddot{C}l$:
benzyl chloride

$PhCH_2—\ddot{O}—CH_2Ph$
dibenzyl ether

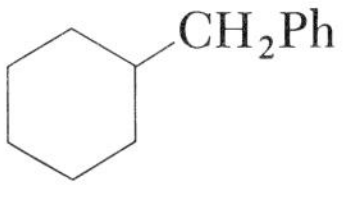

CH_2Ph
benzylcyclohexane

Figure 18.5 Use of *phenyl* and *benzyl* in the nomenclature of organic compounds.

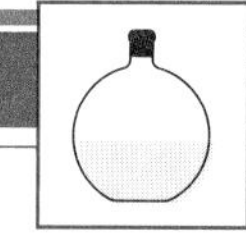

COMPOUND CAPSULE

Paracyclophanes

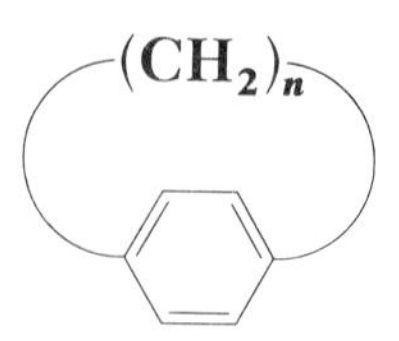

Paracyclophanes are interesting bicyclic compounds in which one of the rings is a benzene ring. Two positions of the benzene ring that are *para* relative to each other serve as bridgeheads. The bridgeheads are connected by a succession of methylene ($-CH_2-$) groups. The compounds are named as [n]-paracyclophanes, where n is the number of methylene groups bridging the *para* positions of the benzene ring. When the number of methylene groups is large, the molecule is relatively unstrained but shows an interesting proton NMR spectrum. Because the chain of methylene groups must pass over the benzene ring, some hydrogen atoms are in a position of high shielding (see Chapter 17). They therefore come into resonance at an unusually upfield chemical shift. For example, for [10]-paracyclophane we observe a signal at δ 0.3 for the hydrogens of the ε-methylene group—usually we observe a signal at about $\delta = 1.0$ for methylene hydrogens that are flanked by neighboring methylene groups.

chemical shift δ 0.3

[10]paracyclophane

If the number of atoms in the bridge linking the *para* positions is small, considerable strain is placed upon the molecule and the benzene ring is forced to twist out of planarity. How far can this twisting be forced by going to shorter and shorter bridges? In the mid-1980s Professor Friedrich Bickelhaupt (Vrije University, Amsterdam) and Professor Yoshito Tobe (University of Osaka) synthesized [5]-paracyclophane, a compound with only five carbon atoms in the bridge. At that time five carbon atoms was the shortest bridge incorporated into a paracyclophane. A few years later Bickelhaupt reported the synthesis of [4]-paracyclophane. Evidently the benzene ring can be bent appreciably. Of course, such bending sacrifices aromatic stability in the process.

PROBLEM 18.6 Draw structures for each of the following:

a. benzyl alcohol
b. 1,3-diphenyl-1,3-butadiene
c. (*E*)-1-phenylpropene
d. *p*-bromobenzyl bromide
e. phenyllithium

THE TERM *ARYL*

An **aryl** group is a general name for any substituted phenyl group. We use the term in the same way that we use *alkyl*. Just as we commonly use the symbol *R* to indicate the generic alkyl group, we use *Ar* to indicate an aryl group.

18.3 Physical Properties

Most benzene derivatives have physical properties similar to those of other hydrocarbons having similar shapes and molecular weights. For example, benzene and its hydrocarbon derivatives have very low solubility in water, like other hydrocarbons. However, hydrogen-bonding substituents change the properties substantially, as we will discuss in later chapters.

18.4 Introduction to Electrophilic Aromatic Substitution Reactions

The most important class of reactions for benzene and its derivatives is **electrophilic aromatic substitution.** In such reactions, an **electrophile** (i.e., an electron-deficient ion or molecule) reacts with benzene or its derivative to form a new benzene derivative. The electrophile takes the place of one of the original ring hydrogens. An example is the bromination of benzene, shown in Equation 18.1.

Eqn. 18.1

$$\text{benzene} \xrightarrow[FeBr_3]{Br_2} \text{bromobenzene (75\% yield)} + H\ddot{Br}:$$

benzene — 75% yield bromobenzene

GENERAL FEATURES OF ELECTROPHILIC AROMATIC SUBSTITUTION

To carry out an electrophilic aromatic substitution reaction, we need a suitable electrophile and a suitable aromatic substrate. Many suitable electrophiles are too reactive to store and thus cannot be obtained directly from a reagent bottle. Instead they must be prepared in situ in the reaction mixture, in the presence of the aromatic substrate. Once formed, the electrophile reacts with the substrate. A two-step mechanism is consistent with experimental observations. The two steps are:

1. The electrophile adds to the aromatic substrate to produce an intermediate carbocation known as a **benzenonium** (or arenonium) **ion.**
2. The intermediate loses a hydrogen ion (or occasionally some other cation) from the site of electrophilic attack to generate the product.

MECHANISM OF REACTION

Electrophilic Aromatic Substitution

Step 1 Addition of the electrophile to the aromatic ring

H E+ → [H E ↔ H E ↔ H E] ≡ H E

Step 2 Abstraction of a proton by a base

H E B: → E + $\overset{+}{B}$—H

Many useful electrophiles are cations, designated by E^+. Some electrophiles are neutral molecules that contain electron-deficient centers. There are many ways of producing electrophiles for reaction with benzene and its derivatives. A few examples are listed in Table 18.1.

Table 18.1 Typical Electrophiles for Aromatic Substitution Reaction

Electrophile* (E^+)	Reactants Used to Generate Electrophile	Product of Aromatic Substitution Reaction
Br^+	$Br_2 + FeBr_3$	a bromobenzene, ArBr
Cl^+	$Cl_2 + FeCl_3$	a chlorobenzene, ArCl
NO_2^+	$HNO_3 + H_2SO_4$	a nitrobenzene, $ArNO_2$
R^+	R—X + AlX_3 (Friedel-Crafts reaction) plus numerous other methods for forming carbocations	an alkylbenzene, ArR
$R—C{\equiv}\ddot{O}^+$	RCOX or ArCOX (acid halide) + AlX_3 (Friedel-Crafts acylation)	an aryl ketone, ArCOR or ArCOAr′
SO_3	SO_3/H_2SO_4	a sulfonic acid, $ArSO_3H$

* The structures of some electrophiles such as Br^+ are simplified in this table (see Section 18.5).

18.5 Bromination of Benzene: A Detailed Look

Although bromine in aqueous or carbon tetrachloride solution adds readily to the double bonds of alkenes, no such addition reaction occurs with benzene and its derivatives. Substitution of a hydrogen atom by a bromine atom occurs instead, but more vigorous conditions are required. We need to use pure (liquid) bromine (rather than a dilute solution) and a Lewis acid catalyst (e.g., $FeBr_3$) in order to cause reaction with most benzene derivatives. The reaction in Equation 18.1 summarizes the required conditions. Often metallic iron (as filings) is used instead of ferric bromide; however, this approach is really no different from the addition of ferric bromide, since bromine reacts readily with metallic iron to form ferric bromide. Ferric bromide, whether used directly or formed from metallic iron, is a Lewis acid that reacts further with bromine.

MECHANISM OF REACTION

Bromination of Benzene

Step 1 Bromine reacts with $FeBr_3$ to form a Lewis acid-base adduct:

$$:\ddot{Br}-\ddot{Br}: \quad FeBr_3 \longrightarrow :\ddot{Br}-\overset{+}{\ddot{Br}}-\overset{-}{Fe}Br_3$$

This adduct is the actual electrophile in the reaction. However, it behaves as if it were $Br^+ \; FeBr_4^-$, that is, as a source of the electrophile Br^+. For simplicity we will consider Br^+ to be the actual electrophile.

Step 2 The electron-rich benzene ring reacts with the electron-deficient electrophile, generating the benzenonium ion intermediate:

$$C_6H_6 + {}^+:\ddot{Br} \; {}^-FeBr_4 \longrightarrow C_6H_6Br^+ + {}^-FeBr_4$$

This reaction is a slow process—it is the rate-determining step of the reaction. It has a high activation energy because it involves the loss of aromaticity.

Step 3 A Lewis base such as $FeBr_4^-$ removes a proton from the benzenonium ion, resulting in reformation of the aromatic ring. This step is a low activation energy process and occurs rapidly.

$$C_6H_6Br^+ + :\ddot{Br}-\overset{-}{Fe}Br_3 \longrightarrow C_6H_5\ddot{Br}: + FeBr_3 + H-\ddot{Br}:$$

Notice that the last step of the reaction regenerates ferric bromide. (Thus there is no net consumption of ferric bromide, consistent with its catalytic role.) Step 3, the proton abstraction that results in the formation of a double bond, is a typical reaction for a carbocation (see Chapter 7, Section 7.6). In this case it occurs particularly readily since it produces an especially stable aromatic ring.

18.6 Other Electrophilic Aromatic Substitution Reactions

The mechanism presented above for the aromatic bromination reaction is mirrored in other electrophilic aromatic substitution reactions. Each reaction involves

1. Initial steps that generate the electrophile
2. Reaction of the electrophile by addition to the aromatic ring to generate a nonaromatic (but resonance-stabilized) benzenonium ion
3. Loss of a cation (usually a proton) from the benzenonium ion ring to regenerate an aromatic ring

PRODUCTION OF THE ELECTROPHILE

Nitration The introduction of a nitro group ($-NO_2$) into a molecule is known as **nitration.** We usually perform nitrations of benzene and its derivatives by heating them with a mixture of nitric and sulfuric acids. This mixture of acids generates the active electrophile $NO_2{}^+$, known as the **nitronium ion.** The formation of the nitronium ion occurs in two steps.

MECHANISM OF REACTION

Formation of the Nitronium Ion

Step 1 Protonation of nitric acid. In this reaction nitric acid acts in an unusual role, as a base. The stronger acid, sulfuric acid, protonates the nitric acid.

$$\mathrm{H{-}\ddot{O}{-}S(=O)_2{-}\ddot{O}{-}H + H{-}\ddot{O}{-}N^{+}(=O){-}O^{-} \longrightarrow H{-}\ddot{O}{-}S(=O)_2{-}\ddot{O}^{-} + H_2\overset{+}{O}{-}N^{+}(=O){-}O^{-}}$$

Step 2 Loss of water.

$$\mathrm{H_2\overset{+}{O}{-}N^{+}(=O){-}O^{-} \longrightarrow H_2\ddot{O} + O{=}N^{+}{=}O}$$

The nitration of benzene is shown in Equation 18.2.

Eqn. 18.2

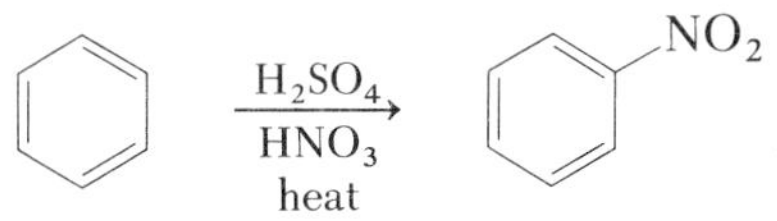

$$\text{benzene} \xrightarrow[\text{HNO}_3,\ \text{heat}]{\text{H}_2\text{SO}_4} \text{C}_6\text{H}_5\text{NO}_2$$

benzene

85% yield
nitrobenzene

PROBLEM 18.7 At times, nitric acid alone (without sulfuric acid) is effective in bringing about nitration. Suggest a mechanism for the production of the nitronium ion, starting with an acid-base reaction between two nitric acid molecules.

PROBLEM 18.8 Deduce the shape of the nitronium ion from its Lewis structure.

Alkylation The usual method for performing alkylations of benzene and its derivatives is the **Friedel-Crafts reaction.** The electrophile is produced by the reaction of an alkyl halide and a Lewis acid catalyst, usually aluminum chloride. The reaction of the two produces a Lewis acid-base complex, as shown in Figure 18.6.

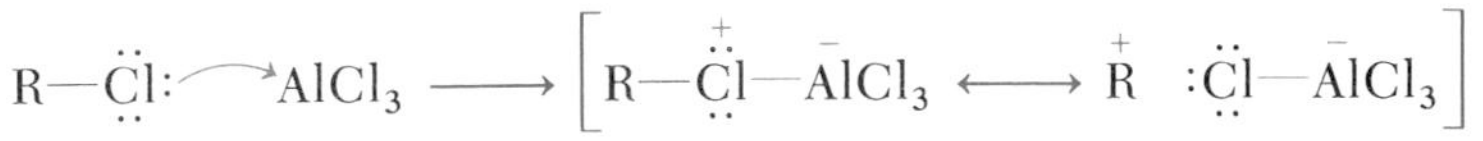

$$R-\ddot{\underset{..}{Cl}}: \curvearrowright AlCl_3 \longrightarrow \left[R-\overset{+}{\underset{..}{Cl}}-\overset{-}{A}lCl_3 \longleftrightarrow \overset{+}{R}\ \ :\ddot{\underset{..}{Cl}}-\overset{-}{A}lCl_3 \right]$$

Figure 18.6 Formation of the electrophile in Friedel-Crafts alkylations.

The Lewis acid-base adduct reacts like a carbocation, that is, as we would expect it to react if the second resonance structure best described its actual structure. However, the degree to which the Lewis acid-base adduct is an actual source of a free carbocation depends on a number of factors. Among these are the stability of R^+ and the solvent used. For example, a more polar solvent will stabilize a free carbocation better than a nonpolar solvent. Free carbocations are implicated as actual intermediates in at least some Friedel-Crafts reactions, since skeletal rearrangements are observed. In these reactions, the second resonance structure of Figure 18.6 must be much the dominant one. We saw earlier (Chapter 7) that rearrangements are common in reactions involving carbocations. Two examples of Friedel-Crafts reactions that are accompanied by rearrangement of the alkyl group are shown in Equations 18.3 and 18.4.

Eqn. 18.3

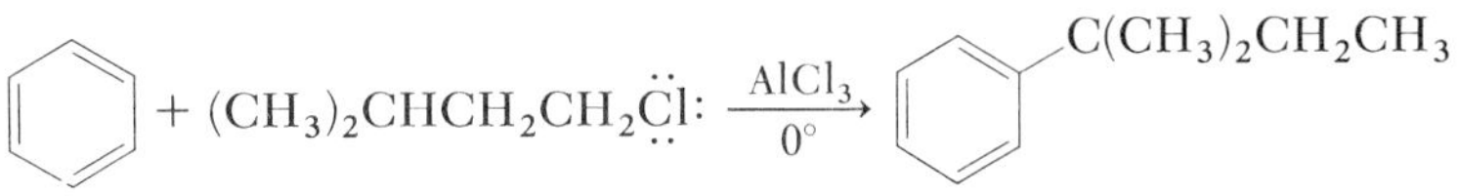

$$\text{C}_6\text{H}_6 + (\text{CH}_3)_2\text{CHCH}_2\text{CH}_2\ddot{\underset{..}{\text{Cl}}}: \xrightarrow[0^\circ]{\text{AlCl}_3} \text{C}_6\text{H}_5\text{C(CH}_3)_2\text{CH}_2\text{CH}_3$$

1-chloro-3-methylbutane

70% yield
2-methyl-2-phenylbutane

Eqn. 18.4

$$C_6H_6 + CH_3CH_2CH_2\ddot{\underset{..}{Cl}}: \xrightarrow{AlCl_3} C_6H_5CH_2CH_2CH_3 + C_6H_5CH(CH_3)_2$$

1-chloropropane; 35% 1-phenylpropane; 65% 2-phenylpropane; product distribution

In Equation 18.4 the major product arises from a rearranged carbocation intermediate, while the minor product is formed from the unrearranged carbocation.

PROBLEM 18.9 Give the structure of the carbocation leading to each of the products shown in Equations 18.3 and 18.4.

The Friedel-Crafts reaction serves as a useful means of alkylating an aromatic ring with a carbocation or carbocation equivalent prepared from an alkyl halide. There are other methods for generating carbocations (we saw several in earlier chapters), and some of these are useful for the synthesis of alkylated aromatics. Four examples are shown in Equations 18.5–18.8.

Eqn. 18.5

$$C_6H_6 \xrightarrow[HF]{PhCH_2OH} C_6H_5CH_2Ph$$

65% yield
diphenylmethane

Eqn. 18.6

$$C_6H_6 \xrightarrow[H_2SO_4]{(CH_3)_2C{=}CH_2} C_6H_5C(CH_3)_3$$

80% yield
tert-butylbenzene

Eqn. 18.7

$$C_6H_6 + C_6H_{10} \xrightarrow{H_2SO_4} C_6H_5\text{-}C_6H_{11}$$

cyclohexene; 75% yield phenylcyclohexane

Eqn. 18.8

$$C_6H_6 + H\ddot{\underset{..}{O}}CH_2CH_2CH_2CH_3 \xrightarrow{BF_3} C_6H_5CH(CH_3)CH_2CH_3$$

1-butanol; 80% yield 2-phenylbutane

The reaction in Equation 18.8 involves a carbocation formation and rearrangement.

PROBLEM 18.10 Give complete mechanisms for the reactions shown in Equations 18.5–18.8.

Each of the reactions in Equations 18.5–18.8 requires an acid catalyst (Brønsted or Lewis). However, not all acids are suitable for the reaction. For example, consider an attempt to prepare cumene by the reaction of benzene with propene in the presence of an acid HX. Protonation of the propene by HX results in the formation of an isopropyl cation. Reaction of benzene with the isopropyl cation will lead to the formation of cumene. However, the anion present, X^-, can *also* react with the isopropyl cation to form a useless side-product, as illustrated in Figure 18.7.

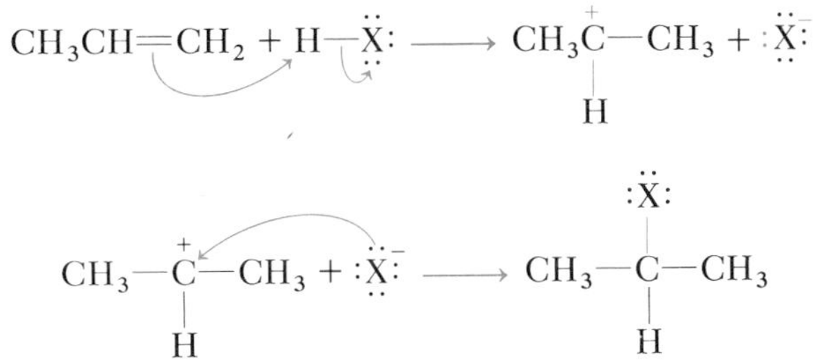

Figure 18.7 Reaction of propene with HX. Although the carbocation is required in order to achieve electrophilic aromatic substitution, it may be captured by an anion prior to reaction with the aromatic ring.

$$CH_3CH{=}CH_2 + H{-}\ddot{X}: \longrightarrow CH_3\overset{+}{C}H{-}CH_3 + :\ddot{X}:^-$$

$$CH_3{-}\overset{+}{C}H{-}CH_3 + :\ddot{X}:^- \longrightarrow CH_3{-}CH(X){-}CH_3$$

We see that if X^- is a sufficiently potent nucleophile, it competes with benzene for capture of the isopropyl cation. Thus acids whose conjugate bases are potent nucleophiles (e.g., HI, HBr, HCl) are not appropriate if the intent is to effect electrophilic aromatic substitution. However, H_2SO_4 and HF often work well since both acids have conjugate bases that are only weakly nucleophilic. Several examples of the use of these acids were shown earlier, and another example is illustrated in Equation 18.9.

Eqn. 18.9

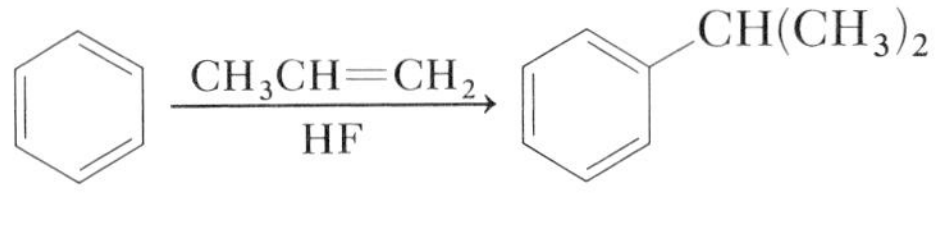

$$C_6H_6 \xrightarrow[HF]{CH_3CH=CH_2} C_6H_5CH(CH_3)_2$$

75% yield
2-phenylpropane

PROBLEM 18.11 Treatment of benzene with either 2-pentanol or 3-pentanol in the presence of the Lewis acid BF_3 gives a 2 : 1 mixture of 2-phenylpentane and 3-phenylpentane. Show a mechanism for the formation of these products and explain the 2 : 1 product distribution found in each case.

PROBLEM 18.12 Treatment of benzene with isobutyl alcohol and BF_3 gives a product that shows only two singlets in its proton NMR spectrum, one at δ 1.30 (9H) and one at δ 7.28 (5H). Give a structure for the product and show a complete mechanism for its formation.

PROBLEM 18.13 When an excess of benzene is treated with tetrachloromethane and aluminum chloride, a compound of formula $C_{19}H_{15}Cl$ is obtained. Give a structure for the product and show a complete mechanism for its formation.

Acylation **Acylation** refers to the introduction of an **acyl group** into a compound, as illustrated in Figure 18.8.

Figure 18.8 Acyl groups and acylation.

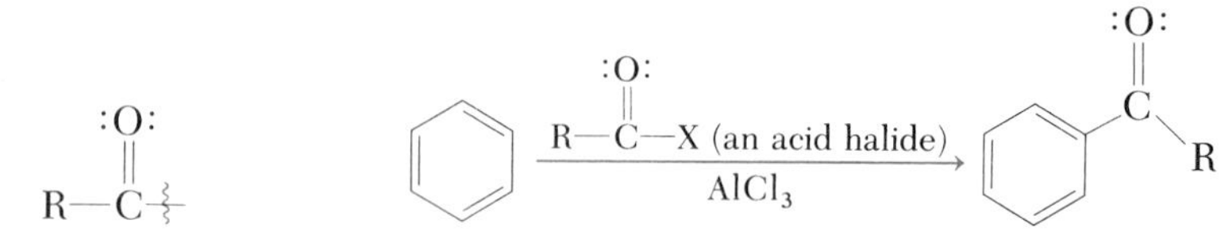

$$\mathrm{R{-}\overset{\overset{\large :O:}{\|}}{C}{-}} \quad \text{an acyl group}$$

$$\text{benzene} \xrightarrow[\mathrm{AlCl_3}]{\mathrm{R{-}\overset{\overset{:O:}{\|}}{C}{-}X}\ \text{(an acid halide)}} \mathrm{C_6H_5{-}\overset{\overset{:O:}{\|}}{C}{-}R}$$

overall acylation of benzene

The acylation of benzene and its derivatives is effected by treating them with an active acyl reagent such as an **acid halide** and a Lewis acid catalyst, usually aluminum chloride. The reaction of the acyl halide with the Lewis acid generates the highly electrophilic **acylium ion.**

MECHANISM OF REACTION

Formation of the Acylium Ion

Step 1 Formation of a complex between the acyl chloride and the aluminum trichloride

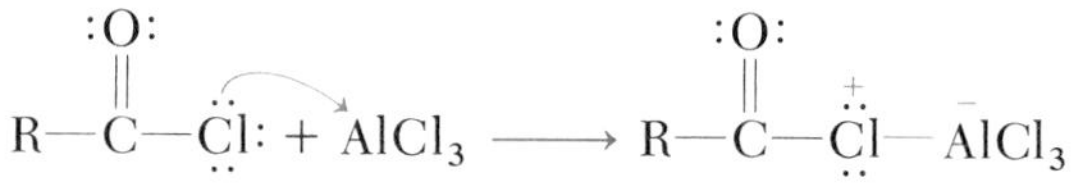

$$\mathrm{R{-}\overset{\overset{:O:}{\|}}{C}{-}\ddot{\underset{..}{Cl}}{:} + AlCl_3 \longrightarrow R{-}\overset{\overset{:O:}{\|}}{C}{-}\overset{+}{\underset{..}{\ddot{Cl}}}{-}\overset{-}{AlCl_3}}$$

Step 2 Dissociation of the complex. In the second resonance structure of the acylium ion (in which the positive charge is located on oxygen) there are complete octets of electrons on both carbon and oxygen. This resonance structure is particularly stable, and it is consistent with the greater stability of an acylium ion compared with an ordinary carbocation.

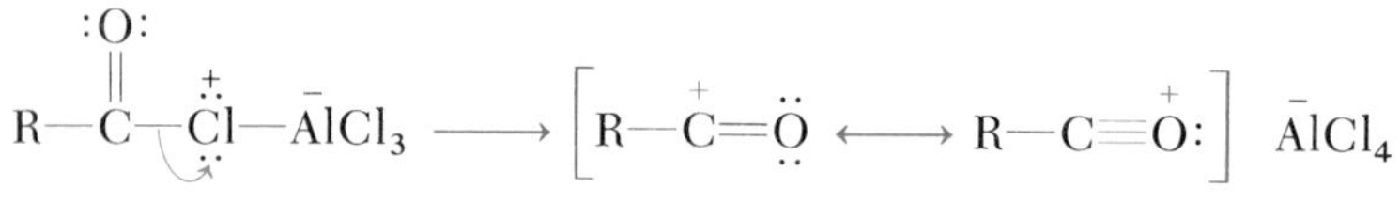

$$\mathrm{R{-}\overset{\overset{:O:}{\|}}{C}{-}\overset{+}{\underset{..}{\ddot{Cl}}}{-}\overset{-}{AlCl_3}} \longrightarrow \left[\mathrm{R{-}\overset{+}{C}{=}\underset{..}{\ddot{O}} \longleftrightarrow R{-}C{\equiv}\overset{+}{O}{:}}\right] \ \mathrm{\overset{-}{AlCl_4}}$$

Rearrangements of the type found in the Friedel-Crafts alkylation reaction do not occur in acylation reactions. An acylium ion is *already* relatively stable; no hydride or alkide shift can lead to a more stable ion.

Acid anhydrides such as acetic anhydride (**18.1**) also react with aluminum halides to give acylium ions. Acid anhydrides therefore constitute alternative starting reagents to acyl halides for effecting acylation of an aromatic ring.

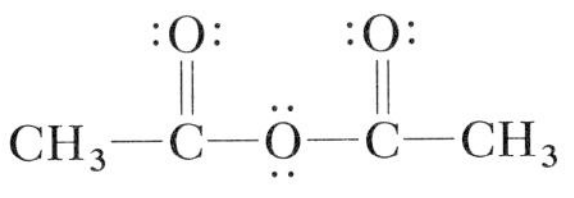

$$CH_3-\overset{\overset{:O:}{||}}{C}-\ddot{\underset{..}{O}}-\overset{\overset{:O:}{||}}{C}-CH_3$$

acetic anhydride

18.1

In the reaction of an acylium ion with benzene and its derivatives, the acylium ion substitutes for one of the hydrogen atoms of the aromatic ring. Three examples of this type of reaction, known as **Friedel-Crafts acylation,** are shown in Equations 18.10–18.12.

Eqn. 18.10

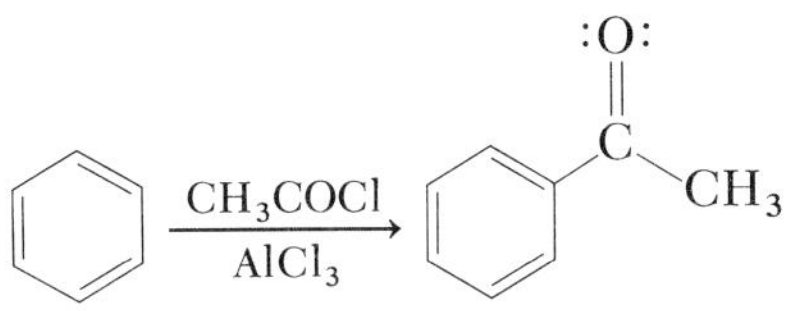

$$C_6H_6 \xrightarrow[AlCl_3]{CH_3COCl} C_6H_5-\overset{\overset{:O:}{||}}{C}-CH_3$$

95% yield
acetophenone

Eqn. 18.11

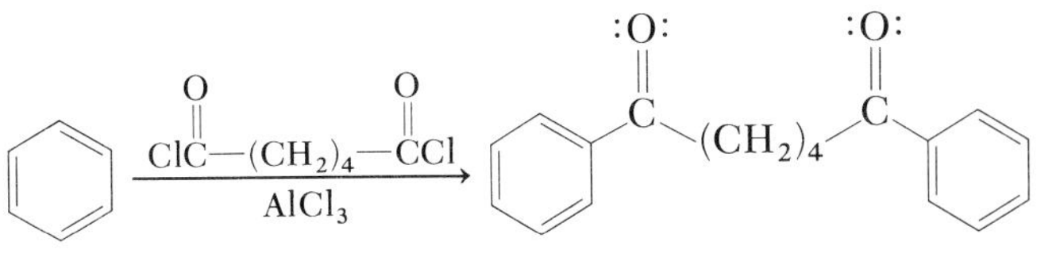

$$C_6H_6 \xrightarrow[AlCl_3]{Cl\overset{O}{\overset{||}{C}}-(CH_2)_4-\overset{O}{\overset{||}{C}}Cl} C_6H_5-\overset{\overset{:O:}{||}}{C}-(CH_2)_4-\overset{\overset{:O:}{||}}{C}-C_6H_5$$

80% yield
1,6-diphenyl-1,6-hexanedione

Eqn. 18.12

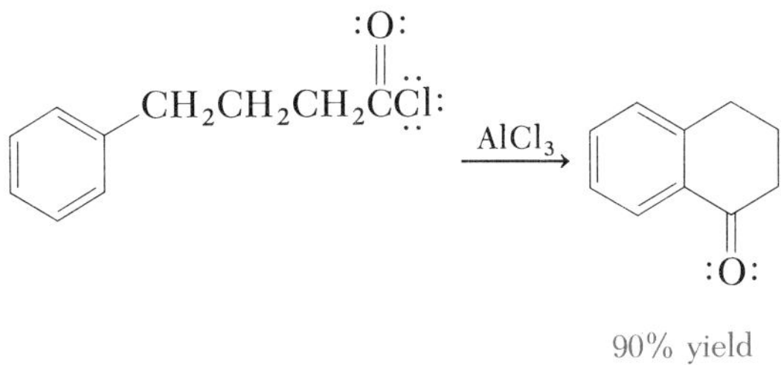

$$C_6H_5-CH_2CH_2CH_2\overset{\overset{:O:}{||}}{C}\ddot{\underset{..}{Cl}}: \xrightarrow{AlCl_3} \alpha\text{-tetralone}$$

4-phenylbutanoyl chloride

90% yield
α-tetralone

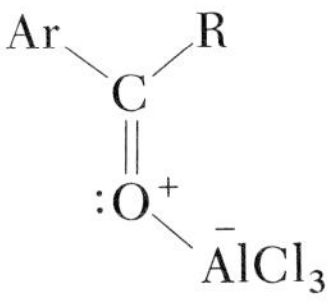

$$Ar-\overset{R}{C}=\overset{+}{O}:-\overset{-}{A}lCl_3$$

Figure 18.9 Association of a ketone with aluminum chloride. This association prevents the aluminum chloride from playing a catalytic role in Friedel-Crafts acylation reactions.

In the reaction shown in Equation 18.11, a diacid halide reacts with two equivalents of benzene. In the reaction shown in Equation 18.12, the reaction is intramolecular. The acid chloride unit is located on a side chain of the aromatic ring. Intramolecular reaction leads to formation of a new ring.

For these reactions it is necessary to use a full equivalent amount of aluminum chloride rather than a catalytic amount. The ketone product that forms associates with aluminum chloride, as shown in Figure 18.9, preventing it from serving as a catalyst for continuing reaction.

PROBLEM 18.14 Write a complete mechanism for the reaction of benzene with acetic anhydride in the presence of aluminum chloride to give a product of formula C_7H_8O.

Steps to Solving the Problem

Solution to Problem 18.14

1. Decide on the initial reaction that generates the active electrophile. Here, aluminum chloride and the acetic anhydride react to form a Lewis acid-base complex which then dissociates into an acylium ion (the electrophile) and an accompanying anion, as shown below.

$$H_3C\overset{O}{\overset{\|}{C}}-\ddot{O}-\overset{O}{\overset{\|}{C}}CH_3 + AlCl_3 \longrightarrow H_3C\overset{O}{\overset{\|}{C}}-\overset{+}{O}(^{-}AlCl_3)-\overset{O}{\overset{\|}{C}}CH_3 \longrightarrow CH_3\overset{+}{C}=\ddot{O} + Cl_3\overset{-}{Al}\ddot{O}\overset{O}{\overset{\|}{C}}CH_3$$

2. We must now decide how the electrophile interacts with the aromatic ring. Reaction occurs to produce an intermediate benzenonium ion, as shown below.

$$C_6H_6 + CH_3\overset{+}{C}=\ddot{O} \longrightarrow \text{benzenonium ion (H, } C(=O)-CH_3\text{)}^{+}$$

3. How is product generated? Rearomatization occurs by loss of a proton from the benzenonium ion. (The aluminum chloride will react with the ketone product. Workup of the reaction mixture with water is required to isolate the target ketone.)

$$\text{benzenonium ion} + CH_3\overset{O}{\overset{\|}{C}}\ddot{O}\overset{-}{Al}Cl_3 \longrightarrow C_6H_5C(=O)CH_3 + CH_3COOH + AlCl_3$$

PROBLEM 18.15 Give a complete mechanism for the formation of the product (α-tetralone) in Equation 18.12.

PROBLEM 18.16 Suggest a synthesis of benzophenone via the Friedel-Crafts acylation of benzene.

PROBLEM 18.17 Give the structures of the products obtained by treating benzene with each of the following cyclic anhydrides in the presence of aluminum chloride, and show the mechanism of each reaction.

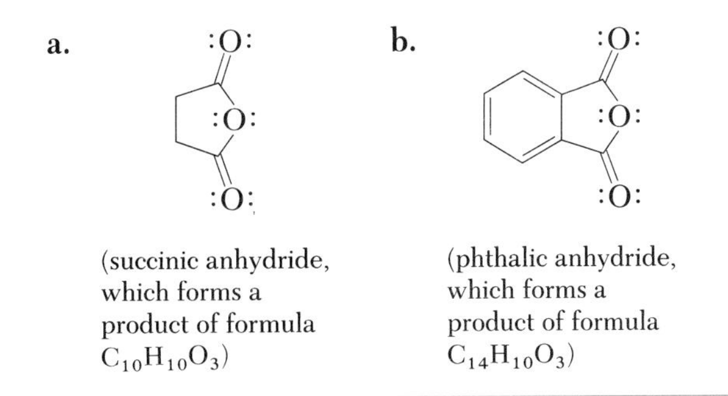

a. (succinic anhydride, which forms a product of formula $C_{10}H_{10}O_3$)

b. (phthalic anhydride, which forms a product of formula $C_{14}H_{10}O_3$)

Sulfonation The structure of sulfur trioxide corresponds to the average of several resonance-contributing forms which are shown in Figure 18.10.

Figure 18.10 Resonance structures for sulfur trioxide. More than eight electrons can be associated with sulfur in some of these resonance structures since sulfur, with available *d* orbitals, can accommodate more than an octet of valence level electrons.

In four of the resonance structures for sulfur trioxide there is an electron deficiency at sulfur. This deficiency is in accord with the ability of sulfur trioxide to function as an electrophile in electrophilic aromatic substitution reactions. Sulfonations are performed with sulfur trioxide dissolved in sulfuric acid (this mixture is known as *fuming sulfuric acid*). An example is shown in Equation 18.13.

Eqn. 18.13

CH_3 $\xrightarrow[H_2SO_4]{SO_3}$ CH_3, SO_3H

100% yield
p-toluenesulfonic acid

18.7 Energetics of Electrophilic Aromatic Substitution: Reaction Progress Diagrams

As we have seen, electrophilic aromatic substitution reactions proceed by a mechanism consisting of two important steps:

1. Attachment of the electrophile to the aromatic ring, with a loss of aromaticity and formation of an intermediate benzenonium ion
2. Rearomatization by loss of a hydrogen ion to some base

The first of these steps is generally much slower than the second since the loss of aromaticity is a relatively high energy process compared to rearomatization. Moreover, the loss of a hydrogen ion for rearomatization occurs faster than reversal of the first step (losing the electrophile). These steps are illustrated in the reaction progress diagram in Figure 18.11.

The reaction progress diagram in Figure 18.11 holds for *most* electrophilic aromatic substitution reactions. An exception is sulfonation, in which the loss of E^+ and H^+ from the intermediate benzenonium ion occur at similar rates. We will say more about the sulfonation reaction in Section 18.12.

Figure 18.11 Reaction progress diagram for electrophilic aromatic substitution.

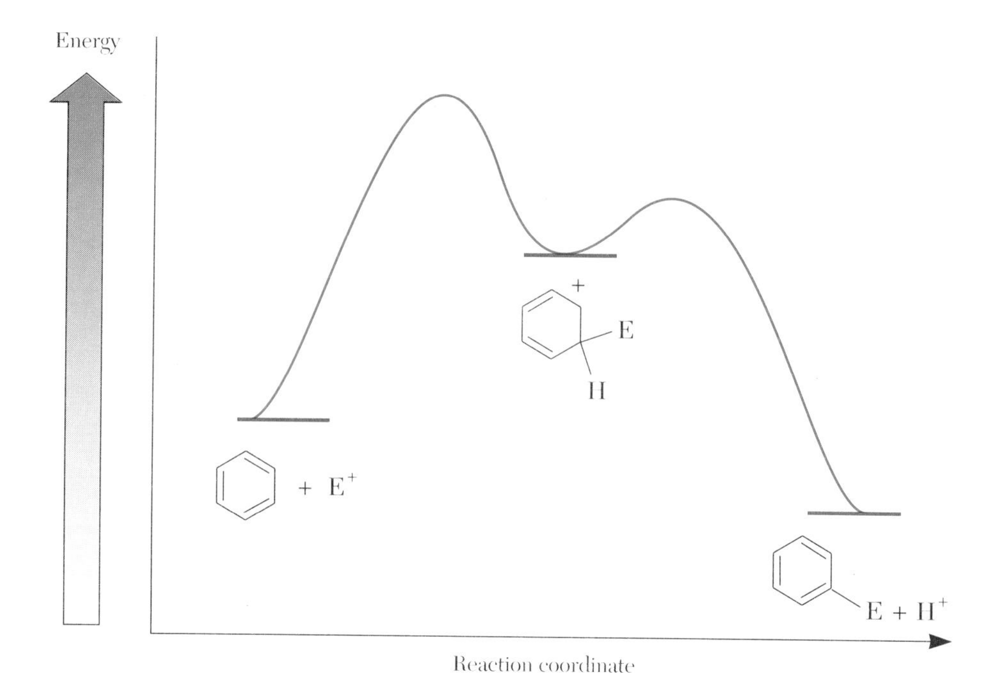

PROBLEM 18.18 Modify the reaction progress diagram in Figure 18.10 to represent the sulfonation of benzene.

18.8 The Effect of Existing Substituents on the Rates and Orientation of Electrophilic Aromatic Substitution Reactions

NO_2 CH_3

< <

slowest fastest

relative rates of reaction with electrophiles

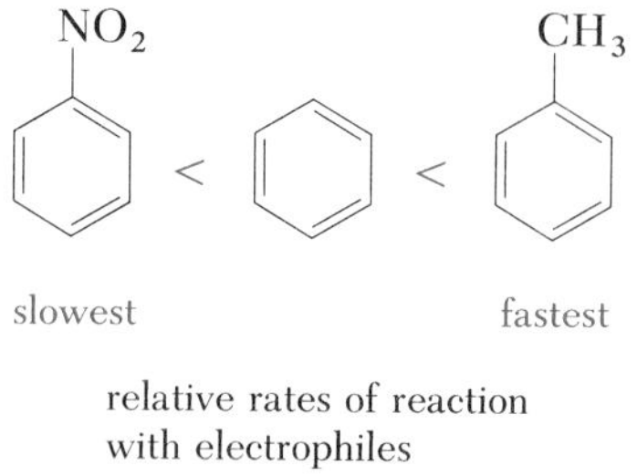

Figure 18.12 Relative rates of reaction of aromatics with electrophiles. A methyl group on the aromatic ring causes reaction to proceed more rapidly than for benzene. On the other hand, a nitro group causes the reaction to proceed more slowly.

Substituents already present on an aromatic ring profoundly influence electrophilic aromatic substitution reactions. There are two particularly important ways in which these substituents affect the reaction. First, substituents influence the *rate* at which the substitution reaction occurs. Second, they affect the *position* (or positions) of the aromatic ring at which the substitution reaction occurs.

Let's consider some specific examples. Under the same experimental conditions, toluene reacts with electrophiles more rapidly than does benzene, but nitrobenzene reacts more slowly than does benzene (see Figure 18.12). As a result of these observations, we classify the methyl group as an *activating group* (relative to hydrogen) toward electrophilic aromatic substitution and the nitro group as a *deactivating group* for this type of reaction.

There is another major difference between the reactions of toluene and nitrobenzene with electrophiles. We can observe it by comparing the products of nitration of each material. Nitration of toluene produces mainly *o*-nitrotoluene and *p*-nitrotoluene, with only small amounts of *m*-nitrotoluene. On the other hand, nitration of nitrobenzene leads principally to *m*-dinitrobenzene. We say that the methyl group is an ***ortho,para*-directing group** while the nitro group is a ***meta*-directing group.** *All* substituents can be classified as *o,p*-directing or *m*-directing. In Table 18.2 we classify commonly encountered substituents according to their rate effect and directing effect. When using the data in Table 18.2 to deduce the effect of a substituent, remember that the effect pertains to the substituent *already present* on the ring rather than to the incoming group.

Table 18.2 Substituent Effects on Electophilic Aromatic Substitution

o,p-Directing Groups	*m*-Directing Groups
Strongly activating	*Strongly Deactivating*
$—\ddot{N}H_2$, $—\ddot{N}HR$, $—\ddot{N}R_2$	$—NO_2$, $—CF_3$, —COOH
$—\ddot{O}H$, $—\ddot{O}R$	—COOR, —C(O)R
Weakly Activating	$—SO_3H$, —CN:
—R, —Ph	
Weakly Deactivating	
$—\ddot{F}:$, $—\ddot{Cl}:$, $—\ddot{Br}:$, $—\ddot{I}:$	

Comparison of the activating/deactivating influences of substituents with their *o,m,p*-directing influences reveals that all *m* directors are also deactivating. Conversely, *most* (but not all) *o,p* directors are activating; the important exception is the halogens, which are *o,p* directors but are weakly deactivating.

These effects result from the electronic nature of the substituents. It is helpful to divide their electronic effects into two classes, **inductive effects** and **resonance effects.** Inductive effects are associated with the electronegativity of the atom or atoms present in the substituent and are generally transmitted through the σ-bonding framework of the molecule. Resonance effects are transmitted through the π-bonding system of the molecule.

Let's compare these two effects for a chlorine atom substituent on a benzene ring. Chlorine is one of the most electronegative elements and thus has a powerful inductive electron-withdrawing effect. The electronegativity of chlorine causes a polarization of nearby bonds, attracting electron density toward the chlorine atom. Thus, in chlorobenzene the chlorine atom causes electron density to be removed from the benzene ring. This inductive effect renders chlorobenzene less reactive toward electrophiles than benzene. The aromatic ring in benzene is electron rich compared to that of chlorobenzene and is more susceptible to attack by an electrophile. Electrophiles seek an electron-rich site, so any factor that diminishes the electron density of the aromatic ring reduces its reactivity toward electrophiles (see Figure 18.13).

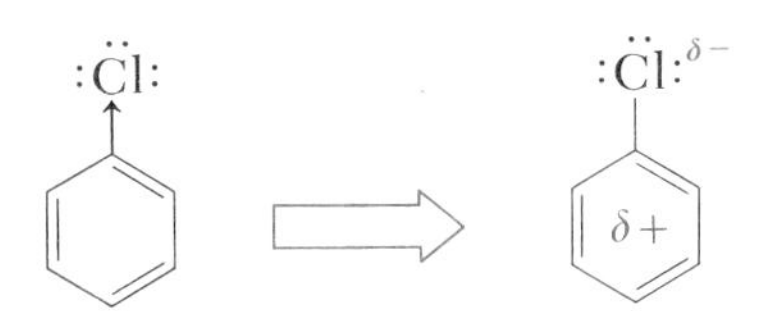

because of its high electronegativity, chlorine siphons electron density away from the benzene ring

as a result, the benzene ring becomes somewhat deficient of electron density

Figure 18.13 Inductive effect of a chlorine atom substituent on a benzene ring.

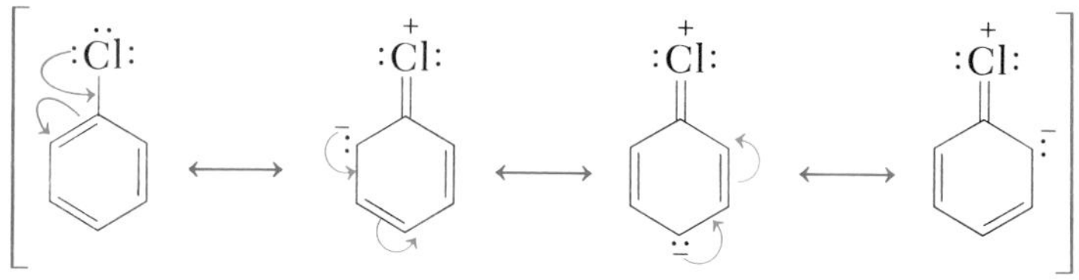

Figure 18.14 Resonance effect of a chlorine atom substituent on a benzene ring. Three of the resonance structures show a positively charged chlorine and a negatively charged benzene ring. The resonance effect tends to make the ring electron rich and thus operates in a direction opposite to the inductive effect. The inductive effect is slightly stronger (although this is not predictable on any simple basis), so the net effect of the chlorine is one of electron withdrawl and deactivation. Notice that the negative charge in each of the three charge-separated resonance structures is located only at the positions *ortho* and *para* to the chlorine substituent. These are the positions attacked by electrophiles.

The electronegativity of chlorine accounts for the observed deactivating effect of a chlorine atom on an aromatic ring. However, the ability of a chlorine atom to exert an electron-donating effect through π electron resonance partly offsets the inductive deactivating effect. For this substituent the resonance effect is in the opposite direction from the inductive effect as we can see by drawing resonance structures for chlorobenzene. These resonance structures show electron donation specifically to the *ortho* and *para* positions of the ring (see Figure 18.14).

While the inductive effect of a halogen atom outweighs its resonance effect, the reverse is true for many other substituents. For example, a hydroxyl group is overall an activating group for electrophilic aromatic substitution. Its electron-donating resonance effect is stronger than the electron-withdrawing inductive effect associated with the electronegative oxygen atom. Similarly, alkoxy groups and amino groups exert an electron-donating resonance effect that is stronger than the electron-withdrawing effect associated with the electronegative oxygen or nitrogen.

In exploring the resonance effect of a substituent on the ring position at which electrophilic aromatic substitution occurs, we must look at the intermediate arenonium ion. Consider chlorobenzene undergoing such a reaction with a generalized electrophile E^+. If the initial addition occurs at a position *ortho* or *para* relative to the chlorine substituent, we can draw resonance structures with a formal positive charge on *chlorine* as well as on the ring carbons. That is, chlorine can donate electron density to the ring. Considered from another point of view, we can say that a chlorine atom stabilizes the positive charge by delocalizing it away from the ring, over a larger region of

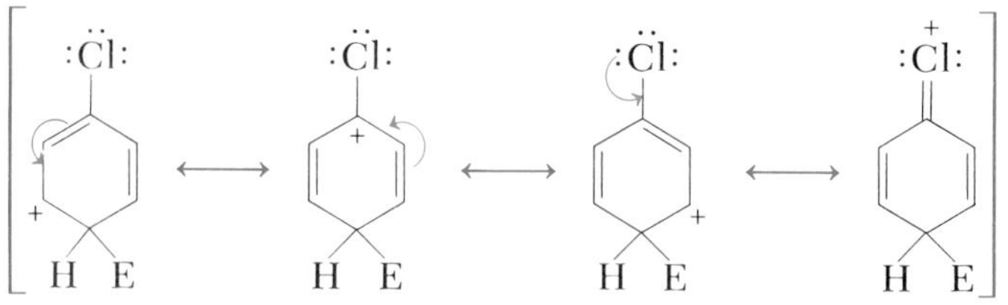

Figure 18.15 Resonance structures for the arenonium ion produced by *ortho* and *para* attack on chlorobenzene. In each case, the final resonance structure is particularly significant because all atoms have a complete noble gas electronic configuration.

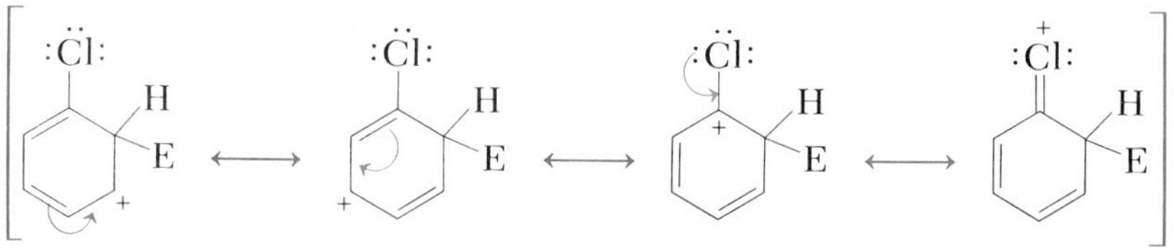

ortho attack

para attack

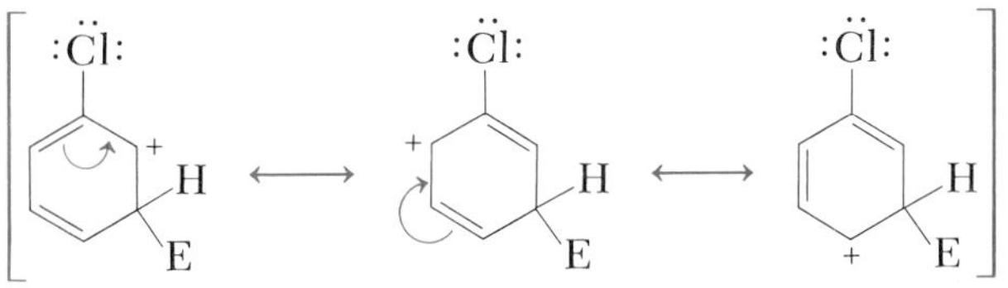

Figure 18.16 Resonance structures for the arenonium ion produced by *meta* attack on chlorobenzene. Only resonance structures in which the positive charge resides on the ring can be drawn. The charge cannot be delocalized off the ring onto the chlorine atom.

the molecule. The resonance structures that involve a positive charge on the chlorine atom are particularly significant since *each atom of the arenonium ion (other than hydrogen) bears a full octet of valence electrons.* These structures are shown in Figure 18.15.

If we consider attack of the electrophile at the *meta* position relative to chlorine, we find that no resonance structure with positive charge on chlorine is possible. The resonance structures that can be drawn are shown in Figure 18.16.

The relative *rates* of *ortho, para,* and *meta* substitution determine the ratio of *ortho-*, *para-*, and *meta-*substituted products. These rates depend on the relative stabilities of the corresponding transition states and therefore (by the Hammond postulate) on the relative stabilities of the corresponding arenonium ion intermediates. The observed preference for *ortho* and *para* substitution when chlorobenzene undergoes electrophilic attack thus correlates with the greater stability of the *ortho-* and *para-*substituted arenonium ions. This greater stability is correctly predicted by comparing resonance structures for the differently substituted arenonium ions, as shown in Figures 18.15 and 18.16.

In Figure 18.17, the competing *para* and *meta* substitution reactions are compared in a reaction progress diagram.

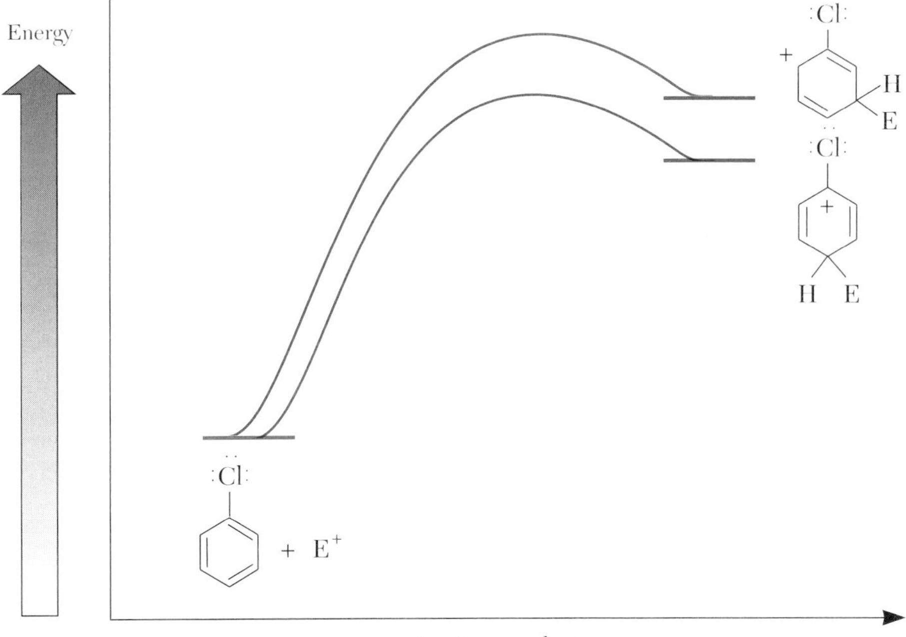

Figure 18.17 Reaction progress diagram for competing processes in electrophilic aromatic substitution of chlorobenzene. The *meta* and *para* positions compete for substitution. The arenonium ion resulting from *para* substitution is lower in energy (more stabilized) than the ion resulting from *meta* substitution. Applying the Hammond postulate, we expect (and find) that the more stable arenonium ion forms more rapidly.

COMPOUND CAPSULE

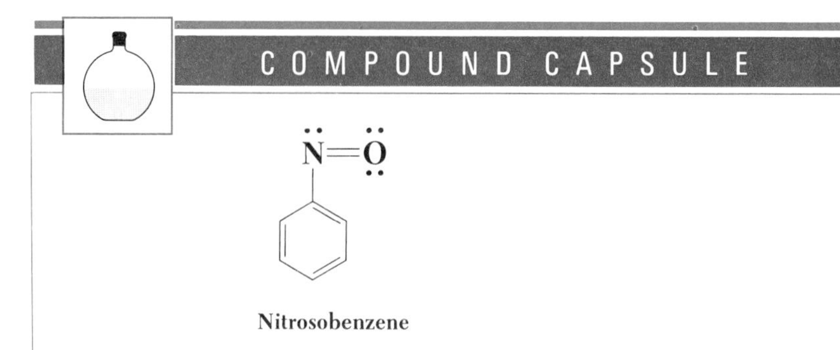

Nitrosobenzene

Nitrosobenzene, when pure, is a colorless solid. However, it undergoes a dramatic color change when melted or dissolved in a solvent. When we melt the solid, we get a green liquid, and when we dissolve it in a solvent we get a green solution. Green is not a very common color in organic chemistry, so the color changes are quite unusual and spectacular. On evaporating the solvent from a solution of nitrosobenzene or on cooling melted nitrosobenzene, we get back the original colorless solid.

The explanation for these effects is that in the *solid* state nitrosobenzene exists as a *dimer*, $(PhNO)_2$, which is colorless. Dissolving the substance in a solvent or melting it produces the monomer, PhNO, which is green.

It is important to note that any substituent with an unshared electron pair on the atom attached directly to the aromatic ring can exert an electron-donating resonance effect. All such substituents stabilize the arenonium ion intermediates for *ortho* and *para* substitution relative to that for *meta* substitution and therefore lower the activation energy for their formation (Hammond postulate). All such substituents are therefore *ortho*- and *para*-directing.

PROBLEM 18.19 Consider electrophilic aromatic substitution occurring on each of the compounds listed below. Do you expect these compounds to undergo reaction with electrophiles principally at the *ortho* and *para* positions or at the *meta* position? Explain your answer.

a. nitrosobenzene [Ph—N̈=Ö̤]

b. phenylboronic acid [Ph—B(Ö̤H)$_2$]

PROBLEM 18.20 Consider the *ortho* bromination of chlorobenzene. Draw a resonance structure for the intermediate arenonium ion such that all atoms (except hydrogen) have a complete octet of valence electrons.

We will now consider further aspects of the role of substitutions in electrophilic aromatic substitution.

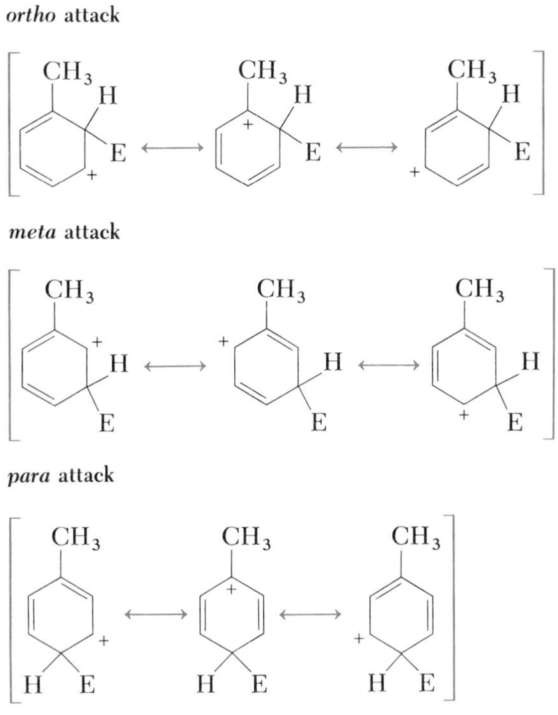

Figure 18.18 Resonance structures for the benzenonium ion produced by *ortho*, *meta*, and *para* attack of E^+ on toluene.

ortho attack

meta attack

para attack

ALKYL SUBSTITUENTS

Alkyl substituents are slightly activating toward electrophilic aromatic substitution. Furthermore, they are *ortho,para* directors. We can use resonance structures to account for this regioselectivity. Consider, for example, electrophilic aromatic substitution on toluene with the generalized electrophile E^+. Resonance structures for the intermediate arenonium ions resulting from attack at the *ortho, meta,* and *para* positions are shown in Figure 18.18.

Only if *ortho* or *para* attack occurs is it possible to have a resonance structure in which the positive charge is delocalized to the carbon atom bearing the methyl substituent, and only then does the arenonium ion have some 3° carbocation character. Thus, the arenonium ion produced by *ortho* or *para* attack is more stable (and more easily produced) than the arenonium ion produced by *meta* attack.

meta-DIRECTING SUBSTITUENTS

Substituents that have no electron-donating ability through inductive, resonance, or hyperconjugative effects are *meta*-directing and deactivating toward electrophilic aromatic substitution. The more commonly encountered groups of this type were summarized in Table 18.2.

The reason for the *meta*-directing influence of such substituents becomes clear if we examine the resonance structures for the intermediate arenonium ions arising from *ortho*, *meta*, and *para* attack. Consider, for example, the bromination of nitrobenzene, as shown in Figure 18.19.

Figure 18.19 Resonance structures for the possible arenonium ions in the bromination of nitrobenzene.

***ortho* bromination**

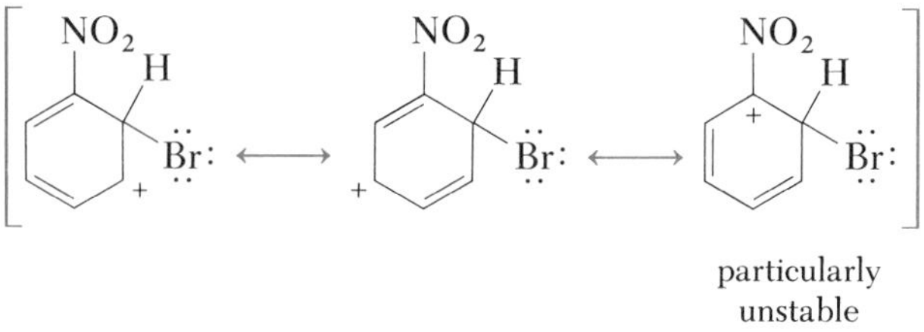

***meta* bromination**

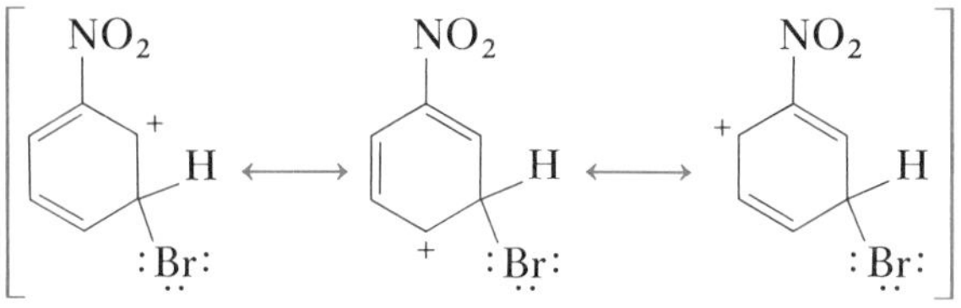

***para* bromination**

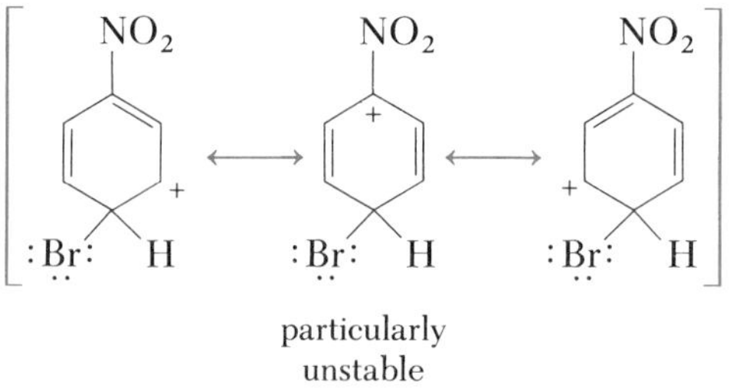

For *ortho* or *para* attack we can draw resonance structures for the intermediate ion in which the positive charge is located adjacent to the electron-withdrawing nitro group. However, with attack at the *meta* position, *no* resonance structure has positive charge delocalized to the carbon atom bearing the nitro group. We anticipate that the *meta*-substituted ion will be more stable (and more easily produced) than the *ortho*- and *para*-substituted ions, and our prediction agrees with the observed (experimental) result.

Remember that the nitro group, unlike the amino group, has *no* unshared valence electron pair on nitrogen. The structures of these two groups are shown in Figure 18.20.

Figure 18.20 Structures of nitro and amino groups. An amino group (but not a nitro group) has an unshared pair of valence electrons on nitrogen. The amino group, like other groups that have an unshared valence electron pair on an atom bonded to the benzene ring, is *ortho*, *para*-directing.

nitro group

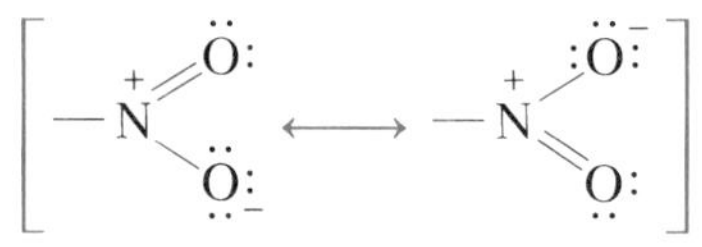

no unshared electron pair on nitrogen

amino group

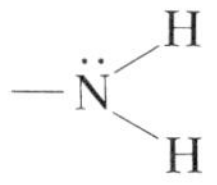

unshared electron pair on nitrogen

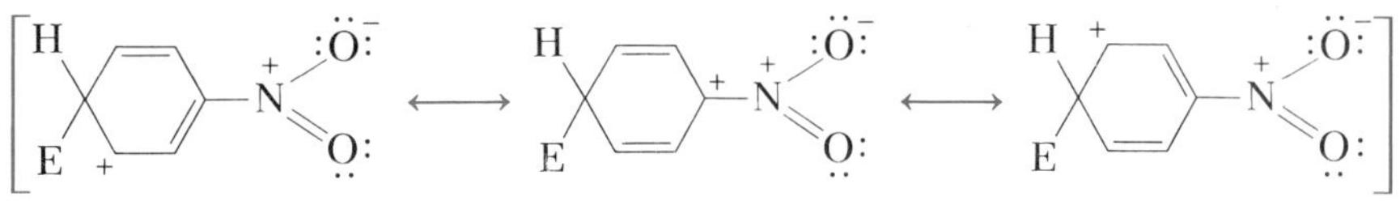

Figure 18.21 Resonance-contributing structures for the arenonium ion formed by *para* attack of an electrophile on nitrobenzene.

H E + N O O ⟷ H E N O O ⟷ H E N O O

very unstable, adjacent positive charges

The nitro group cannot exert an electron-donating resonance effect like that exerted by the amino group. The positive charge of the arenonium ion cannot be delocalized off the ring by a nitro group, and furthermore, one of the standard resonance-contributing forms (with a charge on the ring) is destabilized by the adjacent positive charge of the nitro-group nitrogen, as shown in Figure 18.21.

PROBLEM 18.21 By drawing resonance structures, provide a convincing rationale for the experimental observation that the amino group, unlike a nitro group, is *ortho,para*-directing. In particular, draw structures for the intermediate arenonium ion resulting from *ortho* and *para* attack in which all atoms (except hydrogen) have complete octets of valence electrons.

18.9 The Effect of Multiple Substituents on Electrophilic Aromatic Substitution

The effects of more than one benzene ring substituent on the relative rate of electrophilic substitution reactions are cumulative. For example, xylenes (dimethylbenzenes) and cresols (methylphenols) are more reactive toward electrophiles than either toluene or phenol because each has two activating substituents on the ring. Similarly, the dinitrobenzenes are less reactive to electrophiles than is nitrobenzene because now there are two deactivating groups on the ring. With regard to orientation of reaction, the incoming electrophile reacts preferentially at the most activated (or least deactivated) position of the ring. For example, consider bromination of *p*-cresol (Figure 18.22). The major product is 2-bromo-4-methylphenol because the —OH group activates the position *ortho* to it more strongly than the $-CH_3$ group activates the position *ortho* to it.

What happens when two unlike groups are present on the ring, one activating and the other deactivating (or less activating)? *The more activating substituent exerts the greater influence on the position taken by the incoming*

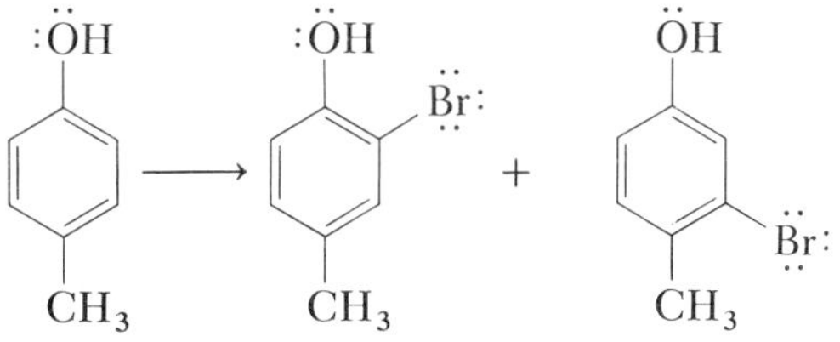

Figure 18.22 Bromination of *p*-cresol.

OH, CH_3 ⟶ OH, Br, CH_3 (major) + OH, Br, CH_3 (minor)

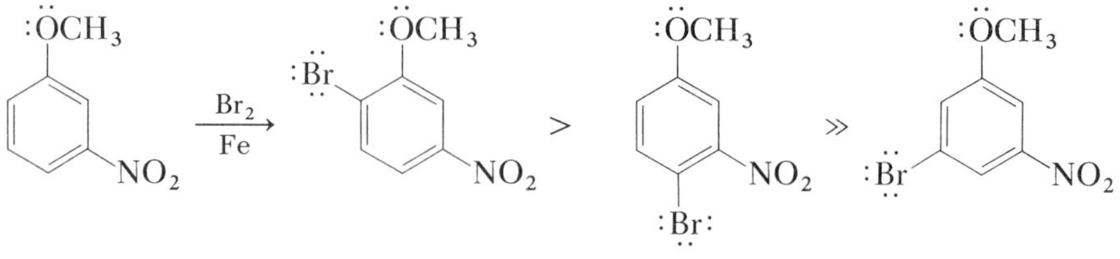

Figure 18.23 Bromination of *m*-nitroanisole. The major products arise from bromine substitution *ortho* and *para* relative to the methoxy group.

electrophile. Consider as an example the bromination of *m*-nitroanisole. Of the two substituents present, one (OCH_3) is activating and *ortho,para*-directing, while the other (NO_2) is deactivating and *meta*-directing. Accordingly, we anticipate that the methoxy substituent will have greater influence than the nitro group. The incoming substituent will occupy a position *ortho* or *para* relative to the methoxy group rather than *meta* relative to the nitro group. Experimental results are in accord with our prediction, as shown in Figure 18.23.

In our analysis thus far of electrophilic aromatic substitution reactions we have noted several important points:

1. Substituents present on an aromatic ring activate it or deactivate it toward electrophilic aromatic substitution.
2. Substituents on the aromatic ring influence the position of the ring at which further electrophilic aromatic substitution occurs.
3. Most *ortho,para*-directing substituents are activating. The halogens are exceptions in that they weakly deactivate the ring for further substitution.
4. All *meta*-directing substituents are deactivating for electrophilic aromatic substitution.
5. The activating/deactivating and directing effects are a result of the electronic influence of the substituent already present. These influences arise from the electronegativities of the atoms in the substituent group and from the ability of the substituent to provide resonance stabilization to the intermediate arenonium ion.
6. All substituents that are bonded to the aromatic ring by an atom with an unshared valence electron pair are *ortho,para*-directors. The unshared electron pair allows the substituent to exert a resonance effect that stabilizes the intermediate arenonium ion formed by attack at the *ortho* or *para* positions of the ring.

PROBLEM 18.22 Predict the major products expected from each of the following reactions:

a. monobromination of *p*-nitrophenol
b. mononitration of *p*-cresol

18.10 Manipulation of Substituent Groups

We have not yet given any preparative procedures for the introduction of several of the substituents whose activating/deactivating and directing influences we have discussed. Specific examples are the amino group ($-NH_2$) and the carboxylic acid group ($-COOH$). There are, in fact, *no* convenient general preparative methods for introducing these substituents *directly* onto a benzene

Figure 18.24 Introduction of the amino group onto an aromatic ring.

$$\text{Ar—H} \xrightarrow[\text{HNO}_3]{\text{H}_2\text{SO}_4} \text{Ar—NO}_2 \xrightarrow{\text{reduction}} \text{Ar—}\ddot{\text{N}}\text{H}_2$$

ring by electrophilic aromatic substitution reactions. Instead, we must first introduce some other substituent by an electrophilic aromatic substitution reaction and then modify it to the desired substituent via a subsequent reaction.

INTRODUCTION OF THE AMINO GROUP

The usual methodology for introducing the amino group (—NH_2) onto a benzene ring begins with the introduction of a nitro group (using nitric and sulfuric acids). Then in a subsequent reaction the nitro group is reduced to an amino group. This general approach is shown in Figure 18.24.

Common methods for converting a nitro group to an amino group include catalytic reduction using hydrogen gas and dissolving-metal reduction. In the latter process we treat the nitro compound with a metal (tin, iron, or zinc) and hydrochloric acid. Aqueous sodium hydroxide is added in the workup to liberate the amine product from its hydrochloride salt. Examples of these reactions are shown in Figures 18.14 and 18.15.

Eqn. 18.14

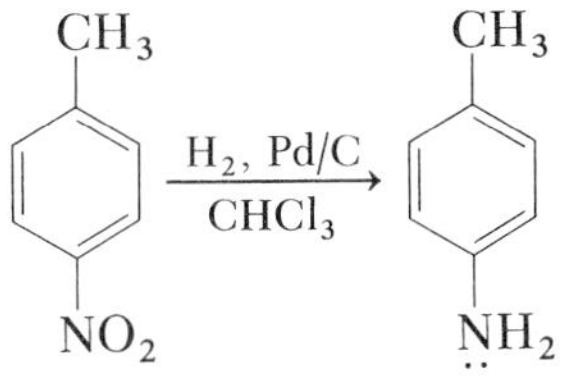

CH_3, NO_2 $\xrightarrow[\text{CHCl}_3]{\text{H}_2\text{, Pd/C}}$ CH_3, $\ddot{N}H_2$

p-nitrotoluene → 90% yield *p*-methylaniline

Eqn. 18.15

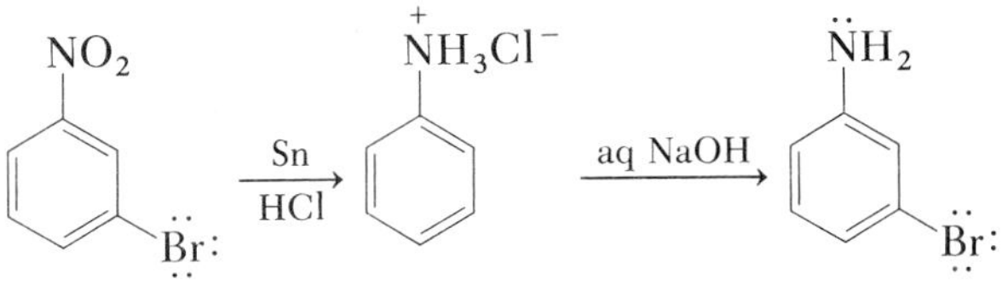

NO_2, $\ddot{Br}$: $\xrightarrow[\text{HCl}]{\text{Sn}}$ $\overset{+}{N}H_3Cl^-$ $\xrightarrow{\text{aq NaOH}}$ $\ddot{N}H_2$, $\ddot{Br}$:

m-nitrobromobenzene → 80% yield *m*-bromoaniline

In later discussions we will consider how further to change an amino group into other useful functional groups.

INTRODUCTION OF THE CARBOXYLIC ACID GROUP

The oxidation of alkylbenzenes is a useful approach for the synthesis of aryl carboxylic acids. We usually perform the oxidation using hot, aqueous potassium permanganate or a Cr(VI) reagent. Common chromium reagents for this purpose include hot, acidic dichromate solution and chromium trioxide in sulfuric acid, although many other oxidizing agents can also be used successfully. Examples of the use of permanganate and Cr(VI) reagents are shown in Equations 18.16–18.18.

Eqn. 18.16

CH_3 Cl: $\xrightarrow[\text{H}_2\text{O (aq acid workup)}]{\text{KMnO}_4}$ COOH Cl:

o-chlorotoluene — 78% yield *o*-chlorobenzoic acid

Eqn. 18.17

CH_3, O_2N, NO_2, NO_2 $\xrightarrow[\text{H}_2\text{SO}_4\text{, heat}]{\text{Na}_2\text{Cr}_2\text{O}_7}$ COOH, O_2N, NO_2, NO_2

2,4,6-trinitrotoluene — 60% yield 2,4,6-trinitrobenzoic acid

Eqn. 18.18

CH_2CH_3 $\xrightarrow[\text{heat}]{\text{CrO}_3/\text{H}_2\text{SO}_4}$ COOH

ethylbenzene — 85% yield benzoic acid

These reactions are referred to as *side-chain oxidations*. The alkyl group, regardless of length, is converted to a carboxylic acid group attached directly to the aromatic ring. The reaction mechanism is quite complex, involving intermediate radicals. For the oxidation reaction to proceed, there must be at least one benzylic carbon-hydrogen bond in the alkylbenzene, as shown in Figure 18.25. For example, *tert*-butyl benzene is resistant to side-chain oxidation since there is no benzylic hydrogen present.

We can often use the products of side-chain oxidation of an unknown benzene derivative to infer the pattern of substituents around the original benzene ring. Since a carboxyl group in the product indicates the presence of an alkyl group in the starting material, the pattern of carboxyl groups on the ring tells us the location of the original substituents. Of course this approach works only if we can identify the structures of the product carboxylic acids. Fortunately, we can usually relate the physical characteristics of these products (such as melting temperature and elemental composition) to the structures of known carboxylic acids.

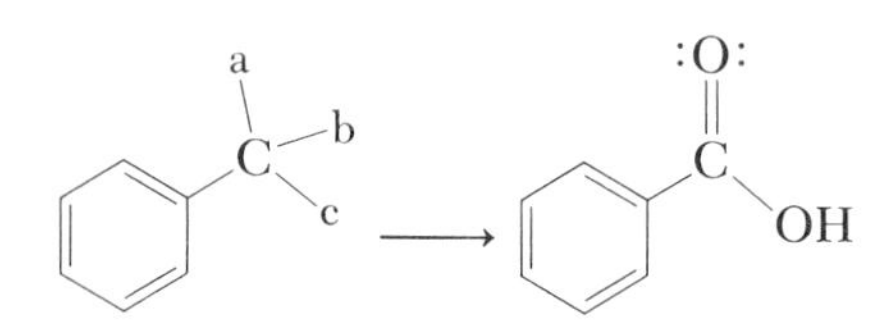

Figure 18.25 Oxidation of a side chain on a benzene ring. At least one of the substituents on the benzylic carbon (a,b,c) *must* be a hydrogen, or no oxidation will occur.

PROBLEM 18.23 A substance of formula C_9H_{12} yields phthalic acid when oxidized with hot alkaline permanganate solution followed by workup in aqueous acid. Suggest a structure for the original substance.

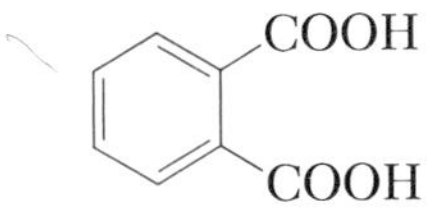

COOH

COOH

phthalic acid

Steps to Solving the Problem

Solution to Problem 18.23

1. What does the product structure tell us about the substitution pattern in the starting compound? The formation of phthalic acid shows us that in the original compound there must have been *two* alkyl groups in *ortho* positions relative to each other.
2. How many carbon and hydrogen atoms did the side chains contain in the starting compound? Subtracting C_6H_4 (phthalic acid minus the carboxyl groups) from the original molecular formula (C_9H_{12}) leaves us with C_3H_8 for the side chains.
3. How can we deduce what two side chains have an overall formulation C_3H_8? There must be one methyl group and one ethyl group. We are left with only one possible structure consistent with the formula C_9H_{12}, *o*-ethyltoluene.

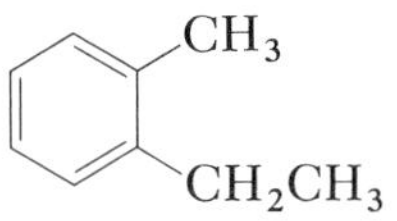

CH_3

CH_2CH_3

PROBLEM 18.24 A substance of formula C_9H_{10} yields phthalic acid upon treatment with permanganate and workup with aqueous acid. The original compound is inert to catalytic hydrogenation unless drastic conditions are used. Suggest a structure for the original compound.

18.11 Substituent Directing Effects and the Order of Synthetic Operations

Because substituent groups have different directing influences, it is important to realize that a different sequence of synthetic operations can result in the formation of different products. For example, if we first nitrate benzene and then brominate it, the major product is *m*-nitrobromobenzene. However, if we reverse the sequence of operations, that is, if we perform the bromination first, the major products are *o*-nitrobromobenzene and *p*-nitrobromobenzene, as illustrated in Figure 18.26.

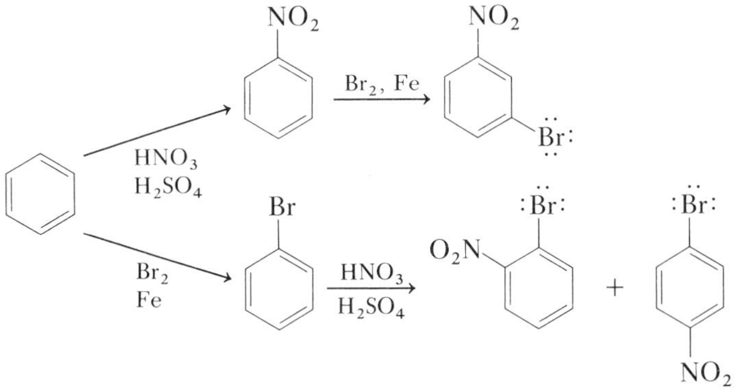

NO_2 NO_2

Br_2, Fe

:Br:

HNO_3
H_2SO_4

Br :Br: :Br:

O_2N

Br_2
Fe

HNO_3
H_2SO_4

+

NO_2

Figure 18.26 Synthesis of bromonitrobenzenes from benzene. The sequence in which the synthetic operations are performed is of paramount importance, as shown in the examples here. Reversal of the order of procedures leads to a different product.

PROBLEM 18.25 Suggest a method to synthesize each of the compounds listed below using benzene or toluene as the organic starting material. Any other nonaromatic organics and inorganics may be used. Assume that *ortho* and *para* isomers can be separated.

a. COOH / COOH (*para*-disubstituted benzene) b. NH_2 / NH_2 (*meta*-disubstituted benzene) c. CH_3, Br, H_2N (trisubstituted benzene)

18.12 Sulfonation and Desulfonation

Reversal of electrophilic aromatic substitution reactions is difficult. For example, there are no simple one-step methods for converting toluene or nitrobenzene to benzene. Sulfonation, however, is exceptional in its relative ease of reversal.

In order to reverse an electrophilic aromatic substitution reaction the normal sequence of mechanistic steps would need to be reversed. To initiate the process we would need to add H^+ to a substituted benzene to generate an intermediate arenonium ion, as illustrated in Figure 18.27. The arenonium ion must then lose E^+ to form the unsubstituted benzene. However, in most cases the energy of activation for the removal of E^+ is too high for the process to occur at any significant rate. Elimination of H^+ occurs instead, since that process has a lower activation energy. However, the arenonium ion containing the sulfonic acid functional group eliminates H^+ or SO_3 with approximately equal ease, as illustrated in the reaction progress diagram in Figure 18.28.

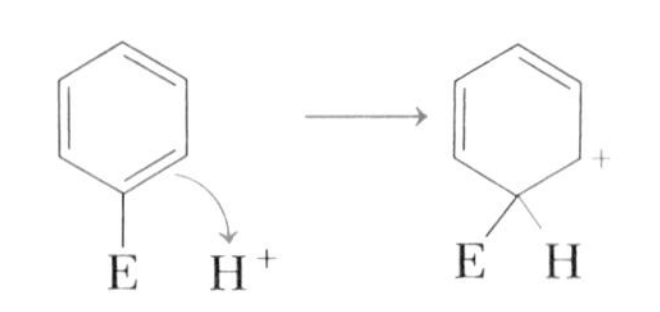

Figure 18.27 Proposed method of reversing an electrophilic aromatic substitution reaction. Acid is required so that H^+ can add to the carbon bearing the substituent to be removed.

Treatment of benzene with sulfuric acid establishes the equilibrium shown in Equation 18.19.

$$\text{benzene} + H_2SO_4 \rightleftharpoons \text{benzenesulfonic acid } (C_6H_5SO_3H) + H_2O$$

benzene benzenesulfonic acid

If we wish the reaction to proceed in the *forward* direction (as written), we use fuming sulfuric acid and continuously remove water from the reaction system by **azeotropic distillation** with benzene (a procedure for the removal of water by azeotropic distillation is discussed at the end of this section). If we wish the reaction to proceed in the *reverse* direction, we treat the sulfonic acid with dilute sulfuric acid and steam so as to drive the equilibrium to the left-hand side.

It is also possible to replace a sulfonic acid group with a hydroxyl group, producing a phenol, ArOH. This type of reaction is known as an alkali fusion reaction and is shown in Figure 18.29. The alkali fusion reaction involves heating the sulfonic acid with sodium hydroxide at ~300 °C. These conditions are quite drastic and are obviously unsuitable when the molecule contains other substituent groups that react with hydroxide ion.

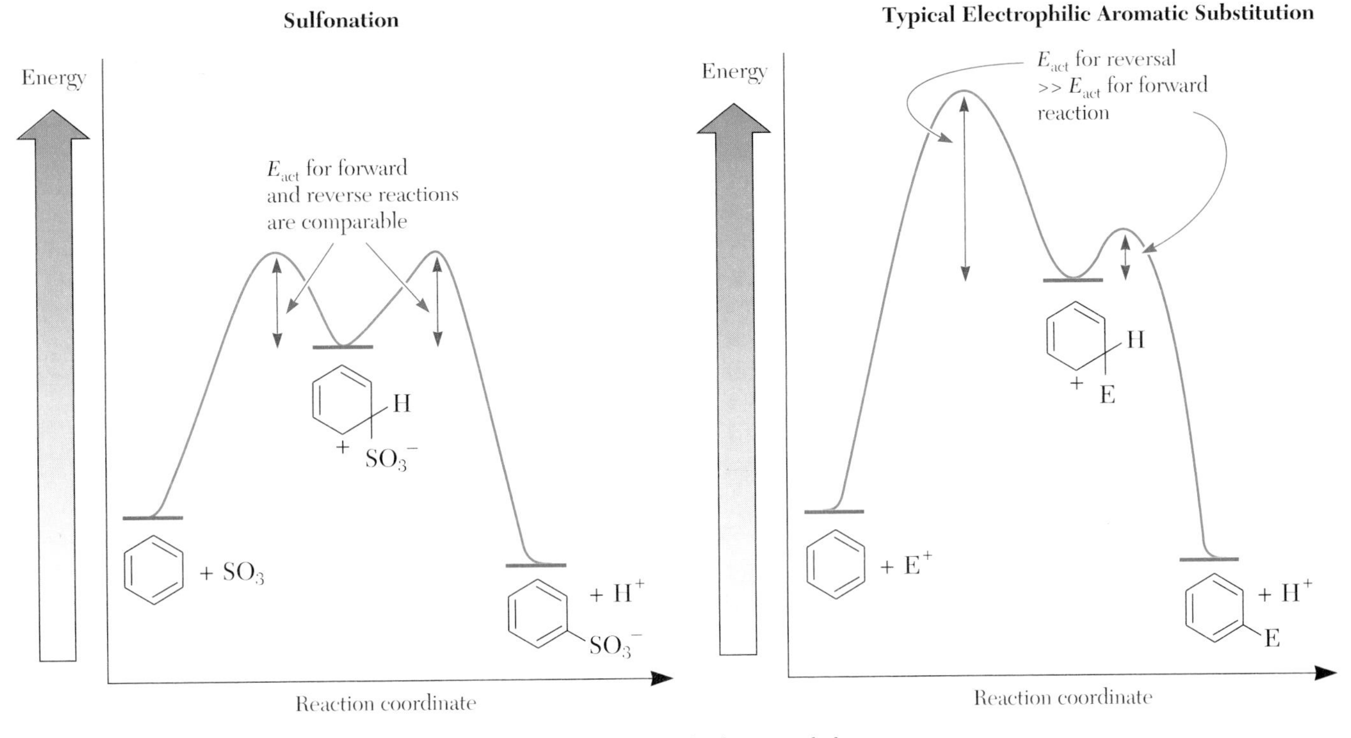

Figure 18.28 Comparison of reaction progress diagrams for sulfonation and other typical electrophilic aromatic substitution reactions.

Figure 18.29 Two methods for the removal of a sulfonic acid linkage from an aromatic ring.

CH_3 ← (H_2SO_4, H_2O / steam) — CH_3, SO_3H — ($NaOH$ / 300 °C) → (acid / workup) → CH_3, :ÖH

desulfonation

alkali fusion reaction

18.13 Some Limitations in the Syntheses of Benzene Derivatives

When planning syntheses of benzene derivatives, we must keep in mind a number of important limitations and caveats:

1. The order of operations in a multistep synthesis is crucial. We have already looked at one example. Bromination of benzene followed by nitration gives mainly *ortho*- and *para*-substituted products. The reverse order, nitration followed by bromination, gives mainly *meta* product.
2. Some groups are so strongly deactivating that certain kinds of electrophilic aromatic substitution reactions do not occur. In particular, Friedel-Crafts alkylations do not occur on benzene derivatives that are more deactivated than halobenzenes. For this reason nitrobenzene proves to be a useful solvent for many Friedel-Crafts reactions on other aromatic compounds. The nitro group so deactivates the ring that alkylation does not occur. Nitrobenzene also has a high boiling temperature, allowing the reaction to be performed at relatively high temperatures, a necessity for some Friedel-Crafts reactions.

SPECIAL TOPIC

Removal Of Water By Azeotropic Distillation

There are many reactions that proceed in low yield because of an unfavorable equilibrium. The formation of aromatic sulfonic acids is one example of this type of reaction. When faced with an unfavorable equilibrium in preparing a compound, we have several methods to improve matters, all based on Le Chatelier's principle.

We can attempt to use an excess of one of the starting materials, or we can constantly remove one of the products as it is formed, or we can do both. For reactions that form water as a by-product, we can cause the equilibrium to shift toward the product side (and thereby improve its yield) by constantly removing the water as it is formed. Water can be removed by azeotropic distillation using a Dean-Stark water separator, as illustrated in the diagram shown below.

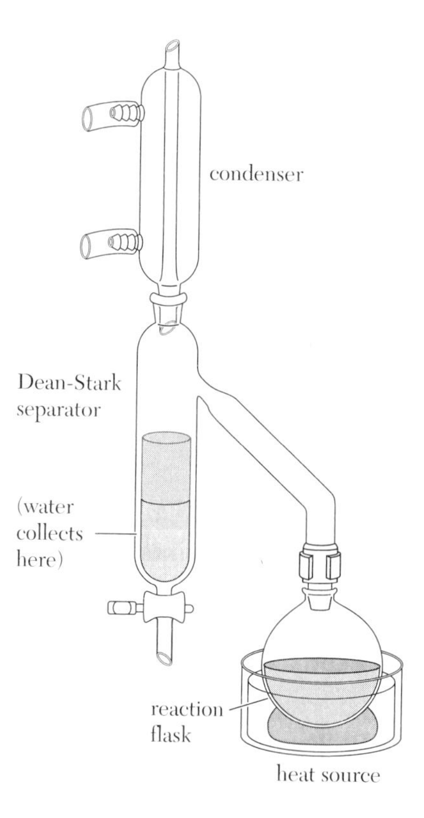

An inert solvent (or an excess of the benzene reactant in the sulfonation of benzene) is heated in the round-bottomed reaction flask and fills the side arm of the water separator. On heating, the refluxing vapors

(continued)

(*continued from previous page*)

consist of an azeotropic mixture of the solvent (benzene or toluene) and water. When these vapors condense in the reflux condenser, they return as a liquid mixture of the solvent and water to the side arm. The water, being the denser of the two materials, sinks to the bottom of the side arm. The solvent simply overflows back into the reaction flask. As the reflux continues, more and more water collects in the side arm, helping the reaction to reach completion. The side arm of a Dean-Stark trap is generally calibrated (in mL) to allow a determination of the extent to which the reaction has progressed.

3. Friedel-Crafts alkylation is also impossible if the benzene ring contains an amino group ($-NH_2$) or a substituted amino group ($-NHR$, or $-NR_2$). The unshared valence electron pair is basic and reacts with the Lewis acid catalyst, as shown in Figure 18.30.

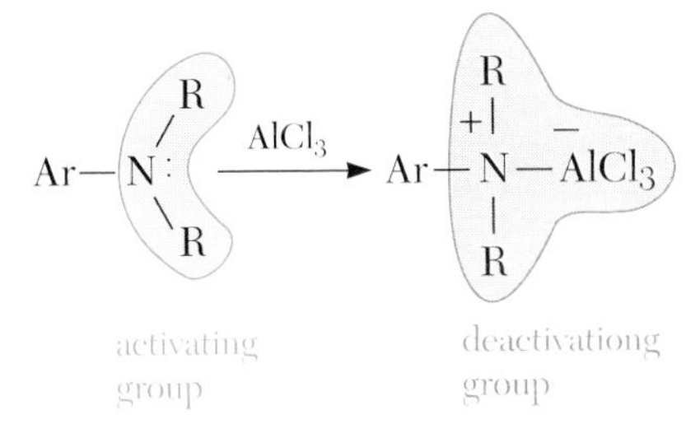

Figure 18.30 Reaction of a Lewis acid ($AlCl_3$) with an amino group attached to an aromatic ring.

4. Nucleophilic displacement of groups from a benzene ring is not a common process. For example, the halobenzenes are essentially inert to the type of nucleophiles that bring about S_N1 and S_N2 reactions on *alkyl* halides. *Aryl* halides undergo nucleophilic substitution reactions only under special circumstances that we will discuss later. We can understand this general inertness to nucleophilic attack in terms of a hindered approach to the back side of the carbon-halogen bond, as is required for S_N2 reaction, and the electrostatic repulsion experienced by the nucleophile upon approaching the electron-rich aromatic ring. Similarly, phenols do not yield aryl halides under the same type of reaction that converts alcohols to alkyl halides; this type of reaction also requires nucleophilic displacement (of H_2O) from the aromatic ring. S_N1 reaction is unfavorable because the $C_6H_5^+$ ion is difficult to form (it is relatively unstable).

5. We must take care to ensure that a synthetic plan is not flawed by incompatibilities of the groups present. For example, if a synthetic plan involves the preparation of an aryl Grignard reagent from an aryl bromide, we must be sure that other functional groups in the aryl bromide cannot cause problems by reacting with the Grignard site.

Table 18.3 Substituents That Are Reactive with Grignard Reagents

Substituent
$-COOH$
$-\ddot{O}H$
$-\ddot{N}H_2$
$-SO_3H$
$-COOR$
$-CN:$
$-NO_2$
$C=\ddot{O}$ of aldehyde or ketone

Let's consider an example. Suppose we wish to convert an aryl bromide, Ar—Br, to an alcohol, Ar—CH_2CH_2—OH. An appealing strategy would be conversion of the aryl halide into a Grignard reagent, followed by reaction with ethylene oxide and workup with aqueous acid, as shown in Figure 18.31. This strategy works well as long as there are no functional groups in the aryl halide that can react with a Grignard. However, the presence of a substituent such as a hydroxyl group on the aromatic ring would cause problems. The hydroxyl group can transfer a proton to the Grignard, thereby destroying it. Similarly, substituents that contain carbonyl groups would invalidate the synthetic strategy since they too react with Grignards. The substituents given in Table 18.3 react

Figure 18.31 Proposed synthesis of a β-arylethyl alcohol from an aryl bromide.

$$Ar-\ddot{B}r: \xrightarrow{Mg,\ ether} Ar-Mg\ddot{B}r: \xrightarrow{\text{ethylene oxide}} \xrightarrow{H_3O^+} Ar-CH_2CH_2-\ddot{O}H$$

with Grignard reagents and therefore must not be contained in the halogen compound used to prepare a Grignard reagent.

PROBLEM 18.26 Propose syntheses of each of the following using benzene or toluene as the starting material.

a. 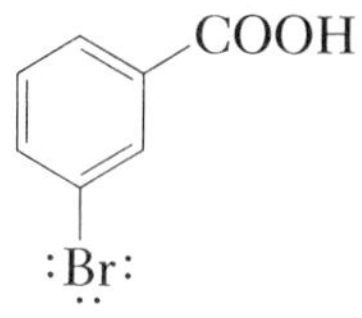 COOH, :Br:

b. 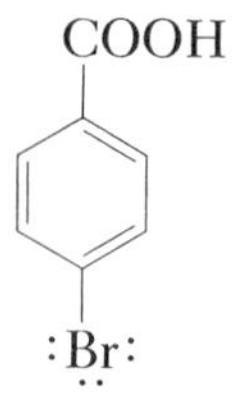 COOH, :Br:

c. 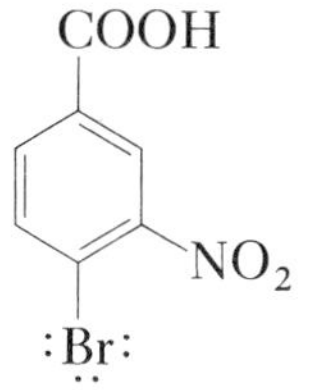 COOH, NO_2, :Br:

d. 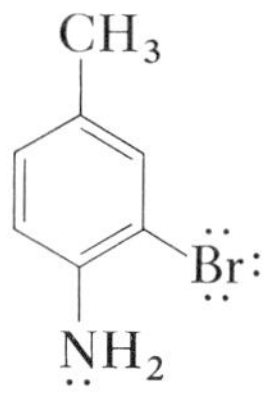 CH_3, :Br:, NH_2

PROBLEM 18.27 Suggest how Grignard methodology can be applied to bring about each of the following conversions. Any nonaromatic or inorganic reagents and any solvents may be used. Assume that *ortho* and *para* isomers can be separated.

a. 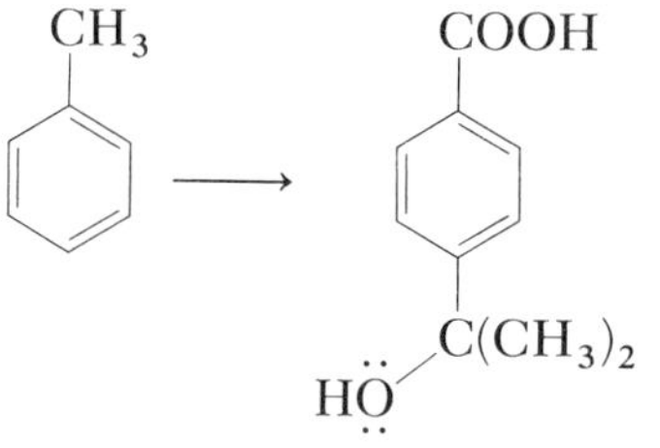 CH_3 ⟶ COOH, $C(CH_3)_2$, HO

b. 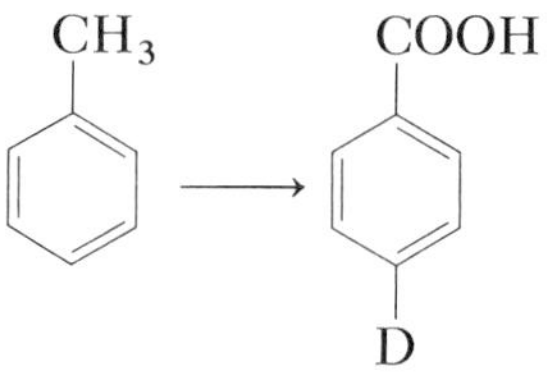 CH_3 ⟶ COOH, D

18.14 The Benzylic Position

STRUCTURE AND STABILIZATION

We often refer to the **benzylic position, benzyl derivatives, benzyl radicals,** and **benzyl cations** in discussions of certain types of aromatic compounds. Although we have met some of these terms earlier, we will review them all here.

In an alkylbenzene, we classify the carbon attached directly to the benzene ring as the *benzylic position. Benzyl derivatives* are compounds in which some substituent is attached to the benzylic carbon atom. **Benzyl radicals, cations,** and **anions** have, respectively, an unpaired electron or a charge of 1+ or 1− at the benzylic carbon. These classifications are summarized in Figure 18.32.

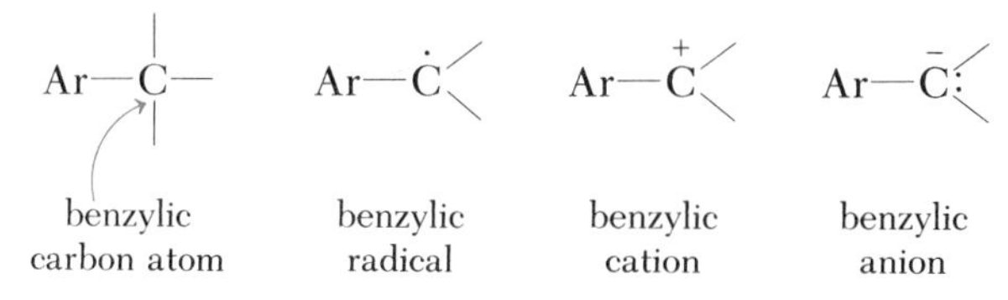

Figure 18.32 Benzylic systems.

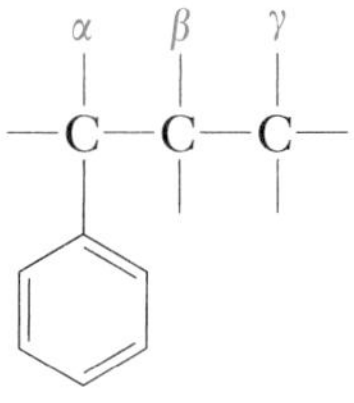

Figure 18.33 Classification of carbon atoms along an alkyl side chain of a benzene ring.

It is also common to label carbon atoms on a benzene side chain as α, β, γ, and so forth. The benzylic carbon is the α-carbon, as shown in Figure 18.33.

Benzyl radicals, cations, and anions have a greater stability and ease of formation than do corresponding saturated species. These characteristics are an expected consequence of the delocalization of the odd electron or the positive or negative charge onto the aromatic ring. For example, resonance structures for a benzylic cation are shown in Figure 18.34.

FREE RADICAL HALOGENATION AT THE BENZYLIC POSITION

Consider an alkylbenzene being heated with chlorine or bromine in the absence of a Lewis acid catalyst. (Alternatively, we can use halogen and light, again with no Lewis acid catalyst present.) Although electrophilic aromatic substitution of the ring does not occur under these conditions, they are appropriate for free radical halogenation to occur on the side chain. The major halogenated product from such a reaction is one in which a halogen takes the place of one of the benzylic hydrogen atoms, as shown in Figure 18.35.

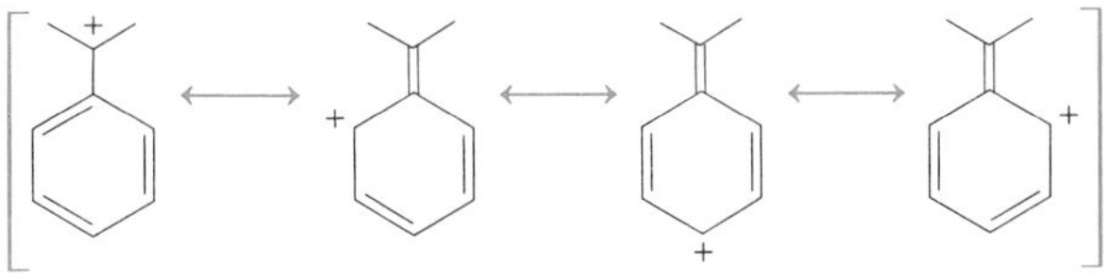

Figure 18.34 Resonance structures for a benzylic cation. Similar resonance structures can be drawn for benzylic radicals and benzylic anions.

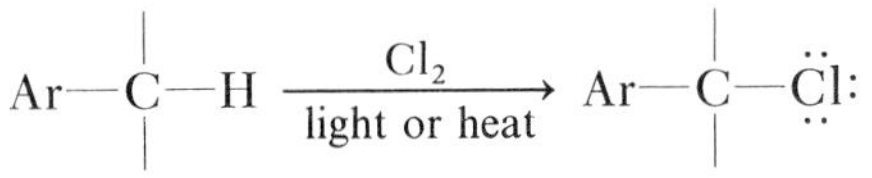

$$\text{Ar—C—H} \xrightarrow[\text{light or heat}]{Cl_2} \text{Ar—C—Cl:}$$

Figure 18.35 Free radical halogenation of the benzylic position. Under these conditions reaction occurs preferentially at the benzylic position rather than on the ring.

A typical reaction of this type is the production of 1-chloro-1-phenylethane from ethylbenzene on irradiation in the presence of chlorine, as shown in Equation 18.20.

Eqn. 18.20

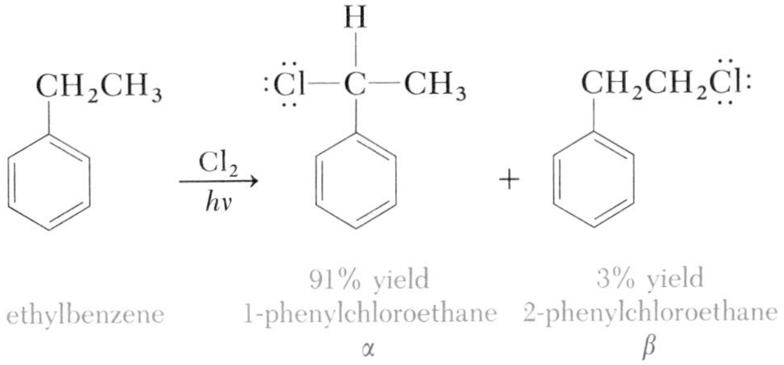

$$C_6H_5CH_2CH_3 \xrightarrow[h\nu]{Cl_2} C_6H_5CH(Cl)CH_3 + C_6H_5CH_2CH_2Cl$$

ethylbenzene; 91% yield 1-phenylchloroethane (α); 3% yield 2-phenylchloroethane (β)

Three steps are involved in the formation of the major product.

MECHANISM OF REACTION

Benzylic Chlorination of an Alkylbenzene

Step 1 Production of chlorine atoms (chain initiation)

$$Cl_2 \xrightarrow{h\nu} 2\,:\ddot{Cl}\cdot$$

Step 2 Abstraction of a hydrogen from the benzylic carbon atom (chain propagation)

$$:\ddot{\text{Cl}}\cdot + \text{Ar}-\overset{|}{\underset{|}{\text{C}}}-\text{H} \longrightarrow \text{Ar}-\overset{|}{\underset{|}{\text{C}}}\cdot + \text{H}\ddot{\text{Cl}}:$$

Step 3 Reaction of the benzylic radical with chlorine (chain propagation)

$$\text{Ar}-\overset{|}{\underset{|}{\text{C}}}\cdot + \text{Cl}_2 \longrightarrow \text{Ar}-\overset{|}{\underset{|}{\text{C}}}-\ddot{\text{Cl}}: + :\ddot{\text{Cl}}\cdot$$

The chlorine atom produced here in Step 3 sets into motion another cycle of reaction.

PROBLEM 18.28 Consider the mechanistic steps for the formation of the *minor* product in the reaction of ethylbenzene with chlorine. Suggest why this route is relatively unimportant in comparison with the competing route to the major product.

PROBLEM 18.29 The ratio of major product to minor product in the chlorination of ethylbenzene is ~30 : 1. Do you expect a larger or smaller ratio than 30 : 1 for the corresponding bromination reaction? *Hint:* Review the Hammond postulate with regard to selectivity of reaction.

PROBLEM 18.30 Suggest how to perform each of the following syntheses.

a. 3-phenyl-1-propanol from ethylbenzene
b. styrene from toluene

REACTIVITY OF BENZYLIC HALIDES TOWARD NUCLEOPHILES

Benzylic halides have reactivities toward nucleophiles that are similar to those of the corresponding allylic halides. Reaction may occur via either the S_N1 or S_N2 mechanism.

The S_N1 reaction of benzylic halides occurs much more rapidly than similar reactions of nonbenzylic halides. Some examples of relative reactivity are given in Table 18.4. The facility of the latter two reactions in Table 18.4 is associated with the improved stability of benzylic carbocations relative to nonbenzylic carbocations. Substituents on the ring also profoundly affect the stability of a benzylic carbocation. For example, a *p*-methoxy group greatly stabilizes a benzylic carbocation. The extra stabilization is the result of the remote oxygen atom exerting an electron-donating resonance effect that helps to delocalize and thereby stabilize the positive charge. One resonance structure is particularly stabilizing because every atom (except hydrogen) has a complete octet of electrons, as shown in Figure 18.36.

PROBLEM 18.31 Predict the major product in the following reaction:

$$\text{C}_6\text{H}_5-\text{C}_6\text{H}_4-\text{CH}=\text{CH}-\text{C}_6\text{H}_5 + \text{H}\ddot{\text{Br}}: \longrightarrow$$

PROBLEM 18.32 Explain the following observation:

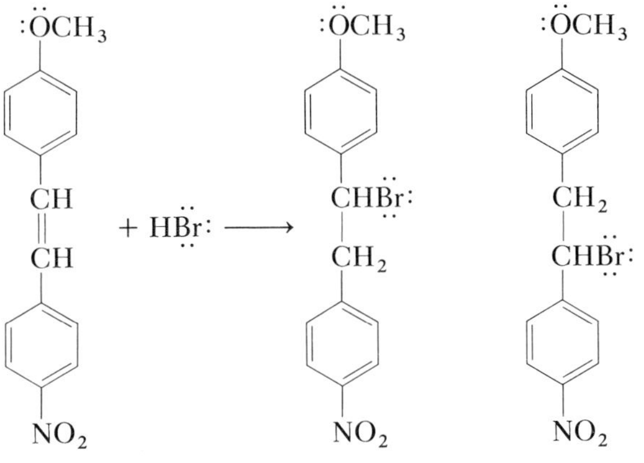

$$p\text{-}CH_3O\text{-}C_6H_4\text{-}CH{=}CH\text{-}C_6H_4\text{-}p\text{-}NO_2 + HBr \longrightarrow p\text{-}CH_3O\text{-}C_6H_4\text{-}CHBr\text{-}CH_2\text{-}C_6H_4\text{-}p\text{-}NO_2 \text{ (major)} + p\text{-}CH_3O\text{-}C_6H_4\text{-}CH_2\text{-}CHBr\text{-}C_6H_4\text{-}p\text{-}NO_2 \text{ (minor)}$$

The S_N2 reactions of benzylic (and allylic) halides are also rapid in comparison with those of other halides. Usually the rate of an S_N2 reaction of a

Table 18.4 Relative Rates of Hydrolysis of Various Halides via S_N1 Reaction

Rates were measured in aqueous acetone at room temperature.

Compound	Relative Rate
$(CH_3)_3C—Cl$ *tert*-butyl chloride	1
$Ph—C(CH_3)_2Cl$ *tert*-cumyl chloride	620
$Ph_3C—Cl$ trityl chloride	> 600,000

$$p\text{-}CH_3O\text{-}C_6H_4\text{-}C^+ \text{ (more stable)} > C_6H_5\text{-}C^+ \text{ (less stable)} \qquad CH_3\overset{+}{O}{=}C_6H_4{=}C$$

Figure 18.36 Stabilization of a benzylic carbocation by a *p*-methoxy group. The resonance structure shown for a *p*-methoxybenzyl carbocation is one in which all carbon and oxygen atoms have a complete octet of electrons.

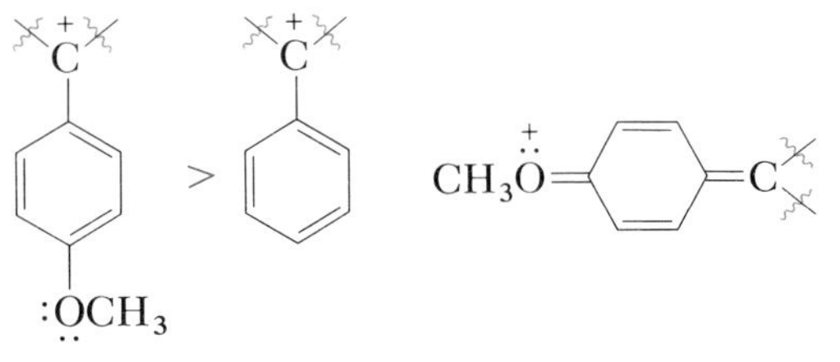

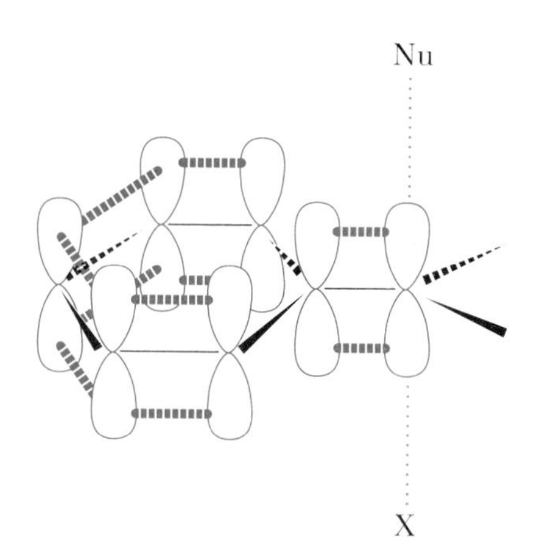

Figure 18.37 Activated complex for the S_N2 displacement of a benzylic halide. The activated complex is stabilized compared with that of a normal S_N2 reaction because of the overlap of a *p* orbital at the site of substitution with the π orbital system of the benzene ring.

benzylic or allylic halide is at least 100 times greater than that of the corresponding ethyl halide. We ascribe this high reactivity to stabilization of the activated complex by orbital overlap, as shown in Figure 18.37.

18.15 Nucleophilic Substitution of Aromatic Halogen Compounds: Introduction

At the beginning of this chapter we focused on electrophilic aromatic substitution reactions, in which an electrophile takes the place of a hydrogen atom on a benzene ring. We noted in passing that nucleophilic aromatic substitution is not common for benzene derivatives; for example, bromobenzene is quite inert to nucleophiles that commonly react with alkyl halides.

Nevertheless, reactions that appear to be nucleophilic substitutions *do* occur with benzene derivatives under special circumstances. Two types of systems are of interest. First, reaction can occur under harsh conditions. For example, hydroxide ion reacts with halobenzenes at high temperature (high pressure also helps) to yield phenols (ArOH). An example is shown in Equation 18.21. Halobenzenes also react with amide ion (NH_2^-) in liquid ammonia solution to yield aromatic amines ($ArNH_2$), as illustrated in Equation 18.22.

Eqn. 18.21

$$C_6H_5\ddot{\underset{..}{Cl}}: \xrightarrow[370\,^\circ C]{NaOH} C_6H_5\ddot{\underset{..}{O}}:^- Na^+ \xrightarrow{HCl} C_6H_5\ddot{\underset{..}{O}}H$$

chlorobenzene — 97% yield phenol

Eqn. 18.22

$$C_6H_5\ddot{\underset{..}{Cl}}: \xrightarrow{NaNH_2,\ liq\ NH_3} C_6H_5\ddot{N}H_2$$

45% yield aniline

A second type of reaction system that allows replacement of halide by a nucleophile to occur on an aromatic ring is one in which the ring also bears one or more strongly electron-withdrawing groups (usually nitro groups) *ortho*

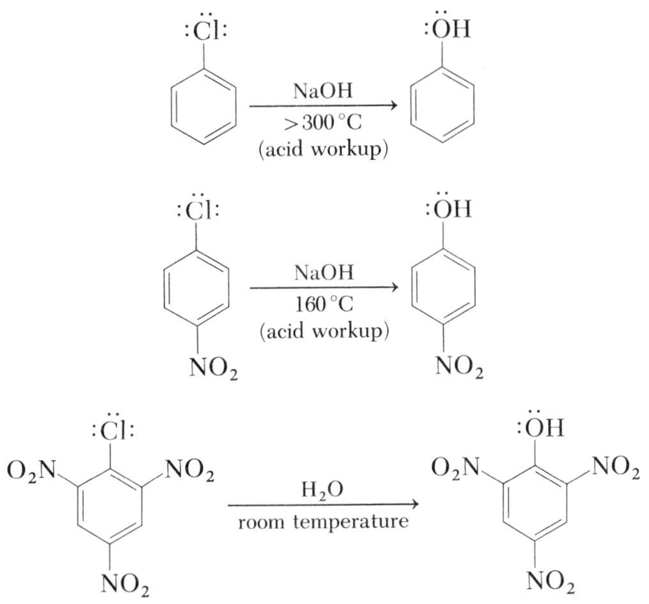

$$\text{chlorobenzene} \xrightarrow[\text{(acid workup)}]{\text{NaOH},\ >300\,^\circ\text{C}} \text{phenol}$$

$$p\text{-}O_2NC_6H_4Cl \xrightarrow[\text{(acid workup)}]{\text{NaOH},\ 160\,^\circ\text{C}} p\text{-}O_2NC_6H_4OH$$

$$2,4,6\text{-}(O_2N)_3C_6H_2Cl \xrightarrow[\text{room temperature}]{H_2O} 2,4,6\text{-}(O_2N)_3C_6H_2OH$$

Figure 18.38 Reactions of aryl chlorides with nucleophiles. Chlorobenzene reacts with hydroxide ion only under extreme conditions of temperature and pressure. *p*-Nitrochlorobenzene reacts with hydroxide ion under relatively normal laboratory conditions. 2,4,6-Trinitrochlorobenzene reacts with water at room temperature.

or *para* relative to the halogen. The contrasting conditions required to displace chloride from the aromatic ring when nitro groups are absent and present are shown in Figure 18.38. As the examples in Figure 18.38 show, the effects of electron-withdrawing groups are cumulative. Thus, even the quite poor nucleophile water is able to convert 2,4,6-trinitrochlorobenzene to 2,4,6-trinitrophenol (picric acid). We will now discuss these reactions in some detail.

18.16 Elimination-Addition

An apparent nucleophilic substitution reaction occurs when halobenzenes are treated with very strong bases such as amide ion. Moderately strong bases such as hydroxide ion also react under conditions of high temperature and pressure. These reactions are, however, different from ordinary nucleophilic substitution reactions in several respects. For example, halobenzenes that have no hydrogen atom *ortho* relative to the halogen are inert to these types of reagents; 2,6-dimethylchlorobenzene, for example, does not react with potassium amide in liquid ammonia.

Furthermore, the entering hydroxyl or amino group does not always occupy the position on the ring that was vacated by the departing halogen. At times the incoming group occupies a position *ortho* (but never *meta* or *para*) relative to the position originally occupied by the halogen. Examples of this type of outcome are shown in Equations 18.23 and 18.24.

Eqn. 18.23

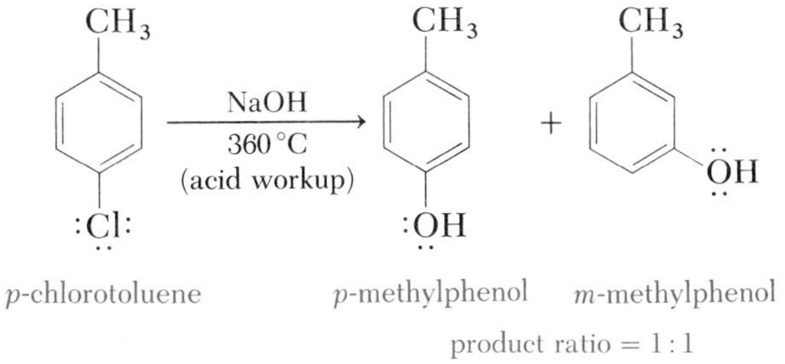

$$\underset{p\text{-chlorotoluene}}{p\text{-}CH_3C_6H_4Cl} \xrightarrow[\text{(acid workup)}]{\text{NaOH},\ 360\,^\circ\text{C}} \underset{p\text{-methylphenol}}{p\text{-}CH_3C_6H_4OH} + \underset{m\text{-methylphenol}}{m\text{-}CH_3C_6H_4OH}$$

product ratio = 1 : 1

Eqn. 18.24

$:\ddot{O}CH_3$ / $\ddot{C}l:$ $\xrightarrow[\text{liq } NH_3]{NaNH_2}$ $:\ddot{O}CH_3$ / $\ddot{N}H_2$

o-chloroanisole — 60% yield *m*-methoxyaniline

These results are not consistent with the nucleophilic substitution mechanisms discussed in earlier chapters. However, all these experimental observations are consistent with an elimination-addition mechanism that proceeds via a highly reactive intermediate known as **benzyne** (**18.2**).

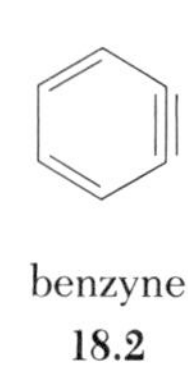

benzyne
18.2

The following mechanism, which shows the elimination-addition reaction that converts chlorobenzene to aniline, illustrates the role of the benzyne intermediate.

MECHANISM OF REACTION

Conversion of Chlorobenzene to Aniline by Elimination-Addition

"Elimination" of HCl

Step 1 The amide ion acts first as a base, abstracting a proton from the position *ortho* relative to the halogen.

$\ddot{C}l:$, H, $^{-}:\ddot{N}H_2$ $\longrightarrow$ $\ddot{C}l:$ $+ H—\ddot{N}H_2$

Step 2 Loss of halide ion occurs to give a highly reactive (not isolable) benzyne intermediate. This is the *elimination* step of the reaction.

$\ddot{C}l:$ $\longrightarrow$ $+ :\ddot{C}l:^{-}$

"Addition" of NH_3

Step 3 The benzyne intermediate is rapidly attacked by the amide ion, which now behaves as a nucleophile. This is the *addition* step of the reaction.

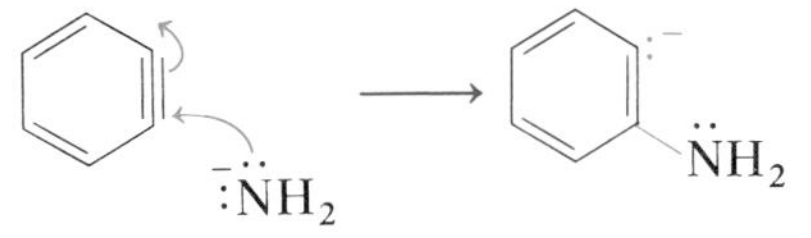

$:\ddot{N}H_2^-$ ⟶ $\ddot{N}H_2$

Step 4 Protonation occurs to give the final product.

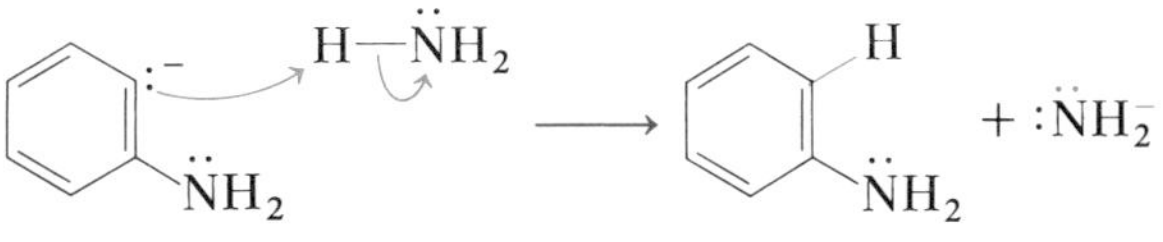

$H-\ddot{N}H_2$ ⟶ H, $\ddot{N}H_2$ $+ :\ddot{N}H_2^-$

Let us now reexamine some of the experimental observations we mentioned earlier in light of the elimination-addition mechanism.

1. Compounds lacking hydrogen at positions *ortho* relative to the halogen cannot undergo this reaction. With no hydrogen to be lost, dehydrohalogenation to a benzyne is impossible.
2. The position taken by the incoming group depends on two factors. The first factor is the orientation of the dehydrohalogenation, that is, which particular benzyne forms. The second factor is the choice of carbon atoms at which nucleophilic attack on the benzyne occurs. Consider, for example, the reaction of *m*-bromoanisole with amide ion. Initial loss of a proton could, in principle, occur from either of the two carbon atoms that are *ortho* relative to the halogen, as shown in Figure 18.39.

Anion (II) of Figure 18.39, with its negative charge adjacent to two electronegative atoms, is more stable than anion (I), and we therefore expect it to form more readily. It follows that the benzyne (**18.3**) forms more rapidly than the benzyne (**18.4**).

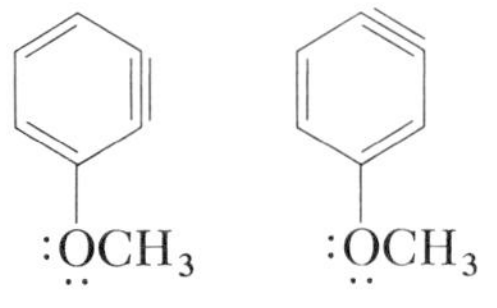

$:\ddot{O}CH_3$ $:\ddot{O}CH_3$

18.3 **18.4**

In considering the attack of amide ion on **18.3**, we again recognize that there are, in principle, two possibilities, as shown in Figure 18.40. We expect there to be a marked preference for mode of attack *a*, which generates an anion whose negative charge is adjacent to two electronegative atoms. Careful analysis of the benzyne mechanism leads us to expect that *m*-bromoanisole in reaction

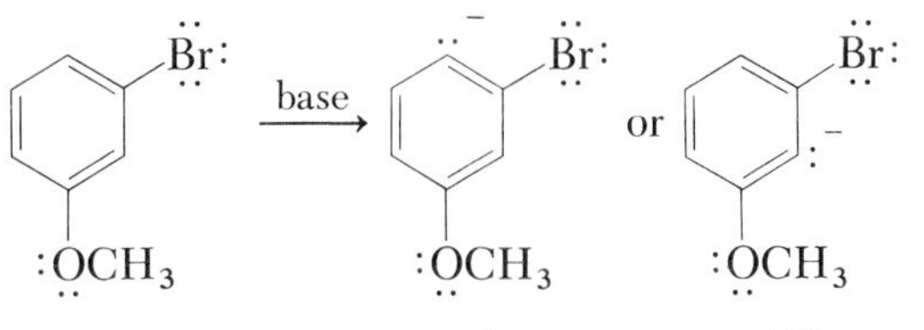

$:\ddot{B}r:$ base ⟶ $:\ddot{B}r:$ or $:\ddot{B}r:$

$:\ddot{O}CH_3$ $:\ddot{O}CH_3$ $:\ddot{O}CH_3$

(I) (II)

Figure 18.39 Reaction of a strong base with *m*-bromoanisole. Loss of a proton from *m*-bromoanisole could, in principle, lead to the formation of either anion (I) or anion (II). Anion (II) is more stable because its negative charge is stabilized by the inductive effect of two adjacent electronegative atoms (Br and O). Neither bromine nor the methoxy group can destabilize the negative charge through an electron-donating resonance effect because the negative charge is located in an sp^2 orbital that is orthogonal to the π system of the benzene ring.

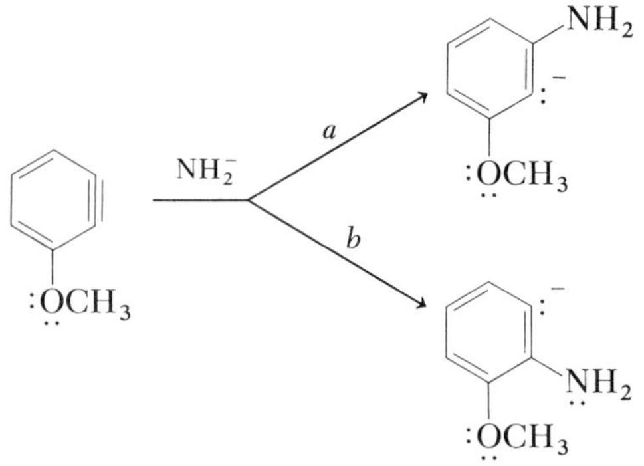

Figure 18.40 Attack of amide ion on a benzyne intermediate. Amide ion could attack the methoxybenzyne by route *a* or route *b* to yield either of the two anions.

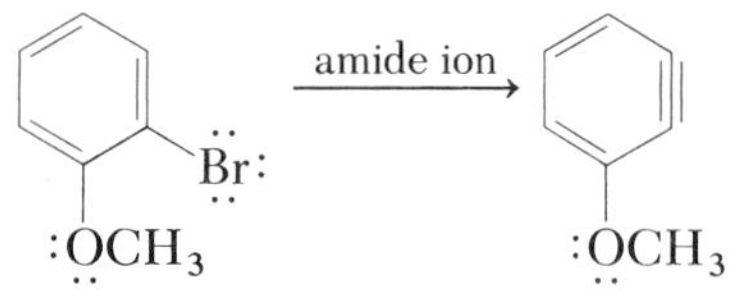

:ÖCH$_3$ — NH_2^- → *a*: $\ddot{N}H_2$, :ÖCH$_3$; *b*: $\ddot{N}H_2$, :ÖCH$_3$

:ÖCH$_3$, :B̈r: —amide ion→ :ÖCH$_3$

Figure 18.41 The benzyne intermediate formed from *o*-bromoanisole. This benzyne is the same as the one formed preferentially from *m*-bromoanisole.

with amide ion should yield mainly *m*-anisidine (*m*-methoxyaniline), and this is the observed result. The incoming group occupies the position vacated by the halogen and does not occupy the position *ortho* to it.

In contrast, consider the reaction of *o*-bromoanisole with amide ion. Because one of the positions *ortho* to bromine is occupied by the methoxy substituent, there is only one possible mode of dehydrohalogenation to a benzyne (see Figure 18.41). In fact, the benzyne produced is identical to that produced from *m*-bromoanisole in reaction with amide ion. We saw earlier that this particular benzyne, in reaction with amide ion, yields *m*-anisidine. We predict and find that both *o*-bromoanisole and *m*-bromoanisole yield the same product (*m*-anisidine) on treatment with amide ion.

PROBLEM 18.33 Give a mechanistic interpretation of the following data:

Fluorobenzene in which both hydrogens *ortho* to the fluorine have been replaced by deuterium is placed with potassium amide in liquid ammonia. After a short time, the reaction is stopped and the products investigated. It is found on investigation of the remaining fluorobenzene that both of the deuterium atoms have been replaced by hydrogen atoms. However, no aniline is present, and none forms even if the reaction proceeds for a longer time, that is:

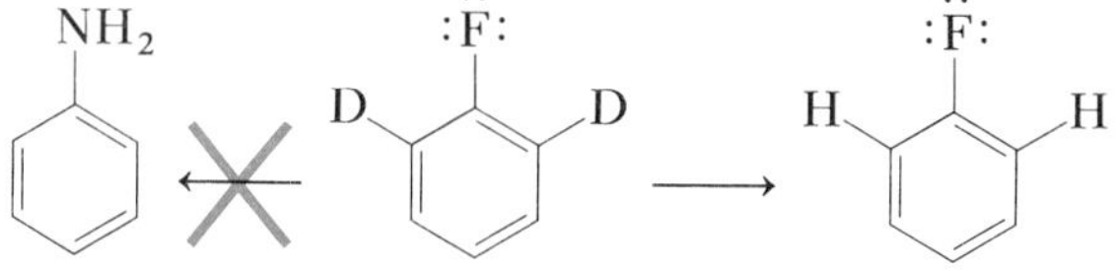

$\ddot{N}H_2$ ✕ :F̈: D D → :F̈: H H

PROBLEM 18.34 Suggest a mechanism for the following reaction:

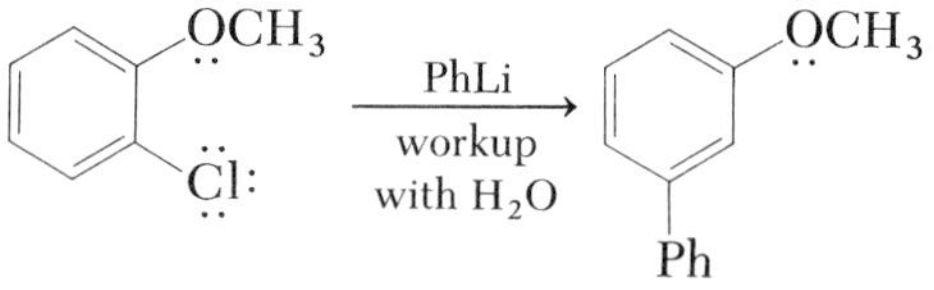

ÖCH$_3$, :C̈l: —PhLi, workup with H_2O→ ÖCH$_3$, Ph

PROBLEM 18.35 Suggest a structure for the product of the reaction shown below, and provide a mechanism for its formation.

$$\text{m-ClC}_6\text{H}_4\text{CH}_2\text{CH}_2\text{CH}_2\text{NH}_2 \xrightarrow[\text{ether}]{\text{PhLi}} \text{C}_9\text{H}_{11}\text{N}$$

(*Hint:* The reaction involves a benzyne intermediate that is attacked intramolecularly.)

18.17 Addition-Elimination

We noted previously that aryl halides that have electron-withdrawing substituents in the positions *ortho* and/or *para* relative to the halogen are reactive with nucleophiles under rather mild conditions. For such reactions, the rate law is the same as that for an S_N2 reaction, that is,

$$\text{rate} = k[\text{aryl halide}][\text{nucleophile}]$$

However, the mechanism of the reaction is decidedly *not* that of a typical S_N2 reaction! While the order of reactivity of alkyl halides in an S_N2 reaction is

$$\text{R—I:} > \text{R—Br:} > \text{R—Cl:} \gg \text{R—F:}$$

the nature of the halogen has little influence on the rate of a nucleophilic aromatic substitution reaction. In fact, aryl fluorides are generally *more* reactive than the other halides in this type of reaction.

The mechanism invoked to explain these data is given below for the specific example of hydroxide ion in reaction with *p*-nitrochlorobenzene.

MECHANISM OF REACTION

Hydroxide Ion Attack on *p*-Nitrochlorobenzene

Step 1 Attack of hydroxide ion leads to the formation of an anionic intermediate.

$$\text{HO:}^- + p\text{-ClC}_6\text{H}_4\text{NO}_2 \xrightarrow[\text{step}]{\text{rate-determining}} \text{[HO, Cl-substituted cyclohexadienyl anion with NO}_2\text{]}$$

Step 2 The anionic intermediate loses chloride ion to form the product.

$$\text{[H—O, Cl anionic intermediate with NO}_2\text{]} \xrightarrow[\text{step}]{\text{rapid}} p\text{-HOC}_6\text{H}_4\text{NO}_2 + \text{:Cl:}^-$$

Several points of interest emerge from considering this mechanism. First, the nucleophile attacks the ***ipso* position** (the ring position to which the halogen is attached). Second, the ring loses its aromatic character in the first step. Thus we expect the first step to be a slow process, which is consistent with the observation that it is the rate-determining step.

Third, we can write several resonance structures for the carbanion intermediate, and they are similar in nature to those we can write for the arenonium ion. In these resonance structures the negative charge is located *only* at positions *ortho* and *para* relative to the site of attack. These resonance structures are shown in Figure 18.42. Consequently, placement of electron-withdrawing groups *ortho* and/or *para* relative to the halogen results in a more stable carbanion intermediate and more rapid reaction. In the absence of such stabilization, reaction by this mechanism is extremely unlikely because it would involve destruction of the resonance stabilization of the ring without any compensation.

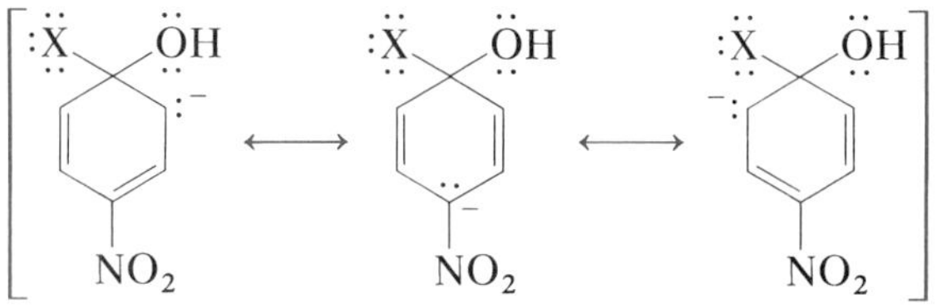

$$\left[\text{:X, OH; } NO_2 \longleftrightarrow \text{:X, OH; } NO_2 \longleftrightarrow \text{:X, OH; } NO_2 \right]$$

Figure 18.42 Resonance structures for the intermediate anion produced by hydroxide ion attack on *p*-nitrochlorobenzene. (Be sure to do Problem 18.36.)

Fourth, the type of halogen atom (I, Br, Cl) has little effect on the rate since the rate-determining step *precedes* the loss of the halide ion. On the other hand, the high electronegativity of fluorine increases the rate of attack at the *ipso* position by stabilizing the resulting anion. This stabilizing effect explains the increased rate of reaction for fluoro derivatives compared to other halogen derivatives.

PROBLEM 18.36 The nitro group is able to stabilize the carbanionic intermediate not only by virtue of its electron-withdrawing inductive effect, but also through an electron-withdrawing resonance effect. Draw a resonance structure for the carbanionic intermediate produced by attack of hydroxide ion on 4-bromonitrobenzene such that both oxygen atoms of the nitro group have a formal charge of 1−.

PROBLEM 18.37 Consider the reaction shown below, where X is a halogen.

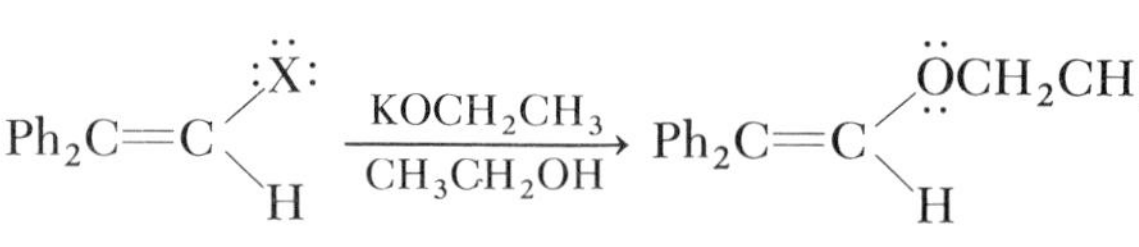

$$Ph_2C{=}C(X)H \xrightarrow[CH_3CH_2OH]{KOCH_2CH_3} Ph_2C{=}C(OCH_2CH_3)H$$

The reaction proceeds most rapidly when X = F. Suggest a mechanism for the reaction. Decide whether the presence of nitro groups in the *ortho* or *para* positions of either phenyl ring will tend to accelerate or retard the reaction compared with the reaction of the unsubstituted compound.

PROBLEM 18.38 One of the chloropyridines shown below is quite reactive in nucleophilic substitution reactions while the other is not. The mechanism by which the reactive material actually reacts is similar to that of the nitrohalobenzenes with nucleophiles. By examining the possible resonance structures for the intermediate carbanions, deduce which chloropyridine is the reactive one with nucleophiles.

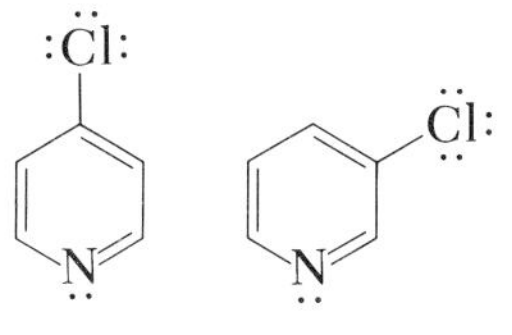

:C̈l: N̈ C̈l: N̈

18.18 Benzene-Chromium Tricarbonyl Complexes

The use of transition metals to activate organic compounds to useful types of reactions is increasing in importance. An interesting family of compounds results when a chromium tricarbonyl group ($—Cr(CO)_3$) is bonded to a benzene ring. The parent compound of this family, benzene-chromium tricarbonyl (**18.5**), is a yellow solid produced by refluxing benzene with chromium hexacarbonyl, as shown in Equation 18.25. An example of a substituted system is shown in Equation 18.26.

Eqn. 18.25

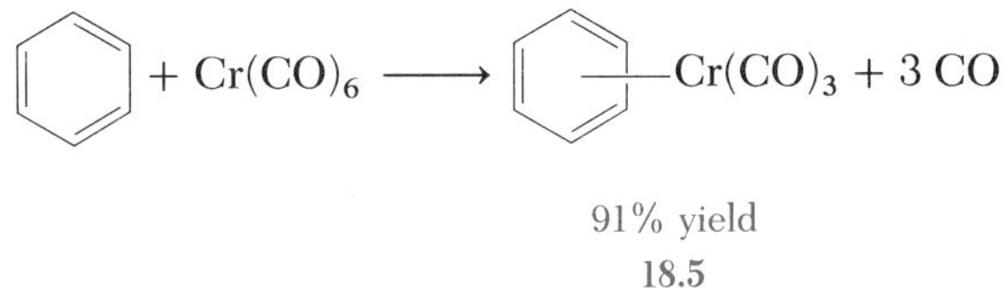

$$C_6H_6 + Cr(CO)_6 \longrightarrow C_6H_6{-}Cr(CO)_3 + 3\ CO$$

91% yield
18.5

Eqn. 18.26

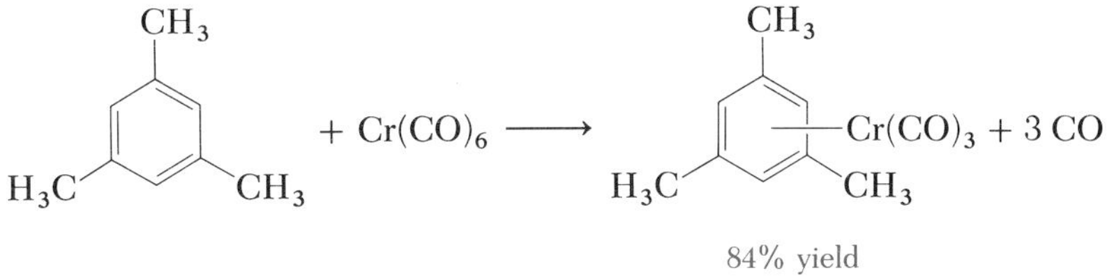

$$C_6H_3(CH_3)_3 + Cr(CO)_6 \longrightarrow C_6H_3(CH_3)_3{-}Cr(CO)_3 + 3\ CO$$

84% yield

Many substituted benzenes and other aromatics react in a similar manner. The bond between the aromatic ring and the chromium atom involves the π electrons of the aromatic ring. In organometallics it is quite possible (and common) to have a bonding interaction of a π nature between a metal and a ligand even though the two are not joined by a σ bond. This type of bond contrasts with π bonds in ordinary organic compounds such as alkenes.

Because the π electrons of the aromatic ring are delocalized, we should not think of the chromium as being bound to any specific carbon atom of the ring. It is bound to the aromatic ring as a whole, and we represent it as shown in Equations 18.25 and 18.26.

The $-Cr(CO)_3$ group removes electron density from the aromatic ring. In this respect its effect is similar to that of an ordinary electron-withdrawing group such as a nitro group. This analogy extends to the reactions of aromatic chromium tricarbonyl compounds. For example, a halogen atom on the aromatic ring readily undergoes nucleophilic substitution reactions (addition-elimination), as shown in Equation 18.27.

Eqn. 18.27

$$\text{(fluorobenzene)}-Cr(CO)_3 \xrightarrow[\text{CH}_3\text{OH, reflux}]{\text{NaOCH}_3} \text{(anisole)}-Cr(CO)_3$$

90% yield

The reactions of the aromatic chromium tricarbonyl compounds parallel those of the nitrohalobenzenes. Complexes of fluorobenzene react more rapidly than those of other halobenzenes.

An advantage of the $-Cr(CO)_3$ group over a nitro group for substitution reactions on the aromatic ring is that the $-Cr(CO)_3$ group can be easily removed once its utility has been exploited. Treatment with either iodine (I_2) or triphenylphosphine (Ph_3P:), a stronger ligand for chromium than an aromatic ring, regenerates the simple aromatic compound. The reaction with iodine is often quantitative. An example is shown in Equation 18.28.

Eqn. 18.28

$$\text{(anisole)}-Cr(CO)_3 \xrightarrow{I_2,\ \text{ether}} \text{(anisole)}$$

100% yield

Thus we can easily add a $-Cr(CO)_3$ group to an aromatic ring to activate it for nucleophilic attack. Once the desired synthetic transformation of the aromatic ring is completed, the $-Cr(CO)_3$ group is easily removed. It is significantly more difficult to remove a nitro group.

18.19 Palladium-Catalyzed Reactions of Aryl Halides

A halogen on an aromatic ring can be replaced with a vinyl or substituted vinyl group through the use of Pd(II) reagents. Two examples of this type of reaction are shown in Equations 18.29 and 18.30.

Eqn. 18.29

$$\text{(}m\text{-iodophenol)} + H_2C{=}CH_2 \xrightarrow[\text{CH}_3\text{CN, (CH}_3\text{CH}_2)_3\text{N}]{\text{Pd(O}_2\text{CCH}_3)_2} \text{(}m\text{-hydroxystyrene, } CH{=}CH_2\text{)}$$

m-iodophenol

73% yield
m-hydroxystyrene

$$\text{2-bromo-1,4-bis}(CH(CH_3)_2)\text{benzene} + H_2C{=}CH{-}CO_2CH_3 \xrightarrow[Ph_3P]{Pd(O_2CCH_3)_2} \text{2,5-bis}(CH(CH_3)_2)C_6H_3{-}CH{=}CH{-}CO_2CH_3$$

Eqn. 18.30

84% yield

The mechanism for this type of transformation follows.

MECHANISM OF REACTION

Palladium-Catalyzed Vinylation of Aryl Halides

Step 1 Formation of the catalytic species. In the initial step, the palladium salt is reduced to the Pd(0) compound $Pd(Ph_3P)_2$ by reaction with triphenylphosphine or another strongly binding ligand. A small amount of the alkene is oxidized in this process.

$$Pd(O_2CCH_3)_2 + (H)C{=}C + 2\,Ph_3P: \longrightarrow Pd(Ph_3P)_2 + HOAc + (H_3CCO_2)C{=}C$$

Step 2 Addition to the aromatic ring. The Pd(0) reagent reacts with the aryl halide.

$$Pd(Ph_3P)_2 + C_6H_5{-}\ddot{X}: \rightleftharpoons C_6H_5{-}Pd(Ph_3P)_2X$$

Step 3 Reaction with the alkene.

$$C_6H_5{-}Pd(Ph_3P)_2X + (H)C{=}C \longrightarrow C_6H_5{-}C(H){-}C{-}Pd(Ph_3P)_2X$$

Step 4 Generation of the vinylated aromatic product. Palladium is eliminated in this step.

$$\text{C}_6\text{H}_5\text{-C(H)-C-Pd(Ph}_3\text{P)}_2\text{X} \longrightarrow \text{C}_6\text{H}_5\text{-C=C} + \text{HPd(Ph}_3\text{P)}_2\text{X}$$

Step 5 Regeneration of the catalytic species. The palladium is again converted to the Pd(0) state for further reaction.

$$\text{HPd(Ph}_3)_2\text{X} + :\text{Base} \longrightarrow \text{Pd(Ph}_3\text{P)}_2 + \text{Base}\overset{+}{-}\text{H} + :\ddot{\text{X}}:^-$$

Ligands other than triphenylphosphine can serve in this reaction, and any available Lewis base can be used in the final step.

This type of reaction is also useful for a variety of haloalkanes. It is of particular significance for *aryl* halides because there are few options for carbon-carbon bond formation to an aromatic ring with displacement of a halide.

PROBLEM 18.39 Three products result from the reaction:

$$\text{Ph}\ddot{\text{I}}: + \text{Ph}-\text{CH}=\text{CH}-\text{CH}_3 \xrightarrow[\text{PPh}_3]{\text{Pd(O}_2\text{CCH}_3)_2}$$

Suggest structures for these three products.

18.20 Aromatic Nucleophilic Substitution by the $S_{RN}1$ Mechanism

The **$S_{RN}1$ mechanism** (unimolecular nucleophilic radical substitution) is another mechanism by which displacement of a halogen (or other leaving group) from an aromatic ring can occur. The reaction is performed in liquid ammonia with a source of electrons such as an electropositive metal. An example of this type of reaction is shown in Equation 18.31.

Eqn. 18.31

$$\text{2,6-}(\text{H}_3\text{C})_2\text{C}_6\text{H}_3\ddot{\text{I}}: \xrightarrow[\text{liq NH}_3]{\text{K}} \text{2,6-}(\text{H}_3\text{C})_2\text{C}_6\text{H}_3\ddot{\text{N}}\text{H}_2$$

2,6-dimethyliodobenzene

64% yield
2,6-dimethylaniline

The $S_{RN}1$ reaction is a free radical chain reaction in which **radical anions** are involved as critical intermediate species. A radical anion is a species that bears an unpaired electron along with a negative charge. The initial radical anion forms by the addition of a solvated electron to the aromatic π system of the aryl halide. This radical anion then loses a halide ion, leaving behind an aromatic radical. The aromatic radical reacts with a nucleophile to form a new radical anion, which subsequently transfers an electron to another molecule of aryl halide and generates the product, which appears to have been formed by simple substitution of the nucleophile for the halide leaving group. For the reaction shown in Equation 18.31, the halide leaving group is iodide and the nucleophile is amide ion.

MECHANISM OF REACTION

The $S_{RN}1$ Reaction

Step 1 Generation of a solvated electron.

$$K^{\cdot} \xrightarrow{\text{liq } NH_3} K^{+}_{(NH_3)} + e^{-}_{(NH_3)}$$

Step 2 Addition of the solvated electron to a π^* orbital of the aromatic. A radical anion is formed.

$$e^{-}_{(NH_3)} + C_6H_5\ddot{X}: \longrightarrow [C_6H_5\ddot{X}:]^{\overline{\cdot}}$$

Step 3 Loss of a halide ion. An aromatic radical is formed.

$$[C_6H_5\ddot{X}:]^{\overline{\cdot}} \longrightarrow C_6H_5^{\cdot} + :\ddot{X}:^{-}$$

Step 4 Addition of a nucleophile to form a new radical anion. The unpaired electron is in a π^* orbital of the aromatic.

$$C_6H_5^{\cdot} + :\ddot{Y}:^{-} \longrightarrow [C_6H_5\ddot{Y}:]^{\overline{\cdot}}$$

Step 5 Electron transfer. The unpaired electron is transferred to another aryl halide molecule.

$$[C_6H_5\ddot{Y}:]^{\overline{\cdot}} + C_6H_5\ddot{X}: \longrightarrow C_6H_5\ddot{Y}: + [C_6H_5\ddot{X}:]^{\overline{\cdot}}$$

Other electropositive metals can be used in the reaction instead of potassium. Sodium works quite well. On dissolving in the liquid ammonia, the metal produces a deep blue color characteristic of the solvated electrons. The substitution reaction works well in the presence of electron-donating groups, such as alkyl groups.

PROBLEM 18.40 The reaction in Equation 18.31 involves an aryl halide in the presence of a strong base (potassium amide forms in the reaction). Why does the reaction proceed via an $S_{RN}1$ mechanism rather than via a benzyne mechanism?

Summary

- Aromatic substances react with a wide range of electrophiles, undergoing substitution reactions.
- In such reactions the electrophilic species generally replaces a hydrogen atom originally attached to the aromatic ring.
- Electrophilic aromatic substitution reactions proceed through an initial slow step that produces a cyclohexadienyl cationic intermediate known commonly as an arenonium ion.
- The arenonium ion ultimately reacts to reform the aromatic ring by losing a proton from the tetracoordinated carbon.
- Table 18.1 lists a series of common electrophiles used in electrophilic aromatic substitution reactions, along with conditions for their generation and the nature of the products formed.
- Substituents that are already attached to an aromatic ring influence the rate at which electrophilic aromatic substitution occurs. They also impose a regioselectivity on the reaction.
- We classify substituents as activating or deactivating for electrophilic aromatic substitution on the basis of their effect on the rate of such reactions.
- We also classify substituents according to their directing effects. Some substituents are *ortho*, *para*-directing, while others are *meta*-directing. The directing influences of some common substituents are summarized in Table 18.2.
- The order of synthetic operations is important in the design of syntheses of benzenoid compounds containing more than one substituent. An inappropriate order of operations often results in the generation of an undesired product.
- Aryl halides are unreactive to *nucleophilic* substitution reactions under ordinary conditions.
- At times we can use special conditions or reagents to accomplish the overall equivalent of nucleophilic substitution. One approach involves the use of aryl halides in which the aromatic ring is electron poor due to the presence of electron-withdrawing substituents *ortho* or *para* to the halogen atom. Such electron-withdrawing groups are commonly nitro or cyano groups. Alternatively, π complexation of the chromium tricarbonyl group with the aromatic ring accomplishes much the same goal.
- Another approach that accomplishes the equivalent of nucleophilic substitution on an aryl halide involves the use of strong bases such as the amide ion. The reaction of amide ion with an aryl halide proceeds first via dehydrohalogenation to a benzyne intermediate. The benzyne then further reacts to form the substituted product. Reactions proceeding via a benzyne intermediate may result in a product that is substituted at the *ipso* site or at the site *ortho* relative to the original halide.

Terms to Remember

phenyl
benzyl
aryl
electrophilic aromatic substitution
electrophile
benzenonium ion
nitration
nitronium ion
Friedel-Crafts reaction
acylation
acyl group
acid halide
acylium ion
Friedel-Crafts acylation
ortho, *para*-directing group
meta-directing group
inductive effects
resonance effects

azeotropic distillation
benzylic position
benzyl derivatives
benzyl radicals
benzyl cations
benzyne
ipso position
$S_{RN}1$ reaction
radical anion

Reactions of Synthetic Utility

95. $ArH \xrightarrow{X_2,\ Fe} ArX$ — 18.5
   X = Br, Cl

96. $ArH \xrightarrow{HNO_3,\ H_2SO_4} ArNO_2$ — 18.6

97. $ArH \xrightarrow{RX,\ AlCl_3} ArR$ — 18.6

98. $ArH \xrightarrow[AlCl_3]{RCOCl\ or\ (RCO)_2O} ArCOR$ — 18.6

99. $ArH \xrightarrow{SO_3,\ H_2SO_4} ArSO_3H$ — 18.6

100. ArH —(alkene; HF or H_2SO_4)→ Ar–(alkyl) — 18.6

101. $ArH \xrightarrow[ROH]{HF\ or\ BF_3} ArR$ — 18.6

102. $ArNO_2 \xrightarrow{Sn,\ HCl} ArNH_2$ — 18.10

103. $ArCHR_2 \xrightarrow[aq\ acid\ workup]{KMnO_4,\ KOH,\ heat} ArCOOH$ — 18.10

104. $ArCHR_2 \xrightarrow{CrO_3,\ H_2SO_4} ArCOOH$ — 18.10

105. $ArSO_3H \xrightarrow{H_2SO_4,\ steam} ArH$ — 18.12

106. $ArSO_3H \xrightarrow[aq\ acid\ workup]{KOH,\ heat} ArOH$ — 18.12

107. $Ar^*X \xrightarrow[aq\ acid\ workup]{KOH,\ heat} Ar^*OH$ — 18.15
   * Strongly electron-withdrawing groups attached; X = F, Cl, Br

108. $ArX \xrightarrow[liq\ NH_3]{NaNH_2} ArNH_2$ — 18.16

109. $ArX \xrightarrow{Cr(CO)_6} ArX\text{–}Cr(CO)_3$ — 18.18

110. $ArX\text{–}Cr(CO)_3 \xrightarrow{NaOR} ArOR\text{–}Cr(CO)_3$ — 18.18
   X = F, Cl, Br

111. $ArX\text{–}Cr(CO)_3 \xrightarrow{I_2} ArX$ — 18.18

112. ArX —(H-alkene, $Pd(O_2CCH_3)_2$; base)→ Ar–alkene — 18.19

113. $ArX \xrightarrow[liq\ NH_3]{K} ArNH_2$ — 18.20

Additional Problems

18.41 Give the structure of each of the following:

a. *o*-nitrophenol
b. *sec*-butylbenzene
c. *p*-nitrobenzyl bromide
d. (*Z*)-2-phenylstyrene
e. 2,4-divinylbenzoic acid
f. 2-cyanobenzoic acid
g. 1-phenylpropanol
h. 2-methyl-4-(*p*-bromophenyl)phenol
i. 2,3-dimethyl-2-phenylpentane
j. (*R*)-1-bromo-1-phenylethane
k. *o*-chlorobenzyl chloride
l. (*E*)-1,2-diphenylethene
m. allylbenzene
n. 4-methyl-2-hydroxyacetophenone
o. all substances of formula C_7H_7Cl containing a benzene ring
p. all substances of formula C_9H_{12} containing a benzene ring

q. 2-methoxy-4-(2-propenyl)phenol (eugenol, derived from clove oil)
r. the xylene that yields one monobromo product on treatment with bromine in the presence of iron
s. the xylene that yields two monobromo products on treatment with bromine in the presence of iron

18.42 Name each of the following structures:

a. 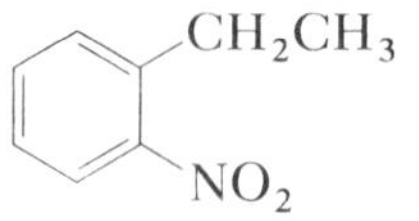 CH_2CH_3, NO_2
b. 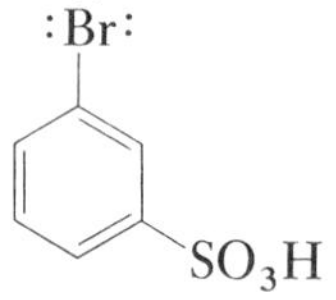 :Br:, SO_3H
c. 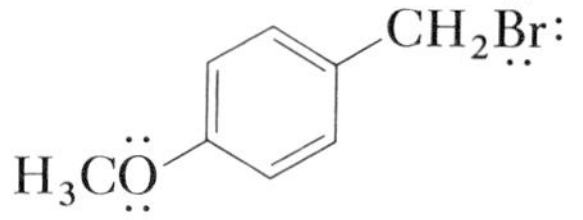 CH_2Br:, H_3CO
d. COOH, :Cl, Cl:
e. CH_3, CH_2CH_3, CH_3
f. COOH, :Br
g. CH=CH_2, O_2N, NO_2
h. CH=CH_2, CH_2=CH
i.

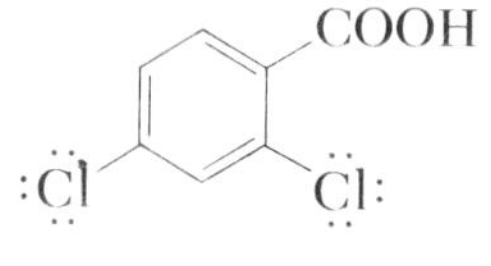

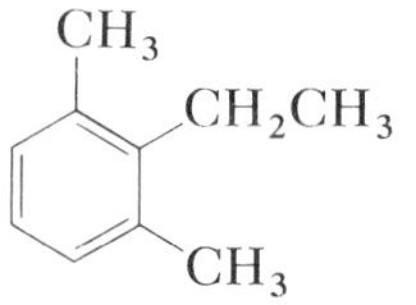

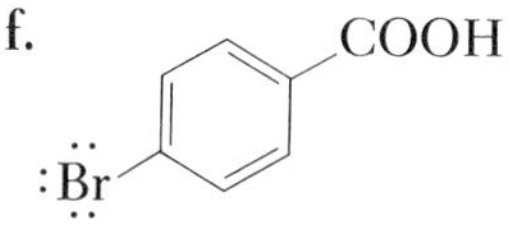

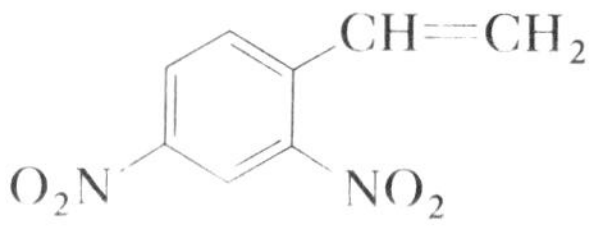

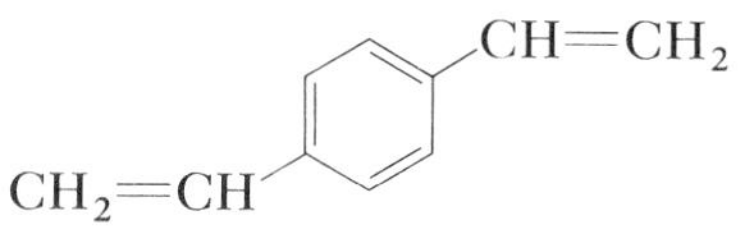

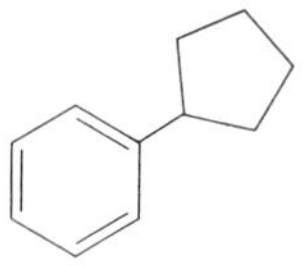

18.43 Give the names and structures of the aromatic compounds that exhibit the following spectrometric characteristics:

a. Proton NMR shows a 5H singlet at δ 7.2, a 2H triplet at δ 2.6, a 2H multiplet at δ 1.8, and a 3H triplet at δ 0.9 (formula, C_9H_{12}).
b. Proton NMR shows a 5H singlet at δ 7.2, a 1H multiplet at δ 2.8, a 2H multiplet at δ 1.8, a 3H doublet at δ 1.3, and a 3H triplet at δ 1.0 (formula, $C_{10}H_{14}$).
c. The IR spectrum shows an absorption at $\sim$1715 cm^{-1} but no absorption above 3100 cm^{-1}. The proton NMR shows a 5H singlet at δ 7.2, a 2H singlet at δ 3.5, and a 3H singlet at δ 1.9 (formula, $C_9H_{10}O$).

18.44 Explain each of the following observations.

a. Both hydroxyl and halogens are *ortho,para*-directing groups, but while hydroxyl groups are activating, halogens are deactivating.
b. Dinitration of diphenyl ether places one nitro group in each of the phenyl rings rather than both in the same ring.
c. The nitroso group (—NO) is *ortho,para*-directing in electrophilic aromatic substitutions, while the nitro group (—NO_2) is *meta*-directing.

18.45 Draw resonance structures that are consistent with the observation that the carbon-chlorine bonds of both chlorobenzene and chloroethene are shorter (1.69 angstrom) than that of chloroethane (1.76 angstrom). In light of your answer, predict which has the greater dipole moment, chlorobenzene or chloroethane.

18.46 Predict the major products of mononitration for each of the following compounds:

a. 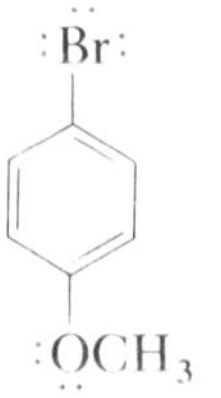 :Br:, :OCH_3
b. 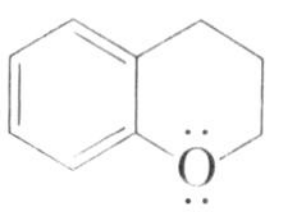 :O:
c. 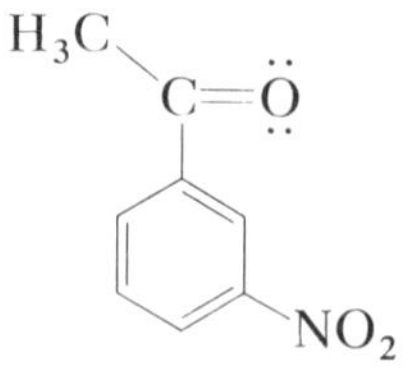 H_3C, C=O:, NO_2

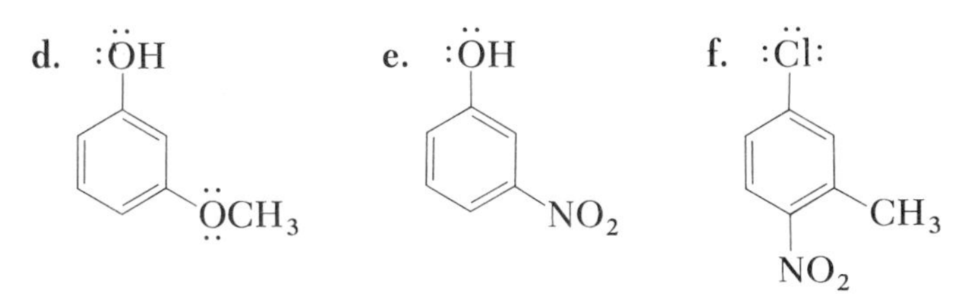

18.47 Predict the major products expected from the following reactions:

a. chlorination of *p*-nitrotoluene
b. nitration of *o*-chloroaniline
c. acetylation of *m*-dibromobenzene
d. sulfonation of 2,3-dinitrotoluene
e. bromobenzene treated with lithium metal in liquid ammonia, followed by workup with water
f. bromobenzene treated with magnesium in ether, followed by the addition of acetone and workup with the addition of water
g. *p*-isopropyltoluene treated with potassium permanganate in aqueous base and workup with aqueous acid

18.48 Predict the major product of monobromination of each of the following compounds:

a. 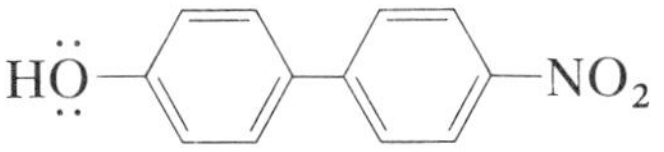 HÖ— —NO2
b. 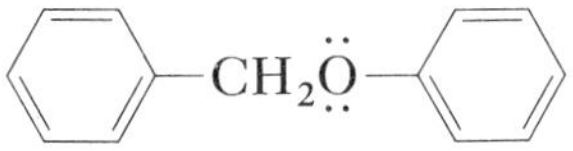 —CH2Ö—
c. 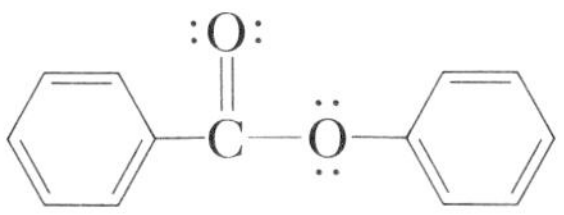 :O: —C—Ö—
d. 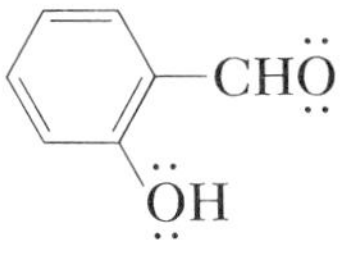 —CHÖ ÖH

18.49 Give synthetic sequences for the preparation of each of the following compounds from benzene.

a. *p*-nitrotoluene
b. *m*-acetyltoluene
c. benzyl bromide
d. styrene
e. *m*-bromobenzoic acid
f. *p*-bromobenzoic acid
g. *m*-bromoaniline
h. 3,5-dinitrochlorobenzene
i. 2-phenylethanol
j. phenylacetylene
k. monodeuteriobenzene

18.50 When anisole is treated with I—Cl, an electrophilic aromatic substitution reaction occurs to give a product in which one of the halogens becomes attached to the aromatic ring. Suggest a structure for the product or products and provide a mechanism for the reaction. Explain why only one of the halogens (I or Cl) becomes incorporated into the product.

18.51 The treatment of benzene with HOBr in sulfuric acid yields bromobenzene. Give a mechanism for the formation of this product.

18.52 Give structures for the major organic products in each of the following reactions, or indicate that there is no reaction.

a. benzyl bromide + KOH/water
b. benzyl bromide + Mg/ether, followed by PhCHO, and worked up with aqueous acid
c. benzyl bromide + benzene/$AlCl_3$
d. benzyl bromide + Mg/ether, followed by benzophenone, and worked up with aqueous acid
e. 2,4-dinitrochlorobenzene + NaSH in water
f. 2-chloro-1,3-dimethylbenzene + Na/liq ammonia
g. *m*-dinitrobenzene + chloromethane/$AlCl_3$
h. benzene + $Cl_2C{=}O/AlCl_3$ (the product has the formula $C_{13}H_{10}O$)
i. 4-chloro-1-phenylpentane heated with $AlCl_3$ in nitrobenzene (the product has the formula $C_{11}H_{14}$)
j. toluene + methylpropene + HF
k. benzene + cyclopentene + HF

18.53 Give a synthesis of the monodeuterated *p*-nitrotoluene shown below, starting with toluene and using Grignard methodology. Be careful with the sequence of reactions.

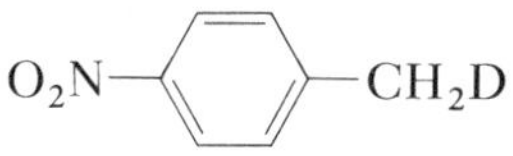

$$O_2N-C_6H_4-CH_2D$$

18.54 Consider the following two-step reaction:

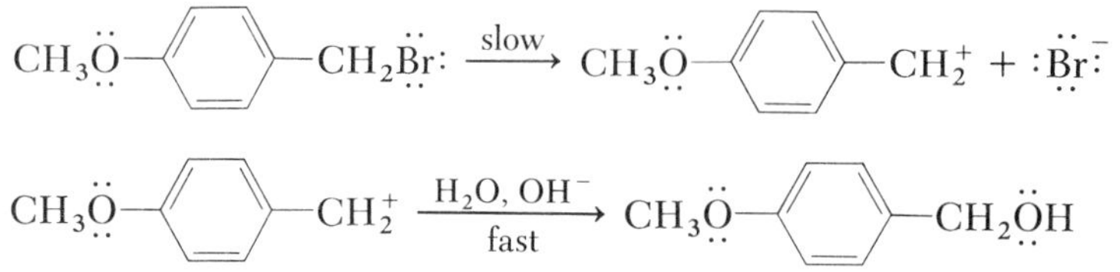

$$CH_3\ddot{O}-C_6H_4-CH_2\ddot{Br}: \xrightarrow{\text{slow}} CH_3\ddot{O}-C_6H_4-CH_2^+ + :\ddot{Br}:^-$$

$$CH_3\ddot{O}-C_6H_4-CH_2^+ \xrightarrow[\text{fast}]{H_2O,\ OH^-} CH_3\ddot{O}-C_6H_4-CH_2\ddot{O}H$$

a. What type of reaction is this?
b. Write a rate law expression for the reaction.
c. Consider the effect of doubling (separately) the concentration of the *p*-methoxybenzyl bromide and the hydroxide ion. How will each of these changes affect the rate constant and the rate of the reaction?
d. Draw a resonance structure for the cation produced in the first step such that each atom (other than hydrogen) has a complete octet of electrons.
e. What would happen to the rate of the reaction if a methyl group were present in place of the methoxy group?

18.55 Both aniline and bromobenzene have approximately the same dipole moment (~1.5 debye). Nitrobenzene has a much larger dipole moment (~3.98 debye). However, one of the pair of compounds shown below has a dipole moment that is larger than that of nitrobenzene and the other has a dipole moment smaller than that of nitrobenzene. Explain these differences. (*Hint:* Compare the relative resonance and inductive effects of the —Br and —NH_2 substituents.) Predict whether *p*-nitroanisole has a larger or smaller dipole moment than that of nitrobenzene. Explain your answer.

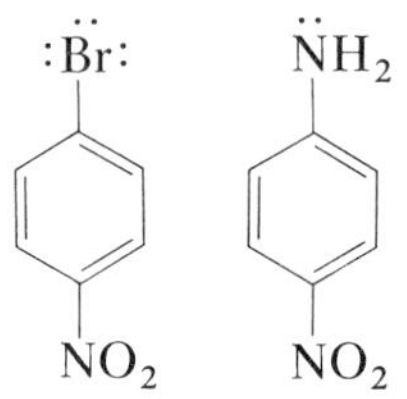

$$:\ddot{Br}:-C_6H_4-NO_2 \qquad \ddot{N}H_2-C_6H_4-NO_2$$

18.56 For one of the pairs of compounds listed below, the *meta* isomer has a higher dipole moment than the *para* isomer. For the other pair, the *meta* isomer has a smaller dipole moment than the *para* isomer. Which pair is which?

m-nitrophenol and *p*-nitrophenol
m-cresol and *p*-cresol

18.57 Phenol and cyclohexanol have significantly different acidities. By considering their conjugate bases, deduce which compound is more acidic. How do you expect the acidity of *p*-nitrophenol to compare with that of phenol?

18.58 Benzene reacts with $CH_3OCH_2CH(CH_3)Cl$ in the presence of $AlCl_3$ to yield $PhCH_2CH(CH_3)OCH_3$. The mechanism involves the formation of an intermediate three-membered cyclic oxonium ion of the formula $C_4H_9O^+$. Deduce the structure of this ion, and explain the formation of the final product.

18.59 Provide a mechanism for the reaction of *p*-dinitrobenzene with KOH/water to yield *p*-nitrophenol. In light of your answer, predict the structure of the product of formula $C_6H_4N_2O_5$ obtained by treating 1,2,4-trinitrobenzene with KOH/water.

18.60 When benzene is heated with 1,4-dichlorobutane in the presence of aluminum trichloride, a product of formula $C_{10}H_{12}$ is formed. Suggest a structure for this product and provide a mechanistic rationale for its formation.

18.61 When styrene is treated with acid a compound of formula $C_{16}H_{16}$ is formed. Suggest a structure for the product and give a mechanism for its formation. (*Hint:* Begin by looking at the protonation of one styrene molecule to give the most stable possible carbocation.)

18.62 Give structures for each of the compounds *A–C*.

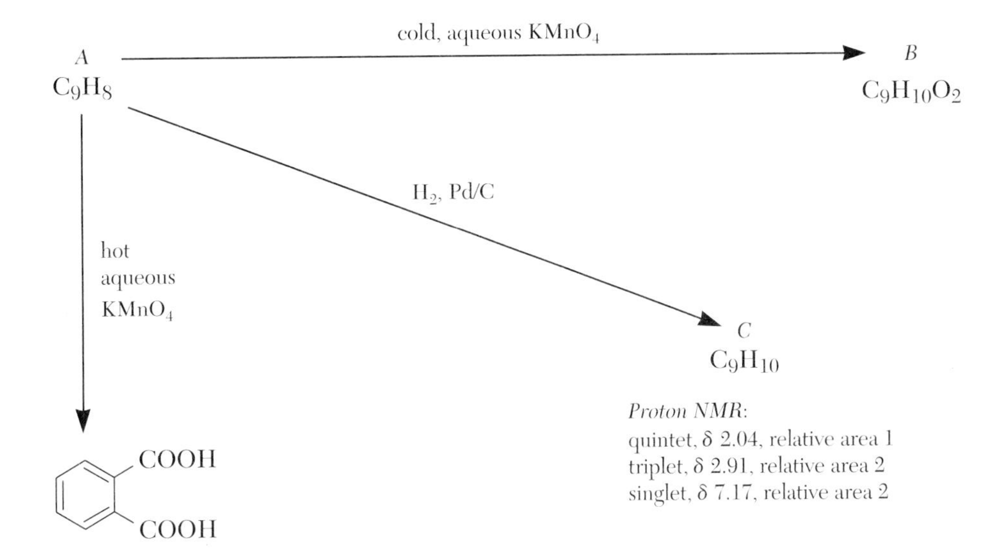

18.63 Give the major organic product(s) in each of the following reactions, or state that there is no reaction.

a. 1,3-diphenylpropyne + H_2/Pd(C) ⟶ $C_{15}H_{16}$

b. HBr: + O_2N–C_6H_4–CH=CH–C_6H_5 ⟶

c. HO:⁻ + 1,2-dichloro-3,5-dinitrobenzene (:Cl: , :Cl, NO_2, NO_2) ⟶ $C_6H_3ClN_2O_5$

d. $Ph(CH_2)_3COCl + AlCl_3$ ⟶ $C_{10}H_{10}O$

e. benzonitrile + $C_2H_5Cl/AlCl_3$ ⟶

f. benzyl phenyl ketone + fuming sulfuric acid ⟶

18.64 Suggest routes to bring about each of the following synthetic conversions.

a. toluene to 1-phenyl-2-propanol

b. toluene to ethyl 4-aminobenzyl ether

c. ethylbenzene to phenylacetylene

d. toluene to *p*-ethoxybenzoic acid

e. bromobenzene to 2,4-diaminophenol
f. benzene to *p*-bromophenol
g. phenylacetylene to acetophenone
h. benzyl alcohol to $Ph(CH_2)_2CH_2OH$
i. *n*-propylbenzene to 1-phenyl-1,2,3-tribromopropane
j. benzenesulfonic acid to *m*-bromophenol

18.65 A substance of formula C_8H_9Br is unreactive to nucleophiles under normal conditions. However, on reaction with potassium amide in liquid ammonia it gives a single product of formula $C_8H_{11}N$. Suggest a structure for the starting materials and the product.

18.66 Provide structures for compounds *D–I*.

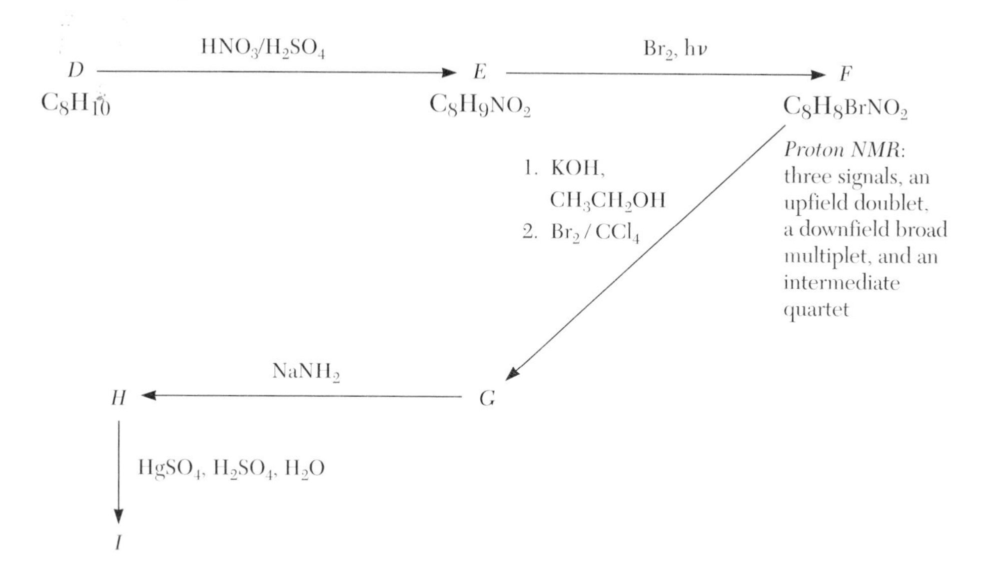

Aldehydes and Ketones: Preparation, Properties, and Nucleophilic Addition Reactions

19.1 Introduction

In this chapter we will be concerned with the chemistry of aldehydes and ketones. Both classes of compounds contain the carbonyl functional group:

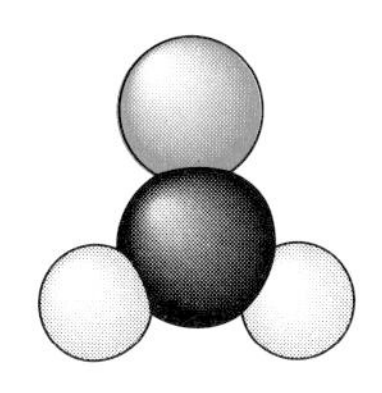

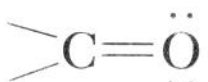

The carbonyl group is polar. The carbon atom is the positive end and the oxygen atom is the negative end of the carbon-oxygen dipole. The carbonyl group undergoes reaction with many nucleophiles. In these reactions, the nucleophile forms a bond to the carbon atom and a pair of electrons from the carbon-oxygen double bond is displaced onto the oxygen atom as a valence level unshared pair. This type of reaction is known as **nucleophilic addition.** We will survey several examples of reactions of this type and discuss their synthetic applications.

Another important property of compounds containing the carbonyl group is the enhanced acidity of hydrogen atoms bound to a carbon atom immediately adjoining the carbonyl group. When a base removes a proton from this position, the anion so produced is resonance-stabilized. This resonance-stabilized conjugate base of a carbonyl compound is known as an **enolate anion.** We will discuss the chemistry of enolate anions briefly in this chapter and in more detail in Chapter 23. They participate in a variety of synthetically useful reactions.

In general, carbonyl compounds have a very rich chemistry. In fact, we find the carbonyl group to be one of the most important of the functional groups as a result of its range of chemical reactions. Compounds containing this functional group abound in nature. Many play important roles in biological processes, and in addition, many have commercial significance.

19.2 Classification and Nomenclature

Aldehydes, ketones, and many other substances contain the carbonyl group. The major possibilities are shown in Figure 19.1. However, for all of these compounds *except* aldehydes and ketones, we think of the carbonyl group as being part of a larger functional group. For example, the carboxylic acid group ($-CO_2H$) contains a hydroxyl group as well as the carbonyl group. There are numerous ways in which the chemistry of aldehydes and ketones is similar to that of these other compounds. However, there are also major differences, so we will look at the chemistry of these other compounds in detail in later chapters.

Figure 19.2 shows the structures of some common naturally occurring aldehydes and ketones.

For simple aldehydes the IUPAC name is derived by changing the final *-e* of the parent alkane name to *-al.* The carbon atom of the carbonyl group is assigned carbon number 1 of the chain, and any substituents or other functional

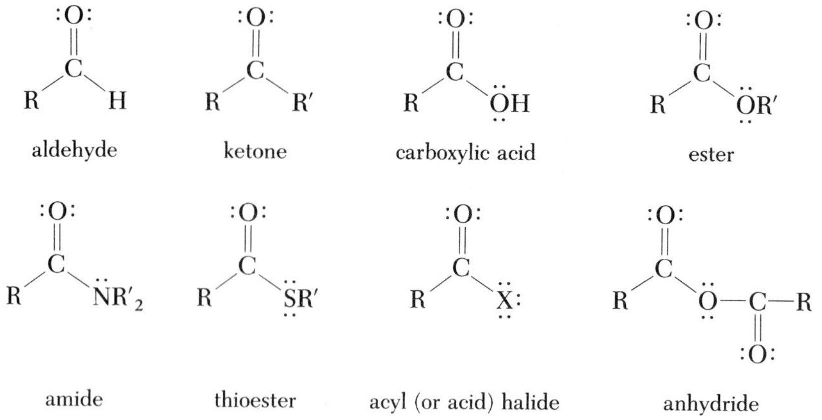

Figure 19.1 Classes of compounds containing the carbonyl group. One particular aldehyde, formaldehyde, has hydrogen as the R group.

aldehyde | ketone | carboxylic acid | ester

amide | thioester | acyl (or acid) halide | anhydride

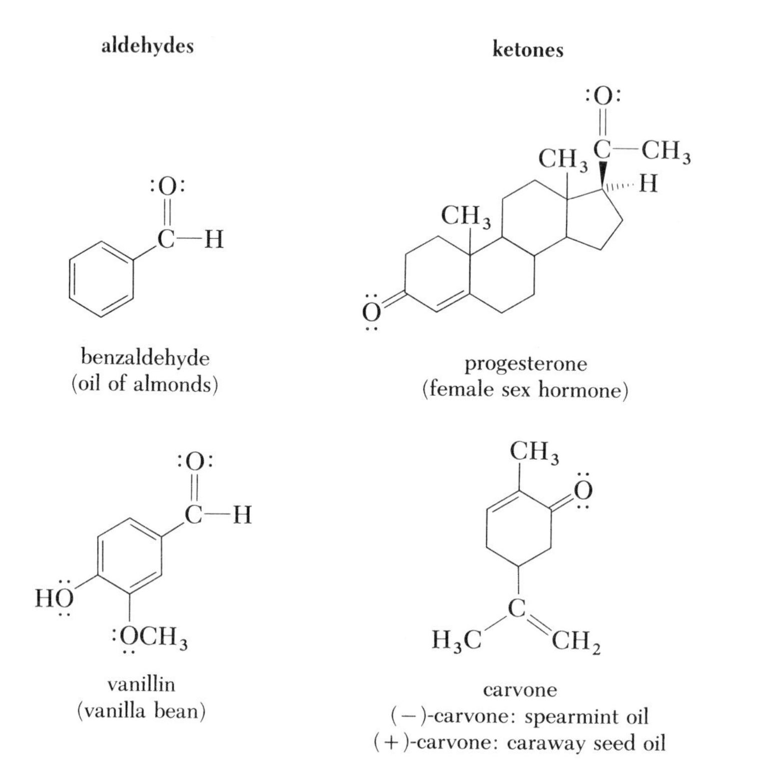

Figure 19.2 Examples of naturally occurring aldehydes and ketones.

groups are named and numbered in the usual way. Several examples are shown in Figure 19.3.

The four simplest aldehydes have common names that are frequently used:

formaldehyde ($H_2C{=}\ddot{O}$)
acetaldehyde ($CH_3CH\ddot{O}$)
propionaldehyde ($CH_3CH_2CH\ddot{O}$)
butyraldehyde ($CH_3CH_2CH_2CH\ddot{O}$)

These names are derived from the common names of the corresponding carboxylic acids (see Chapter 21). A systematic method for naming aldehydes in

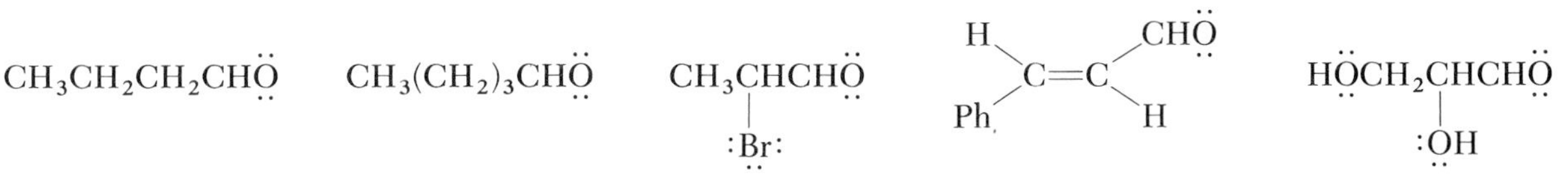

$CH_3CH_2CH_2CHO$ — butanal

$CH_3(CH_2)_3CHO$ — pentanal

$CH_3CHBrCHO$ — 2-bromopropanal

(*E*)-3-phenylpropenal (common name: *trans*-cinnamaldehyde)

$HOCH_2CH(OH)CHO$ — 2,3-dihydroxypropanal (common name: glyceraldehyde)

Figure 19.3 Examples of IUPAC nomenclature of aldehydes.

which the carbonyl group is attached to a cyclic alkyl or aryl group uses the term *carbaldehyde*, as shown in Figure 19.4.

For some nomenclature purposes, we refer to the —CHO group as a **formyl** substituent, and classify reactions that introduce a —CHO group into a molecule as **formylation** reactions. Two examples of aldehydes named under this system are given in Figure 19.5.

To name open-chain ketones according to the IUPAC method, we replace the final *-e* of the parent alkane name with *-one* (pronounced "own") and specify the position of the carbonyl carbon along the chain with a numerical prefix. For cyclic ketones, the carbonyl carbon atom is always given the number 1. Several examples of ketone nomenclature are shown in Figure 19.6.

The simplest ketones also have common names. For example, we usually refer to 2-propanone [$(CH_3)_2C{=}O$], an important solvent and reagent, as *acetone*. 2-Butanone is commonly known as *methyl ethyl ketone* (or MEK), and 3-pentanone is known as *diethyl ketone*.

cyclohexanecarbaldehyde

2-hydroxybenzenecarbaldehyde (usually known as salicylaldehyde, also called 2-hydroxybenzaldehyde)

Figure 19.4 Nomenclature of cyclic aldehydes.

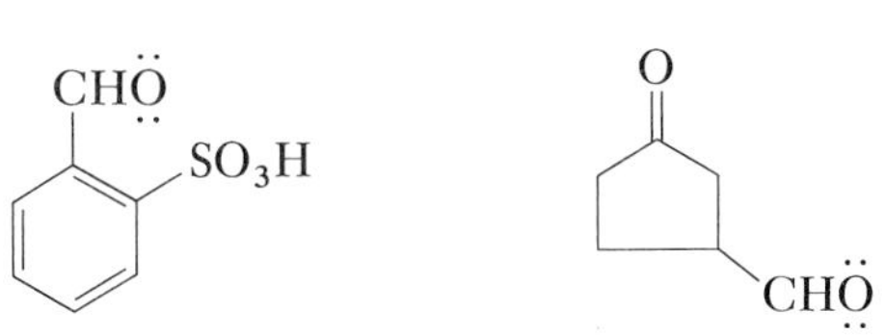

2-formylbenzenesulfonic acid

3-formylcyclopentanone

Figure 19.5 Nomenclature of the —CHO group as a *formyl* substituent. This type of nomenclature is used when the formyl group is present with another group of higher nomenclature priority.

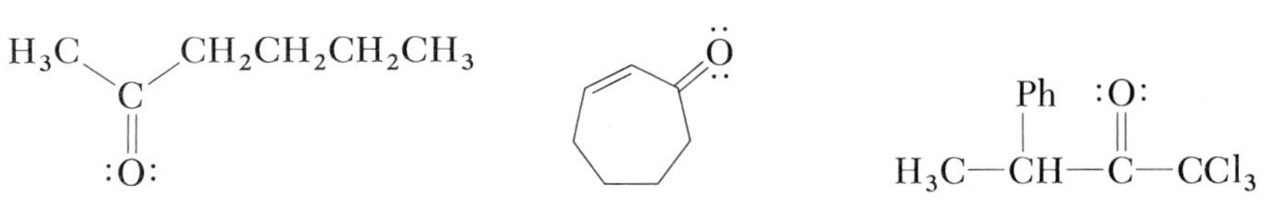

$H_3C-C(=O)-CH_2CH_2CH_2CH_3$ — 2-hexanone

2-cycloheptenone

$H_3C-CH(Ph)-C(=O)-CCl_3$ — 1,1,1-trichloro-3-phenyl-2-butanone

Figure 19.6 Example of IUPAC nomenclature for ketones.

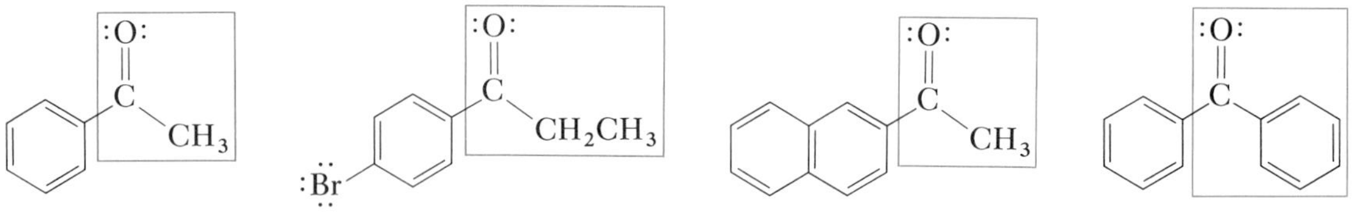

acetophenone | p-bromopropiophenone | acetonaphthone | benzophenone

Figure 19.7 A common nomenclature system for aromatic ketones.

Another nomenclature system is used for ketones in which the carbonyl group is attached directly to an aromatic ring. This system considers the substituent of the aromatic ring as an acyl group. Several examples are shown in Figure 19.7, where blocks are drawn around the acyl substituent.

PROBLEM 19.1 In providing the IUPAC names for acetone and methyl ethyl ketone, it is common not to use a numerical prefix for the position of the carbonyl group. Why not?

PROBLEM 19.2 For each of the structures shown in Figure 19.7, provide an alternative acceptable name.

If a keto functional group is present in a molecule along with another group of higher nomenclature priority, we indicate its presence by the prefix *oxo-*. For example, the following compound has the IUPAC name 2-oxohexanoic acid:

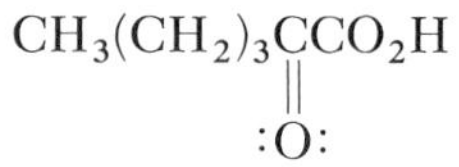

$$CH_3(CH_2)_3\underset{\underset{:O:}{\|}}{C}CO_2H$$

PROBLEM 19.3 Provide IUPAC names for each of the following:

a. formaldehyde **b.** propionaldehyde **c.** isobutyraldehyde
d. diisopropyl ketone **e.** di-*sec*-butyl ketone

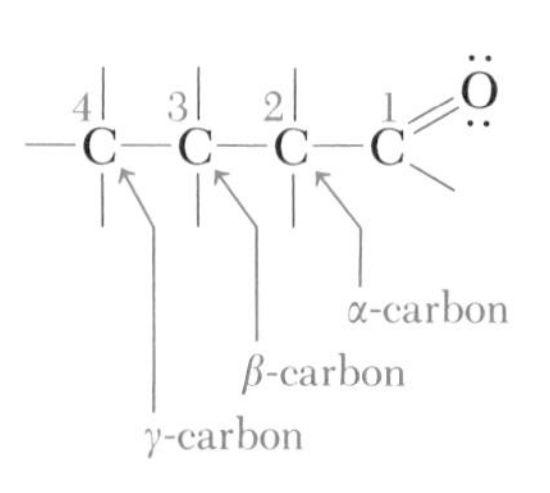

Figure 19.8 Use of Greek letters to designate carbon atoms in an aldehyde or ketone.

A final point of nomenclature concerns the use of Greek letters to designate the carbon atoms of an aldehyde or ketone. We designate a carbon directly attached to a carbonyl carbon as an *α-position*. Moving away from the carbonyl carbon, succeeding carbons have designations of β-, γ-, and so forth, as shown in Figure 19.8.

Greek letters are sometimes used to designate the position of substituents in common (non-IUPAC) names of carbonyl compounds. Several examples are shown in Figure 19.9.

$:\ddot{C}lCH_2CH_2CH\ddot{O}$	$CH_3CH(Ph)CH\ddot{O}$	$CH_3-C(=\ddot{O})-CHCl_2$	$:\ddot{C}lCH_2-C(=\ddot{O})-CH_2\ddot{C}l:$
β-chloropropionaldehyde (3-chloropropanal)	α-phenylpropionaldehyde (2-phenylpropanal)	α,α-dichloroacetone (1,1-dichloro-2-propanone)	α,α′-dichloroacetone (1,3-dichloro-3-propanone)

Figure 19.9 Use of Greek letters to designate position of substituents in common names of carbonyl compounds.

19.3 Bonding about the Carbonyl Group

According to the valence bond model, the carbon atom and the oxygen atom of a carbonyl group are sp^2 hybridized. One of the carbon sp^2 hybrids forms a σ bond to the carbonyl oxygen atom, and the other two form σ bonds to the other two substituents. A carbon-oxygen π bond results from side-to-side overlap of the unhybridized carbon $2p$ and oxygen $2p$ orbitals.

MOLECULAR ORBITAL ANALYSIS

Molecular Orbitals and the Carbonyl Group

The π molecular orbitals of the carbonyl group are considered as arising from the side-to-side interaction of the carbon $2p$ and oxygen $2p$ atomic orbitals, as shown in Figure 19.10. This diagram is similar to those given earlier (e.g.,

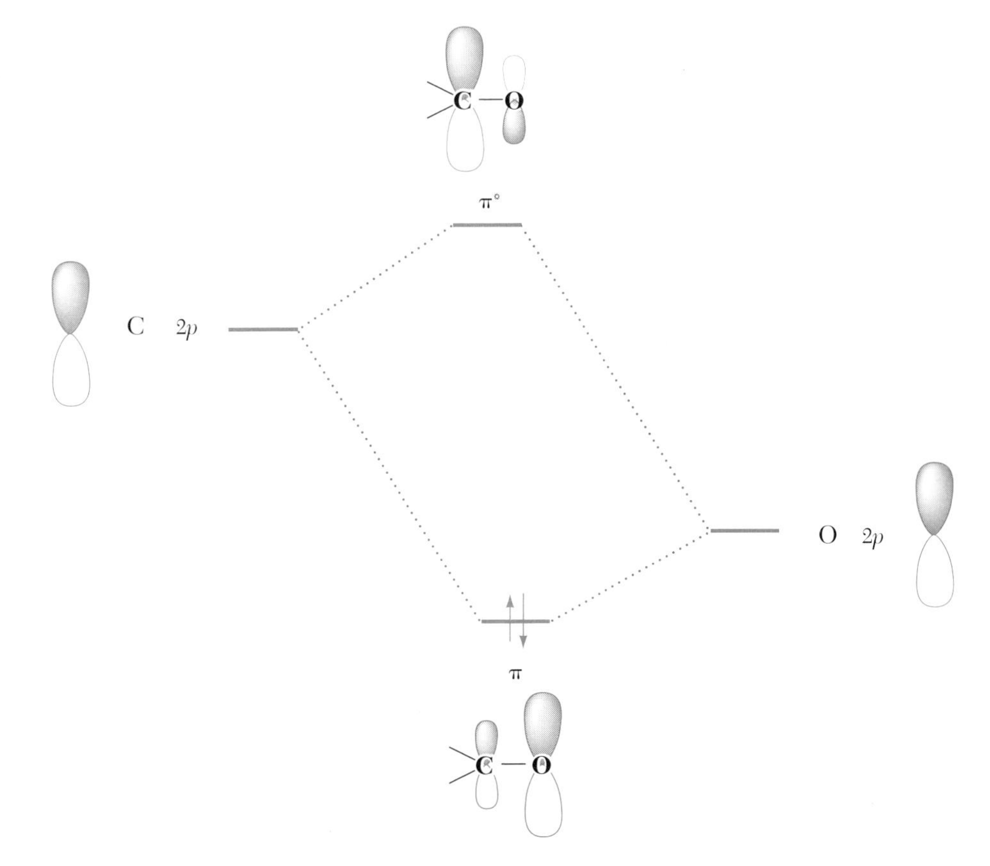

Figure 19.10 Orbital diagram for the π and π* molecular orbitals of the carbonyl group.

Figure 9.12) for the π orbitals of a carbon-to-carbon double bond. However, there is an important difference here. In this case, the two interacting atomic orbitals are not of the same energy—the oxygen $2p$ orbital is lower in energy than the carbon $2p$ orbital. When two orbitals of *unequal* energy interact, they do not contribute equally to the resulting molecular orbitals. Each molecular orbital is more like the atomic orbital that is closer to it in energy. Thus, the bonding π orbital of the carbonyl group has more oxygen $2p$ character than carbon $2p$ character. We indicate this schematically by drawing the lobe on oxygen larger than the lobe on carbon, as in Figure 19.10. For practical purposes, we can say that the electron density in this orbital is greater near the oxygen atom than near the carbon atom. Thus the carbon atom is electron deficient (electrophilic) and the oxygen atom is electron rich. In mathematical terms, the wavefunction for the bonding π orbital is described by Equation 19.1, in which the coefficient on oxygen is larger than the coefficient on carbon, that is, $b > a$.

Eqn. 19.1 $$\Psi(\pi) = a\phi(C_{2p}) + b\phi(O_{2p})$$

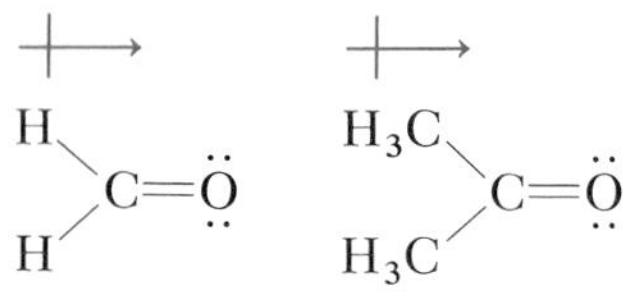

$H_2C{=}\ddot{O}:$ $\mu_D = 2.27$ $(CH_3)_2C{=}\ddot{O}:$ $\mu_D = 2.85$

Figure 19.11 Bond dipole in carbonyl compounds. The polarity of the carbon-oxygen bond results in appreciable dipole moments for most aldehydes and ketones.

Since oxygen is more electronegative than carbon, there is a dipole associated with the carbon-oxygen bond of an aldehyde or ketone, as illustrated in Figure 19.11. This bond polarity is of the utmost importance in the chemistry of aldehydes and ketones. In particular, the carbon atom, which is the positive end of the dipole, is susceptible to nucleophilic attack.

PROBLEM 19.4 Suggest a reason why acetone has a greater dipole moment than does formaldehyde.

Aldehydes and ketones are protonated on the oxygen atom when placed in acidic solution. We correlate this protonation with the presence of the unshared valence level electron pairs on the oxygen atom. The protonation is illustrated in Figure 19.12.

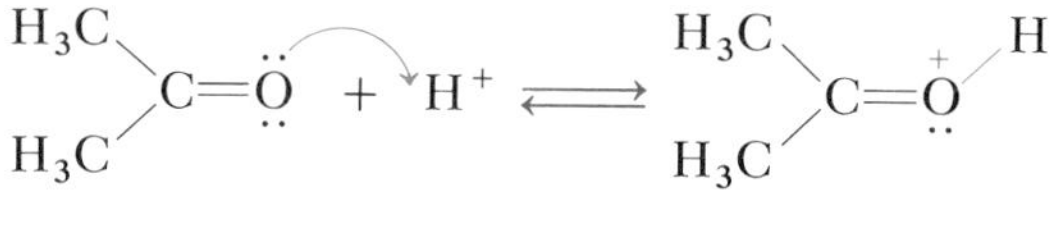

Figure 19.12 Reversible protonation of the oxygen of a carbonyl group.

$$(H_3C)_2C{=}\ddot{O}: + H^+ \rightleftharpoons (H_3C)_2C{=}\overset{+}{\ddot{O}}{-}H$$

This basicity of the carbonyl oxygen also plays an important role in the chemistry of carbonyl compounds, as will become clear in the rest of this chapter.

19.4 Physical Properties of Carbonyl Compounds

Because of their polarities, aldehydes and ketones have boiling temperatures that are higher than those of hydrocarbons of similar molecular weight. However, because aldehyde or ketone molecules cannot hydrogen bond to one another, their ability to aggregate is less than that of alcohols of similar molec-

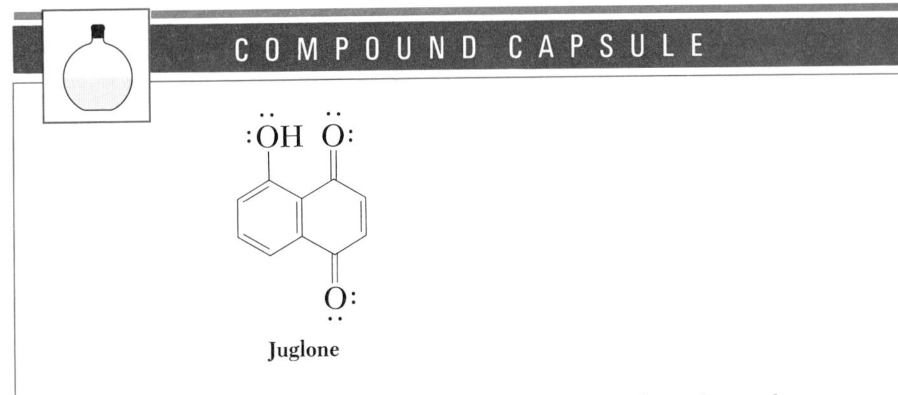

Juglone

It is impossible to grow certain plants near certain other plants, for reasons that are often chemical in origin. One type of plant releases a substance into the soil that prevents the growth of another type of plant. A classical example of this phenomenon occurs with the black walnut tree (*Juglonis nigra*). Plants such as tomatoes and raspberries will not grow near a black walnut tree as a result of the compound *juglone*, which is produced by the black walnut tree and exuded into the soil. This phenomenon is known as *alleopathy*.

The compound juglone is a type of carbonyl compound known as a *quinone*. Its two carbonyl groups are in conjugation with the adjacent ring and the carbon-carbon double bond in their own ring. This compound and others of its type that exhibit alleopathy are of considerable interest as agents for the control of weeds.

ular weight. They are thus more volatile (have lower boiling temperatures) than alcohols of similar molecular weight. Some comparisons of boiling temperatures are shown in Table 19.1.

Table 19.1 Comparison of Boiling Temperatures of an Alkane, an Aldehyde, a Ketone, and an Alcohol of Similar Molecular Weight

Compound	Boiling Temperature (°C)	Molecular Weight
$CH_3CH_2CH_2CH_3$	−0.5	58
$CH_3CH_2CH\ddot{\underset{..}{O}}$	48	58
$(CH_3)_2C{=}\ddot{\underset{..}{O}}$	56	58
$CH_3CH_2CH_2\ddot{\underset{..}{O}}H$	98	60

PROBLEM 19.5 Suggest a reason why acetone has a higher boiling temperature than the isomeric propionaldehyde. (*Hint:* Review the answer to Problem 19.4.)

Table 19.2 Physical Properties of Representative Aldehydes and Ketones

Structure	Name	Melting Temperature (°C)	Boiling Temperature (°C)	Water Solubility (g/100g)
$H_2C{=}\ddot{O}$	formaldehyde (methanal)	−92	−21	∞
$CH_3CH\ddot{O}$	acetaldehyde (ethanal)	−121	21	∞
$CH_3CH_2CH\ddot{O}$	propanal	−81	49	20
$PhCH\ddot{O}$	benzaldehyde	−26	179	0.3
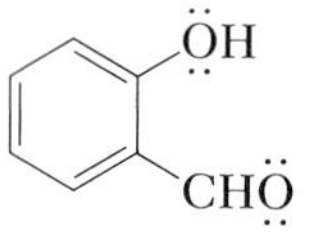 (benzene ring with ortho $\ddot{O}H$ and $CH\ddot{O}$)	salicylaldehyde (2-hydroxybenzaldehyde)	−7	197	slight
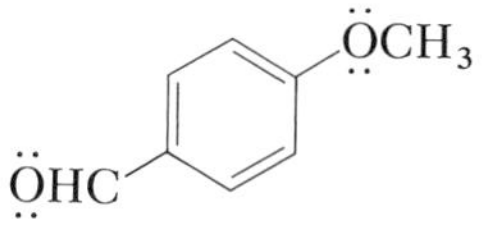 $\ddot{O}HC$–(benzene ring, para)–$\ddot{O}CH_3$	*p*-anisaldehyde (4-methoxybenzaldehyde)	3	248	slight
$(CH_3)_2C{=}\ddot{O}$	acetone (2-propanone)	−95	56	∞
$CH_3{-}C({=}\ddot{O}){-}CH_2CH_3$	2-butanone	−87	80	37
$CH_3{-}C({=}\ddot{O}){-}CH_2CH_2CH_3$	2-pentanone	−78	102	slight
$(CH_3CH_2)_2C{=}\ddot{O}$	3-pentanone	−40	102	4.7
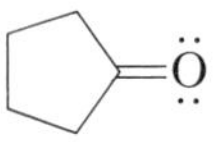 (cyclopentane ring)$={\ddot{O}}$	cyclopentanone	−51	131	43
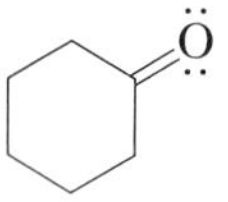 (cyclohexane ring)$={\ddot{O}}$	cyclohexanone	−16	156	slight
$Ph{-}C({=}\ddot{O}){-}CH_3$	acetophenone	20	202	insoluble
$Ph_2C{=}\ddot{O}$	benzophenone	48	306	insoluble

Pure formaldehyde is a gas at low pressure and ordinary temperature. A solution of formaldehyde in water (known as formalin) is used for preserving biological specimens. The other low molecular weight members of the aldehyde and ketone families are liquids with appreciable water solubilities. Hydrogen bonding of these molecules to water is possible, and their water solubility is relatively high. Many of these compounds have characteristic odors (some pleasant, some unpleasant), and they are widely used as flavoring constituents. The properties of some representative aldehydes and ketones are shown in Table 19.2.

19.5 IR and NMR Spectra of Aldehydes and Ketones

The most characteristic spectroscopic signature of a carbonyl compound is an intense absorption band in the IR region 1650–1850 cm^{-1}. All compounds containing a carbonyl linkage, including carboxylic acids, esters, and amides, as well as aldehydes and ketones, give rise to this IR absorption. Thus, we need to apply some caution in making structural assignments based solely on the presence of a *carbonyl band* in the IR spectrum.

Nevertheless, the frequency of the C=O stretching vibration varies considerably with the type of carbonyl group present, and this variation is useful in making structural assignments. In general, the frequency (wavenumber) of the absorption is decreased when the C=O bond is weakened and increased when the bond is strengthened. For example, Figure 19.13 compares the C=O absorption frequencies for acetophenone and a nonaromatic ketone of similar size, cyclohexyl methyl ketone. The relative weakness of the C=Ö bond in acetophenone correlates with its conjugation with the π system of the aromatic ring. We can draw resonance structures showing this conjugation, and they include structures in which a positive charge is located on the ring. These resonance structures are shown in Figure 19.14. No corresponding resonance

Figure 19.13 Comparison of C=O stretching frequencies of acetophenone and cyclohexyl methyl ketone.

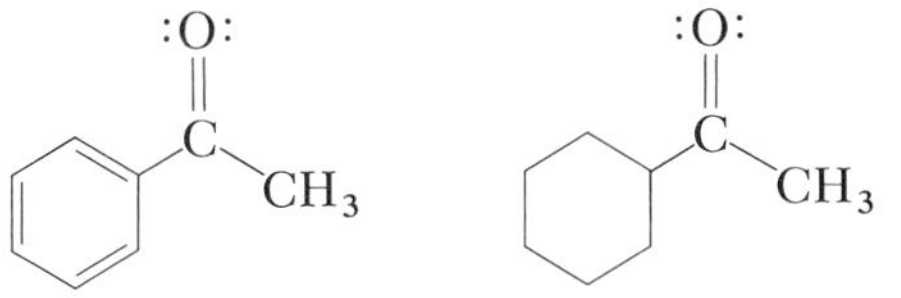

	acetophenone	cyclohexyl methyl ketone
C=O stretching frequency (cm^{-1})	*1685*	*1715*

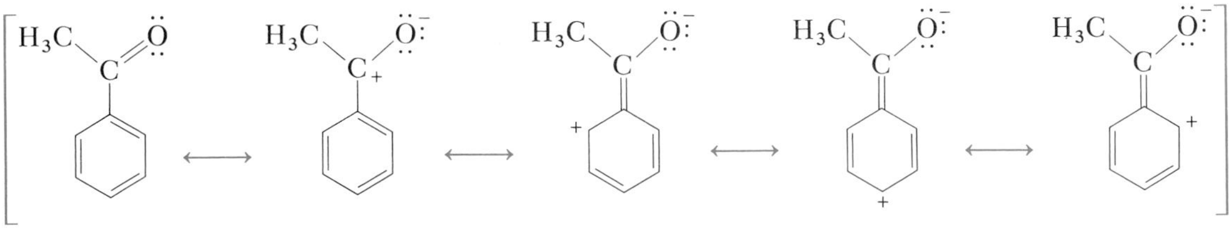

Figure 19.14 Resonance structures for acetophenone. In several structures the carbon-oxygen bond is single. In three of these the carbonyl carbon is involved in a double bond with an adjacent carbon of the aromatic ring. No such structures can be drawn for cyclohexyl methyl ketone. The carbonyl linkage of acetophenone is accordingly longer than that of cyclohexyl methyl ketone and has less double bond character.

structures can be written for cyclohexyl methyl ketone. Because of this delocalization of carbonyl π elecrons, the carbonyl linkage of acetophenone has less double bond character than that of cyclohexyl methyl ketone. Thus, acetophenone absorbs IR light of a lower frequency, because weaker bonds have smaller force constants.

It is often possible to distinguish aldehydes from ketones by the appearance of bands in the 2700–2800 cm^{-1} region of the IR spectra of aldehydes. Unfortunately, these bands are often weak or poorly resolved. A better differentiation comes from the appearance of a very low field (δ 9.5–10.1) signal for the aldehydic hydrogen in the ^1H NMR spectrum.

In the ^1H NMR spectra of methyl ketones, sharp methyl singlets appear at δ ~2.2 for methyl alkyl ketones and at δ ~2.6 for methyl aryl ketones. In the ^{13}C NMR spectra of aldehydes and ketones the carbonyl carbon signal occurs ~200–220 ppm downfield from TMS. Methyl groups (electron-donating groups) attached to the α and β carbons cause moderate downfield shifts of the carbonyl carbon signal. On the other hand, electron-withdrawing substituents at the α-position cause the carbonyl carbon signal to be shifted upfield.

PROBLEM 19.6 Suggest structures for compounds *A–F*, for which analytical data is provided below.

a. *A* Formula: $C_5H_{10}O$; IR: 1715 cm^{-1}; ^1H NMR: exhibits only a triplet and a quartet.

b. *B* Formula: C_4H_8O; IR: 1720, 2710 cm^{-1}; ^1H NMR: δ 1.1 (doublet, relative area 6), δ 2.3 (multiplet, relative area 1), δ 9.6 (closely spaced doublet, relative area 1).

c. *C* Formula: C_4H_8O; IR: 1715 cm^{-1}; ^1H NMR: δ 1.0 (triplet, relative area 3), δ 2.1 (singlet, relative area 3), δ 2.5 (quartet, relative area 2).

d. *D* Formula: $C_4H_8O_2$; ^{13}C NMR (broad-band decoupled): 25.9, 58.8, 77.7, and 205.5 ppm downfield from TMS (under conditions of coupling to directly attached protons, these signals appear respectively as a quartet, a quartet, a triplet, and a singlet).

e. *E* Formula: $C_7H_{14}O$; IR: 1715 cm^{-1}; ^1H NMR: δ 1.0 (singlet, relative area 9), δ 2.2 (singlet, relative area 2), δ 2.3 (singlet, relative area 3).

f. *F* Formula: $C_5H_{10}O$; IR: 1715 cm^{-1}; ^1H NMR: δ 1.1 (doublet, relative area 6), δ 2.1 (singlet, relative area 3), δ 2.3 (multiplet, relative area 1).

PROBLEM 19.7 You have two samples of organic compounds. You know that one of them is *p*-methoxyacetophenone and the other is *p*-nitroacetophenone, but you don't know which is which. On IR analysis, sample *A* exhibits a carbonyl peak at 1700 cm^{-1}, whereas sample *B* exhibits a carbonyl peak at 1685 cm^{-1}. Deduce which structure belongs to sample *A* and which to sample *B*.

19.6 Preparation of Aldehydes and Ketones

FROM ALCOHOLS BY OXIDATION

The most generally important method for the preparation of aldehydes and ketones is the oxidation of alcohols. In Chapter 6 (Section 6.9) we surveyed suitable oxidizing agents for this type of conversion. In general, the oxidation of a secondary alcohol to a ketone proceeds well with a variety of oxidizing agents. However, oxidation of a primary alcohol to an aldehyde requires a careful choice of reagent and/or conditions in order to avoid overoxidation to a carboxylic acid.

The most widely used oxidizing agents for the alcohol-to-carbonyl conversion are Cr(VI) reagents. Chromium trioxide dissolved in acetic acid or sulfuric acid/acetone (the **Jones reagent**) is particularly convenient for the oxidation of secondary alcohols to ketones. Sodium or potassium dichromate in sulfuric acid is also useful for the same purpose.

Chromium trioxide in pyridine is a common choice for the oxidation of primary alcohols to aldehydes. Use of this reagent avoids the problem of overoxidation to a carboxylic acid.

For the present we will limit our attention to the use of Cr(VI) oxidizing agents for the preparation of carbonyl compounds from alcohols. However, many other types of reagents are also well suited for this purpose, and we will meet some of them elsewhere. A number of specific examples of Cr(VI) oxidation of alcohols were given in Chapter 6. Some further examples are shown in Equations 19.2–19.5.

Eqn. 19.2

CH_2OH / OH — CrO_3, pyridine / CH_2Cl_2 → CHO / OH

m-hydroxybenzyl alcohol

87% yield
m-hydroxybenzaldehyde

Eqn. 19.3

CH_3 / CH / OH — CrO_3 / acetic acid → CH_3 / C / O

1-cyclopentylethanol

54% yield
cyclopentyl methyl ketone

Eqn. 19.4

OH — CrO_3, H_2SO_4 / acetone / (Jones reagent) → O

cyclooctanol

95% yield
cyclooctanone

Eqn. 19.5

CH_2CH_3 / :OH — $Na_2Cr_2O_7$, aq H_2SO_4 → CH_2CH_3 / :O:

4-ethylcyclohexanol

90% yield
4-ethylcyclohexanone

Notice that in Equation 19.5 the ethyl substituent is *not* converted into a carboxyl group as it would be if the substituent were attached to a benzene ring (see Section 18.10). Side-chain oxidation occurs only if the side-chain is attached to an *aromatic* ring.

FROM ALKYNES BY HYDRATION

We can convert alkynes into aldehydes or ketones by **hydration,** as was described in Chapter 15 (Section 15.6). The hydration of an alkyne is effected by either a direct hydration procedure or via hydroboration/oxidation. In either case, an enol forms initially, then tautomerizes to an aldehyde or ketone. Examples of these reactions were shown previously in Equations 15.18, 15.19, and 15.21. Additional examples are given in Equations 19.6 and 19.7.

Eqn. 19.6

$$CH_3(CH_2)_6{-}C{\equiv}C{-}H \xrightarrow[H_2SO_4]{HgSO_4,\ H_2O} CH_3(CH_2)_6{-}\underset{\underset{:\ddot{O}:}{\|}}{C}{-}CH_3$$

1-nonyne → 91% yield 2-nonanone

Eqn. 19.7

$$CH_3(CH_2)_5{-}C{\equiv}C{-}H \xrightarrow[2.\ H_2O_2,\ KOH]{1.\ [(CH_3)_2CHCH(CH_3)]_2BH} CH_3(CH_2)_6{-}CH\ddot{\underset{..}{O}}$$

1-octyne → 70% yield octanal

PROBLEM 19.8 Why do we use a substituted borane rather than BH_3 itself in the reaction shown in Equation 19.7?

FROM AROMATIC COMPOUNDS BY ELECTROPHILIC SUBSTITUTION

It is possible to introduce a formyl group $-C(=\ddot{O})H$ or an acyl group $-C(=\ddot{O})R$ onto an aromatic ring by electrophilic aromatic substitution. The Friedel-Crafts acylation method, which was described in Chapter 18, can be used to accomplish this conversion. In Equation 19.8 we see another sample of this type of reaction.

Eqn. 19.8

$$C_6H_5CH_3 \xrightarrow{PhC(=O){-}Cl,\ AlCl_3} p\text{-}CH_3C_6H_4{-}C(=\ddot{O}){-}Ph$$

toluene → 92% yield *p*-tolylphenon

However, this reaction is limited in scope in that some aromatic compounds are too deactivated to undergo the reaction. Moreover, the preparation of aldehydes requires a modified procedure. We would need to use formyl halides (HCOX) to prepare aldehydes, but except for formyl fluoride, such halides are too reactive to be isolable and thus are not available for the standard Friedel-Crafts acylation. However, we can perform the formylation of an aromatic ring by treating the substrate with carbon monoxide and hydrogen chloride in the presence of a Lewis acid. This procedure, known as the **Gatterman-Koch synthesis,** in effect produces formyl chloride in situ. The yields in this reaction are variable but are high enough for the reaction to be of significance for the industrial preparation of some important aldehydes. The reaction involving benzene is shown in Equation 19.9.

Eqn. 19.9

CHO

CO, HCl
$AlCl_3$

benzene

85% yield
benzaldehyde

It is also possible to use formyl fluoride and the Lewis acid BF_3 to accomplish formylation, as shown in Equation 19.10.

Eqn. 19.10

H—C(=O)F
BF_3

CHO

mesitylene

70% yield
2,4,6-trimethylbenzaldehyde

PROBLEM 19.9 Write a mechanism for the reaction of Equation 19.10 using the curved-arrow formalism.

There is also a special reaction for the formylation of phenolic compounds. Formylation *ortho* to the hydroxyl group occurs in the **Reimer-Tiemann reaction,** which involves treating a phenol with chloroform and base. An example is shown in Equation 19.11.

Eqn. 19.11

:OH

$CHCl_3$
NaOH

:OH
CHO

α-naphthol

50% yield
1-hydroxy-2-naphthaldehyde

The reaction of chloroform and base produces dichlorocarbene, a reactive species that we met earlier (Section 12.9). The carbene is electron deficient and behaves like an electrophile toward the electron-rich aromatic ring. Its reaction is typical of other electrophilic aromatic substitutions. However, under these reaction conditions one of the two chlorine atoms is eventually replaced by a hydroxyl group through nucleophilic substitution. This step produces a substance having both a hydroxyl group and a chlorine atom attached to the same carbon atom. Such substances are unstable and undergo facile elimination of HCl to form a carbonyl compound.

MECHANISM OF REACTION

The Reimer-Tiemann Reaction

Step 1 Removal of a proton from chloroform

$$HO^- + H-CCl_3 \longrightarrow HO-H + {}^-{:}CCl_3$$

Step 2 Dissociation of the trichloromethyl anion

$$^-{:}CCl_2-Cl \longrightarrow {:}CCl_2 + Cl^-$$

Step 3 Addition of dichlorocarbene to the phenoxide ion

$$C_6H_5O^- + {:}CCl_2 \longrightarrow \text{cyclohexadienone with } H \text{ and } {}^-CCl_2 \text{ at C-2}$$

Step 4 Abstraction of a proton from water

$$\text{dienone}-{}^-CCl_2 + H-OH \longrightarrow \text{dienone}-CHCl_2 + {}^-OH$$

Step 5 Tautomerization to form a substituted phenol

$$\text{2-(dichloromethyl)cyclohexa-2,4-dienone} \longrightarrow \text{2-(dichloromethyl)phenol } (HO-C_6H_4-CHCl_2)$$

Step 6 Displacement of halide by hydroxide ion

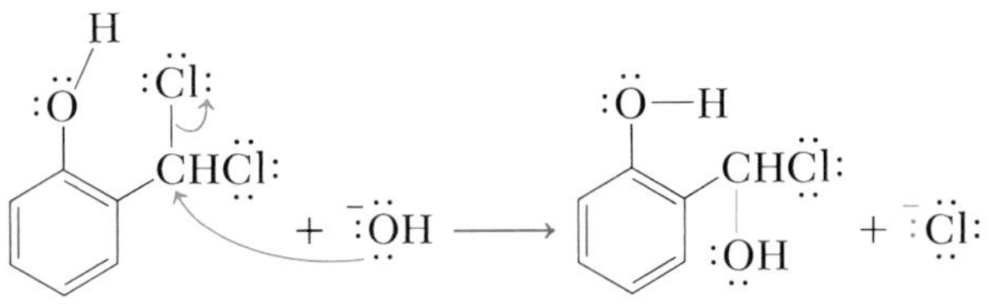

Step 7 Elimination of HCl to form the aldehyde product

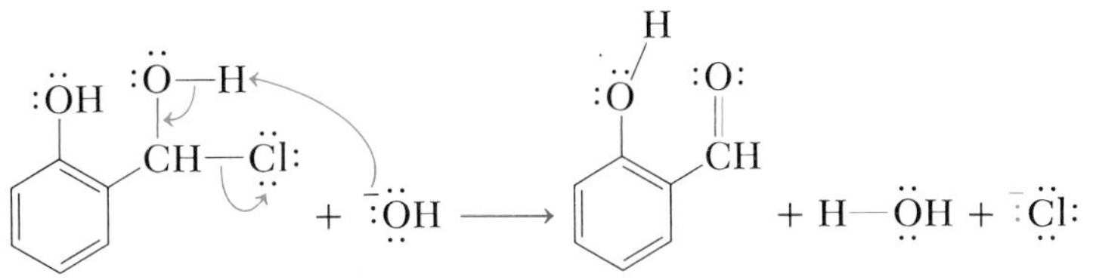

Phenols (and some other aromatics that are particularly reactive toward electrophilic substitution) undergo acylation, usually in good yields, by the **Hoesch reaction.** This reaction involves the following components: the aromatic compound, an acid such as sulfuric or hydrochloric acid, a nitrile, and in some cases a Lewis acid catalyst. An example of the Hoesch reaction is shown in Equation 19.12.

Eqn. 19.12

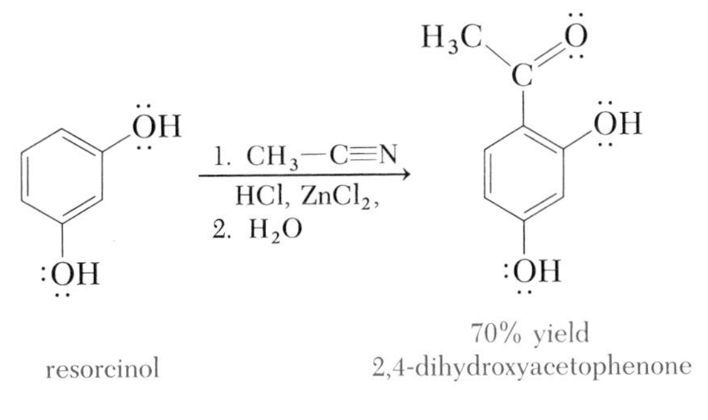

1. $CH_3—C \equiv N$, HCl, $ZnCl_2$, 2. H_2O

resorcinol

70% yield
2,4-dihydroxyacetophenone

After we have discussed additional topics, you will be asked to propose a mechanism for this reaction (Problem 19.53).

FROM 1,2-DIOLS VIA THE PINACOL/PINACOLONE REARRANGEMENT

A mechanistically interesting route to aldehydes and ketones is a reaction of 1,2-diols (glycols) known as the **pinacol/pinacolone rearrangement.** This reaction occurs when a 1,2-diol is treated with a moderately concentrated mineral acid such as sulfuric acid. An example is shown in Equation 19.13; *pinacol* (a trivial name for 2,3-dimethyl-2,3-butanediol) is converted into *pinacolone* (*tert*-butyl methyl ketone).

Eqn. 19.13

$$\underset{\text{pinacol}}{H_3C-\underset{:\ddot{O}H}{\overset{CH_3}{C}}-\underset{:\ddot{O}H}{\overset{CH_3}{C}}-CH_3} \xrightarrow{H_2SO_4} \underset{\substack{70\%\ \text{yield} \\ \text{pinacolone}}}{H_3C-\underset{CH_3}{\overset{CH_3}{C}}-\underset{:O:}{\overset{}{\overset{\|}{C}}}-CH_3}$$

Other 1,2-diols react in a similar manner.

The mechanism of the pinacol/pinacolone rearrangement follows. Reaction begins with the protonation of one of the hydroxyl groups and the loss of water to form a carbocation. In the example shown, the two hydroxyl groups are equivalent and the same carbocation results from protonation of either of them. If the two hydroxyl groups are *not* equivalent, reaction leads to the more stable of the two possible carbocations (see Problem 19.10). The carbocation so formed then rearranges by means of alkyl migration. The driving force for the migration is the formation of a more stable carbocation, one that is resonance stabilized. Even though the initially formed carbocation is tertiary, a rearrangement is still favorable because the rearranged carbocation is resonance stabilized (the rearranged carbocation has a resonance structure in which every atom other than hydrogen has a complete octet of electrons). The rearranged carbocation is a protonated ketone, which exists in equilibrium with the free ketone through an acid-base equilibrium.

MECHANISM OF REACTION

The Pinacol/Pinacolone Rearrangement

Step 1 Protonation of the glycol.

$$(CH_3)_2C(\ddot{O}H)-C(CH_3)_2\ddot{O}H \underset{}{\overset{H_2SO_4}{\rightleftharpoons}} (CH_3)_2C(\ddot{O}H)-C(CH_3)_2\overset{+}{O}H_2$$

Step 2 Loss of water to form a carbocation.

$$(CH_3)_2C(\ddot{O}H)-C(CH_3)_2\overset{+}{O}H_2 \rightleftharpoons (CH_3)_2C(\ddot{O}H)-\overset{+}{C}(CH_3)_2 + \ddot{O}H_2$$

Step 3 Rearrangement of the carbocation. The second resonance structure is especially stable, because all atoms have a noble gas configuration.

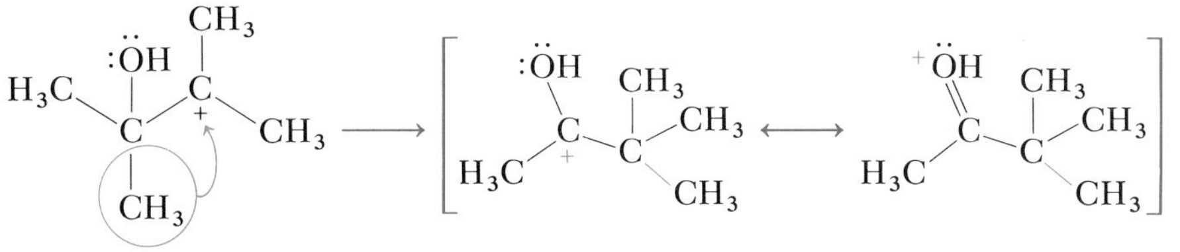

$H_3C-\ddot{C}(:\ddot{O}H)(CH_3)-\overset{+}{C}(CH_3)-CH_3 \longrightarrow \left[H_3C-\overset{+}{C}(:\ddot{O}H)-C(CH_3)_3 \longleftrightarrow H_3C-C(=\overset{+}{\ddot{O}}H)-C(CH_3)_3 \right]$

Step 4 Loss of a proton to yield the product.

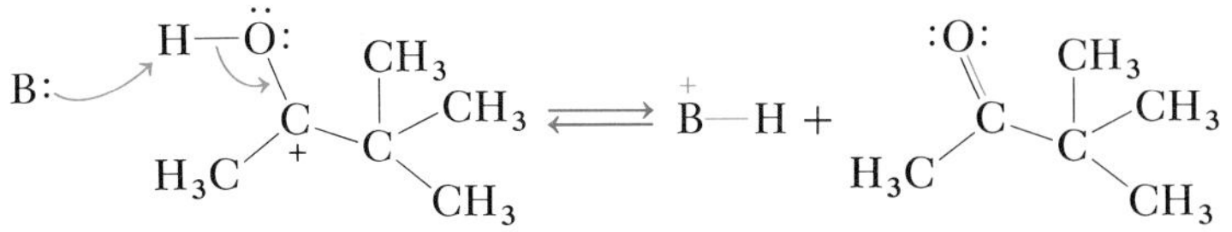

$B: + H-\ddot{O}:-\overset{+}{C}(H_3C)-C(CH_3)_3 \rightleftharpoons \overset{+}{B}-H + H_3C-C(=\ddot{O}:)-C(CH_3)_3$

PROBLEM 19.10 Predict the products of each of the following pinacol/pinacolone rearrangements:

a. 1-phenyl-1,2-ethanediol with sulfuric acid to yield a compound of formula C_8H_8O

b. 2-methyl-1-phenyl-1,2-propanediol with sulfuric acid to yield a compound of formula $C_{10}H_{12}O$

c. 1,2-butanediol with sulfuric acid to yield a compound of formula C_4H_8O

d. 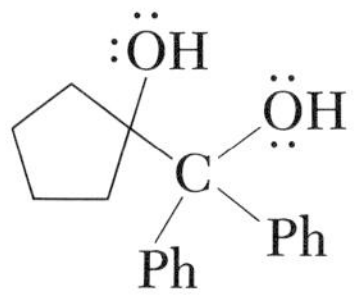 (1-hydroxycyclopentyl)–C(:ÖH)(Ph)(Ph) with sulfuric acid to yield a compound of formula $C_{18}H_{18}O$ that contains no five-membered ring

e. 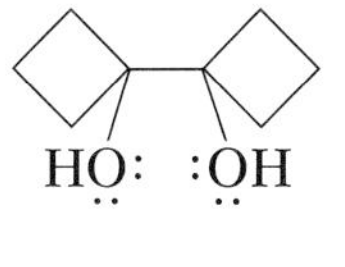 (1-hydroxycyclobutyl)–(1-hydroxycyclobutyl), HÖ: :ÖH, with sulfuric acid to yield a compound of formula $C_8H_{12}O$ that has a spirane structure

Steps to Solving the Problem

Solution to Problem 19.10a

1. Draw the structure of the starting material.

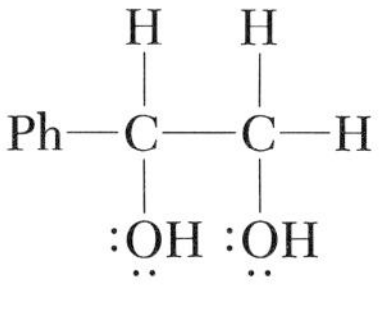

$Ph-CH(:\ddot{O}H)-CH(:\ddot{O}H)-H$

2. Note the site of the initial protonation. The two hydroxyl groups are not equivalent. One will be protonated and lost as water while the other oxygen will be retained in the product. We must decide what will be the fate of each. The secondary hydroxyl will be protonated and lost as water. Protonation and loss of this hydroxyl leads to a benzylic carbocation. Protonation of the other hydroxyl leads to a less stable primary carbocation.

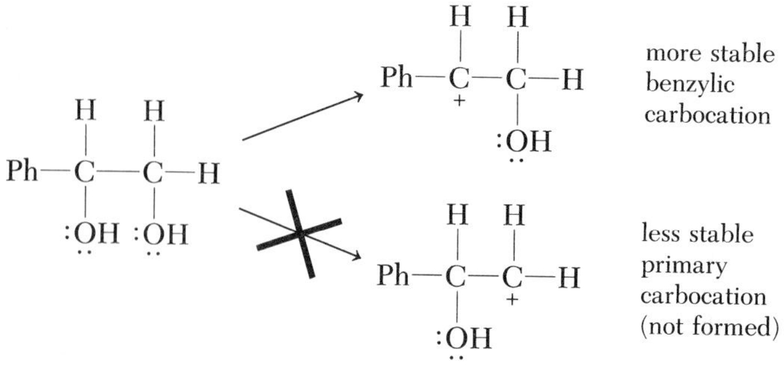

$PhCH(OH)CH_2OH \longrightarrow PhC^{+}HCH_2OH$ — more stable benzylic carbocation

$PhCH(OH)CH_2OH \not\longrightarrow PhCH(OH)C^{+}H_2$ — less stable primary carbocation (not formed)

3. Consider the rearrangement step of the mechanism. A migration of a hydrogen from an adjacent carbon to the carbocation site occurs. We predict the product of the reaction to be 2-phenylethanal.

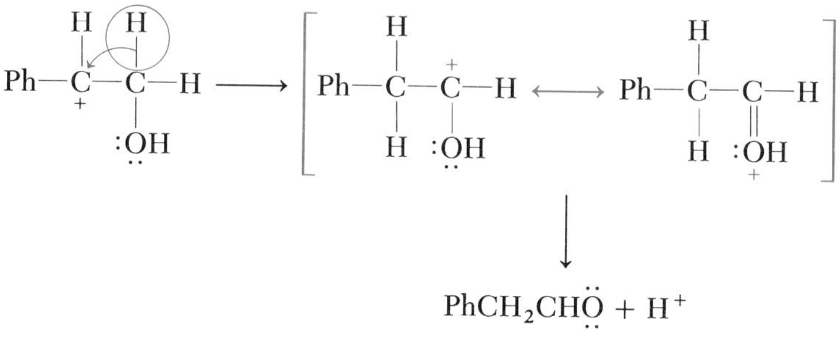

$$Ph\overset{+}{C}H{-}CH_2OH \longrightarrow \left[PhCH_2{-}\overset{+}{C}H{-}\ddot{O}H \longleftrightarrow PhCH_2{-}CH{=}\overset{+}{O}H \right] \longrightarrow PhCH_2CHO + H^+$$

When there is competition among potential migrating groups, an aryl group generally migrates in preference to an alkyl group (see Figure 19.15). However, the propensity of hydrogen to migrate in preference to aryl and alkyl groups varies greatly from compound to compound and is difficult to predict.

FROM ACID HALIDES AND REDUCING AGENTS OR ORGANOMETALLICS

We can prepare aldehydes and ketones from acid halides (compounds of structure RCOX). We have met acid halides previously in the Friedel-Crafts acylation, and we will consider them in detail in Chapter 22. To prepare aldehydes from acid halides we need to perform a reduction, replacing the halogen atom by a hydrogen atom. Several approaches can be used.

One approach is a catalytic hydrogenation procedure known as the **Rosenmund reduction.** In this reaction the catalyst is palladium supported on barium sulfate. Equation 19.14 shows an example of this reaction.

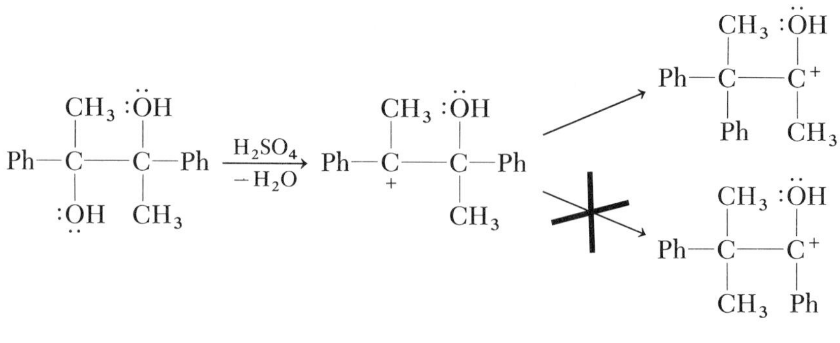

$$Ph{-}C(CH_3)(OH){-}C(CH_3)(OH){-}Ph \xrightarrow[-H_2O]{H_2SO_4} Ph{-}\overset{+}{C}(CH_3){-}C(CH_3)(OH){-}Ph$$

$$\longrightarrow Ph{-}C(CH_3)(Ph){-}C^{+}(OH)(CH_3)$$

$$\not\longrightarrow Ph{-}C(CH_3)(CH_3){-}C^{+}(OH)(Ph)$$

Figure 19.15 Migratory preference in the pinacol/pinacolone rearrangement. An aryl group generally migrates in preference to an alkyl group. We say that an aryl group has a greater *migratory aptitude* than does an alkyl group.

Eqn. 19.14

$$\text{cyclohexyl–CH}_2\text{–C(=O)–Cl} \xrightarrow[\text{Pd/BaSO}_4]{\text{H}_2} \text{cyclohexyl–CH}_2\text{–C(=O)–H}$$

cyclohexylethanoyl chloride

70% yield
cyclohexylethanal

We must use the special supported catalyst so that *further* reduction of the aldehyde to form a primary alcohol does not occur. An alternative procedure is based on hydride chemistry. The complex hydride reagent lithium tri-*tert*-butoxyaluminum hydride effects the same overall conversion, as shown in Equation 19.15. In general, this method provides a high yield preparation of aldehydes.

Eqn. 19.15

$$\text{Cl–C(=O)–C}_6\text{H}_4\text{–NO}_2 \xrightarrow[\text{aq acid workup}]{\text{LiAlH[OC(CH}_3)_3]_3} \text{H–C(=O)–C}_6\text{H}_4\text{–NO}_2$$

p-nitrobenzoyl chloride

85% yield
p-nitrobenzaldehyde

The acid halide required for this reaction is prepared by treatment of the corresponding carboxylic acid with thionyl chloride or some other inorganic acid chloride (Chapter 21). The reducing agent, lithium tri-*tert*-butoxyaluminum hydride, is a reduced-reactivity form of a parent hydride reagent, lithium aluminum hydride ($LiAlH_4$). Lithium aluminum hydride itself, which we will discuss later in this chapter, is too powerful a reducing agent for the preparation of aldehydes from acid halides. It causes a *further* reduction of the aldehyde to a primary alcohol, as shown in Equation 19.16.

Eqn. 19.16

$$\text{C}_6\text{H}_5\text{–C(=O)–Cl} \xrightarrow[\text{aq acid workup}]{\text{LiAlH}_4\text{, (CH}_3\text{CH}_2)_2\text{O}} \text{C}_6\text{H}_5\text{–CH}_2\text{OH}$$

benzoyl chloride

95% yield
benzyl alcohol

In order to prepare ketones from acid halides we use either a lithium dialkyl cuprate reagent (R_2CuLi, Chapter 13) or a dialkyl cadmium reagent (R_2Cd). Representative examples of the use of these reagents are shown in Equations 19.17 and 19.18.

Eqn. 19.17

$$\text{H}_3\text{C–C(=O)–Cl} \xrightarrow[\text{aq acid workup}]{\text{Ph}_2\text{CuLi, (CH}_3\text{CH}_2)_2\text{O}} \text{H}_3\text{C–C(=O)–Ph}$$

acetyl chloride

55% yield
acetophenone

Eqn. 19.18

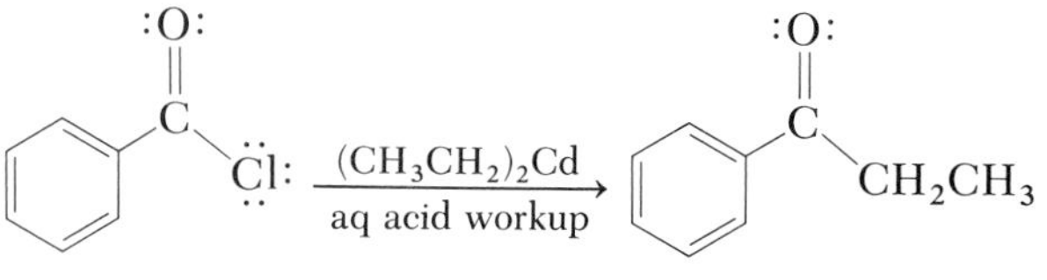

$$\text{C}_6\text{H}_5\text{C(=O)Cl} \xrightarrow[\text{aq acid workup}]{(\text{CH}_3\text{CH}_2)_2\text{Cd}} \text{C}_6\text{H}_5\text{C(=O)CH}_2\text{CH}_3$$

benzoyl chloride

85% yield
propiophenone

The preparation of the lithium dialkyl cuprate reagents was described earlier (Chapter 11). We prepare dialkyl cadmium reagents by the addition of anhydrous cadmium chloride to a solution of a Grignard reagent, as shown in Figure 19.16.

Figure 19.16 Preparation of the dialkyl cadmium reagent. Solid, anhydrous cadmium chloride is added to an ether solution of the Grignard reagent to form the dialkyl cadmium reagent. The dialkyl cadmium reagent, once formed, reacts in situ with other reagents (e.g., an acid chloride) that we add to it.

$$2\,\text{RMgX} + \text{CdCl}_2 \longrightarrow \text{R}_2\text{Cd} + 2\,\text{MgXCl}$$

dialkyl
cadmium
reagent

Both lithium dialkyl cuprates and dialkyl cadmium reagents are organometallics that serve as a source of a carbanion. In effect, the carbanion performs a nucleophilic attack on the acyl halide and displaces halide ion. You might wonder why we do not use a Grignard reagent or alkyllithium reagent to bring about this type of conversion, since both of these can also serve as a carbanion source. The reason is that both are too powerful reagents for the desired conversion. Each *does* convert an acid chloride to a ketone, but it further reacts with the ketone to form a tertiary alcohol. Even if we use only a limited amount of the reagent, we get a mixture of products that is difficult to separate into its components. (At this point you should review Chapter 11, where we discussed the reaction of ketones with Grignard reagents as an effective method for the preparation of tertiary alcohols.)

19.7 Nucleophilic Addition Reactions: Introduction

Aldehydes and ketones react with a wide range of nucleophiles. In general terms we understand this type of reactivity to be related to the electrophilic nature of the carbonyl carbon (see Section 19.3). Nucleophiles, being electron rich, tend to attack the electron-deficient carbon of the carbonyl group, as illustrated in Figure 19.17. The addition process leads to a tetrahedral alkoxide ion. Notice that when the nucleophile attacks the carbonyl carbon, no group is displaced, in contrast to the reaction of nucleophiles with haloalkanes. Thus we refer to the attack of a nucleophile on a carbonyl compound as nucleophilic *addition*, not substitution.

Typically we find that the alkoxide ion so produced becomes protonated, either directly under the reaction conditions or during a subsequent workup of the reaction. The result is the formation of an alcohol. We will illustrate the mechanism of this reaction using the reaction of an acetylide ion (as the nucleophile) with an aldehyde (followed by hydrolysis) as our example.

Figure 19.17 Nucleophilic attack on the carbonyl group. Attack of an anionic nucleophile on a carbonyl group generates a tetrahedral anion with the negative charge on oxygen.

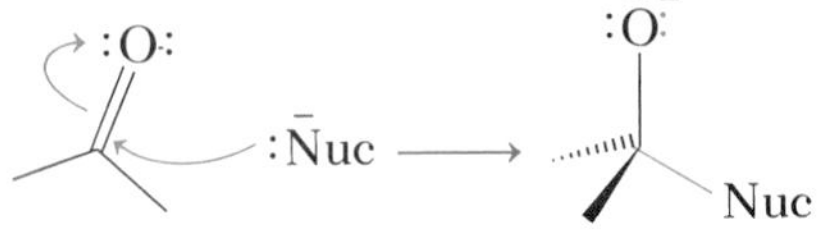

$$\text{R}_2\text{C=O} + :\text{Nuc}^- \longrightarrow \text{R}_2\text{C(O}^-)\text{Nuc}$$

MECHANISM OF REACTION

Nucleophilic Addition at a Carbonyl Carbon

Overall reaction:

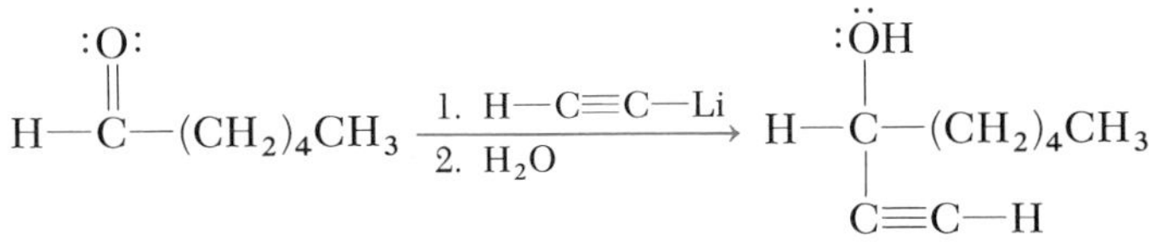

$$\mathrm{H{-}\overset{\overset{:O:}{\|}}{C}{-}(CH_2)_4CH_3 \xrightarrow[2.\ H_2O]{1.\ H{-}C{\equiv}C{-}Li} H{-}\underset{\underset{C\equiv C-H}{|}}{\overset{\overset{:\ddot{O}H}{|}}{C}}{-}(CH_2)_4CH_3}$$

98% yield

Step 1 H—C≡C—Li reacts as $\mathrm{H{-}C{\equiv}C\!:^-\ Li^+}$ and the acetylide ion adds to the carbonyl carbon atom. This is the nucleophilic addition step.

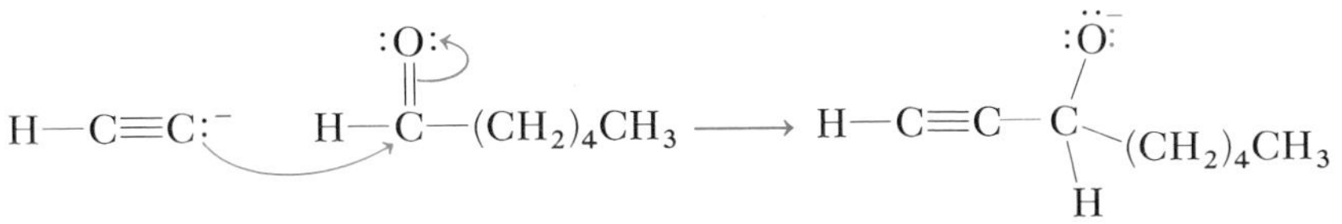

$$\mathrm{H{-}C{\equiv}C\!:^- \quad H{-}\overset{\overset{:O:}{\|}}{C}{-}(CH_2)_4CH_3 \longrightarrow H{-}C{\equiv}C{-}\underset{\underset{H}{|}}{\overset{\overset{:\ddot{O}:^-}{|}}{C}}{-}(CH_2)_4CH_3}$$

Step 2 In the workup of the reaction, the alkoxide ion formed in Step 1 abstracts a proton from a water molecule to generate the alcohol product.

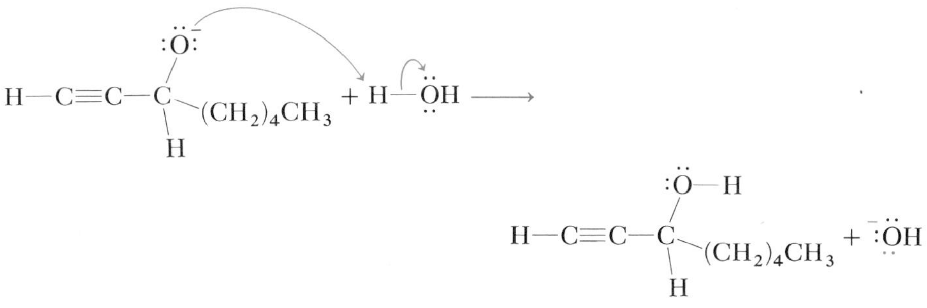

$$\mathrm{H{-}C{\equiv}C{-}\underset{\underset{H}{|}}{\overset{\overset{:\ddot{O}:^-}{|}}{C}}{-}(CH_2)_4CH_3 + H{-}\ddot{O}H \longrightarrow H{-}C{\equiv}C{-}\underset{\underset{H}{|}}{\overset{\overset{:\ddot{O}-H}{|}}{C}}{-}(CH_2)_4CH_3 + {}^-\!:\ddot{O}H}$$

Some nucleophiles react very slowly with aldehydes and ketones, but we can often speed their reaction by the addition of an acid catalyst. The acid protonates the carbonyl oxygen, thereby increasing the susceptibility of the carbonyl carbon to nucleophilic attack, as illustrated in Figure 19.18. Attack of

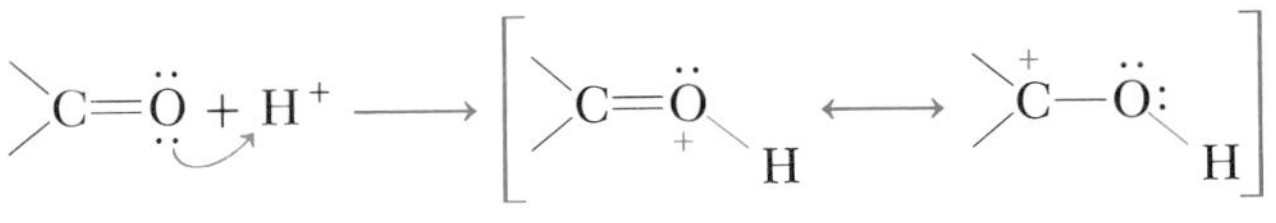

$$\mathrm{{>}C{=}\ddot{O} + H^+ \longrightarrow \left[{>}C{=}\overset{+}{\ddot{O}}{-}H \longleftrightarrow {>}\overset{+}{C}{-}\ddot{O}{:}{-}H \right]}$$

the cation is more prone to nucleophilic attack than is the uncharged parent carbonyl compound

Figure 19.18 Acid catalysis of nucleophilic addition reactions at carbonyl groups. Protonation of the carbonyl group enhances the reactivity of the carbonyl group toward nucleophiles. Aprotic Lewis acids such as BF_3 serve the same purpose as do protic acids.

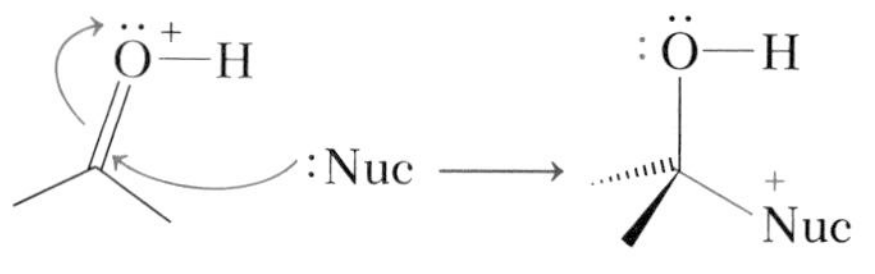

Figure 19.19 Attack of a neutral nucleophile on a protonated carbonyl compound. The reaction leads directly to a product containing a hydroxyl group.

a nucleophile on a protonated aldehyde or ketone leads directly to a compound containing a hydroxyl group, as shown in Figure 19.19. This compound *may* be the observed product of the reaction; however, we may also find that the hydroxyl group is subsequently protonated and lost as water. We will meet several examples of this type of reaction in the following sections.

Steric factors influence the reactivity of aldehydes and ketones toward nucleophiles. Aldehydes are usually more reactive than ketones because the aldehyde presents less steric hindrance to the incoming nucleophile. More precisely, there is less crowding in the aldehyde activated complex for nucleophilic addition than there is in the ketone activated complex. (There is a relatively small hydrogen atom in the activated complex of the aldehyde. When a ketone reacts, a larger alkyl or aryl group is in the place of the hydrogen atom and occupies more space.) The geometry is shown in Figure 19.20.

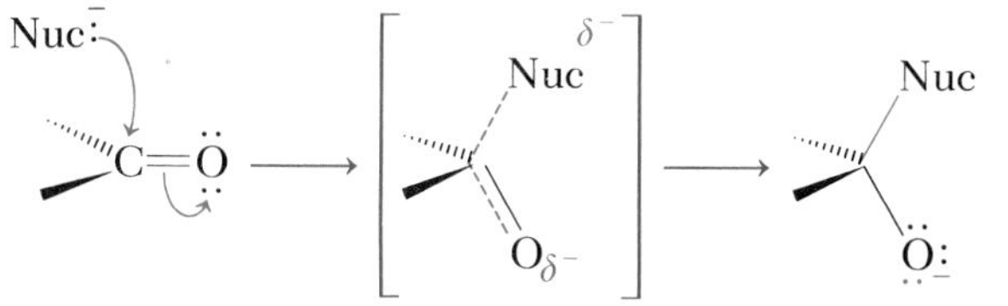

trigonal reactant

activated complex; intermediate between trigonal and tetrahedral

tetrahedral product

Figure 19.20 Activated complex for addition of a nucleophile to a carbonyl carbon. The reaction passes through an activated complex whose geometry is intermediate between that of the trigonal carbonyl compound and that of the tetrahedral product.

19.8 Nucleophilic Attack by Oxygen

WATER

The reaction of aldehydes and ketones with water is illustrated below.

MECHANISM OF REACTION

Reaction of an Aldehyde or Ketone with Water

Overall reaction:

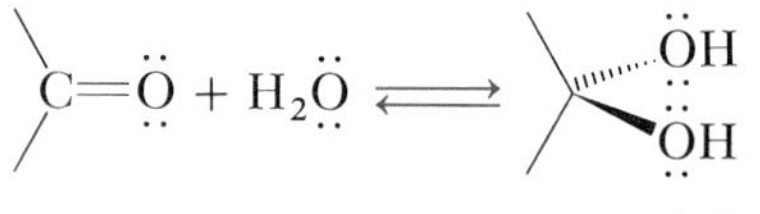

$$>C=\ddot{O} + H_2\ddot{O} \rightleftharpoons >C(OH)_2$$

a gem-diol or hydrate

Step 1 Water performs a nucleophilic addition at the carbonyl carbon atom.

Step 2 A proton transfers from the adduct to another water molecule.

Step 3 The anionic site accepts a proton from the solution to give the product.

The position of equilibrium for the overall reaction varies greatly. Some examples for different carbonyl compounds are given in Table 19.3. In most cases we find that the position of equilibrium strongly favors the carbonyl compound, that is, there is very little *gem*-diol present at equilibrium. In fact, we can rarely isolate *gem*-diols as such. However, there are important exceptions, as Table 19.3 suggests.

We can rationalize the general trends in the values of the equilibrium constant in Table 19.3 by analyzing electronic and steric effects within the carbonyl compounds. In general, factors that stabilize the parent carbonyl compound tend to make K_{eq} smaller, while factors that destabilize it make K_{eq} larger. Compare the K_{eq} values for the hydration of formaldehyde and acetone. They vary by an enormous amount, by a factor of almost one million. Why?

Table 19.3 Hydration of Aldehydes and Ketones

Compound	Hydrate	K_{eq}*	[hydrate]/[$C{=}O$]†
$H_2C{=}O$	$H_2C(OH)_2$	40	999 : 1
CH_3CHO	$CH_3CH(OH)_2$	0.01	1 : 1.8
$(CH_3)_2C{=}O$	$(CH_3)_2C(OH)_2$	0.0001	1 : 10^5
$(CF_3)_2C{=}O$	$(CF_3)_2C(OH)_2$	20,000	10^6 : 1

* For the reaction $C{=}O + H_2O \rightleftharpoons C(OH)_2$

† for a solution in which the total concentration of hydrate and carbonyl forms is 1 *M*

One contributing reason is the stability provided to the carbonyl group by the electron-donating methyl groups of acetone. Recall that the carbonyl group is polar, with the carbon atom being at the positive end of the dipole. Thus this carbonyl carbon has some *carbocation character*. Recall from earlier chapters that a carbocationic center is stabilized by alkyl substitution about that center—alkyl groups donate electron density to an electron-deficient center. Thus acetone is stabilized by its surrounding alkyl groups. Formaldehyde has no alkyl groups to stabilize its electron-deficient carbonyl carbon center, so it adds the elements of water readily when placed in water. In support of this general argument is the huge K_{eq} for the hydration of hexafluoroacetone. The trifluoromethyl groups are strongly electron withdrawing. They greatly destabilize the carbonyl group by pulling electron density away from an already electron-deficient center. In water, hexafluoroacetone is almost completely converted to its hydrate, in which there are no destabilizing effects.

Steric effects are important here, too. In general, groups are crowded together more closely in the tetrahedral *gem*-diol structure than they are in the trigonal aldehyde or ketone structure. The smaller the groups attached to the carbonyl carbon, the more easily it can tolerate the crowding of the hydrated form. Thus the smaller the groups attached to the carbonyl carbon, the greater the amount of *gem*-diol we expect at equilibrium.

ALCOHOLS

If we mix an aldehyde or a ketone with an alcohol, an equilibrium is established in which a **hemiacetal** or a **hemiketal** is present. In Figure 19.21 we see examples of these types of equilibria. There are obvious similarities to the hydration of carbonyl compounds, discussed in the preceding section.

The formation of hydrates, hemiacetals, and hemiketals has little synthetic significance, since these compounds are usually unstable and readily revert to the parent carbonyl compound when we attempt to isolate them. Very few of them can be isolated in the pure state. Later we will see that hemiacetals and hemiketals *are* of significance for many biologically important molecules, generally in solution (see Chapter 24).

Figure 19.21 Hemiacetal and hemiketal formation. Hemiacetals and hemiketals are formed by the addition of an alcohol to aldehydes and ketones. There is a dynamic equilibrium between the adduct and the free carbonyl compound. The attainment of equilibrium is facilitated by the addition of acid (see following discussion). It is becoming common practice to use the term *hemiacetal* to refer to both hemiacetals and hemiketals.

$$CH_3CH\ddot{O} + CH_3\ddot{O}H \rightleftharpoons CH_3CH(\ddot{O}H)(\ddot{O}CH_3)$$

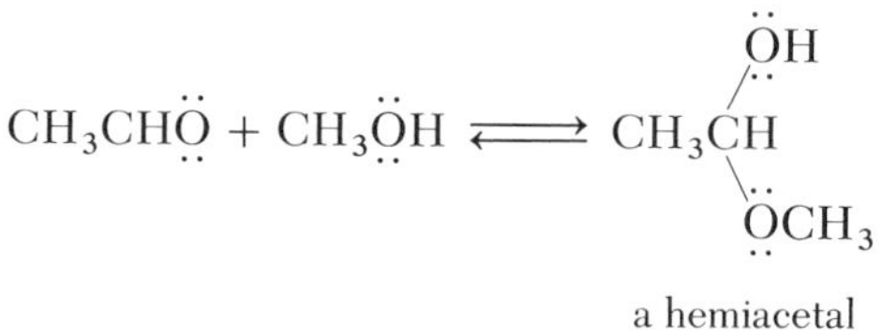

a hemiacetal
(an aldehyde derivate)

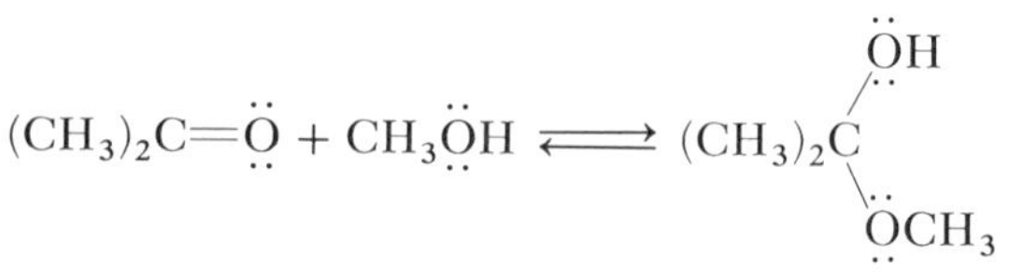

$$(CH_3)_2C{=}\ddot{O} + CH_3\ddot{O}H \rightleftharpoons (CH_3)_2C(\ddot{O}H)(\ddot{O}CH_3)$$

a hemiketal
(a ketone derivative)

Full **acetals** and **ketals** are of more widespread interest and utility for general organic synthetic purposes. These compounds can usually be isolated. We usually form these compounds by allowing an aldehyde or ketone to react with an excess of alcohol in the presence of an anhydrous acid such as *p*-toluenesulfonic acid or hydrogen chloride gas. Equation 19.19 shows an example of acetal formation.

Eqn. 19.19

$$CH_3CHO + 2\,CH_3CH_2OH \xrightarrow{H^+} CH_3CH(OCH_2CH_3)_2 + H_2O$$

60% yield
acetaldehyde
diethyl acetal

All of the mechanistic steps are true equilibria. Thus, the net reaction, the conversion of an aldehyde or a ketone to an acetal or a ketal, is an equilibrium process, the entire sequence of reactions being completely reversible. In order to drive the reaction toward the acetal or ketal, it is often necessary to perform the reaction in an excess of alcohol and/or remove the water as it is formed. A Dean-Stark water separator can be used for the latter purpose (see Chapter 18). The mechanism of this reaction is given below.

MECHANISM OF REACTION

Formation of an Acetal

Step 1 Protonation of the carbonyl oxygen

$$CH_3CHO + H^+ \rightleftharpoons CH_3{-}CH{=}\overset{+}{O}{-}H$$

Step 2 Nucleophilic attack by alcohol on the carbonyl carbon

$$CH_3{-}CH{=}\overset{+}{O}{-}H + CH_3CH_2OH \rightleftharpoons (H)(CH_3)C(OH){-}\overset{+}{O}H{-}CH_2CH_3$$

Steps 3 and 4 Proton transfer through solution to form a hemiacetal

$$B{:} + (H)(CH_3)C(OH){-}\overset{+}{O}H{-}CH_2CH_3 \rightleftharpoons (H)(CH_3)C(OH){-}O{-}CH_2CH_3 + \overset{+}{B}{-}H$$

(a hemiacetal)

$$\overset{+}{B}{-}H + (H)(CH_3)C(OH){-}O{-}CH_2CH_3 \rightleftharpoons (H)(CH_3)C(\overset{+}{O}H_2){-}O{-}CH_2CH_3 + B{:}$$

Step 5 Water loss to solution

$$\text{H}_2\ddot{\text{O}}^{+}\text{–CH(CH}_3\text{)–}\ddot{\text{O}}\text{–CH}_2\text{CH}_3 \rightleftharpoons \text{H}_2\ddot{\text{O}} + \left[\text{H–}\overset{+}{\text{C}}\text{(CH}_3\text{)–}\ddot{\text{O}}\text{–CH}_2\text{CH}_3 \longleftrightarrow \text{H–C(CH}_3\text{)=}\overset{+}{\ddot{\text{O}}}\text{–CH}_2\text{CH}_3 \right]$$

Step 6 Nucleophilic attack by alcohol on the carbocation

$$\text{H}\ddot{\text{O}}\text{CH}_2\text{CH}_3 + \text{H–}\overset{+}{\text{C}}\text{(CH}_3\text{)–}\ddot{\text{O}}\text{CH}_2\text{CH}_3 \rightleftharpoons \text{CH}_3\text{CH}_2\overset{+}{\ddot{\text{O}}}\text{(H)–CH(CH}_3\text{)–}\ddot{\text{O}}\text{–CH}_2\text{CH}_3$$

Step 7 Deprotonation

$$\text{B:} + \text{CH}_3\text{CH}_2\overset{+}{\ddot{\text{O}}}\text{(H)–CH(CH}_3\text{)–}\ddot{\text{O}}\text{–CH}_2\text{CH}_3 \rightleftharpoons \text{CH}_3\text{CH}_2\ddot{\text{O}}\text{–CH(CH}_3\text{)–}\ddot{\text{O}}\text{CH}_2\text{CH}_3 + \overset{+}{\text{B}}\text{–H}$$

PROBLEM 19.11 Calculate how many mL of water would be collected in a Dean-Stark trap if the ketal formation reaction between 20.0 g of cyclohexanone and 150.0 g of 1-pentanol went to completion.

It is usually more efficient to use one equivalent of a 1,2-diol such as 1,2-ethanediol (ethylene glycol, see Chapter 5) than two equivalents of an ordinary alcohol to effect ketal formation. An example of this type of reaction is shown in Equation 19.20.

Eqn. 19.20

$$\text{cyclohexanone} + \text{H}\ddot{\text{O}}\text{CH}_2\text{CH}_2\ddot{\text{O}}\text{H} \xrightarrow{\text{H}_2\text{SO}_4} \text{cyclohexanone ethylene ketal}$$

cyclohexanone — ethylene glycol — 80% yield cyclohexanone ethylene ketal

The use of a 1,2-diol favors acetal or ketal formation through an **entropy** effect that we can appreciate by comparing the reactions shown in Equations 19.19 and 19.20. The first of these reactions involves the conversion of *three* reactant molecules to *two* product molecules, whereas the second involves *two* reactant molecules and produces *two* product molecules. Reactions of the first type, which produce fewer product molecules than reactant molecules, proceed with an increase in the degree of order, that is, they proceed with a decrease in entropy ($\Delta S^\circ < 0$). By contrast, reactions of the second type have an entropy change that is close to zero. Reactions of the type shown in Equation 19.20 therefore have a more favorable ΔS° and thus a more favorable ΔG° than reactions of the type shown in Equation 19.19. With a more favorable ΔG°, they also have a more favorable equilibrium constant.

PROBLEM 19.12 What is the sign (positive or negative) of ΔS° for the reaction shown in Equation 19.19? What must be the sign of ΔH° if the equilibrium constant for the reaction is to be >1? Remember, at constant temperature and pressure

$$\Delta G^\circ = \Delta H^\circ - T\,\Delta S^\circ$$

Acetals and Ketals as Protecting Groups Full acetals and ketals (in contrast to hemiacetals and hemiketals) are generally stable to neutral or basic reaction conditions. However, they revert to the parent carbonyl compound and alcohol (or diol) if we treat them briefly with aqueous acid. We can exploit these properties of acetals and ketals as a means of temporarily protecting the carbonyl group in a synthetic sequence. In Figure 19.22 we pose a synthetic problem in which carbonyl protection is required. We recognize, in general terms, that in order to accomplish the desired conversion an oxidative cleavage of the carbon-carbon double bond is required. Hot, aqueous permanganate solution (see section 10.13) seems to be a reasonable choice. However, the aldehyde functional group is also reactive toward this reagent, and it would be oxidized to a carboxylic acid group, as illustrated in Figure 19.23.

We can avoid this difficulty by protecting the aldehyde group prior to the use of the permanganate. After the permanganate oxidation we *deprotect* it by adding aqueous acid to cleave the acetal. The added acid also converts the carboxylate anion to the free carboxylic acid. The complete sequence of operations is shown in Figure 19.24.

$$(CH_3)_2C{=}CHCH_2CH_2CH_2CH\ddot{O} \xrightarrow{?} HO_2CCH_2CH_2CH_2CH\ddot{O}$$

Figure 19.22 A synthetic conversion requiring protection of the aldehyde group.

$$(CH_3)_2C{=}CHCH_2CH_2CH_2CH\ddot{O} \xrightarrow[\text{2. aq acid workup}]{\text{1. } KMnO_4\text{, KOH, heat}} HO_2CCH_2CH_2CH_2CO_2H$$

Figure 19.23 Formation of a diacid from an unsaturated aldehyde. If the synthesis of the target molecule of Figure 19.22 is attempted using the method shown here, the aldehyde group would be oxidized as well as the carbon-carbon double bond.

PROBLEM 19.13 Suggest how to perform each of the following conversions using a protection-deprotection process.

a. $CH_3CH_2{-}C{\equiv}C{-}CH_2CH_2CH\ddot{O}$ from 1-butyne and 3-bromopropanal
b. 4-deuteriobenzaldehyde from 4-bromobenzaldehyde

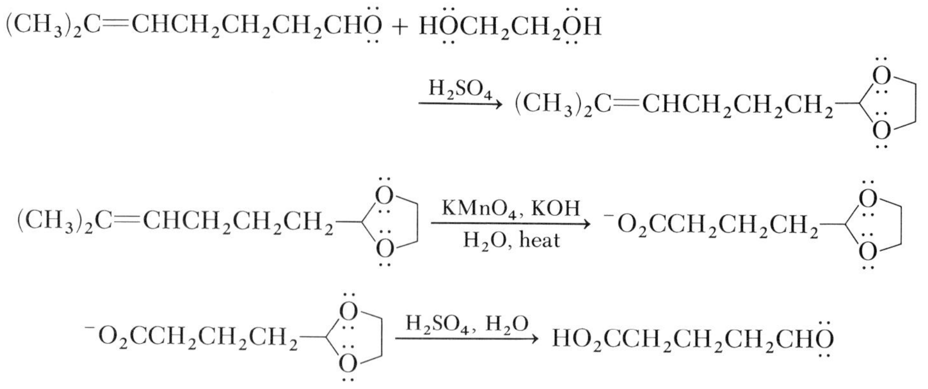

Figure 19.24 Accomplishment of the synthesis proposed in Figure 19.22. First the aldehyde group is protected by formation of the ethylene glycol acetal. Then the double bond is cleaved using permanganate under basic conditions. Finally, the aldehyde group is regenerated using aqueous acid.

$$(CH_3)_2C{=}CHCH_2CH_2CH_2CH\ddot{O} + H\ddot{O}CH_2CH_2\ddot{O}H \xrightarrow{H_2SO_4} (CH_3)_2C{=}CHCH_2CH_2CH_2\text{—(cyclic acetal, 1,3-dioxolane)}$$

$$(CH_3)_2C{=}CHCH_2CH_2CH_2\text{—(1,3-dioxolane)} \xrightarrow[H_2O,\ heat]{KMnO_4,\ KOH} {}^{-}O_2CCH_2CH_2CH_2\text{—(1,3-dioxolane)}$$

$${}^{-}O_2CCH_2CH_2CH_2\text{—(1,3-dioxolane)} \xrightarrow{H_2SO_4,\ H_2O} HO_2CCH_2CH_2CH_2CH\ddot{O}$$

19.9 Nucleophilic Attack by Nitrogen

PRIMARY AMINES

Primary amines have the general structure $R{-}\ddot{N}H_2$, where R is an alkyl or aryl group. (We will discuss the chemistry of amines in detail in the following chapter.) Primary amines generally react with aldehydes and ketones to produce substances known as **imines** or **Schiff bases.** Traces of acid catalyze the reaction by protonating the carbonyl oxygen, thereby making the carbonyl carbon more susceptible to nucleophilic attack. The reaction occurs most readily with aldehydes—imine formation often occurs with mixing or only slight warming. An example of imine formation is shown in Equation 19.21.

Eqn. 19.21

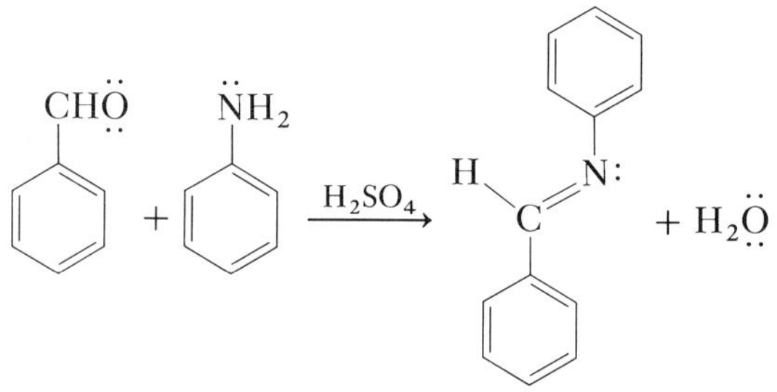

$$C_6H_5CH\ddot{O} + C_6H_5\ddot{N}H_2 \xrightarrow{H_2SO_4} C_6H_5CH{=}\ddot{N}C_6H_5 + H_2\ddot{O}$$

benzaldehyde aniline 85% yield *N*-phenylbenzaldimine

With ketones, the reaction is somewhat more sluggish but occurs when a Lewis acid such as zinc chloride is used. An example is shown in Equation 19.22.

Eqn. 19.22

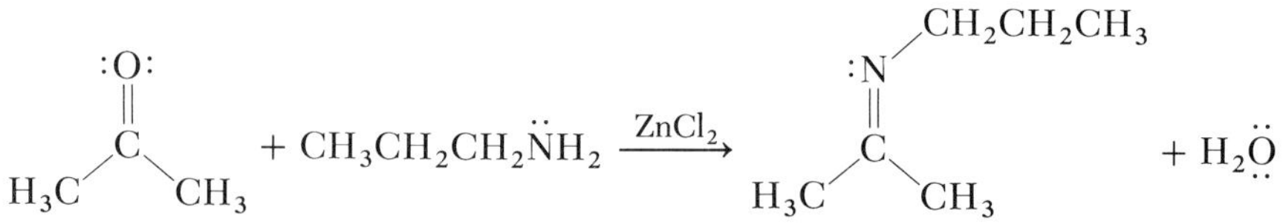

$$(H_3C)_2C{=}\ddot{O}: + CH_3CH_2CH_2\ddot{N}H_2 \xrightarrow{ZnCl_2} (H_3C)_2C{=}\ddot{N}CH_2CH_2CH_3 + H_2\ddot{O}$$

acetone propylamine 85% yield *N*-propylacetoneimine

It is sometimes helpful to use a Dean-Stark trap to remove the water by-product continuously as it is formed. In the reaction mechanism shown below, notice the formation of an intermediate in which a hydroxyl and the RNH groups are attached to the same carbon (sometimes known as a *carbinolamine*). Such substances are unstable with regard to the loss of water. Here the loss of water leads to the formation of an imine. (Imines are also known as Schiff's bases, after the German chemist Hugo Schiff who prepared and identified them in the nineteenth century.) The amine used in these reactions can also play the role of the base B:, which appears in several of the steps.

MECHANISM OF REACTION

Imine Formation from an Aldehyde

Step 1 Protonation of the carbonyl oxygen

$$RCH\ddot{O} + H^+ \rightleftharpoons (R)(H)C{=}\ddot{O}^+{-}H$$

Step 2 Nucleophilic attack by the amine on the carbonyl carbon

$$R'\ddot{N}H_2 + (R)(H)C{=}\ddot{O}^+{-}H \rightleftharpoons R{-}C(H)(R'\overset{+}{N}H_2){-}\ddot{O}{-}H$$

Steps 3 and 4 Proton transfer through solution

$$B: + R{-}C(H)(R'\overset{+}{N}H_2){-}\ddot{O}{-}H \rightleftharpoons R{-}C(H)(R'\ddot{N}H){-}\ddot{O}{-}H + \overset{+}{B}{-}H$$

$$R{-}C(H)(R'\ddot{N}H){-}\ddot{O}H + \overset{+}{B}{-}H \rightleftharpoons R{-}C(H)(R'\ddot{N}H){-}\overset{+}{\ddot{O}}(H){-}H + B:$$

Step 5 Water loss

$$R{-}C(H)(R'\ddot{N}H){-}\overset{+}{\ddot{O}}(H)H \rightleftharpoons \left[(R)(H)\overset{+}{C}{-}\ddot{N}HR' \longleftrightarrow (R)(H)C{=}\overset{+}{N}HR' \right] + H_2\ddot{O}$$

Step 6 Deprotonation

$$R'\ddot{N}{-}H\;(\text{on } C^{+}(R)(H)) + B: \rightleftharpoons R'\ddot{N}{=}C(R)(H) + \overset{+}{B}{-}H$$

Ammonia (NH_3) reacts with aldehydes and ketones in a similar manner to that of primary amines. However, the imines formed are often too reactive to be of general use. In fact, the reaction of ammonia with an aldehyde or ketone often leads to products that are structurally more complex than simple imines because the initially formed imine (or its carbinolamine precursor) undergoes further reaction. Even if we manage to isolate an imine produced by the reaction of a carbonyl compound with ammonia, it is invariably quite sensitive to water and tends to hydrolyze rapidly to form the parent aldehyde or ketone.

PROBLEM 19.14 Write a detailed mechanism for the acid-catalyzed hydrolysis of the imine derived from benzaldehyde and ammonia.

HYDRAZINE AND RELATED COMPOUNDS

Hydrazine has the structure $H_2\ddot{N}{-}\ddot{N}H_2$. In substituted hydrazines, one or more of the hydrogen atoms are replaced by alkyl or aryl groups. Hydrazines with at least one $-\ddot{N}H_2$ group present react with aldehydes and ketones to form substances known as **hydrazones,** which contain the structural unit $>C{=}\ddot{N}{-}\ddot{N}H_2$. These reactions are completely analogous to those discussed in the previous section involving nucleophilic addition and dehydration steps.

PROBLEM 19.15 Give the structure of the product expected from the acid-catalyzed reaction of phenylhydrazine ($PhNH{-}NH_2$) with benzaldehyde. Write a mechanism for this reaction.

Hydrazones are much more stable toward hydrolysis than are simple imines. The hydrolysis reaction begins with protonation of the nitrogen atom of the carbon-nitrogen bond, a process that is much less favorable for a hydrazone than for a simple imine. One explanation for this difference is that the $-NH_2$ group present in a hydrazone exerts an electron-withdrawing inductive effect that lowers the basicity of the adjacent nitrogen atom. Alternatively, it can be argued that protonation of a hydrazone is relatively unfavorable because the conjugate acid so formed is destabilized by the electron-withdrawing effect of this $-NH_2$ group. Both explanations are illustrated in Figure 19.25.

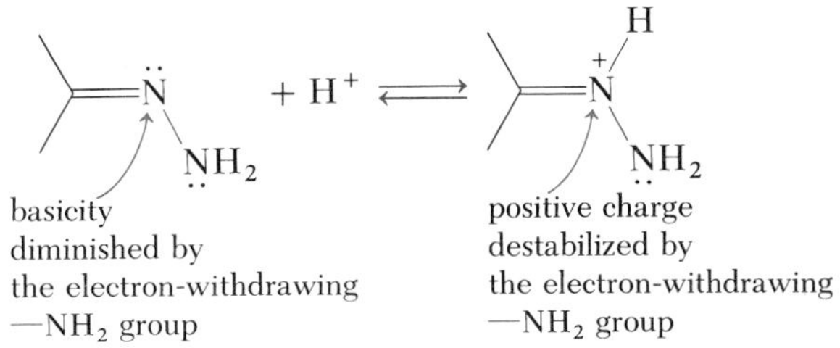

Figure 19.25 Diminished basicity of hydrazones. Hydrazones are less basic than imines of similar structure due to the presence of the $—NH_2$ group.

$$\text{>C=}\ddot{N}\text{–}\ddot{N}H_2 + H^+ \rightleftharpoons \text{>C=}\overset{+}{N}(H)\text{–}\ddot{N}H_2$$

basicity diminished by the electron-withdrawing $—NH_2$ group

positive charge destabilized by the electron-withdrawing $—NH_2$ group

PROBLEM 19.16 Consider the protonated hydrazone structure shown in Figure 19.25. Why is it not possible for the nitrogen of the $—NH_2$ group to exert an electron-donating effect, through resonance (using its unshared valence electron pair) to *stabilize* the adjacent positive charge?

Hydrazones and substituted hydrazones have a useful role in the identification of aldehydes and ketones. In this type of analysis, an unknown carbonyl compound is converted to its hydrazone derivative, which is purified by recrystallization. Its melting temperature is then compared with that of hydrazones of known structure. Two substituted hydrazines, 2,4-dinitrophenylhydrazine (**19.1**) and semicarbazide (**19.2**), are most often used for this purpose, as they lead to highly crystalline solid derivatives.

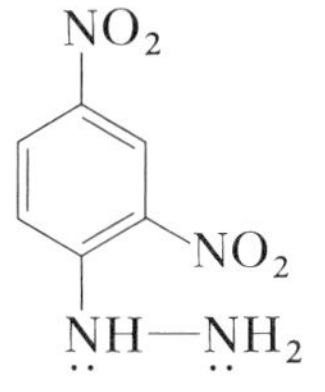

NO_2, NO_2, $\ddot{N}H—\ddot{N}H_2$

2,4-dinitrophenylhydrazine
19.1

$$H_2\ddot{N}—\ddot{N}H—\overset{:O:}{\overset{\|}{C}}—\ddot{N}H_2$$

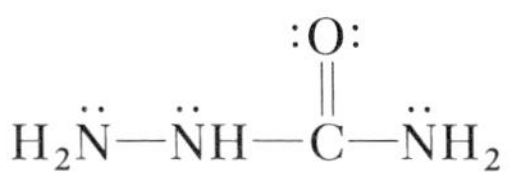

semicarbazide
19.2

PROBLEM 19.17 Notice that semicarbazide (**19.2**) has two $—\ddot{N}H_2$ groups. However, only one is reactive toward carbonyl groups (for example, semicarbazone derivatives of aldehydes have the structure:

$$RCH=\ddot{N}—\ddot{N}H—CO\ddot{N}H_2 \qquad \text{rather than} \qquad RCH=\ddot{N}CO\ddot{N}H\ddot{N}H_2)$$

Suggest a reason for the failure of one of the $—\ddot{N}H_2$ groups to react. *Hint:* Consider a resonance structure that helps to rationalize a diminished nucleophilicity for one of the $—\ddot{N}H_2$ groups.

PROBLEM 19.18 Hydroxylamine, $\ddot{N}H_2\ddot{O}H$, reacts with aldehydes and ketones to produce derivatives known as **oximes.** Suggest a structure for the oxime derivative formed by treating acetone with hydroxylamine.

SECONDARY AMINES

Secondary amines react with aldehydes and ketones to yield substances known as **enamines.** A typical reaction is shown in Equation 19.23.

Eqn. 19.23

$$(CH_3)_2CHCH\ddot{O} + Ph\ddot{N}HCH_3 \xrightarrow{H_2SO_4} (CH_3)_2C{=}CH{-}\ddot{N}(Ph){-}CH_3$$

methylpropanal — *N*-methylaniline — 90% yield *N*,2-dimethyl-*N*-phenyl-1-aminopropene

The mechanistic steps for the formation of an enamine from an aldehyde and a secondary amine are given below. Compare this mechanism with that shown earlier for imine formation. The mechanisms closely parallel each other up to the point of formation of an iminium ion. However, the iminium ion derived from the secondary amine has no hydrogen attached to nitrogen. In Step 6, therefore, a hydrogen atom is removed (as a proton) from *carbon* instead, to give the enamine product.

MECHANISM OF REACTION

Formation of an Enamine from an Aldehyde and a Secondary Amine

Step 1 Protonation of the carbonyl oxygen

$$RCH_2CH\ddot{O} + H^+ \rightleftharpoons RCH_2{-}CH{=}\overset{+}{\ddot{O}}{-}H$$

Step 2 Nucleophilic attack of nitrogen on the carbonyl carbon

$$RCH_2{-}CH{=}\overset{+}{\ddot{O}}{-}H + R'_2\ddot{N}H \rightleftharpoons R'_2\overset{+}{N}H{-}CH(RCH_2){-}\ddot{O}H$$

Steps 3 and 4 Proton transfer through solution

$$B\colon + R'_2\overset{+}{N}H{-}CH(CH_2R){-}\ddot{O}H \rightleftharpoons R'_2\ddot{N}{-}CH(CH_2R){-}\ddot{O}H + \overset{+}{B}{-}H$$

$$R'_2\ddot{N}{-}CH(CH_2R){-}\ddot{O}H + \overset{+}{B}{-}H \rightleftharpoons R'_2\ddot{N}{-}CH(CH_2R){-}\overset{+}{\ddot{O}}H_2 + B\colon$$

Step 5 Water loss

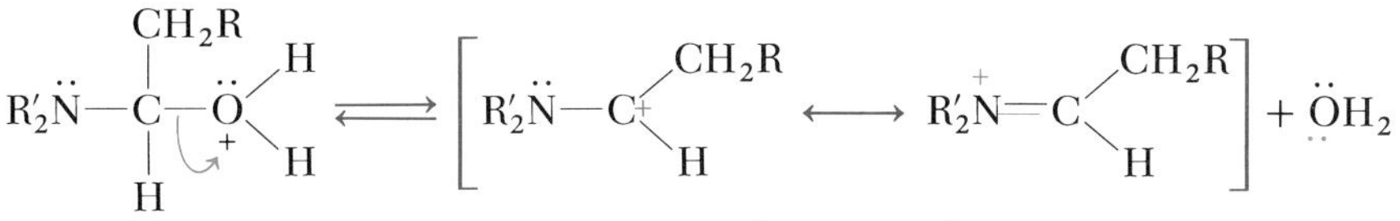

$$R'_2\ddot{N}-\underset{H}{\overset{CH_2R}{C}}-\overset{+}{\ddot{O}}\begin{smallmatrix}H\\H\end{smallmatrix} \rightleftharpoons \left[R'_2\ddot{N}-\overset{+}{C}\begin{smallmatrix}CH_2R\\H\end{smallmatrix} \longleftrightarrow R'_2\overset{+}{N}=C\begin{smallmatrix}CH_2R\\H\end{smallmatrix}\right] + \ddot{O}H_2$$

(iminium ion)

Step 6 Deprotonation

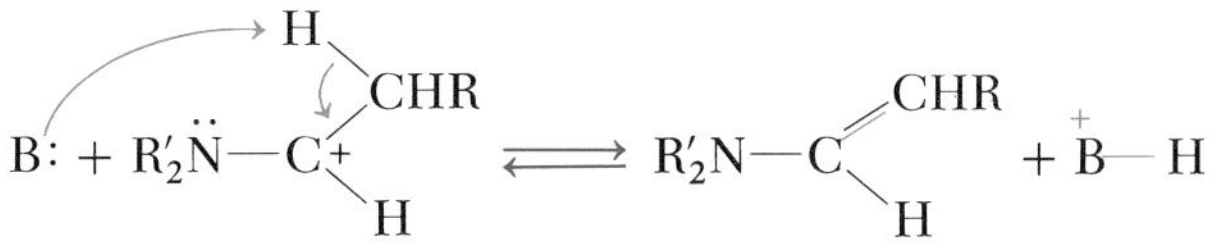

$$B\colon + R'_2\ddot{N}-\overset{+}{C}\begin{smallmatrix}H-CHR\\H\end{smallmatrix} \rightleftharpoons R'_2N-C\begin{smallmatrix}=CHR\\H\end{smallmatrix} + \overset{+}{B}-H$$

PROBLEM 19.19

Not all aldehydes and ketones react with secondary amines to form enamines. In particular those lacking α-hydrogens do not give the reaction. Suggest a reason for this failure of the reaction.

Of course, primary amines could, *in principle*, form enamines (as do secondary amines), just as they could also lose a proton from carbon. However, with a primary amine the imine is the favored product. The imine dominates the equilibrium mixture because it is thermodynamically more stable, as illustrated in Figure 19.26. Secondary amines cannot form imines since their nitrogen atom does not have the required two hydrogens that must be lost in the course of the reaction. The only possible product the secondary amine can form is the enamine.

$$\underset{\text{imine}}{RCH_2CH=\ddot{N}-R} \rightleftharpoons \underset{\text{enamine}}{RCH=CH-\ddot{N}HR}$$

Figure 19.26 Equilibrium of imine and enamine from a primary amine and an aldehyde. The imine is the thermodynamically more stable of the possible structures. The sum of the imine bond strengths is greater than that for the isomeric enamine. At equilibrium, the imine is the dominant species.

19.10 Nucleophilic Attack by Carbon

ORGANOMETALLICS

Many carbon nucleophiles attack the carbonyl carbon of an aldehyde or ketone. Among the most important examples of this type of reagent are organometallic reagents such as the Grignard reagent and alkyllithium reagents. The reactions of these organometallics conform to the general scheme shown in Figure 19.27. This type of reaction provides a most useful synthetic approach to alcohols and hence to compounds derived from alcohols (this reaction was discussed in Section 11.5.)

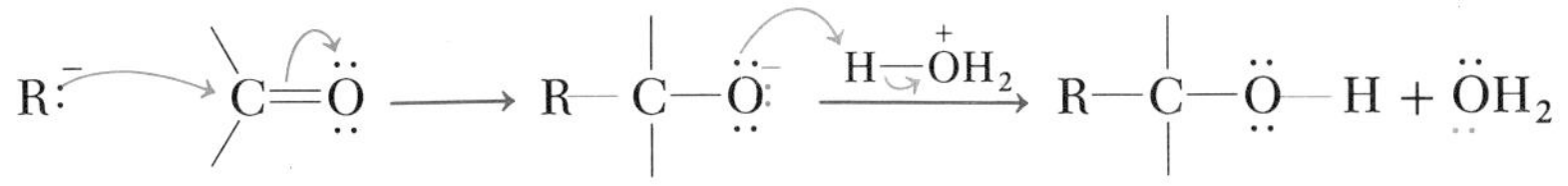

$$R\colon^- + \rangle C=\ddot{O} \longrightarrow R-\underset{|}{\overset{|}{C}}-\ddot{O}\colon^- \xrightarrow{H-OH_2^+} R-\underset{|}{\overset{|}{C}}-\ddot{O}-H + \ddot{O}H_2$$

Figure 19.27 Reaction of a carbanionic organometallic with a carbonyl compound. The organometallic acts as a source of a carbanion, R^-.

PROBLEM 19.20 Perform a retrosynthetic analysis to discover two possible synthetic routes for preparing 2-methyl-2-hexanol from a carbonyl compound and a Grignard reagent. (You may find it helpful to review Section 11.5.)

PROBLEM 19.21 Suggest a synthetic route (involving a Grignard reagent) that will enable you to prepare 1-phenyl-3-methyl-2-butanol from toluene and any alcohol of four or fewer carbon atoms. You will need to perform synthetic manipulations on both the toluene and the alcohol you choose for the route.

ADDITION OF CYANIDE

If we add aqueous mineral acid to a mixture of a carbonyl compound and sodium cyanide, a compound known as a **cyanohydrin** forms. An example of this type of reaction is shown in Equation 19.24.

Eqn. 19.24

$$H_2C\ddot{\underset{..}{O}} + NaCN \xrightarrow[H_2O]{H_2SO_4} H\ddot{\underset{..}{O}}CH_2C{\equiv}N\!:$$

formaldehyde → formaldehyde cyanohydrin (80% yield)

The same overall result is achieved by adding hydrogen cyanide directly to a carbonyl compound. The addition of base catalyzes the reaction as it generates nucleophilic cyanide ion from the weakly acidic hydrogen cyanide. Cyanohydrins are quite useful materials synthetically. The cyano group undergoes facile acid-catalyzed hydrolysis to form a carboxyl group ($-COOH$) or reduction to give the aminomethyl group ($-CH_2NH_2$). We will return to consider these reactions in the context of amines and carboxylic acids (Chapters 20 and 21), and again when we delve into carbohydrate chemistry (Chapter 24).

YLIDES

The Wittig Reaction We now come to a special and most useful reaction, the **Wittig reaction,** which involves the addition of a carbon nucleophile to the carbonyl group. (Georg Wittig received the Nobel Prize in Chemistry in 1979 for his efforts in developing synthetic methodology through this reaction.)

The Wittig reaction converts aldehydes and ketones to alkenes. It relies on the use of a type of substance known as a phosphorus **ylide** (pronounced ilĺ-id). Ylides, in general, are neutral substances for which a Lewis structure can be written with a negatively charged carbon atom and some immediately adjacent positively charged atom, both with complete octets of valence electrons. The type of ylide generally used in the Wittig reaction is a triphenylphosphonium ylide, as shown in Figure 19.28. One resonance structure of the phosphonium ylide has a formal negative charge on carbon. Because of their significant charge separation, ylides behave as a carbanions, that is, as carbon nucleophiles. We will now discuss several aspects of the Wittig reaction.

SPECIAL TOPIC

Cyanohydrins in Biological Systems

The addition of hydrogen cyanide to aldehydes and ketones is a reversible reaction whose eqilibrium constant depends on the structure of the carbonyl compound.

$$\mathrm{RR'C{=}\ddot{O}: + HCN: \rightleftharpoons RR'C(\ddot{O}H)(CN:)}$$

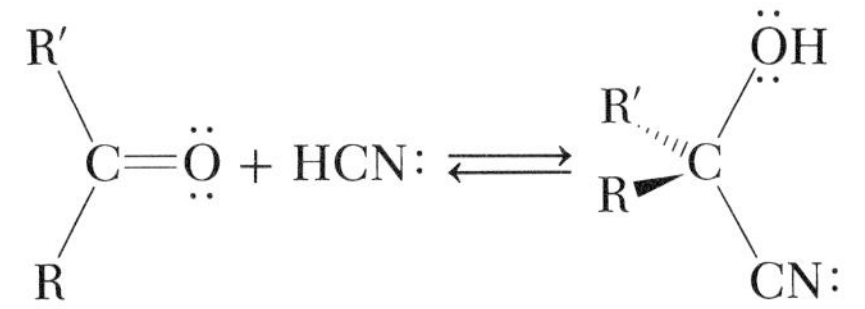

$$K_{eq} = \frac{[\text{cyanohydrin}]}{[\text{carbonyl compound}]\,[\text{HCN}]}$$

The value of the equilibrium constant varies considerably, but it is generally quite large (>100) for most aldehydes. It is rather small (<0.02) for many open-chain ketones but large for cyclic ketones (cyclohexanone, 500; cycloheptanone, 10,000; cyclooctanone, 100).

Addition of alkali to a cyanohydrin displaces the position of equilibrium toward the carbonyl compound. Numerous enzymes also cause reversal of the reaction. This reversibility is of considerable interest in biological systems. Several plants, including some forage plants, synthesize cyanohydrins. After the plants are eaten, the cyanohydrins revert to carbonyl compound and the highly toxic hydrogen cyanide. Death of grazing animals due to cyanide poisoning can be a serious problem for farmers.

The pits of cherries and other *Prunus* species (including plums, apricots, and peaches, as well as bitter almonds) contain considerable quantities of cyanohydrins and should not be eaten in quantity. Some people describe the odor of hydrogen cyanide as being that of *bitter almonds*. In fact, when we crush the kernels of bitter almonds, we obtain an oil that contains up to 4% hydrogen cyanide. The source of this hydrogen cyanide is a cyanohydrin precursor.

Cyanohydrins also play a role in lives of insects. The millipede (*Apheloria corrigate*) possesses an enzyme that causes rapid dissociation of a cyanohydrin stored in its defense glands into a mixture of benzaldehyde and hydrogen cyanide. When a millipede is attacked, it squirts this noxious mixture onto its potential predator in order to defend itself—a rather sophisticated form of chemical warfare.

$$\left[\mathrm{AB C{=}PPh_3 \longleftrightarrow AB\ddot{C}^{-}{-}\overset{+}{P}Ph_3}\right] + \mathrm{RR'C{=}\ddot{O}} \longrightarrow \mathrm{ABC{=}CRR'} + \mathrm{Ph_3\overset{+}{P}{-}\ddot{O}:^{-}}$$

triphenylphosphonium ylide — aldehyde or ketone — alkene product (geometric isomers are possible)

Figure 19.28 Reaction of a triphenylphosphonium ylide with a carbonyl compound. The product derived from the aldehyde or ketone is an alkene. The oxygen of the carbonyl compound has been replaced by the carbon function from the ylide. The by-product of the reaction is triphenylphosphine oxide. An ylide resonance form in which there is no charge separation is also shown.

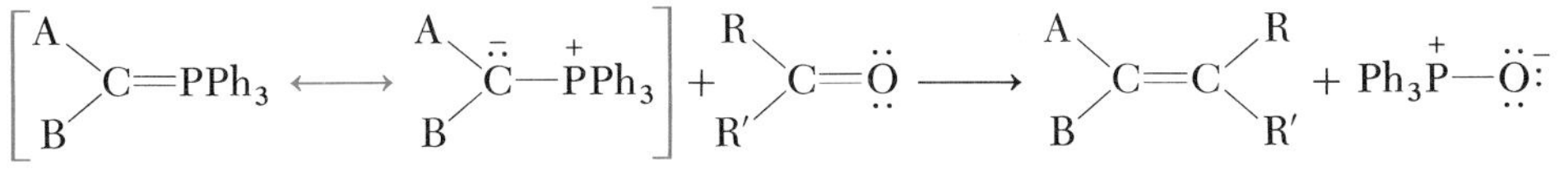

Figure 19.29 Formation of a triphenylphosphonium salt.

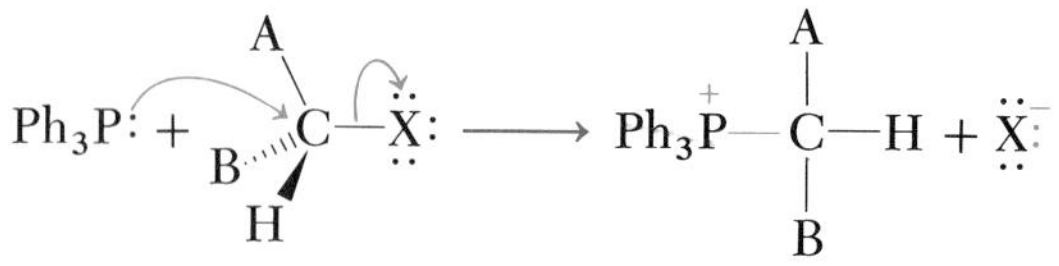

$$Ph_3P: + \text{B}\cdots\text{C(A)(H)}-\ddot{X}: \longrightarrow Ph_3\overset{+}{P}-\text{C(A)(B)}-H + :\ddot{X}:^-$$

a triphenylphosphonium salt

Preparation of the Ylide Phosphonium ylides are prepared by a two-step procedure. First, triphenylphosphine is allowed to react with a suitable haloalkane. The reaction, which proceeds via the S_N2 mechanism, produces a phosphonium salt, as shown in Figure 19.29.

Triphenylphosphine is able to function as a potent nucleophile but only as a weak base. Thus, we may use a methyl, primary, or secondary haloalkane without being concerned that large amounts of the competing elimination reaction will take place. Tertiary haloalkanes are not useful in this procedure since the carbon carrying the halide substituent needs at least one hydrogen attached to it for the subsequent ylide formation.

After we have prepared the phosphonium salt, we treat it with a strong base to remove a hydrogen ion from the carbon attached to phosphorus. Organolithium reagents are commonly used for this procedure, as shown in Figure 19.30.

Mechanism of the Wittig Reaction An example of the Wittig reaction is shown in Equation 19.25.

Eqn. 19.25

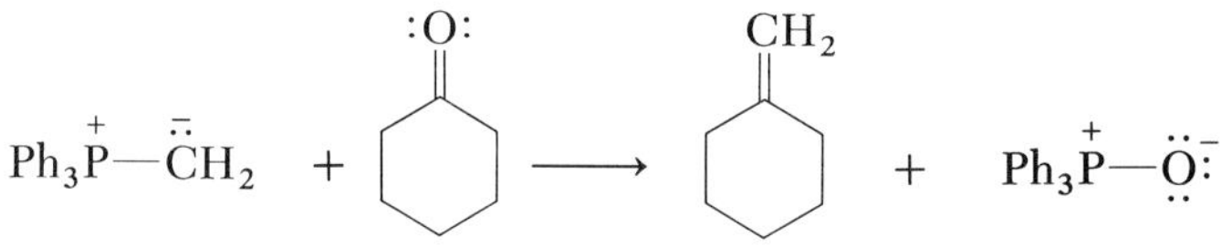

$$Ph_3\overset{+}{P}-\overset{..-}{C}H_2 + \text{cyclohexanone} \longrightarrow \text{methylenecyclohexane} + Ph_3\overset{+}{P}-\ddot{\underset{..}{O}}:^-$$

triphenylmethylenephosphorane; cyclohexanone; 86% yield methylenecyclohexane; triphenylphosphine oxide

The mechanism for this reaction is illustrated below. The ylide performs a nucleophilic attack on the carbonyl carbon using its electron-rich carbon site. The substance generated in this process has a positive charge on phosphorus and negative charge on oxygen and is known as a **betaine.** The betaine closes to an *oxyphosphorane* (five bonds to phosphorus, at least one of them involving oxygen) and then fragments to give the product.

Figure 19.30 Formation of a phosphorus ylide for the Wittig reaction.

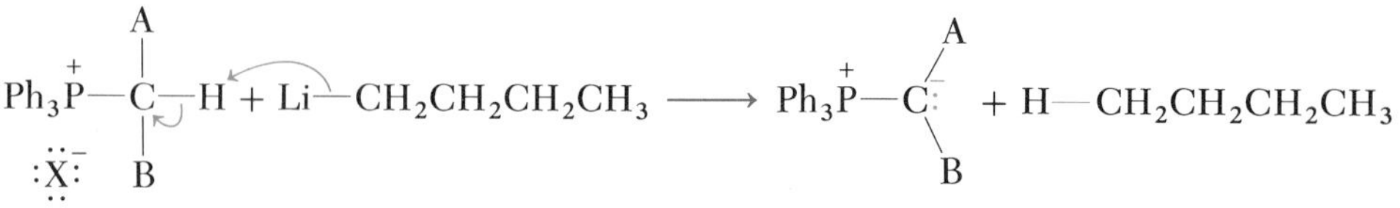

$$Ph_3\overset{+}{P}-\text{C(A)(B)}-H + Li-CH_2CH_2CH_2CH_3 \quad :\ddot{X}:^- \longrightarrow Ph_3\overset{+}{P}-\ddot{C}\text{(A)(B)} + H-CH_2CH_2CH_2CH_3$$

MECHANISM OF REACTION

The Wittig Reaction

Step 1 The electron-rich carbon of the ylide attaches to the carbonyl carbon atom.

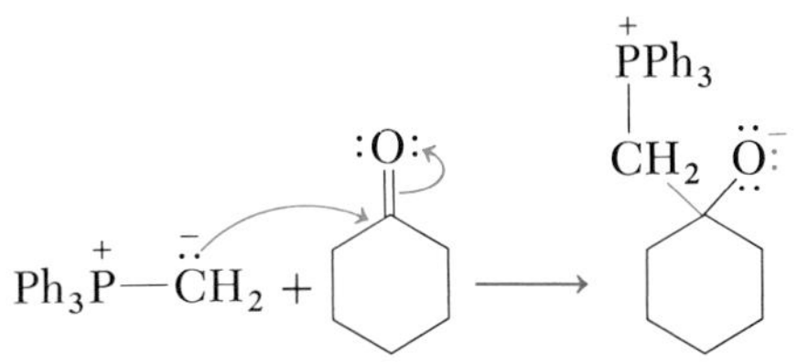

$$Ph_3\overset{+}{P}-\overset{\cdot\cdot -}{C}H_2 + \text{cyclohexanone} \longrightarrow \text{betaine}$$

a betaine

Step 2 The betaine closes to an oxyphosphorane.

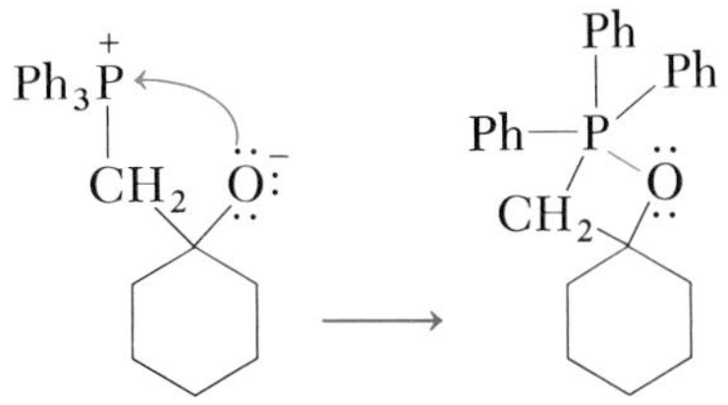

an oxyphosphorane

Step 3 The oxyphosphorane decomposes to yield the product.

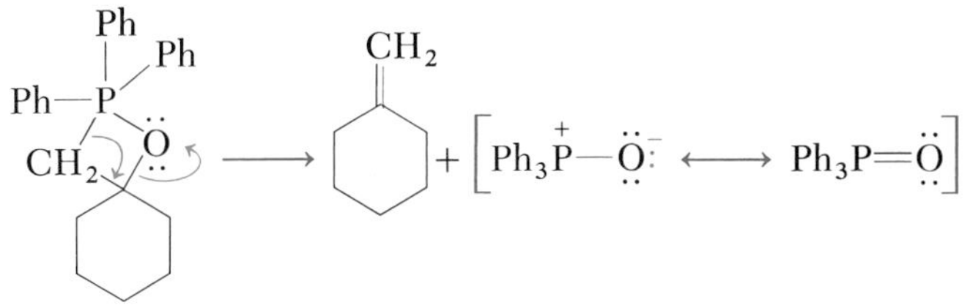

$$\longrightarrow \text{methylenecyclohexane} + \left[Ph_3\overset{+}{P}-\ddot{O}:^- \longleftrightarrow Ph_3P{=}\ddot{O}\right]$$

PROBLEM 19.22 Plan a synthetic route for each of the following compounds using Wittig reaction methodology.

a. 1-hexene
b. styrene
c. 2,3-dimethyl-2-butene
d. 1,1-diphenylethylene

Steps to Solving the Problem

Solution to Problem 19.22a

1. Perform a retrosynthetic analysis for the target material. A retrosynthetic analysis reveals that two possible combinations of carbonyl compound and

ylide will yield 1-hexene:

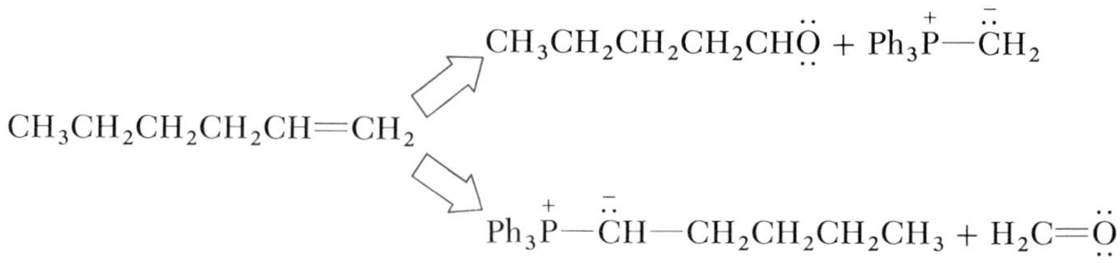

$$CH_3CH_2CH_2CH_2CH{=}CH_2 \Rightarrow CH_3CH_2CH_2CH_2CH\ddot{\underset{..}{O}} + Ph_3\overset{+}{P}{-}\overset{-}{\ddot{C}}H_2$$

$$CH_3CH_2CH_2CH_2CH{=}CH_2 \Rightarrow Ph_3\overset{+}{P}{-}\overset{-}{\ddot{C}}H{-}CH_2CH_2CH_2CH_3 + H_2C{=}\ddot{\underset{..}{O}}$$

2. Decide on the better of the two possible routes. It is common to find two possible approaches to an alkene via the Wittig reaction. Here, as in other cases, both approaches are feasible. We make our choice of which route to follow based on the availability of the starting materials. Suppose we start with pentanal as the carbonyl component. This choice entails using methyl iodide to prepare the phosphonium salt and ylide, as becomes clear from a further retrosynthetic analysis.

$$Ph_3\overset{+}{P}{-}\overset{-}{\ddot{C}}H_2 \Longrightarrow Ph_3\overset{+}{P}{-}CH_3 \Longrightarrow Ph_3P{:} + CH_3\ddot{\underset{..}{I}}{:}$$

3. Summarize the analysis. Putting everything together, we summarize our plan of synthesis as shown below.

$$CH_3\ddot{\underset{..}{I}}{:} \xrightarrow{Ph_3P} Ph_3\overset{+}{P}{-}CH_3\ {:}\ddot{\underset{..}{I}}{:}^{-} \xrightarrow{LiCH_2CH_2CH_2CH_3} Ph_3\overset{+}{P}{-}\overset{-}{\ddot{C}}H_2$$

$$Ph_3\overset{+}{P}{-}\overset{-}{\ddot{C}}H_2 \xrightarrow{CH_3CH_2CH_2CH_2CHO} CH_3CH_2CH_2CH_2CH{=}CH_2$$

19.11 Nucleophilic Attack by Sulfur

BISULFITE ION

Nucleophilic attack at the carbonyl carbon occurs with certain carbonyl compounds when they are shaken with a concentrated solution of sodium bisulfite, $NaHSO_3$. Reaction is limited, however, to aldehydes and to sterically unhindered ketones (generally methyl ketones and cyclic ketones). We refer to the product of the reaction as a *bisulfite addition compound* or a *bisulfite adduct*. These adducts are water-soluble salts that are insoluble in common organic solvents. The general nature of the reaction is shown in Figure 19.31.

Bisulfite adducts, with the exception of that formed from formaldehyde, revert readily to the starting carbonyl compound upon the addition of strong

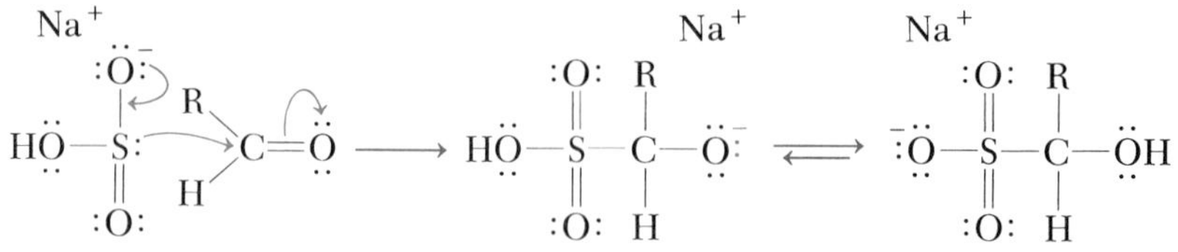

$$Na^+\ HO{-}\underset{\|\ O}{\overset{O^-}{|}}{S}{:} + \underset{H}{\overset{R}{}}C{=}\ddot{O} \longrightarrow HO{-}\underset{\|\ O}{\overset{\|\ O}{S}}{-}\underset{H}{\overset{R}{C}}{-}\ddot{O}{:}^-\ Na^+ \rightleftharpoons {}^-{:}\ddot{O}{-}\underset{\|\ O}{\overset{\|\ O}{S}}{-}\underset{H}{\overset{R}{C}}{-}\ddot{O}H\ Na^+$$

a bisulfite adduct

Figure 19.31 Formation of a bisulfite adduct with an aldehyde.

aqueous acid or base. This property provides a useful method for the purification of aldehydes and ketones. The carbonyl compound is first converted to the bisulfite adduct, which is water soluble. Insoluble organic contaminants are removed. The aqueous solution is then treated with acid or base to regenerate the carbonyl compound, which is generally insoluble in water.

THIOLS

A **thiol** is another type of sulfur nucleophile that reacts with aldehydes and ketones. Thiols are compounds of the general formula RSH, and thus they are sulfur analogues of alcohols, ROH.

PROBLEM 19.23 Suggest a synthetis of $CH_3CH_2CH_2CH_2SH$ from $CH_3CH_2CH_2CH_2OH$.

Recall that alcohols react with aldehydes and ketones to form acetals and ketals. Thiols behave similarly, forming thioacetals and thioketals. A common procedure for the preparation of thioacetals and thioketals involves treating the carbonyl compound with a *dithiol* (such as 1,2-ethanedithiol or 1,3-propanedithiol). This procedure produces a cyclic thioacetal or thioketal with the same favorable entropy factor as we found for the formation of cyclic acetals and ketals. An example of this type of reaction is shown in Equation 19.26.

Eqn. 19.26

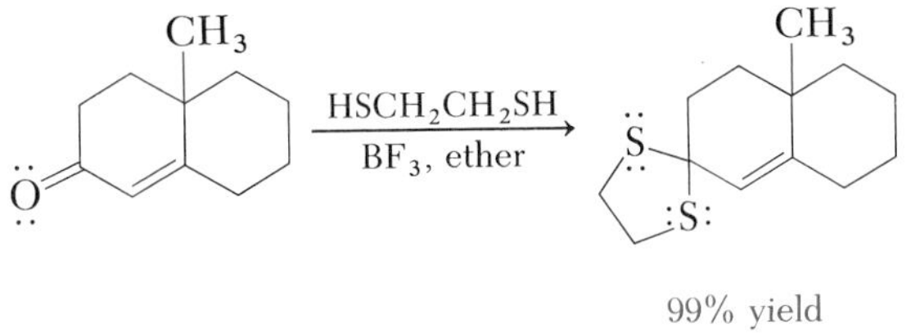

CH_3 ... $\xrightarrow[BF_3,\ ether]{HSCH_2CH_2SH}$ ... CH_3

99% yield

This reaction, like the formation of acetals and ketals, is acid-catalyzed and is accompanied by the formation of water. In contrast to ordinary ketals, thioketals are less sensitive to the action of aqueous acid and thus are more easily manipulated in synthetic operations.

Thioacetals and thioketals have several uses. One use lies in the ready cleavage of carbon-sulfur bonds in the presence of Raney nickel. (Raney nickel is a finely divided nickel on the surface of which is adsorbed molecular hydrogen. It is prepared by the treatment of a nickel-aluminum alloy with aqueous base.) In the product, carbon-hydrogen bonds replace the original carbon-sulfur bonds. An example of this reaction is shown in Equation 19.27.

Eqn. 19.27

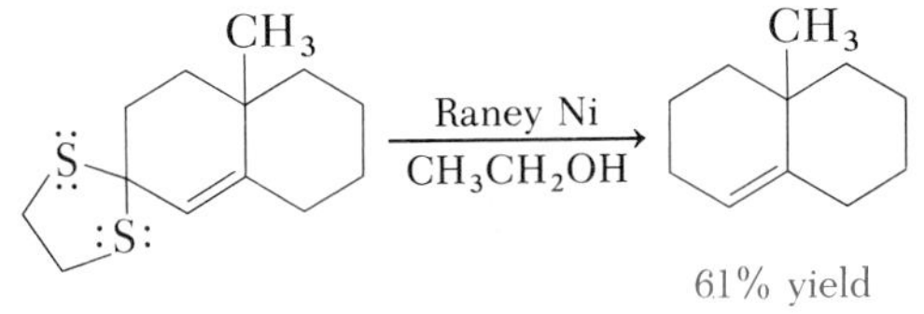

CH_3 ... $\xrightarrow[CH_3CH_2OH]{Raney\ Ni}$ ... CH_3

61% yield

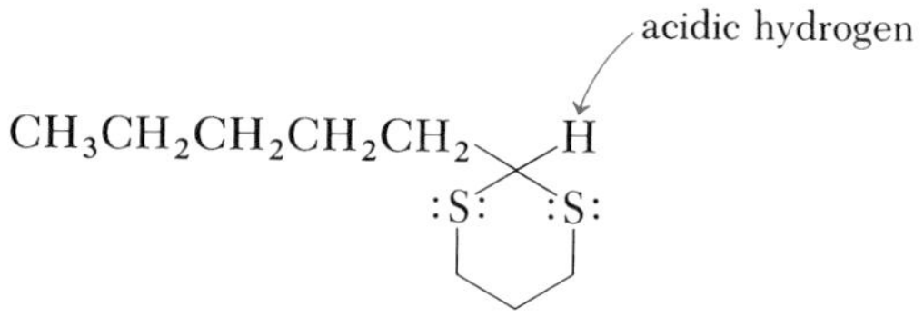

Figure 19.32 Cyclic dithioacetal of hexanal. The hydrogen of enhanced acidity is indicated.

acidic hydrogen

$CH_3CH_2CH_2CH_2CH_2$ H
:S: :S:

The net effect of converting an aldehyde or ketone to a thioacetal or thioketal followed by Raney nickel desulfurization is to reduce the carbonyl group ($>C=O$) to a methylene group ($>CH_2$).

Another use of thioacetals results from the increased acidity in the thioacetals of the hydrogen(s) attached to the original aldehyde carbonyl carbon. This increased acidity is particularly pronounced in the cyclic dithioacetals derived from 1,3-propanedithiol. The appropriate thioacetal of hexanal is shown in Figure 19.32 with the acidic hydrogen noted.

A strong base, such as an alkyllithium reagent, can remove the acidic hydrogen of a dithiane to produce a nucleophilic carbanion. This new carbanion then is capable of performing nucleophilic substitution or addition reactions. Notice that conversion of the carbonyl group to a dithioacetal, followed by removal of the proton, constitutes an *umpolung* (see Chapter 11) in that the initially electron-deficient carbon atom of the carbonyl bond becomes electron rich in the carbanion formed after proton removal. An example of this *umpolung* in a synthetic scheme is shown in Equation 19.28.

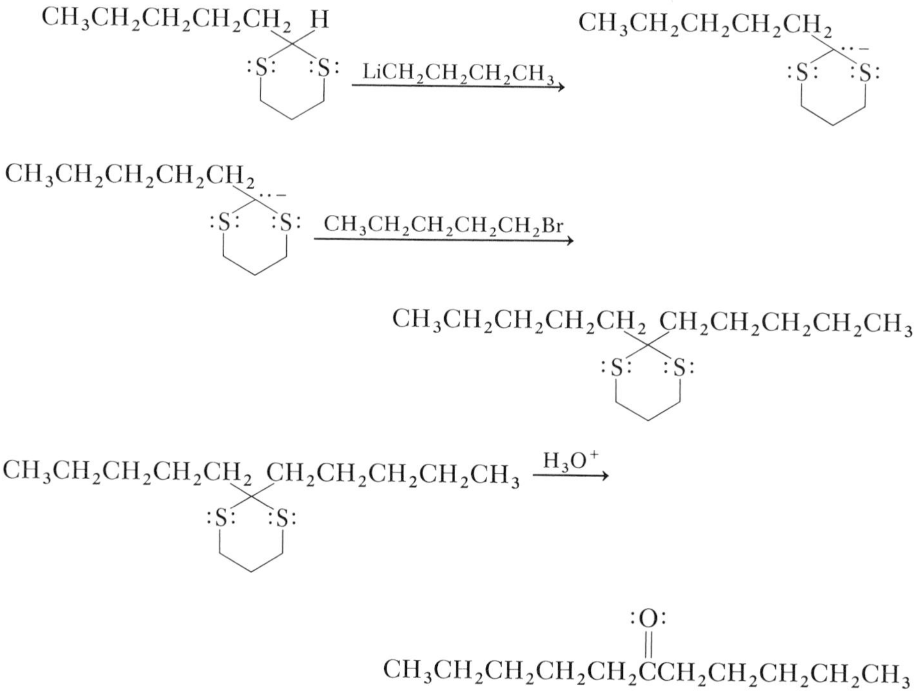

$CH_3CH_2CH_2CH_2CH_2$ H
:S: :S: $\xrightarrow{LiCH_2CH_2CH_2CH_3}$ $CH_3CH_2CH_2CH_2CH_2$ (carbanion, :S: :S:)

$CH_3CH_2CH_2CH_2CH_2$ (carbanion, :S: :S:) $\xrightarrow{CH_3CH_2CH_2CH_2CH_2Br}$

$CH_3CH_2CH_2CH_2CH_2$ $CH_2CH_2CH_2CH_2CH_3$
:S: :S:

$CH_3CH_2CH_2CH_2CH_2$ $CH_2CH_2CH_2CH_2CH_3$ $\xrightarrow{H_3O^+}$
:S: :S:

:O:
||
$CH_3CH_2CH_2CH_2CH_2CCH_2CH_2CH_2CH_2CH_3$

85% yield
6-undecanone

This sequence of reactions provides a method of converting aldehydes into ketones.

PROBLEM 19.24 1,3-Dithiane (shown below) is a commercially available material. Give the structures of compounds *A–C* in the following reaction scheme involving 1,3-dithiane.

1,3-dithiane

$$\text{1,3-dithiane} \xrightarrow[\text{2. } CH_3CH_2Br]{\text{1. } LiCH_2CH_2CH_2CH_3} A \quad (C_6H_{12}S_2)$$

$$A \xrightarrow[\text{2. } (CH_3)_2CHI]{\text{1. } LiCH_2CH_2CH_2CH_3} B \quad (C_9H_{18}S_2)$$

$$B \xrightarrow[\text{water, methanol}]{H_2SO_4} C \quad (C_6H_{12}O) + H\ddot{S}CH_2CH_2CH_2\ddot{S}H$$

19.12 Acidity of α-Hydrogen Atoms

An extremely important aspect of the chemistry of aldehydes and ketones is the enhanced acidity of hydrogens attached to the α-carbon atoms. Figure 19.33 emphasizes the α-carbon atom and the acidic hydrogen attached to it in a carbonyl compound.

The relatively high acidity of the α-hydrogens of a carbonyl compound correlates with the relatively high stability of the conjugate base formed upon removal of the hydrogen ion. The conjugate base is stabilized by delocalization of the charge to the carbonyl oxygen as well as to the carbon. The contributing resonance structures are shown in Figure 19.34.

As noted previously, the name *enolate anion* is commonly given to this type of conjugate base. This name reflects the importance of the second resonance structure, which is the conjugate base of an enol, (it is an enol that has lost a proton from its hydroxyl group).

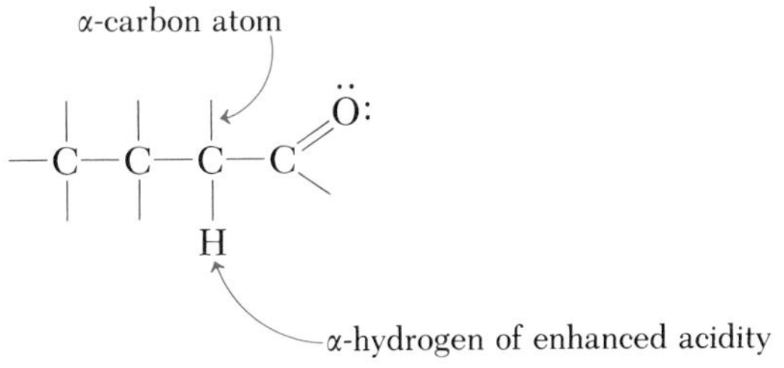

α-carbon atom

α-hydrogen of enhanced acidity

Figure 19.33 The α-position of a carbonyl compound. Hydrogen atoms attached at the α-carbon atom of a carbonyl compound have enhanced acidity compared with ordinary aliphatic hydrogen atoms.

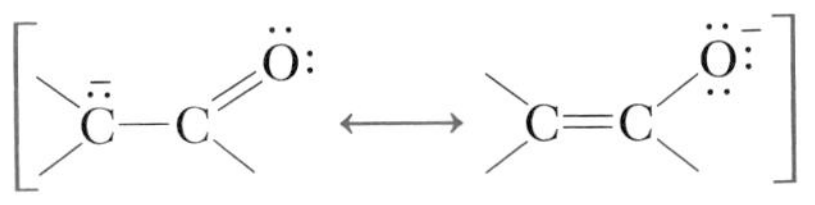

Figure 19.34 Contributing resonance structures for the anion generated upon removal of the α-hydrogen of a carbonyl compound. The delocalization of the negative charge stabilizes the ion.

A quantitative measure of the acidity of hydrogens at the α-position of a carbonyl compound is obtained by looking at the pK_a values for acetone and propane, as shown in Table 19.4.

The acidity of acetone is much closer to that of alcohols and water than to that of an alkane. Alkoxide ions and hydroxide ions are thus able to generate small but significant quantities of enolate anions when added to aldehydes and ketones bearing α-hydrogens, as is illustrated in Figure 19.35.

PROBLEM 19.25 Calculate the equilibrium constant for the reaction of ethoxide ion with acetone by using the appropriate pK_a values.

Table 19.4 Comparison of the Acidities of Acetone and Propane.

Compound	pK_a
$CH_3-C(=\ddot{O}:)-CH_3$	19
$CH_3-CH_2-CH_3$	50

The pK_a of acetone is 31 units smaller than that of propane. Thus the ratio of the K_a values of the two compounds is about $10^{31}:1$—they vary by a factor 16 million times greater than the Avogadro number!

If the enolate anion enters into further reaction with some added reagent, the equilibrium of Figure 19.35 is constantly driven to the right-hand side. With time, more and more of the carbonyl compound reacts to generate enolate anion, which then reacts with the added reagent.

There are many consequences of the enhanced acidity associated with α-hydrogens of carbonyl compounds. The main focus of Chapter 23 is the reactions of enolate anions that result in the formation of new carbon-carbon bonds. In this chapter we will look at some other properties and reactions associated with the acidic α-hydrogens of carbonyl compounds.

BASE-CATALYZED RACEMIZATION OF CHIRAL ALDEHYDES AND KETONES HAVING α-HYDROGEN ATOMS

Suppose we have an optically active aldehyde or ketone in which the source of optical activity is a stereogenic α-carbon atom bearing a hydrogen. When we place such an optically active compound in basic solution there is a rapid loss of optical activity, that is, racemization occurs. It occurs because the added base sets in motion a series of acid-base reactions involving the α-hydrogen. Suppose we are working with (*R*)-2-methyl-1-phenyl-1-butanone (**19.3**).

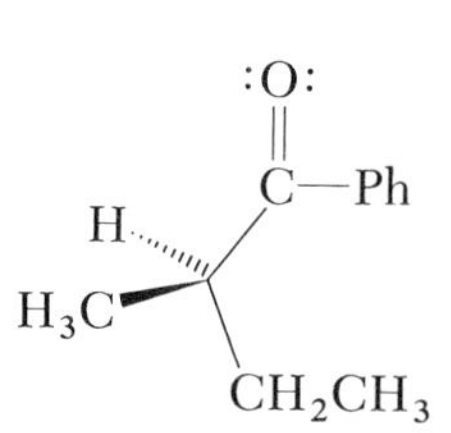

:O:
C—Ph
H
H_3C
CH_2CH_3

(*R*)-2-methyl-1-phenyl-1-butanone
19.3

$$-\overset{|}{\underset{|}{C}}-C(=\ddot{O}:) + H\ddot{O}:^- \rightleftharpoons \ddot{C}^--C(=\ddot{O}:) + H-\ddot{O}H$$

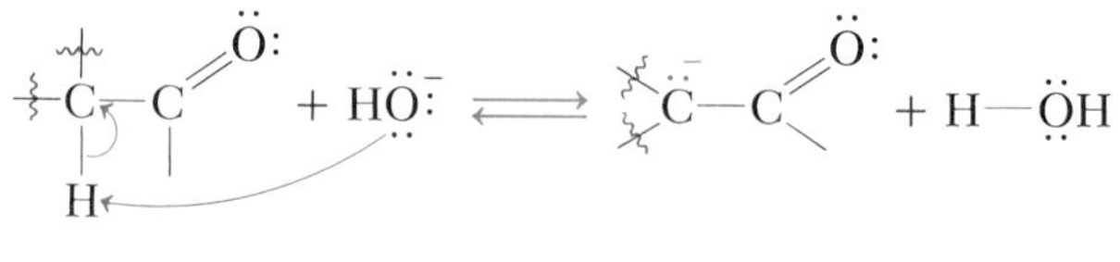

Figure 19.35 Conversion of a carbonyl compound to an enolate anion by hydroxide ion. The reaction is an acid-base equilibrium.

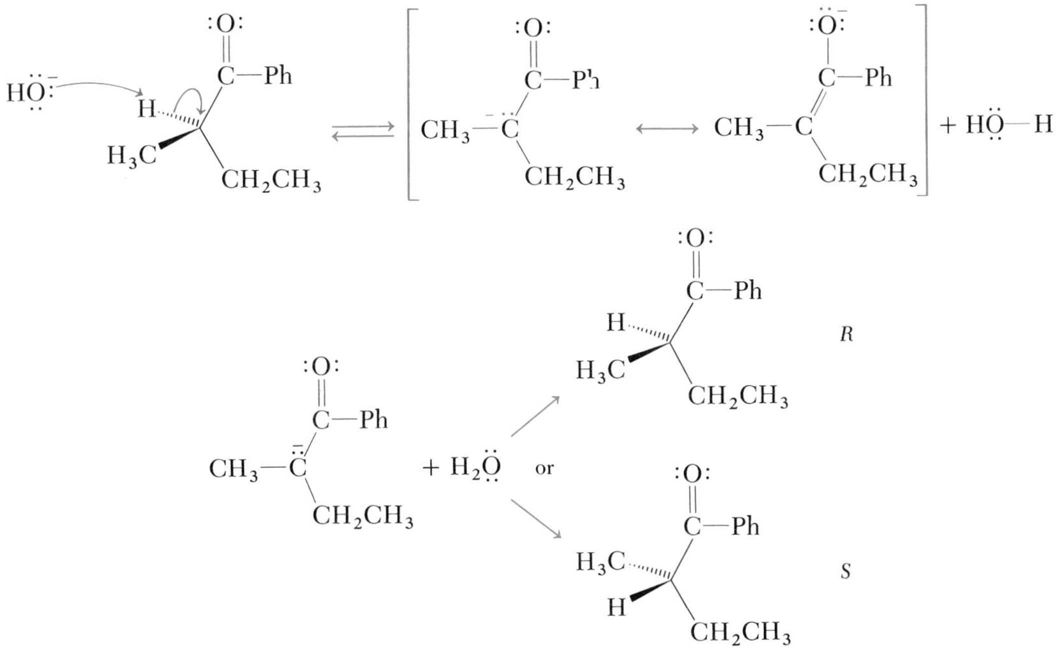

Figure 19.36 **Base-induced racemization of optically active 2-methyl-1-phenyl-1-butanone.** The base removes a proton from the stereogenic α-carbon atom, forming an achiral enolate anion. When the planar enolate anion regains a proton from water, there is equal likelihood that the *R* or *S* form will be generated. The result is the formation of a racemic mixture.

The base is able to remove α-hydrogens from some of the molecules of (**19.3**), thus breaking a bond to the stereogenic center. This acid-base reaction is reversible, that is, the α-carbon atom of the enolate ion can regain a proton. However, there is an equal likelihood of an *R* or an *S* configuration 2-methyl-1-phenyl-1-butanone being generated in this process. Since deprotonation and protonation occur rapidly, a racemic mixture is produced in a short period of time, as illustrated schematically in Figure 19.36.

PROBLEM 19.26 We can also racemize chiral carbonyl compounds in acidic solution. The process is catalytic with regard to the concentration of hydronium ion. Suggest a mechanism for the acid-catalyzed racemization of (*R*)-2-methyl-1-phenyl-1-butanone. *Hint:* An enol intermediate is involved.

SELECTIVE DEUTERATION

If an aldehyde or ketone is placed in a solution of NaOD in D_2O, the α-hydrogens will be replaced by deuterium atoms. This deuteration process again involves a series of acid-base equilibria. In the presence of a base, the carbonyl compound loses the α-hydrogens, as noted previously. The enolate anion thus produced can then regain a proton or (more likely in an excess of D_2O) pick up a deuteron. In a short period of time the α-deuteration is essentially complete.

Deuteration in this manner is quite helpful in the determination of organic structures. We can observe this exchange of deuterium for hydrogen quite readily in the ^1H NMR spectrum (see Chapter 17). Furthermore, each deuterium atom that replaces a hydrogen atom increases the molecular weight of the compound by one unit. Thus, by measuring the molecular weight of a compound before and after deuteration, we can determine very easily the number of α-hydrogen atoms present in the original compound.

PROBLEM 19.27 A ketone containing just one carbonyl group is found to have a molecular weight of 100 g/mole. The ketone is shaken with NaOD in D_2O. On isolation of the organic product the molecular weight is found to have increased to 103 g/mole. Suggest all possible structures for the starting ketone.

SELECTIVE HALOGENATION—THE HALOFORM REACTION

It is possible to halogenate aldehydes and ketones selectively at the α-position, replacing any α-hydrogen atoms originally present. The reaction is accelerated by bases such as hydroxide ion. This reaction, like those of the previous section, involves an enolate anion as an intermediate. Here the enolate anion reacts with the halogen to give overall halogen substitution for the original α-hydrogen. Under basic conditions it is difficult to control the reaction; thus we find that *all* available α-hydrogen atoms are replaced by halogen.

There is one special case of this reaction that occurs when *methyl ketones* react with halogens (chlorine, bromine, iodine) under aqueous basic conditions. As might be anticipated, halogens rapidly replace all three hydrogen atoms of the methyl group. However, the trihalomethyl ketone that is formed is still reactive under these reaction conditions. Hydroxide ion acts as a nucleophile and displaces the trihalomethyl anion from the carbonyl carbon in two steps.

The reaction consists of a series of acid-base and substitution reactions. Each successive removal of an α-hydrogen from the carbonyl intermediates proceeds more readily than the previous one. The halogen stabilizes the charge on the anion. With each replacement by halogen, the remaining α-hydrogen(s) becomes more acidic. Finally, when there are no more α-hydrogens for replacement, the hydroxide adds to the carbonyl carbon. The trihalomethyl group departs as the anion, being stabilized by the presence of the three halogens. The products of the reaction are haloform and carboxylate anion. Because it produces a haloform (HCX_3, e.g., $CHCl_3$ (chloroform)), this process is commonly referred to as the **haloform reaction.**

MECHANISM OF REACTION

The Haloform Reaction

Step 1 Deprotonation of the methyl ketone

$$H_2C(H)-C(=\ddot{O}:)-R + {}^{-}:\ddot{O}-H \rightleftharpoons \left[H_2\bar{C}-C(=\ddot{O}:)-R \longleftrightarrow H_2C=C(-\ddot{O}:^{-})-R \right] + H\ddot{O}-H$$

Step 2 Halogenation of the enolate anion

$$H_2\bar{C}{-}C(=O){-}R + X{-}X \longrightarrow H_2C(X){-}C(=O){-}R + X^-$$

Step 3 Deprotonation of the halogenated ketone

$$XCH(H){-}C(=O){-}R + {}^-OH \rightleftharpoons \left[X\bar{C}H{-}C(=O){-}R \longleftrightarrow XCH{=}C(O^-){-}R \right] + HO{-}H$$

Step 4 Halogenation of the enolate anion

$$X\bar{C}H{-}C(=O){-}R + X{-}X \longrightarrow XCH(X){-}C(=O){-}R + X^-$$

Step 5 Deprotonation of the intermediate ketone

$$X_2C(H){-}C(=O){-}R + {}^-OH \rightleftharpoons X_2\bar{C}{-}C(=O){-}R + HO{-}H$$

Step 6 Halogenation of the enolate anion

$$X_2\bar{C}{-}C(=O){-}R + X{-}X \longrightarrow X_2C(X){-}C(=O){-}R + X^-$$

Step 7 Nucleophilic displacement of the trihalomethyl anion

$$X_3C{-}C(=O){-}R + {}^-OH \longrightarrow X_3C{-}C(O^-)(OH){-}R \longrightarrow X_3C^- + HO{-}C(=O){-}R$$

Step 8 Proton abstraction to generate haloform

$$X_3C^- + H{-}O{-}H \longrightarrow X_3C{-}H + {}^-O{-}H$$

Step 9 Anion formation with the carboxylic acid

$$R-\overset{\overset{:O:}{\parallel}}{C}-\ddot{O}-H + :\ddot{O}^{-}-H \longrightarrow R-\overset{\overset{:O:}{\parallel}}{C}-\ddot{O}:^{-} + H-\ddot{O}-H$$

This reaction has two applications. First, it serves as a method for the synthesis of carboxylic acids from methyl ketones. A typical example of this synthesis is shown in Equation 19.29.

Eqn. 19.29

$$(CH_3)_3C-\overset{\overset{:O:}{\parallel}}{C}-CH_3 \xrightarrow[2.\ H_3O^+]{1.\ Br_2,\ NaOH,\ H_2O} HCBr_3 + (CH_3)_3C-COOH$$

3,3-dimethyl-2-butanone; 74% yield 2,2-dimethylpropanoic acid

Second, the reaction is used as a diagnostic test for the presence of a methyl ketone. If we use iodine as the halogen, the haloform product is iodoform, a yellow solid that is insoluble in the test solution. The formation of the yellow precipitate serves as a positive iodoform test.

There is a limitation to the use of this reaction as a diagnostic tool. Alcohols of the type $CH_3CH(OH)R$ (where $R = H$ or an alkyl or aryl group) *also* give a positive iodoform test because iodine in aqueous base is a sufficiently strong oxidizing agent to convert a primary or secondary alcohol to a carbonyl compound. Accordingly, any alcohol that produces a methyl ketone (or ethanal) on oxidation also gives a positive iodoform test.

PROBLEM 19.28 Which of the following compounds do you expect to give a positive iodoform test?

2-pentanone	acetophenone
3-pentanone	benzyl alcohol
2-pentanol	benzophenone
3-pentanol	

PROBLEM 19.29 Consider the reaction of acetone with bromine in aqueous basic solution. Using the curved-arrow formalism, write the two mechanistic steps leading to the formation of monobromoacetone. Given that the rate law for the reaction is

$$\text{rate} = k[\text{acetone}][\text{hydroxide ion}]$$

which of the two steps is faster? Predict whether iodine or bromine will react more rapidly with acetone under base-catalyzed conditions.

We can restrict halogenation of a methyl ketone to the addition of a single halogen to the α-carbon site by using acidic reaction conditions. This reaction proceeds efficiently and in good yield. An example is shown in Equation 19.30.

Eqn. 19.30

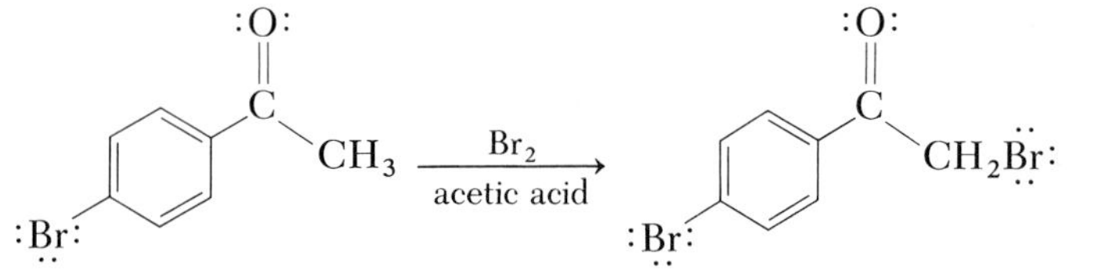

p-bromoacetophenone $\xrightarrow[\text{acetic acid}]{Br_2}$ p-bromophenyl bromomethyl ketone (70%)

PROBLEM 19.30 The reaction of acetone with bromine in aqueous acid is catalytic with regard to hydronium ion concentration. Suggest a mechanism for this process, noting which step is rate-determining, given the following information:

- acid-catalyzed hydrogen-deuterium exchange and acid-catalyzed bromination occur with the same rate constants.
- acid-catalyzed iodination and acid-catalyzed racemization of a chiral ketone (such as 2-methyl-1-phenyl-1-butanone) occur with the same rate constants.

19.13 Oxidation and Reduction

Aldehydes are oxidized to carboxylic acids very readily, while ketones are inert to most oxidizing agents. In contrast, both aldehydes and ketones undergo reduction by the same types of reducing reagents. Depending on the reducing agent used, we can reduce the carbonyl group to either a carbinol or a methylene group. In this section we will survey the specific conditions needed for the oxidation and reduction of aldehydes and ketones.

increasing level of oxidation ↑

RCO_2H carboxylic acid

$RCHO$ aldehyde

RCH_2OH primary alchol

RCH_3 alkane

Figure 19.37 Position of aldehydes in the hierarchy of oxidation states.

THE OXIDATION OF ALDEHYDES

Let us first recall the position of aldehydes in the hierarchy of oxidation states, which is shown schematically in Figure 19.37. Most oxidizing agents that oxidize primary alcohols to aldehydes also oxidize aldehydes to carboxylic acids. (Recall from Chapter 6 that we need to use special reaction conditions and/or reagents to stop the oxidation of a primary alcohol at the aldehyde stage.) Most oxidizing agents convert a primary alcohol to a carboxylic acid. Two further examples of the oxidation of aldehydes to carboxylic acids are shown in Equations 19.31 and 19.32.

Eqn. 19.31

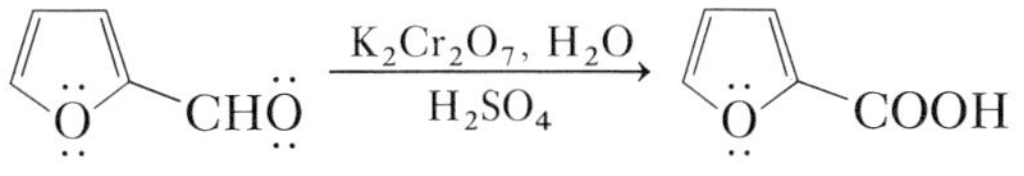

furfural $\xrightarrow[H_2SO_4]{K_2Cr_2O_7,\ H_2O}$ 2-furoic acid (75% yield)

Eqn. 19.32

$$CH_3CH_2CH_2CH_2CH_2CH_2CHO \xrightarrow[\text{2. aq acid}]{\text{1. } KMnO_4,\ KOH,\ H_2O} CH_3CH_2CH_2CH_2CH_2CH_2COOH$$

heptanal → heptanoic acid (77% yield)

The high susceptibility of aldehydes to oxidation has a number of practical consequences. Even the oxygen in air can oxidize aldehydes to carboxylic acids at ordinary temperature. For example, if we open a bottle of benzaldehyde (a liquid) that has been stored for even a relatively short period of time, we usually find that it contains some crystals of benzoic acid because the benzaldehyde invariably comes into contact with small amounts of air. A sample of benzaldehyde stored for a long period of time might even be completely solid (i.e., completely oxidized to benzoic acid). For this reason we must carefully check all aldehydes for purity before we use them.

Aldehydes can be oxidized to carboxylic acids in the presence of other sensitive functional groups. A group of very mild oxidizing agents that can be used in the selective oxidation of aldehydes to carboxylic acids is based on Ag(I). These reagents are sufficiently mild that they oxidize aldehydes to carboxylic acids without affecting primary or secondary alcohol functions that are also present. Stronger oxidizing agents would oxidize both aldehyde and alcohol functional groups.

One example of this type of oxidizing agent is the **Tollens' reagent**, $[Ag(NH_3)_2]^+$. A solution containing this ion can be prepared by adding concentrated aqueous ammonia to a solution of a silver salt such as silver nitrate. Aldehydes react with this cation in aqueous solution to generate the carboxylate salt, reducing the complex silver ion to metallic silver, Ag(0), which forms as a mirror on the walls of the reaction flask. We sometimes use this reaction as a diagnostic test for the presence of an aldehyde functional group ("the silver mirror test"). A similar reagent is a suspension of silver oxide in aqueous alkali solution. An example of the use of this type of reagent is shown in Equation 19.33.

Eqn. 19.33

2-thiophenecarboxaldehyde (thiophene ring with CHO) $\xrightarrow[\text{2. aq acid}]{\text{1. } Ag_2O,\ NaOH,\ H_2O}$ 2-thiophenecarboxylic acid (thiophene ring with COOH), 96% yield

THE OXIDATION OF KETONES

Most ketones are resistant to most oxidizing agents. Methyl ketones, however, constitute an exception. Under the special conditions of the haloform reaction, methyl ketones undergo oxidation to carboxylic acids (see Section 19.12). Other ketones give no reaction with most of the common oxidizing agents we have met. Oxidation occurs only under extreme conditions that result in the cleavage of a carbon-carbon bond. The product of such a reaction is often a mixture of carboxylic acids, making such reactions of little synthetic value. (An exception is the Baeyer-Villiger oxidation, which we will discuss in a later chapter.)

THE REDUCTION OF ALDEHYDES AND KETONES TO ALCOHOLS

The reduction of an aldehyde or ketone to an alcohol is a process of great synthetic value. Two common approaches are **catalytic hydrogenation** and the use of **complex metal hydrides** such as sodium borohydride ($NaBH_4$) and lithium aluminum hydride ($LiAlH_4$).

Catalytic hydrogenation occurs readily in the presence of a variety of catalysts; the catalysts are finely divided metals, sometimes held on the surface of a support medium such as charcoal. Palladium, platinum, rubidium, and nickel are most commonly used. (The metals palladium and rubidium are generally supported on a carbon powder. Platinum is often in the form of PtO_2, *Adam's catalyst*, which reacts with hydrogen immediately to form finely divided Pt(0). Nickel is usually in the form of Raney nickel.) An example of the reduction of a simple ketone using catalytic hydrogenation is shown in Equation 19.34.

Eqn. 19.34

$$\text{cyclohexanone} \xrightarrow[\text{ethanol } 25^\circ]{H_2 \text{ (3 atm.)}, PtO_2} \text{cyclohexanol (98\% yield)}$$

cyclohexanone — 98% yield cyclohexanol

However, this method has the disadvantage of being of low selectivity. Other functional groups such as alkene double bonds also undergo reduction under these conditions. An example is shown in Equation 19.35.

Eqn. 19.35

$$\text{methyl 4-cyclohexenyl ketone} \xrightarrow[\text{Ni}]{H_2 \text{ (1 atm)}} \text{1-cyclohexylethanol (96\% yield)}$$

methyl 4-cyclohexenyl ketone — 96% yield 1-cyclohexylethanol

Metal hydride reducing agents are more selective. The two reagents of this type that are most commonly used are sodium borohydride and lithium aluminum hydride. Of the two, lithium aluminium hydride is more potent and therefore less selective. Sodium borohydride is a relatively mild reagent. While it is usually effective for the reduction of the carbonyl group of aldehydes and ketones, it has no effect on many other groups that would undergo reduction with lithium aluminium hydride.

Both reagents act, in effect, as sources of nucleophilic hydride ion. We can think of the reduction as involving a nucleophilic addition of a hydride ion delivered by the metal hydride reagent to the carbonyl carbon. Interestingly, simple metal hydrides such as sodium hydride, NaH, are not effective for this reduction. (You should remember that there is no free hydride ion floating around in solution with any of these reagents at any time. "Hydride ion" is in a bound state, and the complex ion donates a hydrogen nucleus along with a pair of electrons.) Examples of the use of these metal hydride reducing agents are shown in Equations 19.36 and 19.37.

Eqn. 19.36

$$\text{cyclobutanone} \xrightarrow[\text{2. aq acid}]{\text{1. } LiAlH_4, \text{ ether}} \text{cyclobutanol (82\% yield)}$$

cyclobutanone — 82% yield cyclobutanol

Eqn. 19.37

$$H_2C{=}CHCH_2CH_2CH\ddot{\underset{..}{O}} \xrightarrow{NaBH_4,\ H_2O} H_2C{=}CHCH_2CH_2CH_2OH$$

4-pentenal — 85% yield, 4-penten-1-ol

PROBLEM 19.31 Choose the reagent or combination of reagents you would use to accomplish each of the following conversions:

a. crotonaldehyde ($CH_3CH{=}CH{-}CH\ddot{\underset{..}{O}}$) to 1-butanol

b. cinnamaldehyde ($PhCH{=}CH{-}CH\ddot{\underset{..}{O}}$) to cinnamyl alcohol ($PhCH{=}CH{-}CH_2\ddot{\underset{..}{O}}H$)

There are a variety of methods for the conversion of a carbonyl group to a methylene group. We have already seen one of these methods earlier in this chapter—the desulfurization of thioacetals or thioketals using Raney nickel. Two other important (and complementary) methods are the **Clemmensen reduction** and the **Wolff-Kishner reduction.** While the Raney nickel desulfurization occurs under essentially neutral conditions, the Clemmensen reduction occurs in acidic solution and the Wolff-Kishner reduction occurs in basic medium. The experimental conditions for each of these methods are summarized in Table 19.5.

You might wonder why we need several alternative ways for effecting the same functional group transformation. Why wouldn't a single method suffice (there would be a lot less for the student to learn)? If we worked only with simple compounds containing only one functional group, one method probably *would* suffice most of the time. However, when working with complex molecules containing many functional groups, we must make certain that changing one

Table 19.5 Experimental Conditions for the Reduction of a Carbonyl Group to a Methylene Group

Method	Experimental Conditions and Procedures
Raney nickel desulfurization of thioketals	The carbonyl compound is first converted to the dithioketal using 1,3-propanedithiol with acid catalysis. Under neutral conditions the dithioketal is treated with freshly prepared Raney nickel.
Clemmensen reduction	The carbonyl compound is treated with a zinc amalgam (a solution of zinc in mercury, generally written Zn(Hg)) in concentrated hydrochloric acid.
Wolff-Kishner reduction	The carbonyl compound is heated with hydrazine to form the hydrazone. The hydrazone is heated strongly with sodium or potassium hydroxide in a high-boiling alcohol such as diethylene glycol.

functional group does not at the same time change other functional groups that are present and that we wish to keep intact. For example, suppose we wish to reduce a carbonyl group to a methylene group. If our molecule also contains an alcohol function, we would not choose the Clemmensen reduction method because the strong acid could react with the hydroxyl group and cause rearrangements, eliminations, or substitutions to occur. Similarly, if our compound contained a remote halogen substituent, we would not choose either the Raney nickel desulfurization (carbon-halogen bonds can undergo hydrogenolysis) or the Wolff-Kishner reduction (the strong alkali could cause an elimination reaction at the halide site).

Examples of the use of the Clemmensen and Wolff-Kishner reductions are shown in Equations 19.38 and 19.39, respectively.

Eqn. 19.38

$$\text{3-methoxy-5-hydroxybenzaldehyde} \xrightarrow[\text{ethanol, reflux}]{\text{Zn (Hg), HCl, } H_2O} \text{3-methoxy-5-hydroxytoluene}$$

:ÖCH$_3$ / HÖ / CHÖ — 3-methoxy-5-hydroxybenzaldehyde

:ÖCH$_3$ / HÖ / CH$_3$ — 65% yield 3-methoxy-5-hydroxytoluene

Eqn. 19.39

$$O{=}C(CH_2CH_2CH_2CH_2COOH)_2 \xrightarrow[\text{2. KOH, } H_2O\text{, heat; 3. aq acid}]{\text{1. } H_2NNH_2} H_2C(CH_2CH_2CH_2CH_2COOH)_2$$

6-oxoundecandioic acid

90% yield
undecandioic acid

Although the mechanism of the Clemmensen reduction is beyond the scope of this course, the mechanism of the Wolff-Kishner reduction is not. In fact, it is a rather interesting mechanism involving a series of acid-base equilibria that are pushed to the product side by the irreversible evolution of nitrogen, one of the reaction products. The acid-base reactions essentially transfer hydrogen from the terminal nitrogen to the carbon. The mechanism given below begins with the preformed hydrazone (from reaction of the carbonyl compound with hydrazine).

MECHANISM OF REACTION

The Wolff-Kishner Reduction

Step 1 Deprotonation of the hydrazone.

$$R_2C{=}\ddot{N}{-}\ddot{N}H(H) + {}^{-}:\ddot{O}H \rightleftharpoons [R_2\bar{C}{-}\ddot{N}{=}\ddot{N}H \longleftrightarrow R_2C{=}\ddot{N}{-}\bar{N}H] + H{-}\ddot{O}H$$

Step 2 Acid-base reaction with water.

$$R_2\ddot{C}^{-}-\ddot{N}=\ddot{N}H + H-\ddot{O}-H \rightleftharpoons R_2C(H)-\ddot{N}=\ddot{N}H + {}^{-}:\ddot{O}H$$

Step 3 Deprotonation of the intermediate.

$$R_2CH-\ddot{N}=\ddot{N}-H + {}^{-}:\ddot{O}-H \rightleftharpoons R_2CH-\ddot{N}=\ddot{N}:^{-} + H-\ddot{O}H$$

Step 4 Decomposition of the intermediate. This rate-determining step is essentially irreversible because of the evolution of nitrogen gas from the reaction mixture. The driving force for the generation of the carbanion in this step is the great stability of the bond in the nitrogen molecule.

$$R_2CH-\ddot{N}=\ddot{N}:^{-} \xrightarrow{\text{slow}} R_2\underline{\ddot{C}}H + :N\equiv N:$$

Step 5 Another acid-base reaction with water.

$$R_2\underline{\ddot{C}}H + H-\ddot{O}-H \longrightarrow R_2CH(H) + {}^{-}:\ddot{O}H$$

Summary

- Aldehydes and ketones both contain the carbonyl functional group

$$\rangle C=\ddot{O}$$

- In aldehydes, at least one hydrogen atom is attached to the carbon of the carbonyl group.
- In ketones, the carbon of the carbonyl group is bonded only to other carbon atoms.
- Aldehydes and ketones can be prepared in a variety of ways. The most important general method is oxidation of primary or secondary alcohols. Primary alcohols yield aldehydes under controlled oxidation conditions. Secondary alcohols are oxidized by a variety of reagents to ketones.
- Other general methods for the preparation of aldehydes and ketones include the hydration of alkynes, the pinacol/pinacolone rearrangement, and the treatment of acid halides with reducing agents (to produce aldehydes) or with certain organometallic compounds (to produce ketones).
- There are also some special methods for producing aromatic aldehydes and ketones. Aromatic aldehydes can sometimes be prepared by means of the Reimer-Tiemann reaction of a phenol with dichlorocarbene, and aromatic ketones can be made by Friedel-Crafts acylation.
- The carbonyl group is attacked by nucleophiles, resulting in nucleophilic addition. The nucleophile adds to the carbon of the carbonyl group, and a pair of electrons is displaced from the carbon-oxygen double bond to become an unshared valence level pair on oxygen.
- In many cases of carbonyl addition, such as the addition of cyanide or a Grignard reagent, a substance containing the hydroxyl group is obtained (after aqueous workup).

- Water and alcohols add to the carbonyl group to form unstable hydrates, hemiacetals, and hemiketals.
- Relatively more stable full acetals or ketals can be obtained by the reaction of alcohols with aldehydes and ketones in the presence of anhydrous acid, with the removal of water from the reaction system as it is formed.
- Full acetals and ketals are not cleaved by basic or nucleophilic reagents. They thus provide a method for protecting a carbonyl group.
- Cyclic acetals, ketals, thioacetals, and thioketals can be prepared by allowing aldehydes or ketones to react with diols or dithiols.
- When a nitrogen-containing nucleophile attacks an aldehyde or ketone using an unshared valence level electron pair on nitrogen, the initially formed product contains a hydroxyl group, but it may then eliminate water to form a product with a carbon-nitrogen (or a carbon-carbon) double bond.
- Phosphorus ylides (compounds containing a negatively charged carbon atom and an adjacent positively charged phosphorus atom) function as nucleophiles toward the carbonyl group. The reaction, known as the Wittig reaction, is of major importance because it leads to the formation of a new carbon to carbon double bond.
- Aldehydes, but not ketones, undergo facile oxidation. Aldehydes yield carboxylic acids upon reaction with many oxidizing agents. Even very mild oxidizing agents allow this reaction to occur.
- Aldehydes and ketones can be reduced to alcohols with complex hydride reagents such as sodium borohydride.
- The carbonyl group can be reduced to a methylene group ($>CH_2$) by a variety of methods including the Clemmensen reduction, the Wolff-Kischner reduction, or Raney nickel reduction of a thioacetal.
- Cyclic thioacetals formed by reaction of an aldehyde with a 1,3-dithiol can be deprotonated by strong base. The hydrogen removed is the one attached to the carbon atom that was originally the carbonyl carbon. The deprotonation produces a nucleophilic carbanionic reagent that reacts with electrophiles such as haloalkanes. The products of these reactions can be hydrolyzed to form ketones.

Terms to Remember

nucleophilic addition
enolate anion
formyl
formylation
Jones reagent
hydration
Gatterman-Koch synthesis
Reimer-Tiemann reaction
Hoesch reaction
pinacol/pinacolone rearrangement
Rosenmund reduction
hemiacetal
hemiketal
acetal
ketal
entropy
imine
Schiff base
hydrazone
oxime
enamine
cyanohydrin
Wittig reaction
ylide
betaine
thiol
haloform reaction
Tollens' reagent
catalytic hydrogenation
complex metal hydride
Clemmensen reduction
Wolff-Kishner reduction

Reactions of Synthetic Utility

114. $ArH \xrightarrow[AlCl_3]{CO,\ HCl} ArCHO$ 19.6

115. R–(C₆H₄)–OH $\xrightarrow[NaOH]{CHCl_3}$ R–(C₆H₃)(OH)(CHO) (ortho) 19.6

116. $RCOCl \xrightarrow[Pd/BaSO_4]{H_2} RCHO$ 19.6

117. $RCOCl \xrightarrow{LiAlH[OC(CH_3)_3]_3} RCHO$ 19.6

118. $RCOCl \xrightarrow{R'_2CuLi} RR'C{=}O$ 19.6

119. $RCOCl \xrightarrow{R'_2Cd} RR'C{=}O$ 19.6

120. $RR'C{=}O \xrightarrow[acid]{HOCH_2CH_2OH}$ RR'C(–O–CH₂CH₂–O–) (1,3-dioxolane) 19.8

121. $RR'C{=}O \xrightarrow{H_2NX,\ acid} RR'C{=}NX$ 19.9

122. $R{-}C({=}O){-}CH\!<\ \xrightarrow{HNR'_2,\ acid}\ R{-}C(NR'_2){=}C\!<$ 19.9

123. $RR'C{=}O \xrightarrow{NaCN,\ acid} RR'C(OH)(CN)$ 19.10

124. $RR'C{=}O \xrightarrow{Ph_3\overset{+}{P}{-}\overset{-}{C}R''_2} RR'C{=}CR''_2$ 19.10

125. $RR'C{=}O \xrightarrow[acid]{HSCH_2CH_2SH}$ RR'C(–S–CH₂CH₂–S–) (1,3-dithiolane) 19.11

126. RR'C(–S–CH₂CH₂–S–) $\xrightarrow{Raney\ Ni} RR'CH_2$ 19.11

127. $RCHO \xrightarrow{NaHSO_3} RCH(OH)SO_3Na$ 19.11

128. RC(H)(–S–CH₂CH₂CH₂–S–) (1,3-dithiane) $\xrightarrow{1.\ CH_3CH_2CH_2CH_2Li;\ 2.\ R'X;\ 3.\ acid} RR'C{=}O$ 19.11

129. $R{-}C({=}O){-}CH_3 \xrightarrow[H_2O]{X_2,\ NaOH} RCO_2H$ 19.12

130. $R{-}C({=}O){-}CH_3 \xrightarrow[acetic\ acid]{X_2} R{-}C({=}O){-}CH_2X$ 19.12

131. $RCHO \xrightarrow[2.\ acid]{1.\ Ag_2O,\ NaOH,\ H_2O} RCOOH$ 19.13

132. $RR'C{=}O \xrightarrow{H_2,\ PtO_2} RR'CH{-}OH$ 19.13

133. $RR'C{=}O \xrightarrow[\text{2. acid}]{\text{1. LiAlH}_4} RR'CH{-}OH$ 19.13

134. $RR'C{=}O \xrightarrow{\text{NaBH}_4} RR'CH{-}OH$ 19.13

135. $RR'C{=}O \xrightarrow{\text{Zn(Hg), HCl}} RR'CH_2$ 19.13

136. $RR'C{=}NNH_2 \xrightarrow[\text{heat}]{\text{KOH, H}_2\text{O}} RR'CH_2$ 19.13

Additional Problems

19.32 Write structural formulas for each of the following:

a. (Z)-2-butenal
b. benzyl phenyl ketone
c. isobutyraldehyde
d. 3-chloropentanal
e. 2-bromo-8-methyl-7-oxo-3-nonyne
f. (*E*)-3-methylcyclobutanecarbaldehyde
g. 3-formylcyclohexanone
h. (Z)-3-phenylpropenal
i. β-bromobutyl neopentyl ketone
j. the semicarbazone of butanone
k. the 2,4-dinitrophenylhydrazone of benzaldehyde
l. the cyclic ketal formed by treating acetophenone with 1,2-ethanediol in the presence of anhydrous acid
m. a phosphorus ylide that will react with benzaldehyde to form

Ph
=C
H

n. a chiral substance of formula $C_7H_{14}O$ that is *not* racemized when placed in aqueous basic solution but does give a yellow precipitate in the iodoform test
o. the enamine produced from acetone and diethylamine
p. a substance of formula $C_9H_{15}N$ produced by the reaction of cyclopentanone and pyrrolidine in the presence of acid

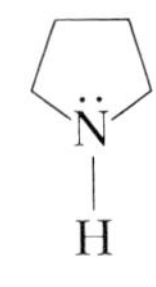

pyrrolidine

q. a substance of formula $C_5H_{10}O$ that forms a phenylhydrazone derivative, gives a negative test with Tollens' reagent, and gives a negative iodoform test
r. the aldehyde or ketone isomer of formula C_3H_5ClO that most readily forms a hydrate (i.e., a *gem*-diol derivative)
s. a substance that is in tautomeric equilibrium with acetophenone
t. a substance of formula C_4H_7N that is formed along with water when 4-aminobutanal is treated with acid

u. a substituted cyclohexanol of formula $C_7H_{14}O$ that cannot be made by reduction of a ketone or an aldehyde with sodium borohydride
v. a ketone that on Clemmensen reduction yields 4-isobutyltoluene
w. an alkene formed by treating iodoethane initially with triphenylphosphine followed by strong base and then with acetone
x. a substance of formula $C_8H_8O_2$ that shows IR absorptions at $\sim$3400 and $\sim$1700 cm^{-1} and that is oxidized to benzene-1,4-dicarboxylic acid by the action of potassium permanganate in aqueous base
y. the product obtained by treating benzophenone with methyl Grignard followed by dilute sulfuric acid
z. a methyl ketone that can be used to prepare $(CH_3)_2CHCOOH$ by a haloform reaction

19.33 Substance *A* has the molecular formula C_4H_9Br. When *A* is boiled with aqueous NaOH, *B* is formed. Compound *B* can be oxidized by hot, aqueous dichromate in sulfuric acid to yield *C*, of formula C_4H_8O. Compound *C* forms a derivative when treated with 2,4-dinitrophenylhydrazine but gives a negative Tollens' test. Suggest structures for compounds *A–C*. Which of the compounds *A–C* gives a positive iodoform test?

19.34 Show how to prepare each of the following compounds using a Grignard reagent.
a. 2-methyl-2-pentanol b. 1-phenyl-1-propanol c. 3-pentanol

19.35 What organic products are anticipated when benzaldehyde is treated with each of the following reagents:
a. hot, aqueous potassium dichromate in sulfuric acid
b. 1,2-ethanediol and anhydrous acid
c. Tollens' reagent
d. lithium aluminum hydride, followed by workup with aqueous acid
e. sodium cyanide and dilute sulfuric acid
f. sodium bisulfite
g. a mixture of concentrated nitric and sulfuric acids
h. hydrogen in the presence of a nickel catalyst
i. 1,3-propanedithiol and anhydrous acid
j. ethanol and anhydrous acid
k. ethylamine and anhydrous acid
l. sodium acetylide followed by hydrolysis with aqueous acid
m. hydrazine followed by KOH in a high-boiling alcohol solvent
n. bromine and iron

19.36 Compound *D* is a haloalkane. *D* reacts with magnesium in ether to form a Grignard reagent that yields butane on treatment with water. The Grignard reagent reacts with acetaldehyde to form 3-methyl-2-pentanol (after workup with aqueous acid). What is the structure of *D*?

19.37 Give the structure of the anticipated organic product (if any) upon treatment of acetophenone with each of the following:
a. bromine in aqueous sodium hydroxide, followed by acidification
b. excess of sodium deuteroxide in deuterium oxide
c. chromic anhydride in sulfuric acid
d. lithium aluminum hydride, followed by workup with aqueous acid
e. diethylamine with an anhydrous acid
f. zinc amalgam and concentrated hydrochloric acid
g. silver oxide and sodium hydroxide in water
h. chromic anhydride in pyridine
i. bromine in acetic acid

19.38 Suggest routes for the synthesis of acetophenone from each of the following:
a. benzene b. phenylacetylene c. acetaldehyde

19.39 Suggest a series of reactions that will yield the compound shown below using cyclopentanone as the only organic starting material.

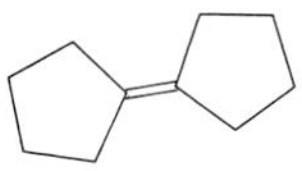

19.40 Suppose 2,3-diphenyl-2,3-butanediol is treated with 40% sulfuric acid so as to induce a pinacol/pinacolone rearrangement to occur. This reaction forms *E*, of formula $C_{16}H_{16}O$. When *E* is treated with aqueous sodium hydroxide and iodine, a yellow precipitate forms. After acidification of the reaction mixture, a carboxylic acid *F*, of formula $C_{15}H_{14}O$, forms. Suggest structures for *E* and *F*.

19.41 Suppose acetaldehyde is treated with 1,3-propanedithiol, followed by strong base, followed by 2-ethyloxirane. On hydrolysis of the resulting reaction mixture a substance of formula $C_6H_{12}O_2$ is isolated. Suggest a structure for this product and explain its formation.

19.42 Give reagents and reaction conditions for accomplishing the following syntheses:

a. 1,1-diphenylethene using Wittig reagent chemistry, starting from any alkyl halide and any carbonyl compound of your choice
b. *sec*-butyl methyl ether from butanone
c. pentanal from 1-pentene
d. *m*-chloroethylbenzene from benzene (*Hint:* finish the synthesis with a Clemmensen reduction.)
e. 1-phenylethanol from acetophenone
f. 4-deuteriocyclohexanone from 4-hydroxycyclohexanone

19.43 Give a complete mechanism for the reaction of acetone, ethylene glycol, and anhydrous acid to form a cyclic ketal.

19.44 When cyclobutanecarbaldehyde is heated with acid, it is converted to a substance of formula C_5H_8O that forms a 2,4-dinitrophenylhydrazone derivative but does not react with Tollens' reagent. Using mechanistic principles you have learned throughout the course, suggest a likely structure for the product and give a mechanism for its formation. (*Hint:* Where is the starting material most likely to become protonated? Draw the protonated structure, then draw a resonance structure of it, then consider possible skeletal rearrangements, ...)

19.45 In a manner similar to that used in Problem 19.44, propose a mechanism for the conversion shown below.

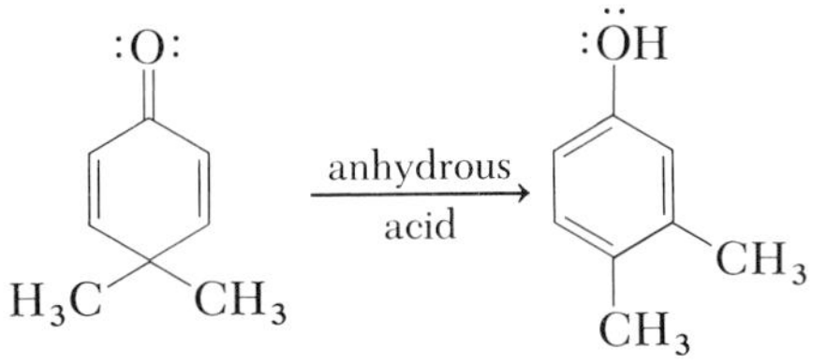

:O: — H_3C — CH_3 —(anhydrous acid)→ :ÖH — CH_3 — CH_3

19.46 When 4-hydroxybutanal is dissolved in methanol containing HCl, the acetal shown below forms. Suggest a mechanism for its formation.

:O: — H — $\ddot{O}CH_3$

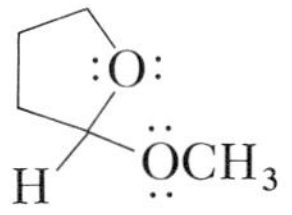

19.47 Suppose 2-methyl-2-cyclohexenone is dissolved in a large excess of CH_3OD containing base. After some time, an extraction is performed and the organic substance present is isolated. It is found to be identical to the starting material, except that four hydrogen atoms have been replaced by deuterium atoms. Use your mechanistic knowledge to decide which four hydrogen atoms have been replaced.

19.48 Suggest a structure for the compound of formula $C_7H_{12}O_2$ that reacts with iodine in aqueous sodium hydroxide solution to produce iodoform, and after acidification, a compound of formula $C_5H_8O_4$ that exhibits broad IR absorption between 2500 and 3400 cm^{-1} and whose ^1H NMR spectrum consists of two singlets.

19.49 When benzene is heated with *G* (formula C_4H_7ClO) in the presence of aluminum chloride, the reaction yields *H* (formula $C_{10}H_{12}O$). Compound *H* exhibits a band near 1700 cm^{-1} in its IR spectrum and yields *I* (formula $C_{10}H_{14}$) on treatment with zinc amalgam and hydrochloric acid. The ^1H NMR spectrum of *I* exhibits the following signals: δ 0.88, 6 H, doublet; δ 1.86, 1 H, multiplet; δ 2.45, 2 H, doublet; δ 7.12, 5 H, singlet. Give structures for compounds *G–I*.

19.50 Compound *J* (formula $C_{10}H_{12}O$) exhibits a signal in its IR spectrum near 1700 cm^{-1}. Upon treatment with methyl Grignard and workup with aqueous acid, *J* yields *K*, which exhibits the following ^1H NMR signals: δ 0.8, 3 H, triplet; δ 1.3, 6 H, singlet; δ 1.5, 2 H, quartet; δ 5.3, 1 H, broad singlet; δ 7.0, 4 H, AA′BB′ quartet. Suggest structures for compounds *J* and *K*.

19.51 Provide structures for the compounds *L–R* in the reaction scheme shown below.

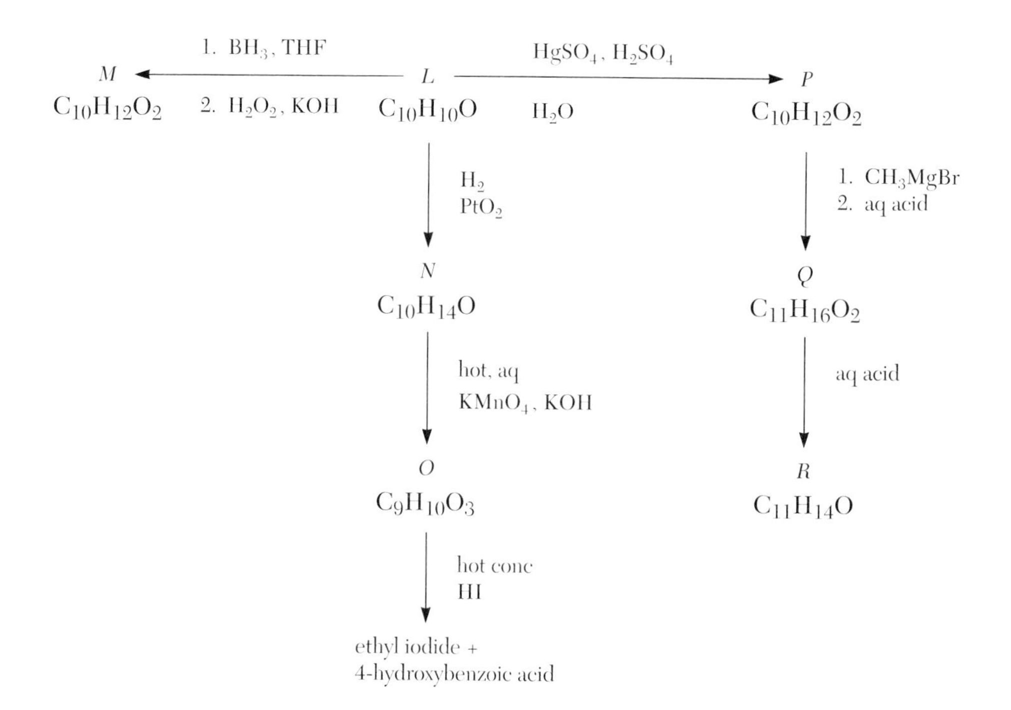

19.52 The ketal shown below (exobrevicomin) has been identified as a pheromone of the Western pine beetle.

:O:

O CH$_2$CH$_3$

CH$_3$

Give the structure of a dihydroxyketone that on treatment with anhydrous acid will undergo intramolecular conversion to the ketal shown. Show how to synthesize the ketal starting with 6-bromo-2-hexanone. *Hint:*

First find the carbon that is the carbonyl carbon atom of the dihydroxyketone. How can you tell which one it is? You arrive at the structure of the dihydroxyketone by then imagining a hydrolysis to regenerate the carbonyl group.

19.53 Propose a mechanism for the Hoesch reaction as illustrated in Equation 19.12.

19.54 A hydrocarbon S (C_8H_{14}) is oxidized by osmium tetroxide to a diol *T* ($C_8H_{16}O_2$). Treatment of *T* with sulfuric acid in acetic acid yields a ketone *U* ($C_8H_{14}O$), which exchanges two hydrogen atoms for deuterium on treatment with alkaline deuterium oxide. Wolff-Kischner reduction of *U* gives a saturated hydrocarbon that is not identical with that derived from S on hydrogenation. Compound *U* can be reduced to an alcohol *V* ($C_8H_{16}O$) that on acid catalyzed dehydration yields two hydrocarbons, *W* and *X*, that are isomeric with S. Ozonolysis of *W* gives a diketone *Y* ($C_8H_{14}O_2$), which is oxidized to $HOOC(CH_2)_4COOH$ upon treatment with aqueous KOH/bromine. Give structures for compounds S–*W* and *Y*. Describe the mechanisms for the conversion of *T* to *U* and of *V* to *W* and *X*. What are the possible structures of *X*?

20 CHAPTER Amines And Related Compounds

20.1 Introduction

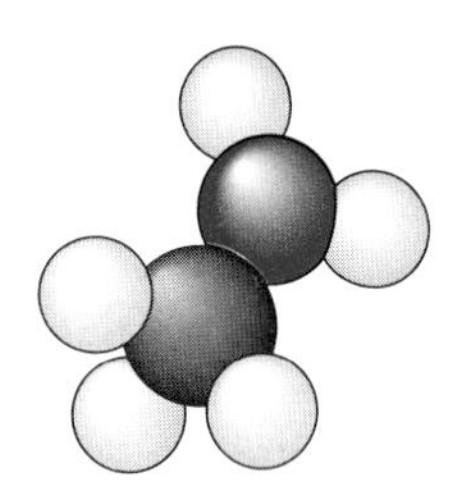

The replacement of one or more of the hydrogen atoms of ammonia by alkyl or aryl groups produces an **amine.** Like ammonia, most amines are moderately basic. The unshared valence electron pair on nitrogen is the basic site, since it has the ability to bind a proton. The basicity of amines, although relatively weak, is considerably greater than that of other families of organic compounds we have met. Amines are the strongest bases present in living organisms, and they are the bases in many physiological acid-base reactions. Amines can also act as nucleophiles toward suitable substrates. This reaction type is of widespread importance both in the synthetic arsenal of the organic chemist and in biological systems.

The amine functional group is found in many important groups of naturally occurring compounds, including amino acids, peptides, proteins (Chapter 26) and nucleic acid heterocyclic bases (Chapter 28). Alkaloids are organic bases that occur in plants. Figure 20.1 shows some familiar alkaloids. Many alkaloids have profound physiological effects on humans. Some have medicinal uses, so this group of compounds has attracted considerable attention as a source of therapeutic pharmaceuticals. Unfortunately, many alkaloids are also toxic and addictive—addictive drugs are often alkaloids.

In this chapter we explore the chemistry of relatively simple amines. An understanding of their chemistry is a crucial step in our effort to understand the role of biologically active nitrogen compounds.

Figure 20.1 Structures of some familiar alkaloids.

nicotine (major alkaloid of tobacco leaf)

mescaline (a cactus alkaloid that is a hallucinogen)

cocaine (chief alkaloid of the leaves of the coca bush)

atropine (from the belladonna plant; used in dilute solution to dilate the pupil of the eye; also used in symptomatic treatment of toxic inhibition of acetylcholinesterase)

Figure 20.2 Geometry of ammonia and amines. Ammonia and the simple amines have a pyramidal shape. This correlates with the sp^3 hybridization of the valence orbitals of nitrogen. Nitrogen uses three of the hybrid orbitals to form bonds to attached atoms. The fourth hybrid orbital accommodates the unshared valence electron pair. The bond angles of ammonia are slightly less than the theoretical tetrahedral value of 109°28′. They are, however, much larger than the 90° bond angles that would be present if only atomic *p* orbitals were used. The decrease in bond angle from 109°28′ is sometimes considered to be a result of electron-electron repulsion between the unshared electron pair and the electrons of the hydrogen-nitrogen bond.

20.2 Structure and Geometry

Ammonia and the amines have a pyramidal geometry, as shown in Figure 20.2. The observed geometry is rationalized by invoking sp^3 hybridization for the valence level atomic orbitals of nitrogen.

Ammonia and amines are more basic than neutral oxygen compounds such as water and alcohols. A nitrogen atom has a lower electronegativity than an oxygen atom, and the less electronegative nitrogen atom is a better electron pair donor. (However, amines are much weaker bases than bases with *negatively* charged oxygen atoms such as the hydroxide ion and alkoxide ions.)

The conjugate acids of ammonia and amines are, respectively, **ammonium ion** and substituted ammonium ions. Such ions have tetrahedral shapes, as shown in Figure 20.3 for the ammonium ion.

Quaternary ammonium ions, ions in which four alkyl (or aryl) groups are attached to a positively charged nitrogen, also have a tetrahedral geometry. An example of a quaternary ammonium salt is tetramethylammonium iodide (**20.1**). Such salts can be prepared by the reaction of an amine with an alkyl halide, as we will discuss later.

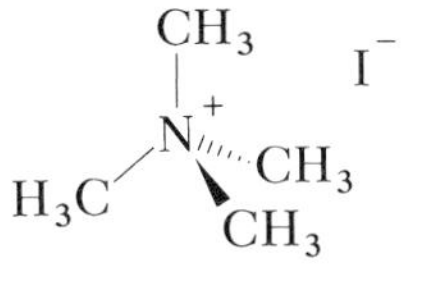

$$(CH_3)_4N^+ \; I^-$$

tetramethylammonium iodide
20.1

$$H_3N: + H{-}X: \longrightarrow NH_4^+ + :X:^-$$

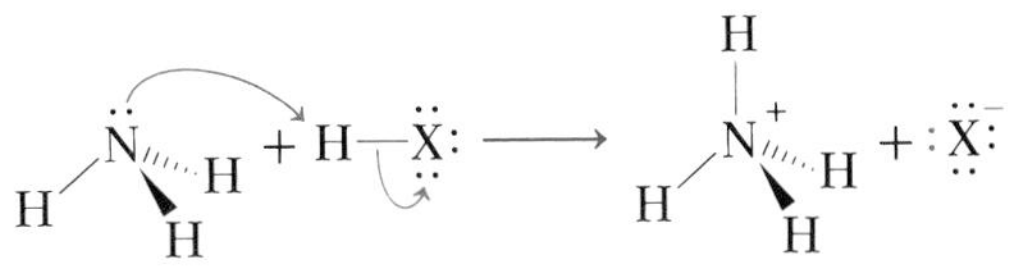

Figure 20.3 The ammonium ion. On reaction of ammonia with a Brønsted acid, the ammonium ion forms. Like a methane molecule, the ammonium ion has a perfect tetrahedral geometry. All bond angles in the ammonium ion are 109°28′.

20.3 Nomenclature

AMINES

The IUPAC system requires amines to be named as *amino*-substituted hydrocarbons. Simple amines also have common names that we devise by stringing together the names of the alkyl groups attached to nitrogen in alphabetical sequence. Several examples showing both the IUPAC and the common names are given in Figure 20.4.

When the amine contains a benzene ring attached directly to nitrogen, it is named as a derivative of the parent arylamine, aniline (**20.2**). Several examples are shown in Figure 20.5.

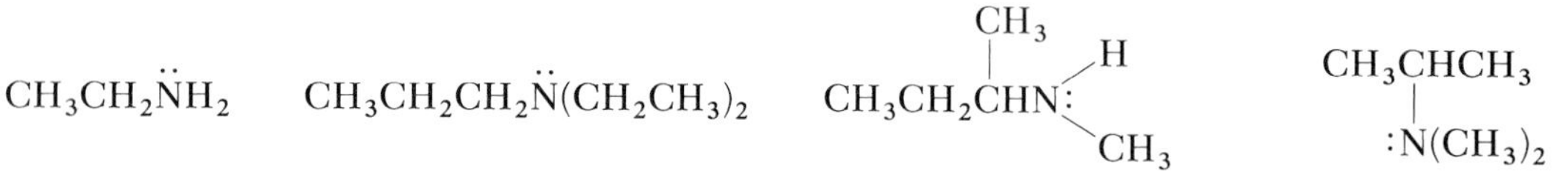

Figure 20.4 Nomenclature of simple alkylamines. The IUPAC name derives from the parent hydrocarbon with an *amino*-substituent. Common names are shown in parentheses beneath the IUPAC names.

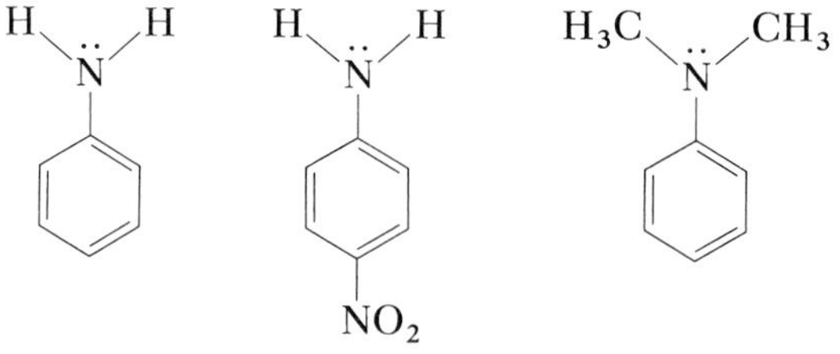

$CH_3CH_2\ddot{N}H_2$ — aminoethane (ethylamine)

$CH_3CH_2CH_2\ddot{N}(CH_2CH_3)_2$ — 1-(diethylamino)propane (diethylpropylamine)

$CH_3CH_2CH(CH_3)\ddot{N}H(CH_3)$ — 2-(methylamino)butane (*sec*-butylmethylamine)

$CH_3CH(CH_3)\ddot{N}(CH_3)_2$ — 2-(dimethylamino)propane (dimethylisopropylamine)

Figure 20.5 Nomenclature of arylamines. Compounds are named as derivatives of the parent arylamine, aniline. The prefix *N* designates a substituent located on the amino nitrogen.

$C_6H_5\ddot{N}H_2$ — aniline **20.2**

$p\text{-}O_2NC_6H_4\ddot{N}H_2$ — *p*-nitroaniline

$C_6H_5\ddot{N}(CH_3)_2$ — *N*,*N*-dimethylaniline

PRIMARY, SECONDARY, AND TERTIARY AMINES

Amines are classified as 1°, 2°, or 3° according to the number of alkyl (or aryl) groups attached to nitrogen. Amines with a single alkyl or aryl group attached to nitrogen are *primary amines*. Similarly, those with two groups attached to nitrogen are *secondary amines*, and those with three groups attached are *tertiary amines*.

PROBLEM 20.1 Tell which of the structures given in Figures 20.1, 20.4, and 20.5 are secondary amines and which are tertiary amines.

PROBLEM 20.2 Draw the structures for each of the following compounds:

a. 3-aminopentane
b. 4-dimethylamino-3-methylheptane
c. 2-ethylamino-3-pentanol

Steps to Solving the Problem

Solution to Problem 20.2a

1. The name *3-aminopentane* indicates that the compound is a derivative of pentane with a substituent at the 3-position.
2. The substituent at the 3-position is the amino group, $-NH_2$. We write the structure as we would for any 3-substituted pentane:

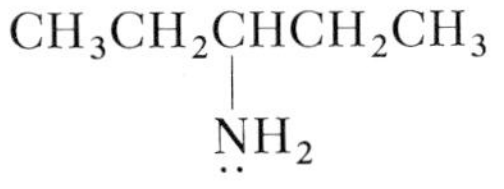

$$CH_3CH_2\underset{\substack{|\\ \ddot{N}H_2}}{C}HCH_2CH_3$$

PROBLEM 20.3 Provide systematic names for each of the following structures:

a. 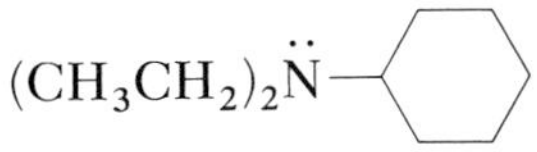 $(CH_3CH_2)_2\ddot{N}$—(cyclohexyl)

b. 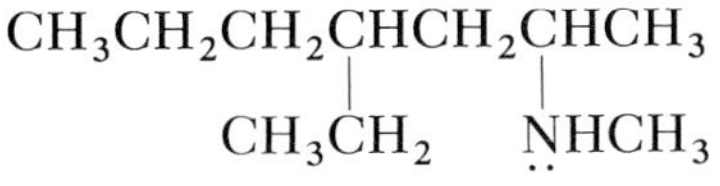 $CH_3CH_2CH_2\underset{\substack{|\\ CH_3CH_2}}{C}HCH_2\underset{\substack{|\\ \ddot{N}HCH_3}}{C}HCH_3$

c. (3-chlorophenyl)—$\ddot{N}HCH_2CH_3$ (ring bearing :Cl: substituent)

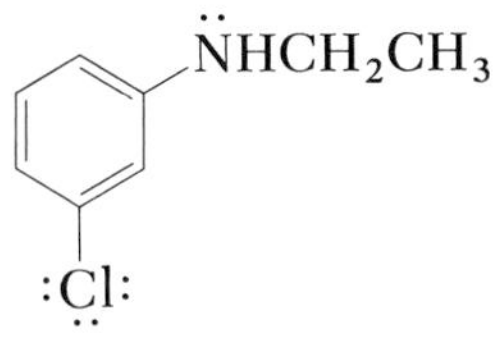

AMMONIUM IONS

Substituted ammonium ions are named by adding the standard names for each attached alkyl group to the suffix *ammonium*. For arylamines, such as derivatives of aniline, the names of any alkyl groups are accompanied by the suffix *anilinium*. Several examples are shown in Figure 20.6.

IMINES

We first met imines in Chapter 19. They are usually named as derivatives of the carbonyl compounds from which they are commonly prepared. Their names consist of the name of the parent carbonyl compound followed by the term *imine*. Several examples are shown in Figure 20.7.

The imines illustrated in Figure 20.7 are all derived from symmetrical ketones. If the imine is derived from an unsymmetrical ketone or an aldehyde, its stereochemistry must be specified in its name. The double bond of an imine is similar to that of an alkene in that there is no free rotation; thus geometric

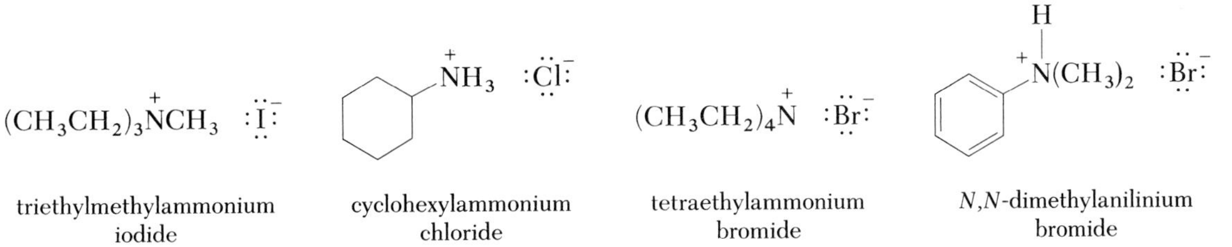

Figure 20.6 Nomenclature of ammonium ions and salts. An alternative common name is often used to name ammonium halide salts in which a hydrogen is attached to nitrogen. The common name consists of the name of the parent amine followed by *hydrohalide*. For example, the common name for *N*,*N*-dimethylanilinium bromide is *N*,*N*-dimethylaniline hydrobromide.

$(CH_3CH_2)_3\overset{+}{N}CH_3$ $:\ddot{I}:^-$ — triethylmethylammonium iodide

(cyclohexyl)$\overset{+}{N}H_3$ $:\ddot{Cl}:^-$ — cyclohexylammonium chloride

$(CH_3CH_2)_4\overset{+}{N}$ $:\ddot{Br}:^-$ — tetraethylammonium bromide

(phenyl)$\overset{+}{N}H(CH_3)_2$ $:\ddot{Br}:^-$ — *N*,*N*-dimethylanilinium bromide

Figure 20.7 Nomenclature of imines.

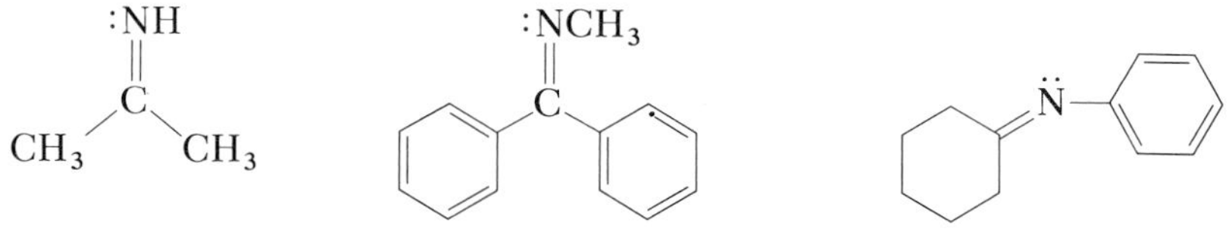

acetone imine　benzophenone *N*-methylimine　cyclohexanone *N*-phenylimine

Figure 20.8 Nomenclature of unsymmetrical imines.

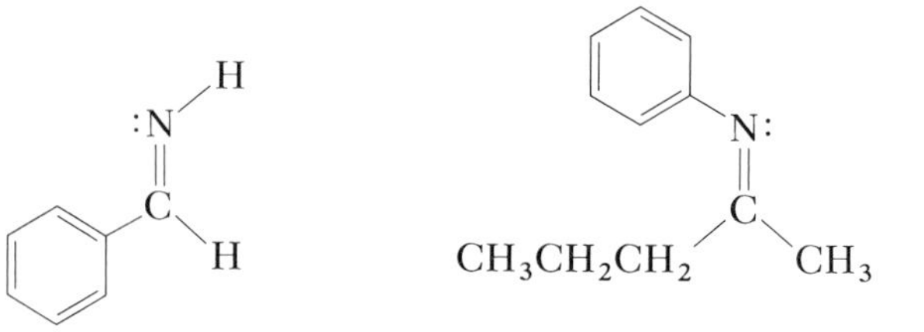

anti-benzaldehyde imine or ((*E*)-benzaldehyde imine)　*syn*-2-pentanone *N*-phenylimine or ((Z)-2-pentanone *N*-phenylimine)

isomers can exist. In naming the isomers, we specify the position of the substituent attached to the nitrogen relative to the group of higher priority at the imine carbon. We refer to compounds in which these groups are across from each other as *anti* and those in which the groups are on the same side of the double bond as *syn*. The *E*/*Z* notation system can also be used. Examples of nomenclature are shown in Figure 20.8.

PROBLEM 20.4 Provide structures for each of the following named compounds:

a. benzylethylammonium chloride
b. *p*-nitroanilinium iodide
c. *syn*-2-methyl-3-hexanone *N*-methylimine
d. *anti*-3-chlorobenzaldehyde *N*-phenylimine

PROBLEM 20.5 Provide systematic names for each of the following structures:

a.

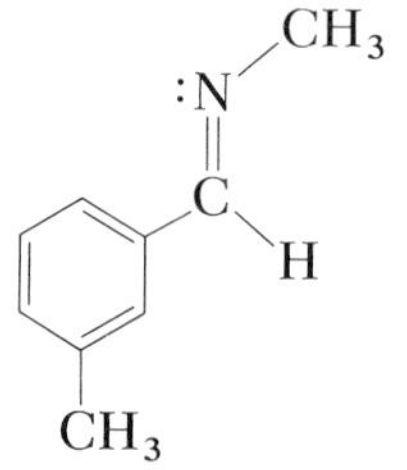

b. $CH_3CH_2CH_2\overset{+}{N}H(CH_2CH_3)_2\ Br^-$

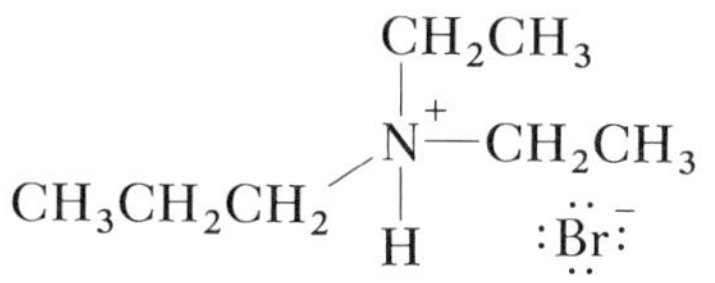

c.

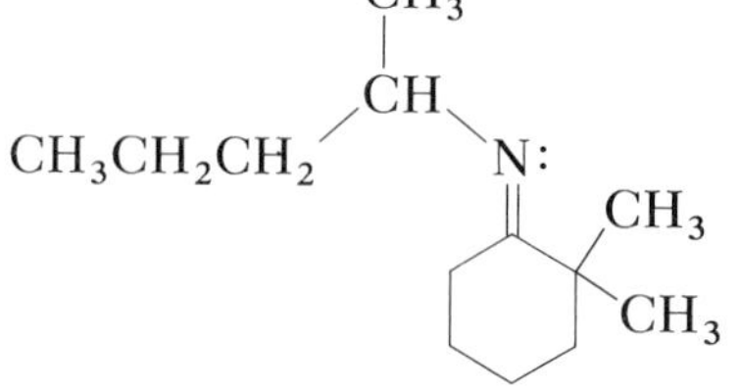

d.

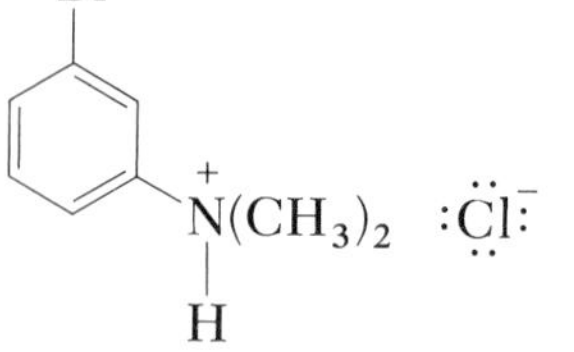

20.4 Basicity and Nucleophilicity of Amines

THE DEFINITION OF BASICITY

Earlier we defined Lewis basicity in terms of the donation of a pair of electrons in a reaction. We also differentiated the ways in which Lewis basicity can be expressed. If a species donates an electron pair to form a new bond to a hydrogen, we simply say it is acting as a base. However, if a species donates an electron pair to form a new bond to some atom other than hydrogen, we say it is acting as a nucleophile. We will briefly review these concepts in the context of amines.

Generally, when we speak about the basicity of an amine, we are referring to its ability to form a new bond to hydrogen using its unshared valence electron pair. In order to consider the relative basicities of two or more amines, we need to specify a standard reaction system for comparison. The equilibrium established upon reaction of the amine with water is most commonly used. We compare the basicities of various amines by looking at the positions of their equilibria in this reaction (see Figure 20.9).

$$R\ddot{N}H_2 + H_2\ddot{O} \rightleftharpoons R\overset{+}{N}H_3 + H\ddot{O}:^- \qquad K_b = \frac{[R\overset{+}{N}H_3][H\ddot{O}:^-]}{[R\ddot{N}H_2]}$$

Figure 20.9 Comparing the base strengths (basicities) of amines. The stronger the base, the farther the equilibrium lies to the right, and the larger the value of K_b.

A complementary approach is to compare the *acidities* of the conjugate acids of the amines. The more acidic the conjugate acid, the weaker the amine base, as is illustrated in Figure 20.10.

The values of K_b and K_a for an amine-ammonium ion pair are related as shown in Equation 20.1.

$$(K_a)(K_b) = K_w = 10^{-14} \qquad \text{Eqn. 20.1}$$

It has become standard practice to report relative base strengths of amines in terms of the pK_a values of their conjugate acids. (Remember, pK_a = − log K_a.) Be careful not to confuse these pK_a values of ammonium ions with the pK_a values of the amines themselves! For example, ammonia *itself* has a pK_a of −35, while its conjugate acid, NH_4^+, has a pK_a of 7.2. *The more positive the* pK_a *of the conjugate acid, the more basic the amine.* The pK_a values for the conjugate acids of several amines are given in Table 20.1.

$$R\overset{+}{N}H_3 + H_2\ddot{O} \rightleftharpoons H_3\overset{+}{\ddot{O}} + R\ddot{N}H_2 \qquad K_a = \frac{[H_3\overset{+}{\ddot{O}}][R\ddot{N}H_2]}{[R\overset{+}{N}H_3]}$$

Figure 20.10 Measurement of amine basicity through the acidity of the conjugate acids. The farther this equilibrium lies to the right, the larger the K_a of the conjugate acid RNH_3^+ and the weaker the base RNH_2.

PROBLEM 20.6 Verify that Equation 20.1 is a valid relationship of K_a and K_b.

PROBLEM 20.7 Two primary amine hydrochlorides *A* and *B* (general formula RNH_3Cl) have as their respective pK_a values in water 8.5 and 9.3. Which has the stronger conjugate base (RNH_2)? What is the pK_b value for each of the conjugate bases (RNH_2)?

Table 20.1 Aqueous Solution Basicities of Amines as Measured by pK_a of Their Conjugate Acids

The entries are listed in order of decreasing basicity of the amine.

Parent Base		pK_a of Conjugate Acid
Structure	Name	
	guanidine	13.5
	quinuclidine	10.6
$(CH_3CH_2)_2\ddot{N}H$	diethylamine	9.1
$(CH_3)_2\ddot{N}H$	dimethylamine	8.8
$CH_3CH_2\ddot{N}H_2$	ethylamine	8.7
$(CH_3CH_2)_3N:$	triethylamine	8.6
$CH_3\ddot{N}H_2$	methylamine	8.6
$(CH_3)_3N:$	trimethylamine	7.8
$\ddot{N}H_3$	ammonia	7.2
	N,*N*-dimethylaniline	5.1
	aniline	4.6
	pyridine	3.1
	p-nitroaniline	1.0
	N-phenyl-*p*-nitroaniline	−2.5
	2,4-dinitroaniline	−4.5

STRUCTURAL RELATIONSHIPS OF AMINE BASICITY

Primary, Secondary, and Tertiary Alkyl Amines If an amine is protonated, the alkylammonium ion that forms has a charge of 1+. From our earlier discussions, we would expect this positive charge to be better stabilized with increasing numbers of alkyl substituents. Thus we expect the conjugate acid of a tertiary amine to be intrinsically more stable than the conjugate acids of primary and secondary amines. Put another way, a reasonable expectation of the relative basicities of amines would seem to be

$$\ddot{N}H_3 < R\ddot{N}H_2(1°) < R_2\ddot{N}H(2°) < R_3\ddot{N}(3°)$$

least basic most basic

Indeed, proton transfer to amines *in the gas phase* is in accord with these predictions. However, we are usually concerned with reactions *in solution*, and as we have seen, amine basicities are usually compared in terms of equilibria established in aqueous solution. Interestingly, the order of basicities follows no simple trend under these conditions, as shown by the following series:

$$\ddot{N}H_3 < CH_3CH_2\ddot{N}H_2 < (CH_3CH_2)_3\ddot{N} < (CH_3CH_2)_2\ddot{N}H$$

least basic most basic

We met this type of phenomenon before, when we compared the relative acidities of alcohols in the gas phase and in solution (see Section 6.5). We can infer that some type of solvation effect must be operating to reverse the gas phase trends. The dominant effect seems to involve the conjugate acid of the amine, that is, the substituted ammonium ion. We find that while alkyl groups increase the ability of an alkylammonium ion to disperse and thus to stabilize a positive charge, they *also* diminish the ability of the ion to engage in hydrogen bonding with water molecules. Diminished solvation means diminished stability. The measured basicity in solution reflects these opposing trends. Secondary amines are most basic because their conjugate acids have the best combination of inherent stability (owing to electron release from the two alkyl groups) and degree of solvation. For a given series of amines (RNH_2, R_2NH, R_3N, with the same alkyl group throughout), the secondary amine is usually stronger than the primary amine, but the tertiary amine is usually weaker than one or both of the others, that is:

$$R_2\ddot{N}H > R_3\ddot{N} > R\ddot{N}H_2$$

or

$$R_2\ddot{N}H > R\ddot{N}H_2 > R_3\ddot{N}$$

The Importance of Hybridization Other factors being equal, the basicities of amines and other compounds containing an unshared valence electron pair on nitrogen correlate with the hybridization of the nitrogen atom. The unshared electron pair can be considered as occupying one of the hybrid orbitals, and for each type of hybridization there is a different fraction of p character. The more p character in the hybrid orbital, the higher its energy. The fractions of p character for the various types of hybrids are: three-fourths for sp^3, two-thirds for sp^2, and one-half for sp. Thus the predicted order of orbital energies is $sp^3 > sp^2 > sp$. Furthermore, an electron pair in a higher-energy orbital is more available (more basic) than one in a lower-energy orbital. Thus, compounds containing sp^3-hybridized nitrogen are predicted to be most basic, and those with sp-hybridized nitrogen are predicted to be least basic. These predictions are in accord with the observed basicities of amines, imines, and nitriles:

$$RCH_2\ddot{N}H_2 > RCH{=}\ddot{N}H > R{-}C{\equiv}N{:}$$

Substituent Effects on the Basicity of Arylamines Consider aniline, $PhNH_2$. The phenyl group attached to the amine nitrogen causes a diminished basicity in solution. This effect is opposite to that produced by an attached alkyl group. Now consider *N*,*N*-dimethylaniline. We might expect that the methyl groups would enhance the basicity compared to that of aniline, and we find this to be the case. As shown in Table 20.1, *N*,*N*-dimethylaniline *is* more basic than aniline (its conjugate acid is less acidic than the anilinium ion).

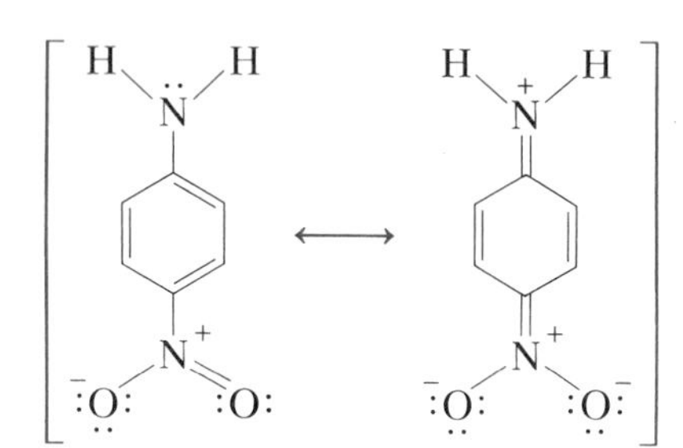

Figure 20.11 Resonance structures of *p*-nitroaniline. The resonance effect of the nitro group is to withdraw electron density from both the aromatic ring and the amino group nitrogen, resulting in the diminished basicity of *p*-nitroaniline in comparison to aniline itself.

Substituents attached to the aromatic ring also affect the basicity of nitrogen in aniline derivatives. Again referring to Table 20.1, notice that nitro groups attached to the aromatic ring greatly decrease the basicity of the aniline nitrogen. Nitro groups are strongly electron withdrawing and remove electron density from the basic nitrogen site. If the nitro group is *ortho* or *para* relative to the amino group, it can exert both its resonance and its inductive effects. The pertinent resonance structures for *p*-nitroaniline are shown in Figure 20.11.

In general, electron-withdrawing groups attached to the aromatic ring render the amino group less basic than otherwise. (These groups are the same ones that are *deactivating* toward electrophilic aromatic substitution.) Electron-donating groups attached to the ring render the amino group *more* basic than it is in aniline.

We must always be careful when we try to understand variations in the basicities or acidities of compounds. It is often true that *many* factors, including electronic effects, steric effects, and solvation effects, influence these properties. Often it is inappropriate to try to account for differences in basicity by invoking differences in a single property such as electronic effects, particularly when we are comparing compounds with significant structural differences. However, when comparing a series of structurally related compounds such as *p*-substituted anilines, we are on reasonably safe ground in relating differences in basicity mainly to one influence, namely, electronic effects, because solvation and steric effects are relatively constant for all members of the series.

PROBLEM 20.8 Arrange the following derivatives of aniline in increasing order of basicity in aqueous solution. Assume solvation effects to be roughly the same for the entire series of molecules.

$\ddot{N}H_2$ $\ddot{N}H_2$ (with $C{\equiv}N{:}$) $\ddot{N}H_2$ (with CH_3) $\ddot{N}HCH_3$ (with CH_3) $\ddot{N}H_2$ (with $C{\equiv}N{:}$ and $C(=\ddot{O})CH_3$)

Pyridine and Pyrrole Pyridine (**20.3**) and pyrrole (**20.4**) are two nitrogen compounds that are aromatic but are structurally different from aniline and its derivatives.

pyridine **20.3** pyrrole **20.4**

Both are less basic in aqueous solution than aniline. Moreover, pyrrole is significantly less basic than pyridine. (The pK_a values for the conjugate acids of pyridine and pyrrole are 3.1 and 0.4, respectively.) How can we rationalize this large difference in the basicity of the two compounds? We start by considering the orbitals bearing the basic electron pair for each molecule.

In pyridine, the unshared valence electron pair of nitrogen is located in an sp^2 hybrid orbital that is orthogonal to the aromatic ring. To a first approximation, there is zero interaction of this orbital with the π system of the aromatic ring. However, in pyrrole the electron pair on nitrogen is in a *p* orbital that is an integral part of the aromatic system. The unshared valence electron pair of nitrogen constitutes a portion of the aromatic sextet of electrons, as illustrated in Figure 20.12.

When pyridine accepts a proton, the aromatic six-π-electron system remains intact. With pyrrole, however, protonation at nitrogen leads to a conjugate acid that is *not* aromatic. Since aromatic stabilization is lost in the conjugate acid of pyrrole, protonation of pyrrole is an unfavorable process (see Figure 20.13). Thus pyrrole is much less basic than pyridine. (Pyrrole can be protonated by strong acids—however, protonation occurs on one of the ring carbon atoms, not on the nitrogen atom.)

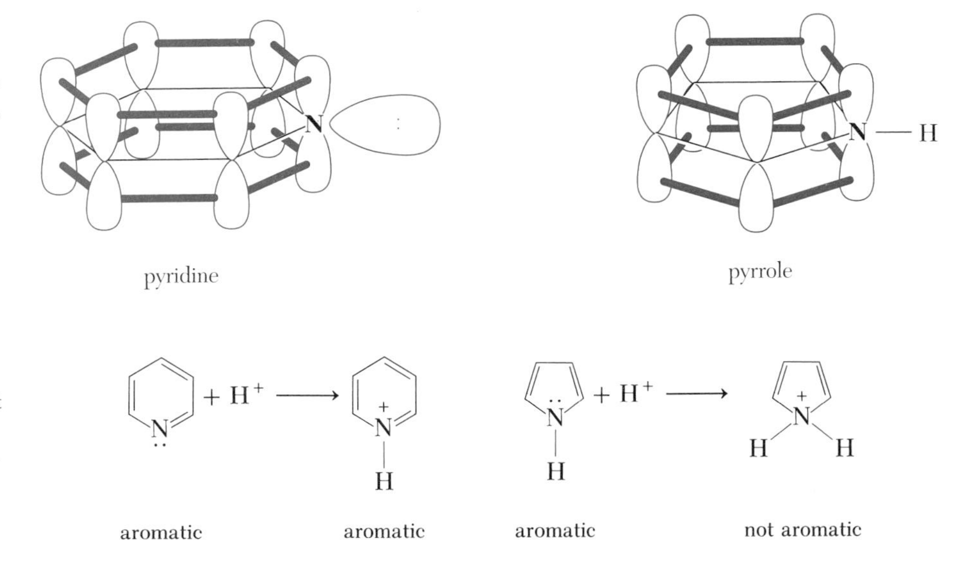

Figure 20.12 Electronic structure of pyridine and pyrrole. In pyridine the unshared valence electron pair of nitrogen is orthogonal to the aromatic ring. However, in pyrrole the nitrogen lone pair is an integral part of the aromatic π electron system.

Figure 20.13 Comparison of protonation of the nitrogen atom of pyridine and pyrrole. The conjugate acid of pyrrole is not aromatic, since there is no continuous sequence of *p* orbitals about the entire ring. Once the pyrrole molecule has been protonated, there is no longer an available *p* orbital on nitrogen.

NUCLEOPHILICITY OF AMINES

The presence of an unshared valence electron pair on nitrogen gives all amines the potential to act as nucleophiles. We find that amines participate in both nucleophilic substitution and **nucleophilic addition reactions.** Although there is usually a rough correlation between the basicities and the nucleophilicities of amines, exceptions arise if the amine is sterically congested. Consider, for example, *cis*-2,6-di-*tert*-butylpiperidine (**20.5**). This amine is an effective base, but it is not nucleophilic. The steric congestion near the nitrogen atom does not decrease the ability of the amine to bind to a small hydrogen atom. However, it *does* restrict the ability of the amine to approach more sterically hindered sites.

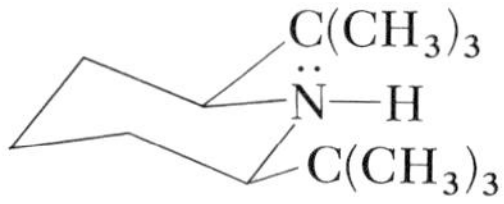

$C(CH_3)_3$
$\ddot{N}-H$
$C(CH_3)_3$

cis-2,6-di-*tert*-butylpiperidine
20.5

Molecules in which an atom with one or more unshared valence electron pairs of its own is bound directly to a nitrogen atom show a significant enhancement in the nucleophilicity of that nitrogen. Two molecules that show this effect are hydrazine (**20.6**) and hydroxylamine (**20.7**).

$H_2\ddot{N}-\ddot{N}H_2$ — hydrazine **20.6**

$H_2\ddot{N}-\ddot{O}H$ — hydroxylamine **20.7**

While both substances are relatively weak bases in aqueous solution, both are potent nucleophiles. For example, they readily undergo nucleophilic addition reactions with aldehydes, as we discussed in Chapter 19. Their enhancement of nucleophilicity is known as the **α-effect.** The name relates to the presence of an atom with unshared valence electron pair(s) in an α position relative to the atom performing the nucleophilic attack.

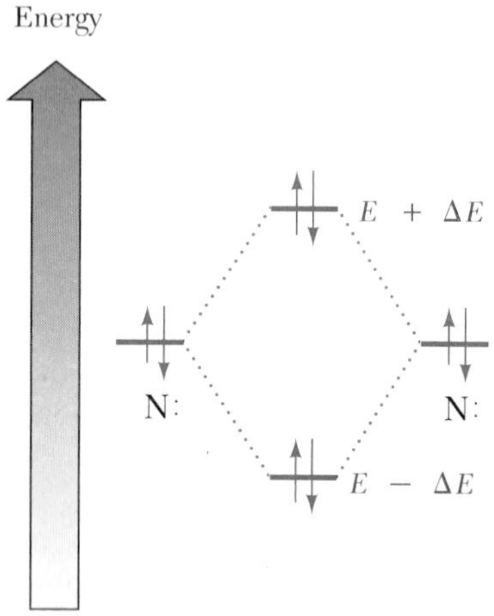

Energy

$E + \Delta E$

N: N:

$E - \Delta E$

interaction of the two nitrogen unshared valence electron pairs of hydrazine

Figure 20.14 Molecular orbital occupation in hydrazine.

MOLECULAR ORBITAL ANALYSIS

Frontier Molecular Orbitals and the α-Effect

The enhanced nucleophilicity associated with the α-effect correlates with a lowering of the energy gap between the HOMO of the nucleophile and the LUMO of the substrate. We can think of the raising of the HOMO energy in the following way: consider hydrazine. The two side-by-side unshared valence electron pairs, in the absence of any interaction, would each be accommodated in orbitals of the same energy, E. However, there is really an interaction between them that is similar to the interaction between the two side-by-side p orbitals of ethylene. This interaction generates two π molecular orbitals, one of energy $E + \Delta E$, and the other of energy $E - \Delta E$ (see Chapter 16), as illustrated in Figure 20.14. In a hydrazine molecule both of these molecular orbitals are fully occupied. The HOMO is the orbital with the energy $E + \Delta E$. Thus the HOMO energy is higher as a result of the interaction, and the energy gap between this HOMO and the LUMO of the substrate is correspondingly decreased.

20.5 The Synthesis of Aliphatic Amines

NUCLEOPHILIC SUBSTITUTION REACTIONS

Consider the reaction of ammonia with a haloalkane. We know that haloalkanes are good substrates for nucleophilic attack, and we also know that ammonia can function as a nucleophile. The reaction between ammonia and a haloalkane thus can serve as a means of creating a nitrogen-carbon bond and thereby provide a route to primary amines.

MECHANISM OF REACTION

Nucleophilic Substitution Reaction of Ammonia with a Haloalkane

Step 1 Nucleophilic attack on the haloalkane. This reaction is a nucleophilic substitution reaction (S_N2). It is virtually irreversible under usual reaction conditions.

$$H_3N\!: + R{-}\ddot{\underset{..}{X}}\!: \longrightarrow H_3\overset{+}{N}{-}R + :\ddot{\underset{..}{X}}\!:^-$$

Step 2 Abstraction of a proton from the alkylammonium ion. The free product amine is liberated at the expense of an additional equivalent of ammonia.

$$R{-}\overset{+}{N}H_2(H) + :NH_3 \longrightarrow R{-}\ddot{N}H_2 + H{-}\overset{+}{N}H_3$$

By analogy, it would seem that secondary amines could be prepared by reaction of a primary amine with a haloalkane and that tertiary amines could be prepared by alkylation of a secondary amine with a haloalkane. However, there are difficulties that limit the applicability of these reactions for preparative purposes. The main problem is that it is difficult to limit the reaction to a single alkylation. For example, in the reaction of ammonia and a haloalkane, the product is a primary amine, and like the beginning ammonia, it is a potential nucleophile. As the concentration of the primary amine builds up, it competes more and more effectively with the ammonia reactant for reaction with the haloalkane substrate. If the primary amine does react, the product will be a secondary amine—another nucleophile that can also compete for reaction with the haloalkane! In fact, continuing reaction can lead all the way to a quaternary ammonium salt, as shown in the following scheme.

MECHANISM OF REACTION

The Reaction of Ammonia and Amines with Haloalkanes

Step 1 Nucleophilic attack

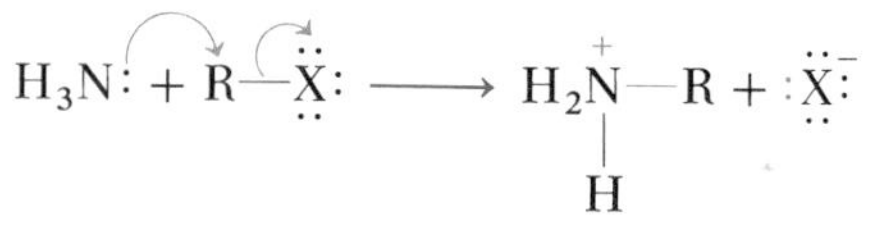

$$H_3N\!: + R{-}\ddot{\underset{..}{X}}\!: \longrightarrow H_2\overset{+}{N}(H){-}R + :\ddot{\underset{..}{X}}\!:^-$$

Step 2 Brønsted acid/base reaction

$$H_2\overset{+}{N}(H){-}R + :NH_3 \longrightarrow H_2\ddot{N}{-}R + H{-}\overset{+}{N}H_3$$

1° amine

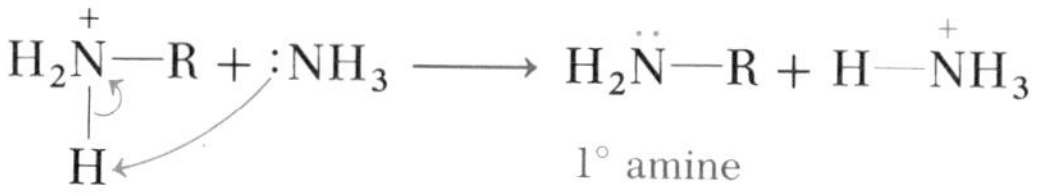

Step 3 Nucleophilic attack

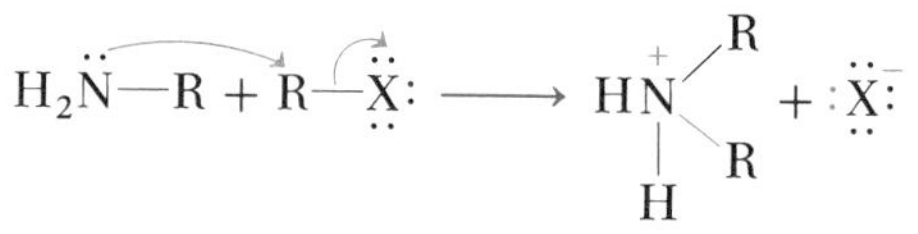

$$H_2\ddot{N}{-}R + R{-}\ddot{\underset{..}{X}}\!: \longrightarrow H\overset{+}{N}(H)R_2 + :\ddot{\underset{..}{X}}\!:^-$$

Step 4 Brønsted acid/base reaction

$$H{-}\overset{+}{N}R_2(H) + :NH_3 \longrightarrow H{-}\ddot{N}R_2 + H{-}\overset{+}{N}H_3$$

2° amine

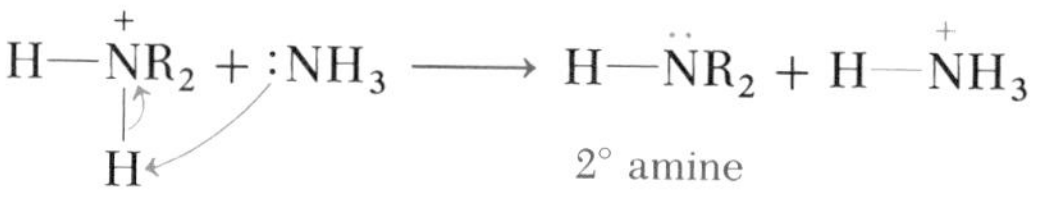

Step 5 Nucleophilic attack

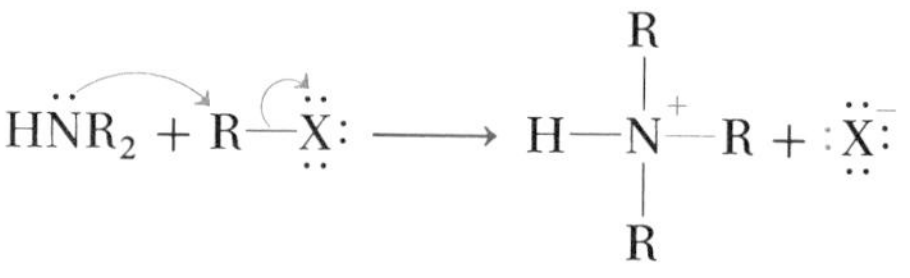

$$H\ddot{N}R_2 + R{-}\ddot{\underset{..}{X}}\!: \longrightarrow H{-}\overset{+}{N}R_2{-}R + :\ddot{\underset{..}{X}}\!:^-$$

Step 6 Brønsted acid/base reaction

$$H{-}\overset{+}{N}R_3 + :NH_3 \longrightarrow :NR_3 + H{-}\overset{+}{N}H_3$$

3° amine

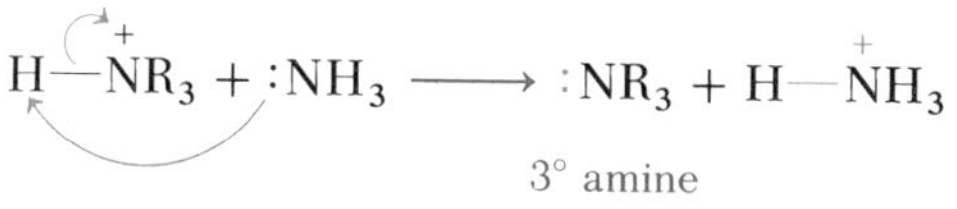

Step 7 Nucleophilic attack

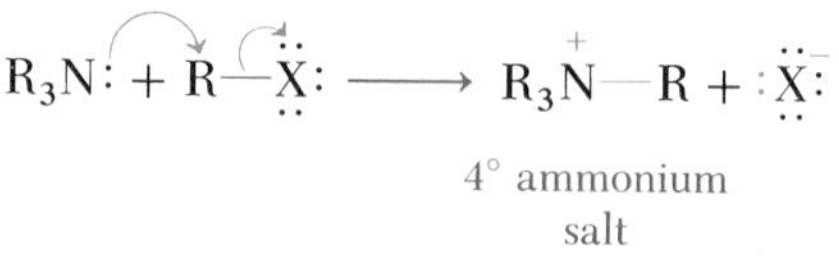

$$R_3N\!: + R{-}\ddot{\underset{..}{X}}\!: \longrightarrow R_3\overset{+}{N}{-}R + :\ddot{\underset{..}{X}}\!:^-$$

4° ammonium salt

The difficulty posed by the continuing sequence of reactions is not easy to overcome. If we try to use only one equivalent each of ammonia and alkyl halide, we are likely to produce a useless mixture of all of the possible products with some ammonia left unreacted. The best solution for the successful synthesis of primary amines is to use a large excess of ammonia. In this way the available haloalkane is always more likely to encounter another molecule of ammonia than a primary amine molecule (the initial product). An example of a successful synthesis of this type is shown in Equation 20.2.

Eqn. 20.2

$$CH_3CH_2CH_2CH_2CH_2CH_2CH_2\ddot{\underset{\cdot\cdot}{Br}}: \xrightarrow[CH_3OH]{NH_3\text{ (large excess)}} CH_3CH_2CH_2CH_2CH_2CH_2CH_2\ddot{N}H_2$$

1-bromoheptane

47% yield
1-aminoheptane

If a primary or secondary amine is of sufficiently simple structure and available for use in large excess, we can similarly use the reaction for the preparation of secondary or tertiary amines. An example is shown in Equation 20.3.

Eqn. 20.3

(large excess) N-methylaniline + 2-chlorocyclopentanone ⟶ N-methyl-N-phenyl-2-aminocyclopentanone (50% yield)

In general, however, this is *not* a method of choice, because most amines are too precious to waste.

Of course the preparation of quaternary ammonium compounds from tertiary amines faces no complication of continuing reaction. The quaternary ammonium ion produced cannot undergo further nucleophilic substitution reaction because it has no unshared valence electron pair on nitrogen. We can effect these quaternization reactions efficiently and in good yield, as shown in Equation 20.4.

Eqn. 20.4

$$C_6H_5CH_2\ddot{N}H_2 \xrightarrow[NaHCO_3]{\text{large excess } CH_3I} C_6H_5CH_2\overset{+}{N}(CH_3)_3\ :\ddot{\underset{\cdot\cdot}{I}}:^-$$

benzylamine

72% yield
benzyltrimethylammonium iodide

In this example an inorganic base (sodium bicarbonate) facilitates the early stages of the reaction by converting the amine hydroiodide salts to the free amines.

Finally, we must note that elimination is a competing side reaction in this system. In the preceding examples we have considered ammonia or an amine acting as a nucleophile toward a molecule of haloalkane. However, amines and ammonia can also act as bases, and thus an elimination reaction can compete with our intended nucleophilic substitution reaction if we make a poor choice of reagents. For that reason we usually use this route only with primary haloalkanes as the substrate. Many secondary and most tertiary haloalkanes react with amines to give largely alkene by-product via an E2 reaction. Thus, reactions of secondary or tertiary haloalkanes with ammonia or amines are usually of little synthetic value.

ALTERNATIVES TO NUCLEOPHILIC SUBSTITUTION BY AMMONIA

The Gabriel Synthesis The **Gabriel synthesis** of primary amines involves a nucleophilic substitution reaction but is free of the major difficulty associated with direct attack by ammonia on a haloalkane. In the Gabriel synthesis the nucleophile is not ammonia but rather an anion derived from phthalimide (**20.8**).

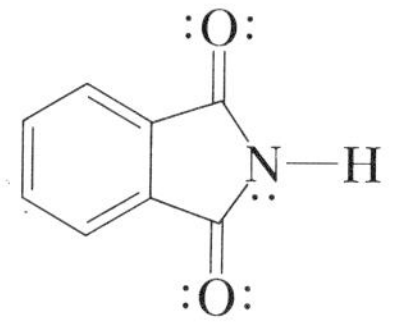

phthalimide
20.8

On treatment with a strong base such as KOH, phthalimide gives up a proton to generate an anion that is a good nucleophile. Upon addition of a suitable substrate, a nucleophilic substitution reaction (S_N2) ensues to generate a substituted phthalimide. An example is shown in Equation 20.5.

Eqn. 20.5

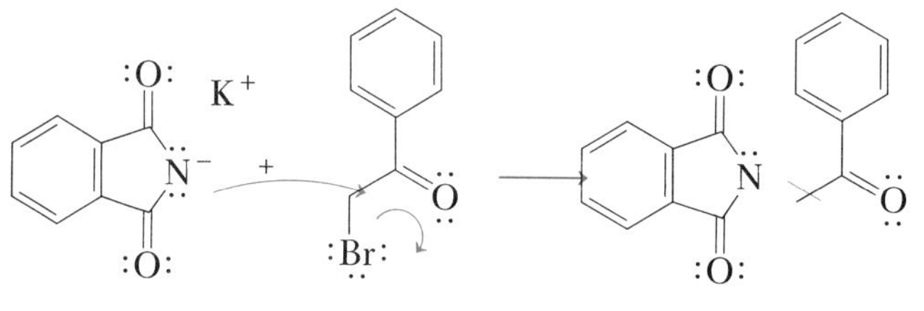

potassium phthalimide + α-bromoacetophenone → N-phenacylphthalimide (92% yield)

The substituted phthalimide product of such a reaction is not nucleophilic. Thus, further alkylation cannot occur. The substituted phthalimide product can be converted into the target amine by various means. One method is shown in Equation 20.6. The mechanism for hydrolysis reactions of this type will be described in Chapter 22.

Eqn. 20.6

KOH / H_2O → K^+ K^+ + H_2N

80% yield
α-aminoacetophenone

PROBLEM 20.9 Explain why the compound shown below on the left is nucleophilic while that on the right is not.

N—CH_3 N—CH_3

PROBLEM 20.10 A student plans to convert 3,4-dimethylbromobenzene to 3,4-dimethylaniline via the Gabriel procedure. However, he is disappointed to find that his synthesis does not work. Can you suggest a reason why it didn't?

Two other examples of the use of the Gabriel synthesis for the preparation of primary amines are shown in Equations 20.7 and 20.8.

Eqn. 20.7

benzyl bromide → potassium phthalimide → 79% yield → H_2N—NH_2 / CH_3CH_2OH → 95% yield benzylamine

Eqn. 20.8

3-brompo-1,2-propanediol acetonide → potassium phthalimide → 25% yield → KOH / H_2O → 62% yield 3-amino-1,2-propanediol acetonide

PROBLEM 20.11 Show the Gabriel approach for the synthesis of each of the following primary amines:

a. 1-amino-2-methylpropane
b. *p*-nitrobenzylamine
c. 3-cyclohexyl-1-aminopropane

$$R{-}\ddot{X}: \xrightarrow[\text{DMSO}]{\text{NaCN}} R{-}C{\equiv}N:$$

$$R{-}C{\equiv}N: \xrightarrow{\text{reduction}} R{-}CH_2\ddot{N}H_2$$

Figure 20.15 Preparation of primary amines from haloalkanes. The haloalkane is first converted to a nitrile by a nucleophilic substitution reaction (S_N2), then the nitrile is reduced. The procedure works best with primary haloalkanes having minimal branching at the β-position. Several methods are available for the nitrile reduction.

The Reduction of Nitriles Cyanide ion can act as a nucleophile in reaction with haloalkanes. This substitution reaction, which is easily controlled, yields a nitrile. The nitrile can serve as a precursor in the preparation of primary amines with minimum side-product formation. Starting from a haloalkane, RX, we can prepare a primary alkylamine of formula RCH_2NH_2 in two steps. This is summarized in Figure 20.15. Examples of the synthesis of nitriles from haloalkanes were shown earlier in our discussion of nucleophilic substitution reactions.

Two examples of the reduction of nitriles for the preparation of primary amines are shown below.

Eqn. 20.9

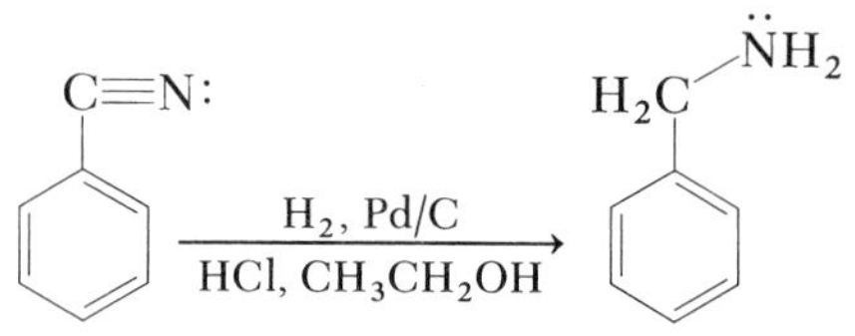

$$C_6H_5{-}C{\equiv}N: \xrightarrow[\text{HCl, } CH_3CH_2OH]{H_2\text{, Pd/C}} C_6H_5{-}CH_2\ddot{N}H_2$$

benzonitrile — 95% yield benzylamine

Eqn. 20.10

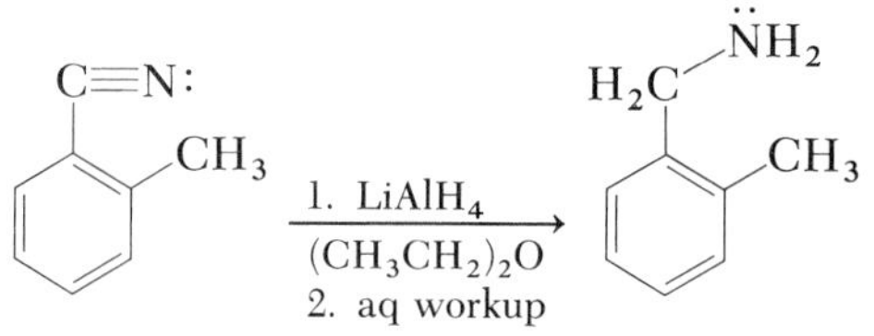

$$o\text{-}CH_3C_6H_4{-}C{\equiv}N: \xrightarrow[\text{2. aq workup}]{\text{1. } LiAlH_4\text{, } (CH_3CH_2)_2O} o\text{-}CH_3C_6H_4{-}CH_2\ddot{N}H_2$$

o-methylbenzonitrile — 88% yield *o*-methylbenzylamine

20.6 The Synthesis of Arylamines

A common approach for the synthesis of arylamines is the reduction of aryl nitro compounds. You should recall from our discussion of electrophilic aromatic substitution reactions that the nitration of an aromatic ring is easily achieved. Moreover, we can control both the position of nitro group introduction and the number of nitro groups introduced.

There are several common methods available for the reduction of nitro groups, each with its own particular utility and selectivity. While each method allows the same conversion of $-NO_2$ to $-NH_2$, it is important to have more than one method available. We decide which approach to use in any particular case based on the compatibility of the reagent with other functional groups present in the molecule.

One approach to the reduction of nitro groups involves the use of a hydride reagent in the presence of a Lewis acid. An example is shown in Equation 20.11.

Eqn. 20.11

NO_2 / CH_3 —($NaBH_4$, $NiCl_2$)→ $\ddot{N}H_2$ / CH_3

p-nitrotoluene

95% yield
p-methylaniline

We very commonly use a metal (such as iron, tin, or zinc) in an acidic solution to reduce aromatic nitro compounds to amines. Two examples of this type of reduction are shown in Equations 20.12 and 20.13.

Eqn. 20.12

:O: NO_2 —(acetic acid, Fe (workup with base))→ :O: $\ddot{N}H_2$

o-nitrobenzophenone

89% yield
o-aminobenzophenone

Eqn. 20.13

:F: NO_2 —(Sn, HCl (workup with base))→ :F: $\ddot{N}H_2$

m-fluoronitrobenzene

89% yield
m-fluoroaniline

The procedure using iron in acetic acid (the **Bechamp reduction**) is a relatively mild method and can be used to reduce a nitro group selectively in compounds containing both nitro groups and carbonyl groups. The reduction of both types of groups can occur with many other dissolving metal reduction procedures. In this context, remember that the Clemmensen reduction uses zinc metal in hydrochloric acid to reduce carbonyl groups. If we treated a compound containing a nitro group *and* a carbonyl group under the conditions of the Clemmensen reduction, *both* groups would be reduced.

Catalytic reduction of aromatic nitro groups occurs readily under relatively mild conditions. An example of the formation of an aromatic amine by catalytic reduction of an aryl nitro compound is shown in Equation 20.14. This particular procedure uses a *soluble* hydrogenation catalyst, although heterogeneous catalytic systems also can be used (e.g., hydrogen gas in the presence of PtO_2).

Eqn. 20.14

H_3C / NO_2 / NO_2 —($RuCl_2(PPh_3)_3$, H_2)→ H_3C / NO_2 / $\ddot{N}H_2$

2,4-dinitrotoluene

91% yield
2-methyl-5-nitroaniline

This particular reaction shows a selectivity in that only one nitro group is reduced, but this type of selectivity is difficult to predict. A problem with catalytic reduction is that other functional groups (carbonyl groups, carbon-carbon double and triple bonds, and carbon-halogen linkages) also react with hydrogen under these conditions.

A final method for the reduction of a nitro group involves reaction of an aryl nitro compound with an inorganic polysulfide in the presence of a protic solvent. An example is shown in Equation 20.15.

Eqn. 20.15

$$3\text{-}O_2N\text{-}C_6H_4\text{-}C{\equiv}CH \xrightarrow[H_2O]{CoS_x} 3\text{-}H_2\ddot{N}\text{-}C_6H_4\text{-}C{\equiv}CH$$

(3-nitrophenyl) acetylene → 90% yield (3-aminophenyl) acetylene

PROBLEM 20.12 Describe how you would synthesize each of the following compounds starting with 1-bromobutane.

a. 1-aminobutane **b.** 1-aminopentane

PROBLEM 20.13 Describe how you would synthesize each of the following compounds starting with either benzene or toluene.

a. 4-bromoaniline **b.** 3-bromoaniline
c. benzylamine **d.** 2,5-dimethylaniline

20.7 The Use of Imines in the Synthesis of Amines

Primary amines undergo nucleophilic addition reactions with aldehydes and ketones to form imines (Schiff's bases) as described in the previous chapter. The reaction shown in Equation 20.16 is an example of this type of reaction.

Eqn. 20.16

$$C_6H_{10}{=}\ddot{O}{:} + (CH_3)_3C{-}\ddot{N}H_2 \xrightarrow[\text{benzene}]{\text{acid}} C_6H_{10}{=}\ddot{N}{-}C(CH_3)_3 + H_2\ddot{O}$$

cyclohexanone + *tert*-butylamine → 85% yield *N-tert*-butylcyclohexanone imine

Imines are useful compounds that play a significant role in biological processes and undergo synthetically useful reactions.

SPECIAL TOPIC

Imines in Biological Systems

Although imines (Schiff's bases) are rather reactive species, they are not simply interesting structures that we can produce in the chemical laboratory. They are also important intermediates occurring in biological processes. For example, pyridoxal, a form of vitamin B_6, forms imines in reaction with enzymic amino groups in the transamination process. (Transamination is the reversible exchange of an amino group of an amino acid for a carbonyl function.) The imine interacts with the amino group of an α-amino acid to assist in its removal and replacement by a carbonyl function. This process is summarized below.

pyridoxal + (protein with free amino group) ⇌ (imine)

(imine) + $RCH(NH_2)COOH$ ⇌ [protein–NH_2 / pyridoxal imine with $RCHCOO^-$ on $\overset{+}{N}$–H]

[protein :NH_2 / $\overset{+}{N}$H=CH–pyridoxal, $RCHCOO^-$] ⇌ [protein :NH_2 / $RC(=\overset{+}{N}H)COO^-$–$CH_2$–pyridoxal]

[protein :NH_2 / $RC(=\overset{+}{N}H)COO^-$–$CH_2$–pyridoxal] + $H_2\ddot{O}$ ⇌ [protein :NH_2 / $\overset{+}{N}H_3$–CH_2–pyridoxal] + $RC(=O)COO^-$

THE REDUCTION OF IMINES

It is possible to reduce imines to amines using a variety of reagents. In these reactions the net effect is always the addition of one hydrogen atom to the carbon atom and one hydrogen atom to the nitrogen atom of the carbon-nitrogen double bond. Catalytic hydrogenation and complex hydride reduction are two convenient ways of achieving this reduction. Examples are shown in Equations 20.17 and 20.18.

Eqn. 20.17

$$CH_3CH_2CH_2CH_2\text{—}\ddot{N}{=}CH\text{—}CH_2CH_2CH_3 \xrightarrow[CH_3CH_2OH]{H_2,\ PtO_2} CH_3CH_2CH_2CH_2\text{—}\ddot{N}(H)\text{—}CH_2CH_2CH_2CH_3$$

butyraldehyde *N*-butylimine — 65% yield dibutylamine

Eqn. 20.18

$$CH_3CH_2CH_2CH_2\text{—}\ddot{N}{=}C(CH_3)_2 \xrightarrow[H_2O]{NaBH_4} CH_3CH_2CH_2CH_2\text{—}\ddot{N}(H)\text{—}CH(CH_3)_2$$

acetone N-butylimine — 63% yield butylisopropylamine

In a useful synthetic procedure known as **reductive amination,** we allow a carbonyl compound to react with ammonia or a primary amine in the presence of a reducing agent. Under these conditions an imine is initially formed but is not isolated. Instead, it is reduced to the observed amine product. Examples of reductive amination are shown in Equations 20.19 and 20.20.

Eqn. 20.19

$$C_6H_5CH\ddot{O} \xrightarrow[\text{ethanol}]{NH_3,\ H_2,\ Ni} C_6H_5CH_2\ddot{N}H_2$$

benzaldehyde — 89% yield benzylamine

Eqn. 20.20

$$(CH_3)_2CHCH\ddot{O} + CH_3CH_2CH_2CH_2\ddot{N}H_2 \xrightarrow[\text{ethanol}]{H_2,\ PtO_2} (CH_3)_2CHCH_2\ddot{N}H\text{—}CH_2CH_2CH_2CH_3$$

isobutyraldehyde — butylamine — 92% yield butylisobutylamine

The use of boron-containing reducing agents provides a convenient alternative to the use of catalytic hydrogenation. One reagent of this type is $NaBH_3CN$ (sodium cyanoborohydride). An example of its use is given in Equation 20.21.

Eqn. 20.21

$$PhCH\ddot{O} + CH_3CH_2\ddot{N}H_2 \xrightarrow[\text{methanol}]{NaBH_3CN} PhCH_2\ddot{N}HCH_2CH_3$$

benzaldehyde — ethylamine — 91% yield benzylethylamine

If we perform the reductive amination using a carbonyl compound with a *secondary* amine in the presence of a reducing agent, the product is a tertiary amine. An example of this type of reaction is shown in Equation 20.22. As shown, this reaction proceeds via an intermediate **iminium ion.**

Eqn. 20.22

$$\text{piperidine} + CH_3CH_2CH_2CHO \xrightarrow[CH_3CH_2OH]{H_2,\ Ni} [\text{iminium ion } (C_5H_{10}N^+{=}CHCH_2CH_2CH_3)\ \ HO^-] \longrightarrow C_5H_{10}N{-}CH_2CH_2CH_2CH_3$$

piperidine butyraldehyde

93% yield
N-butylpiperidine

Oximes (RCH=NOH, Chapter 19) can also be reduced to primary amines. Only *primary* amines can be formed from oximes because there is only one carbon group attached to nitrogen in the oxime. The preparation of amines from oximes involves not only the reduction of the double bond but also a cleavage of the nitrogen-oxygen bond. This bond is relatively weak and is easily cleaved under catalytic or hydride reduction conditions. An example of the use of an oxime for the synthesis of a primary amine is shown in Equation 20.23.

Eqn. 20.23

$$\text{3-indolyl}{-}CH{=}NOH \xrightarrow[(CH_3CH_2)_2O]{LiAlH_4} \text{3-indolyl}{-}CH_2NH_2$$

3-indolecarboxaldehyde oxime

87% yield
3-aminomethylindole

THE CLARKE-ESCHWEILER SYNTHESIS

Earlier in this chapter we encountered the problem of *overalkylation* in the reaction of ammonia and amines with haloalkanes. It is difficult to control this type of reaction so that only one or two alkyl groups substitute for hydrogen on nitrogen.

In this regard, consider a specific synthetic objective: the conversion of a primary amine, RNH_2, to a tertiary amine, $RN(CH_3)_2$, without any accompanying overalkylation to form the quaternary ammonium ion. Similarly, consider the conversion of a secondary amine, R_2NH to a tertiary amine, R_2NCH_3, again with no formation of quaternary ammonium ion. In both cases we need to replace all of the hydrogens originally attached to nitrogen with methyl groups, without adding an additional methyl group. We refer to this type of

$$R{-}\ddot{N}H_2 \longrightarrow R{-}\ddot{N}(CH_3)_2 \not\longrightarrow R{-}\overset{+}{N}(CH_3)_3 \qquad R_2\ddot{N}H \longrightarrow R_2\ddot{N}{-}CH_3 \not\longrightarrow R_2\overset{+}{N}(CH_3)_2$$

primary amine — tertiary amine — quaternary ammonium ion; secondary amine

Figure 20.16 A synthetic problem: permethylation of an amine *without* formation of a quaternary ammonium salt. Simple alkylation of the amine with a halomethane *cannot* give us the desired result.

process as **permethylation.** The synthesis problem is summarized in Figure 20.16.

A suitable procedure for these syntheses is the **Clarke-Eschweiler synthesis.** It involves the reaction of a primary or secondary amine with formaldehyde and formic acid. The formaldehyde is used in its polymeric form, $(-OCH_2-)_x$, commonly known as paraformaldehyde, which under the reaction conditions acts as a source of formaldehyde molecules. Examples of the Clarke-Eschweiler synthesis are shown in Equations 20.24 and 20.25.

Eqn. 20.24

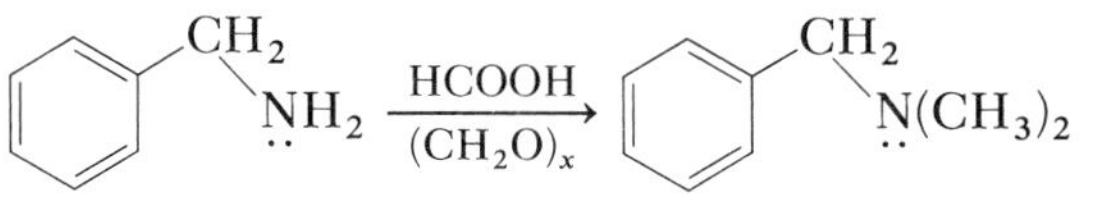

$$C_6H_5CH_2\ddot{N}H_2 \xrightarrow[(CH_2O)_x]{HCOOH} C_6H_5CH_2\ddot{N}(CH_3)_2$$

benzylamine — 80% yield *N,N*-dimethylbenzylamine

Eqn. 20.25

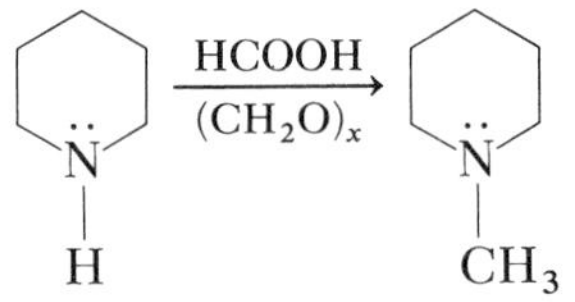

$$C_5H_{10}\ddot{N}{-}H \xrightarrow[(CH_2O)_x]{HCOOH} C_5H_{10}\ddot{N}{-}CH_3$$

piperidine — 80% yield *N*-methylpiperidine

Consider a Clarke-Eschweiler synthesis with a primary amine. The amine first reacts with formaldehyde to form an imine. The imine is then protonated by formic acid, and the resulting iminium ion is reduced in situ to a secondary amine that differs from the original amine in having a methyl group in place of a hydrogen atom. The secondary amine then undergoes a further cycle of reactions with formaldehyde and formic acid to form a tertiary amine. At this point reaction stops—the tertiary amine has no hydrogen atoms bonded to nitrogen and thus cannot form an imine or iminium ion.

MECHANISM OF REACTION

The Clarke-Eschweiler Synthesis

Step 1 Formation of an imine (see Chapter 19 for the full mechanism).

$$R\ddot{N}H_2 + H_2C{=}\ddot{O} \longrightarrow R{-}\ddot{N}{=}CH_2 + H_2\ddot{O}$$

Step 2 Protonation of the imine.

$$H_2C{=}\ddot{N}{-}R + H{-}\ddot{O}{-}C(=O){-}H \longrightarrow \left[H_2\overset{+}{C}{-}\ddot{N}(H){-}R \longleftrightarrow H_2C{=}\overset{+}{N}(H){-}R \right] + {}^{-}\ddot{O}{-}C(=O){-}H$$

iminium ion formate ion

Step 3 Reduction of the iminium ion formed in Step 2. Formate ion acts as the reducing agent by delivering a hydrogen atom with a pair of electrons (i.e., a hydride ion) to the iminium ion.

$$R{-}\overset{+}{N}(H){=}CH_2 + H{-}C(=O){-}\ddot{O}^{-} \longrightarrow R{-}\ddot{N}(H){-}CH_2{-}H + O{=}C{=}O$$

Step 4 The secondary amine from Step 3 reacts further with formaldehyde to form a new iminium ion.

$$R{-}\ddot{N}H(CH_3) + H_2C{=}\ddot{O} \longrightarrow R{-}\overset{+}{N}(CH_3){=}CH_2 + H_2\ddot{O}$$

Step 5 The new iminium ion is reduced to the tertiary amine product.

$$R{-}\overset{+}{N}(CH_3){=}CH_2 + H{-}C(=O){-}\ddot{O}^{-} \longrightarrow R{-}N(CH_3){-}CH_2{-}H + O{=}C{=}O$$

PROBLEM 20.14 Consider the mechanism of the Clarke-Eschweiler synthesis. An oxidation-reduction occurs in this reaction. What species is oxidized?

PROBLEM 20.15 Rationalize the fact that no quaternary ammonium salt forms in the Clarke-Eschweiler synthesis.

20.8 The Reactions of Amines with Nitrous Acid

Nitrous acid (H—O—N=O) is an unstable substance that does not survive storage. However, a dilute solution can be prepared by the reaction of a nitrite salt with a cold solution of a strong acid, usually sulfuric acid, as shown in Figure 20.17. A solution of nitrous acid prepared in this way survives sufficiently

$$\ddot{O}{=}\ddot{N}{-}\ddot{O}:^- + H_2SO_4 \rightleftharpoons \ddot{O}{=}N{-}\ddot{O}{-}H + HSO_4^-$$

stronger base | stronger acid | weaker acid | weaker base

Figure 20.17 Equilibrium formation of nitrous acid.

long for us to perform useful reactions with it. Under the reaction conditions, nitrous acid acts as a source of the **nitrosonium ion** (NO^+), which is the active reagent in reactions of amines with nitrous acid.

MECHANISM OF REACTION

Generation of the Nitrosonium Ion

Step 1 Formation of nitrous acid

$$NaNO_2 + H_2SO_4 \rightleftharpoons NaHSO_4 + H\ddot{O}{-}\ddot{N}{=}\ddot{O}$$

Step 2 Protonation of nitrous acid

$$H\ddot{O}{-}\ddot{N}{=}\ddot{O} + H_2SO_4 \rightleftharpoons H_2\overset{+}{\ddot{O}}{-}\ddot{N}{=}\ddot{O} + HSO_4^-$$

Step 3 Loss of water

$$H_2\overset{+}{\ddot{O}}{-}\ddot{N}{=}\ddot{O} \rightleftharpoons H_2\ddot{O} + \left[\overset{+}{N}{=}\ddot{O} \longleftrightarrow :N{\equiv}\overset{+}{O}:\right]$$

In the following sections we will be concerned with the reactions of the nitrosonium ion with amines and the utility of the species thus generated for organic syntheses.

THE DIAZOTIZATION OF PRIMARY AMINES

The Formation of Diazonium Ions **Diazotization** refers to the conversion of a primary amine (RNH_2 or $ArNH_2$) into the corresponding **diazonium salt** ($RN_2^+X^-$ or $ArN_2^+X^-$). We generally perform this conversion by adding the primary amine to a cold (0–5 °C) solution of sodium nitrite in dilute sulfuric acid or hydrochloric acid. The nitrosonium ion formed from the nitrous acid reacts with the primary amine to form the diazonium ion in a series of acid-base type reactions. Notice that a *N*-nitrosamine is formed as a reaction intermediate. Had the starting amine been a secondary amine, reaction would have ceased at this point. However, *N*-nitrosamines of primary amines are not stable and the reaction continues as shown.

MECHANISM OF REACTION

The Diazotization of a Primary Amine

Overall Reaction:

$$R-\ddot{N}H_2 \longrightarrow R-N_2^{\oplus}$$

Step 1 Addition of nitrosonium ion to the amine

$$R-\ddot{N}H_2 + \overset{+}{N}=\ddot{O} \rightleftharpoons R-\overset{+}{N}H_2(-N=\ddot{O})$$

Step 2 Hydrogen transfer. The base B: can be a water molecule, a molecule of amine, or simply the anion accompanying the nitrosonium ion.

$$R-\overset{+}{N}H(-H)(-N=\ddot{O}) + :B \rightleftharpoons R-\ddot{N}H(-N=\ddot{O}) + H-\overset{+}{B}$$

intermediate
N-nitrosamine

Steps 3 and 4 Tautomeric equilibrium

$$R-\ddot{N}H(-N=\ddot{O}) + H-\overset{+}{B} \rightleftharpoons B: + \left[R-\ddot{N}H(-N=\overset{+}{\ddot{O}}-H) \longleftrightarrow R-\overset{+}{N}H(=N-\ddot{O}-H)\right]$$

$$R-\overset{+}{N}(-H)(=N-\ddot{O}-H) + :B \rightleftharpoons R-\ddot{N}=\ddot{N}-\ddot{O}-H + H-\overset{+}{B}$$

diazenol
(unstable at low pH)

Step 5 Protonation

$$R-\ddot{N}=\ddot{N}-\ddot{O}-H + H-\overset{+}{B} \rightleftharpoons R-\ddot{N}=\ddot{N}-\overset{+}{\ddot{O}}H_2 + :B$$

Step 6 Water loss

$$R-\ddot{N}=\ddot{N}-\overset{+}{O}H_2 \rightleftharpoons R-\overset{+}{N}\equiv N: + H_2\ddot{O}$$

PROBLEM 20.16 Draw a Lewis structure for the nitrosonium ion such that both atoms have complete valence level octets of electrons.

PROBLEM 20.17 Draw a pair of resonance-contributing Lewis structures for the benzene diazonium ion, PhN_2^+.

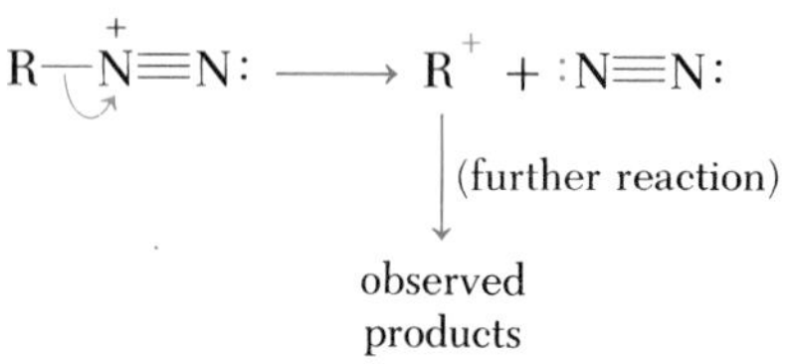

$$R-\overset{+}{N}\equiv N: \longrightarrow R^+ + :N\equiv N:$$

(further reaction) → observed products

Figure 20.18 Decomposition of alkyl diazonium ions. The reaction occurs rapidly even at 0° as the diazonium ions are generated in aqueous acidic solution.

The Nature of Diazonium Salts Most diazonium salts are highly reactive species that are stable to decomposition only in solution at reduced temperatures. The stability of alkyl diazonium salts is so slight that even in solution at 0 °C, they decompose to form nitrogen (an excellent leaving group) and carbocations. The carbocations react further as illustrated in Figure 20.18 (also see Problem 20.18).

Because of their very high reactivity, alkyl diazonium ions are relatively unimportant for organic syntheses. Aryl diazonium ions, however, are extremely useful in this context. In general, aryl diazonium ions are reasonably stable in aqueous acid solution at 0 °C. Furthermore, with the appropriate counterion, a few aryl diazonium salts are isolable as solids. We will consider the utility of diazonium salts in the following sections.

PROBLEM 20.18 When butylamine reacts with sodium nitrite in dilute hydrochloric acid, a mixture of the following compounds is formed.

1-butanol	(*E*)-2-butene
2-butanol	1-butene
1-chlorobutane	(Z)-2-butene
2-chlorobutane	

Suggest a mechanism for the formation of each of these products.

PROBLEM 20.19 Suggest a mechanism for the overall reaction shown below.

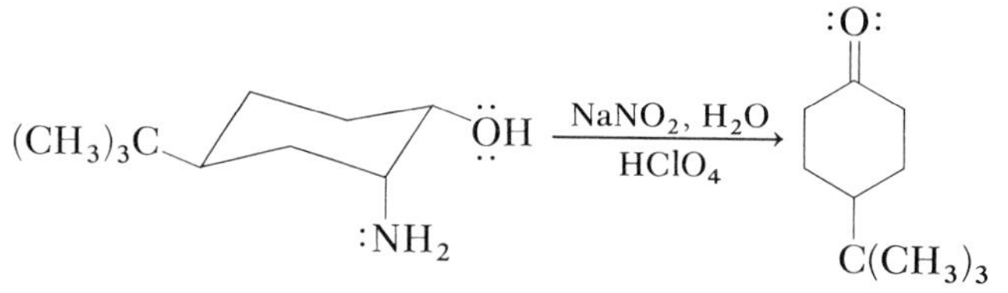

$(CH_3)_3C$–cyclohexane(–$\ddot{O}H$)(–$:NH_2$) $\xrightarrow[HClO_4]{NaNO_2,\ H_2O}$ 4-$C(CH_3)_3$-cyclohexanone ($:\ddot{O}:$)

Replacement Reactions of Aromatic Diazonium Ions Aryl diazonium ions undergo a variety of reactions in which the $-N_2^+$ substituent is lost as nitrogen and replaced by a new substituent. Common reactions of synthetic utility are summarized in Table 20.2.

The overall deamination of an arylamine can be effected by diazotization followed by treatment with hypophosphorous acid (H_3PO_2). As Table 20.2 shows, this process results in the replacement of $-N_2^+$ with $-H$. Examples are shown in Equations 20.26 and 20.27.

Table 20.2 Replacement Reactions of Aromatic Diazonium Ions

Replacing Substituent	Reagent
hydrogen	H_3PO_2 (deamination; reduction)
chloride, bromide, cyanide	CuX (Sandmeyer reaction)
fluoride	HBF_4 (Schieman reaction)
iodide	KI
hydroxide	aqueous acid

Eqn. 20.26

2-methyl-4-nitroaniline $\xrightarrow[2.\ H_3PO_2]{1.\ NaNO_2,\ H_2SO_4}$ *m*-nitrotoluene (75% yield)

Eqn. 20.27

6-bromo-2,4-diethylaniline $\xrightarrow[2.\ H_3PO_2]{1.\ NaNO_2,\ H_2SO_4}$ 3,5-diethylbromobenzene (70% yield)

In performing these reactions we first form the diazonium salt in aqueous solution at 0°. Then the reducing agent is added and the reaction mixture is warmed to room temperature.

To replace a primary aromatic amino substituent by a halide, the procedure used depends on the halide to be introduced. The **Sandmeyer reaction** is useful for introducing a chloride, bromide, or cyanide substituent. In the Sandmeyer reaction we again form the diazonium salt at 0 °C, and then we add the cuprous halide or cyanide and warm the reaction mixture to room temperature. Hydrochloric acid can be used to accomplish the diazotization when a chloride is to replace the amino substituent. Sulfuric acid is used when other replacements are to be made. Examples of syntheses using the Sandmeyer reactions are shown in Equations 20.28–20.30.

Eqn. 20.28

m-aminobenzaldehyde $\xrightarrow[2.\ CuCl]{1.\ NaNO_2,\ H_2SO_4}$ *m*-chlorobenzaldehyde (79% yield)

Eqn. 20.29

CHO, NH_2 → (1. $NaNO_2$, H_2SO_4; 2. CuBr) → CHO, Br:

65% yield
m-bromobenzaldehyde

Eqn. 20.30

NH_2, CH_3 → (1. $NaNO_2$, H_2SO_4; 2. CuCN) → C≡N:, CH_3

o-methylaniline

o-methylbenzonitrile

To prepare aryl iodides from arylamines, potassium iodide can be used instead of cuprous iodide. An example is shown in Equation 20.31.

Eqn. 20.31

NH_2 → (1. $NaNO_2$, H_2SO_4; 2. KI) → :I:

aniline

76% yield
iodobenzene

If we wish to replace an amino function by a fluorine atom, the tetrafluoroborate salt of the diazonium ion must be used. These tetrafluoroborate salts are significantly more stable than other diazonium salts. They can be isolated and dried, while many other diazonium salts explode if isolated and dried. Heating the dry tetrafluoroborate salt results in the formation of the aryl fluoride. Two examples are shown in Equations 20.32 and 20.33.

Eqn. 20.32

:OCH_3, H_2N, NO_2 → (1. $NaNO_2$, H_2SO_4; 2. HBF_4; 3. heat) → :OCH_3, :F, NO_2

3-nitro-5-methoxyaniline

93% yield
3-fluoro-5-nitroanisole

Eqn. 20.33

NH_2 → (1. $NaNO_2$, H_2SO_4; 2. HBF_4; 3. heat) → F:

4-aminobiphenyl

94% yield
4-fluorobiphenyl

Aryl diazonium salts react with hot water to form **phenols** (i.e., hydroxyaromatic compounds). Such reactions provide us with a method for converting a —NH_2 group on a benzene ring to an —OH group. We first diazotize the amine in the usual manner, in dilute aqueous sulfuric acid. Then, upon heating the reaction mixture, nucleophilic attack by water occurs, displacing a nitrogen molecule. An example is shown in Equation 20.34.

Eqn. 20.34

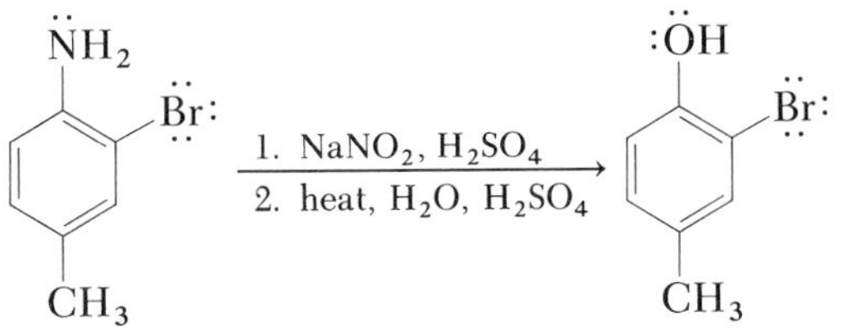

NH_2 ... Br: → 1. $NaNO_2$, H_2SO_4 2. heat, H_2O, H_2SO_4 → :OH ... Br:

CH_3 CH_3

2-bromo-4-methylaniline

92% yield
2-bromo-4-methylphenol

PROBLEM 20.20 Give the reagents and conditions required for each of the following preparations:

a. 4-iodotoluene from 4-methylaniline
b. 4-fluorotoluene from 4-methylaniline
c. 4-bromotoluene from *p*-nitrotoluene

Aromatic Syntheses Using Diazonium Replacement Reactions Aryl diazonium replacement reactions provide us with versatility in the synthesis of aromatic compounds. These reactions can be used as alternatives to or complements of the nucleophilic and electrophilic aromatic substitution reactions we discussed in earlier chapters.

In syntheses using diazonium replacement reactions the critical initial substituent is the *nitro* group. If we can introduce a nitro group at a particular position on the aromatic ring, we can then reduce it to a primary amino group, which we can subsequently convert to a diazonium ion and then replace with halogen, cyanide, hydroxyl, or hydrogen. Thus an efficient synthesis of a molecule such as *m*-dibromobenzene becomes feasible. If we were to try to synthesize *m*-dibromobenzene using only electrophilic aromatic substitution reactions, there would be a major problem. We could introduce one bromine atom into the benzene ring easily, but the second bromine atom would be placed *ortho* or *para* relative to the first, since bromine is an *ortho,para*-directing group. The synthesis of *m*-dibromobenzene using diazonium salt chemistry is shown in Figure 20.19.

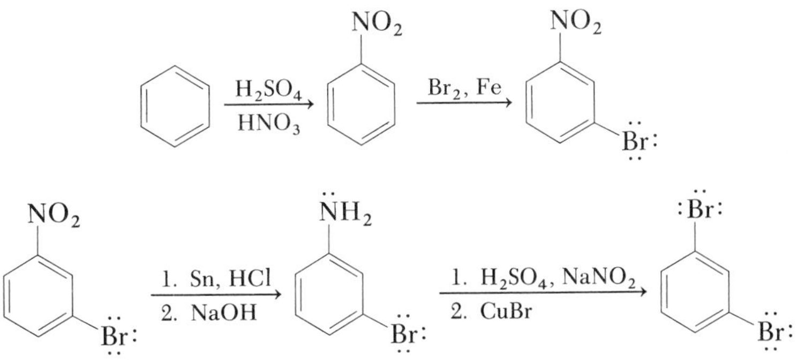

Figure 20.19 Synthesis of *m*-dibromobenzene from benzene. The initial introduction of the nitro group allows electrophilic aromatic substitution with *meta* orientation. Once the nitro group is reduced, introduction of the desired substituent is possible via diazotization.

benzene → H_2SO_4, HNO_3 → NO_2 → Br_2, Fe → NO_2 ... Br:

NO_2 ... Br: → 1. Sn, HCl 2. NaOH → NH_2 ... Br: → 1. H_2SO_4, $NaNO_2$ 2. CuBr → :Br: ... Br:

Consider also the use of diazonium ion chemistry to prepare *o*-chlorobromobenzene, free of the *p*-isomer. The route is shown in Figure 20.20. Here we introduce a nitro group simply to block the *p*-position. After the bromination step, the nitro group is discarded by converting it to an amino group, diazotizing the amino group, and finally treating the diazonium salt with H_3PO_2.

Figure 20.20 Synthesis of *o*-chlorobromobenzene. The nitro group is used to block the *para* position (relative to the chlorine) while bromine substitution is performed. The nitro group is then removed by reduction to an amino group followed by diazotization and further reduction.

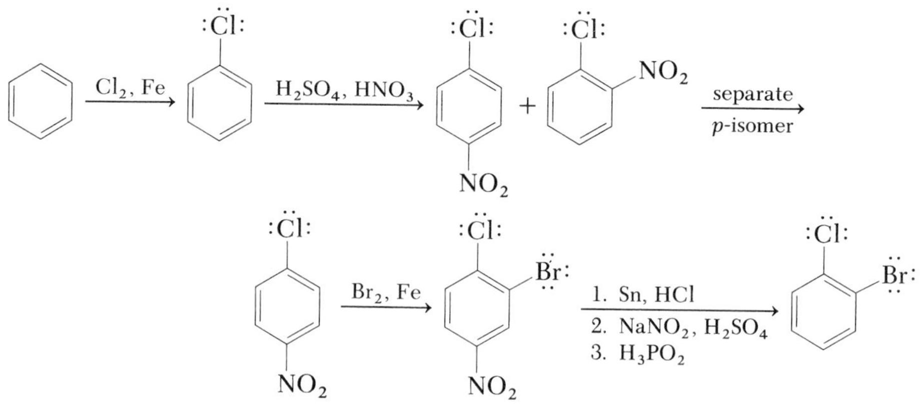

:Cl: Cl_2, Fe ; H_2SO_4, HNO_3 ; NO_2 + NO_2 ; separate *p*-isomer ; Br_2, Fe ; Br: ; 1. Sn, HCl 2. $NaNO_2$, H_2SO_4 3. H_3PO_2

Clearly, the use of diazonium salts greatly expands the armory of preparative procedures we can use to introduce substituents into specific locations on an aromatic ring.

Diazo Coupling Reactions One feature of all of the diazonium salt chemistry we have discussed thus far is the loss of nitrogen in their reactions. Diazonium salts also undergo a reaction known as *coupling*, in which no nitrogen is lost. In these coupling reactions diazonium ions serve as electrophiles that react with sufficiently activated aromatic rings, usually those with amino or hydroxyl substituents. Two examples are shown in Equations 20.35 and 20.36.

Eqn. 20.35

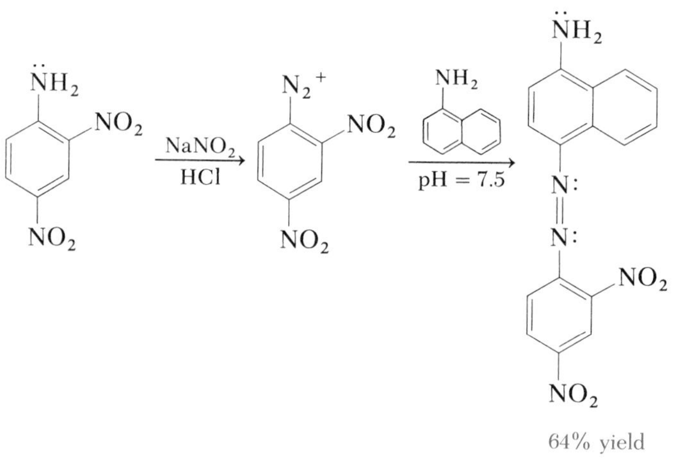

NH_2, NO_2, NO_2 ; $NaNO_2$, HCl ; N_2^+, NO_2, NO_2 ; NH_2 (naphthylamine), pH = 7.5 ; NH_2, N:=N:, NO_2, NO_2

64% yield

Eqn. 20.36

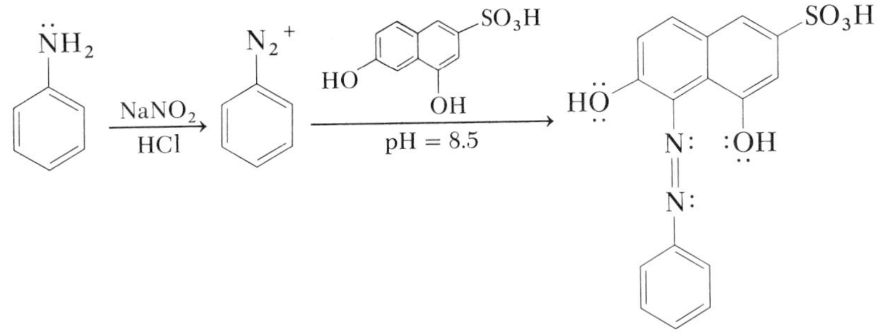

NH_2 benzene $\xrightarrow[HCl]{NaNO_2}$ N_2^+ benzene $\xrightarrow[pH = 8.5]{\text{HO, OH, } SO_3H \text{ naphthalene}}$ azo product (SO_3H, HO, :OH, N=N, benzene)

58% yield

The products of diazo coupling reactions contain a nitrogen-nitrogen double bond, are highly colored, and are referred to as **azo compounds.** Historically, they provided the foundation for the German aniline-dye industry, which helped spur the development of industrial organic chemistry.

Compounds containing the azo linkage generally absorb light in the visible region of the electromagnetic spectrum. They therefore have a color that is complementary to the light they absorb. By the proper choice of substituents it is possible to produce compounds providing almost a continuum of colors through the visible spectrum.

Notice that in Equation 20.35 the azo group enters the left-hand of the two benzene rings, *para* to the amino substituent. The other ring is unaffected because it is insufficiently reactive toward the weakly electrophilic diazonium ion. In general, only $-NH_2$, $-NHR$, $-NR_2$, and $-OH$ groups are sufficiently activating when attached to a benzene ring to permit the formation of azo compounds by reaction with a diazonium ion.

PROBLEM 20.21 *N,N*-Dimethylaniline reacts under diazotization reaction conditions to give a green product. Suggest a structure for this product, whose formula is $C_8H_{10}N_2O$.

PROBLEM 20.22 Predict the product obtained by the reaction of benzene diazonium chloride with the compound shown below.

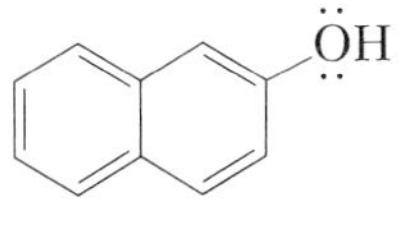

(naphthalene with :OH)

Furthermore, the successful performance of a diazonium coupling reaction depends on careful control of the solution pH. If the solution is highly acidic ($pH < 5$) or highly basic ($pH \geq 11$), coupling does not occur. For example, at $pH < 5$ phenols are unreactive. Although phenols are reactive in many electrophilic aromatic substitution reactions, a diazonium ion is only very weakly electrophilic. No reaction will occur unless the benzene ring is very strongly activated, and a hydroxyl group is insufficiently activating for such coupling reactions. However, when a phenol is converted to a phenoxide ion (at higher

SPECIAL TOPIC

Diazotization and Mutagenesis

Concern has been expressed regarding the use of inorganic nitrates and nitrites to retard food spoilage. This concern centers around the ability of nitrites to cause the diazotization of amino functions. (Inorganic nitrates are also of concern because they can be reduced in vivo to nitrites.) Under the acidic conditions commonly present in the stomach, nitrite ion generates nitrous acid and can diazotize free amino functions such as the aromatic primary amino substituent of a cytidine residue in a nucleic acid. Diazotization followed by reaction with water (as occurs in the absence of any other reactant for the diazonium ion) produces hydroxyl substitution for the original amino function. That is, a hydroxyl substituent results where there was originally an amino substituent. This substitution is shown schematically below for cytidine in a nucleic acid.

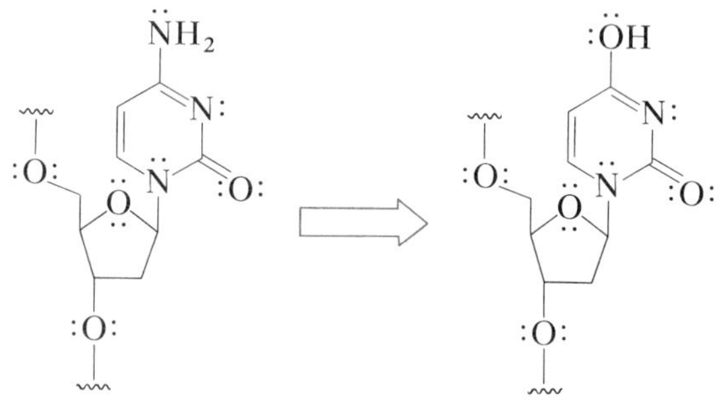

NH_2 :N: :O: :O: :O: N :O: ⟹ :OH :N: :O: :O: :O: N :O:

cytidine residue uridine residue

The cytidine residue in the nucleic acid is converted to a uridine residue. If this change occurs along a portion of genetic nucleic acid that serves as a code for peptide synthesis, a change in one of the amino acids along the peptide chain could be produced. Depending on the other nearby nucleotide residues, the amino acid isoleucine might be placed in the peptide chain being synthesized instead of the amino acid threonine, or phenylalanine instead of serine. The change of a single amino acid along the chain of a peptide critical for any number of biological processes can seriously disrupt that process. Sickle-cell anemia is a classical example of a genetic disease resulting from single amino acid mutation. Other types of diseases can result as well. At times this type of mutation produces cancerous growths. Agents (such as nitrite ion) that lead to such mutagenic or carcinogenic events are known as *mutagens* or *carcinogens*, respectively.

pH), the benzene ring is then sufficiently activated to react with the diazonium ion. (An —$\ddot{O}$:⁻ group is more activating than an —$\ddot{O}$H group.) There is a caveat, however, which is discussed below. Similarly, we know that arylamines are protonated in acidic solutions. Under acidic conditions, the benzene ring of an arylamine is deactivated and no reaction occurs with a diazonium ion.

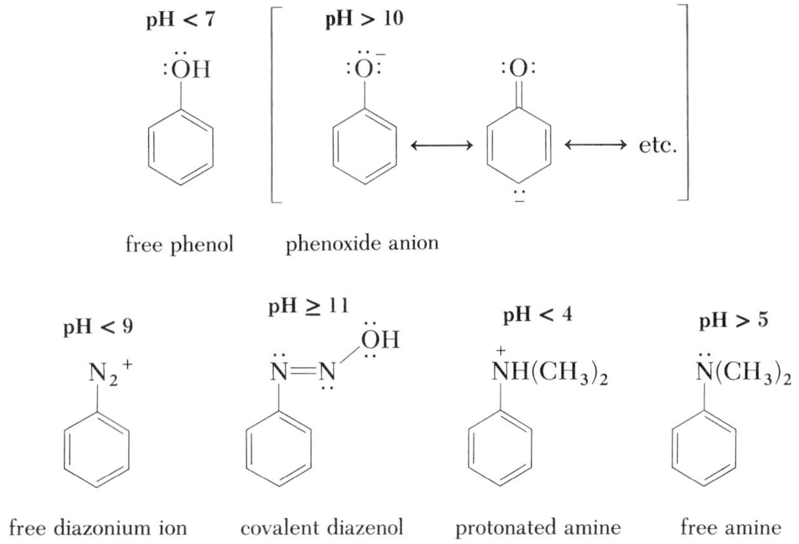

Figure 20.21 States of reactants in diazonium coupling reactions as the pH varies. A diazonium coupling reaction requires a free diazonium ion and a substrate that is highly reactive toward electrophilic aromatic substitution. For a phenol, the most reactive state is as the phenoxide ion, where extra electron density is donated to the aromatic ring. With an amine, the most reactive state is the free amine. Diazonium coupling reactions occur most readily at a pH of approximately 7. Even though the concentration of phenoxide ion is not large at that pH, it is sufficient to allow the coupling reaction to occur. Overall, the pH factor must be balanced to provide reasonable concentrations of each reactant at the same time.

pH < 7 — free phenol; pH > 10 — phenoxide anion (etc.)

pH < 9 — free diazonium ion (N_2^+); pH ≥ 11 — covalent diazenol (N=N–OH); pH < 4 — protonated amine ($\overset{+}{N}H(CH_3)_2$); pH > 5 — free amine ($N(CH_3)_2$)

Under basic conditions, amines are present as the reactive free amine and phenols are in the form of the highly reactive phenoxide ions. However, the diazonium ions do not exist as free cations under these conditions. Instead, they add hydroxide ion to form the covalent diazenols. These species are no longer electrophiles and cannot perform electrophilic aromatic substitution reactions. For the coupling reaction to be successful, the diazonium species must be present as the free ion and the substrate in the form of the free amine or phenoxide ion. The effects of pH on these species are summarized in Figure 20.21.

REACTIONS OF SECONDARY AMINES WITH NITROUS ACID

Secondary amines react with nitrous acid to form *N*-nitrosamines. Earlier we noted that *N*-nitrosamines are formed as intermediates in the reaction of primary amines with nitrous acid. When a secondary amine reacts with nitrous acid, reaction stops at the *N*-nitrosamine stage because the *N*-nitrosamine formed from a secondary amine cannot undergo tautomerization to a diazenol (why not?).

Since *N*-nitrosamines are extremely weak bases, they are insoluble in dilute aqueous acid. They separate from solution as yellow or orange solids or oils. An example of *N*-nitrosamine formation is shown in Equation 20.37.

Eqn. 20.37

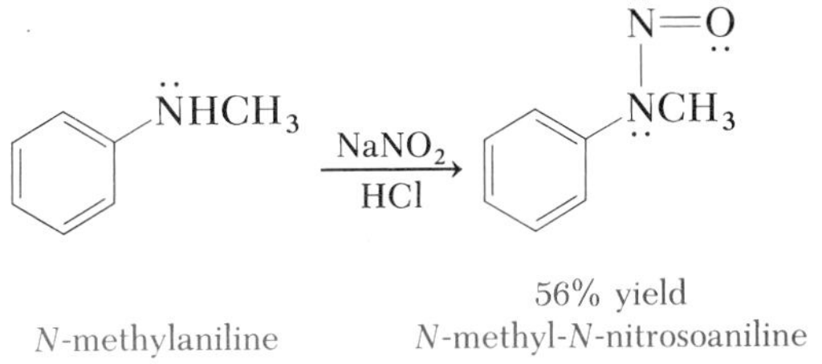

$$C_6H_5NHCH_3 \xrightarrow[HCl]{NaNO_2} C_6H_5N(CH_3)N{=}O$$

N-methylaniline → 56% yield *N*-methyl-*N*-nitrosoaniline

The *N*-nitrosamines are carcinogenic and must be handled with extreme care.

REACTIONS OF TERTIARY AMINES WITH NITROUS ACID

Tertiary alkylamines give no net reaction with nitrosonium ion. However, tertiary arylamines do react to form nitroso compounds. In these reactions the nitrosonium ion acts as an electrophile toward the highly activated aromatic ring of the arylamine.

PROBLEM 20.23 Propose a mechanism for the formation of the green compound discussed in Problem 20.21.

20.9 Cleavage of Carbon-Nitrogen Bonds

The carbon-nitrogen bond of an amine is not easily cleaved because the amino group would need to be displaced as an amide ion (e.g., NH_2^-), a very poor leaving group. We can make an analogy with alcohols. In earlier chapters we discussed the difficulties associated with removing a hydroxyl group from an alcohol. Since hydroxide ion is a relatively strong base, it is a very poor leaving group for either nucleophilic substitution or elimination reactions. Because the amide ion is an even stronger base than the hydroxide ion, it is even less likely to act as a leaving group. To induce the cleavage of the carbon-nitrogen bond of an amine with the accompanying loss of the amino function, we must choose conditions similar to those necessary for cleaving the carbon-oxygen bond of alcohols. Specifically, we must convert the amino nitrogen into a substituent that is a weaker base and therefore a better leaving group. One method is by conversion of an $-NH_2$ group to a $-N_2^+$ group, as described previously. *Exhaustive methylation* is also useful. In this reaction any hydrogen atoms attached to the nitrogen of the amino group are replaced by methyl groups through reaction with iodomethane, and one *additional* methyl group is added to the nitrogen to produce a quaternary ammonium salt. The quaternary ammonium salt has a positive charge on nitrogen and is a good leaving group.

THE HOFMANN DEGRADATION OF AMINES

When heated with base, quaternary ammonium salts undergo an elimination reaction to form alkenes. The sequence of reactions that converts an amine to an alkene via a quaternary ammonium salt is known as the **Hofmann degradation.** The overall process is illustrated in Figure 20.22.

The Hofmann degradation of amines is of greatest synthetic utility when only one product can be formed. Three examples are shown in Equations 20.38–20.40.

Eqn. 20.38

$$\text{3-aminocyclohexene } (:NH_2) \xrightarrow[CH_3I]{\text{excess}} \xrightarrow[\text{heat}]{Ag_2O,\ H_2O} \text{1,3-cyclohexadiene}$$

3-aminocyclohexene

99% yield
1,3-cyclohexadiene

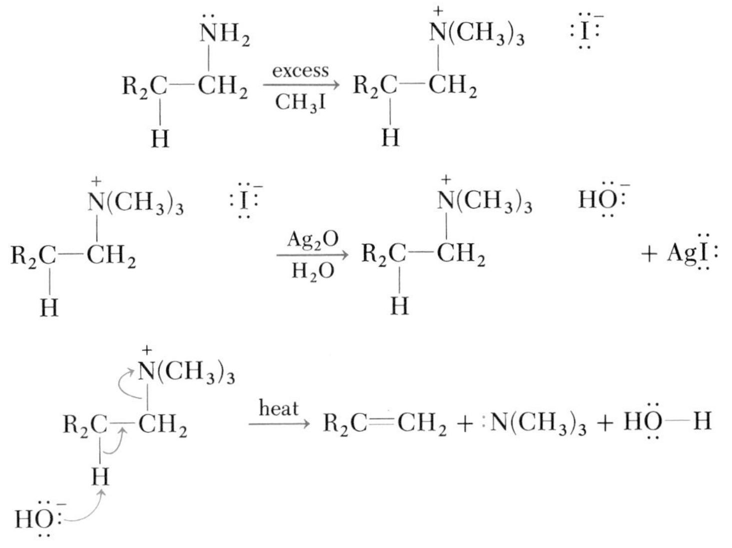

Figure 20.22 The Hofmann degradation of amines. After exhaustive methylation of the amino nitrogen to produce a quaternary iodide salt, treatment with aqueous silver oxide generates the quaternary ammonium hydroxide. Silver iodide precipitates from the reaction mixture, driving the equilibrium to the right, and is removed by filtration. On heating the quaternary ammonium hydroxide solution, an elimination reaction occurs in which the hydroxide ion acts as the base. The elimination is shown here as a classical E2 process; however, subtle variations in the mechanism often need to be considered.

$$R_2CH-CH_2\ddot{N}H_2 \xrightarrow[CH_3I]{\text{excess}} R_2CH-CH_2\overset{+}{N}(CH_3)_3\ :\ddot{I}:^-$$

$$R_2CH-CH_2\overset{+}{N}(CH_3)_3\ :\ddot{I}:^- \xrightarrow[H_2O]{Ag_2O} R_2CH-CH_2\overset{+}{N}(CH_3)_3\ H\ddot{O}:^- + Ag\ddot{I}:$$

$$H\ddot{O}:^- + R_2CH-CH_2\overset{+}{N}(CH_3)_3 \xrightarrow{\text{heat}} R_2C{=}CH_2 + :N(CH_3)_3 + H\ddot{O}-H$$

Eqn. 20.39

$$\text{piperidine} \xrightarrow[CH_3I]{\text{excess}} \xrightarrow[\text{heat}]{Ag_2O,\ H_2O} (CH_3)_2\ddot{N}CH_2CH_2CH_2CH{=}CH_2$$

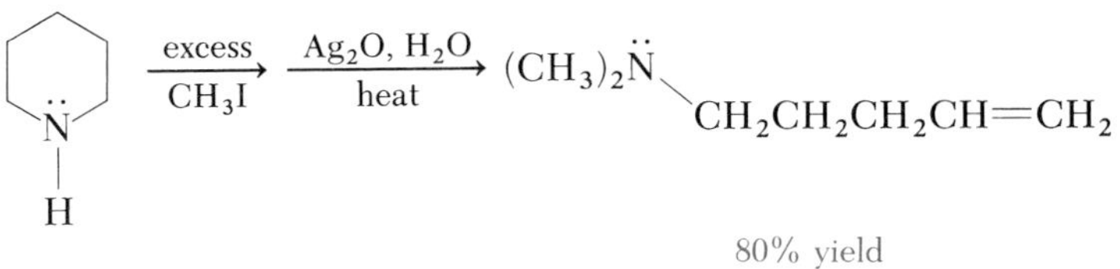

piperidine

80% yield
4-dimethylamino-1-pentene

Eqn. 20.40

$$[(CH_3)_2CH]_2CHCH_2\ddot{N}H_2 \xrightarrow[CH_3I]{\text{excess}} \xrightarrow[\text{heat}]{Ag_2O,\ H_2O} [(CH_3)_2CH]_2C{=}CH_2$$

73% yield

Recall that when haloalkanes undergo elimination reactions, it is often possible for a mixture of alkene products to form. The major product in such reactions is the *most* highly substituted alkene (Zaitzev orientation). It is also possible for quaternary ammonium ions to undergo elimination reactions that produce mixtures of alkenes. In such reactions we find that the *least* highly substituted alkene is the major product. This preference is known as **Hofmann orientation** and is illustrated in Figure 20.23. The major product of Hofmann orientation is the thermodynamically *less* stable alkene.

Figure 20.23 Competition of Hofmann and Zaitzev orientations for elimination. When the leaving group, X, is iodide ion, the Hofmann product accounts for only 30% of the elimination product. The remainder occurs with Zaitzev orientation, yielding the more highly substituted alkenes. However, if the leaving group is trimethylamine (the starting material being a quaternary ammonium salt), the Hofmann product predominates (89%).

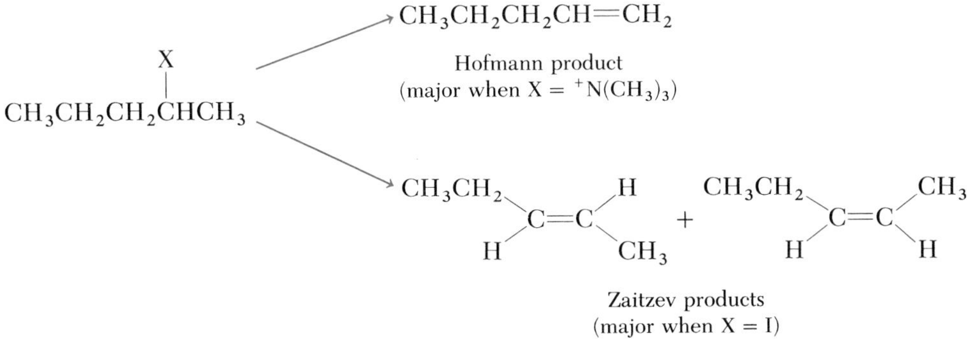

$$CH_3CH_2CH_2CH(X)CH_3 \longrightarrow CH_3CH_2CH_2CH{=}CH_2$$

Hofmann product
(major when X = $^+N(CH_3)_3$)

$$CH_3CH_2CH_2CH(X)CH_3 \longrightarrow CH_3CH_2CH{=}CHCH_3\ (trans) + CH_3CH_2CH{=}CHCH_3\ (cis)$$

Zaitzev products
(major when X = I)

Hofmann orientation can be rationalized by surmising that the mechanism for the elimination deviates from the mechanism involved in the usual E2 reaction. Specifically, we infer that carbon-hydrogen bond breaking is further developed in the activated complex of the rate-determining step than is carbon-nitrogen bond breaking.

In an extreme case, the β-hydrogen is removed *completely* before the leaving group departs. We refer to this mechanism as **E1cb** (elimination, first order, conjugate base), and it is shown in more detail below. In the Hofmann degradation of amines, the elimination mechanism *approaches* this extreme. There is greater carbon-hydrogen bond breaking in the activated complex than there is carbon-nitrogen bond breaking.

The question of orientation arises when there is more than one type of hydrogen atom attached to a carbon adjacent to the C—X bond. In the E1cb mechanism or in mechanisms approaching E1cb, the base preferentially removes a proton from the least highly substituted carbon atom, generating the more stable carbanion (or carbanionlike species). Secondary carbanions are less stable than primary carbanions because of the destabilizing electron donation by two alkyl groups rather than only one.

MECHANISM OF REACTION

The (Extreme) E1cb Reaction

Step 1 A base removes a proton to generate a carbanion.

$$R_2C(\ddot{X}:)-CH_2(H) + :B \rightleftharpoons R_2C(\ddot{X}:)-\ddot{C}H_2^{-} + H-\overset{+}{B}$$

Step 2 The halide departs to generate the alkene.

$$R_2C(\ddot{X}:)-\ddot{C}H_2^{-} \longrightarrow R_2C{=}CH_2 + :\ddot{X}:^{-}$$

An example of the selectivity of the Hofmann degradation of amines is given in Equation 20.41.

Eqn. 20.41

$$\text{ethylpropylamine} \xrightarrow[CH_3I]{\text{excess}} \text{ethylpropyldimethylammonium } :\ddot{I}:^{-} \xrightarrow[\text{heat}]{Ag_2O,\ H_2O} \underset{\substack{98\%\ \text{yield}\\ \text{ethene}}}{H_2C{=}CH_2} + \underset{\substack{2\%\ \text{yield}\\ \text{propene}}}{H_2C{=}CHCH_3}$$

The major alkene product is derived from the alkyl group with the less highly substituted β-carbon.

PROBLEM 20.24 The hydroxyl group is a poor leaving group. Upon protonation, however, it is changed to a good leaving group. Why could we not use protonation rather than methylation to convert an amino group from a poor to a good leaving group for an elimination reaction?

PROBLEM 20.25 For each of the synthetic conversions shown in Equations 20.38–20.40, write the structure of all intermediate compounds produced in the reaction sequence.

PROBLEM 20.26 In the Hofmann degradation of amines we use iodomethane to generate a quaternary ammonium salt. What is the advantage of iodomethane over iodoethane?

PROBLEM 20.27 In the famous synthesis of cyclooctatetraene by Richard Willstatter with E. Waser and M. Heidelberger, the Hofmann degradation of amines was used three times. The last step of the synthesis is as shown below.

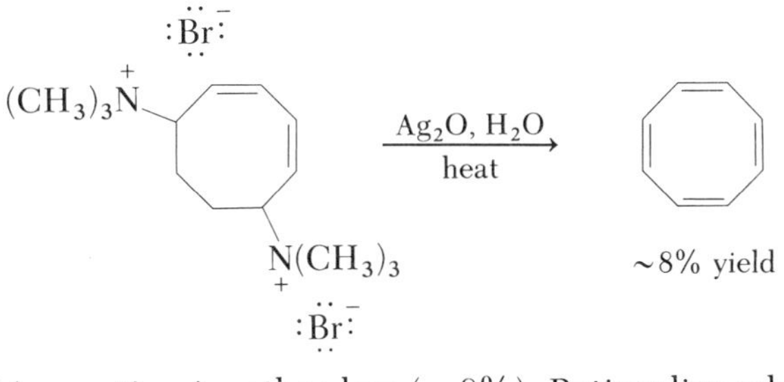

$:\ddot{Br}:^-$ $(CH_3)_3\overset{+}{N}$ — cyclooctadiene — $\overset{+}{N}(CH_3)_3$ $:\ddot{Br}:^-$ $\xrightarrow[\text{heat}]{Ag_2O,\ H_2O}$ cyclooctatetraene

~8% yield

The yield in this reaction is rather low (~8%). Rationalize why this reaction might still be more efficient than the direct dehydrohalogenation of the dibromide structure shown below (also an intermediate in the overall synthesis). Your explanation should take into account the mechanisms for the two processes and the stereochemistry of the system.

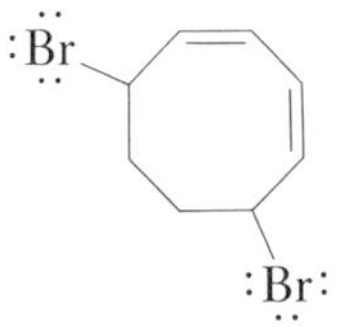

$:\ddot{Br}$ — cyclooctadiene — $:\ddot{Br}:$

THE COPE ELIMINATION

The **Cope elimination** is another method for the cleavage of carbon-nitrogen bonds of amines. This approach again involves the creation of a positive charge at the nitrogen of the linkage to be broken, but in a decidedly different manner. In the Cope elimination we treat a *tertiary* amine with hydrogen peroxide to generate a tertiary **amine oxide.** An amine oxide is a zwitterion (an ion with two charged atoms). There is a positive charge on nitrogen and a negative charge on the oxygen atom directly attached to it. Triethylamine oxide (**20.9**) is an example of an amine oxide.

$$(CH_3CH_2)_3\overset{+}{N}-\ddot{\underset{..}{O}}:^-$$

triethylamine oxide

20.9

On heating, an amine oxide undergoes an intramolecular proton abstraction reaction with cleavage of the carbon-nitrogen bond. The synthesis of methylenecyclopentane via an amine oxide is given below as an illustration of the mechanism.

MECHANISM OF REACTION

The Cope Elimination

Step 1 Oxidation of the tertiary amine

$$\text{C}_5\text{H}_8(\text{H})-\text{CH}_2-\ddot{\text{N}}(\text{CH}_3)_2 \xrightarrow[\text{H}_2\text{O}]{\text{H}_2\text{O}_2} \text{C}_5\text{H}_8(\text{H})-\text{CH}_2-\overset{+}{\text{N}}(\text{CH}_3)_2-\ddot{\text{O}}{:}^-$$

Step 2 Concerted intramolecular elimination

$$\text{C}_5\text{H}_8(\text{H})-\text{CH}_2-\overset{+}{\text{N}}(\text{CH}_3)_2-\ddot{\text{O}}{:}^- \xrightarrow{\text{heat}} \text{C}_5\text{H}_8{=}\text{CH}_2 + \text{H}-\ddot{\text{O}}-\ddot{\text{N}}(\text{CH}_3)_2$$

61% yield   dimethylhydroxylamine

Notice that the base that removes the β-proton in the Cope elimination is the negatively charged oxygen atom of the amine oxide group. For this intramolecular concerted reaction to occur efficiently, the β-proton must be accessible to the amine oxide oxygen atom. It has been demonstrated that elimination is *syn*—the eliminated groups are lost from the same face of the developing double bond. Figure 20.24 depicts the stereospecific nature of the elimination.

Two more examples of Cope eliminations are given in Equations 20.42 and 20.43.

Eqn. 20.42

$$\text{C}_7\text{H}_{13}-\ddot{\text{N}}(\text{CH}_3)_2 \xrightarrow[\text{2. heat}]{\text{1. H}_2\text{O}_2,\ \text{H}_2\text{O}} \text{C}_7\text{H}_{12}$$

N,N-dimethylcycloheptylamine   92% yield cycloheptene

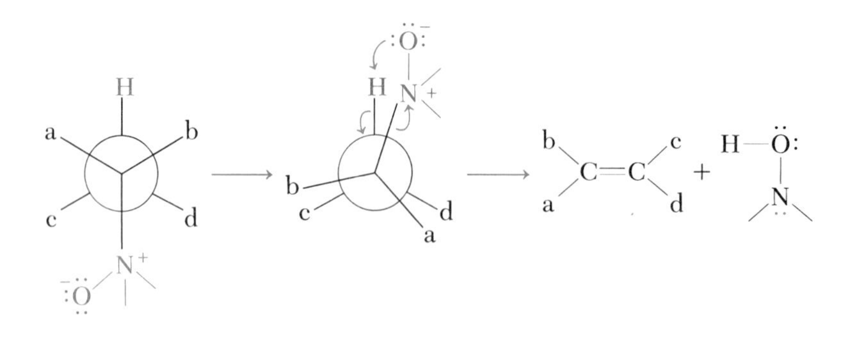

Figure 20.24 Stereochemistry of the Cope elimination. The eliminating groups must adopt a *syn*-periplanar relationship so that concerted intramolecular reaction can occur. This relationship is achieved in the eclipsed conformation.

Eqn. 20.43

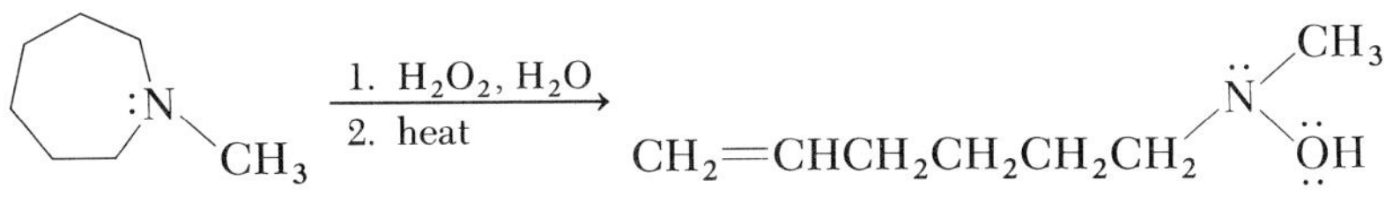

$$\text{N-methylhomopiperidine} \xrightarrow[\text{2. heat}]{\text{1. } H_2O_2,\ H_2O} CH_2{=}CHCH_2CH_2CH_2CH_2N(CH_3)OH$$

N-methylhomopiperidine — N-6-(1-hexenyl)-N-methylhydroxylamine, 53% yield

If there is more than one type of β-hydrogen position that can participate in the elimination reaction, the product distribution is generally the statistically expected one. That is, the greater the number of β-hydrogens of a particular type available, the greater the amount of product that results from the removal of one of them.

PROBLEM 20.28 Use stereochemical drawings to show why the intramolecular Cope elimination of *N*-methylpiperidine-*N*-oxide (shown below) does not occur.

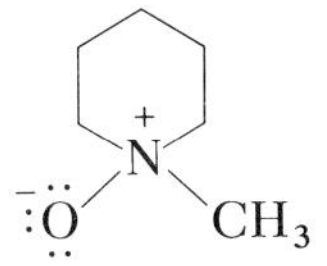

PROBLEM 20.29 Suppose you wish to convert 2,3-dimethyl-3-aminopentane to 2,4-dimethyl-2-pentene using a Cope elimination. It is first necessary to prepare the tertiary amine by substituting two methyl groups for hydrogens on the amino function. How would you accomplish this initial conversion without the formation of a significant amount of quaternary ammonium salt?

PROBLEM 20.30 Consider the Cope elimination applied to (2*R*,3*R*)-3-dimethylamino-4,4-dimethyl-2-phenylpentane. Give the structure of the expected product, keeping in mind the concerted nature of the reaction. Is this product different from that expected from the (2*S*,3*S*)- or (2*R*,3*S*)- isomers? Explain.

AN EXCURSION INTO ALKENE SYNTHESES USING ANALOGUES OF THE COPE ELIMINATION

The Cope elimination and the Hofmann degradation of amines are useful reactions for the cleavage of carbon-nitrogen bonds of amines and the formation of alkenes. Often, as in the Willstatter synthesis of cyclooctatetraene, it is advantageous to convert a haloalkane to an amine before performing an elimination reaction to synthesize an alkene. However, there are sometimes difficulties with these elimination reactions. Alternative but analogous methods for the synthesis of alkenes from haloalkanes have been devised to complement the Cope elimination. We will consider two of these methods here.

We can consider sulfoxides and selenoxides to be analogues of amine oxides. Sulfoxides and selenoxides bear an oxygen atom with a formal negative charge in much the same manner as do amine oxides. Moreover, these compounds are readily available from haloalkanes, as are the amine oxides, and they also undergo a facile *syn* elimination process. Two alkene syntheses proceeding through *selenoxide* intermediates are shown in Equations 20.44 and 20.45.

Eqn. 20.44

$$C_{10}H_{21}-CH_2-CH_2-\ddot{\underset{..}{Br}}: \xrightarrow[\text{ethanol}]{C_6H_5SeNa} C_{10}H_{21}-CH_2-CH_2-\ddot{\underset{..}{Se}}-C_6H_5$$

1-bromododecane

$$C_{10}H_{21}-CH_2-CH_2-\ddot{\underset{..}{Se}}-C_6H_5 \xrightarrow[20°,\ 20\text{ hr}]{H_2O_2,\ THF} C_{10}H_{21}-CH=CH_2$$

77% yield (overall) 1-dodecene

Eqn. 20.45

$$C_6H_{11}-CH_2\ddot{\underset{..}{Br}}: \xrightarrow{C_6H_5SeNa,\ \text{ethanol}} C_6H_{11}-CH_2\ddot{\underset{..}{Se}}C_6H_5$$

bromomethylcyclohexane

$$C_6H_{11}-CH_2-\ddot{\underset{..}{Se}}C_6H_5 \xrightarrow[25°,\ 9.5\text{ hr}]{H_2O_2,\ THF} C_6H_{10}=CH_2$$

92% yield (two steps) methylenecyclohexane

Both of these examples involve selenoxide intermediates that decompose readily even under the mild conditions of their formation. The hydrogen peroxide generates the selenoxide intermediate, just as it generates amine oxides. However, even at room temperature the selenoxide undergoes the *syn* elimination.

MECHANISM OF REACTION

Syn Elimination of Selenoxides

Step 1 Oxidation of the organoselenium compound

$$\underset{H}{RCH}-\underset{:\underset{..}{Se}C_6H_5}{CH_2} \xrightarrow{H_2O_2} \underset{H}{RCH}-\underset{\overset{+}{\underset{..}{Se}}C_6H_5(-\ddot{\underset{..}{O}}:^-)}{CH_2} + H_2\ddot{\underset{..}{O}}$$

Step 2 Concerted elimination reaction

$$\underset{H}{RCH}-\underset{\overset{+}{Se}C_6H_5(-\ddot{\underset{..}{O}}:^-)}{CH_2} \longrightarrow RCH=CH_2 + H-\ddot{\underset{..}{O}}-\ddot{\underset{..}{Se}}C_6H_5$$

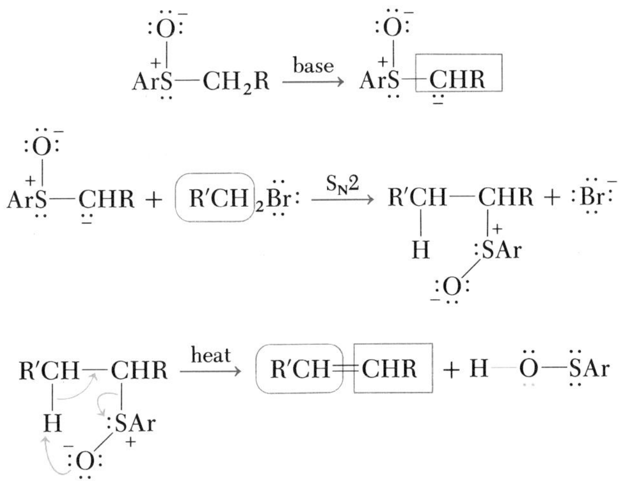

Figure 20.25 Use of a sulfoxide for the synthesis of an olefin. The boxed portions of each of the reagents are combined in the alkene product. The alkylation of the sulfoxide proceeds most favorably with primary haloalkanes (typical of S_N2 reactions). The thermolysis of the sulfoxide proceeds with *syn* elimination as do the previously discussed reactions.

$$\mathrm{Ar\overset{+}{S}(O^-)\!-\!CH_2R \xrightarrow{\text{base}} Ar\overset{+}{S}(O^-)\!-\!\ddot{C}HR}$$

$$\mathrm{Ar\overset{+}{S}(O^-)\!-\!\ddot{C}HR + R'CH_2Br: \xrightarrow{S_N2} R'CH(H)\!-\!CHR(\overset{+}{S}Ar\!-\!O^-) + :Br:^-}$$

$$\mathrm{R'CH(H)\!-\!CHR(\overset{+}{S}Ar\!-\!O^-) \xrightarrow{\text{heat}} R'CH\!=\!CHR + H\!-\!\ddot{O}\!-\!\ddot{S}Ar}$$

A variation on this procedure involves reaction of a suitable sulfoxide with base and a haloalkane (see Figure 20.25). An example of the use of this process for the synthesis of an alkene is shown in Equation 20.46.

Eqn. 20.46

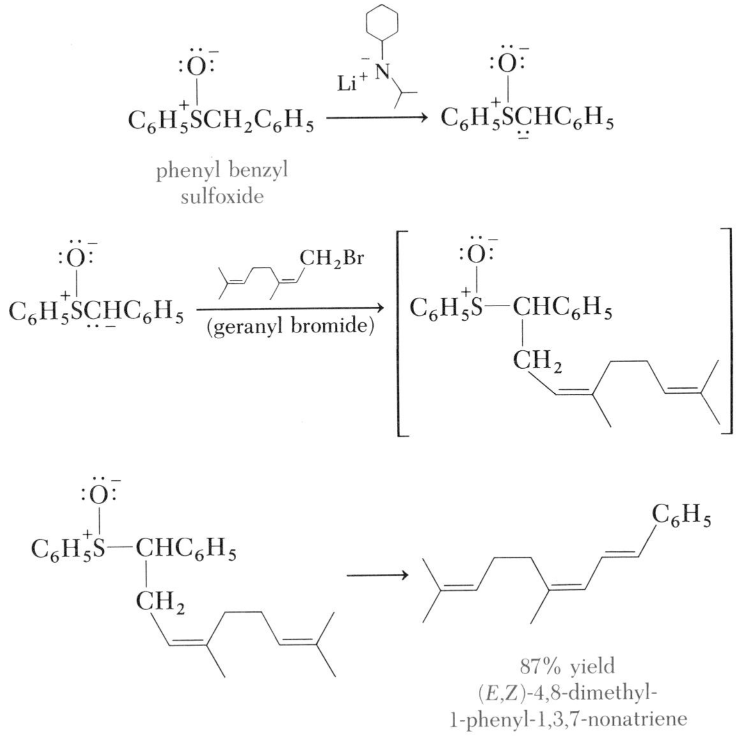

$$\mathrm{C_6H_5\overset{+}{S}(O^-)CH_2C_6H_5 \xrightarrow{Li^+\ ^-N(C_6H_{11})(CH(CH_3)_2)} C_6H_5\overset{+}{S}(O^-)\ddot{C}HC_6H_5}$$

phenyl benzyl sulfoxide

$$\mathrm{C_6H_5\overset{+}{S}(O^-)\ddot{C}HC_6H_5 \xrightarrow[\text{(geranyl bromide)}]{CH_2Br} \left[C_6H_5\overset{+}{S}(O^-)\!-\!CHC_6H_5(CH_2\text{-geranyl})\right]}$$

$$\mathrm{C_6H_5\overset{+}{S}(O^-)\!-\!CHC_6H_5(CH_2\ldots) \longrightarrow}$$

87% yield
(*E*,*Z*)-4,8-dimethyl-1-phenyl-1,3,7-nonatriene

The entire reaction scheme of Equation 20.46 is a *one-pot* synthesis, that is, it is performed without isolation of any intermediates. The base used to generate the anion from benzyl phenyl sulfoxide is lithium cyclohexyl isopropyl amide, a strong, non-nucleophilic base. Notice that the α-hydrogen atoms of sulfoxides are rather like those of aldehydes and ketones in that they are somewhat acidic and can be removed as protons by suitable bases.

20.10 Structural Elucidation of Amines

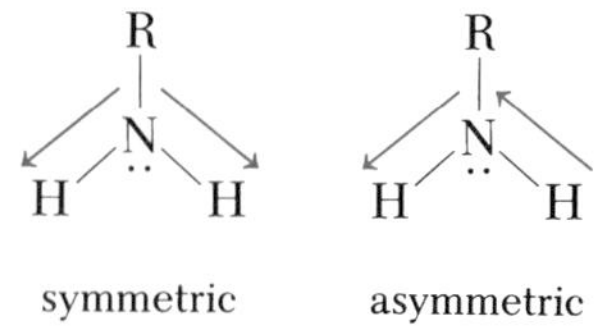

R R
N N
H H H H

symmetric asymmetric

Figure 20.26 Symmetric and asymmetric stretching of RNH_2. Primary amines exhibit two nitrogen-hydrogen stretching bands in the 3300–3500 cm^{-1} of the infrared spectrum. These two bands are associated with the symmetric and asymmetric stretchings of the two nitrogen-hydrogen bonds.

INFRARED SPECTRA

Primary and secondary amines exhibit characteristic nitrogen-hydrogen stretching bands in the 3300–3500 cm^{-1} region of the infrared spectrum. We can sometimes differentiate primary from secondary amines by their absorptions in this region. Primary amines exhibit *two* bands in this region because of symmetric and asymmetric stretching of the nitrogen-hydrogen bonds. These vibrational modes are shown in Figure 20.26. Secondary amines have only one type of nitrogen-hydrogen stretch and correspondingly exhibit only a single absorption band.

Figures 20.27 and 20.28 show the IR spectra of typical primary and secondary amines.

Tertiary amines have no nitrogen-hydrogen bonds and thus exhibit no bands in the 3300–3500 cm^{-1} region. You should suspect that any basic organic compound exhibiting no IR absorption in this region is a tertiary amine.

^1H NMR SPECTRA

The ^1H NMR spectra of amines exhibit characteristic signals for H—C—N hydrogens near δ 2.7. The position of the amino hydrogens themselves varies considerably because of different degrees of hydrogen bonding (we have noted a similar effect with the hydroxyl hydrogens of alcohols). Furthermore, rapid

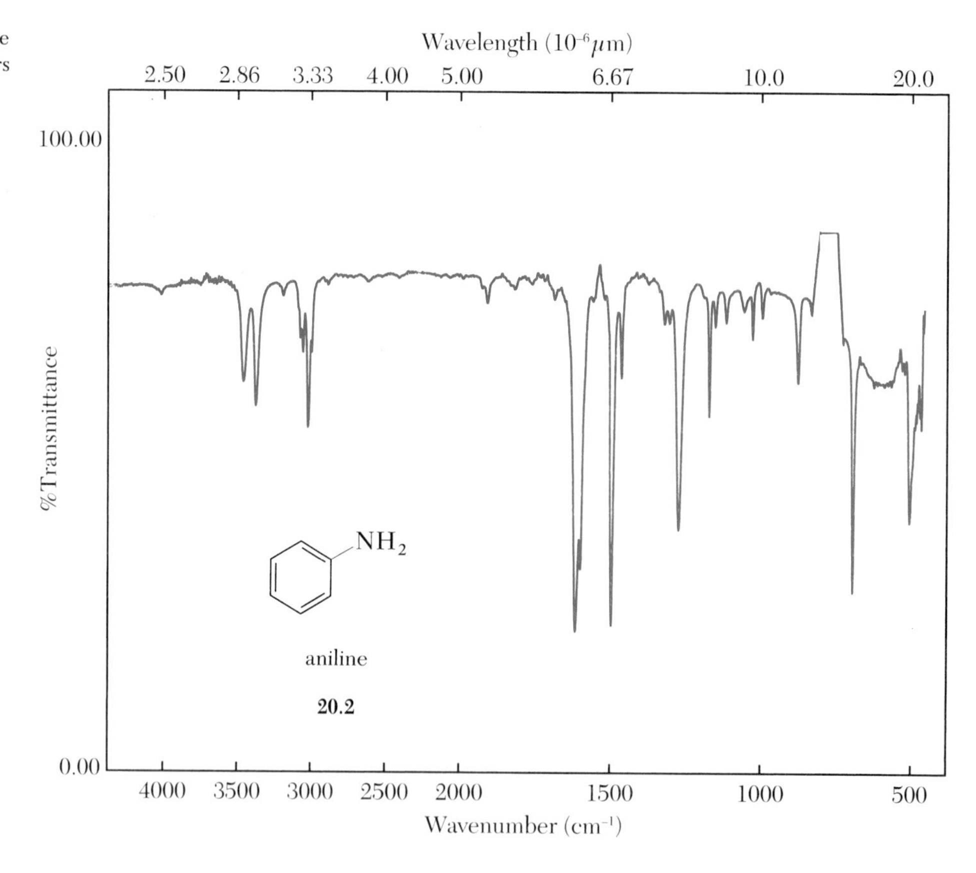

Figure 20.27 IR spectrum of aniline. The nitrogen-hydrogen stretching band appears as two peaks between 3300 and 3500 cm^{-1}.

Figure 20.28 IR spectrum of *N*-methylaniline. The IR spectrum of this secondary amine exhibits a single sharp band in the region 3300–3500 cm^{-1}.

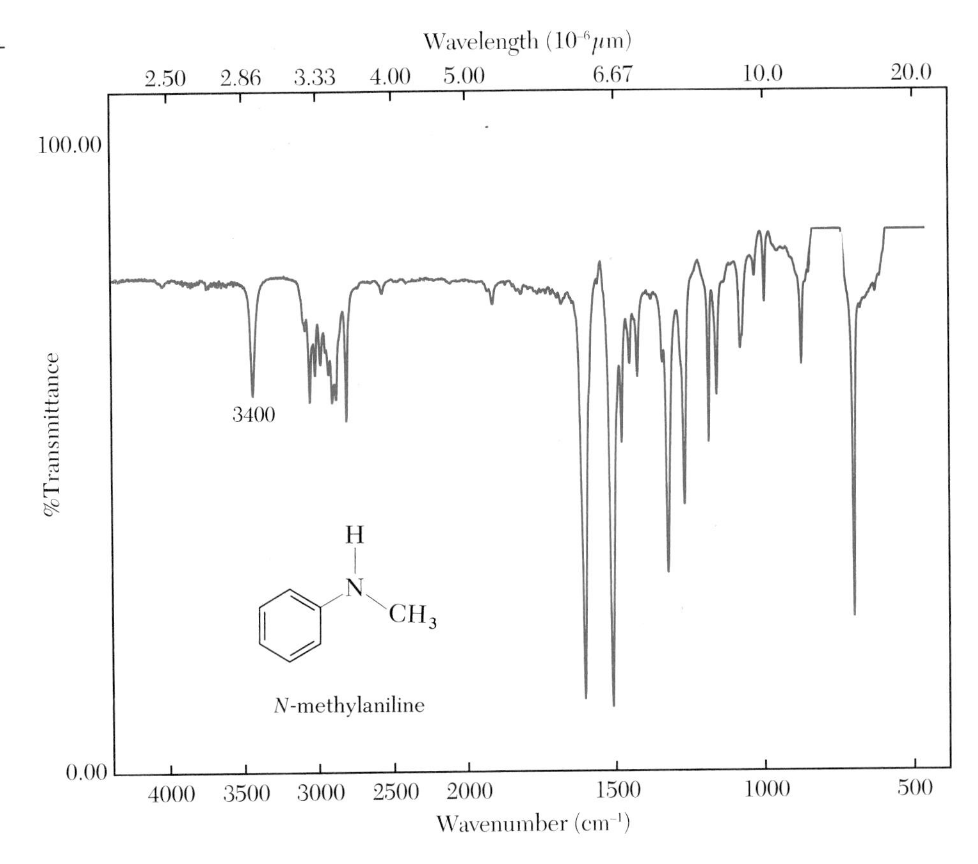

exchange of the amino hydrogens occurs in the presence of trace amounts of acidic substances. This exchange removes any coupling that might otherwise have been present. For example, in the spectrum of diethylamine we see only the ordinary signals (triplet + quartet) for the two equivalent ethyl groups and a singlet for the hydrogen attached to nitrogen. We see no coupling between the amino hydrogen and the methylene hydrogens because rapid exchange removes coupling that otherwise would be expected.

PROBLEM 20.31 Suggest structures that produce each of the following sets of data:

a. an amine of formula $C_4H_{11}N$ that exhibits no IR absorption in the region 3300–3500 cm^{-1}

b. all amines of formula $C_4H_{11}N$ that exhibit two IR peaks in the region 3300–3500 cm^{-1}

c. an amine of formula $C_4H_{11}N$ that exhibits a ^{1}H NMR spectrum consisting of two singlets

d. an amine of formula $C_4H_{11}N$ that exhibits a ^{13}C NMR spectrum consisting of four signals

e. an amine of formula $C_6H_{15}N$ that exhibits a single IR peak in the region 3300–3500 cm^{-1} and a ^{1}H NMR spectrum as follows: δ 0.4, broad, relative area 1; δ 1.0, doublet, relative area 12; δ 2.8, septet, relative area 2.

PROBLEM 20.32 On comparing the ^{13}C NMR spectra of methanol and methylamine we find that one compound exhibits a signal at 26.9 ppm downfield from TMS while the other has a signal at 48.0 ppm downfield from TMS. Which compound produces which signal? Explain your answer.

CHEMICAL METHODS

Since amines are basic, we can titrate them with standardized acid solutions to determine their equivalent weights. If we also know the molecular weight of the amine (e.g., by mass spectrometry, Chapter 25) we can deduce the number of amino groups present.

PROBLEM 20.33 Cadaverine, a basic compound responsible for the odor of decaying flesh, has a molecular weight of 102 g/mole. Moreover, it exhibits two bands in the IR region 3300–3500 cm^{-1}. In titration of cadaverine with a standardized acid solution, a 0.51 g sample of the amine requires 50.0 mL of a 0.2 *M* solution of hydrochloric acid to be exactly neutralized. How many amino groups are present per molecule of cadaverine? Suggest a structure for cadaverine, given that its ^{13}C NMR spectrum consists of three peaks.

We sometimes find it useful to employ the Hofmann exhaustive methylation and elimination procedure to assist in the structural determination of complex amines. Working back from the observed products, we can determine the structure of the starting amine.

For example, consider an application of this approach to determining the structure of amphetamine, a central nervous system stimulant. Amphetamine is an optically active substance of formula $C_9H_{13}N$. It exhibits two IR peaks in the region 3300–3500 cm^{-1} and produces benzoic acid on oxidation with hot, aqueous potassium permanganate.

The evidence presented thus far suggests that amphetamine is a chiral primary amine that is also a monosubstituted benzene derivative. The two structures shown in Figure 20.29 fit these experimental observations.

When we perform the exhaustive methylation followed by the Hofmann elimination, the product is 3-phenyl-1-propene. This product can arise only from structure **20.10.** The alternative structure, **20.11,** would produce 2-phenyl-1-propene in this reaction sequence.

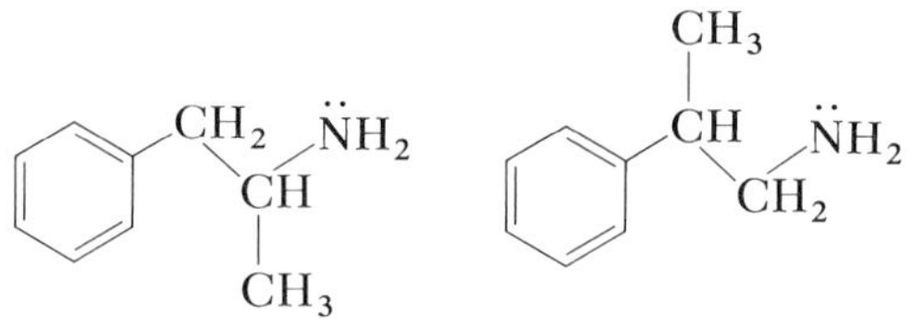

Figure 20.29 Possible structures for amphetamine based on preliminary evidence.

C_6H_5–CH_2–$CH(\ddot{N}H_2)$–CH_3 **20.10**

C_6H_5–$CH(CH_3)$–CH_2–$\ddot{N}H_2$ **20.11**

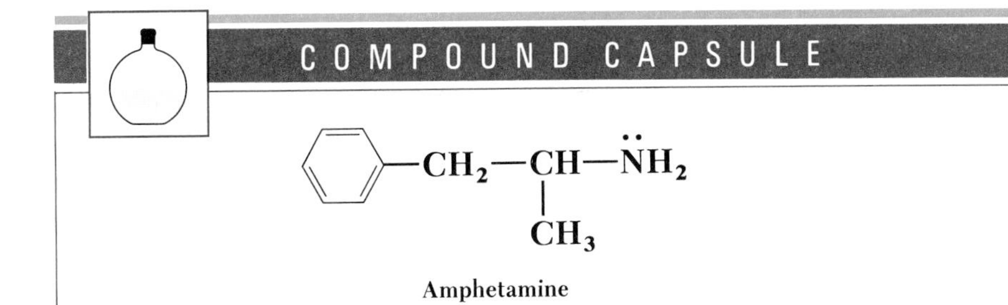

Amphetamine

Amphetamines, as a group, are amines related to α-benzylethylamine, (2-amino-1-phenylpropane). The simplest amphetamine structurally is 2-amino-1-phenylpropane itself, which is known commonly as *amphetamine*. Unfortunately, amphetamines have been widely abused as illegal drugs because they act as stimulants. Their legitimate uses include the treatment of narcolepsy (a sleep disorder) and hyperactivity in children.

In fact, amphetamine does not exist as a single compound but as two enantiomers. Being chiral, the two enantiomers interact differently with enzymes and thus differ in their physiological effects. The (+) enantiomer is more potent in its biological activity than is the (−) enantiomer. The pure (+) enantiomer has the trade name *dexedrine*, while the racemic mixture is known as *benzedrine*.

A structurally related amphetamine is *methadrine*, shown below. Methadrine is a heavily abused drug commonly known as "speed."

$$C_6H_5-CH_2-\underset{\underset{CH_3}{|}}{CH}-\ddot{N}H-CH_3$$

PROBLEM 20.34 The active compound in the venom of the red fire ant has the formula $C_{17}H_{35}N$. When it is treated with an excess of iodomethane and the product warmed with silver oxide and water, we obtain a mixture of the following products:

$$H_2C{=}CHCH_2CH_2CH_2\overset{\overset{\ddot{N}(CH_3)_2}{|}}{C}HCH_2(CH_2)_9CH_3$$

$$CH_3\overset{\overset{\ddot{N}(CH_3)_2}{|}}{C}HCH_2CH_2CH{=}CHCH_2(CH_2)_9CH_3$$

$$CH_3\overset{\overset{\ddot{N}(CH_3)_2}{|}}{C}HCH_2CH_2CH_2CH{=}CHCH_2(CH_2)_8CH_3$$

Suggest a structure for the active compound.

Summary

- Amines are organic bases, significantly weaker in strength than hydroxide or alkoxide bases, but nonetheless sufficiently basic to serve as proton acceptors in a variety of reactions.
- The base strength of a particular amine depends on the availability of an electron pair for donation, solvent stabilization of the protonated amine, and on steric interference with its approach to an acidic site.
- Amines, like ammonia, can also serve as nucleophiles in both substitution and addition reactions.
- In these substitution reactions, more highly substituted amines or quaternary ammonium salts are formed.
- Nucleophilic addition reactions of amines, particularly with carbonyl compounds, provide us with a host of useful synthetic techniques.
- Primary alkyl and aromatic amines undergo reaction with nitrosonium ion to generate alkyl (or aryl) diazonium ions. These species are highly reactive and undergo a variety of subsequent reactions.
- Alkyl diazonium ions rapidly break apart to form nitrogen and carbocations. The organic products of diazotization of primary alkylamines are those of carbocation reaction.
- Aromatic diazonium ions are significantly more stable than are alkyl diazonium ions. Thus we are able to use them in a variety of synthetic procedures. These procedures complement and supplement the previously discussed electrophilic aromatic substitution reactions for organic syntheses.
- It is difficult to cleave the carbon-nitrogen bond of an amine. To facilitate its cleavage we must first render the nitrogen positively charged; it can then leave as part of a neutral species rather than as a negatively charged species. The Hofmann degradation and the Cope elimination are two viable approaches.

Terms to Remember

amine
ammonium ion
quaternary ammonium ion
nucleophilic addition reaction
α-effect
Gabriel synthesis
Bechamp reduction
reductive amination
iminium ion
permethylation
Clarke-Eschweiler synthesis
nitrosonium ion
diazotization
diazonium salt
Sandmeyer reaction
phenol
azo compound
Hofmann degradation
Hofmann orientation
E1cb
Cope elimination
amine oxide

Reactions of Synthetic Utility

137. $RX + R'_2NH \longrightarrow RR'_2N$ — 20.5

overalkylation occurs

138. $RX + NH_3 \longrightarrow R_4N^+X^-$ — 20.5

139. $RX + \text{potassium phthalimide} \longrightarrow \xrightarrow[\text{aq base or } H_2N\text{—}NH_2]{\text{aq acid or}} RNH_2$ — 20.5

140. $RCN \xrightarrow{\text{reducing agent}} RCH_2NH_2$ reducing agents: $LiAlH_4$, H_2, Pd/C	**20.5**
141. $ArNO_2 \xrightarrow[NiCl_2]{NaBH_4} ArNH_2$	**20.6**
142. $ArNO_2 \xrightarrow[\text{with acid}]{\text{electropositive metal}} ArNH_2$ reagents: Fe/acetic acid, Sn/HCl	**20.6**
143. $ArNO_2 \xrightarrow[RuCl_2(PPh_3)_3]{H_2} ArNH_2$	**20.6**
144. $ArNO_2 \xrightarrow[CoS_x]{H_2O} ArNH_2$	**20.6**
145. $RN{=}CR'_2 \xrightarrow{\text{reducing agent}} RNHCHR'_2$ reducing agents: H_2/PtO_2, $NaBH_4$	**20.7**
146. $R_2NH + R'CHO \xrightarrow{\text{reductive amination}} R_2NCH_2R'$ reducing agents: H_2/Ni, H_2/PtO_2, $NaBH_3CN$	**20.7**
147. $R_2C{=}NOH \xrightarrow{LiAlH_4} R_2CHNH_2$	**20.7**
148. $RNH_2 \xrightarrow[HCOOH]{H_2C{=}O} RN(CH_3)_2$ permethylation	**20.7**
149. $ArNH_2 \xrightarrow[H_2SO_4]{1.\ NaNO_2} \xrightarrow{2.\ H_3PO_2} ArH$	**20.8**
150. $ArNH_2 \xrightarrow[H_2SO_4]{1.\ NaNO_2} \xrightarrow{2.\ CuX} ArX$ X = Cl, Br, CN	**20.8**
151. $ArNH_2 \xrightarrow[H_2SO_4]{1.\ NaNO_2} \xrightarrow{2.\ KI} ArI$	**20.8**
152. $ArNH_2 \xrightarrow[H_2SO_4]{1.\ NaNO_2} \xrightarrow[3.\ \text{heat}]{2.\ HBF_4} ArF$	**20.8**
153. $ArNH_2 \xrightarrow[H_2SO_4]{1.\ NaNO_2} \xrightarrow[\text{heat}]{2.\ H_2O} ArOH$	**20.8**
154. $ArNH_2 \xrightarrow[H_2SO_4]{1.\ NaNO_2} \xrightarrow{2.\ Ar'X} Ar{-}N{=}N{-}Ar'X$ X = —OH, —NR_2	**20.8**
155. $R_2NH \xrightarrow{NaNO_2,\ H_2SO_4} R_2N{-}N{=}O$	**20.8**
156. $-\underset{H}{\underset{\mid}{\overset{\mid}{C}}}-\underset{\mid}{\overset{^{+}N(CH_3)_3}{\overset{\mid}{C}}}- \xrightarrow{Ag_2O,\ \text{heat}} \;>C{=}C<$	**20.9**

157. $-\overset{|}{\underset{\mathrm{H}}{\mathrm{C}}}-\overset{\mathrm{N(CH_3)_2}}{\underset{|}{\mathrm{C}}}-\ \xrightarrow[\text{heat}]{H_2O_2,\ H_2O}\ \ >C=C<$ 20.9

158. $-\overset{|}{\underset{|}{\mathrm{C}}}-\overset{|}{\underset{\mathrm{SePh}}{\mathrm{C}}}-\ \xrightarrow{H_2O_2}\ \ >C=C<$ 20.9

Additional Problems

20.35 Draw structures for each of the following compounds:

a. dibenzylamine
b. *tert*-butylamine
c. *N*,*N*-dimethylaniline
d. *N*-nitroso-*N*-methylaniline
e. trimethylammonium chloride
f. *meso*-2,3-diaminobutane
g. cyclobutyltrimethylammonium iodide
h. *N*-methyl-2-(1-cyclohexylpropyl) amine
i. benzenediazonium chloride
j. triisobutylamine
k. methylbutylamine
l. 2-(2-methylbutyl) amine
m. acetophenone *N*-methylimine
n. cyclohexanone *N*-benzylimine

20.36 From each pair of compounds, choose the one that has the indicated characteristic (do not use tables of data). Explain your choice in each case.

a. higher boiling temperature: *n*-propylamine or ethylmethylamine
b. more basic: 4-nitroaniline or 4-methoxyaniline
c. more basic: pyridine or piperidine (shown below)

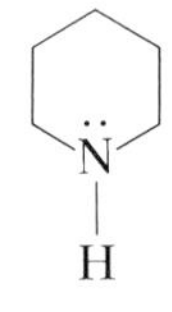

piperidine

d. more basic: pyridine or pyrrole
e. forms enamines in reaction with ketones: 1-propylamine or ethylmethylamine
f. forms an *N*-nitrosamine on treatment with nitrous acid: 4-ethylaniline or *N*-ethylaniline
g. undergoes a diazo coupling reaction with benzenediazonium ion: phenol or chlorobenzene
h. cannot be prepared by reduction of a nitrile: 1-propylamine or ethylmethylamine
i. fails to react with iodomethane to give a quaternary salt: pyrrole or pyrrolidine (shown below)

pyrrolidine

20.37 Many amines are shipped by chemical suppliers in the form of their hydrochloride salts. Describe the laboratory operations you would perform to transform the hydrochloride salt to the free amine.

20.38 Describe the laboratory operations you would need to perform to separate a mixture of aniline and nitrobenzene (without using distillation).

20.39 Give the organic product in each of the following reactions:
a. 3,5-dichloronitrobenzene treated with Zn/HCl
b. isopropylamine treated with an excess of iodomethane
c. aniline treated with hydrogen chloride
d. *N*,*N*-dimethyl-1-amino-4-pentene *N*-oxide upon heating
e. 2,3-butanedione treated with 1,2-diaminobenzene (product has the formula $C_{10}H_{10}N_2$)

20.40 Give the products you would obtain by treating 4-methoxybenzenediazonium sulfate with each of the following:
a. cuprous chloride
b. hypophosphorous acid
c. HBF_4, followed by heating
d. *p*-cresol

20.41 Suggest how to accomplish each of the following conversions. (More than one step may be required in each.)
a. benzene to aniline
b. aniline to benzylamine
c. benzene to 1,3,5-tribromobenzene
d. 2-propanol to isopropylamine
e. 2-nitroaniline to *o*-nitrobenzonitrile
f. aniline to *p*-dimethylaminoazobenzene
g. 1-pentanol to 1-pentylamine
h. acetophenone to $PhCOCH_2NH_2$
i. toluene to 3-bromo-4-methylaniline
j. toluene to 2,6-dibromo-4-methylaniline
k. *N*,*N*-diethylaniline to 4-nitroso-*N*,*N*-diethylaniline
l. benzene to *p*-bromobenzonitrile

20.42 In very dilute solution, 1-(3-bromopropyl)dimethylamine undergoes an intramolecular reaction to form a crystalline salt of formula $C_5H_{12}NBr$. What is the structure of this product? Explain how it forms.

20.43 Deduce the structure of a compound of formula $C_3H_{10}N_2$ that is obtained by treating 1,3-dibromopropane with potassium phthalimide, followed by treatment with hydrazine and water.

20.44 When cyclopentylcarbinylamine (structure shown below) is treated with sodium nitrite in cold dilute sulfuric acid there is formed in 76% yield a product of formula $C_6H_{12}O$ that does not contain a five-membered ring. Suggest a structure for this product and a mechanism for its formation.

$CH_2\ddot{N}H_2$

cyclopentylcarbinylamine

20.45 A ketone shows no evidence of containing carbon-carbon double bonds. Its ^1H NMR spectrum shows no indication of methyl groups being present. On treatment with ammonia in the presence of hydrogen and nickel, the ketone is converted to an amine. A sample of the amine weighing 0.28 g is neutralized by 28.3 mL of 0.100 *M* hydrochloric acid solution. Suggest a structure for the ketone.

20.46 Compound *A*, of formula C_7H_7Cl, reacts with excess ammonia to produce *B*. A sample of *B* weighing 0.45 g is exactly titrated with 42.0 mL of 0.100 *M* hydrochloric acid solution. Treatment of *B* with hot, aqueous alkaline potassium permanganate solution yields *C* upon workup with aqueous acid. Compound *C* exhibits a broad IR absorption between 2500 and 3400 cm^{-1}. A sample of *C* weighing 0.14 g is exactly titrated by 11.5 mL of 0.100 *M* aqueous NaOH. Suggest structures for compounds *A*–*C*.

20.47 When 0.61 g of an amine is treated with nitrous acid, it evolves 187 mL of nitrogen gas, measured at STP. An alcohol isolated from the reaction mixture is found to give a positive iodoform test. Suggest a structure for the amine.

20.48 Hydrolysis of piperine (an alkaloid responsible for the sharp taste of pepper) yields an amine *D* of formula $C_5H_{11}N$. The IR and ^1H NMR spectra of *D* are shown below.

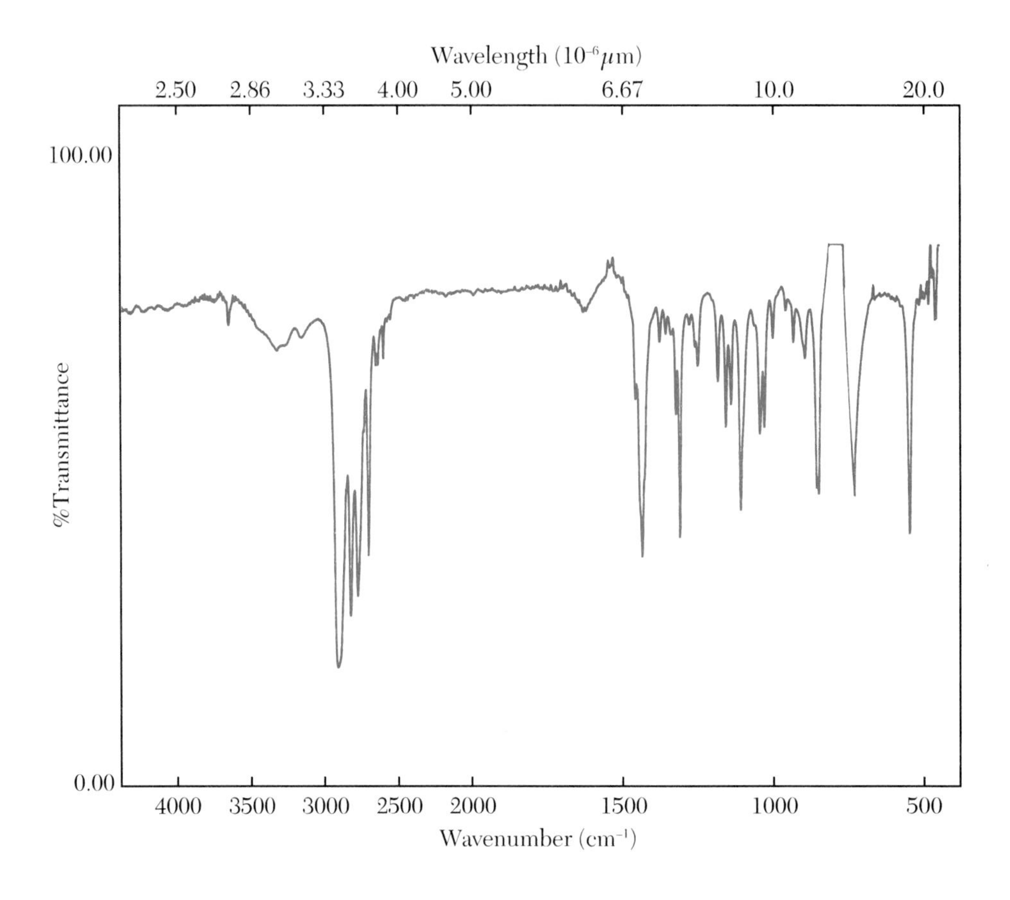

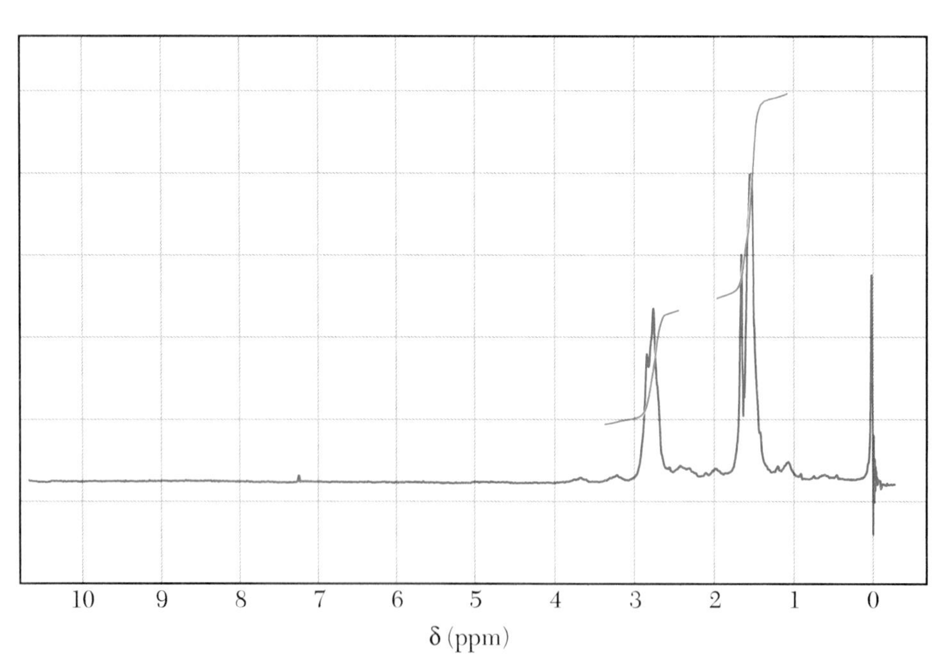

When D is treated with excess iodomethane, a quaternary salt is formed. Heating this salt with silver oxide/water yields E, of formula $C_7H_{15}N$. Compound E is also converted into a quaternary salt on treatment with excess iodomethane. Heating this quaternary salt with silver oxide/water yields F, of formula C_5H_8, whose IR and ^{1}H NMR spectra are shown below.

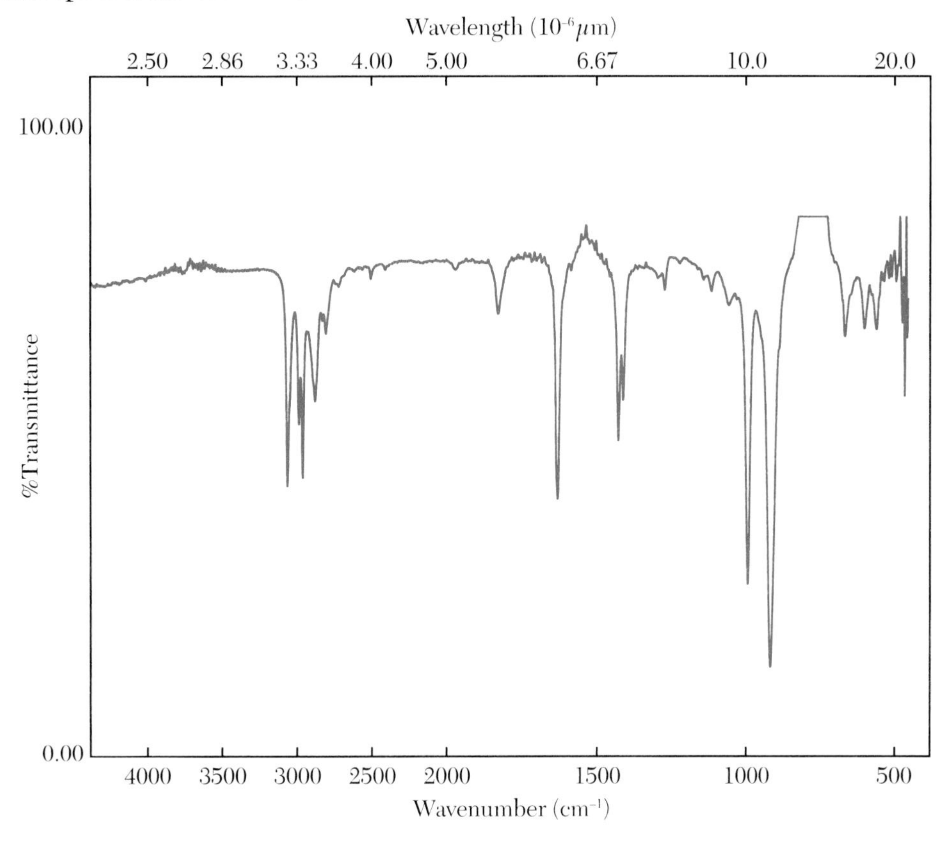

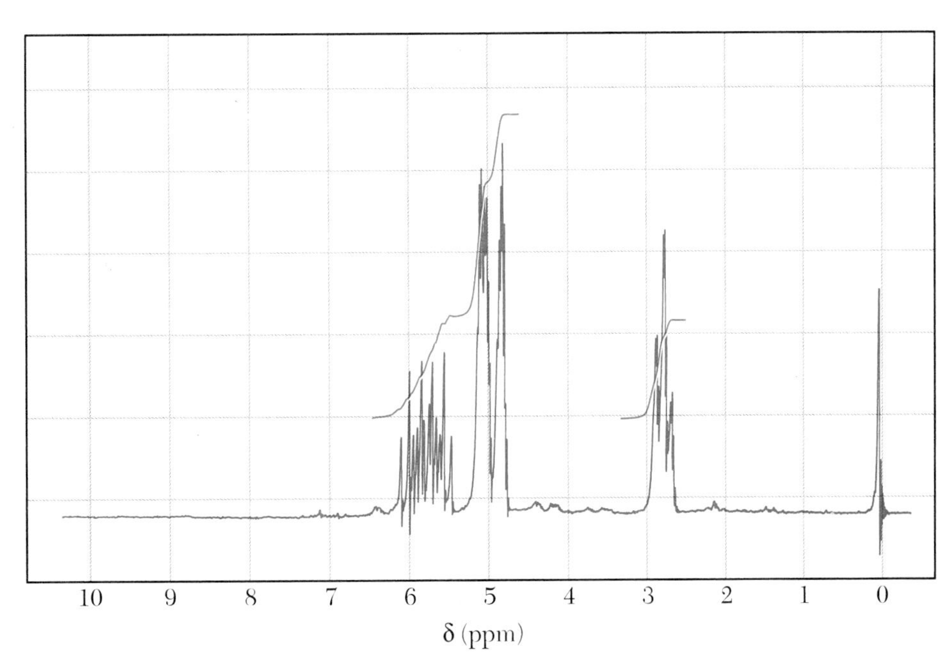

The ^{13}C NMR spectrum of *F* exhibits only three peaks (25.9, 27.8, and 47.9 ppm downfield from TMS). Suggest structures for compounds *D*, *E*, and *F*.

20.49 Suggest structures for compounds *G*–*K*.

$$\text{cyclopentanone} \xrightarrow[H_2/PtO_2]{NH_3} G\ (C_5H_{11}N)$$

$$G + \text{nitrous acid} \longrightarrow H\ (C_5H_8,\ \text{plus other products})$$

$$H + \text{1,3-butadiene} \longrightarrow I\ (C_9H_{14})$$

$$I + \text{cold, aq permanganate} \longrightarrow J$$

$$J + \text{acetone} \xrightarrow{\text{acid}} K\ (C_{12}H_{20}O_2,\ \text{a tricyclic compound})$$

20.50 Suggest structures for compounds *L*–*P*.

$$L\ (C_7H_6O_2NCl) + \text{hot, aq } Na\ddot{\underset{..}{O}}H \longrightarrow M\ (C_7H_7O_3N)$$

$$M \xrightarrow[H_2SO_4]{CrO_3} N\ (C_7H_5O_4N,\ {}^1H\ \text{NMR shown below})$$

$$N \xrightarrow{Sn/HCl} O$$

$$O \xrightarrow[H_2O]{Br_2} P\ (C_7H_4O_2NBr_3)$$

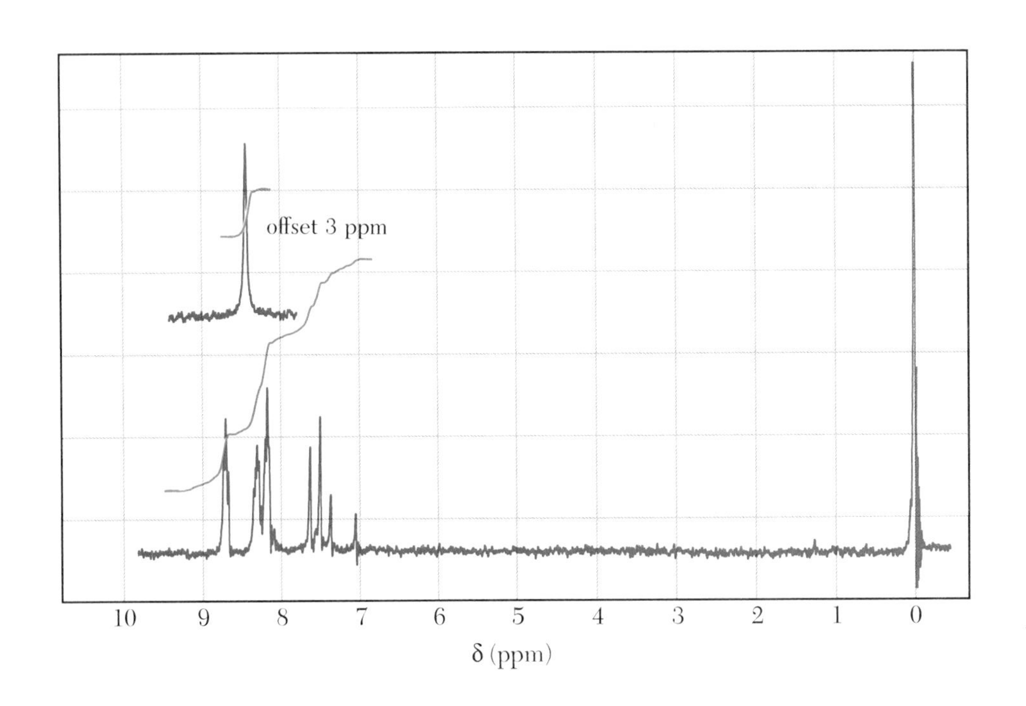

20.51 When (1S,2S)-1,2-diphenyl-2-aminoethanol is treated with excess iodomethane and the resulting quaternary ammonium salt is heated with silver oxide and water, the compound shown below is formed. Suggest a mechanism for the formation of this compound.

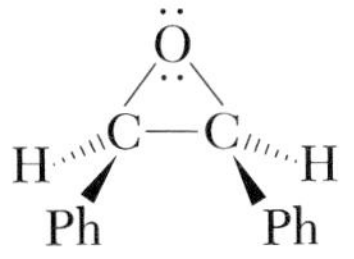

20.52 A primary amine was subjected to exhaustive methylation. The resulting quaternary ammonium salt was heated with silver oxide/water to give trimethylamine and an alkene. Ozonolysis and workup of the alkene yielded acetone as the only organic product. Suggest a structure for the amine.

20.53 The acid/base indicator methyl orange is an azo dye of the structure shown below. Suggest a route by which it could be synthesized using an azo coupling reaction.

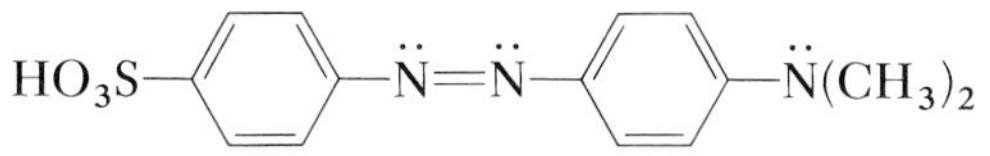

$HO_3S-C_6H_4-N{=}N-C_6H_4-N(CH_3)_2$

The use of methyl orange as an acid/base indicator depends on there being different colors for the parent compound and its protonated form. On which nitrogen do you expect protonation to occur? (*Hint:* Consider the possible resonance structures of the various conjugate acids that are possible.)

20.54 Diazomethane, H_2CN_2 (Chapter 13), undergoes interesting and useful reactions with many organic compounds. Suggest a mechanism for the following reaction:

cyclopentanone + $H_2\bar{C}-\overset{+}{N}{\equiv}N{:}$ ⟶ cyclohexanone + N_2

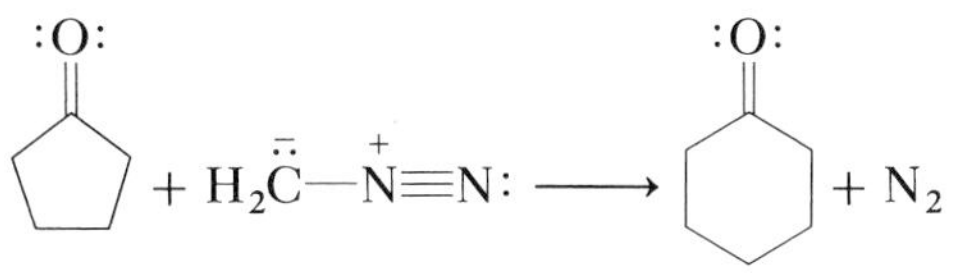

20.55 Suggest mechanisms for each of the following reactions:

a. o-phenylenediamine $\xrightarrow[\text{acid}]{\text{HONO}}$ benzotriazole (N–H)

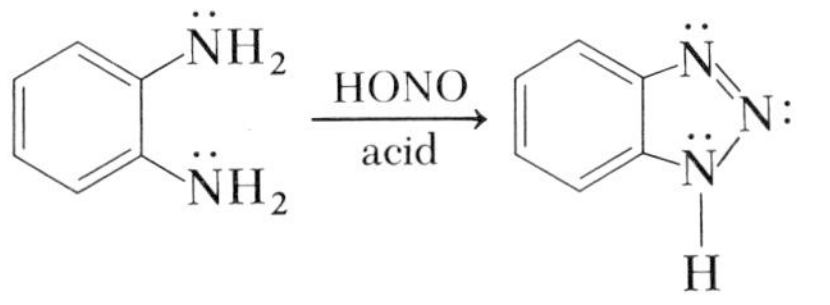

b. cycloheptenylmethanol (CH_2OH) $\xrightarrow{\text{PhSeCl}}$ bicyclic ether with SePh $\xrightarrow{H_2O_2}$ bicyclic ether with double bond

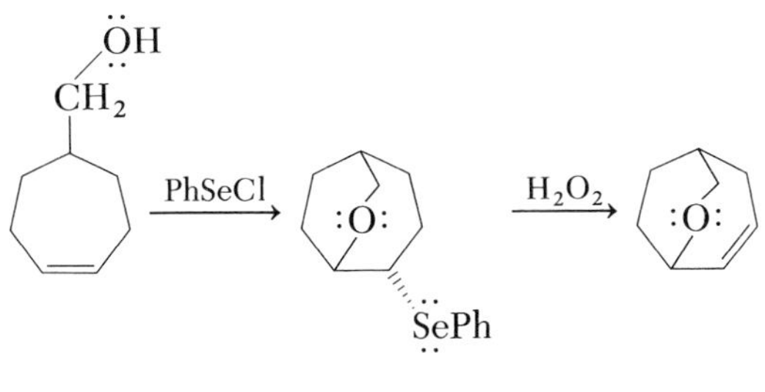

(*Hint:* Consider first electrophilic addition of PhSeCl to the double bond.)

20.56 Give structures for each of the compounds *Q*–*W*.

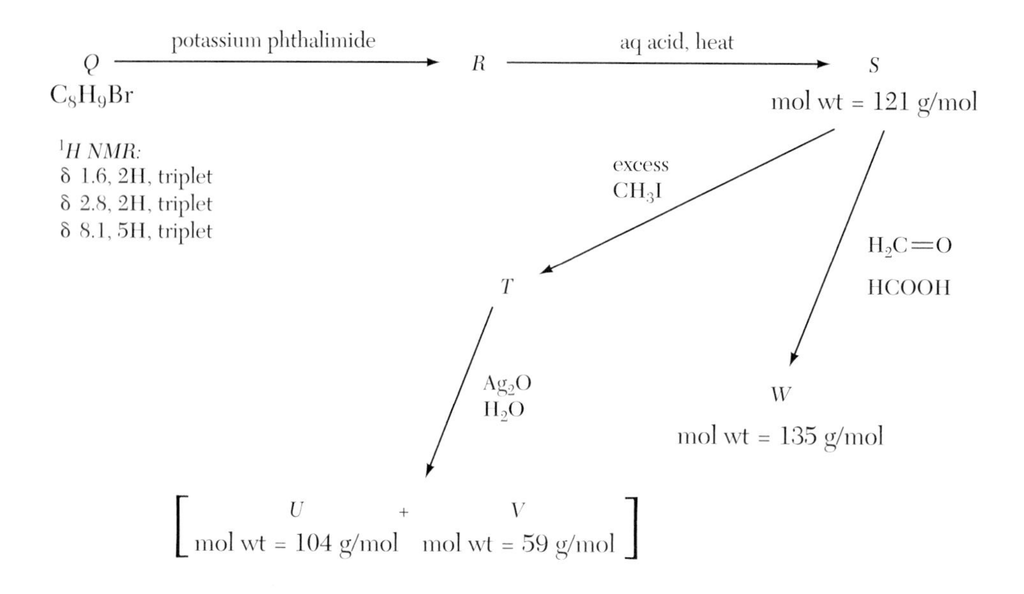

21 CHAPTER Carboxylic Acids

21.1 Introduction

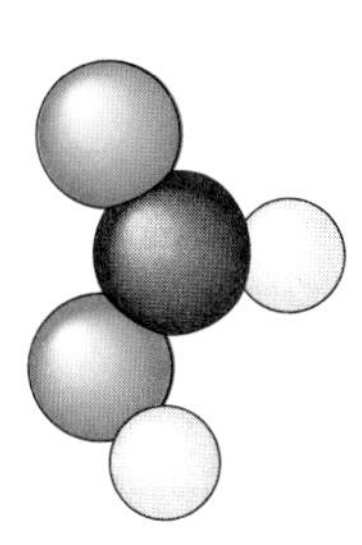

FUNDAMENTALS OF STRUCTURE

Carboxylic acids, as a group, are moderately acidic, with pK_a values typically in the 3–5 range. They are significantly stronger than weakly acidic organic compounds such as alcohols, alkynes, and phenols, but are much weaker than mineral acids such as sulfuric acid and hydrochloric acid (these strong acids are able to convert salts of carboxylic acids into the free carboxylic acids themselves).

The general structure of a carboxylic acid molecule is shown in Figure 21.1. A carboxylic acid consists of three parts: a hydroxyl group, a carbonyl group, and the "remainder." The carbonyl group and the hydroxyl group together constitute the **carboxyl group:**

$$-\underset{\underset{:\ddot{O}:}{\|}}{C}-\ddot{O}H$$

COMMON CARBOXYLIC ACIDS

The simplest carboxylic acids are colorless liquids with acrid odors. Formic acid, (HCOOH), for example, is a liquid with a highly irritating odor. It is the active component of the sting of some ants.

Acetic acid, CH_3COOH, produced by the oxidation of ethanol, is responsible for the characteristic odor and flavor of vinegar. In vinegar, acetic acid is usually present to the extent of ~4–5%. Acetic acid is also an important industrial chemical that finds extensive use in the production of plastics. Pure acetic acid freezes at 17 °C, allowing it to be purified of the presence of water by a freezing process. The pure acid is referred to as *glacial acetic acid.*

The odor of simple carboxylic acids is a dominant characteristic. Butyric acid, $CH_3CH_2CH_2COOH$, is responsible for the odor of rancid butter. Caproic,

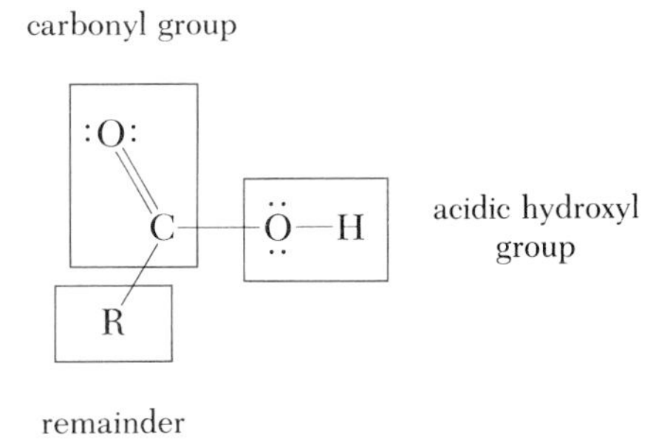

Figure 21.1 The parts of a carboxylic acid molecule. There is a structural resemblance both to alcohols and to aldehydes and ketones. However, the reactivity of both the hydroxyl and the carbonyl groups in carboxylic acids is significantly modified by their juxtaposition.

Table 21.1 Structures of Simple Carboxylic Acids Found in the Skin Secretions of Goats

Structure	Common Name
$CH_3CH_2CH_2CH_2CH_2COOH$	caproic acid
$CH_3CH_2CH_2CH_2CH_2CH_2CH_2COOH$	caprylic acid
$CH_3CH_2CH_2CH_2CH_2CH_2CH_2CH_2CH_2COOH$	capric acid

Table 21.2 Structures of Some Common Saturated Fatty Acids
The general formula is $CH_3(CH_2)_xCOOH$.

x	Name of Acid	Source
10	lauric acid	coconut oil
12	myristic acid	nutmeg seed
14	palmitic acid	palm oil
16	stearic acid	animal fats

caprylic, and capric acids, shown in Table 21.1, are all present in the skin secretions of goats and are responsible for the characteristic odor of these animals. The common names of all of these acids are derived from the Latin word for goat, *caper*. Caprylic and capric acids also occur in coconut oil.

Notice that each of the acids in Tables 21.1 and 21.2 contains an even number of carbon atoms. Other long-chain naturally occurring carboxylic acids also contain even numbers of carbon atoms. We commonly refer to such naturally occurring carboxylic acids containing 10–22 carbon atoms as **fatty acids.** The characteristic of having an even number of carbon atoms reflects their common mode of biosynthesis from units containing two carbon atoms. Some common fatty acids are listed in Table 21.2.

The metabolism of carboxylic acids in biological systems shows that chains are also cleaved by successive removal of two-carbon units. For example, when animals are fed synthetic carboxylic acids of the type $Ph(CH_2)_nCOOH$, the ultimate biological degradation product depends on whether n is odd or even. If n is an even number, benzoic acid forms at the end of the degradation process and is excreted by the animal. However, if n is an odd number, phenylacetic acid is the ultimate product. These degradations are illustrated in Figure 21.2.

$$Ph{-}(CH_2)_n{-}COOH \longrightarrow \longrightarrow Ph{-}COOH$$
n = even — benzoic acid

$$Ph{-}(CH_2)_n{-}COOH \longrightarrow \longrightarrow Ph{-}CH_2{-}COOH$$
n = odd — phenylacetic acid

Figure 21.2 Metabolism of synthetic carboxylic acids. Experiments reveal that degradation occurs through a succession of reactions that remove two carbon atoms at a time from the chain. Degradation stops when no $-CH_2CH_2-$ units remain.

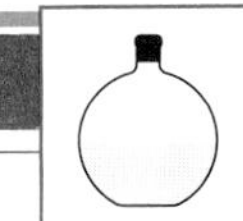

COMPOUND CAPSULE

$(CH_3CH_2CH_2)_2CHCOOH$

Valproic acid

Valproic acid (2-propylpentanoic acid, also known as *DPA* (di-*n*-propylacetic acid) is used as an anticonvulsant and as an antiepileptic. Its antiepileptic properties were discovered quite by chance in 1963, when Pierre Eymard was investigating the properties of a series of substances (unrelated to valproic acid) that he had synthesized in his laboratory as potential pharmaceutical agents. The synthesized compounds proved to have poor solubilities in water and other common solvents, and this severely hampered their pharmacological testing. Eymard discovered, however, that the substances were soluble in valproic acid, and the testing proceeded. It was found that the solutions provided good protection against epileptic seizures in rabbits. However, a blank experiment performed with only valproic acid itself proved just as effective! This discovery led to the marketing of valproic acid as an antiepileptic in 1967.

This type of discovery, in which we find something that we were not looking for, is often referred to as *serendipity*. Such accidental discoveries have played an important role in the development of chemistry and medicine.

Some fatty acids contain carbon-carbon double bonds along the chain. Two examples are oleic acid (**21.1**) and arachidonic acid (**21.2**).

$CH_3(CH_2)_6CH_2 \quad CH_2(CH_2)_5CH_2COOH$

C=C

H H

oleic acid

21.1

$CH_3(CH_2)_3CH_2 \quad CH_2 \quad CH_2 \quad CH_2 \quad CH_2CH_2CH_2COOH$

C=C C=C C=C C=C

H H H H H H H H

arachidonic acid

21.2

Arachidonic acid is an example of the **polyunsaturated fatty acids.** It contains four carbon-carbon double bonds, all of them of *cis* geometry.

Carboxylic acids containing additional hydroxyl groups are also common in nature. Examples of this type of compound include lactic acid (**21.3**), citric acid (**21.4**), and tartaric acid (**21.5**).

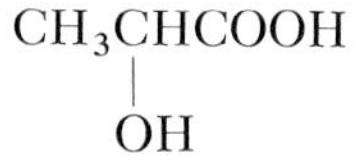

$CH_3CHCOOH$ with OH on C-2	$HOOCCH_2-C(OH)(COOH)-CH_2COOH$	$CH(OH)-COOH$ / $CH(OH)-COOH$
lactic acid (from milk) **21.3**	citric acid (from citrus fruits) **21.4**	tartaric acid (from grapes) **21.5**

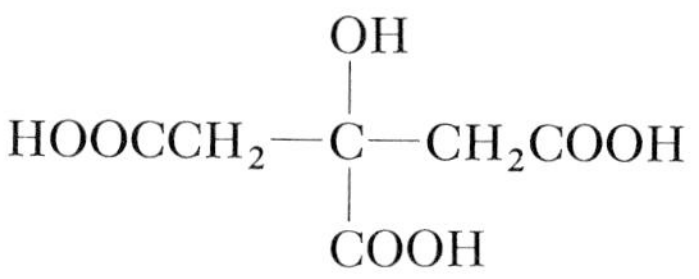

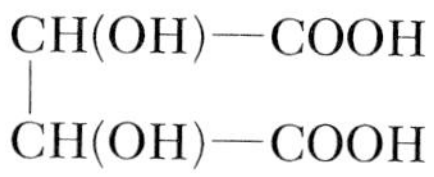

21.2 Nomenclature of Carboxylic Acids

The IUPAC nomenclature of aliphatic carboxylic acids uses the name of the parent alkane and changes the ending from *-e* to *-oic acid*. Several examples, along with their common names are shown in Figure 21.3.

$HCOOH$	CH_3COOH	$CH_3CH_2CH_2COOH$	$(CH_3)_2CHCH_2CH_2COOH$	$Cl_2CHC(CH_3)_2COOH$
methanoic acid (formic acid)	ethanoic acid (acetic acid)	butanoic acid (butyric acid)	4-methylpentanoic acid	3,3-dichloro-2,2-dimethylpropanoic acid

Figure 21.3 Nomenclature of aliphatic carboxylic acids.

The names of aromatic carboxylic acids (in which the carboxylic acid functional group is attached directly to the aromatic ring) are based on the particular aromatic ring structure involved. Several examples are shown in Figure 21.4.

COOH, 8, 9, 1, COOH, 7, 2, 6, 10, 3, 5, 4, COOH, Cl:, COOH, H_3C, COOH, :Br:

benzoic acid

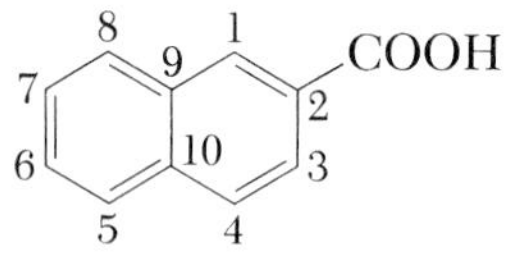

2-naphthoic acid

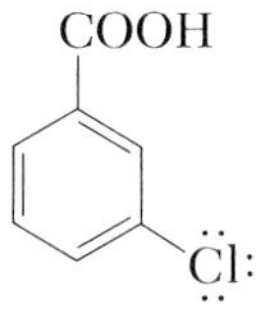

3-chlorobenzoic acid

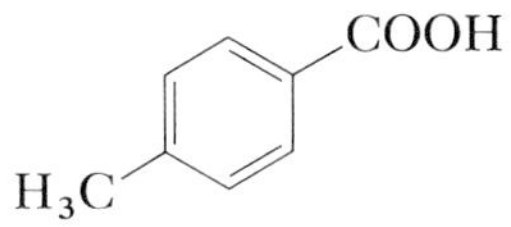

4-methylbenzoic acid (*p*-toluic acid)

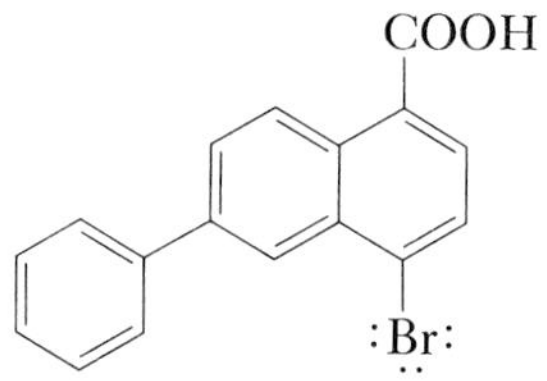

4-bromo-6-phenylnaphthoic acid

Figure 21.4 Nomenclature of aromatic carboxylic acids. The numbering system for the naphthalene ring is illustrated with 2-naphthoic acid.

The carboxylic acid group has a higher nomenclature priority than any other functional group. Thus, compounds that contain the carboxylic acid group along with other groups are named as derivatives of the parent carboxylic acid (e.g., the compound $HO-(CH_2)_3-COOH$ is named as 4-hydroxybutanoic acid.)

PROBLEM 21.1 Give the IUPAC name of each of the following structures:

a. $(CH_3CH_2)_2C(Cl)CH_2CH_2COOH$

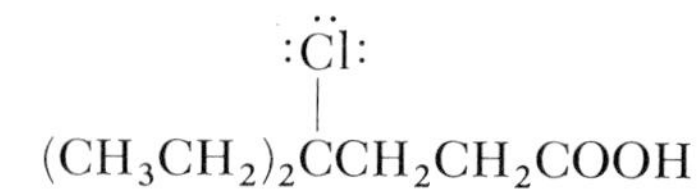

b. $C_6H_5-C(CH_3)_2-CH_2CH_2COOH$ (H₃C, CH₃, C, CH₂CH₂COOH)

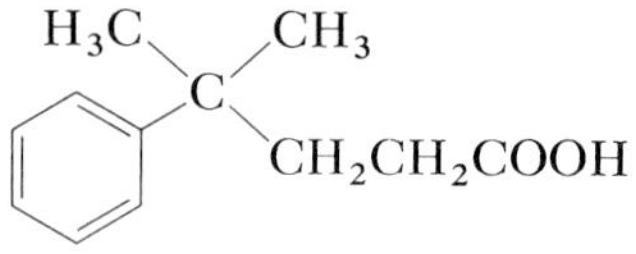

c. H_3C, CH_2, COOH, CH_3CH_2, :OH

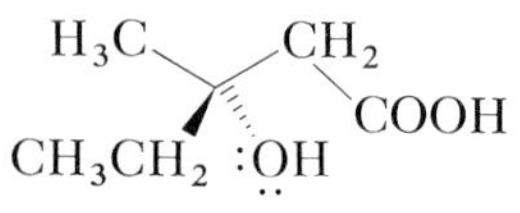

d. $CH_3CH_2-O-CH_2CH_2COOH$

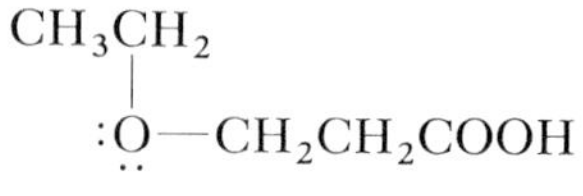

e. (benzene ring with COOH and $CH_2CH_2CH_2\ddot{O}H$ substituents in meta positions)

COOH

$CH_2CH_2CH_2\ddot{O}H$

PROBLEM 21.2 Draw structures for each of the following compounds:

a. 2-bromo-3-ethyl-3-hydroxypentanoic acid
b. 4-(2-aminoethyl)-2-hydroxybenzoic acid
c. (*R*)-2-aminopropanoic acid

There are also many common and important dicarboxylic acids. Several of these are listed in Table 21.3.

In addition to the aliphatic dicarboxylic acids of the type shown in Table 21.3, there are also important aromatic dicarboxylic acids. Several of these are shown in Figure 21.5.

Some dicarboxylic acids occur naturally in plants. For example, oxalic acid occurs in spinach and rhubarb, and glutaric acid and adipic acids occur in sugar beets.

Table 21.3 Common Dicarboxylic Acids

Structure	Common Name	IUPAC Name
HOOC—COOH	oxalic acid	ethanedioic acid
HOOC—CH_2—COOH	malonic acid	1,3-propanedioic acid
HOOC—$(CH_2)_2$—COOH	succinic acid	1,4-butanedioic acid
HOOC—$(CH_2)_3$—COOH	glutaric acid	1,5-pentanedioic acid
HOOC—$(CH_2)_4$—COOH	adipic acid	1,6-hexanedioic acid

SPECIAL TOPIC

Carboxylic acids as Pheromones

Some carboxylic acids serve as pheromones. For example, oleic acid is a death pheromone in some species of ant. Upon the death of an ant, by whatever cause, free oleic acid is emitted by the remains. When the oleic acid is detected by another living ant, it acts to remove the deceased ant from the communal area to a refuse pile.

Other simple carboxylic acids serve as sex pheromones in the rhesus monkey. The ovulating rhesus monkey emits a mixture of six carboxylic acids (acetic acid, propanoic acid, 2-methylpropanoic acid, butanoic acid, 4-methylpentanoic acid, and 3-methylbutanoic acid) that produces a sexual mating response in the male.

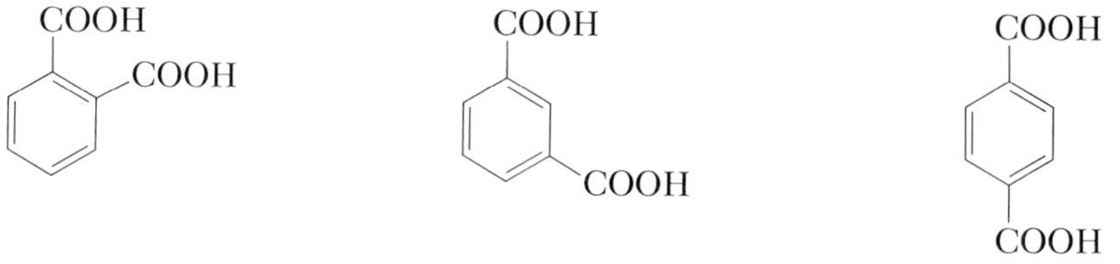

COOH COOH | COOH COOH | COOH COOH

(1,2-benzenedicarboxylic acid) | isophthalic acid (1,3-benzenedicarboxylic acid) | terephthalic acid (1,4-benzenedicarboxylic acid)

Figure 21.5 Some aromatic dicarboxylic acids.

PROBLEM 21.3 Suggest a synthesis for adipic acid, beginning with cyclohexanol.

21.3 Physical Properties of Carboxylic Acids

The physical properties of carboxylic acids are heavily influenced by their ability to form hydrogen bonds. Carboxylic acids form hydrogen bonds either to neighboring carboxylic acid molecules or to other appropriate molecules such as water. Carboxylic acids exhibit even higher boiling temperatures than do alcohols of comparable molecular weight. For example, butanoic acid boils at 164 °C, while 1-pentanol boils at 138 °C. Even in the vapor phase, many carboxylic acid molecules exist as dimers, as shown in Figure 21.6. As a result, measurements of the molecular weight of carboxylic acids often indicate a value twice what is expected on the basis of the simple structure RCOOH.

Figure 21.6 Acetic acid dimer structure. Two acetic acid molecules associate through a pair of hydrogen bonds.

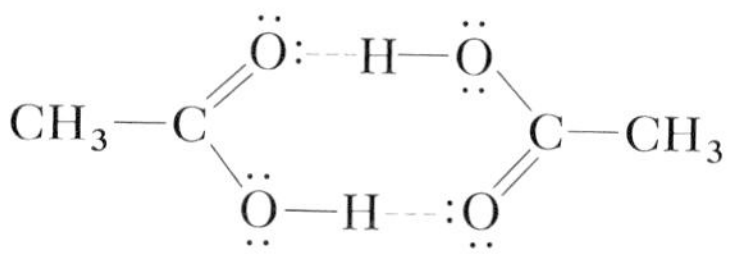

$$CH_3-C(=O\cdots H-O)(-O-H\cdots O=)C-CH_3$$

21.4 The Acidity of Carboxylic Acid

Why is a carboxylic acid so much more acidic than an alcohol? The answer lies in the structure of the conjugate base for each type of compound. In Figure 21.7 we compare the equilibria of acetic acid and of 2-propanol in reaction with water. The conjugate base of a carboxylic acid is known as a **carboxylate ion.** It is less basic than an alkoxide ion since the negative charge is delocalized over *two* oxygen atoms. Figure 21.8 shows two contributing resonance structures consistent with this charge delocalization. An alkoxide ion is more basic than is a carboxylate ion; the negative charge of the alkoxide ion is concentrated on *one* oxygen atom. As always, a less basic conjugate base correlates with a more acidic parent acid.

Figure 21.7 Acid-base reactions of acetic acid and 2-propanol with water.

$$CH_3-\overset{O}{\overset{\|}{C}}-OH + H_2O \rightleftharpoons CH_3-\overset{O}{\overset{\|}{C}}-O^- + H_3O^+$$

$$K_a = 1.74 \times 10^{-5}$$

$$(CH_3)_2CHOH + H_2O \rightleftharpoons (CH_3)_2CHO^- + H_3O^+$$

$$K_a = 10^{-18}$$

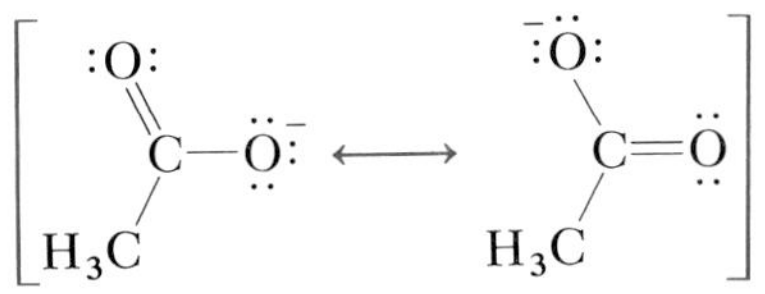

$$\left[\begin{array}{c} :\ddot{O}: \\ \| \\ H_3C-C-\ddot{O}:^- \end{array} \longleftrightarrow \begin{array}{c} :\ddot{O}:^- \\ | \\ H_3C-C=\ddot{O} \end{array} \right]$$

Figure 21.8 Contributing resonance structures for the acetate anion. The delocalization of negative charge stabilizes the anion.

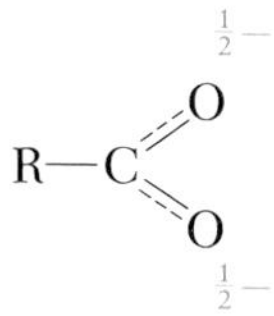

$$R-C\begin{matrix} \overset{\frac{1}{2}-}{O} \\ \underset{\frac{1}{2}-}{O} \end{matrix}$$

Figure 21.9 A carboxylate anion. The four-atom system (two oxygens, the carboxylate carbon, and the R atom attached directly to the carboxylate carbon) is planar, that is all four atoms lie in the same plane. Each of the two oxygen atoms bears one-half of the negative charge. The two carbon-oxygen bond distances are the same.

MOLECULAR ORBITAL ANALYSIS

A Molecular Orbital View of Carboxylate Ions

The molecular orbital model provides a description of carboxylate anions that complements the valence-bond resonance description. Qualitatively, a carboxylate anion is similar to the allyl anion (Figures 16.14–16.16) in that it has the same type of π molecular orbitals. The HOMO has electron density at each of the two ends of the system (the two oxygen atoms). A representation of the delocalized carboxylate ion is shown in Figure 21.9.

Several factors influence the acidities of carboxylic acids. One factor is the nature of the R group. Electron-withdrawing groups increase acidity and electron-donating groups decrease acidity. Selected carboxylic acid pK_a values are shown in Table 21.4. In every case, loss of a proton leads to a carboxylate ion, RCO_2^-, that is the conjugate base of the parent acid. When an electronegative atom is bound close to the carboxyl group, the conjugate base is stabilized because the electronegative atom allows the negative charge of the carboxylate ion to be delocalized, increasing the stability of the ion and rendering it less basic. The corollary is that the parent acid is strengthened by such an effect. Indeed, we find that electronegative groups increase the acidity of carboxylic acids.

We also know from our past dealings with alcohols and amines that solvent effects can play a major role in determining the strengths of acids and bases. How important are such effects with carboxylic acids? It has been determined

Table 21.4 Acidities of Selected Carboxylic Acids

Acid	pK_a
Cl_3CCOOH	0.65
$Cl_2CHCOOH$	1.29
$[(CH_3)_3NCH_2COOH]^+$	1.83
FCH_2COOH	2.66
$ClCH_2COOH$	2.86
p-O_2N-C_6H_4COOH	3.42
m-NC-C_6H_4COOH	3.51
$HCOOH$	3.77
m-F-C_6H_4COOH	3.86
C_6H_5COOH	4.20
m-H_2N-C_6H_4COOH	4.36
p-CH_3-C_6H_4COOH	4.37
p-H_3CO-C_6H_4COOH	4.47
CH_3COOH	4.76
CH_3CH_2COOH	4.88
$(CH_3)_3CCOOH$	5.05

that entropy effects related to solvation are extremely important in influencing the strengths of carboxylic acids. When a carboxylic acid dissociates, there is a change in solvation. In general, the conjugate base, being an anion, is solvated to a much greater extent than the parent acid, a neutral molecule. An ordering of solvent molecules accompanies the dissociation process. However, the degree of ordering (i.e., ΔS for the dissociation process) differs depending on the nature of the parent carboxylic acid and its conjugate base. For example, compare acetic acid and formic acid in aqueous solution. Both are solvated, but acetic acid is solvated to a lesser degree because its methyl group, like alkyl groups in general, is hydrophobic, disfavoring interaction with solvent molecules. On dissociation of the two acids, formate and acetate ions are formed. Both are more highly solvated than their parent acids, but formate anion is only slightly more solvated than acetate anion. The main factor influencing solvation of the carboxylate ions is their negative charge. The negative charge greatly favors solvation and largely overwhelms the effect of the hydrophobic methyl group. As a result, there is more ordering when acetic acid dissociates to actetate ion in aqueous solution than when formic acid dissociates to formate ion. This entropy effect is the main reason for the diminished acidity of acetic acid compared to formic acid.

Dicarboxylic acids have two pK_a values, one corresponding to each of the acidic functional groups. Consider oxalic acid. The first (pK_{a1}) is 1.27, indicating that the acid is significantly more acidic than acetic acid. We can understand this by considering the conjugate base of oxalic acid, $HOOC{-}COO^-$. In the oxalate anion the electron-withdrawing carboxyl group stabilizes the immediately adjacent carboxylate anion. Furthermore, a *statistical* factor is involved here. Since there are two equivalent carboxylic acid functions in oxalic acid, there immediately is a doubled likelihood of donating a hydrogen ion in an acid/base reaction. The second pK_a (pK_{a2}) is 4.26, indicating that the second acidic hydrogen is less acidic than acetic acid. We rationalize this difference rather easily. Removal of a hydrogen ion from the oxalate anion leads to a dianion, $^-O_2C{-}CO_2^-$, in which *two* negative charges are in close proximity and therefore repel one another. The formation of this dianion is relatively more difficult than formation of a monoanion.

PROBLEM 21.4 Which acid, oxalic or malonic, would you expect to have the larger K_{a1}/K_{a2} ratio? Explain your answer.

PROBLEM 21.5 You might expect that K_{a1}/K_{a2} for very long chain dicarboxylic acids ($HOOC{-}(CH_2)_n{-}COOH$, where n is a large number) would have a value of unity (1) since the carboxylic acid groups would act independently. Actually, the value of K_{a1}/K_{a2} for such molecules is 4. Propose an explanation for this observation. (This problem is challenging, as it requires a thoughtful analysis. Do some library research, if necessary.)

Since carboxylic acids are acids, they undergo neutralization with bases. This reaction produces a carboxylate salt, as illustrated in Figure 21.10. We name carboxylate salts by first naming the cation and then adding the name

Figure 21.10 Formation of a carboxylate salt.

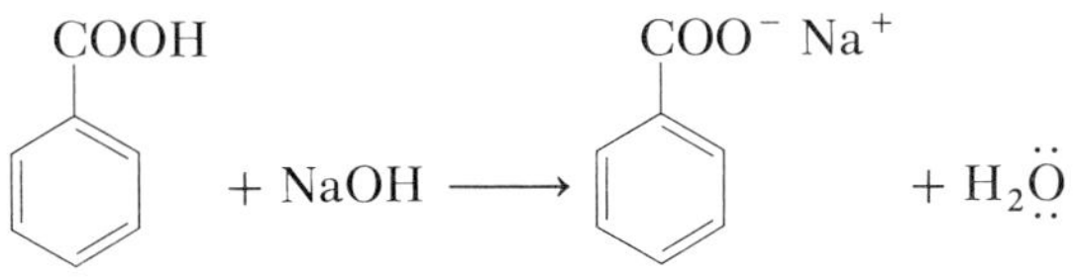

$$C_6H_5COOH + NaOH \longrightarrow C_6H_5COO^- Na^+ + H_2\ddot{O}$$

sodium benzoate (a common food preservative)

of the carboxylate anion. In adding the anion name we change the *-ic acid* ending of the free acid to *-ate*. We can isolate such salts by evaporating the water (formed in the reaction and often used as the solvent).

Salts of long chain fatty acids are **soaps**, materials that contain both a highly polar region (the anionic site) that can interact with water molecules and a nonpolar region (the alkyl chain) that can interact with other nonpolar materials. (See the "Special Topic," page 798.)

PROBLEM 21.6 Draw a structure for potassium 3-chloropropanoate and describe how to prepare and isolate it using 3-chloropropanoic acid as a starting material.

PROBLEM 21.7 What volume of 0.200 M sodium hydroxide is needed to titrate exactly 0.25 g of benzoic acid to neutrality?

21.5 Syntheses of Carboxylic Acids

There are many ways of introducing a carboxylic acid group into an organic molecule. In earlier chapters we introduced several important methods involving oxidation of some other group. We begin here by briefly reviewing these methods.

OXIDATIONS OF ALDEHYDES AND PRIMARY ALCOHOLS

Both aldehydes and primary alcohols are oxidized to carboxylic acids by the action of common oxidizing agents. If our starting material is a primary alcohol, oxidation proceeds via an intermediate aldehyde (recall that aldehydes undergo oxidation so readily that we must use special conditions if we wish to prevent their continuing oxidation to carboxylic acids). Equations 21.1 and 21.2 give examples of the use of Cr(VI) and Mn(VII) oxidizing agents for the oxidation of primary alcohols to carboxylic acids.

Eqn. 21.1

$$:\ddot{F}CH_2(CH_2)_8CH_2\ddot{O}H \xrightarrow[H_2SO_4,\ H_2O]{CrO_3} :\ddot{F}CH_2(CH_2)_8COOH$$

10-fluoro-1-decanol → 93% yield 10-fluorodecanoic acid

Eqn. 21.2

$$Cl_3C(CH_2)_3CH_2\ddot{O}H \xrightarrow[H_2O]{KMnO_4} Cl_3C(CH_2)_3COOH$$

(aq acid workup)

5,5,5-trichloro-1-pentanol → 92% yield 5,5,5-trichloropentanoic acid

SPECIAL TOPIC

Soap

The manufacture of soap dates back to ancient times. For example, early Roman writers tell of how the Phoenicians made soap by heating goat fat with ashes. Until quite recently it remained common practice for people to make their own soap from animal fats and lye (basic components from wood ash). The mixture of fat and aqueous base was heated in a vat and the soap would form and rise to the surface of the mixture. On cooling, the soap would solidify. A dilute solution of glycerol would also form. This method of preparing soap is simply a hydrolysis of the esters present in the animal fat, as shown below.

$$\begin{array}{l} H_2C-O-C(=O)-(CH_2)_{16}CH_3 \\ \quad | \\ HC-O-C(=O)-(CH_2)_{16}CH_3 \\ \quad | \\ H_2C-O-C(=O)-(CH_2)_{16}CH_3 \end{array} \xrightarrow[\text{H}_2\text{O, heat}]{\text{NaOH}} \begin{array}{l} H_2C-OH \\ \quad | \\ HC-OH \\ \quad | \\ H_2C-OH \end{array} + 3\,Na^+\ {}^-O_2C-(CH_2)_{16}CH_3$$

glycerol — sodium stearate (a soap)

The action of soap depends on the presence of two regions within each molecule. One is a polar, hydrophilic region (the carboxylate anion region), and the other is a nonpolar, hydrophobic region (the alkyl chain). Most water-insoluble contaminants (dirt) we wish to remove from surfaces are composed of oily, hydrophobic hydrocarbon or hydrocarbon-like substances. On adding soap with water to the contaminated item, an emulsion consisting of small drops suspended in the water is formed. These small drops are characterized by an ordered structure known as a micelle. In the spherical structure of a soap micelle, the hydrophobic contaminant is located at the center of the sphere, surrounded by the soap species. The

(*continued*)

(continued from previous page)
hydrophobic regions of the soap are directed *inward* toward the hydrophobic contaminant, interacting with it through van der Waals type interactions. The hydrophilic regions of the soap are directed *outward* toward the aqueous solution. A schematic representation of a micelle in water is shown below.

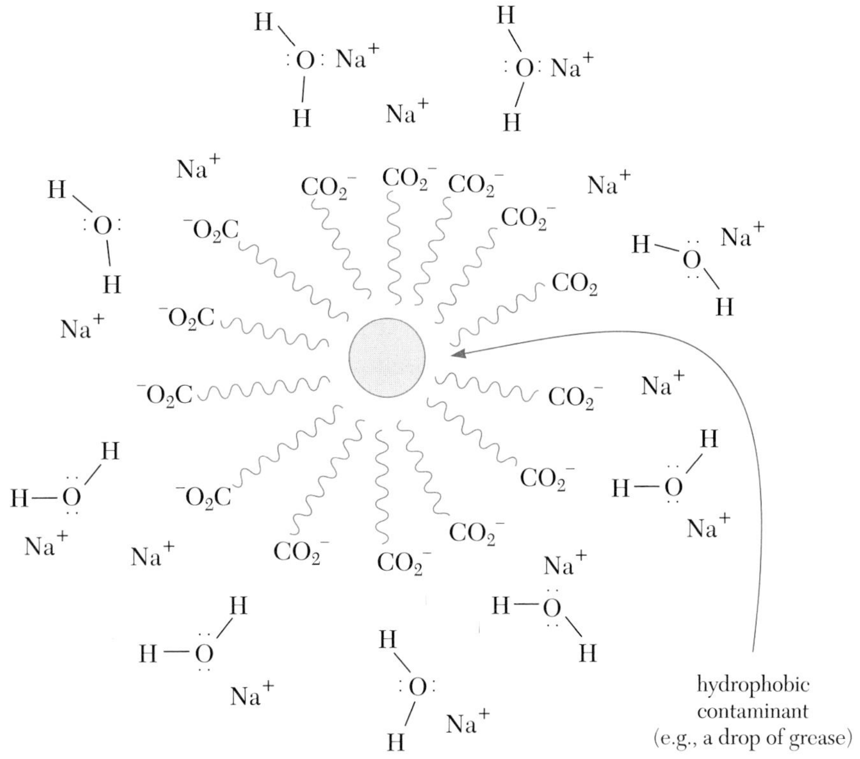

hydrophobic contaminant (e.g., a drop of grease)

These same reagents convert aldehydes to carboxylic acids, as illustrated in Equation 21.3.

Eqn. 21.3

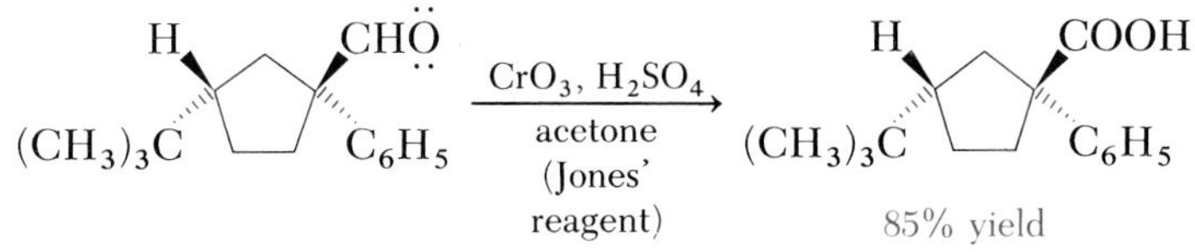

$$\text{(E)-3-}tert\text{-butyl-1-phenylcyclopentanecarboxaldehyde} \xrightarrow[\text{acetone (Jones' reagent)}]{CrO_3,\ H_2SO_4} \text{(E)-3-}tert\text{-butyl-1-phenylcyclopentanecarboxylic acid (85\% yield)}$$

(E)-3-*tert*-butyl-1-phenylcyclopentanecarboxaldehyde

85% yield
(E)-3-*tert*-butyl-1-phenylcyclopentanecarboxylic acid

Many other reagents also oxidize aldehydes to carboxylic acids, for example, dilute nitric acid (Equation 21.4) and hypochlorite ion (Equation 21.5).

Eqn. 21.4

2,3,6-trichlorobenzaldehyde $\xrightarrow[H_2O]{HNO_3}$ 2,3,6-trichlorobenzoic acid (24% yield)

Eqn. 21.5

cyclohexanecarboxaldehyde $\xrightarrow[H_2O]{Ca(OCl)_2}$ cyclohexanecarboxylic acid (77% yield)

If we wish to oxidize an aldehyde group selectively in the presence of other functional groups that are also susceptible to oxidation, we need to use another type of reagent. Reagents involving Ag(I) as the oxidizing agent (such as the Tollens' reagent—see Section 19.13) are convenient for this purpose. These reagents are very mild oxidizing agents and affect only very easily oxidized groups.

SIDE-CHAIN OXIDATION OF SUBSTITUTED AROMATIC COMPOUNDS

The Cr(VI) and Mn(VII) reagents discussed earlier also oxidize the side chains of benzene and other aromatic rings to carboxylic acid groups. We discussed this type of reaction in earlier chapters. Two additional examples of this type of oxidation are shown in Equations 21.6 and 21.7.

Eqn. 21.6

1-phenylpropane ($C_6H_5CH_2CH_2CH_3$) $\xrightarrow[H_2SO_4,\ H_2O,\ heat]{CrO_3}$ benzoic acid (C_6H_5COOH) (60% yield)

Eqn. 21.7

tetralin $\xrightarrow[Na_2CO_3,\ H_2O,\ heat,\ (aq\ acid\ workup)]{KMnO_4}$ phthalic acid ($C_6H_4(COOH)_2$) (27% yield)

OXIDATIVE CLEAVAGE REACTIONS

Molecules containing carbon-carbon double or triple bonds undergo oxidative cleavage reactions to yield carboxylic acids. Generally these oxidative cleavage methods (e.g., ozonolysis) result in the fragmentation of a larger molecule into two smaller molecules. However, oxidative cleavage of an appropriate cyclic alkene (or alkyne) results in an open-chain dicarboxylic acid and constitutes a

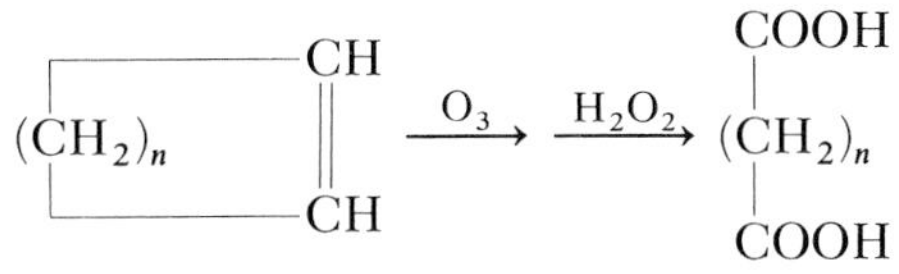

Figure 21.11 Ozonolysis of a cyclic alkene. The cleavage product is a single molecule containing two carboxyl groups.

$$\text{cyclic }(CH_2)_n\text{-CH=CH} \xrightarrow{O_3} \xrightarrow{H_2O_2} HOOC-(CH_2)_n-COOH$$

useful approach to this type of compound, as is illustrated in the general scheme shown in Figure 21.11.

THE HALOFORM REACTION

The haloform reaction, introduced in Section 19.12, is a special method for oxidizing methyl ketones to carboxylic acids. Additional examples are shown in Equations 21.8 and 21.9.

Eqn. 21.8

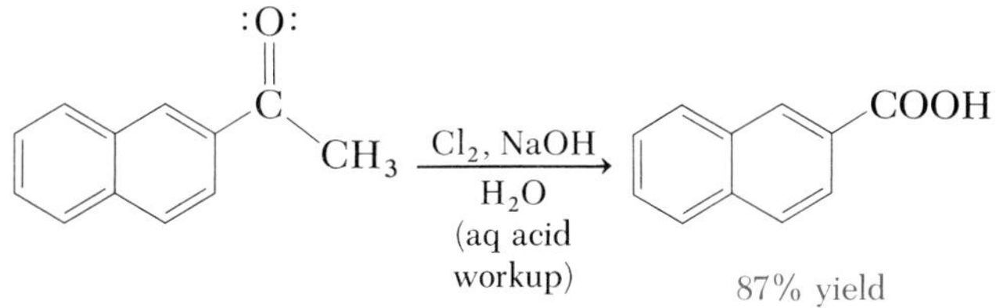

$$\text{methyl 2-naphthyl ketone} \xrightarrow[\text{(aq acid workup)}]{Cl_2,\ NaOH,\ H_2O} \text{2-naphthoic acid (87\% yield)}$$

Eqn. 21.9

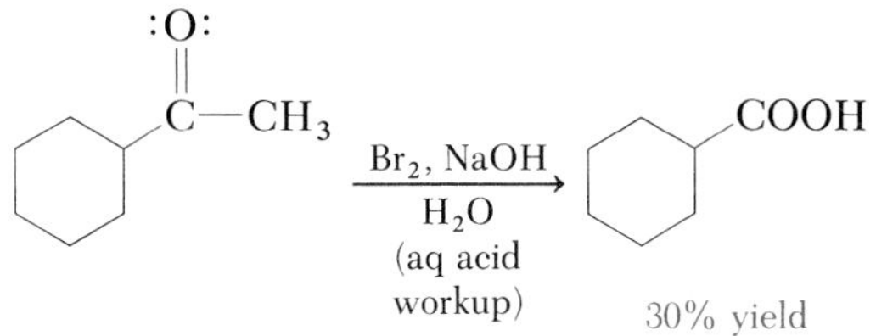

$$\text{methyl cyclohexyl ketone} \xrightarrow[\text{(aq acid workup)}]{Br_2,\ NaOH,\ H_2O} \text{cyclohexanecarboxylic acid (30\% yield)}$$

You should recall that secondary alcohols of the type $RCH(OH)CH_3$ are also converted to carboxylic acids under these reaction conditions. Such alcohols are first oxidized to a methyl ketone; then the methyl ketone undergoes the haloform reaction to form the carboxylic acid.

THE CARBONATION OF ORGANOMETALLICS

In Chapter 11 we discussed the ability of organometallics to behave as powerful nucleophiles. One important type of reaction is that of organometallics such as Grignard reagents with a carbonyl group. In a completely analogous reaction, adding carbon dioxide to an organometallic (**carbonation**) leads immediately to a carboxylate anion. The organometallic reagent performs a nucleophilic attack on the carbon of carbon dioxide. This approach allows the preparation of carboxylic acids bearing one more carbon atom than the alkyl or aryl halide used to make the Grignard reagent, as is illustrated in Figure 21.12.

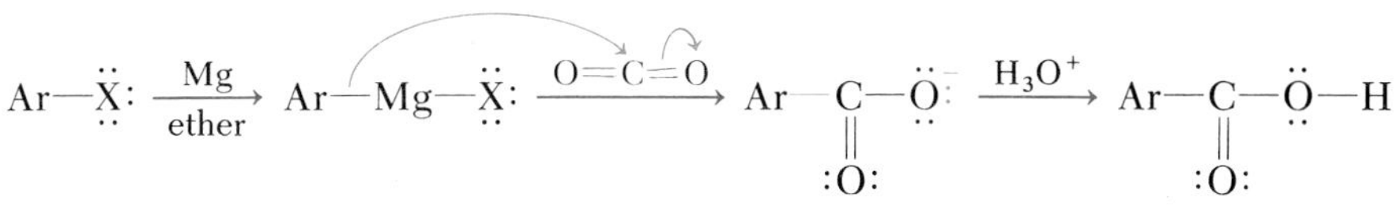

Figure 21.12 Carbonation of a Grignard reagent. Overall, the reaction allows the synthesis of a carboxylic acid from an alkyl or aryl halide. In effect, a carboxylate group replaces the original halogen atom.

$$Ar-X \xrightarrow[\text{ether}]{Mg} Ar-Mg-X \xrightarrow{O=C=O} Ar-C(=O)-O^- \xrightarrow{H_3O^+} Ar-C(=O)-O-H$$

Dry ice (solid carbon dioxide) is commonly used as the source of CO_2 in these reactions. It is added to a solution of the organometallic reagent. After the reaction is complete, aqueous mineral acid is added to protonate the carboxylate anion and form a free carboxylic acid. Two examples are shown in Equations 21.10 and 21.11.

Eqn. 21.10

$$\underset{\text{:Cl:}}{CH_3CH_2\underset{|}{C}HCH_3} \xrightarrow[\text{2. } CO_2 \text{ 3. aq acid}]{\text{1. Mg, ether}} \underset{\text{COOH}}{CH_3CH_2\underset{|}{C}HCH_3}$$

2-chlorobutane

86% yield
2-methylbutanoic acid

Eqn. 21.11

$$\text{1-chloronaphthalene} \xrightarrow[\text{2. } CO_2 \text{ 3. aq acid}]{\text{1. Mg, THF}} \text{1-naphthoic acid}$$

1-chloronaphthalene

56% yield
1-naphthoic acid

Aryllithium species are also highly reactive toward carbon dioxide and give carboxylic acids in good yield. An example is shown in Equation 21.12.

Eqn. 21.12

$$C_6H_5Br \xrightarrow[\text{2. } CO_2 \text{ 3. aq acid}]{\text{1. Li, ether}} C_6H_5COOH$$

bromobenzene

58% yield
benzoic acid

THE HYDROLYSIS OF NITRILES

In our earlier discussion of nucleophilic substitution reactions (Section 12.3), we considered the formation of aliphatic nitriles through cyanide displacement of halide ion from haloalkanes. Aromatic nitriles can be prepared by means of the Sandmeyer reaction of aryl diazonium ions with cuprous cyanide (Section 20.8). Thus, we have facile access to both alkyl and aromatic nitriles. These nitriles are easily converted to the corresponding carboxylic acids by boiling with aqueous acid. Two examples are shown in Equations 21.13 and 21.14.

Eqn. 21.13

$$2,4,6\text{-}(CH_3)_3C_6H_2CH_2CN \xrightarrow[\text{heat}]{H_2SO_4,\ H_2O} 2,4,6\text{-}(CH_3)_3C_6H_2CH_2COOH$$

(2,4,6-trimethyl phenyl)acetonitrile

87% yield
(2,4,6-trimethyl-phenyl)acetic acid

Eqn. 21.14

$$\text{1-naphthonitrile (CN)} \xrightarrow[\text{heat}]{H_3PO_4,\ H_2O} \text{1-naphthoic acid (COOH)}$$

1-naphthonitrile

90% yield
1-naphthoic acid

The acid-catalyzed hydrolysis of nitriles proceeds according to the following mechanism, which consists of a series of acid-base reactions. Notice that no oxidation-reduction occurs in the entire reaction sequence. Each step of the reaction is reversible. The equilibria favor the carboxylic acid product in acid solution because of the protonation of ammonia. Once protonated, the ammonia no longer has an available unshared pair of valence electrons and thus is unable to participate in the reverse process.

MECHANISM OF REACTION

Acid-Catalyzed Hydrolysis of Nitriles

Step 1 Protonation of the nitrile

$$R{-}C{\equiv}N{:} + H^+ \rightleftharpoons [R{-}C{\equiv}\overset{+}{N}{-}H \longleftrightarrow R{-}\overset{+}{C}{=}\ddot{N}{-}H]$$

Step 2 Nucleophilic attack by water

$$R{-}\overset{+}{C}{=}\ddot{N}{-}H + H_2\ddot{O}{:} \rightleftharpoons R{-}C(\overset{+}{O}H_2){=}\ddot{N}{-}H$$

Steps 3 and 4 Proton transfer (B is some convenient base in solution)

$$B{:} + R{-}C(\overset{+}{O}H_2){=}\ddot{N}{-}H \rightleftharpoons \overset{+}{B}{-}H + R{-}C(\ddot{O}H){=}\ddot{N}H$$

$$R{-}C(\ddot{O}H){=}\ddot{N}H + H{-}\overset{+}{B} \rightleftharpoons$$

$$\left[R{-}C(\ddot{O}H){=}\overset{+}{N}H_2 \longleftrightarrow R{-}\overset{+}{C}(\ddot{O}H){-}\ddot{N}H_2 \longleftrightarrow R{-}C(={\overset{+}{O}H}){-}\ddot{N}H_2\right] + B{:}$$

Step 5 Nucleophilic attack by water

$$R-\overset{+}{C}(\ddot{O}H)-\ddot{N}H_2 + H_2\ddot{O} \rightleftharpoons R-C(\ddot{N}H_2)(\ddot{O}H)-\overset{+}{\ddot{O}}H_2$$

Steps 6 and 7 Proton transfer

$$B\!: + R-C(\overset{+}{O}H_2)(\ddot{O}H)-\ddot{N}H_2 \rightleftharpoons R-C(\ddot{O}-H)(\ddot{O}-H)-\ddot{N}H_2 + \overset{+}{B}-H$$

$$R-C(\ddot{O}-H)(\ddot{O}-H)-\ddot{N}H_2 + H-\overset{+}{B} \rightleftharpoons R-C(\ddot{O}-H)(\ddot{O}-H)-\overset{+}{N}(H)(H)-H + B\!:$$

Step 8 Loss of ammonia

$$R-C(\ddot{O}-H)(\ddot{O}-H)-\overset{+}{N}H_3 \rightleftharpoons \ddot{N}H_3 +$$

$$\left[R-\overset{+}{C}(\ddot{O}-H)(\ddot{O}-H) \longleftrightarrow R-C(=\overset{+}{\ddot{O}}-H)(\ddot{O}-H) \longleftrightarrow R-C(\ddot{O}-H)(=\overset{+}{\ddot{O}}-H) \right]$$

Step 9 Proton loss

$$B\!: + R-\overset{+}{C}(:\!O\!:-H)(:\!O\!:-H) \rightleftharpoons R-C(=\!:\!O\!:)-\ddot{O}-H + \overset{+}{B}-H$$

Nitriles can also be hydrolyzed under basic conditions by refluxing with aqueous hydroxide. Under these conditions a solution of a carboxylate salt is obtained. Usually, the reaction mixture is subjected to workup with an aqueous solution of a mineral acid so that the free carboxylic acid is produced. The sequence in Equation 21.15 is typical.

Eqn. 21.15 H_3C–(3-methylphenyl)cyclohexane–CN $\xrightarrow[(HOCH_2CH_2)_2O]{KOH,\ H_2O}$ H_3C–(3-methylphenyl)cyclohexane–COO^- K^+ $\xrightarrow[H^+]{H_2O}$ H_3C–(3-methylphenyl)cyclohexane–COOH

1-(3-methylphenyl)cyclohexanecarbonitrile

93% yield
1-(3-methylphenyl)cyclohexanecarboxylic acid

PROBLEM 21.8 Write a mechanism for the reaction shown in Equation 21.15.

PROBLEM 21.9 Outline a synthesis of $HOOC—(CH_2)_5—COOH$ starting with cyclopentene. (*Hint:* Simple ozonolysis will not work, because you need two additional carbon atoms.)

PROBLEM 21.10 Show how to accomplish each of the following syntheses:

a. pentanoic acid from 1-pentene
b. butanoic acid from 1-pentene
c. hexanoic acid from 1-pentene
d. *rac*-2-methylbutanoic acid from 1-butene
e. benzoic acid from benzene
f. *p*-nitrobenzoic acid from benzene

21.6 Reactions of Carboxylic Acids

CARBOXYLIC ACID DERIVATIVES

In addition to undergoing the typical reactions of weak acids, carboxylic acids also undergo a variety of other reactions. Of particular importance is their conversion to various types of **carboxyl derivatives.** We will consider these derivatives in detail in this and the following two chapters. Many of them have another group in place of the —OH portion of the parent carboxylic acid. Several examples are shown in Table 21.5.

Nitriles, R—C≡N, are often viewed as derivatives of carboxylic acids. In a formal sense, nitriles are related to amides in that dehydration of a primary amide produces a nitrile. In the laboratory we can often accomplish this dehydration amide using a dehydrating agent such as phosphorus pentoxide (P_2O_5) or thionyl chloride ($SOCl_2$). The relationship of nitriles to carboxylic acids and other derivatives is reflected in their common nomenclature. Several examples are shown in Table 21.6.

Table 21.5 Some Derivatives of Carboxylic Acids
R can be an alkyl or an aryl group.

$$R-\overset{\overset{\displaystyle :O:}{\|}}{C}-G$$

G	Type of Compound
$-\ddot{\underset{..}{O}}H$	carboxylic acid
$-\ddot{\underset{..}{X}}:$ (halide)	carboxylic acid (or acyl) halide
$-\ddot{\underset{..}{O}}R$	ester
$-\ddot{N}R_2$, $-\ddot{N}HR$, $\ddot{N}H_2$	amide
$-\ddot{\underset{..}{O}}-\underset{\underset{\displaystyle :O:}{\|}}{C}-R$	anhydride

Table 21.6 Nomenclature of Nitriles
We name nitriles by dropping *-ic acid* from the ending of the name of the parent acid and adding *-nitrile*.

Nitrile	Nitrile Name	Parent Carboxylic Acid
CH_3CN	acetonitrile	acetic acid
CH_3CH_2CN	propionitrile	propionic acid
C_6H_5CN	benzonitrile	benzoic acid

The derivatives of carboxylic acids are important classes of compounds not only for synthetic organic chemistry but also for a wide variety of industrial applications and virtually all biological processes. In the following section we will look at the preparation of these derivatives from the parent carboxylic acids.

The Preparation of Carboxylic Acid Chlorides In general, an acid halide is a derivative of an oxyacid in which a halogen takes the place of the hydroxyl group of the oxyacid. Several examples of such acid halides are shown in Figure 21.13.

Carboxylic acid halides (chlorides in particular) are extremely useful for organic syntheses, as we saw in earlier chapters, (e.g., in Friedel-Crafts acylation reactions (Chapter 18)). Carboxylic acid halides are in general the most reactive of the carboxylic acid derivatives. Many nucleophiles react readily with carboxylic acid halides, and the overall result is displacement of the halogen atom as a halide ion.

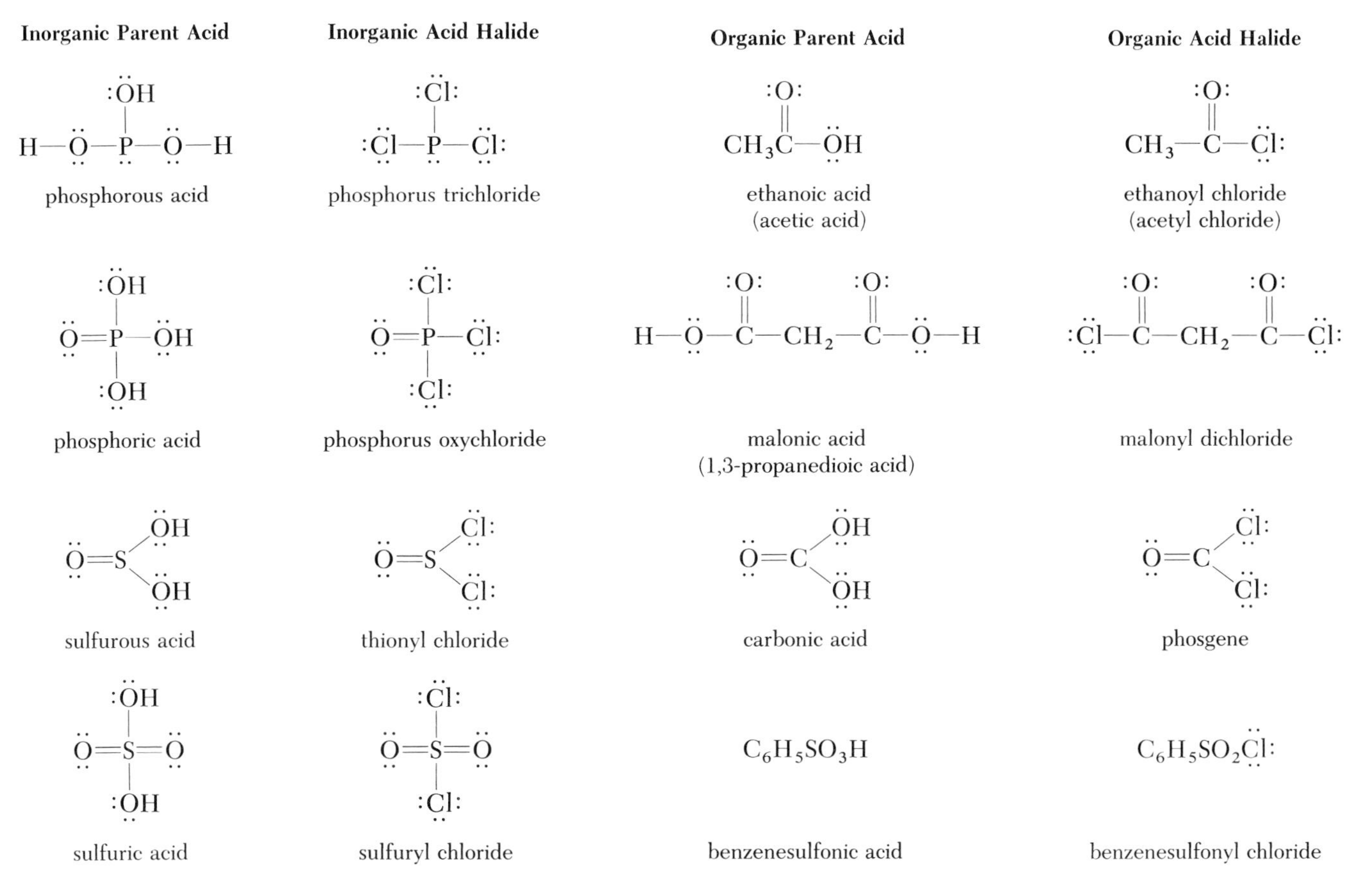

Figure 21.13 Examples of inorganic and organic acid halides (chlorides).

PROBLEM 21.11 Based on leaving-group ability, predict the relative reactivities of the following derivatives toward nucleophiles:

anhydrides	amides
esters	carboxylic acids

(The order predicted by leaving-group ability is the experimentally found order. However, see Section 22.2 for further discussion.)

There are several ways to prepare acid halides from their parent carboxylic acids. A common method is the treatment of the carboxylic acid with an inorganic acid chloride such as thionyl chloride, phosphorus trichloride, or phosphorus pentachloride. Several examples are shown in Equations 21.16–21.19.

Eqn. 21.16

$$\underset{\text{trichloroacetic acid}}{Cl_3C{-}COOH} \xrightarrow{SOCl_2} \underset{\substack{\text{89\% yield} \\ \text{trichloroacetyl chloride}}}{Cl_3C{-}\overset{\overset{\displaystyle :\ddot{O}:}{\|}}{C}{-}\ddot{\underset{..}{Cl}}:}$$

Eqn. 21.17

$$C_6H_5CH_2COOH \xrightarrow{PCl_3} C_6H_5CH_2{-}C({=}O){-}Cl$$

phenylacetic acid — 83% yield phenylacetyl chloride

Eqn. 21.18

$$p\text{-}H_3C{-}C_6H_4{-}COOH \xrightarrow{PBr_3} p\text{-}H_3C{-}C_6H_4{-}C({=}O){-}Br$$

p-toluic acid — 65% yield *p*-methylbenzoyl bromide

Eqn. 21.19

$$CH_3(CH_2)_{16}COOH \xrightarrow[C_6H_6]{PCl_5} CH_3(CH_2)_{16}C({=}O){-}Cl$$

octadecanoic acid — 70% yield octadecanoyl chloride

A disadvantage of these procedures is that the inorganic acid halides used are highly reactive toward other functional groups. Thus, the reagents are not particularly selective. Furthermore, when these inorganic acid halides react, they generate hydrogen chloride or other acidic by-products that can affect acid-sensitive molecules.

A milder method involving no potentially harmful acidic by-products utilizes triphenylphosphine in the presence of tetrahalomethanes. An example is shown in Equation 21.20.

Eqn. 21.20

$$C_6H_5COOH \xrightarrow[CCl_4]{Ph_3P} C_6H_5C({=}O){-}Cl + Ph_3PO$$

benzoic acid — 88% yield benzoyl chloride

The acid halide is isolated by filtering off the insoluble triphenylphosphine oxide and allowing unreacted tetrahalomethane to evaporate. (Some CHX_3 forms as a by-product; it also is removed by evaporation.) Related phosphine reagents are also effective. For example, triphenylphosphine dichloride (**21.6**) works nicely.

$$(C_6H_5)_3PCl_2$$

triphenylphosphine dichloride

21.6

An ingenious modification involves the attachment of the reactive phosphorus compound to an insoluble polymer, generally a polystyrene derivative. This type of reagent is insoluble in the solvent systems used for the substrate carboxylic acid, and the reaction occurs at the surface of the polymer. The byproduct is also insoluble in the reaction solvent, so purification of the product is simplified. The polymeric reagent provides very mild reaction conditions and an expedited workup procedure. An example is shown in Equation 21.21.

Eqn. 21.21

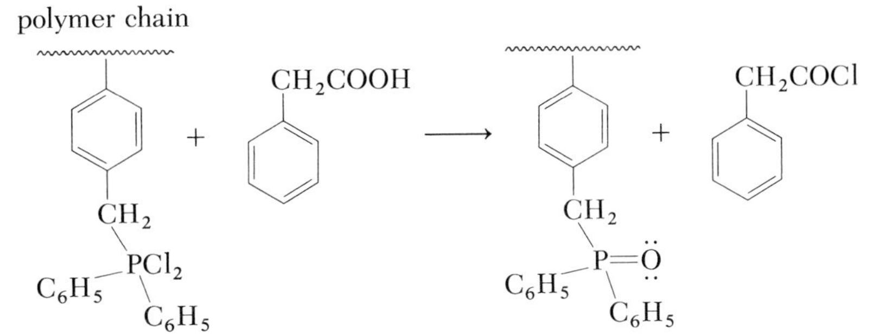

polymer chain

CH_2 PCl_2 C_6H_5 C_6H_5 + CH_2COOH ⟶ CH_2 $P{=}O$ C_6H_5 C_6H_5 + CH_2COCl

phenylacetic acid

100% yield phenylacetyl chloride

Reactions in which one of the participants is bound to an insoluble polymer have proven invaluable in accomplishing efficient multistep syntheses. Of particular interest is the application of this methodology to the synthesis of complex molecules such as peptides, as we will describe in Chapter 26.

Carboxylic Acid Anhydrides The name **anhydride** literally means "without water." Inorganic acid anhydrides have a composition corresponding to the removal of the elements of water from an oxyacid. For example, sulfur trioxide (SO_3) is the anhydride of sulfuric acid (H_2SO_4), and chromium trioxide (CrO_3), sometimes known as chromic anhydride, is the anhydride of chromic acid (H_2CrO_4).*

The simplest carboxylic acid, formic acid, yields carbon monoxide (CO) upon dehydration. However, other simple carboxylic acids form anhydrides in which one molecule of water is removed from *two* molecules of the acid. Two common examples of this type of anhydride are acetic anhydride (**21.7**) and benzoic anhydride (**21.8**). If the two carboxyl groups of dicarboxylic acids are properly oriented, dehydration leads to a *cyclic* anhydride such as maleic anhydride (**21.9**) and phthalic anhydride (**21.10**).

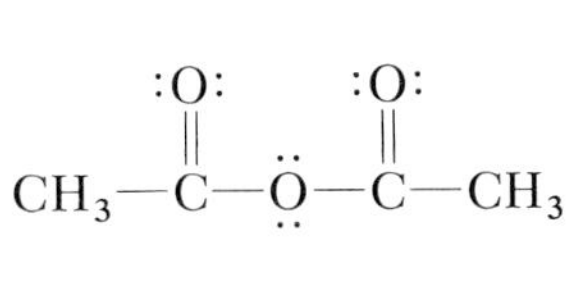

$CH_3-C(=O)-O-C(=O)-CH_3$

acetic anhydride

21.7

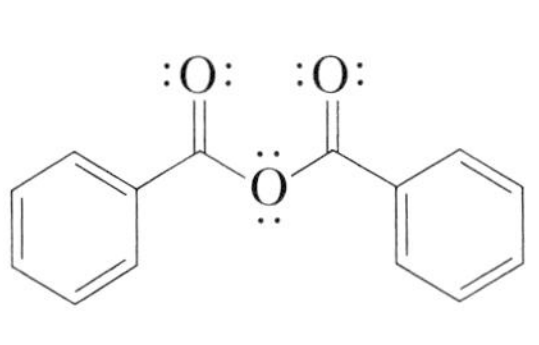

benzoic anhydride

21.8

* Although chromic acid itself is unstable and cannot be isolated, its anhydride is a common (although reactive) laboratory reagent.

maleic anhydride **21.9**

phthalic anhydride **21.10**

Anhydrides of straight-chain carboxylic acids containing up to twelve carbons are liquids. The most common of these, acetic anhydride, is a very use-

SPECIAL TOPIC

Biological Anhydrides

Anhydride linkages are present in a variety of molecules that are involved in the normal metabolic processes of living organisms. Any anhydride is generally reactive toward nucleophilic reagents. In biological systems, anhydrides facilitate the formation of a new bond between the original acidic center and an attacking nucleophile.

Biological anhydrides are generally not of the symmetrical carboxylic type; usually at least one part is related to an inorganic acid. Two biologically important anhydrides, acetyl phosphate and adenosine diphosphate, are shown below, along with a schematic representation of their chemical origins in parent acids. A similar schematic is shown for acetic anhydride to demonstrate the related natures of organic and biological anhydrides.

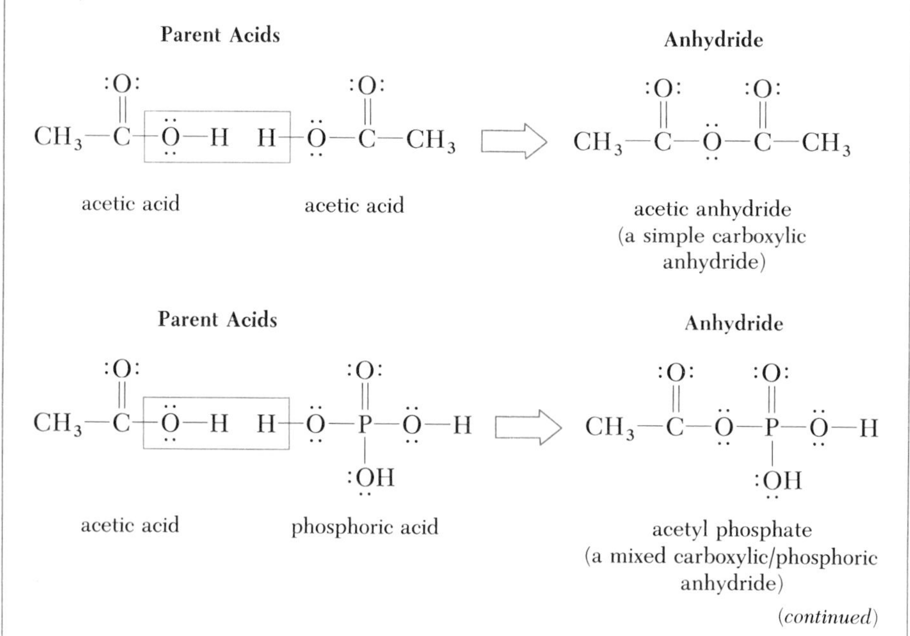

(*continued*)

(continued from previous page)

Parent Acids

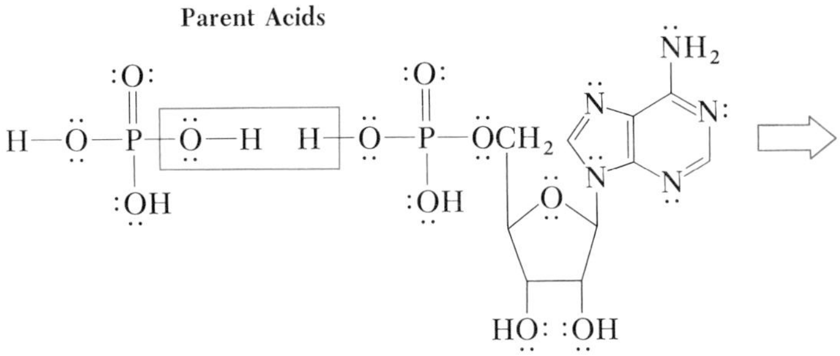

phosphoric acid

adenosine monophosphate (AMP)

Anhydride

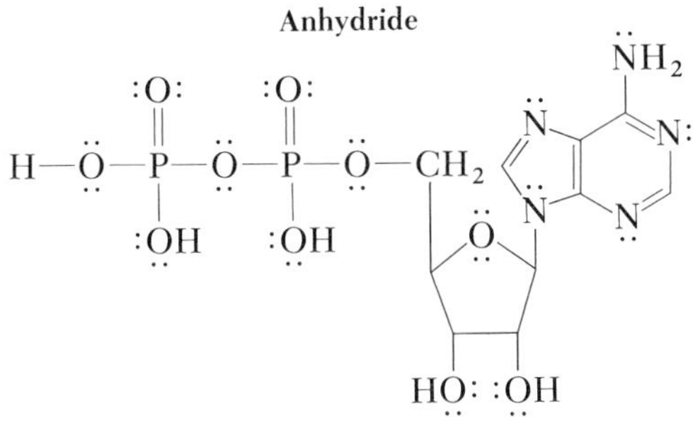

adenosine diphosphate (ADP)
(a phosphoric anhydride)

Anhydrides of this general type are involved in biological systems in the formation of a variety of types of ester linkages such as phosphate esters, which were previously discussed in Chapter 6 and will be studied in more detail in Chapter 28.

ful laboratory reagent commonly used to introduce the acetyl group, $CH_3—C[O]—$ into organic compounds. It is a mobile liquid with a sharp, irritating odor.

Anhydrides are less sensitive to nucleophilic attack than are acid halides. For example, while acetyl chloride reacts instantly and violently with water to form acetic acid, acetic anhydride needs to be boiled for several minutes with water to effect total hydrolysis. In cold water, acetic anhydride hydrolyzes rather slowly, requiring several hours to reach completion. Figure 21.14 shows the hydrolysis reaction of an anhydride.

Although special methods exist for the preparation of individual anhydrides, one general method of considerable utility involves the reaction of a carboxylate salt with an acid halide. An example of this type of reaction is shown in Equation 21.22.

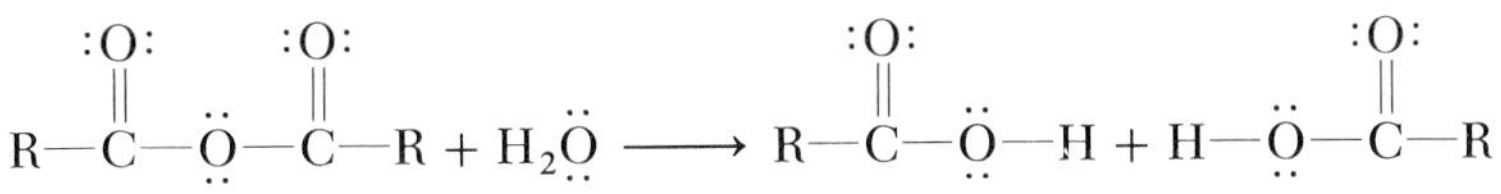

Figure 21.14 Reaction of a carboxylic anhydride with water. Two equivalents of the carboxylic acid form in this reaction. Reversal of the reaction requires a dehydrating agent to remove one molecule of water from the two carboxylic acid molecules.

$$R—C(=O)—O—C(=O)—R + H_2O \longrightarrow R—C(=O)—O—H + H—O—C(=O)—R$$

Eqn. 21.22

$$CH_3(CH_2)_5\overset{\overset{:O:}{\|}}{C}-\ddot{\underset{..}{O}}:^{-}\ Na^+ + CH_3(CH_2)_5\overset{\overset{:O:}{\|}}{C}-\ddot{\underset{..}{Cl}}: \longrightarrow CH_3(CH_2)_5\overset{\overset{:O:}{\|}}{C}-\ddot{\underset{..}{O}}-\overset{\overset{:O:}{\|}}{C}(CH_2)_5CH_3$$

sodium heptanoate — heptanoyl chloride — 60% yield heptanoic anhydride

We can use this method to prepare either symmetric or unsymmetric anhydrides. In general, unsymmetric anhydrides (derived from two *different* carboxylic acids) are of little use for organic synthesis. Mixed anhydrides of carboxylic acids and other acids are of some interest and are particularly important in biological processes.

PROBLEM 21.12 Describe two ways to prepare acetic benzoic anhydride.

PROBLEM 21.13 Name the organic products you would expect from the reaction of acetic anhydride with each of the following:
a. methanol **b.** ammonia

PROBLEM 21.14 Ketene ($H_2C{=}C{=}O$) can be prepared by the pyrolysis of acetic acid at 700 °C. Ketene reacts with acetic acid to form acetic anhydride. Write a mechanism for this preparation of acetic anhydride.

PROBLEM 21.15 What products would you expect from the reaction of ketene (see Problem 21.14) with each of the following compounds:
a. hydrogen chloride **b.** ammonia **c.** ethanol

Carboxylic Acid Esters We discussed esters previously (Chapter 6) in our study of alcohols. Structurally, we can view esters as molecules derived from a parent alcohol and a parent acid, as is illustrated schematically in Figure 21.15.

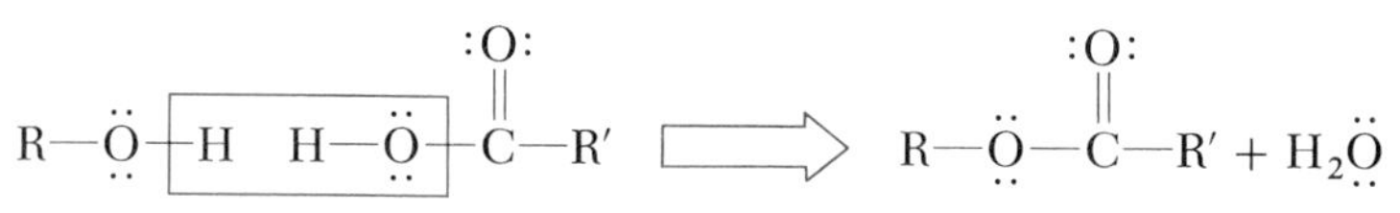

$$R-\ddot{\underset{..}{O}}-H\quad H-\ddot{\underset{..}{O}}-\overset{\overset{:O:}{\|}}{C}-R' \Longrightarrow R-\ddot{\underset{..}{O}}-\overset{\overset{:O:}{\|}}{C}-R' + H_2\ddot{\underset{..}{O}}$$

Figure 21.15 Schematic relationship of an ester to a carboxylic acid and an alcohol. The nomenclature of esters reflects the names of the parent acid and alcohol. For example, the ester formed from benzyl alcohol and acetic acid is benzyl acetate.

PROBLEM 21.16 Write the structure of benzyl acetate, which is formed in the esterification of acetic acid with benzyl alcohol.

PROBLEM 21.17 Name the esters whose structures are shown.

a. 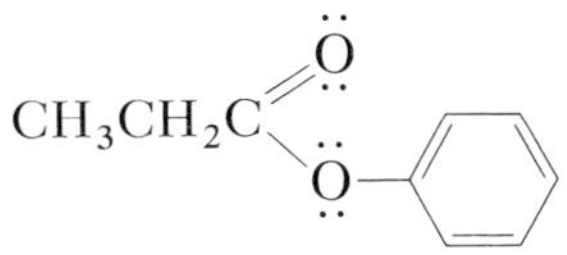 $CH_3CH_2C(=O)-O-C_6H_5$ b. 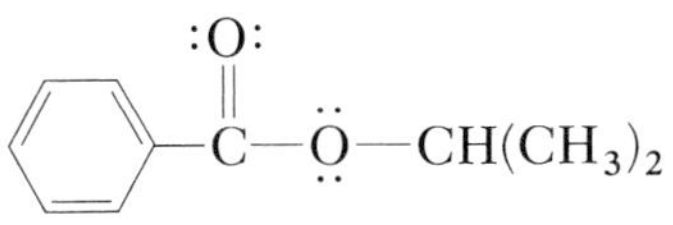 $C_6H_5-C(=O)-O-CH(CH_3)_2$

Esters of carboxylic acids can be prepared in numerous ways. The simplest is direct reaction of a carboxylic acid with an alcohol under conditions of acid catalysis, a procedure known as **Fischer esterification.** A molecule of water is produced as the by-product. An example of this reaction is shown in Equation 21.23.

Eqn. 21.23

$$(CH_3)_3CCH_2COOH + CH_3CH_2OH \xrightarrow{H_2SO_4} (CH_3)_3CCH_2-C(=O)-OCH_2CH_3$$

3,3-dimethylbutanoic acid → 77% yield ethyl 3,3-dimethylbutanoate

The mechanism involves a series of acid-base reactions.

MECHANISM OF REACTION

Acid-Catalyzed Esterification of a Carboxylic Acid

Step 1 Protonation of the carboxylic acid

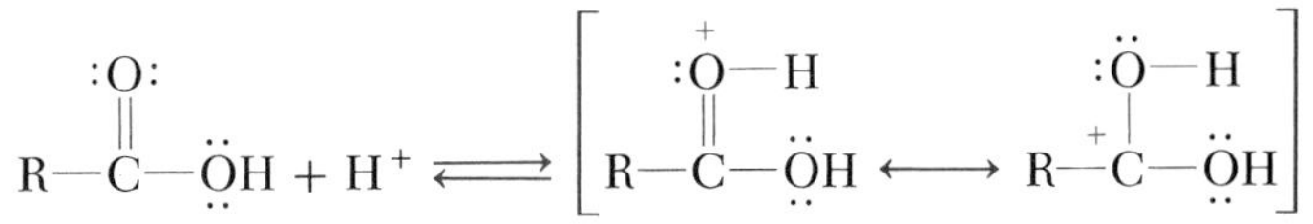

$$R-C(=O)-OH + H^+ \rightleftharpoons \left[R-C(=\overset{+}{O}-H)-OH \longleftrightarrow R-\overset{+}{C}(-OH)-OH \right]$$

Step 2 Nucleophilic attack by an alcohol

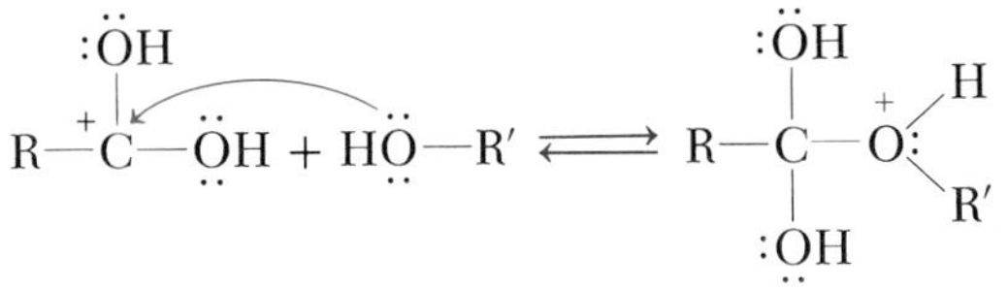

$$R-\overset{+}{C}(OH)-OH + HO-R' \rightleftharpoons R-C(OH)(OH)-\overset{+}{O}(H)R'$$

Steps 3 and 4 Proton transfer (B: is some suitable base present in solution)

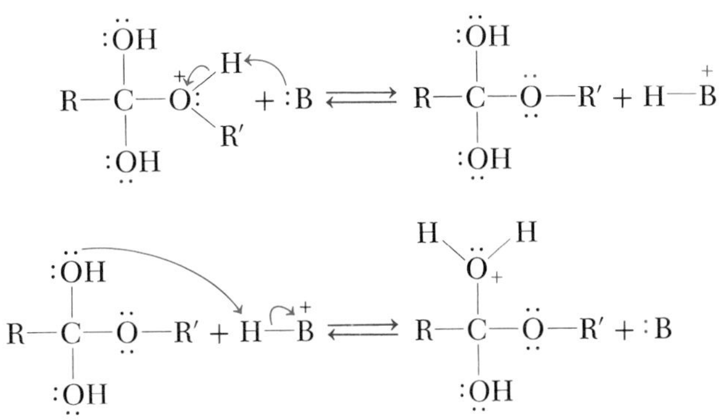

$$R-C(OH)(OH)-\overset{+}{O}(H)R' + :B \rightleftharpoons R-C(OH)(OH)-O-R' + H-\overset{+}{B}$$

$$R-C(OH)(OH)-O-R' + H-\overset{+}{B} \rightleftharpoons R-C(\overset{+}{O}H_2)(OH)-O-R' + :B$$

Step 5 Water loss

$$\mathrm{R{-}\overset{\overset{+\ddot{O}H_2}{|}}{\underset{\underset{:\ddot{O}H}{|}}{C}}{-}\ddot{O}{-}R'} \rightleftharpoons \left[\mathrm{R{-}\overset{+}{\underset{\underset{:\ddot{O}H}{|}}{C}}{-}\ddot{O}{-}R'} \longleftrightarrow \mathrm{R{-}\underset{\underset{+\ddot{O}H}{\|}}{C}{-}\ddot{O}{-}R'}\right] + H_2\ddot{O}$$

Step 6 Deprotonation

$$\mathrm{B{:}} + \mathrm{R{-}\overset{+}{\underset{\underset{H-\ddot{O}:}{|}}{C}}{-}\ddot{O}{-}R'} \rightleftharpoons \mathrm{R{-}\underset{\underset{:O:}{\|}}{C}{-}\ddot{O}{-}R'} + \overset{+}{\mathrm{B}}{-}\mathrm{H}$$

This mechanism is quite important and has several points that we need to consider. First, all steps are equilibrium reactions, so the whole sequence is completely reversible. Thus, we should be able to synthesize a carboxylic acid from an ester as well as an ester from the carboxylic acid. This is in fact the case. We can cause the reaction to proceed either toward the ester or toward the acid by choosing the appropriate reaction conditions. If we wish to prepare an ester from a carboxylic acid, we generally use an excess of the alcohol and/or remove one of the products of the reaction (water) as it is formed (see Chapter 19). To prepare an acid from an ester, we choose conditions that shift the equilibrium in the opposite direction. Specifically, the ester is heated with a large excess of water and a catalytic amount of acid; we say that we are *hydrolyzing* the ester to its parent carboxylic acid and alcohol.

A second important point is that this mechanism explains the experimental observation that the two oxygen atoms of the product arise from different sources. The *carbonyl-type oxygen* is derived from the carboxylic acid, but the *ether-type oxygen* comes from the alcohol.

PROBLEM 21.18 Verify that the mechanism illustrated above is truly catalytic in acid. Specifically, note the number of steps in which H^+ is consumed and the number in which it is generated.

PROBLEM 21.19 Suppose we treat benzoic acid under each of the sets of conditions listed below. At the end of the reaction, where will the ^{18}O isotopic label be located in the product? Estimate the percentage of the product molecules that contain the ^{18}O label.

a. Benzoic acid (containing only ^{16}O) in reaction with ethanol ($CH_3CH_2{}^{18}OH$, 100% isotopically pure) in benzene with a catalytic amount of sulfuric acid. Water is removed using a Dean-Stark trap.

b. Benzoic acid (one of the two oxygens in each molecule is ^{18}O) in reaction with ethanol (containing only ^{16}O) in benzene with a catalytic amount of sulfuric acid. Water is removed using a Dean-Stark trap.

c. Benzoic acid (containing only ^{18}O) is heated with an aqueous solution of sulfuric acid in which all of the oxygen is ^{16}O.

Molecules containing both a hydroxyl and a carboxylic acid group can undergo *intramolecular* ester formation. The product of such a reaction is a cyclic ester known as a **lactone.** An example is shown in Equation 21.24.

Eqn. 21.24

$$HOCH_2CH_2CH_2CH_2CH_2COOH \xrightarrow[\text{heat, } C_6H_6]{p\text{-}CH_3C_6H_4SO_3H}$$ (seven-membered lactone ring, carbons labeled α, β, γ, δ, ε)

6-hydroxyhexanoic acid

43% yield
ε-caprolactone

Lactones form most readily when the ring contains five, six, or seven members. We refer to these respectively as γ-, δ-, and ε-lactones. Thus, the lactone shown in Equation 21.24 is an ε-lactone. Smaller (≤ 4) rings form only with difficulty because of the strain involved in forming the ring. Larger (≥ 8) rings form with poor efficiency as a result of the statistical improbability that the two distant ends of a single, open-chain precursor will come close enough to react.

PROBLEM 21.20 An organic chemistry student attempted to perform the reaction shown in Equation 21.24 using 20 grams of the 6-hydroxyhexanoic acid in a solution of benzene with a total volume of 100 mL. He obtained a less than 10% yield of the target material along with a much larger quantity of intractable high molecular weight "garbage." What went wrong in this reaction? How could he have prevented this difficulty and obtained a better yield of the target material?

Dicyclohexylcarbodiimide (DCC, **21.11**) facilitates ester formation from a carboxylic acid and an alcohol. An example of the use of this reagent is shown in Equation 21.25.

$$C_6H_{11}\text{—}N{=}C{=}N\text{—}C_6H_{11}$$

dicyclohexylcarbodiimide
21.11

Eqn. 21.25

$$C_6H_5CH_2CH_2COOH + (CH_3)_2CHOH \xrightarrow[p\text{-}CH_3C_6H_5SO_3H]{DCC}$$

2-phenylpropanoic acid; 2-propanol

$$C_6H_5CH_2CH_2C({=}O)\text{—}O\text{—}CH(CH_3)_2$$

99% yield
isopropyl 2-phenylpropanoate

DCC has two roles. First, it converts the —OH of the carboxyl group into a much better leaving group, and second, it picks up the elements of water that are eliminated in the ester-forming reaction, thus preventing the reaction from reversing. The reaction proceeds by a series of acid-base reactions and usually requires a catalytic amount of acid, such as *p*-toluenesulfonic acid or phosphoric acid, for initiation. The details of the mechanism are given below.

MECHANISM OF REACTION

DCC-Mediated Coupling of a Carboxylic Acid and an Alcohol

Step 1 Protonation of DCC. R represents the cyclohexyl group.

$$R{-}\ddot{N}{=}C{=}\ddot{N}{-}R + H^+ \rightleftharpoons \left[R{-}\ddot{N}{=}C{=}\overset{H}{\underset{+}{N}}{-}R \longleftrightarrow R{-}\ddot{N}{=}\underset{+}{C}{-}\overset{H}{\ddot{N}}{-}R \right]$$

Step 2 Nucleophilic attack by the carboxylic acid.

$$R{-}\ddot{N}{=}\underset{+}{C}{-}\overset{H}{N}{-}R + R'{-}\underset{\|\ :O:}{C}{-}\ddot{O}{-}H \longrightarrow R{-}\ddot{N}{=}C(\ddot{N}HR)({-}\overset{+}{O}(H){-}C({=}O){-}R')$$

Step 3 Proton transfer.

$$B{:} + R{-}\ddot{N}{=}C(\ddot{N}HR)({-}\overset{+}{O}(H){-}C({=}O){-}R') \rightleftharpoons R{-}\ddot{N}{=}C(\ddot{N}HR)({-}\ddot{O}{-}C({=}O){-}R') + \overset{+}{B}{-}H$$

Step 4 Nucleophilic addition by the alcohol.

$$R{-}\ddot{N}{=}C(\ddot{N}HR)({-}\ddot{O}{-}C({=}O){-}R') + H{-}\ddot{O}{-}R'' \longrightarrow R{-}\ddot{N}{=}C(\ddot{N}HR)({-}\ddot{O}{-}C(R')(:\ddot{O}:^-)({-}\overset{+}{O}(H){-}R''))$$

Step 5 Proton transfer.

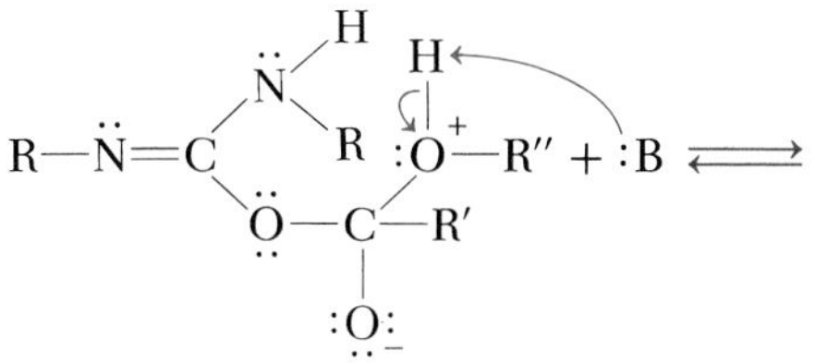

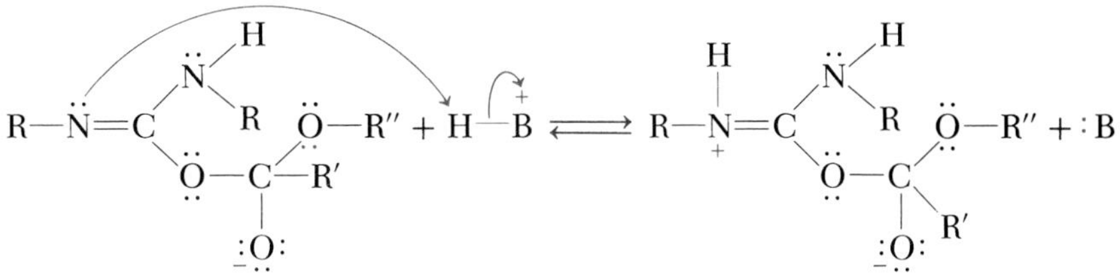

Step 6 Formation of products. Dicyclohexylurea is formed as a by-product.

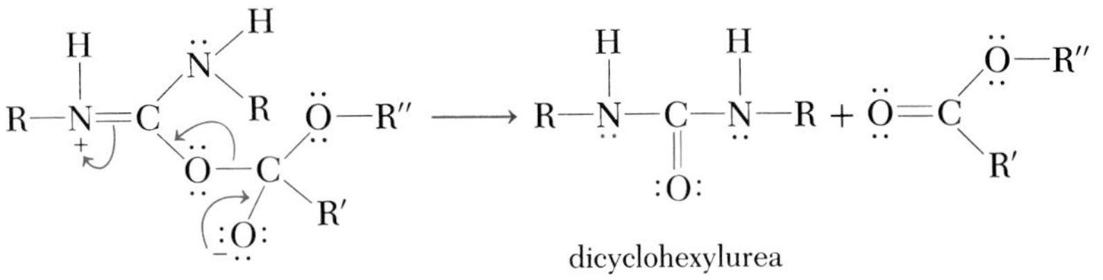

dicyclohexylurea

PROBLEM 21.21 In the first step of the mechanism shown above, two resonance structures for a resonance-stabilized cation are shown. Give a third resonance structure for this cation.

PROBLEM 21.22 Draw structures for each of the following:

a. cyclohexyl acetate
b. *sec*-butyl formate
c. *p*-nitrobenzyl benzoate
d. isobutyl 3-phenylpropanoate
e. ethyl α-bromopropanoate
f. diethyl adipate
g. methyl 2-methylbutanoate

PROBLEM 21.23 Suggest a structure for a compound of formula $C_6H_8O_4$ that is formed when lactic acid ($CH_3CH(OH)COOH$) is heated.

PROBLEM 21.24 Propose syntheses for each of the following esters from the indicated starting materials and methanol or ethanol, using any needed inorganic reagents.

a. methyl 2,2-dimethylpropanoate from 3,3-dimethyl-2-butanone
b. ethyl hexanoate from 1-hexanol
c. methyl pentanoate from 1-bromobutane

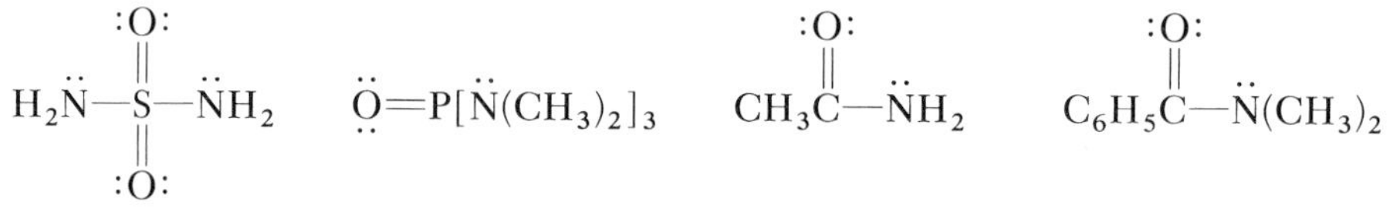

Figure 21.16 Inorganic and carboxylic acid amides. We can think of a carboxylic amide as being derived from a parent amine (or ammonia) and a parent carboxylic acid. This derivation is reflected in their nomenclature, as shown.

$$H_2\ddot{N}-S(=O)_2-\ddot{N}H_2 \qquad \ddot{O}=P[\ddot{N}(CH_3)_2]_3 \qquad CH_3C(=O)-\ddot{N}H_2 \qquad C_6H_5C(=O)-\ddot{N}(CH_3)_2$$

sulfamide — hexamethyl phosphorictriamide — ethanamide (acetamide) — *N*,*N*-dimethylbenzamide

Carboxylic Acid Amides Amides are derivatives of oxyacids in which an $-NR_2$ (or $-NH_2$ or $-NHR$) group is present in place of the $-OH$ of the parent acid. Examples of inorganic and carboxylic acid amides are shown in Figure 21.16.

PROBLEM 21.25 Draw structures for each of the following:
a. *N*-phenylacetamide b. *N*,*N*-dimethylbutyramide
c. phenylacetamide

Amides can be prepared by the reaction of ammonia or an amine with a suitable derivative, as shown in Figure 21.17.

Carboxylic acids (**G** = OH) are not good substrates for this reaction. Instead, carboxylic acids react with amines and ammonia to form salts of the general form $RCOO^-\ R_3NH^+$. In such reactions, the ammonia (or amine) acts as a Brønsted base rather than as a nucleophile. The $-OH$ group is not involved in any way as a leaving group.

PROBLEM 21.26 You might think that amide formation from ammonia and a carboxylic acid would be promoted by a catalytic amount of acid that, in principle, could convert the poor leaving group, $-OH$, into a better leaving group, $-OH_2^+$, and encourage nucleophilic attack by ammonia. However, while the treatment of benzoic acid with methanol in the presence of a catalytic amount of acid is effective for the preparation of methyl benzoate, treating benzoic acid and ammonia with a catalytic amount of sulfuric acid is not effective for the preparation of benzamide. Explain why the latter preparation is not feasible.

It is possible to convert the ammonium salts of some carboxylic acids into amides by heating. The carboxylic acid is heated strongly with ammonia or an amine. Under these conditions, the salt that forms initially decomposes to form an amide. An example is shown in Equation 21.26.

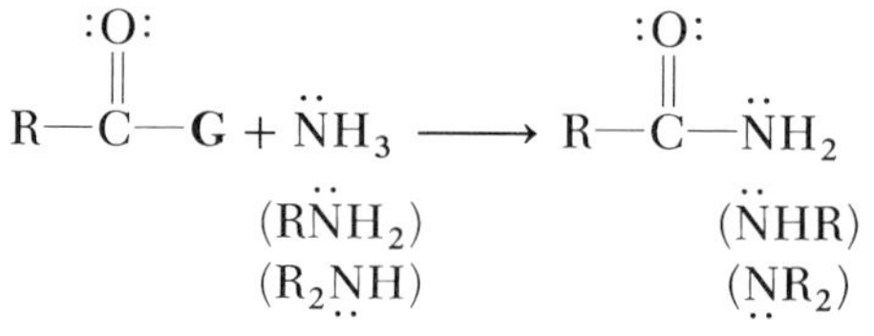

Figure 21.17 Preparation of amides. The reaction involves nucleophilic attack by ammonia or an amine on the carboxyl carbon. The group **G** is displaced.

$$R-C(=\ddot{O}:)-\mathbf{G} + \ddot{N}H_3\ (R\ddot{N}H_2)\ (R_2\ddot{N}H) \longrightarrow R-C(=\ddot{O}:)-\ddot{N}H_2\ (\ddot{N}HR)\ (\ddot{N}R_2)$$

Eqn. 21.26

$$CH_3(CH_2)_5COOH \xrightarrow[190\,^\circ C]{NH_3} CH_3(CH_2)_5C(=O)NH_2$$

heptanoic acid — 75% yield heptanamide

In general, however, this is not the method of choice for preparing amides.

A much better way of preparing amides is to treat the acid chloride with ammonia or an amine. An example is shown in Equation 21.27.

Eqn. 21.27

$$C_6H_{11}C(=O)Cl + HN(CH_3)_2 \longrightarrow C_6H_{11}C(=O)N(CH_3)_2$$

cyclohexanecarbonyl chloride — dimethylamine — 86% yield *N*,*N*-dimethylcyclohexanecarboxamide

DCC can also be used to couple amines and carboxylic acids. An example is shown in Equation 21.28. This use is analogous to its previously discussed use for coupling alcohols and carboxylic acid to produce esters.

Eqn. 21.28

$$BrCH_2CH_2COOH + 3,5\text{-}(CH_3O)_2C_6H_3NH_2 \xrightarrow[CH_2Cl_2]{DCC} BrCH_2CH_2C(=O)NH\text{-}C_6H_3(OCH_3)_2$$

3-bromopropanoic acid — 3,5-dimethoxyaniline — 78% yield *N*-(3,5-dimethoxyphenyl)-3-bromopropionamide

---

PROBLEM 21.27 Write out in detail the mechanism for the DCC-mediated coupling of an amine (RNH_2) and a carboxylic acid, ($R'COOH$) to form an amide. (*Hint:* See the mechanism shown earlier for the use of DCC in ester formation.)

PROBLEM 21.28 If ammonia is heated with carbon dioxide, we obtain a compound known as ammonium carbamate. With continued heating, ammonium carbamate decomposes to urea (CH_4N_2O) and water. Suggest structures for ammonium carbamate and urea. More than 10^{10} pounds of urea are produced annually in the United States by this method. The urea is used mainly as a fertilizer.

THE α-HALOGENATION OF CARBOXYLIC ACIDS

The preparation of an α-halocarboxylic acid directly from the parent carboxylic acid is an important reaction. It provides starting material for the preparation of other α-substituted acid derivatives. A common approach is to allow the parent acid to react with a mixture of halogen (generally bromine) and a phosphorus trihalide (such as phosphorus tribromide). This treatment produces the α-haloacid halide, which, upon workup with water, gives the free α-haloacid. The procedure is known as the **Hell-Volhard-Zelinskii reaction.**

The reagents originally used in this reaction were bromine and elemental phosphorus. It was soon recognized, however, that the initial reaction involved the formation of phosphorus tribromide by reaction of the elemental phosphorus and the bromine. Bromine itself does not accomplish the conversion. The role of the phosphorus tribromide is to convert the carboxylic acid to the acid bromide. The enol form of the acid bromide then reacts with elemental bromine to form the α-bromoacid bromide. The mechanism is summarized below.

MECHANISM OF REACTION

The Hell-Volhard-Zelinskii Reaction

Overall reaction:

$$RCH_2C(=O)-OH \xrightarrow[PBr_3]{Br_2} RCH(Br)-C(=O)-OH$$

Step 1 Acid bromide formation. The mechanism is like that in Section 6.7.

$$RCH_2C(=O)-OH + :PBr_3 \longrightarrow RCH_2C(=O)-Br: + HOPBr_2$$

Step 2 Keto-enol tautomerism. (See Chapter 15 for a discussion of this process.)

$$RCH_2C(=O)-Br: \rightleftharpoons RC(H)=C(OH)-Br:$$

Step 3 Bromination.

$$RC(H)=C(OH)-Br: + :Br-Br: \longrightarrow RCH(Br)-C(=O)-Br: + :Br:^- + H^+$$

Steps 4–6 Hydrolysis.

$$\mathrm{RCH(Br)}-\mathrm{C}(=\mathrm{O})-\mathrm{Br} + \mathrm{H_2O} \longrightarrow \mathrm{RCH(Br)}-\mathrm{C}(\mathrm{O^-})(\mathrm{Br})-\overset{+}{\mathrm{O}}\mathrm{H_2}$$

$$\mathrm{RCH(Br)}-\mathrm{C}(\mathrm{O^-})(\mathrm{Br})-\overset{+}{\mathrm{O}}\mathrm{H_2} \longrightarrow \mathrm{RCH(Br)}-\mathrm{C}(=\mathrm{O})-\overset{+}{\mathrm{O}}\mathrm{H_2} + \mathrm{Br^-}$$

$$\mathrm{RCH(Br)}-\mathrm{C}(=\mathrm{O})-\overset{+}{\mathrm{O}}\mathrm{H_2} + \mathrm{Br^-} \longrightarrow \mathrm{RCH(Br)}-\mathrm{C}(=\mathrm{O})-\mathrm{O}-\mathrm{H} + \mathrm{H}-\mathrm{Br}$$

An example of the Hell-Volhard-Zelinskii reaction is shown in Equation 21.29. With proper care, the intermediate α-halogenated acid halide is isolable.

Eqn. 21.29

$$\underset{\text{hexadecanoic acid}}{\mathrm{CH_3(CH_2)_{13}CH_2COOH}} \xrightarrow[\mathrm{PBr_3}]{\mathrm{Br_2}} \underset{96\%\text{ yield}}{\mathrm{CH_3(CH_2)_{13}CHBrC(=O)-Br}}$$

$$\mathrm{CH_3(CH_2)_{13}CHBrC(=O)-Br} \xrightarrow{\mathrm{H_2O}} \underset{\substack{92\%\text{ yield}\\ \text{2-bromohexadecanoic acid}}}{\mathrm{CH_3(CH_2)_{13}CHBrC(=O)-OH}}$$

In later chapters we will see reactions that use α-halocarboxylic acids for the preparation of a variety of useful compounds.

REDUCTIONS OF CARBOXYLIC ACIDS

Carboxylic acids represent the highest oxidation state of carbon in the series:

hydrocarbon < 1° alcohol < aldehyde < carboxylic acid

Therefore, the conversion of carboxylic acids to aldehydes, alcohols, and hydrocarbons requires reduction. Several methods of reduction will be described.

Lithium Aluminum Hydride Reduction Carboxylic acids undergo reaction with the powerful reducing agent lithium aluminum hydride ($LiAlH_4$) to give alkoxide salts. The free alcohol is obtained upon workup of the reaction with aqueous acid. Since lithium aluminum hydride also reacts with a variety of other functional groups, we cannot use it to reduce a carboxyl group selectively in the presence of other reducible functional groups such as aldehydes and ketones.

A general difficulty associated with lithium aluminum hydride reductions of carboxylic acids is the selection of a solvent in which both reactants dissolve. Many carboxylic acids dissolve well in protic polar solvents such as alcohols, but these solvents are incompatible with the use of $LiAlH_4$ (they would immediately react with it, producing hydrogen gas). Instead, ether solvents must be used, but typically the carboxylic acid has only limited solubility in ether solvents. Reduction can nevertheless be effected, even under these circumstances, as shown in Equation 21.30.

Eqn. 21.30

$$C_6H_5COOH \xrightarrow[\text{2. aq acid}]{\text{1. LiAlH}_4\text{, THF, 3 hours, heat}} C_6H_5CH_2\ddot{O}H$$

benzoic acid — 91% yield benzyl alcohol

Because of the solubility problem, it is often more convenient to reduce a *derivative* of a carboxylic acid, such as an ester, instead of the carboxylic acid itself. This procedure will be discussed further in Chapter 22.

PROBLEM 21.29 Treatment of 0.1 mole of benzoic acid with 0.04 mole of lithium aluminum hydride provides reduction of only a portion of the acid to the alcohol. All of the lithium aluminum hydride is consumed, in spite of the fact that each mole of lithium aluminum hydride provides *four* moles of reducing hydride. Explain the observed result.

Borane Reductions Complexes of borane such as the borane-tetrahydrofuran complex provide a convenient alternative to lithium aluminum hydride. Reduction of the carboxyl group occurs rapidly to form a primary alcohol at room temperature without disturbing other functional groups that are sensitive to lithium aluminum hydride. An example is shown in Equation 21.31. If lithium aluminum hydride were used for this conversion, reduction of the —CN group to $—CH_2NH_2$ would also occur.

Eqn. 21.31

COOH / CN (benzene ring) $\xrightarrow{H_3\bar{B}—\overset{+}{O}\text{(THF ring)}}$ $CH_2\ddot{O}H$ / CN (benzene ring)

p-cyanobenzoic acid — 82% yield *p*-cyanobenzyl alcohol

DECARBOXYLATION OF CARBOXYLIC ACIDS

Direct Decarboxylation The *removal* of a carboxyl group from an organic molecule and its replacement (by hydrogen, halogen, or some other atom or group) is known as **decarboxylation.**

The ease with which carboxylic acids undergo decarboxylation varies greatly with structure. Some carboxylic acids undergo decarboxylation readily upon heating. Others, in reactions that have little synthetic utility, require more drastic treatment.

Two types of carboxylic acids that undergo decarboxylation under particularly mild conditions are those related to malonic acid (**21.12**) and acetoacetic acid (**21.13**).

$$HOOC{-}CH_2{-}COOH \qquad HOOC{-}CH_2{-}\overset{\overset{:O:}{\|}}{C}{-}CH_3$$

malonic acid **21.12** — acetoacetic acid **21.13**

Examples of two facile decarboxylations of carboxylic acids in these categories are shown in Equations 21.32 and 21.33.

Eqn. 21.32

$$CH_3CH_2\underset{\underset{CH_3}{|}}{C}HCH(COOH)_2 \xrightarrow[\text{heat}]{H_2SO_4} CH_3CH_2\underset{\underset{CH_3}{|}}{C}HCH_2COOH$$

65% yield

Eqn. 21.33

$$CH_3\overset{\overset{:O:}{\|}}{C}\underset{\underset{COOH}{|}}{C}HCH_2CH_2CH_2CH_3 \xrightarrow[\text{heat}]{H_2SO_4} CH_3\overset{\overset{:O:}{\|}}{C}CH_2CH_2CH_2CH_2CH_3$$

61% yield

The mechanism by which a β-ketocarboxylic acid decarboxylates is illustrated below. The reaction occurs via a cyclic six-membered activated complex. The acidic hydrogen of the carboxyl group is transferred intramolecularly to the oxygen at the β-position with the accompanying loss of carbon dioxide. The immediate product of this fragmentation is the decarboxylated species, the enol form of the simple ketone. At equilibrium the keto form by far dominates the initially formed enol structure.

MECHANISM OF REACTION

Decarboxylation of a β-Ketocarboxylic Acid

Step 1 Intramolecular transfer of hydrogen with simultaneous carbon-carbon bond cleavage

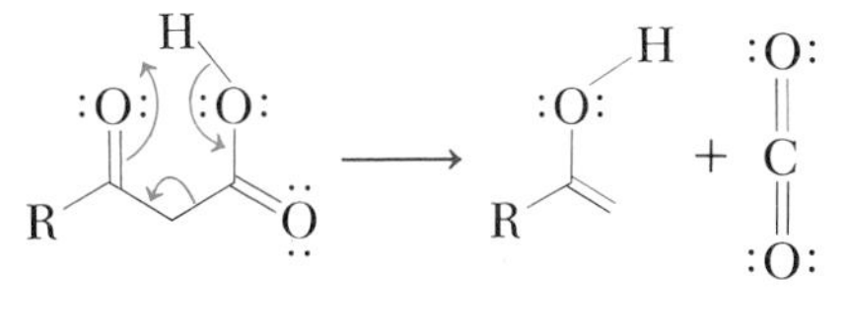

$$R\text{-}C(=\ddot{O}:)\text{-}CH_2\text{-}C(=\ddot{O}:\cdots H)\text{-}\ddot{O} \longrightarrow R\text{-}C(\text{-}\ddot{O}\text{-}H)=CH_2 + :\ddot{O}=C=\ddot{O}:$$

Step 2 Keto-enol tautomerism

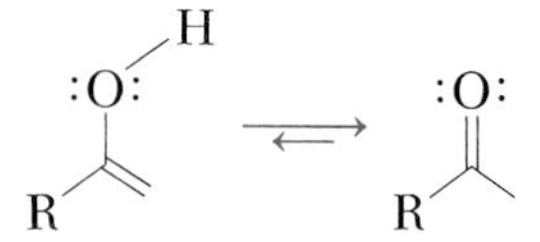

PROBLEM 21.30 Using the above mechanism of β-ketocarboxylic acid decarboxylation, propose a mechanism for the decarboxylation of $CH_3CH_2CH(COOH)_2$ to butanoic acid.

The intermediate enol form of the decarboxylated product is crucial to the decarboxylation. If such an enol cannot form or is highly destabilized, decarboxylation will not occur. A rather interesting example of this phenomenon exists with certain bicyclic systems. If the enol that would be formed has a double bond to a bridgehead carbon atom, it is highly destabilized and will not form. The reason for the instability lies in the structural constraints imposed by the bicyclic system, as illustrated in Figure 21.18.

PROBLEM 21.31 Using a set of molecular models, demonstrate the difficulty involved in the formation of the enol form of the proposed ketone product shown in Figure 21.18.

PROBLEM 21.32 In organic chemistry there is a rule known as *Bredt's rule*, which states that double bonds to a bridgehead carbon atom are very weak. However, chemists have been able to prepare such compounds if the bridge is sufficiently long. Explain why increasing the length of the bridge (increasing the value of n in the structure shown below) should improve the stability of the double bond. Use molecular models to demonstrate this phenomenon.

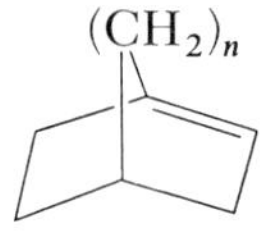

$(CH_2)_n$

Figure 21.18 Lack of decarboxylation for a bicyclic β-ketoacid. The enol form of the potential product is highly unstable because it involves a double bond to the bridgehead carbon of a bicyclo[2.2.1]-heptane structure. The contributing p orbitals for the π bond of such an enol structure cannot be parallel, and thus the π bond is greatly weakened. Because the intermediate does not form, no overall decarboxylation occurs.

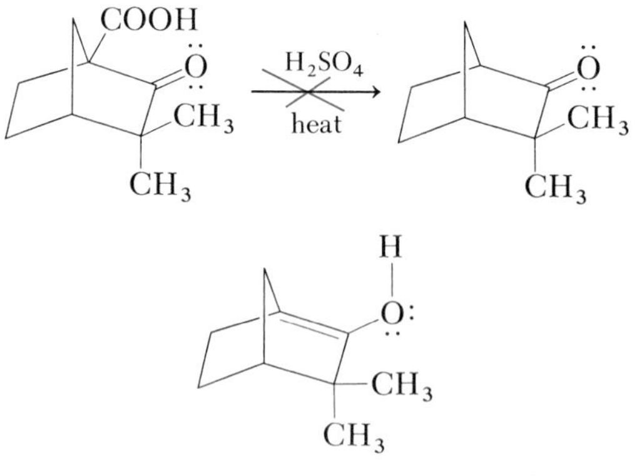

COOH, CH_3, CH_3 — H_2SO_4, heat — CH_3, CH_3

H, CH_3, CH_3

Enol cannot form because it is highly destablized.

The Hunsdiecker Reaction In the **Hunsdiecker reaction** a bromine atom takes the place of a carboxylic acid group. Thus, the overall reaction is conversion of RCOOH to RBr. To bring about the reaction, a silver salt of a carboxylic acid is allowed to react with bromine. Two examples of the Hunsdiecker reaction are shown in Equations 21.34 and 21.35.

Eqn. 21.34

$$CH_3(CH_2)_9CH_2COOAg \xrightarrow[CCl_4]{Br_2} CH_3(CH_2)_9CH_2Br$$

silver dodecanoate → 67% yield 1-bromoundecane

Eqn. 21.35

$$p\text{-}O_2N\text{-}C_6H_4\text{-}COOAg \xrightarrow[CCl_4]{Br_2} p\text{-}O_2N\text{-}C_6H_4\text{-}Br$$

silver *p*-nitrobenzoate → 79% yield *p*-nitrobromobenzene

The Hunsdiecker reaction occurs according to the mechanism shown below.

MECHANISM OF REACTION

The Hunsdiecker Reaction

Step 1 Nucleophilic attack of carboxylate on bromine

$$R{-}C({=}O){-}O^-\ Ag^+ + Br{-}Br \longrightarrow R{-}C({=}O){-}O{-}Br + AgBr$$

Step 2 Chain-initiating step

$$R{-}C({=}O){-}O{-}Br \xrightarrow{\text{heat}} R{-}C({=}O){-}O\cdot + \cdot Br$$

Steps 3 and 4 Chain-propagation steps

$$R{-}C({=}O){-}O\cdot \longrightarrow R\cdot + O{=}C{=}O$$

$$R\cdot + Br{-}O{-}C({=}O){-}R \longrightarrow R{-}Br + \cdot O{-}C({=}O){-}R$$

Step 5 Chain-termination step

$$R\cdot + \cdot\ddot{Br}: \longrightarrow R-\ddot{Br}:$$

In the preceding discussion of reductions, no mention was made of reagents that will reduce a carboxylic acid to an aldehyde because there is no good, general, one-step method. The conversion of a —COOH group to a —CHO group is usually done in two steps. A common procedure is to convert the carboxylic acid into a derivative, such as an acid chloride, for which a reagent is available for reduction to an aldehyde (see Chapter 22). Alternatively, the carboxylic acid can be reduced to an alcohol, and then the alcohol oxidized under controlled conditions (can you give the conditions?) to an aldehyde.

REACTIONS WITH ORGANOMETALLICS

Carboxylic acids react as Brønsted acids upon treatment with organometallic substances. Even acids as weak as carboxylic acids react immediately with the strong basic sites of typical organometallics. Once the carboxylate anion is formed, further reaction with the organometallic is retarded. With organometallics such as Grignard reagents, the carboxylate anion undergoes *no* further reaction. However, alkyllithium (and aryllithium) reagents are sufficiently nucleophilic that they attack the carboxyl carbon of carboxylate anions. These reagents are of use for the synthesis of ketones from carboxylic acids. Two examples are shown in Equations 21.36 and 21.37 (see Section 11.5 for a discussion of this type of reaction).

Eqn. 21.36

$$C_6H_5CH_2COOH \xrightarrow[\text{ether (aq acid workup)}]{CH_3Li} C_6H_5CH_2-\overset{\overset{:\ddot{O}:}{\|}}{C}-CH_3$$

phenylacetic acid → 76% yield benzyl methyl ketone

Eqn. 21.37

$$CH_3CH_2COOH \xrightarrow[\text{ether (aq acid workup)}]{C_6H_5Li} CH_3CH_2-\overset{\overset{:\ddot{O}:}{\|}}{C}-C_6H_5$$

propanoic acid → 82% yield propiophenone

While these reactions proceed in reasonable yield based on the starting carboxylic acid, they consume an extra equivalent of the organometallic. The first equivalent of organometallic reacts with the carboxylic acid as a base to form the carboxylate salt. The second equivalent of alkyllithium (aryllithium) reagent attacks the carboxyl carbon as a nucleophile to form the ketone. The reaction requires workup using aqueous acid. The final step of the mechanism is loss of water from the ketone hydrate to the ketone itself (this type of process was discussed in section 19.8).

MECHANISM OF REACTION

Reaction of an Alkyllithium (or Aryllithium) Reagent with a Carboxylic Acid

Step 1 Deprotonation

$$R-CH_2-\overset{\overset{:O:}{\|}}{C}-\ddot{\underset{..}{O}}-H + R'-Li \longrightarrow R-CH_2-\overset{\overset{:O:}{\|}}{C}-\ddot{\underset{..}{O}}:^{-}\ Li^+ + R'-H$$

Step 2 Nucleophilic addition

$$R-CH_2-\overset{\overset{:O:}{\|}}{C}-\ddot{\underset{..}{O}}:^{-}\ Li^+ + R'-Li \longrightarrow R-CH_2-\overset{:\ddot{O}:^{-}\ Li^+}{\underset{R'}{C}}-\ddot{\underset{..}{O}}:^{-}\ Li^+$$

Step 3 Protonation

$$R-CH_2-\overset{:\ddot{O}:^{-}\ Li^+}{\underset{R'}{C}}-\ddot{\underset{..}{O}}:^{-}\ Li^+ + 2\ H_2\ddot{\underset{..}{O}} \longrightarrow R-CH_2-\overset{:\ddot{O}H}{\underset{R'}{C}}-\ddot{\underset{..}{O}}H + 2\ Li\ddot{\underset{..}{O}}H$$

Step 4 Loss of water

$$R-CH_2-\overset{:\ddot{O}H}{\underset{R'}{C}}-\ddot{\underset{..}{O}}H \rightleftharpoons R-CH_2-\overset{\overset{:O:}{\|}}{C}-R' + H_2\ddot{\underset{..}{O}}$$

Most other organometallic reagents, such as Grignard reagents, are insufficiently nucleophilic to add to the carboxyl carbon of a carboxylate anion. A Grignard reagent simply removes the acidic hydrogen from the carboxylic acid (Step 1 in the preceding mechanism), and there is no further reaction.

PROBLEM 21.33 For Step 4 of the preceding mechanism, show a complete stepwise loss of water using the curved-arrow formalism.

21.7 IR and NMR Spectra of Carboxylic Acids

IR SPECTRA IN SOLUTION

The most characteristic IR signature of a carboxylic acid is a very broad absorption band stretching from $\sim 2500\ cm^{-1}$ to above $3000\ cm^{-1}$. We associate this band with a hydrogen-bonded O—H stretch. (A *free* hydroxyl band appears at higher frequency.) In the carbonyl region of the IR, carboxylic acids exhibit bands near 1760 cm^{-1} (monomer form) and 1710 cm^{-1} (dimer form). (Refer to Section 21.3 to review the monomer and dimer forms of carboxylic acids.) If there is conjugation of the carboxyl group with other π linkages, these values are lower by $\sim$20 cm^{-1}.

Salts of carboxylic acids exhibit none of the above features. Instead, they exhibit characteristic bands in the 1550–1610 cm^{-1} region and at $\sim$1400 cm^{-1}.

PROBLEM 21.34 Explain why salts of carboxylic acids do not exhibit a typical carbonyl stretch in their IR spectra.

^{1}H NMR SPECTRA

The acidic proton of a carboxylic acid produces a signal that is usually broad and appears in the region δ 10–13. This proton is exchangeable with D_2O. Thus, the signal disappears when a carboxylic acid is examined in D_2O solution. Protons at the α-carbon position come into resonance in the same region as those of aldehydes and ketones.

^{13}C NMR SPECTRA

The carboxyl carbon atom produces a signal in the region 170–180 ppm downfield from TMS in the ^{13}C NMR spectrum.

Summary

- Carboxylic acids are organic compounds that are weakly acidic on an absolute scale but are significantly more acidic than most other organic compounds.
- Upon removal of the acidic hydrogen from the free carboxylic acid molecule, a resonance-stabilized carboxylate anion forms. Its negative charge is delocalized over the pair of oxygen atoms.
- Substituents located near the carboxyl group have an important influence on the acidity of the substance. For example, electron-donating groups destabilize the anion and thus reduce the acidity of the parent molecule.
- Solvation effects are also important in influencing acidity.
- There is a variety of methods for the synthesis of carboxylic acids, including oxidations of alcohols, aldehydes, and methyl ketones and the carbonation of organometallics.
- Carboxylic acids can also be prepared by the hydrolysis of nitriles.
- Many simple derivatives of carboxylic acids can be prepared with relative ease. The most important of these are acid halides, acid anhydrides, esters, and amides.
- The carboxyl group can be reduced to a primary alcohol with relative ease. Stopping the reaction at the intermediate aldehyde requires special reaction conditions or the preliminary preparation of one of the carboxylic acid derivatives.
- Decarboxylation reactions remove a carboxyl group from a molecule. Molecules containing other nearby functional groups with which the carboxyl group can interact (such as a carbonyl group or another carboxyl group) undergo facile decarboxylation. The carboxyl group is replaced by hydrogen. In the absence of such proximate functional groups, we can still achieve decarboxylation by using the Hunsdiecker reaction to replace the carboxyl carbon with a halogen.

- A halogen atom can be introduced at the α-position of the carboxylic acid by reaction with a phosphorus trihalide and halogen.
- Most organometallic reagents simply remove the acidic hydrogen from a carboxylic acid, forming a carboxylate ion. However, alkyllithium (and aryllithium) reagents are sufficiently nucleophilic that they react further, attacking the carboxylate anion. This method is used for the synthesis of ketones from carboxylic acids.

Terms to Remember

carboxyl group
fatty acids
polyunsaturated fatty acids
carboxylate ion
soaps
carbonation
carboxyl derivative
anhydride
Fischer esterification
lactone
Hell-Volhard-Zelinskii reaction
decarboxylation
Hunsdiecker reaction

Reactions of Synthetic Utility

159. $RMgX \xrightarrow[\text{2. aq acid}]{\text{1. } CO_2} RCOOH$ — 21.5

160. $RCN \xrightarrow{\text{aq acid, heat}} RCOOH$ — 21.5

161. $RCOOH \xrightarrow[\text{halides}]{\text{inorganic acid}} RCOCl$ — 21.6

($SOCl_2$, PCl_3, PCl_5)

162. $RCOOH \xrightarrow{Ph_3P,\ CCl_4} RCOCl$ — 21.6

163. $RCOCl + R'COO^-M^+ \longrightarrow RC(=O)—O—C(=O)R'$ — 21.6

164. $RCOOH + R'OH \xrightarrow{\text{acid}} RC(=O)—OR'$ — 21.6

165. $RCOOH + R'OH \xrightarrow{\text{DCC}} RC(=O)—OR'$ — 21.6

166. $R—C(=O)—G + HNR_2 \longrightarrow R—C(=O)—NR_2$ — 21.6

$G = Cl,\ OC(=O)R,\ OR$

167. $RCOOH + HNR_2 \xrightarrow{\text{DCC}} RC(=O)NR_2$ — 21.6

168. $R_2CHCOOH \xrightarrow[2.\ H_2O]{1.\ PBr_3,\ Br_2} R_2CBrCOOH$ 21.6

169. $RCOOH \xrightarrow[\text{aq acid workup}]{LiAlH_4} RCH_2OH$ 21.6

170. $RCOOH \xrightarrow{H_3B-THF} RCH_2OH$ 21.6

171. $CH_3COCH_2COOH \xrightarrow{\text{heat}} CH_3COCH_3$ 21.6

172. $RCOO^-Ag^+ \xrightarrow[CCl_4]{Br_2} RBr$ 21.6

173. $RCOOH \xrightarrow[\text{acid workup}]{R'Li} RCOR'$ 21.6

Additional Problems

21.35 Draw structures for each of the following compounds:

a. 2-phenylbutanoic acid
b. 2-hydroxy-2-phenylacetic acid
c. propenoic acid
d. (Z)-9-octadecenoic acid
e. benzoic heptanoic anhydride
f. succinic anhydride
g. 3-methylbutanamide
h. *N*-isopropyl-*N*-methylbenzamide
i. 2-methylpropanenitrile (2-methylpropionitrile)
j. isobutyronitrile
k. *sec*-butyl 3,5-dinitrobenzoate
l. *N*-(4-bromophenyl)acetamide
m. methoxyacetic acid
n. α,β,γ-tribromo-*n*-butyric acid
o. β-methylglutaric acid
p. potassium propanoate
q. isobutyryl chloride
r. a substance of formula $C_6H_{12}O$ that reacts with I_2/NaOH in water to produce iodoform and, after acidification, a carboxylic acid of formula $C_5H_{10}O_2$. The ^1H NMR spectrum of the carboxylic acid consists of two singlets.
s. a substance of formula $C_4H_4N_2$ that on refluxing with aqueous mineral acid yields a dicarboxylic acid. On heating, the dicarboxylic acid forms a monomeric anhydride that has a single peak in its ^1H NMR spectrum.

21.36 Provide a systematic name for each of the following compounds:

a. $H_2C{=}CH{-}CH_2CH_2COOH$
b. $HOCH_2CH(CH_3)COOH$
c. $(CH_3CH_2)_3CCOOH$
d. $H_2C{=}CHCH_2COOCH(CH_3)CH_2CH_3$

21.37 Choose the compound in each pair with the indicated property. Explain your choice.

a. stronger acid: fluoroacetic acid or bromoacetic acid
b. stronger acid: $(CH_3)_3CCH_2COOH$ or CH_3OCH_2COOH
c. stronger acid: one with $pK_a = 4$ or $pK_a = 5$
d. stronger acid: $HOOCCH_2COOH$ or $HOOCCH_2CH_2COOH$
e. forms a cyclic anhydride: *cis*- or *trans*-cyclopentanedicarboxylic acid
f. contains C—O bonds of different length: formic acid or sodium formate

g. contains the longer C—O bonds: sodium formate or calcium carbonate
h. decarboxylates most readily on heating: 1,1-cyclobutanedicarboxylic acid or *cis*-1,2-cyclobutanedicarboxylic acid
i. undergoes the Hell-Volhard-Zelinskii reaction: benzoic acid or cyclohexanecarboxylic acid
j. most reactive with water: propionyl chloride or propionic anhydride
k. most readily forms a lactone: *cis*- or *trans*-3-hydroxycyclohexanecarboxylic acid

21.38 Give the reaction product of $PhCH_2CH_2COOH$ with each of the following:
a. aq NaOH
b. aq Na_2CO_3
c. cold, aq ammonia
d. lithium aluminum hydride
e. Ph_3P/CCl_4
f. Br_2/PBr_3
g. 1-butanol in the presence of acid
h. ethylene glycol in the presence of acid
i. phenyllithium in ether solution
j. methylmagnesium bromide in ether solution
k. hot, aq potassium dichromate in sulfuric acid

21.39 Primary amides form hydrogen-bonded dimers similar to those formed by carboxylic acids. Show the structure of such a dimer.

21.40 Outline the series of laboratory operations you would use to separate a carboxylic acid and an alcohol.

21.41 Which reagent or combination of reagents would you use to convert *p*-toluic acid (4-methylbenzoic acid) into each of the following:
a. sodium 4-methylbenzoate
b. terephthalic acid
c. *p*-toluamide
d. 4-methylbenzyl alcohol
e. 4-methylbenzaldehyde

21.42 Propose methods to acomplish each of the following conversions:
a. benzoic acid into *m*-nitrobenzoic acid
b. benzoic acid into *m*-bromobenzoic acid
c. bromobenzene into benzoic acid
d. acetophenone into benzoic acid
e. toluene into 3-nitrobenzoic acid
f. toluene into *p*-toluic acid
g. phenylacetic acid into phenylmalonic acid
h. acetophenone into *m*-ethylbenzoic acid
i. 4-methylaniline into *p*-toluic acid
j. 2-pentanol into 2-hydroxy-2-methylpentanoic acid
k. toluene into *N*-methyl-*p*-nitrobenzamide
l. cyclohexene into 1-hydroxy-1-cyclohexanecarboxylic acid
m. cyclopentane into cyclopentanecarboxylic acid
n. cyclohexene into 3-cyclohexylpropanoic acid
o. propanoic acid into ethyl 2-chloropropanoate
p. *p*-nitrotoluene into *p*-nitrophenylacetic acid
q. 3-methylbutanoic acid into isopropylmalonic acid
r. succinic acid into 2,5-dimethyl-2,4-hexadiene
s. ethanol into malonic acid

21.43 Propose a mechanism for the reaction of benzene with succinic anhydride in the presence of aluminum trichloride to produce $PhCOCH_2CH_2COOH$.

21.44 Propose structures for compounds *A*–*O*.

a. $CH_3CH(COOH)_2 + Br_2 \xrightarrow{PBr_3} A \xrightarrow{\text{heat with acid}} B$

A ($C_4H_5BrO_4$), B ($C_3H_5BrO_2$)

b. $(CH_3)_2CHBr + Ph_3P: \longrightarrow C$

$C + CH_3CH_2CH_2CH_2Li \longrightarrow D$

$D + CO_2 \longrightarrow E$

$E + H_2\ddot{O} \longrightarrow F + Ph_3P{=}\ddot{O}$

$(C_4H_8O_2)$

c. $G + NaBH_4 \xrightarrow{\text{aq acid workup}}$ [six-membered lactone ring: C=O (:O:), ring :O:, methyl substituent]

$(C_6H_{10}O_3)$

d. $H \xrightarrow{\text{heat with aq acid}} I$

$(C_5H_8O_4)$ $(C_4H_8O_2)$

^{1}H NMR (H):
δ 1.3: singlet, relative area 3
δ 12.1: singlet, relative area 1
IR: 2500–3400 cm^{-1}

^{1}H NMR (I):
δ 1.2: doublet, relative area 6
δ 2.5: multiplet, relative area 1
δ 12.2: singlet, relative area 1

e. $J \xrightarrow{H_2,\ PtO_2} K$

$(C_{10}H_{16}O_2)$ optically active; $(C_{10}H_{18}O_2)$ optically inactive

K (as silver salt) $+ Br_2 \longrightarrow L + CO_2$

$(C_9H_{17}Br)$

$L \xrightarrow{\text{KOH, ethanol, heat}} M$

(C_9H_{16})

$M + N$-bromosuccinimide $\longrightarrow N$

$(C_9H_{15}Br)$

$N \xrightarrow{\text{KOH, ethanol, heat}} O$

$O \xrightarrow{\text{ozone, oxidative workup}}$ cyclopentanecarboxylic acid

21.45 On treatment with lithium aluminum hydride, compound *P*, of formula $C_5H_{10}O_2$ (^{1}H NMR and IR follow) yields compound *Q*, of formula $C_5H_{12}O$ (^{1}H NMR shown below). Compound *Q* reacts further with aqueous sulfuric acid to form compound *R* (^{1}H NMR shown below). Give structures for compounds *P–R*.

^{1}H NMR Spectrum of *P*

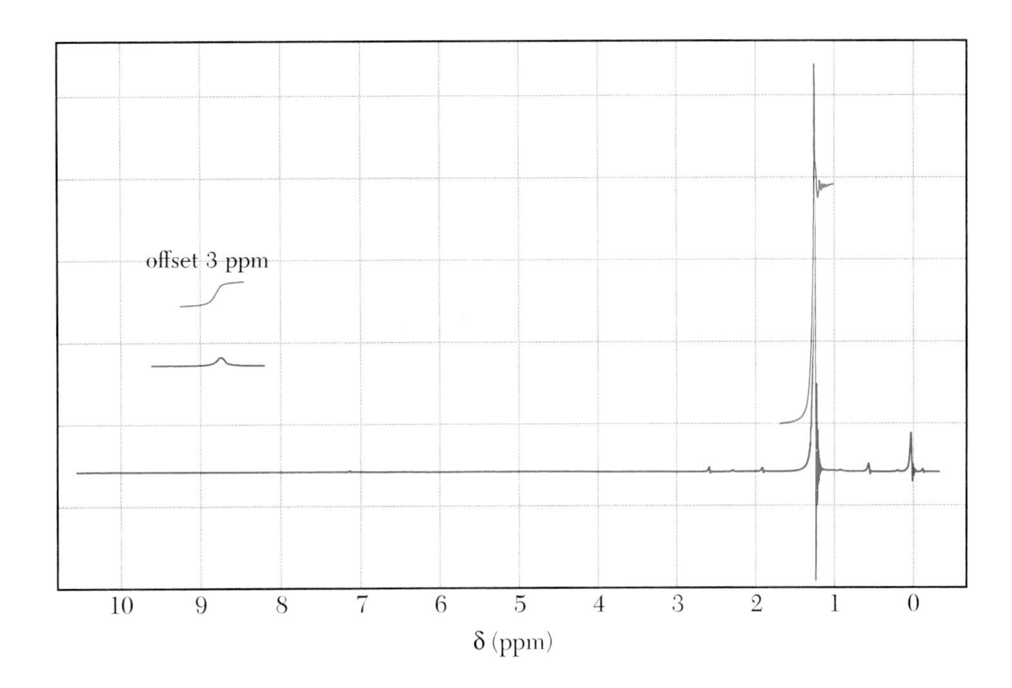

IR Spectrum of *P*

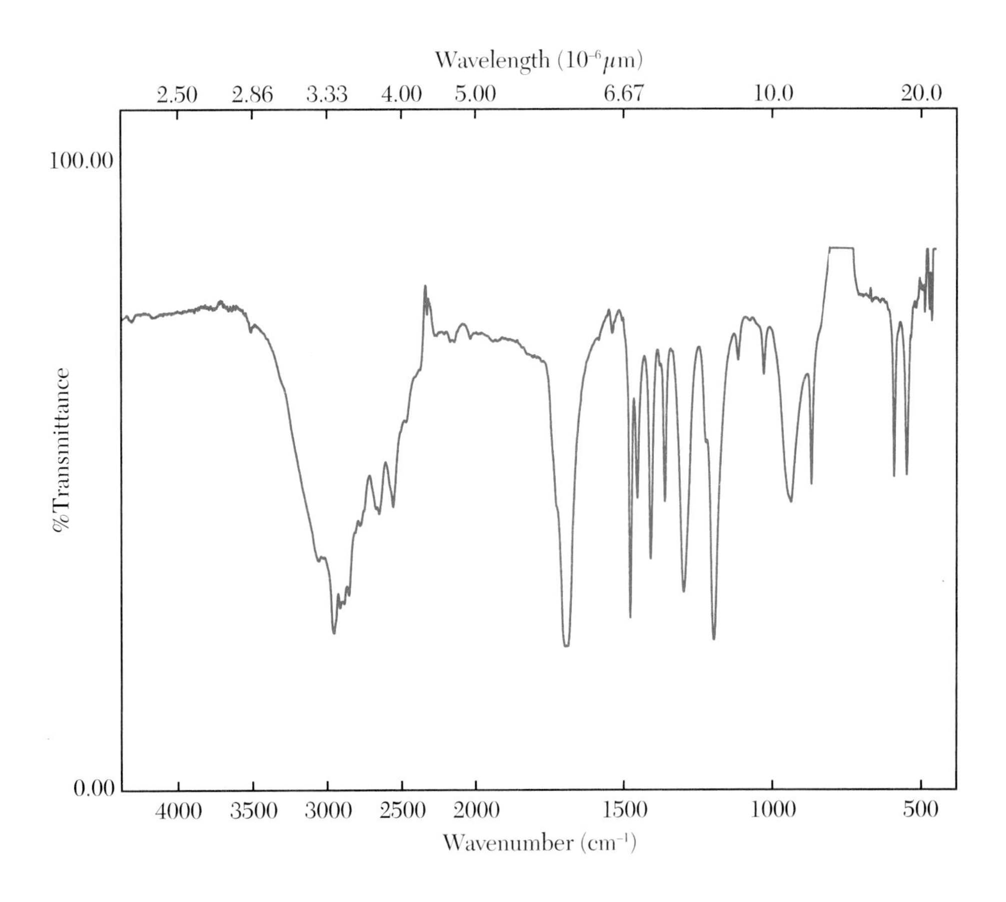

^{1}H NMR Spectrum of *Q*

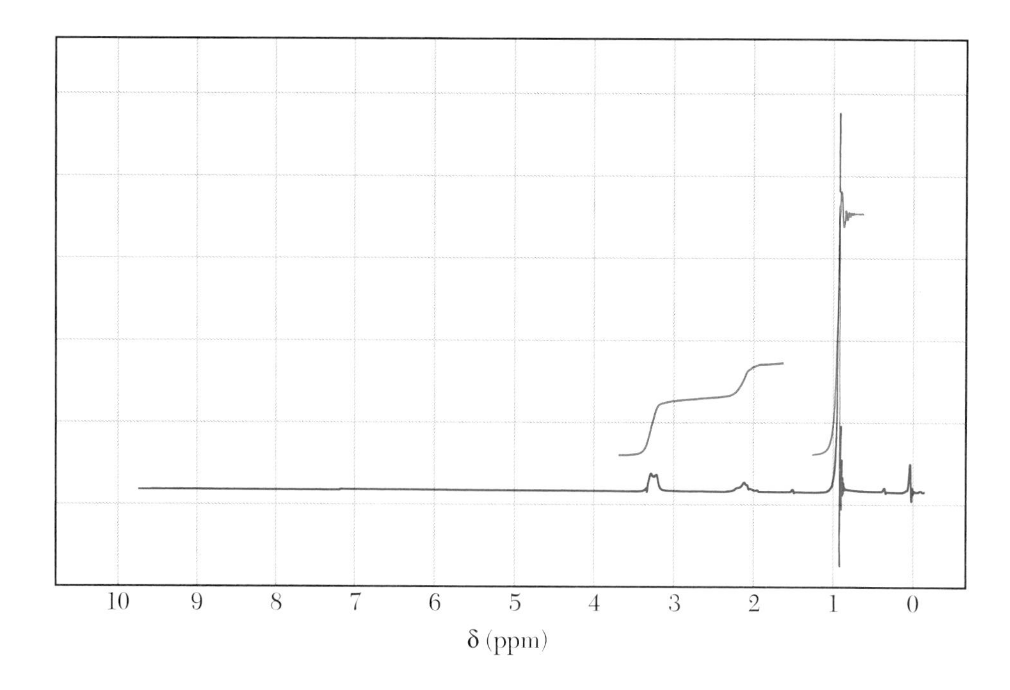

^{1}H NMR Spectrum of *R*

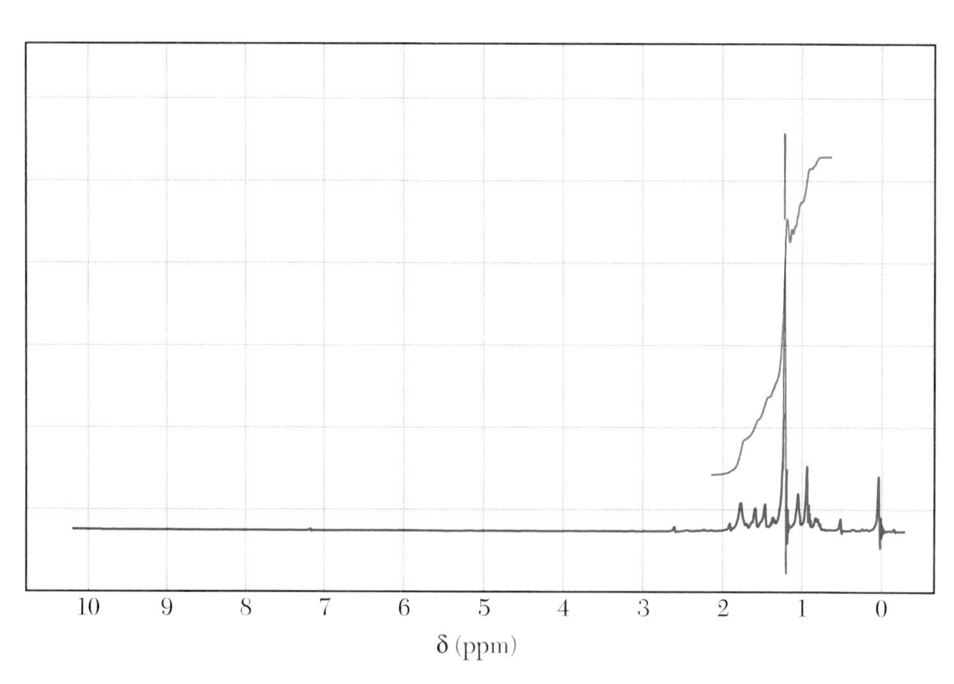

21.46 Compound S, which contains only carbon, hydrogen, and oxygen, gives the following carbon/hydrogen analysis:

C: 40.00%, H: 6.67%

An aqueous solution of S is acidic and 0.183 g can be neutralized by titrating with exactly 19.80 mL of a 0.103 *M* NaOH solution. Compound S is oxidized by hot, aqueous $KMnO_4$ solution to *T*, which is also acidic. On heating, *T* loses carbon dioxide to form *U*, another acidic compound. A sample of *U* weighing 0.0750 g is neutralized by titration with exactly 25.0 mL of a 0.050 *M* NaOH solution. Assign structures to compounds *S–U* that are consistent with the information given.

21.47 Compound *V*, of formula $C_{13}H_{18}$, yields *W* (of formula C_8H_8O) and *X* (of formula $C_5H_{10}O$) upon ozonolysis followed by workup with zinc and water. Compound *W* has an IR band at 1690 cm^{-1} and yields *Y* (of formula $C_7H_6O_2$) when treated with chlorine and aqueous sodium hydroxide followed by workup with dilute sulfuric acid. The IR spectrum of *X* has a band at 1710 cm^{-1}. The ^1H NMR spectrum of *X* shows two signals, a triplet and a quartet. Suggest structures for compounds *V–Y* consistent with these data.

21.48 Decarboxylation of salts of carboxylic acids can be performed by an electrochemical method known as the Kolbe electrolysis. If sodium acetate is electrolyzed, the acetate ion undergoes a one-electron oxidation at the anode and then loses carbon dioxide, ultimately yielding a molecule of ethane for every two carbon dioxide molecules formed. Use fish-hook arrows to show a mechanism for the Kolbe electrolysis, accounting for the formation of ethane in the electrolysis of sodium acetate.

21.49 Compound Z is formed upon treatment of toluene with chlorine gas in the presence of light. Heating Z with aqueous sodium hydroxide and followed by workup with mineral acid yields benzoic acid. Give a structure for Z and explain the formation of benzoic acid.

21.50 We can prepare methyl esters of carboxylic acids by allowing them to react with diazomethane (H_2CN_2). Propose a mechanism for the conversion of benzoic acid to methyl benzoate using this reagent.

21.51 The treatment of a nitrile, RCN, with a Grignard reagent, R′MgX, yields (after workup with aqueous acid) a ketone of structure RCOR′. Suggest a mechanism for this conversion.

21.52 An amide *AA* (formula C_4H_9NO) exhibits the following features in its ^1H NMR spectrum: δ 1.2, 6H, doublet; δ 2.4, 1H, septet; δ 5.9, 2H, broad singlet. The compound *AA* is dehydrated upon treatment with the inorganic anhydride phosphorus pentoxide to yield compound *BB* (formula C_4H_7N). Compound *BB* reacts with phenylmagnesium bromide to yield (after workup with water) compound *CC* (formula $C_{10}H_{12}O$). Compound *CC* reacts with the ylide Ph_3PCH_2 to yield 3-methyl-2-phenyl-1-butene. Suggest structures for compounds *AA–CC*.

22

CHAPTER

Derivatives of Carboxylic Acids

22.1 Introduction

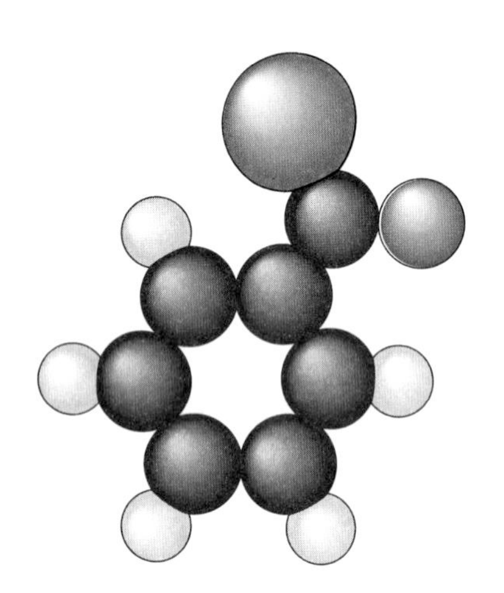

STRUCTURES OF THE COMMON DERIVATIVES

In the previous chapter we introduced the common derivatives of carboxylic acids—esters, amides, acid chlorides, anhydrides, and nitriles. Structures **22.1–22.5** show these derivatives for benzoic acid.

$C_6H_5C(=O)OCH_2CH_3$
ethyl benzoate
22.1

$C_6H_5C(=O)N(CH_3)_2$
N,*N*-dimethylbenzamide
22.2

$C_6H_5C(=O)Cl$
benzoyl chloride
22.3

$C_6H_5C(=O)OC(=O)C_6H_5$
benzoic anhydride
22.4

$C_6H_5C{\equiv}N$
benzonitrile
22.5

Most common carboxylic acid derivatives can be thought of as being derived from two parent compounds. For each derivative, one parent is a carboxylic acid and the other parent varies according to the derivative. For example, an ester can be thought of as being derived from a carboxylic acid and an alcohol, and an amide as being derived from a carboxylic acid and an amine. The chemistry of carboxylic acid derivatives reflects these relationships—they can be hydrolyzed to their parent compounds under the appropriate conditions. These structural relationships are illustrated in Figure 22.1.

THE ELECTROPHILIC NATURE OF THE CARBOXYL CARBON ATOM

A common characteristic of carboxylic acid derivatives is the electron-deficient (i.e., electophilic) nature of the carboxyl group carbon atom. It is therefore not surprising that many nucleophiles react with carboxylic acid derivatives, forming a new bond to the carboxyl carbon atom. The mechanism for these reactions

Figure 22.1 Structural relationships among carboxylic acid derivatives. Each derivative can be thought of as being derived from two parent molecules, one of which is always a carboxylic acid.

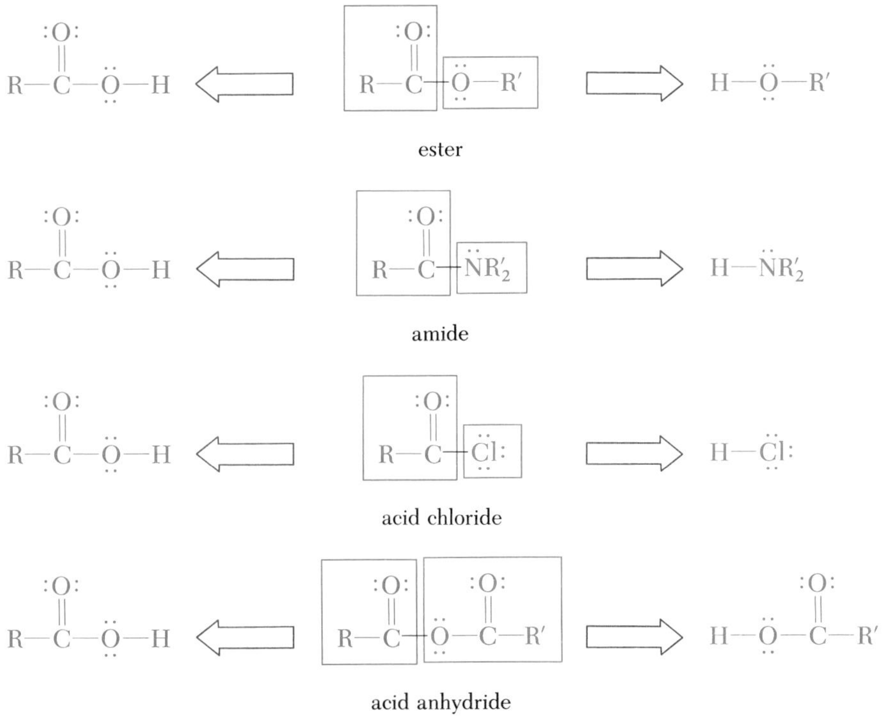

$$R-C(=O)-O-H \Leftarrow R-C(=O)-O-R' \Rightarrow H-O-R'$$

ester

$$R-C(=O)-O-H \Leftarrow R-C(=O)-NR'_2 \Rightarrow H-NR'_2$$

amide

$$R-C(=O)-O-H \Leftarrow R-C(=O)-Cl \Rightarrow H-Cl$$

acid chloride

$$R-C(=O)-O-H \Leftarrow R-C(=O)-O-C(=O)-R' \Rightarrow H-O-C(=O)-R'$$

acid anhydride

follows a common course. Nucleophilic attack produces a tetrahedral intermediate, which then decomposes to provide the product. The mechanism of the reaction between an alcohol and an acid chloride is representative.

MECHANISM OF REACTION

Reaction of an Alcohol with an Acid Chloride

Overall reaction:

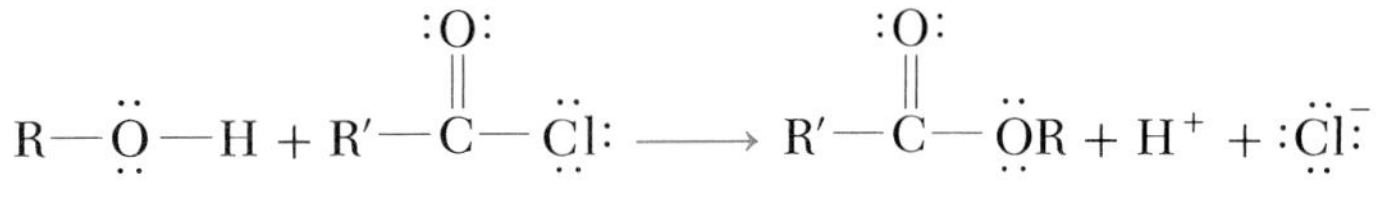

$$R-\ddot{O}-H + R'-C(=O)-\ddot{Cl}: \longrightarrow R'-C(=O)-\ddot{O}R + H^+ + :\ddot{Cl}:^-$$

Step 1 Nucleophilic addition to form a tetrahedral intermediate.

$$R-\ddot{O}-H + R'-C(=O)-\ddot{Cl}: \longrightarrow R'-C(-O^-)(-\ddot{Cl}:)-O^+(R)H$$

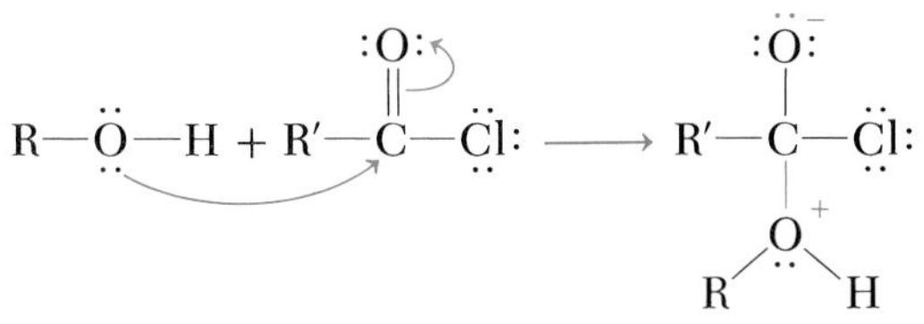

Step 2 Decomposition of the intermediate with ejection of a leaving group.

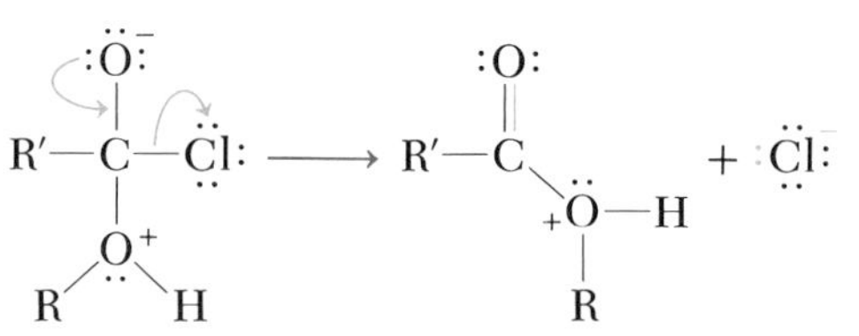

$$R'-\overset{\overset{\displaystyle :\ddot{O}:^{-}}{|}}{\underset{\underset{\displaystyle R\diagup\ddot{O}^{+}\diagdown H}{|}}{C}}-\ddot{Cl}: \longrightarrow R'-\overset{\overset{\displaystyle :O:}{\|}}{C}-\underset{\underset{\displaystyle R}{|}}{\overset{+}{\ddot{O}}}-H + :\ddot{Cl}:^{-}$$

Step 3 Deprotonation. The base B: can be one of several species (e.g., the anion displaced in Step 2, or a molecule of alcohol).

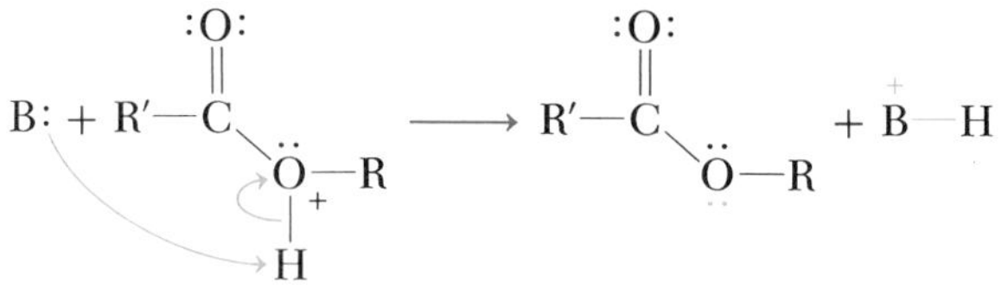

$$B: + R'-\overset{\overset{\displaystyle :O:}{\|}}{C}-\underset{\underset{\displaystyle H}{|}}{\overset{+}{\ddot{O}}}-R \longrightarrow R'-\overset{\overset{\displaystyle :O:}{\|}}{C}-\ddot{\underset{..}{O}}-R + \overset{+}{B}-H$$

The relative reactivities of the different kinds of carboxylic acid derivatives toward nucleophiles correlate with the relative leaving-group abilities, as shown below:

relative reactivity: acid chloride > anhydride > ester > amide

$$\text{leaving group:} \quad -\ddot{\underset{..}{Cl}}: \; > -\ddot{\underset{..}{O}}-\overset{\overset{\displaystyle :O:}{\|}}{C}-R > -\ddot{\underset{..}{O}}R > -\ddot{N}R_2$$

However, it is important to note that the rate-determining step in these reactions is formation of a tetrahedral intermediate and not the loss of a leaving group. It so happens that the same factors that improve leaving-group ability also stabilize the tetrahedral intermediates.

22.2 The Interconversion of Carboxylic Acid Derivatives

ESTERS AND AMIDES FROM ACID CHLORIDES AND ANHYDRIDES

In Chapter 21 we described the preparation of esters and amides directly from the parent carboxylic acids. However, it is usually more efficient to prepare these derivatives from either an acid chloride or an anhydride. These compounds are especially reactive toward attack by nucleophiles. Although acid chlorides are generally more reactive than the corresponding anhydrides, anhydrides *do* react at a reasonable rate for synthetic purposes. In fact, the use of an anhydride is often preferred as reaction is less violent and more easily controlled. Several examples of ester formation from acid chlorides and anhydrides are shown in Equations 22.1–22.4.

Eqn. 22.1

$$C_6H_5CH_2CH(C_6H_5){-}\ddot{O}H \xrightarrow[\text{benzene}]{2,4,6\text{-}(CH_3CH_2)_3C_6H_2COCl} C_6H_5CH_2CH(C_6H_5){-}\ddot{O}{-}C(=O){-}C_6H_2(CH_2CH_3)_3$$

1,2-diphenylethanol 2,4,6-triethylbenzoyl chloride

69% yield
1,2-diphenylethyl
2,4,6-triethylbenzoate

Eqn. 22.2

$$p\text{-}H_3CC_6H_4C(=O){-}\ddot{Cl}: \xrightarrow[(CH_3)_3COLi]{(CH_3)_3COH} p\text{-}H_3CC_6H_4C(=O){-}\ddot{O}{-}C(CH_3)_3$$

p-methylbenzoyl chloride

82% yield
tert-butyl *p*-methylbenzoate

Eqn. 22.3

$$p\text{-}C_6H_5C_6H_4\ddot{O}H \xrightarrow{\text{propionic anhydride}} p\text{-}C_6H_5C_6H_4\ddot{O}{-}C(=O)CH_2CH_3$$

p-phenylphenol

73% yield
4-biphenyl propanoate

Eqn. 22.4

$$HOCH_2C{\equiv}CCH_2OH \xrightarrow{\text{acetic anhydride}} CH_3{-}\overset{\overset{:O:}{\|}}{C}{-}\ddot{O}{-}CH_2C{\equiv}CCH_2{-}\ddot{O}{-}\overset{\overset{:O:}{\|}}{C}{-}CH_3$$

butyne-1,4-diol

85% yield
butyne-1,4-diol diacetate

PROBLEM 22.1 Write a curved-arrow mechanism for the reaction depicted in Equation 22.3.

Methods for the preparation of amides are often analagous to those used for preparing esters. For example, a common procedure is to react an acid chloride (or anhydride) with ammonia (or a primary or secondary amine). Several examples are given in Equations 22.5–22.8.

Eqn. 22.5

$$(CH_3)_2CH\text{—}C(=\ddot{O}:)\ddot{Cl}: \xrightarrow[\text{water workup}]{NH_3} (CH_3)_2CH\text{—}C(=\ddot{O}:)\ddot{N}H_2$$

isobutyroyl chloride — 70% yield isobutyramide

Eqn. 22.6

$$C_8H_{17}CH{=}CH(CH_2)_7COCl \xrightarrow[\text{hexane}]{C_4H_9NH_2} C_8H_{17}CH{=}CH(CH_2)_7C(=\ddot{O}:)\text{—}\ddot{N}HC_4H_9$$

oleoyl chloride — 83% yield *N*-butyloleamide

Eqn. 22.7

$$C_6H_5COCl + (CH_3CH_2)_2\ddot{N}\text{—}H \longrightarrow C_6H_5C(=\ddot{O}:)\text{—}\ddot{N}(CH_2CH_3)_2$$

benzoyl chloride, diethylamine — 75% yield *N,N*-diethylbenzamide

Eqn. 22.8

$$C_6H_5\ddot{N}H_2 + CH_3\text{—}C(=\ddot{O}:)\text{—}\ddot{O}\text{—}C(=\ddot{O}:)\text{—}CH_3 \longrightarrow CH_3\text{—}C(=\ddot{O}:)\text{—}\ddot{N}HC_6H_5$$

aniline, acetic anhydride — 89% yield *N*-phenylacetamide

PROBLEM 22.2 A student treats each of the compounds ammonia, aniline, diethylamine, and triethylamine with benzoyl chloride. Upon mixing the reagents, each reaction system liberates heat, indicating that an exothermic reaction has occurred. Upon workup with water the student isolates the appropriate amide product from the reactions involving ammonia, aniline, and diethylamine. However, the student isolates benzoic acid from the reaction system using triethylamine. Give the structure of each of the products in the first three reactions, and explain why benzoic acid was isolated from the triethylamine reaction.

Esters and amides can also be prepared from other activated forms of the carboxyl group. These activated forms have structural similarities to simple anhydrides and acid chlorides. For example, in Chapter 21 we considered the formation of esters from carboxylic acids and alcohols using dicyclohexylcarbodiimide (DCC) as a coupling/dehydrating agent. The active intermediate in this process bears a structural resemblance to a simple anhydride, as is shown in Figure 22.2.

A special reagent is required if we wish to prepare an ester or an amide of formic acid, because neither formic anhydride nor formyl chloride exist as stable, usable materials. However, we can prepare formic acetic anhydride (**22.6**) by the reaction of sodium formate with acetyl chloride, as shown in Figure 22.3. This reagent preferentially transfers the formyl group upon reaction

Figure 22.2 Comparison between an anhydride and the intermediate in DCC-mediated coupling of a carboxylic acid and an alcohol. The two are structurally similar, and both are highly reactive toward nucleophiles.

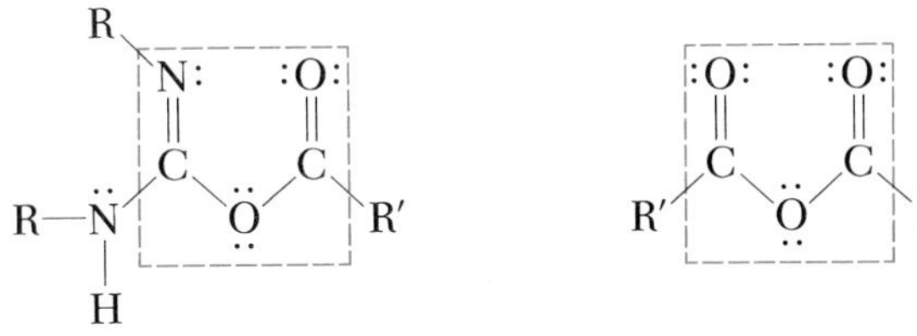

intermediate in DCC-mediated coupling of an acid and an alcohol

anhydride

Figure 22.3 A preparation of formic acetic anhydride. The reagent is useful for the preparation of formate esters.

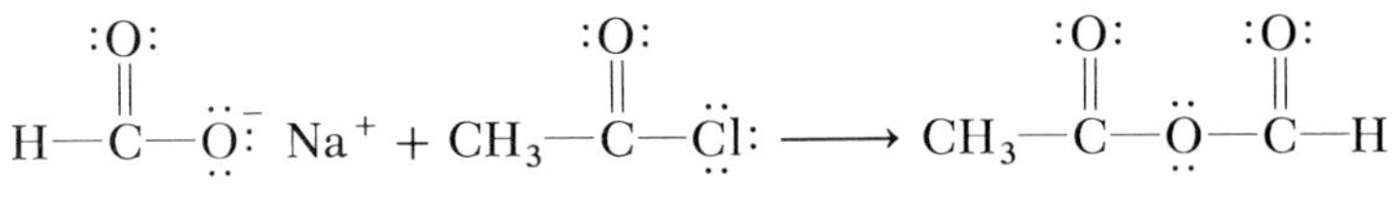

$$\mathrm{HC(=O)O^-\ Na^+ + CH_3C(=O)Cl \longrightarrow CH_3C(=O)OC(=O)H}$$

formic acetic anhydride
22.6

with an alcohol to give the formate ester. The use of formic acetic anhydride for the preparation of a formate ester is shown in Equation 22.9.

Eqn. 22.9

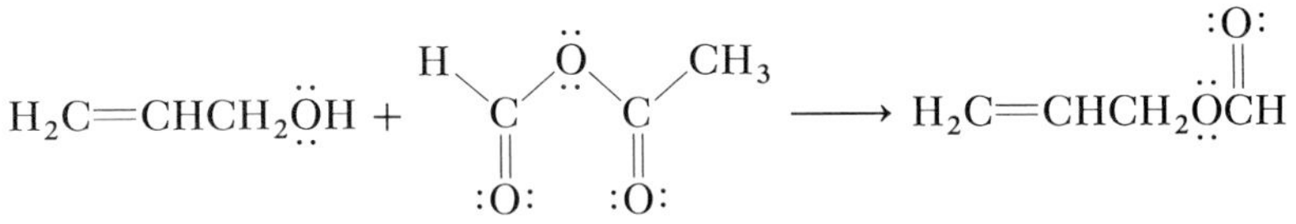

$$\mathrm{H_2C{=}CHCH_2OH + HC(=O)OC(=O)CH_3 \longrightarrow H_2C{=}CHCH_2OCH(=O)}$$

allyl alcohol — formic acetic anhydride — 98% yield allyl formate

PROBLEM 22.3 Write a mechanism for the reaction shown in Equation 22.9. Why does the alcohol attack the formyl rather than the acetyl carboxyl carbon atom? (That is, why does *formylation* occur rather than *acetylation*?)

PROBLEM 22.4 Predict the major organic product in each of the following reactions:

a. 2,2-dimethylpropanoyl chloride with ethanol
b. benzoic anhydride with 4-methylaniline
c. 2,2-dimethylpropanoyl chloride with ammonia
d. benzoyl chloride with diethylamine

PROBLEM 22.5 Give a set of reagents and reaction conditions for the preparation of each of the following esters from the parent alcohol:

a. cyclohexyl propanoate **b.** ethyl 4-nitrobenzoate
c. *tert*-butyl acetate **d.** 1-hexyl formate

PROBLEM 22.6 Give the reagents and reaction conditions for the preparation of each of the following amides from the parent acids:

a. *N*,*N*-diethylbenzamide **b.** *N*-4-methoxyphenylpropanamide
c. phenylacetamide

TRANSESTERIFICATION

Transesterification is the conversion of one ester into another by treatment with an appropriate alcohol under either acidic or basic conditions. Equation 22.10 shows the conversion of a methyl ester into an *n*-decyl ester under acid catalysis. The mechanism of this reaction involves a series of equilibria. In order to drive the reaction to the desired product we use an excess of the alcohol whose ester we require. An example of transesterification under basic conditions is shown in Equation 22.11.

Eqn. 22.10
$$H_2C{=}CHCOCH_3 \xrightarrow[HOCH_2(CH_2)_8CH_3]{H_2SO_4} H_2C{=}CHCOCH_2(CH_2)_8CH_3 + CH_3OH$$

methyl acrylate → 83% yield *n*-decyl acrylate

Eqn. 22.11
$$C_6H_5O{-}C({=}O){-}OCH_3 \xrightarrow{C_6H_5O^-Na^+} C_6H_5O{-}C({=}O){-}OC_6H_5 + CH_3OH$$

methyl phenyl carbonate → 70% yield diphenyl carbonate

PROBLEM 22.7 Write a complete mechanism for the reaction shown in Equation 22.10. (*Hint:* See Section 21.6.)

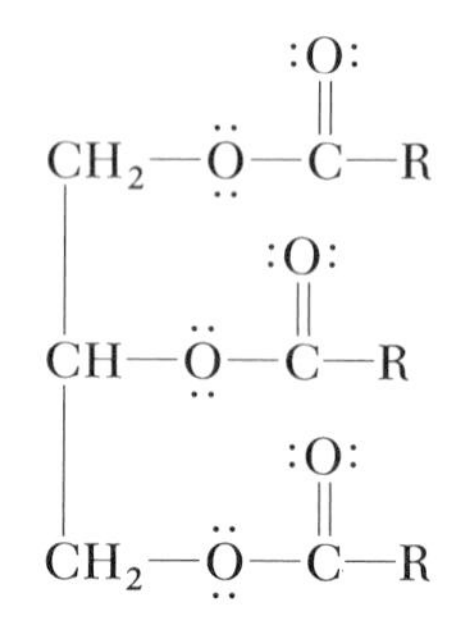

Figure 22.4 General structure of a triglyceride.

The usual synthetic application of transesterification reactions is in the preparation of desired esters from cheap, naturally occurring esters. An example is the preparation of simple esters of fatty acids from the naturally occurring fatty acid esters. **Triglycerides** are triesters of fatty acids and glycerol (1,2,3-propanetriol). (Triglycerides were introduced in our discussion of soaps in Chapter 21.) Coconut oil consists mainly of triglycerides of the type shown in Figure 22.4, where the carboxylic acid portion (RCO_2—) is octanoyl, dodecanoyl (twelve carbon atoms), or tetradecanoyl (fourteen carbon atoms). If we reflux coconut oil with ethanol and sulfuric acid, transesterification occurs, producing the ethyl esters of octanoic, dodecanoic, and tetradecanoic acids.

PROBLEM 22.8 What organic by-product is formed along with the ethyl esters of the fatty acids when a coconut oil triglyceride is refluxed with ethanol and sulfuric acid?

PROBLEM 22.9 Refluxing a *tert*-butyl ester [$RCOOC(CH_3)_3$] with ethanol and sulfuric acid produces an alkene (2-methylpropene). Suggest a mechanism for the formation of 2-methylpropene. Why are alkenes not formed when esters of primary and secondary alcohols are refluxed with ethanol and sulfuric acid?

SPECIAL TOPIC

Esters and Flavoring

Because many esters of simple carboxylic acids have fragrant, fruity odors, they are often used as flavoring agents. Some examples are shown below.

Compound	Structure	Aroma
ethyl formate	$H{-}C({=}O){-}O{-}CH_2CH_3$	rum
1-pentyl ethanoate	$CH_3{-}C({=}O){-}O{-}CH_2CH_2CH_2CH_2CH_3$	banana
3-methylbutyl ethanoate	$CH_3{-}C({=}O){-}O{-}CH_2CH_2CH(CH_3)_2$	banana
1-octyl ethanoate	$CH_3{-}C({=}O){-}O{-}CH_2CH_2CH_2CH_2CH_2CH_2CH_2CH_3$	orange
methyl butanoate	$CH_3CH_2CH_2{-}C({=}O){-}O{-}CH_3$	apple
ethyl butanoate	$CH_3CH_2CH_2{-}C({=}O){-}O{-}CH_2CH_3$	pineapple
1-pentyl butanoate	$CH_3CH_2CH_2{-}C({=}O){-}O{-}CH_2CH_2CH_2CH_2CH_3$	apricot
methyl salicylate	benzene ring bearing OH and $C({=}O){-}OCH_3$ (ortho)	oil of winter-green

ESTER-AMIDE INTERCONVERSIONS

We can convert an ester to an amide (or the reverse) under conditions similar to those used for transesterification. The preparation of an ester from an amide generally involves the use of an acidic catalyst. Boron trifluoride is a powerful Lewis acid that serves well for this purpose. An example is shown in Equation 22.12.

COMPOUND CAPSULE

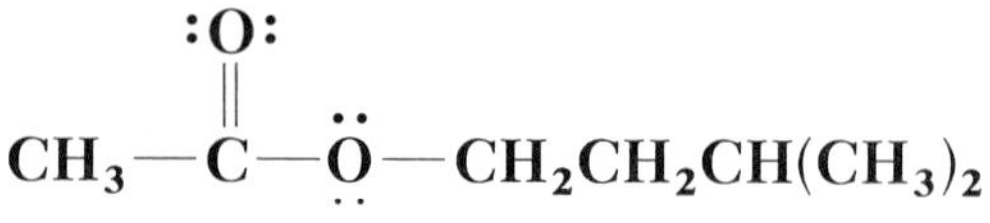

$$CH_3-\overset{\overset{:O:}{\|}}{C}-\ddot{\underset{..}{O}}-CH_2CH_2CH(CH_3)_2$$

Isoamyl acetate

Isoamyl acetate (3-methylbutyl ethanoate) is an ester that has the sweet odor of bananas. In the insect world it elicits a less-than-sweet response from honeybees. Bees release this ester upon stinging, and the ester attracts other bees to the same location. Thus there is a chemical explanation for a phenomenon that has long been observed: a single sting increases the probability of attack by more bees.

A variety of relatively simple chemicals play a major role in the whole social order of the beehive. A compound known as *queen substance* is produced in the mandibular gland of a queen bee and is spread to worker bees during feeding and other social contact. The substance prevents the worker bees from developing ovaries, thus preventing them from becoming new queens. A closely related compound, *queen scent*, keeps workers clustered around a queen bee. Citral and geranial are used by bees to mark a food source, while 2-heptanone is produced during times of danger, causing an angry, aggressive response in the bees.

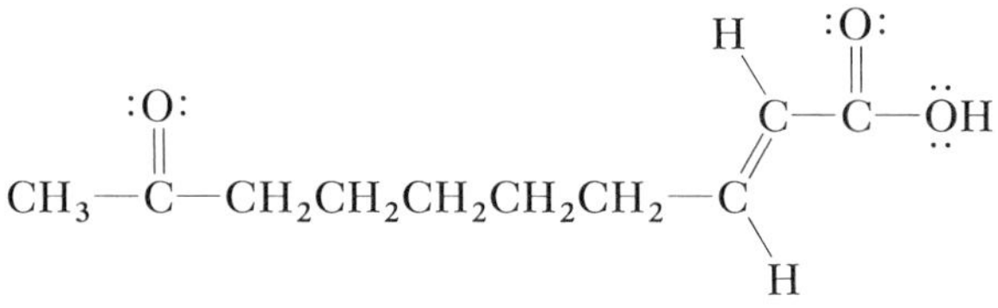

$$CH_3-\overset{\overset{:O:}{\|}}{C}-CH_2CH_2CH_2CH_2CH_2-CH=CH-\overset{\overset{:O:}{\|}}{C}-\ddot{\underset{..}{O}}H$$

queen substance

$$CH_3-\underset{\underset{H}{|}}{\overset{\overset{:\ddot{O}H}{|}}{C}}-CH_2CH_2CH_2CH_2CH_2-CH=CH-\overset{\overset{:O:}{\|}}{C}-\ddot{\underset{..}{O}}H$$

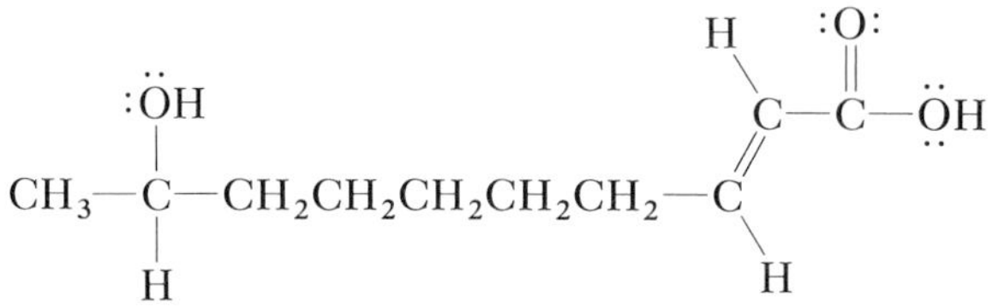

queen scent

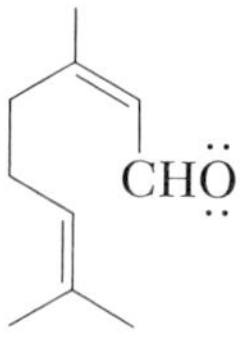

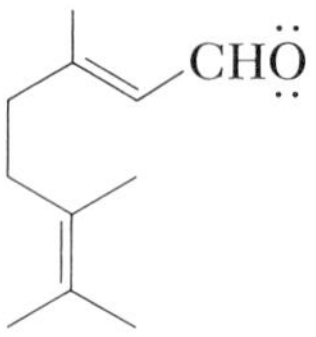

citral geranial

Eqn. 22.12

$$C_6H_5{-}\overset{\overset{\large :O:}{\|}}{C}{-}\ddot{N}H_2 \xrightarrow[105\,°C]{CH_3OH,\ BF_3} C_6H_5{-}\overset{\overset{\large :O:}{\|}}{C}{-}\ddot{\underset{..}{O}}CH_3$$

benzamide — 100% yield, methyl benzoate

The reverse process, the preparation of an amide from an ester, is effected by heating the ester with an excess of the amine, as shown in Equation 22.13.

Eqn. 22.13

$$C_6H_5{-}\overset{\overset{\large :O:}{\|}}{C}{-}CH_2{-}\overset{\overset{\large :O:}{\|}}{C}{-}\ddot{\underset{..}{O}}{-}CH_2CH_3 \xrightarrow[heat]{C_6H_5NH_2} C_6H_5{-}\overset{\overset{\large :O:}{\|}}{C}{-}CH_2{-}\overset{\overset{\large :O:}{\|}}{C}{-}\ddot{N}HC_6H_5$$

ethyl 3-oxo-3-phenylpropanoate — 84% yield, *N*-phenyl-3-oxo-3-phenylpropanamide

PROBLEM 22.10

a. In the amide-to-ester conversion shown in Equation 22.12, boron trifluoride acts as a catalyst for the methanol attack on the amide but is consumed in a later step of the overall reaction; at least an equivalent amount of boron trifluroide is required for the reaction. Show the product formed when boron trifluoride is consumed in this reaction.

b. Write a mechanism for the overall reaction in Equation 22.12.

Steps to Solving the Problem

Solution to Problem 22.10a

1. What kind of a reagent is boron trifluoride? Boron trifluoride is a powerful Lewis acid and will react with Lewis bases that are present.
2. What substance is available in the reaction mixture and could serve as a Lewis base for irreversible reaction with boron trifluoride? Ammonia, a moderate base, is a by-product of the simple amide-to-ester reaction. The boron trifluoride reacts with ammonia to form a salt whose structure is shown below.
3. What is the effect of this reaction on the desired amide-to-ester conversion? This reaction has two effects. First, we need more than a simple catalytic amount of boron trifluoride to complete the reaction, since it is consumed by reaction with the by-product. Second, the ammonia generated cannot attack the ester under these conditions since it is converted to the non-nucleophilic salt.

$$F_3\overset{-}{B}{-}\overset{+}{N}H_3$$

DEHYDRATION OF AMIDES

The preferred method for the synthesis of nitriles is the S_N2 reaction of cyanide ion with a haloalkane (Chapter 12). However, we can also prepare nitriles by the dehydration of an appropriate amide. Generally, thionyl chloride or phosphorus pentoxide is used as the dehydrating agent. An example is shown in Equation 22.14.

Eqn. 22.14

$$Cl_3C-\overset{\overset{\large :O:}{\|}}{C}-\ddot{N}H_2 \xrightarrow[\text{heat}]{P_2O_5} Cl_3C-C\equiv N:$$

trichloracetamide — 80% yield trichloroacetonitrile

SPECIAL TOPIC

Polyesters and Polyamides

We have seen that carboxylic acids react with alcohols under acid-catalyzed conditions to produce esters (Fischer esterification). If we use a *di*carboxylic acid and a *diol* under conditions of Fischer esterification, we are able to form a *polyester*, as shown in the following equation:

$$HOOC-C_6H_4-COOH + HOCH_2CH_2OH \xrightarrow{\text{acid}} HOCH_2CH_2-O-[C(=O)-C_6H_4-C(=O)-OCH_2CH_2-O]_n-C(=O)-C_6H_4-C(=O)-OH$$

This particular polyester can be spun into fibers known as *Dacron*. *Polyamides* can also be spun into fibers. The best known of these, nylon,

(*continued*)

(*continued from previous page*)

can be made by the reaction of a diamine with a diacyl halide:

$$\text{:}\ddot{\text{Cl}}\text{—}\overset{\text{:O:}}{\overset{\|}{\text{C}}}\text{—(CH}_2)_n\text{—}\overset{\text{:O:}}{\overset{\|}{\text{C}}}\text{—}\ddot{\text{Cl}}\text{:} + \text{H}_2\ddot{\text{N}}\text{—(CH}_2)_{n'}\text{—}\ddot{\text{N}}\text{H}_2 \longrightarrow$$

$$\text{H}_2\ddot{\text{N}}\text{—(CH}_2)_{n'}\text{—}\ddot{\text{N}}\text{H—}\left[\text{C(=}\ddot{\text{O}}\text{)—(CH}_2)_n\text{—C(=}\ddot{\text{O}}\text{)—}\ddot{\text{N}}\text{H—(CH}_2)_{n'}\text{—}\ddot{\text{N}}\text{H}\right]_m\text{—}\overset{\text{:O:}}{\overset{\|}{\text{C}}}\text{—(CH}_2)_n\text{—}\overset{\text{:O:}}{\overset{\|}{\text{C}}}\text{—}\ddot{\text{Cl}}\text{:}$$

The particular nylon produced in this type of reaction is classified according to the values of n and n'. For example, nylon 6,6 is made on an industrial scale by heating adipic acid with hexamethylenediamine under vacuum. For a more detailed description of these and other polymers, see Chapter 29.

PROBLEM 22.11

The product of Equation 22.14 is trichloroacetonitrile, which is used in coupling reactions of alcohols with phosphoric acid to give phosphate esters. Its role is similar to that of DCC—it generates an intermediate whose structure is similar to and that acts much like an anhydride. Overall, trichloroacetonitrile removes the elements of water from the two reactants in this type of reaction. Write a mechanism for the coupling reaction of an alcohol, (ROH) and phosphoric acid (H_3PO_4) in the presence of trichloroacetonitrile.

22.3 Hydrolysis of Acid Derivatives

The term **hydrolysis** means a *cleavage by water*. The hydrolysis of any derivative of a carboxylic acid produces the free carboxylic acid.

In general, a catalyst is necessary for the hydrolysis of esters, amides, and nitriles, but many acid chlorides and anhydrides are hydrolyzed by water alone. Both acids and bases catalyze or promote the hydrolysis of esters, albeit by different mechanisms. The specific mechanism of hydrolysis for a given ester depends on the nature of the ester as well as the reaction conditions. We will review the most common mechanisms of ester hydrolysis in the following section. Amides and nitriles also undergo hydrolysis under conditions of acid catalysis. Hydrolyses of many carboxylic acid derivatives are catalyzed by specific enzymes in biological systems. We will note the organic synthetic utility of these reactions, but discussions of their mechanisms are beyond the scope of this course.

HYDROLYSIS OF ESTERS

Acid-Catalyzed Hydrolysis Esters of carboxylic acids are subject to cleavage to the free acid and alcohol by the action of aqueous acid. The mechanism by which *most* carboxylic acid esters undergo acid-catalyzed hydrolysis is shown below. It is the same mechanism we saw earlier for the formation of an ester from an alcohol and an acid (see Chapter 21) except that it is reversed. The role of the acid catalyst is to facilitate the attack of water at the carboxylate carbon. Protonation of the *carbonyl* oxygen makes the carboxyl carbon even more susceptible to attack by a nucleophile than it is before protonation. Once water has added to the carboxyl carbon, a series of acid-base reactions leads to the loss of a molecule of alcohol and the formation of a resonance-stabilized cation, the protonated carboxylic acid. The further reaction of the protonated carboxylic acid with water leads to the neutral carboxylic acid. All reactions involved in this overall mechanism are reversible.

Acid-Catalyzed Hydrolysis of Carboxylate Esters

Overall reaction:

$$\mathrm{R{-}\overset{\overset{:O:}{\|}}{C}{-}\ddot{\underset{\cdot\cdot}{O}}R' + H_2\ddot{\underset{\cdot\cdot}{O}} \xrightarrow{H^+} R{-}\overset{\overset{:O:}{\|}}{C}{-}\ddot{\underset{\cdot\cdot}{O}}H + R'\ddot{\underset{\cdot\cdot}{O}}H}$$

Step 1 Protonation of the ester

$$\mathrm{R{-}\overset{\overset{:O:}{\|}}{C}{-}\ddot{\underset{\cdot\cdot}{O}}R' + H^+ \rightleftharpoons \left[R{-}\overset{\overset{:\overset{+}{O}{-}H}{\|}}{C}{-}\ddot{\underset{\cdot\cdot}{O}}R' \longleftrightarrow R{-}\overset{\overset{:\ddot{O}{-}H}{|}}{\underset{+}{C}}{-}\ddot{\underset{\cdot\cdot}{O}}R' \right]}$$

Step 2 Nucleophilic attack by water

$$\mathrm{R{-}\overset{\overset{:\ddot{O}{-}H}{|}}{\underset{+}{C}}{-}\ddot{\underset{\cdot\cdot}{O}}R' + \ddot{\underset{\cdot\cdot}{O}}H_2 \rightleftharpoons R{-}\overset{\overset{:\ddot{O}H}{|}}{\underset{\underset{H\diagup\overset{+}{\underset{\cdot\cdot}{O}}\diagdown H}{|}}{C}}{-}\ddot{\underset{\cdot\cdot}{O}}R'}$$

Steps 3 and 4 Proton transfer

$$R-C(OH)(OR')(O^{+}H_2) + :B \rightleftharpoons R-C(OH)(OR')(OH) + \overset{+}{B}-H$$

$$R-C(OH)_2-OR' + H-\overset{+}{B} \rightleftharpoons R-C(OH)_2-\overset{+}{O}(H)R' + B:$$

Step 5 Loss of alcohol

$$R-C(OH)_2-\overset{+}{O}(H)R' \rightleftharpoons \left[R-\overset{+}{C}(OH)_2 \longleftrightarrow R-C(=\overset{+}{O}H)(OH) \right] + R'OH$$

Step 6 Deprotonation

$$B: + R-C(=\overset{+}{O}H)(OH) \rightleftharpoons R-C(=O)(OH) + \overset{+}{B}-H$$

All the steps in this mechanism are completely reversible. We can cause the reaction to proceed in either desired direction (toward ester or toward acid and alcohol) by properly choosing the reaction conditions. For ester formation we use an excess of alcohol and/or remove the water as it is generated to force the equilibrium toward the ester side. For hydrolysis, we provide a large excess of water to force the equilibrium toward the side of acid and alcohol.

Two examples of acid-catalyzed ester hydrolysis for the preparation of carboxylic acids are shown in Equations 22.15 and 22.16.

Eqn. 22.15

$$BrCH_2CH(Br)-C(=O)-OCH_3 \xrightarrow[H_2O]{HBr} BrCH_2CH(Br)-C(=O)-OH$$

methyl 2,3-dibromopropanoate

72% yield

2,3-dibromopropanoic acid

Eqn. 22.16

$$p\text{-}C_6H_4(COOCH_3)_2 \xrightarrow[HCOOH,\ H_2O]{CH_3SO_3H} p\text{-}C_6H_4(COOH)_2$$

dimethyl terephthalate — 99% yield terephthalic acid

Base-Promoted Hydrolysis The hydrolysis of carboxylate esters can also be effected under basic conditions. We often refer to this method as **saponification,** a term that is derived from the preparations of soaps by the basic hydrolysis of natural esters of fatty acids. The mechanism of hydrolysis varies with the nature of the carboxylate ester. One mechanism that is much more common than the others is illustrated below.

MECHANISM OF REACTION

Base-Promoted Hydrolysis of Carboxylic Acid Esters

Overall reaction:

$$R{-}C(=O){-}OR' + {}^{-}OH \longrightarrow R{-}C(=O){-}O^{-} + R'OH$$

Step 1 Nucleophilic attack by hydroxide ion

$$R{-}C(=O){-}OR' + {}^{-}OH \rightleftharpoons R{-}C(O^{-})(OH){-}OR'$$

Step 2 Collapse of the tetrahedral intermediate

$$R{-}C(O^{-})(OH){-}OR' \rightleftharpoons R{-}C(=O){-}OH + {}^{-}O{-}R'$$

Steps 3 and 4 Proton transfer reactions

$$R'{-}O^{-} + H{-}OH \rightleftharpoons R'{-}O{-}H + {}^{-}OH$$

$$R{-}C(=O){-}O{-}H + {}^{-}OH \rightleftharpoons R{-}C(=O){-}O^{-} + H{-}OH$$

We generally workup these reactions by adding aqueous acid to the reaction mixture to ensure the complete conversion of the alkoxide ion to the free alcohol. If we wish to isolate the free acid, this approach also readily permits extraction of the acid from the reaction medium. Examples of the use of base-promoted hydrolysis of esters are shown in Equations 22.17–22.19.

Eqn. 22.17

$$CH_3(CH_2)_8CH{=}C(CH_3){-}C({=}O)OCH_3 \xrightarrow[\text{(aq acid workup)}]{\text{KOH, ethanol}} CH_3(CH_2)_8CH{=}C(CH_3){-}C({=}O)OH$$

methyl 2-methyl-2-dodecenoate

83% yield
2-methyl-2-dodecenoic acid

Eqn. 22.18

$$C_7H_7{-}C({=}O){-}OCH_3 \xrightarrow[\text{methanol, water (aq acid workup)}]{\text{NaOH, NaHCO}_3} C_7H_7{-}C({=}O){-}OH$$

methyl
cycloheptatrienecarboxylate

92% yield
cycloheptatrienecarboxylic
acid

Eqn. 22.19

$$2\text{-}CH_3C_6H_4{-}CH_2{-}O{-}C({=}O){-}CH_3 \xrightarrow[\text{2. methanol water (aq acid workup)}]{\text{1. NaOH}} 2\text{-}CH_3C_6H_4{-}CH_2{-}OH$$

2-methylbenzyl acetate

97% yield
2-methylbenzyl alcohol

Although all ester hydrolyses produce a carboxylic acid and an alcohol, we are often interested in isolating only one of these two products. For example, in Equations 22.17 and 22.18 the target of interest is the carboxylic acid. However, in Equation 22.19 the target is the alcohol. The by-product in Equations 22.17 and 22.18 is methanol, whereas in Equation 22.19 it is acetic acid.

Enzymatic Hydrolysis of Esters Esters play important roles in biological systems. They undergo catalyzed hydrolysis in normal metabolic processes. However, the strong acids and bases we use as catalysts in the laboratory are not compatible with living cells. For an organism's metabolism to proceed, hydrolyses must be catalyzed and occur under very mild conditions. The catalysts for these processes in biological systems are known as **enzymes.** Enzymes are macromolecules composed of many amino acids (see Chapter 26) coupled by amide linkages. In general, enzymes activate the substrate and hold it in a suitable position for reaction.

In recent years the number and variety of enzymes isolated and purified from biological systems has been increasing rapidly. Furthermore, organic chemists have begun to overcome their early reluctance to use enzymes in the performance of organic syntheses in the laboratory. We previously noted (Chapter 8) the use of enzymes for performing resolutions of racemic mixtures. The hydrolysis of carboxylate esters is another reaction type for which enzymes find increasing synthetic utility. Two examples are shown in Equations 22.20 and 22.21.

Eqn. 22.20

baker's yeast
pH = 7.0
water

78% yield

Eqn. 22.21

pig liver esterase
H_2O

86% yield

PROBLEM 22.12 When we treat ethyl acetate with water and sodium hydroxide that are enriched in ^{18}O and stop the reaction before all of the ethyl acetate has been hydrolyzed, we find ^{18}O incorporation into the unhydrolyzed ethyl acetate. Explain in terms of the mechanism how the incorporation of ^{18}O occurs.

HYDROLYSIS OF AMIDES

Acid-Catalyzed Hydrolysis We usually hydrolyze amides by refluxing them with water under relatively strong acidic conditions. Examples of this type of reaction are shown in Equations 22.22 and 22.23.

Eqn. 22.22

$$(CH_3CH_2)_2CH-\overset{\overset{:O:}{\|}}{C}-\ddot{N}H_2 \xrightarrow[H_2O]{H_2SO_4} (CH_3CH_2)_2CHCOOH$$

2-ethylbutanamide

80% yield
2-ethylbutanoic acid

Eqn. 22.23

$$\text{N-(2-bromo-4-methylphenyl)acetamide} \xrightarrow[\text{(NaOH workup)}]{HCl,\ H_2O} \text{2-bromo-4-methylaniline}$$

N-(2-bromo-4-methylphenyl)acetamide

67% yield
2-bromo-4-methylaniline

If we wish to isolate the amine product, we need to follow the acidic hydrolysis step with an aqueous basic workup. This procedure generates the amine in its free base form and converts the acid to the carboxylate anion. The amine is then easily extracted into an organic solvent, leaving the carboxylic acid portion in the aqueous solution. To isolate the carboxylic acid product of hydrolysis, we simply extract the strongly acidic solution with an organic solvent. The amine is in the form of its ammonium ion under these conditions and will remain in the aqueous solution. The usual mechanism for the acid-catalyzed hydrolysis of amides is shown below.

MECHANISM OF REACTION

Acid-Catalyzed Hydrolysis of Amides

Overall reaction:

$$R-\overset{\overset{:O:}{\|}}{C}-\ddot{N}H_2 + H_2\ddot{O} \xrightarrow{H^+} R-\overset{\overset{:O:}{\|}}{C}-\ddot{O}H + \overset{+}{N}H_4$$

Step 1 Protonation of amide

$$R-\overset{\overset{:O:}{\|}}{C}-\ddot{N}H_2 + H^+ \rightleftharpoons \left[R-\overset{\overset{:\overset{+}{O}-H}{\|}}{C}-\ddot{N}H_2 \longleftrightarrow R-\overset{\overset{:\ddot{O}-H}{|}}{\overset{+}{C}}-\ddot{N}H_2 \right]$$

Step 2 Nucleophilic attack by water

$$R-\overset{\overset{:\ddot{O}H}{|}}{\underset{+}{C}}-\ddot{N}H_2 + \ddot{O}H_2 \rightleftharpoons R-\overset{\overset{:\ddot{O}H}{|}}{\underset{\underset{H-\overset{+}{\ddot{O}}H}{|}}{C}}-\ddot{N}H_2$$

Steps 3 and 4 Proton transfer

$$\text{B:} + \text{R—C(OH)(NH}_2\text{)—}\overset{+}{\text{O}}\text{H}_2 \rightleftharpoons \text{R—C(OH)(OH)—NH}_2 + \overset{+}{\text{B}}\text{—H}$$

$$\text{R—C(OH)(OH)—NH}_2 + \text{H—}\overset{+}{\text{B}} \rightleftharpoons \text{R—C(OH)(OH)—}\overset{+}{\text{N}}\text{H}_3 + \text{:B}$$

Step 5 Loss of ammonia

$$\text{R—C(OH)(OH)—}\overset{+}{\text{N}}\text{H}_3 \rightleftharpoons \left[\text{R—C}^+\text{(OH)(OH)} \longleftrightarrow \text{R—C(=}\overset{+}{\text{O}}\text{H)(OH)} \longleftrightarrow \text{R—C(OH)(=}\overset{+}{\text{O}}\text{H)}\right] + \text{:NH}_3$$

Steps 6 and 7 Proton transfer

$$\text{B:} + \text{R—C}^+\text{(OH)(OH)} \rightleftharpoons \text{R—C(=O)(OH)} + \overset{+}{\text{B}}\text{—H}$$

$$\overset{+}{\text{B}}\text{—H} + \text{:NH}_3 \rightleftharpoons \text{H—}\overset{+}{\text{N}}\text{H}_3 + \text{:B}$$

We can also hydrolyze amides using alkaline conditions by refluxing the amide with aqueous sodium hydroxide or potassium hydroxide. An example is shown in Equation 22.24.

Eqn. 22.24

$$\text{N-(4-methoxy-2-nitrophenyl)acetamide} \xrightarrow[\text{methanol, heat}]{\text{KOH, } H_2O} \text{4-methoxy-2-nitroaniline (97\% yield)}$$

N-(4-methoxy-2-nitrophenyl)acetamide

97% yield
4-methoxy-2-nitroaniline

PROBLEM 22.13 The alkaline hydrolysis of amides proceeds by means of a mechanism analogous to that involved in the alkaline hydrolysis of esters (given earlier in this chapter). Write out the mechanism for the base-catalyzed hydrolysis of amides. Would you expect amides or esters to hydrolyze more readily under alkaline conditions? Explain your choice.

PROBLEM 22.14 What product would you expect to form upon refluxing ε-caprolactam (shown below) with hydrochloric acid? (A lactam is a cyclic amide.)

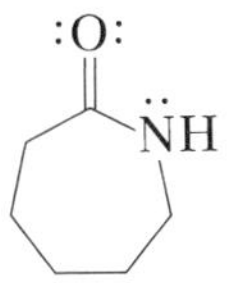

:O:

NH

Enzymatic Hydrolysis of Amides Like carboxylate esters, amides in biological systems undergo hydrolysis catalyzed by enzymes. With the availability of purified enzyme preparations, organic chemists have increasingly turned to the use of these biological catalysts for synthetic purposes. An example is shown in Equation 22.25. Here an enzyme from a bacterium efficiently accomplishes an amide hydrolysis. Because the starting material is sensitive to a variety of reagents, the highly selective enzymatic procedure is preferable. Harsh catalysts would not be able to effect the selective cleavage of the amide; other competing processes would occur with their use. Organic chemists sometimes say that the reactant would be "chewed up" under such harsh conditions.

Eqn. 22.25

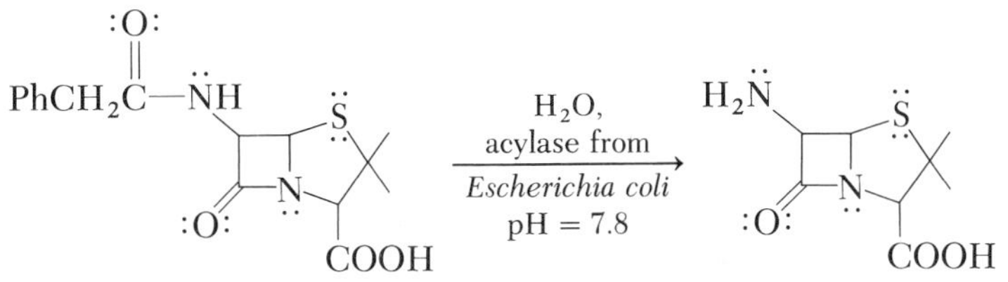

:O:
$PhCH_2C$—NH S N :O: COOH

$\xrightarrow[\text{pH = 7.8}]{\text{H}_2\text{O, acylase from } \textit{Escherichia coli}}$

H_2N S N :O: COOH

benzylpenicillin

90% yield
penicillamine

HYDROLYSIS OF NITRILES

Nitriles undergo hydrolysis to carboxylic acids and ammonia upon heating with aqueous acid. The reaction proceeds through the intermediate amide, which then undergoes acid-catalyzed hydrolysis (see the preceding "Mechanism of Reaction"). The mechanism of the nitrile hydrolysis reaction, up to the point of amide formation is given below. Under ordinary reaction conditions, the amide would continue to react, the end products being a carboxylic acid and ammonium ion. The reaction *can* be stopped at the amide stage by using sulfuric acid with an exactly calculated equivalent amount of water.

MECHANISM OF REACTION

Acid: Catalyzed Hydrolysis of Nitriles to Amides

Step 1 Protonation of nitrile

$$R-C\equiv N\!: + H^+ \rightleftharpoons \left[R-C\equiv\overset{+}{N}-H \longleftrightarrow R-\overset{+}{C}=\ddot{N}-H\right]$$

Step 2 Nucleophilic attack by water

$$R-\overset{+}{C}=\ddot{N}-H + \ddot{O}H_2 \rightleftharpoons R-C(\overset{+}{O}H_2)=\ddot{N}-H$$

Steps 3, 4, and 5 Proton transfers

$$B\!: + R-C(\overset{+}{O}H_2)=\ddot{N}-H \rightleftharpoons R-C(\ddot{O}H)=\ddot{N}-H + \overset{+}{B}-H$$

$$\overset{+}{B}-H + R-C(\ddot{O}H)=\ddot{N}-H \rightleftharpoons \left[R-C(\ddot{O}H)=\overset{+}{N}H_2 \longleftrightarrow R-\overset{+}{C}(\ddot{O}H)-\ddot{N}H_2\right] + B\!:$$

$$B\!: + R-\overset{+}{C}(\ddot{O}H)-\ddot{N}H_2 \rightleftharpoons R-C(=\ddot{O})-\ddot{N}H_2 + \overset{+}{B}-H$$

PROBLEM 22.15 Nitriles can also be hydrolyzed under alkaline conditions. Write a mechanism for this reaction.

The hydrolysis of nitriles provides a convenient synthetic route to carboxylic acids from compounds of one fewer carbon atom. For example, haloalkanes (R—X) produce carboxylic acids (R—COOH) after nucleophilic displacement by cyanide ion and hydrolysis of the resulting nitrile; and aldehydes (R—CHO) lead to α-hydroxycarboxylic acids, RCH(OH)—COOH, upon cyanohydrin formation (Chapter 19) and subsequent hydrolysis. Examples are shown in Equations 22.26 and 22.27.

Eqn. 22.26

$$C_6H_5CH_2\ddot{B}r: \xrightarrow[H_2O]{KCN} C_6H_5CH_2C{\equiv}N \xrightarrow[H_2O]{H_2SO_4} C_6H_5CH_2CO_2H$$

benzyl bromide — 80% yield phenylacetic acid

Eqn. 22.27

$$C_6H_5CH\ddot{O} \xrightarrow[H_2O]{HCN} C_6H_5CH(\ddot{O}H)C{\equiv}N: \xrightarrow[H_2O]{HCl} C_6H_5CH(\ddot{O}H)CO_2H$$

benzaldehyde — 52% yield α-hydroxyphenylacetic acid

PROBLEM 22.16 When phenylacetonitrile is refluxed with ethanol and sulfuric acid, an 85% yield of a compound of formula $C_{10}H_{12}O_2$ is obtained. Suggest a structure for this product.

PROBLEM 22.17 Acid-catalyzed hydrolysis of the compound shown below yields a product of formula $C_9H_{14}O_5$. Suggest a structure for this product.

(cyclic ketal: 1,3-dioxolane ring with two $(CH_2)_3CN$ groups on C-2)

22.4 Reductions of Acids and Their Derivatives

In carboxylic acids and their derivatives, carbon is in the highest oxidation state in which it can occur in organic compounds. Reduction of carboxylic acids is an important process. Organic chemists have been especially interested in the development of controlled methods for converting carboxylic acids into aldehydes and into alcohols. Several types of methods are used for this process, the most important of which are hydride reductions, dissolving-metal reductions, and catalytic hydrogenation. We briefly considered some of these topics in the previous chapter. In the next sections we further examine these methods and their applications.

HYDRIDE REDUCTIONS OF CARBOXYLIC ACID DERIVATIVES

Esters Although carboxylic acids themselves can be reduced directly to alcohols, it is often preferable to follow a two-step procedure. The acid is first converted to its methyl ester, and then the ester is reduced. Among the advantages of this procedure are the improved ether-solubility properties of the ester over the carboxylic acid and the wider range of convenient reducing agents for the ester (compared with the acid). For example, we can use either $LiAlH_4$ or $NaBH_4$ to reduce esters; the latter has no effect on the parent acid. Sodium borohydride is much milder and safer to use than $LiAlH_4$. However, to reduce an ester efficiently with $NaBH_4$ we must use a Lewis acid (such as aluminum trichloride) in the reaction. (The Lewis acid associates with the carbonyl oxygen of the ester, making the carboxyl carbon more susceptible to attack by a nucleophile such as the complex hydride ion.)

We also use a solvent such as diglyme (diethyleneglycol dimethyl ether, $CH_3OCH_2CH_2OCH_2CH_2OCH_3$), since it has a high boiling temperature that allows us to conduct the reaction at a high temperature. Two examples of hydride reduction of esters are shown in Equations 22.28 and 22.29.

Eqn. 22.28

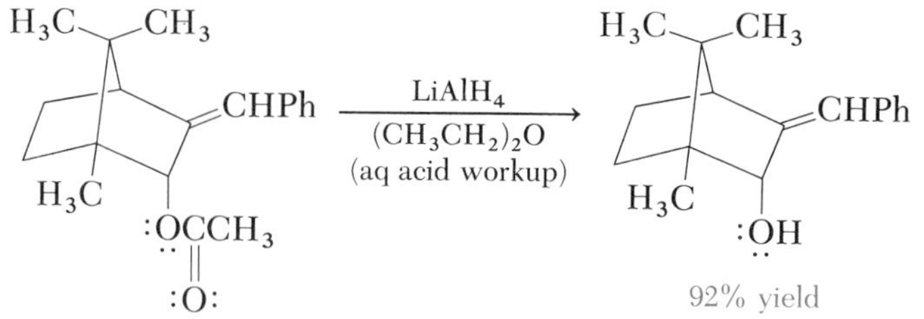
H3C CH3
CHPh
H3C
:OCCH3
:O:
LiAlH4
(CH3CH2)2O
(aq acid workup)
H3C CH3
CHPh
H3C
:OH
92% yield

Eqn. 22.29

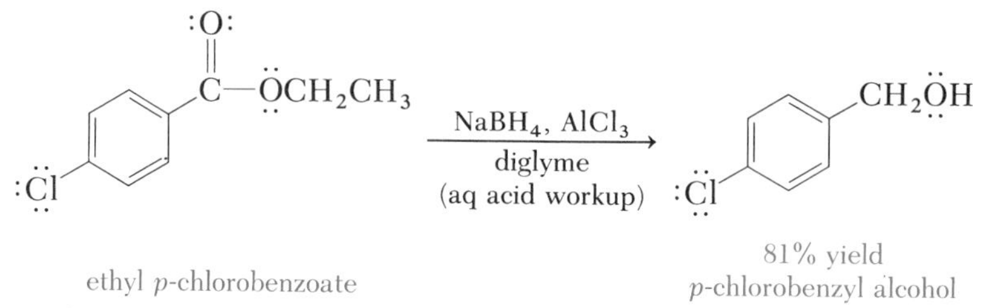
:O:
C—OCH2CH3
:Cl
NaBH4, AlCl3
diglyme
(aq acid workup)
CH2OH
:Cl
81% yield
ethyl p-chlorobenzoate
p-chlorobenzyl alcohol

Hydride reductions of esters proceed in stages. Initially, a tetrahedral intermediate (see Figure 22.5) forms; the intermediate then breaks down to an aldehyde and an alkoxide ion. The aldehyde undergoes further reduction to the alkoxide ion of the primary alcohol.

PROBLEM 22.18 For each of the reactions in Equations 22.28 and 22.29, give the structure of the organic by-product that is formed along with the indicated product.

Amides The reduction of carboxylic amides occurs with ease using any of the hydride reagents already mentioned in this section. However, there is a fundamental difference in the nature of the reduction product of amides compared

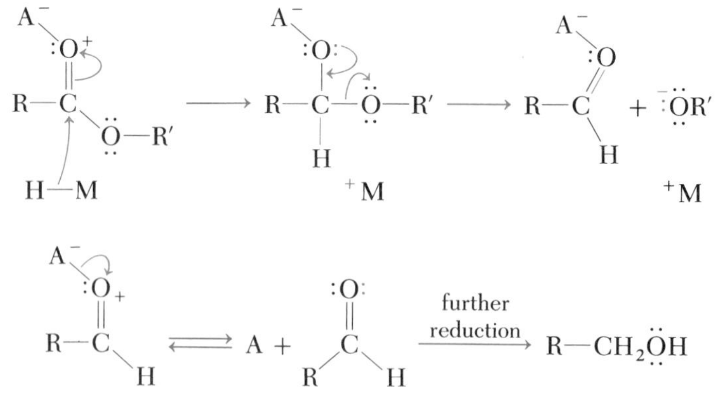
A
:O+
R—C
O—R′
H—M
A
:O:
R—C—O—R′
H
+M
A
:O
R—C
H
+ :OR′
+M
A
:O+
R—C
H
A +
:O:
C
R
H
further
reduction
R—CH2OH

Figure 22.5 Hydride reduction of a carboxylate ester. Attack of the hydride reagent at the carboxyl carbon is facilitated by complexation of a Lewis acid (A) at the carbonyl oxygen atom. The complex metal hydride transfers a hydrogen with a pair of electrons to the electron-deficient carboxyl carbon atom. The tetrahedral intermediate thus formed breaks down to an aldehyde and an alkoxide ion. The aldehyde undergoes further hydride reduction in the reaction medium.

with that of esters: the carboxyl carbon-nitrogen bond of the amide remains intact upon reduction, whereas the carboxyl carbon-oxygen bond of an ester is cleaved. The product of amide reduction is an amine. Examples of amide reduction are shown in Equations 22.30–22.32.

Eqn. 22.30

$$PhOCH_2-\overset{\overset{\displaystyle :O:}{\|}}{C}-NH_2 \xrightarrow[(CH_3CH_2)_2O]{LiAlH_4} PhOCH_2-CH_2-NH_2$$

phenoxyacetamide → 80% yield 2-phenoxyethylamine

Eqn. 22.31

$$CH_3CH_2CH_2-\overset{\overset{\displaystyle :O:}{\|}}{C}-NH_2 \xrightarrow[\text{CoCl}_2,\ \text{methanol}]{NaBH_4} CH_3CH_2CH_2-CH_2-NH_2$$

butanamide → 70% yield butylamine

Eqn. 22.32

$$CH_3(CH_2)_4-\overset{\overset{\displaystyle :O:}{\|}}{C}-NHCH_3 \xrightarrow{THF-BH_3} CH_3(CH_2)_4-CH_2-NHCH_3$$

N-methylhexamide → 98% yield hexylmethylamine

The reduction of amides provides us with an additional powerful method for the preparation of amines. We can easily obtain an amine ($RCH_2NR'_2$) from an acid halide (RCOCl) and another amine (HNR'_2) (or ammonia). The acid halide and amine react to give an amide, $RC(O)NR'_2$. We can then reduce the amide as described above. This approach is similar to that discussed in Chapter 20 for reduction of nitriles. However, while the reduction of nitriles can lead only to primary amines, amine synthesis through the amide can be used for the preparation of primary, secondary, and tertiary amines.

PROBLEM 22.19 Show how you would prepare each of the following amines using a reaction sequence of amide formation followed by amide reduction.
a. benzylamine **b.** cyclohexylethylamine **c.** tri(1-propyl)amine

PROBLEM 22.20 Show how you would synthesize each of the following amines starting from ammonia and using an amide reduction reaction.
a. dibenzylamine **b.** cyclohexylethylamine

Acid Chlorides We have already described (Chapter 19) how acid chlorides can be reduced to aldehydes using the reduced-reactivity hydride reagent lithium tri-*tert*-butoxy aluminum hydride. If we use lithium aluminum hydride itself with an acid chloride, rapid reaction occurs to generate a primary alcohol. However, this reaction is difficult to control because of the extremely high reactivity of $LiAlH_4$. If we wish to generate a primary alcohol from an acid chloride, we usually use sodium borohydride rather than lithium aluminum hydride so that the reduction is easier to control and safer. An example is shown in Equation 22.33.

Eqn. 22.33

$$CH_3(CH_2)_{14}COCl \xrightarrow[\text{dioxane (aq workup)}]{NaBH_4} CH_3(CH_2)_{14}CH_2\ddot{O}H$$

hexadecanoyl chloride — 87% yield hexadecanol

DISSOLVING-METAL REDUCTIONS OF CARBOXYLIC ACIDS AND THEIR DERIVATIVES

An older but useful method for the reduction for carboxylic acids and their derivatives involves the addition of an electropositive metal to a solution of the substrate in a protic solvent. Most commonly, lithium and sodium are the *dissolving metals,* which react through free radical processes to effect the reduction of the carboxyl group. Although esters are the most common substrates for this type of reduction, acids and nitriles also undergo facile reaction. Examples are shown in Equations 22.34–22.36.

Eqn. 22.34

$$CH_3(CH_2)_{10}-\overset{\overset{:O:}{\|}}{C}-\ddot{O}CH_2CH_3 \xrightarrow[\text{ethanol, toluene}]{Na} CH_3(CH_2)_{10}-CH_2\ddot{O}H$$

ethyl dodecanoate — 75% yield dodecanol

Eqn. 22.35

$$CH_3CH_2CH_2CH_2C{\equiv}N: \xrightarrow[\text{ethanol, toluene}]{Na} CH_3CH_2CH_2CH_2CH_2\ddot{N}H_2$$

1-cyanobutane — 67% yield pentylamine

Eqn. 22.36

$$CH_3(CH_2)_3-COOH \xrightarrow[CH_3NH_2]{Li} CH_3(CH_2)_3-CH\ddot{O}$$

pentanoic acid — 61% yield pentanal

The reduction of the carboxylic acid (Equation 22.36) is noteworthy in that an aldehyde is formed rather than the primary alcohol. This partial reduction of the carboxyl group is a useful tranformation.

HYDROGENATION OF CARBOXYLIC ACIDS AND THEIR DERIVATIVES

In Chapter 19 we saw that we can reduce acid chlorides to aldehydes under simple hydrogenation conditions using a *reduced-reactivity catalyst* (Rosenmund reduction, Equation 19.14). If we use an ordinary hydrogenation catalyst such as PtO_2 or Pd/C, the acid chloride is reduced to a primary alcohol.

Acid chlorides are the exceptions with regard to hydrogenation. Carboxylic acids and derivatives other than acid chlorides do not undergo such facile hydrogenation. Special catalysts, high temperatures, and high pressures of hydrogen are usually necessary for their reduction. Two examples are shown in Equations 22.37 and 22.38.

Eqn. 22.37

$$C_6H_5COOH \xrightarrow[ReO_3,\ H_2O]{H_2\ (250\ atm)} C_6H_5CH_2\ddot{O}H$$

benzoic acid → 43% yield benzyl alcohol

Eqn. 22.38

$$CH_3(CH_2)_4-\overset{:O:}{\overset{\|}{C}}-\ddot{O}CH_3 \xrightarrow[\text{copper chromite } 250^\circ]{H_2\ (200\ atm)} CH_3(CH_2)_4-CH_2-\ddot{O}H$$

methyl hexanoate → 78% yield 1-hexanol

Because of the drastic reaction conditions for these processes (hydrogen pressures of several hundred atmospheres), they are *not* standard laboratory procedures. They require special pressure apparatus and often special buildings isolated from other laboratories and personnel because of the explosion hazard. Not surprisingly, organic chemists generally prefer to use the alternative methods of reduction discussed earlier!

22.5 Reactions of Organometallics with Carboxylic Acid Derivatives

In Chapters 19 and 21 we introduced the reactions that carboxylic acids and acid chlorides undergo with organometallic reagents. Esters, nitriles, and amides also undergo reaction with these highly active reagents. Such reactions are of significant synthetic utility. In all cases the driving force for reaction is the interaction of the electron-rich carbon of the organometallic species with the electron-deficient carboxyl carbon atom.

ESTERS

Esters are the carboxylate derivatives most commonly used as substrates for reaction with organometallics. Esters react with both Grignard reagents and organolithium reagents to form tertiary alcohols. Ketones form as intermediates in this reaction, but they are susceptible to continued attack by an additional unit of the organometallic reagent. The general reaction system is outlined below, wherre M is some metal.

MECHANISM OF REACTION

Reaction of an Organometallic with an Ester

Overall reaction:

$$R-\overset{:O:}{\overset{\|}{C}}-\ddot{O}R' \xrightarrow{R''-M} \xrightarrow[\text{workup}]{\text{aq acid}} R-\underset{R''}{\overset{:\ddot{O}H}{C}}-R'' + R'\ddot{O}H$$

Step 1 Attack of the carbanionic reagent at the carboxyl carbon atom.

$$R{-}\overset{\overset{:O:}{\|}}{C}{-}\ddot{O}R' + R''{-}M \longrightarrow R{-}\underset{\underset{R''}{|}}{\overset{\overset{:\ddot{O}:^{-}\ M^{+}}{|}}{C}}{-}\ddot{O}R'$$

Step 2 Decomposition of the tetrahedral intermediate.

$$R{-}\underset{\underset{R''}{|}}{\overset{\overset{:\ddot{O}:^{-}\ M^{+}}{|}}{C}}{-}\ddot{O}R' \longrightarrow R{-}\overset{\overset{:O:}{\|}}{C}{-}R'' + {}^{-}:\ddot{O}R' \quad M^{+}$$

Step 3 Attack of the carbanionic reagent at the carbonyl carbon atom. The ketone intermediate undergoes continuing reaction with a second equivalent of organometallic.

$$R{-}\overset{\overset{:O:}{\|}}{C}{-}R'' + R''{-}M \longrightarrow R{-}\underset{\underset{R''}{|}}{\overset{\overset{:\ddot{O}:^{-}\ M^{+}}{|}}{C}}{-}R''$$

Step 4 Protonation of the alkoxide ion upon the addition of aqueous acid. A tertiary alcohol is the ultimate product.

$$H_2\overset{+}{\ddot{O}}{-}H + R{-}\underset{\underset{R''}{|}}{\overset{\overset{{}^{-}:\ddot{O}:\ M^{+}}{|}}{C}}{-}R'' \longrightarrow R{-}\underset{\underset{R''}{|}}{\overset{\overset{H{-}\ddot{O}}{|}}{C}}{-}R'' + H_2\ddot{O} + M^{+}$$

Since we are unable to stop the reaction at the intermediate ketone stage, the main use of this reaction is for the preparation of tertiary alcohols. Examples are shown in Equations 22.39 and 22.40.

Eqn. 22.39

$$CH_3(CH_2)_{14}{-}\overset{\overset{:O:}{\|}}{C}{-}\ddot{O}CH_3 \xrightarrow[\substack{(CH_3CH_2)_2O \\ \text{(aq acid workup)}}]{CH_3CH_2MgBr} CH_3(CH_2)_{14}{-}\underset{\underset{CH_2CH_3}{|}}{\overset{\overset{:\ddot{O}H}{|}}{C}}{-}CH_2CH_3$$

methyl hexadecanoate

96% yield
3-ethyl-3-octadecanol

Eqn.22.40

$$Ph{-}\overset{\overset{:O:}{\|}}{C}\ddot{O}CH_3 \xrightarrow[\substack{THF \\ \text{(aq acid workup)}}]{CH_3Li} Ph{-}\underset{\underset{CH_3}{|}}{\overset{\overset{:\ddot{O}H}{|}}{C}}{-}CH_3$$

methyl benzoate

74% yield
2-phenyl-2-propanol

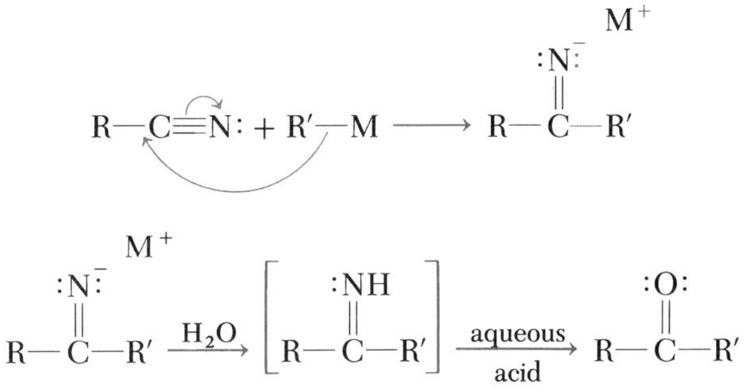

Figure 22.6 Reaction of a nitrile with an organometallic reagent. The reaction forms an anionic intermediate that is unreactive to the organometallic reagent. On workup with aqueous acid, a ketone forms.

$$R—C{\equiv}N: + R'—M \longrightarrow R—C(=\ddot{N}:^{-}\ M^{+})—R'$$

$$R—C(=\ddot{N}:^{-}\ M^{+})—R' \xrightarrow{H_2O} \left[R—C(=\ddot{N}H)—R'\right] \xrightarrow[\text{acid}]{\text{aqueous}} R—C(=\ddot{O}:)—R'$$

NITRILES

Unlike esters, nitriles *do* yield ketones upon reaction with either Grignard reagents or organolithium reagents. The reaction proceeds (as shown in Figure 22.6) to an anionic intermediate that remains in solution until the reaction is subjected to workup with aqueous acid. Workup produces an imine, which further hydrolyzes to the observed ketone product. Thus the carbonyl group is not generated until *after* the aqueous acid workup. At this time no organometallic reagent remains, so there can be no continuing reaction of the ketone. Two examples of the use of this reaction for the synthesis of ketones are shown in Equations 22.41 and 22.42.

Eqn. 22.41

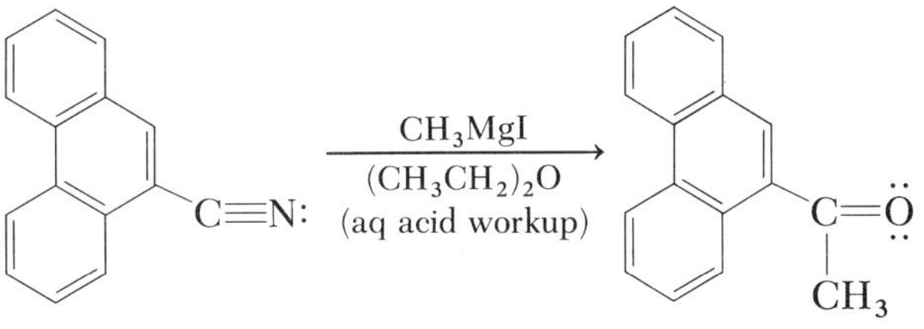

9-cyanophenanthrene (phenanthrene–C≡N:) $\xrightarrow[\text{(aq acid workup)}]{CH_3MgI,\ (CH_3CH_2)_2O}$ 9-acetophenanthrone (phenanthrene–C(=Ö)–CH_3)

59% yield

Eqn. 22.42

$CH_3CHCH_2C{\equiv}N:$ (with 4-methylcyclohex-3-enyl substituent, CH_3) $\xrightarrow[\text{heptane (aq acid workup)}]{(CH_3)_2CHCH_2Li,\ (CH_3CH_2)_2O}$ $CH_3CHCH_2C(=\ddot{O}:)CH_2CH(CH_3)_2$ (with 4-methylcyclohex-3-enyl substituent, CH_3)

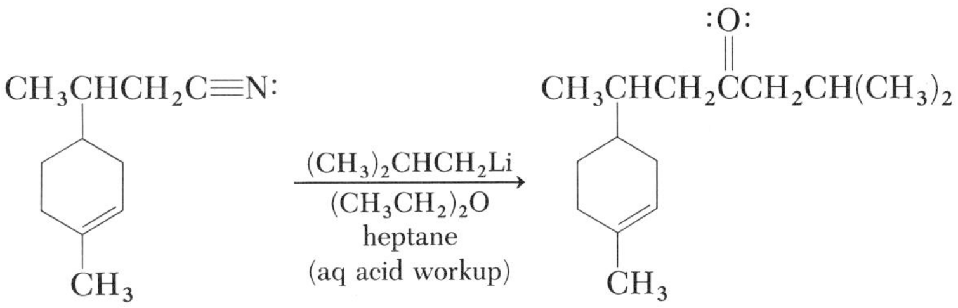

76% yield

PROBLEM 22.21 Write a mechanism for the last step in the reaction sequence shown in Figure 22.6 (i.e., the formation of ketone after treatment with aqueous acid).

PROBLEM 22.22 Give the reagents and reaction conditions required for the synthesis of each of the following ketones from the indicated starting nitriles using a Grignard reaction.

a. *p*-bromophenyl ethyl ketone from *p*-bromobenzonitrile
b. ethyl isobutyl ketone from propionitrile
c. 2,6-dimethyl-3-heptanone from isobutyronitrile

Steps to Solving the Problem

Solution to Problem 22.22a

1. Consider the structures of the target material and the required starting material. Remember that the cyano-carbon of the starting material becomes the carbonyl carbon of the product. The remaining portion of the product (boxed in the structure shown) must originate with the Grignard reagent.

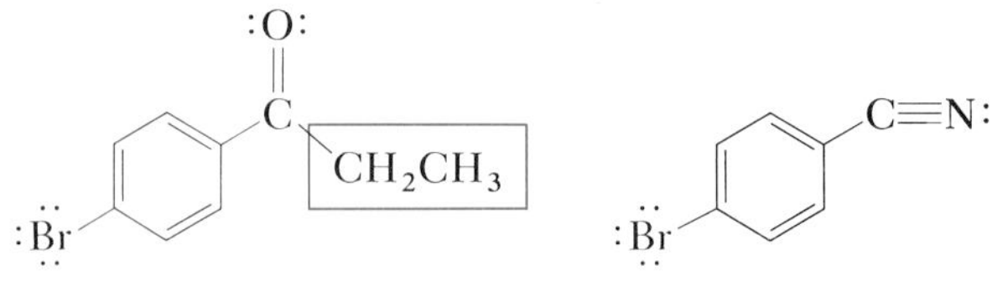

:O: C CH_2CH_3 :Br: — target material

C≡N: :Br: — starting material

2. We must decide on the organometallic reagent to be used with the nitrile. Since the carbon portion to be added to the starting nitrile is an ethyl group, we need to use the ethyl Grignard reagent in the synthesis. The required reaction is shown below.

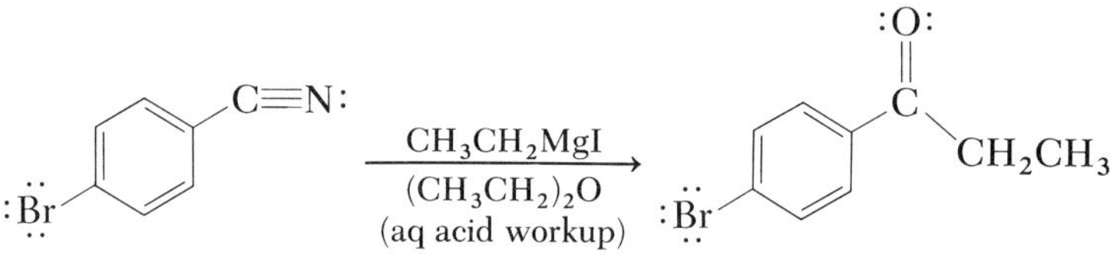

$$p\text{-BrC}_6\text{H}_4\text{C}\equiv\text{N:} \xrightarrow[\text{(aq acid workup)}]{\text{CH}_3\text{CH}_2\text{MgI},\ (\text{CH}_3\text{CH}_2)_2\text{O}} p\text{-BrC}_6\text{H}_4\text{C(=O)CH}_2\text{CH}_3$$

PROBLEM 22.23 How would you prepare *p*-bromobenzonitrile, the given starting material in Problem 22.22, starting from benzene?

22.6 Carbon-Carbon Bond Cleavages Involving Derivatives of Carboxylic Acids

THE HOFMANN REARRANGEMENT

The **Hofmann rearrangement** involves the conversion of a primary amide to an amine with removal of the carboxyl carbon. The overall conversion is shown in Figure 22.7. It is one of several mechanistically similar reactions.

We usually effect Hofmann rearrangement by treating a primary amide with a solution of bromine in aqueous base. The reaction begins with the base removing a proton from nitrogen to generate an anion. This anion reacts further with bromine to form an *N*-bromoamide. The *N*-bromoamide then loses another proton to a base. These initial three steps are completely analogous to the halogenation of a ketone under basic conditions. In the fourth step the rearrangement occurs as the R group of the original amide displaces the halogen from the nitrogen with the formation of an isocyanate (R—N=C=O; see the "Compound Capsule" later in this chapter). The isocyanate then undergoes hydrolysis (solvolysis) to yield the product amine. The carbon-carbon bond that is broken is that between the carboxyl carbon and the R group. The complete mechanism follows.

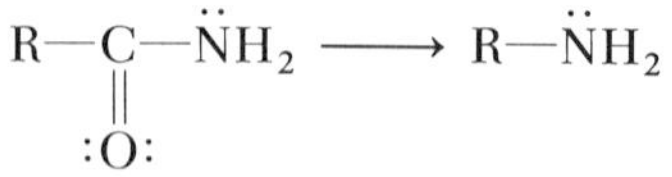

$$\text{R—C(=O:)—}\ddot{\text{N}}\text{H}_2 \longrightarrow \text{R—}\ddot{\text{N}}\text{H}_2$$

Figure 22.7 Overall course of the Hofmann rearrangement. The carboxyl carbon atom and its associated oxygen atom are eliminated in the formation of the amine product.

MECHANISM OF REACTION

The Hofmann Rearrangement

Step 1 Removal of a proton from nitrogen by a base.

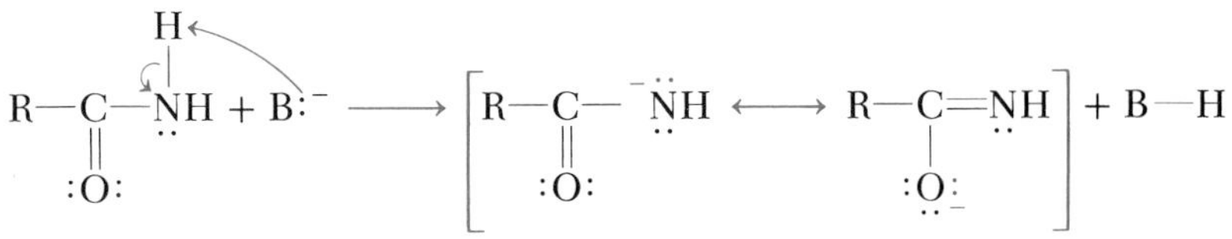

$$R{-}C({=}O){-}NH_2 + B^- \longrightarrow \left[R{-}C({=}O){-}\ddot{N}H^- \longleftrightarrow R{-}C(O^-){=}NH\right] + B{-}H$$

Step 2 Attack of the intermediate anion on a bromine molecule

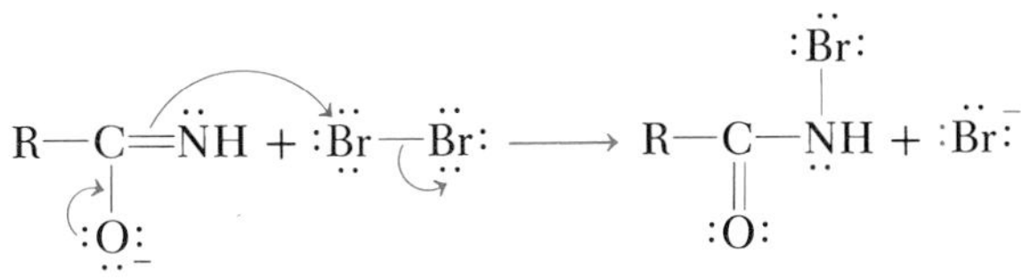

$$R{-}C(O^-){=}NH + Br{-}Br \longrightarrow R{-}C({=}O){-}NH{-}Br + Br^-$$

Step 3 Removal of a proton from the *N*-bromoamide by base

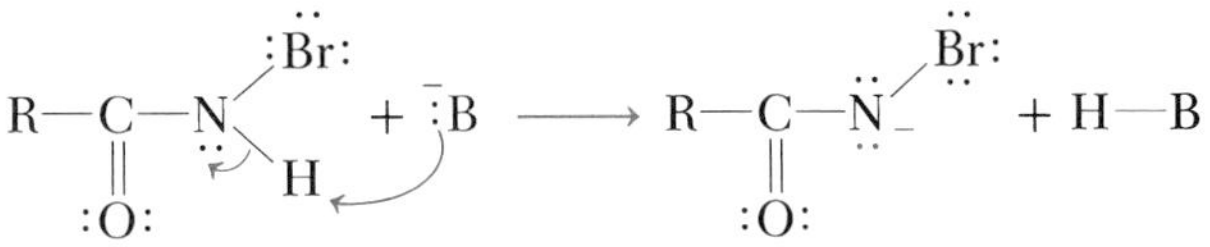

$$R{-}C({=}O){-}N(Br)H + {:}B^- \longrightarrow R{-}C({=}O){-}N^-{-}Br + H{-}B$$

Step 4 Decomposition of the anion and formation of an isocyanate

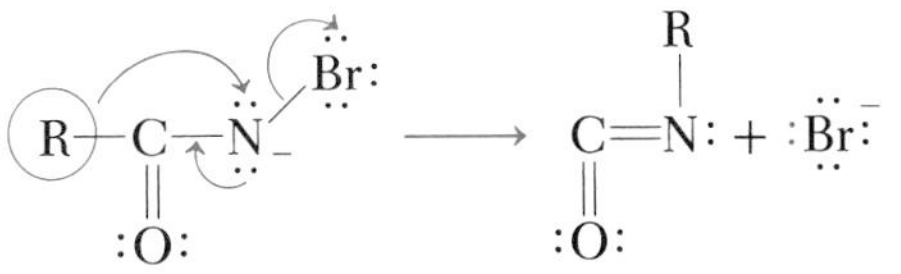

$$R{-}C({=}O){-}N^-{-}Br \longrightarrow R{-}N{=}C{=}O + Br^-$$

Step 5 Hydrolysis of the isocyanate to the amine

$$R{-}\ddot{N}{=}C{=}\ddot{O} \xrightarrow[R'OH/H_2O\text{ solvent}]{\text{Base}} R{-}\ddot{N}H_2 + CO_2$$

In the process of migration (rearrangement), the R group does *not* become free. Instead, it *slides* along the carbon-nitrogen linkage, with the new carbon-nitrogen bond forming as the old carbon-carbon bond is breaking. Thus the migration occurs with *retention* of configuration at the carbon that is migrating. We see this retention clearly when we use an amide that is stereogenic at its α-carbon atom. We also see it in the facile reaction of the bicyclic compound shown in Figure 22.8.

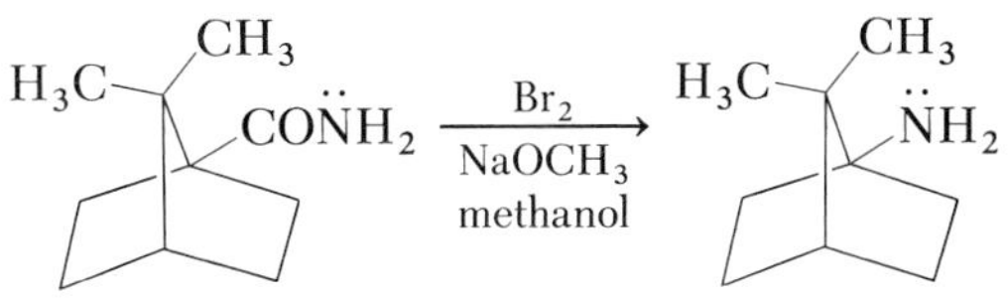

$$\text{bicyclic }(H_3C,\ CH_3)\text{-}CONH_2 \xrightarrow[\text{methanol}]{Br_2,\ NaOCH_3} \text{bicyclic }(H_3C,\ CH_3)\text{-}NH_2$$

Figure 22.8 Hofmann rearrangement of a bridgehead bicyclic amide. The reaction necessarily proceeds with retention of configuration at the migrating carbon atom.

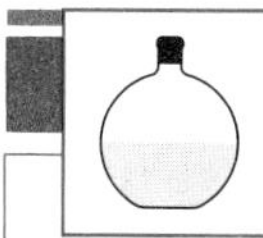

COMPOUND CAPSULE

$$CH_3-\ddot{N}=C=\ddot{O}:$$

Methyl isocyanate

We saw that isocyanates are produced as intermediates in the Hofmann rearrangement. Methyl isocyanate is an industrial chemical that is produced and used in bulk quantities.

In December 1984, large quantities of methyl isocyanate escaped from a storage container at a chemical plant near the town of Bhopal, India. The vapors of the material quickly spread across the town and caused the worst catastrophe in the history of industrial chemistry in terms of death and suffering. In the first week after the incident, 2,500 people died and over 100,000 others suffered from debilitating injuries, particularly to the eyes and respiratory tract. The great toxicity of the compound is explained by its high reactivity with nucleophiles. Upon exposure to methyl isocyanate, the water in the mucous membranes reacts with it and severe dehydration results. Methylamine and carbon dioxide are also produced in this reaction.

Two examples of the Hofmann rearrangement that are used for synthetic purposes are shown in Equations 22.43 and 22.44.

Eqn. 22.43

$$(CH_3)_2CHCH_2CO\ddot{N}H_2 \xrightarrow[H_2O]{KOH,\ Br_2} (CH_3)_2CHCH_2\ddot{N}H_2$$

3-methylbutanamide → 90% yield, 2-methyl-1-aminopropane

Eqn. 22.44

quinoline 3-carboxamide (quinoline ring with $-C(=\ddot{O})-\ddot{N}H_2$ at C-3) $\xrightarrow[\text{methanol}]{KOH,\ Br_2}$ 3-aminoquinoline (quinoline ring with $\ddot{N}H_2$ at C-3)

75% yield, 3-aminoquinoline

PROBLEM 22.24 Explain why the Hofmann rearrangement reaction does not work with *N*-methylbenzamide. What product do you expect to form upon treatment of *N*-methylbenzamide with bromine in aqueous sodium hydroxide solution?

PROBLEM 22.25 Consider the last step in the Hofmann rearrangement. Propose a detailed mechanism for the formation of the amine from the isocyanate.

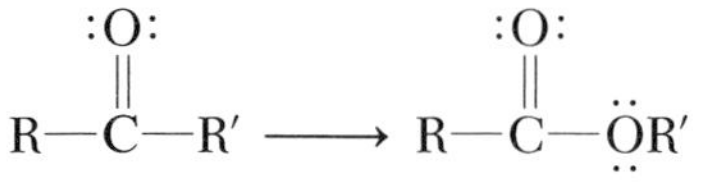

$$R-C(=O)-R' \longrightarrow R-C(=O)-OR'$$

Figure 22.9 Direct conversion of a carbonyl compound (ketone or aldehyde) to an ester by the Baeyer-Villiger reaction.

THE BAEYER-VILLIGER REACTION

The **Baeyer-Villiger oxidation** is a reaction in which a ketone (or aldehyde) is oxidized to an ester. The general conversion is shown in Figure 22.9. Overall, it *appears* that an oxygen is *inserted* between the carbonyl carbon and an α-carbon position in this reaction. Normally, we effect the conversion by simply heating a carbonyl compound with a peroxy carboxylic acid such as peroxybenzoic acid or peroxytrifluoroacetic acid. (We discussed peroxy carboxylic acids in connection with the epoxidation of alkenes in Chapter 10.) Three examples of the use of this reaction are shown in Equations 22.45–22.47.

Eqn. 22.45

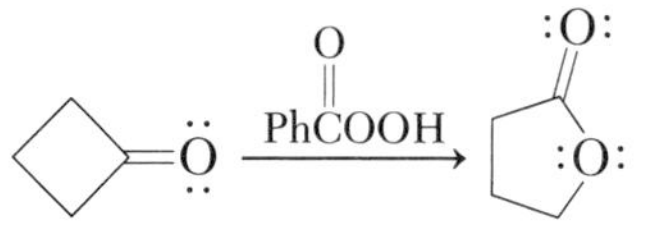

cyclobutanone $\xrightarrow{PhC(=O)OOH}$ γ-butyrolactone, 70% yield

Eqn. 22.46

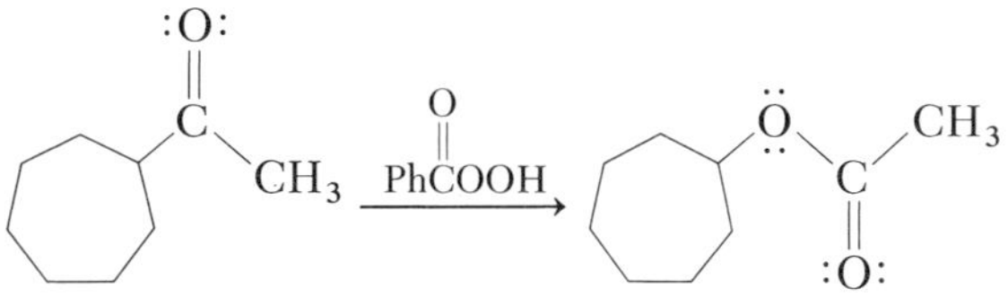

cycloheptyl methyl ketone $\xrightarrow{PhC(=O)OOH}$ cycloheptyl acetate, 69% yield

Eqn. 22.47

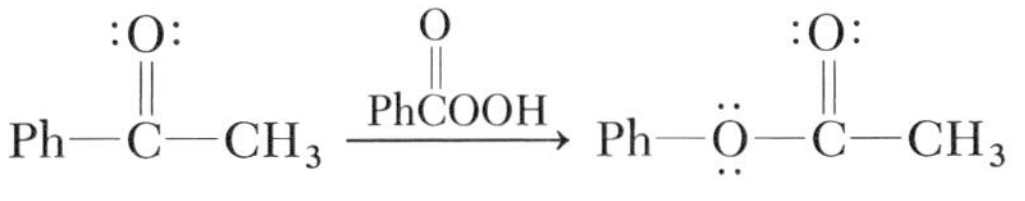

$$Ph-C(=O)-CH_3 \xrightarrow{PhC(=O)OOH} Ph-O-C(=O)-CH_3$$

acetophenone → phenyl acetate, 84% yield

The mechanism of the reaction is presented below.

MECHANISM OF REACTION

The Baeyer-Villiger Reaction

Step 1 Protonation of the ketone

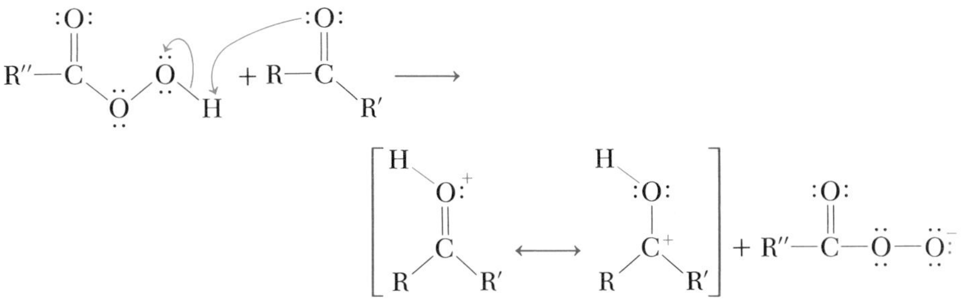

$$R''-C(=O)-O-O-H + R-C(=O)-R' \longrightarrow \left[R-C(=\overset{+}{O}H)-R' \longleftrightarrow R-\overset{+}{C}(OH)-R' \right] + R''-C(=O)-O-O^-$$

Step 2 Addition of the peroxycarboxylate anion to the protonated ketone

$$R-\overset{+}{C}(OH)-R' + R''-\overset{\overset{O}{\|}}{C}-O-O^{-} \longrightarrow R-C(OH)(R')-O-O-\overset{\overset{O}{\|}}{C}-R''$$

Step 3 Rearrangement of the adduct

$$R-C(OH)(R')-O-O-\overset{\overset{O}{\|}}{C}-R'' \longrightarrow \left[{}^{+}C(OH)(R')(O-R) \longleftrightarrow R'-\overset{\overset{{}^{+}O-H}{\|}}{C}-O-R \right] + {}^{-}O-\overset{\overset{O}{\|}}{C}-R''$$

Step 4 Deprotonation

$$B^{-} + {}^{+}C(OH)(R')(O-R) \longrightarrow R'-\overset{\overset{O}{\|}}{C}-O-R + B-H$$

The Baeyer-Villiger reaction has its greatest synthetic utility in the oxidation of *symmetrical* ketones, whether cyclic or acyclic, because an unsymmetrical ketone can give a mixture of products since either of the two groups can migrate. The Baeyer-Villiger reaction with unsymmetrical ketones can have synthetic value, however, when the different types of groups present migrate with different abilities. The more highly substituted the α-carbon of an alkyl group of a ketone, the more readily the group migrates. Since methyl groups migrate very slowly, the reaction can be used with methyl ketones for the preparation of esters of acetic acid. Aryl groups migrate more readily than primary alkyl groups but less readily than secondary alkyl groups.

22.7 Pyrolysis of Esters

THE PYROLYSIS OF ACETATE ESTERS

In Chapter 9 we discussed the formation of alkenes by acid-catalyzed dehydration of alcohols. Often such reactions are of little synthetic value because of carbocation rearrangements that alter the carbon skeleton.

If we first prepare esters from the alcohols, however, alkene syntheses can often be accomplished without skeletal rearrangements. **Pyrolyses,** that is, cleavages by heating, of the esters lead to the formation of alkenes.

Ordinary carboxylate esters undergo controlled, concerted cleavages upon heating to relatively high temperatures. In principle, any acid can serve as the

Figure 22.10 Mechanism of acetate ester pyrolysis. The reaction involves a concerted shifting of electrons.

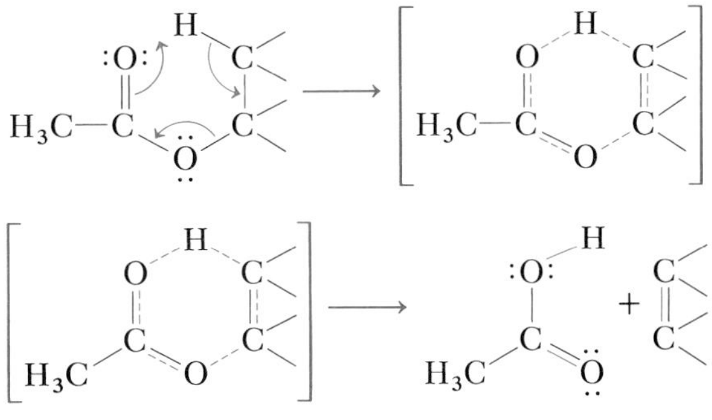

acid portion of the ester, but for practical purposes esters of acetic acid (i.e., acetates) are usually used. On heating, acetates undergo cleavage through a concerted rearrangement of electrons with a cyclic activated complex as illustrated in Figure 22.10. The elimination has a *syn* stereospecificity.

The major structural requirement is the presence of at least one hydrogen on the second carbon (the β-carbon) of the alcohol portion of the ester. Without at least one hydrogen in this position the reaction cannot proceed. An example of a synthetically useful acetate pyrolysis reaction is shown in Equation 22.48.

Eqn. 22.48

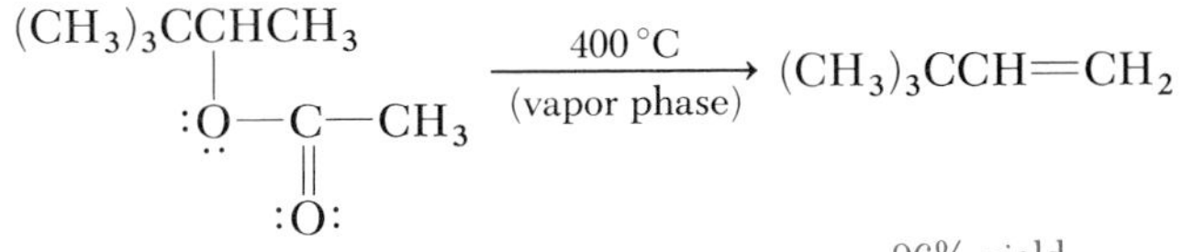

$$(CH_3)_3CCH(OCOCH_3)CH_3 \xrightarrow[\text{(vapor phase)}]{400\,°C} (CH_3)_3CCH{=}CH_2$$

3,3-dimethyl-2-butyl acetate → 96% yield 3,3-dimethyl-1-butene

We need to use care in devising alkene syntheses using this approach. If there is more than one type of β-hydrogen within the alcohol portion of the ester, a mixture of products can (and usually will) form. Equation 22.49 shows a simple reaction in which a mixture of two products results.

Eqn. 22.49

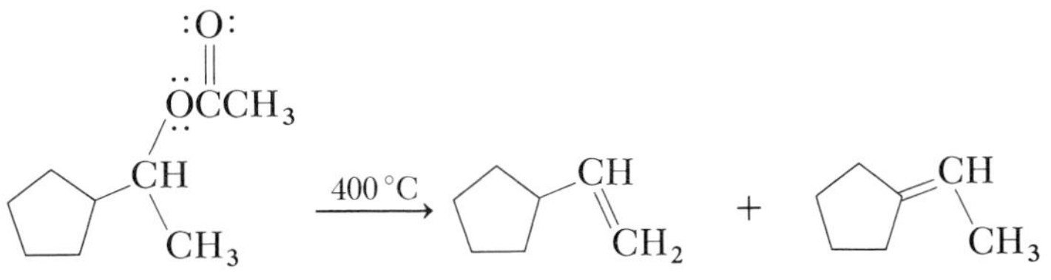

1-cyclopentylethyl acetate $\xrightarrow{400\,°C}$ vinylcyclopentane (87% yield) + ethylidenecyclopentane (13% yield)

PROBLEM 22.26 Consider the products formed in the reaction shown in Equation 22.49. What *statistical* ratio of products would we anticipate based on the number of each type of hydrogen available for removal? Explain why there is a greater amount of the 1-alkene formed than we would anticipate from statistical considerations. (*Hint:* Draw the conformations of the activated complexes required for the formation of each of the products.)

PROBLEM 22.27 Predict the alkene products that would result from the pyrolysis of each of the following acetate esters. Which of these pyrolyses would you expect to be of value as a synthetic procedure?

a. 3-octyl acetate
b. 2-phenylethyl acetate
c. *trans*-2-methylcyclohexyl acetate

XANTHATE PYROLYSES—THE CHUGAEV REACTION

Compounds known as **xanthate esters** (of the general formula shown in Figure 22.11) undergo pyrolysis to yield alkenes at lower temperatures than do the corresponding acetates. We commonly refer to this reaction as the **Chugaev reaction.** The lower temperatures at which the Chugaev reaction occurs allow structurally more complex alcohols to be used in alkene syntheses. The overall procedure for xanthate ester formation and pyrolysis is shown in Figure 22.11.

Two examples of alkene syntheses using the Chugaev reaction are shown in Equations 22.50 and 22.51.

Eqn. 22.50

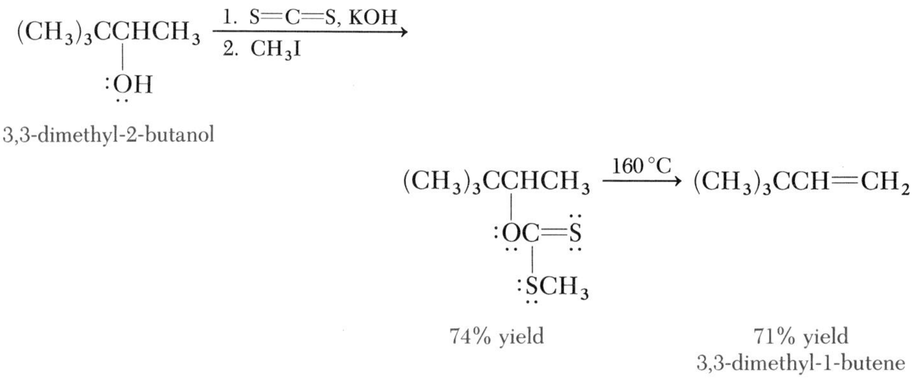

$$(CH_3)_3CCH(OH)CH_3 \xrightarrow[2.\ CH_3I]{1.\ S{=}C{=}S,\ KOH} (CH_3)_3CCH(OC(=S)SCH_3)CH_3 \xrightarrow{160\,°C} (CH_3)_3CCH{=}CH_2$$

3,3-dimethyl-2-butanol; 74% yield; 71% yield 3,3-dimethyl-1-butene

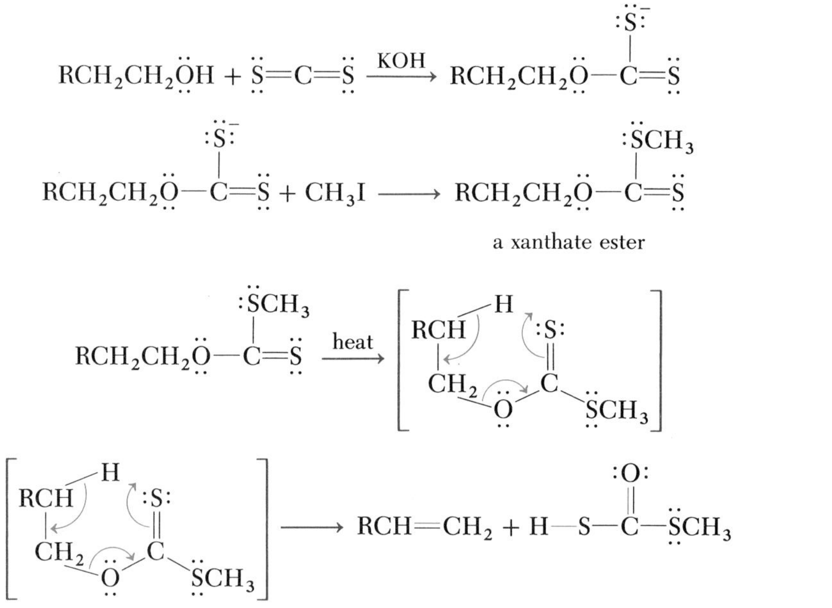

Figure 22.11 Formation and pyrolysis of xanthate esters. The xanthate ester is formed by the reaction of an alcohol with carbon disulfide in the presence of base, followed by a displacement reaction of the anion on methyl iodide. The pyrolysis occurs in the same manner as does the pyrolysis of acetate esters, except that it requires lower temperatures. The elimination occurs with *syn* stereospecificity.

$$RCH_2CH_2OH + S{=}C{=}S \xrightarrow{KOH} RCH_2CH_2O{-}C(S^-){=}S$$

$$RCH_2CH_2O{-}C(S^-){=}S + CH_3I \longrightarrow RCH_2CH_2O{-}C(SCH_3){=}S$$

a xanthate ester

$$RCH_2CH_2O{-}C(SCH_3){=}S \xrightarrow{heat} \left[\text{cyclic transition state: RCH(H)–CH}_2\text{–O–C(=S)SCH}_3\right]$$

$$\left[\text{cyclic transition state}\right] \longrightarrow RCH{=}CH_2 + H{-}S{-}C(=O){-}SCH_3$$

Eqn. 22.51

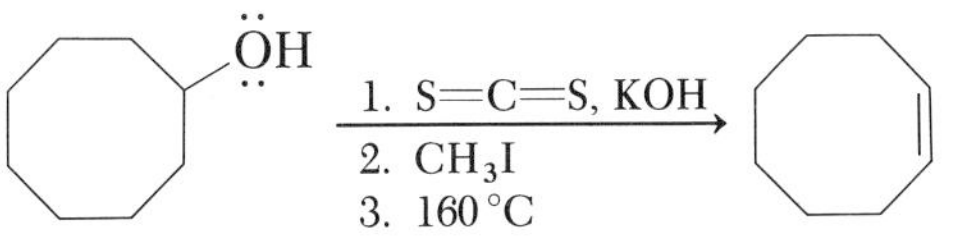

cyclooctanol $\xrightarrow[\text{2. } CH_3I \text{ 3. } 160\,°C]{\text{1. } S{=}C{=}S,\ KOH}$ cyclooctene (88% yield)

PROBLEM 22.28 Explain why we use iodomethane rather than iodoethane in the formation of the xanthate ester for use in the Chugaev reaction.

22.8 Spectroscopic Properties of Carboxylic Acid Derivatives

INFRARED

All carboxylic acid derivatives exhibit a C=O stretching band in their IR spectra. The *exact position* of this band is quite sensitive to the environment of the C=O linkage. The variation of the position of this band for different substituents is shown in Table 22.1.

Recall that a stretching frequency is related to the strength of a bond. We see that the C=O bond is appreciably stronger in acid halides and anhydrides than it is in carboxylic acids, but it is appreciably weaker in amides. We can understand these trends by taking into account the resonance structures of the molecules.

Consider an acid chloride. The chlorine is extremely electronegative, resulting in a high polarity for the C—Cl bond. We might thus represent an acid halide as a resonance hybrid of covalent and ionic structures, as shown in Figure 22.12. The ionic structures involve an acylium ion, $(RCO)^+$. The best resonance structure we can draw for an acylium ion is the one with the positive charge on the oxygen. In this structure each atom has a complete valence level octet of electrons. This charge delocalization provides *triple-bond character* to the carbon-oxygen linkage of an acyl halide. This triple-bond character is consistent with the increased bond strength and increased carbonyl stretching frequency of such compounds compared with their parent carboxylic acids.

Table 22.1 Variation of C=O Stretching Frequency with Carboxylic Acid Derivative

Compound Type	C=O Stretching Frequency (cm^{-1})
Carboxylic acid	1705–1725
Carboxylate ester	1735–1750
Carboxylic amide	1630–1680
Carboxylic acid chloride	1790–1800
Carboxylic anhydride	1740–1760 and 1800–1850

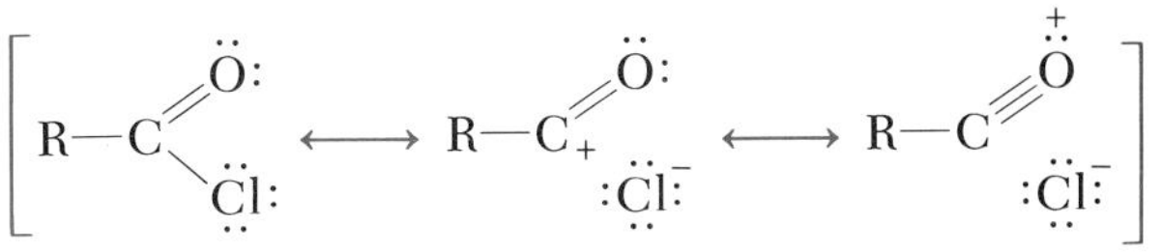

Figure 22.12 Contributing resonance hybrid structures for an acid chloride.

$$\left[R{-}C(=\ddot{O}:){-}\ddot{Cl}: \longleftrightarrow R{-}C^{+}(=\ddot{O}:)\ :\ddot{Cl}:^{-} \longleftrightarrow R{-}C{\equiv}\overset{+}{O}:\ :\ddot{Cl}:^{-} \right]$$

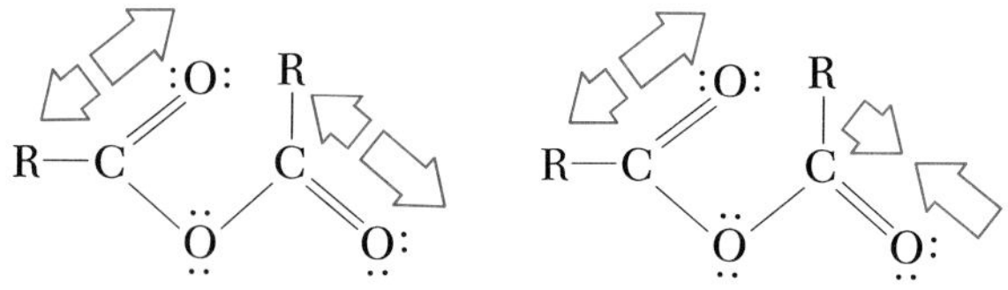

Figure 22.13 **Stretching modes of carboxylic anhydrides.** The arrows indicate the direction of motion of the atoms in each type of vibration.

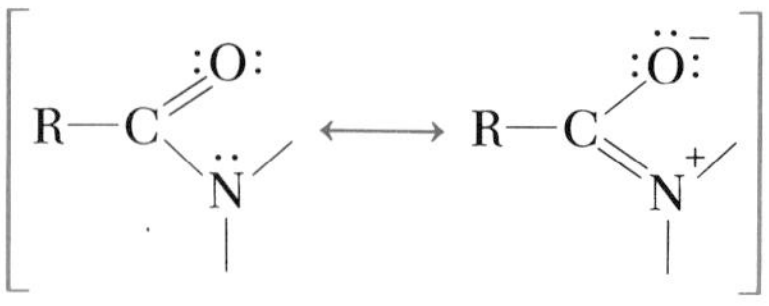

in-phase
1740–1760 cm^{-1}

out-of-phase
1800–1850 cm^{-1}

Figure 22.14 **Resonance structures for a carboxylic amide.** Because nitrogen can express a strong resonance effect, carboxylic amides have one significant resonance structure in which the carbon-oxygen linkage is a single bond.

We can make similar arguments about the structure of carboxylic acid anhydrides and, to a lesser degree, esters. The two carbon-oxygen stretching bands we observe for anhydrides relate to a coupling of two C=O vibrations, one *in-phase* and one *out-of-phase*, as shown in Figure 22.13.

Amides have a C=O bond that is weaker than those of the other carboxylate derivatives. We associate this relative weakness with the ability of a nitrogen atom to exert a resonance effect that is stronger than its inductive effect. A resonance structure in which the carbon-oxygen bond is only a single bond is significant (see Figure 22.14).

Thus, the carbon-oxygen bond in an amide is less than a full double bond.

Table 22.2 Chemical Shifts of α-Hydrogens in Carboxylate Compounds

Compound Type	Approximate Chemical Shift (δ)
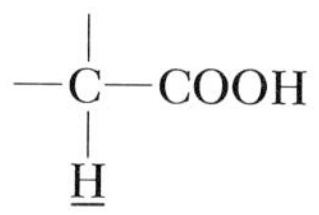 H–C–COOH	2.20–2.40
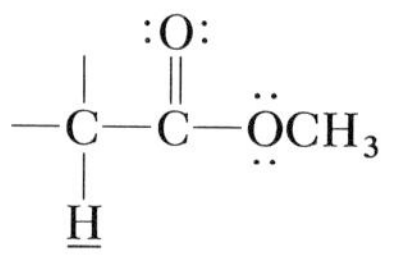 H–C–C(=O)–OCH_3	2.10–2.36
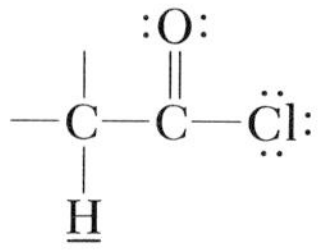 H–C–C(=O)–Cl	2.67
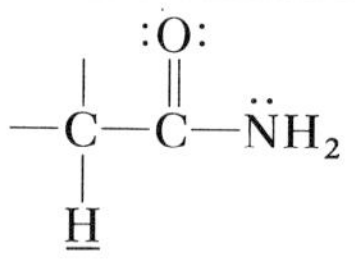 H–C–C(=O)–NH_2	2.08–2.23
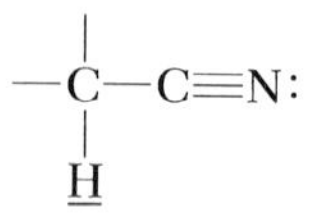 H–C–C≡N:	2.00–2.28

^{1}H NMR SPECTRA

Hydrogen atoms attached to a carbon atom that is α-relative to the C=O of a carboxylic acid or a carboxylate derivative are slightly deshielded and therefore come into resonance at $\delta \sim 2.0$–2.5 in a ^{1}H NMR spectrum. Common values for these chemical shifts are shown in Table 22.2

Protons attached to the carbon atom adjacent to the alcohol-type oxygen of a carboxylate ester also give rise to a characteristic signal. Such protons produce a signal at lower field (by ~0.4–0.8 ppm) than do the analogous protons on simple alcohols, as illustrated in Figure 22.15.

Figure 22.15 Chemical shifts of hydrogens in ethyl alcohol and ethyl acetate.

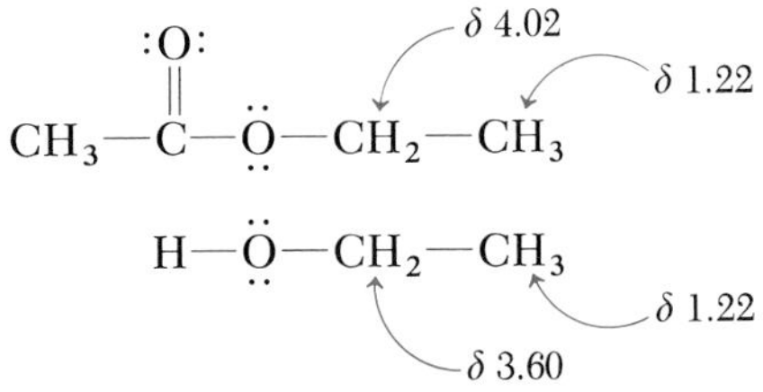

$$CH_3-\overset{\overset{:O:}{\|}}{C}-\ddot{O}-CH_2-CH_3 \quad (\delta\ 4.02,\ \delta\ 1.22)$$

$$H-\ddot{O}-CH_2-CH_3 \quad (\delta\ 3.60,\ \delta\ 1.22)$$

PROBLEM 22.29 The ^{1}H NMR spectrum of *N,N*-dimethylformamide exhibits two nonequivalent methyl resonance peaks at $\delta \sim 2.9$ and $\delta \sim 3.0$ when measured at low temperature. At higher temperatures, a single methyl peak appears. Offer an explanation for this observation. (*Hint*: Consider the resonance structures shown for an amide in Figure 22.14.)

^{13}C NMR SPECTRA

The main feature associated with a carboxyl group in ^{13}C NMR is a resonance associated with the carboxyl carbon atom. It occurs in the region 160–210 ppm downfield from TMS.

PROBLEM 22.30 Substance *A* (formula $C_{10}H_{11}ClO$) exhibits an IR absorption band at ~1790 cm^{-1}. On treatment of *A* with aluminum chloride, the compound shown below forms. Suggest a structure for substance *A*.

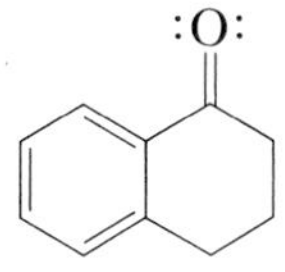

:O:

PROBLEM 22.31 The two ^{1}H NMR spectra shown below are those of methyl propanoate and ethyl acetate. Decide which spectrum corresponds to which compound and explain your decision.

a.

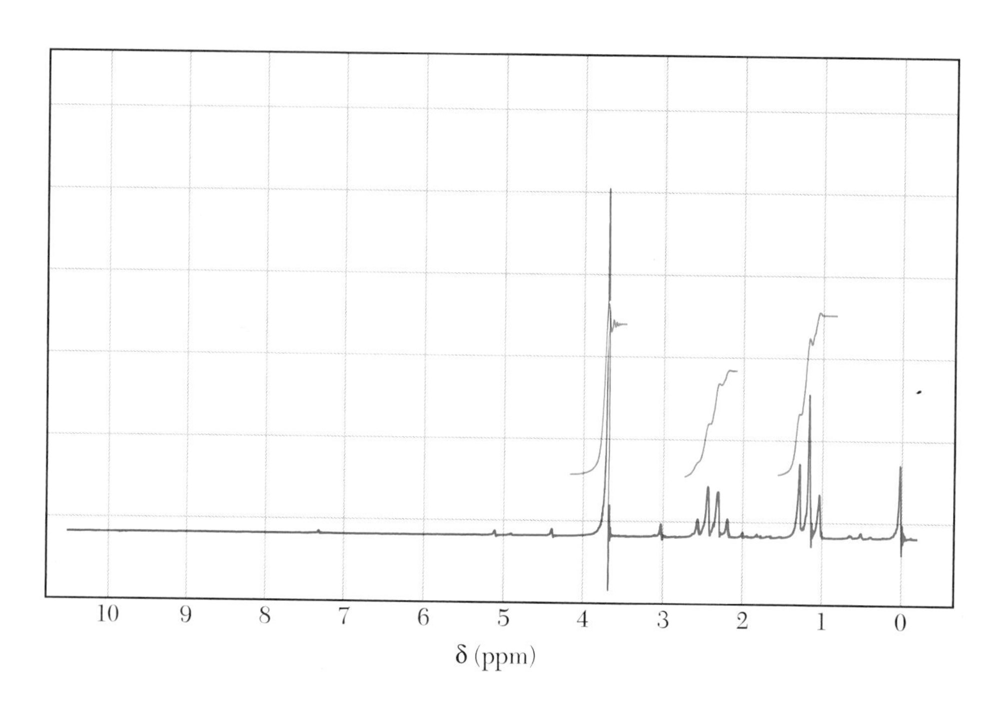

b.

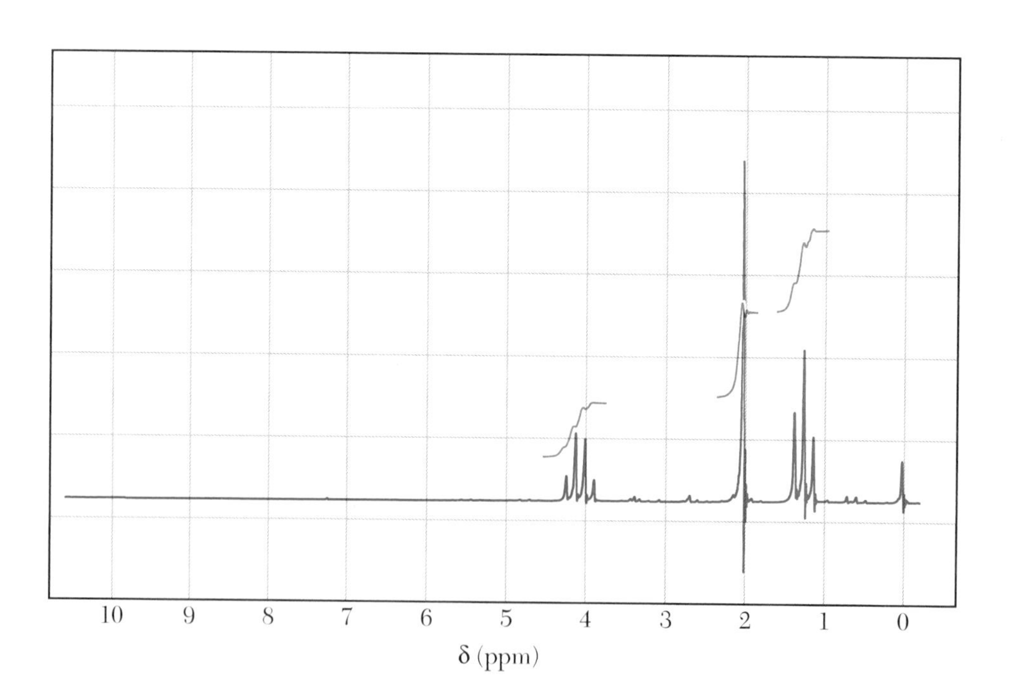

PROBLEM 22.32 Give the structures of compounds *B*–*E*.

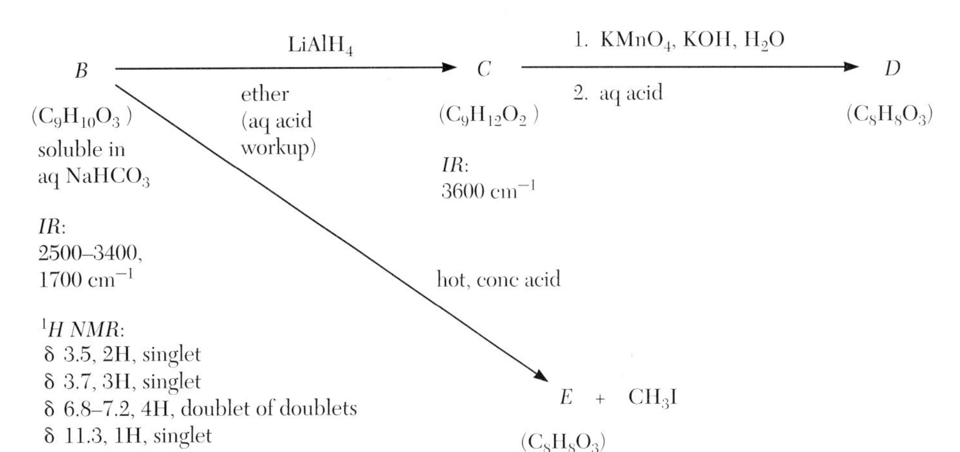

Summary

- In the common carboxylic acid derivatives, another functional group is present in place of the —OH group of the parent carboxylic acid.
- Table 22.3 summarizes the synthetic methods available for the interconversions among carboxylic acids and their derivatives.
- Acid halides, anhydrides, esters, and amides are all reactive toward nucleophiles. The nucleophile attacks the carbon of the carboxyl group.
- The order of reactivity toward nucleophiles is:

  acid halide > anhydride > ester > amide

Table 22.3 Synthetic Methods for Carboxylate Derivative Interconversion

Starting Compound	Target Compound			
	R—C(=O)—OH	R—C(=O)—Cl	RC(=O)—OR′	RC(=O)—NR′R″
RCOOH		PCl_3, or $SOCl_2$, or CCl_4/Ph_3P:	R′OH/acid, or R′OH/DCC	R′R″NH, DCC
RCOCl	H_2O		R′OH	R′R″NH
RCO_2R'	H_2O/acid, H_2O/base	—		R′R″NH, heat
RCONR′R″	H_2O/acid, H_2O/base	—	R′OH, heat	

- Nitriles are useful reagents because they can be hydrolyzed to carboxylic acids or reduced to amines.
- Carboxylic acid derivatives can be reduced by complex metal hydrides to aldehydes or primary alcohols. The reagents for oxidative and reductive interconversions among alcohols, aldehydes, ketones, and carboxylic acids are summarized in Figure 22.16.
- Organometallic reagents react with carboxylic acid derivatives to form ketones. Continuing reaction may occur to generate a tertiary alcohol.

Figure 22.16 The Reagents for Oxidative and Reductive Interconversions among Alcohols, Aldehydes, Ketones, and Carboxylic Acids.

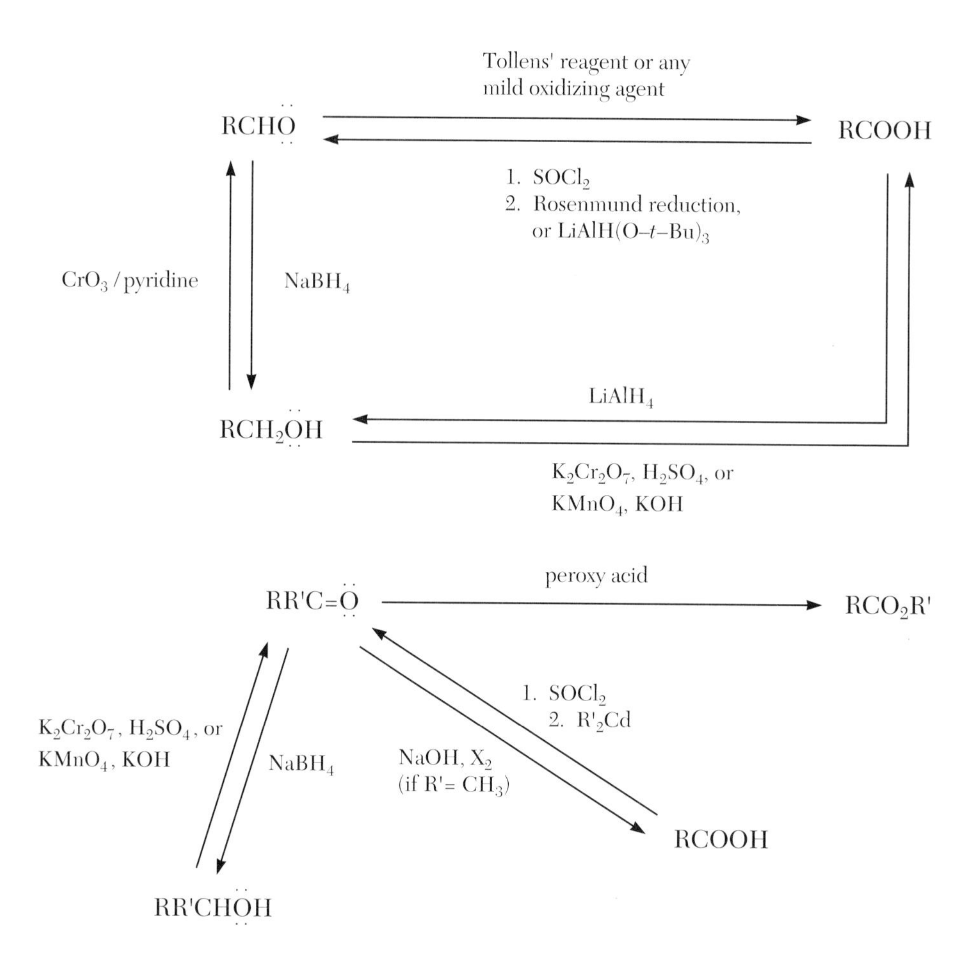

Terms to Remember

transesterification
triglyceride
hydrolysis
saponification
enzymes
Hofmann rearrangement
Baeyer-Villager oxidation
pyrolysis
xanthate ester
Chugaev reaction

Reactions of Synthetic Utility

174. $ROH + R'COCl \longrightarrow R'C(=O)OR$ **22.2**

175. $ROH + R'C(=O)—O—C(=O)—R' \longrightarrow R'C(=O)OR$ 22.2

176. $R_2NH + R'COCl \longrightarrow R'C(=O)—NR_2$ 22.2

177. $R_2NH + R'C(=O)—O—C(=O)R' \longrightarrow R'C(=O)—NR_2$ 22.2

178. $ROH + R'C(=O)OR'' \xrightarrow{\text{acid}} R'C(=O)OR + R''OH$ 22.2

179. $R_2NH + R'C(=O)OR'' \longrightarrow R'C(=O)NR_2 + R''OH$ 22.2

180. $RCONH_2 \xrightarrow{P_2O_5} RC{\equiv}N$ 22.2

181. $RC(=O)OR' \xrightarrow{\text{aq acid}} RCOOH + R'OH$ 22.3

182. $RC(=O)OR' \xrightarrow{\text{MOH, water}} RCOO^-M^+ + R'OH$ 22.3

183. $RC(=O)NR'_2 \xrightarrow{\text{aq acid}} RCOOH + R_2\overset{+}{N}H_2$ 22.3

184. $R—C{\equiv}N \xrightarrow{\text{aq acid}} RCOOH$ 22.3

185. $RCOOH \xrightarrow{BH_3} RCH_2OH$ 22.4

186. $RC(=O)OR' \xrightarrow{LiAlH_4} RCH_2OH + R'OH$ 22.4

187. $RC(=O)OR' \xrightarrow[AlCl_3]{NaBH_4} RCH_2OH + R'OH$ 22.4

188. $RC(=O)NR'_2 \xrightarrow{LiAlH_4} RCH_2NR'_2$ 22.4

189. $RCOCl \xrightarrow[\text{dioxane}]{NaBH_4} RCH_2OH$ 22.4

190. $RC(=O)OR' \xrightarrow[\text{ethanol}]{Na} RCH_2OH$ 22.4

191. $RC{\equiv}N \xrightarrow[\text{ethanol}]{\text{Na}} RCH_2NH_2$ 22.4

192. $RCOR' \xrightarrow[\text{aq workup}]{R''M} RC(OH)R''_2$ (ester $RC(=O)OR'$ gives tertiary alcohol $R-C(OH)(R'')-R''$) 22.5

R″M = Grignard; alkyllithium

193. $RC{\equiv}N \xrightarrow[\text{aq workup}]{R'M} RC(=O)R'$ 22.5

R′M = Grignard; alkyllithium

194. $RC(=O)NH_2 \xrightarrow[Br_2]{H_2O,\ KOH} RNH_2$ 22.6

195. $RC(=O)R \xrightarrow{R'CO_3H} RC(=O)OR$ 22.6

196. $CH_3C(=O)-O-\overset{|}{\underset{|}{C}}-\overset{H}{\underset{|}{C}}- \xrightarrow{\text{heat}} \,>C{=}C<$ 22.7

197. $RCH_2CH_2OH \xrightarrow[2.\ CH_3I]{1.\ CS_2,\ KOH} RCH_2CH_2-OC(=S)-SCH_3 \xrightarrow{\text{heat}} RCH{=}CH_2$ 22.7

Additional Problems

22.33 Give the systematic name of each of the following structures:

a. $PhOC(=\ddot{O})CH_2CH_3$

b. $CH_3\ddot{O}C(=\ddot{O})Ph$

c. $PhCH_2\ddot{O}C(=\ddot{O})Ph$

d. $PhC(=\ddot{O})-\ddot{N}(CH_3)_2$

e. $H_2C{=}C{=}\ddot{O}$

f. $CH_3C(=\ddot{O})-\ddot{N}(CH_3)_2$

g. $:\ddot{Br}-C_6H_4-CN:$ (para-substituted benzene ring)

h. $CH_3CH_2CN:$

i. $C_6H_{11}-\ddot{N}{=}C{=}\ddot{N}-C_6H_{11}$ (cyclohexyl rings)

j. $CH_3CH_2CH_2COO^-Na^+$

k. six-membered cyclic ester (ring :O: with C=:O: adjacent)

l. five-membered ring with :N—CH_3 and adjacent C=:O:

22.34 Give the products resulting from each of the following reactions:

a. methyl formate + ammonia
b. acetic anhydride + 2-propanol
c. butanoic anhydride + HCl gas
d. sodium propanoate + acetyl chloride
e. the Rosenmund reduction of propanoyl chloride
f. ketene + 1,2-ethanediol (to give a product $C_6H_{10}O_4$)
g. benzoyl chloride + *sec*-butylamine
h. 2-butanol + formic acetic anhydride
i. ethyl acetate refluxed with excess methanol and sulfuric acid
j. benzamide heated with phosphorus pentoxide
k. γ-butyrolactone refluxed with excess methanol and sulfuric acid
l. *N*-methylbutanamide treated with sodium borohydride in the presence of cobalt (II) chloride and methanol
m. ethyl decanoate treated with sodium in ethanol
n. propionitrile treated with sodium in ethanol
o. hexanoic acid treated with lithium in liquid methylamine
p. methyl benzoate treated with excess methylmagnesium bromide and worked up with aqueous acid
q. benzonitrile treated with phenylmagnesium bromide and worked up with aqueous acid
r. benzamide + bromine in aqueous sodium hydroxide
s. *N*-ethylisobutanamide treated with lithium aluminum hydride
t. methyl acetate heated with excess methylamine
u. phthalic anhydride + 2-propanol (1 mole of each)

22.35 What reagent or combination of reagents would you use to accomplish each of the following:

a. reduction of an ester to an alcohol
b. reduction of an acid chloride to an aldehyde
c. conversion of a lactone to a diol
d. conversion of an amide to an amine containing the same number of carbon atoms
e. conversion of an amide to an amine containing one fewer carbon atom
f. conversion of an ester into a carboxylic acid
g. conversion of a ketone into an ester
h. conversion of an acid chloride into the ester of a tertiary alcohol
i. conversion of a ketone to a primary amine

22.36 Suggest methods for the conversion of benzamide to each of the following:

a. ethyl benzoate b. benzylamine c. acetophenone d. aniline

22.37 From each pair of substances, choose the one that exhibits the indicated property and give an explanation for your choice:

a. more reactive toward nucleophiles: acetic anhydride or formic acetic anhydride
b. hydrolyzes more rapidly under basic conditions: ethyl benzoate or ethyl *p*-nitrobenzoate
c. more basic: methylamine or acetamide
d. more acidic: methylamine or acetamide
e. contains the more acidic hydrogen: benzamide or phthalimide
f. forms a *p*-brominated product on treatment with bromine: methyl benzoate or phenyl acetate
g. is not the ester of a naturally occurring fatty acid: $CH_3(CH_2)_{14}COOCH_3$ or $CH_3(CH_2)_{13}COOCH_3$
h. exhibits a carbonyl IR absorption $<1700\ cm^{-1}$: benzoyl chloride or benzamide
i. exhibits the lower carbon-oxygen stretching frequency: methyl *p*-aminobenzoate or methyl *p*-nitrobenzoate
j. readily forms an anhydride on heating: *cis*-1,2-ethenedicarboxylic acid or *trans*-1,2-ethenedicarboxylic acid

22.38 Give the structure of each of the following compounds:

a. Compound *F* (aspirin, formula $C_9H_8O_4$) is produced by the reaction of *o*-hydroxybenzoic acid with acetic anhydride.

b. Lactone *G* (formula $C_5H_8O_2$) contains a three-proton doublet in its ^1H NMR spectrum.

c. Compound *H* (formula $C_{10}H_{11}OCl$) reacts with aluminum chloride to form the structure shown below:

:O:

d. Compound *I* (formula $C_8H_{16}O_3$) is formed by refluxing the lactone shown below with ethanol and sulfuric acid.

:O:

H_3C :O:

e. Compound *J* (coumarin, formula $C_9H_6O_2$, a compound responsible for the odor of freshly cut grass) has the following spectra:

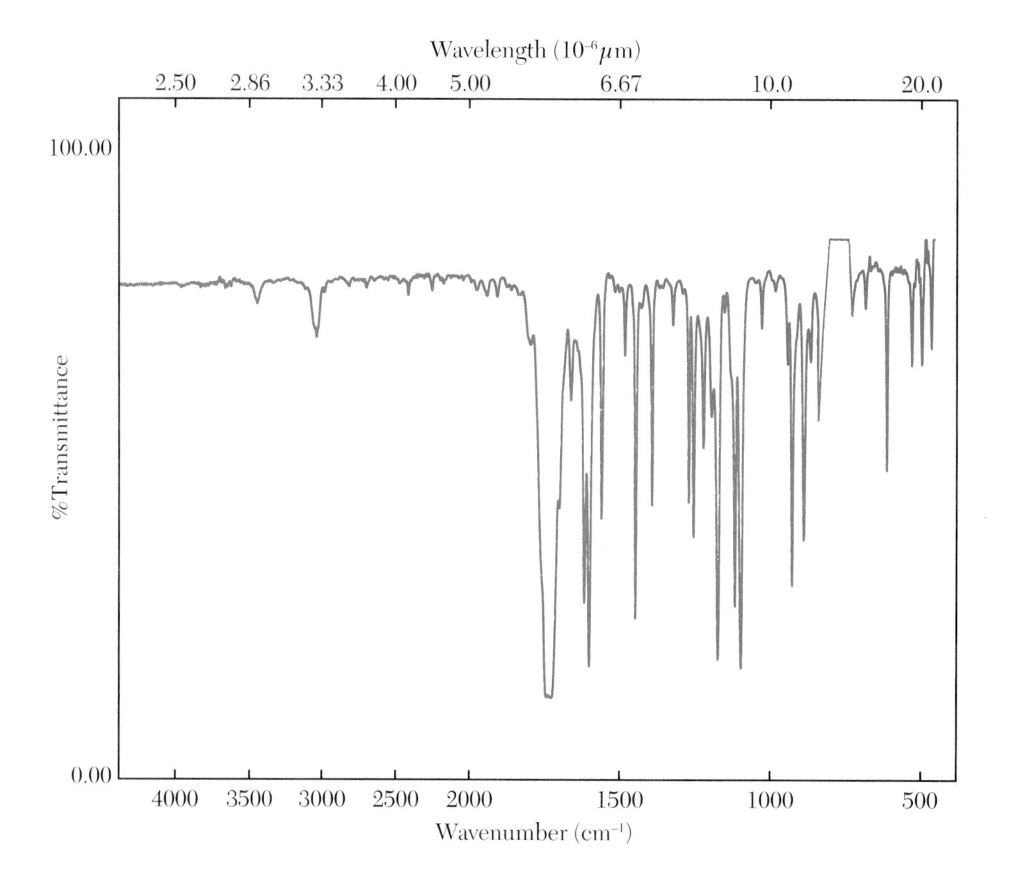

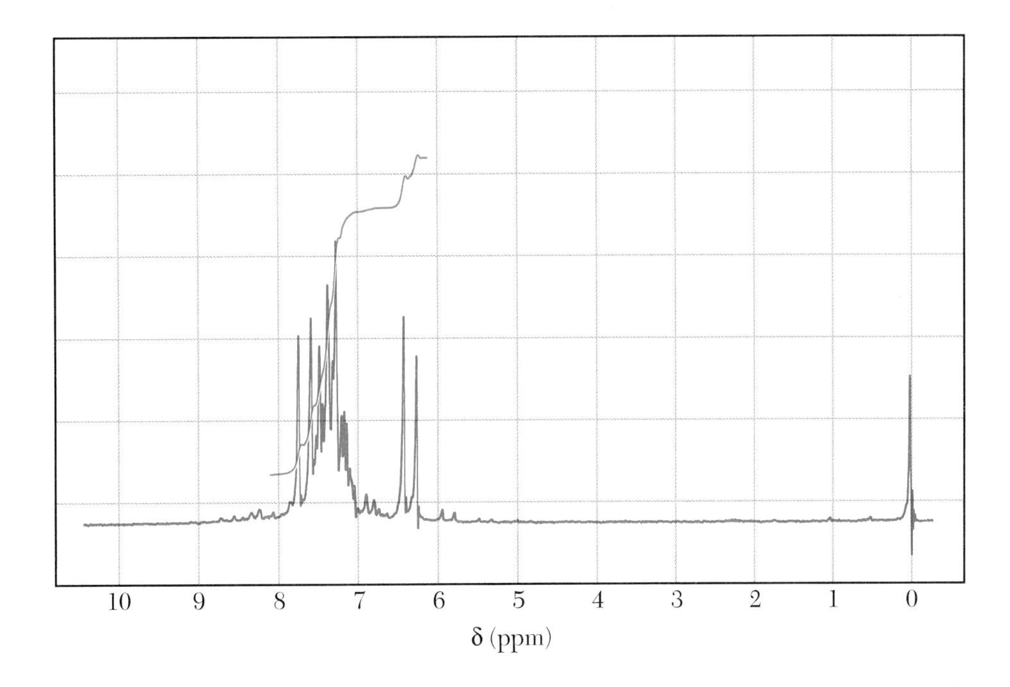

f. Compound *K* (formula $C_5H_{11}NO$), on treatment with bromine and aqueous sodium hydroxide, yields *L* (formula $C_4H_{11}N$), which exhibits a ^1H NMR spectrum consisting of two singlets.

g. Compound *M* (formula $C_{10}H_{14}O$) has the following properties:
- (i) reacts with acetic anhydride to give a sweet-smelling liquid
- (ii) produces a yellow precipitate when treated with iodine in aqueous sodium hydroxide
- (iii) reacts with sodium metal (bubbles form)
- (iv) reacts with chromic anhydride in sulfuric acid, immediately giving a blue-green color to the solution
- (v) yields benzoic acid upon treatment with hot, alkaline potassium permanganate solution followed by workup with aqueous acid
- (vi) gives no reaction with bromine in carbon tetrachloride

h. Compound *N* (formula $C_{14}H_{20}O_3$) is optically active. Refluxing in aqueous potassium hydroxide solution converts *N* to *O* (formula $C_9H_{12}O$), which is optically active, and *P* (formula $C_5H_{10}O_3$), which is optically inactive. On oxidation with potassium permanganate, *O* yields benzoic acid. Compound *P* has the following spectroscopic properties: IR absorptions at 2500–3000 and 1720 cm^{-1}; ^1H NMR (in order from low field to high): 1 H singlet, 2 H singlet, 1 H septet, 6 H doublet.

i. Compound *Q* (formula $C_6H_{12}O_2$) exhibits IR absorption at ~1740 cm^{-1} and is reduced by lithium aluminum hydride to a single organic product *R* (formula C_3H_8O).

j. Compound S (formula $C_{16}H_{16}O_2$) has the following ^1H NMR spectrum: δ 2.8, triplet, 2H; δ 3.4, singlet, 2H; δ 4.2, triplet, 2H; δ 7.1, singlet, 10H. On treatment with lithium aluminum hydride followed by aqueous acid workup, S yields an organic product *T* of formula $C_8H_{10}O$.

k. Compound *U* (formula $C_{11}H_{15}NO$) is hydrolyzed by refluxing aqueous alkali to yield *V* (formula $C_8H_{11}N$). On treatment with an excess of aqueous bromine, *V* is converted to *W* (formula $C_8H_9Br_2N$). Compound *V* reacts with cold sodium nitrite in hydrochloric acid, and when cuprous cyanide is added to the reaction mixture compound *X* is formed. On refluxing with hot, aqueous potassium permanganate followed by workup with aqueous acid, *X* yields *Y* (formula $C_8H_6O_4$) whose ^1H NMR spectrum consists of a singlet at δ 8.0 (relative area 2) and a singlet at δ 11.0 (relative area 1).

l. Reflux of compound Z (formula $C_5H_{11}NO$) with aqueous sodium hydroxide forms *AA*. A 2.2-g sample of *AA* is neutralized by titration with exactly by 25.0 mL of 1.0 *M* hydrochloric acid.

22.39 Give the structures of compounds *BB*–DD.

:O:

$\xrightarrow{\text{HCN}}$ *BB* $\xrightarrow[\text{heat}]{\text{aq acid}}$ *CC* $\xrightarrow[\text{heat}]{\text{acid}}$ *DD*

(C_6H_9NO) ($C_6H_{10}O_3$) ($C_{12}H_{16}O_4$)

22.40 Substance *EE* (formula $C_7H_{16}O_3$) has the following spectroscopic properties: no IR bands above 3150 cm^{-1} and no bands in the 1700–1800 cm^{-1} region; ^1H NMR: δ 1.2, triplet, 9H; δ 3.6, quartet, 6H; δ 5.1, singlet, 1H. Compound *EE* reacts with cyclohexylmagnesium bromide to yield cyclohexanecarboxaldehyde in 73% yield after workup with aqueous acid. Deduce the structure of *EE*.

22.41 Sketch the expected ^1H NMR spectrum of $CH_3CO_2CH_2CH_2CD_2CH_3$.

22.42 A student decides to attempt the reaction of benzamide with ethylmagnesium bromide. He observes that reaction occurs (bubbling with the evolution of a gas). However, after workup of the reaction with aqueous acid he recovers his starting material in almost quantitative yield! What happened? Which gas was evolved?

22.43 A different student tries the reaction of *N,N*-diethylbenzamide with ethylmagnesium bromide. This student observes no gas evolution. She works up the reaction with aqueous acid and obtains a good yield of the ketone Ph—C(=:O:)—CH_2CH_3. Give a mechanism for the reaction that occurred in this case. Why did this amide react differently than the amide in the previous problem?

22.44 Deduce the structure of compound *FF*, which results from the following series of reactions:

H_3C ... CH_3 $\xrightarrow[\text{heat}]{N\text{-bromosuccinimide}}$ $C_{14}H_{12}Br_2$ $\xrightarrow{\text{KCN}}$ $C_{16}H_{12}N_2$ $\xrightarrow{\text{HCl, } H_2O}$ $C_{16}H_{10}O_4$ $\xrightarrow{SOCl_2}$ $C_{16}H_8O_2Cl_2$ $\xrightarrow{AlCl_3}$ *FF*

22.45 When *o*-nitrosobenzamide is treated with aqueous sodium hydroxide solution, nitrogen gas is evolved and the sodium salt of benzoic acid forms. The initial reaction leads to the formation of a reactive intermediate with the structure shown below. Write a complete mechanism (using the curved-arrow formalism) for the formation of this intermediate and its continuing reaction to yield the final products.

:O: N: N

22.46 When cyclopentyl methyl ketone is subjected to Baeyer-Villiger oxidation, a 61% yield of cyclopentyl acetate is obtained. Which group migrates more readily, the secondary cyclopentyl group or the methyl group?

22.47 In the Baeyer-Villiger oxidation we usually find that the more nucleophilic group migrates. Predict the product of the following Baeyer-Villiger oxidation.

$$\text{4-methoxybenzophenone} \xrightarrow[\text{heat}]{PhCO_3H}$$

22.48 Provide a mechanism for the following reaction.

$$\text{2-aminobenzamide} \xrightarrow[HCl]{NaNO_2} \text{4-hydroxy-1,2,3-benzotriazine}$$

22.49 Give structures for compounds *GG–II*.

$$H{-}C{\equiv}C{-}CH_2OH + \text{3,4-dihydro-2H-pyran} \xrightarrow{\text{acid}} GG \; (C_8H_{12}O_2) \text{ (a ketal)}$$

$$GG + CH_3CH_2MgBr \xrightarrow{THF} HH \quad C_8H_{11}O_2MgBr$$

$$HH + CO_2 \xrightarrow[\text{workup}]{\text{aq acid}} II \quad C_4H_4O_3$$

22.50 Explain why the synthesis of *II* in the previous problem could not be shortened by using the following sequence of reactions.

$$H{-}C{\equiv}CH_2OH \xrightarrow[\text{2. } CO_2 \text{ 3. aq acid}]{\text{1. } CH_3CH_2MgBr} II$$

22.51 Propose syntheses for each of the following compounds from benzene or toluene.

a. *N,N*-diethyl-*m*-toluamide (the active ingredient in "Off" insect repellent)
b. ethyl *p*-aminobenzoate (benzocaine)
c. ethyl phenylacetate
d. *N*-benzylbenzamide
e. 2-phenylethylamine
f. triphenylmethanol
g. *p*-nitrobenzoyl chloride
h. *m*-nitrobenzoyl chloride

22.52 A lactone of formula $C_5H_8O_2$ forms when 4-pentenoic acid is treated with sulfuric acid. Suggest a structure for the lactone and write a mechanism for its formation.

Enamines, Enolates, and α,β-Unsaturated Carbonyl Compounds

23.1 Introduction

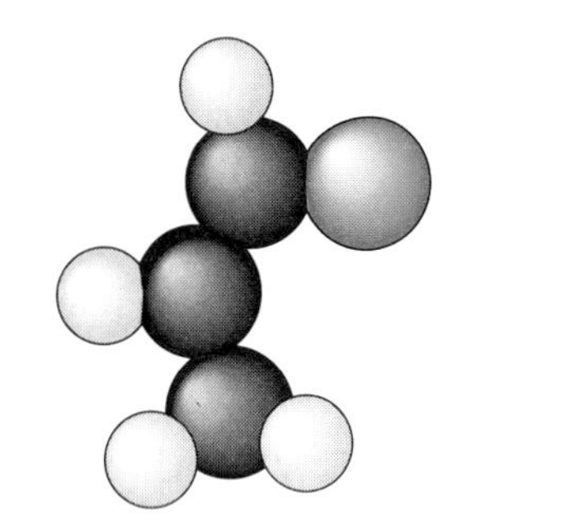

In earlier chapters we discussed methods for preparing carbanionic reagents. We saw that two important classes of such reagents, organometallics and ylides, can be prepared from haloalkane precursors, as shown in Figure 23.1. These reagents are of great value for synthetic work because they are a source of nucleophilic carbon.

Carbonyl compounds (aldehydes and ketones) and related compounds (particularly esters) can also be used as convenient precursors to carbanionic reagents. In this chapter we will see how such species can serve as carbon nucleophiles for organic syntheses.

This chapter will also discuss the chemistry of α,β-unsaturated carbonyl compounds, with particular emphasis on their reactivity toward carbanionic reagents.

23.2 Enamines and Enolate Ions: Structure and Reactivity

Recall (Section 19.9) that enamines are prepared by allowing a secondary amine to react with an aldehyde or ketone and removing water as it is formed. Another example of this type of reaction is shown in Equation 23.1.

Eqn. 23.1

$$\mathrm{Ph{-}\overset{\overset{\displaystyle :\!O\!:}{\|}}{C}{-}CH_3} + \text{morpholine (N–H)} \xrightarrow{H^+} \mathrm{Ph{-}\underset{\text{N-morpholinyl}}{C}{=}CH_2} + H_2\ddot{O}$$

acetophenone morpholine 60% yield

One reaction in which enamines participate is the overall alkylation of carbonyl compounds, as shown in Equation 23.2.

Eqn. 23.2

$$\text{cyclohexanone} \xrightarrow[\text{pyrrolidine}]{\text{pyrrolidine (N–H)}} \text{1-(1-pyrrolidinyl)cyclohexene} \xrightarrow[\text{2. aq acid}]{\text{1. } CH_3I} \text{2-methylcyclohexanone } (CH_3)$$

cyclohexanone 80% yield α-methylcyclohexanone

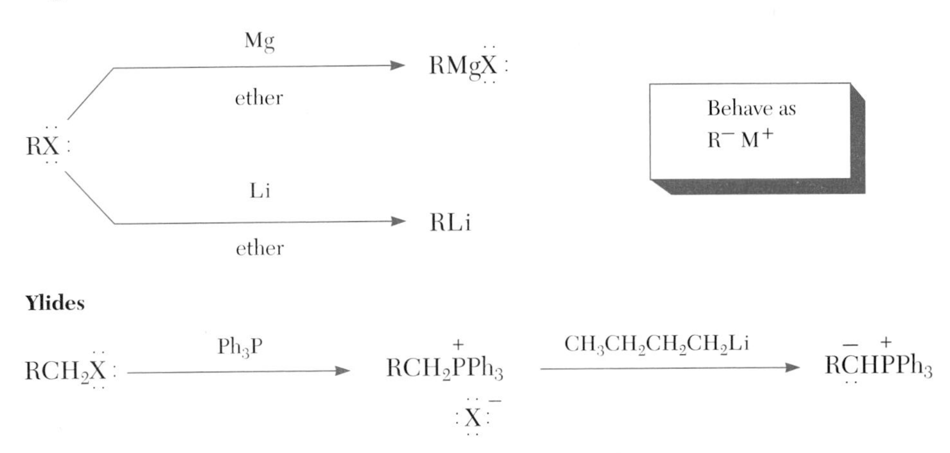

Figure 23.1 Preparation of organometallics and ylides from haloalkanes. Both organometallics and ylides are carbanionic. Both have the potential to act as nucleophiles through the negatively charged carbon atom.

To understand why enamines behave as carbon nucleophiles, we must consider their bonding. An enamine has two resonance structures, as shown in Figure 23.2. In one structure a negative charge is located at the α-carbon atom. We anticipate (and find) that this carbon atom has the potential to serve as a nucleophile. We will see specific examples of this reactivity later in this chapter.

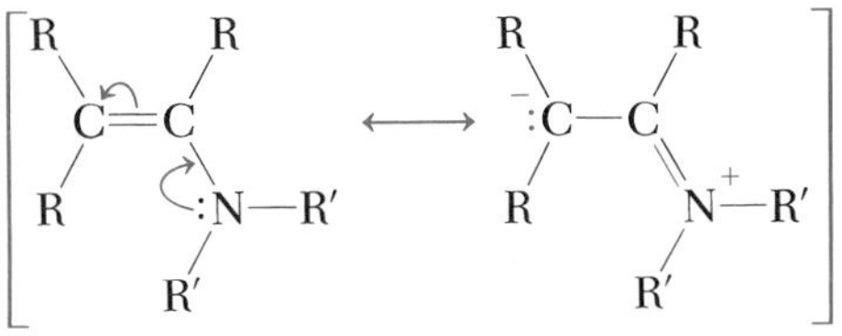

Figure 23.2 Resonance structures for an enamine. In one of the pair of resonance structures representing an enamine, carbon bears a formal negative charge, giving the enamine the potential to function as a nucleophile.

MOLECULAR ORBITAL ANALYSIS

A Molecular Orbital View of Enamines

We can also correlate the nucleophilicity of an enamine with the nature of its highest occupied molecular orbital (HOMO). As Figure 23.3 shows, there is a similarity between the structure of an enamine and that of an allyl anion. Enamines have the same type of π orbitals as do allylic anions whose π molecular orbitals we studied in Chapter 15. In each case the HOMO has a node at the central atom. The electron density of the HOMO is concentrated at the two ends of the three-atom system, suggesting that enamines behave as nucleophiles by using either the terminal carbon or the terminal nitrogen of the >C=C—N< unit. We find this to be the case, with the two types of reaction competing with each other. However, the dominant mode of reaction is through the carbon atom in alkylation reactions. We thus have a synthetically useful reaction system; examples of its applications will be given in the following section.

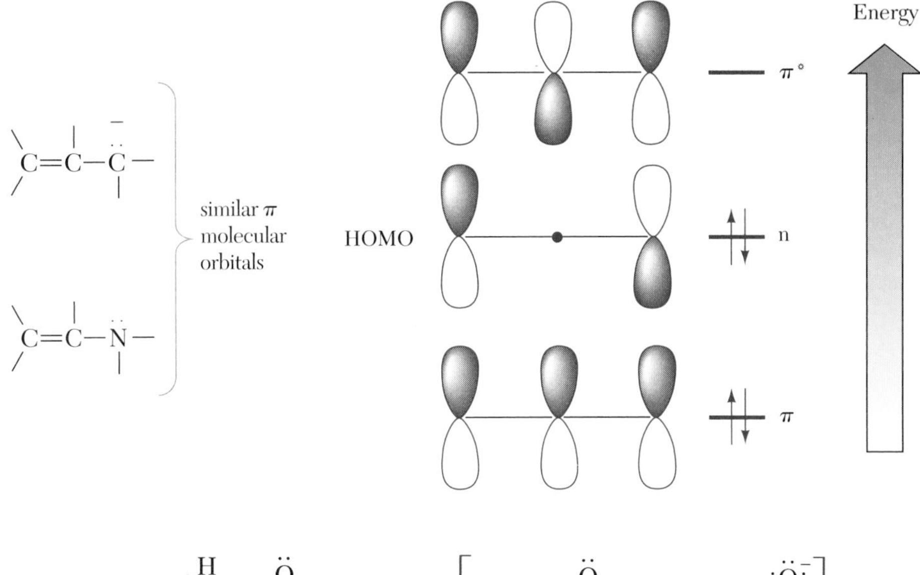

Figure 23.3 The π molecular orbitals of an enamine and an allyl anion. These molecular orbitals are fundamentally similar. The HOMO of each bears electron density only at the terminal atoms.

$$B:^- + -\overset{H}{C}-C(=\ddot{O}) \rightleftharpoons B-H \quad \left[-\ddot{C}^- -C(=\ddot{O}) \longleftrightarrow C=C(-\ddot{O}:^-) \right]$$

Figure 23.4 Formation of an enolate ion. An enolate ion forms when a hydrogen is abstracted by a base from the α-carbon atom of a carbonyl compound.

We also anticipate that **enols** should behave much like enamines. Enols and enamines have similar structures (and similar π molecular orbitals—see Figure 23.3). However, enols are generally unavailable for synthetic work because they tautomerize to the corresponding carbonyl compounds.

Although enols themselves are generally of limited synthetic use, **enolate ions** are extremely useful. We prepare enolate ions by allowing a carbonyl compound bearing at least one α-hydrogen to react with a base, as illustrated in Figure 23.4. There are two ways in which we use bases to generate enolate ions from carbonyl compounds. One method involves the use of a full molar equivalent of a base that is sufficiently strong to convert all of the carbonyl compound to its enolate ion. The other method involves using a weaker base that establishes an equilibrium in which the concentration of enolate ion may be quite small. Both of these methods have their uses (see Section 23.4).

Enolate ions, like enamines, can function as nucleophiles through either the oxygen atom or the α-carbon atom. The synthetically more important reaction is nucleophilic attack through the α-carbon, and there are many important reactions in which this reaction mode is dominant.

23.3 The Use of Enamines in Synthesis

Figure 23.5 shows a synthetic sequence in which enamine chemistry plays the pivotal role. The net result of the reaction sequence is the conversion of a ketone to an α-substituted ketone. This specific example shows how enamines can be used to achieve substitution at the α-carbon atom of an aldehyde or ketone.

Let's consider the details of this reaction sequence. First, we form the enamine by reaction of the ketone starting material (cyclohexanone in this example) with a suitable secondary amine. (Cyclic secondary amines generally

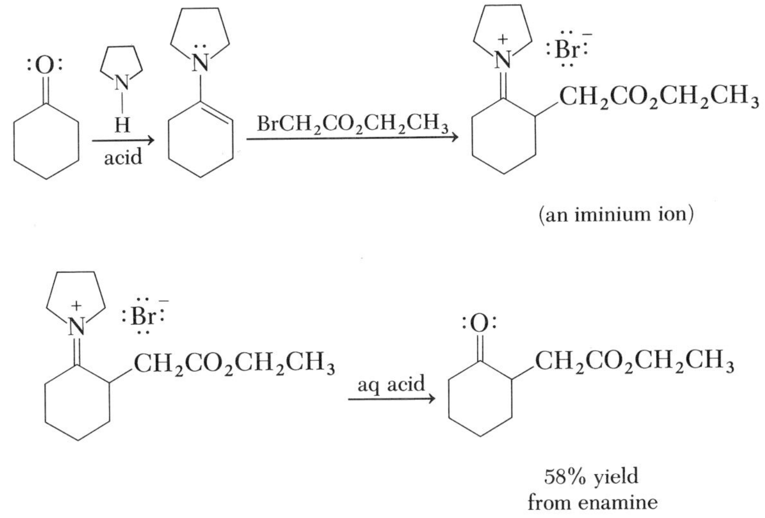

Figure 23.5 Use of an enamine in a synthetic sequence resulting in α-substitution of cyclohexanone. Another example is given in Equation 23.2.

give better results because they are more nucleophilic than acyclic secondary amines and form the enamine more readily.) Then we allow the enamine to react with a suitable substrate (here, ethyl α-bromopropionate). Nucleophilic attack by the enamine leads to an iminium ion and bromide ion. The iminium salt so formed is then subjected to hydrolysis under acidic conditions to form the target α-substituted carbonyl compound (here a ketoester).

PROBLEM 23.1 How would you prepare the ethyl α-bromopropionate used in the reaction in Figure 23.5 from propanoic acid?

PROBLEM 23.2 Write a mechanism for the hydrolysis of the iminium salt shown in Figure 23.5.

Some simple haloalkanes react with enamines to give a mixture of N- and C-alkylated products. An example is shown in Figure 23.6.

The minor product of the alkylation step in Figure 23.6 is an N-alkylated enamine, a simple quaternary ammonium salt that does not undergo hydrolysis in the final aqueous acid workup. Because this product does not undergo hydrolysis, the two products can be separated with relative ease. The N-alkylated product remains in the aqueous solution (quaternary ammonium salts are generally quite soluble in water), while the ketone product of the hydrolysis step does not. We isolate the ketone product by extraction with a suitable organic solvent followed by evaporation of the solvent. The α-alkylated ketone produced in the reaction in Figure 23.6 can be isolated in satisfactory yield despite the competing N-alkylation reaction.

PROBLEM 23.3 In principle, a different enamine could have formed in the first reaction in Figure 23.6. Show its structure. Explain why this enamine did not form in preference to the one shown.

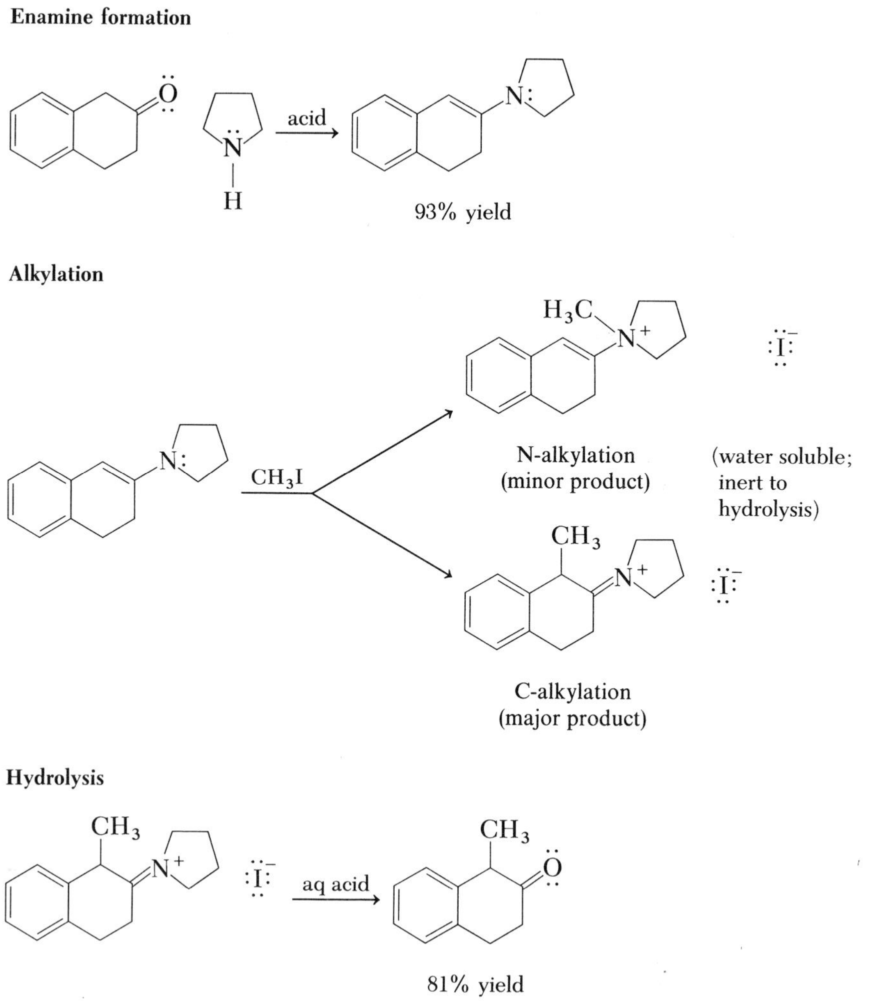

Figure 23.6 Competing N- and C-alkylation reactions of an enamine with a haloalkane.

Enamine formation

acid

H

93% yield

Alkylation

H_3C N^+ $:\ddot{I}:^-$

CH_3I

N-alkylation (minor product)

(water soluble; inert to hydrolysis)

CH_3 N^+ $:\ddot{I}:^-$

C-alkylation (major product)

Hydrolysis

CH_3 N^+ $:\ddot{I}:^-$ aq acid CH_3

81% yield

PROBLEM 23.4 Plan a synthesis for each of the following materials using enamine chemistry:

a. $CH_3CH_2CH_2CH_2CH(CH_3)CH\ddot{O}$ b. :O: CH_2CH_3

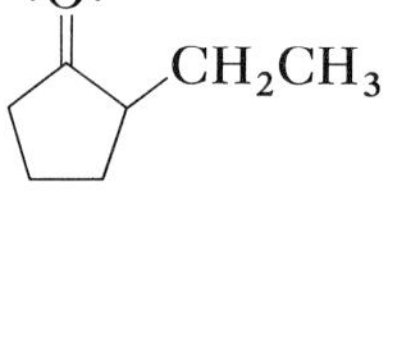

Steps to Solving the Problem

Solution to Problem 23.4a

1. We begin planning our synthetic route by using the structure of the target material to perform a retrosynthetic analysis. An enamine synthesis involves a substitution reaction (here an alkylation) at the α-position relative to the original carbonyl carbon. In this target compound *two* alkyl groups (*n*-butyl and methyl) are joined to the α-carbon. Either of these groups could be added to a parent structure using an enamine procedure, as shown in the following retrosynthetic analysis scheme.

$$CH_3CH_2CH_2CH_2\underset{\substack{|\\ CH_3}}{CH}CH\ddot{O} \Rightarrow CH_3CH_2CH_2CH_2CH{=}CH{-}\ddot{N}R_2 + CH_3\ddot{I}:$$

or

$$\Rightarrow CH_3CH_2CH_2CH_2\ddot{I}: + CH_3CH{=}CH{-}\ddot{N}R_2$$

2. Having performed the retrosynthetic analysis, we need to decide on the actual reagents for the synthesis. The analysis revealed two possible enamine syntheses leading to the target compound. The enamine of either hexanal or propanal can be used for the synthesis. The sequences of steps for these two possibilities are shown below.

$$CH_3CH_2CH_2CH_2CH_2CH\ddot{O} \xrightarrow[\text{acid}]{\text{pyrrolidine (N–H)}} CH_3CH_2CH_2CH_2CH{=}CH{-}\text{(pyrrolidinyl N)} \xrightarrow[\text{2. aq acid}]{\text{1. }CH_3I} CH_3CH_2CH_2CH_2\underset{\substack{|\\ CH_3}}{CH}CH\ddot{O}$$

or

$$CH_3CH_2CH\ddot{O} \xrightarrow[\text{acid}]{\text{pyrrolidine (N–H)}} CH_3CH{=}CH{-}\text{(pyrrolidinyl N)} \xrightarrow[\text{2. aq acid}]{\text{1. }CH_3CH_2CH_2CH_2I} CH_3CH_2CH_2CH_2\underset{\substack{|\\ CH_3}}{CH}CH\ddot{O}$$

PROBLEM 23.5 How would you prepare each of the following molecules, starting with cyclohexanone and using enamine chemistry as part of the synthetic sequence? (*Hint:* One problem involves *acylation* of an enamine rather than *alkylation*—that is, an acid halide must be used rather than an alkyl halide).

a. 2-propanoylcyclohexanone (cyclohexanone bearing $C(=\ddot{O})CH_2CH_3$ at the α carbon)

b. 2-ethylcyclohexanol (cyclohexane bearing $:\ddot{O}H$ and adjacent CH_2CH_3)

23.4 The Formation of Enolate Ions

In the previous section we saw a general method for the α-alkylation (or acylation) of aldehydes and ketones using enamine chemistry. In principle we can achieve the same result using enolate chemistry—Figure 23.7 shows in general terms how the α-alkylation of cyclohexanone could be accomplished.

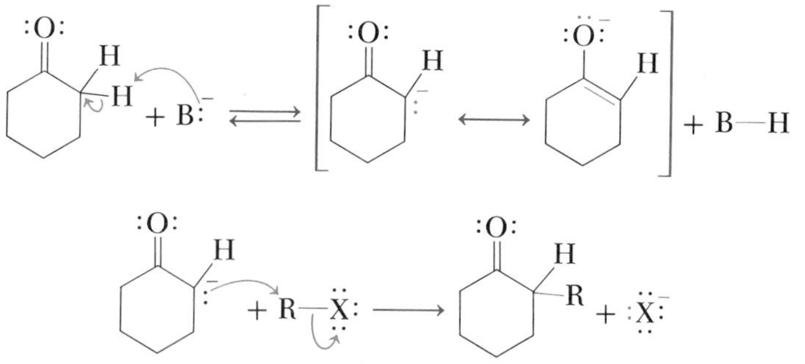

Figure 23.7 Alkylation of an enolate ion. A carbonyl compound can be alkylated at the α-carbon atom by first converting it to an enolate ion and then using the enolate ion as a nucleophile in a substitution reaction on an alkyl halide or other suitable substrate.

The practicality of this approach depends on a number of factors. Among the most important are the acidity of the carbonyl compound and the strength of the base used to abstract the α-hydrogen. These factors govern the degree to which the carbonyl compound can be converted into the enolate ion. If the conversion is complete or almost complete, the method can (with some care) be viable for α-alkylation or acylation. However, if the conversion is inefficient, a small amount of enolate and a large amount of the parent carbonyl compound would be present in the equilibrium mixture; under these conditions the enolate often reacts with a molecule of the parent carbonyl compound.

In general we would like to know if a given combination of carbonyl compound and base will generate a large or a small equilibrium concentration of enolate ion. We can determine this by considering the quantitative acid/base properties (pK_a values) of the carbonyl compound and the base. *For relatively complete conversion of carbonyl compound to enolate ion, the acidity of the carbonyl compound must be much greater than that of the conjugate acid (HB) corresponding to the base (B^-) used* (that is, the pK_a of the carbonyl compound must be much smaller).

Consider, for example, the reaction of a typical ketone, acetone, with various bases. Acetone has a pK_a value of approximately 19. If we add hydroxide ion to acetone, only a small fraction of the acetone is converted to the enolate ion, as shown in Figure 23.8.

On the other hand, bases much stronger than hydroxide ion are able to bring about the rapid and essentially complete conversion of a ketone to its enolate. However, we must be careful in our choice of which strong base to use. One potential problem is that many strong bases can also function as potent nucleophiles. If we add such a base to an aldehyde or ketone, nucleophilic addition to the carbonyl group competes with enolate formation. If we make a poor choice of base, nucleophilic addition will dominate completely over enolate formation. For example, we know that Grignard reagents and alkyllithium reagents can serve as sources of carbanions. Such reagents are strongly

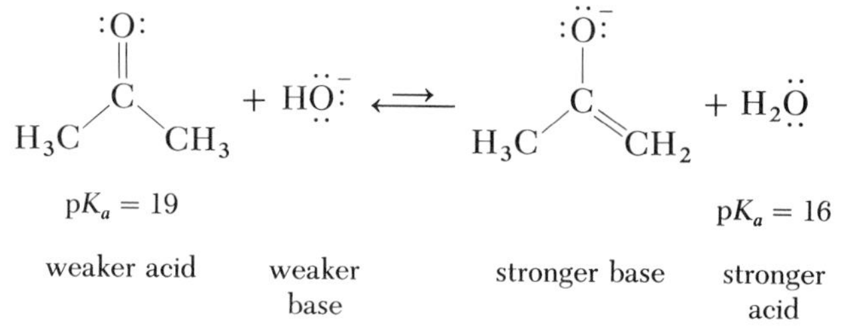

Figure 23.8 Reversible enolate formation with acetone and a relatively weak base.

$pK_a = 19$ weaker acid; weaker base; stronger base; $pK_a = 16$ stronger acid basic, but usually we *cannot* use them to produce enolates from carbonyl compounds because nucleophilic addition rather than enolate formation takes place.

PROBLEM 23.6 Which product will you obtain (after workup with aqueous acid) by adding phenylmagnesium bromide to acetone?

We need a strong, nonnucleophilic base to achieve selective enolate formation. Lithium diisopropyl amide (LDA, **23.1**) is ideal.

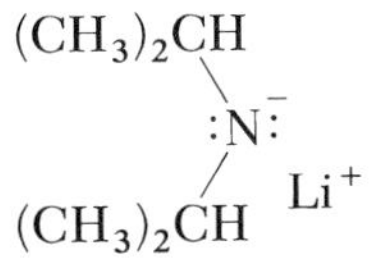

$$[(CH_3)_2CH]_2\ddot{N}:^- \; Li^+$$

lithium diisopropyl amide

23.1

LDA can be prepared by adding butyllithium to diisopropylamine, as shown in Figure 23.9.

LDA is useful in this type of reaction because it is a strong base, but a weak nucleophile. Its weak nucleophilicity results from the relatively large size of the isopropyl groups, which hinder the approach of LDA to the carbonyl carbon, rendering nucleophilic addition difficult. Equation 23.3 shows an example of the use of LDA in the α-alkylation of a ketone.

Eqn. 23.3

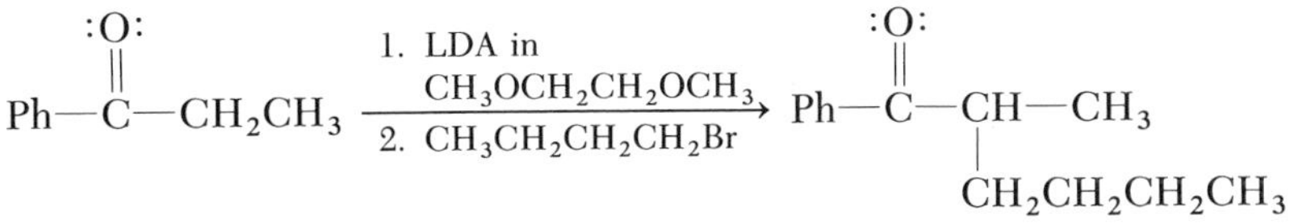

$$\underset{\text{propiophenone}}{Ph{-}\overset{:O:}{\overset{\|}{C}}{-}CH_2CH_3} \xrightarrow[\text{2. } CH_3CH_2CH_2CH_2Br]{\text{1. LDA in } CH_3OCH_2CH_2OCH_3} Ph{-}\overset{:O:}{\overset{\|}{C}}{-}\underset{CH_2CH_2CH_2CH_3}{\underset{|}{CH}}{-}CH_3$$

75% yield

phenyl 2-hexyl ketone

This approach is generally not useful for the α-alkylation of aldehydes. Unless the aldehyde is converted very rapidly and quantitatively to its enolate, nucleophilic attack by the enolate on the carbonyl group of an unreacted aldehyde molecule will occur. This reaction is known as an **aldol condensation,** a process that we will explore in detail in Section 23.7.

However, we *can* alkylate esters at the carbon α to the carboxylate group using reaction conditions similar to those noted for the alkylation of ketones. Such reactions normally proceed in good to excellent yield, as illustrated by Equation 23.4.

$$[(CH_3)_2CH]_2\ddot{N}{-}H + CH_3CH_2CH_2CH_2Li \longrightarrow [(CH_3)_2CH]_2\ddot{N}:^- \; Li^+ + \text{butane}$$

Figure 23.9 Preparation of LDA.

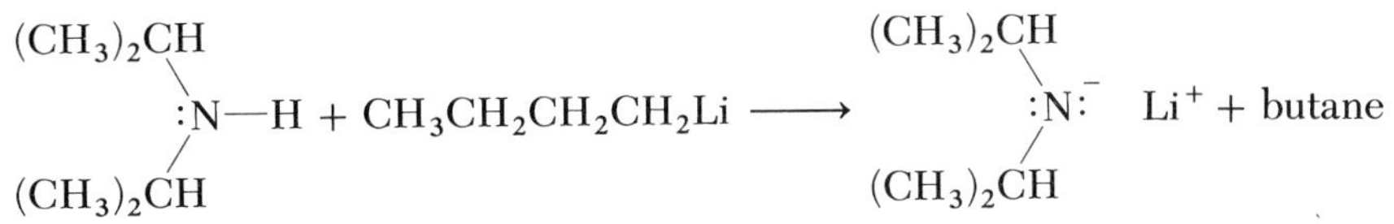

Eqn. 23.4

$$\underset{\text{methyl butanoate}}{CH_3CH_2CH_2COOCH_3} \xrightarrow[\text{2. } CH_3I]{\text{1. LDA } (-78\,^\circ C)} \underset{\substack{\text{98\% yield} \\ \text{methyl 2-methylbutanoate}}}{CH_3CH_2\underset{\displaystyle CH_3}{\underset{|}{C}}HCOOCH_3}$$

PROBLEM 23.7 Give the structures of compounds *A* and *B* in the reaction scheme shown below. (*Hint:* The reaction involves nucleophilic addition by an enolate ion rather than nucleophilic substitution.)

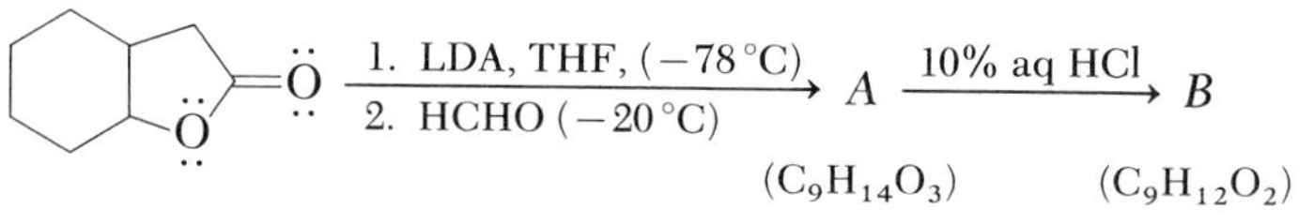

$$\xrightarrow[\text{2. HCHO } (-20\,^\circ C)]{\text{1. LDA, THF, } (-78\,^\circ C)} \underset{(C_9H_{14}O_3)}{A} \xrightarrow{\text{10\% aq HCl}} \underset{(C_9H_{12}O_2)}{B}$$

Bases other than LDA can be used in these types of reactions. For example, we can convert ethyl phenylacetate to its enolate by reaction with sodium amide in liquid ammonia. This enolate undergoes alkylation quite efficiently, as shown in Equation 23.5.

Eqn. 23.5

$$\underset{\text{ethyl phenylacetate}}{PhCH_2\overset{:O:}{\overset{\|}{C}}-\ddot{O}CH_2CH_2} \xrightarrow[\text{2. } PhCH_2CH_2Br]{\text{1. } NaNH_2\text{, liq } NH_3} \underset{\substack{\text{80\% yield} \\ \text{ethyl 2,4-diphenylbutanoate}}}{Ph\underset{\displaystyle CH_2CH_2Ph}{\underset{|}{C}}H\overset{:O:}{\overset{\|}{C}}-\ddot{O}CH_2CH_3}$$

PROBLEM 23.8 What problem would you anticipate if we tried the reaction in Equation 23.5 with phenylacetic acid itself instead of one of its esters?

An unsymmetrical ketone can form isomeric enolates upon deprotonation. The question of kinetic versus thermodynamic control in the formation of the ion comes into play with such systems. An example of these two possible reaction paths is shown in Figure 23.10.

When we treat the ketone shown in Figure 23.10 with Ph_3CLi (lithium triphenylmethide, a strong organometallic base) using dimethoxyethane (an

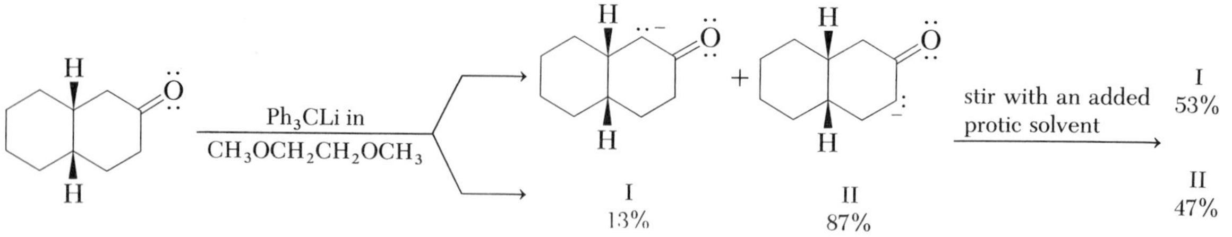

Figure 23.10 Thermodynamic versus kinetic control in enolate formation. Deprotonation of an unsymmetrical ketone leads to the formation of a pair of isomeric enolate ions. The relative proportion of these enolate ions depends on the experimental conditions.

Ph_3CLi in $CH_3OCH_2CH_2OCH_3$ → I 13% + II 87% → stir with an added protic solvent → I 53%, II 47%

aprotic solvent) as the solvent, we form a mixture of enolate ions I and II in the ratio 13/87. However, when we stir the solution for an additional period of time after adding an excess of a protic solvent, the ratio of I to II changes to 53/47. We infer from this observation that enolate ion I is *thermodynamically* more stable than enolate ion II. However, in the initial reaction of the ketone, enolate ion II is favored *kinetically* over enolate ion I. Recall that the thermodynamically more stable of a pair of isomers is dominant *if an equilibrium can be established*. We can produce the product of kinetic control only if we can prevent an equilibrium from being established. To form the enolate of kinetic control preferentially, we must choose experimental conditions that deprotonate the parent ketone extremely rapidly and irreversibly—we generally use a strong base in an aprotic solvent and avoid the use of excess ketone. To produce the thermodynamically favored enolate ion, we use an excess of the ketone and/or a protic solvent.

PROBLEM 23.9 Explain the ability of a protic solvent and the failure of an aprotic solvent to establish an equilibrium in the reaction scheme in Figure 23.10. Why would an excess of the starting ketone be conducive to the formation of the thermodynamically favored enolate ion?

PROBLEM 23.10 When *tert*-butyl ethyl ketone undergoes deprotonation, two diastereoisomeric (*E* and *Z*) enolate ions can form. Draw the structures of these two enolate ions. Which enolate ion do you expect to be favored by treating the ketone with LDA in tetrahydrofuran?

23.5 Particularly Acidic Carbonyl Compounds

We have noted that a strong base must be used to effect the quantitative deprotonation of simple ketones and esters since they are only very weakly acidic. However, some carbonyl compounds have considerably enhanced acidities. Important examples of such compounds include β-diketones, β-ketoesters, and diesters of malonic and substituted malonic acids. Figure 23.11 shows the general structures of these classes of compounds.

Table 23.1 compares the pK_a values of several examples of these particularly acidic compounds with those of ordinary carbonyl compounds. The greatly enhanced acidities of compounds of the types shown in Figure 23.11 reflect the special stabilization of their conjugate bases. This stabilization results from

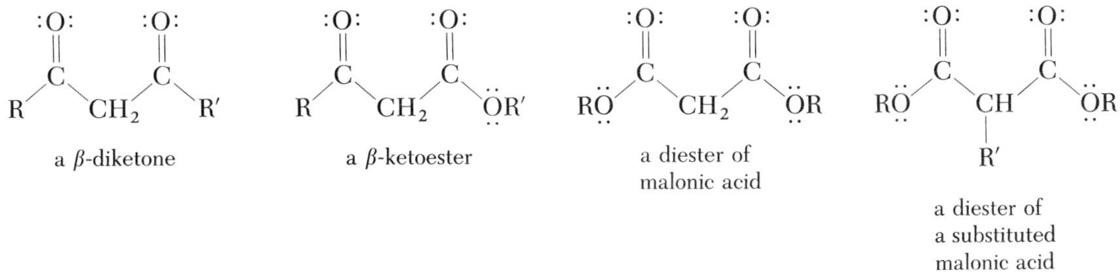

Figure 23.11 General structures of particularly acidic carbonyl compounds. A compound containing a $-CH_2-$ or $-CHR-$ group in an α-position relative to *two* C=O linkages is particularly acidic.

$R-C(=O)-CH_2-C(=O)-R'$ — a β-diketone

$R-C(=O)-CH_2-C(=O)-OR'$ — a β-ketoester

$RO-C(=O)-CH_2-C(=O)-OR$ — a diester of malonic acid

$RO-C(=O)-CH(R')-C(=O)-OR$ — a diester of a substituted malonic acid

Table 23.1 pK_a Values for Some Ordinary and Some Particularly Acidic Carbonyl Compounds

Compound	pK_a
$CH_3-C(=O)-N(CH_3)_2$	30
$CH_3-C(=O)-OCH_3$	25
$CH_3-C(=O)-CH_3$	19
$CH_3-C(=O)-H$	17
$CH_3O-C(=O)-CH_2-C(=O)-OCH_3$	13
$CH_3-C(=O)-CH_2-C(=O)-OCH_3$	11
$CH_3-C(=O)-CH_2-C(=O)-CH_3$	9

an extra delocalization of the negative charge of the enolate ion. A third resonance structure can be drawn for these enolates, while only two can be drawn for the enolate anion of an ordinary carbonyl compound, as is illustrated in Figure 23.12.

Because of the increased acidity of the *β*-dicarbonyl compounds, we can use relatively mild conditions to generate their enolate ions. There is no need to use extremely strong bases such as LDA. Examples of the use of mild bases for the alkylation of 2,4-pentanedione are shown in Equations 23.6 and 23.7.

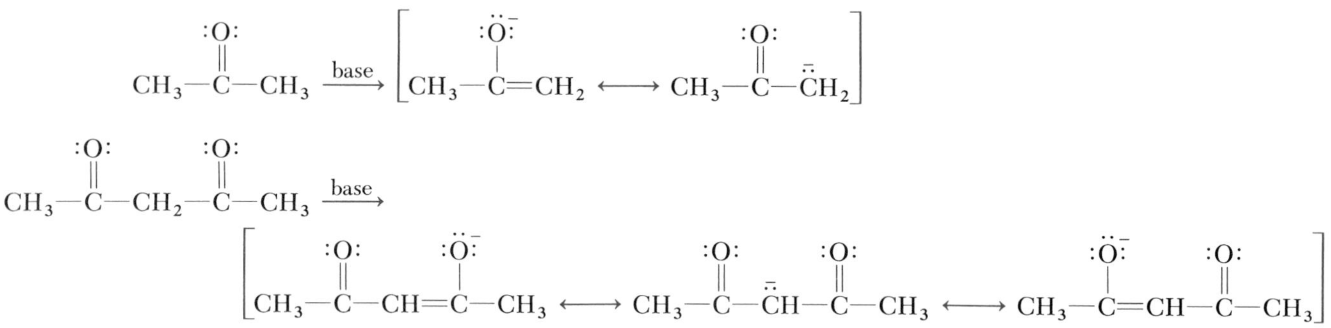

Figure 23.12 Resonance structures for enolate ions of a simple ketone and a *β*-diketone. The enolate ion of the *β*-diketone has one more resonance structure than the enolate ion of the simple ketone. The greater the dispersal of charge, the greater the degree of stabilization.

$$CH_3-C(=O)-CH_3 \xrightarrow{\text{base}} \left[CH_3-C(-O^-)=CH_2 \longleftrightarrow CH_3-C(=O)-\bar{C}H_2\right]$$

$$CH_3-C(=O)-CH_2-C(=O)-CH_3 \xrightarrow{\text{base}}$$

$$\left[CH_3-C(=O)-CH=C(-O^-)-CH_3 \longleftrightarrow CH_3-C(=O)-\bar{C}H-C(=O)-CH_3 \longleftrightarrow CH_3-C(-O^-)=CH-C(=O)-CH_3\right]$$

Eqn. 23.6

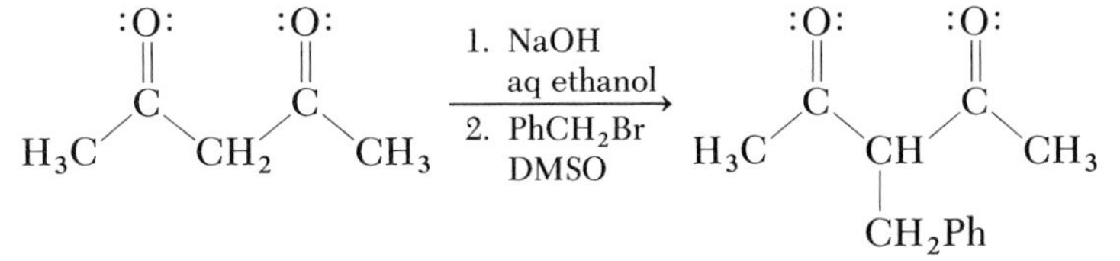

$$H_3C-C(=O)-CH_2-C(=O)-CH_3 \xrightarrow[\text{2. } PhCH_2Br,\ DMSO]{\text{1. NaOH, aq ethanol}} H_3C-C(=O)-CH(CH_2Ph)-C(=O)-CH_3$$

acetylacetone

65% yield
3-benzyl-2,4-pentanedione

Eqn. 23.7

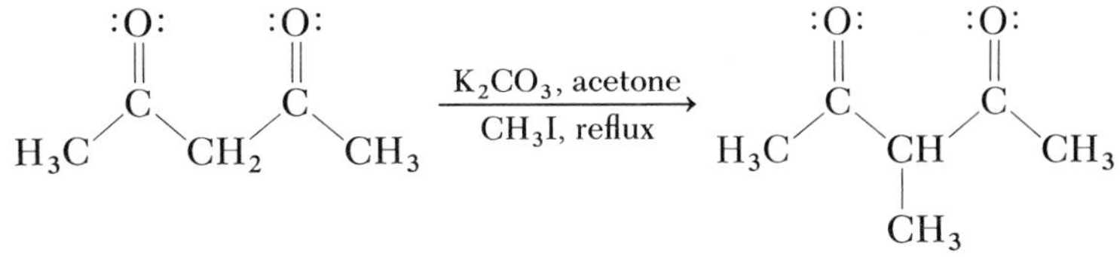

$$H_3C-C(=O)-CH_2-C(=O)-CH_3 \xrightarrow[CH_3I,\ \text{reflux}]{K_2CO_3,\ \text{acetone}} H_3C-C(=O)-CH(CH_3)-C(=O)-CH_3$$

75% yield
3-methyl-2,4-pentanedione

PROBLEM 23.11 Outline a synthesis of the compound shown below, starting with propene and 1,3-cyclohexanediol.

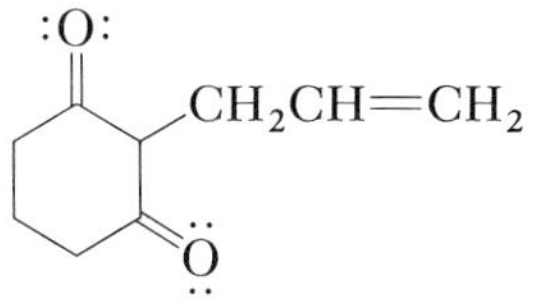

(2-allyl-1,3-cyclohexanedione: cyclohexane ring with C=O at C1 and C3, $CH_2CH{=}CH_2$ at C2)

Several important synthetic procedures are based on the facile production of enolate ions of the type shown in Figure 23.12. Two important types start with diethyl malonate (**malonic ester**) or ethyl acetoacetate (**acetoacetic ester**). In the following sections we will discuss the use of these synthetic procedures.

THE MALONIC ESTER SYNTHESIS: A GENERAL ROUTE FOR THE SYNTHESIS OF CARBOXYLIC ACIDS

The malonic ester synthesis is a generally useful route for the preparation of carboxylic acids. The overall conversion is that of diethyl malonate to a carboxylic acid, as illustrated in Figure 23.13.

The sequence of operations involved in the malonic ester synthesis is as follows:

1. Treat diethyl malonate with sodium ethoxide in ethanol to generate an enolate ion.
2. Add a haloalkane (RX) to the solution with the enolate anion; this step results in displacement of the halide by the enolate ion.

Figure 23.13 Overall result of the malonic ester synthesis. We use a series of reactions, beginning with diethyl malonate, to synthesize a carboxylic acid.

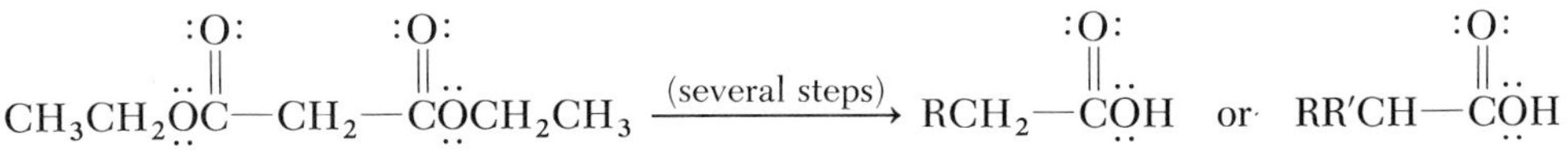

$$CH_3CH_2OC(=O)-CH_2-C(=O)OCH_2CH_3 \xrightarrow{\text{(several steps)}} RCH_2-C(=O)OH \quad \text{or} \quad RR'CH-C(=O)OH$$

Figure 23.14 **Use of the malonic ester synthesis for the preparation of pentanoic acid.** The initial treatment with KOH/ethanol is in the cold so that no hydrolysis of the ester groups occurs.

Formation of the enolate and alkylation

$$CH_2(CO_2CH_2CH_3)_2 \xrightarrow[\text{2. } CH_3(CH_2)_3Br]{\text{1. KOH/ethanol}} CH_3(CH_2)_3CH(CO_2CH_2CH_3)_2$$

Hydrolysis of the alkylated ester

$$CH_3(CH_2)_3CH(CO_2CH_2CH_3)_2 \xrightarrow[\text{2. dilute } H_2SO_4]{\text{1. KOH/water, heat}} CH_3(CH_2)_3CH(CO_2H)_2$$

Decarboxylation

$$CH_3(CH_2)_3CH(CO_2H)_2 \xrightarrow{\text{heat, hydrochloric acid}} CH_3(CH_2)_4CO_2H$$

68% yield

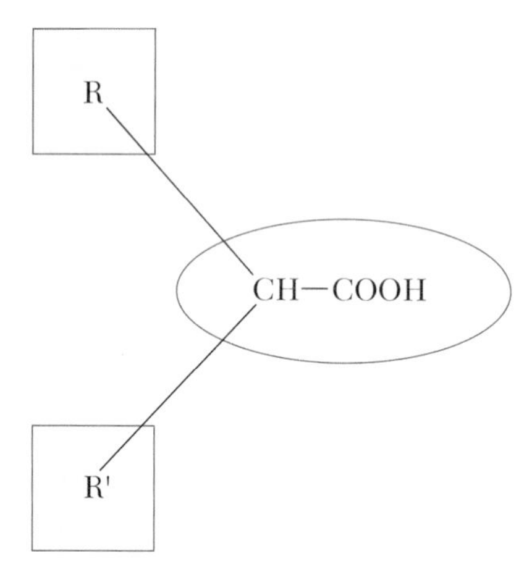

Figure 23.15 **Outlining a malonic ester synthesis by considering the structure of the target acid.** The two groups R and R′ (boxed) are derived from haloalkanes RX and R′X. The remainder of the target molecule (circled) is derived from the malonic ester.

3. If a second alkyl group is to be introduced, add a second equivalent of sodium ethoxide, followed by a second haloalkane, R′X.
4. Hydrolyze the resulting malonic ester to the free substituted malonic acid.
5. Decarboxylate the substituted malonic acid (see Chapter 21) by heating it.

Figure 23.14 shows the application of the malonic ester synthesis to the preparation of pentanoic acid.

The malonic ester synthesis for the preparation of carboxylic acids is summarized in Figure 23.15. We can use this approach as long as one hydrogen remains on the α-carbon site of the target carboxylic acid and only *alkyl* groups are to be attached to that carbon. A further important point is that it must be possible to introduce both the R and the R′ group by S_N2 reactions; that is, ideally R and R′ should be methyl or primary alkyl groups.

PROBLEM 23.12 We can use the malonic ester synthesis to prepare 3-phenylpropanoic acid but not to prepare phenylacetic acid. How would you prepare 3-phenylpropanoic acid? Why could you not prepare phenylacetic acid by this route?

PROBLEM 23.13 You are assigned the task of preparing 2-ethyl-3-methylbutanoic acid via the malonic ester route. Which haloalkanes would you need? Outline the entire synthesis.

PROBLEM 23.14 When we treat diethyl malonate with sodium ethoxide followed by 1,3-dibromopropane and then by an additional equivalent of sodium ethoxide, we isolate compound *C* (formula $C_{10}H_{16}O_4$), which exhibits *no* C=C stretching band in the IR spectrum. On hydrolysis followed by heating, *C* yields product *D* (formula $C_5H_8O_2$). Suggest structures for *C* and *D*.

PROBLEM 23.15 Using the strategy introduced in Problem 23.14, outline a synthesis of cyclopentanecarboxylic acid using the malonic ester synthesis.

PROBLEM 23.16 Tell which haloalkanes you would require for the malonic ester synthesis of each of the following carboxylic acids:
a. octanoic acid b. 2-ethyloctanoic acid
c. 2-cyclohexylpropanoic acid

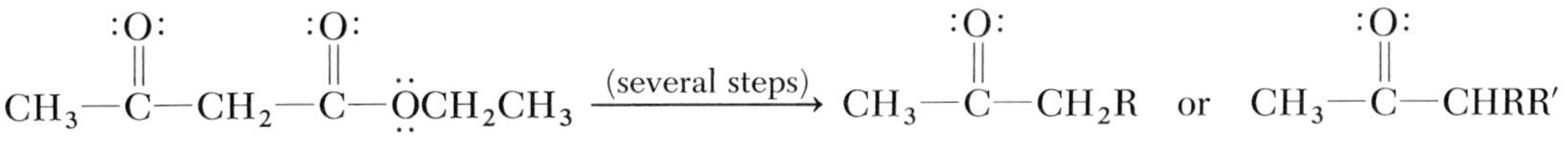

$$CH_3-\overset{\overset{:O:}{\|}}{C}-CH_2-\overset{\overset{:O:}{\|}}{C}-\ddot{O}CH_2CH_3 \xrightarrow{\text{(several steps)}} CH_3-\overset{\overset{:O:}{\|}}{C}-CH_2R \text{ or } CH_3-\overset{\overset{:O:}{\|}}{C}-CHRR'$$

Figure 23.16 Overall result of the acetoacetic ester synthesis. In the acetoacetic ester synthesis we use a series of reactions to convert ethyl acetoacetate to a methyl ketone.

THE ACETOACETIC ESTER SYNTHESIS: A GENERAL ROUTE FOR THE SYNTHESIS OF KETONES

Acetoacetic ester is a common name for the β-ketoester ethyl acetoacetate (ethyl 3-oxobutanoate) (**23.2**).

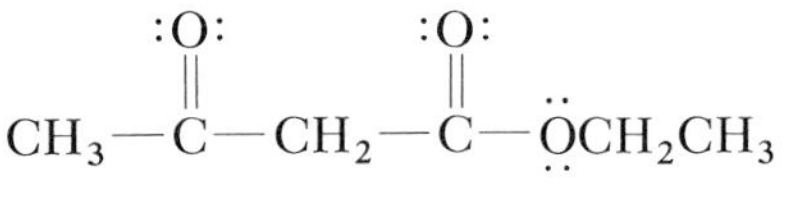

$$CH_3-\overset{\overset{:O:}{\|}}{C}-CH_2-\overset{\overset{:O:}{\|}}{C}-\ddot{O}CH_2CH_3$$

ethyl acetoacetate
(ethyl 3-oxobutanoate)
23.2

The acetoacetic ester synthesis is a general method for converting ethyl acetoacetate into ketones. The overall conversion is shown in Figure 23.16. The sequence of steps in an acetoacetic ester synthesis closely parallels the malonic ester synthesis. Figure 23.17 shows the series of steps for the preparation of 2-heptanone via the acetoacetic ester route.

Compare the sequence of reactions in Figure 23.17 with those for the malonic ester synthesis in Figure 23.14. The same steps are involved, that is, formation of an enolate ion, alkylation, hydrolysis, and decarboxylation. Both procedures rely upon facile decarboxylation in the final step. Use of the acetoacetic ester synthesis for the preparation of methyl ketones is summarized in Figure 23.18.

Figure 23.17 Synthesis of 2-heptanone using acetoacetic ester.

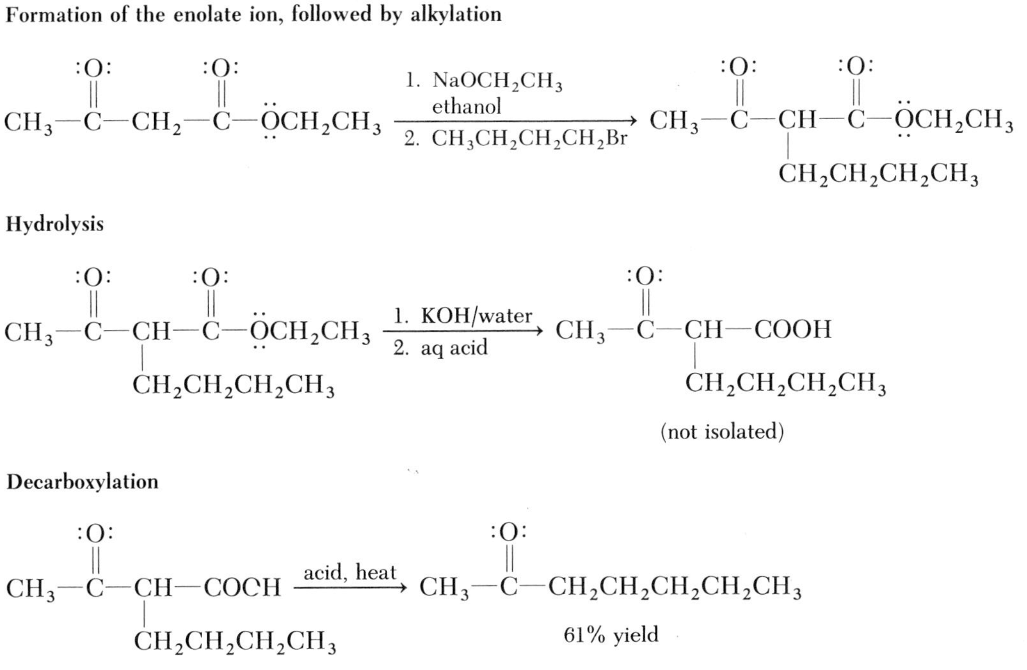

Formation of the enolate ion, followed by alkylation

$$CH_3-\overset{\overset{:O:}{\|}}{C}-CH_2-\overset{\overset{:O:}{\|}}{C}-\ddot{O}CH_2CH_3 \xrightarrow[\text{2. } CH_3CH_2CH_2CH_2Br]{\text{1. } NaOCH_2CH_3 \text{, ethanol}} CH_3-\overset{\overset{:O:}{\|}}{C}-\underset{\underset{CH_2CH_2CH_2CH_3}{|}}{CH}-\overset{\overset{:O:}{\|}}{C}-\ddot{O}CH_2CH_3$$

Hydrolysis

$$CH_3-\overset{\overset{:O:}{\|}}{C}-\underset{\underset{CH_2CH_2CH_2CH_3}{|}}{CH}-\overset{\overset{:O:}{\|}}{C}-\ddot{O}CH_2CH_3 \xrightarrow[\text{2. aq acid}]{\text{1. KOH/water}} CH_3-\overset{\overset{:O:}{\|}}{C}-\underset{\underset{CH_2CH_2CH_2CH_3}{|}}{CH}-COOH$$

(not isolated)

Decarboxylation

$$CH_3-\overset{\overset{:O:}{\|}}{C}-\underset{\underset{CH_2CH_2CH_2CH_3}{|}}{CH}-COOH \xrightarrow{\text{acid, heat}} CH_3-\overset{\overset{:O:}{\|}}{C}-CH_2CH_2CH_2CH_2CH_3$$

61% yield

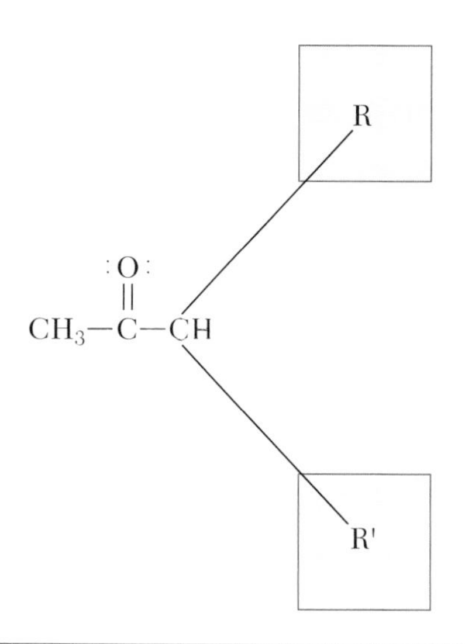

Figure 23.18 Use of the acetoacetic ester synthesis for the preparation of methyl ketones. The *alkyl* groups R and R′ are derived from haloalkanes RX and R′X. The remainder of the target molecule is derived from the ethyl acetoacetate. Both R and R′ should be methyl or primary alkyl groups.

PROBLEM 23.17 Show the curved-arrow mechanism for the decarboxylation step in Figure 23.16. (*Hint:* Review the decarboxylation reaction given in Chapter 21.)

PROBLEM 23.18 Plan syntheses for each of the following compounds using acetoacetic ester as a starting reagent.

a. 4-phenyl-2-butanone **b.** 2-pentanone
c. 2,5-hexanedione **d.** 3-methyl-2-hexanol

PROBLEM 23.19 A beginning graduate student needs a supply of methyl *tert*-butyl ketone. Recognizing that the acetoacetic ester synthesis is a general route for the preparation of methyl ketones, she first contemplates but then rules out this method of preparing the compound. What problem did she foresee?

23.6 Enols as a Source of Nucleophilic Carbon: The Mannich Reaction

We mentioned earlier that enols, in principle, should be able to serve as carbon nucleophiles in the same way that enamines do. However, we also noted that most enols are *not* viable laboratory reagents for this process since they exist in very unfavorable tautomeric equilibria with carbonyl compounds. Nevertheless, enols present in a keto-enol equilibrium can be utilized as effective sources of nucleophilic carbon in a process known as the **Mannich reaction.**

The reagents involved in a Mannich reaction are formaldehyde, a carbonyl compound that can undergo enolization (that is, one that has at least one enolizable α-hydrogen), and an amine (usually a secondary amine). The reaction is performed under mildly acidic conditions, the source of the acid often being the hydrochloride salt of the amine used as a reactant. An example of the Mannich reaction is shown in Equation 23.8.

$$(CH_3)_2\ddot{N}H + H_2C{=}\ddot{O} + (CH_3)_2CHCH\ddot{O} \xrightarrow{HCl}$$

Eqn. 23.8 dimethylamine formaldehyde isobutyraldehyde

$$(CH_3)_2\ddot{N}{-}CH_2C(CH_3)_2{-}CH\ddot{O}$$

80% yield
2,2-dimethyl-
3-(dimethylamino)propanal

The mechanism of the Mannich reaction follows. The reaction begins with the formation of a highly reactive methyleneiminium ion resulting from the reaction of formaldehyde with the secondary amine. This highly electrophilic intermediate ion reacts with the enol form of the enolizable carbonyl compound. An acid-base equilibrium produces the final product, known as a Mannich base. The Mannich base has the same fundamental structure as the initial enolizable carbonyl compound, except that an aminomethyl group ($—CH_2NR_2$) has taken the place of the enolizable hydrogen at the α-carbon atom.

MECHANISM OF REACTION

The Mannich Reaction

Overall reaction:

$$R_2\ddot{N}H + H_2C{=}\ddot{O} + H_3C{-}\overset{:O:}{\overset{\|}{C}}{-}R' \longrightarrow R_2\ddot{N}{-}CH_2{-}CH_2{-}\overset{:O:}{\overset{\|}{C}}{-}R'$$

Step 1 Formation of the methyleneiminium ion by nucleophilic addition of nitrogen at carbon followed by loss of water

$$R_2\ddot{N}H + H_2C{=}\ddot{O} \xrightarrow{H^+} R_2\overset{+}{N}{=}CH_2 + H_2\ddot{O}$$

Step 2 Nucleophilic attack on the iminium ion by the enol form of the carbonyl compound

$$R_2\overset{+}{N}{=}CH_2 + H_2C{=}C(\ddot{O}{-}H)R' \longrightarrow R_2\ddot{N}{-}CH_2{-}CH_2{-}C({=}\overset{+}{O}{-}H)R'$$

Step 3 Establishment of an acid-base equilibrium generating the product

$$R_2\ddot{N}{-}CH_2{-}CH_2{-}C({=}\overset{+}{O}{-}H)R' + B: \rightleftharpoons R_2\ddot{N}{-}CH_2{-}CH_2{-}C({=}\ddot{O}:)R' + \overset{+}{B}{-}H$$

PROBLEM 23.20 Provide a curved-arrow mechanism for the formation of the methyleneiminium ion in the first step of the reaction scheme shown above.

PROBLEM 23.21 Explain how acidic conditions favor the efficient accomplishment of the Mannich reaction.

In Mannich reactions, we usually use a *secondary* amine since the complication of dialkylation arises with primary amines. Also, using the hydrochloride salt of a secondary amine precludes the need for adding acid.

PROBLEM 23.22 What is the structure of the dialkylation product you might anticipate if methylamine were used instead of dimethylamine in the reaction shown in Equation 23.8?

PROBLEM 23.23 Deduce the structure of the cyclic compound *E* (formula $C_{15}H_{25}NO_5$) obtained from the following reaction.

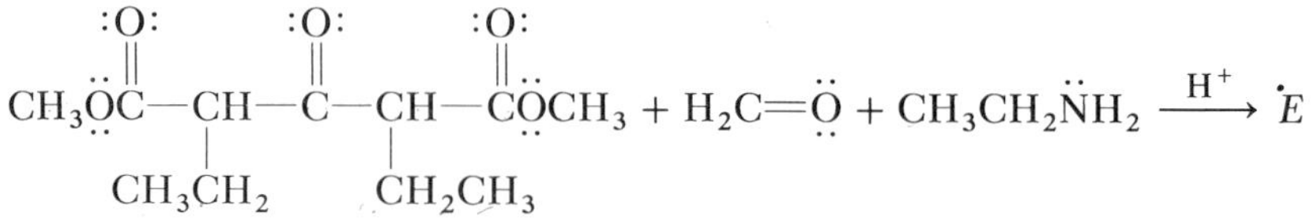

$$CH_3O\overset{O}{\overset{\|}{C}}-\underset{CH_3CH_2}{\underset{|}{CH}}-\overset{O}{\overset{\|}{C}}-\underset{CH_2CH_3}{\underset{|}{CH}}-\overset{O}{\overset{\|}{C}}OCH_3 + H_2C{=}O + CH_3CH_2NH_2 \xrightarrow{H^+} E$$

Explain the steps involved in the formation of *E*.

PROBLEM 23.24 Devise syntheses for the following compounds starting with formaldehyde and any other reagents deemed necessary:

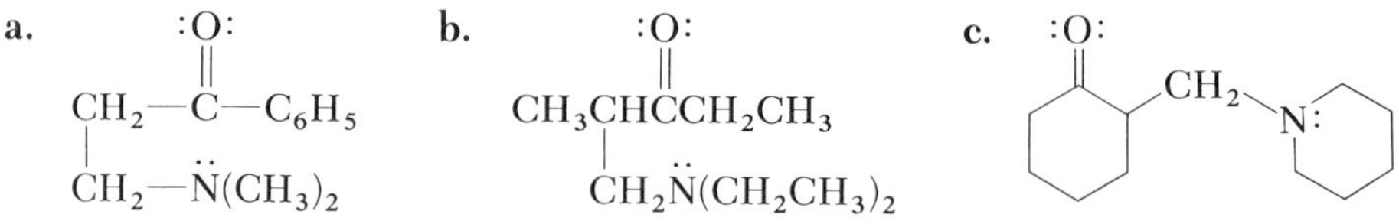

a. $\underset{CH_2-N(CH_3)_2}{\underset{|}{CH_2}}-\overset{O}{\overset{\|}{C}}-C_6H_5$

b. $CH_3\underset{CH_2N(CH_2CH_3)_2}{\underset{|}{CH}}\overset{O}{\overset{\|}{C}}CH_2CH_3$

c. 2-(piperidin-1-ylmethyl)cyclohexanone (cyclohexanone ring with C=O, CH_2–N: of a piperidine ring on the adjacent carbon)

Steps to Solving the Problem

Solution to Problem 23.24a

1. Consider the structure of the target compound. There are two carbon atoms between the amino nitrogen and the carbonyl group, indicating that this compound should be amenable to synthesis via the Mannich reaction.
2. To visualize the Mannich reaction, we break the molecule into three parts:

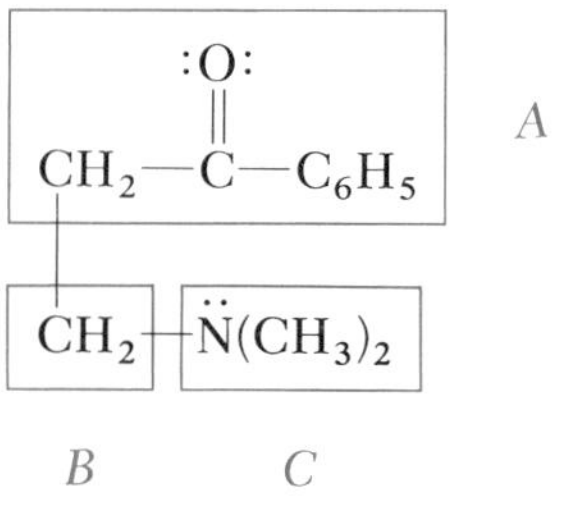

$$\boxed{CH_2-\overset{O}{\overset{\|}{C}}-C_6H_5}\ A$$
$$\underset{B}{\boxed{CH_2}}\ \underset{C}{\boxed{N(CH_3)_2}}$$

Part *A* is derived from the ketone component of the reaction. In this case the appropriate ketone is acetophenone. The linker component *B* is derived from formaldehyde, and the secondary amine required for *C* is dimethylamine.

3. The required reaction is:

$$(CH_3)_2NH + H_2C{=}O + CH_3\overset{O}{\overset{\|}{C}}C_6H_5 \xrightarrow{HCl} (CH_3)_2NCH_2CH_2\overset{O}{\overset{\|}{C}}C_6H_5$$

23.7 Aldol Reactions and Condensations

Treatment of ethanal (acetaldehyde) with cold, aqueous sodium hydroxide or potassium hydroxide yields 3-hydroxybutanal, as shown in Equation 23.9.

Eqn. 23.9

$$CH_3CHO \xrightarrow[5°C]{KOH/water} CH_3CH(OH)CH_2CHO$$

ethanal → 3-hydroxybutanal (50% yield)

The product in Equation 23.9 has the trivial name *aldol* because it contains both an aldehyde and a hydroxyl group. Other aldehydes and ketones that contain at least one α-hydrogen atom can undergo similar reactions (to be discussed later). For example, butanal yields 2-ethyl-3-hydroxyhexanal when treated with aqueous base, as shown in Equation 23.10.

Eqn. 23.10

$$CH_3CH_2CH_2CHO \xrightarrow[8°C]{KOH/water} CH_3CH_2CH_2CH(OH)CH(CH_2CH_3)CHO$$

butanal → 2-ethyl-3-hydroxyhexanal (75% yield)

The general name for this type of reaction is the **aldol addition reaction.** In each case the product is a **β-hydroxyaldehyde** or a **β-hydroxyketone.**

MECHANISM OF THE ALDOL ADDITION REACTION

We can understand the course of the aldol addition reaction using our previous knowledge of the chemistry of enolates and the nature of aldehydes and ketones. When an aldehyde reacts with aqueous hydroxide ion, a small equilibrium concentration of the enolate ion is produced in the presence of a high concentration of the aldehyde. As we have seen, an enolate ion is quite nucleophilic, while an aldehyde is very susceptible to nucleophilic attack, so it is not surprising that there is a reaction between the enolate ion and the parent aldehyde. This reaction leads to the formation of the observed aldol-type product. The mechanism is illustrated below for the reaction shown in Equation 23.10.

MECHANISM OF REACTION

The Aldol Reaction of Butanal

Step 1 An acid-base equilibrium is established.

$$CH_3CH_2CH(H)CHO + {}^-OH \rightleftharpoons \left[CH_3CH_2\bar{C}H{-}CHO \longleftrightarrow CH_3CH_2CH{=}CH{-}O^-\right] + H{-}OH$$

Step 2 The enolate anion performs a nucleophilic addition on a molecule of aldehyde.

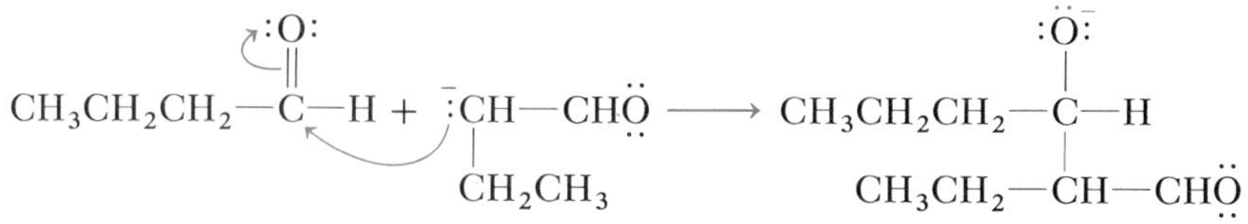

$$CH_3CH_2CH_2-\overset{\overset{:O:}{\|}}{C}-H + \underset{\underset{CH_2CH_3}{|}}{\bar{:}CH}-CH\ddot{O} \longrightarrow CH_3CH_2CH_2-\overset{\overset{:\ddot{O}:^-}{|}}{\underset{\underset{CH_3CH_2-CH-CH\ddot{O}}{|}}{C}}-H$$

Step 3 Proton transfer from solvent generates the product.

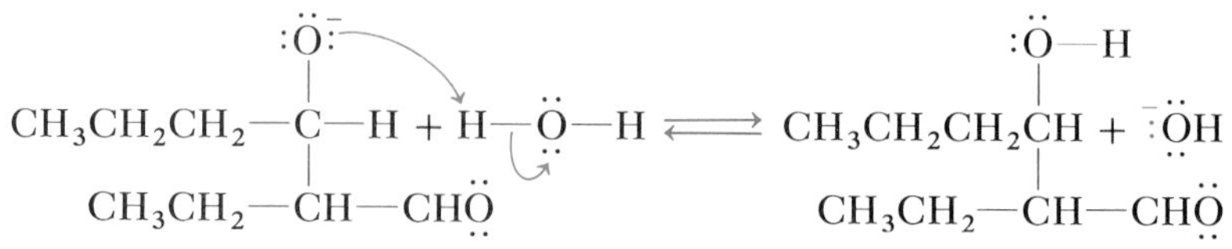

$$CH_3CH_2CH_2-\overset{\overset{:\ddot{O}:^-}{|}}{\underset{\underset{CH_3CH_2-CH-CH\ddot{O}}{|}}{C}}-H + H-\ddot{O}-H \rightleftharpoons CH_3CH_2CH_2\overset{\overset{:\ddot{O}-H}{|}}{\underset{\underset{CH_3CH_2-CH-CH\ddot{O}}{|}}{C}H} + {}^-:\ddot{O}H$$

Ketones are generally less reactive toward aldol formation than are aldehydes, which generally have greater reactivities toward nucleophiles (see Chapter 19). The second step of the aldol addition reaction involves the nucleophilic addition of an enolate ion to a carbonyl carbon. This step is significantly less favorable for a ketone than it is for an aldehyde; for simple ketones, the equilibrium does not favor the nucleophilic addition product. However, in some cases an appropriate experimental set-up can be used to drive the equilibrium to the aldol product. In such cases we can obtain a good yield of the aldol product from ketones, as shown in Equation 23.11.

Eqn. 23.11

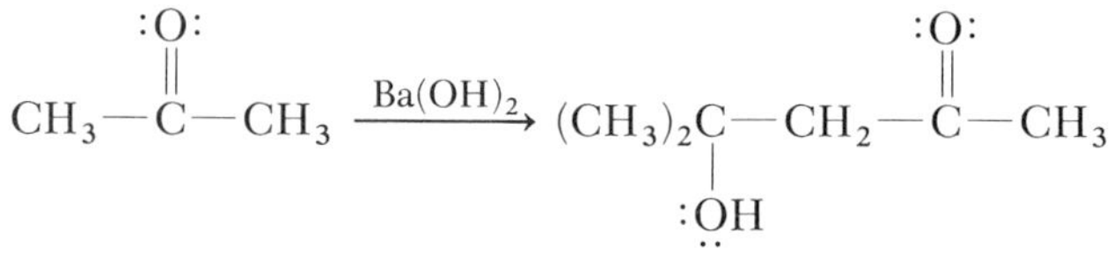

$$\underset{\text{acetone}}{CH_3-\overset{\overset{:O:}{\|}}{C}-CH_3} \xrightarrow{Ba(OH)_2} \underset{\substack{71\%\ \text{yield} \\ \text{4-hydroxy-4-methyl-} \\ \text{2-pentanone}}}{(CH_3)_2\underset{\underset{:\ddot{O}H}{|}}{C}-CH_2-\overset{\overset{:O:}{\|}}{C}-CH_3}$$

DEHYDRATION IN THE ALDOL ADDITION REACTION

On heating, the aldol product undergoes dehydration to form an ***α,β*-unsaturated carbonyl compound.** Figure 23.19 shows the general result of this process.

In α,β-unsaturated carbonyl compounds, the olefinic π bond and the carbonyl π bond are conjugated. (Recall that a conjugated system contains alternating double and single bonds; see Chapter 16.) Conjugated systems are generally more stable than nonconjugated systems, and thus the dehydration

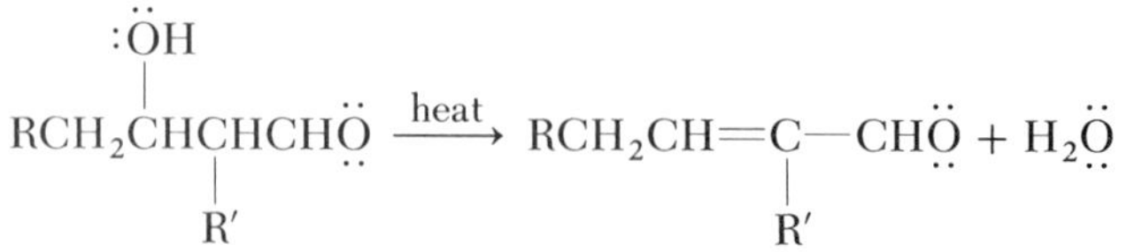

Figure 23.19 Dehydration of an aldol product to an *α,β*-unsaturated carbonyl compound.

$$RCH_2\overset{\overset{:\ddot{O}H}{|}}{C}H\underset{\underset{R'}{|}}{C}HCH\ddot{O} \xrightarrow{\text{heat}} RCH_2CH=\underset{\underset{R'}{|}}{C}-CH\ddot{O} + H_2\ddot{O}$$

of an aldol product proceeds much more readily than the dehydration of a simple alcohol. The activation energy for dehydration leading to the conjugated product is lower than that for simple alcohol dehydration because of the additional orbital overlap as the bonds of the product begin to form.

Many aldol reactions proceed directly to an α,β-unsaturated product. The initially formed β-hydroxyaldehyde or β-hydroxyketone dehydrates faster than it can be isolated. We can prevent this by avoiding the use of vigorous reaction conditions. Hence low temperatures are needed for the reactions in Equations 23.9 and 23.10.

However, it is very often desirable to have the reaction proceed to the α,β-unsaturated carbonyl compound. Such compounds are particularly valuable starting materials for further synthetic manipulation. We generally refer to a reaction that proceeds to the α,β-unsaturated carbonyl compound as an *aldol condensation*. A condensation reaction, in general, is one in which two smaller molecules combine to form a larger molecule and another small molecule such as water is eliminated.

With ketones there is a further experimental advantage in using conditions that favor dehydration of the initially formed aldol addition product. The advantage lies in the special stability of the α,β-unsaturated carbonyl compound. Even though the equilibrium for the nucleophilic addition of the enolate ion to the ketone may be quite unfavorable, as discussed earlier, it has little consequence for the isolation of the *dehydrated* product. Once dehydration occurs to yield the α,β-unsaturated carbonyl compound, return to starting materials is highly unlikely. Thus the aldol adduct is automatically removed from the equilibrium system as it is formed. According to LeChatelier's principle, more aldol adduct will now form, and it too will dehydrate to the α,β-unsaturated carbonyl compound. Thus we obtain a good yield of the final product, as is illustrated in Equation 23.12.

Eqn. 23.12

$$C_6H_5-\overset{\overset{\displaystyle :\ddot{O}:}{\|}}{C}-CH_3 \xrightarrow[\text{xylene, }100^\circ]{Al[OC(CH_3)_3]_3} C_6H_5-\underset{\underset{\displaystyle CH_3}{|}}{C}=CH-\overset{\overset{\displaystyle :\ddot{O}:}{\|}}{C}-C_6H_5$$

acetophenone

77% yield
1,3-diphenylbut-2-ene-1-one

The experimental conditions shown in Equation 23.12 involve heating the ketone with aluminum tri-*tert*-butoxide in xylene. These conditions are generally applicable for performing the aldol condensation of ketones.

This reaction system illustrates a generally important principle. In a reaction such as the aldol condensation, which involves a series of equilibria, we can often tolerate several unfavorable equilibria as long as the *final* equilibrium is favorable for product formation. We will find another example of this type of phenomenon in the Claisen condensation (Section 23.8).

PROBLEM 23.25 Draw the structure of the β-hydroxyketone precursor to the final product of Equation 23.12.

PROBLEM 23.26 Which product would you expect upon heating cyclohexanone with aluminum tri-*tert*-butoxide?

PROBLEM 23.27 It is possible to achieve an aldol condensation using acid rather than base as the catalyst. Give a mechanism for the acid-catalyzed condensation of acetone.

PROBLEM 23.28 Some β-hydroxyaldehydes undergo reactions other than dehydration. For example, upon standing β-hydroxybutyraldehyde undergoes a dimerization to the product shown below. What kind of a reaction is this dimerization? Write a mechanism for it.

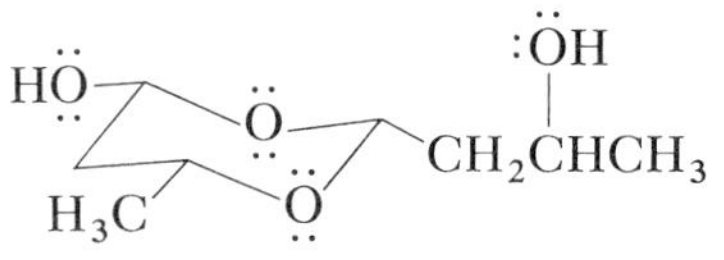

HO, H_3C, O, O, :OH, CH_2CHCH_3

CROSSED ALDOL REACTIONS

Consider what happens when aqueous sodium hydroxide is added to a *mixture* of carbonyl compounds. For example, suppose we mix two aldehydes, *A* and *B*, both having α-hydrogen atoms, and add aqueous sodium hydroxide to the mixture. Several different aldol reactions are possible. The enolate ion of *A* could add to the carbonyl carbon of either another molecule of *A* or a molecule of *B*. Similarly, the enolate ion of *B* could add to the carbonyl carbon of either *A* or *B*. Thus four possible aldol products are possible in such a case. We call reactions of this type, in which we add base to a mixture of carbonyl compounds, **crossed** (or *mixed*) **aldol reactions.**

PROBLEM 23.29 Show the four aldol addition products we could expect from the addition of aqueous sodium hydroxide to a mixture of propanal and butanal.

PROBLEM 23.30 How many different aldol addition products are possible upon the addition of aqueous sodium hydroxide to a mixture of 2-butanone and 2-pentanone? Draw their structures.

Crossed aldol reactions that yield many products are of no use for synthetic purposes. However, *some* crossed aldol reactions *are* of synthetic value. In general, we must choose the mixture of carbonyl compounds carefully so that the formation of a single product is favored.

A usual first requirement for a crossed aldol reaction is that only *one* of the carbonyl compounds have an α-hydrogen—then only this carbonyl compound can form an enolate ion. We must then choose the reaction conditions so that this enolate ion preferentially attacks the carbonyl carbon of the *other* starting carbonyl compound.

Consider, for example, the addition of aqueous base to a mixture of acetophenone and benzaldehyde. Of the two starting compounds, only acetophenone has an α-hydrogen atom and thus it is the only starting material that can form an enolate ion. Once formed, this enolate ion could attack either the carbonyl group of another acetophenone molecule or that of a benzaldehyde molecule. However, attack on benzaldehyde proceeds more efficiently, mainly for steric reasons. Benzaldehyde is an aldehyde whereas acetophenone is a ketone, and nucleophilic attack occurs much more readily on the less hindered carbonyl carbon of aldehydes than on ketones. As a result, a very good yield of the single aldol condensation product is obtained, as shown in Equation 23.13.

Eqn. 23.13

$$\text{Ph—CHO} + \text{Ph—C(=O)—CH}_3 \xrightarrow[\text{H}_2\text{O}]{\text{NaOH}} \text{PhCH=CH—C(=O)—Ph}$$

benzaldehyde | acetophenone | 85% yield 1,3-diphenylprop-2-ene-1-one

We can also choose conditions for this type of reaction to minimize the small amount of attack by the enolate ion on another molecule of its precursor. One technique is to add the enolizable carbonyl compound slowly to a solution of base and the nonenolizable carbonyl compound. In this way (for the example of acetophenone and benzaldehyde) there is always an excess of the nonenolizable carbonyl compound (benzaldehyde) available for reaction with the enolate ion from the enolizable one (acetophenone). However, very little of the enolizable compound (acetophenone) is ever available for reaction with its enolate ion.

A crossed aldol condensation involving an aromatic aldehyde is known as a **Claisen-Schmidt condensation.** Such reactions always proceed all the way to the α,β-unsaturated product.

PROBLEM 23.31 Predict the major product of a crossed aldol reaction between formaldehyde and 2-methylbutanal.

PROBLEM 23.32 In the reaction shown in Equation 23.13 there are actually *two* possible crossed aldol condensation products. Write the structure of each and tell which you would expect to be the major product.

PROBLEM 23.33 Name the reagents you would use to form each of the following compounds using a crossed aldol condensation. If more than one product forms in the reaction you show, tell which you would expect to be the major product.

a. (2-furyl)CH=CH—C(=O)—Ph

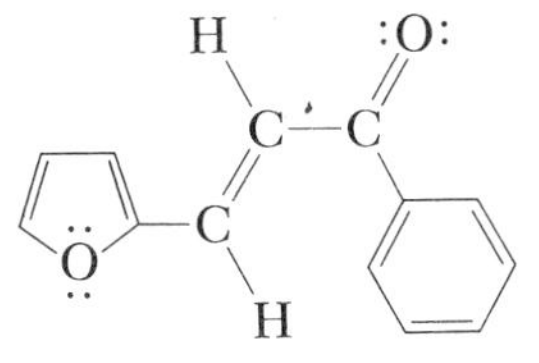

b. $(CH_3)_3C$—CH=CH—C(=O)—CH_3

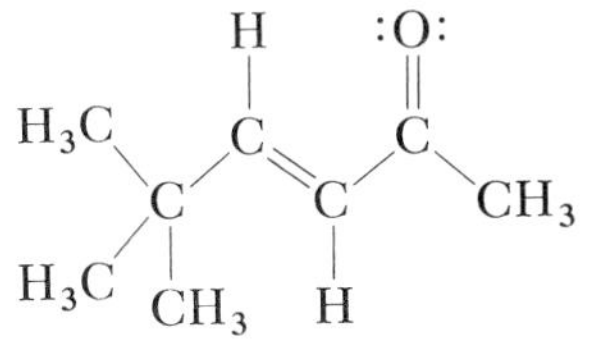

c. [structure: 2-benzylidenecyclohexanone; :O:, H, C, Ph]

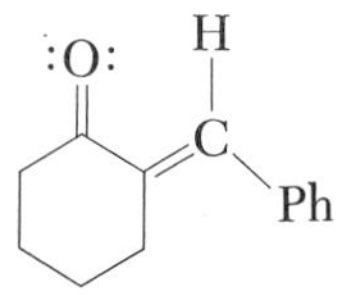

Steps to Solving the Problem

Solution to Problem 23.33a

1. When we consider a structure as a candidate for synthesis in a crossed aldol condensation, we need to decide which portions come from which reagent. For an α,β-unsaturated carbonyl target material, we look to the carbon-carbon double bond as the point of disconnection, as shown below.

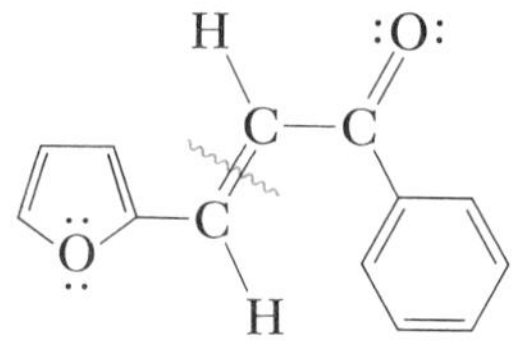

[structure: furyl–CH=CH–C(=O)–phenyl with wavy disconnection line across the C=C; labels H, :O:, C—C, Ö, C, H]

2. What reagent leads to each part of the product? The portion containing the carbonyl group (to the right) is derived from the enolate ion, whereas the remainder is derived from the substrate of enolate attack. The two components for the reaction are shown below with the reaction conditions.

$$\text{furan-CHO} + CH_3\text{—}\overset{\overset{\text{:O:}}{\|}}{C}\text{—Ph} \xrightarrow[H_2O,\ CH_3OH]{NaOH} \text{furan—CH=CH—}\overset{\overset{\text{:O:}}{\|}}{C}\text{—Ph}$$

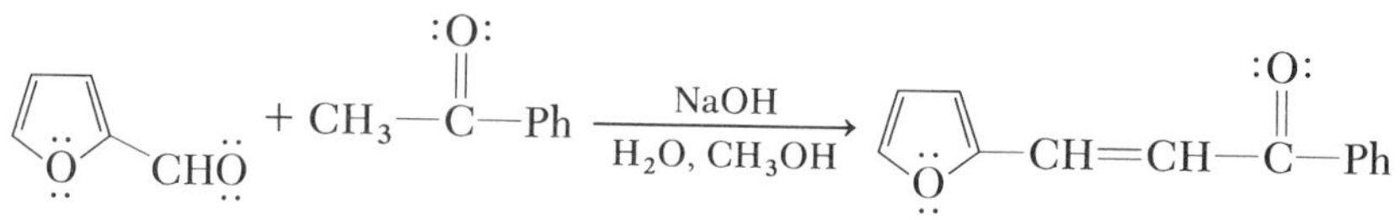

PROBLEM 23.34 Give the reagents and the reaction conditions you would use for the preparation of 4-methoxyphenyl-3-buten-2-one using a crossed aldol condensation.

INTRAMOLECULAR ALDOL REACTIONS

Substances containing two carbonyl groups within a single molecule can undergo **intramolecular aldol condensations.** In such reactions an enolate ion forms by removal of an α-hydrogen from a site adjacent to one of the carbonyl groups. This enolate ion then performs an intramolecular nucleophilic attack at the molecule's other carbonyl carbon atom. The result of this reaction is the formation of a cyclic α,β-unsaturated carbonyl compound. An example of this type of reaction is shown in Equation 23.14.

Eqn. 23.14

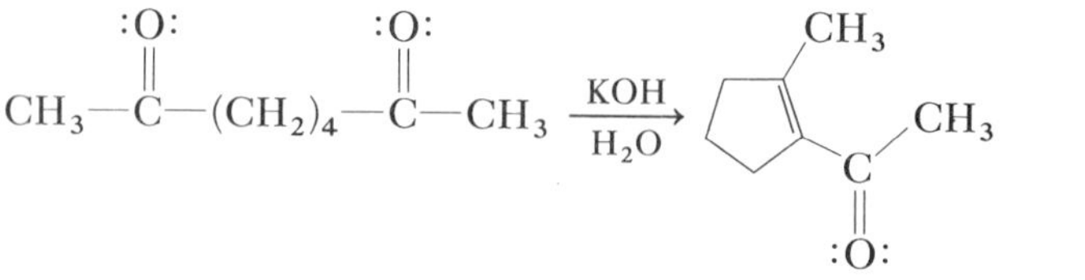

$$CH_3\text{—}\overset{\overset{\text{:O:}}{\|}}{C}\text{—}(CH_2)_4\text{—}\overset{\overset{\text{:O:}}{\|}}{C}\text{—}CH_3 \xrightarrow[H_2O]{KOH} \text{[cyclopentene with } CH_3 \text{ and } C(=\text{:O:})CH_3\text{]}$$

2,7-octanedione

83% yield
2-acetyl-1-methylcyclopentene

If a five- or six-membered ring can form, the intramolecular aldol condensation generally occurs more rapidly than the corresponding intermolecular reaction. In fact, organic chemists use the intramolecular aldol condensation as a convenient and useful synthetic route to prepare cyclic compounds.

PROBLEM 23.35 Why would an intramolecular aldol condensation leading to a five- or six-membered ring occur more rapidly than the competing intermolecular aldol condensation?

PROBLEM 23.36 Give a complete mechanism for the reaction shown in Equation 23.14.

PROBLEM 23.37 What would be the major product of an intramolecular aldol condensation for each of the carbonyl compounds shown below.

a. 2,6-heptanedione

b. 2-(3-oxobutyl)cyclohexanone (structure: cyclohexanone ring bearing $CH_2CH_2C(=O)CH_3$)

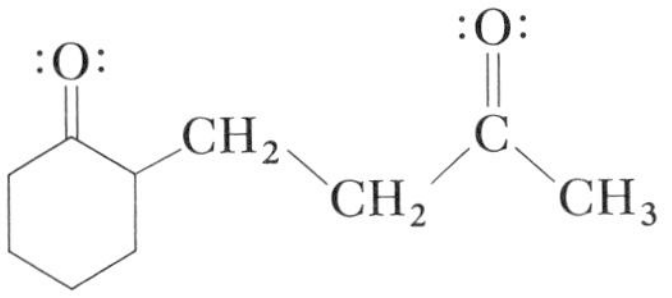

PROBLEM 23.38 Propose a synthetic route for the overall conversion shown below.

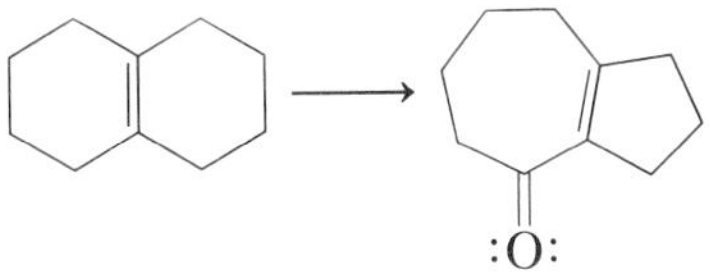

(bicyclic octalin with central double bond $\longrightarrow$ bicyclic enone: cycloheptenone fused to cyclopentene)

RETRO-ALDOL REACTIONS

Both acid- and base-catalyzed aldol reactions proceed via a series of equilibria. Thus, reaction can proceed in either direction. So far we have been concerned with the forward reaction (the pivotal step in the forward reaction is the nucleophilic addition of an enolate ion to a carbonyl group). The *reverse* reaction is referred to as a **retro-aldol reaction.**

Retro-aldol reactions are common with β-hydroxyketones and α,β-unsaturated ketones. Consider, for example, the previously discussed aldol product from acetone (Equation 23.11). The equilibrium for the formation of this aldol product is unfavorable—in order to prepare the aldol addition product in a reasonable yield we need to use special conditions to remove one of the products from the reaction mixture and force the equilibrium to the product side. If we expose the aldol addition product to experimental conditions that reestablish equilibrium, the addition product reverts to acetone. Heating with strong base produces this effect, as shown in Equation 23.15.

Eqn. 23.15

$$CH_3-\overset{\overset{\displaystyle :O:}{\|}}{C}-CH_2\overset{\overset{\displaystyle :\ddot{O}H}{|}}{C}(CH_3)_2 \xrightarrow[H_2O]{NaOH} 2\ CH_3-\overset{\overset{\displaystyle :O:}{\|}}{C}-CH_3$$

4-hydroxy-4-methyl-2-pentanone

95% yield acetone

PROBLEM 23.39 Propose a mechanism for the reaction shown below.

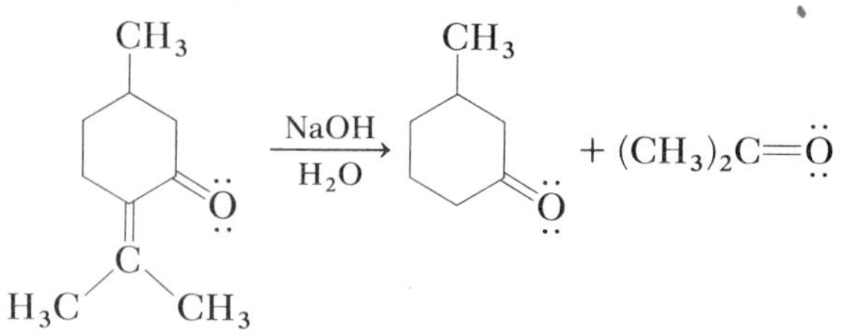

$$\text{(2-isopropylidene-5-methylcyclohexanone)} \xrightarrow[H_2O]{NaOH} \text{(3-methylcyclohexanone)} + (CH_3)_2C{=}\ddot{O}$$

PROBLEM 23.40 What product would you expect to result from a retro-aldol reaction on the compound shown below?

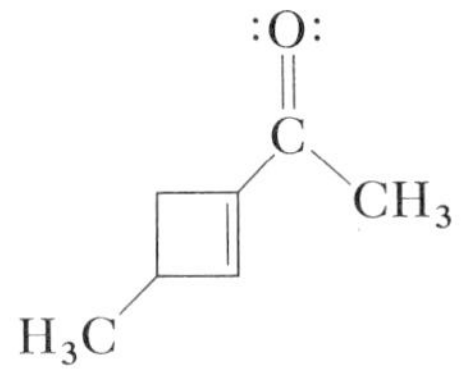

(Structure: cyclobutene bearing $CH_3C(=O)$– and H_3C– substituents)

23.8 Condensation Reactions of Esters

THE CLAISEN CONDENSATION

Esters of the general formula RCH_2CO_2R' undergo an important reaction known as the **Claisen condensation.** The simplest example of the Claisen condensation is shown in Equation 23.16. In this example R = H and R′ = CH_2CH_3. Notice that the product is ethyl acetoacetate, which is the starting material in the acetoacetic ester synthesis of ketones (discussed earlier in this chapter).

Eqn. 23.16

$$\underset{\text{ethyl acetate}}{CH_3{-}\overset{:O:}{\overset{\|}{C}}{-}\ddot{O}CH_2CH_3} \xrightarrow[\text{HOCH}_2\text{CH}_3\ \text{(aq acid workup)}]{\text{NaOCH}_2\text{CH}_3} \underset{\substack{75\%\ \text{yield} \\ \text{ethyl acetoacetate}}}{CH_3{-}\overset{:O:}{\overset{\|}{C}}{-}CH_2{-}\overset{:O:}{\overset{\|}{C}}{-}\ddot{O}CH_2CH_3}$$

The Claisen condensation, in general, occurs when we treat an appropriate ester with sodium ethoxide in ethanol. We use aqueous acid to workup the reaction and isolate the β-ketoester product.

The mechanism of the Claisen condensation is shown below. Several aspects of the reaction and its mechanism merit comment. A full equivalent amount of sodium ethoxide (rather than a catalytic amount) must be used to accomplish the reaction because of the presence of several unfavorable equilibria at the beginning of the reaction mechanism. (Recall from our previous discussion that we can obtain useful yields of product in spite of initial unfavorable equilibria if some final, favorable equilibrium follows the unfavorable ones.) The favorable final equilibrium in the Claisen condensation is the formation of the enolate ion of the β-ketoester product. To ensure the conversion of the β-ketoester entirely to its enolate ion, we need to use a full equivalent of base. Driving this last equilibrium toward the enolate-ion side brings the reaction to completion. Workup of the reaction with aqueous acid converts the enolate of the β-ketoester to the free β-ketoester product.

MECHANISM OF REACTION

The Claisen Condensation

Step 1 Formation of enolate ion

$$CH_3CH_2\ddot{O}:^- + H{-}CH_2{-}\overset{\overset{:O:}{\|}}{C}{-}\ddot{O}CH_2CH_3 \rightleftharpoons$$

weaker base — weaker acid

$$^-:CH_2{-}\overset{\overset{:O:}{\|}}{C}{-}\ddot{O}CH_2CH_3 + CH_3CH_2\ddot{O}H$$

stronger base — stronger acid

Step 2 Nucleophilic attack by the enolate ion on the carboxylate carbon atom

$$CH_3{-}\overset{\overset{:O:}{\|}}{C}{-}\ddot{O}{-}CH_2CH_3 + {}^-:CH_2{-}\overset{\overset{:O:}{\|}}{C}{-}\ddot{O}CH_2CH_3 \rightleftharpoons$$

$$CH_3{-}\overset{\overset{:\ddot{O}:^-}{|}}{\underset{\underset{:\ddot{O}CH_2CH_3}{|}}{C}}{-}CH_2{-}\overset{\overset{:O:}{\|}}{C}{-}\ddot{O}CH_2CH_3$$

Step 3 Cleavage of the carbon-oxygen bond, eliminating ethoxide ion

$$CH_3{-}\overset{\overset{:\ddot{O}:^-}{|}}{\underset{\underset{:\ddot{O}CH_2CH_3}{|}}{C}}{-}CH_2{-}\overset{\overset{:O:}{\|}}{C}{-}\ddot{O}CH_2CH_3 \rightleftharpoons$$

$$CH_3{-}\overset{\overset{:O:}{\|}}{C}{-}CH_2{-}\overset{\overset{:O:}{\|}}{C}{-}\ddot{O}CH_2CH_3 + CH_3CH_2\ddot{O}:^-$$

Step 4 Formation of a new enolate ion

$$CH_3{-}\overset{\overset{:O:}{\|}}{C}{-}\underset{\underset{H}{|}}{CH}{-}\overset{\overset{:O:}{\|}}{C}{-}\ddot{O}CH_2CH_3 + {}^-:\ddot{O}CH_2CH_3 \rightleftharpoons$$

stronger acid — stronger base

$$CH_3{-}\overset{\overset{:O:}{\|}}{C}{-}\underset{\ddot{-}}{CH}{-}\overset{\overset{:O:}{\|}}{C}{-}\ddot{O}CH_2CH_3 + H{-}\ddot{O}CH_2CH_3$$

weaker base — weaker acid

Step 5 Protonation of the enolate ion upon acid workup to yield product

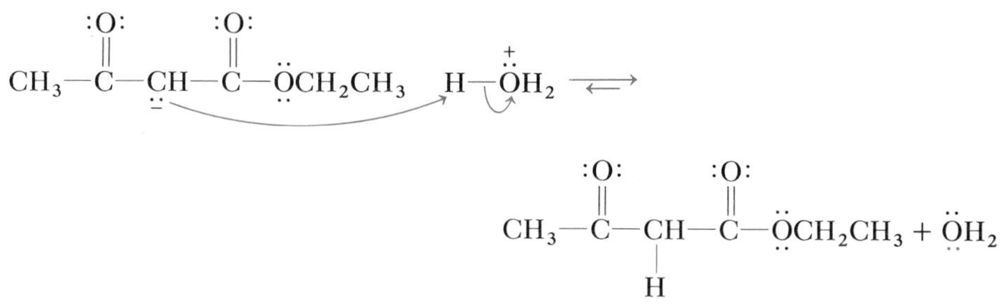

$$CH_3-\overset{\overset{\large :O:}{\|}}{C}-\underset{..}{C}H-\overset{\overset{\large :O:}{\|}}{C}-\ddot{O}CH_2CH_3 \quad H-\overset{+}{\ddot{O}}H_2 \rightleftharpoons$$

$$CH_3-\overset{\overset{\large :O:}{\|}}{C}-\underset{\underset{H}{|}}{C}H-\overset{\overset{\large :O:}{\|}}{C}-\ddot{O}CH_2CH_3 + \ddot{O}H_2$$

Our analysis of the mechanism of the Claisen condensation shows that the starting ester should have *two* α-hydrogen atoms. One of these α-hydrogen atoms is involved in the formation of the initial enolate ion. The second is involved in the equilibrium step, allowing the overall reaction to go to completion. In accord with this analysis, we find that esters such as ethyl isobutyrate (**23.3**) do not undergo the Claisen condensation when treated with sodium ethoxide in ethanol.

$$(CH_3)_2CH-\overset{\overset{\large :O:}{\|}}{C}-\ddot{O}CH_2CH_3$$

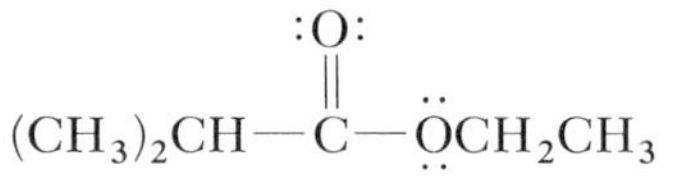

ethyl isobutyrate
23.3

Successful conversion of such esters as ethyl isobutyrate to β-ketoesters requires special reaction conditions (a base that is much stronger than ethoxide ion or the continuous removal of a volatile product from the reaction mixture (or both)). Sodium hydride can sometimes be used as the base in such reactions. Hydride ion is a very strong base; when it removes the α-hydrogen, the products are the enolate ion and hydrogen gas. The gas escapes the reaction mixture, making the reaction irreversible.

PROBLEM 23.41 β-Ketoesters that cannot be formed under the usual conditions of the Claisen condensation often undergo retro (reverse) Claisen condensations. Propose a complete mechanism for the reaction of ethyl 2,2,4-trimethyl-3-oxopentanoate with sodium ethoxide in ethanol to form ethyl isobutyrate.

PROBLEM 23.42 What problem (or problems) do you foresee in using sodium hydroxide rather than sodium ethoxide in an attempted Claisen condensation?

PROBLEM 23.43 Give the structure of the Claisen condensation products you would expect by treating each of the following with sodium ethoxide in ethanol.
a. ethyl butanoate **b.** ethyl phenylethanoate

CROSSED CLAISEN CONDENSATIONS

Ester-Ester Condensations We can perform crossed (or mixed) Claisen condensations between two different esters, but a useless mixture of products results unless the starting esters are carefully chosen. The usual strategy for executing a useful crossed Claisen condensation is similar to the strategy for a crossed aldol condensation. Of the two esters used, only one should have α-hydrogens, while the other should be particularly susceptible to nucleophilic attack. Among the useful esters lacking α-hydrogens are esters of benzoic acid, substituted benzoic acids, formic acid, and oxalic acid. Examples of synthetically useful crossed Claisen condensations using these types of esters are shown in Equations 23.17–23.19.

$$\underset{\text{methyl benzoate}}{Ph{-}C({=}O){-}OCH_3} + \underset{\text{methyl propanoate}}{CH_3CH_2{-}C({=}O){-}OCH_3} \xrightarrow[\substack{CH_3OH \\ \text{(aq acid workup)}}]{NaOCH_3} \underset{\substack{\text{60\% yield} \\ \text{methyl 2-methyl-3-phenyl-3-oxopropanoate}}}{Ph{-}C({=}O){-}CH(CH_3){-}C({=}O){-}OCH_3}$$

Eqn. 23.17

$$\underset{\text{ethyl formate}}{H{-}C({=}O){-}OCH_2CH_3} + \underset{\text{ethyl phenylacetate}}{PhCH_2{-}C({=}O){-}OCH_2CH_3} \xrightarrow[\substack{CH_3CH_2OH \\ \text{(aq acid workup)}}]{NaOCH_2CH_3} \underset{\substack{\text{75\% yield} \\ \text{ethyl 2-formyl-2-phenylacetate}}}{PhCH(CHO){-}C({=}O){-}OCH_2CH_3}$$

Eqn. 23.18

$$\underset{\text{ethyl propanoate}}{CH_3CH_2{-}C({=}O){-}OCH_2CH_3} + \underset{\text{diethyl oxalate}}{CH_3CH_2O{-}C({=}O){-}C({=}O){-}OCH_2CH_3} \xrightarrow[\substack{CH_3CH_2OH \\ \text{(aq acid workup)}}]{NaOCH_2CH_3} \underset{\substack{\text{70\% yield} \\ \text{diethyl 2-methyl-3-oxosuccinate}}}{CH_3CH(C({=}O){-}C({=}O){-}OCH_2CH_3){-}C({=}O){-}OCH_2CH_3}$$

Eqn. 23.19

Ester-Ketone Condensations A useful variation of the crossed Claisen condensation involves the reaction of an ester and a ketone. In this type of reaction we must again be careful in our choice of starting materials so that a useless mixture of products does not result. A nonenolizable ester (one with no α-hydrogens) is commonly used for this purpose. Again, the esters of benzoic, substituted benzoic, formic, or oxalic acids prove useful for this type of reaction. A typical example is shown in Equation 23.20.

Eqn. 23.20

$$Ph-\overset{\overset{:O:}{\|}}{C}-\ddot{O}CH_2CH_3 + CH_3-\overset{\overset{:O:}{\|}}{C}-Ph \xrightarrow[\substack{CH_3CH_2OH \\ \text{(aq acid workup)}}]{NaOCH_2CH_3} Ph-\overset{\overset{:O:}{\|}}{C}-CH_2-\overset{\overset{:O:}{\|}}{C}-Ph$$

ethyl benzoate; acetophenone; 65% yield 1,3-diphenyl-1,3-propanedione

PROBLEM 23.44 Suggest synthetic routes for the preparation of each of the following materials using a crossed ester-ketone condensation reaction.

a. 2-formylcyclohexanone (cyclohexanone ring with CHO on the carbon adjacent to C=O)

b. $CH_3-\underset{\underset{:O:}{\|}}{C}-CH_2-\underset{\underset{:O:}{\|}}{C}-(CH_2)_4CH_3$

c. $CH_3CH_2\ddot{O}-\overset{\overset{:O:}{\|}}{C}-\overset{\overset{:O:}{\|}}{C}-\underset{\underset{C_6H_5}{|}}{CH}-\overset{\overset{:O:}{\|}}{C}-C_6H_5$

THE INTRAMOLECULAR CLAISEN CONDENSATION

Earlier we pointed out that dialdehydes and diketones undergo intramolecular aldol condensations to give cyclic products. Diesters similarly undergo an intramolecular condensation known as the **Dieckmann condensation.** Like the cyclic aldol reaction, Dieckmann condensation is generally most useful for preparing rings of five and six members, although rings of other sizes are also accessible. A simple example of the Dieckmann condensation is shown in Equation 23.21.

Eqn. 23.21

$$CH_3CH_2\ddot{O}-\overset{\overset{:O:}{\|}}{C}-(CH_2)_4-\overset{\overset{:O:}{\|}}{C}-\ddot{O}CH_2CH_3 \xrightarrow[\text{(aq acid workup)}]{\substack{NaOCH_2CH_3 \\ CH_3CH_2OH}}$$

diethyl adipate

(cyclopentanone ring with C=O and adjacent $-\overset{\overset{:O:}{\|}}{C}-\ddot{O}CH_2CH_3$)

80% yield
2-carboethoxycyclopentanone

PROBLEM 23.45 Provide a complete mechanism for the reaction shown in Equation 23.21.

PROBLEM 23.46 Predict the product obtained from a Dieckmann condensation of the compound whose structure is shown below. (*Hint:* This substance has two different types of α-hydrogen atoms. Thus two different products are in principle possible, but only one of these products actually forms.)

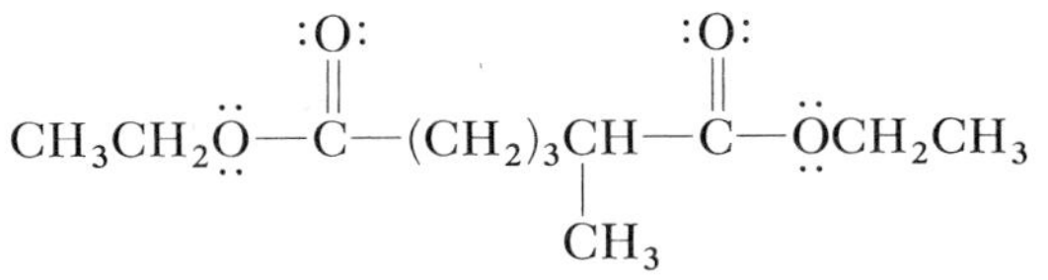

$$CH_3CH_2\ddot{O}-\overset{\overset{:O:}{\|}}{C}-(CH_2)_3\underset{\underset{CH_3}{|}}{CH}-\overset{\overset{:O:}{\|}}{C}-\ddot{O}CH_2CH_3$$

A reaction that is very similar to the Dieckmann condensation occurs with 4-oxo- and 5-oxoesters. Cyclic diketones are obtained from such reactions. An example is given in Equation 23.22.

Eqn. 23.22

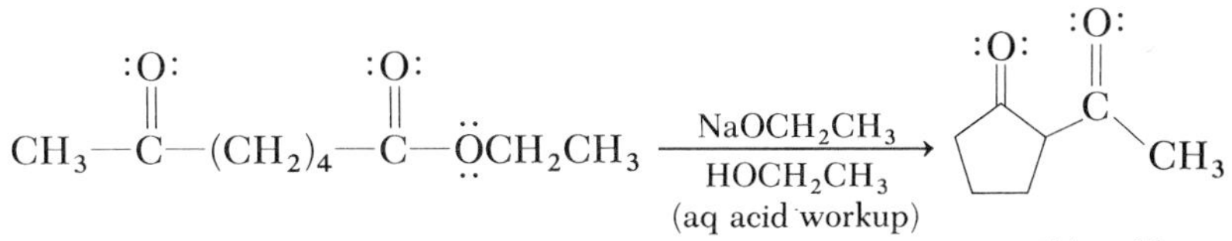

$$CH_3-\overset{\overset{:O:}{\|}}{C}-(CH_2)_4-\overset{\overset{:O:}{\|}}{C}-\ddot{O}CH_2CH_3 \xrightarrow[\text{HOCH}_2\text{CH}_3\ (\text{aq acid workup})]{\text{NaOCH}_2\text{CH}_3}$$ 2-acetylcyclopentanone

ethyl 6-oxoheptanoate; 90% yield 2-acetylcyclopentanone

PROBLEM 23.47 Give the reagents and reaction conditions needed to accomplish the conversion shown below.

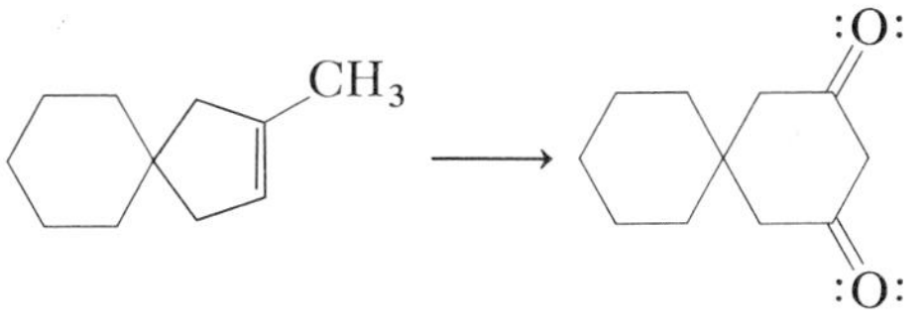

[spiro[4.5]dec-2-ene with CH_3 on the double bond → spiro[5.5]undecane-2,4-dione]

23.9 Reactions Related to the Aldol and Claisen Condensations

Both the aldol and the Claisen condensations involve the addition of a carbanion to a carbonyl carbon atom. We will now consider several other condensation reactions of this type.

THE PERKIN CONDENSATION

In the **Perkin condensation** an acid anhydride bearing an α-hydrogen atom serves as the source of the carbanion (that is, the enolate anion). We use a weak base, typically the sodium or potassium salt of the acid whose anhydride is involved, to produce the enolate of the anhydride. The carbonyl compound that is attacked by the enolate anion is generally an aromatic aldehyde. Aromatic aldehydes have no α-hydrogen atoms and thus cannot yield an enolate anion on their own.

The overall effect of the Perkin condensation is to produce an α,β-unsaturated carboxylic acid. Usually we find that the major stereoisomer of the product is the one in which the carboxylate group is *trans* relative to the larger group attached to the β-carbon atom. An example of the Perkin condensation is given in Equation 23.23.

Eqn. 23.23

$$CH_3C(=O)-O-C(=O)CH_3 + PhCHO \xrightarrow[2.\ \text{aq acid}]{1.\ CH_3CO_2K} (Ph)(H)C{=}C(H)(CO_2H)$$

acetic anhydride   benzaldehyde   60% yield *trans*-cinnamic acid

The mechanistic steps involved in the Perkin condensation are given below.

MECHANISM OF REACTION

The Perkin Condensation

Overall reaction:

$$R-C(=O)-O-C(=O)-R + ArCHO \xrightarrow[2.\ H_2O]{1.\ RC(=O)-O^-Na^+} ArCH{=}CH-C(=O)-OH$$

(must have an α-hydrogen)

Step 1 Formation of enolate of the anhydride by reaction with a carboxylate anion

$$CH_3-C(=O)-O-C(=O)-CH_2-H + {}^-O-C(=O)-CH_3 \longrightarrow CH_3-C(=O)-O-C(=O)-\overset{-}{C}H_2 + H-O-C(=O)-CH_3$$

Step 2 Nucleophilic attack by the enolate ion on an aromatic aldehyde

$$ArC(=O)-H + {}^-CH_2-C(=O)-O-C(=O)-CH_3 \longrightarrow Ar-CH(O^-)-CH_2-C(=O)-O-C(=O)-CH_3$$

Step 3 Intramolecular acylation of the alkoxide site

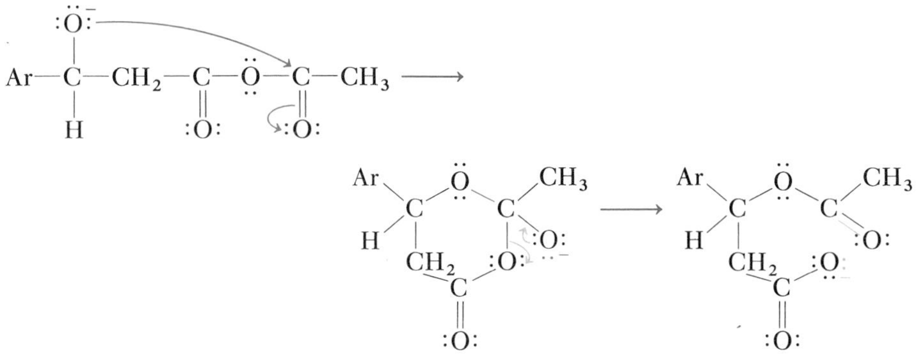

$$Ar-\underset{H}{\overset{:\ddot{O}:^-}{C}}-CH_2-\underset{\|}{C}(=O)-\ddot{O}-C(=O)-CH_3 \longrightarrow$$

$$\text{cyclic tetrahedral intermediate} \longrightarrow \text{cyclic product}$$

Step 4 Anhydride formation by transacylation

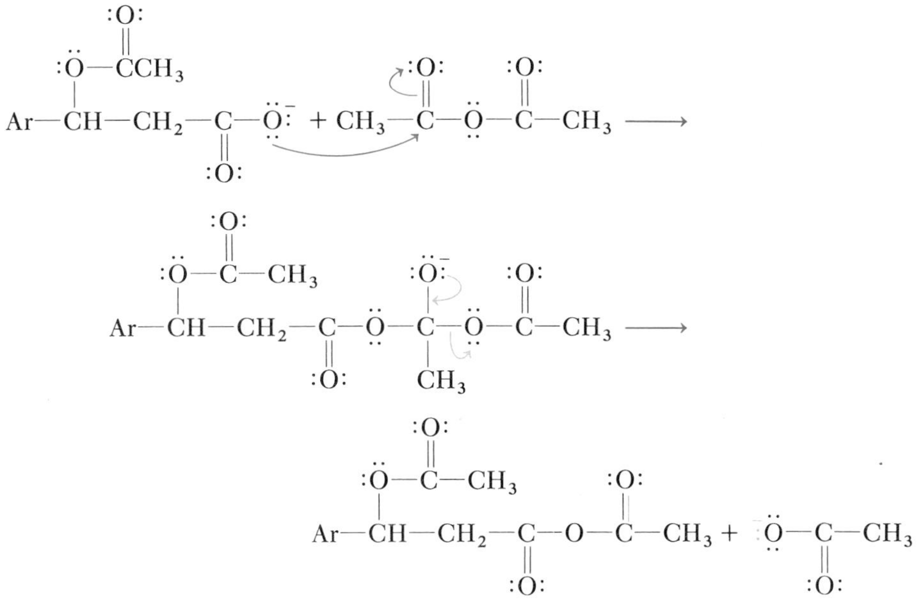

$$Ar-CH(OCCH_3)-CH_2-C(=O)-\ddot{O}:^- + CH_3-C(=O)-\ddot{O}-C(=O)-CH_3 \longrightarrow$$

$$Ar-CH(O-C(=O)-CH_3)-CH_2-C(=O)-\ddot{O}-C(\ddot{O}:^-)(CH_3)-\ddot{O}-C(=O)-CH_3 \longrightarrow$$

$$Ar-CH(O-C(=O)-CH_3)-CH_2-C(=O)-O-C(=O)-CH_3 + {}^-:\ddot{O}-C(=O)-CH_3$$

Step 5 Elimination (E2)

$$B:^- + Ar-CH(O-C(=O)-CH_3)-CH(H)-C(=O)-\ddot{O}-C(=O)-CH_3 \longrightarrow$$

$$ArCH=CH-C(=O)-\ddot{O}-C(=O)-CH_3 + H-B + {}^-:\ddot{O}-C(=O)-CH_3$$

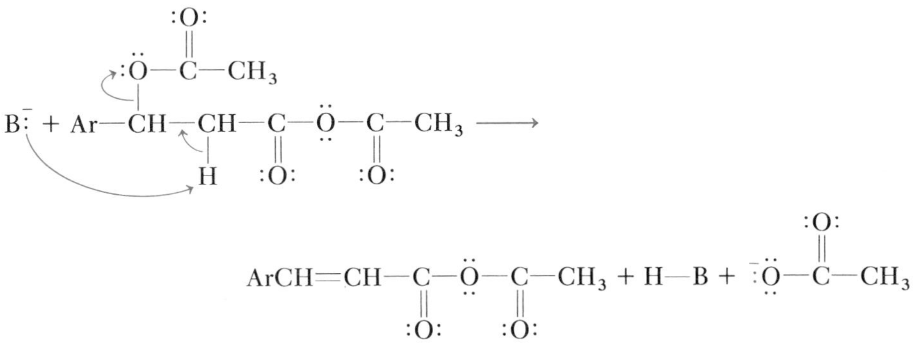

Step 6 Hydrolysis upon workup with aqueous acid

$$ArCH{=}CH{-}\underset{\underset{:O:}{\|}}{C}{-}\ddot{O}{-}\underset{\underset{:O:}{\|}}{C}{-}CH_3 + H_2\ddot{O} \longrightarrow ArCH{=}CH{-}CO_2H + CH_3CO_2H$$

PROBLEM 23.48 At high temperatures the product of Step 3 in the Perkin condensation mechanism undergoes a competing reaction to give $ArCH{=}CH_2$. Write a mechanism for this reaction using the curved-arrow formalism.

PROBLEM 23.49 Suggest a structure for the product of the reaction shown below.

$$\text{(o-HOC}_6\text{H}_4\text{CHO)} + CH_3\overset{\overset{:O:}{\|}}{C}{-}\ddot{O}{-}\overset{\overset{:O:}{\|}}{C}{-}CH_3 \xrightarrow[\text{2. aq acid}]{\text{1. } CH_3CO_2K} C_9H_6O_2$$

THE KNOEVENAGEL CONDENSATION

In the **Knoevenagel condensation** the source of enolate ion is a particularly acidic carbonyl compound such as diethyl malonate or ethyl acetoacetate. Reaction is effected by treating an aldehyde or ketone with one of these particularly acidic carbonyl compounds in the presence of a catalytic amount of ammonia (or a primary or secondary amine) and a small amount of a carboxylic acid. The reactions are normally performed in refluxing benzene in an apparatus equipped with a Dean-Stark trap to remove water as it is formed. The continuous removal of water from the reaction mixture shifts the reaction equilibrium toward the product side. Three examples of the Knoevenagel condensation are shown in Equations 23.24–23.26.

Eqn. 23.24

$$PhCH\ddot{O} + H_2C(CO_2CH_2CH_3)_2 \xrightarrow[PhCO_2H]{\text{piperidine (N–H)}} PhCH{=}C(CO_2CH_2CH_3)_2 + H_2\ddot{O}$$

benzaldehyde; diethyl malonate; 90% yield ethyl 3-phenyl-2-carboethoxyacrylate

In the reaction shown in Equation 23.26, ammonia is used in the form of ammonium acetate. Ethyl cyanoacetate is the acidic organic compound in this reaction; it has a high reactivity in this type of reaction and is often a preferred reagent for condensation reactions with less reactive ketones.

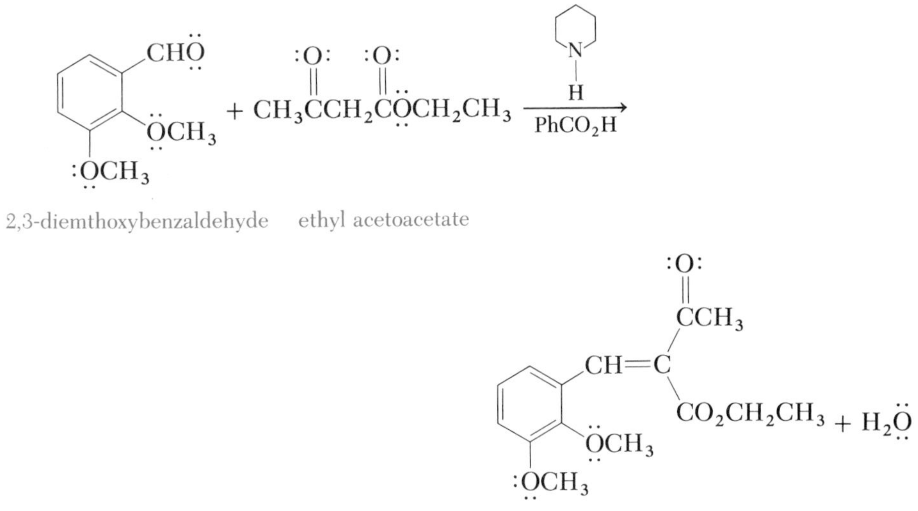

Eqn. 23.25

2,3-diemthoxybenzaldehyde + ethyl acetoacetate $\xrightarrow[\text{PhCO}_2\text{H}]{\text{piperidine}}$ 3-carboethoxy-4-(2,3-dimethoxyphenyl)butenone (70% yield) + H_2O

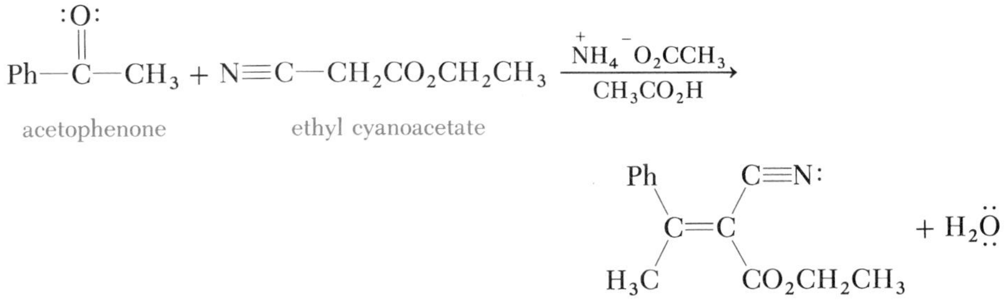

Eqn. 23.26

$$\text{Ph—C(=O)—CH}_3 + \text{N≡C—CH}_2\text{CO}_2\text{CH}_2\text{CH}_3 \xrightarrow[\text{CH}_3\text{CO}_2\text{H}]{\overset{+}{\text{N}}\text{H}_4\ \overset{-}{\text{O}}_2\text{CCH}_3} (\text{Ph})(\text{H}_3\text{C})\text{C=C}(\text{C≡N:})(\text{CO}_2\text{CH}_2\text{CH}_3) + H_2\ddot{O}$$

acetophenone; ethyl cyanoacetate

55% yield
ethyl (Z)-2-cyano-3-phenyl-2-butenoate

CONDENSATIONS WITH NITRO- AND CYANO- COMPOUNDS

The ease of formation of the carbanions we have discussed thus far correlates with their resonance stabilization. We can draw resonance structures for these carbanions in which the negative charge is delocalized from carbon to the oxygen of a neighboring carbonyl or carboxyl group. Groups other than the carbonyl and carboxyl groups can also stabilize carbanions by resonance, as shown in Figure 23.20 for the nitro and cyano groups. Not surprisingly, we find

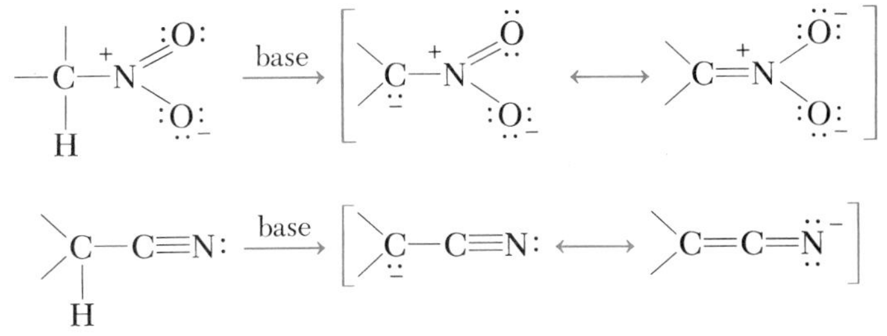

Figure 23.20 Resonance stabilization of carbanions from cyano- and nitro-compounds.

$$\text{H—C—}\overset{+}{\text{N}}\text{O}_2^- \xrightarrow{\text{base}} [\ddot{\text{C}}^-\text{—}\overset{+}{\text{N}}(=\text{O})\text{O}^- \longleftrightarrow \text{C=}\overset{+}{\text{N}}(\text{O}^-)\text{O}^-]$$

$$\text{H—C—C≡N:} \xrightarrow{\text{base}} [\ddot{\text{C}}^-\text{—C≡N:} \longleftrightarrow \text{C=C=}\ddot{\text{N}}^-]$$

that nitro- and cyano- compounds can enter into reactions similar to those we have discussed in this chapter. For example, such compounds undergo aldol-type condensations with carbonyl compounds, as illustrated in Equations 23.27 and 23.28.

Eqn. 23.27

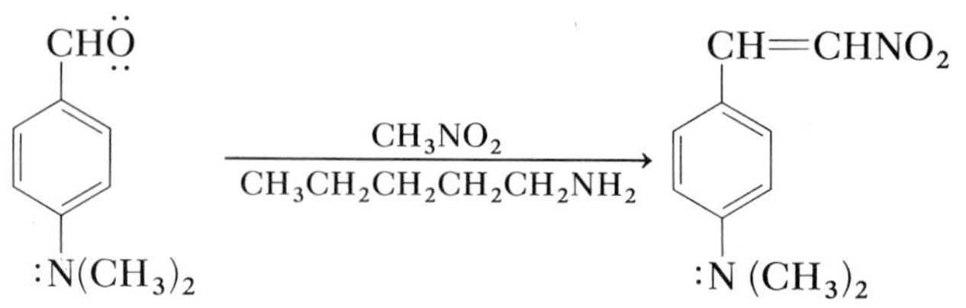

4-(dimethylamino)benzaldehyde (p-$(CH_3)_2N$–C_6H_4–CHO) $\xrightarrow[CH_3CH_2CH_2CH_2CH_2NH_2]{CH_3NO_2}$ p-$(CH_3)_2N$–C_6H_4–$CH{=}CHNO_2$

83% yield
2-(4-dimethylaminophenyl)-1-nitroethene

Eqn. 23.28

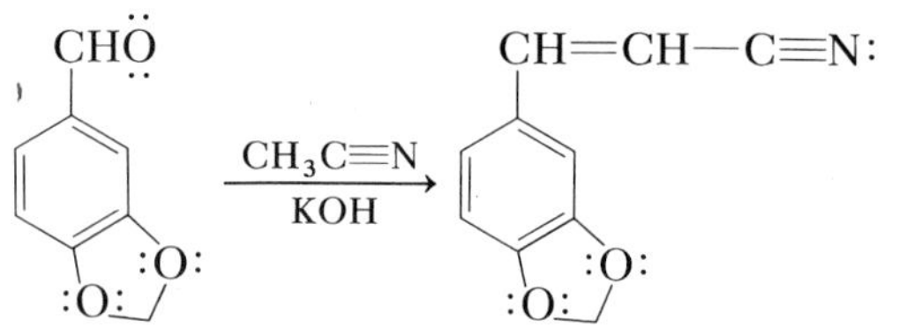

3,4-methylenedioxybenzaldehyde $\xrightarrow[KOH]{CH_3C{\equiv}N}$ 3,4-methylenedioxyphenyl–$CH{=}CH{-}C{\equiv}N$:

86% yield
3-(3,4-methylenedioxyphenyl)-acrylonitrile

23.10 α,β-Unsaturated Carbonyl Compounds: Michael Addition

The aldol condensation provides a convenient route to α,β-unsaturated carbonyl compounds. These compounds themselves undergo a number of important reactions that depend on the interaction of the conjugated carbon-carbon and carbon-oxygen π-bonds.

Consider, for example, the reaction of cyanide ion with an α,β-unsaturated carbonyl compound. First, think about the reactions of *isolated* alkenes and carbonyl linkages with cyanide ion. If we were to treat a simple alkene with cyanide ion, there would be no reaction at the carbon-carbon double bond,

Figure 23.21 Reaction of cyanide ion with α,β-unsaturated carbonyl compounds. Although cyanide ion fails to react with an ordinary alkene double bond, it does undergo reaction at the carbon-carbon double bond of an α,β-unsaturated carbonyl compound.

$$H_2C{=}CH_2 + :CN:^- \longrightarrow \text{no reaction}$$

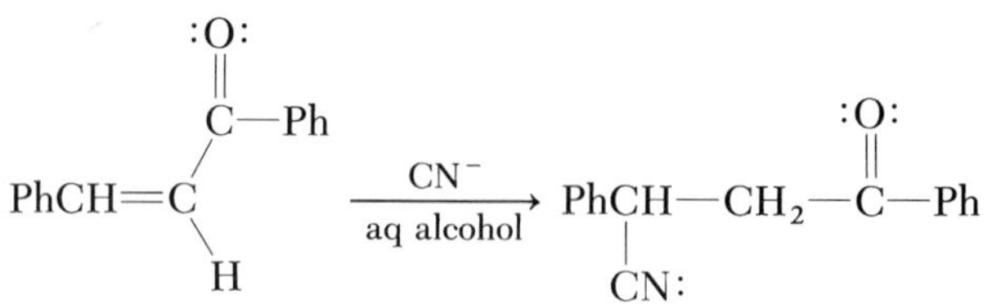

$$PhCH{=}C(H){-}C({=}O){-}Ph \xrightarrow[\text{aq alcohol}]{CN^-} PhCH(CN){-}CH_2{-}C({=}O){-}Ph$$

95% yield

because alkenes are generally inert toward nucleophiles. On the other hand, we know that carbonyl compounds are quite reactive toward nucleophiles—cyanide ion reacts with aldehydes and ketones to form cyanohydrins. Naively, then, we might expect cyanide ion to attack the carbonyl carbon atom of an α,β-unsaturated carbonyl compound rather than the carbon-carbon double bond. However, we find that this does *not* happen. Cyanide ion instead attacks the carbon-carbon double bond, as shown in Figure 23.21.

Many other nucleophiles react in the same way that cyanide ion reacts—they undergo addition to the β-carbon atom of the α,β-unsaturated carbonyl unit. We call such a reaction **conjugate addition.** Additional examples of conjugate addition reactions are shown in Equations 23.29 and 23.30.

Eqn. 23.29

$$(CH_3)_2C{=}CH{-}\overset{\overset{:O:}{\|}}{C}{-}CH_3 \xrightarrow{CH_3NH_2} (CH_3)_2\underset{\underset{:NHCH_3}{|}}{C}{-}CH_2{-}\overset{\overset{:O:}{\|}}{C}{-}CH_3$$

4-methylpent-3-ene-2-one

75% yield
4-methyl-4-methylamino-
2-pentanone

Eqn. 23.30

$$PhCH{=}CH{-}\overset{\overset{:O:}{\|}}{C}{-}Ph \xrightarrow{H_2S} Ph{-}\underset{\underset{:\ddot{S}H}{|}}{CH}{-}CH_2{-}\overset{\overset{:O:}{\|}}{CH}{-}Ph$$

1,3-diphenylprop-
2-ene-1-one

62% yield
1,3-diphenyl-3-oxo-
1-propanethiol

Although these results may appear surprising at first, careful analysis shows that they conform to rational mechanistic considerations. As shown in Figure 23.22, conjugate addition by a nucleophile yields a more stable intermediate anion than would be produced by addition to the carbonyl carbon atom. The intermediate anion produced by conjugate addition can be represented by two resonance structures, while that produced by addition to the carbonyl carbon atom has only one structure.

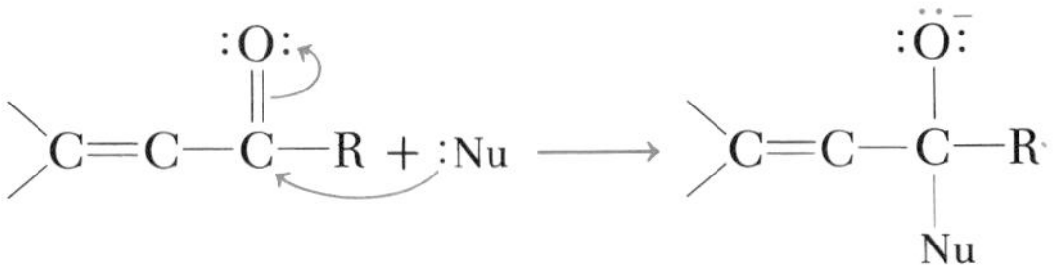

Figure 23.22 Conjugate addition compared to addition at the carbonyl carbon atom. A more stable anion results when the nucleophile adds to the β-carbon atom of the α,β-unsaturated carbonyl linkage than to the carbonyl carbon atom.

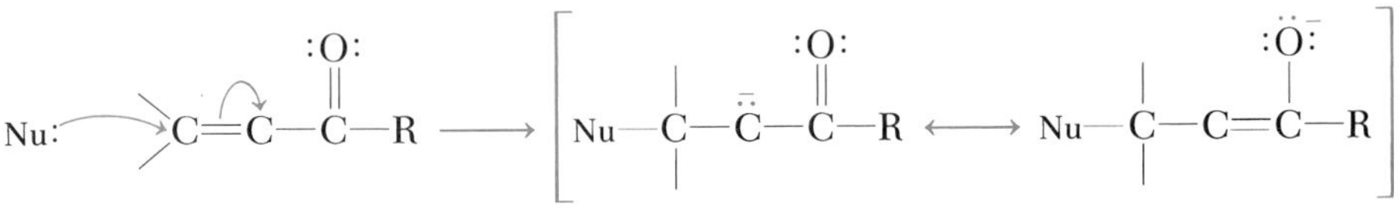

Conjugate addition

$$Nu{:}^- + {>}C{=}C{-}\overset{\overset{:O:}{\|}}{C}{-}R \longrightarrow \left[Nu{-}\overset{|}{\underset{|}{C}}{-}\ddot{\bar{C}}{-}\overset{\overset{:O:}{\|}}{C}{-}R \longleftrightarrow Nu{-}\overset{|}{\underset{|}{C}}{-}C{=}\overset{\overset{:\ddot{O}:^-}{|}}{C}{-}R \right]$$

Addition to the carbonyl carbon

$$>C{=}C{-}\overset{\overset{:O:}{\|}}{C}{-}R + {:}Nu \longrightarrow >C{=}C{-}\overset{\overset{:\ddot{O}:^-}{|}}{\underset{\underset{Nu}{|}}{C}}{-}R$$

PROBLEM 23.50 Attack by the nucleophile on the *oxygen* atom of the carbonyl group of an α,β-unsaturated carbonyl compound would also produce an anion with two resonance structures. Suggest reasons why attack at oxygen does not occur.

When a carbanion is the attacking nucleophile, the conjugate addition process is known as **Michael addition.** Several examples of Michael addition reactions are shown in Equations 23.31–23.33. In general, we find that resonance-stabilized carbanions and lithium dialkylcuprate reagents give predominantly conjugate addition when added to α,β-unsaturated carbonyl compounds.

Eqn. 23.31

$$CH_3-\overset{\overset{\displaystyle :O:}{\|}}{C}-CH=CH_2 \xrightarrow[NaOCH_2CH_3,\ CH_3CH_2OH]{CH_2(CO_2CH_2CH_3)_2} CH_3-\overset{\overset{\displaystyle :O:}{\|}}{C}-CH_2CH_2CH(CO_2CH_2CH_3)_2$$

methyl vinyl ketone

70% yield
ethyl 2-carboethoxy-5-oxohexanoate

Eqn. 23.32

$$PhCH=CH-\overset{\overset{\displaystyle :O:}{\|}}{C}-CH_3 \xrightarrow[(CH_3CH_2)_2NH]{CH_3CH_2CH_2NO_2} \underset{\underset{\displaystyle CH_3CH_2CHNO_2}{|}}{PhCH}-CH_2-\overset{\overset{\displaystyle :O:}{\|}}{C}-CH_3$$

methyl 2-styryl ketone

90% yield
5-nitro-4-phenyl-2-heptanone

Eqn. 23.33

$$\text{3-methylcyclohex-2-enone} \xrightarrow{(CH_3)_2CuLi} \text{3,3-dimethylcyclohexanone (3-}CH_3\text{, 3-}CH_3\text{)}$$

3-methylcyclohex-2-enone

98% yield
3,3-dimethylcyclohexanone

Michael additions to other α,β-unsaturated systems are also observed. Equations 23.34 and 23.35 illustrate Michael additions to α,β-unsaturated esters and nitriles.

Eqn. 23.34

$$\text{2-methylcyclopentanone} \xrightarrow[KOC(CH_3)_3]{H_2C=CHCO_2CH_3} \text{cyclopentanone with 2-}CH_3\text{, 2-}CH_2CH_2CO_2CH_3$$

2-methylcyclopentanone

53% yield
2-methyl-2-(2-carbomethoxy)ethyl-cyclopentanone

Eqn. 23.35

$$Ph-CH(C{\equiv}N{:})-CO_2CH_2CH_3 \xrightarrow[KOH,\ HOC(CH_3)_3]{H_2C{=}CH-C{\equiv}N} Ph-C(C{\equiv}N{:})(CO_2CH_2CH_3)-CH_2CH_2-C{\equiv}N{:}$$

ethyl α-cyanophenylacetate

75% yield
ethyl 2,4-dicyano-2-phenylbutanoate

We should introduce a word of caution here. Not *all* additions to α,β-unsaturated carbonyl compounds are conjugate additions. Sometimes we observe additions to the carbonyl carbon atom. In particular, alkyllithium reagents and lithium aluminum hydride give principally products of addition at the carbonyl carbon atom, as shown in Equations 23.36 and 23.37.

Eqn. 23.36

$$(CH_3)_2C{=}CH-C({=}\ddot{O}{:})-CH_3 \xrightarrow[2.\ H_2O]{1.\ C_6H_5Li} (CH_3)_2C{=}CH-C(:\ddot{O}H)(C_6H_5)-CH_3$$

4-methyl-3-pentene-2-one

65% yield
4-methyl-2-phenyl-3-pentene-2-ol

Eqn. 23.37

$$\text{3-methyl-2-cyclohexenone } (:O:,\ CH_3) \xrightarrow[2.\ \text{aq acid}]{1.\ LiAlH_4,\ (CH_3CH_2)_2O} \text{3-methyl-2-cyclohexenol } (:\ddot{O}H,\ CH_3)$$

3-methyl-2-cyclohexenone

98% yield
3-methyl-2-cyclohexenol

Consider the lithium aluminum hydride reaction. You should recall that this reagent, in effect, serves as a source of nucleophilic hydride ion. It attacks the polar carbonyl linkage at the carbon atom faster than it attacks the carbon-carbon double bond. The thermodynamically less stable anion (from addition of the carbonyl carbon atom) forms faster than the more stable anion (from conjugate addition). If there were a mechanism to establish an equilibrium between the two ions, the more stable ion (from conjugate addition) would predominate. However, hydride, once attached, cannot be displaced, so an equilibrium cannot be established and we observe the formation of the product of *kinetic control*.

Additions of this type give us a useful way of reducing selectively the carbonyl group of an α,β-unsaturated carbonyl compound, leaving the carbon-carbon double bond intact. If we wish to reduce the carbon-carbon double bond, we can use a catalytic hydrogenation method. Under catalytic hydrogenation conditions we can reduce *only* the carbon-carbon double bond, or *both* the carbon-carbon and carbon-oxygen double bonds, depending on the conditions and catalysts used. Examples of these reductions are shown in Figure 23.23.

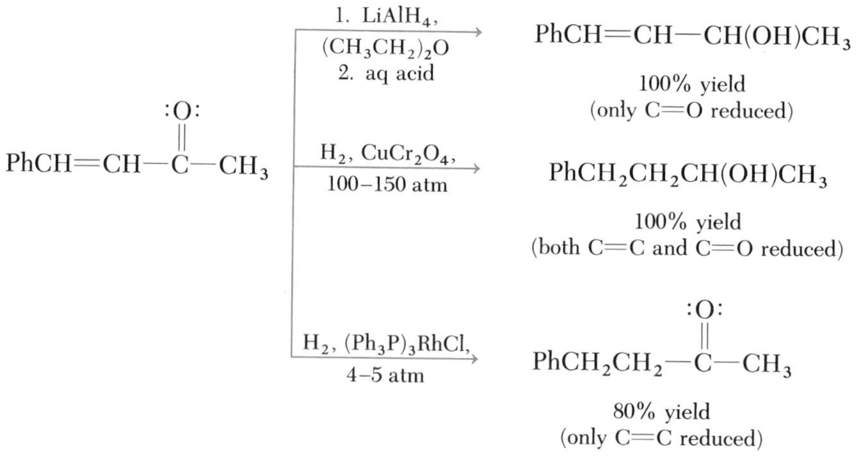

Figure 23.23 Methods for reducing α,β-unsaturated carbonyl compounds. By choosing the proper reaction conditions, we can reduce either of the π bonds of the α,β-unsaturated carbonyl compound or *both* of them.

$$PhCH{=}CH{-}\overset{\overset{\displaystyle :O:}{\|}}{C}{-}CH_3$$

- 1. $LiAlH_4$, $(CH_3CH_2)_2O$; 2. aq acid → $PhCH{=}CH{-}CH(OH)CH_3$ — 100% yield (only C=O reduced)
- H_2, $CuCr_2O_4$, 100–150 atm → $PhCH_2CH_2CH(OH)CH_3$ — 100% yield (both C=C and C=O reduced)
- H_2, $(Ph_3P)_3RhCl$, 4–5 atm → $PhCH_2CH_2{-}\overset{\overset{\displaystyle :O:}{\|}}{C}{-}CH_3$ — 80% yield (only C=C reduced)

PROBLEM 23.51 Consider the addition of HCl gas to $H_2C{=}CH{-}CHO$. The first mechanistic step is protonation of the organic compound to give the more stable of the possible cationic intermediates. What is this cation? What final product do you expect in the overall reaction?

PROBLEM 23.52 Deduce the structure of the product (formula $C_7H_{14}O_2$) you would expect on the addition of methanol and sulfuric acid to $(CH_3)_2C{=}CH{-}\underset{\underset{\displaystyle :O:}{\|}}{C}{-}CH_3$. Show a complete mechanism for the formation of this product.

PROBLEM 23.53 Devise syntheses for each of the following compounds:

a. $Ph{-}\overset{\overset{\displaystyle :O:}{\|}}{C}{-}CH_2{-}\underset{\underset{\displaystyle Ph}{|}}{CH}{-}\overset{\overset{\displaystyle CO_2CH_2CH_3}{|}}{CH}{-}CO_2CH_2CH_3$

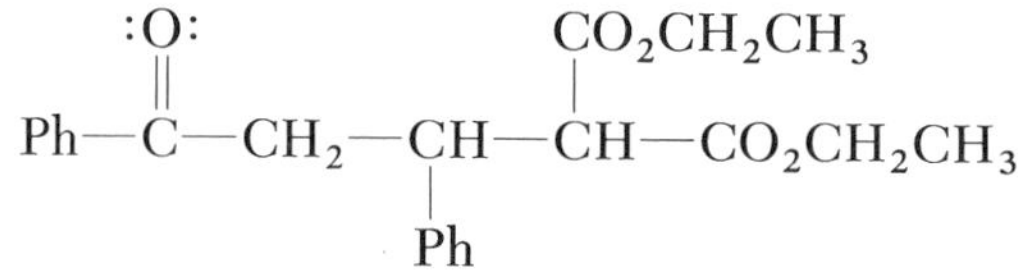

b. 2-substituted cyclopentane-1,3-dione (two ring C=O, :O:) bearing $-CH(CH_3){-}CH_2{-}\underset{\underset{\displaystyle :O:}{\|}}{C}{-}CH_3$

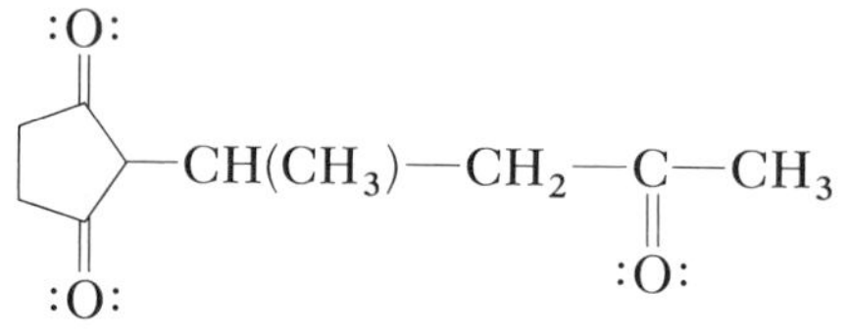

c. cyclopentanone (:O:) bearing $CH_2CO_2CH_3$ at the 3-position

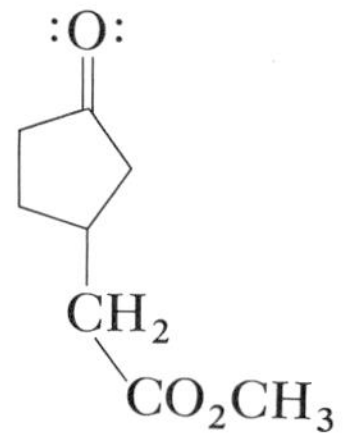

Steps to Solving the Problem

Solution to Problem 23.53a

1. From its structure we recognize that the target material is a 1,5-dicarbonyl compound. A Michael addition can therefore be used in its preparation, so we seek a strategy involving the addition of an enolate to an α,β-unsaturated carbonyl compound.

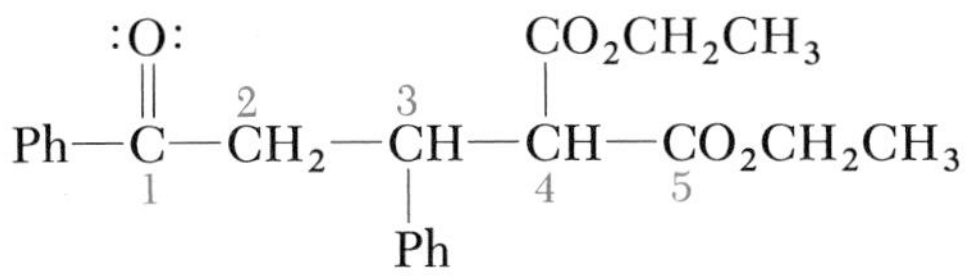

$$\mathrm{Ph{-}\overset{\overset{\displaystyle :O:}{\|}}{\underset{1}{C}}{-}\overset{2}{CH_2}{-}\overset{3}{\underset{\displaystyle Ph}{CH}}{-}\underset{4}{\overset{\overset{\displaystyle CO_2CH_2CH_3}{|}}{CH}}{-}\underset{5}{CO_2CH_2CH_3}}$$

2. Perform a retrosynthetic analysis to find a suitable combination of enolate and α,β-unsaturated carbonyl compound for the synthesis.

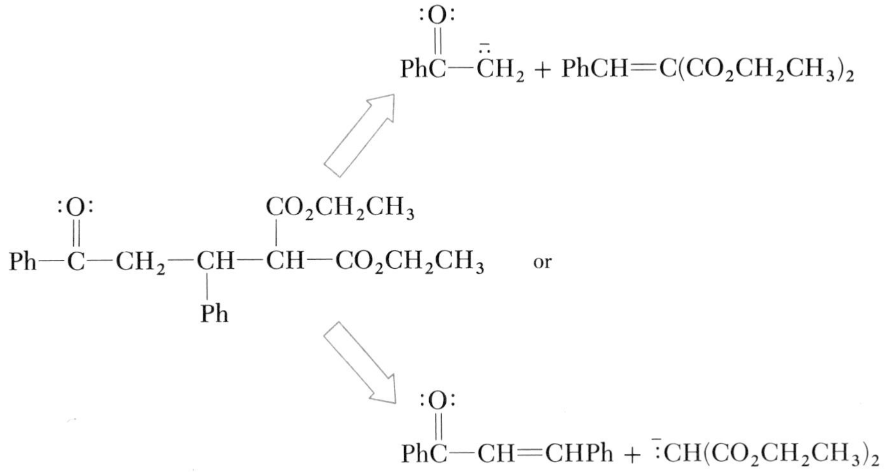

$$\mathrm{Ph{-}\overset{\overset{\displaystyle :O:}{\|}}{C}{-}CH_2{-}\underset{\displaystyle Ph}{CH}{-}\overset{\overset{\displaystyle CO_2CH_2CH_3}{|}}{CH}{-}CO_2CH_2CH_3} \Rightarrow \mathrm{Ph\overset{\overset{\displaystyle :O:}{\|}}{C}{-}\ddot{C}H_2^{-} + PhCH{=}C(CO_2CH_2CH_3)_2}$$

or

$$\Rightarrow \mathrm{Ph\overset{\overset{\displaystyle :O:}{\|}}{C}{-}CH{=}CHPh + {}^{-}\!:CH(CO_2CH_2CH_3)_2}$$

We see that two possible combinations of reagents need to be considered.

3. Comparing the possibilities, we prefer to use the enolate anion from diethyl malonate because it is easily prepared under mild conditions.
4. We can then summarize the overall synthetic procedure as shown below. If PhC(O)CH=CHPh were unavailable, we would of course need to synthesize it from suitable precursors.

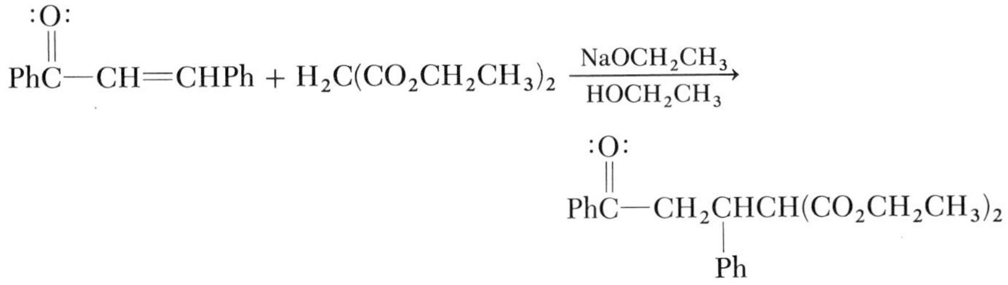

$$\mathrm{Ph\overset{\overset{\displaystyle :O:}{\|}}{C}{-}CH{=}CHPh + H_2C(CO_2CH_2CH_3)_2 \xrightarrow[\text{HOCH}_2\text{CH}_3]{\text{NaOCH}_2\text{CH}_3} Ph\overset{\overset{\displaystyle :O:}{\|}}{C}{-}CH_2\underset{\displaystyle Ph}{CH}CH(CO_2CH_2CH_3)_2}$$

Earlier in this chapter we saw enamines acting as carbon nucleophiles. Enamines also add in a Michael sense to α,β-unsaturated carbonyl compounds. Hydrolysis of the reaction mixture yields a 1,5-carbonyl compound, as shown in the example in Equation 23.38.

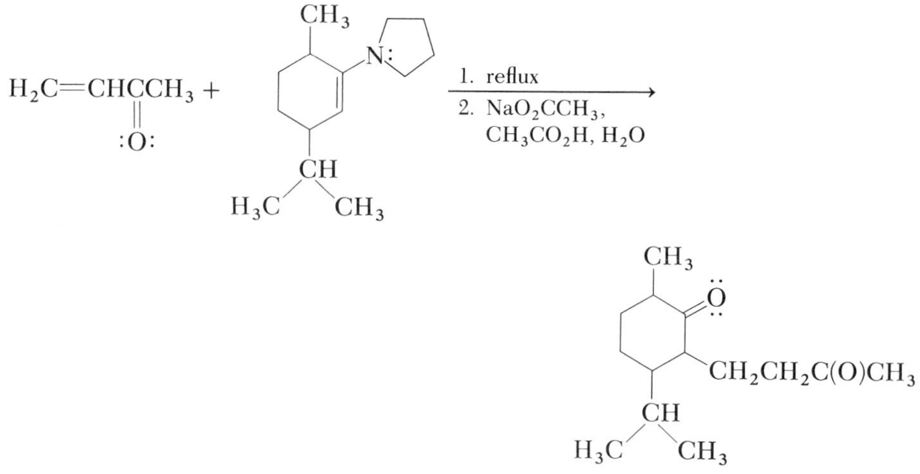

Eqn. 23.38

$$H_2C{=}CHCCH_3 \text{ (C=O)} + \text{enamine (pyrrolidine, } CH_3, CH(CH_3)_2\text{)} \xrightarrow[\text{2. } NaO_2CCH_3,\ CH_3CO_2H,\ H_2O]{\text{1. reflux}} \text{product } CH_2CH_2C(O)CH_3$$

66% yield

PROBLEM 23.54 Give the complete mechanism for the reaction of Equation 23.38 using the curved-arrow formalism.

23.11 The Robinson Annulation

Michael addition plays a crucial role in a ring-forming reaction known as the **Robinson annulation.** An example of this important process is shown in Equation 23.39. The Robinson annulation has been widely used as a synthetic strategy for constructing the six-membered ring components of natural products such as steroids.

Eqn. 23.39

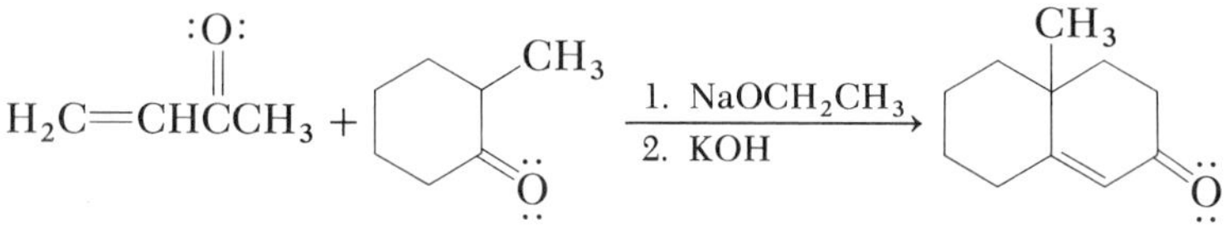

$$H_2C{=}CHCCH_3 \text{ (:O:)} + \text{2-methylcyclohexanone} \xrightarrow[\text{2. KOH}]{\text{1. } NaOCH_2CH_3} \text{bicyclic enone } (CH_3)$$

40% yield

The Robinson annulation essentially consists of a Michael addition followed by an intramolecular aldol (or related) condensation. The base needed to generate an enolate ion for the Michael addition also promotes the condensation reaction. The mechanism of the overall reaction shown in Equation 23.39 is given below.

MECHANISM OF REACTION

The Robinson Annulation

Step 1 Generation of an enolate ion

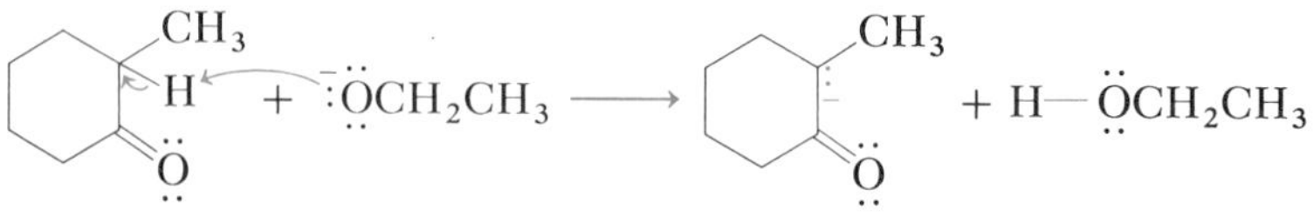

$$\text{2-methylcyclohexanone (H, } CH_3\text{)} + {:}\ddot{O}CH_2CH_3 \longrightarrow \text{enolate } (CH_3) + H{-}\ddot{O}CH_2CH_3$$

Step 2 Michael addition

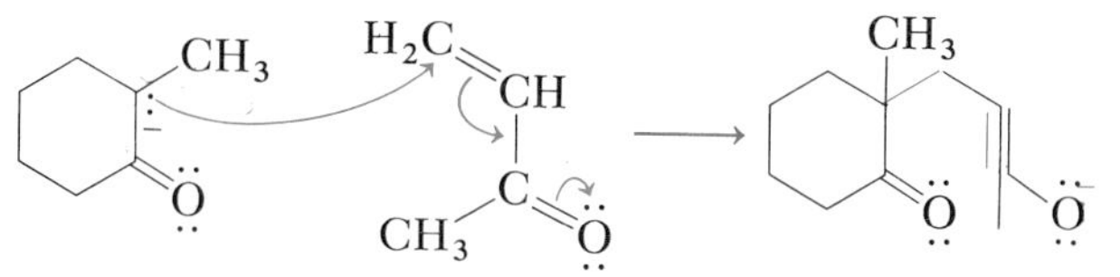

CH_3 H_2C CH CH_3 C O → CH_3 O O

Step 3 Proton transfer through solution and re-enolization

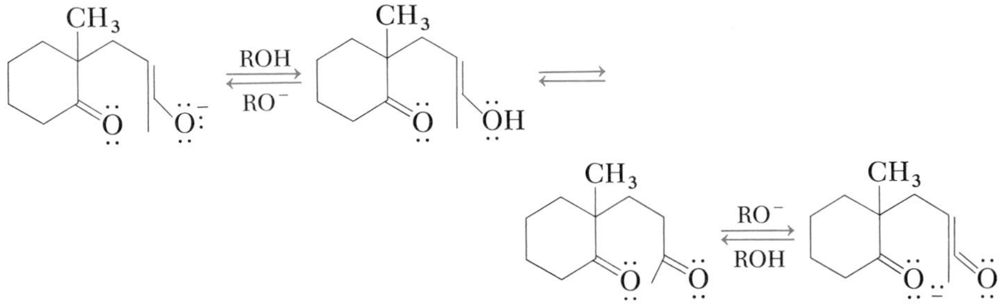

CH_3 O O: ROH / RO^- CH_3 O OH ⇌

CH_3 O O RO^- / ROH CH_3 O O

Step 4 Intramolecular aldol addition

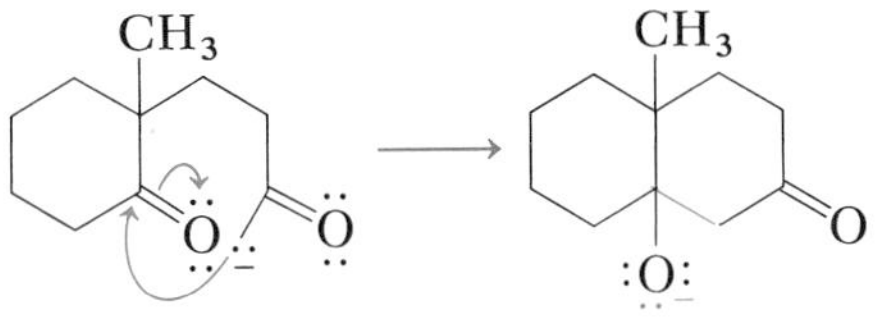

CH_3 O O → CH_3 :O: O

Step 5 Protonation from solvent and dehydration

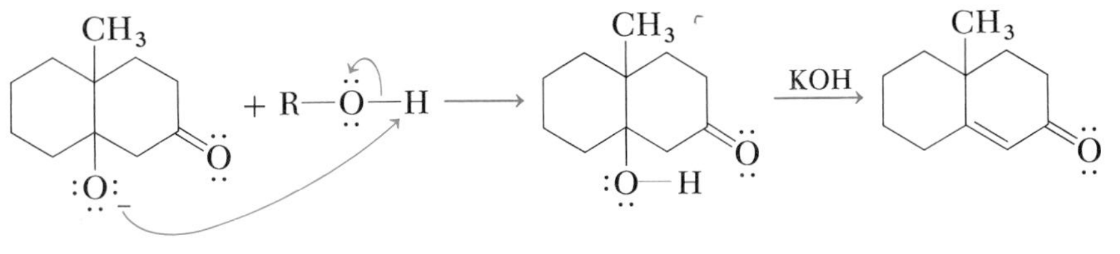

CH_3 O :O: + R—O—H → CH_3 O :O—H KOH → CH_3 O

PROBLEM 23.55 Predict the product of the Robinson annulation reaction that occurs when cyclohexanone and PhCH=CH—C(=O)—CH_3 are treated with sodium amide.

PROBLEM 23.56 A mixture of $(CH_3)_2C{=}C(CH_3)C(O)CH_3$ and diethyl malonate is treated with sodium ethoxide. After initial enolate formation and Michael addition, a Dieckmann reaction occurs to give a 95% yield of a product of formula $C_{12}H_{18}O_4$. Suggest a structure for this product.

PROBLEM 23.57 Suggest a synthesis for the compound shown below using the Robinson annulation procedure.

Summary

- Carbonyl compounds and their derivatives are a rich source of nucleophilic carbon.
- Enamines and enolate ions act as sources of nucleophilic carbon, a phenomenon we can relate to their bonding. We can draw resonance structures for them with a formal negative charge on carbon.
- To convert an aldehyde or ketone *completely* to its enolate ion, we must use a very strong, nonnucleophilic base. Lithium diisopropylamide (LDA) is a common choice for such a base. Having formed the enolate ion, we can use it as a nucleophile toward haloalkanes and other substances prone to nucleophilic attack.
- Some carbonyl compounds (e.g., β-ketoesters and diesters of malonic acid) are unusually acidic. They are converted to enolate ions by much milder bases than LDA. The malonic ester synthesis and the acetoacetic ester synthesis are based on their ease of conversion to enolate ions.
- The malonic ester synthesis provides a general route to substituted acetic acids, and the acetoacetic ester synthesis is a general route to methyl ketones.
- If we treat an aldehyde or a ketone with a base that does *not* convert it completely to its enolate ion, we find that the enolate ion that is formed reacts with the parent carbonyl compound. The result is an aldol addition or aldol condensation reaction. This type of reaction is also useful in syntheses.
- *Intramolecular* reactions of compounds containing two carbonyl groups lead to cyclic products.
- Reactions similar to the aldol condensation are observed with a variety of other carbonyl-related compounds. Many of these reactions have names—the Claisen, Dieckmann, Perkin, and Knoevenagel reactions.
- α,β-Unsaturated carbonyl compounds react readily with many nucleophiles. Often addition takes place at the β-carbon atom of such molecules. We call such reactions *conjugate addition*. If a carbon nucleophile is adding in this manner, the reaction is called a *Michael addition*.
- The Robinson annulation is an important method for preparing cyclic compounds. It consists of a Michael addition followed by an intramolecular aldol condensation.

Terms to Remember

enol
enolate ion
aldol condensation
malonic ester
acetoacetic ester
Mannich reaction
aldol addition reaction
β-hydroxyaldehyde
β-hydroxyketone
α,β-unsaturated carbonyl compound
crossed aldol reaction
Claisen-Schmidt condensation
intramolecular aldol condensation
retro-aldol reaction
Claisen condensation
Dieckmann condensation
Perkin condensation
Knoevenagel condensation
conjugate addition
Michael addition
Robinson annulation

Reactions of Synthetic Utility

198. (enamine) $\xrightarrow{RX}$ (iminium salt, X^-, R) $\xrightarrow{\text{aq acid}}$ (ketone with R) — 23.3

199. (A-CO-CH₂-H) $\xrightarrow[\text{2. RX}]{\text{1. LDA}}$ (A-CO-CH₂-R) — 23.4

$A = H, R', OR'$

200. $H_2C(CO_2R)_2 \xrightarrow[\text{2. R'X; 3. aq acid, heat}]{\text{1. base}} R'CH_2CO_2H$ — 23.5

201. (β-keto ester, OR) $\xrightarrow[\text{2. R'X; 3. aq acid, heat}]{\text{1. base}}$ (methyl ketone with R′) — 23.5

202. $R_2NH + H_2CO + R'C(=O)CH \longrightarrow R'C(=O)CCH_2NR_2$ — 23.6

203. $2\ {>}CH{-}C(=O)A \xrightarrow[\text{cool}]{\text{base}} {>}C(C(=O)A){-}C(A)(OH){-}CH{<}$ — 23.7

$A = H, R, OR$

204. $2\ RCH_2{-}C(=O)A \xrightarrow[\text{heat}]{\text{base}} R{-}C(C(=O)A){=}C(A){-}CH_2{-}$ — 23.7

$A = H, R, OR$

205. $RCH_2C(=O)OC(=O)CH_2R + ArCHO \xrightarrow[\text{2. aq acid}]{\text{1. } R'CH_2COO^-} ArCH{=}C(COOH)R$ — 23.9

206. $ArCHO + H_2C(CO_2R)_2 \xrightarrow{Ar'COOH,\ R''_2NH} ArCH{=}C(CO_2R)_2$ — 23.9

207. (α,β-unsaturated carbonyl, A) $+ :Nu \xrightarrow[\text{workup}]{\text{acid}}$ (β-:Nu carbonyl, A) — 23.10

$A = H, R, OR$; $Nu = CN^-, R_2NH, R_2CuLi$, enolate

Additional Problems

23.58 From each pair of compounds, choose the one with the indicated property, and explain your choice.

a. is racemized when placed in basic solution: (*R*)-4-methyl-2-hexanone or (*R*)-3-methyl-2-hexanone
b. forms an enamine when treated with a ketone: diethylmethylamine or diethylamine
c. has the higher frequency carbonyl stretching band in the IR spectrum: cyclohexanone or 2-cyclohexenone
d. has the higher frequency carbonyl stretching band in the IR spectrum: *p*-nitroacetophenone or *p*-methoxyacetophenone
e. is more acidic in aqueous solution: nitromethane or nitrobenzene
f. is more acidic in aqueous solution: 2-butanone or 2,4-pentanedione
g. is more acidic in aqueous solution:

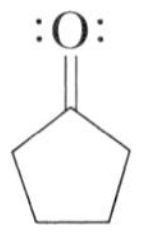

:O: or :O:

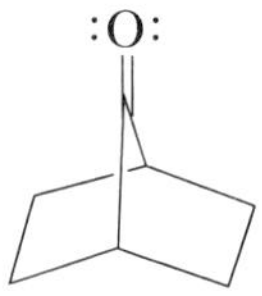

h. is an α,β-unsaturated carbonyl compound: 5-phenyl-2-hexenal or 5-phenyl-3-hexenal

23.59 Give the structure of each of the following:

a. a chiral substance of formula $C_7H_{14}O$ that is not racemized when placed in aqueous basic solution but gives a yellow precipitate when treated with an aqueous solution containing KOH and I_2.
b. a compound of formula $C_{10}H_{16}O_2$ that yields the compound shown below via an intramolecular aldol condensation on treatment with aqueous NaOH.

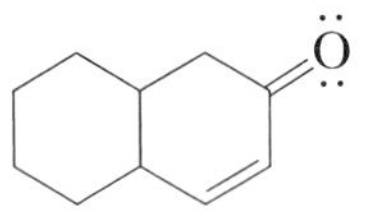

:O:

c. a compound of formula $C_{19}H_{18}O_2$ that forms upon heating a mixture of Ph—C(=O)—C(=O)—Ph and 3-pentanone in KOH/ethanol solution. (*Hint:* The product is formed by two aldol additions and one dehydration.)

23.60 Draw structures of the products (there may be more than one) of each of the following reactions.

a. a base-catalyzed mixed aldol condensation of cyclohexanone and 2-propanone
b. a base-catalyzed mixed aldol condensation between isobutyraldehyde and formaldehyde
c. an intramolecular aldol condensation of 2,8-nonanedione
d. a Claisen condensation of ethyl propanoate
e. a mixed Claisen condensation of ethyl formate with 2-propanone
f. a mixed Claisen condensation of ethyl oxalate with cyclohexanone
g. a reaction in which an enamine derived from 3-pentanone is allowed to react with methyl acrylate (methyl propenoate) and the resulting intermediate is hydrolyzed to a ketoester
h. a reaction in which ethyl phenylacetate (ethyl phenylethanoate) and diethyl malonate are allowed to react in the presence of sodium ethoxide
i. a reaction in which *p*-nitrobenzaldehyde is allowed to react with acetic anhydride and sodium acetate
j. a reaction in which cyclohexanone is treated with nitroethane and sodium methoxide

23.61 Propose synthetic routes for the preparation of each of the following:

a. 4-hydroxy-2-butanone by an aldol condensation
b. 4-methyl-2-pentanone from ethyl acetoacetate

c. 4-phenyl-2-butanol from benzaldehyde and 2-propanone
d. 2-methylcyclopentanone from cyclopentanol
e. 5-hydroxy-2-pentanone from ethyl acetoacetate
f. 2-methylpropanoic acid from diethyl malonate
g. γ-butyrolactone from diethyl malonate
h. 3-methylcyclohexanone from 2-cyclohexenone
i. 1-phenyl-1,4-pentanedione from ethyl acetoacetate

23.62 Give the structures of compounds *A*–*W*.

a. Compound *A* (C_3H_6O) reacts with *B* ($C_{13}H_{10}O$) in the presence of NaOH in a mixed aldol condensation to give *C* ($C_{16}H_{14}O$), which exhibits the following ^{1}H NMR signals: δ 7.2, 10H, singlet; δ 2.3, 3H, singlet; δ 5.3, 1H, singlet.

b. 2-propanone is treated with barium hydroxide followed by acid workup of the reaction to give *D* ($C_6H_{10}O$). In turn, *D* reacts with chlorine in aqueous sodium hydroxide solution to give *E* ($C_5H_8O_2$) along with chloroform. Compound *E* reacts with hydrogen gas in the presence of platinum catalyst to form *F* ($C_5H_{10}O_2$).

c. Ethyl acetoacetate, on treatment with sodium ethoxide followed by the addition of 1-bromo-2-propanone yields *G* ($C_9H_{12}O_4$). On treatment with aqueous sodium hydroxide followed by heating with aqueous acid, *G* yields *H* ($C_6H_{10}O_2$). Finally, on treatment with sodium ethoxide, *H* yields *I* (C_6H_8O).

d. In the presence of an acid catalyst 3-pentanone reacts with pyrrolidine [a cyclic amine of formula $(CH_2)_4NH$] to form *J* ($C_9H_{17}N$). Compound *J* in turn reacts with methyl vinyl ketone (after aqueous workup) to form *K* ($C_9H_{16}O_2$). Finally, *K* reacts with sodium ethoxide to yield *L* ($C_9H_{14}O$).

e. Methyl propenoate reacts with methylamine to form *M* ($C_9H_{17}O_2N$). Compound *M* in turn reacts with sodium methoxide to form *N* ($C_8H_{13}NO_3$).

f. A mixture of methyl vinyl ketone and ethyl acetoacetate reacts in the presence of sodium ethoxide to yield *O* ($C_{10}H_{16}O_4$). On treatment with aqueous acid followed by heating, *O* yields *P* ($C_7H_{12}O$). On treatment with $NaBH_4$, *P* forms *Q* ($C_7H_{16}O_2$).

g. Compound *R* ($C_5H_{11}Br$) reacts with cyanide ion to form S ($C_6H_{11}N$), which on heating with aqueous acid yields *T* ($C_6H_{12}O_2$). Heating compound *T* with ethanol in the presence of an acid catalyst forms *U* ($C_8H_{16}O_2$). Compound *U* does not undergo a Claisen condensation.

h. 2-Methylpropanal on treatment with formaldehyde and base yields *V* ($C_5H_{10}O_2$). On treatment with sodium cyanide in the presence of an acid catalyst and workup by refluxing with aqueous acid, *V* yields *W* ($C_6H_{10}O_3$).

23.63 Propose a reasonable mechanism to account for the fact that 3-butenal is isomerized to 2-butenal when treated with base. In light of your answer, decide which of the substances *X* or *Y* would *not* isomerize to Z on treatment with base.

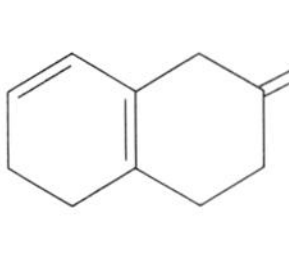

X 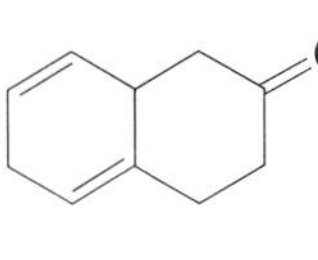 Y 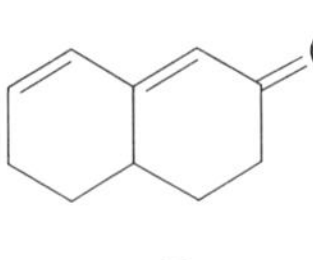 Z

23.64 Propose mechanisms to account for each of the following transformations.

a. Nitriles of the type $RCH_2C{\equiv}N$, when treated with sodium hydride followed by aqueous acid, are converted to substances of the structure

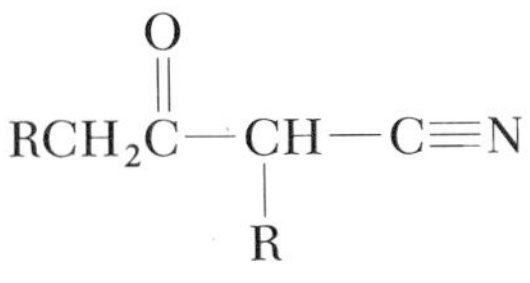

$$RCH_2\overset{\overset{\displaystyle O}{\|}}{C}-\underset{\underset{\displaystyle R}{|}}{CH}-C{\equiv}N$$

b. The ketoester *AA* is isomerized to *BB* when treated with sodium ethoxide in ethanol.

:O: CH_3 $CO_2CH_2CH_3$ $\xrightarrow[HOCH_2CH_3]{NaOCH_2CH_3}$ H_3C :O: $CO_2CH_2CH_3$

AA *BB*

(*Hint:* No methyl migration occurs here. The correct mechanism involves an opening and closing of the ring through a series of equilibria.)

c. Benzaldehyde and ethyl acetoacetate react in the presence of a base to give *CC*.

:O: :O: $CH_3CH_2\ddot{O}C$ Ph CH_3 $CO_2CH_2CH_3$

CC

d. $PhCH_2CPh$ (:O:) + $(CH_3)_2C{=}CH{-}C{-}CH_3$ (:O:) $\xrightarrow{NaOCH_2CH_3}$:O: H_3C H_3C Ph Ph

e. H_3C H C=C H $CO_2C_2H_5$ + $Ph\ddot{N}H\ddot{N}H_2$ $\longrightarrow$ H H_3C :Ö: N–N H Ph

23.65 Provide structures for the compounds *DD–JJ* based on the information given.

Compound *DD* ($C_6H_{10}O_4$) is neutral to litmus. On alkaline hydrolysis of *DD* followed by workup with mineral acid, it is converted to *EE* ($C_4H_6O_4$). Compound *EE* has a broad IR absorption band from 2500–3500 cm^{-1}. On heating, *EE* readily yields *FF* ($C_4H_4O_3$). None of the substances *DD–FF* decolorize aqueous potassium permanganate solution. Condensation of *DD* with ethyl formate in the presence of sodium ethoxide yields *GG* ($C_7H_{10}O_5$). When *GG* is boiled with dilute aqueous sulfuric acid, it is converted to a carboxylic acid *HH* and carbon dioxide is evolved. Treatment of *HH* with Tollens' reagent gives metallic silver and carboxylic acid *EE*. Reduction of *HH* with sodium borohydride yields carboxylic acid *II*, which has a molecular weight of 104 g/mole. When heated, *II* forms *JJ* ($C_4H_6O_2$). The ^1H NMR spectrum of *JJ* appears moderately complex because of overlapping signals. It can be interpreted, however, as being composed of two triplets (each of relative area 1) and a pentuplet (also of relative area 1).

23.66 Give the structures of compounds *KK—NN* in the following sequence.

Treatment of benzaldehyde with propanoic anhydride in the presence of sodium propanoate yields *KK*. *LL* is formed on treatment of *KK* with hydrogen over a platinum catalyst. *LL* reacts further with thionyl chloride ($SOCl_2$) to yield *MM*. Compound *MM* reacts in the presence of aluminum chloride to form *NN* ($C_{10}H_{10}O$).

23.67 Provide the missing reagents, intermediates, or products (*OO*–*RR*) in the following reaction scheme.

$$PhCHO + (CH_3)_2C{=}O \xrightarrow[HOCH_2CH_3]{NaOCH_2CH_3} OO \xrightarrow{PP} PhCH{=}CH{-}CH(OH){-}CH_3 \xrightarrow{30\%\ aq\ H_2SO_4} QQ\ (C_{10}H_{10}) \xrightarrow[\text{heat (Diels-Alder reaction)}]{RR} \text{2-phenylcyclohex-3-enecarbaldehyde (Ph, CHO)}$$

23.68 Provide structures for each of the materials *SS*–*ZZ* in the following sequence.

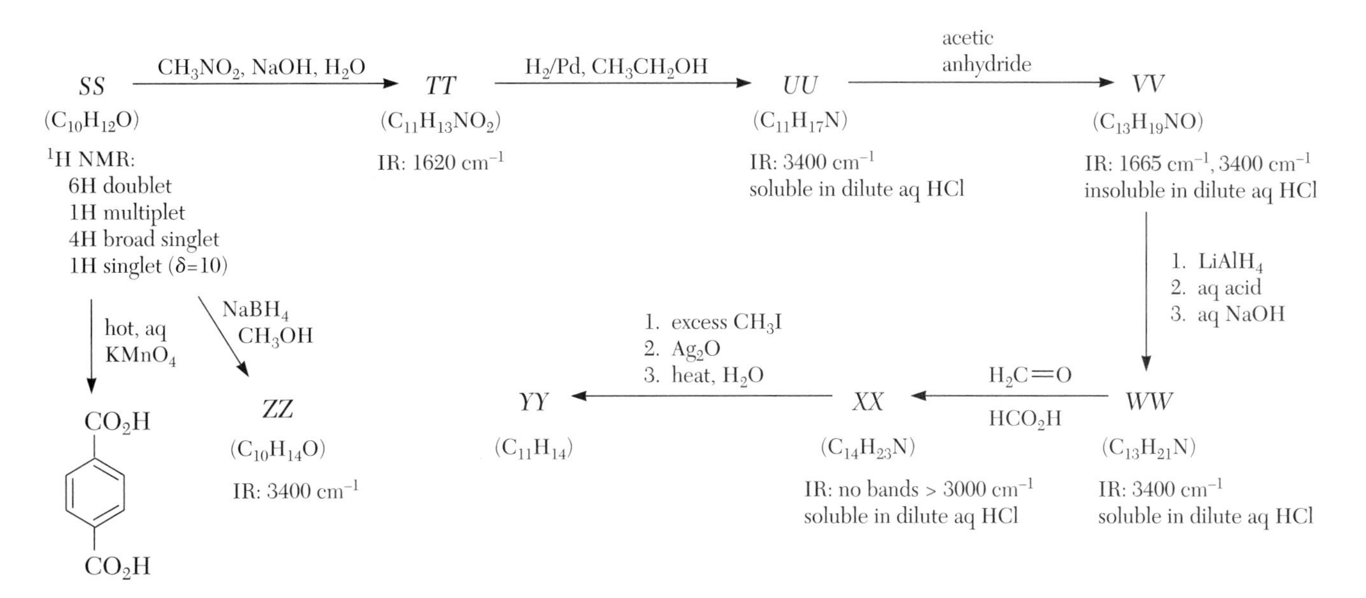

24 CHAPTER Carbohydrates

24.1 Introduction

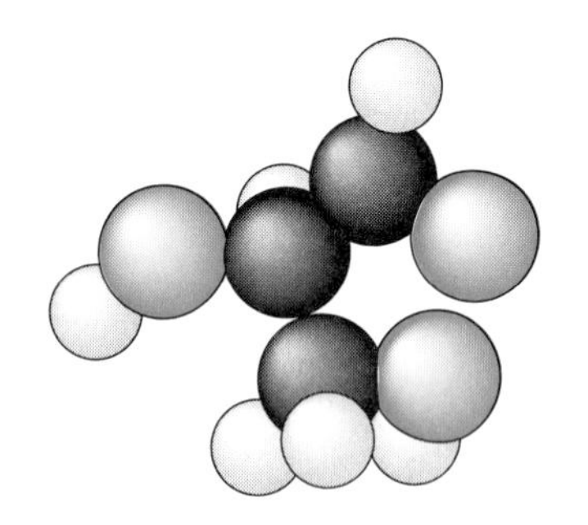

SIGNIFICANCE

Carbohydrates are one of the most abundant and significant types of biological compounds. They serve as one of the fundamental food groups and are a major source of calories for most animals. In the body they are broken down into simpler molecules through a sequence of metabolic reactions known as **catabolism.** Catabolism allows the energy of the chemical bonds of carbohydrates to be used in other life processes. It is a major source of the energy needed to drive these chemical processes.

Carbohydrates play another role in living organisms. The structural elements of the walls of most cells are composed of large carbohydrate molecules, and some of these carbohydrates also serve as sites of specific recognition (receptor sites) on the cell wall surfaces to regulate interaction with other cells and molecules.

In recent years synthetic organic chemists have increasingly turned to naturally occurring carbohydrates as convenient sources of optically active reagents. Such carbohydrates serve as starting materials for synthesizing chiral organic molecules of highly complex structure or as reagents for the purification of organic compounds.

In discussing carbohydrates, we move to a new level in our excursion through organic chemistry. So far we have usually been concerned with the chemical and physical characteristics conferred on a molecule by a single functional group. Carbohydrate molecules contain at least *two* (and often several more) functional groups. The chemistry of a particular carbohydrate molecule depends on the interrelationship among these functional groups as well as on the molecule's interactions with other molecules.

Thus the organic chemistry of carbohydrates is a complex matter, and the full realm of chemistry associated with carbohydrates has by no means been explored. (This chapter provides only a brief introduction to this vast topic.) To understand the chemistry of carbohydrate molecules we must pay very close attention to the details of their structure and stereochemistry. However, we should not look at the structural complexity of carbohydrates as a negative factor. It is this very complexity that allows carbohydrates to serve both as highly specific reagents in biological processes and as construction materials in organic synthesis.

FUNDAMENTALS OF STRUCTURE

The name *carbohydrate* was coined because the general formula for most members of this class, $C_n(H_2O)_n$, suggested that they were hydrates of carbon.

SPECIAL TOPIC

Biological Carbohydrates of Nonlinear Structure

Although they are not as common as the carbohydrates of linear structure, a few carbohydrates of nonlinear structure do occur in biological systems. Some, such as D-apiose, are similar to the linear carbohydrates in that they have a single carbonyl group and a hydroxyl group at each of the remaining carbon atoms; however, their carbon chains are branched. There are also cyclic carbohydrates such as *myo*-inositol in which no carbonyl group is present. There is a secondary hydroxyl group at each carbon atom.

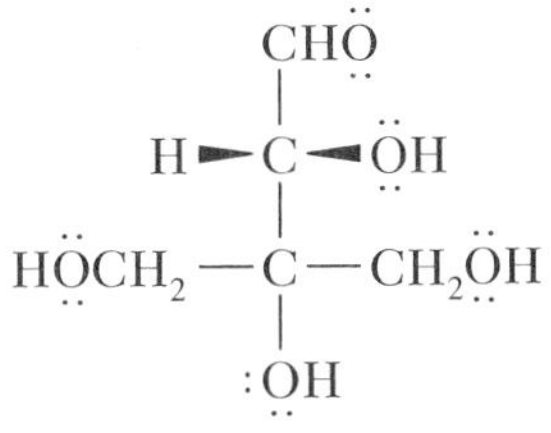

CHO
H—C—OH
$HOCH_2$—C—CH_2OH
OH

D-apiose

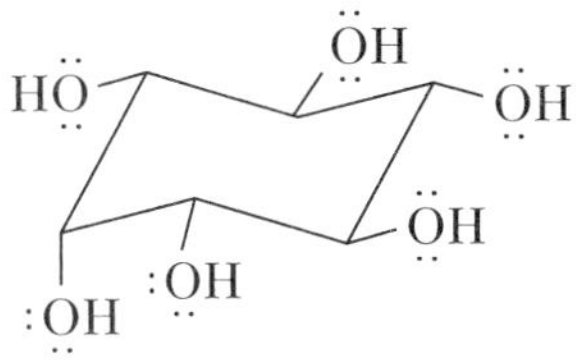

myo-inositol

myo-Inositol (in phosphorylated form) has been implicated as a species of major significance for the intracellular transmission of biological signals and calcium ion binding.

However, structural studies quickly established that carbohydrates are *not* hydrates in the sense that inorganic compounds are hydrates. That is, they contain no intact water molecules. Carbohydrates are actually polyhydroxy-aldehydes, polyhydroxyketones, or molecules with related structures.

The carbon atoms of a carbohydrate are usually joined in a continuous sequence without branching. We use the term *straight-chain* or *linear carbohydrate* for such structures. The common straight-chain simple carbohydrates fall into the two structural categories shown in Figure 24.1. In one category the carbonyl group is an aldehyde. We refer to such compounds generically as **aldoses,** the *-ose* ending indicating that the compound is a carbohydrate and the *ald-* prefix indicating that an aldehyde group is present. The other category contains a ketone function as its carbonyl group. We classify these compounds as **ketoses.**

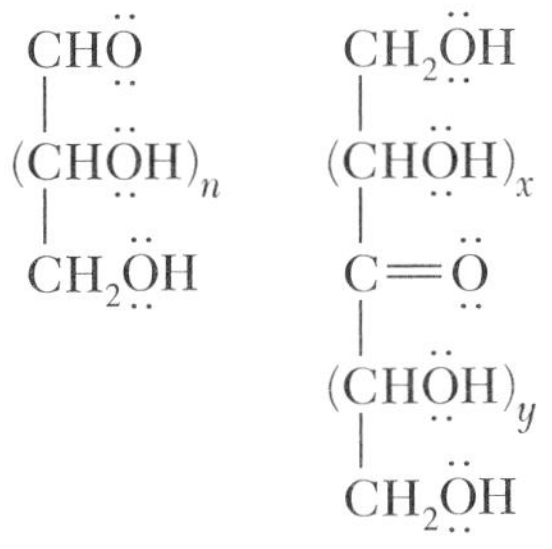

We also classify carbohydrates according to the number of carbon atoms they contain using the generic terms shown in Table 24.1.

A major factor in the structural complexity of the linear carbohydrates arises from the fact they contain stereogenic carbon atoms equal in number to the number of secondary hydroxyl groups present. Since there are n stereogenic carbon atoms in an aldose (an aldose contains $n + 2$ total carbon atoms; see Figure 24.1) and no possibility of a plane of symmetry, there will be 2^n stereoisomers for each category of aldose.

aldose	ketose
CHO	CH_2OH
$(CHOH)_n$	$(CHOH)_x$
CH_2OH	C=O
	$(CHOH)_y$
	CH_2OH

Figure 24.1 General structures of aldoses and ketoses. In an aldose, one of the hydroxyl groups is primary and the remainder are secondary. In a ketose, two hydroxyl groups are primary and the remainder are secondary.

Table 24.1 Classification Terms for Carbohydrates

Carbon Atoms	General Term	Aldehyde	Ketone
3	triose	aldotriose	ketotriose
4	tetrose	aldotetrose	ketotetrose
5	pentose	aldopentose	ketopentose
6	hexose	aldohexose	ketohexose
7	heptose	aldoheptose	ketoheptose
⋮	⋮	⋮	⋮

PROBLEM 24.1 For each structural type listed below, tell how many stereoisomers can exist. Also, tell which are enantiomers and which are diastereoisomers.

a. the aldotetroses **b.** the aldopentoses

PROBLEM 24.2 Give the structure of a ketose that is not optically active.

Steps to Solving the Problem

Solution to Problem 24.1a

1. Draw the general structure for an aldotetrose. The generic aldotetrose is represented by:

$$\begin{array}{l} \mathrm{CHO} \\ | \\ \mathrm{CHOH} \\ | \\ \mathrm{CHOH} \\ | \\ \mathrm{CH_2OH} \end{array}$$

2. Determine the number of stereogenic atoms present. There are two secondary hydroxyl groups and two stereogenic carbon centers as well. Furthermore, there can be no plane of symmetry. Thus there are 2^2 (or four) possible optical isomers.
3. Draw out the structures in greater detail and thus verify that there are two pairs of enantiomers, each pair being diastereoisomeric with the other pair.

$$\begin{array}{cccc} \mathrm{CHO} & \mathrm{CHO} & \mathrm{CHO} & \mathrm{CHO} \\ \mathrm{H{-}C{-}OH} & \mathrm{HO{-}C{-}H} & \mathrm{HO{-}C{-}H} & \mathrm{H{-}C{-}OH} \\ \mathrm{H{-}C{-}OH} & \mathrm{HO{-}C{-}H} & \mathrm{H{-}C{-}OH} & \mathrm{HO{-}C{-}H} \\ \mathrm{CH_2OH} & \mathrm{CH_2OH} & \mathrm{CH_2OH} & \mathrm{CH_2OH} \end{array}$$

enantiomeric pair (first two); enantiomeric pair (last two)

diastereoisomers

Later we will consider the matter of carbohydrate stereochemistry in greater detail.

We often classify carbohydrates and related molecules as **monosaccharides, disaccharides,** and so forth. These terms describe the complexity of the compound. For example, in a disaccharide molecule there are two separate carbohydrate units (monosaccharide units) linked by an acetal or ketal linkage. If many monosaccharide units are so linked, the molecule is a **polysaccharide.** We will provide examples and discuss the formation and properties of such compounds after surveying the simplest carbohydrates, the monosaccharides.

24.2 The Natural Occurrence of Linear Carbohydrates

Biological systems provide many examples of carbohydrates of the types listed in Table 24.1. Several monosaccharides of natural importance are shown in Figure 24.2 with their common names and classifications. In some cases the naturally occurring form is a derivative form of the parent carbohydrate.

STEREOCHEMISTRY IN NATURALLY OCCURRING CARBOHYDRATES

The structures in Figure 24.2 are drawn to emphasize an important stereochemical feature that is common to all but the ketotriose. Notice that each structure is oriented so that the carbon chain is shown *vertically*. Furthermore, the structure is drawn so that the carbonyl carbon is at the top (or as close as possible to the top) of this vertical chain. Finally, bonds to substituents along the chain are shown horizontally and have a direction *out* of the plane in which they are drawn. This style of depicting carbohydrate structures is standard for organic chemists.

Figure 24.2 Naturally occurring carbohydrates. Selected aldoses and ketoses containing three to seven carbon atoms are shown. D-Glucose is the most important of the simple carbohydrates.

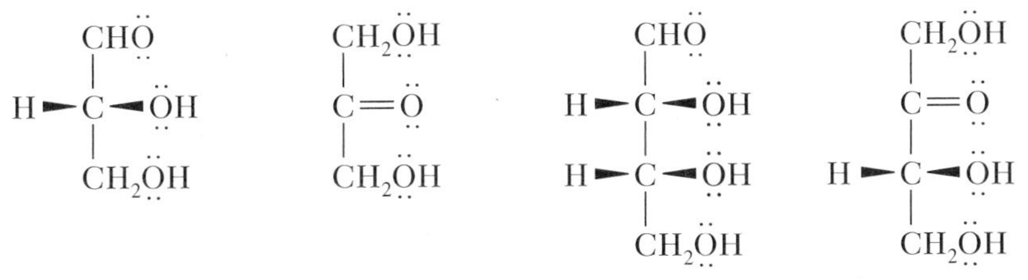

D-glyceraldehyde (an aldotriose)

dihydroxyacetone (the *only* ketotriose)

D-erythrose (an aldotetrose)

D-erythulose (a ketotetrose)

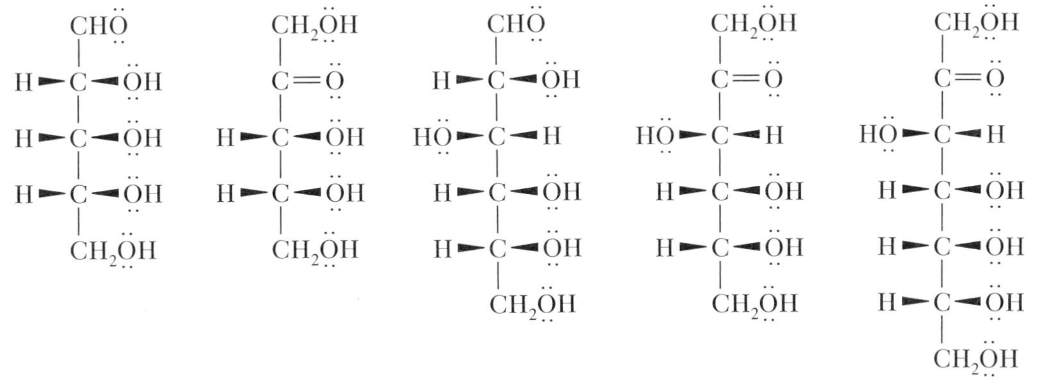

D-ribose (an aldopentose)

D-ribulose (a ketopentose)

D-glucose (an aldohexose)

D-fructose (a ketohexose)

D-sedoheptulose (a ketoheptose)

Figure 24.3 The enantiomers of glyceraldehyde. The dextrorotatory enantiomer is the parent member of the D family of carbohydrates.

CHO / H—C—OH / CH_2OH CHO / HO—C—H / CH_2OH

D-(+)-glyceraldehyde   L-(−)-glyceraldehyde

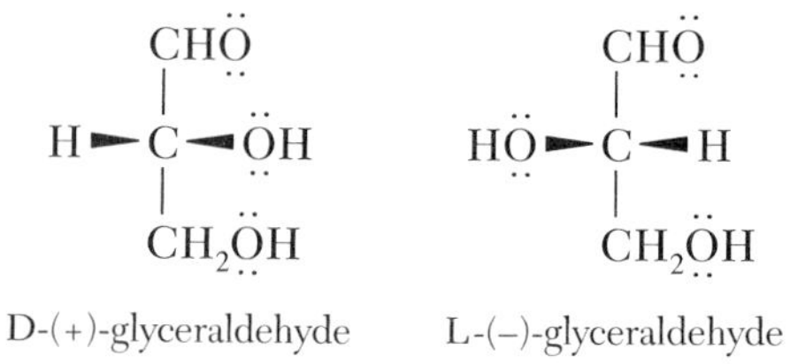

The common stereochemical feature we wish to emphasize concerns the stereogenic carbon atom that is furthest from the carbonyl group. For all of the molecules in Figure 24.2 (except the ketotriose, which has no stereogenic carbon atom) this stereogenic carbon atom is next to the bottom of the chain. (The very bottom carbon atom is not stereogenic because it does not have four different groups attached to it.) Notice that in all of the molecules shown the hydroxyl group attached to this bottom stereogenic carbon atom is drawn to the *right*. According to the *R*/*S* notation system we classify this stereogenic carbon atom as *R*. Most naturally occurring carbohydrates have an *R* configuration at this stereocenter. We say that such compounds belong to the *D family* of carbohydrates. If the configuration at this stereocenter is S, we say that the compound belongs to the *L family* of carbohydrates. The terms *D* and *L* originated from early studies of carbohydrates and indicate stereochemical relationship to the two enantiomers of glyceraldehyde, as shown in Figure 24.3. (The *R*/*S* notation system was introduced long after extensive studies of carbohydrate structure had been performed.) The stereochemical relationship can be established by the synthesis of higher carbohydrates from D- or L-glyceraldehyde, using reactions in which no bonds to the original stereogenic center are broken.

The dextrorotatory enantiomer of glyceraldehyde is designated *D* and the levorotatory molecule is designated *L*. Other carbohydrates are classified as *D* or *L* according to whether they have the same configuration at the stereocenter most distant from the carbonyl group as that in D- or L-glyceraldehye. (Remember that before the 1950s chemists had not developed the specific X-ray diffraction techniques needed to distinguish between enantiomers and therefore had no way of determining the spatial arrangement of groups in the dextrorotatory and levorotatory isomers. The structures for the two enantiomers (Figure 24.3) could be confirmed only after these techniques became available.) The D/L system has remained in use for naming carbohydrates and amino acids (Chapter 26).

Figure 24.4 shows the enantiomers of erythrose and ribose with their D and L labels.

Figure 24.4 Classification of D and L carbohydrates. The structural feature used for the classification is the stereogenic center furthest from the carbonyl group. A carbohydrate is designated as D if the hydroxyl group bonded to this stereocenter is on the right in a standard structural representation (i.e., with the carbonyl group top and primary alcohol group bottom) and as L if it is on the left.

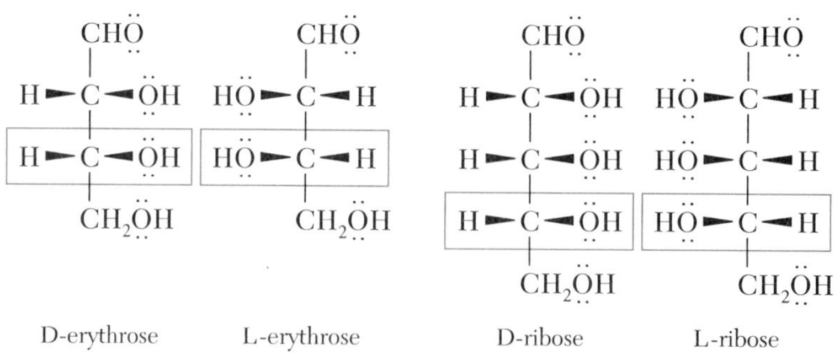

CHO / H—C—OH / H—C—OH / CH_2OH CHO / HO—C—H / HO—C—H / CH_2OH CHO / H—C—OH / H—C—OH / H—C—OH / CH_2OH CHO / HO—C—H / HO—C—H / HO—C—H / CH_2OH

D-erythrose   L-erythrose   D-ribose   L-ribose

PROBLEM 24.3 Would you expect D-ribose and D-erythrose to *necessarily* be dextrorotatory? Explain.

Fischer projections are often used to depict carbohydrate structures. The corresponding wedge and Fischer projections for D-ribose are shown in Figure 24.5.

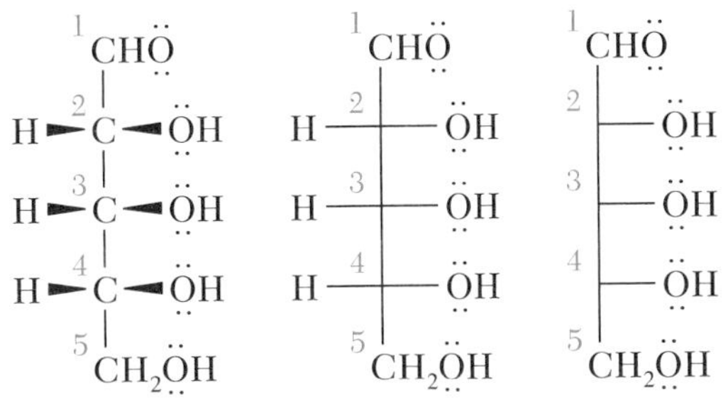

Figure 24.5 Representations of D-ribose. On the left is the wedge projection in the standard orientation. In the center is a Fischer projection of the same molecule; we understand that the horizontal bonds come out from the plane in which the structure is drawn. On the right is an abbreviated form of the Fischer projection in which only the hydroxyl groups (and not the hydrogens) at the stereogenic carbon atoms are shown.

Almost all of the common naturally occurring carbohydrates are in the D family. This interesting phenomenon is the result of the biosynthesis processes for carbohydrates. These biochemical pathways involve a buildup at the carbonyl end of D-glyceraldehyde. (There are, nevertheless, some naturally occurring carbohydrates that have the L configuration, but they are generally produced by secondary processes from D configuration carbohydrates.)

Proving that all of the common naturally occurring carbohydrates are of the D family was one of the triumphs of organic chemistry. This determination required the systematic degradation of each of the larger carbohydrates, removing one chain carbon at a time until only D-glyceraldehyde remained. We will describe how this degradation can be done a little later.

We will also explore the sequential addition of carbon atoms to D-glyceraldehyde in syntheses leading to higher molecular weight aldoses. The structural relationships linking the linear aldoses of the D family are summarized in Figure 24.6.

PROBLEM 24.4 Write the structure of each of the compounds shown in Figure 24.2 as a Fischer projection. Then write the structure of its enantiomer as a Fischer projection.

PROBLEM 24.5 Consider some early experiments that revealed useful information about the structure of (+)-glucose.

a. (+)-Glucose reacts with Tollens' reagent. On the basis of this observation, what functional group is present in (+)-glucose? What is the organic product of this reaction? (Use the structure of (+)-glucose given in Figure 24.6.)

b. (+)-Glucose reacts with phenylhydrazine to yield a compound of formula $C_{12}H_{18}O_5N_2$. Which functional group is suggested by this reaction? Again, draw the structure of the product of the reaction.

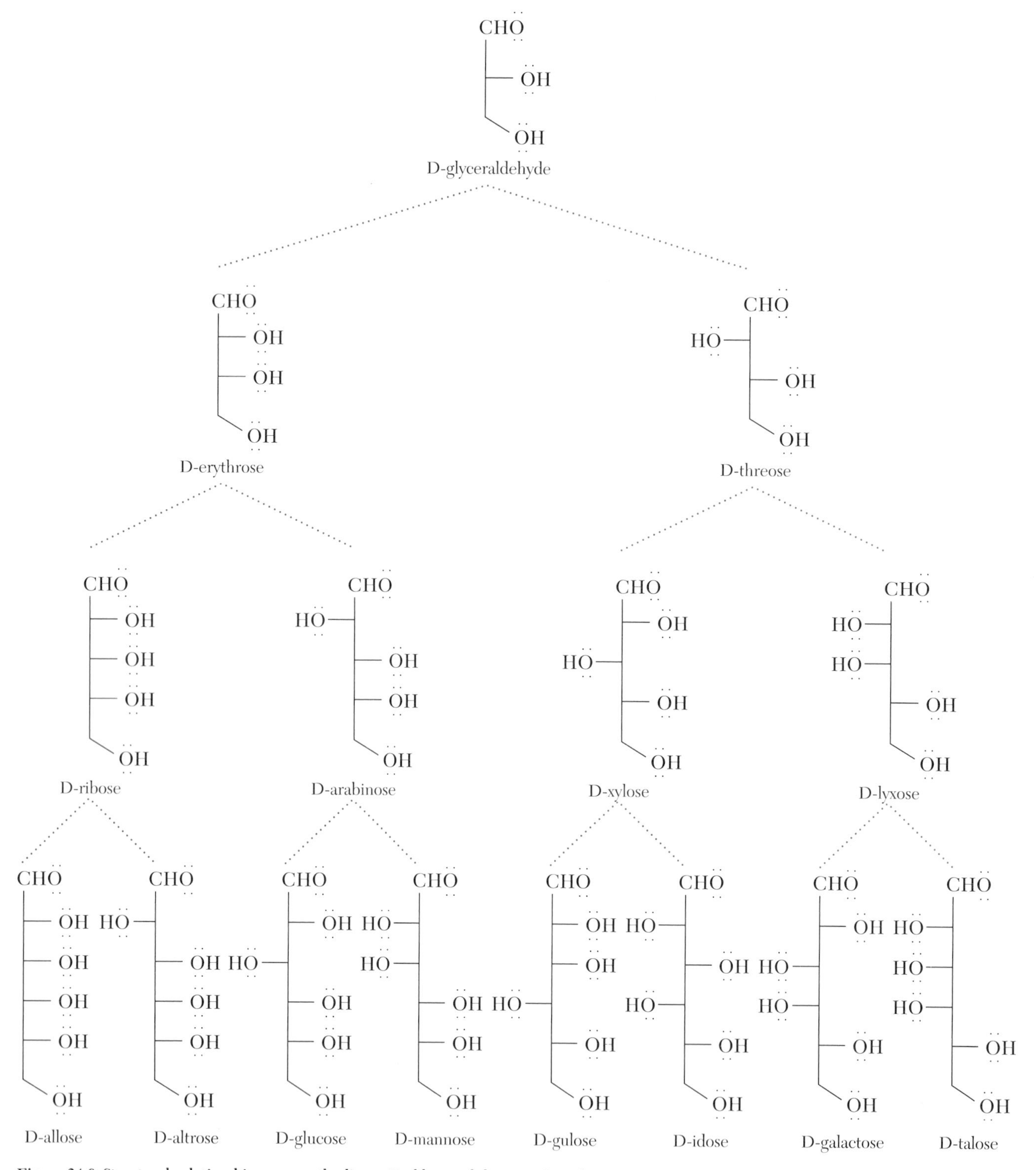

Figure 24.6 Structural relationships among the linear D-aldoses of three to six carbon atoms.

c. The presence of hydroxyl groups in (+)-glucose was established by reaction with acetic anhydride. This reaction converts the hydroxyl groups to ester linkages. Predict the maximum number of moles of acetic anhydride that would react with one mole of (+)-glucose. Show the structure of the fully esterified product.

d. Observations such as those just described suggested to early chemists that (+)-glucose is a pentahydroxyaldehyde. Why do you think that a structure in which the hydroxyl groups are attached to separate carbon atoms was considered more likely than a structure in which two hydroxyl groups are attached to a single carbon atom?

24.3 Cyclic Forms of Linear Carbohydrates

CYCLIC HEMIACETALS AND HEMIKETALS IN CARBOHYDRATES

Consider again the aldopentoses. The structures shown in Figure 24.6 are polyhydroxyaldehydes. We see that each molecule contains an aldehydic carbonyl group and four hydroxyl groups. We know that aldehydes react with alcohols to form hemiacetals (Chapter 19). Is it possible that the aldehyde group of an aldose could undergo an intramolecular reaction with one of the hydroxyl groups to form a cyclic hemiacetal? We find this indeed to be the case. As we might expect, intramolecular reaction leads preferentially to either five- or six-membered rings. We refer to the five-membered rings as **furanose** rings and the six-membered rings as **pyranose** rings. Figure 24.7 shows the formation of furanose and pyranose rings from D-ribose.

Ketoses can also form cyclic ketals, as is illustrated for D-fructose in Figure 24.8.

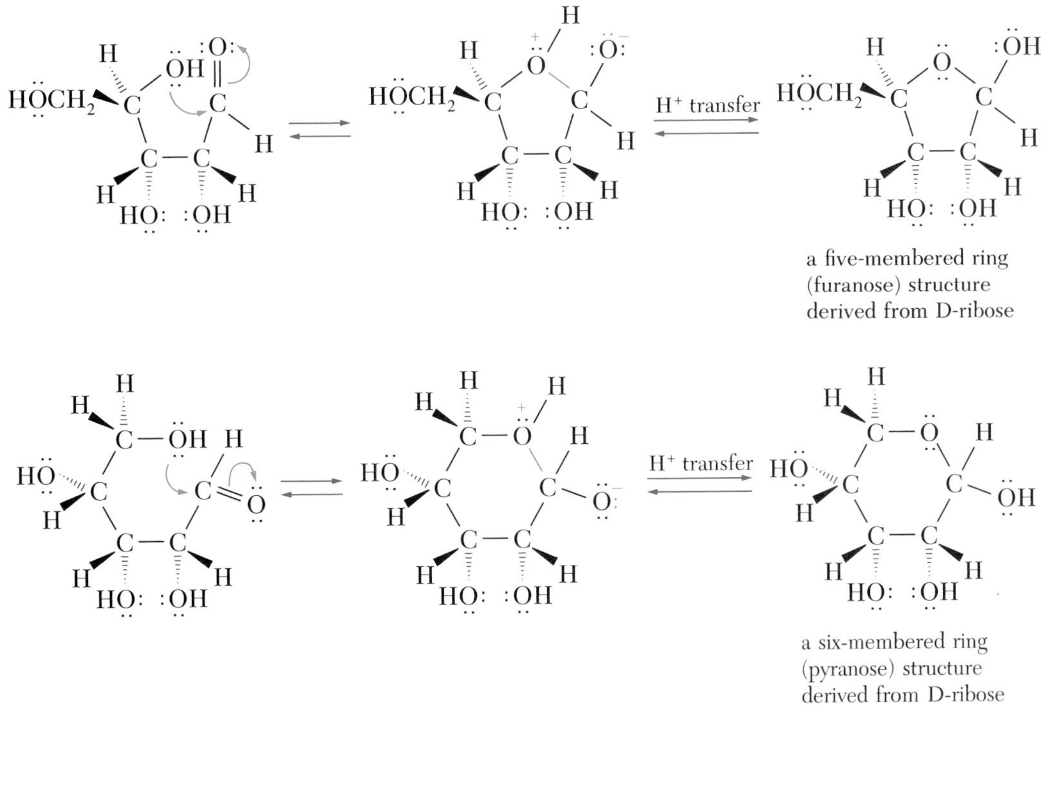

Figure 24.7 Cyclic hemiacetal formation from D-ribose. A six-membered hemiacetal is referred to as a furanose structure after the five-membered cyclic ether, furan (see Figure 14.3). A six-membered hemiacetal is referred to as a pyranose structure after the six-membered cyclic ether, pyran (also shown in Figure 14.3). The closure and opening of the hemiacetal ring occurs under all pH conditions. The reaction is shown under neutral conditions.

H⁺ transfer

a five-membered ring (furanose) structure derived from D-ribose

H⁺ transfer

a six-membered ring (pyranose) structure derived from D-ribose

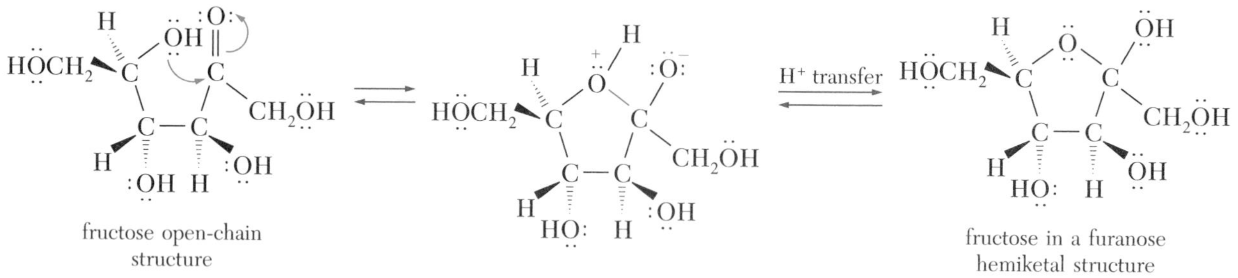

fructose open-chain structure

H^+ transfer

fructose in a furanose hemiketal structure

Figure 24.8 Furanose hemiketal formation with fructose.

PROBLEM 24.6 Compare the open-chain structures of D-ribose shown in Figure 24.7. Use models to verify that they are simply different conformations of the same structure.

PROBLEM 24.7 Use models and draw wedge structures to show the generation of pyranose and furanose forms of D-glucose.

Notice that the open-chain and the cyclic hemiacetal (hemiketal) structures are isomeric. No special conditions are needed to prepare the cyclic structures because the carbohydrates *naturally prefer the cyclic form*. When we work with a carbohydrate such as D-ribose, most of the molecules are in a cyclic form. When we dissolve a solid carbohydrate in water, some of the rings revert to the open-chain form. The open-chain form is present in very low concentration, but we can still observe *some* of the classical reactions of the carbonyl group, for example, the Tollens' reagent reaction with aldehydes. However, less reactive reagents such as bisulfite give no reaction with aldoses because at equilibrium there is an insufficient amount of the open-chain form to give reaction.

THE EXISTENCE OF ANOMERIC FORMS OF CARBOHYDRATES

If you have worked out Problem 24.7 using molecular models, or if you have studied in detail the hemiacetal and hemiketal structures we have thus far drawn, you may have realized that the cyclization of the open-chain form produces a *new* stereogenic center. If you did not notice this or are unsure how the new center is formed, consider Figure 24.7 again. Notice that while the carbonyl carbon atom is not a stereogenic center in the open-chain form, it becomes stereogenic in the cyclic form—there are four different groups attached to it. In fact, the carbonyl carbon atom is originally a *prochiral center* (see Chapter 10 for a discussion of prochirality) since it becomes stereogenic upon addition of a new group. Two diastereoisomers result from the addition of the hydroxyl oxygen to different faces of the carbonyl group, as is illustrated in Figure 24.9.

Now consider the formation of a furanose hemiacetal from the open-chain form of D-ribose. Two possible structures can result, because the aldehyde site is prochiral. Since the D-ribose molecule contains stereogenic centers, the two

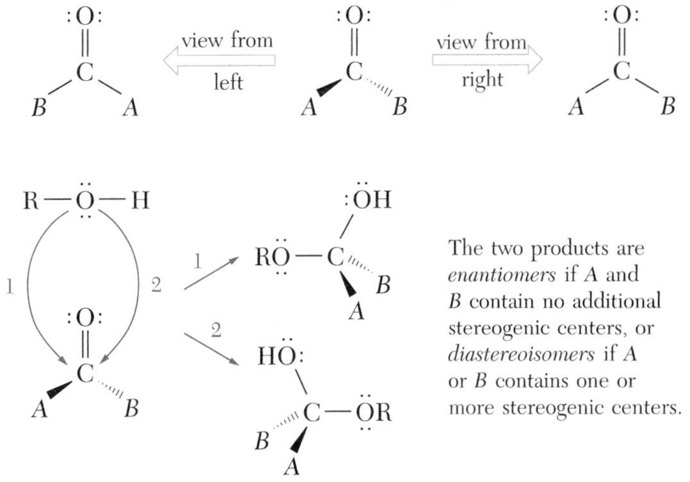

Figure 24.9 A prochiral carbonyl center. The carbonyl group is planar and in itself not a stereogenic center, but it is *prochiral* as long as *A* and *B* are not identical. In such a case, the two faces of the group are not identical, as shown at the top of the diagram. Viewed on one face, *A*, O, and *B* are arranged in clockwise order about the carbon; viewed on the opposite face, the arrangement of *A*, O, and *B* is counterclockwise. When a new group adds to this carbonyl carbon, addition to the different faces generates stereoisomers. These stereoisomers are enantiomers if *A* and *B* do *not* contain any other stereogenic centers. If either *A* or *B* (or both) contains one or more stereogenic centers, the resultant adducts are diastereoisomers.

view from left

view from right

The two products are *enantiomers* if A and B contain no additional stereogenic centers, or *diastereoisomers* if A or B contains one or more stereogenic centers.

possible structures are *diastereoisomers* rather than enantiomers. We refer to diastereoisomers related in this way as **anomers** and to the carbon that is the source of this stereoisomerism as an **anomeric carbon atom.** The generation of the furanose anomers of D-ribose is illustrated in Figure 24.10.

Usually we adopt a standard form (known as a **Haworth projection**) for depicting cyclic anomers. This form is illustrated for the two furanose anomers of D-ribose in Figure 24.11.

We differentiate the anomers by using a prefix to the name to indicate the direction of the anomeric hydroxyl in the standard view. If the hydroxyl is *down* in the standard view we refer to the anomer as an **α-anomer.** The anomer in which the hydroxyl is *up* in the standard view is the **β-anomer.** To specify the compounds shown in Figure 24.11 completely, we also indicate the size of the ring using the furanose/pyranose designation. Thus, the complete name of the first compound shown in Figure 24.11 is β-D-ribofuranose, and that of its anomer, shown at the bottom, is α-D-ribofuranose.

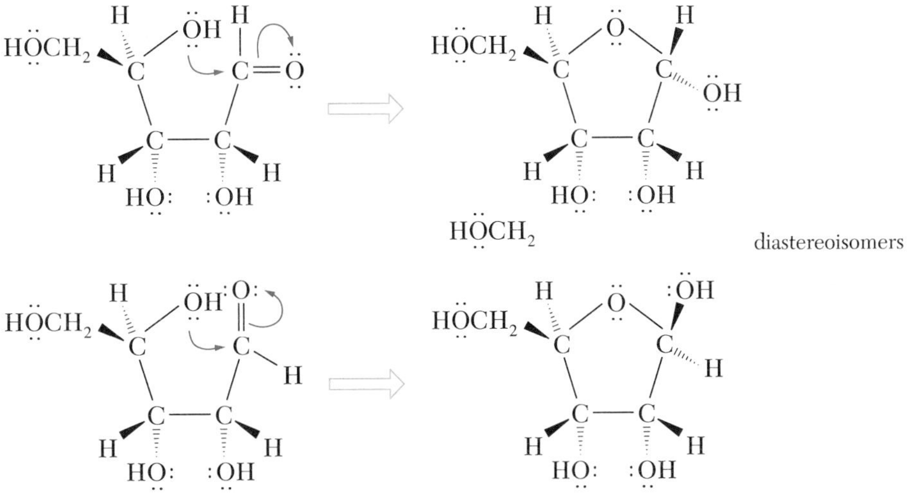

Figure 24.10 Formation of the pair of furanose anomers of D-ribose. Each of the anomers contains four stereogenic centers. Three of these centers (the original three of the open-chain D-ribose) have the same configuration in the two structures, but the fourth (the anomeric center) is different. The structures are diastereoisomers.

diastereoisomers

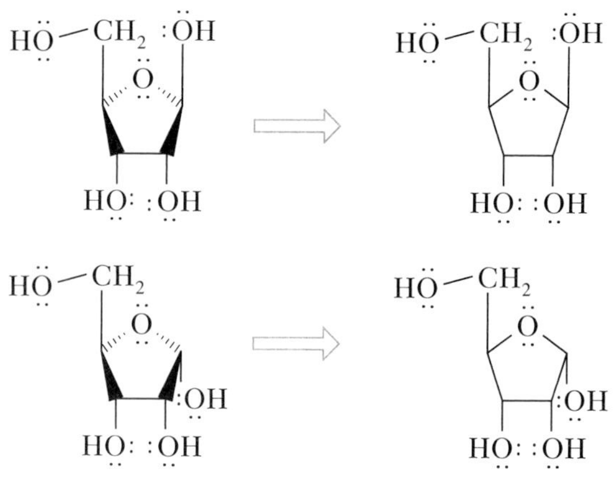

Figure 24.11 Standard representations of the furanose anomers of D-ribose. In the standard view (for all D-carbohydrates) the oxygen of the ring is located in the back and the anomeric carbon on the right, as is shown most clearly by the structures on the left. When using structures like those on the right (Haworth projections), we *understand* that the directions of the bonds relative to the plane of the paper is as shown on the left.

PROBLEM 24.8 What is the absolute configuration designation (R/S) for the anomeric carbon in each of the α and β forms of D-ribofuranose? Does this designation depend on the D-carbohydrate under consideration or is it the same for all? Does this designation depend on the size of the ring (furanose or pyranose)? Explain your conclusion.

PROBLEM 24.9 Use the R/S system to designate the absolute configuration about each stereogenic center in the anomers of D-ribofuranose. What is the stereochemical relationship between the two structures?

PROBLEM 24.10 Give the complete name of each of the following structures:

a.

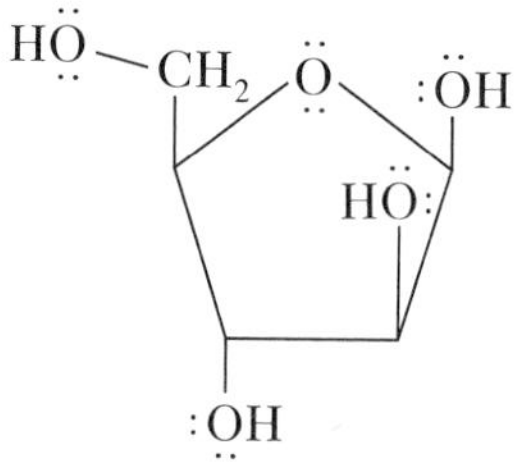

b.

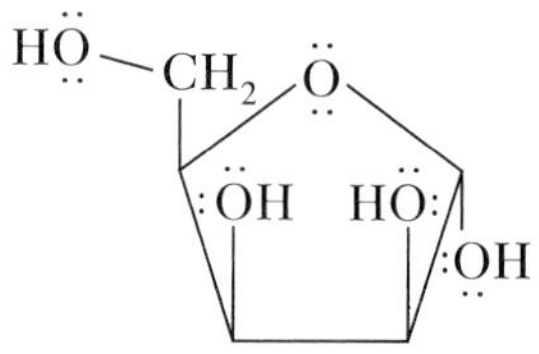

c.

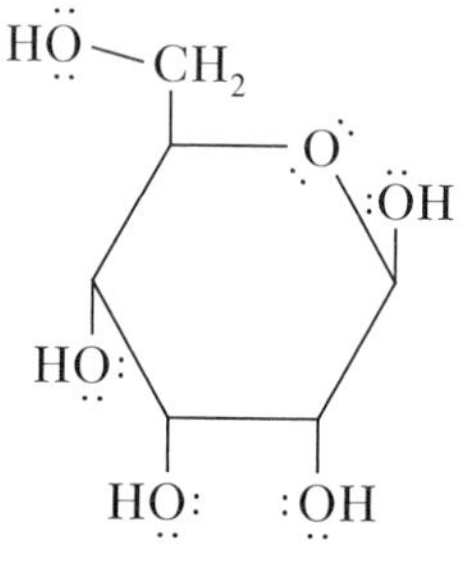

PROBLEM 24.11 Draw and name the two anomeric forms of each of the following:
a. D-fructofuranose b. D-glucopyranose

Steps to Solving the Problem

Solution to Problem 24.11a

1. Start with the open-chain structure of D-fructose. View it from the left side, and redraw the compound, bending the carbon chain so that it begins to resemble a ring. Place the carbonyl carbon at the far right.

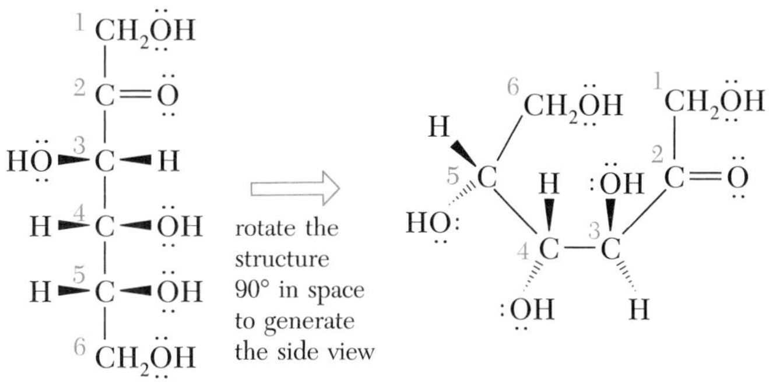

rotate the structure 90° in space to generate the side view

2. Determine which hydroxyl group will enter into hemiketal formation. Since we need a furanose structure, the hydroxyl on the fifth carbon of the chain must be the one that forms the bond with the carbonyl group. Therefore we must rotate about the bond between the fourth and fifth carbons to place the hydroxyl group in proper position for interaction with the carbonyl group; this involves a rotation of 120°.

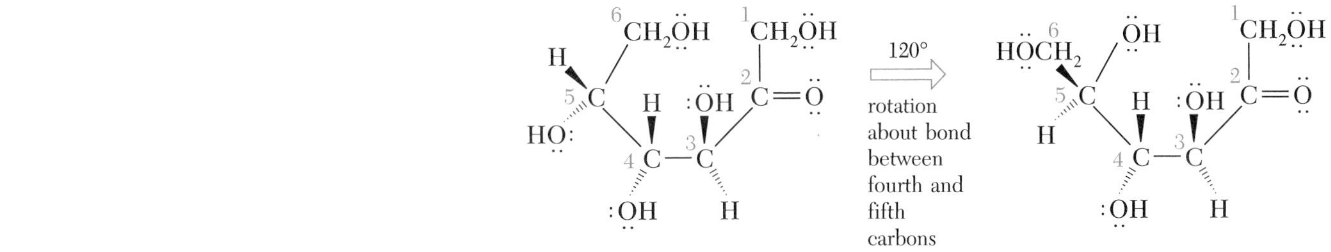

120° rotation about bond between fourth and fifth carbons

3. We are now ready to draw the cyclic anomers.

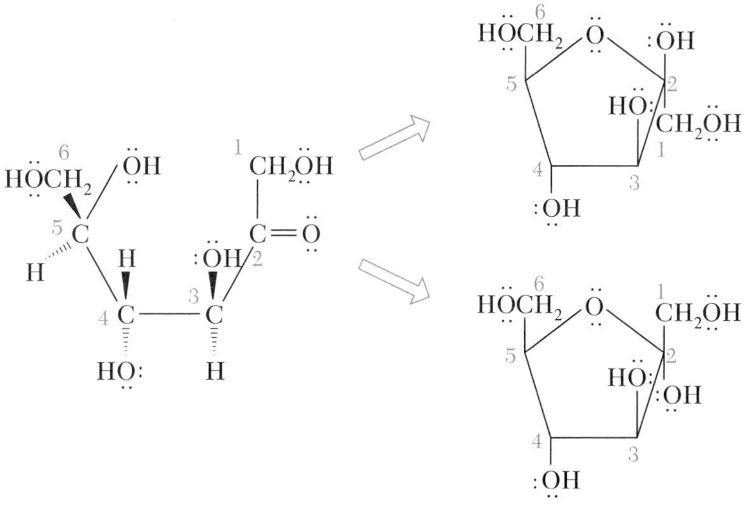

4. The upper structure is β-D-fructofuranose, and the lower is α-D-fructofuranose.

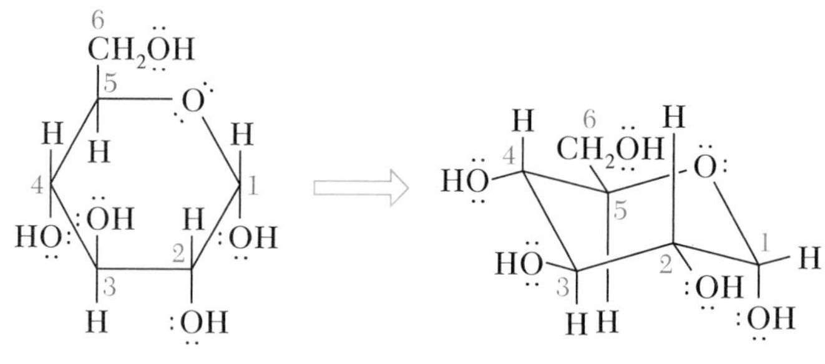

Figure 24.12 Chair conformations of α- and β-D-glucopyranose.

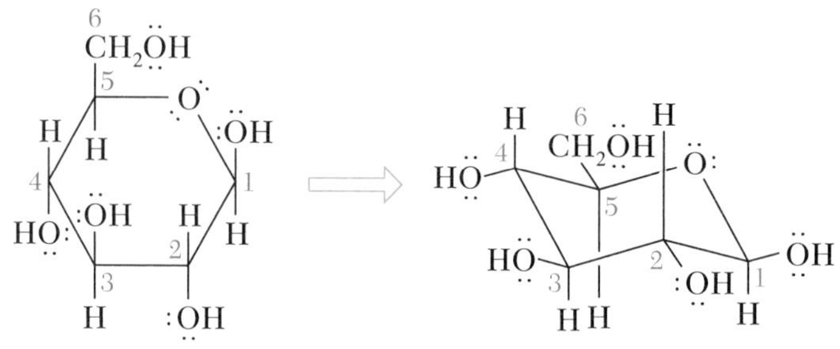

6 CH_2OH 5 O H H H 4 1 HO: :OH H :OH 2 3 H :OH

H 6 H 4 CH_2OH O: HO 5 HO 2 1 H 3 :OH H H :OH

α-anomer

6 CH_2OH 5 O :OH H H 4 1 HO: :OH H H 2 3 H :OH

H 6 H 4 CH_2OH O: HO 5 HO 2 OH 3 :OH 1 H H H

β-anomer

As you might expect by analogy with cyclohexane derivatives (Chapter 13), carbohydrates with a pyranose ring adopt chair conformations. Taking into account the equatorial and axial positions of substituents about a pyranose ring enables us to evaluate the relative stabilities and reactivities of anomers. Consider, for example, the α- and β-anomers of D-glucopyranose. While the β-anomer can adopt a conformation in which all of the larger groups are in equatorial positions, the α-anomer cannot. In the α-anomer, the hydroxyl group at the C-1 position must occupy an axial position if the other large groups are to occupy equatorial positions. These conformations are shown in Figure 24.12.

PROBLEM 24.12 Two crystalline forms of glucose can be obtained by recrystallization. They correspond to the α- and β-anomers of D-glucose. Crystallization from a cold solution yields a crystalline form that has a melting point of 146°C and a specific rotation of +112° (sodium vapor lamp). The other crystalline form results from crystallization from a hot solution.

a. Do you expect the crystals obtained from the high temperature crystallization to melt at 146 °C? Explain.
b. Do you expect the crystals obtained from the high temperature crystallization to have a specific rotation of +112°, −112°, or some other value? Explain your answer.

PROBLEM 24.13 Draw the two possible chair conformations of each of the following:

a. α-D-mannopyranose b. β-D-galactopyranose

EQUILIBRIA OF ANOMERIC FORMS

The structures we have drawn for the anomeric forms of simple carbohydrates are hemiacetals and hemiketals. We recall from our discussion of the chemistry of carbonyl compounds (Chapter 19) that hemiacetals and hemiketals are labile in aqueous solution at all pH values. Thus, for a given carbohydrate in aqueous solution, the open-chain form and all of its cyclic hemiacetal (or hemiketal) forms are in dynamic equilibrium. Although one particular structure often dominates at a given pH and temperature, it does not exist to the total exclusion of the alternative forms. Figure 24.13 illustrates the dynamic equilibrium of open-chain, pyranose, and furanose forms of D-glucose.

When crystals of α-D-glucopyranose are dissolved in water and the specific rotation of the solution is measured, we *initially* find it to have a value of $+112°$. However, the value of the specific rotation decreases with time, first rapidly and then more slowly, until it becomes constant at 53°. If we start with a fresh solution prepared from crystals of β-D-glucopyranose, the initial specific rotation

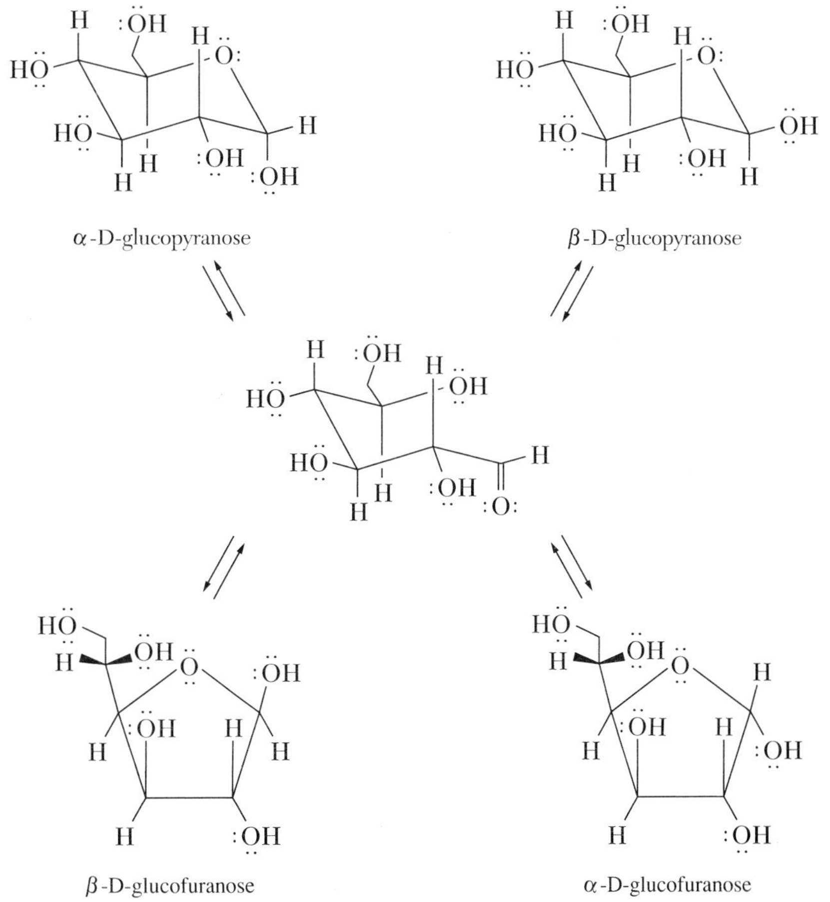

Figure 24.13 Dynamic equilibrium of the forms of D-glucose. The interconversion of all cyclic hemiacetal forms proceeds through the open-chain form.

α-D-glucopyranose

β-D-glucopyranose

β-D-glucofuranose

α-D-glucofuranose

is +19°. With time the specific rotation of this solution increases, eventually reaching the same constant value (53°) as that reached by the solution of the α-D-glucopyranose. This phenomenon is observed with many carbohydrates and is known as **mutarotation.** It involves the establishment of a dynamic equilibrium of all of the possible forms of the carbohydrate in solution; the observed specific rotation is the weighted average for all of the species present.

GLYCOSIDES

The cyclic forms of carbohydrates we have seen so far have all been hemiacetals or hemiketals. **Glycosides** are carbohydrate derivatives in which the anomeric carbon is bound in a *full* acetal (or ketal) linkage. We say that such compounds contain a *glycosidic linkage*.

In our earlier discussion of carbonyl chemistry (Chapter 19) we pointed out that formation of a full acetal (or ketal) requires the interaction of *two* hydroxyl groups with the carbonyl carbon, along with the loss of the elements of water. In a glycoside, one of these hydroxyl groups is provided intramolecularly (as in the cyclic hemiacetal or hemiketal form) and the second comes from another molecule. The general structures of glycosides of D-glucose are shown in Figure 24.14. The R group in Figure 24.14 can be a simple alkyl group (such as methyl) or a more complex group. With R = $—CH_3$, the glycosides in Figure 24.14 are methyl α-D-glucopyranoside (**24.1**) and methyl β-D-glucopyranoside (**24.2**).

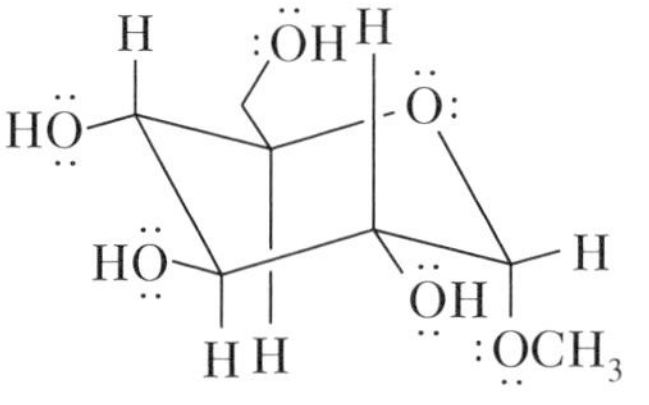

methyl α-D-glucopyranoside
24.1

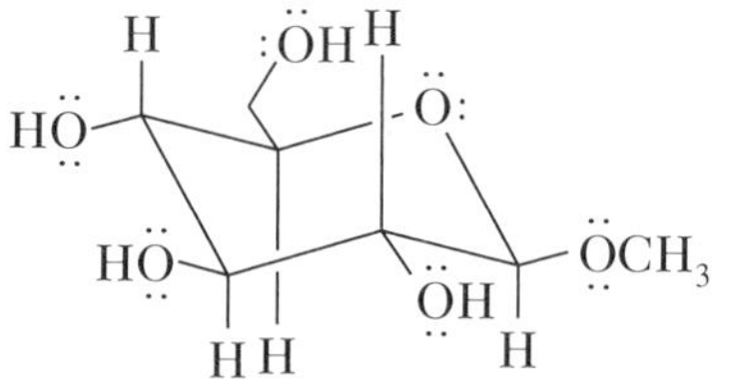

methyl β-D-glucopyranoside
24.2

To name glycosides, we use the name of the parent carbohydrate (with its configurational and anomeric designations) but change the *-ose* ending to *-oside*. We then add as a prefix the name of the alkyl group forming the glycoside.

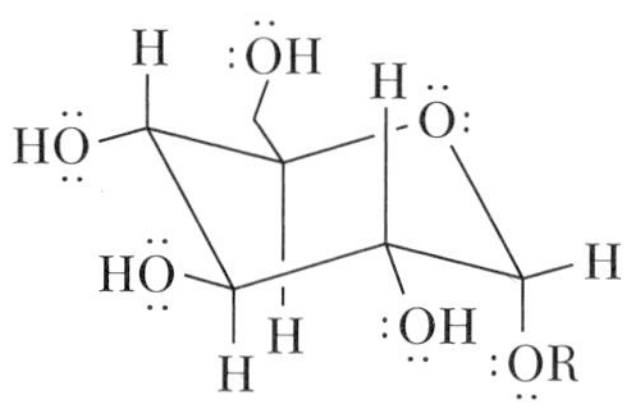

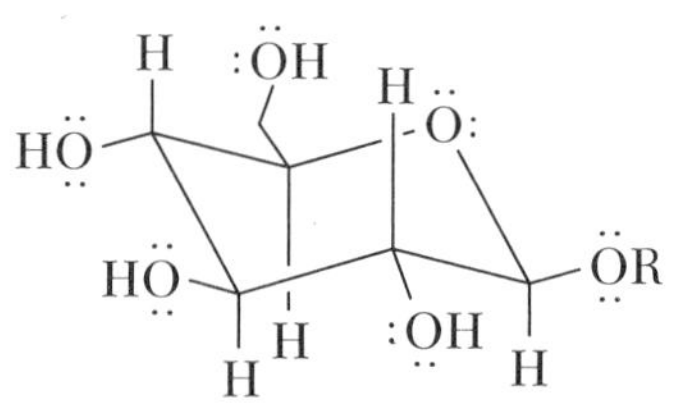

Figure 24.14 General structure of six-membered-ring glycosides of D-glucose. The compounds shown are both acetals.

R = alkyl, but *not* H

an α-D-glucopyranoside

a β-D-glucopyranoside

PROBLEM 24.14 Name each of the following glycosides:

a.

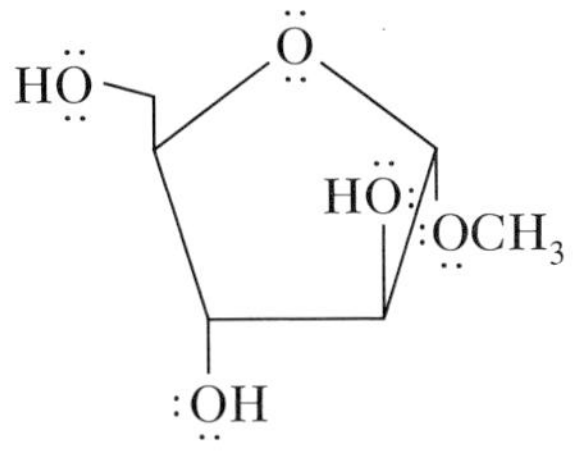

b.

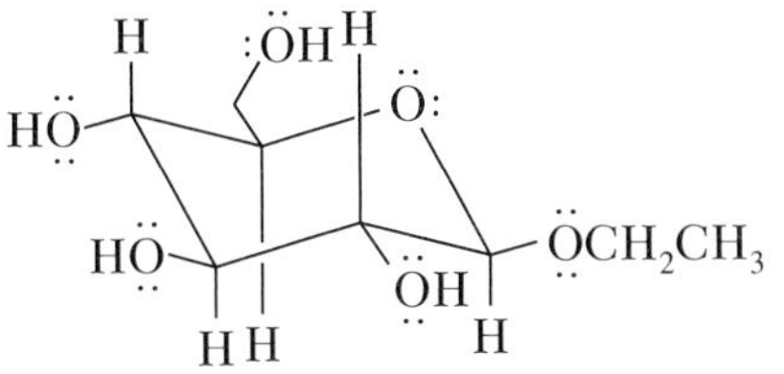

c.

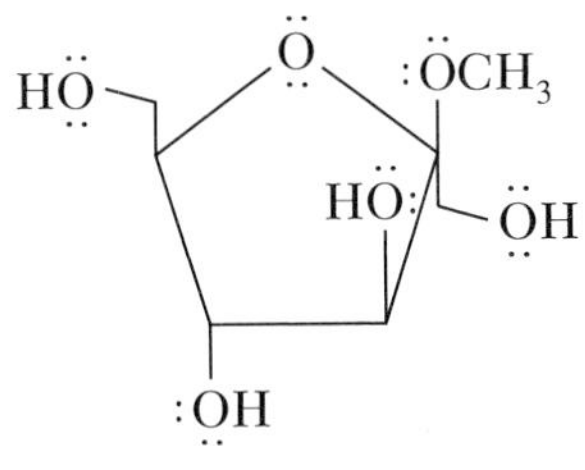

Steps to Solving the Problem

Solution to Problem 24.14a

1. First determine the parent carbohydrate for this glycoside. We see from the Haworth projection that it is an aldopentose of the D-series, specifically D-arabinose (see Figure 24.6).
2. Now consider the *form* of the glycoside. It is a five-membered ring, making it a furanoside structure.
3. What alcohol forms the acetal linkage in the glycoside, and what is its orientation? We see that the glycosidic linkage is formed using methanol. Thus it is a *methyl* glycoside, and it has an α-orientation (the anomeric oxygen is down when the structure is shown in the standard position).
4. We thus name the compound methyl α-D-arabinofuranoside.

The source of the second hydroxyl group for the generation of the glycosidic linkage is often more complex than the simple alcohols thus far indicated. Of particular significance are structures in which the second hydroxyl group belongs to another carbohydrate molecule. Such substances are disaccharides and polysaccharides, whose structure and chemistry will be discussed later in this chapter.

PROBLEM 24.15 Draw the structure for each of the following glycosides:

a. methyl β-D-ribofuranoside b. ethyl α-D-allopyranoside
c. methyl α-D-arabinofuranoside

PROBLEM 24.16 Under what conditions would you expect the glycosides listed in Problem 24.15 to undergo mutarotation? Explain your answer.

Formation of Glycosides Like ordinary acetals and ketals, glycosides form by the reaction of the hemiacetal (or hemiketal) form of the carbohydrate with an alcohol under conditions of acid catalysis. The formation of a methyl glycoside of ribose is illustrated below. The reaction is completely reversible under acidic conditions. *Both α- and β-anomers can form from the cationic intermediate.* The formation of the β-anomer is shown.

MECHANISM OF REACTION

Acid-Catalyzed Glycoside Formation

Step 1 Protonation of the C-1 hydroxyl group

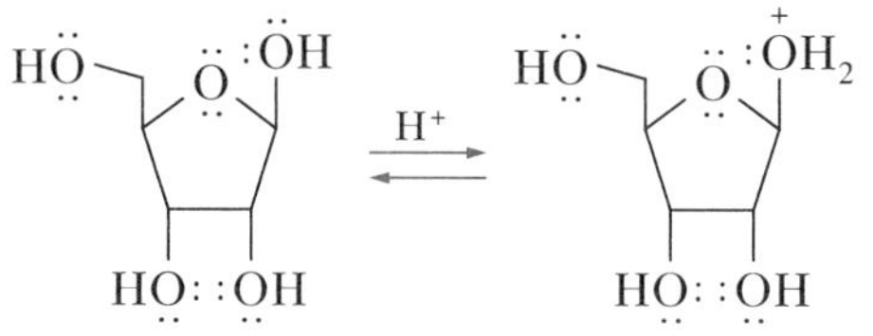

Step 2 Loss of water to form a resonance-stabilized cation

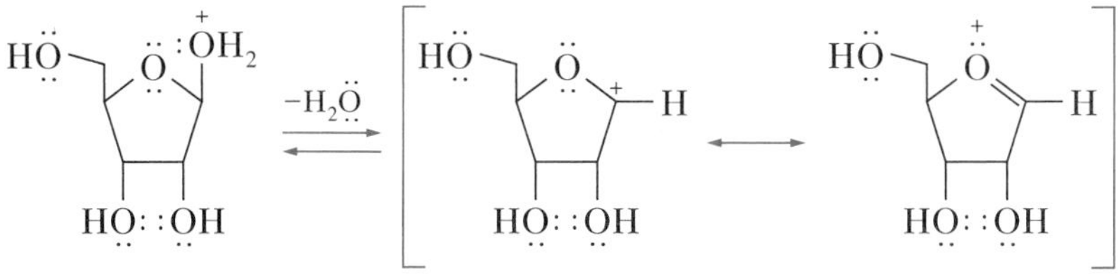

Step 3 Nucleophilic attack by methanol

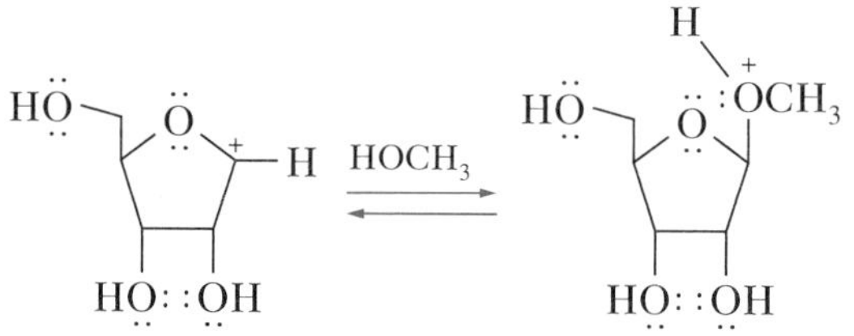

Step 4 Loss of a proton

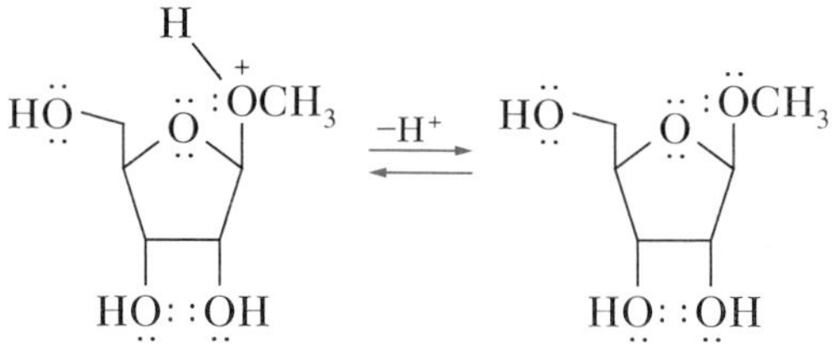

PROBLEM 24.17 Show how the cationic intermediate of Step 2 in the acid-catalyzed glycoside formation mechanism can lead to the α-anomer. Why would you *not* expect equal amounts of the α- and β-anomers to form in this reaction?

Glycoside formation reactions occur strictly at the anomeric site of the carbohydrate. To synthesize glycosides of this type, we force the equilibrium toward the desired product either by using a large excess of the alcohol or by removing the by-product (water) as it forms.

The relative stabilities of α- and β-anomers of *pyranosides* are interesting. The anomer having the exocyclic (outside the ring) oxygen in an *axial* position is found to be more stable than the anomer in which it is in an equatorial position. For example, methyl α-D-glucopyranoside is thermodynamically more stable than methyl β-D-glucopyranoside. This order is, of course, the *opposite* of the order we would anticipate based on the usual preference of a large group for an equatorial position. This unusual situation, in which a substituent favors an axial position over an equatorial one, is known as the **anomeric effect.**

MOLECULAR ORBITAL ANALYSIS

A Molecular Orbital Explanation of the Anomeric Effect

We normally expect substituents bulkier than hydrogen, if at all possible, to preferentially occupy equatorial positions about six-membered rings. Thus, the anomeric effect is an anomaly. There must be some factor that either stabilizes the substituent when it is in the axial position or destabilizes it when it is in the equatorial position. One explanation for this anomaly arises from consideration of the molecular orbitals involved.

When a polar substituent is singly bound to carbon, the major lobe of the σ^* orbital lies behind the carbon atom on the side opposite the attached electronegative atom. When the polar substituent is in an axial position at an anomeric carbon, this major lobe of the *empty* σ^* orbital is in an excellent position for interaction with the *full* nonbonding orbital of the ring oxygen. This interaction between the empty and full orbitals leads to a stabilization of the system. If the substituent were located in an equatorial position, the σ^* and nonbonding orbitals would not have a relative orientation suitable for interaction. Thus, the axial orientation of a polar substituent at the anomeric position has a particular stabilizing factor. The orbital orientations and interactions are illustrated in Figure 24.15.

Glycosidic linkages join the monosaccharide units of disaccharides and polysaccharides. We have seen that a glycosidic linkage results from the interaction of two molecules. One of these molecules is a carbohydrate with a hemiacetal (or hemiketal) site at an anomeric carbon atom, and the other is

Axial polar substituent at the anomeric position:

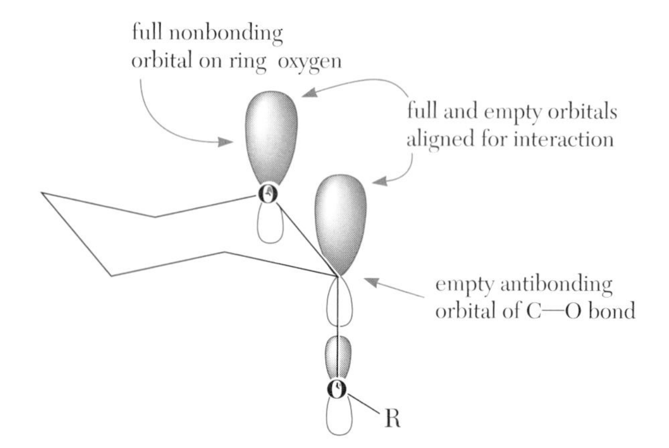

Equatorial polar subtituent at the anomeric position:

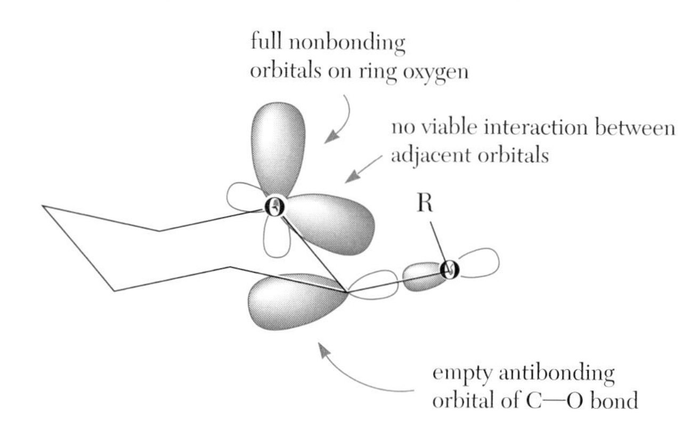

Figure 24.15 Orbital interactions in the anomeric effect. A stabilizing interaction between the unshared valence level electron-pair orbital of the ring oxygen and the antibonding orbital of the exocyclic carbon-oxygen linkage results in a stabilization of the system.

an alcohol molecule. A disaccharide forms when the needed alcohol group is provided by one monosaccharide and the anomeric carbon by another. An example of a disaccharide (maltose) is shown in Figure 24.16.

REACTIVITY OF GLYCOSIDIC LINKAGES

All the steps in the acid-catalyzed formation of a glycoside are equilibria, just as they are for the formation of any other acetal or ketal. Thus the overall transformation is fully reversible. Accordingly, we can displace the overall equilibrium to the free carbohydrate side by using a large excess of water. A glycoside can therefore be hydrolyzed to its carbohydrate and alcohol precursors by treatment with an excess of water in the presence of an acid.

However, glycosides are inert toward aqueous base (typical behavior for acetals and ketals). Notice this contrast between the behavior of a glycoside and that of the parent carbohydrate in its cyclic hemiacetal form, which is dynamically labile at *all* aqueous pH values. Thus we can perform synthetic manipulations on glycosides under basic conditions without disturbing the glycosidic linkage (we will see some examples of such manipulations in later sections).

Figure 24.16 A glycosidic linkage between two monosaccharide units. The monosaccharide unit on the left uses its anomeric carbon and that on the right uses its 4-position hydroxyl to form the glycosidic linkage. This disaccharide is maltose. Notice that the monosaccharide unit on the right has a hemiacetal linkage at its anomeric carbon (it could serve as a component of a glycosidic linkage to a *third* monosaccharide unit in a trisaccharide or polysaccharide).

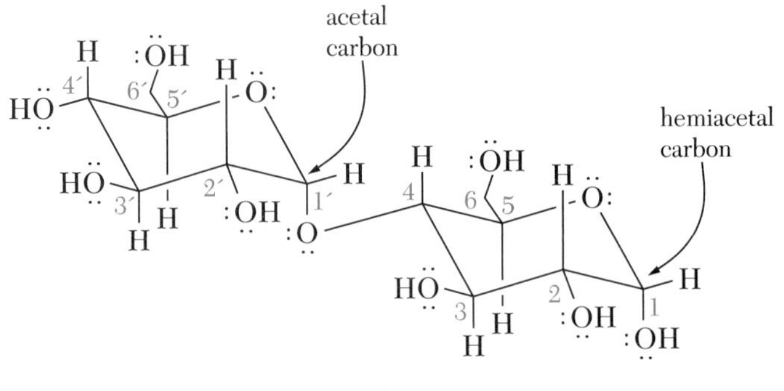

acetal carbon

hemiacetal carbon

maltose

24.4 Synthesis, Reactions, and Degradations of Carbohydrates

Carbohydrate chemistry has a rich history. From both structural determinations and synthetic efforts, organic chemists have developed numerous important techniques, procedures, and thinking processes that can be applied to carbohydrates. In this section we will survey some of these. Our discussion will draw upon and enhance our earlier studies of stereochemistry and will provide a basis for the application of carbohydrate chemistry to current problems in organic chemistry.

THE KILIANI-FISCHER SYNTHESIS

The **Kiliani-Fischer synthesis** is a sequence of reactions for increasing the number of carbon atoms in a carbohydrate by one. Figure 24.17 shows how D-glyceraldehyde can be converted to D-erythrose and D-threose by the Kiliani-Fischer method. The procedure involves two stages. First, the starting carbohydrate (here, D-glyceraldehyde) is converted to a diastereomeric mixture of cyanohydrins. After the diastereoisomers are separated, the cyano group of each is converted to an aldehyde group.

Figure 24.17 The Kiliani-Fischer method applied to the conversion of D-glyceraldehyde to aldotetroses. Notice that the D-stereochemistry is preserved throughout the sequence.

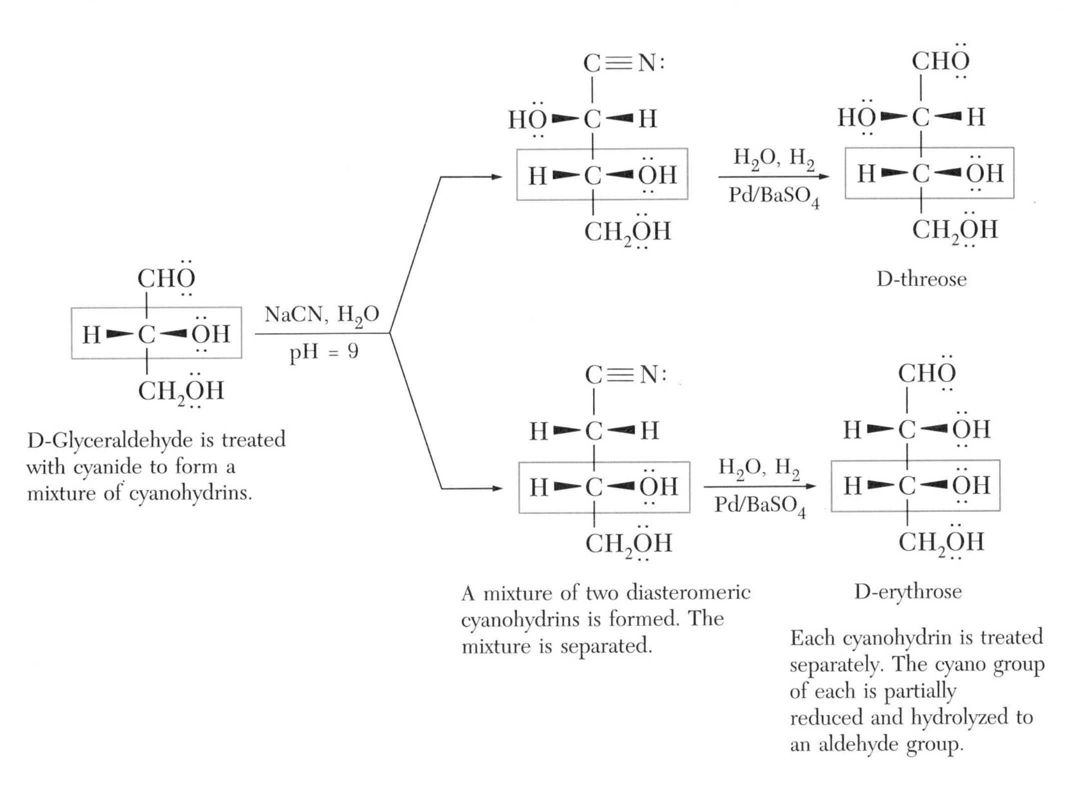
CHO
H—C—OH
CH2OH
NaCN, H2O
pH = 9
D-Glyceraldehyde is treated with cyanide to form a mixture of cyanohydrins.
C≡N:
HO—C—H
H—C—OH
CH2OH
H2O, H2
Pd/BaSO4
CHO
HO—C—H
H—C—OH
CH2OH
D-threose
C≡N:
H—C—H
H—C—OH
CH2OH
H2O, H2
Pd/BaSO4
CHO
H—C—OH
H—C—OH
CH2OH
D-erythrose
A mixture of two diasteromeric cyanohydrins is formed. The mixture is separated.
Each cyanohydrin is treated separately. The cyano group of each is partially reduced and hydrolyzed to an aldehyde group.

PROBLEM 24.18 Which substance, D-erythrose or D-threose, would yield an optically active product upon reduction with sodium borohydride?

PROBLEM 24.19 Suppose you used D-erythrose as the starting material in a Kiliani-Fischer synthesis. Which two pentoses would you produce?

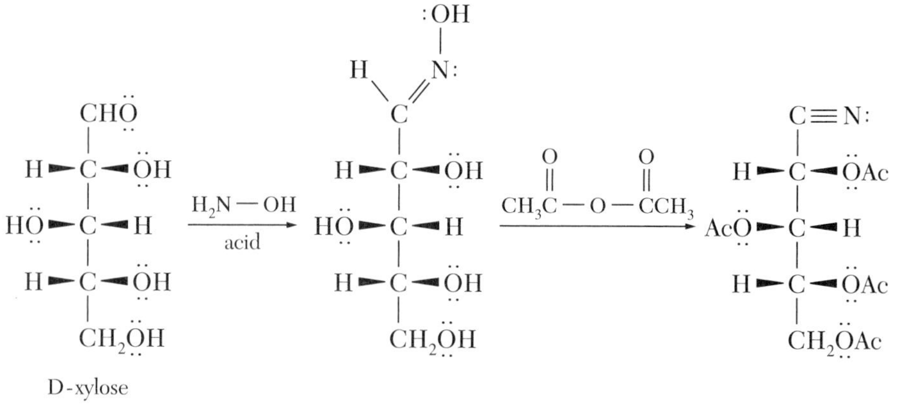

Figure 24.18 The first two steps in the Wohl degradation of D-xylose. In the first step, the free carbonyl group is converted to an oxime. Once this is accomplished, acetic anhydride is used to dehydrate the oxime to a nitrile. The hydroxyl groups are also converted to ester linkages, a process that must be reversed in the remainder of the degradation process. (The ACO— group = acetate, $CH_3—C(=O)—O—$.)

D-xylose: CHO / H—C—OH / HO—C—H / H—C—OH / CH_2OH $\xrightarrow[\text{acid}]{H_2N—OH}$ HC=N—OH / H—C—OH / HO—C—H / H—C—OH / CH_2OH $\xrightarrow{CH_3C(=O)—O—C(=O)CH_3}$ C≡N / H—C—OAc / AcO—C—H / H—C—OAc / CH_2OAc

DEGRADATIONS OF CARBOHYDRATES

The Kiliani-Fischer synthesis is a method for *ascending* the carbohydrate series, that is, increasing the chain length. Methods have also been devised for *descending* the series, that is, decreasing the number of carbon atoms in a carbohydrate molecule. Both methods are useful, and with them the structures of the entire range of aldoses can be related.

The Wohl Degradation The series of reactions known as the **Wohl degradation** is a four-step procedure. It begins with treatment of an aldose with hydroxylamine (H_2NOH) to produce an oxime. The oxime is then allowed to react with an excess of acetic anhydride, which causes dehydration of the oxime to a nitrile. It also converts all hydroxyl groups in the carbohydrate to acetates. These two steps of the Wohl degradation, beginning with D-xylose, are illustrated in Figure 24.18.

PROBLEM 24.20 Provide a complete mechanism for the oxime-forming step of Figure 24.18. (*Hint:* Review Chapter 19).

Following the dehydration reaction, the acetate ester linkages are converted to free hydroxyl groups by treatment with an excess of ammonia. The two products of this reaction are acetamide and the cyanohydrin of the aldotetrose D-threose. Finally, D-threose is produced by a reversal of the normal cyanohydrin-forming reaction. Treatment of the cyanohydrin with silver oxide precipitates silver cyanide and silver hydroxide, leaving D-threose. These two steps are shown in Figure 24.19.

The cyanohydrin decomposition merits comment. In Section 19.10 we discussed cyanohydrin formation as an equilibrium process. Knowing this, we can predict that if cyanide ion is removed from the reaction system, the equilibrium will shift toward the free carbonyl side. In the final reaction in Figure 24.19, the addition of silver ion causes cyanide to be removed from the cyanohydrin as insoluble silver cyanide.

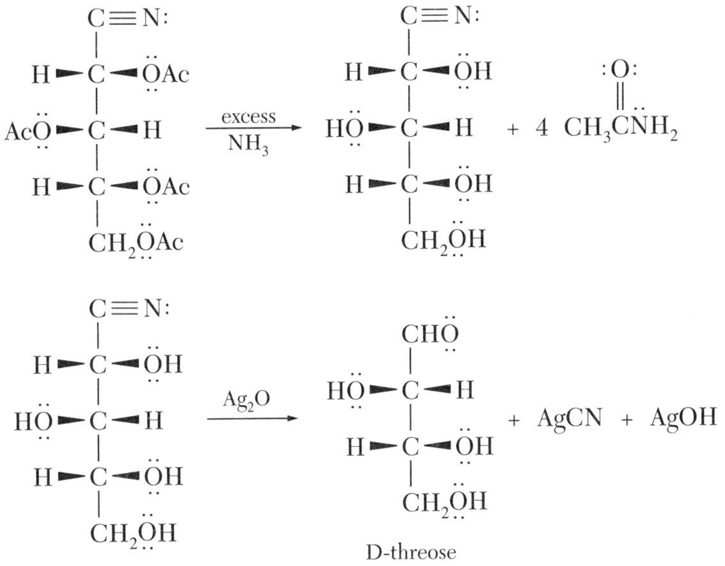

Figure 24.19 Completion of the Wohl degradation of D-xylose. The reaction of the tetraacetate with excess ammonia is an ester to amide conversion of type discussed in Chapter 22. The final reaction (with Ag_2O) brings about the decomposition of a cyanohydrin.

This type of systematic degradation of the carbohydrate molecule has been of great utility in establishing the D configuration of natural carbohydrates. Sequential degradations of higher aldoses eventually lead to glyceraldehyde. Comparison of the glyceraldehyde isolated in these processes with that from natural systems (assigned the D configuration) leads to the conclusion that all have the same configuration about the stereogenic center most distant from the carbonyl group.

The Ruff Degradation An alternative to the Wohl degradation is the **Ruff degradation,** which accomplishes the same end with a different set of reagents. The Ruff degradation also proceeds in four steps. It begins with a controlled oxidation of the aldehyde group of an aldose to a carboxylic acid using bromine in water, followed by conversion of the free acid to the calcium salt using calcium carbonate. These two steps are illustrated in Figure 24.20 for the conversion of D-threose to D-glyceraldehyde. When treated with a ferric salt and hydrogen peroxide, the secondary hydroxyl group adjacent to the carboxylate anion site becomes oxidized to a ketone (see Figure 24.21). On acidification and heating, the free acid undergoes decarboxylation facilitated by the β-hydroxyl group, as shown in Figure 24.21.

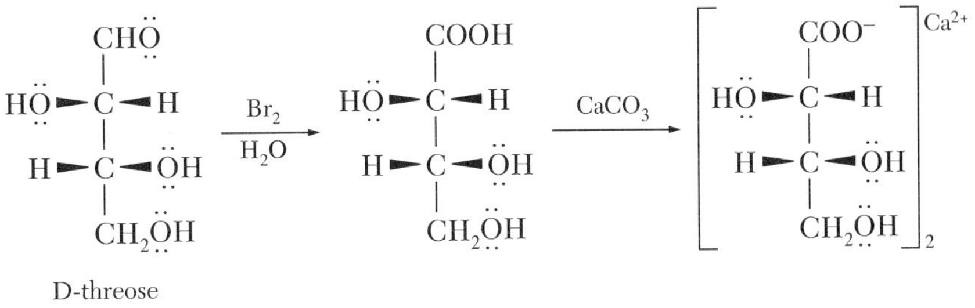

Figure 24.20 First two steps of the Ruff degradation of D-threose. A mild oxidation using bromine in water converts the aldehyde function to a carboxylic acid. Then, the free acid is converted to a calcium salt using calcium carbonate.

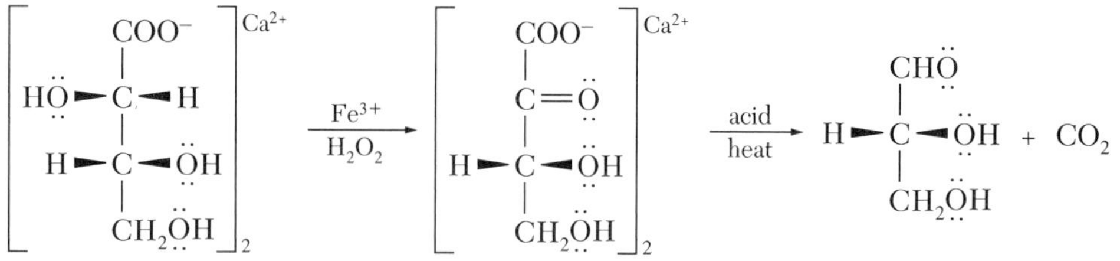

Figure 24.21 Completion of the Ruff degradation of D-threose. Overall, one carbon atom has been removed from the carbonyl terminus of the aldose. The position originally adjacent to the carbonyl group becomes the carbonyl carbon atom in the product. The stereochemistry about the other original stereogenic centers is maintained throughout the reaction sequence.

ESTER FORMATION

The hydroxyl groups of carbohydrates are of two types. While most are of the normal alcohol type, some (those bonded to an anomeric carbon atom) are part of a hemiacetal or hemiketal function. The two types of hydroxyl groups behave differently with some reagents and similarly with others (we have already seen some examples of this difference).

We can esterify *all* of the hydroxyl groups of carbohydrates by the usual methods. The most common types of ester derivatives are acetates. To prepare acetates we usually treat the carbohydrate with acetic anhydride and a basic catalyst, as is illustrated in Figure 24.22 for reaction of D-glucose.

PROBLEM 24.21

If the reaction in Figure 24.22 is performed at a higher temperature, the α-anomer of the pentaacetate is also formed. Explain why.

Consider the sequence of reactions shown in Figure 24.23. The starting compound is a methyl glycoside. The glycoside ring is unaffected by treatment with acetic anhydride, but all of the hydroxyl groups are acylated. When the acylated glycoside is treated with cold, dilute aqueous acid, the highly sensitive glycoside (acetal) linkage is hydrolyzed, but the acetate ester groups remain intact (refluxing with aqueous acid is required to hydrolyze them). The final product has three acetate groups and one free hydroxyl group. The position of the hydroxyl group reflects the size of the initial ring. The reaction started with a furanose, so the free hydroxyl group is at the fourth carbon atom of the chain. If the initial ring had six members (a pyranose system), the free hydroxyl group would have been at the fifth carbon atom of the chain. Thus if we are working with a ring of unknown size, we can carry out a series of reactions like those shown in Figure 24.23 to help us to determine the ring size.

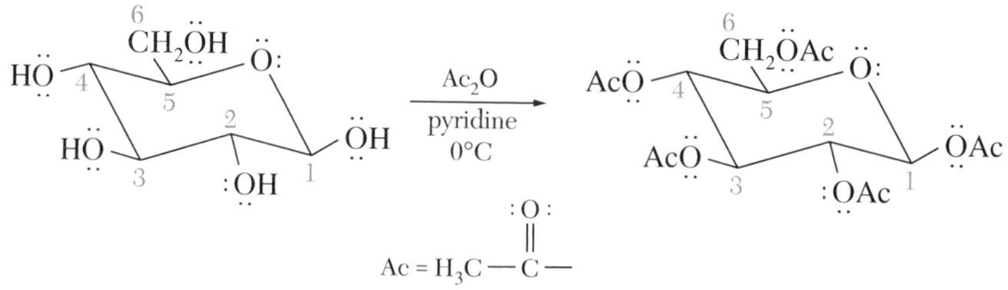

Figure 24.22 Conversion of β-D-glucose to a pentaacetate. β-D-Glucose is converted to a pentaacetate by treatment with acetic anhydride in pyridine at 0°C.

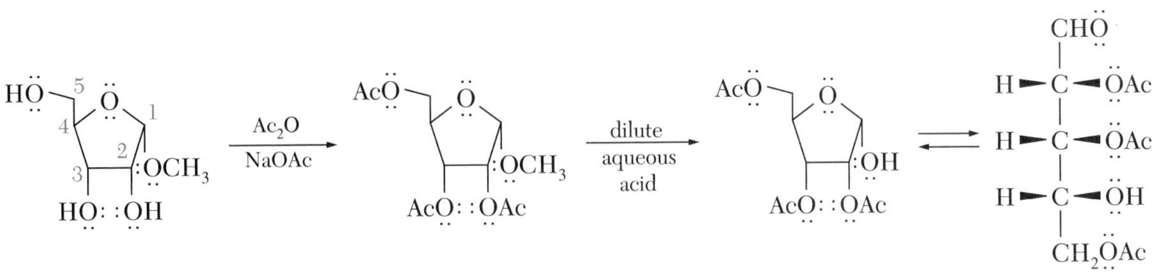

Figure 24.23 Acetylation and ring opening of a glycoside. The position of the free hydroxyl group in the open-chain structure reflects the ring size of the original structure.

ETHER FORMATION

The different types of hydroxyl groups of a carbohydrate differ greatly in their ease of conversion of alkoxy groups. As we have seen, a hemiacetal hydroxyl group is easily converted to a full acetal alkoxy group (that is, a glycosidic linkage) by refluxing with an alcohol and an anhydrous acid catalyst. However, ordinary alcohol hydroxyl groups are unaffected under these conditions—they are *not* converted into ether linkages by treatment with an alcohol and anhydrous acid. However, they can be converted into ethers using the Williamson method.

The structural determination of carbohydrates has often depended on studies of their *methyl* ethers. To prepare such methyl ethers the carbohydrate is treated with base (usually sodium hydroxide) and a methylating agent. The base converts the weakly nucleophilic hydroxyl groups to strongly nucleophilic alkoxide groups. The methylating agent can be any convenient reagent that has a good leaving group attached to a methyl group. Iodomethane or dimethyl sulfate is commonly used. (For syntheses involving carbohydrates as reagents, other ether linkages are more convenient than methyl.)

In such ether-forming reactions we must be careful to protect the anomeric carbon site. Generally, this is done by transforming the site into a glycosidic linkage. This protection is necessary because the hemiacetal is in equilibrium with the open-chain structure, which is reactive under the basic conditions required for the ether-forming reaction (see Section 24.3). Figure 24.24 shows a reaction sequence that converts the hydroxyl groups of D-ribose to methyl ether linkages. Notice how the anomeric position is protected, and note that the position of the free hydroxyl group in the final open-chain structure reflects the size of the ring in the starting material.

The ether derivatives of carbohydrates are named by designating the *oxygen* of the carbon at which the ether linkage is located. For example, the final product of the sequence of reactions shown in Figure 24.24 is named 2,3,5-tri-*O*-methyl-D-ribose. When an alkyl group is part of the glycosidic linkage, we precede the fundamental name of the carbohydrate with the name of

Figure 24.24 Methylation of a glycoside. This sequence of reactions illustrates the significant differences between the chemistry of the different hydroxyl groups in carbohydrates. In the first reaction the hydroxyl group at the anomeric position is methylated by treatment with methanol under conditions of *acid* catalysis. The remaining hydroxyl groups are unaffected by this treatment. However, these other hydroxyl groups are methylated on treatment with *base* and dimethyl sulfate (the Williamson method). Finally, treatment with dilute mineral acid cleaves the glycosidic linkage but leaves the ordinary ether linkages intact.

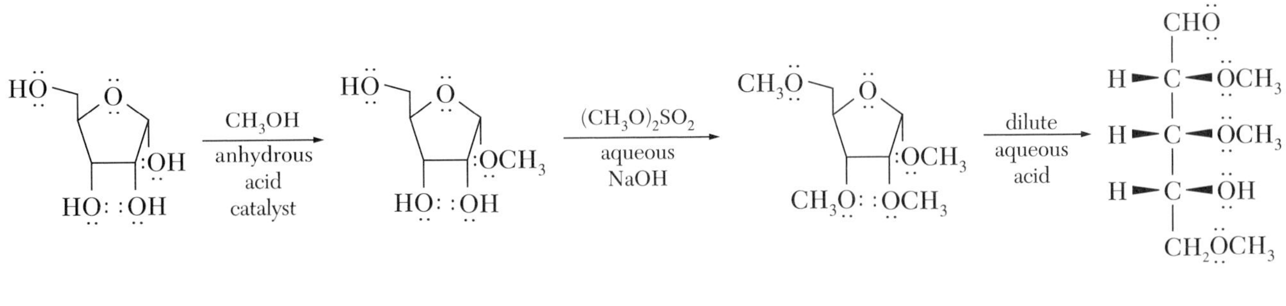

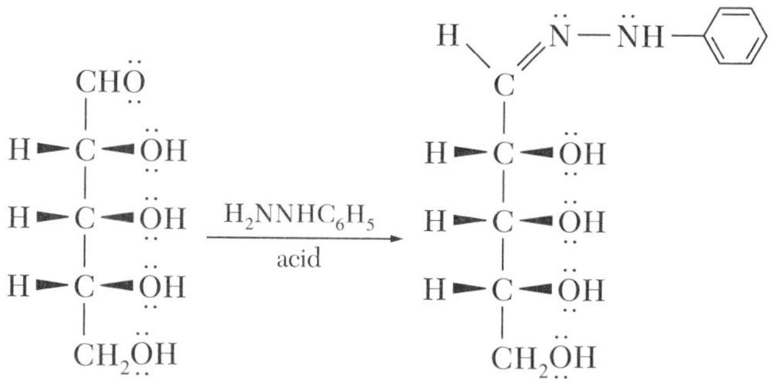

Figure 24.25 Phenylhydrazone formation from D-ribose.

that alkyl group. For example, the third structure in the reaction sequence in Figure 24.24 is named methyl 2,3,5-tri-*O*-methyl-α-D-ribofuranoside.

OSAZONE FORMATION

Carbohydrates undergo many reactions typical of ordinary aldehydes and ketones. Among these is the reaction with primary amines to form imines, as discussed in Chapter 19. We saw an example of this type of reaction in the Wohl degradation with the formation of an oxime from an aldose. As a further example, aldoses react with phenylhydrazine under conditions of acid catalysis to yield phenylhydrazones, as illustrated in Figure 24.25.

In the presence of *excess* phenylhydrazine, the initially formed phenylhydrazone undergoes an oxidation at the site adjacent to the first reaction, and the carbonyl group thus generated reacts again with phenylhydrazine. The product of this double reaction with phenylhydrazine is known as an **osazone.** Once formed, the osazone generally precipitates from solution and no further reaction occurs. Osazone formation with D-ribose is illustrated in Figure 24.26.

Osazones have played a significant role in the history of carbohydrate chemistry. One of their principal uses was in the determination of the stereochemical relationships among carbohydrates. For example, of the aldohexoses, only D-mannose forms the same osazone as does D-glucose. This observation allowed early investigators to establish that these two aldohexoses differ only in their stereochemistry at the second carbon atom of the chain, as is illustrated in Figure 24.27.

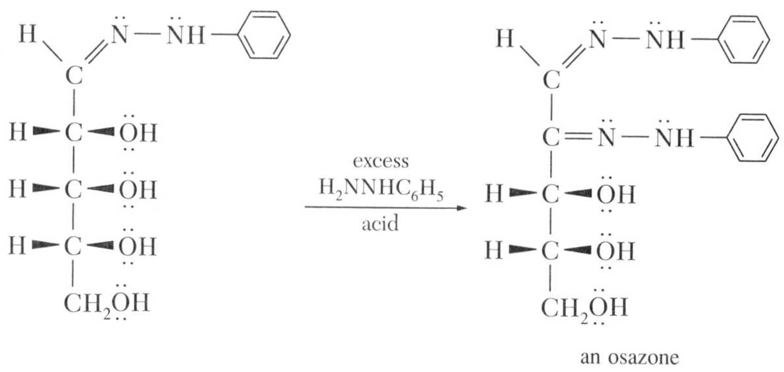

Figure 24.26 Osazone formation from D-ribose.

an osazone

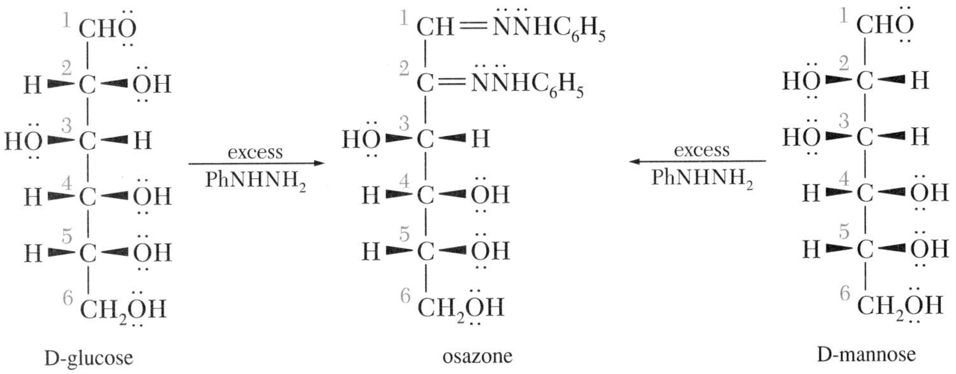

D-glucose — excess $PhNHNH_2$ → osazone ← excess $PhNHNH_2$ — D-mannose

Figure 24.27 Osazone formation from D-glucose and D-mannose. D-Glucose and D-mannose form the same osazone. This observation allowed early investigators to infer that the parent carbohydrates must differ *only* in their stereochemistry at the second carbon atom of the chain.

PROBLEM 24.22 Which pairs of D-aldoses in Figure 24.6 yield identical osazone products?

CONTROLLED OXIDATIONS OF CARBOHYDRATES AND THEIR DERIVATIVES

Mild Oxidation The two most easily oxidized groups in aldoses are the aldehyde group and the primary alcohol group. We can oxidize *both* of these groups using dilute nitric acid, or we can oxidize *only* the aldehyde group using bromine in a solution buffered to pH ~ 5.5. (Although we are accustomed to using bromine as a brominating agent, we should always remember that it is also an oxidizing agent, as are the other halogens.) These reactions are summarized in Figure 24.28.

It is also possible to oxidize the aldehyde group of aldoses with Tollens' reagent (silver nitrate in aqueous ammonia), Fehling's solution (cupric tartrate in aqueous solution), or Benedict's reagent (a cupric salt in aqueous sodium citrate). All three of these are used to provide revealing visual tests for what

Figure 24.28 Oxidation of aldoses to aldaric and aldonic acids.

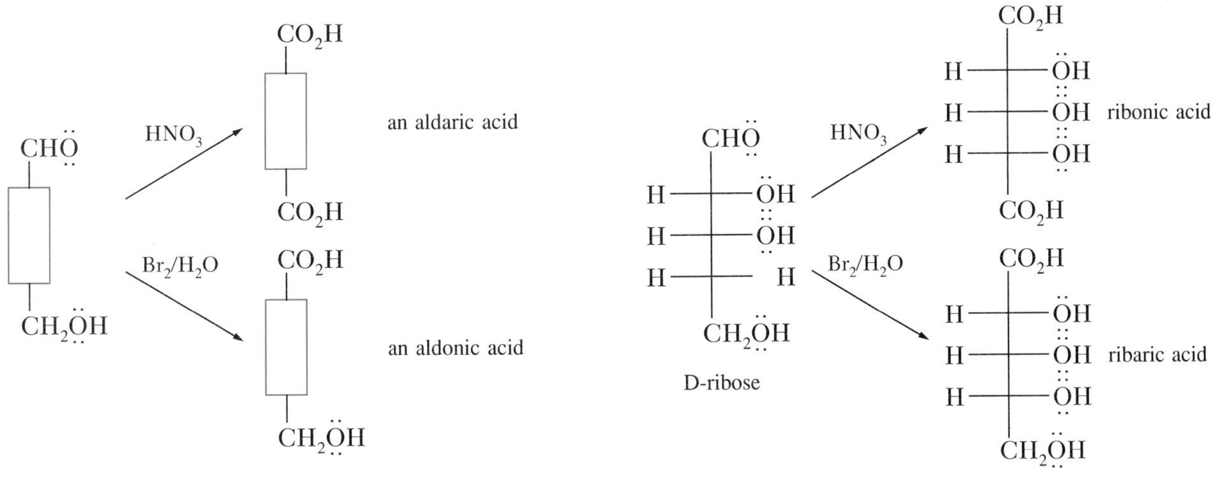

HNO_3 → an aldaric acid; Br_2/H_2O → an aldonic acid

D-ribose: HNO_3 → ribonic acid; Br_2/H_2O → ribaric acid

are known as **reducing sugars.** In each case the sugar (carbohydrate) reduces the metal ion of the test reagent. A reducing sugar is defined as one that gives a positive test with these reagents (i.e, one that is easily oxidized by mild reagents). These tests are summarized in the following paragraphs.

- *Tollens' Test.* The carbohydrate is treated with silver nitrate in aqueous ammonia. The diamminesilver(I) ion $[Ag(NH_3)_2]^+$ is present in this solution and serves as the oxidizing agent. If the carbohydrate is a reducing sugar, the silver(I) species is reduced to metallic silver (Ag(0)), which appears as a shiny, silver mirror on the inside of the test vessel.
- *Fehling's and Benedict's Tests.* The carbohydrate is mixed with a cupric salt (Cu^{2+}) in the presence of tartrate or citrate ion. The cupric ion serves as the oxidizing agent. If the carbohydrate is a reducing sugar, the copper(II) is reduced to copper(I). A red precipitate of Cu_2O forms, constituting the positive test for a reducing sugar. Test kits for sugar in urine are based on Benedict's reagent.

What kinds of carbohydrates are reducing sugars? First, we can say that all aldoses are reducing sugars since they contain an aldehyde group. You might be skeptical of this general rule, since you have learned that aldoses exist principally in the cyclic hemiacetal form. However, since the cyclized hemiacetal and open-chain forms of aldoses are in dynamic equilibrium over the whole pH range, the equilibrium can shift to generate more free aldehyde. Thus there is always free aldehyde form present to be oxidized and allow a positive test. In contrast, if a ring *cannot* open to the open-chain free aldehyde form, it *cannot* give a positive test with these reagents. For example, methyl glycosides do not give a positive test for reducing sugars with these reagents. The full acetal linkage in such compounds does not open in neutral or basic aqueous solutions.

The situation with ketoses is not as straightforward as with aldoses. We might anticipate that ketoses would not be reducing sugars since ketones are generally inert toward even strong oxidizing agents. However, simple ketoses such as fructose *are* reducing sugars—they give a positive reaction with the various test reagents. How can this be? To understand this phenomenon we must consider the reactions that a ketose such as D-fructose can undergo in aqueous basic solution.

We will consider D-fructose in aqueous basic solution as our prototypical example. In such a solution, an equilibrium is established involving the free ketone and an enolate anion, just as it would be for other aliphatic carbonyl compounds placed in a basic solution. Other acid/base equilibria are also established. The equilibrium of significance for our present discussion is shown in Figure 24.29. Proceeding through an **enediol** intermediate species, D-fructose is equilibrated with D-glucose and D-mannose, and these aldoses are in fact responsible for the positive test for D-fructose with the mild oxidizing reagents.

PROBLEM 24.23 Name all of the aldohexoses that will give optically active dicarboxylic acids on treatment with nitric acid.

PROBLEM 24.24 Examine the structure of maltose shown in Figure 24.16. Do you expect it to be a reducing sugar? Explain why or why not.

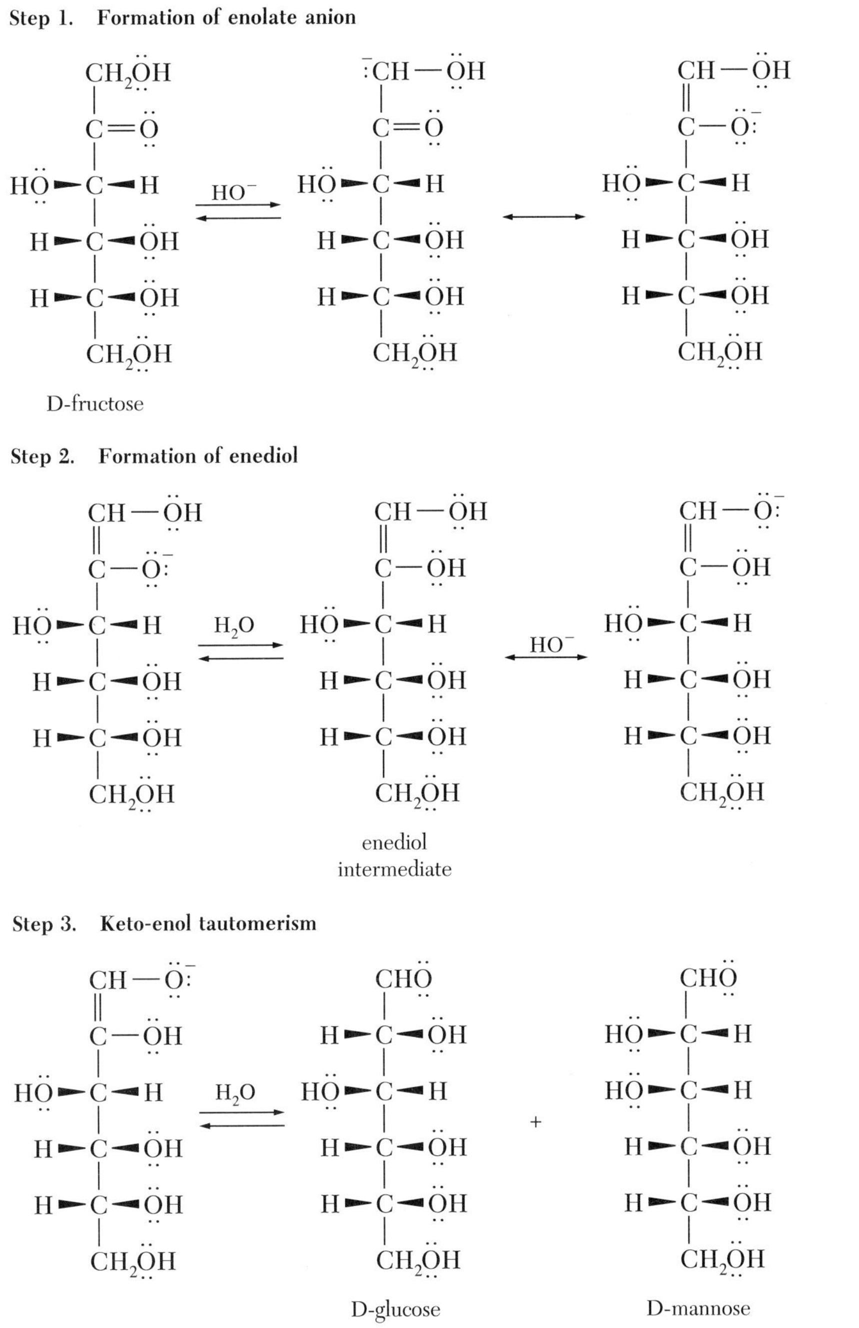

Figure 24.29 Isomerization of D-fructose to a pair of aldoses in aqueous base. D-Fructose gives a positive test as a reducing sugar because it is isomerized to a pair of aldoses under the test conditions. The equilibrium proceeds through an intermediate enediol in which hydroxyl groups are attached to each of a pair of doubly bound carbon atoms.

Step 1. Formation of enolate anion

D-fructose

Step 2. Formation of enediol

enediol intermediate

Step 3. Keto-enol tautomerism

D-glucose

D-mannose

PROBLEM 24.25 Try to deduce the structures of D-(+)-xylose, D-(−)-idose, and D-(−)-gulose *solely* from the data given in this problem. Do *not* use Figure 24.6 to help. By working this problem in this way you will follow the same thought processes as early carbohydrate chemists did in inferring the structures of the carbohydrates. Use only the following data:

D-(+)-Xylose is an aldopentose. On oxidation with nitric acid it is converted to an optically inactive dicarboxylic acid. When the Kiliani-Fischer synthesis is applied to D-(+)-xylose, a mixture to two aldohexoses, D-(−)-gulose and D-(−)-idose is obtained. Both of these hexoses are oxidized by nitric acid to optically active dicarboxylic acids. No other aldose of either the D- or L-family is oxidized to the same dicarboxylic acid as the one formed on oxidation of D-(−)-idose. However, the dicarboxylic acid obtained from the oxidation of D-(−)-gulose is also obtained by the oxidation of an L-series aldohexose. In addition to working out the structures of the three required D-aldopentoses, also suggest a structure (and a name—you can now look at Figure 24.6) for the L-family aldohexose referred to above.

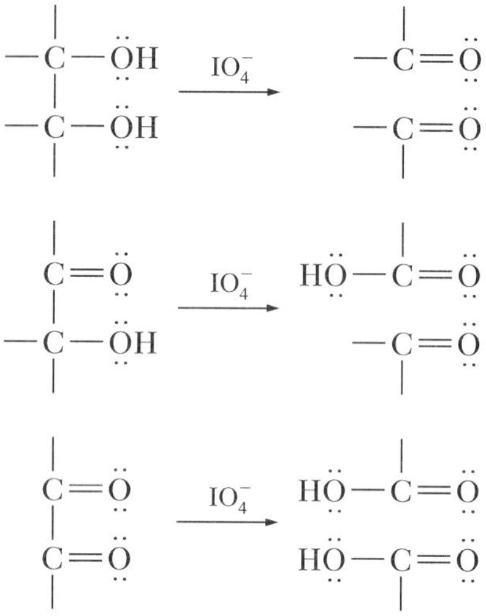

Periodate Oxidation of Glycosides If we add periodate ion (IO_4^-) to compounds containing two or more hydroxyl or carbonyl groups attached to adjacent carbon atoms, an oxidative cleavage occurs. The carbon-carbon bond linking these adjacent centers is broken, and the level of oxidation of each of these carbon atoms increases. This cleavage is illustrated in Figure 24.30.

The presence of either a hydroxyl group or a carbonyl group at each carbon of a carbohydrate makes it a candidate for extensive oxidation by periodate. By careful performance of the periodate oxidation (that is, by measuring the amount of periodate consumed and the amount of each product formed), we can use this reaction for a degradative structural analysis of a carbohydrate substrate.

Although simple carbohydrates *are* oxidized by periodate, in practice we commonly use the reaction only with glycosides. Periodate oxidation of a simple carbohydrate tells us only if the carbohydrate is an aldose or a ketose and how many carbons are present. With a glycoside we can also determine the size of the ring, and often we can deduce whether the glycoside is derived from a D- or L-carbohydrate.

Consider the periodate oxidation of a simple glycoside to demonstrate the analytical utility of the reaction. The complete (quantitative) oxidation of methyl α-D-ribofuranoside by periodate followed by acid workup is shown in Figure 24.31. The three fragments tell us that the substrate was a D-carbohydrate

Figure 24.30 Cleavage of carbon-carbon bonds by periodate ion. The cleavage of a carbon-carbon bond by periodate ion requires the presence of either a hydroxyl group or a carbonyl group on each of the carbons.

methyl α-D-ribofuranoside
The bond cleaved by periodate is indicated by ～～.

glyoxal D-glyceraldehyde

Figure 24.31 Periodate oxidation of methyl α-D-ribofuranoside. The oxidation is allowed to go to completion prior to the addition of acid. The substrate has only one site for oxidation by periodate—the carbon-carbon bond between the second and third carbon atoms. No other adjacent pair of carbon atoms bears free hydroxyl or carbonyl groups. After acid workup, some products have adjacent carbons bearing free hydroxyl or carbonyl groups, but at this stage periodate is no longer present to oxidize such linkages.

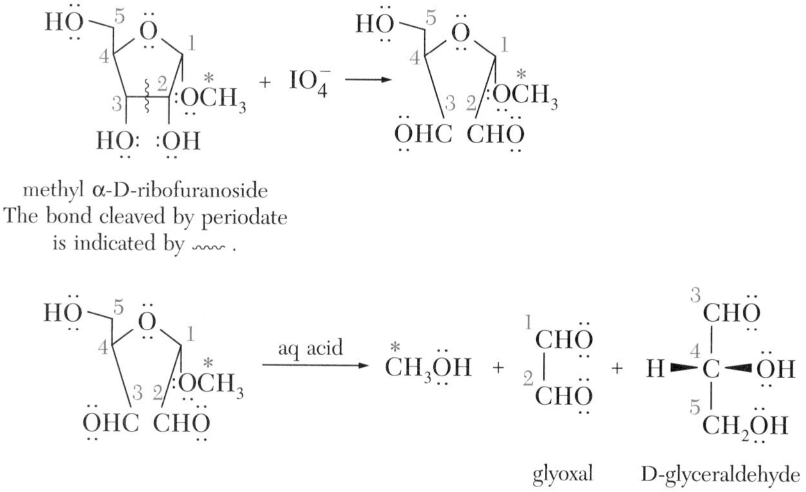

derivative, that it was a methyl glycoside, and that it was an aldopentose. Only one equivalent of periodate was consumed, indicating that only one carbon-carbon bond was cleaved. The D-glyceraldehyde product results from the third, fourth, and fifth carbon atoms of the substrate, and the glyoxal results from the first and second carbon atoms.

The periodate oxidation does *not* tell us certain points about the structure of the substrate. These points involve the stereochemistry at the carbon atoms that are oxidized. Specifically, we learn nothing about the stereochemistry of the anomeric carbon or the second and third carbons of the substrate. Either an α- or β-glycoside of any D-aldopentose would yield the same products.

PROBLEM 24.26 Show how you could differentiate between methyl β-D-glucopyranoside and methyl β-D-glucofuranoside using periodate cleavage reactions. Could you use this method to differentiate between methyl α-D-glucopyranoside and methyl β-D-glucopyranoside?

PROBLEM 24.27 Predict the products of periodate oxidation followed by aqueous acid workup for each of the compounds listed below. Also indicate the relative amount of each product formed and the relative amount of periodate consumed in the reaction.

a. methyl β-D-mannopyranoside
b. ethyl α-D-galactofuranoside
c. methyl α-D-apiofuranoside (see "Biological Carbohydrates of Nonlinear Structure," earlier in this chapter)

Steps to Solving the Problem

Solution to Problem 24.27a

1. Consider the structure of the glycoside of interest and note which bonds will be cleaved. The structure of the glycoside substrate in this oxidation is shown below, and the carbon-carbon bonds that are susceptible to periodate cleavage are indicated.

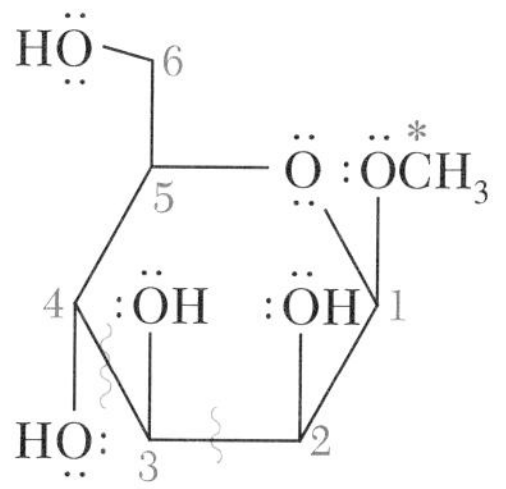

HO 6 / 5 O :OCH$_3$ * / 4 :OH :OH 1 / HO: 3 2

2. How much periodate will be consumed in this oxidation? Each cleaved bond requires one equivalent of periodate, so two equivalents will be consumed. The immediate products of the periodate cleavage are shown below in the same relative positions as in the substrate. Note that the third carbon atom of the mannose structure is oxidized to formic acid by the cleavage of *two* of its bonds.

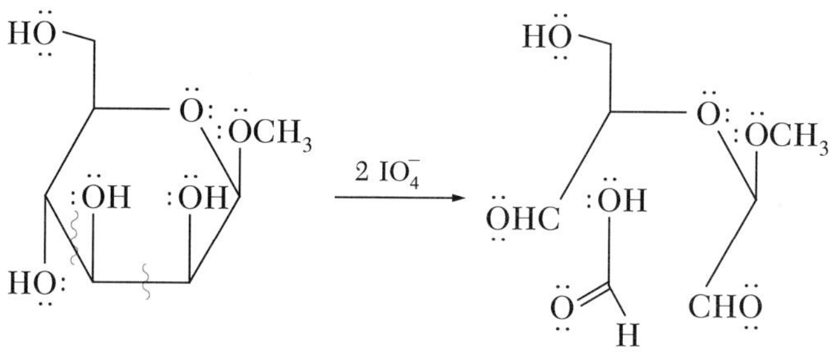

HO: —; O:; :OCH$_3$; :OH; :OH; HO: $\xrightarrow{2\ IO_4^-}$ HO —; O:; :OCH$_3$; OHC; :OH; O=; H; CHO

3. What organic products will we isolate from this oxidation? On workup with aqueous acid the acetal linkage is cleaved, yielding the final products.

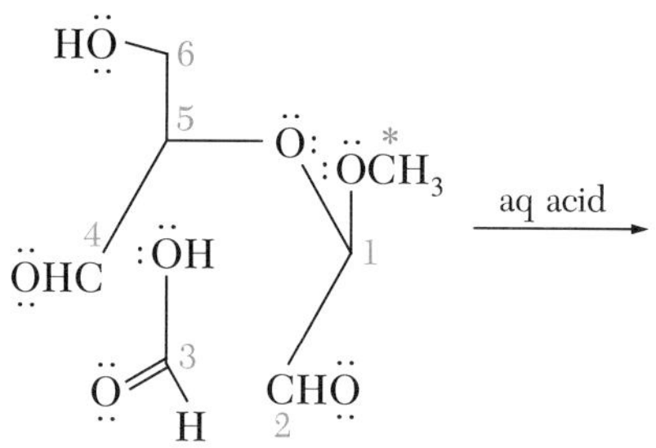

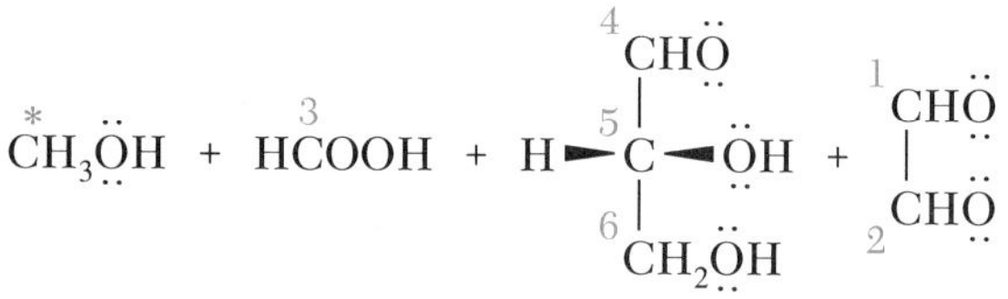

HO 6; 5; O:; * :OCH$_3$; 4 OHC; :OH; 1; 3 O=; H; CHO 2 $\xrightarrow{\text{aq acid}}$

$\overset{*}{CH_3OH}$ + $\overset{3}{HCOOH}$ + H—C(5)(CHO 4)(CH$_2$OH 6)—OH + CHO(1)—CHO(2)

PROBLEM 24.28 The following products are isolated after periodate oxidation of a glycoside with aqueous acid workup:

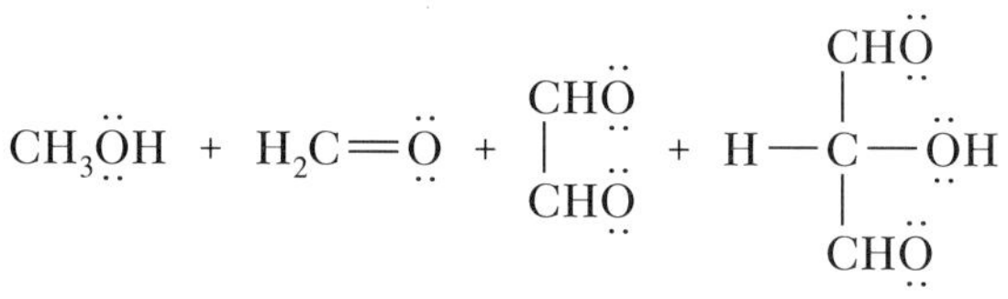

CH_3OH + $H_2C{=}O$ + CHO—CHO + H—C(CHO)(CHO)—OH

The oxidation procedure uses two equivalents of periodate for each equivalent of the glycoside. Propose a structure for the starting glycoside. What structural features of the starting glycoside can you *not* specify, given this data about the products and the periodate consumption.

24.5 Applications of Carbohydrate Chemistry to Organic Synthesis

When chemists first began the systematic study of carbohydrates and their derivatives, the main problems of interest were the determination of the structures of different carbohydrates and the development of methods for their synthesis. With these goals firmly accomplished, the interest of organic chemists in carbohydrates has turned in more recent years in other directions. One area that has become particularly significant is the use of carbohydrates as reagents for the synthesis of other organic compounds. Since carbohydrates bear several stereogenic centers and are isolable in pure form from natural sources, they can be important starting materials for the syntheses of other complex compounds that also contain one or more stereogenic centers.

In this section we will look at an example in which a carbohydrate is used for this purpose. In Chapter 29 we will consider another example of the use of a carbohydrate as a chiral starting material for the laboratory synthesis of a complex organic molecule related to a nucleoside. This area is an ongoing field of endeavour for organic chemists; it involves the development not only of new syntheses but also of new reagents and new methods for syntheses.

MANNITOL AS A CHIRAL STARTING MATERIAL FOR ORGANIC SYNTHESES

The Source of the Chiral Reagent If we reduce the carbonyl group of D-mannose by catalytic hydrogenation or some other method, we obtain the hexadiol D-mannitol (**24.3**). (D-mannitol also occurs *naturally* in numerous sources, including manna and seaweed.) D-mannitol is thus readily available to organic chemists.

CH_2OH
HO—C—H
HO—C—H
H—C—OH
H—C—OH
CH_2OH

D-mannitol
24.3

The structure of D-mannitol is intriguing in that the *upper* and *lower* halves have a relationship analogous to that of the two arms of a single-bladed propellor. We can see this relationship in the IUPAC name for the material, (2*R*,3*R*,4*R*,5*R*)-1,2,3,4,5,6-hexanehexadiol. If we could chemically cut this molecule in the center, between the third and fourth carbon atoms, we would have two stereochemically identical halves.

In fact, we *can* cleave the D-mannitol molecule in this way. We obtain from one equivalent of D-mannitol two equivalents of an important reagent bearing a single stereogenic center and having stereochemical purity identical to that of the natural starting material. We accomplish the cleavage by first treating the D-mannitol with acetone in the presence of an acid catalyst. Under the proper conditions, this procedure binds four of the hydroxyl groups into a pair of ketal linkages, as shown in Equation 24.1. (Recall the formation of ketals from Chapter 19.) The ketal linkages formed between acetone and hydroxyls on adjacent carbon atoms are known as *acetonide linkages*, *isopropylidene linkages*, or more rigorously, 2,2-dimethyldioxolanes. (Other ketal products can be obtained from D-mannitol and acetone using modified reaction conditions.)

Eqn. 24.1

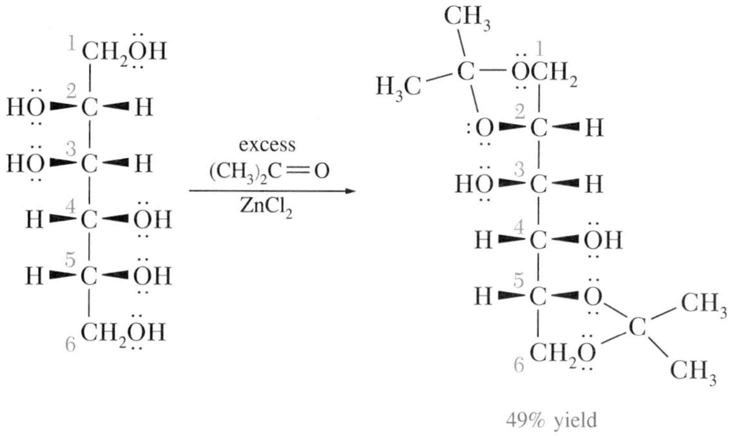

excess $(CH_3)_2C{=}O$, $ZnCl_2$

49% yield

We refer to the product in Equation 24.1 as D-mannitol diacetonide, or 1,2:5,6-di-*O*-isopropylidene-D-mannitol. It contains a pair of hydroxyl groups on adjacent (the third and fourth) carbon atoms, leaving the carbon-carbon bond between these atoms susceptible to cleavage by reagents such as periodate. The cleavage of this linkage yields two identical halves, as shown in Equation 24.2.

Eqn. 24.2

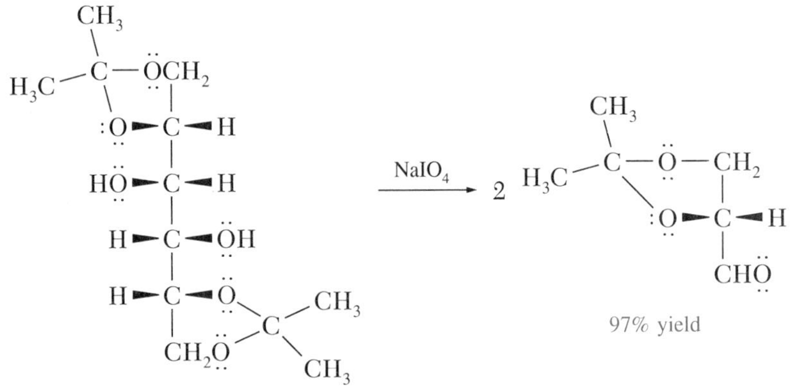

$NaIO_4$

97% yield

You should recognize the product in Equation 24.2 as the acetonide derivative of D-glyceraldehyde. (Its preparation from D-mannitol is more efficient than from D-glyceraldehyde itself. D-Glyceraldehyde in pure form dimerizes rapidly and thus is difficult to use in syntheses. The acetonide of D-glyceraldehyde also polymerizes rapidly when pure and therefore must be kept in solution and used immediately after preparation.)

The product in Equation 24.2 can now serve as a convenient reagent for the introduction of a stereogenic center in a synthetic target without the necessity of resolving enantiomers. The carbohydrate starting material provides the chiral reagent in optically pure form. It can then be used in a variety of syntheses where a target material bearing a single stereogenic center in optically pure form is required. An example of the use of this carbohydrate-derived chiral reagent is shown in the following section.

The Synthesis of (*R*)-Glycerol 3-Phosphate (*R*)-Glycerol 3-phosphate (**24.4**) is a naturally occurring material that forms in cells via numerous routes. Once generated by normal metabolic pathways, (*R*)-glycerol 3-phosphate reacts further to produce, among other substances, the phospholipids that constitute the major components of cell walls. A convenient *laboratory* synthesis of (*R*)-glycerol 3-phosphate uses D-mannitol as a chiral starting material.

CH_2OH — HO–C–H — CH_2–O–P(=O)$(OH)_2$

(*R*)-glycerol 3-phosphate

24.4

The route to (*R*)-glycerol 3-phosphate from the acetonide of D-glyceraldehyde is shown in Equations 24.3 and 24.4. The first step (Equation 24.3) involves a catalytic reduction of the aldehyde group to a primary alcohol. This step is followed by reaction of the primary alcohol with phosphorus oxychloride (Equation 24.4), which forms an ester linkage between the alcohol and the phosphorus. In the workup, water addition yields the free acid, which is ultimately isolated as the barium salt.

Eqn. 24.3

acetonide (CHO) $\xrightarrow[Ni]{H_2}$ acetonide (CH_2OH)

73% yield

Eqn. 24.4

acetonide (CH_2OH) $\xrightarrow{POCl_3}$ acetonide ($CH_2OP(O)Cl_2$) $\xrightarrow{H_2O}$ acetonide ($CH_2OP(O)(OH)_2$)

acetonide ($CH_2OP(O)(OH)_2$) $\xrightarrow{Ba(OH)_2}$ CH_2OH — HO–C–H — CH_2O–PO_3Ba

37% yield

This approach to the synthesis of (*R*)-glycerol 3-phosphate avoids all of the difficulties associated with the resolution of enantiomers that would occur if we were to use an achiral starting reagent. From this point the entire range of natural phospholipids are available for laboratory chemical synthesis in optically pure form.

PROBLEM 24.29 Consider the variety of methods available for the reduction of an aldehyde to a primary alcohol. What other method(s) might have been used for the conversion in Equation 24.3?

24.6 Disaccharides and Polysaccharides

In our earlier discussion of glycosides we pointed out that a hydroxyl group of one monosaccharide unit could participate in glycoside formation with the anomeric carbon site of another monosaccharide unit. The resultant glycoside is a *disaccharide*. If many monosaccharide units are linked in this manner, the resulting species is a *polysaccharide*.

Disaccharides and polysaccharides are substances of great biological significance. As *complex carbohydrates* they serve as major caloric sources for animal species. Moreover, they constitute major portions of the structural components of cell walls and specific recognition sites at cell surfaces. In this section we will briefly consider some structural aspects of specific di- and polysaccharides along with their chemistry and biochemistry.

CHARACTERISTICS OF DI- AND POLYSACCHARIDES

Maltose Maltose is one of the simplest disaccharides. Although we can isolate maltose from plant sources, it is probably not present in plants as the free molecule. Instead, it is a component of more complex structures (starch) that are hydrolyzed to maltose and other simpler substances by enzymatic degradation.

We can learn about the structure of maltose by performing a series of chemical and biochemical reactions with it. If the glycosidic linkage of maltose is hydrolyzed, D-glucose is the only monosaccharide produced. Thus, we infer that maltose consists of two D-glucose units joined by a glycosidic linkage.

However, maltose is a reducing sugar; that is, it is oxidized by silver nitrate in aqueous ammonia and produces silver metal from the oxidizing agent. To understand this result, we need to recognize that there are two anomeric carbon atoms in a disaccharide, one in each monosaccharide unit. The glycosidic linkage present in maltose involves only one of the two anomeric carbons. The other anomeric carbon remains free (or as a hemiacetal).

One of the ordinary hydroxyls of one glucose unit is involved in the glycosidic linkage with the anomeric carbon of the second glucose unit. If the free hydroxyl groups of maltose are methylated prior to hydrolysis, it can be determined that the hydroxyl group involved in the glycosidic linkage is at the 4-position of the glucose.

The configuration of the glycosidic linkage is the only remaining structural feature we need to determine for the maltose molecule. We can do this in several ways. With modern techniques of nuclear magnetic resonance, we would look for the chemical shift of the hydrogen at the glycosidic carbon. From the spectra of other model compounds we know that a hydrogen locked into an equatorial position on a six-membered ring comes into resonance slightly downfield (by ~0.5 ppm) from a hydrogen in an axial position. In the ^1H NMR spectrum of maltose we indeed find the signal for the hydrogen of the glycosidic linkage downfield from the chemical shift we would anticipate if it were in an axial position.

We can now draw the structure of maltose. We draw the glycosidic glucose ring in the more stable of the possible chair conformations with the maximum number of bulky groups in equatorial positions. We then place the anomeric hydrogen in an equatorial position, leaving the oxygen joining the two monosaccharide units in an axial position. (This position is *not* unfavorable—remember the anomeric effect.) The structure we thus obtain for maltose involves an α-glycosidic linkage, as shown in Figure 24.32.

Maltose is a trivial name that by itself does not convey structural information. We name maltose in a systematic manner by considering the glycosidic glucose portion as a substituent at the 4-*O*-position of the hemiacetal glucose portion. We thus name the structure shown in Figure 24.32 4-*O*-(α-D-glucopyranosyl)-α-D-glucopyranose.

The configuration of the glycosidic anomeric carbon of maltose was determined using biochemical techniques prior to the advent of NMR methods. The hydrolysis of maltose can be catalyzed by enzymes such as α-D-glucosidase from yeast, which also catalyzes the hydrolysis of methyl α-D-glucopyranoside. However, maltose hydrolysis is not catalyzed by enzymes such as β-D-glucosidase from almonds, which catalyzes the hydrolysis of methyl β-glucopyranoside.

Since maltose *does* contain an α-glycosidic linkage, it is a useful caloric source for humans. The human digestive system contains enzymes (α-amylases) that catalyze the hydrolysis of di- and polysaccharides with α-glycosidic linkages but not those with β-glycosidic linkages.

Cellobiose Cellobiose is another disaccharide that does not occur as a free species in natural systems but is produced by the partial degradation of plant materials such as cotton or wood (cellulose). If the same structural determination experiments we discussed for maltose are performed on cellobiose, we find fundamental similarities in the structures of the two materials.

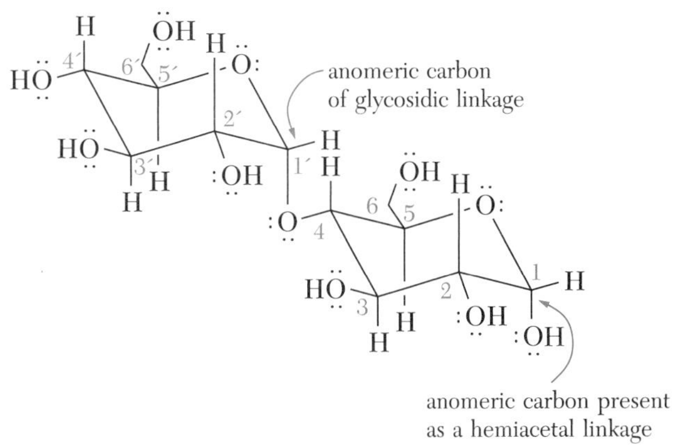

anomeric carbon of glycosidic linkage

anomeric carbon present as a hemiacetal linkage

Figure 24.32 The structure of the disaccharide maltose. The glucopyranoside ring shown at the upper left has its anomeric carbon bound in a glycosidic linkage. The external oxygen to this anomeric carbon is *down* in this standard view; thus the structure is that of an α-glycoside. The glucopyranose ring shown on the lower right uses the 4-position hydroxyl to form the glycosidic linkage with the other monosaccharide unit. This glucopyranose ring is shown here as an α-hemiacetal linkage.

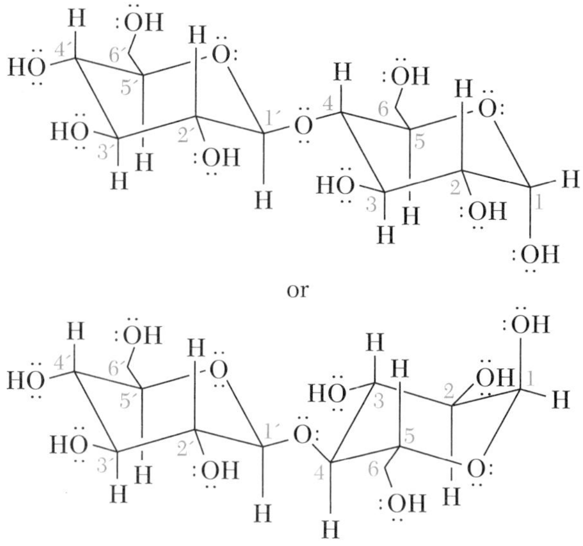

Figure 24.33 Structure of cellobiose, 4-*O*-(*β*-D-glucopyranosyl)-*β*-D-glucopyranose. The disaccharide contains two D-glucose units joined by a *β*-glycosidic linkage. In these structures the hemiacetal linkage of the reducing sugar portion of the compound has an *α*-configuration. Two representations of cellobiose are shown. The lower structure shows the glycosidic linkage (C—O—C) with a more realistic bond angle than does the upper structure. However, the upper structure shows both rings in the standard view for carbohydrate rings and may make it simpler to visualize the monosaccharide components. Both types of representations will be used in our future discussions, depending on the structural point to be emphasized.

or

Cellobiose is a reducing sugar that yields two equivalents of D-glucose on complete hydrolysis. That is, one glycosidic linkage holds together two D-glucose units, and one of the anomeric sites is not bound into a glycosidic linkage. Moreover, studies of the products of methylation and hydrolysis of cellobiose indicate that the 4-position hydroxyl of one D-glucose unit is bound with the anomeric site of the other D-glucose unit, as in maltose.

However, there is a fundamental difference between these two disaccharides. Cellobiose is virtually inert toward the *α*-glucosidase that catalyzes the hydrolysis of maltose, but it undergoes hydrolysis rapidly in the presence of *β*-glucosidase. The ^{1}H NMR of cellobiose also indicates its glycosidic linkage to be of the *β*-configuration. Thus we infer the structure of cellobiose to be that shown in Figure 24.33. Since the human digestive tract contains *α*-glycosidases but not *β*-glycosidases, cellobiose is *not* useful as a human food.

Lactose Lactose is a disaccharide that makes up ~5% of the milk of all mammals; there is slightly more lactose in human milk than in milk from cows. The structure of lactose is shown in Figure 24.34. The disaccharide is composed of one D-glucose and one D-galactose unit (both are pyranoses). The D-galactose unit contributes its anomeric carbon atom to the glycosidic linkage. The D-glucose portion uses its 4-position hydroxyl group to bind to the D-galactose anomeric site, while its anomeric carbon is a hemiacetal. Accordingly, the systematic name for lactose is 4-*O*-(*α*-D-galactopyranosyl)-*α*-D-glucopyranose.

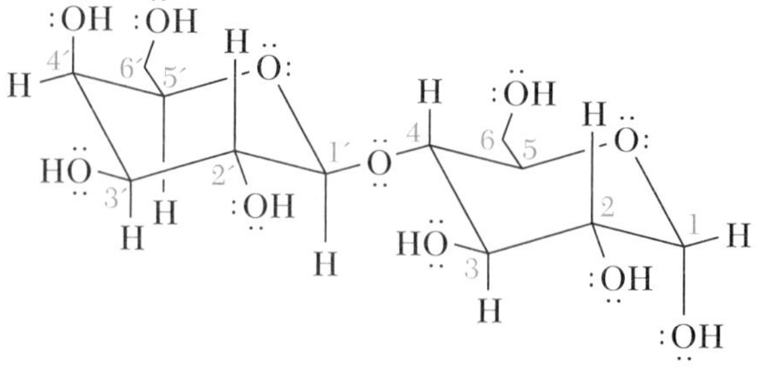

Figure 24.34 Structure of lactose.

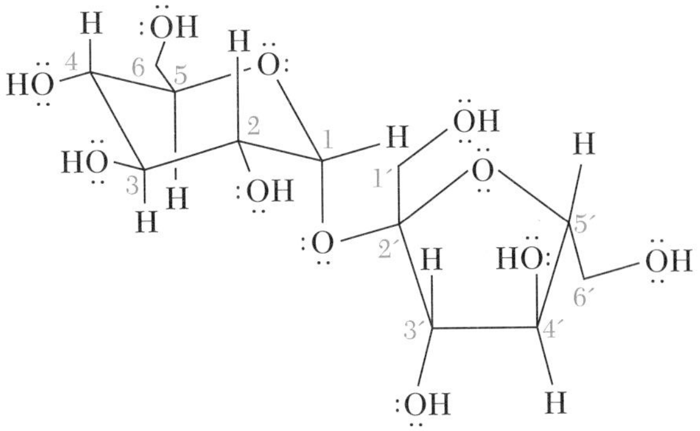

Figure 24.35 Structure of sucrose. The anomeric carbons of the D-glucose and D-fructose units are connected in a glycosidic linkage. Sucrose is not a reducing sugar.

PROBLEM 24.30 Outline the experiments you would perform to determine the complete structure of lactose. Describe the anticipated results of those experiments and explain how they would provide evidence of the structure.

Sucrose Hydrolysis of sucrose (common table sugar obtained from sugar cane and sugar beet) yields one equivalent each of D-fructose and D-glucose. Sucrose contains both a ketose and an aldose monosaccharide unit. However, the most intriguing difference between sucrose and the other disaccharides we have studied so far is that sucrose is not a reducing sugar. The anomeric carbon of each monosaccharide unit is involved in a glycosidic linkage—the anomeric sites are connected *to each other* by an oxygen atom. The structure of sucrose is shown in Figure 24.35.

From the perspective of the D-glucose unit, the glycosidic linkage of sucrose has an α-configuration, so sucrose is susceptible to hydrolysis catalyzed by α-glycosidases and can serve as a caloric source for humans. When viewed from the fructose end of the disaccharide, however, the glycosidic linkage has the β-configuration.

PROBLEM 24.31 Figure 24.35 shows the D-glucose unit (but not the D-fructose unit) in the standard orientation. Make a model of sucrose and draw the structure such that the D-fructose portion has the standard orientation. Verify that the glycosidic linkage has a β-configuration with regard to the D-fructose unit.

The sucrose molecule can be named in either of two ways; each name uses one of the monosaccharide units as the parent and the other as a substituent. These names are α-D-glucopyranosyl-β-D-fructofuranoside and β-D-fructofuranosyl-α-D-glucopyranoside.

Starch We refer to the polysaccharide consisting of an indefinite number of D-glucose units joined by α-glycosidic linkages as **starch.** Starch is a complex carbohydrate that serves as the most important caloric source for humans.

In the forms commonly stored by plants, starch consists of two types of D-glucopyranoside polymers. One of these forms, *soluble starch*, contains only linkages of the type we find in maltose; that is, the glycosidic linkages are all of the α-configuration and join the anomeric site of one D-glucose unit to the

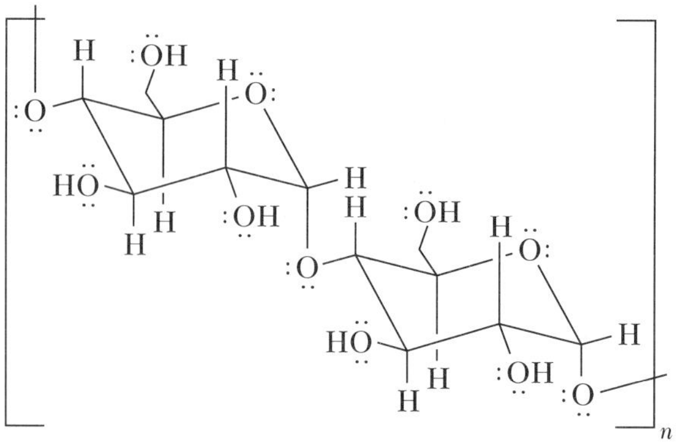

Figure 24.36 Structure of soluble starch (amylose). Soluble starch is a polymer of D-glucose units with linkages between the anomeric carbon and the 4-position hydroxyl oxygen of adjacent units. At one end of the polymeric chain there is a free anomeric center, while at the other end there is a free 4-position hydroxyl group.

4-position hydroxyl of the adjacent D-glucose unit. Soluble starch thus has a *polymaltose* structure, as shown in Figure 24.36. We refer to amylose as *soluble starch* because it is readily soluble in hot water. Crude starch from plants consists of a mixture of this polymaltose material and another *branched* poly-D-glucoside material.

The branched polymaltose components of crude starch, sometimes known as **amylopectin,** again contain only D-glucose units, but the glycosidic linkages are of two types. A varying number ($\sim$5%) of these glycosidic linkages join the anomeric carbon of one unit to the 6-position hydroxyl of the adjacent unit. Figure 24.37 shows a trisaccharide section of amylopectin containing both types of glycosidic linkages. In those glycosidic linkages involving the 6-position hydroxyl there is still an α-configuration at the anomeric center.

Cellulose **Cellulose** is another polymeric D-glucoside; it differs from starch in that the glycosidic linkages all have the β-configuration. Virtually all of the glycosidic linkages in ordinary cellulose join the anomeric center and the 4-position hydroxyl of adjacent monosaccharide units. Thus we can describe cellulose as *polycellobiose*. Its structure is shown in Figure 24.38.

Cellulose is a major constituent of the structural skeleton of plants (wood). It also is present in other parts of plants, for example, in the fruit of the cotton

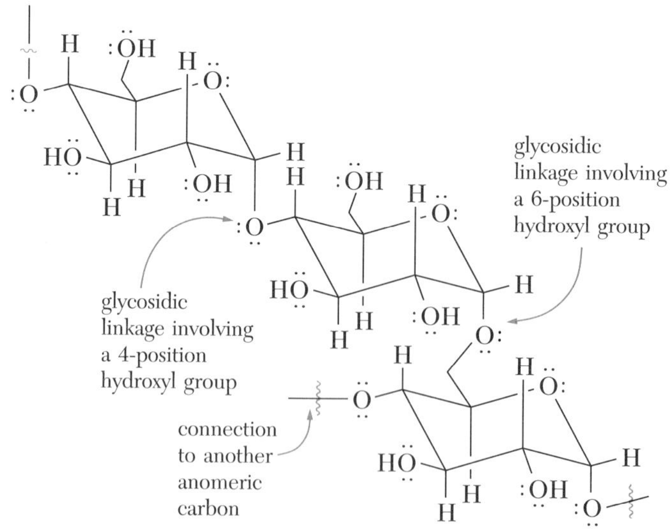

Figure 24.37 A portion of the structure of amylopectin. Two glycosidic linkages, one involving a 4-position hydroxyl and one involving a 6-position hydroxyl, are shown. Those involving 6-position hydroxyl groups account for $\sim$5% of the glycosidic linkages in amylopectin. The disaccharide unit on the right, in which an α-glycosidic linkage joins the anomeric center and the 6-hydroxyl group of adjacent monosaccharide units, is known as gentiobiose.

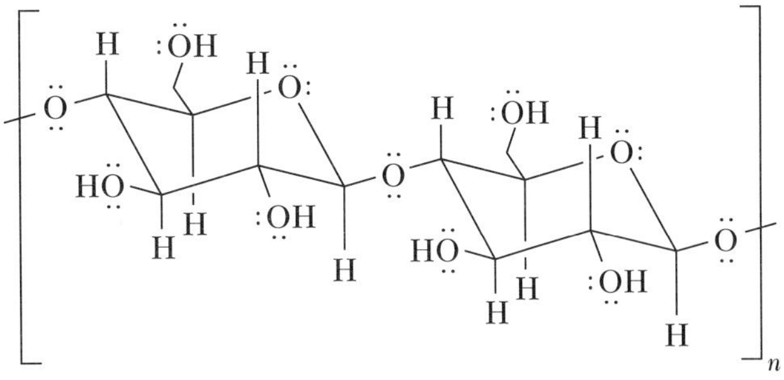

Figure 24.38 Structure of cellulose. Cellulose consists of D-glucose units joined by β-configuration glycosidic linkages between the 4-position hydroxyl and the anomeric center of adjacent units. In order to show the pyranose rings in the standard view, the C—O—C glycosidic bond angle is distorted here.

plant. Since cellulose contains only β-glycosidic linkages, it cannot be digested by humans. However, the rumina of mammals such as cows and goats contain bacteria that secrete β-glycosidases and thus allow the animal to utilize cellulose and similar polysaccharides.

PROBLEM 24.32 Draw the complete structure of each of the following disaccharides:

a. 6-*O*-(β-D-glucopyranosyl)-α-D-glucopyranose (also known as gentiobiose)

b. 6-*O*-(α-D-galactopyranosyl)-α-D-mannopyranose (also known as epimelibiose)

PROBLEM 24.33 Give the systematic name of each of the following disaccharides:

a.

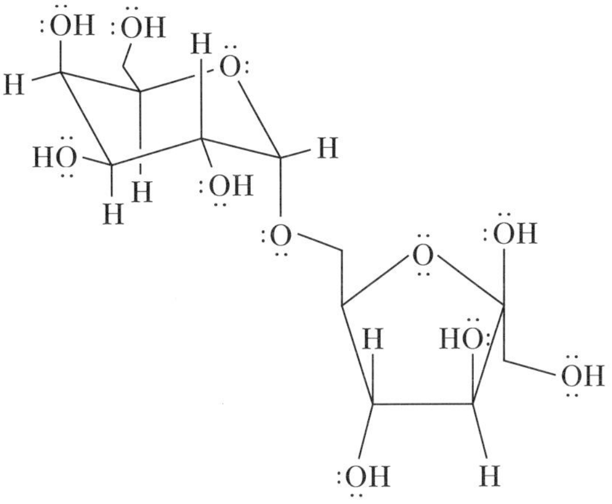

b.

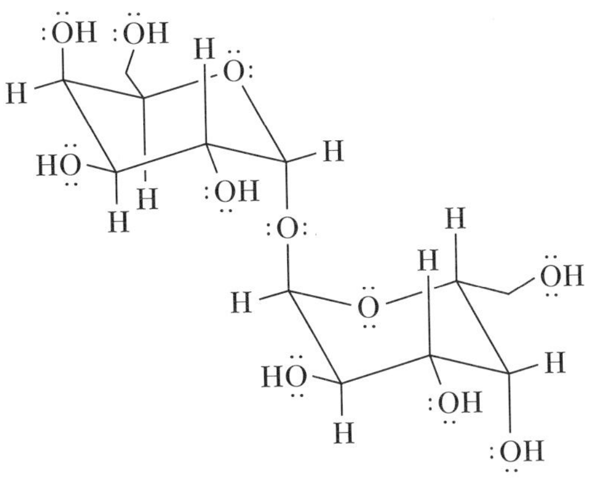

PROBLEM 24.34 On treatment with a β-glycosidase, the trisaccharide gentianose yields D-fructose and gentiobiose (see Figure 24.37). On treatment with an α-glycosidase, gentianose yields two equivalents of D-glucose and one equivalent of D-fructose. What is the structure of gentianose? (*Hint:* Gentianose is a nonreducing sugar.)

24.7 Natural Materials Structurally Related to Carbohydrates

DEOXYCARBOHYDRATES

Structure and Occurrence A **deoxycarbohydrate** is a simple carbohydrate in which a hydrogen atom takes the place of one of the hydroxyl groups. For example, D-2-deoxyribose (**24.5**) and D-ribose (**24.6**) are shown in Figure 24.39.

Although such deoxycarbohydrates occasionally occur in the free state in organisms, they are usually components of larger, structurally more complex materials. We can isolate the fundamental deoxycarbohydrate unit by degradation of the larger material. Deoxycarbohydrates are not synthesized from simpler molecules in biological systems—the known deoxycarbohydrates in biological systems form by reduction of derivatives of the ordinary carbohydrates.

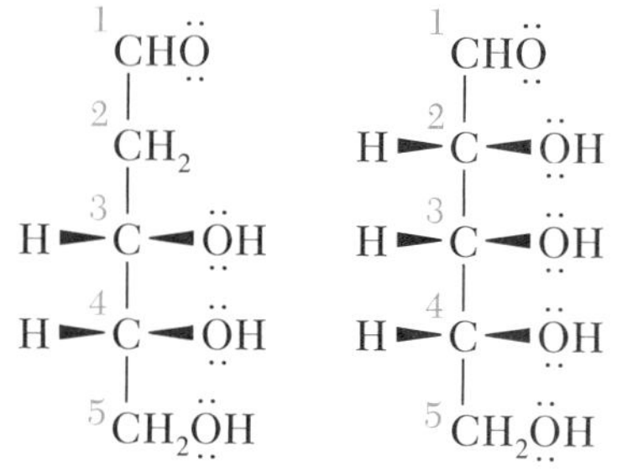

D-2-deoxyribose **24.5** D-ribose **24.6**

Figure 24.39 Comparison of the structures of D-2-deoxyribose and D-ribose. In the deoxy structure there is a hydrogen in place of one of the hydroxyl groups usually present in a carbohydrate. The numerical prefix in the name indicates the position in which the hydroxyl group has been replaced.

D-2-Deoxyribose D-2-Deoxyribose is the most familiar deoxycarbohydrate. It does not occur free in biological systems but is found as a component of deoxyribonucleic acid (DNA) and deoxyribonucleotides (Chapter 28). The D-2-deoxyribose component of a section of DNA is shown in Figure 24.40. We can isolate the parent D-2-deoxyribose by treating the nucleic acid with aqueous acid. Hydrolysis of both of the phosphate ester linkages occurs under these conditions, along with cleavage of the glycosidic linkage.

In biological systems, the D-2-deoxyribose components arise from enzymatic reduction of D-ribose derivatives. There is no separate biosynthetic route for D-2-deoxyribose, nor is it produced as a free component. Its synthesis occurs with a heterocyclic base already in place at the anomeric carbon and one phosphate ester linkage already present.

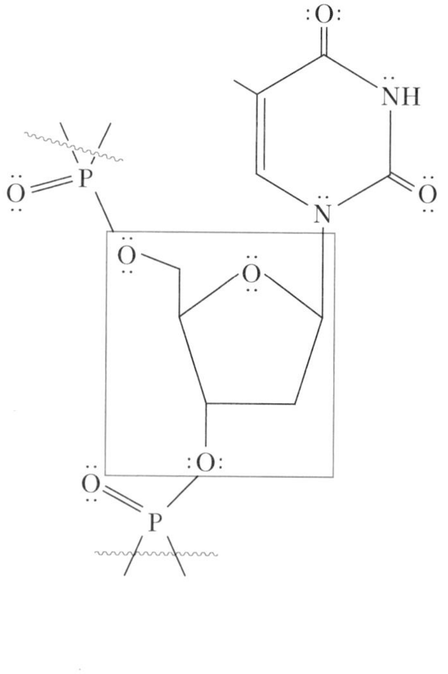

Figure 24.40 Section of DNA. The D-2-deoxyribose portion is enclosed in the box. Other components of the DNA (a heterocyclic base and phosphate ester linkages) are also shown. The anomeric carbon of the D-2-deoxyribose is bound in a glycosidic linkage involving a nitrogen of the heterocyclic base. The other hydroxyl groups of the D-2-deoxyribose portion are bound in phosphate ester linkages.

6-Deoxyhexoses The number of naturally occurring L-family carbohydrates and carbohydrate-related substances is small. However, several of them have significant roles in biological systems. One example is L-rhamnose (**24.7**), a 6-deoxyhexose.

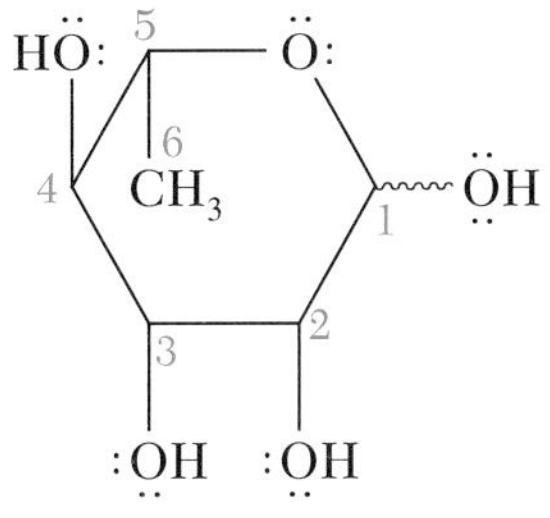

L-rhamnose
24.7

Unlike D-2-deoxyribose, L-rhamnose *does* occur in the free form in certain biological systems (it is found in the leaves of poison ivy and poison sumac). However, it occurs more often in glycosidic form, both in plants and in bacterial cell walls. Like D-2-deoxyribose, L-rhamnose does not have an independent biosynthetic source. It is formed from derivatives of D-glucose through a series of rearrangements and reduction.

The 6-deoxyhexose L-fucose (**24.8**) also arises biochemically from derivatives of D-glucose. It is a rather common deoxycarbohydrate that is found in a variety of biological sites, including human blood and milk; it is also a structural component in seaweed.

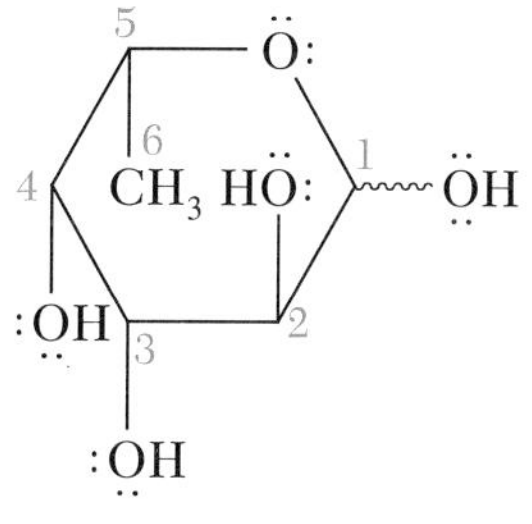

L-fucose
24.8

PROBLEM 24.35 Consider the structures of L-fucose and L-rhamnose. What specific changes in configuration and state of oxidation are required for their biosynthesis from D-glucose?

PROBLEM 24.36 D-fucose is a 6-deoxyaldohexose that occurs in biological systems. It is found in a variety of plants, including the roots of the jalapeño pepper plant. Draw the structure of D-fucose in an α-pyranose form. Compare this structure to that of D-glucose and show what changes in configuration must occur for the biosynthesis of D-fucose from that source.

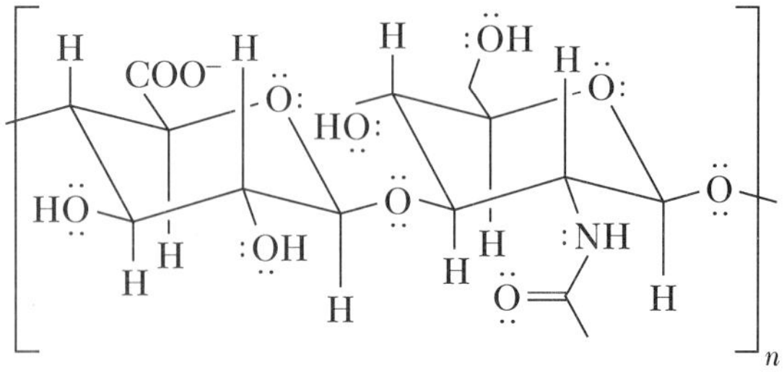

through phosphodiester linkage to complex carbohydrate units

through oligopeptide to another murein chain

repeating unit of hyaluronate, a viscous, jellylike substance occurring between the cells of animal tissues

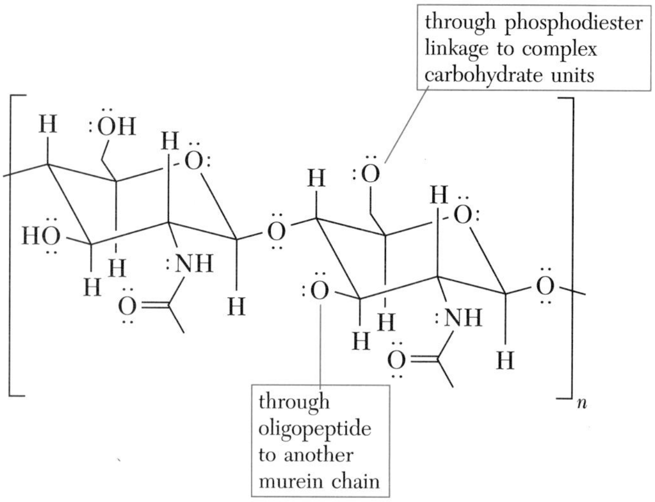

repeating unit of murein of bacterial cell walls

Figure 24.41 General structures of hyaluronate and murein. These structural materials both contain the N-acetyl derivative of D-glucosamine bound in glycosidic form. The glycosidic linkages in both species have the β-configuration. In hyaluronate the alternating carbohydrate derivative unit is glucuronic acid, a D-glucose derivative in which the 6-position hydroxyl is oxidized to a carboxylic acid function.

AMINODEOXY SUGARS

The **aminodeoxy sugars** are the final category of carbohydrate-related species that we will consider here. In an aminodeoxy sugar, an amino group ($—NH_2$) is present in place of one of the usual hydroxyl groups of a carbohydrate. Two common examples of aminodeoxy sugars are chondrosamine (3-amino-3-deoxy-D-galactose) (**24.9**) and glucosamine (2-amino-2-deoxy-D-glucose) (**24.10**).

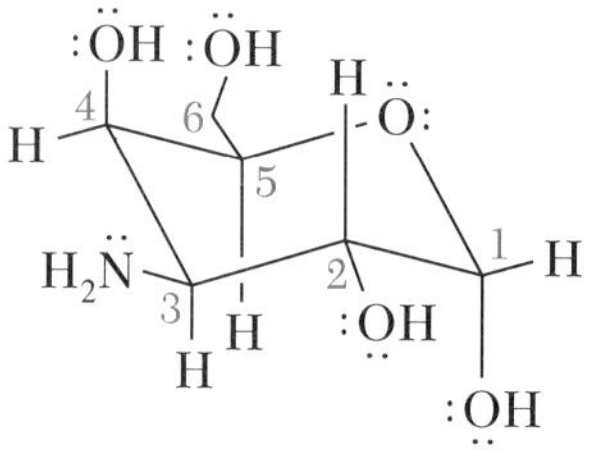

chondrosamine
24.9

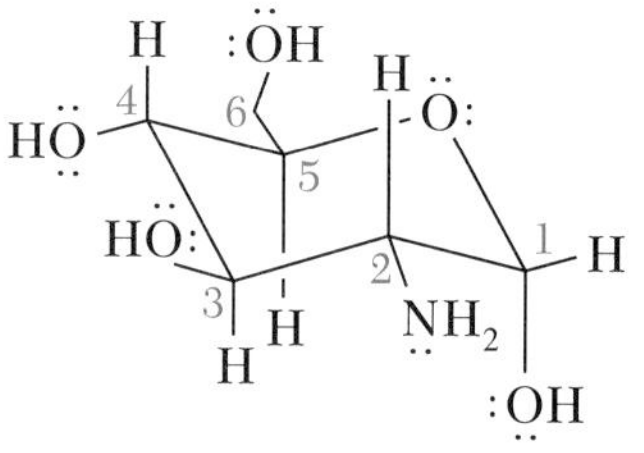

glucosamine
24.10

Both of these aminodeoxy sugars have their biochemical origins in derivatives of fructose; they are produced by isomerization and transamination reactions. In derivative forms, as glycosides and amides of acetic acid, they are important structural components of numerous biological systems, including the murein of bacterial cell walls and hyaluronic acid of animal connective tissue. General structural representations of hyaluronate and murein are shown in Figure 24.41.

Many aminodeoxy sugars exist in nature. They are ubiquitous in biological systems.

Summary

- Carbohydrates are classified in various ways.
- First, we classify them according to the number of carbon atoms present, that is, as tetroses, pentoses, hexoses, and so forth.

- They are also classified as aldoses or ketoses depending on whether the carbonyl group present is an aldehyde or a ketone.
- We further classify carbohydrates as monosaccharides, disaccharides, and so forth. This classification reflects the number of simple carbohydrate units that we can discern in the total structure.
- Carbohydrates are also classified as belonging to D- or L-families. This classification is based on the stereochemistry of the stereogenic carbon atom located farthest from the carbonyl group (the reference carbon atom).
- For convenience we often draw open-chain structures depicting linear carbohydrates as polyhydroxyaldehydes or polyhydroxyketones, but they normally exist as cyclic hemiacetals (or hemiketals) in five- or six-membered rings known as furanoses or pyranoses.
- We envision ring formation through the association of a hydroxyl group of the open-chain structure with the carbon atom of the carbonyl group. This cyclization process generates a new stereogenic center, and thus there are two cyclic diastereoisomers for each open-chain structure. We designate these diastereoisomers as α and β, depending on the relative stereochemistry of the anomeric carbon atom. We commonly use Fischer projections to represent open-chain structures and Haworth projections or chairs to represent cyclic forms of carbohydrates.
- Glycosides are derivatives of carbohydrates in which the anomeric carbon atom is bound in a full acetal or ketal linkage. Glycosides are inert to neutral or basic reagents in aqueous solution but are hydrolyzed by aqueous acid. Glycosidic linkages join monosaccharide units to form disaccharides and polysaccharides.
- Reducing sugars are easily oxidized by mild reagents such as Tollens' reagent, Fehling's solution, and Benedict's solution. The carbonyl group of aldoses can be oxidized to a carboxylic acid group by bromine water. Nitric acid also oxidizes this group and in addition oxidizes any primary alcohol groups present to carboxylic acid groups.
- We can *ascend* the series of aldoses using the Kiliani-Fischer synthesis and *descend* the series using either the Ruff or Wohl degradations.
- Carbohydrates also serve as convenient sources of chiral reagents for the synthesis of other stereochemically complex molecules.

Terms to Remember

carbohydrate
catabolism
aldose
ketose
monosaccharide
disaccharide
polysaccharide
furanose
pyranose
anomer
anomeric carbon atom
Haworth projection
α-anomer
β-anomer
mutarotation
glycoside
anomeric effect
Kiliani-Fischer synthesis
Wohl degradation
Ruff degradation
osazone
reducing sugar
enediol
starch
amylopectin
cellulose
deoxycarbohydrate
aminodeoxy sugar

Additional Problems

24.37 Draw Haworth projection structures for each of the following:

a. α-D-allopyranose **b.** β-D-ribofuranose **c.** α-D-arabinofuranose
d. methyl α-D-mannopyranoside **e.** methyl β-D-galactopyranoside

24.38 Show the products obtained by performing each of the following reactions (or series of reactions) on D-galactose:

a. subjecting it to Ruff degradation
b. treating it with base, leading to an equilibrium mixture containing D-galactose, another aldose, and a ketose

c. warming it with aqueous bromine
d. treating it with sodium borohydride in ethanol
e. treating it with an excess of phenylhydrazine
f. treating it with acetic anhydride
g. dissolving it in methanol and bubbling anhydrous hydrogen chloride through the solution
h. treating the product of reaction **g** (above) with sodium periodate followed by workup with aqueous acid

24.39 Draw Fischer projection structures for each of the following:
a. a D-aldotetrose that yields an optically active product on being reduced with sodium borohydride
b. an aldohexose that gives the same osazone as D-idose
c. a ketose, D-tagatose, that yields the same osazone as D-galactose
d. L-galactose

24.40 Show the two chair conformations of methyl α-D-idopyranoside. Which chair conformation do you think is more stable? Explain your answer.

24.41 Draw the more stable chair conformations for each of the following:
a. methyl β-D-galactopyranoside b. methyl β-D-xylopyranoside c. methyl α-D-arabinopyranoside

24.42 One mole of a compound reacts with one mole of sodium periodate to form one mole of $HO_2C(CH_2)_4CHO$. Suggest a structure for the initial compound.

24.43 One mole of a compound reacts with three moles of sodium periodate to form two moles of formic acid, one mole of acetaldehyde, and one mole of formaldehyde. Suggest a structure for the initial compound.

24.44 Predict all products from the sodium periodate cleavage of methyl α-D-galactopyranoside, after aqueous acid workup.

24.45 You perform the reactions of the Kiliani-Fischer synthesis, starting with D-talose, and you isolate a pair of aldoheptoses. Draw the structures of these two aldoheptoses and tell in detail the chemical conversions and the physical measurements you would make to assign the correct absolute configuration to each.

24.46 Give the correct set of reagents and reaction conditions for each of the conversions labeled I–V in the sequence shown below. More than one step may be required for each conversion.

HO ... :OH, HO: :OH —I→ HO ... :OCH_2CH_3, HO: :OH —II→ HO ... :OCH_2CH_3, :O O: —III→ CHO ... :OCH_2CH_3, :O O: —IV→ ... :OCH_2CH_3, :O O: —V→ CH_2OH, H–OH, :OCH_2CH_3, :O O: + CH_2OH, HO–H, :OCH_2CH_3, :O O:

24.47 The structure of melezitose, a naturally occurring trisaccharide found in numerous plants, is shown below.
a. Is melezitose a reducing sugar? Why or why not?
b. What products are obtained upon treatment of melezitose with aqueous acid? Name them.

c. Upon treatment of melezitose with sodium periodate followed by aqueous acid workup, what products form and in what relative amounts?

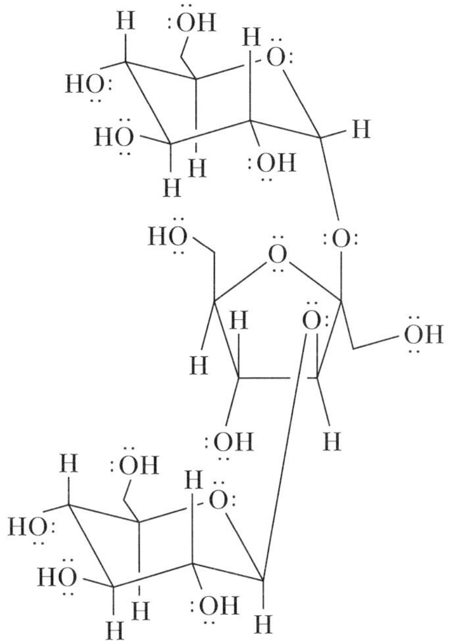

24.48 Compound *A* is a D-aldopentose that can be oxidized to an optically inactive aldaric acid, *B*. On Kiliani-Fischer chain extension, *A* is converted into *C* and *D*. Both *C* and *D* are converted to aldaric acids by nitric acid oxidation, *C* yielding an optically active product, *E*, and *D* yielding an optically inactive product *F*. Give the structures of the compounds *A–F*.

24.49 Draw the structure of the disaccharide turanose, which has the systematic name 3-*O*-(α-D-glucopyranosyl)-α-D-fructofuranose.

24.50 Melibiose, *G*, is a disaccharide whose hydrolysis is catalyzed by α-glycosidases but not by β-glycosidases. On hydrolysis of melibiose to monosaccharides, one equivalent of D-glucose and one equivalent of D-galactose form. If melibiose is treated with methanol and acid, its methyl glycoside, *H*, forms. Further treatment of *H* with dimethylsulfate forms compound *I*, which bears methyl ether linkages in place of the seven free hydroxyl groups of *H*. Hydrolysis of *I* with aqueous acid forms the two products shown below. Give the complete structure of compounds *G–I*.

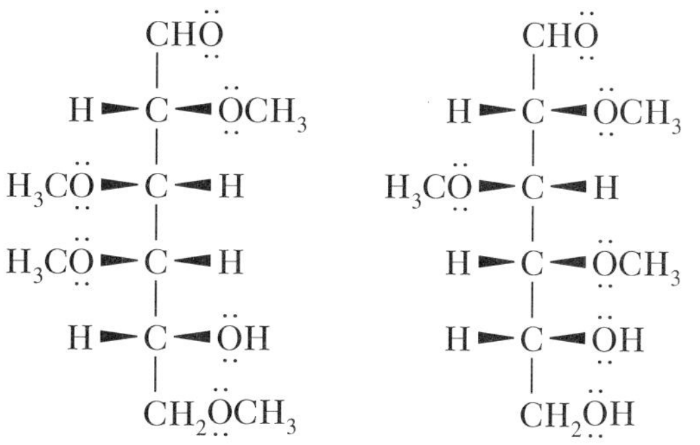

CHO	CHO
H—C—OCH_3	H—C—OCH_3
H_3CO—C—H	H_3CO—C—H
H_3CO—C—H	H—C—OCH_3
H—C—OH	H—C—OH
CH_2OCH_3	CH_2OH

24.51 On hydrolysis catalyzed by β-glycosidases, a trisaccharide yields one equivalent each of D-fructose and melibiose (see Problem 24.50). On hydrolysis catalyzed by α-glycosidases, it yields one equivalent each of D-fructose, D-glucose, and D-galactose. Give a complete structure for the trisaccharide.

24.52 Describe all reactions and reagents you would use in the synthesis of (S)-hexane-1,2-diol starting with an aldohexose. (Choose the particular aldohexose that is most convenient for this overall conversion.)

24.53 Two D-aldotetroses, *J* and *K*, undergo reaction with sodium borohydride to yield compounds *L* and *M*, respectively, both of formula $C_4H_{10}O_4$. On treatment with dilute sulfuric acid, both *L* and *M* undergo dehydration to yield compounds *N* and *O*, respectively, each of formula $C_4H_8O_3$. On treatment with acetone in the presence of an acidic catalyst, *N* reacts to form an acetonide but *O* does not form an acetonide. Give structures for compounds *J–O*.

24.54 Consider the structures of the cyclic hexitols (the inositols or, formally, the cyclohexane-1,2,3,4,5,6-hexaols). Draw the structures for all of the stereoisomers and tell which are optically active.

24.55 On treatment with periodate followed by acid workup, the methyl glycoside of D-tagatose yields the products illustrated below.

CHO / H—C—OH / CH_2OH CH_2OH / C=O / CHO CH_3OH

D-Tagatose itself is resistant to oxidation with bromine in water, although it is a reducing sugar. The methyl glycoside of D-tagatose yields an acetonide upon treatment with acetone in the presence of an acid catalyst. Upon treatment with sodium borohydride, D-tagatose yields two hexaols, one of which is optically inactive and identical to that obtained by a similar reduction of D-allose. Deduce the structures of the methyl glycoside of D-tagatose and D-tagatose itself.

24.56 Show all reagents and reaction conditions required for the conversion of D-ribose to 5-deoxy-5-amino-D-ribose.

Ultraviolet/Visible and Mass Spectrometry

25.1 Introduction

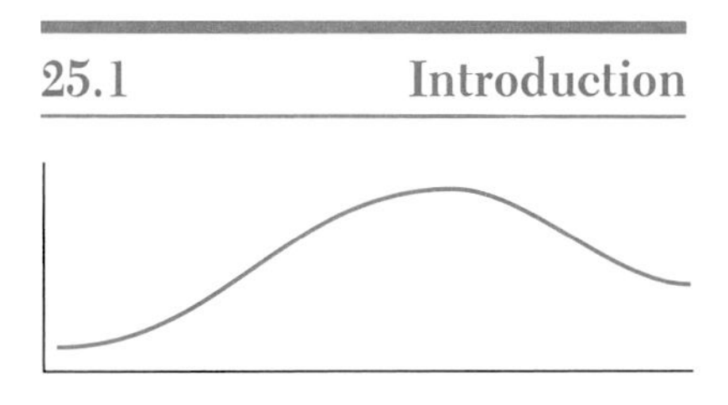

In Chapter 17 we began our discussion of the ways in which spectra provide information about the structures of molecules. The two techniques discussed there, infrared and nuclear magnetic resonance spectrometry, are the spectrometric methods most frequently used by organic chemists. Nevertheless, other techniques can also provide important information about molecular structure. In this chapter we focus on the uses of ultraviolet/visible (UV/VIS) **electronic absorption spectrometry** and **mass spectrometry.**

25.2 Ultraviolet/Visible Spectrometry

FUNDAMENTAL PRINCIPLES

In Chapter 17 we discussed infrared absorption spectrometry. Recall how an infrared analysis is performed. The amount of infrared electromagnetic radiation absorbed by a sample is measured at various wavelengths and the data are plotted to provide an *infrared spectrum,* which is a record of the variation of absorption intensity with the wavelength or wavenumber of the radiation used. An ultraviolet/visible spectrophotometer has the same fundamental design as an infrared spectrophotometer. The principal difference between the two is the source of the radiation used.

In an ultraviolet/visible spectrometer, the source provides radiation of significantly higher energy per photon than in an infrared spectrometer. The higher-energy photons cause a different kind of change than is involved in infrared spectrometry. Electrons are promoted from their ground state orbitals to higher-energy (excited state) orbitals. Of course, the usual quantum restrictions hold for these excitation processes. An electron can be promoted *only* if a molecule receives exactly the right energy from an impacting photon. The energy of the photon, $h\nu$, must match the difference in energy, ΔE, between the ground state and the excited state, according to Planck's law, $\Delta E = h\nu$.

By convention we generally refer to visible and ultraviolet radiation by its wavelength (expressed in nanometers, nm) rather than by its frequency (as for infrared radiation). Visible light has wavelengths in the range ~400 nm (violet) to ~750 nm (red). Ultraviolet radiation has wavelengths shorter than 400 nm.

Most ultraviolet/visible spectrophotometers are able to measure absorption processes in the 200–750 nm range. There are experimental difficulties associated with measuring absorption of radiation with wavelengths less than 200 nm. Most cell materials and the atmospheric gases themselves absorb light of these short wavelengths. A specially designed apparatus is needed to perform measurements at wavelengths <200 nm, the region commonly known as the

vacuum ultraviolet region. Fortunately, absorptions by organic molecules at wavelengths >200 nm can provide us with useful structural information.

If a compound absorbs light in the visible region, it appears to us to have a color complementary to that of the light absorbed. For example, a sample that absorbs in the violet region of the visible range appears yellow. Sometimes the simple fact that a compound has a color provides us with structural information.

INSTRUMENTATION

The basic design of a typical ultraviolet/visible absorption spectrometer is shown in Figure 25.1. The sample cell is usually constructed of quartz. Quartz is transparent through the entire ultraviolet/visible region to a wavelength of 200 nm. Ordinary glass cells can be used if we are interested only in the visible and not the ultraviolet region.

TERMINOLOGY

A UV/VIS absorption spectrum is a plot of **absorbance** of light as a function of the wavelength of the incident light. Absorbance is defined as shown in Equation 25.1:

Eqn. 25.1

$$A = \log(I_0/I)$$

where A is the absorbance, I_0 is the intensity of light incident upon the sample, and I is the intensity of light transmitted by the sample. Notice that in UV/VIS spectrometry we are generally concerned with *absorbance* rather than *transmittance*. [The percent transmittance is related to absorbance, since percent transmittance is $100(I/I_0)$.]

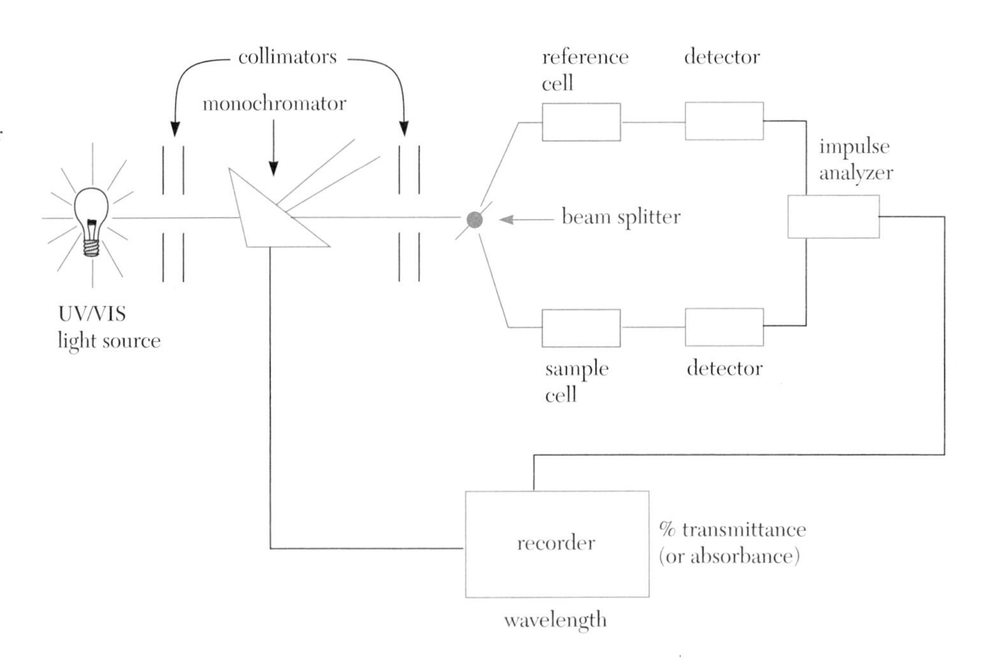

Figure 25.1 Schematic of a UV/VIS (electronic) spectrometer. The source of light is generally a tungsten filament bulb for the visible region and a mercury vapor lamp for the ultraviolet region. The spectrum is shown as % transmittance (or absorbance) versus wavelength.

The actual value of the absorbance of a sample depends on the concentration of the sample in the solution, the length of the cell, and the nature of the excitation process. The **molar absorptivity** is obtained by dividing the absorbance by the product of the sample concentration and the cell length, as shown in Equation 25.2, where c is the molar concentration of the sample, l is the cell length in cm, and the symbol ε represents the molar absorptivity. (In older literature the molar absorptivity is commonly referred to as the molar extinction coefficient.)

Eqn. 25.2
$$\varepsilon = A/cl$$

You should recall a similar treatment of concentration and cell length in our discussion of optical rotation in Chapter 8. By dividing by these factors we obtain a characteristic property of the compound that is independent of the amount of material we are considering. The quantity ε depends only on the molecular structure of the substance. Experimentalists making measurements with different cells, different concentrations, and different instruments will all obtain the same value of ε for a given substance.

A UV/VIS spectrum generally has a relatively simple appearance, consisting of one or more rather broad bands. A typical example of a UV/VIS spectrum (that of 3,5,5-trimethyl-2-cyclohexen-1-one) is shown in Figure 25.2. The wavelength at which a maximum absorbance occurs is known as λ_{max} for that substance. When we summarize data obtained from a UV/VIS spectrum, we generally specify each λ_{max} along with the corresponding ε value.

PROBLEM 25.1 A solution is prepared from 2.50 mg of a substance having a molecular weight of 150 by dissolving it in ethanol and diluting to 25.0 mL. The UV/VIS spectrum of the sample is measured in a cell with a length of 1.00 cm. The sample exhibits a λ_{max} at 380 nm with an absorbance of 1.50. Calculate the molar absorptivity of the compound at 380 nm.

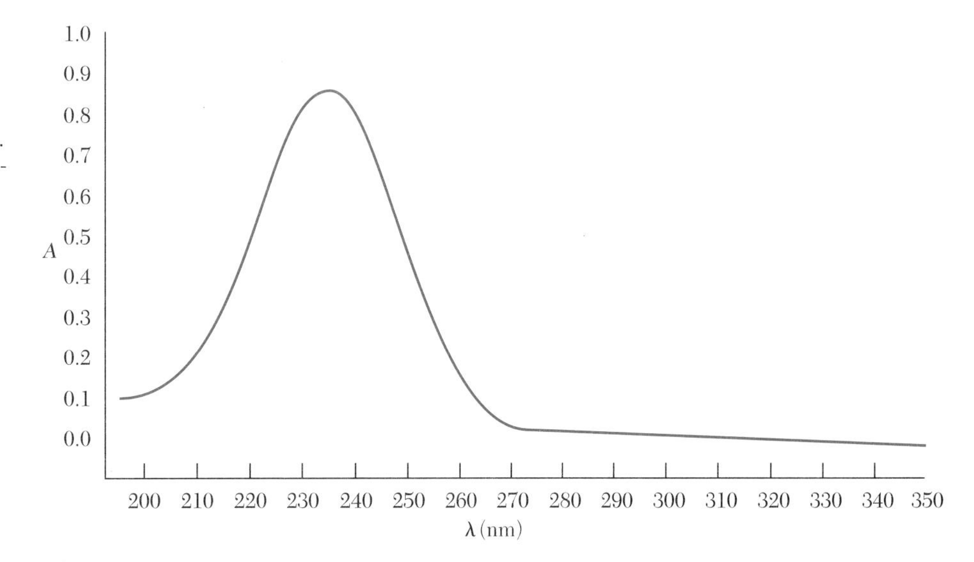

Figure 25.2 UV/VIS absorption spectrum of 3,5,5-trimethyl-2-cyclohexen-1-one. The spectrum was measured in methanol solution. The sample exhibits a strong absorption peak with a maximum at 235 nm. Using a concentration of 0.70 mM, the absorbance observed is 0.83 in a 0.10 cm cell. We thus calculate the molar absorptivity (ε) to be 1.2×10^4.

PROBLEM 25.2 A mixture consists of a major component that does not absorb light at 450 nm and a minor component (an impurity) that has a λ_{max} at 450 nm with $\varepsilon = 1.05 \times 10^3$. A sample of the mixture is placed in a 1.00-cm cell and its visible spectrum is measured. If the measured absorbance at 450 nm is 0.020, what is the molar concentration of the impurity in the solution?

TYPES OF ELECTRONIC TRANSITIONS

Each band of a UV/VIS absorption spectrum corresponds to an electronic transition, that is, the promotion of an electron from an orbital of lower energy to one of higher energy. In principle, an electron in *any* occupied orbital can be excited to any of the unoccupied orbitals if radiation of the correct energy (wavelength) is provided. It is often useful to classify transitions by specifying the natures of the two orbitals involved in the transition. The following abbreviations are commonly used:

- n a nonbonding orbital
- π a bonding π molecular orbital
- σ a bonding σ molecular orbital
- π^* an antibonding π molecular orbital
- σ^* an antibonding σ molecular orbital

Transitions between these types of orbitals are designated using the abbreviations given above and an arrow showing the direction of the transition, as illustrated in Figure 25.3.

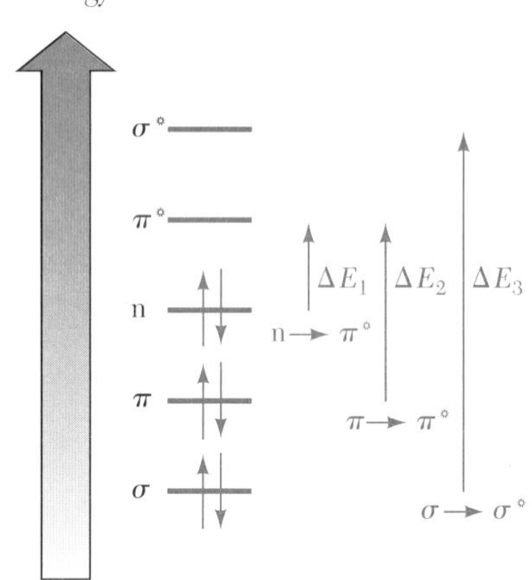

Figure 25.3 Some electronic transitions in organic molecules. Other transitions are possible, depending on the availability of the orbitals and the application of light of the proper energy.

Usually only one or a few bands are seen in a UV/VIS spectrum because only one or a few of the possible transitions are in the energy range probed by the experiment (200–750 nm). The commonly observed bands are generally the result of $\pi \rightarrow \pi^*$ or $n \rightarrow \pi^*$ transitions of relatively low energy. The higher-energy transitions occur in the wavelength region below 200 nm, which is inaccessible for ordinary experimental measurement.

STRUCTURAL INFORMATION

Not all organic molecules exhibit significant or structurally identifying UV/VIS absorptions. For example, molecules containing only σ and σ^* molecular orbitals exhibit no absorptions in the entire accessible UV/VIS region. The possible $\sigma \rightarrow \sigma^*$ transitions occur at energies corresponding to wavelengths less than 200 nm. Furthermore, only certain types of molecules containing n and π (and π^*) orbitals exhibit useful absorptions. The $\pi \rightarrow \pi^*$ transitions prove to be most useful to organic chemists seeking structural information, particularly information about the degree of conjugation and substitution of unsaturated linkages.

Simple alkenes such as ethylene exhibit bands due to $\pi \rightarrow \pi^*$ transitions only in the vacuum ultraviolet region (very short wavelength), but conjugated dienes and molecules with other conjugated unsaturated linkages absorb at longer wavelengths. If many unsaturated linkages are conjugated, as in β-carotene (Chapter 9), the compound absorbs visible light and therefore has a color. (β-Carotene is deep red-purple when pure. It appears pale yellow in dilute solution.)

MOLECULAR ORBITAL ANALYSIS

Molecular orbital theory provides an explanation of the progressive shift to longer wavelengths for $\pi \rightarrow \pi^*$ absorptions as the degree of conjugation increases. According to molecular orbital theory, the lowest-energy electronic transition in a molecule is the promotion of an electron from the HOMO to the LUMO. For alkenes and polyenes, the HOMO is the highest-energy π orbital and the LUMO is the lowest-energy π^* orbital. The data given by UV/VIS spectrometry can be correlated with the energy difference between these two orbitals. Molecular orbital theory tells us that the energy difference between the HOMO and the LUMO decreases as conjugation increases, as illustrated in Figure 25.4.

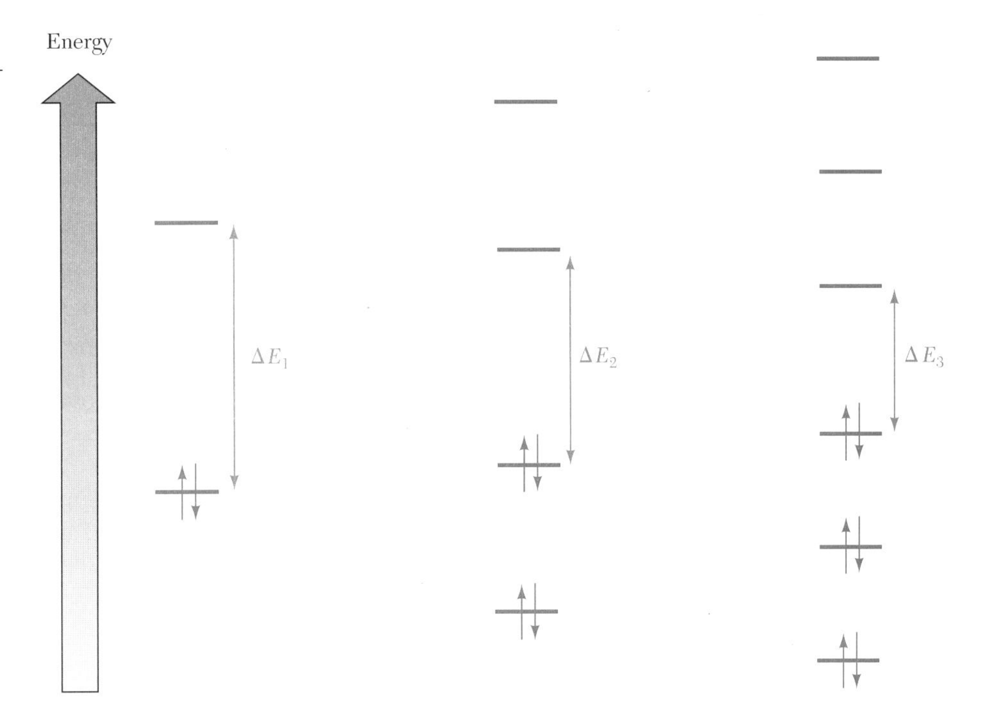

Figure 25.4 π-Molecular orbital energy levels. As the number of π bonds in conjugation increases, the HOMO–LUMO energy gap decreases. The HOMO–LUMO gaps for an alkene, an alkadiene, and an alkatriene are indicated by ΔE_1, ΔE_2, and ΔE_3, respectively.

The HOMO–LUMO gap can also be correlated with the number of nodes in the orbitals. Comparison of 1,3-butadiene and 1,3,5-hexatriene provides a good example of this correlation. With 1,3-butadiene the HOMO and LUMO have one and two nonlinear nodes, respectively. The LUMO has twice as many nonlinear nodes as does the HOMO, and the HOMO–LUMO gap is relatively large. However, with 1,3,5-hexatriene the HOMO and LUMO have two and three nonlinear nodes, respectively. The LUMO has only 1.5 times as many nonlinear nodes as does the HOMO. Thus, the HOMO–LUMO gap in 1,3,5-hexatriene is less than it is in 1,3-butadiene.

The observed values of the $\pi \rightarrow \pi^*$ bands for ethene, 1,3-butadiene, and 1,3,5-hexatriene are shown in Figure 25.5.

$H_2C{=}CH_2$ — 171 nm $H_2C{=}CH{-}CH{=}CH_2$ — 217 nm $H_2C{=}CH{-}CH{=}CH{-}CH{=}CH_2$ — 258 nm

Figure 25.5 The observed λ_{max} values for the $\pi \rightarrow \pi^*$ absorption in an alkene, a conjugated diene, and a conjugated triene.

PROBLEM 25.3 Predict which molecule in each of the following sets exhibits the longer wavelength $\pi \rightarrow \pi^*$ transition band in the UV/VIS spectrum.

a. 1,3,5-hexatriene or 1,3,5,7-octatetraene

b. 1,3-pentadiene or 1,4-pentadiene

c. or

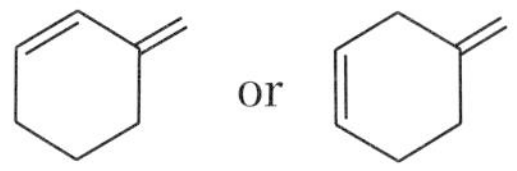

PROBLEM 25.4 Compound *A* (formula C_6H_8) exhibits a UV/VIS absorption band between 250 and 260 nm. It also exhibits two groups of signals in the ^1H NMR spectrum, one at δ 1.5–2.0 and the other at δ 5.0–5.7. On catalytic hydrogenation *A* is converted to *B* (formula C_6H_{12}), which exhibits a single ^1H NMR signal at δ 1.4. Suggest structures for *A* and *B*.

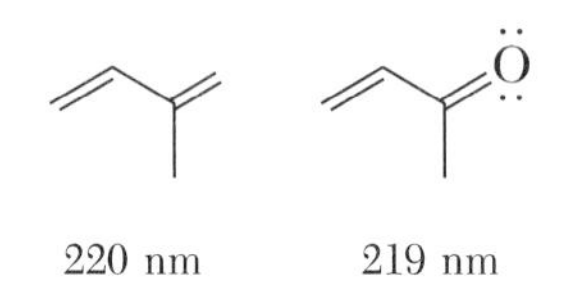

Figure 25.6 The $\pi \rightarrow \pi^*$ absorption bands for 2-methyl-1,3-butadiene and methyl vinyl ketone. The $\pi \rightarrow \pi^*$ absorption bands for conjugated dienes and α,β-unsaturated aldehydes and ketones of similar structure occur at approximately the same wavelength.

Conjugated carbonyl compounds exhibit a similar type of $\pi \rightarrow \pi^*$ absorption band in the UV/VIS spectrum, as do dienes, trienes, and so forth. Simple α,β-unsaturated aldehydes and ketones absorb at approximately the same wavelengths as do the corresponding dienes (see Figure 25.6).

Many carbonyl compounds exhibit *additional* weak bands in their UV/VIS spectra due to n $\rightarrow \pi^*$ transitions. One of the oxygen nonbonded valence level electrons is promoted to a π^* level upon absorption of light of the proper energy. For example, consider the spectrum of 4-methyl-3-penten-2-one (commonly known as mesityl oxide), shown in Figure 25.7.

Even a very dilute solution (10^{-4} to 10^{-5} *M*), shows a strong absorption band for the $\pi \rightarrow \pi^*$ transition. However, under these conditions there is no

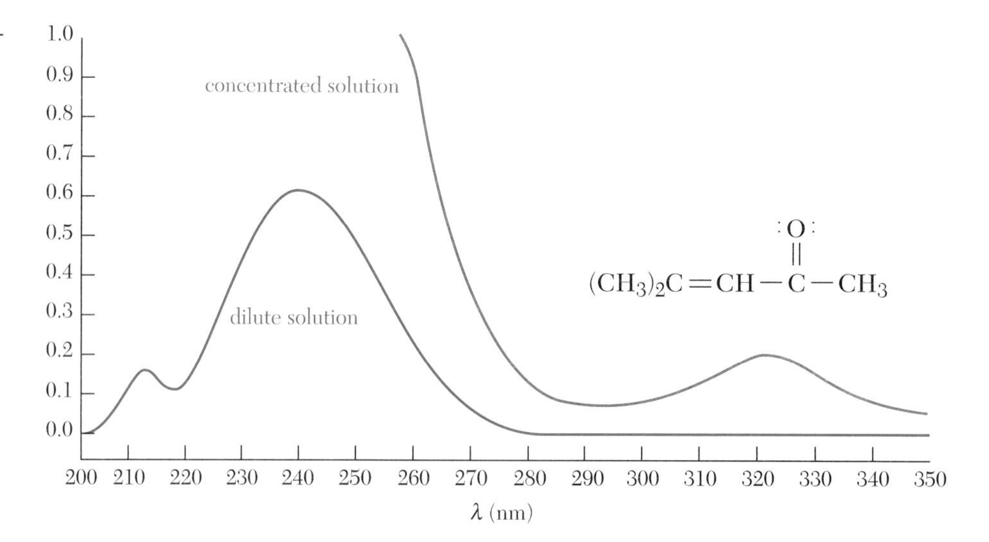

Figure 25.7 The UV/VIS absorption spectrum of mesityl oxide. The upper trace was obtained with a solution 100 times more concentrated than that used to obtain the lower trace.

obvious indication of a n → π^* absorption. This weaker band is detected only when we examine a much more concentrated solution. The spectra in Figure 25.7 are typical. The molar absorptivities (ε) for $\pi \rightarrow \pi^*$ transitions in α,β-unsaturated carbonyl compounds are of the order 10^4, but they are generally 10^2 or less for the n → π^* transitions.

The anticipated λ_{max} values for the $\pi \rightarrow \pi^*$ transitions of conjugated molecules can be calculated with good accuracy by adding together various contributions due to substituents and degrees of unsaturation. A set of contributing values was determined empirically by the late Professor R. B. Woodward of Harvard University. **Woodward's rules** are summarized below.

Woodward's Rules for Diene $\pi \rightarrow \pi^*$ Absorption Wavelengths

1. The *base value* of the $\pi \rightarrow \pi^*$ absorption wavelength for a conjugated diene depends on the conformation associated with the diene linkage. For a diene that is held rigidly in a *transoid* geometry or is capable of free rotation about the central carbon-carbon single bond, the base value is 215 nm. If the diene is held rigidly in a *cisoid* geometry, the base value is 253 nm.

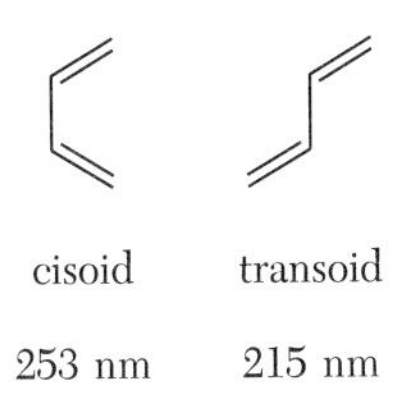

2. Add 5 nm to the appropriate base value for any alkyl group, alkoxy group, or halogen atom attached to any of the carbons of the conjugated system.
3. Add 30 nm to the appropriate base value for any additional double bond conjugated with those in the base unit.
4. Add 5 nm to the appropriate base value for any π bond exocyclic to a five- or six-membered ring.

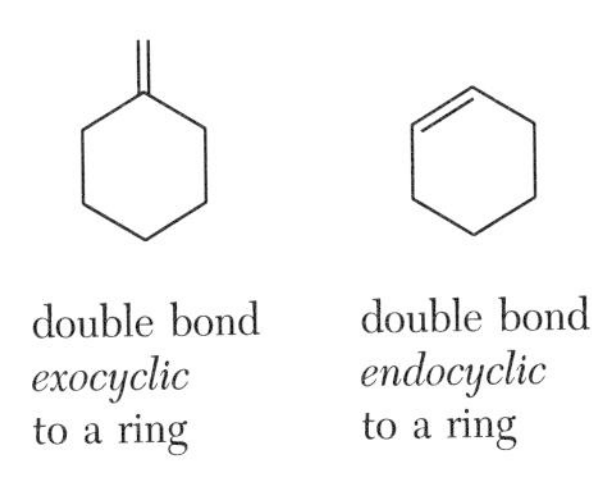

PROBLEM 25.5 Use Woodward's rules to calculate the $\pi \rightarrow \pi^*$ λ_{max} for each of the following compounds.

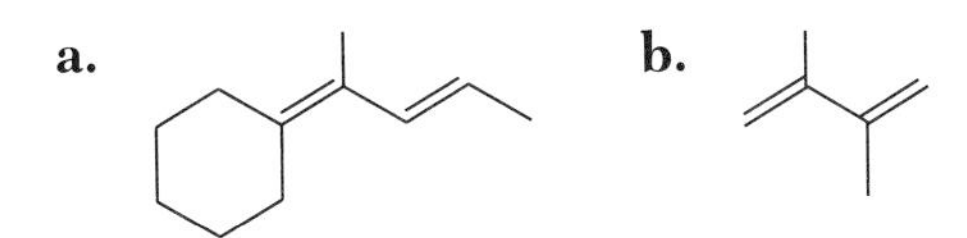

c.

d.

Steps to Solving the Problem

Solution to Problem 25.5a

1. Identify the basic conjugated diene unit in the molecule.

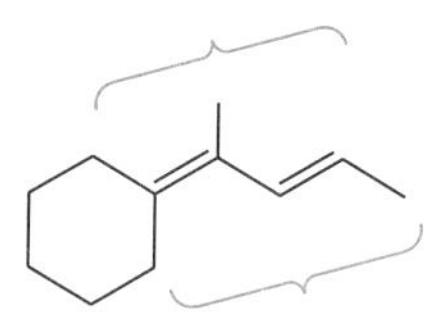

diene unit of molecule

We see that it is a diene unit in which free rotation about the central carbon-carbon bond is possible. Thus the base value is 215 nm.

2. Look to see if the diene unit is exocyclic to a five- or six-membered ring.

exocyclic juncture of diene and a six-membered ring

Since there is an exocyclic juncture of the diene unit with a six-membered ring, we need to add 5 nm to the base value.

3. Consider how many (if any) substituents are present on the carbons of the diene linkage.

alkyl groups attached to the basic diene linkage

We see that there are four alkyl groups attached to the basic diene linkage. Since each alkyl group contributes 5 nm, we add 20 nm to the base value.

4. Add the total contributions to calculate λ_{max} for the compound.

$$215 + 5 + 20 = 240 \text{ nm}$$

We predict λ_{max} for the $\pi \rightarrow \pi^*$ absorption band of this compound to be 240 nm.

Woodward's Rules for Enone $\pi \rightarrow \pi^*$ Absorption

1. The *base value* for a $\pi \rightarrow \pi^*$ absorption of an enone depends on the fundamental structure of the system. If the enone system is acyclic or part of a six-membered ring, the base value is 215 nm. If the enone system is part of a five-membered ring, the base value is 202 nm. If the conjugated system is an acyclic dienone, the base value is 245 nm.

acyclic enone or six-membered ring enone: 215 nm

five-membered ring enone: 202 nm

acyclic dienone: 245 nm

2. Add 30 nm to the appropriate base value for any carbon-carbon double bond extending the conjugation
3. Add 39 nm to the appropriate base value for the presence of a homocyclic diene component.

a homocyclic diene component (both carbon-carbon double bonds are within the same ring)

4. To the appropriate base value, make additions for groups or atoms attached to carbon atoms of the conjugated system. The amount to be added depends on the specific carbon site to which the group or atom is attached and the nature of the attached group or atom. The additions are summarized below.

	Position			
Substituent	α	β	γ	δ
alkyl group	10	12	18	18
—ÖH	35	30	—	50
—ÖC(O)R	6	6	—	6
—ÖCH$_3$	35	30	17	31
—Cl:	15	12	—	—
—Br:	25	30	—	

PROBLEM 25.6 Predict the UV/VIS λ_{max} for the $\pi \rightarrow \pi^*$ absorption for each of the following compounds.

a. b.

c. d.

Steps to Solving the Problem

Solution to Problem 25.6a

1. Identify the basic enone unit in the molecule.

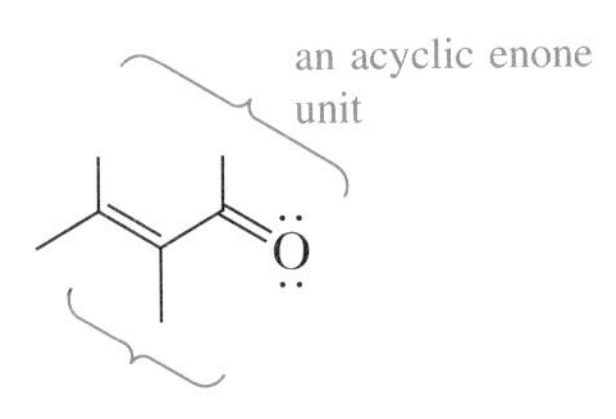

   Since the basic enone unit is a simple acyclic enone, the base value is 215 nm.

2. Look for any substituents associated with the base unit. There is no extended conjugation or ring component. There are, however, three pertinent substituents.

two β substituents

one α substituent

   The α substituent is an alkyl group, so it adds 10 nm to the base value. The two β substituents are both alkyl groups, each adding 12 nm to the base value.

3. We can calculate the predicted λ_{max}:

$$215 + 10 + 12 + 12 = 249 \text{ nm}$$

One final note should be made regarding the UV/VIS spectra of enones. There are slight variations in the $\pi \rightarrow \pi^*$ absorption λ_{max} values depending on the solvent used. Polar solvents tend to shift the λ_{max} to slightly higher values than are found for nonpolar solvents. This shift occurs only with the enones; it does not occur with dienes.

PROBLEM 25.7 A material known as α-cyperone was isolated from natural sources. Fundamental chemical tests led to the postulation of two possible structures for α-cyperone, as shown below.

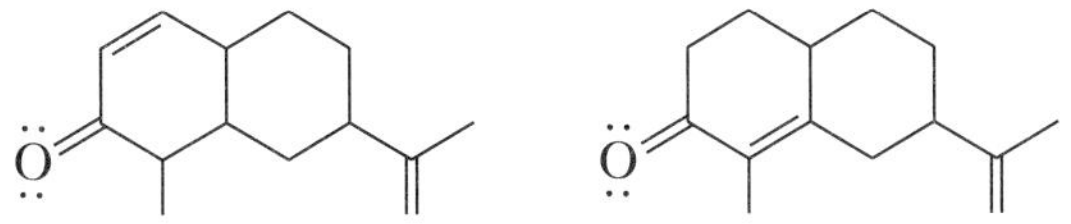

The UV/VIS spectrum of α-cyperone exhibits a λ_{max} at 252 nm with an ε of 19,000. Use Woodward's rules to decide upon the actual structure of α-cyperone.

25.3 Mass Spectrometry

INTRODUCTION

In a **mass spectrometer** a sample is vaporized in a vacuum ($\sim 10^{-6}$ torr, 1.3×10^{-4} Pa) and ionized by one of several methods. A common approach is to bombard the sample molecules with medium-energy electrons, that is, electrons having energies in the range 50–110 eV (1 eV (electron volt) = 96.4 kJ/mole = 23.1 kcal/mole). Under these conditions, molecules of the sample are converted into various types of positive and negative ions. The mass spectrometer allows us to determine the masses of these ions. (Some radicals and neutral molecules are also produced in this bombardment, but they are not detected in mass spectrometric analysis.)

A mass spectrometer can be configured to provide the masses of either the positive or the negative ions. However, in most studies of organic molecules only the positive ions are investigated; useful structural information can be inferred from these measurements alone.

Strictly speaking, a mass spectrometer sorts ions by their *mass-to-charge ratios* (m/e), not simply their masses. However, most of the positive ions produced bear a single unit of charge (+1), so measurement of their values of m/e provides a direct measurement of their masses (m).

The sorting of the ions can be effected in various ways. One common method uses a magnetic sector analyzer, as illustrated in Figure 25.8. Ions with different values of m/e follow different paths under the influence of the magnetic field in the analyzer section. For any given magnetic field strength, only those ions with a specific value of m/e are able to exit the analyzer and be counted by a suitable detector. Other ions (with inappropriate values of m/e) follow paths that send them into the walls of the analyzer section; the radii of the circular paths they follow are either too short or too long to focus them on the exit slit of the analyzer.

To obtain a mass spectrum (an m/e spectrum) we vary the strength of the analyzing magnetic field and measure the number of ions collected. As the magnetic field is decreased, ions with progressively larger values of m/e are brought to focus on the analyzer exit slit. (The degree of bending of the path of a moving, charged particle is inversely proportional to m/e.) The mass spectrum shows the relative number of each ion reaching the detector versus the value of m/e for the ion.

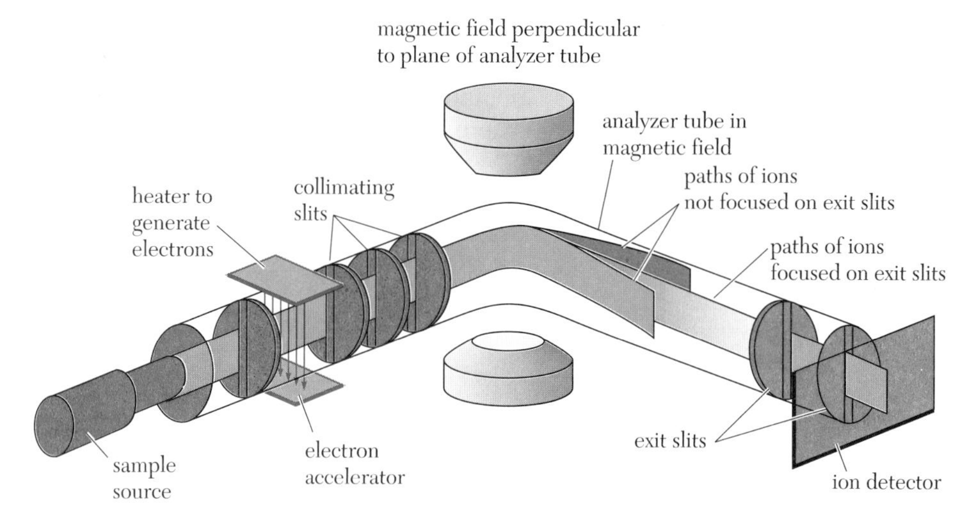

Figure 25.8 Schematic diagram of a mass spectrometer. The particular instrument shown employs an *electron impact source* to generate the ions from the sample molecules and a *magnetic sector analyzer* for separating the ions according to m/e. A mass spectrum of a particular sample is produced by plotting the number of ions detected versus their mass-to-charge ratio (m/e).

AN INTRODUCTORY LOOK AT TWO SIMPLE MASS SPECTRA

The fundamental utility of mass spectrometry is best illustrated by considering the mass spectra of some structurally simple compounds. The mass spectra of two isomers, 3-pentanone (**25.1**) and 3-methyl-2-butanone (**25.2**), are shown in Figure 25.9. The spectra consist of plots of relative ion abundance versus the mass-to-charge ratio of the ions. We will use the spectra of these isomers to introduce the basic terminology of mass spectrometry and some of the salient features of the interpretation of mass spectra.

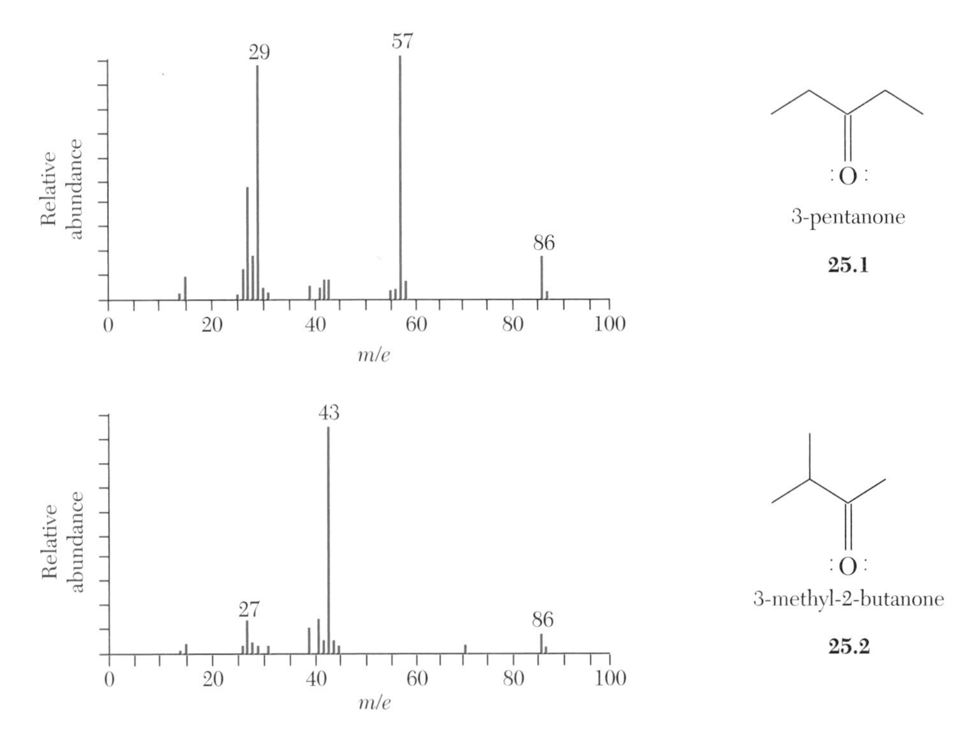

Figure 25.9 Electron impact mass spectra of 3-pentanone and 3-methyl-2-butanone.

The spectra of both **25.1** and **25.2** exhibit peaks at $m/e = 86$. The formula of these isomeric compounds ($C_5H_{10}O$) indicates a molecular weight of 86. We can therefore infer that upon impact with an energetic electron (70 eV), *some* of the molecules undergo a simple loss of an electron to yield a positive ion but do not break into fragments. This process is represented by Equation 25.3.

Eqn. 25.3

$$C_5H_{10}O + e^- \longrightarrow \underset{m/e\,=\,86}{C_5H_{10}O^{+\cdot}} + 2e^-$$

Ions produced by the loss of a single electron without fragmentation (such as $C_5H_{10}O^{\dot{+}}$ in Equation 25.3) are known as **molecular ions.** Notice that the formula for the molecular ion includes both a dot and a positive charge sign to indicate that the species is both an ion and a radical (a *radical cation*).

In general, the designation $M^{\dot{+}}$ (or M^+ or M) is used to indicate a molecular ion. Most (but not all) samples exhibit recognizable molecular ion peaks in their mass spectra. If we are dealing with an unknown sample, we can *usually* use the molecular ion peak to infer the molecular weight of the sample, since the molecular weight of the sample and that of the molecular ion differ only by the (negligible) mass of an electron. Under ordinary conditions, the molecular ion is the heaviest (largest m/e) ion in the mass spectrum.

Notice, however, that there are also some lower intensity peaks at m/e values above the molecular ion peak (greater than $m/e = 86$). We refer to them as the M + 1, M + 2, . . . , peaks, to indicate that they are one, two, or more mass units heavier than the molecular ion. In the spectra shown in Figure 25.9, the M + 1 peaks for each compound are barely discernible. If we were to record these spectra using higher sensitivity, these peaks would become more obvious, and we would also see M + 2 peaks. These peaks at m/e values higher than that of the molecular ion result from the presence of heavy isotopes of carbon, hydrogen, and oxygen in the samples. In any sample of an organic material, including the ketones **25.1** and **25.2**, some of the molecules contain ^{13}C as one of the carbon atoms (rather than the usual ^{12}C) and ^2H (D) rather than the usual ^1H. These heavier isotopes occur naturally, so they must be present in some molecules. The molecular ion produced when such a molecule is ionized has a mass one unit greater than that of a usual molecular ion. Mass spectrometry is a very sensitive analytical technique, so we can easily detect these M + 1 ion peaks. Sample molecules containing two ^{13}C, or two ^2H per molecule (or one of each) give rise to an M + 2 peak. Similarly, sample molecules containing an ^{18}O isotope (rather than a ^{16}O) produce an M + 2 peak. As we will see later, measurement of the exact relative intensities of the M, M + 1, and M + 2 peaks gives us detailed knowledge of the formula of an ion as well as its mass.

Molecules containing the heavier isotopes are always present in our samples. Recall that we rely on the presence of naturally occurring ^{13}C when we perform ^{13}C NMR spectrometric analyses. (Because their natural abundances are low, we do not *usually* detect the presence of these heavier isotopes in IR spectrometry. However, if samples are enriched in heavier isotopes, it is sometimes possible to observe IR stretching bands that are shifted from those of normal absorptions.)

PROBLEM 25.8 Which isotopic change will most affect a carbon-hydrogen stretching frequency in the IR spectrum, changing the carbon atom from ^{12}C to ^{13}C or changing the ^{1}H to a ^{2}H? Explain your reasoning. If the $^{12}C—^{1}H$ stretching frequency is 3000 cm^{-1}, calculate stretching frequencies for the $^{13}C—^{1}H$ and $^{12}C—^{2}H$ bonds (see Chapter 17).

Notice that in the spectra shown in Figure 25.9 there are many peaks at m/e values smaller than that of the molecular ion. These peaks result from **fragment ions.** Consider, for example, the large peak at $m/e = 57$ in the spectrum of 3-pentanone. We infer that when 3-pentanone undergoes ionization in an electron impact mass spectrometer, many molecules fragment to produce an ion of $m/e = 57$. A useful strategy for deducing structural information from a mass spectrum is to express the mass of fragment ion peaks in the form $M - x$; for example, we would refer to the m/e peak at 57 in the 3-pentanone spectrum as $M - 29$ (it is 29 mass units lighter than the molecular ion peak). Put another way, the molecular ion has broken into two fragments, one of $m/e = 57$ and another of 29 mass units. The latter, however, is neutral and is therefore not detected.

This fragmentation is related to the structure of 3-pentanone. We might guess that an ethyl radical was cleaved from the molecular ion of 3-pentanone. This hypothesis seems reasonable, because the ethyl group is a structural element of the 3-pentanone molecule. When some molecular ions formed from 3-pentanone fragment, we see the other product in the mass spectrum; that is, the molecular ion fragments to form the ethyl cation and a neutral species of 57 mass units. We then see a peak of $m/e = 29$ in the mass spectrum of 3-pentanone and assign the ethyl cation structure to it. These two routes of fragmentation for 3-pentanone are shown in Equation 25.4.

Eqn. 25.4

$$CH_3—CH_2—\overset{\overset{:\dot{O}^{+}}{\|}}{C}—CH_2—CH_3 \quad (m/e = 86,\ M^{+})$$

$$\longrightarrow CH_3—CH_2—\overset{\overset{:O:}{\|}}{C^{+}} + \cdot CH_2—CH_3 \quad (m/e = 57,\ M - 29)$$

$$\longrightarrow CH_3\overset{+}{C}H_2 + \cdot\overset{\overset{:O:}{\|}}{C}—CH_2—CH_3 \quad (m/e = 29,\ M - 57)$$

Now consider the spectrum of 3-methyl-2-butanone (Figure 25.9). This spectrum does *not* show a peak at $m/e = 57$. No ethyl group is cleaved from this molecule, either as a cation or a radical fragment. This observation is consistent with the structure of 3-methyl-2-butanone—no ethyl group is attached to the carbonyl carbon atom. However, we *do* see a small peak at

$m/e = 71$ and larger one at $m/e = 43$, corresponding to M − 15 and M − 43, respectively. These peaks are consistent with the loss of CH_3 and C_3H_7 groups from the carbonyl carbon (these structural units *are* present in 3-methyl-2-butanone). These fragmentation routes are illustrated in Equation 25.5.

Eqn. 25.5

$$(CH_3)_2CH{-}\overset{\overset{+}{:O\cdot}}{\overset{\|}{C}}{-}CH_3 \longrightarrow (CH_3)_2CH{-}\overset{:O:}{\overset{\|}{C^+}} + \cdot CH_3$$

$$(CH_3)_2CH{-}\overset{\overset{+}{:O\cdot}}{\overset{\|}{C}}{-}CH_3 \longrightarrow CH_3{-}\overset{:O:}{\overset{\|}{C^+}} + \cdot CH(CH_3)_2$$

$m/e = 86$ (M^+)

$m/e = 71$ (M − 15)

$m/e = 43$ (M − 43)

In a mass spectrum we see *relative* intensities of the peaks. These intensities are measured and reported as a fraction of the largest peak in the spectrum, which we refer to as the **base peak.** Thus, the peak at $m/e = 43$ in the spectrum of 3-methyl-2-butanone is the base peak for that mass spectrum, the peak to which all other peaks in the spectrum are referenced. We report the intensity of each peak as a percentage of the intensity of the base peak, which is assigned the relative intensity of 100.

You may wonder why some peaks are larger than others in a particular mass spectrum. The peak intensities reflect the relative probabilities of each of the different modes of fragmentation occurring. Generally, fragmentations that lead to more stable ions occur more readily than fragmentations leading to the less stable ions. Thus the larger peaks in a mass spectrum often represent the more highly stabilized of the possible positive ion fragments. For example, the loss of an alkyl radical from the molecular ion of an alkyl ketone, as shown in Equation 25.6, is a favored route of fragmentation because it leads to the particularly stable acylium ion. (Recall the nature of the acylium ion from our discussion of the Friedel-Crafts reaction in Chapter 18.) The largest peaks in each of the spectra in Figure 25.9 correspond to acylium ions.

Eqn. 25.6

$$R_2C{=}\overset{+}{\ddot{O}}\cdot \longrightarrow \left[R{-}\overset{+}{C}{=}\ddot{O} \longleftrightarrow R{-}C{\equiv}\overset{+}{O}: \right] + R$$

molecular ion

acylium ion

In general, intense fragment ion peaks can be expected to correspond to relatively stable positive ions. For example, we can expect fragmentations that lead to the formation of allylic, benzylic, and tertiary carbocations to occur more readily than fragmentations that lead to secondary, primary, or methyl carbocations.

Fragmentations that produce small, neutral, stable molecules such as water, hydrogen cyanide, acetylene, ethylene, and carbon monoxide also tend to occur relatively readily. In later sections we will see examples of these types of fragmentations.

Although fragmentations provide us with information about the *structure* of the sample molecule, they do so at the expense of the intensity of the molecular ion peak. When we measure a mass spectrum using an electron impact ion source, the molecular ion forms with a significant amount of excess energy. The impacting electrons (70 eV) have energies greatly in excess of that needed to ionize the molecule. This excess energy leads to bond cleavage and fragmentation of the molecular ion. In some cases, so few molecular ions survive that it is not possible to discern the molecular ion peak—its intensity is zero, or very close to zero.

Increasing intensity of fragment ion peaks is bought at the cost of decreasing intensity of the molecular ion peak. We therefore must be on guard in the interpretation of mass spectra, realizing that the peak of highest m/e ratio *may not represent a molecular ion*—it could represent a fragment ion.

If we suspect that a molecular ion is not visible, that is, it is undergoing rapid, complete fragmentation, we can use a different method of ionization to minimize fragmentation. One type of ion source that serves this purpose is the **field ionization source.** In a field ionization source, the electron gun of an electron impact source is replaced by a field emitter, usually a collection of microneedles grown on a fine wire edge. A high potential ($\sim$10 kV) is placed between the entrance slit of the mass spectrometer and the field emitter. This potential produces a large electric field that causes electrons to be ejected from the sample molecules by a tunneling mechanism that requires much less energy than electron impact ionization. It results in an increased relative abundance of the molecular ion at the expense of fragment ions. We gain information about the molecular weight of the sample in this way, but we lose details of structure that are derived from fragment ion formation. Another way to minimize fragmentation is to use a conventional electron impact source but moderate the impact energy.

PROBLEM 25.9 The mass spectra of three isomeric alkanes of formula $C_{12}H_{26}$ (*n*-dodecane, 4-methylundecane, and 2,2,4,4,6-pentamethylheptane) are shown below. They were measured using a 70-eV electron impact ion source. Match each spectrum with the correct structure.

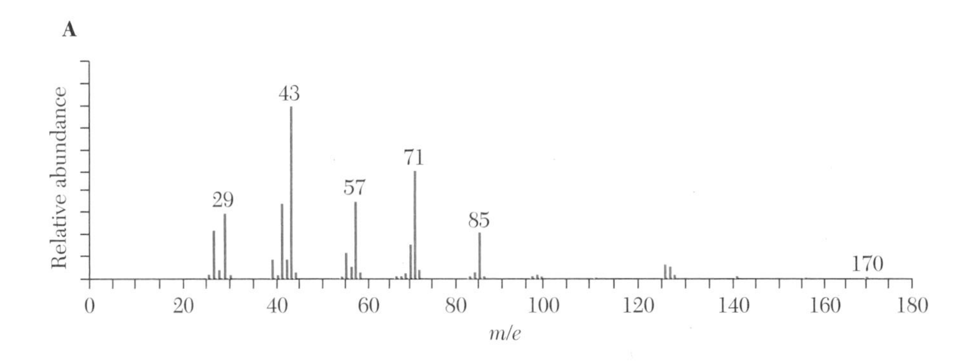

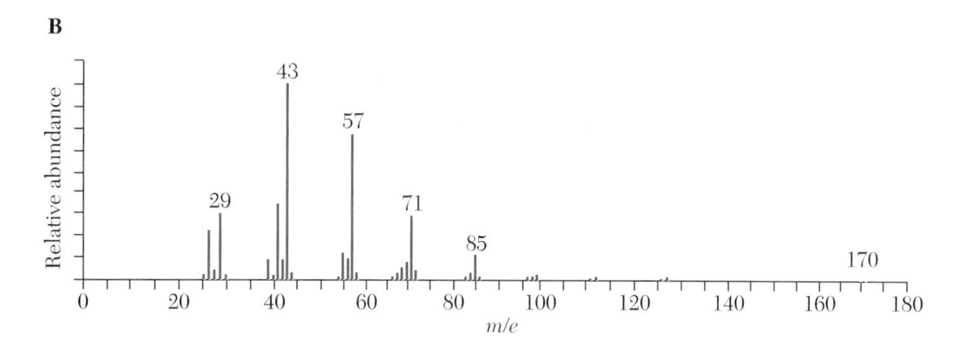

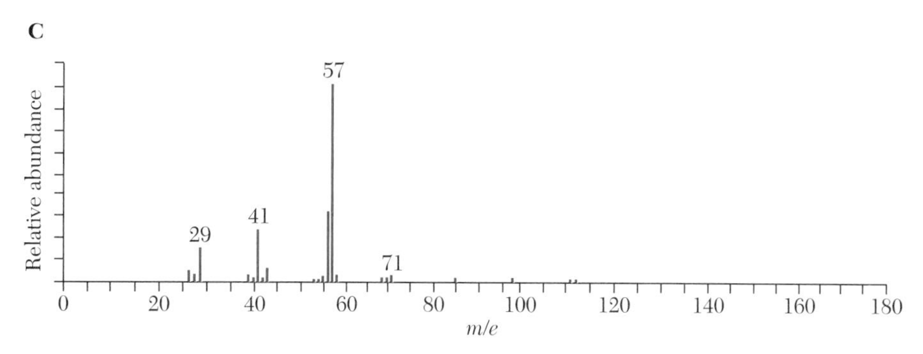

THE IMPORTANCE OF ISOTOPES IN MASS SPECTROMETRY

Suppose we are considering the mass spectrum of an unknown substance. We find a molecular ion peak at $m/e = 68$, several fragment ion peaks, and peaks at $m/e = 69$ and 70 (M + 1 and M + 2 peaks). As we have noted, peaks with m/e values greater than that of the molecular ion are caused by the presence of heavy isotopes in the molecular ion species. You might think initially that these peaks are of little value in structural analysis, but this is, in fact, far from the actual case. In a simple but ingenious way these peaks help us determine the molecular formula of the compound. For example, we can use them to determine whether an unknown compound with a molecular ion peak at $m/e = 68$ has the formula C_5H_8, C_4H_4O, or $C_3H_4N_2$.

The intensities of the M + 1 and M + 2 peaks relative to that of the M peak depend on the relative abundances of the heavy isotopes. Table 25.1 lists the natural relative abundances of some common heavy isotopes. These relative abundances can be used to predict the relative intensities of the M, M + 1, and M + 2 peaks for any given formula. To a close approximation, we can calculate the relative intensities of the M and M + 1 peaks using the following formula:

$$
\begin{aligned}
&\text{M} + 1 \text{ intensity as a percentage of (M) intensity} \\
&\quad = (\text{number of C atoms})(\text{abundance of } {}^{13}\text{C}) \\
&\quad + (\text{number of H atoms})(\text{abundance of } {}^{2}\text{H}) \\
&\quad + (\text{number of N atoms})(\text{abundance of } {}^{15}\text{N}) \\
&\quad + (\text{similar terms for any other atoms present})
\end{aligned}
$$

Table 25.1 Relative Isotopic Abundances

Element	Most Abundant Isotope	Heavy Isotope Abundance*	
		M + 1	M + 2
H	^{1}H	^{2}H (0.016%)	
C	^{12}C	^{13}C (1.08%)	
N	^{14}N	^{15}N (0.38%)	
O	^{16}O	^{17}O (0.04%)	^{18}O (0.20%)
S	^{32}S	^{33}S (0.78%)	^{34}S (4.40%)
Cl	^{35}Cl		^{37}Cl (32.5%)
Br	^{79}Br		^{81}Br (98.0%)

* Each entry is expressed as a percentage of the abundance of the most abundant isotope.

Similarly, the relative intensities of the M and M + 2 peaks can be predicted using the same type of calculation. When these calculations are performed for the formulas C_5H_8, C_4H_4O, and $C_3H_4N_2$, the results shown in Table 25.2. are obtained.

Our next step in deducing a molecular formula is to measure the *experimental* values from the mass spectrum and compare them with the calculated values (Table 25.2). The molecular formula is the one that predicts the intensities most closely in agreement with the experimental values.

There is a useful shortcut to this method for many organic compounds. For most organic compounds, carbon makes the greatest contribution to the intensity of the M + 1 peak because the ^{13}C isotope is *relatively* abundant (about 1.1% of all carbon atoms are ^{13}C, whereas only ~0.01% for all hydrogen atoms are ^{2}H). We can often calculate the number of carbon atoms in a molecular ion using the formula given in Equation 25.7.

Eqn. 25.7

$$\frac{(\text{M} + 1 \text{ intensity})}{(\text{M intensity})(0.011)} = \text{number of C atoms}$$

Table 25.2 Calculated intensities of M + 1 and M + 2 peaks for several formulas*

Formula	M + 1	M + 2
C_5H_8	5.53	0.12
C_4H_4O	4.43	0.28
$C_3H_4N_2$	4.07	0.06

* Each value is expressed as a percentage of the intensity of the M peak.

This simplified calculation works particularly well for compounds containing only carbon, hydrogen, oxygen, and halogens. It works less well when nitrogen is present because the natural abundance of ^{15}N is relatively high (0.38%).

With the general availability of higher-resolution mass spectrometric equipment, an alternative approach to determining the molecular formula associated with a molecular ion (or fragment species) has become increasingly available. This method involves the determination of the *exact mass* of a charged species observable in the mass spectrometer. The determination of an ion's exact mass allows us to specify a formula for the species where previously, with only the nominal mass, we could not.

For example, consider three possible formulas for an ion of $m/e = 68$, as noted earlier. Simply noting the nominal mass (as $m/e = 68$) does not distinguish among the possibilities of C_4H_4O, $C_3H_4N_2$, and C_5H_8. However, the exact mass of each of these species is different: their exact masses are 68.0262 (C_4H_4O), 68.0375 ($C_3H_4N_2$), and 68.0626 (C_5H_8). Using a mass spectrometer with resolution to 1 part in 10,000, we can easily distinguish among these possibilities. Although it is not a routine technique to make such measurements for *all* peaks in a given mass spectrum, it is possible to make these determinations for selected peaks.

PROBLEM 25.10 Compound *D* contains only carbon, hydrogen, and oxygen. The intensity of the molecular ion peak is 38% of the intensity of the base peak, and the intensity of the M + 1 peak is 2.5% of the intensity of the base peak. How many carbon atoms are there per molecule of *D*?

PROBLEM 25.11 Compound *E* exhibits an IR absorption at 1715 cm^{-1}, and its mass spectrum exhibits an M + 1 peak at $m/e = 171$ that is 13.2% as intense as the peak for the molecular ion. Suggest a formula (not a structure) for *E*.

PROBLEM 25.12 Substance *F*, which contains only carbon, hydrogen, and oxygen, exhibits an M + 1 peak at $m/e = 95$ that is 6.6% as intense as the peak for the molecular ion. Suggest a formula for *F*.

Notice in Table 25.1 that heavy isotopes of large abundance exist for chlorine and bromine. The ^{37}Cl isotope is approximately one-third as abundant as ^{35}Cl, and the abundance of ^{81}Br is almost equal to that of ^{79}Br. (Note that although we use ~80 as the atomic weight of bromine for stoichiometric calculations, no individual bromine atoms have a mass of 80 amu. The atomic weight reflects the weighted average of the masses of the ^{79}Br and ^{81}Br isotopes.) Because of the high abundance of the heavy isotopes of chlorine and bromine, large M + 2 peaks are present in the mass spectra of compounds containing a single chlorine or bromine atom. (By convention we refer to the peak corresponding to the isotopic combination having the lowest m/e as the M^+ peak, and those of higher m/e as being $M + x$). The mass spectrum of

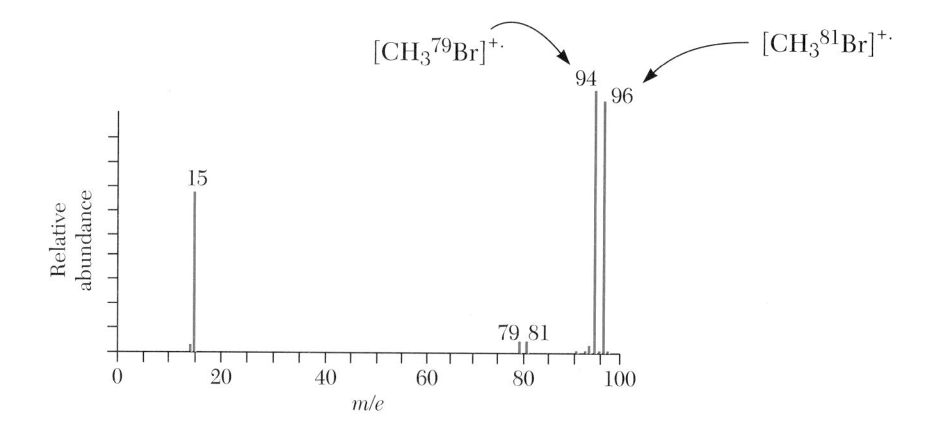

Figure 25.10 Mass spectrum of bromomethane.

bromomethane, shown in Figure 25.10, illustrates this phenomenon. The M + 2 peak reflects the high abundance of the heavy ^{81}Br isotope.

Suppose you had *not* been told that the mass spectrum in Figure 25.10 was that of bromomethane but had simply been given it as the spectrum of an unknown compound. How would you know that the peak at $m/e = 96$ is an M + 2 peak and not the M peak? There are two aspects of the spectrum that should indicate that the $m/e = 96$ peak is not an M peak. First, M − 2 peaks are not usually very intense peaks in mass spectra. An M − 2 peak would represent the loss of a hydrogen molecule or the loss of two hydrogen atoms, neither of which are common processes. Thus we would be suspicious of a large $m/e = 94$ peak representing such a fragment ion. Furthermore, look at the intensity of the $m/e = 97$ peak, which is only about 1% the intensity of the $m/e = 96$ peak. Such a small peak would indicate only a single ^{13}C atom, an unlikely possibility for a molecule of molecular weight 96 amu without a halogen atom.

PROBLEM 25.13 What is the origin of the peak at $m/e = 95$ in Figure 25.10? Explain its relative intensity ($\sim$1% the intensity of each of the $m/e = 94$ and 96 peaks) compared to the other peaks in the spectrum.

Now consider a substance containing *two* bromine atoms per molecule, such as 1,2-dibromoethane. In some molecules both bromine atoms are ^{79}Br, while in others both are ^{81}Br atoms, and yet others contain one ^{79}Br atom and one ^{81}Br atom. For the first of these types of molecules we observe an M peak, while for the second type we observe an M + 4 peak, and for the third we observe an M + 2 peak. We can rapidly estimate the relative intensities of these three peaks by making the approximation that the two bromine isotopes are equally abundant. We readily see that the probability of a molecule containing one of each of the isotopes is twice the probability that it contains two of the same isotope. The peak intensities reflect the relative numbers of molecules leading to these three types of ions; thus the relative peak intensities are approximately 1 : 2 : 1 for the M : M + 2 : M + 4 peaks, as is illustrated in Figure 25.11.

PROBLEM 25.14 Again making the approximation that the ^{79}Br and ^{81}Br isotopes have the same relative abundance, calculate the general appearance of the cluster of peaks at the highest *m/e* value in the mass spectra of compounds containing:
a. three bromine atoms **b.** four bromine atoms

PROBLEM 25.15 For simplicity, make the approximation that the ^{35}Cl and ^{37}Cl isotopes exist naturally in the ratio of 3 : 1. Sketch the general appearance of the cluster of peaks at the highest *m/e* value in the mass spectrum of each of the following compounds:
a. chloromethane **b.** 1,2-dichloroethane **c.** 1,2,3-trichloropropane

PROBLEM 25.16 Making the same simplifying assumption as in Problem 25.15, calculate the intensity of the M + 3 peak in the spectrum of 1,2-dichloroethane relative to:
a. the M peak **b.** the M + 1 peak

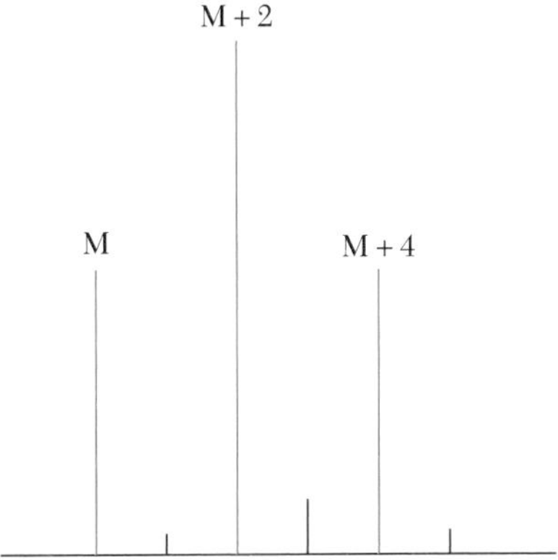

Figure 25.11 General appearance of the M, M + 2 and M + 4 peaks in the mass spectrum of compounds containing two bromine atoms.

One final point needs to be made with regard to the presence of heavy isotopes. Fragment ions also exhibit peak clusters similar to those of molecular ions. For example, consider a dibromoalkane undergoing fragmentation to yield an ion containing one bromine atom. Two peaks with relative intensities of approximately 1 : 1 result from such a fragment ion. This result reflects the fact that the bromine atom in the fragment has an almost equal likelihood of being ^{79}Br or ^{81}Br.

AN INTRODUCTION TO SOME COMMON FRAGMENTATION PROCESSES

Single-Bond Cleavage Processes The simplest type of fragmentation occurs through cleavage of one of the single bonds of the molecular ion. We saw one type of such **single-bond cleavage** earlier when we looked at the ketone mass spectra.

The most probable bond cleavages are those that lead to more stable fragments. For example, fragmentation occurs more readily at a carbon chain branch point than along a linear portion of a carbon chain. Bond breaking at a branch point leads to a more highly substituted and hence more stable carbocation than bond breaking along a linear portion of the chain. This point is illustrated by the mass spectrum of 3-methyloctane, whose base peak is at *m/e* = 57. Its fragmentation process is illustrated in Figure 25.12.

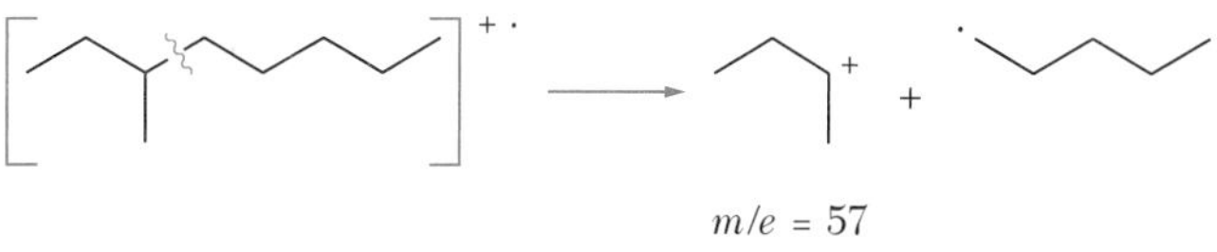

Figure 25.12 Fragmentation of the molecular ion of 3-methyloctane. Cleavage of a bond associated with a branch point generally leads to a more stable fragment than do other bond cleavages. The fragment with *m/e* = 57 is the base peak in the mass spectrum of 3-methyloctane.

m/e = 57

PROBLEM 25.17 What other ions would you anticipate to be of high abundance in the mass spectrum of 3-methyloctane? Explain your answer.

PROBLEM 25.18 The molecular ion for 3-methyloctane (Figure 25.12) does not indicate the orbital from which the electron was removed. From which molecular orbital would you expect the electron to have been removed for the molecular ion fragmenting as shown in Figure 25.12? Consider the other ions of relatively high abundance in the mass spectrum of 3-methyloctane (Problem 25.17). Would such ions form from the same molecular ion as the $m/e = 57$ ion or a *different* molecular ion? Explain your reasoning.

PROBLEM 25.19 Which peak, the peak at $m/e = 71$ or the peak at $m/e = 57$, would you expect to be larger in the mass spectrum of each of the following compounds?
a. 2-methylpentane **b.** 3-methylpentane

Cleavage of a single bond occurs especially readily when it leads to the formation of a resonance-stabilized cation, as occurs in the facile fragmentation of alcohol molecular ions. For example, the 3-hexanol molecular ion undergoes facile cleavages of the bond between carbons 3 and 4 or the bond between carbons 2 and 3 to yield abundant fragments with m/e values of 59 and 73. Figures 25.13 and 25.14 show the mass spectrum of 3-hexanol and these major fragmentation processes.

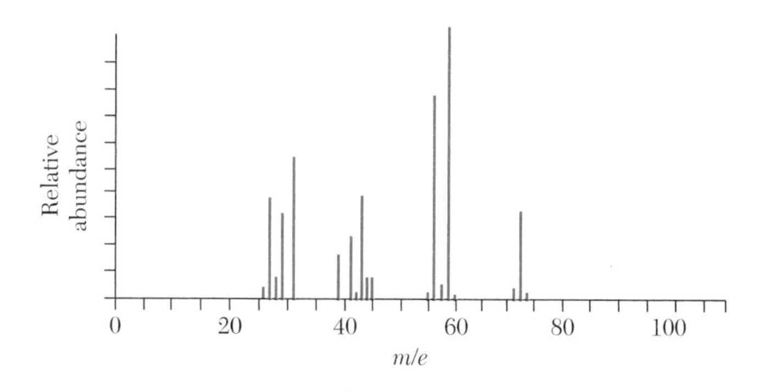

Figure 25.13 Mass spectrum of 3-hexanol. The molecular weight of 3-hexanol is 102 g/mole.

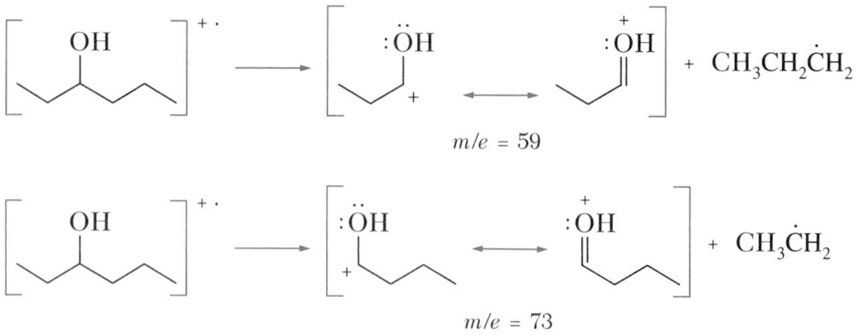

OH $]^{+\cdot}$ → [:ÖH ↔ $:\overset{+}{O}H$] + $CH_3CH_2\dot{C}H_2$

$m/e = 59$

OH $]^{+\cdot}$ → [:ÖH ↔ $:\overset{+}{O}H$] + $CH_3\dot{C}H_2$

$m/e = 73$

Figure 25.14 Major routes of fragmentation of the molecular ion of 3-hexanol. Single-bond cleavage adjacent to the hydroxyl-bearing carbon leads to resonance-stabilized carbocations.

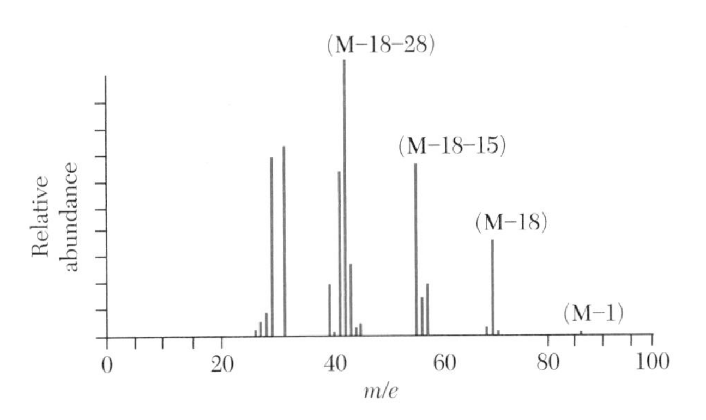

Figure 25.15 Mass spectrum of 1-pentanol.

PROBLEM 25.20 The mass spectrum of dibutyl ether exhibits a major peak at $m/e = 87$. This peak is associated with a resonance-stabilized carbocation. Draw the resonance structures for this carbocation.

PROBLEM 25.21 The mass spectra of isobutylamine and *tert*-butylamine have base peaks at $m/e = 30$ and $m/e = 58$, respectively. Draw two resonance structures for each of these two fragment ions.

Two-Bond Cleavage Processes **Two-bond cleavage** is the term given to a common type of fragmentation in which *two* single bonds are broken in the same fragmentation and a neutral molecule (not a radical) is produced along with a cation. Alcohols are illustrative of species that undergo this type of cleavage.

Most alcohols exhibit M − 18 peaks in their mass spectra. These peaks correspond to the loss of a molecule of water from the parent molecular ion. For example, the spectrum of 1-pentanol shows a prominent M − 18 peak at $m/e = 70$, as illustrated in Figure 25.15. Notice that we observe no peak for the molecular ion in this mass spectrum. This behavior is typical for alcohols. Water is lost so readily from the molecular ion that none of them survive to be analyzed. The loss of water from an alcohol molecular ion necessarily involves the cleavage of *two* bonds, the oxygen-carbon bond and a carbon-hydrogen bond. The manner in which this two-bond cleavage occurs in 1-pentanol is illustrated in Figure 25.16.

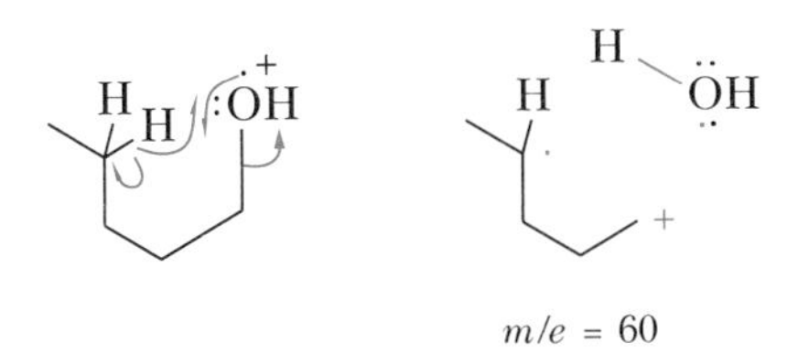

Figure 25.16 Fragmentation resulting in loss of water from the molecular ion of 1-pentanol. Two bonds are cleaved, leading to the formation of a molecule of water and a new radical cation.

Fragmentation by the McLafferty Rearrangement The **McLafferty rearrangement** is a mechanistically interesting fragmentation owing its name to Professor Fred McLafferty of Cornell University. The McLafferty rearrangement is a six-membered cyclic process that transfers a hydrogen atom and splits out an alkene molecule. This type of fragmentation commonly occurs in molecules containing a linear alkyl group of three or more carbon atoms attached to a carbonyl group. The general nature of the McLafferty rearrangement is shown in Figure 25.17. This type of fragmentation process is a major producer of intense fragment ions in the mass spectra of ketones, aldehydes, and carboxylate derivatives.

A similar but not identical rearrangement process accounts for the base peak in the mass spectrum of 1-pentanol (shown in Figure 25.15). The base

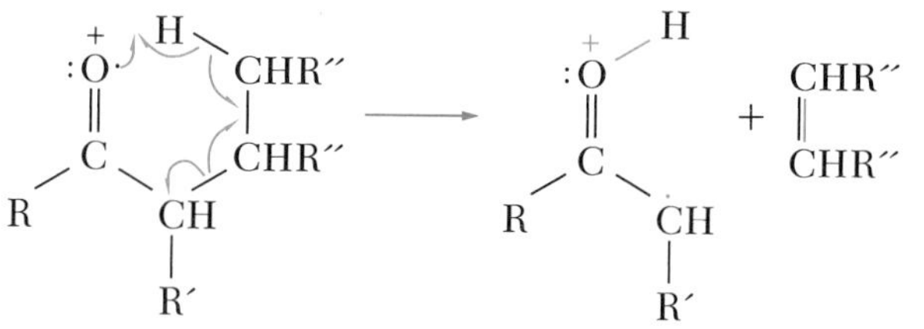

Figure 25.17 The McLafferty rearrangement of the molecular ion of a ketone. A hydrogen atom is transferred from the γ-position of the alkyl chain to the carbonyl oxygen, accompanied by extrusion of an alkene molecule. Note that for a simple ketone the molecular ion has an *even m/e* ratio, as does the product ion of the McLafferty rearrangement.

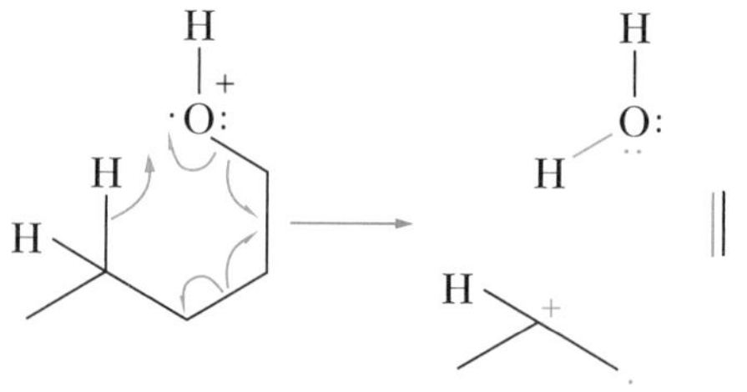

Figure 25.18 Cyclic fragmentation-rearrangement of the 1-pentanol molecular ion.

peak in that spectrum ($m/e = 42$) was described as M − 18 − 28. This peak results from cleaving *two* stable, neutral molecules from the molecular ion in a cyclic six-membered process, as shown in Figure 25.18.

PROBLEM 25.22 In the mass spectra of the compounds listed below, what peaks would result from McLafferty rearrangement of the molecular ions?
a. 2-hexanone **b.** 2-methylbutanal **c.** 3-methylbutanal

PROBLEM 25.23 Methyl octanoate exhibits an intense peak in its mass spectrum at $m/e = 74$. This peak is assigned the structure corresponding to a McLafferty rearrangement product of the molecular ion. Give a structure for this fragment ion.

Summary

- In ultraviolet/visible spectrometry we measure the molecular absorption of light over the wavelength range 200 nm to ~800 nm.
- Molecules absorbing this radiation undergo electronic transitions in which an electron is promoted from a bonding (or nonbonding) molecular orbital to an antibonding molecular orbital.
- The wavelength of light absorbed depends critically on the degree of unsaturation and conjugation in the molecule.
- Increasing conjugation brings bonding and antibonding molecular orbitals closer in energy. A longer wavelength of light is absorbed to produce such transitions.
- Empirically determined factors (Woodward's rules) allow us to calculate the approximate absorption wavelengths for various types of conjugated systems.
- In mass spectrometry a sample of the material to be studied is ionized by one of several means, including electron bombardment (electron impact) or field ionization.
- The mass-to-charge ratios and relative abundances of the resultant ions are measured to provide information about the molecular weight, molecular formula, and structure of the sample.
- The molecular ion (M) of a mass spectrum is the species produced by the removal of a single electron from the parent molecule.

- Measurement of the mass-to-charge ratio of the molecular ion provides information about the molecular weight and molecular formula of the sample.
- Structural information about the sample is provided by studying the fragment ions produced from the molecular ion. Many of these fragment ions result from simple bond cleavages from the molecular ion. However, more complex fragmentations, including rearrangements, also occur.
- An important aspect of mass spectrometry is that it reveals separate peaks for ions of different isotopic composition. The relative intensities of these peaks reflect the natural abundances of the isotopes of elements contained in the sample.

Terms to Remember

electronic absorption spectrometry
mass spectrometry
vacuum ultraviolet
absorbance
molar absorptivity
Woodward's rules
mass spectrometer
molecular ion
fragment ion
base peak
field ionization source
single-bond cleavage
two-bond cleavage
McLafferty rearrangement

Additional Problems

25.24 A solution containing 2.50×10^{-3} g/L of 1,3-cyclopentadiene is placed in a 1-cm long quartz cell for measurement of its UV spectrum. The solution produces an absorption band with a maximum at 244 nm and an absorbance at this wavelength of 9.95×10^{-2}. Calculate the molar absorptivity of 1,3-cyclopentadiene.

25.25 From each of the following pairs, choose the one that matches the given characteristic and give a brief explanation of your choice.

a. more energy per photon: IR light or UV light

b. type of ionization source that gives a greater proportion of molecular ion peak in mass spectrometry: high-energy electron bombardment or low-energy electron bombardment

c. good solvent for UV spectrometry: benzene or cyclohexane

d. gives M, M + 2, and M + 4 peaks in the mass spectrum of intensities in the approximate ratio 1 : 2 : 1: *p*-dibromobenzene, *p*-dichlorobenzene, or *p*-dinitrobenzene

e. exhibits a UV absorption band that disappears upon the addition of acid: trimethylamine or *tert*-butyl chloride

25.26 Choose the compound with the longer wavelength UV absorption from each of the following pairs:

a. 1,3-pentadiene or 1,4-pentadiene

b. or

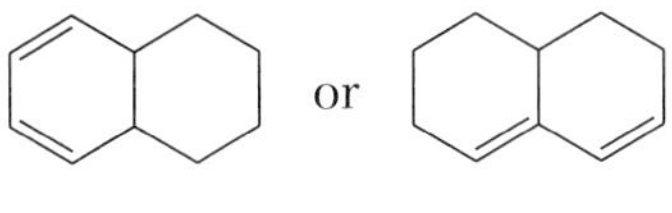

c. Ö or Ö

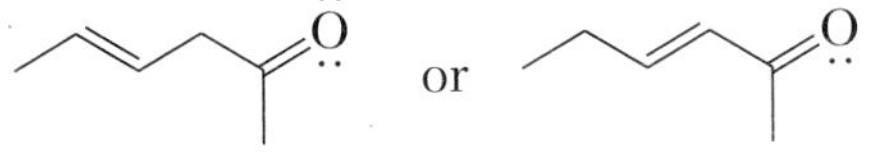

d. Ö or :O:

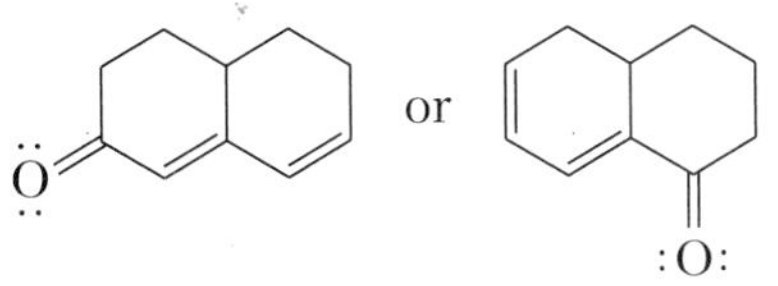

25.27 A compound of formula C_4H_6O exhibits two absorption bands in the UV region. One of these bands has $\lambda_{max} = 320$ nm with $\varepsilon = 30$, and the other has $\lambda_{max} = 218$ nm with $\varepsilon = 18{,}000$.

a. Suggest the types of electronic transitions responsible for the two bands.

b. Suggest possible structures that are consistent with the observed data.

25.28 The structure of an unknown compound has been narrowed down to the two possibilities shown below.

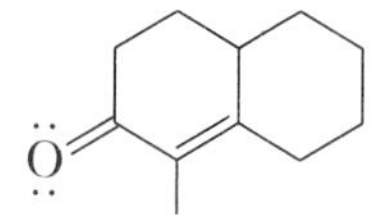

and

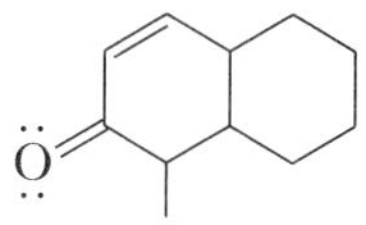

Given that the compound exhibits a UV absorption band at $\lambda_{max} = 225$ nm, which structure do you favor? Would you expect this band to remain present after the compound is subjected to catalytic hydrogenation?

25.29 Suggest formulas (not structures) for compounds exhibiting M and M + 1 peaks of the following relative intensities at $m/e = 148$ and 149, respectively, in their mass spectra:

a. M + 1, 12.14% of M **b.** M + 1, 6.83% of M **c.** M + 1, 8.83% of M

25.30 The mass spectrum of an unknown compound exhibits the following cluster of peaks in the region expected for the molecular ion:

m/e	112	113	114	115
relative intensity	100.0	6.9	32.1	2.1

Suggest a formula for the compound.

25.31 The mass spectrum of the compound considered in Problem 25.30 also exhibits a large fragment ion peak at $m/e = 77$. On this basis, suggest a structure for the compound.

25.32 Calculate the approximate ratio of the intensities of the peaks at $m/e = 394$ and 396 in the mass spectrum of 1,2,3,4-tetrabromobenzene.

25.33 Deduce the structure of an unknown acetal from the following spectrometric data:

a. The mass spectrum of the compound exhibits its peaks of highest m/e at $m/e = 168$ and 170. These two peaks are of approximately equal intensities.

b. The ^{1}H NMR spectrum exhibits the following three signals:

a doublet at δ 3.2 of relative intensity 2

a singlet at δ 3.5 of relative intensity 6

a triplet at δ 4.3 of relative intensity 1

25.34 Choose the molecular formula that accommodates the observed exact mass molecular ion mass spectrometric determination for each sample given below. (You will need to refer to a table of exact masses for the nuclides involved.)

a. 130.1471 $C_7H_{14}O_2$ or $C_7H_{18}N_2$ **b.** 84.0940 C_5H_8O or C_6H_{12}

26 CHAPTER

Amino Acids, Peptides, and Proteins

26.1 Introduction

Proteins constitute one of the most important groups of biochemicals. They are the main organic components of muscle, skin, blood, hair, and connective tissue. Enzymes, the catalysts of biochemical reactions, are also proteins. Proteins are very large molecules with molecular weights in the tens or hundreds of thousands (or more). However, there is an underlying order to their structures—all are composed basically of **α-amino acid** units connected through amide linkages. Figure 26.1 shows the general structure of an α-amino acid along with a portion of a protein.

If we wish to break down a protein into its component α-amino acids, we must hydrolyze all of the amide linkages. This can be done by using the customary laboratory methods for hydrolyzing amides. Complete hydrolysis is the usual first step in the overall structural elucidation of a protein. Thus we first learn which α-amino acids are present and in what relative amounts. After that we need to determine the sequence in which the α-amino acids are joined. This **sequencing** task is more difficult than determining the gross composition. Later in this chapter we will review the methods that chemists use to sequence proteins.

The amide linkages [—C(O)—NH—] joining the α-amino acids of proteins are often referred to as **peptide bonds**. When only a few α-amino acids are connected by peptide linkages, we refer to the molecule as a **polypeptide** (or simply a **peptide**). The term *protein* is generally reserved for polypeptides of about 50 or more α-amino acid units (*residues*). Some protein molecules have portions that are *not* composed of α-amino acids; these portions are called **prosthetic groups**. We will have more to say about them later.

Our aims in this chapter are to examine the structure and chemistry of α-amino acids, to examine the way in which α-amino acids are combined in peptides and proteins, and to introduce the relationship between the structure of proteins and their ability to perform specific tasks in living cells.

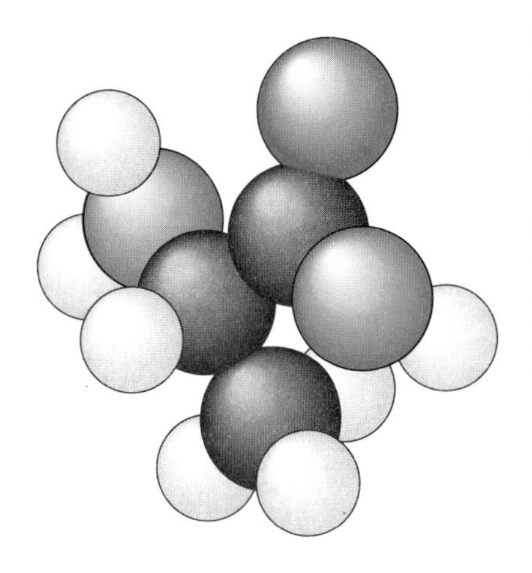

Figure 26.1 General structure of α-amino acids and proteins. A protein consists of α-amino acids connected by amide linkages. In the protein, the R, R′, and R″ substituents may be the same or different. The wavy lines indicate the end of the portion of the protein shown. Each end is connected to the remainder of the protein by additional amide linkages.

$$H_2\ddot{N}-\underset{\displaystyle R}{\underset{|}{C}H}-CO_2H$$

General structure of an α-amino acid

$$\sim\ddot{N}H-\overset{R}{\overset{|}{C}H}-\underset{:O:}{\underset{\|}{C}}-\ddot{N}H-\overset{R'}{\overset{|}{C}H}-\underset{:O:}{\underset{\|}{C}}-\ddot{N}H-\overset{R''}{\overset{|}{C}H}-\underset{:O:}{\underset{\|}{C}}-\sim$$

amide linkages

Structure of a portion of a protein

Table 26.1 Major Naturally Occurring α-amino Acids

All of the α-amino acids listed here (except for the achiral glycine) occur naturally in the L-configuration. Two of those listed (isoleucine and threonine) contain an additional stereogenic center of configuration as shown. The structures are shown in the zwitterionic form (see text). The existence of several values of pK_a for each α-amino acid is also explained in the text.

Name	Abbreviation	Structure	pK_{a1}	pK_{a2}	pK_{a3}
		Nonpolar side chains			
alanine	Ala	$CH_3CH(^+NH_3)—COO^-$	2.35	9.69	—
glycine	Gly	$HCH(^+NH_3)—COO^-$	2.34	9.60	—
isoleucine	Ile	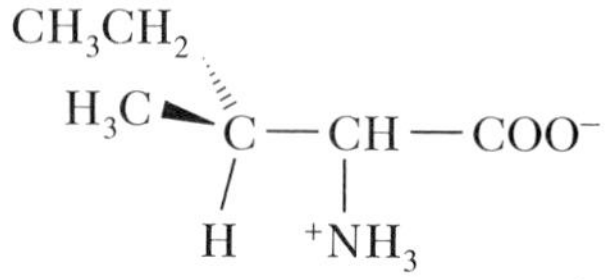 $CH_3CH_2(H_3C)(H)C—CH(^+NH_3)—COO^-$	2.36	9.68	—
leucine	Leu	$(CH_3)_2CHCH_2CH(^+NH_3)COO^-$	2.36	9.60	—
phenylalanine	Phe	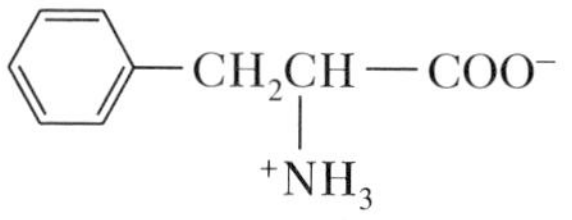 $C_6H_5—CH_2CH(^+NH_3)—COO^-$	1.83	9.13	—
proline	Pro	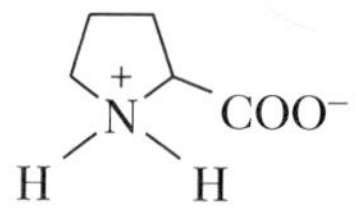 pyrrolidine ring, $^+N(H)$, ring CH(H)—COO^-	1.99	10.60	—
valine	Val	$(CH_3)_2CHCH(^+NH_3)COO^-$	2.32	9.62	—
		Polar, neutral side chains			
asparagine	Asn	$H_2\ddot{N}—C(=\!:\!O\!:)—CH_2CH(^+NH_3)—COO^-$	2.02	8.08	—
cysteine	Cys	$H\ddot{S}CH_2CH(^+NH_3)—COO^-$	1.71	8.33	10.78
glutamine	Gln	$H_2\ddot{N}—C(=\!:\!O\!:)—CH_2CH_2CH(^+NH_3)—COO^-$	2.17	9.13	—

—*Continued*

Table 26.1—Continued

Name	Abbreviation	Structure	pK_{a1}	pK_{a2}	pK_{a3}
Polar, neutral side chains-continued					
methionine	Met	$H_3CSCH_2CH_2CH(^+NH_3)—COO^-$	2.28	9.21	—
serine	Ser	$HOCH_2CH(^+NH_3)—COO^-$	2.21	9.15	—
threonine	Thr	$H_3C—C(H)(HO)—CH(^+NH_3)—COO^-$	2.63	10.43	—
tryptophan	Trp	(indol-3-yl)$—CH_2CH(^+NH_3)—COO^-$	2.38	9.39	—
tyrosine	Tyr	$HO—C_6H_4—CH_2CH(^+NH_3)—COO^-$	2.20	9.11	10.07
Acidic side chains					
aspartic acid	Asp	$HO_2CCH_2CH(^+NH_3)COO^-$	2.09	3.86	9.82
glutamic acid	Glu	$HO_2CCH_2CH_2CH(^+NH_3)—COO^-$	2.19	4.25	9.67
Basic side chains					
arginine	Arg	$H_2N—C(=NH)—NHCH_2CH_2CH_2CH(^+NH_3)—COO^-$	2.17	9.04	12.48
histidine	His	(imidazol-4-yl, N—H)$—CH_2CH(^+NH_3)COO^-$	1.82	6.00	9.17
lysine	Lys	$H_2NCH_2CH_2CH_2CH_2CH(^+NH_3)—COO^-$	2.18	8.95	10.53

26.2 Occurrence and Structure of Amino Acids

THE FUNDAMENTALS OF α-AMINO ACID STRUCTURE

Consider the general structure of an α-amino acid as shown in Figure 26.1. The number of possible α-amino acids with this general structure is almost limitless, since the R group is capable of almost limitless variation. In spite of this possible range of structure, fewer than 30 α-amino acids are common in nature. Of these, only 20 are commonly found incorporated in protein structures. The structures of these common, naturally occurring α-amino acids, along with their names and standard abbreviations, are shown in Table 26.1. Each naturally occurring α-amino acid has been assigned a three-letter abbreviation (e.g., Gly for glycine and Ala for alanine). Chemists and biochemists use these abbreviations extensively when referring to the structures of peptides and proteins. Thus it is useful to commit to memory not only the structures and their names but also their abbreviations.

You should note that all of the α-amino acids listed in Table 26.1 (with the exception of glycine) have a stereogenic carbon atom at the α-position (attached to the carboxyl carbon atom). These natural α-amino acids (with the exception of the achiral glycine) occur in optically active forms. Usually only one enantiomer occurs in nature (although there are exceptions). All common chiral α-amino acids belong to the L stereochemical family; that is, they have the same relative configuration about the stereogenic carbon as L-glyceraldehyde, as shown in Figure 26.2. (The D/L notation system was introduced in Chapter 24.)

PROBLEM 26.1 Assign the *R*/*S* stereochemical descriptors to the stereogenic centers in each of the following naturally occurring amino acids.
a. alanine b. tryptophan c. tyrosine

PROBLEM 26.2 Naturally occurring alanine is dextrorotatory. Would you expect all naturally occurring α-amino acids to be similarly dextrorotatory? Explain your answer.

Not all of the 20 α-amino acids listed in Table 26.1 and found in proteins can be synthesized in the human body. Those that cannot be synthesized in vivo must be obtained from the diet. We refer to the amino acids required on a regular basis in the human diet as **essential amino acids** (see Table 26.2). Humans obtain these essential amino acids by the digestion of protein from

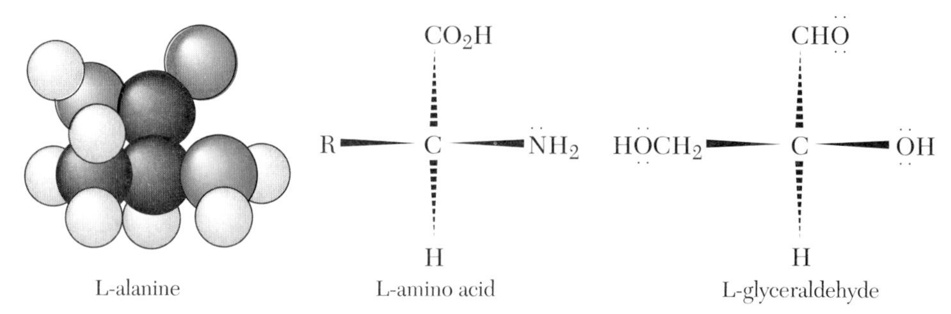

Figure 26.2 General structure of an L-α-amino acid relative to L-glyceraldehyde. Natural α-amino acids generally have the L configuration about the α-carbon site. When α-amino acids of the D configurational family occur in nature, they have been formed by racemization of an L-α-amino acid rather than by their own biosynthetic route. A space-filling model of one L-α-amino acid, L-alanine, is shown. For L-alanine, R = methyl.

Table 26.2 Essential α-Amino Acids in the Diet of Humans*

L-leucine
L-lysine
L-methionine
L-phenylalanine
L-threonine
L-tryptophan
L-valine

* L-Arginine and L-histidine are sometimes listed as essential α-amino acids for children. However, recent determinations call these requirements into question.

other sources (plants and animals). These proteins are hydrolyzed to their constituent α-amino acids, which in turn are reassembled in the proper sequence to produce the required proteins.

The properties of α-amino acids in aqueous solution and in the solid phase suggest that they exist largely in the form of **zwitterions** (German; hybrid), as shown in Table 26.1 and Figure 26.3. The preponderance of the zwitterionic form can be rationalized in terms of a general rule we have used frequently: *an acid-base equilibrium favors the formation of the weaker acid and weaker base.* Thus, the equilibrium in Figure 26.3 favors the zwitterionic form.

High dipole moments, high water solubility, low solubility in less polar solvents, and high melting temperatures (typical of salts) are among the properties consistent with the zwitterionic structure. Furthermore, an α-amino acid such as glycine is a much weaker base and a much weaker acid than would be expected for a compound containing a free amino group ($—NH_2$) or a free carboxyl group ($—COOH$). The observed low acidity, however, is similar to that of an ammonium salt, and the observed low basicity is similar to that of a carboxylate salt. The saltlike zwitterionic structure is particularly important for the biological activity of α-amino acids. Because of the increased water solubility of the zwitterionic structure (compared to an un-ionized structure), α-amino acids can exist in significant concentrations in the interiors of cells, where the homogeneous environment is conducive to efficient reactions with other substances.

ACID-BASE PROPERTIES OF α-AMINO ACIDS

Consider glycine in an aqueous solution of low pH. Protonation of glycine occurs under these acidic conditions, converting the zwitterionic structure to a cationic form. Similarly, when glycine is placed in a solution of high pH, deprotonation of the zwitterionic form occurs, leading to an anion. Formation of these cationic and anionic forms is illustrated in Figure 26.4. The zwitterionic, cationic, and anionic forms of an α-amino acid may all be present simultaneously in significant quantities in aqueous solution. The relative proportions of these forms depend on the pH of the solution and the structure of the α-amino acid itself. Different forms dominate at different pH values.

It is useful to define the **isoelectric point** or *isoelectric pH*, a property of α-amino acids that is related to their acidity and basicity. The isoelectric point, usually designated pI, is defined as the pH at which the concentration of the cationic and anionic forms are equal. It is also the pH at which the concentration

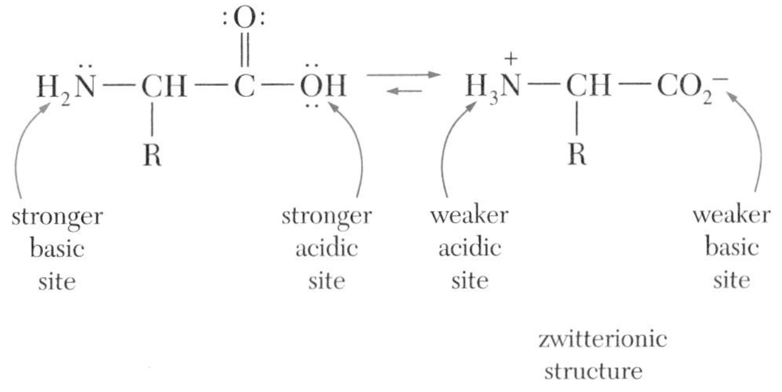

Figure 26.3 The zwitterionic structure of α-amino acids.

$$H_2\ddot{N}—\underset{\displaystyle R}{\underset{|}{CH}}—\overset{\displaystyle :O:}{\overset{\|}{C}}—\ddot{O}H \rightleftharpoons H_3\overset{+}{N}—\underset{\displaystyle R}{\underset{|}{CH}}—CO_2^-$$

stronger basic site; stronger acidic site; weaker acidic site; weaker basic site

zwitterionic structure

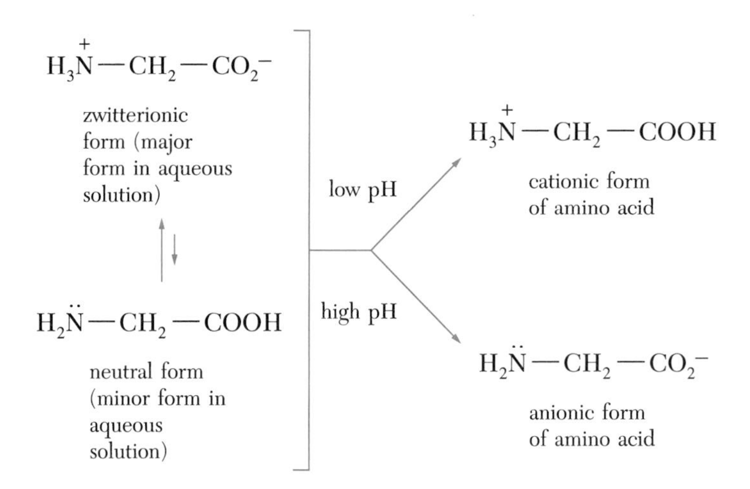

Figure 26.4 Protonation and deprotonation of glycine.

of the zwitterionic form is at a maximum. We will now explore the relation between the isoelectric pH and the pK_a values of the α-amino acids.

Consider the two acid-base equilibria shown in Figure 26.5. The equilibrium constants for the two equilibria are the K_{a1} and K_{a2} of the α-amino acid. The equilibrium constants for the reactions in Figure 26.5 can be expressed in terms of the concentrations of the zwitterionic, cationic, and anionic forms of the α-amino acid, as shown in Equations 26.1 and 26.2.

Eqn. 26.1
$$K_{a1} = \frac{[\text{zwitterion}][H_3O^+]}{[\text{cation}]}$$

Eqn. 26.2
$$K_{a2} = \frac{[\text{anion}][H_3O^+]}{[\text{zwitterion}]}$$

We can rearrange these equations to obtain expressions for the concentrations of the cationic and anionic forms of the α-amino acid, as shown in Equations 26.3 and 26.4.

Eqn. 26.3
$$[\text{cation}] = \frac{[\text{zwitterion}][H_3O^+]}{K_{a1}}$$

Eqn. 26.4
$$[\text{anion}] = \frac{[\text{zwitterion}]K_{a2}}{[H_3O^+]}$$

The isoelectric point is the pH at which the concentrations of the anionic and cationic forms are equal. Thus, we can obtain an expression for pI in terms

Figure 26.5 Acid-base equilibria with α-amino acids in aqueous solution.

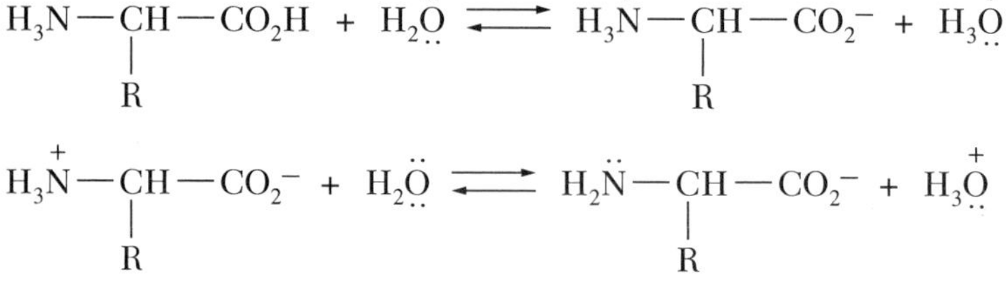

$$H_3\overset{+}{N}-\underset{R}{\underset{|}{C}H}-CO_2H + H_2\ddot{\underset{..}{O}} \rightleftharpoons H_3\overset{+}{N}-\underset{R}{\underset{|}{C}H}-CO_2^- + H_3\overset{+}{\underset{..}{O}}$$

$$H_3\overset{+}{N}-\underset{R}{\underset{|}{C}H}-CO_2^- + H_2\ddot{\underset{..}{O}} \rightleftharpoons H_2\ddot{N}-\underset{R}{\underset{|}{C}H}-CO_2^- + H_3\overset{+}{\underset{..}{O}}$$

of the pK_a values for the equilibria shown in Figure 26.5:

At the isoelectric point

Eqn. 26.5
$$\frac{[\text{zwitterion}][H_3O^+]}{K_{a1}} = \frac{[\text{zwitterion}]K_{a2}}{[H_3O^+]}$$

Eqn. 26.6
$$(K_{a1})(K_{a2}) = [H_3O^+]^2$$

Eqn. 26.7
$$\log K_{a1} + \log K_{a2} = 2\log[H_3O^+]$$

Eqn. 26.8
$$pI = \frac{pK_{a1} + pK_{a2}}{2}$$

This analysis shows that the isoelectric pH (the pI) of an α-amino acid is simply the mean of its two pK_a values. This relationship is clearly true for those α-amino acids bearing only a single amino group and a single carboxylic acid group. However, some naturally occurring α-amino acids are structurally more complex. Consider, for example, the structures of aspartic acid and glutamic acid. Each of these α-amino acids bears an additional carboxyl group on the side chain. Thus, these two α-amino acids have an extra acidic site. We refer to them as *acidic α-amino acids*, and we need to consider *three* pK_a values (pK_{a1}, pK_{a2}, and pK_{a3}) for them rather than two. If there is a basic substituent on the side chain, we refer to the α-amino acid as a *basic α-amino acid*, and again there is an additional pK_a value to consider. We can use a simple approach to understand the effect of an additional acidic or basic substituent group on the pI value of an α-amino acid.

Consider an α-amino acid that has a carboxylic acid substituent on the side chain. It will be considerably more acidic than α-amino acids with no carboxyl group on the side chain, and it will therefore dissociate to a greater degree, producing a higher concentration of its anionic form, as shown in Figure 26.6. Recall that the pI is the pH at which the concentrations of anionic and cationic forms are equal. In order to reach the pI, we need to adjust the pH to suppress the higher concentration of anion resulting from dissociation of the carboxyl group on the side chain. We therefore add acid to drive the equilibrium of Figure 26.6 to the left. It follows that the pI will be at an acidic pH.

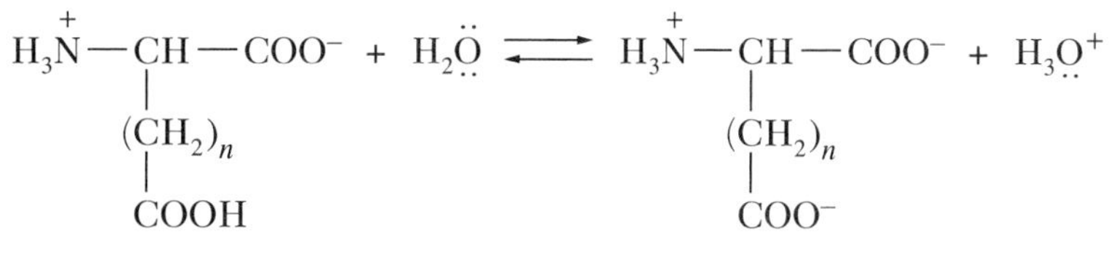

Figure 26.6 Anionic form of an acidic α-amino acid.

$$H_3\overset{+}{N}-CH(COO^-)-(CH_2)_n-COOH + H_2\ddot{O} \rightleftharpoons H_3\overset{+}{N}-CH(COO^-)-(CH_2)_n-COO^- + H_3O^+$$

anionic form of an acidic amino acid

PROBLEM 26.3 Write equations for the reactions associated with K_{a1}, K_{a2}, and K_{a3} for each of the following α-amino acids:

a. aspartic acid **b.** lysine

PROBLEM 26.4 For each of the following α-amino acids, deduce whether pI is the mean value of pK_{a1} and pK_{a2}, or pK_{a2} and pK_{a3}.
a. aspartic acid **b.** lysine

PROBLEM 26.5 The monosodium salt of glutamic acid (MSG) is used to flavor food. Suggest a structure for this compound.

PROBLEM 26.6 The pI of tyrosine is 5.65. At pH = 6 do you expect the cationic form or the anionic form to be present in higher concentration?

26.3 Availability and Synthesis of α-Amino Acids

We can obtain α-amino acids from natural protein sources or by laboratory synthesis. Optically active α-amino acids can be isolated from protein sources, but synthetic methods generally lead to racemic mixtures. Since many applications require the biologically active pure L enantiomer, we usually need to follow up a synthetic route to an α-amino acid with a resolution step. For some L configuration α-amino acids, the more cost-effective preparation is to use a natural protein source rather than a synthesis. For such α-amino acids the cost of the L enantiomer from a chemical supply house is often much less than that of a racemic mixture of the same material, which can be produced only by synthesis. (The D-enantiomer of such an α-amino acid is also correspondingly expensive.)

Nevertheless, the syntheses of α-amino acids that do *not* occur naturally, as well as the syntheses of some that are naturally occurring, are important and economically feasible. We will consider here three methods for the synthesis of α-amino acids; all lead to racemic mixtures.

SYNTHESIS FROM CARBOXYLIC ACIDS

If we use a carboxylic acid as our starting material for the preparation of an α-amino acid, the synthetic task is to introduce an amino group onto the α-carbon atom. There is currently no convenient one-step laboratory procedure for accomplishing this, but we can achieve the result in two steps.

The first step in this procedure is the introduction of a bromine atom at the α-position by means of the Hell-Volhard-Zelinsky reaction, which we discussed in Chapter 21 (Reaction 168). The introduction of a bromine atom is followed by a displacement reaction with ammonia. Ammonia displaces a bromide ion from the α-carbon atom in an S_N2 reaction. An example of the overall reaction is shown in Equation 26.9.

Eqn. 26.9

$$CH_3CH_2CO_2H \xrightarrow[Br_2]{PBr_3} \underset{\displaystyle Br}{CH_3CHCO_2H} \xrightarrow{NH_3} \underset{\displaystyle {}^+NH_3}{CH_3CHCO_2^-}$$

56% yield

We learned earlier (Chapter 20) that the preparation of amines by the reaction of haloalkanes with ammonia is often unsatisfactory because of overalkylation. This problem is less serious when we prepare α-aminocarboxylic acids from α-bromocarboxylic acids. The nitrogen in the α-amino acid product is considerably less nucleophilic than nitrogen in ammonia. Thus, a second alkylation of the nitrogen is much less likely than the first. Satisfactory yields of the target α-amino acid are obtained through the use of an excess of ammonia.

PROBLEM 26.7 Outline a method for the preparation of isoleucine from a carboxylic acid.

PROBLEM 26.8 What problem(s) do you envision in the preparation of serine from a carboxylic acid using the method described above?

SYNTHESIS FROM MALONIC ESTER

Several variations of the malonic ester synthesis (Chapter 23) are used to prepare α-amino acids. One procedure is in essence a blend of the malonic ester and Gabriel syntheses (Chapter 20), as shown in Figure 26.7. In the first step, malonic ester is subjected to bromination. The resultant α-bromomalonic ester is then allowed to react with potassium phthalimide to produce an *N*-phthalimidomalonic ester, which in turn is alkylated at the α-carbon atom. Hydrolysis and the accompanying decarboxylation liberate the racemic α-amino acid. The synthesis of racemic methionine using this approach is illustrated in Equation 26.10.

Eqn. 26.10

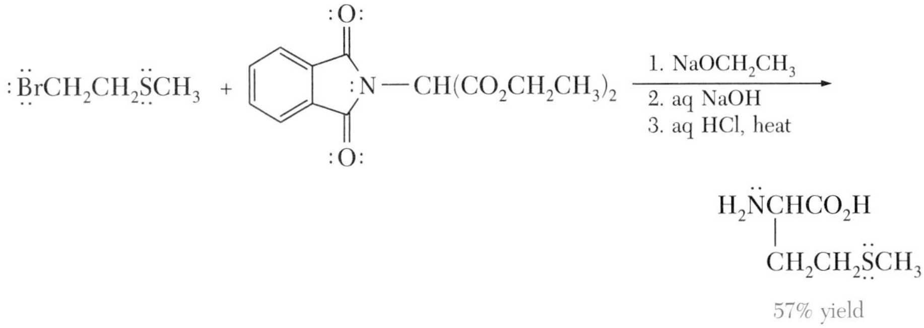

$$:\ddot{B}rCH_2CH_2\ddot{S}CH_3 + \text{(phthalimido)}:N-CH(CO_2CH_2CH_3)_2 \xrightarrow[\text{2. aq NaOH} \\ \text{3. aq HCl, heat}]{\text{1. NaOCH}_2\text{CH}_3} H_2\ddot{N}CHCO_2H \text{ (with } CH_2CH_2\ddot{S}CH_3\text{)}$$

57% yield

Figure 26.7 Malonic ester route for the synthesis of an α-amino acid.

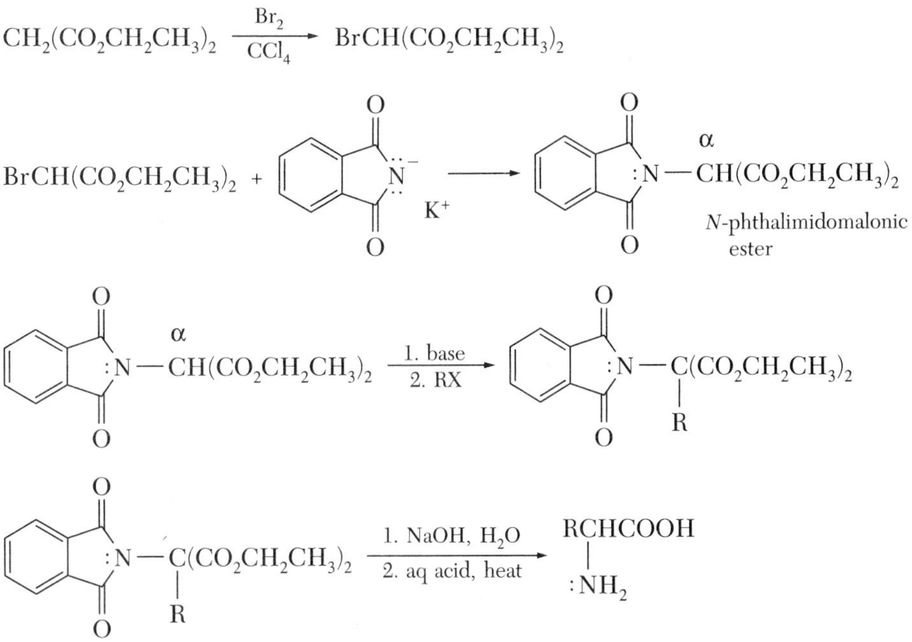

$$CH_2(CO_2CH_2CH_3)_2 \xrightarrow[CCl_4]{Br_2} BrCH(CO_2CH_2CH_3)_2$$

$$BrCH(CO_2CH_2CH_3)_2 + \text{(phthalimide } \ddot{N}^- K^+) \longrightarrow \text{(phthalimido)}:N-CH(CO_2CH_2CH_3)_2$$

N-phthalimidomalonic ester

$$\text{(phthalimido)}:N-\overset{\alpha}{C}H(CO_2CH_2CH_3)_2 \xrightarrow[\text{2. RX}]{\text{1. base}} \text{(phthalimido)}:N-C(R)(CO_2CH_2CH_3)_2$$

$$\text{(phthalimido)}:N-C(R)(CO_2CH_2CH_3)_2 \xrightarrow[\text{2. aq acid, heat}]{\text{1. NaOH, H}_2\text{O}} RCH(:NH_2)COOH$$

PROBLEM 26.9 Draw the structure of the substituted malonic acid that would result from hydrolysis of the ester linkages of the substituted *N*-phthalimidomalonic ester in the scheme shown in Figure 26.7.

PROBLEM 26.10 Propose a synthesis of valine using the phthalimidomalonic ester route.

PROBLEM 26.11 When diethyl *N*-phthalimidomalonate is treated with ethyl acrylate and sodium ethoxide, a compound of formula $C_{20}H_{23}O_8N$ is obtained. This compound is hydrolyzed by hot hydrochloric acid to an acidic α-amino acid of formula $C_5H_9O_4N$. Suggest structures for the intermediate substituted phthalimide and the product α-amino acid.

A variation of this procedure uses **acetamidomalonic ester** rather than phthalimidomalonic ester. The preparation of histidine using this approach is shown in Equation 26.11.

Eqn. 26.11

$$CH_3\overset{\overset{:O:}{\|}}{C}\ddot{N}HCH(CO_2CH_2CH_3)_2 \xrightarrow[\text{3. hot aq HCl}]{\text{1. }NaOCH_2CH_3 \quad \text{2. (4-imidazolyl)}CH_2Cl} \text{(4-imidazolyl)}CH_2CH(NH_2)CO_2H$$

acetamidomalonic ester

35% yield histidine

PROBLEM 26.12 When acetamidomalonic ester is treated with sodium hydroxide and formaldehyde, a compound of formula $C_8H_{17}O_6N$ is produced. Treatment of this compound with hot hydrochloric acid results in the formation of an α-amino acid. Suggest structures for the intermediate compound and for the product α-amino acid.

THE STRECKER SYNTHESIS

We have seen that the hydrolysis of a cyano group is a useful route for the preparation of carboxylic acids (see Chapter 21). In principle, therefore, we should be able to prepare α-amino acids by the hydrolysis of α-aminonitriles, as illustrated in Equation 26.12. The α-aminonitriles needed for this preparation can be obtained from the treatment of aldehydes with ammonia and cyanide ion (in the form of a salt such as ammonium cyanide, NH_4CN). The preparation of alanine by this route is shown in Equation 26.13.

Eqn. 26.12

$$R-\underset{\underset{\ddot{N}H_2}{|}}{CH}-CN \xrightarrow{\text{hydrolysis}} R-\underset{\underset{\ddot{N}H_2}{|}}{CH}-COOH$$

Eqn. 26.13

$$CH_3CH\ddot{O} + NH_4CN \longrightarrow CH_3-\underset{\underset{\ddot{N}H_2}{|}}{CH}-CN \xrightarrow[\text{2. aq NaOH}]{\text{1. aq HCl, heat}} CH_3-\underset{\underset{\overset{+}{N}H_3}{|}}{CH}-CO_2^-$$

60% yield
alanine

This method for the preparation of α-amino acids is known as the **Strecker synthesis**.

PROBLEM 26.13 Outline a preparation of phenylalanine using the Strecker synthesis.

PROBLEM 26.14 What problem(s) do you foresee in an attempted preparation of lysine using the Strecker synthesis? How might you get around such a problem(s)?

PROBLEM 26.15 The mechanism for the formation of α-aminonitriles by the reaction of an aldehyde with cyanide ion and ammonia is thought to involve an imine intermediate. Write a mechanism using the curved-arrow formalism for the formation of $CH_3CH(CN)NH_2$ by the reaction of acetaldehyde with ammonia and ammonium cyanide.

26.4 Reactions of α-Amino Acids

α-Amino acids undergo many of the reactions typical of amines and carboxylic acids. However, in order to cause these typical reactions to occur it is often necessary to adjust the pH of the reaction medium carefully. Remember that α-amino acids exist in different forms depending on the pH and that the zwitterionic form is dominant at intermediate pH values.

AMIDE FORMATION

Basic conditions are required for the efficient conversion of the amino group of an α-amino acid to an amide linkage. Under basic conditions the zwitterionic form of the α-amino acid is converted to the anionic form, in which the carboxylate group is negatively charged and the amino group is neutral. The free amino group thus undergoes the same types of reactions as do simple amines. For example, the free $-NH_2$ group reacts with acyl halides to form amides. The synthesis of hippuric acid using this approach is shown in Figure 26.8.

$$H_3\overset{+}{N}CH_2CO_2^- \xrightarrow{\text{NaOCH}} H_2\ddot{N}CH_2CO_2^-\ Na^+ \xrightarrow{\overset{O}{\|}{PhCCl}} Ph\overset{:O:}{\overset{\|}{C}}\ddot{N}HCH_2CO_2^-\ Na^+$$

$$Ph\overset{:O:}{\overset{\|}{C}}\ddot{N}HCH_2CO_2^-\ Na^+ \xrightarrow[\text{aq acid}]{\text{dilute}} Ph\overset{:O:}{\overset{\|}{C}}\ddot{N}HCH_2CO_2H$$

80% yield
hippuric acid

Figure 26.8 The synthesis of hippuric acid from glycine. Hippuric acid (*N*-benzoylglycine) is a natural product found in horse urine. Its name is derived from the Greek words for horse (*hipp-*) and urine (*-uric*). It is produced biologically from benzoic acid in the diet. It is also present to a small degree in human urine (the amount may increase at Thanksgiving because cranberries are rich in benzoic acid).

PROBLEM 26.16 Which substance, hippuric acid or glycine, would you expect to cause effervescence when added to an aqueous solution of sodium bicarbonate? Explain your answer.

PROBLEM 26.17 Write the structure of *N*-acetylalanine. How would you synthesize *N*-acetylalanine from alanine?

ESTER FORMATION

Ester formation is another important reaction of α-amino acids. For example, it is often a necessary step in peptide syntheses, as we will discuss later. Conditions similar to those used for the esterification of simple carboxylic acids also serve for amino acids. For example, we can add an alcohol to the α-amino acid in the presence of a strong acid. A large excess of hydrogen chloride gas is usually used as the acidic reagent. It protonates the zwitterionic form of the α-amino acid, thereby forming a high concentration of the cationic form. The latter contains a free carboxyl group suitable for ester formation. Figure 26.9 shows the preparation of the methyl ester of phenylalanine using this approach.

Other strong acids such as benzenesulfonic acid ($PhSO_3H$) may also be used in this type of esterification reaction. The equilibrium for the ester formation can, as usual, be driven toward the product by continuous removal of water using azeotropic distillation (Dean-Stark technique, Chapter 18).

THE NINHYDRIN REACTION

Ninhydrin (**26.1**) is a compound that gives a useful color reaction with α-amino acids (except proline). If we add a few drops of a dilute solution of ninhydrin in ethanol to a solution of an α-amino acid, the original colorless mixture becomes violet. This color test is known as the **ninhydrin test**. It detects the $-NH_2$ group of α-amino acids and proteins. The reaction is summarized in Figure 26.10.

The mechanistic steps of the ninhydrin reaction involve some processes we have met previously—the establishment of an equilibrium between a carbonyl compound and its hydrate, imine formation and hydrolysis, decarboxylation, and simple acid-base chemistry.

Figure 26.9 Synthesis of the methyl ester of phenylalanine.

$$PhCH_2CH(\overset{+}{N}H_3)CO_2^- \xrightarrow[HCl]{anhyd} PhCH_2CH(\overset{+}{N}H_3)CO_2H\ :\ddot{Cl}:^- \xrightarrow[HCl]{CH_3OH} PhCH_2CH(\overset{+}{N}H_3)C(=\ddot{O})\ddot{O}CH_3\ :\ddot{Cl}:^-$$

$$PhCH_2CH(\overset{+}{N}H_3)C(=\ddot{O})\ddot{O}CH_3\ :\ddot{Cl}:^- \xrightarrow[aq\ NaOH]{dilute,\ cold} PhCH_2CH(\ddot{N}H_2)C(=\ddot{O})\ddot{O}CH_3$$

90% yield

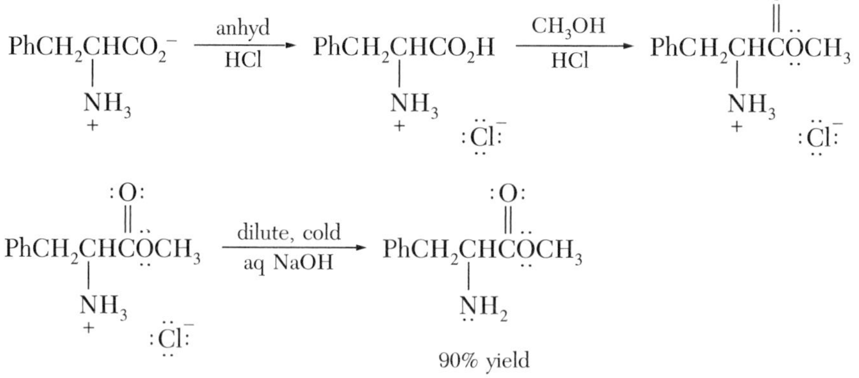

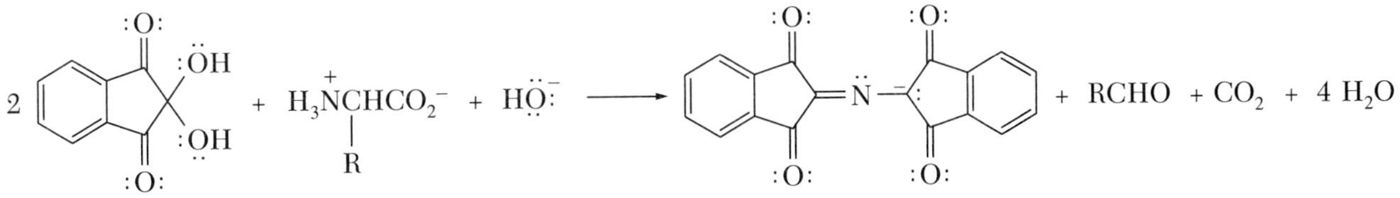

$$2\ \text{ninhydrin} + H_3\overset{+}{N}CH(R)CO_2^- + HO^- \longrightarrow \text{(purple color)} + RCHO + CO_2 + 4\,H_2O$$

ninhydrin
26.1

(purple color)

Figure 26.10 Overall reaction of ninhydrin with an α-amino acid. Two equivalents of ninhydrin react with one of the α-amino acid. The side chain of the α-amino acid and the α-carbon atom itself ultimately form an aldehyde, RCHO.

MECHANISM OF REACTION

The Ninhydrin Reaction

Step 1 An equilibrium is established between the *gem*-diol form of ninhydrin and the tricarbonyl form.

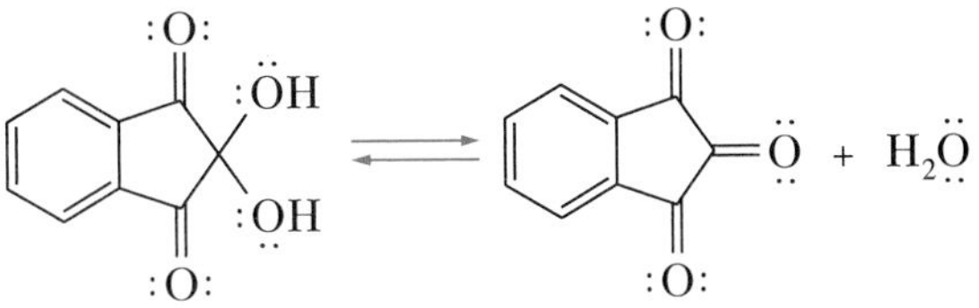

$$\text{ninhydrin (gem-diol)} \rightleftharpoons \text{tricarbonyl form} + H_2O$$

Step 2 The amino group of the α-amino acid forms an imine with the tricarbonyl form of ninhydrin.

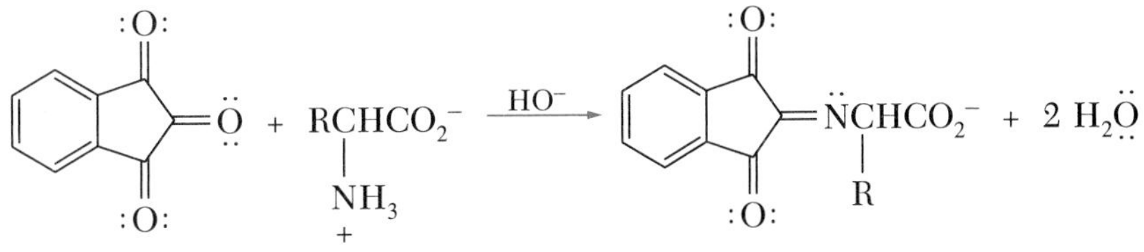

$$\text{tricarbonyl form} + RCH(\overset{+}{N}H_3)CO_2^- \xrightarrow{HO^-} \text{imine}{=}NCH(R)CO_2^- + 2\,H_2O$$

Step 3 Decarboxylation of the imine occurs to generate a new imine.

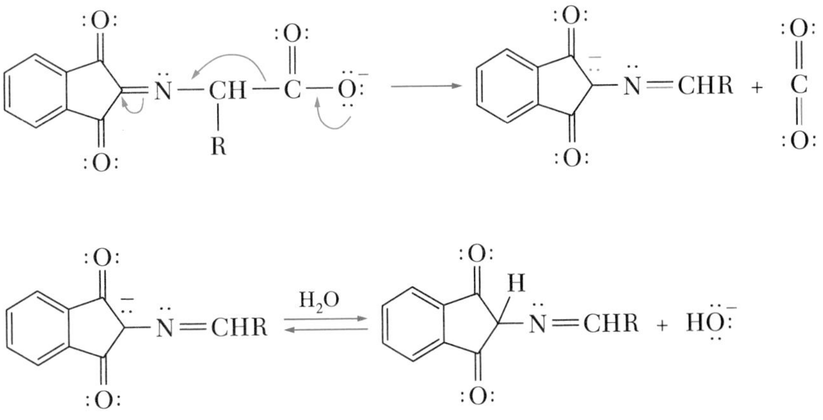

$$\text{imine}{=}N{-}CH(R){-}CO_2^- \longrightarrow \text{carbanion}{-}N{=}CHR + CO_2$$

$$\text{carbanion}{-}N{=}CHR \underset{}{\overset{H_2O}{\rightleftharpoons}} \text{H-substituted}{-}N{=}CHR + HO^-$$

Step 4 The imine undergoes hydrolysis to an aldehyde and an amine.

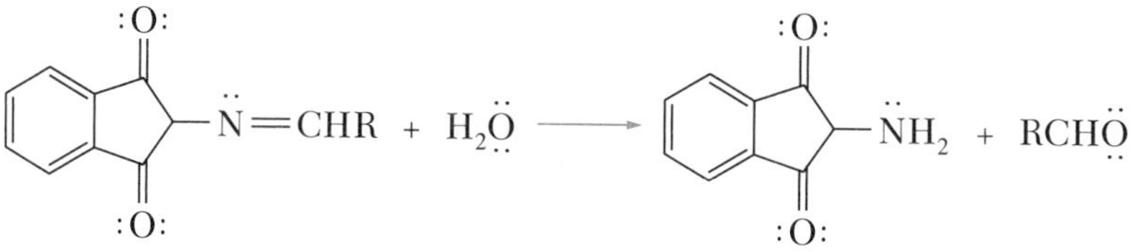

Step 5 The amino group forms an imine with a second molecule of ninhydrin (tricarbonyl form).

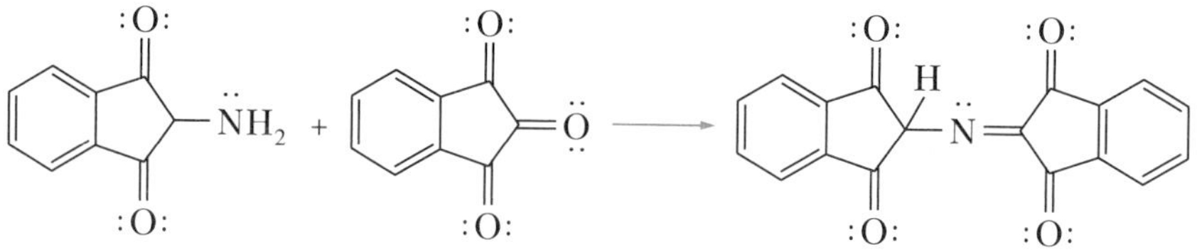

Step 6 Base deprotonates the imine, forming its conjugate base, which is violet in color.

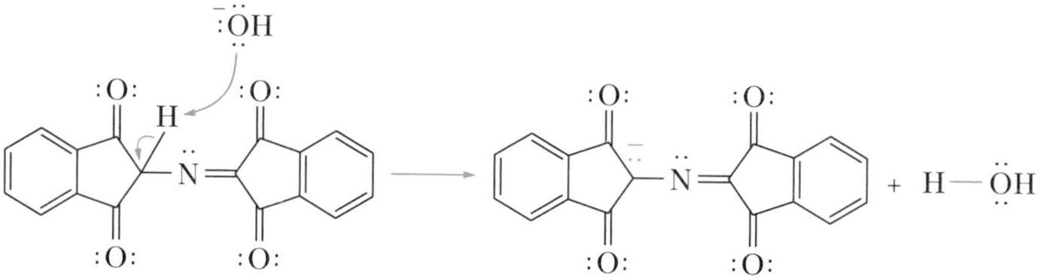

charge is highly delocalized; ion is violet in color

The ninhydrin color test is extremely sensitive—it can detect as little as 10^{-10} mole of an α-amino acid. For this reason we need to be extremely careful when performing such tests. Even touching a clean sheet of filter paper can transfer sufficient α-amino acid from the fingers to the filter paper to produce a violet color upon spraying the paper with the ninhydrin reagent.

PROBLEM 26.18 Ninhydrin is a gem-diol. Such species exist in dynamic equilibrium with a carbonyl compound and water. Normally, the equilibrium is unfavorable for the *gem*-diol (see Chapter 19). Rationalize the stability of the hydrated form in the case of ninhydrin.

PROBLEM 26.19 α-Amino acids give a positive ninhydrin test. Would you expect simple primary amines also to give a positive ninhydrin test? Explain your answer and propose an explanation for the failure of proline to give a positive test with ninhydrin.

26.5 The Separation and Identification of α-Amino Acids

We mentioned earlier that peptides and proteins can be degraded to their α-amino acid components by hydrolysis of all of the peptide bonds. Once the individual α-amino acid components have been generated by this means, we can use various analytical techniques to separate and identify them and to determine their relative amounts. Paper chromatography is one simple laboratory technique that can be used to accomplish this separation and analysis. (Paper chromatography is one example of a general method of separation known as *absorption chromatography*. Organic chemists commonly use a variety of other absorption chromatography techniques for the separation and purification of reaction product mixtures.)

In paper chromatography of a peptide hydrolysate, a dilute mixture of the α-amino acids is placed as a small spot close to one end of a rectangular piece of chromatography or filter paper. The end of the paper is dipped into a solvent so that the solvent rises along the length of the paper (by capillary action), passing through the spot containing the analysis mixture and continuing toward the top of the strip of paper. The individual α-amino acids dissolve in the solvent and are carried up the length of paper, proceeding different distances depending on their particular structures.

The different α-amino acids are thus separated because they are transported different distances along the chromatography paper. Their separation depends on their partitioning between two solvents. One of these solvents (the **mobile phase**) is the one in which we dip the paper; it moves by capillary action along the paper. The other solvent (the **stationary phase**) is water that is bonded by hydrogen bonds to the surface of the paper. The different α-amino acids become separated because of the continual displacement of their equilibrium distribution between the mobile and stationary phases.

We select the mobile phase solvent to emphasize the differences in the solubilities of the α-amino acids present. The more soluble an α-amino acid is in the mobile phase, the further along the paper it will be carried. Those with relatively poor solubility in the mobile phase move a relatively short distance along the strip of chromatography paper.

After performing the chromatographic separation of the α-amino acids, we allow the paper to dry and then spray it with the ninhydrin reagent. The α-amino acids (with the exception of proline, of course), which by themselves are colorless, react with the ninhydrin to produce violet spots at the points to which each has migrated. By measuring the relative distances traveled by *authentic* samples of each α-amino acid and comparing those distances with the results of the separation of the unknown mixture, we can identify the particular α-amino acids present in that mixture. An illustration of the technique is shown in Figure 26.11.

Paper chromatographic techniques are useful for determining the *identities* of the α-amino acids present in a mixture but generally not their *quantities*. In principle, the intensity of the violet color of the spot on the paper (after treatment with ninhydrin) could be used to determine the *amount* of material that produced that spot (Chapter 25). In practice, however, such analysis would be difficult to accomplish with paper chromatography.

Another type of chromatography, **ion exchange chromatography**, has been developed and is used in an automated instrument known as an **amino acid analyzer**. This is the method of choice for the quantitative analysis of the complex mixtures of α-amino acids encountered in biochemical research. In this method,

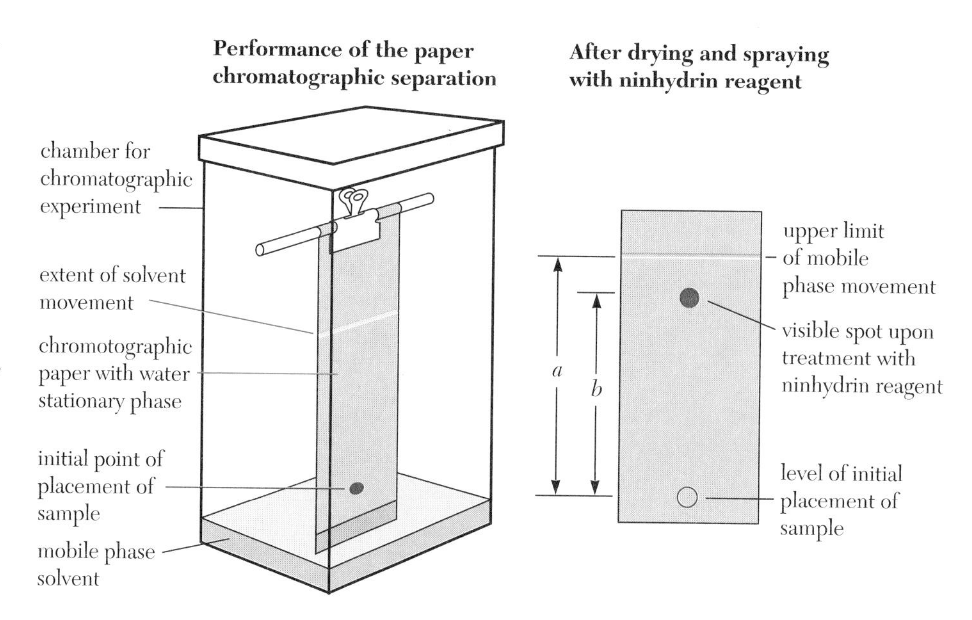

Figure 26.11 Paper chromatography in α-amino acid analysis. For a given solvent system (mobile phase) and type of paper, the distance traveled along the paper by the α-amino acid (b) relative to the distance traveled by the solvent (a) is a fundamental characteristic of that particular α-amino acid. We refer to the ratio b/a as the $\boldsymbol{R_f}$ **value** (retardation factor) for the particular α-amino acid under the conditions of measurement. By the comparison of the R_f values of known α-amino acids and the unknowns of the analysis mixture, we can determine the identity of the α-amino acids present.

the mixture of amino acids is passed through a column containing a **cation exchange resin**. A cation exchange resin is a high molecular weight polymer with anionic functional groups attached to the polymer backbone. Cations (such as protonated amino acids) are free to associate with the water-insoluble, polymer-bound anionic sites and to be exchanged with other cations in solution. The amino acid solution is passed down the column and eluted under carefully controlled pH conditions. The pH is controlled by using a series of aqueous buffers as the mobile phase. At a given pH, each amino acid has a characteristic passage time through the column and can be identified accordingly.

As the α-amino acids emerge from the column, they are mixed with ninhydrin, producing the violet-colored ion previously discussed. The intensity of the violet color is measured on a spectrophotometer (Chapter 25), and the color intensity is displayed on a chart recorder. Each emerging α-amino acid produces a peak on the chart recorder, and the areas of the peaks are proportional to the amounts of the different α-amino acids. The ion exchange analysis of a group of α-amino acids is illustrated schematically in Figure 26.12.

PROBLEM 26.20 Refer to the elution chart shown in Figure 26.12. Why do the α-amino acids on the right-hand side of the chart require a less acidic buffer for elution than those on the left-hand side of the chart?

It is also possible to separate α-amino acids using **electrophoresis**. In electrophoresis, a solution of the α-amino acid mixture is placed at the center of a piece of wet paper or a conducting gel. The paper or gel is moistened using an aqueous buffer solution of a chosen pH. Electrodes are attached to the ends to provide a potential difference (voltage drop) across the length of the paper

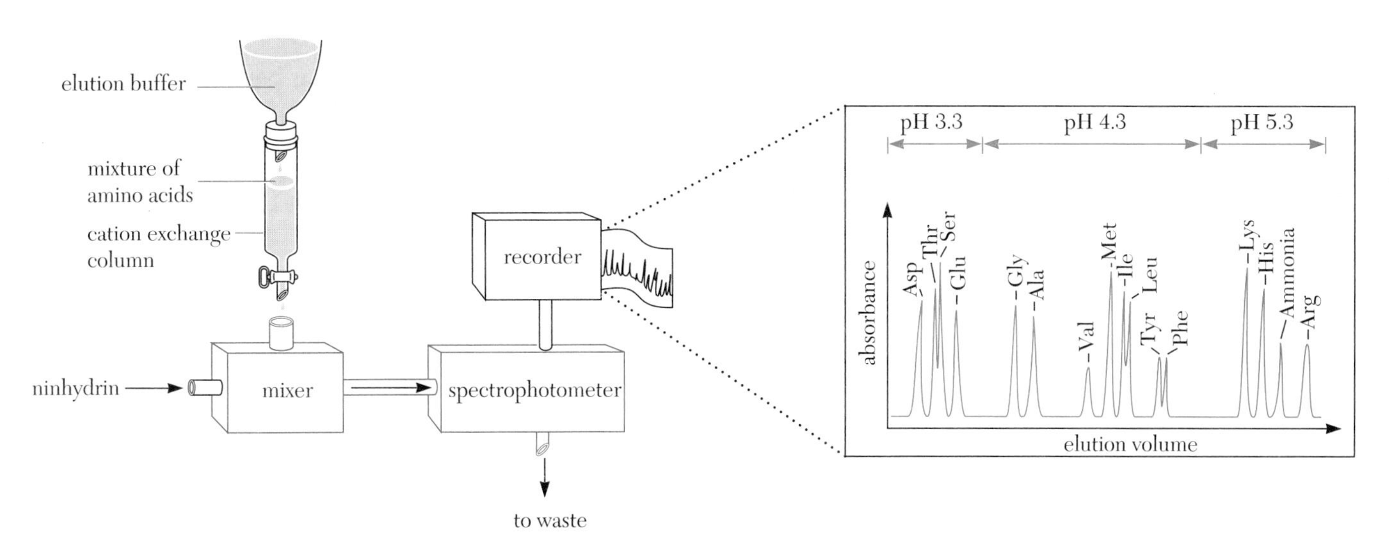

Figure 26.12 Analysis of an α-amino acid mixture using automated cation exchange chromatography. The pH of the eluting buffer solution is changed during the elution as indicated. Ammonia is added as a reference. This procedure is useful for the quantitative analysis of an α-amino acid mixture obtained from the hydrolysis of a peptide or protein.

or gel. When the electrical circuit is completed, the α-amino acids begin to migrate away from the center; their direction and rate of motion depend on their charge.

If an α-amino acid is in its anionic form at the pH used (because its pI is below the pH of the buffer), it will migrate toward the positive electrode (the anode). However, if the α-amino acid is in its cationic form (its pI is greater than the pH of the buffer), the α-amino acid migrates toward the negative electrode (the cathode). An α-amino acid predominantly in its zwitterionic form (pI equal to the buffer pH) migrates very little or not at all. In general, the rate and direction of migration of an α-amino acid depend on its pI and the pH of the buffer. Figure 26.13 illustrates separation of a mixture of alanine, lysine, and glutamic acid by electrophoresis at pH = 6.

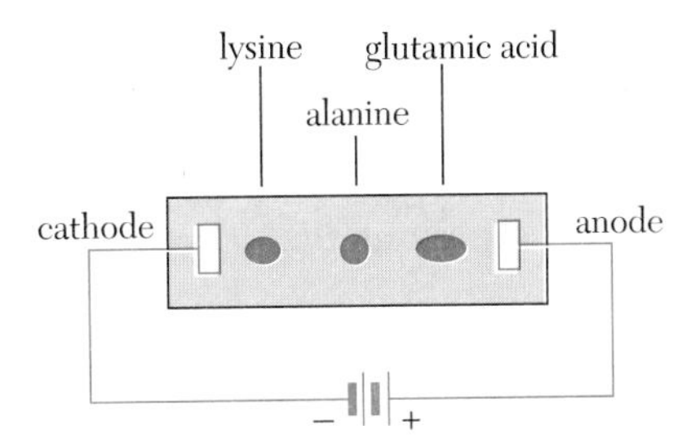

Figure 26.13 Separation of a mixture of lysine, alanine, and glutamic acid by electrophoresis at pH = 6. The pH used is close to the pI of alanine; thus alanine migrates very little in this experiment. The pI of lysine is 9.74, well above the pH of the buffer, so lysine exists mainly in its cationic form and migrates toward the cathode. On the other hand, the pI of glutamic acid is 3.22, well below the pH of the buffer. Glutamic acid therefore exists principally in the anionic form at this pH, and it migrates toward the anode.

PROBLEM 26.21

How will a mixture of aspartic acid, glycine, phenylalanine, and arginine behave when subjected to electrophoresis at pH = 6? Make a sketch similar to the one in Figure 26.13, showing their relative positions on the electrophoresis paper after a voltage has been applied for a sufficient period of time to produce separation.

26.6 Peptide Linkages in Simple Peptides

Consider the union of the two simplest α-amino acids, glycine and alanine, through a peptide linkage. If there is a peptide linkage between the carboxyl group of glycine and the amino group of alanine, we have the dipeptide glycylalanine (**26.2**), also known as Gly-Ala. On the other hand, if there is a peptide linkage between the carboxyl group of alanine and the amino group of glycine, we have a *different* dipeptide, alanylglycine (**26.3**), also known as Ala-Gly.

$$H_2\ddot{N}-CH_2-\overset{\overset{:\ddot{O}:}{\|}}{C}-\ddot{N}H-\underset{\underset{CH_3}{|}}{CH}-COOH$$

glycylalanine
26.2

$$H_2\ddot{N}-\underset{\underset{CH_3}{|}}{CH}-\overset{\overset{:\ddot{O}:}{\|}}{C}-\ddot{N}H-CH_2-COOH$$

alanylglycine
26.3

Notice that these dipeptides, like simple amino acids, have both an amino group and a carboxyl group. In solution we expect (and find) a distribution of zwitterionic, cationic, and anionic forms similar to what we find for simple α-amino acids.

By convention we show the structures of peptides with the amino group (or modified amino group) on the left and the carboxyl group (or modified carboxyl group) on the right. We often use the terms *N terminus* and *C terminus* to designate these respective ends of the peptide chain. Since the chemical structures of large peptides and proteins can be extremely complex, we often do not draw them out completely. Instead, we use the notations for individual α-amino acids listed in Table 26.1. The shorthand notation for a peptide consists of the abbreviations for the constituent α-amino acids listed in sequence from the N terminus to the C terminus, left to right. For example, **26.2** is Gly-Ala, and **26.3** is Ala-Gly.

PROBLEM 26.22 How many different tripeptides (three α-amino acids, two peptide linkages) contain one of each of the following α-amino acid residues: phenylalanine, alanine, glycine? Use the abbreviated notation system to designate the structure of each of the possible tripeptides.

PROBLEM 26.23 Draw the full structure of the tripeptide Ala-Ile-Pro.

Now we will consider a possible complication in the structure of peptides that is best understood with an illustration. The tripeptide glutathione (**26.4**)

SPECIAL TOPIC

Small Peptides With Biological Activity

Several small peptides have profound biological activity. Glutathione is one example. Several others are noted here.

Enkephalins. The enkephalins are the body's natural pain killers. These brain peptides contain five α-amino acid residues. Two examples are Tyr-Gly-Gly-Phe-Met and Tyr-Gly-Gly-Phe-Leu. These peptides act by occupying pain-relief receptor sites in the brain. Some artificial pain-killers such as morphine operate by duplicating the ability of the enkephalins to fit onto these receptor sites.

Bradykinin. Bradykinin is a nonapeptide found in blood plasma. Its structure is summarized as: Arg-Pro-Pro-Gly-Phe-Ser-Pro-Phe-Arg. Bradykinin plays an important role in the regulation of blood pressure.

Oxytocin. Oxytocin is a hormone secreted by the pituitary gland. It brings about smooth muscle contraction, induces labor prior to childbirth, and enhances the ejection of milk from the mammary glands. It is used as a drug to facilitate childbirth. The structure of oxytocin, shown below, has two interesting features. First, it is a cyclic nonapeptide—a disulfide cysteine linkage completes the ring. Second, the C terminus is not a free carboxylic acid linkage but is present as the amide.

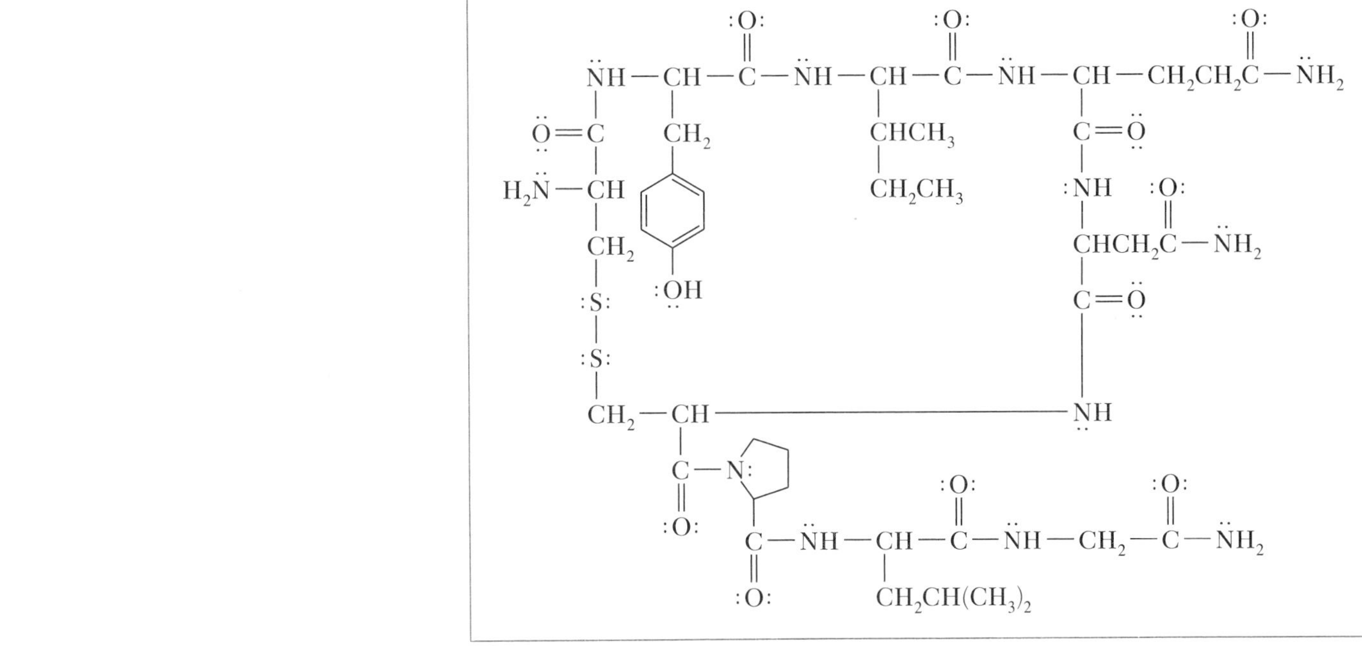

```
                  :O:               :O:                     :O:
                  ||                ||                      ||
      NH — CH — C — NH — CH — C — NH — CH — CH2CH2C — NH2
      |     |              |                |
   O==C    CH2            CHCH3             C==O
      |     |              |                |
 H2N—CH   (C6H4)          CH2CH3           :NH    :O:
      |     |                               |      ||
     CH2   :OH                             CHCH2C — NH2
      |                                     |
     :S:                                    C==O
      |                                     |
     :S:                                    |
      |                                     |
     CH2 — CH ——————————————————————————— NH
            |
            C — N:(pyrrolidine ring)
            ||    |          :O:              :O:
           :O:    |          ||               ||
                  C — NH — CH — C — NH — CH2 — C — NH2
                  ||        |
                 :O:       CH2CH(CH3)2
```

is present in almost all living cells. It acts as a catalyst in certain biological redox reactions. The three α-amino acids present in glutathione are (from the N terminus to the C terminus) glutamic acid, cysteine, and glycine. However, if we write the structure of glutathione as Glu-Cys-Gly, an ambiguity arises because glutamic acid (**26.5**) has two carboxyl groups, one α- and one γ-relative to the amino group. Which carboxyl group is involved in the amide linkage to cysteine? Structural analysis of glutathione indicates that it is the γ-carboxyl group. We thus write the structure of glutathione as γ-Glu-Cys-Gly to make this structural point clear.

$$H_2\ddot{N}-\underset{\displaystyle |}{\overset{\displaystyle COOH}{\overset{|}{C}H}}-CH_2CH_2-\overset{\displaystyle :O:}{\overset{\|}{C}}-\ddot{N}H-\underset{\displaystyle CH_2SH}{\underset{|}{C}H}-\overset{\displaystyle :O:}{\overset{\|}{C}}-\ddot{N}H-CH_2-COOH$$

glutathione
26.4

$$H_2\ddot{N}-\underset{\displaystyle CH_2CH_2COOH}{\underset{|}{C}H}-COOH$$

glutamic acid
26.5

Another interesting point arises when we consider the structures of peptides. In addition to the amide linkages that join individual α-amino acids in linear chains, there are often additional linkages between cysteine residues located at relatively distant points within the peptide chain. These linkages are **disulfide bridges** ($-S-S-$) that result from the oxidative combination of two thiol linkages ($-S-H + H-S-$) of the cysteine residues. These disulfide bridges are a major factor in giving particular shapes to peptide chains.

26.7 The Primary Structure of Peptides and Proteins: Determining the Sequence of Constituent α-Amino Acids

The sequence of α-amino acids in a peptide or protein is referred to as its **primary structure**. Knowledge of the primary structure of a peptide is of the utmost importance to anyone working with these compounds that are so central to all living things. The usual approach for determining the primary structure of a peptide involves first hydrolyzing all of the amide linkages to establish the identity and amount of each α-amino acid present. This relatively straightforward procedure was described in the previous section. More difficult is the task of determining the order in which the α-amino acids are present in the parent peptide. To simplify the task of determining the primary structure, we again subject a sample of the peptide to conditions that will cleave amide linkages. However, our aim now is not a complete breakdown of the peptide into its constituent α-amino acids but rather a *partial* breakdown into fragments that contain a much smaller number of α-amino acids than the original peptide. This is accomplished by using either relatively mild hydrolysis conditions or, more commonly, enzymes (biological catalysts) that facilitate the hydrolysis of only certain types of linkages between α-amino acids.

Once these peptide fragments have been separated by chromatographic procedures, the sequence of α-amino acids in the fragments is determined. Since the fragments are relatively short, containing only a few α-amino acid units, this determination is much easier than attacking the entire peptide at once. Having determined the sequences of the fragments, we can then establish the original order of the parent peptide by piecing together *overlapping sequences* of the fragments.

fragments	Gly—Val
	Gly—Val—Ala
	Val—Ala—Phe
	Ala—Phe
	Ala—Phe—Leu
	Phe—Leu—Ser
	Leu—Ser
sequence in original hexapeptide	Gly—Val—Ala—Phe—Leu—Ser

Figure 26.14 Determining the original primary structure of a hexapeptide by reconstruction of fragments from its partial hydrolysis.

Let's look at a very simple example that illustrates this overall procedure. Suppose the hexapeptide Gly-Val-Ala-Phe-Leu-Ser is subjected to mild hydrolysis. Mild hydrolysis conditions cause some molecules to cleave in one way and other molecules to cleave in a different way. The peptide fragments formed in this hydrolysis are separated and identified. The fragment structures are then written in a way that reveals overlapping α-amino acid sequences. As shown in Figure 26.14, the overlapping α-amino acid sequences allow a reconstruction of the original hexapeptide structure.

PROBLEM 26.24 An unknown peptide, on partial hydrolysis, yields a mixture of the following fragments: Phe-Gly, Tyr-Cys-Ala, Ala-Leu-Ile, Cys-Ala-Leu, Val-Tyr-Cys, Gly-Val-Tyr. Complete hydrolysis of the peptide shows that all of the α-amino acids of the peptide are present in equimolar quantities. What is the simplest possible structure for the original peptide?

Proteolytic enzymes, biological catalysts that bring about the scission of *particular* amide linkages of peptides, are often used to effect the partial hydrolysis of a peptide. (The word *proteolytic* means "protein-cleaving.") Some of the commonly used enzymes are listed below with their reaction characteristics.

- *Carboxypeptidase.* Carboxypeptidase is an enzyme that specifically catalyzes the hydrolysis of an amide linkage to a C-terminal α-amino acid.
- *Chymotrypsin.* Chymotrypsin selectively catalyzes the hydrolysis of amide linkages involving the carboxyl carbon atom of α-amino acids containing a benzene ring in the side chain, that is, phenylalanine, tryptophan, and tyrosine.
- *Trypsin.* Trypsin selectively catalyzes the hydrolysis of amide linkages involving the carboxyl carbon atom of the basic α-amino acids lysine and arginine.
- *Aminopeptidase.* Aminopeptidase acts as a catalyst for the hydrolysis of the amide linkages of terminal α-amino acids possessing a free amino group.
- *Thermolysin.* Thermolysin acts as a catalyst for the hydrolysis of amide linkages involving the carboxyl carbon atom of isoleucine, leucine, and valine.

How do we obtain these enzymes? Proteolytic enzymes are found in the gastrointestinal tract of animals, where their combined action is responsible for hydrolyzing dietary proteins to α-amino acids. In structural elucidation, we use such enzymes to facilitate the cleavage of the peptides into fragments sufficiently short to allow determination of the sequence of α-amino acids with relative ease.

PROBLEM 26.25 A tetrapeptide is known to contain the four α-amino acids alanine, glycine, phenylalanine, and glutamic acid. Shortly after treating this tetrapeptide with carboxypeptidase, we detect free glutamic acid. A different sample of the tetrapeptide is treated with chymotrypsin; two dipeptides are subsequently found to be present. Suggest two possible structures for the original tetrapeptide.

Partial hydrolysis of a peptide using proteolytic enzymes generally leads to rather long peptide fragments. A method devised by Pehr Edman of the University of Lund (Sweden) proves to be very useful in sequencing these long fragments. The **Edman degradation** procedure has been automated, adding to its convenience.

The Edman degradation is based on two fundamental steps. The long peptide fragment is first treated with phenyl isothiocyanate (**26.6**).

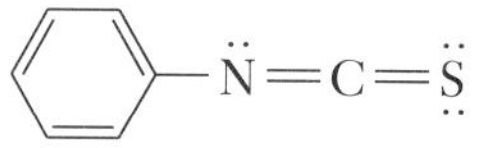

$$C_6H_5-\ddot{N}=C=\ddot{S}$$

phenyl isothiocyanate
26.6

An addition reaction occurs between the phenyl isothiocyanate and the free amino group at the N terminus of the peptide. It produces a derivatized form of the peptide, as shown in Figure 26.15.

When this derivatized peptide is treated with trifluoroacetic acid, cleavage of the amide linkage between the N-terminal α-amino acid (the derivatized site) and the adjacent α-amino acid occurs, leading to the formation of two fragments. One fragment is derived from the original N-terminal α-amino acid, and the other is the remainder of the peptide with the original N-terminal α-amino acid removed. The derivative of the original N-terminal α-amino acid is known as a *phenylthiohydantoin derivative*, and it has chromatographic characteristics that allow us to identify its α-amino acid precursor.

The new, shortened peptide is then subjected to another cycle of the Edman degradation to determine the identity of the new N-terminal α-amino acid. In this way we sequentially remove and identify α-amino acids from one end of the peptide (the N terminus). The overall procedure for two cycles of the Edman degradation is illustrated in Figure 26.16.

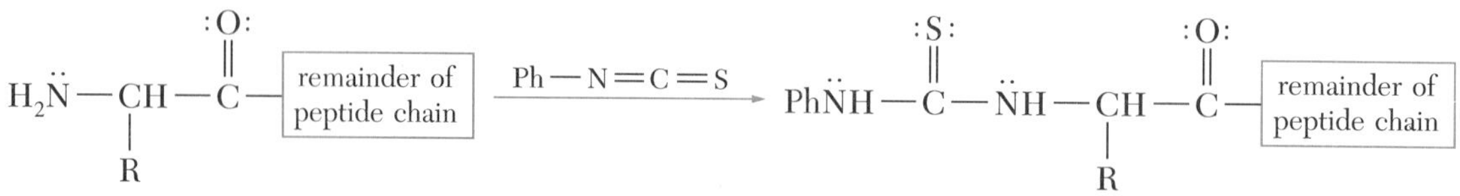

$$H_2\ddot{N}-CH(R)-C(=\ddot{O})-[\text{remainder of peptide chain}] \xrightarrow{Ph-N=C=S} Ph\ddot{N}H-C(=\ddot{S})-\ddot{N}H-CH(R)-C(=\ddot{O})-[\text{remainder of peptide chain}]$$

Figure 26.15 Addition of phenyl isothiocyanate to the N terminus of a peptide. The type of derivative formed is known as a thiourea. A nitrogen-hydrogen bond of the amino group adds across the carbon-nitrogen double bond of the phenyl isothiocyanate.

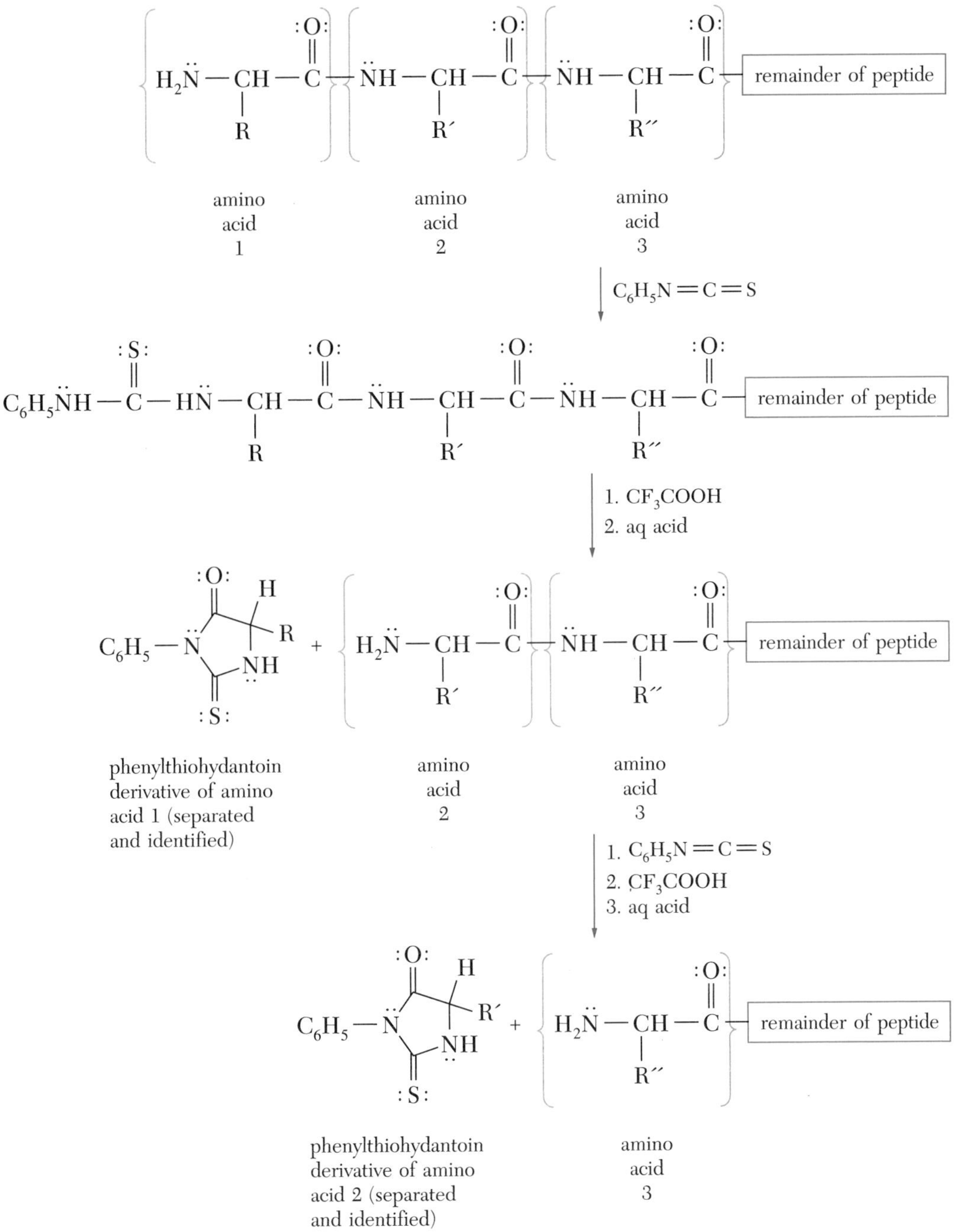

$H_2\ddot{N}$—CH(R)—C(=O)—$\ddot{N}$H—CH(R′)—C(=O)—$\ddot{N}$H—CH(R″)—C(=O)— remainder of peptide

amino acid 1 | amino acid 2 | amino acid 3

↓ $C_6H_5N{=}C{=}S$

$C_6H_5\ddot{N}H$—C(=S)—$H\ddot{N}$—CH(R)—C(=O)—$\ddot{N}$H—CH(R′)—C(=O)—$\ddot{N}$H—CH(R″)—C(=O)— remainder of peptide

↓ 1. CF_3COOH
2. aq acid

C_6H_5—N(ring: C=O, C(H)(R), NH, C=S) + $H_2\ddot{N}$—CH(R′)—C(=O)—$\ddot{N}$H—CH(R″)—C(=O)— remainder of peptide

phenylthiohydantoin derivative of amino acid 1 (separated and identified) | amino acid 2 | amino acid 3

↓ 1. $C_6H_5N{=}C{=}S$
2. CF_3COOH
3. aq acid

C_6H_5—N(ring: C=O, C(H)(R′), NH, C=S) + $H_2\ddot{N}$—CH(R″)—C(=O)— remainder of peptide

phenylthiohydantoin derivative of amino acid 2 (separated and identified) | amino acid 3

Figure 26.16 The Edman degradation of a peptide. The N-terminal α-amino acids are derivatized with phenyl isothiocyanate and are cleaved sequentially. In this way we determine the primary structure of the peptide starting at the N terminus.

In principle, we can continue the Edman degradation procedure until we have worked our way along the entire peptide chain. In practice, this is possible only if the peptide chain is of an experimentally reasonable length (no more than about 50–60 α-amino acids). Problems arise in working with longer peptides because we end up working with extremely small amounts of material, and side products begin to accumulate and obscure the interpretation of the results. If we need to sequence a very long peptide, we first use proteolytic enzymes

COMPOUND CAPSULE

Insulin

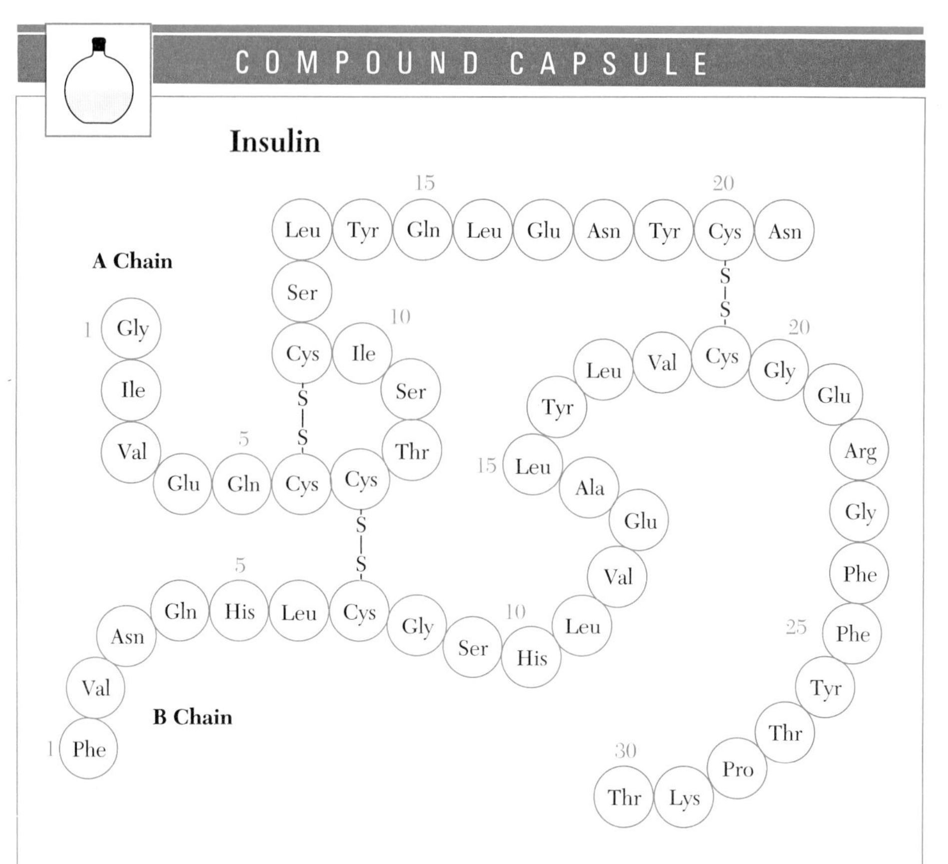

The structure shown above is that of human insulin. It consists of two peptide chains joined by disulfide bridges. Each chain is numbered from the N terminus. The A chain contains 21 α-amino acids, and the B chain contains 30. Insulins from other animal sources have a very similar sequence of α-amino acids. Generally, only two regions are found to differ among the mammalian insulins. One region involves the α-amino acids 8–10 on the A chain, and the other involves the C terminus of the B chain. These variations are summarized below.

Species	A8	A9	A10	B30
human	Thr	Ser	Ile	Thr
pig, dog, sperm whale	Thr	Ser	Ile	Ala
horse	Thr	Gly	Ile	Ala
bovine	Ala	Ser	Val	Ala
sheep, goat	Ala	Gly	Val	Ala

These similarities have made it possible to treat many human diabetics with insulin isolated from the pancreas of cows and pigs.

Insulin's role in the body is the regulation of the blood sugar level. In a healthy human, a rise in blood sugar level triggers the production of insulin

(continued)

(continued from previous page)

by the pancreas. Insulin in turn reduces the blood sugar level by stimulating the passage of glucose out of the blood and into cells. There the sugar can be used in exoergic processes to produce energy for other functions of life, converted to fat, or polymerized and stored as glycogen. If insulin is *not* produced by the pancreas, a condition of hyperglycemia (high blood sugar) is said to exist.

In one form of diabetes the body produces no insulin at all. In another form, insulin is produced but does not trigger an appropriate level of biochemical response. If no insulin is produced at all, injections of insulin are needed to ward off hyperglycemia. Injections may also help a patient whose own insulin production is insufficient to achieve the proper level of biochemical response. On the other hand, if the production of insulin by the pancreas is excessive, hypoglycemia (low blood sugar) results. This condition, like hyperglycemia, is dangerous and requires medical attention.

to cleave it into smaller fragments conducive to the Edman degradation. Then the method of overlapping sequences can be used to deduce the structure of the original peptide chain.

The pioneering work in peptide sequencing was extremely difficult and tedious. A notable landmark was achieved in 1953 by Frederick Sanger, a researcher at Cambridge University in England. In that year Sanger published his findings on the α-amino acid sequence of insulin, a hormone having 51 α-amino acids. All of this work was done without the aid of the automated sequencers available today. The determination of the primary structure of insulin was a crucial step in demonstrating that the molecular structures of large molecules could be determined, and it led to the automated procedures we now use. With these automated procedures it is possible to determine the primary structure of peptides containing more than a thousand α-amino acids. In 1958 Sanger was awarded the Nobel prize for his work in determining the primary structure of insulin.

PROBLEM 26.26 Much of Sanger's early work was done prior to the development of the Edman degradation. Sanger developed the use of the reagent 2,4-dinitrofluorobenzene (DNFB) for derivatizing peptides at the N terminus. The amino group at the N terminus attacks the DNFB reagent, displacing fluoride ion. DNFB reacts faster in this procedure than does any other 2,4-dinitrohalobenzene.

a. What is the mechanism of reaction of DNFB with the peptide?
b. What is the structure of the DNFB derivative of Ala-Gly?
c. Determine the structure of an unknown tetrapeptide with the following reaction characteristics: On reaction with DNFB followed by hydrolysis, the tetrapeptide yields the DNFB derivative of glycine, along with free alanine, leucine, and tyrosine. On reaction of the tetrapeptide with chymotrypsin, two dipeptides are formed. On treatment with carboxypeptidase, the tetrapeptide initially releases leucine.

26.8 The Secondary Structure of Peptides and Proteins

The sequence of α-amino acids in a peptide or protein is referred to as its primary structure. In a polypeptide chain there are many bonds and therefore many different possible conformations that could result from rotations about these bonds. However, we find that each protein generally has a preferred, fixed geometric structure (a preferred conformation). We use the term **secondary structure** to describe any fixed arrangement of the polypeptide chain.

The specific shapes adopted by peptide chains are rooted in the geometry of the amide bond itself and in the interactions that can occur between α-amino acids in different regions of the peptide chain.

Consider first the geometry of the amide linkage. X-ray crystallography indicates that the atoms immediately associated with the carbon-nitrogen bond of the amide linkage all lie in the same plane. The geometry of the amide linkage of a peptide is illustrated in Figure 26.17. Notice that the bond angles about the amide nitrogen are close to 120°. These angles and the planar geometry about nitrogen suggest that the hybridization scheme for this nitrogen atom is sp^2. This hybridization allows significant resonance delocalization (and stabilization), as shown in Figure 26.18.

Given that rotation is restricted about the carbon-nitrogen amide bond, we recognize that *cisoid* and *transoid* conformations (see Figure 26.19) should be possible, as with alkenes. Moreover, we expect (and find) that the *transoid* conformation is the more stable one, just as it is with alkenes.

In the *transoid* conformation, it is impossible for the hydrogen attached to nitrogen to participate in hydrogen bonding with the carbonyl oxygen of its own amide linkage. This point is crucial for the secondary structure of proteins.

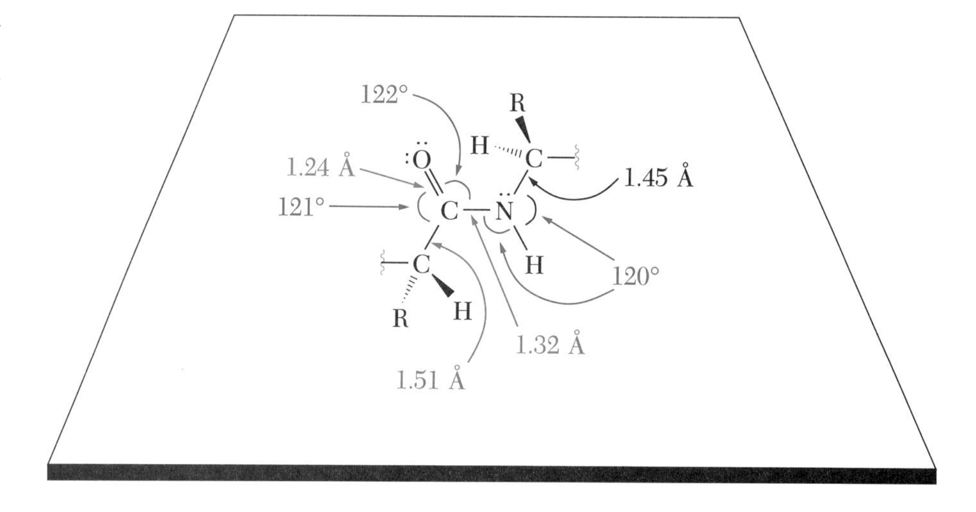

Figure 26.17 The amide linkage in a peptide. In the amide linkage, the atoms of the carbon-nitrogen bond and the four atoms immediately bound to them all lie in the same plane (shown here as the plane of the paper). Typical bond angles and bond lengths are also shown.

Figure 26.18 Resonance delocalization in an amide linkage. The linkage is best viewed as a resonance hybrid of the two structures shown. The carbon-nitrogen bond has some double-bond character, which restricts rotation about the carbon-nitrogen bond. This point is important for the three-dimensional geometry of peptides.

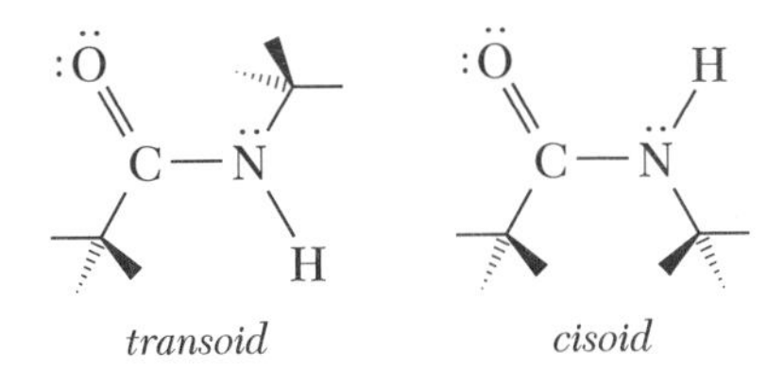

Figure 26.19 The *transoid* and *cisoid* conformations of amide linkages. The *transoid* conformation is the more stable of the two possibilities.

The carbonyl oxygen and the hydrogen attached to nitrogen are thus left free to participate in hydrogen bonding with other amino acid sites along the polypeptide chain. Because hydrogen bonding is a stabilizing interaction, we can anticipate that the polypeptide chain will bend or coil to maximize these intramolecular hydrogen-bonding interactions. One type of coiling known as the α-helix was originally proposed by Linus Pauling and Robert Corey and is commonly found with peptide chains. The α-helix structure is shown in Figure 26.20. In α-helical structures, appropriate α-amino acids three or four positions apart along the peptide chain are in position to hydrogen bond with each other. These hydrogen bonds fix the peptide chain in the α-helical conformation. The peptide chain naturally takes up this conformation because it provides greater stabilization than a random twisting of the chain.

Earlier in our discussion of stereochemistry (Chapter 8) we noted that helical objects have an inherent chirality. In principle, the helical conformation adopted by a polypeptide chain could be left-handed or right-handed. A right-handed helix twists *away* from you and a left-handed helix twists *toward* you if you turn the helix clockwise. (Think of right-handed and left-handed screws as an analogy.) For peptides composed of L-α-amino acids, the right-handed helix is more stable than a left-handed helix. The two forms have different stabilities because they are diastereoisomeric.

In many proteins, large portions of the peptide chains consist of α-helix conformations. Two important examples are the oxygen-carrying proteins hemoglobin and myoglobin. More than 50% of their peptide chain regions are coiled

Figure 26.20 Three representations of the right-handed α-helix of a polypeptide. This coiled structure is commonly adopted by polypeptides or portions of the chains of polypeptides. Hydrogen bonding occurs between α-amino acids three or four positions apart along the chain. These hydrogen-bonding interactions stabilize and maintain the conformation.

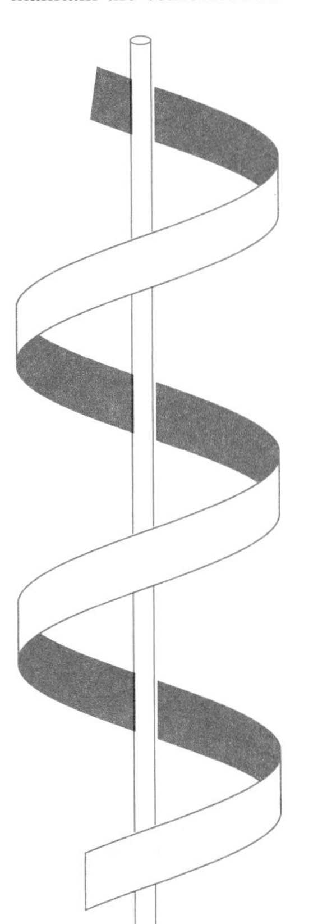

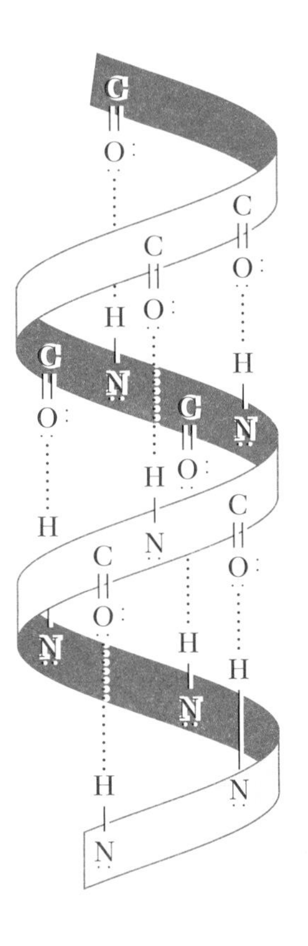

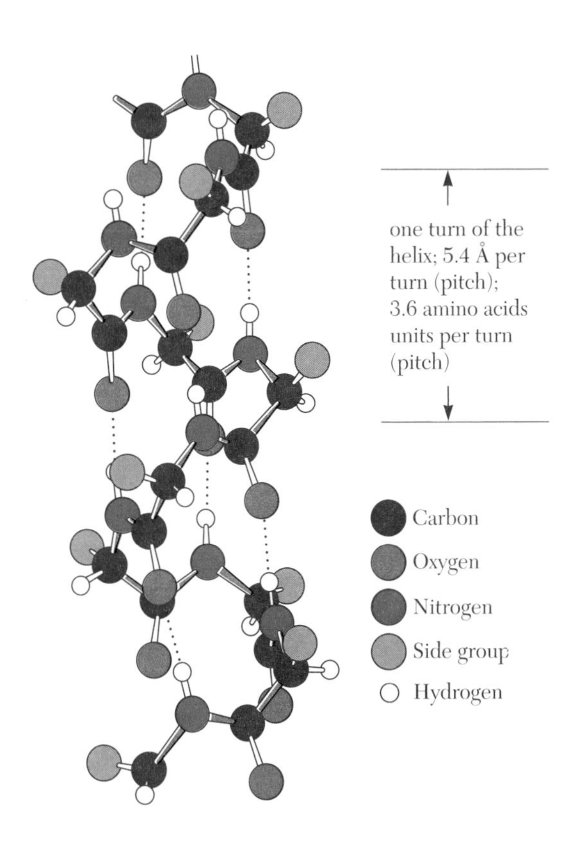

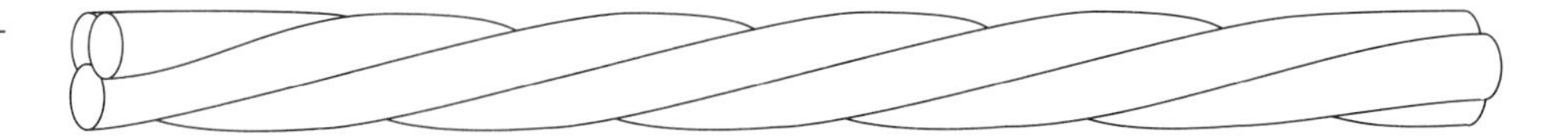

Figure 26.21 The supracoiling of three α-helices in the keratins of hair and wool.

into an α-helix structure. In some molecules, several α-helices coil about one another, as shown in Figure 26.21.

Not all peptide chains adopt an α-helix conformation. Another common ordered arrangement for peptide chains is known as the *β-sheet* or *pleated sheet*. In the pleated sheet conformation, hydrogen bonds link the α-amino acids of one peptide chain with those of another chain. An illustration of the pleated sheet is shown in Figure 26.22.

The different physical characteristics of wool and silk can be traced to differences in the secondary structures of their peptide chains. Wool is flexible. We can stretch it a significant distance without breaking it, and it returns to its original length when the tension is removed. The polypeptide chains of wool are arranged in α-helical form. We can stretch wool easily because all we need to do is to break the hydrogen bonds along the turns of the α-helix. Releasing the tension allows the hydrogen bonds and the favored conformation to reform.

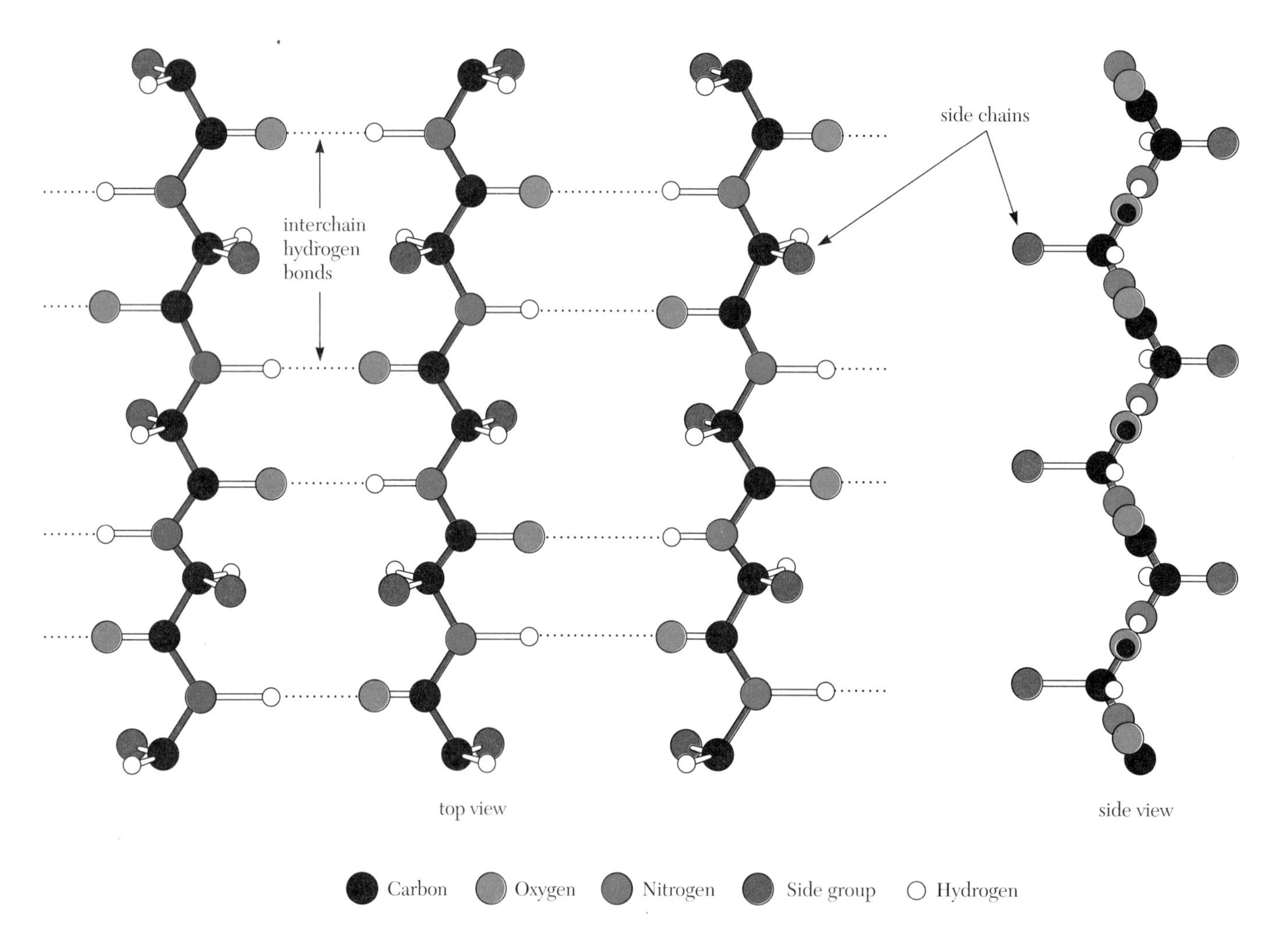

Figure 26.22 Pleated sheet structure of protein chains. The pleated sheet structure is stabilized by hydrogen bonds between α-amino acids that lie opposite each other in adjacent chains. The side chains lie above and below the plane of the pleated sheet.

In contrast, the polypeptides in silk are arranged in the pleated sheet conformation. In the pleated sheet there are hydrogen bonds between *each* pair of α-amino acids on adjacent chains. The resulting structure is relatively inflexible. Even if we break a few hydrogen bonds, many others remain intact to provide rigidity to the structure. Accordingly, silk (unlike wool) is relatively resistant to stretching.

26.9 The Tertiary Structure of Proteins

The tertiary structure of a protein refers to its overall three-dimensional shape. The hydrogen-bonding interactions discussed in the context of secondary structure certainly contribute to this overall shape. However, other types of interactions are also important. Interactions among the side chains and between the side chains and the surrounding solvent (water) molecules are of particular significance.

Let's consider some examples. Several of the naturally occurring α-amino acids contain nonpolar side chains. Two examples are alanine ($-CH_3$) and phenylalanine ($-CH_2Ph$). We say that such side chains are **hydrophobic** (water fearing); they do not undergo bonding interactions with the polar water molecules. We generally expect water-soluble proteins to adopt a shape that places as many hydrophobic side chains as possible away from the surface of the protein, where they would be in contact with water molecules. That is, we expect hydrophobic side chains to be turned to the *inside* of the protein conformation, away from the surrounding water. Furthermore, we would expect the protein to adopt a shape that places hydrophobic side chains from different parts of the molecule in close proximity to each other (see Figure 26.23).

Conversely, polar side chains, such as those in serine and aspartic acid, are **hydrophilic** (water loving). Hydrophilic side chains can form hydrogen bonds with water molecules. Thus we expect that the protein will fold so as to place the hydrophilic side chains on the *outside* surface, in position to participate in stabilizing hydrogen bonding with surrounding water molecules.

Consider the space-filling model of the enzyme lysozyme shown in Figure 26.24. Lysozyme is an example of a **globular protein**. Globular proteins have

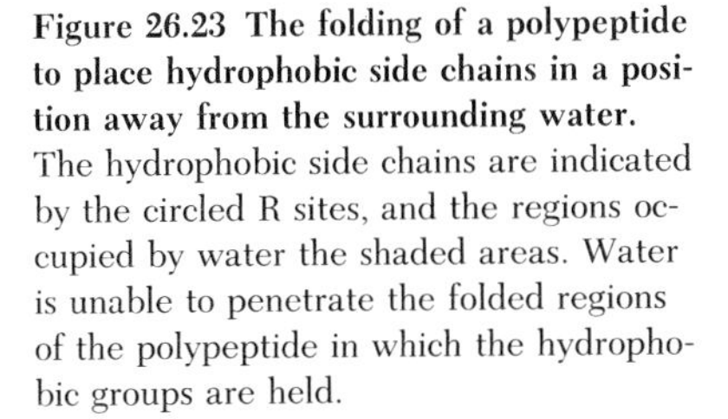

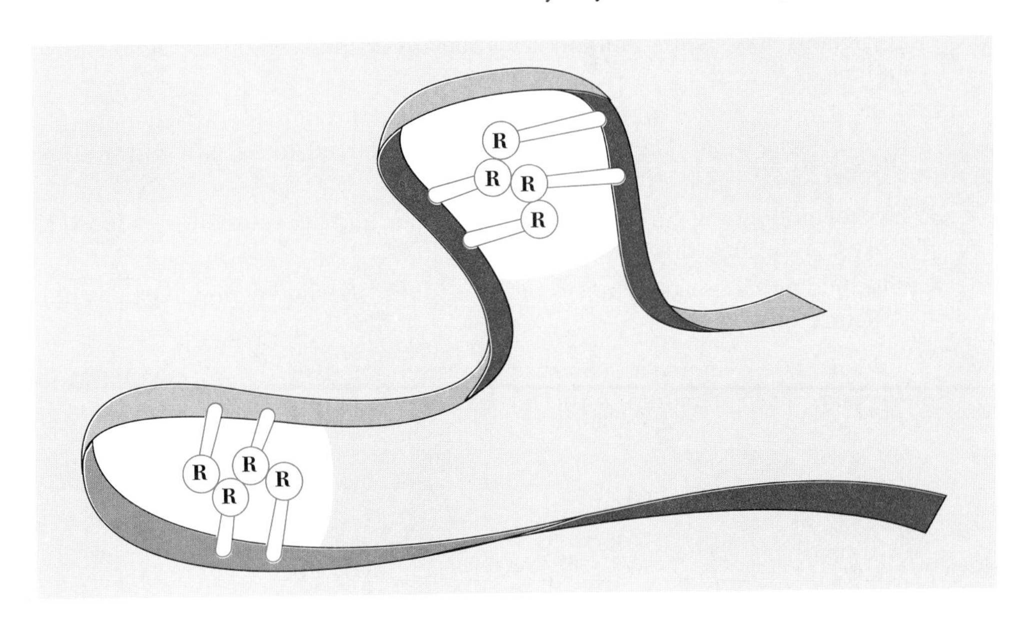

Figure 26.23 The folding of a polypeptide to place hydrophobic side chains in a position away from the surrounding water. The hydrophobic side chains are indicated by the circled R sites, and the regions occupied by water the shaded areas. Water is unable to penetrate the folded regions of the polypeptide in which the hydrophobic groups are held.

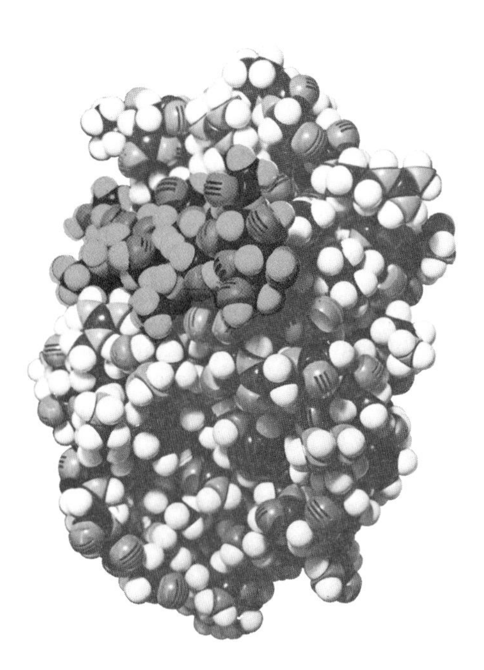

Figure 26.24 The lysozyme molecule and an associated polysaccharide. Lysozyme is an enzyme found in egg white and human tears. It acts as a catalyst for the hydrolysis of polysaccharides in the protective cell walls of some types of bacteria. Approximately 40% of its 129 α-amino acids lie in the α-helical arrangement. This conformation leaves a crevice in one side of the molecule; the polysaccharide that the lysozyme acts upon fits into this crevice. The polysaccharide molecule is the orange region.

Illustration © Irving Geis.

a compact shape that is almost spherical or elliptical. Most of the hydrophobic side chains are inside the globular structure, and most of the hydrophilic side chains are outside, facing the aqueous medium. Globular proteins tend to have more hydrophobic than hydrophilic side chains. Thus, they adopt a shape having a minimal surface area in order to expose as few as possible of the hydrophobic side chains to the water.

Several other types of interactions among the side chains contribute to tertiary structure. These interactions are summarized below.

1. Electrostatic attractive forces between positively charged ammonium ion sites and negatively charged carboxylate anion sites can exist between the side chains of α-amino acids having free amino or carboxyl groups. Such attractions occur with α-amino acids such as lysine, arginine, glutamic acid, and aspartic acid.
2. Two or more acidic α-amino acids can be linked through interaction mediated by a metal cation. These interactions are referred to as **salt bridges** (see Figure 26.25).
3. Hydrogen bonding can occur between donor and acceptor sites of the side chains. An example is shown in Figure 26.26.
4. Disulfide bridges can join cysteine residues, as shown previously in the structure of insulin.

Figure 26.27 shows a schematic representation of the various types of interactions that contribute to the tertiary structure of proteins.

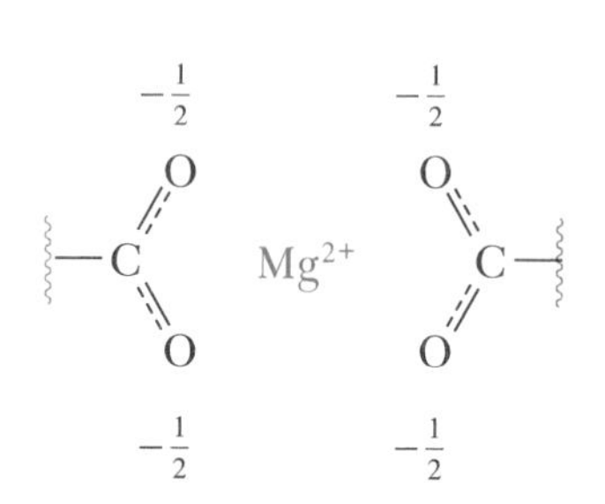

salt bridge between two regions of the peptide chain

Figure 26.25 A salt bridge between acidic side chains along a peptide chain. Coordination of the carboxylate groups with a metal ion binds two regions of the peptide chain.

Figure 26.26 Hydrogen bonding between side chains of α-amino acids.

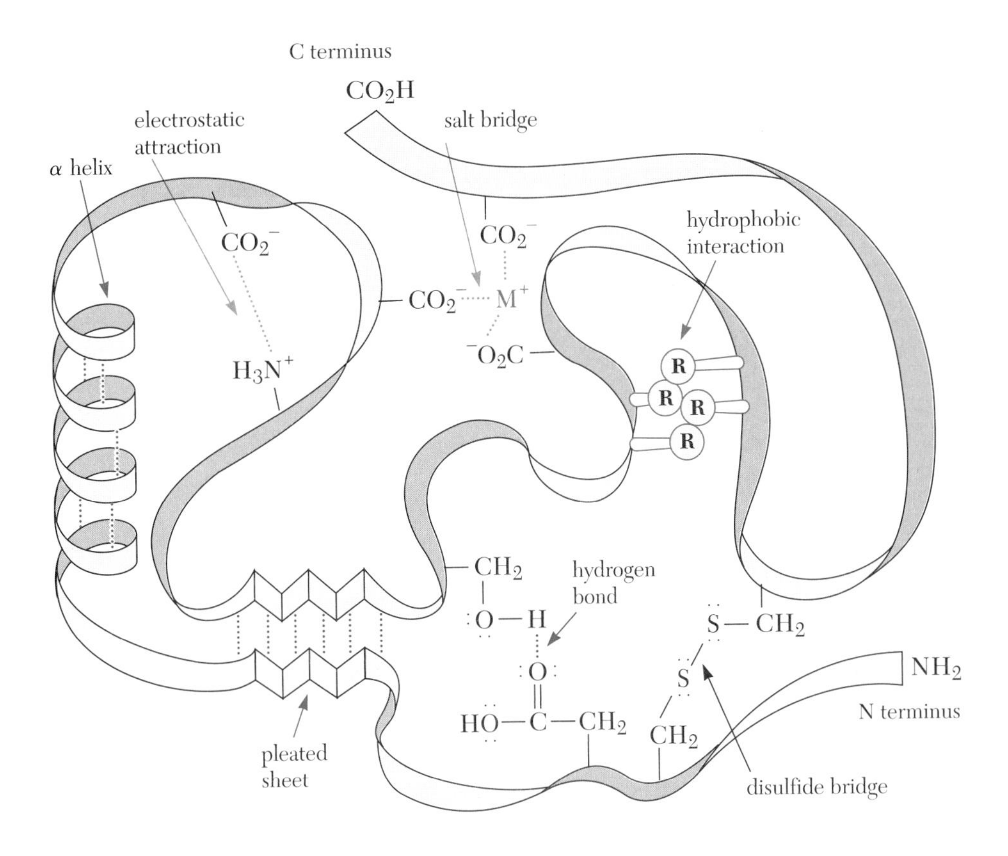

Figure 26.27 Interactions providing tertiary structure to a protein.

26.10 Oxygen-Binding Proteins and Quaternary Structure

We mentioned previously that some protein molecules contain portions that are not polypeptide in nature. These portions are referred to as *prosthetic groups*. Important examples of nonpeptidic prosthetic groups are found in the oxygen-carrying proteins myoglobin and hemoglobin.

Diving mammals such as whales and seals use large quantities of myoglobin to store oxygen in muscle tissues. Myoglobin consists of a peptide chain and a nonpeptidic prosthetic unit. The peptide chain of myoglobin is composed of 153 α-amino acid residues. The nonpeptidic prosthetic group, which is the site of oxygen binding, is known as the **heme** group. Heme is also present in the oxygen-carrying protein hemoglobin.

Heme consists of a planar ring system containing interconnected pyrrole units. At its center is an iron atom in the + 2 oxidation state. The ring of heme serves as a tetradentate chelating ligand that holds the iron in place. An iron atom in the + 2 oxidation state can accommodate a total of six ligands. Interaction with the pyrrole nitrogens of the ring fills four of these ligand sites. The remaining two sites lie above and below the plane of the heme ring. When both of these sites are occupied, there is an approximately octahedral distribution of six atoms about the central Fe(II) atom. In myoglobin, a nitrogen atom of a histidine residue in the polypeptide chain fills the site on one side of the plane of the heme ring. The sixth position is available for binding to an oxygen molecule. The detailed structure of the myoglobin molecule, (its molecular architecture) ensures that the oxygen can bind efficiently and reversibly to the Fe(II) atom. When the oxygen is coordinated with the Fe(II) atom in

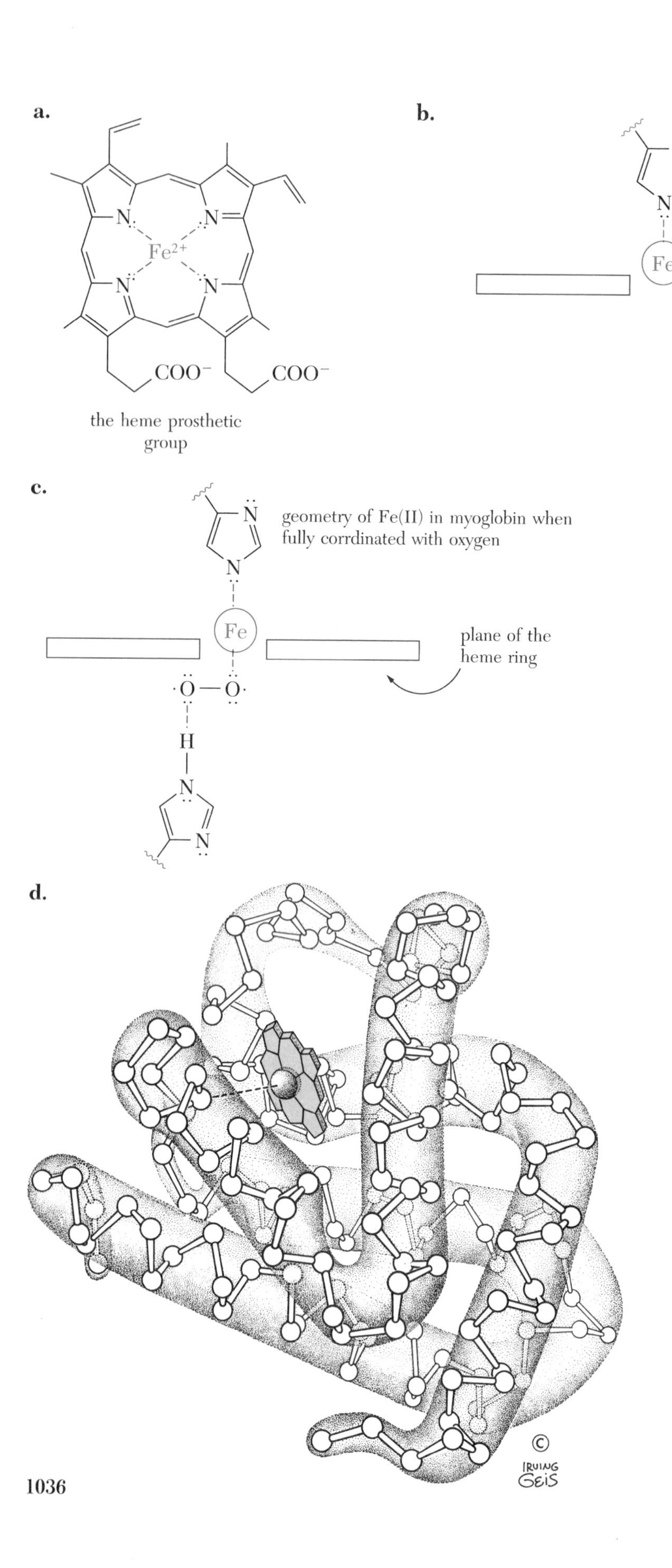

Figure 26.28 Heme and myoglobin. (*a*) The structure of the heme ring with Fe(II) coordinated in the center. (*b*) The coordination of Fe(II) with the heme ring and the histidine residue from the polypeptide chain in the absence of oxygen. Note that the Fe(II) is slightly out of the plane of the heme ring. (*c*) The coordination of the Fe(II) with an oxygen molecule. A second histidine residue from the polypeptide coordinates with the oxygen as well. Here Fe(II) is six-coordinated. (*d*) The myoglobin molecule showing the heme unit and the polypeptide.

the heme unit, it is in a stored form, but it is capable of facile release when required for metabolic oxidations. Figure 26.28 shows the heme unit and its relationship to the polypeptide portion of the myoglobin molecule.

Hemoglobin is another oxygen-carrying protein species. Hemoglobin constitutes approximately 90% of the protein in red blood cells. Its structure is considerably more complex than that of myoglobin—it has four peptide chains and four heme rings (compared to one for myoglobin). The peptide chains of hemoglobin are of two types: there are two identical chains of 141 α-amino acids each (known as α-chains) and two identical chains of 146 α-amino acids each (known as β-chains). The complete three-dimensional structure of normal adult hemoglobin is shown in Figure 26.29.

Hemoglobin, unlike myoglobin, has a quaternary structure. The term quaternary structure refers to the way in which the individual peptide chains of a complex protein pack together. Having only one peptide chain, myoglobin has no quaternary structure. Hemoglobin consists of four globular units, each containing a heme prosthetic unit. As in myoglobin, the heme group is located in a crevice near the surface of the molecule. Interestingly, the four peptide chains of hemoglobin with their respective heme units pack in a tetrahedral array about the center of the entire molecule.

The protein and heme structure of hemoglobin is such that oxygen can bind and be released efficiently. Even miniscule changes in the total structure

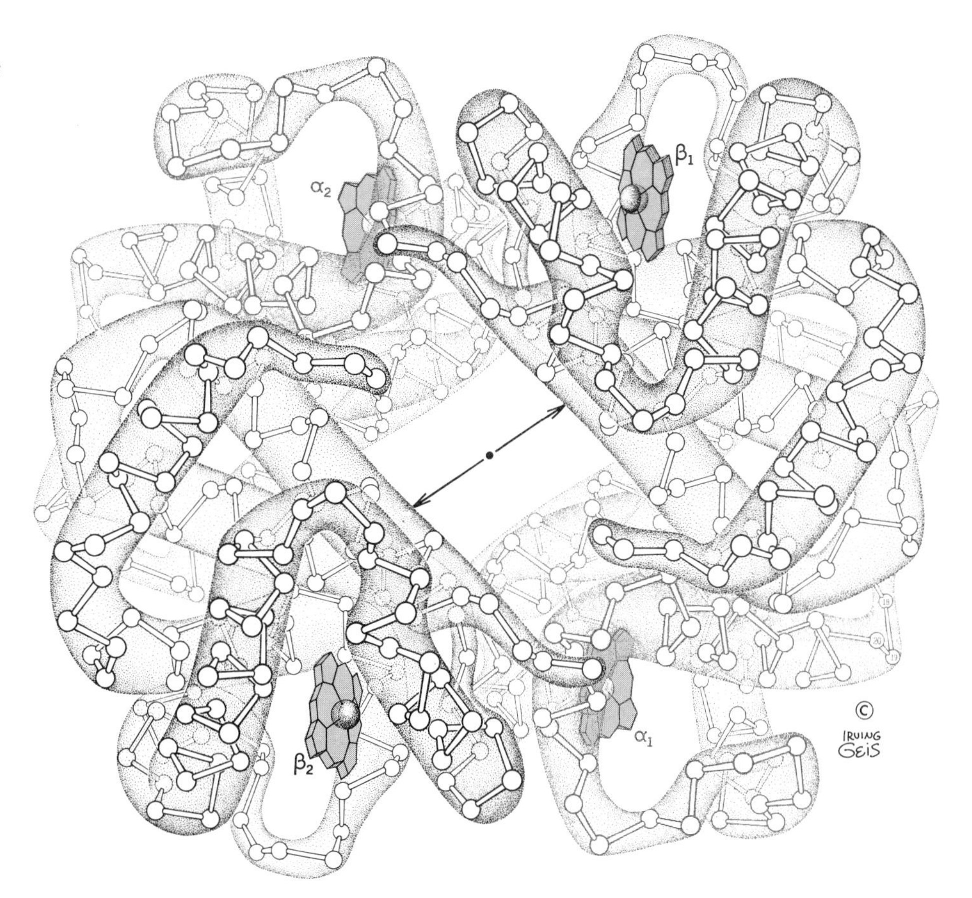

Figure 26.29 The structure of hemoglobin. The hemoglobin molecule consists of four peptide chains and four associated heme units. The locations of the heme units are indicated in orange.

can severely compromise the ability of hemoglobin to perform its oxygen-carrying task. Sickle-cell anemia is an example of a genetic disease in which a modification of the peptide structure of hemoglobin has a seriously deleterious effect. In the hemoglobin of individuals afflicted with sickle-cell anemia, a single α-amino acid in each of the β-chains is different from that in normal hemoglobin. The sixth α-amino acid from the N terminus is glutamic acid in normal hemoglobin but valine in individuals suffering from sickle-cell anemia. The presence of a hydrophobic α-amino acid (valine) in place of an acidic one (glutamic acid) in a region of the protein normally exposed to the external surface (near the external water) results in a crucial change in the shape of the protein. In Chapter 28 we will consider in more detail the chemical nature of genetic diseases.

Notice that the biological function of myoglobin and hemoglobin depends on the ability of an oxygen molecule to act as a ligand binding to Fe(II). If another ligand binds instead of oxygen, it can prevent the molecule from serving its oxygen-carrying function. Carbon monoxide is an extremely toxic substance simply because it binds more strongly to Fe(II) than does oxygen. Carbon monoxide quickly saturates all of the available hemoglobin binding sites (producing carboxyhemoglobin). Oxygen starvation and ultimately death result.

PROBLEM 26.27

In 1949 Linus Pauling and his coworkers found that normal hemoglobin and hemoglobin from victims of sickle-cell anemia behaved differently when subjected to electrophoresis. Which type of hemoglobin would you expect to migrate faster toward the positive electrode? Explain your reasoning.

26.11 The Synthesis of Peptides

How can we synthesize a polypeptide chain and ensure that the constituent α-amino acids are connected in the correct order? Two types of synthetic methodology are currently used. The first approach, which will be the focus of our discussion, uses synthetic strategies introduced in earlier chapters. A second approach involves recombinant DNA techniques, which are sometimes referred to as *genetic engineering*. This approach will be discussed in Chapter 28.

THE GENERAL STRATEGY OF PEPTIDE SYNTHESIS: PREPARATION OF A DIPEPTIDE

A brief analysis of the synthesis of even a simple dipeptide reveals that considerable ingenuity is required to devise an efficient route for peptide synthesis. Suppose we want to devise a synthesis of alanylglycine (Ala-Gly). Clearly we must start with alanine and glycine and arrange for them to couple in the proper sequence.

You should recall from our earlier discussions (Chapter 21) that dicyclohexylcarbodiimide (DCC) is an effective reagent for the dehydrative coupling of carboxylic acids and amines to form amides. Perhaps we could simply treat a mixture of alanine and glycine with DCC under the appropriate conditions to form Ala-Gly? Unfortunately, it is not that simple. This approach would produce some Ala-Gly, but its efficiency is doomed to be low because it is possible for *four different* dipeptides to be formed—Ala-Gly, Ala-Ala, Gly-Ala, and Gly-Gly. Moreover, there is nothing to prevent coupling of these dipeptides with other molecules of alanine or glycine to yield higher peptides.

Figure 26.30 Cumulative yields of successive coupling reactions. After four coupling reactions, each with only a 25% yield, the overall yield of the pentapeptide would be only 0.39%.

	Cumulated Yield
$A_1 + A_2 \longrightarrow A_1{-}A_2$	25%
$A_1{-}A_2 + A_3 \longrightarrow A_1{-}A_2{-}A_3$	6.25%
$A_1{-}A_2{-}A_3 + A_4 \longrightarrow A_1{-}A_2{-}A_3{-}A_4$	1.56%
$A_1{-}A_2{-}A_3{-}A_4 + A_5 \longrightarrow A_1{-}A_2{-}A_3{-}A_4{-}A_5$	0.39%

All of these coupling reactions will occur simultaneously and with similar efficiencies. Even under the best of circumstances, we could not expect better than a 25% yield of the target Ala-Gly. Clearly such inefficiency cannot be tolerated in the preparation of long polypeptide chains. If we recover only 25% of the target material after each cycle of coupling, we would isolate only a miniscule yield of polypeptide after just five α-amino acid residues were joined! The decreasing yield after successive couplings is shown schematically in Figure 26.30. To improve this situation we need to use protecting (or blocking) groups to prevent the undesired coupling reactions from occurring. We will see how this approach can provide an efficient synthesis of Ala-Gly from alanine and glycine.

Alanine is to be the N-terminal unit of the dipeptide. Therefore, we need to protect the amino group of alanine prior to coupling to ensure that it will not participate in any coupling reactions of its own. An amino group is usually protected by converting it to a *tert*-butyl or benzyl carbamate linkage. Figure 26.31 shows this procedure for alanine. This reaction protects the alanine amino group and thus allows the alanine molecule to enter into amide bond formation *only* through its carboxyl group.

At this point several options are available. We can choose to use DCC as a dehydrative coupling agent, in which case we need to protect the carboxyl group of glycine prior to coupling with the *N-t*-BOC-Ala. If we did not protect the glycine carboxyl group, a significant amount of Gly-Gly would be generated in the reaction. Alternatively, we can activate the carboxyl group of the *N-t*-BOC-Ala so that it will readily form an amide linkage when challenged with a free amine. We will consider both of these approaches.

If we wish to perform a dehydrative coupling (such as with DCC) to generate Ala-Gly, the carboxyl group of the glycine must be protected. One way to do this is by forming an ester at the glycine carboxyl group. An example of this approach is shown in Figure 26.32. Remember that when we add a

Figure 26.31 Protection of the amino group of alanine prior to coupling. Other protecting groups may also be used. The protecting group shown is commonly referred to as *t*-BOC.

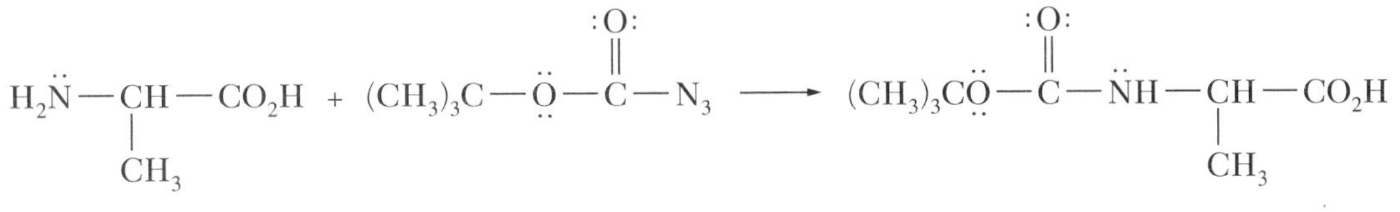

$$H_2\ddot{N}{-}CH(CH_3){-}CO_2H + (CH_3)_3C{-}\ddot{O}{-}C({=}O){-}N_3 \longrightarrow (CH_3)_3C\ddot{O}{-}C({=}O){-}\ddot{N}H{-}CH(CH_3){-}CO_2H$$

alanine; *t*-butylazidoformate; *N-t*-BOC-Ala

Figure 26.32 Protection of the carboxyl group of glycine.

$$H_2\ddot{N}{-}CH_2{-}CO_2H + (CH_3)_2C{=}CH_2 \xrightarrow{H_2SO_4} H_2\ddot{N}{-}CH_2{-}C({=}O){-}\ddot{O}{-}C(CH_3)_3$$

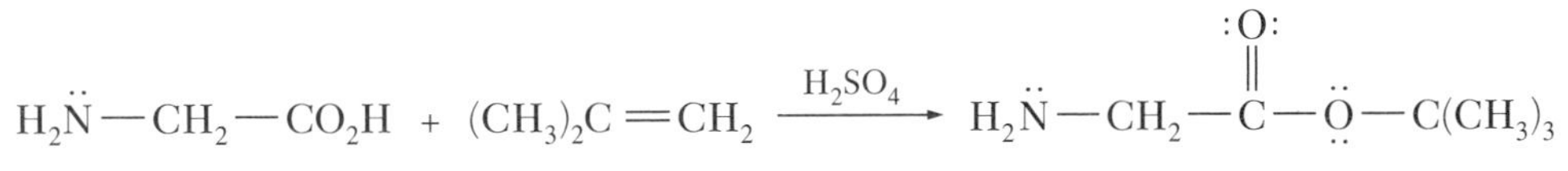

glycine *t*-butyl ester

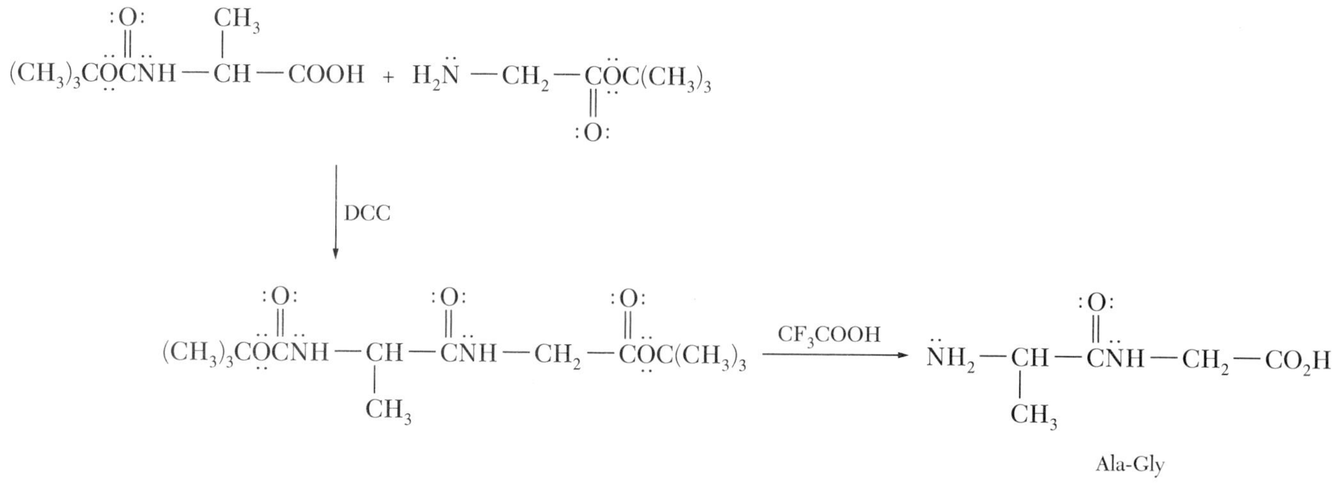

$$(CH_3)_3COC(=O)NH-CH(CH_3)-COOH + H_2N-CH_2-C(=O)OC(CH_3)_3 \xrightarrow{DCC} (CH_3)_3COC(=O)NH-CH(CH_3)-C(=O)NH-CH_2-C(=O)OC(CH_3)_3 \xrightarrow{CF_3COOH} NH_2-CH(CH_3)-C(=O)NH-CH_2-CO_2H$$

Ala-Gly

Figure 26.33 Coupling and deprotection in the synthesis of Ala-Gly.

protecting group we must be able to remove it with relative ease. In addition, we must not cleave the desired linkage when we remove the protecting group.

After protecting the glycine carboxyl group, we are ready for the dehydrative coupling step. The protecting groups allow *only* the sequence Ala-Gly to be generated. Deprotection to isolate the target material is accomplished by adding trifluoroacetic acid. These steps are shown in Figure 26.33.

Alternatively, we can perform a preliminary activation of the carboxyl group of the protected alanine to facilitate amide formation. Several methods for performing this activation are available. In one method a reactive anhydride linkage using a partial ester/partial acid chloride derivative of carbonic acid is formed. The preparation and use of isobutyl chloroformate, a common reagent of this type, is illustrated in Figure 26.34.

Once the carboxyl group has been activated in this manner, it is ready for amide formation upon treatment with an α-amino acid. The amino group of the α-amino acid serves as a nucleophile to attack the anhydride linkage forming the amide. Protection of the carboxyl group of the attacking α-amino acid is not required in this case since the amino function is much more nucleophilic

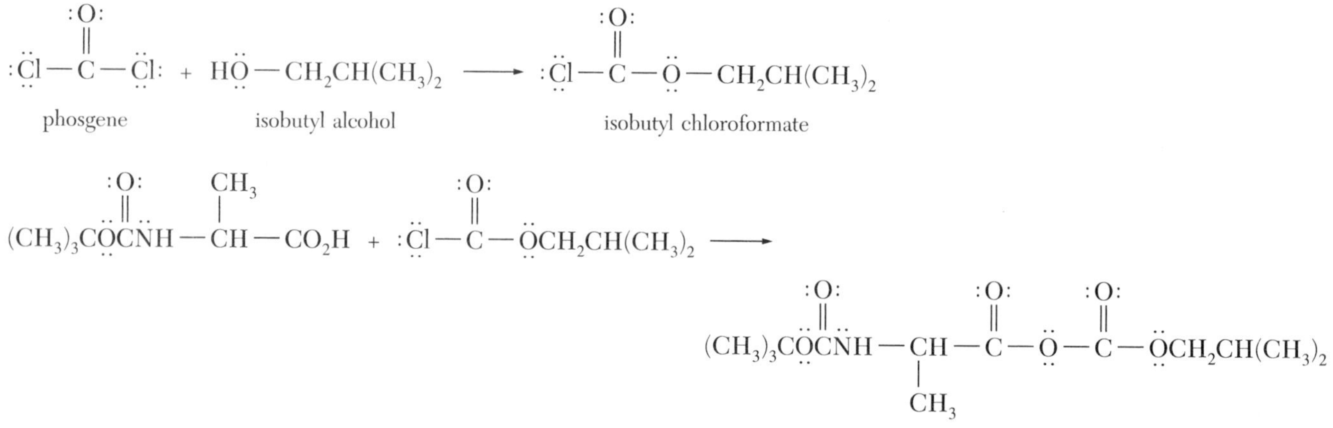

Figure 26.34 Preparation and use of isobutyl chloroformate. Isobutyl chloroformate is prepared by reaction of isobutyl alcohol with one equivalent amount of phosgene. The remaining chloride site is reactive with nucleophiles such as a carboxylate group. Reaction with a carboxylic acid forms an anhydride, an active form of the carboxylic acid for derivative formation.

$$Cl-C(=O)-Cl + HO-CH_2CH(CH_3)_2 \longrightarrow Cl-C(=O)-O-CH_2CH(CH_3)_2$$

phosgene — isobutyl alcohol — isobutyl chloroformate

$$(CH_3)_3COC(=O)NH-CH(CH_3)-CO_2H + Cl-C(=O)-OCH_2CH(CH_3)_2 \longrightarrow (CH_3)_3COC(=O)NH-CH(CH_3)-C(=O)-O-C(=O)-OCH_2CH(CH_3)_2$$

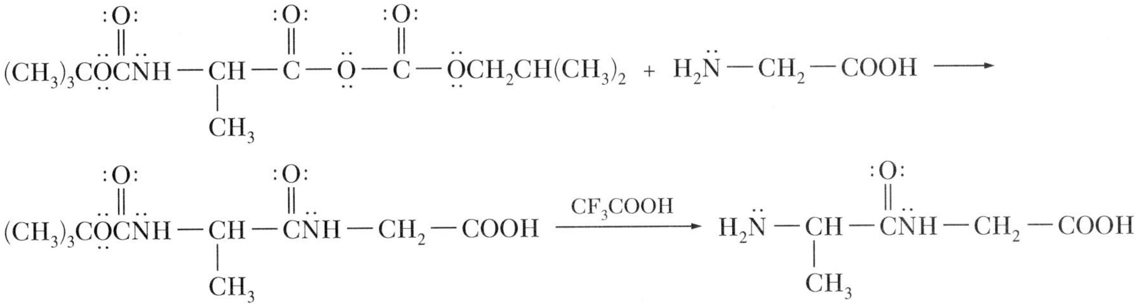

$$(CH_3)_3COCNH-\underset{CH_3}{CH}-\overset{O}{\overset{\|}{C}}-O-\overset{O}{\overset{\|}{C}}-OCH_2CH(CH_3)_2 + H_2N-CH_2-COOH \longrightarrow$$

$$(CH_3)_3COCNH-\underset{CH_3}{CH}-\overset{O}{\overset{\|}{C}}NH-CH_2-COOH \xrightarrow{CF_3COOH} H_2N-\underset{CH_3}{CH}-\overset{O}{\overset{\|}{C}}NH-CH_2-COOH$$

Figure 26.35 Peptide formation using an activated ester procedure with final deprotection.

than the carboxylic acid group. The overall procedure, including the final deprotection, is shown in Figure 26.35.

Each of these approaches requires several laboratory operations, the actual coupling of the α-amino acid residues being only one. Can these strategies be applied fruitfully to the synthesis of long polypeptide chains? Very high yields are required at every stage of the procedure, or else the overall yield will be miniscule. Suppose that by working with protecting groups we achieve a yield of 80% for each cycle of reactions that adds one α-amino acid to the growing polypeptide chain. This yield would seem to be a significant improvement over the 25% we previously considered. However, in practical terms, we are still in trouble. Our overall yield would tumble to only ~10% after the nine cycles required to prepare a decapeptide. The difficulties involved are still quite formidable.

In spite of these difficulties, Vincent du Vigneaud accomplished the synthesis of oxytocin (a nonapeptide) in the early 1950s. This accomplishment was acknowledged by awarding him a Nobel Prize. In the early 1960s the synthesis of insulin (51 α-amino acid residues) was reported. However, the work was tedious and incredibly time-consuming. The procedure involved the performance of hundreds of consecutive reactions with purifications all along the way.

If we wish to prepare very long polypeptide chains, we require extraordinarily high yields for each reaction, along with a means to facilitate purification. At this stage in your organic chemistry laboratory career, you realize that an 80% yield is generally considered quite good. To synthesize complex polypeptides, we need an approach that will give us yields in the 99+% range with simple operational procedures.

THE SOLID-PHASE SYNTHESIS OF PEPTIDES

Professor R. B. Merrifield of Rockefeller University was responsible for the revolutionary advance needed to solve these problems in the synthesis of polypeptides. Merrifield concluded that conventional laboratory procedures would not suffice for this type of preparation. Small losses of material during extraction, filtration, and other workup procedures are unavoidable, and their cumulative effect was intolerable for these syntheses. Merrifield's developmental idea was to build the polypeptide chain on a solid, insoluble support.

The overall procedure can be summarized as follows. First, one α-amino acid residue is attached to the inert solid support. Then a suitably protected second α-amino acid is added by a coupling reaction. This procedure is repeated

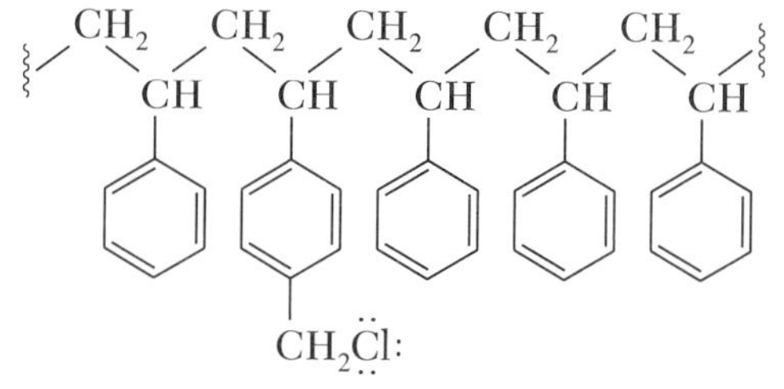

Figure 26.36 Support used in the Merrifield solid-phase peptide synthesis. The material is a modified form of polystyrene. About 10% of the benzene rings have a chloromethyl substituent at the *para* position.

until the entire polypeptide chain has been attached to the solid support. After each reaction, reagents and by-products are rinsed away. None of the developing polypeptide is lost because it remains chemically anchored to the insoluble support. Finally, the polypeptide chain is chemically removed from the solid support after it is fully assembled.

This scheme lends itself to mechanization. In 1969 Merrifield described the use of a protein-synthesizing machine for the synthesis of the enzyme ribonuclease, a polypeptide containing 124 α-amino acid residues. The synthesis involved 369 separate chemical reactions and almost 12,000 separate operations. The *overall* yield was 17%, meaning that each of the 369 reactions had an average yield of 99.5%. The synthesis took only six weeks to accomplish. Merrifield was awarded the Nobel Prize in 1984 for his efforts.

A modified form of polystyrene is used as the solid support for most solid-phase syntheses. Approximately one out of ten benzene rings present in polystyrene has a chloromethyl group attached to it, as illustrated in Figure 26.36.

In performing a peptide synthesis using the Merrifield method, we begin with the C terminus of the chain. The α-amino acid located at the C terminus is used in its amino-protected form (e.g., as the *t*-BOC derivative) and converted to its anionic form using base. This anionic form is brought into contact with the solid support (in the form of small beads), and the carboxylate group displaces the chloride ion of the polystyrene by an S_N2 reaction, thus attaching the α-amino acid to the support, as illustrated in Figure 26.37.

PROBLEM 26.28 Why is it necessary to use the amino-protected α-amino acid in anchoring the C terminus of the potential peptide to the polymer?

Figure 26.37 Attachment of a C-terminal α-amino acid to the Merrifield polymer at the beginning of a peptide synthesis.

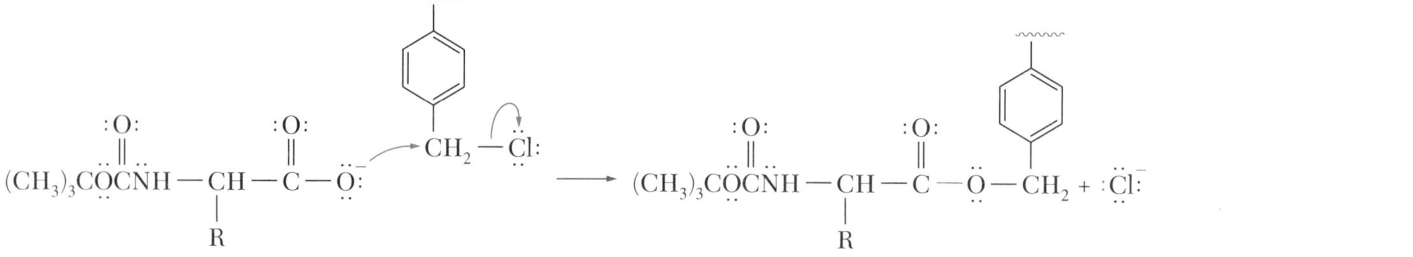

The next step in the overall peptide synthesis involves deprotecting the amino group of the C-terminal α-amino acid attached to the solid support. We accomplish this using standard procedures, for example, treatment with trifluoroacetic acid. The C-terminal α-amino acid, which is insoluble in the solvent systems used, is now ready for the attachment of the next α-amino acid in the chain. The next unit of the growing peptide is added as an amino-protected, carboxyl-activated α-amino acid of the type illustrated in Figure 26.34. After the addition, a new reactive amino group for further development of the peptide chain is generated by treatment with trifluoroacetic acid. These steps are shown in Figure 26.38.

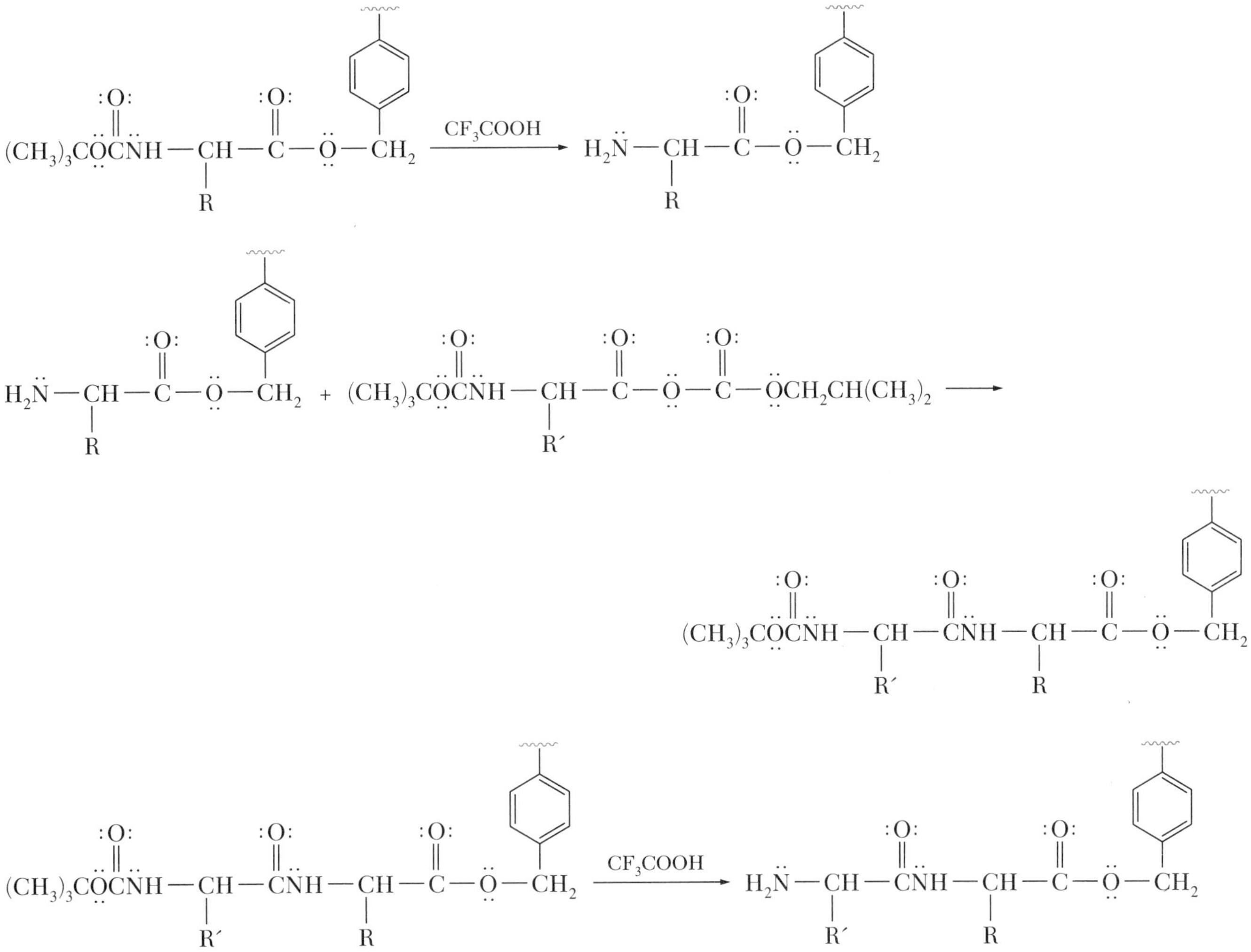

$$(CH_3)_3COC(=O)NH-CH(R)-C(=O)-O-CH_2-C_6H_4\text{~} \xrightarrow{CF_3COOH} H_2N-CH(R)-C(=O)-O-CH_2-C_6H_4\text{~}$$

$$H_2N-CH(R)-C(=O)-O-CH_2-C_6H_4\text{~} + (CH_3)_3COC(=O)NH-CH(R')-C(=O)-O-C(=O)-OCH_2CH(CH_3)_2 \longrightarrow$$

$$(CH_3)_3COC(=O)NH-CH(R')-C(=O)NH-CH(R)-C(=O)-O-CH_2-C_6H_4\text{~}$$

$$(CH_3)_3COC(=O)NH-CH(R')-C(=O)NH-CH(R)-C(=O)-O-CH_2-C_6H_4\text{~} \xrightarrow{CF_3COOH} H_2N-CH(R')-C(=O)NH-CH(R)-C(=O)-O-CH_2-C_6H_4\text{~}$$

Figure 26.38 Attachment of the second α-amino acid residue in the Merrifield approach to peptide synthesis. After the last step shown, the growing peptide chain is ready for the attachment of the next unit.

We attach the third, fourth, ... α-amino acids in a completely analogous manner. At each stage, any by-products and excess reagents are washed away from the solid-phase polymer and its attached peptide chain by rinsing with suitable solvents.

When all of the desired α-amino acid residues have been added to complete the target peptide chain, we need to cleave it from the polymer. We accomplish this by the addition of HBr in trifluoroacetic acid as shown in Figure 26.39.

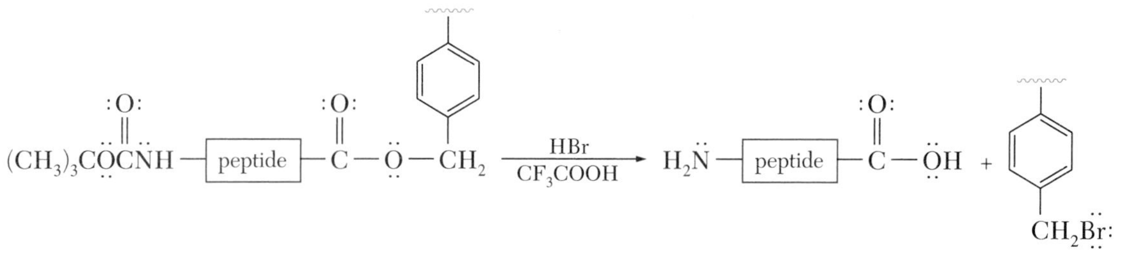

$$(CH_3)_3COCNH-\boxed{\text{peptide}}-C(=O)-O-CH_2-C_6H_4-\text{~~~} \xrightarrow[CF_3COOH]{HBr} H_2N-\boxed{\text{peptide}}-C(=O)-OH + \text{~~~}-C_6H_4-CH_2Br$$

Figure 26.39 Cleavage of the complete peptide chain from the solid-phase support.

This method can be used for the rapid synthesis of extremely large peptides in relatively good yields. This general approach—performing syntheses with a solid-phase support of the substrate—has also been applied to other types of organic synthesis problems.

PROBLEM 26.29 Show all of the steps in the synthesis of Phe-Ala-Val using the Merrifield method.

Summary

- Polypeptides and proteins are large molecules composed of α-amino acid units joined by amide linkages that are often referred to as *peptide bonds*.
- Only 20 α-amino acids are commonly found in proteins. In all of these α-amino acids (with the exception of glycine) the carbon atom bearing the amino and carboxyl groups is stereogenic.
- Most natural α-amino acids have the same configuration at this stereogenic center. Such compounds are commonly known as L-α-amino acids by analogy with L-glyceraldehyde.
- In solution, α-amino acids exist in cationic, anionic, and zwitterionic forms, depending on their structures and the pH of the solution. The pH at which the concentrations of the cationic and anionic forms are equal is known as the isoelectric point (pI) of that α-amino acid.
- α-Amino acids can be synthesized from α-halocarboxylic acids, from malonic ester, and from α-aminonitriles. These synthetic routes produce racemic mixtures that must be resolved in order to obtain the optically active forms.
- α-Amino acids undergo many of the usual reactions of simple amines and simple carboxylic acids. However, we often need to adjust the pH carefully in order to effect reaction.
- The structural determination of polypeptides and proteins requires several steps. First, we need to hydrolyze all of the peptide linkages and separate the resulting mixture of α-amino acids. Automated chromatographic and electrophoretic techniques are used in this process. This type of determination tells us which α-amino acids are present and in what amount.
- Following this analysis, a sample of the protein is sequenced. The Edman procedure is commonly used for this determination. The α-amino acids are derivatized and removed from the peptide, one at a time, starting at the N terminus. For very large peptides it is first necessary to cleave the molecule into fragments and sequence each fragment. The structure of the original peptide is then reconstructed using the method of overlapping sequences.
- Peptide synthesis requires special experimental procedures. Merrifield's solid-phase method has been used successfully to prepare molecules containing hundreds of α-amino acids.

Terms to Remember

protein
α-amino acid
sequencing
peptide bond
polypeptide
peptide
prosthetic group
essential amino acid
zwitterion
isoelectric point
acetamidomalonic ester
Strecker synthesis
ninhydrin test
mobile phase
stationary phase
R_f value
ion exchange chromatography
amino acid analyzer
cation exchange resin
electrophoresis
disulfide bridge
primary structure
proteolytic enzyme
Edman degradation
secondary structure
hydrophobic
hydrophilic
globular protein
salt bridge
heme

Additional Problems

26.30 From each of the following pairs, choose the substance that has the indicated property and explain your selection.

a. has a pI > 7: a basic or an acidic α-amino acid
b. reacts faster with acetic anhydride under basic conditions: a simple aliphatic amine or an α-amino acid
c. is the naturally occurring enantiomer of threonine: *R* or *S*
d. gives a positive iodoform test: serine or threonine
e. produces N_2 gas upon treatment with nitrous acid: aspartic acid or proline
f. has a higher concentration of cationic form at physiological pH (i.e., pH ~ 6–7): an α-amino acid of *low* or *high* pI
g. upon electrophoresis at pH = 4, it migrates toward the cathode: Gly-Ala-Val or Asp-Ala-Gly
h. upon electrophoresis at pH = 7, it migrates toward the cathode: Ala-Lys-Gly or Tyr-Gly-Ala
i. under physiological conditions the α-amino acid more likely to be found in the interior of a globular protein than at its surface: Phe or Glu
j. cannot participate in the hydrogen bonding involved in the α-helix structure of proteins: Pro or Val
k. is more acidic: glycine in the cationic form or propanoic acid

26.31 What are the products obtained by treatment of the octapeptide Gly-Ser-Thr-Lys-Ala-Arg-Ser-Gly with trypsin?

26.32 Consider the tetrapeptide Ser-Phe-Ala-Glu:

a. Estimate its pI value.
b. Tell the sign of the electrode to which it will migrate upon electrophoresis at pH = 7.
c. Tell which products would result from its treatment with each of the following reagents: (i) chymotrypsin, (ii) carboxypeptidase, (iii) phenylisothiocyanate followed by trifluoroacetic acid and finally by aqueous acid.

26.33 Draw structures for each of the following:

a. *N*-acetylalanine
b. Phe-Leu
c. the ethyl ester of glycine
d. phenylalanine hydrochloride
e. the product of the reaction of glycine hydrochloride and thionyl chloride
f. a cyclic product of formula $C_4H_6O_2N_2$ obtained upon heating glycine

g. the product of the reaction of alanine with benzyl chloroformate
h. the product of the reaction of glycine with aqueous KOH
i. the product of the reaction of glycine with ethanol in the presence of an acid catalyst

26.34 Give systematic names for each of the following:
a. alanine b. phenylalanine c. tyrosine

26.35 A recently developed method for the synthesis of α-amino acids begins with methyl nitroacetate ($O_2NCH_2CO_2CH_3$). Outline the steps needed to convert this starting material into α-amino acids of the general structure $H_2NCH(R)COOH$.

26.36 Suggest a synthesis of $H_2NCH_2{}^{14}COOH$ using $^{14}CO_2$ as your source of ^{14}C.

26.37 Deduce the primary structure of a heptapeptide from the following data: (i) On treatment with 3 *M* hydrochloric acid, 1 mmole of the peptide yields 1 mmole each of Leu, Phe, Ser, Tyr, and Pro, along with 2 mmole of Ala. (ii) On treatment with 1 *M* hydrochloric acid, the peptide yields a mixture of five tripeptides, Ser-Leu-Ala, Phe-Ala-Tyr, Pro-Phe-Ala, Leu-Ala-Pro, and Ala-Pro-Phe. (iii) On treatment of the peptide with carboxypeptidase, a hexapeptide is obtained along with Tyr. (iv) After one cycle of the Edman degradation, a hexapeptide is obtained along with the compound of structure shown below.

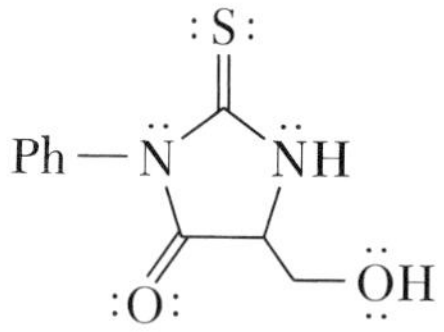

:S:
Ph—N NH
:O: OH

26.38 Show all steps in the Merrifield solid-phase synthesis of Ala-Phe-Gly.

26.39 Using the synthetic routes discussed in this chapter, show all the steps involved in the synthesis of a racemic mixture of each of the following α-amino acids:
a. aspartic acid b. isoleucine

26.40 Provide the missing reagents and intermediates (*A–E*) in the following synthesis of racemic tyrosine.

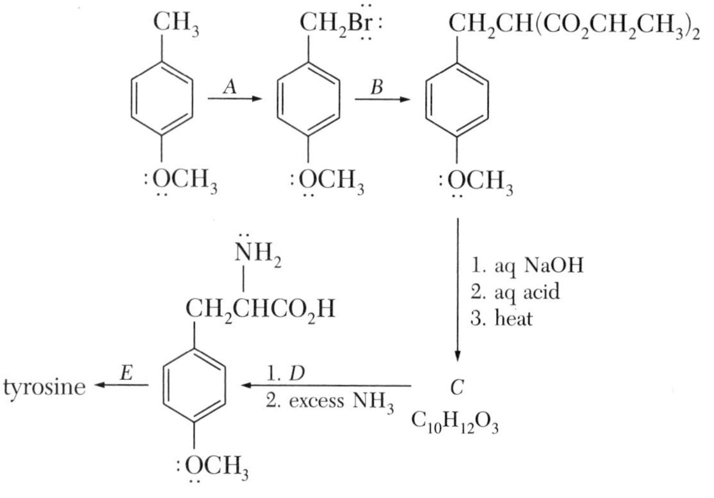

CH_3 $\xrightarrow{A}$ CH_2Br $\xrightarrow{B}$ $CH_2CH(CO_2CH_2CH_3)_2$
:OCH_3 :OCH_3 :OCH_3

1. aq NaOH
2. aq acid
3. heat

C
$C_{10}H_{12}O_3$

1. *D*
2. excess NH_3

NH_2
CH_2CHCO_2H
:OCH_3

tyrosine ← *E*

26.41 Draw structures for all the intermediates in the following reaction sequence for the preparation of an α-amino acid.

potassium phthalimide + $BrCH(CO_2CH_2CH_3)_2$ ⟶ *F*

$$F \xrightarrow[\text{2. 1,3-dibromopropane}]{\text{1. NaH}} \underset{C_{18}H_{20}O_6NBr}{G}$$

$$G + \text{potassium acetate} \longrightarrow \underset{C_{20}H_{23}O_8N}{H}$$

$$H \xrightarrow[\text{2. heat, aq acid}]{\text{1. heat, aq NaOH}} \underset{C_5H_{11}O_3N}{I}$$

$$I + HCl \longrightarrow \underset{C_5H_{10}O_2NCl}{J}$$

$$J \xrightarrow{\text{heat}} \underset{C_5H_9NO_2}{K}$$

26.42 A peptide has been determined to have an N-terminal residue of Val and a C-terminal residue of Leu. One method of partial hydrolysis of the peptide yields a mixture of the following four smaller peptide fragments along with arginine:

Val-Gly-Ser-Lys Asp-Gln-Tyr-Ala
Ala-Ser-Phe-Gly-Lys Tyr-Gly-Leu

A different partial hydrolysis of another sample of the same peptide yields the following five fragment species:

Val-Gly-Ser-Lys-Ala-Ser-Phe Ala-Arg-Tyr
Gly-Lys-Asp-Gln Gly-Leu
Tyr

Propose a structure for the original peptide.

CHAPTER 27 Heterocyclic Compounds

27.1 Introduction

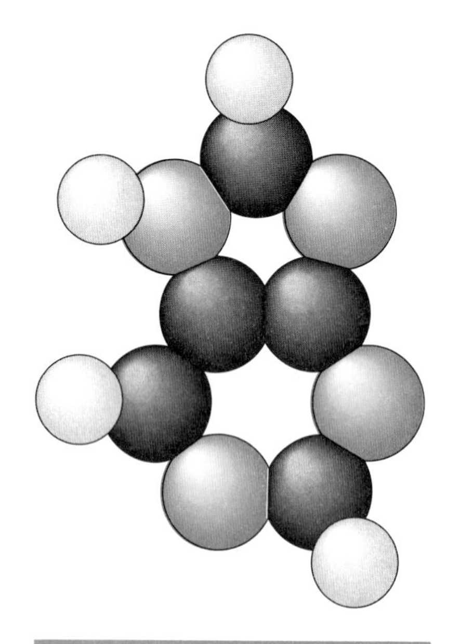

Heterocyclic compounds or **heterocycles** are compounds whose molecules contain a ring in which at least one atom is not carbon. Any ring atoms that are *not* carbon are referred to as **heteroatoms.** The heteroatoms most commonly found in heterocyclic compounds are nitrogen, oxygen, and sulfur. Figure 27.1 shows examples of common three-, four-, five-, and six-membered saturated heterocyclic compounds containing nitrogen and/or oxygen. You should recall meeting some of these heterocyclic compounds in earlier chapters.

In addition to the saturated compounds shown in Figure 27.1, heterocycles can be aromatic, as we discussed in Chapter 16. Indeed, aromatic heterocycles constitute an extremely important class of organic substances, and there are many naturally occurring aromatic heterocycles. Of particular importance are the base components of nucleic acids (Chapter 28), which play the central role in the action of genes. Figure 27.2 shows the structures and names of several important aromatic heterocyclic (often called **heteroaromatic**) compounds.

27.2 Nonaromatic Heterocycles

Nonaromatic heterocycles are usually prepared from open-chain compounds. A useful strategy is to arrange that two functional groups of an open-chain compound can interact to form a ring. The reaction shown in Equation 27.1 illustrates this strategy. This synthesis of oxetane is simply an intramolecular version of the Williamson ether synthesis (Chapter 12).

Eqn. 27.1

$$HO{-}CH_2CH_2CH_2{-}Cl \xrightarrow{NaOH} \underset{CH_2-O^-}{\overset{Cl}{CH_2-CH_2}} \longrightarrow \text{oxetane}$$

PROBLEM 27.1

Each of the following reactions results in the formation of a heterocyclic compound. For each reaction, provide the structure of the heterocyclic product and a mechanism for its formation.

a. $BrCH_2C(CH_3)_2CH_2NHCH_3 \xrightarrow[100\ °C]{50\%\ aq\ KOH} C_6H_{13}N$

b. $\underset{\displaystyle CH_2\ddot{\underset{\cdot\cdot}{Cl}}:}{PhCH{-}CO_2H} \xrightarrow[\text{room temp}]{\text{NaOH, } H_2O} C_9H_8O_2$

c. 3-pyridyl–$CHICH_2CH_2CH_2\ddot{N}HCH_3 \xrightarrow{\text{heat}}$ nicotine

PROBLEM 27.2 Suggest a structure for the bicyclic compound of formula $C_6H_{10}SO$ formed in the following reaction:

$$\text{epoxycyclopentyl–}CH_2\ddot{I}: + Na_2\ddot{S} \xrightarrow{H_2O} C_6H_{10}SO$$

Figure 27.1 Structures and names of some heterocyclic compounds. In naming substituted heterocycles, the heteroatom (or one of the heteroatoms) is assigned the 1-position.

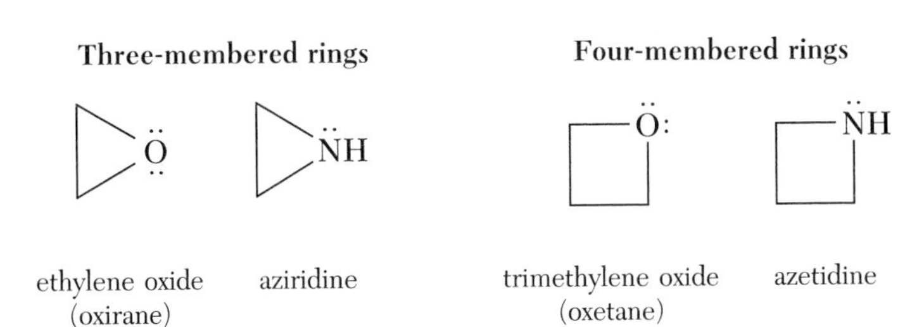

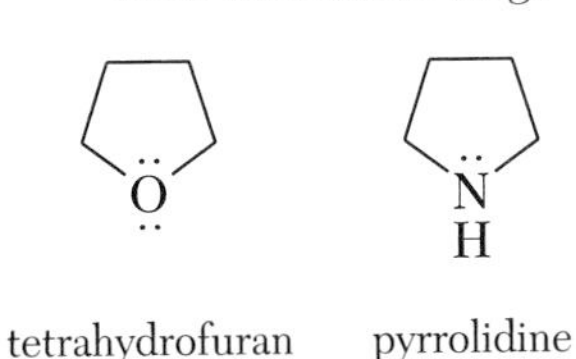

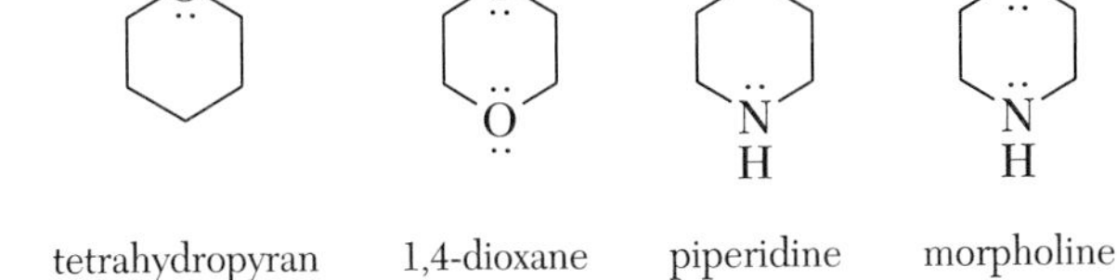

Figure 27.2 Structures and names of some heteroaromatic compounds.

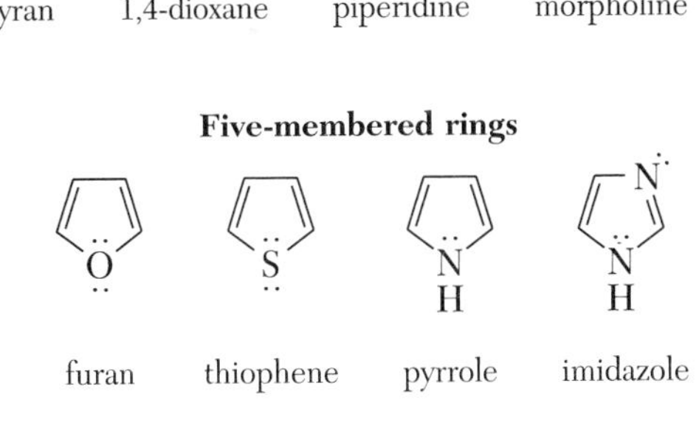

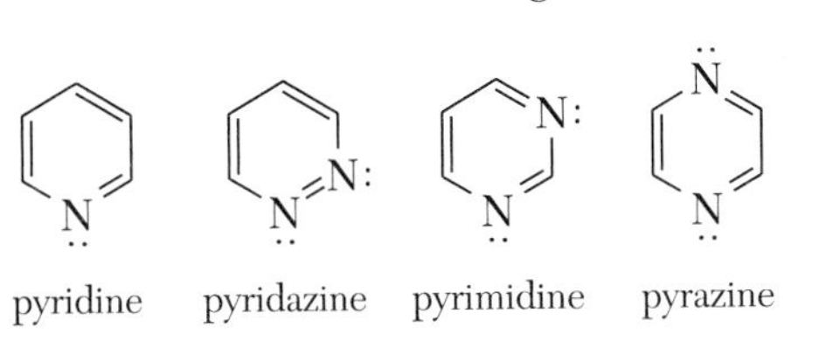

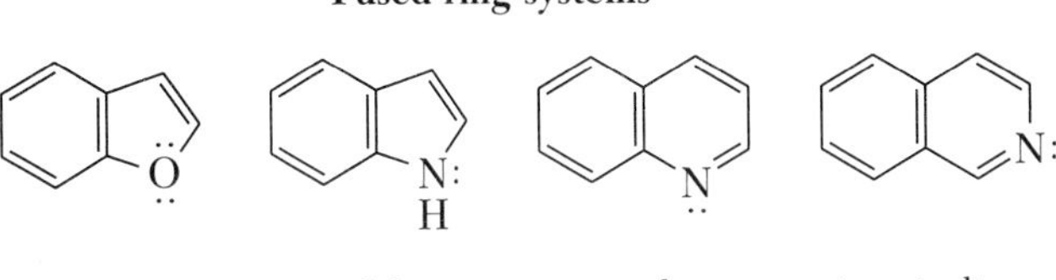

The efficiency of ring formation in this type of reaction depends on two factors related to the size of the ring. The first of these factors is *enthalpic* and depends heavily on the degree of strain in the ring being produced. For a given reaction type producing a ring, the more highly strained the ring, the higher the activation enthalpy for its formation. The second factor is *entropic* and is related to the probability that the two ends of the open-chain molecule will come into contact so that reaction can occur. The entropic factor becomes increasingly less favorable as the ring size increases. The enthalpic factor follows the order of ring stability we discussed in Chapter 13.

The overall ease of ring formation reflects a balance of the enthalpic and entropic factors. In most cases the ease of ring formation decreases in the order: 5- > 6- > 3- > 7- > 4-membered-ring. Interestingly, five-membered rings generally form more readily than do the more stable (less strained) six-membered rings. Presumably the entropic factor outweighs the enthalpic factor for these rings. Rings containing more than seven members are often difficult to prepare because of a relatively unfavorable entropic factor. The probability that the two ends of molecule will meet and react *intramolecularly* to form a large ring is quite low. *Intermolecular* reaction (between two separate molecules) is then more likely.

The reactions of nonaromatic heterocyclic compounds are very similar to those of their open-chain counterparts for rings of intermediate or large size. However, if the ring containing the heteroatom is small, ring strain may be a dominant factor in its chemistry. We noted this effect with epoxides (Chapter 14), which are much more reactive than other cyclic or open-chain ethers. Ring-opening occurs in the reactions of epoxides, relieving the strain present in the small ring.

27.3 Aromatic Heterocyclic Compounds

The most important aromatic heterocycles contain heteroatoms in either five- or six-membered rings. Many of these compounds can be obtained from natural sources, at times in such great quantities that they serve for industrial chemical use.

The principal natural sources of furans and related materials are agricultural residues such as corncobs, oat hulls, and cottonseed hulls. These materials contain complex polysaccharides known as **pentosans,** which yield only pentoses on hydrolysis. Dehydration of the pentoses leads readily to furfural (2-furancarbaldehyde), an extremely useful reagent shown in Figure 27.3.

Furan and substituted furans are manufactured from furfural. Furfural undergoes facile oxidation to 2-furoic acid (**27.1**), a carboxylic acid that in turn

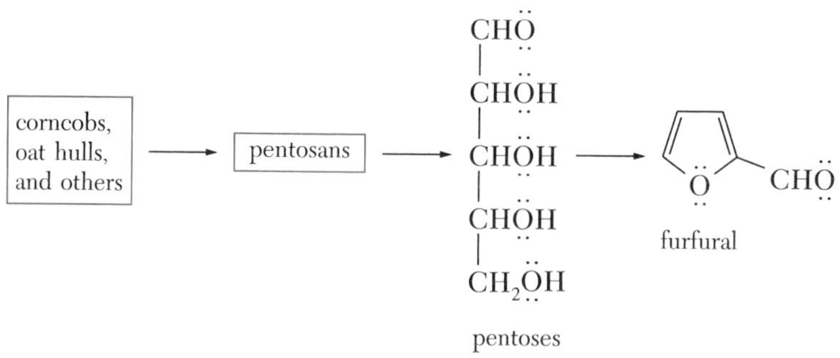

Figure 27.3 Preparation of furfural from natural materials. Corncobs and other agricultural products provide a convenient source of furfural. Polysaccharides in the vegetable product are hydrolyzed to pentoses, which are in turn dehydrated to form the furfural. Other derivatives are then synthesized from the furfural.

corncobs, oat hulls, and others → pentosans → CHO–CHOH–CHOH–CHOH–CH_2OH (pentoses) → furfural (CHO) is decarboxylated to furan. The important solvent tetrahydrofuran (THF) (**27.2**) is manufactured by catalytic hydrogenation of furan.

2-furoic acid **27.1** tetrahydrofuran **27.2**

PROBLEM 27.3 Describe the laboratory synthesis of each of the following materials, starting with furfural.

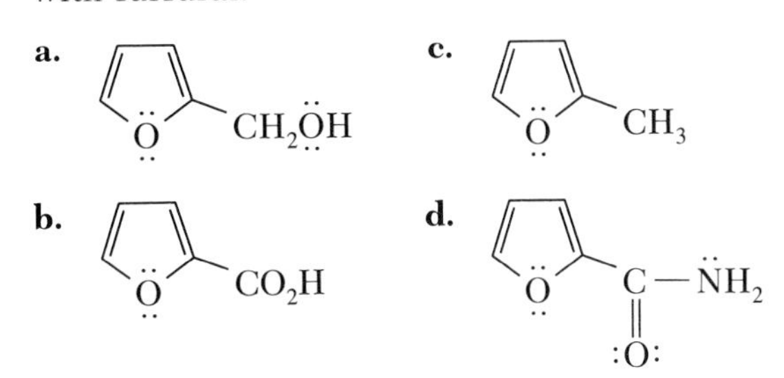

PROBLEM 27.4 Describe the methods you would use to convert tetrahydrofuran to each of the following materials:
a. 1,4-dibromobutane **b.** 1,4-dicyanobutane
c. 1,6-hexanedioic acid

Furan is also a commercially important material for the preparation of pyrrole and thiophene, as illustrated in Figure 27.4.

Coal tar is a rich source of pyridines and methyl-substituted pyridines. Many fractions are obtained from the distillation of coal tar. Pyridine and the methylpyridines are present in the light (relatively low boiling) fractions, from which they are isolated easily by extraction into mineral acid solution. The monomethylpyridines are frequently described as α-, β-, or γ-picolines depending on the position of the methyl group. Pyridines substituted with two methyl groups are known commonly as lutidines. Structures of the picolines and one of the lutidines are shown in Figure 27.5.

Figure 27.4 Preparation of pyrrole and thiophene from furan. Pyrrole and thiophene can be manufactured from furan by heating with ammonia or hydrogen sulfide, respectively, in the presence of alumina.

NH_3, Al_2O_3, 450 °C
H_2S, Al_2O_3, 450 °C

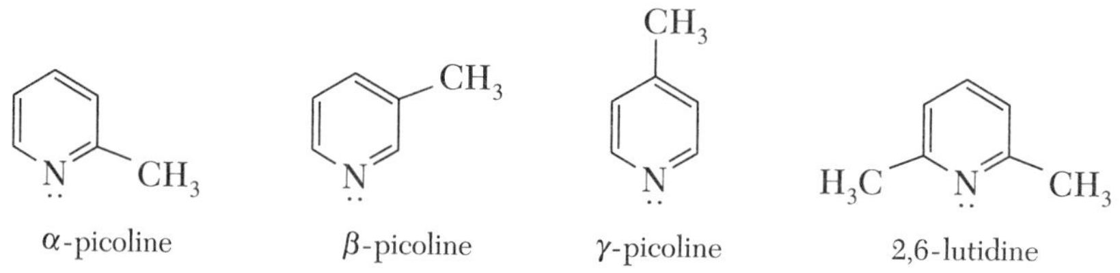

Figure 27.5 Nomenclature of methyl-substituted pyridines.

α-picoline β-picoline γ-picoline 2,6-lutidine

27.4 Contrasting Reactivities of Five- and Six-Membered Heteroaromatics

ELECTROPHILIC AROMATIC SUBSTITUTION

Heteroaromatic compounds undergo reactions typical of other aromatic compounds such as benzene and its derivatives. For example, aromatic electrophilic substitution reactions such as halogenation, nitration, and sulfonation can be accomplished with both five-membered heteroaromatics such as pyrrole and six-membered aromatics such as pyridine. However, there are significant differences in the reactivities of these heteroaromatic compounds. In general, the five-membered heteroaromatics are much *more* reactive than benzene toward electrophilic reagents, while the corresponding six-membered heteroaromatics are much *less* reactive than benzene toward the same reagents. These differences are summarized in Figure 27.6.

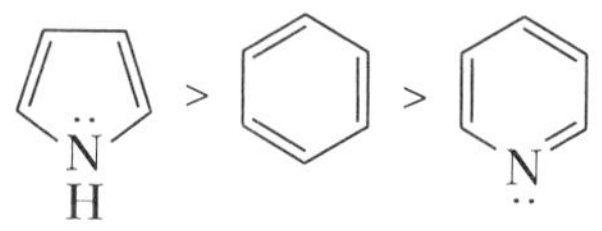

Figure 27.6 Relative reactivity of aromatics toward electrophilic reagents. Other five-membered heteroaromatics are similarly more reactive than benzene toward electrophilic reagents.

Relative reactivity toward electrophilic reagents

pyrrole > benzene > pyridine

Bromination provides an example of these differing reactivities. While pyrrole reacts almost explosively with bromine, benzene reacts with bromine only in the presence of a Lewis acid catalyst, and pyridine reacts with bromine only at very high temperature.

PROBLEM 27.5 Although pyridine itself undergoes electrophilic bromine substitution only under extreme conditions, 2-aminopyridine undergoes bromination in the 5-position readily upon being mixed with bromine in acetic acid. Account for the difference in reactivities of these two materials. Would you expect 2-picolinic acid to be similar to 2-aminopyridine in its reactivity? Explain your reasoning.

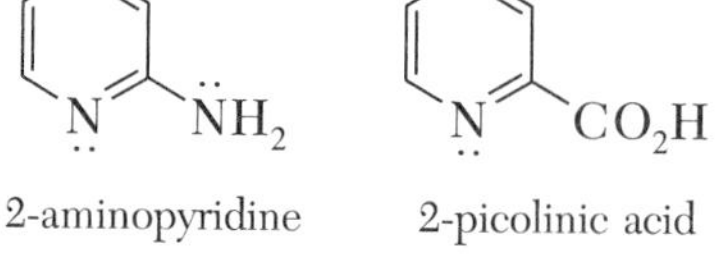

2-aminopyridine 2-picolinic acid

We find further that pyrrole, furan, and thiophene undergo electrophilic aromatic substitution principally at the α-position relative to the heteroatom.

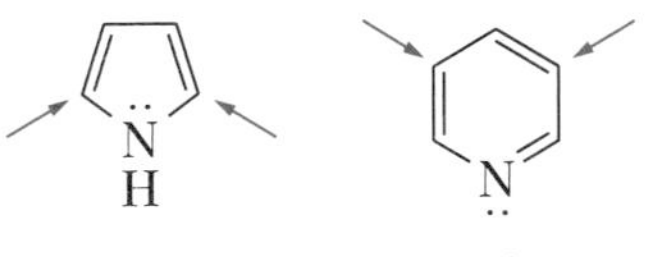

pyrrole pyridine

Figure 27.7 Comparison of regioselectivity of electrophilic substitution in pyrrole and pyridine. Electrophilic attack occurs at the arrowed positions.

On the other hand, when pyridine reacts, it does so principally at the β-position relative to the heteroatom, as illustrated in Figure 27.7.

The rationalization for these patterns of electrophilic substitution is rooted in the mechanism of the reaction. In electrophilic aromatic substitution (review Chapter 18), the rate-determining step is generally the attachment of the electrophilic reagent to the aromatic ring. When different positions of the ring are available for reaction, addition occurs to generate the more stable of the possible cationic intermediates. For a five-membered heteroaromatic molecule such as pyrrole, addition at the α-position leads to a more stable carbocation than does addition at the β-position. We can draw three resonance structures providing charge delocalization to stabilize the former intermediate but only two such structures for the latter intermediate (see Figure 27.8).

These resonance structures also help us rationalize the increased reactivity of pyrrole (compared to benzene) in electrophilic aromatic substitution reactions. The first resonance structure shown for addition at the 2-position (like the first resonance structure shown for addition at the 3-position) has a complete octet of electrons associated with each atom of the ring. We have seen that our ability to draw such particularly favorable Lewis resonance structures correlates with improved stability (and ease of formation) of the species. No such resonance structures can be drawn for electrophilic substitution reactions occurring on benzene. No resonance structure with a complete octet of electrons at each atom of the ring can be drawn for benzenonium ions. Thus we rationalize the greater reactivity of pyrrole over benzene in electrophilic aromatic substitution reactions to be due to the greater stabilization of the pyrrole reaction intermediate compared to the benzene intermediate.

PROBLEM 27.6 Would you expect nitrobenzene or aniline (both derivatives of benzene) to more closely resemble pyrrole in its reactivity toward electrophilic reagents for substitution? Explain your answer.

Now consider pyridine in electrophilic aromatic substitution reactions. An electrophile, in principle, could attack any one of three different positions about the pyridine ring, that is, it could attack *ortho-*, *meta-*, or *para-* relative to the ring nitrogen atom. In each case there are three resonance structures for the cationic intermediate, as shown in Figure 27.9.

Figure 27.8 Resonance structures for the intermediate cations formed by attack of an electrophile (E) on the 2- and 3-positions of pyrrole. More resonance structures can be drawn for the 2-substituted cation, suggesting that it is more stable than the 3-substituted cation.

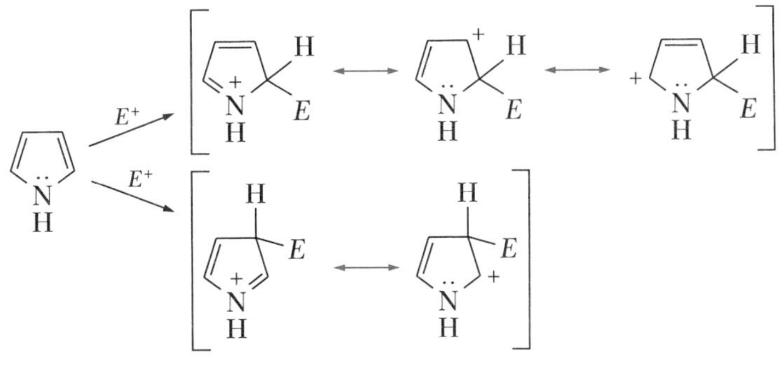

Figure 27.9 Resonance structures for the cationic intermediate formed by attack of an electrophile on pyridine. Attack of the electrophile can occur at the 2-, 3-, or 4-position. Each route leads to cations described by a trio of resonance structures. However, the energies of the contributing resonance structures for each possible intermediate cation are not equivalent.

Electrophilic attack at the 2-position (*ortho* to the ring N)

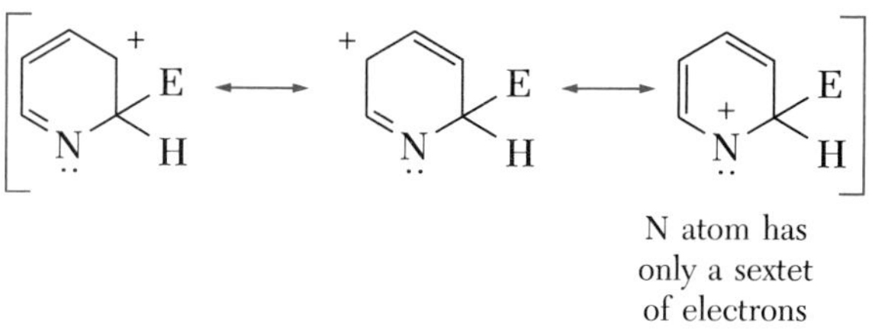

N atom has only a sextet of electrons

Electrophilic attack at the 3-position (*meta* to the ring N)

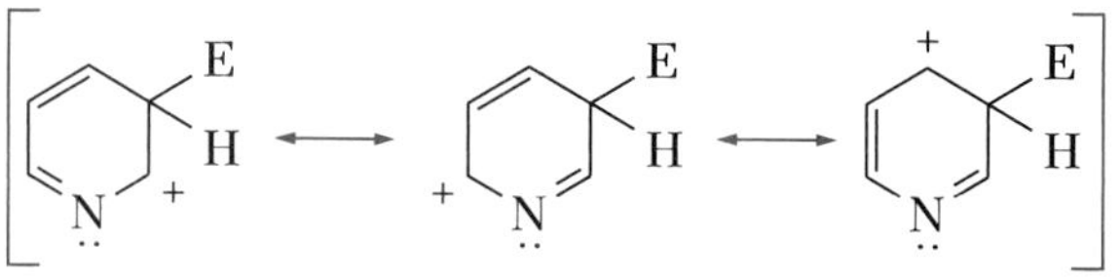

Electrophilic attack at the 4-position (*para* to the ring N)

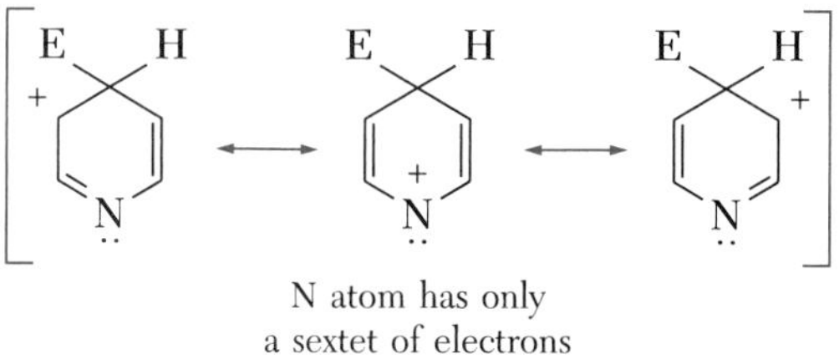

N atom has only a sextet of electrons

Each resonance structure in Figure 27.9 is less stable than the corresponding one resulting from attack on a benzene ring because of the presence of the electron-withdrawing nitrogen atom. This difference in stability correlates with the lowered reactivity of pyridine compared to benzene in this type of reaction.

These contributing resonance structures also account for the experimental observation that pyridine preferentially undergoes electrophilic aromatic substitution at the 3-position. The three sets of resonance structures in Figure 27.9 are *not* equivalent. Attack at the 2- or 4-position is relatively *disfavored* since the positive charge is delocalized to the electronegative nitrogen atom in one of the contributing structures for each route, and the nitrogen in those structures has only a sextet of electrons. In contrast, the intermediate formed by attack at the 3-position has no highly unfavorable resonance structure of this type.

PROBLEM 27.7 Consider the pyrimidine molecule (Figure 27.2):

a. Predict the primary position of attack in electrophilic aromatic substitution reactions with pyrimidine.
b. Do you expect pyrimidine to be more reactive or less reactive than pyridine toward electrophilic attack? Explain your answer.

AROMATIC NUCLEOPHILIC REACTIONS OF PYRIDINES

In its reactivity toward electrophiles, the pyridine ring behaves like a benzene ring bearing strongly electron-withdrawing substituents. This similarity extends to its reactivity with nucleophilic reagents. Recall that although nucleophilic displacement reactions on a benzene ring are generally not observed, such reactions can occur if suitable electron-withdrawing substituents are present (Chapter 18). Since the pyridine ring contains an electron-withdrawing nitrogen atom as a component of the ring itself, it is perhaps not surprising that the pyridine ring is quite reactive toward nucleophilic substitution. There is, however, a selectivity to these reactions. Nucleophilic displacement occurs preferentially when the leaving group is at the 2- or 4-position of the pyridine ring. An example in which a chlorine atom is displaced from the 2-position of a pyridine ring is shown in Equation 27.2. (A chlorine atom is *not* similarly displaced from the *3-position* of the ring.)

Eqn. 27.2

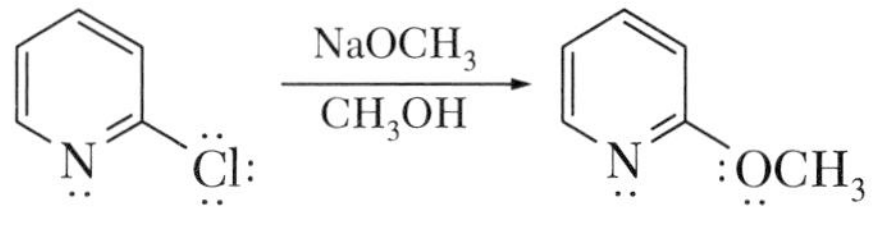

2-chloropyridine $\xrightarrow[CH_3OH]{NaOCH_3}$ 2-methoxypyridine (OCH_3)

95% yield

The mechanism for this and similar reactions involves addition of the nucleophile followed by elimination of the leaving group. This addition-elimination mechanism is analogous to the mechanism for nucleophilic substitution reactions on benzene rings bearing electronegative substituents (see Chapter 18).

MECHANISM OF REACTION

Nucleophilic Substitution Reaction for 2-Chloropyridine

Step 1 Addition of the nucleophile:

$^-$:OCH_3 + 2-chloropyridine ⟶

[N$^-$ / OCH_3 / Cl ⟷ OCH_3 / Cl ⟷ OCH_3 / Cl]

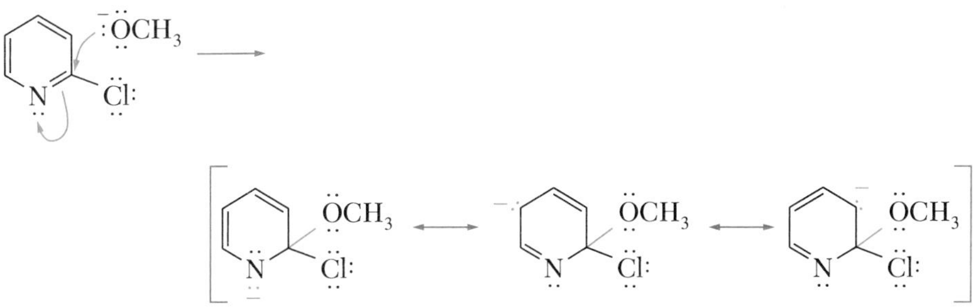

Step 2 Loss of the leaving group:

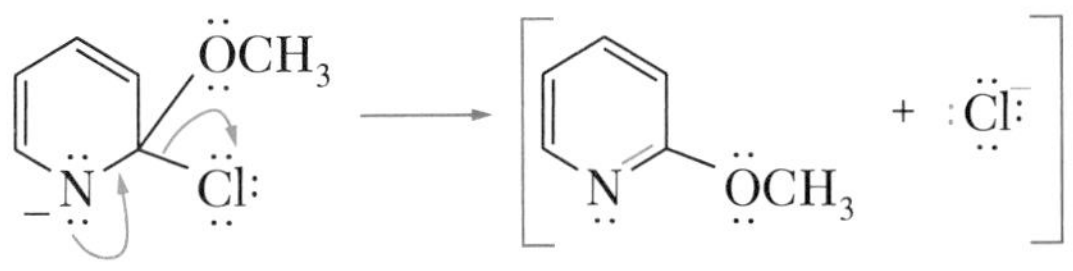

N$^-$ / OCH_3 / Cl ⟶ [2-methoxypyridine (OCH_3) + :Cl:$^-$]

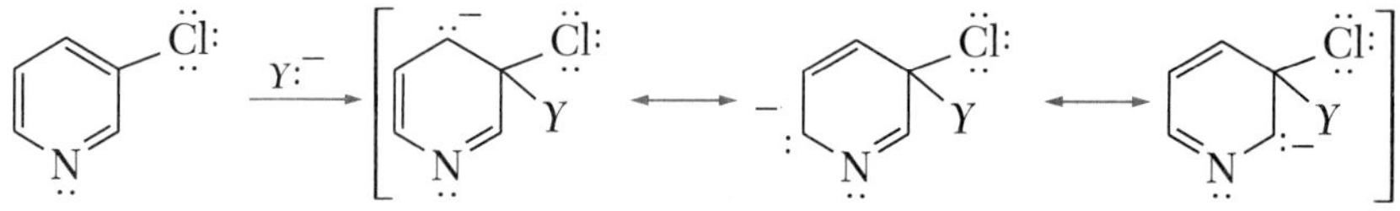

Figure 27.10 Nucleophilic attack on pyridine with a substituent in the 3-position of the ring. Substituents in the 3-position of pyridine rings are not easily displaced by nucleophiles. The anion formed upon addition of the nucleophile does not delocalize negative charge onto the ring nitrogen atom. The resulting lack of stability is reflected in a very low rate formation of the anion.

Notice that in the intermediate anion, the negative charge is delocalized onto the electronegative nitrogen atom of the pyridine ring. This delocalization stabilizes the anion, making reaction possible. If no such delocalization is possible, the anion is less stable and forms at a negligibly slow rate—no net reaction is observed. Thus, a halogen present in the 3-position of a pyridine ring is not displaced by nucleophiles (see Figure 27.10).

PROBLEM 27.8 Predict the structure of the organic product in the following reaction:

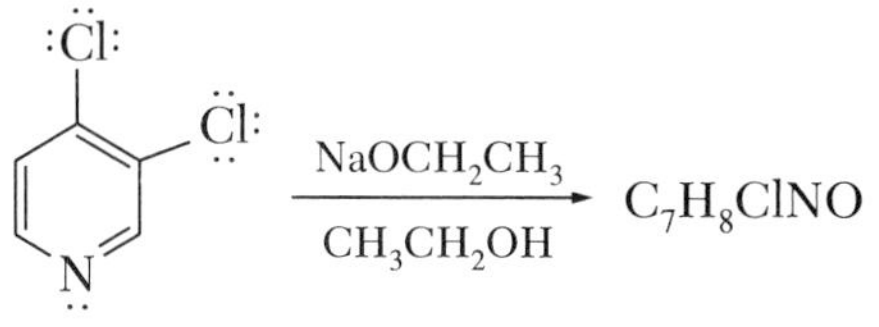

$$\xrightarrow[CH_3CH_2OH]{NaOCH_2CH_3} C_7H_8ClNO$$

PROBLEM 27.9 4-Chloropyridine is commercially available in the form of its hydrochloride salt.

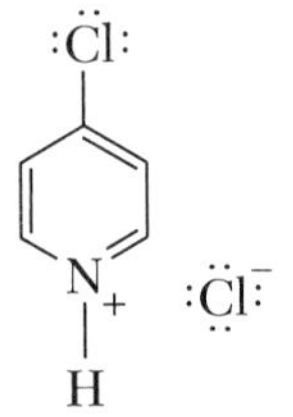

hydrochloride salt of 4-chloropyridine

a. What chemical operations would you perform in the laboratory to obtain a pure sample of free 4-chloropyridine from its hydrochloride salt?
b. When freshly isolated, 4-chloropyridine is a clear liquid, but on standing, it is converted to a solid polymeric material. Explain the formation of this polymeric material.

It is possible to use a potent nucleophile to effect the loss of hydride ion from the α-position of pyridines. The most important example of this type of reaction is the **Tschichibabin reaction,** in which pyridine is heated with sodium amide in a suitable solvent such as *N,N*-diethylaniline. The reaction is worked up by addition of water, as shown in Equation 27.3, to give an α-aminopyridine.

Eqn. 27.3

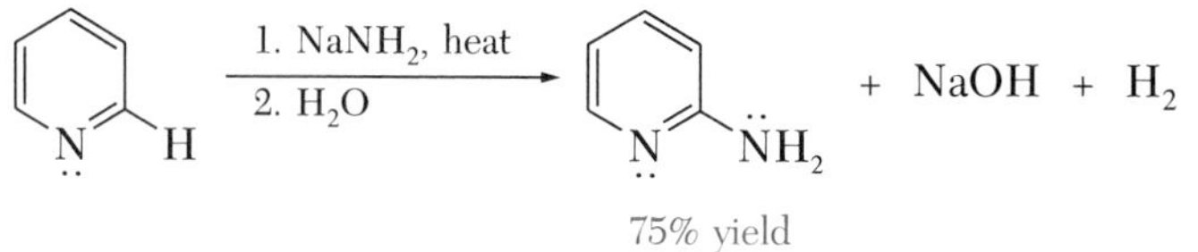

$$\xrightarrow[2.\ H_2O]{1.\ NaNH_2,\ heat} \quad + NaOH + H_2$$

75% yield

The mechanism of the Tschichibabin reaction involves addition to the aromatic ring followed by loss of hydride ion.

MECHANISM OF REACTION

The Tschichibabin Reaction

Step 1 Addition of amide ion to the ring

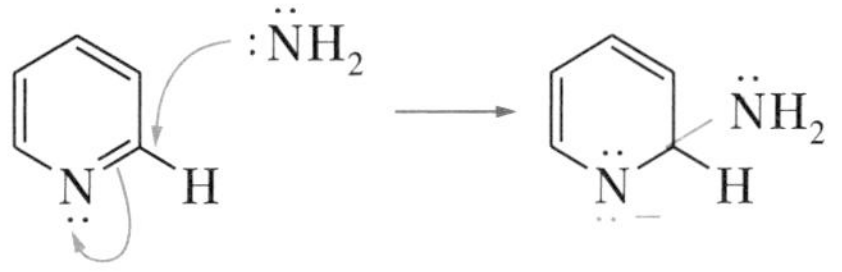

Step 2 Loss of hydride ion to a nearby electrophile

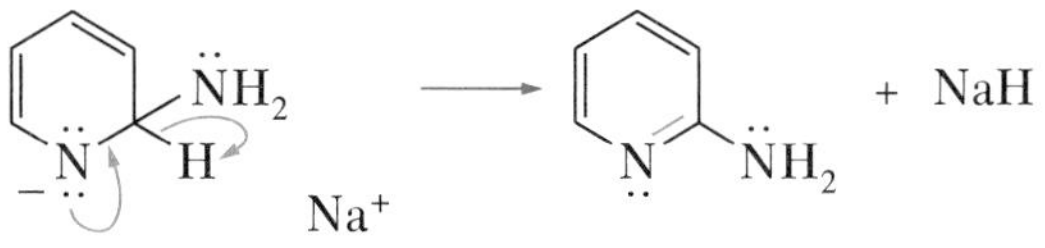

Na^+ + NaH

Step 3 Abstraction of an amine hydrogen by hydride

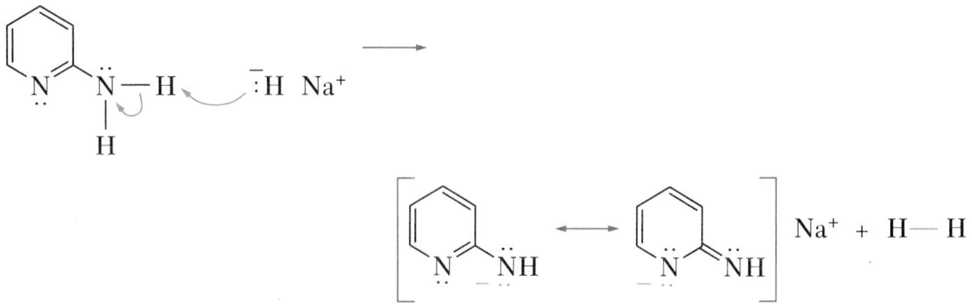

$\text{:}\bar{\text{H}}\ \text{Na}^+$ → Na^+ + H—H

Step 4 Protonation by water

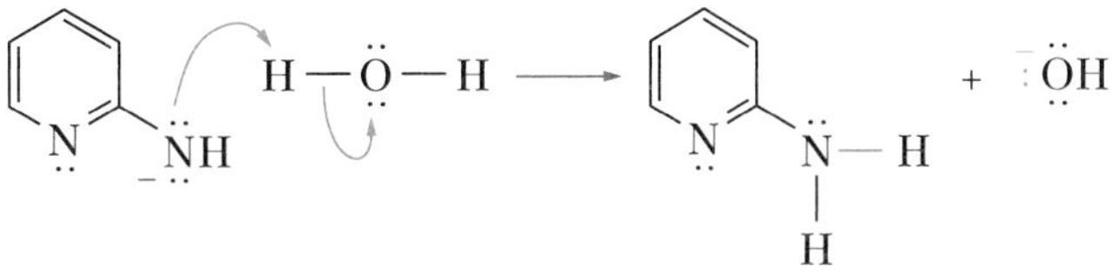

H—Ö—H → + $^-$:ÖH

The 2-aminopyridines produced by this reaction are useful starting materials for the synthesis of other substituted pyridines. For example, diazotization of the aminopyridine generates a diazonium salt that can be converted easily to a halopyridine or a hydroxypyridine (see Chapter 18 for the chemistry of diazonium salts).

Phenyllithium reacts with pyridines in a manner similar to that of sodium amide. Again, the overall effect is replacement of a hydrogen from an α-carbon site, in this case by a phenyl group, as shown in Equation 27.4.

Eqn. 27.4

C_6H_5Li, toluene; pyridine (2-H) → 2-C_6H_5-pyridine, 50% yield

BASICITIES OF THE NITROGEN HETEROCYCLES

The basicities of pyrrole and pyridine differ greatly from each other and from those of the corresponding saturated molecules, pyrrolidine and piperidine. The pK_a values of their conjugate acids are given in Figure 27.11. Remember that the larger the pK_a of the conjugate acid, the stronger the parent base.

How can we rationalize these differences in basicity? First, we note that the two nonaromatic heterocycles have approximately the same basicity, which is quite similar to what we observe for open-chain secondary amines. There appears to be nothing particularly unusual about the basicity of these heterocycles.

However, both pyridine and pyrrole are significantly less basic than either of their saturated counterparts. Furthermore, there is a large difference in the basicities of pyrrole and pyridine. We can begin to understand this difference by considering the hybridization of the unshared valence electron pair on nitrogen. For any one of these compounds to act as a base, a nitrogen unshared valence electron pair must be used to bind to a proton. In the cases of pyrrolidine and piperidine, the nitrogen unshared valence electron pair occupies an sp^3 hybrid orbital, whereas in pyridine it occupies an sp^2 hybrid orbital. The percentage of *s* character for the unshared valence electron pair in piperidine (and pyrrolidine) is 25% whereas it is 33% with pyridine. The greater the *s* character of a hybrid orbital, the more tightly electrons occupying it are held to the parent nucleus, and correspondingly, the *less* available they are for binding to an acidic proton. This analysis explains the reduced basicity of pyridine compared to piperidine and pyrrolidine. We used this type of reasoning earlier in analyzing the enhanced acidity of terminal alkynes compared to other hydrocarbons (Chapter 15) and in comparing the basicities of amines, imines, and nitriles (Chapter 20).

The remaining question concerns the very weak basicity of pyrrole. In Chapter 20 we considered this point, noting that with pyrrole the nitrogen uses its (nominally) unshared valence electron pair to complete the aromatic sextet of the ring. On protonation pyrrole thus loses its aromatic character. Protonation of pyrrole is therefore a relatively unfavorable process.

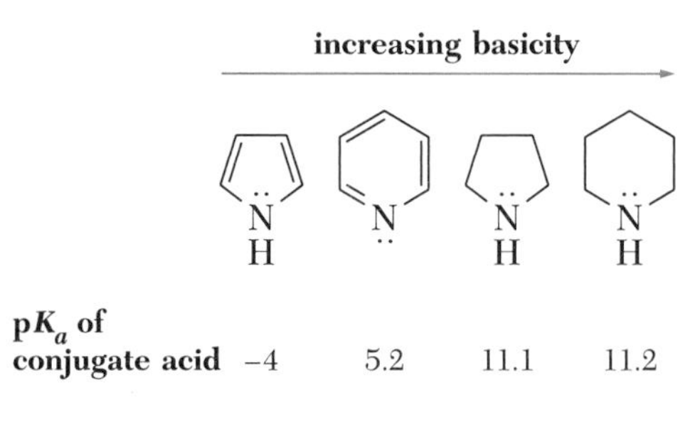

Figure 27.11 Variation in the basicities of nitrogen heterocycles.

PROBLEM 27.10 Pyrimidine (Figure 27.2) is a weaker base than pyridine, but imidazole is a stronger base than pyrrole. Account for these relative basicities.

PROBLEM 27.11 In considering Problem 27.10, a student suggested that because imidazole is a stronger base than pyrrole, it must be a weaker acid than pyrrole. Criticize this suggestion. Based on their structures, which compound, pyrrole or imidazole, would you expect to be more acidic? Explain your answers.

27.5 Special Reactions of Five-Membered Ring Heterocycles

REACTIONS WITH ACIDS

Although pyrrole is a very weak base, it can be protonated by strong acid. However, protonation occurs not at nitrogen but instead at the α-carbon atom. Protonation at *any* position of pyrrole necessarily destroys the aromatic character of the system. However, protonation at the α-carbon atom produces a cation that is resonance stabilized. Protonation at nitrogen produces a cation without such stabilization, as illustrated in Figure 27.12.

In fact, pyrrole *polymerizes* when treated with strong acid. The polymerization process begins with the interaction of a protonated pyrrole molecule with a nonprotonated molecule, and the adduct continues to react with further nonprotonated molecules. There is considerable interest in polypyrroles as electrically conducting organic polymers.

PROBLEM 27.12 Account for the preferential protonation of pyrrole at the α-carbon atom rather than at the β-carbon atom.

PROBLEM 27.13 Suggest a structure for polypyrrole.

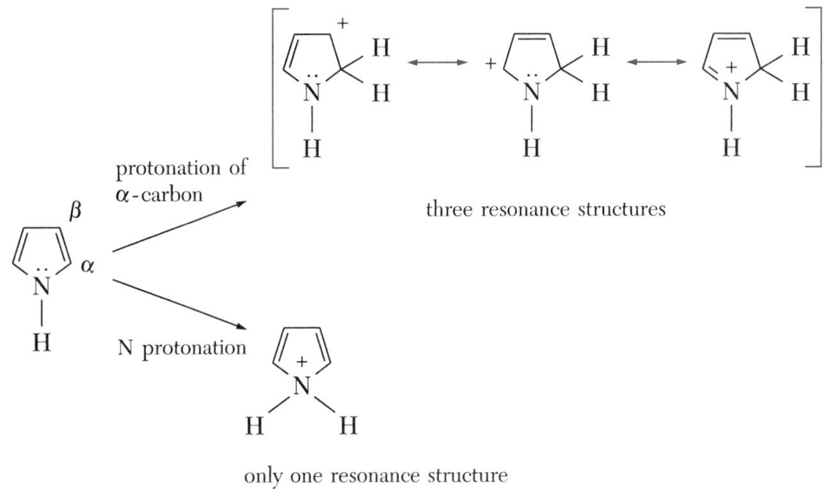

Figure 27.12 Comparison of protonation of pyrrole at the nitrogen and at the α-carbon site. The cation formed on protonation at the α-carbon is resonance stabilized.

protonation of α-carbon

three resonance structures

N protonation

only one resonance structure

Furan reacts almost explosively with strong acids. However, with *dilute* mineral acids a controlled reaction occurs, leading to an opened-ring product, a 1,4-dicarbonyl compound. An example of this ring-opening reaction is shown in Equation 27.5.

Eqn. 27.5

H_3C Ö CH_3 —(H_2O, CH_3CO_2H / H_2SO_4, heat)→ :O: :O:

90% yield

The mechanism of this reaction involves an initial protonation of the furan ring at the β-carbon atom. Protonation is followed by a nucleophilic attack by water on the α-carbon to form a hemiketal. The hemiketal then opens to form the diketone product.

MECHANISM OF REACTION

Reaction of Furan with Strong Acids

Step 1 Protonation of the β-carbon of the furan ring. (Protonation of the α-carbon also occurs, but cannot lead to the observed products.)

H—$\ddot{O}SO_3H$ Ö CH_3 →

H H CH_3 Ö CH_3 ⟷ H H CH_3 O CH_3 + $^-$:$\ddot{O}SO_3H$

Step 2 Nucleophilic attack by water

H Ö H H H CH_3 Ö CH_3 ⇌ H H $\ddot{O}H_2$ CH_3 Ö CH_3

Step 3 Acid-base equilibria involving the cyclic hemiketal

H H $\ddot{O}H_2$ CH_3 Ö CH_3 ⇌(H_2O / H_3O^+) H H $\ddot{O}H$ CH_3 Ö CH_3 ⇌(H_3O^+ / H_2O) H H $\ddot{O}H$ CH_3 +O CH_3 H

Step 4 Ring opening

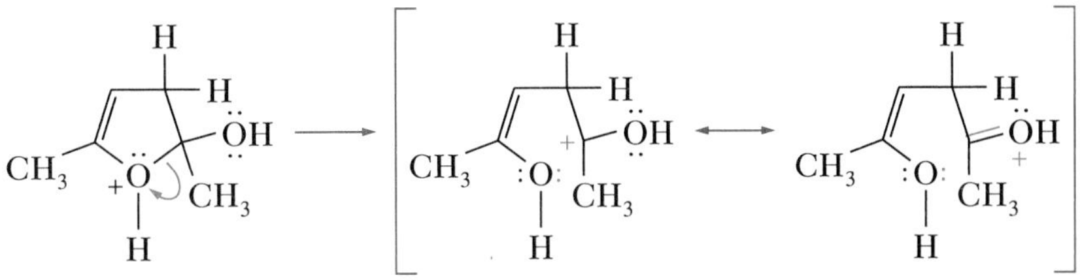

H H H H H H
CH$_3$ +O CH$_3$ ÖH CH$_3$:O: CH$_3$ ÖH CH$_3$:O: CH$_3$ ÖH
H H H

Step 5 Deprotonation

H H H H
CH$_3$:O: CH$_3$ Ö+ H ÖH$_2$ CH$_3$:O: CH$_3$ Ö + H—ÖH$_2$ +
H H

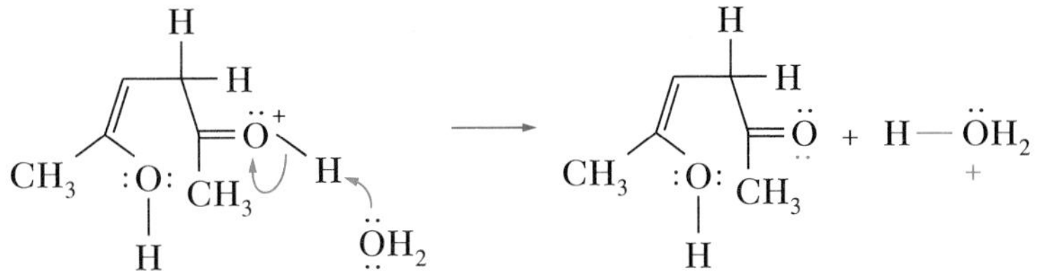

Step 6 Keto-enol tautomerism

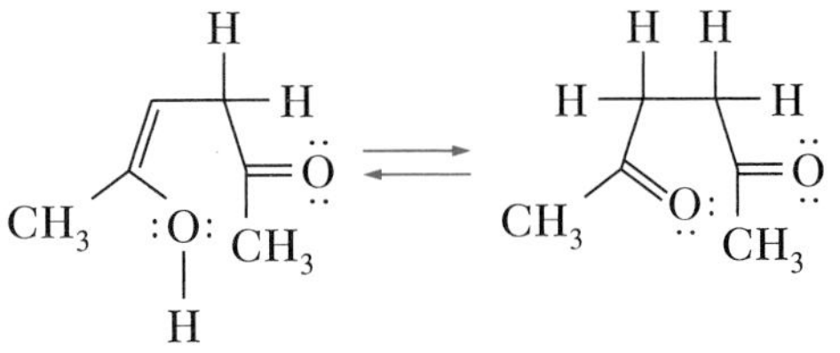

H H H H H H
CH$_3$:O: CH$_3$ Ö CH$_3$ O: CH$_3$ Ö
H

Thiophene, unlike pyrrole and furan, is stable to acidic conditions.

DIELS-ALDER REACTIONS

Another area in which there is a marked difference in the reactivity of the three common five-membered ring heterocycles is their ability to participate in the Diels-Alder reaction as the diene component. Furan and its derivatives react readily with typical dienophiles, as illustrated in Equation 27.6, while pyrroles are either inert to such reactions or proceed only with great difficulty.

Eqn. 27.6

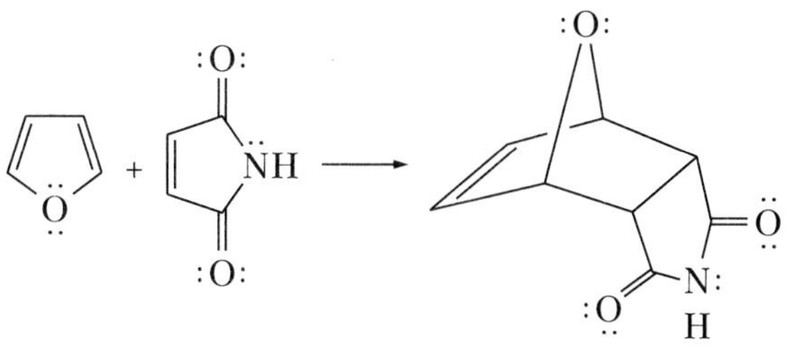

Ö + :O: NH :O: ⟶ :O: Ö N: H :O

95% yield

In all of these reaction we detect a pattern in reactivity. The general order of reactivity is:

furan > pyrrole > thiophene

The heteroatom appears to participate in the aromatic stabilization to the greatest extent in thiophene and the least extent in furan. This observation is consistent with the idea that oxygen holds its unshared valence electron pairs closest to itself and participates in delocalization the least.

27.6 Special Reactions of Pyridines

N-OXIDE FORMATION AND REACTIVITY

Like ordinary tertiary amines, pyridines are oxidized by hydrogen peroxide to form **N-oxides.** An example is shown in Equation 27.7.

Eqn. 27.7

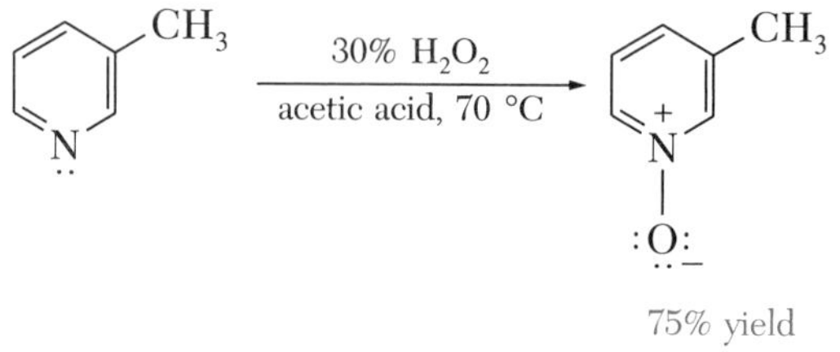

3-methylpyridine $\xrightarrow[\text{acetic acid, 70 °C}]{30\%\ H_2O_2}$ 3-methylpyridine N-oxide

75% yield

The pyridine *N*-oxides are useful materials. For example, they are much more reactive in electrophilic substitution reactions than are their parent pyridines. In Figure 27.13 the reactivities of pyridine and pyridine *N*-oxide toward nitration are compared. Even under drastic reaction conditions, the parent pyridine furnishes a poor yield of nitration product, while pyridine *N*-oxide provides a 90% yield. Notice as well that there is a difference in the regioselectivity of the two reactions. With pyridine, substitution occurs primarily at the β-position, while with the *N*-oxide, substitution occurs primarily at the γ-position.

Pyridine $\xrightarrow[\text{330 °C}]{HNO_3,\ KNO_3}$ 3-nitropyridine (NO_2)

15% yield

Pyridine N-oxide $\xrightarrow[H_2SO_4,\ 90\ °C]{\text{fuming } HNO_3}$ 4-nitropyridine N-oxide (NO_2)

90% yield

Figure 27.13 Comparison of nitration reactions of pyridine and pyridine *N*-oxide.

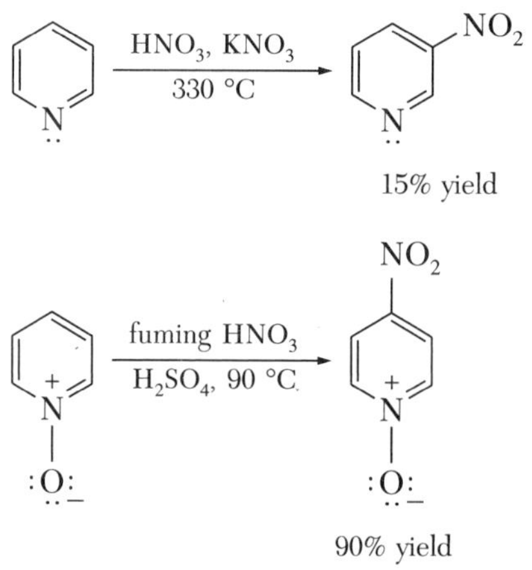

PROBLEM 27.14 Nitration of pyridine *N*-oxide follows the usual mechanism of electrophilic aromatic substitution. Nitronium ion adds to the aromatic ring in the rate-

determining step to form an intermediate cation of the formula $C_5H_5N_2O_3^+$. Draw resonance structures illustrating why nitration occurs principally at the 4-position (and 2-position) rather than at the 3-position.

PROBLEM 27.15 One of the substances illustrated below is nitrated chiefly at the 4-position, while the other substance is nitrated mainly at the 3-position. Which substance is nitrated principally at the 4-position? Explain your answer.

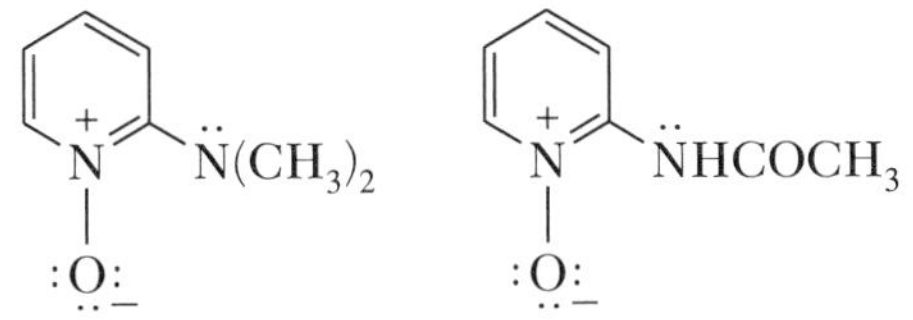

$N(CH_3)_2$ $NHCOCH_3$

Various methods are available for the deoxygenation of pyridine *N*-oxides. A common procedure involves heating the *N*-oxide with phosphorus trichloride. You might wonder why we would introduce an oxygen at the nitrogen of a pyridine only to remove it. The explanation is that this operation is useful in organic syntheses. For example, 4-nitropyridine can be synthesized from pyridine with relative ease proceeding through the *N*-oxide. Direct nitration of pyridine to obtain the 4-nitro derivative is unproductive, but if we first convert the pyridine to its *N*-oxide, then nitrate it, and finish with treatment with phosphorus trichloride, we obtain the 4-nitropyridine in good yield.

Pyridine *N*-oxides also react with organometallics, undergoing attack by the nucleophile at the 2-position, and they react at the oxygen with alkyl and acyl halides.

PROBLEM 27.16 Pyridine *N*-oxide reacts with phenylmagnesium bromide in tetrahydrofuran solution to give 2-phenylpyridine in 67% yield. Suggest a mechanism for this conversion.

ALKYL SIDE-CHAIN REACTIVITY

Alkyl groups attached to pyridine rings behave in some ways like those attached to benzene rings. However, they also have some special properties attributable to the electron-withdrawing effect of the nitrogen atom in the ring.

The greatest similarity between alkyl groups on pyridine rings and alkyl groups on benzene rings is in their oxidation to ring-attached carbonyl groups. An example of the reaction for a pyridine derivative is shown in Equation 27.8.

Eqn. 27.8

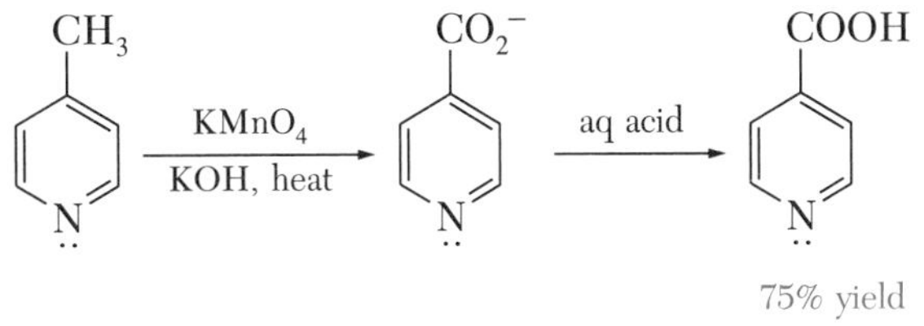

CH_3 $\xrightarrow[\text{KOH, heat}]{KMnO_4}$ CO_2^- $\xrightarrow{\text{aq acid}}$ COOH

75% yield

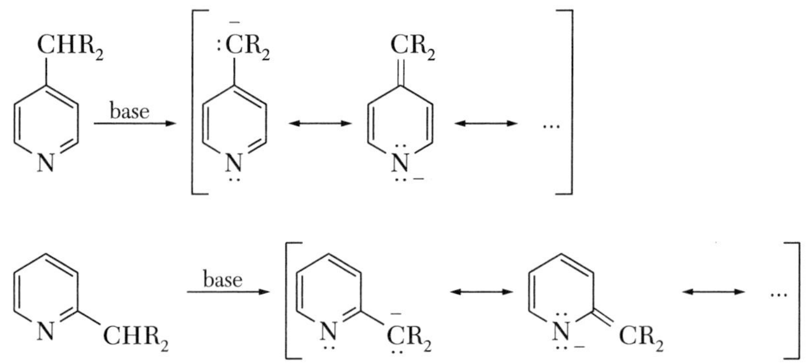

Figure 27.14 Resonance structures for the conjugate bases of 2- and 4-alkylpyridines. In both molecules, the negative charge of the anion is delocalized to the electron-withdrawing nitrogen atom of the ring. With alkylbenzenes, there is no electron-withdrawing atom in the ring to provide special stabilization for the negative charge.

A significant difference in the nature of alkyl-substituted pyridines and benzenes lies in the markedly enhanced acidities of protons at the α-positions of the alkyl groups of 2- and 4-alkyl pyridines. We rationalize the enhanced acidity of these compounds by considering the stabilization afforded the conjugate base formed upon proton removal, as illustrated in Figure 27.14.

As a result of their enhanced acidity, we can use weaker bases to remove a proton from 2- and 4-alkylpyridines than we can with alkylbenzenes. The conjugate bases produced from the alkyl pyridines function as efficient carbon nucleophiles in a variety of reactions. For example, it is possible to effect alkylation as illustrated in Equation 27.9.

Eqn. 27.9

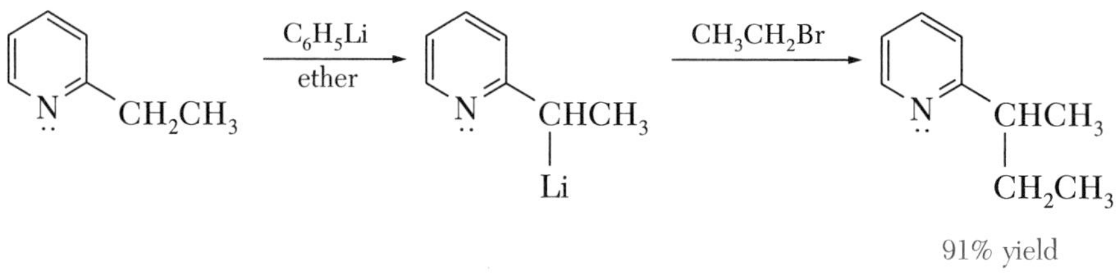

C_6H_5Li, ether; CH_3CH_2Br

91% yield

We also find that 2- and 4-methylpyridines undergo aldol-like condensations with aldehydes, as shown in Equation 27.10.

Eqn. 27.10

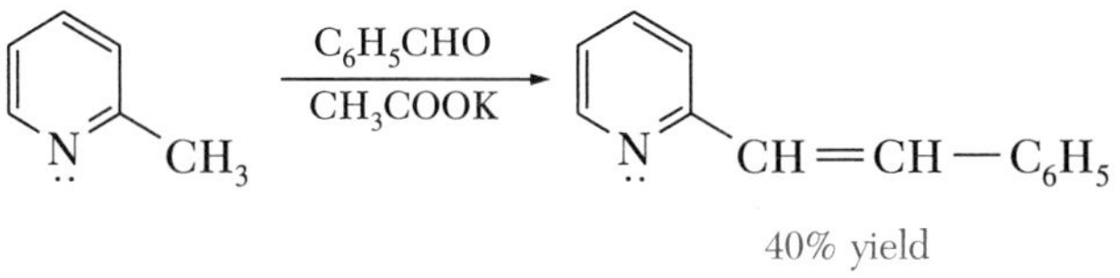

C_6H_5CHO, CH_3COOK; $CH{=}CH{-}C_6H_5$

40% yield

PROBLEM 27.17 Suggest a mechanism for the reaction in Equation 27.10.

PROBLEM 27.18 Starting with 4-methylpyridine and toluene, suggest a synthesis for the compound shown below.

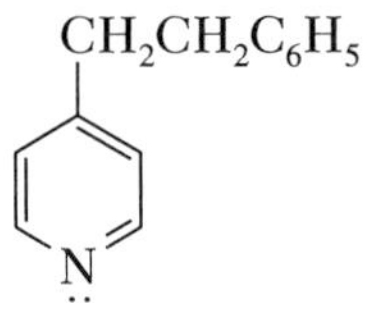

$CH_2CH_2C_6H_5$

27.7 Quinoline, Isoquinoline, and Indole

Quinoline, isoquinoline, and indole are **fused-ring heterocycles** in which a pyridine (in quinoline and isoquinoline) or a pyrrole (in indole) ring is fused to a benzene ring. The chemistry of these substances and their derivatives is a blend of the chemistry of a benzene ring and a heteroaromatic compound. Many derivatives of these fused-ring heterocycles are important natural products or drugs. Several examples are shown in Figure 27.15.

Figure 27.15 Examples of physiologically active derivatives of quinoline, isoquinoline, and indole.

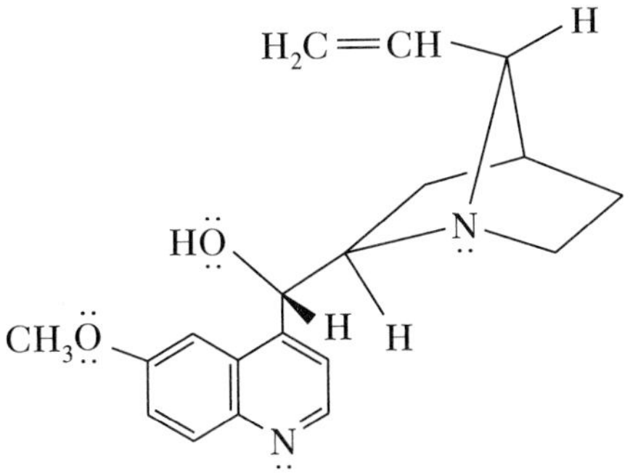

quinine

a quinoline heterocycle from the bark of the *chinchona* tree, used as an antimalarial drug

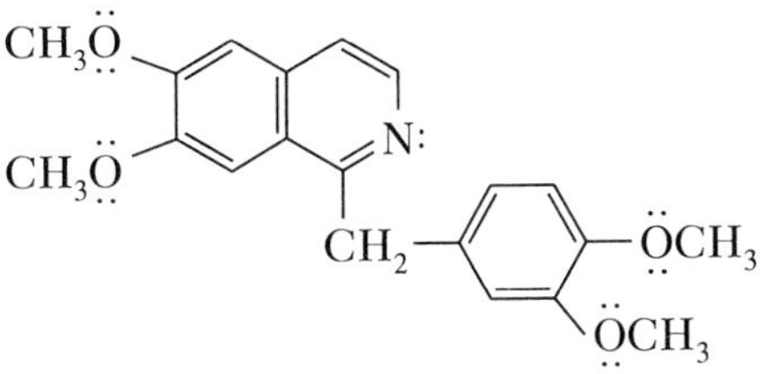

papaverive

an isoquinoline heterocycle from the seeds of *papaver somniferum*, the opium poppy

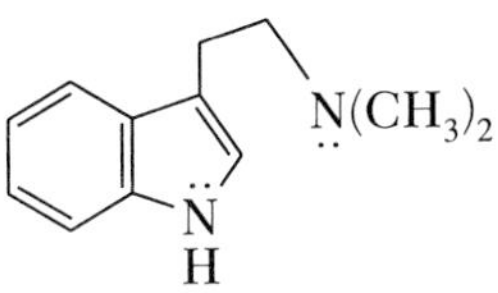

N,N-dimethyltryptamine

an indole heterocycle that acts as a hallucinogen

PREPARATIVE METHODS

Quinolines The **Skraup synthesis** is a general route to quinolines starting from an aromatic amine (aniline or a substituted aniline). In a typical procedure, the aromatic amine is heated with a mixture of glycerol, sulfuric acid, and an oxidizing agent such as nitrobenzene. The synthesis of quinoline using these reagents is shown in Equation 27.11.

Eqn. 27.11

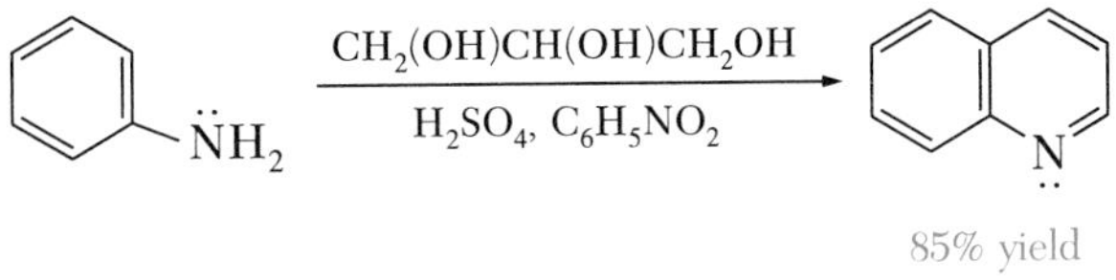

$$C_6H_5NH_2 \xrightarrow[H_2SO_4,\ C_6H_5NO_2]{CH_2(OH)CH(OH)CH_2OH} \text{quinoline}$$

85% yield

The general mechanism of the Skraup synthesis is shown below.

MECHANISM OF REACTION

The Skraup Synthesis

Step 1 Dehydration of glycerol to acrolein

$$CH_2(OH)-CH(OH)-CH_2OH \xrightarrow{H_2SO_4} CH_2{=}CH-C({=}O)-H$$

The details of acid-catalyzed alcohol dehydration have been covered in detail previously. You should write out the individual steps of this overall process as an exercise. Acrolein cannot be used directly as a reagent in the Skraup synthesis because at high concentrations it undergoes polymerization under the reaction conditions and does not lead to quinoline. The acrolein must be generated in situ in low concentration.

Step 2 Conjugate addition of the aromatic amine to the acrolein

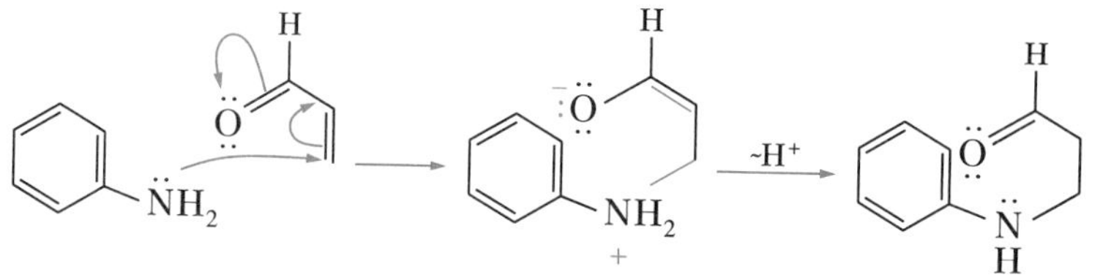

H O NH_2 → H O NH_2 + $\xrightarrow{-H^+}$ H O N H

(Conjugate additions and the subsequent proton transfers were discussed in Chapter 23.)

Step 3 Ring closure through electrophilic aromatic substitution

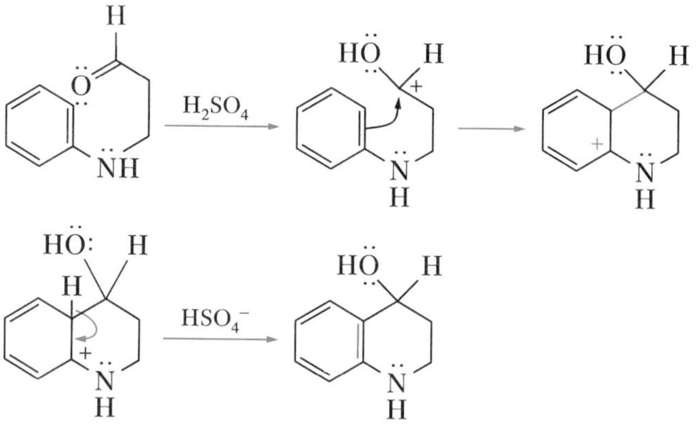

H O NH $\xrightarrow{H_2SO_4}$ HO H + N H → HO H + N H

HO: H H + N H $\xrightarrow{HSO_4^-}$ HO H N H

Step 4 Dehydration

HO H N H $\xrightarrow{H_2SO_4}$ N H + H_2O

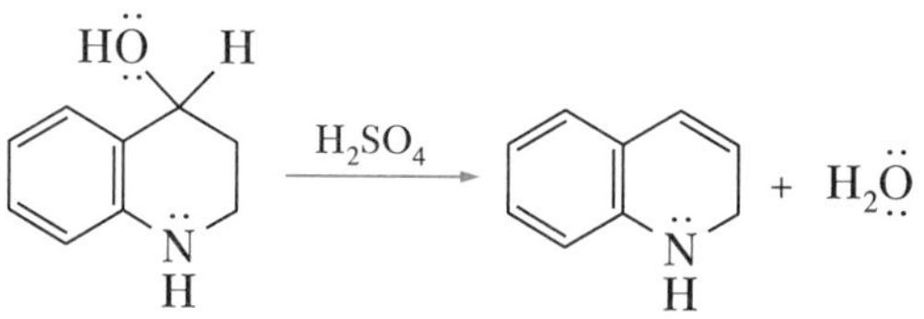

Step 5 Oxidation

N H $\xrightarrow{C_6H_5NO_2}$ N + H_2O + $C_6H_5N{=}O$

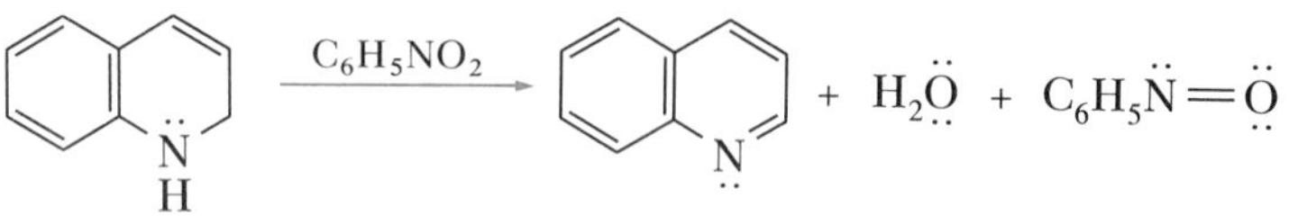

The oxidant illustrated in Step 5 is nitrobenzene—the original reagent used in the Skraup synthesis. An improvement in the reaction procedure uses phosphoric acid (H_3PO_4) to replace the sulfuric acid and the nitrobenzene. Phosphoric acid serves both as the strong acid for the reaction and the oxidizing agent yielding phosphorous acid (H_3PO_3) as the by-product.

Quinolines substituted in the benzene ring portion are available via the Skraup synthesis using appropriately substituted anilines.

PROBLEM 27.19 What substituted anilines would you use to prepare each of the following quinolines using the Skraup synthesis?

a. CH_3, H_3C, N

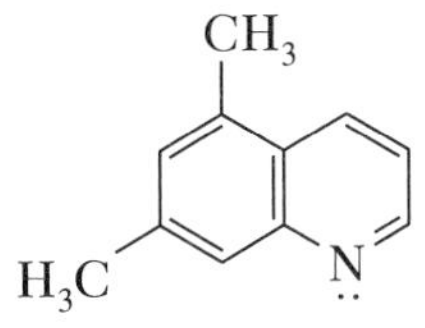

5,7-dimethylquinoline

b. $CH_3\ddot{O}$, N, NO_2

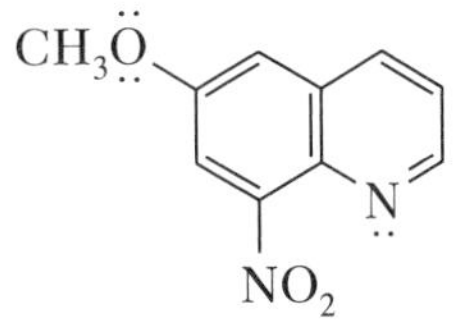

6-methoxy-8-nitroquinoline

Isoquinolines The **Bischler-Napieralksi synthesis** is a general route to isoquinolines. A phenylethylamine reacts with a carboxylic acid halide to form an amide, which is cyclyzed, with loss of water, to form a 3,4-dihydroxyquinoline. Aromatization is effected with Pd/C. The preparation of 1-methylisoquinoline using this method is illustrated in Figure 27.16.

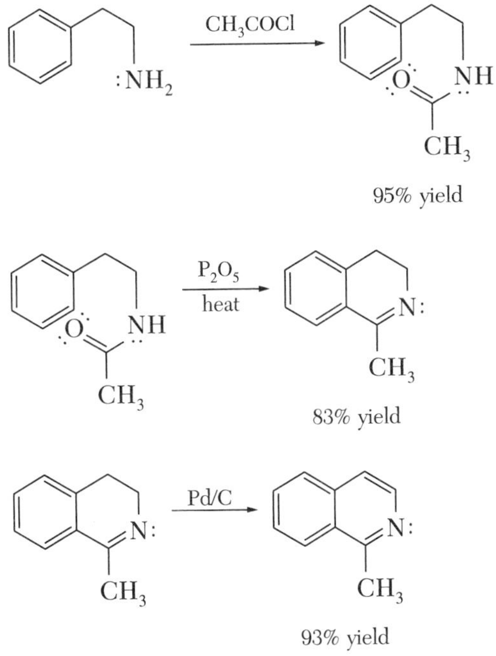

Figure 27.16 Preparation of 1-methylisoquinoline using the Bischer-Napieralski method. The overall route produces 1-methylisoquinoline in 73% yield.

:NH_2 → (CH_3COCl) → $\ddot{O}$, NH, CH_3

95% yield

$\ddot{O}$, NH, CH_3 → (P_2O_5, heat) → N:, CH_3

83% yield

N:, CH_3 → (Pd/C) → N:, CH_3

93% yield

Indoles The parent material indole (Figure 27.2) is found in jasmine and orange-blossom oils and can be isolated along with some of its derivatives from coal tar. The most important general method for the preparation of indole derivatives (but not indole itself) is the **Fischer indole synthesis.** The process involves heating the phenylhydrazone derivative of an aldehyde, ketone, or ketoacid with an acid catalyst such as polyphosphoric acid, zinc chloride, or boron trifluoride etherate. The preparation of two substituted indoles using this approach is shown in Equations 27.12 and 27.13.

Eqn. 27.12

H_3C C_6H_5 N: NH —polyphosphoric acid, 100 °C→ indole with C_6H_5, N H

75% yield

Eqn. 27.13

$CH_3CH_2CH_2$ CH_3 N: NH —CuCl 200 – 250 °C→ indole with $CH_2CH_2CH_3$, CH_3, N H

PROBLEM 27.20 How would you prepare the starting materials for the reactions shown in Equations 27.12 and 27.13?

The conversion of a phenylhydrazone to an indole follows the mechanistic steps as shown below.

MECHANISM OF REACTION

Conversion of a Phenylhydrazone to an Indole

Step 1 Protonation and tautomerization of the phenylhydrazone.

R CH_3 N: N H ⇌(acid) R CH_3 N: $\overset{+}{N}$ H H ⇌ R CH_2 NH $\overset{+}{N}$ H H

This step requires the presence of at least one α-hydrogen atom in the original carbonyl compound and its phenylhydrazone derivative.

Step 2 Electrocyclic rearrangement. (The nature of this type of rearrangement will be discussed in Chapter 30.)

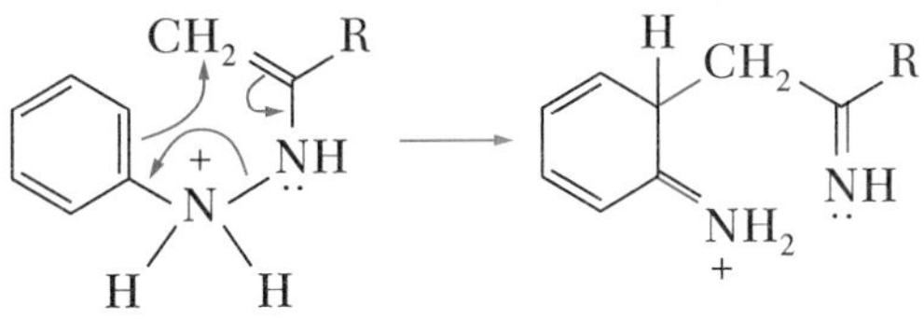

Step 3 Proton loss and aromatization. Any base present in the system (e.g., the conjugate base of the acid used) can remove the proton from the ring.

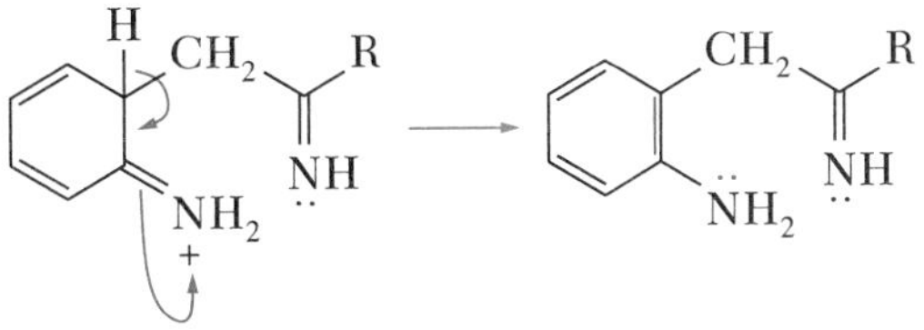

Step 4 Protonation and nucleophilic addition.

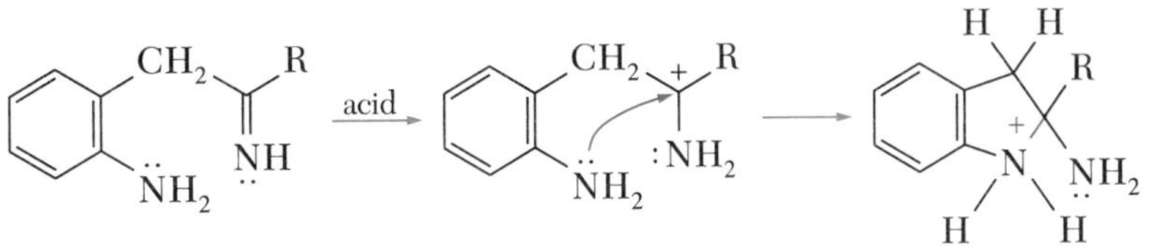

Step 5 Tautomerization and loss of ammonia. Again, any base present in the system can cause the elimination of ammonia to occur. Note that the completion of this step requires the presence of a *second* α-hydrogen in the original carbonyl compound and its phenylhydrazone derivative.

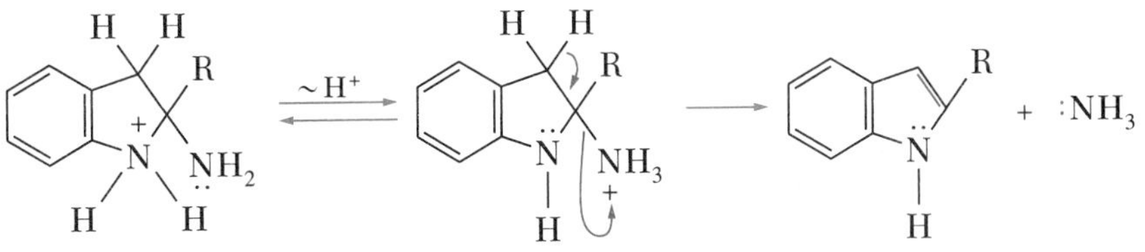

REACTIONS

Quinoline, isoquinoline, and indole all undergo electrophilic aromatic substitution reactions. With quinoline and isoquinoline, reaction occurs principally in the benzene ring, as is illustrated in Figure 27.17. This result is understandable because benzene is more reactive toward electrophiles than is pyridine.

Indole, on the other hand, undergoes electrophilic aromatic substitution principally in the heterocyclic portion of the molecule. This result is consistent with the greater reactivity of pyrrole compared to benzene in such reactions. An example is shown in Equation 27.14.

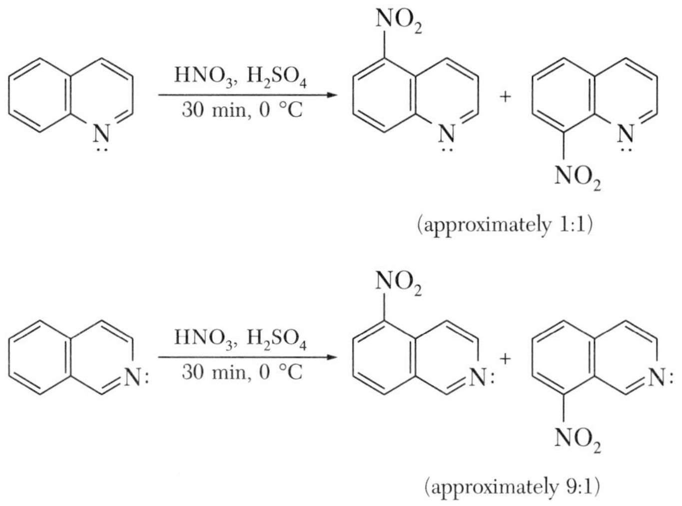

Figure 27.17 Electrophilic aromatic substitution in quinoline and isoquinoline. Reaction occurs principally in the benzene ring portion of the molecule.

HNO_3, H_2SO_4
30 min, 0 °C

NO_2 + NO_2

(approximately 1:1)

HNO_3, H_2SO_4
30 min, 0 °C

NO_2 + NO_2

(approximately 9:1)

Eqn. 27.14

benzoyl nitrate
acetonitrile, 0 °C

NO_2

35% yield

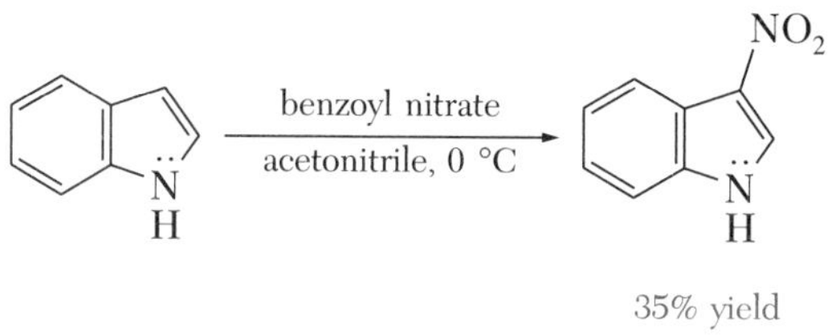

PROBLEM 27.21 Predict the relative reactivities of quinoline and indole to electrophilic aromatic substitution of bromine.

PROBLEM 27.22 Use resonance structures to account for the fact that indole undergoes electrophilic aromatic substitution principally in the 3-position, in contrast to pyrrole, which reacts chiefly at the 2-position.

Summary

- Nonaromatic heterocycles can usually be prepared from difunctional open-chain compounds. The functional group containing the desired heteroatom generally acts as a nucleophilic site and attacks the second functional group (such as a halogen), which serves as a leaving group in a nucleophilic substitution reaction.
- The reactions of nonaromatic heterocycles are generally similar to those of their open-chain counterparts. Special reactivity is observed if there is strain in the ring, as with an epoxide. This strain results in facile ring-opening reactions.
- The most common heteroaromatics are those containing the heteroatom in a five- or six-membered ring. The five-membered ring compounds are generally more reactive than benzene to electrophilic aromatic substitution, and reaction occurs principally at the α-carbon site. The six-membered heteroaromatics are less reactive than benzene toward electrophilic aromatic substitution, and substitution occurs principally at the β-carbon site of the ring.
- The regioselectivity of these reactions can be understood by considering the resonance structures for the

cationic intermediates formed in the electrophilic addition.

- Nucleophilic displacement reactions are observed to occur at the α- and γ-positions of pyridine rings. Not only can halogen be substituted at these positions, but so can hydrogen under suitable conditions. The most important example of hydrogen substitution in such systems is the Tschichibabin reaction in which a pyridine compound is heated with sodium amide to yield an aminopyridine.
- Fused-ring heterocycles contain a heteroaromatic ring fused to another ring, generally a benzene ring. The properties of such compounds are a blend of the properties of those two ring systems.

Terms to Remember

heterocycle
heteroatom
heteroaromatic
pentosan
Tschichibabin reaction
N-oxide
fused-ring heterocycle
Skraup synthesis
Bischler-Napieralski synthesis
Fischer indole synthesis

Reactions of Synthetic Utility

208. pyridine (N) $\xrightarrow[\text{2. } H_2O]{\text{1. } NaNH_2}$ 2-aminopyridine (N, NH_2) **27.4**

209. pyridine (N) $\xrightarrow{H_2O_2}$ pyridine N-oxide (N^+—O^-) **27.6**

210. aniline (NH_2) $\xrightarrow[H_3PO_4]{\text{glycerol}}$ quinoline (N) **27.7**

211. phenylhydrazone (NH—N=C(R′)CH_2R) $\xrightarrow{\text{acid}}$ indole (3-R, 2-R′, N—H) **27.8**

Additional Problems

27.23 Draw structures for each of the following compounds:

a. 1,2-diisobutylaziridine
b. 2,5-diphenylpyridine
c. 5-chloroindole
d. 6-chloro-2-methylquinoline
e. 3-acetyl-2,5-dimethylthiophene
f. 1-(4-chlorophenyl)pyrrole
g. 2-methyl-5-(4-methoxyphenyl)thiophene
h. 4-chloromethylpyridine

i. 2-chloro-4,6-dimethyl-3-cyanopyridine j. 4-chloropyridine hydrochloride
k. 4-chloroquinoline-*N*-oxide

27.24 Provide names for each of the following structures:

a. N, NH_2

b. S, $CHCH_2CH_3$, CH_3

c. O_2N, NO_2, N, Cl:

d.

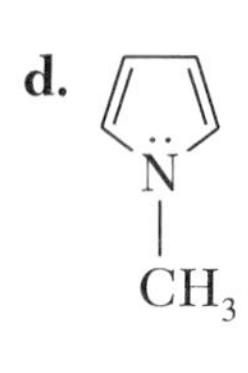

e. N, :OCH_3

f. $CH_2CH(CH_3)_2$, N, H

g. :O:, CH_3, CH_3

h. N, CH_2CH_3

i. :Cl:, :Br:, O

27.25 From each of the following pairs, choose the compound that exhibits the indicated property and explain your choice.

a. more reactive toward bromine: pyridine or pyrrole
b. more basic: pyridine or pyrrole
c. more acidic: pyrrole or imidazole
d. more basic: pyridine or 3-nitropyridine
e. undergoes electrophilic aromatic substitution reactions on the benzene ring portion: quinoline or indole
f. undergoes electrophilic aromatic substitution reactions more readily: furan or 2-furoic acid
g. more reactive toward dienophiles: furan or thiophene
h. more reactive toward nucleophiles: 2-chloropyridine or 2-chloropyrrole
i. more reactive toward nucleophiles: 3-chloropyridine or 4-chloropyridine
j. undergoes more rapid condensation reaction with benzaldehyde under basic conditions to give a compound of formula $C_{13}H_{11}N$: 2-picoline or 3-picoline
k. reacts with sodium amide to form a primary amine: pyridine or pyrrole
l. is the stronger acid:

$\overset{+}{N}H$, N, H or $\overset{+}{N}H$, O

m. fails to form a quaternary ammonium salt on treatment with excess iodomethane: pyridine or pyrrole

27.26 Provide structures for the organic products of each of the following reactions.

a. thiophene treated with bromine and ferric bromide to yield a compound of formula C_4H_3BrS
b. the product of reaction **a** in reaction with magnesium followed by treatment with carbon dioxide and workup with aqueous acid
c. pyridine in reaction with a mixture of fuming nitric and sulfuric acids
d. pyridine treated with hydrogen peroxide in acetic acid
e. the product of reaction **c** treated with a mixture of concentrated nitric and sulfuric acids

f. the product of reaction **d** treated with phosphorus trichloride
g. pyridine treated with iodomethane
h. 4-picoline treated with hot, aqueous alkaline potassium permanganate and worked up with aqueous acid
i. 4-penten-1-ol treated with mercuric acetate in water followed by sodium borohydride to yield a cyclic ether of formula $C_5H_{10}O$
j. pyridine treated with phenyllithium
k. pyrrolidine treated with acetic anhydride
l. furfural treated with propanone in the presence of base
m. pyridine treated with benzyl chloride
n. 2,5-diethylfuran treated with sulfuric acid and water to yield a compound of formula $C_8H_{14}O_2$
o. 3-aminopyridine treated with glycerol in the presence of phosphoric acid

27.27 When 3,4-dimethylpyridine is treated with one equivalent amount of butyllithium followed by iodomethane, a product of formula $C_8H_{11}N$ is formed. Give a structure for this product.

27.28 There exists a tautomeric equilibrium between 2-pyridone and 2-hydroxypyridine as shown below.

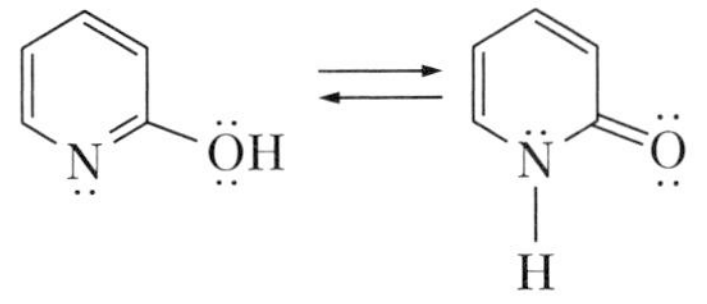

N ÖH ⇌ N O H

Would you anticipate that a similar equilibrium would exist for 3-hydroxypyridine? Explain why or why not.

27.29 Give synthetic procedures for the preparation of each of the following, starting with benzene or simple derivatives of benzene.
a. 1-benzylisoquinoline
b. 6-quinolinecarboxylic acid
c. 5-methoxy-4,7-phenanthroline (shown below)

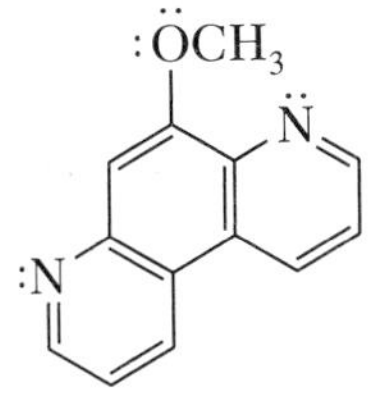

:ÖCH$_3$ N :N

27.30 Each of the following compounds is an important analytical reagent. Give reaction sequences for their preparation starting with the indicated materials.
a. 8-hydroxyquinoline from a disubstituted benzene derivative using a Skraup synthesis
b. 1,10-phenanthroline (structure given below), starting with a disubstituted benzene derivative and using a Skraup synthesis
c. 4-(2-pyridylazo) resorcinol (structure given below), starting with a monosubstituted pyridine and a disubstituted benzene derivative and using a diazo coupling reaction

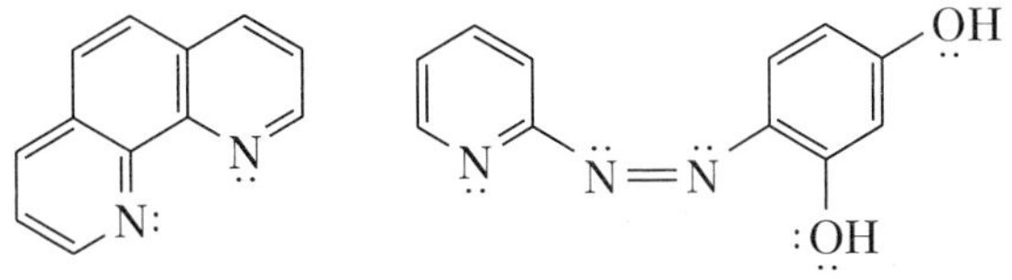

N N: N N=N ÖH :OH

1,10-phenanthroline 4-(2-pyridylazo)resorcinol

27.31 Tell how each of the following synthetic conversions could be accomplished.

a. CH_3 → CH_2OH

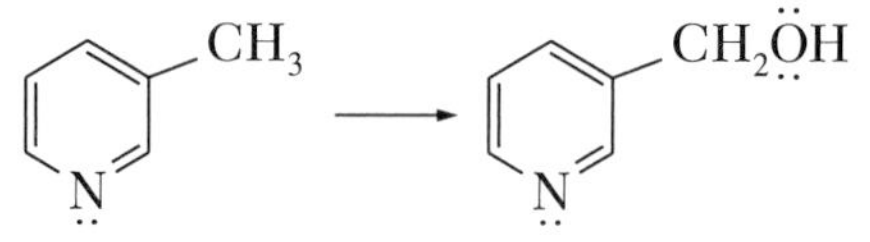

b. N → NHC—CH_3 (:O:)

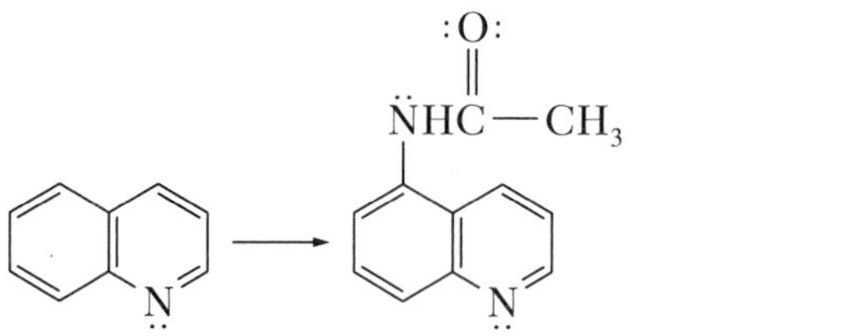

c. CH_3 → NO_2, COOH (N)

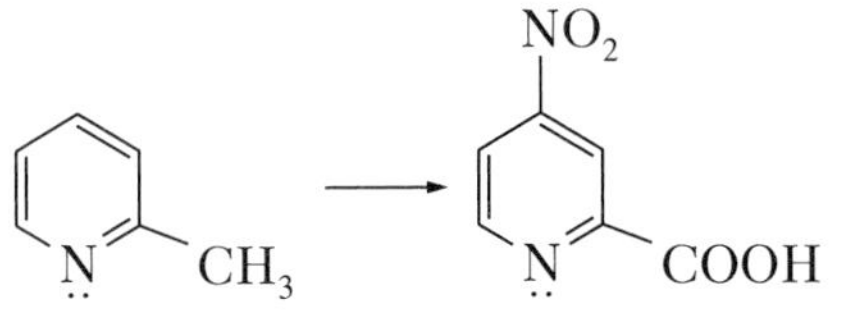

d. CHO → C—OCH_2CH_3 (:O:)

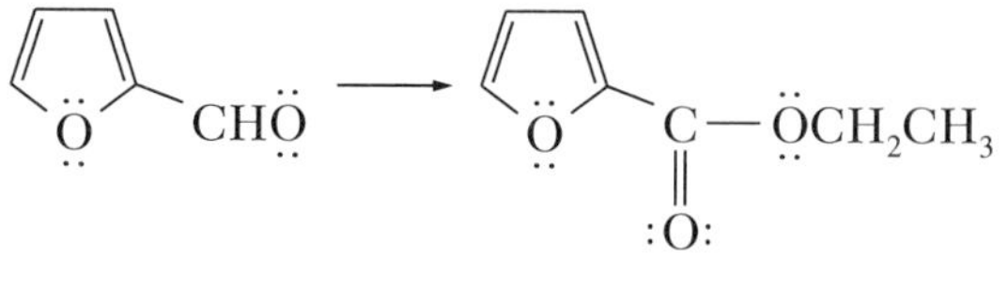

e. CHO → CH=CH—C—CH_3 (:O:)

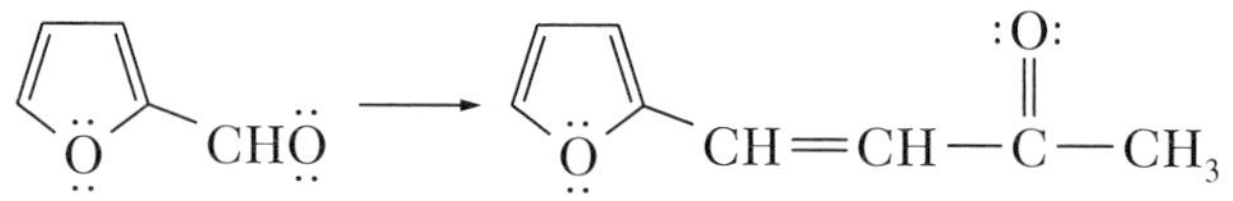

f. COOH → $N(CH_3)_2$ (S)

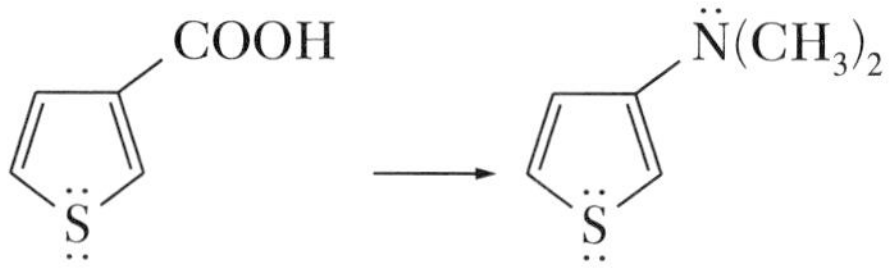

27.32 Consider the synthetic route shown below for the preparation of the unsaturated lactone *D*. Give the structures of compounds *A*, *B*, and *C*.

$$H{-}C{\equiv}C{-}CO_2H + 2\text{ equiv LiN}[CH(CH_3)_2]_2 \longrightarrow A$$

$C_3O_2Li_2$

A —(1. :O: epoxide, CH_3 CH_3; 2. aq acid)→ *B* —(H_2, Pd/$BaSO_4$)→ *C* —(aq acid)→ *D* (H_3C, H_3C)

B: $C_7H_{10}O_3$
broad IR absorption
in the range 2500 – 3500 cm^{-1}

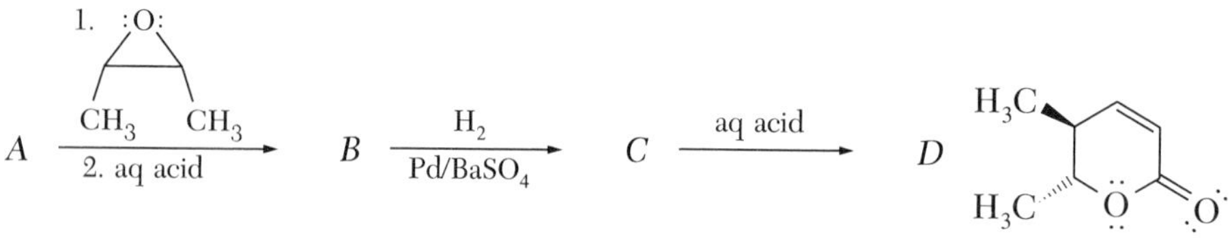

27.33 Suggest mechanisms for each of the following conversions.

a. :O: —(aq acid)→ :O:

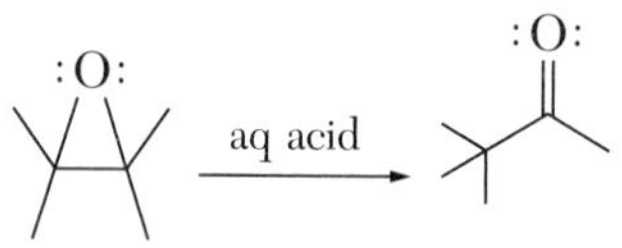

b. S —($H_2C{=}O$, HCl)→ S, CH_2OH

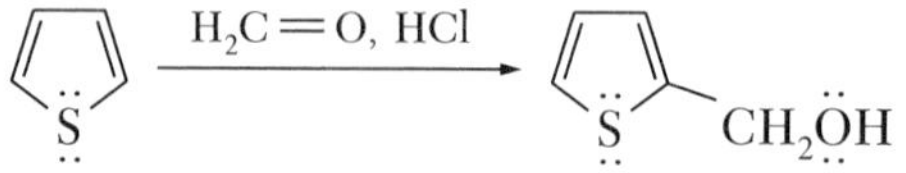

c. $(C_6H_5)_2C$—CO_2H, CH_2Cl: —(NaOH, H_2O)→ C_6H_5, C_6H_5, :O:, O:

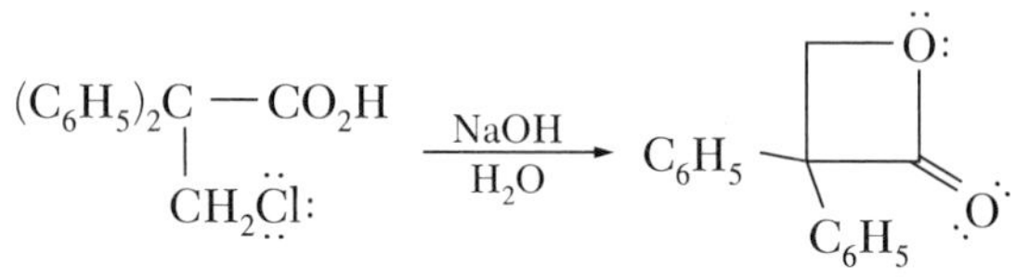

d.

$H_2NCH_2CH_2NH_2$, acid

e.

CH_3CO_2H, aq dioxane; $H_2\ddot{N}-\ddot{N}H_2$

f.

$CH_3O_2C-C\equiv C-CO_2CH_3$ ... $+ CH_3C\equiv N:$

g.

NaOH, H_2O, heat

h.

heat

28 CHAPTER Nucleosides, Nucleotides, and Nucleic Acids

28.1 Introduction

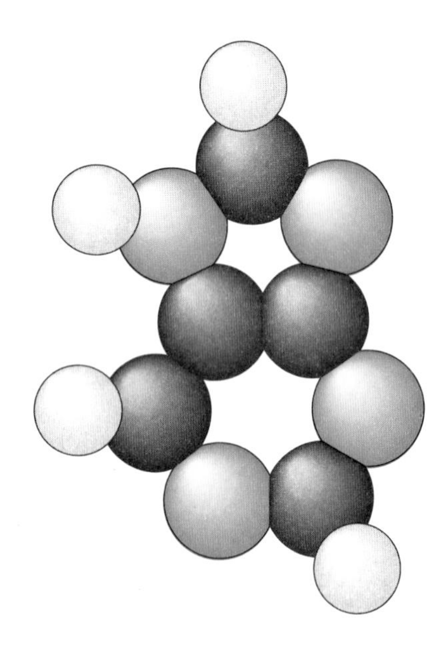

In 1869, Friederich Miescher isolated a phosphorus-containing compound from the nuclei of white blood cells. Later it was discovered that similar phosphorus-containing compounds could be isolated from the nuclei of all cells. Because these compounds were acidic, the term **nucleic acid** was coined for them, although their structure was not known at the time.

In spite of their early discovery (early considering the total time span of the systematic study of organic and biological chemistry), it is only in recent years that the role and even the molecular structures of nucleic acids have been uncovered. In 1944, Oswald T. Avery obtained data that implicated nucleic acids as the carriers of genetic information. In 1953, Francis Crick and James Watson (Nobel Prize winners in 1962) elucidated the three-dimensional structure of **deoxyribonucleic acid (DNA),** one structural type of nucleic acid. Their work led to an understanding of the mechanism by which genetic information is copied and marked the beginning of modern molecular biology.

In 1957, a specific cellular function was found for another structural type of nucleic acid, **ribonucleic acid (RNA).** RNA was found to play pivotal roles in the synthesis of enzymes, complex proteins that are the catalysts of chemical reactions in living systems (Chapter 26). It is the different collections of enzymes in different living species that account for variations within species and from species to species. Nucleic acids, which direct and facilitate enzyme synthesis, are passed from generation to generation in the reproductive process and account for hereditary similarities. Nucleic acids determine which amino acids are to be assembled to make the enzyme molecules and in which order they are to be assembled.

The chemical instructions for the assembly of the enzymes are contained in the sequence of subunits of nucleic acids. Just as the sequence of statements in a computer program determines the order in which a series of computational processes is performed, the sequence of subunits in a nucleic acid determines the order in which amino acids are assembled into enzymes. Different living species and different members of the same species have different sets of nucleic acids, which account not only for the different natures of various species but also for the unique nature of each individual within a species. Furthermore, each cell of each individual carries the nucleic acid to direct the synthesis of all of the particular enzymes of that individual.

A first step toward understanding the nature of nucleic acids and their biological role is to consider the structural components of these large molecules. We will do so in light of our earlier discussions of carbohydrates, esters, and heterocyclic compounds.

28.2 Nucleic Acid Structure

The structures of nucleic acids are best appreciated by first focusing on their components. Nucleic acids consist of individual units known as **nucleosides,** which are joined to each other through phosphate diester linkages (Chapter 6). Individual nucleosides differ in the identity of their carbohydrate and heterocyclic portions. A specific nucleic acid molecule is defined by the identity of the carbohydrate that all of its nucleoside units contain and by the sequence of nitrogenous heterocyclic portions along its linear chain.

NUCLEOSIDES

General Structure A nucleoside consists of two parts—a carbohydrate and a nitrogenous heterocycle usually referred to as a "base." The anomeric position (see Section 24.3) of the carbohydrate is linked to a nitrogen atom of the heterocyclic base. The nucleoside molecule is therefore a type of acetal in which one of the two electronegative atoms bound to the anomeric carbon is nitrogen and the other is oxygen (see Figure 28.1).

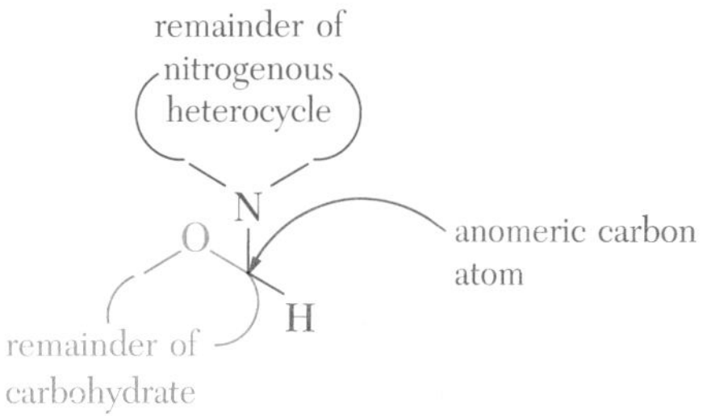

remainder of nitrogenous heterocycle
N
O
H
anomeric carbon atom
remainder of carbohydrate

Figure 28.1 General structure of a nucleoside. The nitrogenous heterocycle is bound through a nitrogen atom to the anomeric carbon atom of the carbohydrate portion of the molecule.

The Carbohydrate Portion of Nucleosides The carbohydrate portion of nucleosides is usually derived from one of two carbohydrates—D-ribose (**28.1**) or D-2-deoxyribose (**28.2**). Within a particular nucleic acid molecule, all of the nucleoside components contain the same carbohydrate portion. If the nucleic acid contains only D-ribose, it is classified as a ribonucleic acid (RNA), and if it contains only D-2-deoxyribose, it is classified as a deoxyribonucleic acid (DNA).

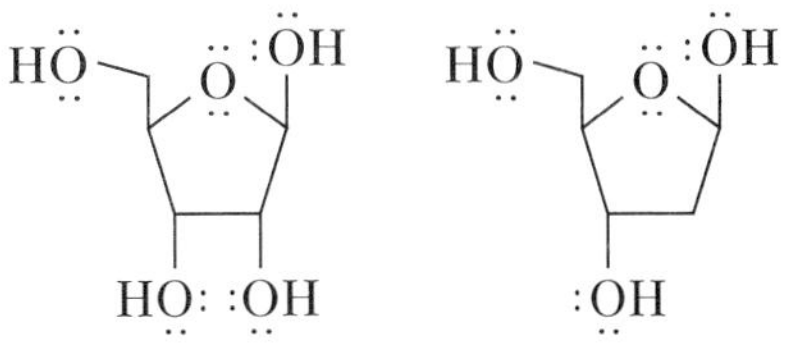

HO O :OH HO: :OH
D-ribose
28.1

HO O :OH :OH
D-2-deoxyribose
28.2

PROBLEM 28.1 Do the structures shown for D-ribose and D-2-deoxyribose represent α- or β-anomeric forms of the compounds? (Refer to Chapter 23.)

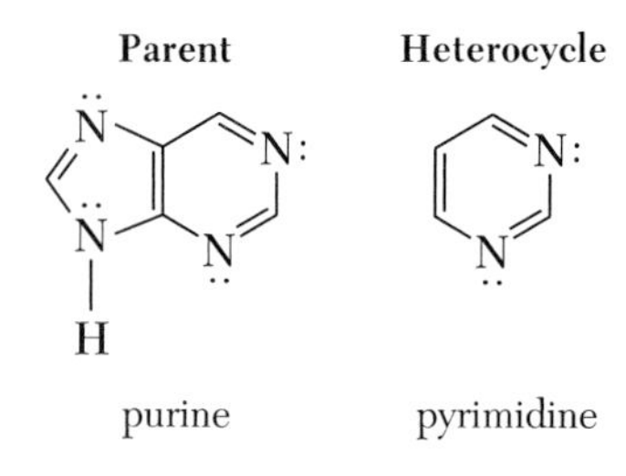

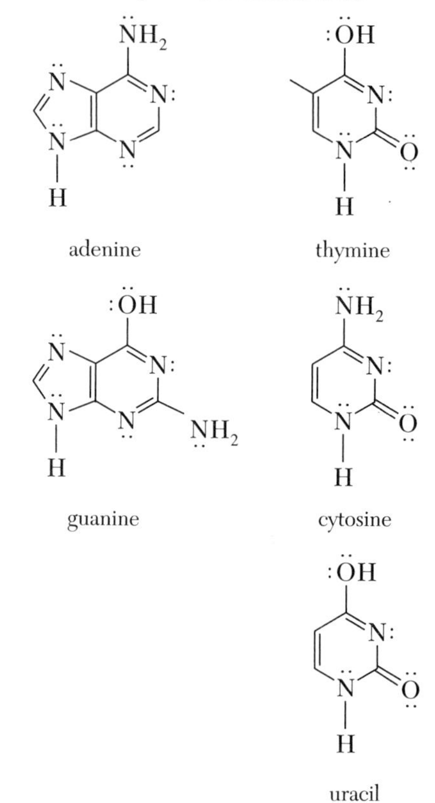

Figure 28.2 The nitrogenous heterocycles found in nucleic acids. The parent heterocycles **purine** and **pyrimidine** are shown at the top. There are two purines found in nucleic acids, adenine and guanine. In ribonucleic acids (RNA) the two pyrimidine bases are cytosine and uracil, but in deoxyribonucleic acids (DNA) cytosine and thymine are found.

The Base Portion of Nucleosides The five nitrogenous heterocycles commonly found in the nucleosides of nucleic acids are shown in Figure 28.2.

In nucleosides, these nitrogenous heterocycles are bound to the anomeric carbon atom (carbon 1) of the carbohydrate component. Several examples of naturally occurring nucleosides are shown in Figure 28.3.

PROBLEM 28.2 Using the nitrogenous heterocycle component structures shown in Figure 28.2, draw the structures for each of the following nucleosides:

a. D-2′-deoxycytidine **b.** D-2′-deoxyguanosine
c. uridine **d.** adenosine

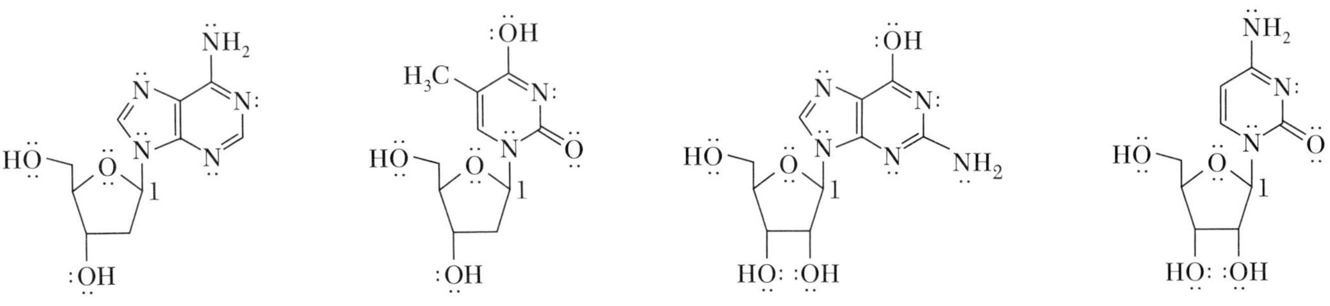

deoxyadenosine deoxythymidine guanosine cytidine

Figure 28.3 Naturally occurring nucleosides in the D-2-deoxyribose and D-ribose series.

NUCLEOTIDES

A **nucleotide** is a nucleoside in which one (or more) of the hydroxyl oxygen atoms of the carbohydrate is bound in a phosphate ester linkage. Several examples of nucleotides and their names are shown in Figure 28.4.

The numbering of positions within nucleosides and nucleotides requires some clarification. Two series of numbers are used. The positions within the nitrogenous heterocycle are numbered consecutively as indicated in Figure 28.5. The positions in the carbohydrate portion are also numbered consecutively, starting at the anomeric carbon site, but these numbers are supplemented with a prime symbol (′).

Figure 28.4 Representative examples of nucleotides. Nucleotides are named as phosphate esters of the corresponding nucleosides. At times the 5′-nucleoside monophosphates are named as *-ylic acids*, for example, AMP is adenylic acid.

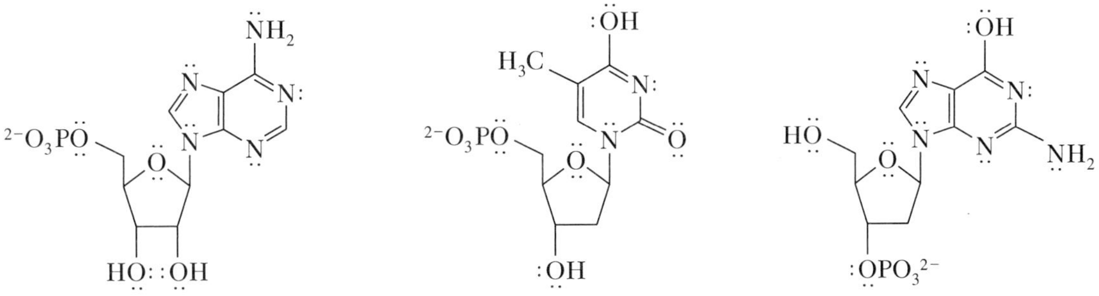

adenosine-5′-monophosphate (AMP) deoxythymidine-5′-monophosphate (dTMP) deoxyguanosine-3′-monophosphate

Figure 28.5 Numbering of the positions of the nitrogenous heterocycle and carbohydrate portions of nucleosides and nucleotides.

purines **pyrimidines** **carbohydrate components**

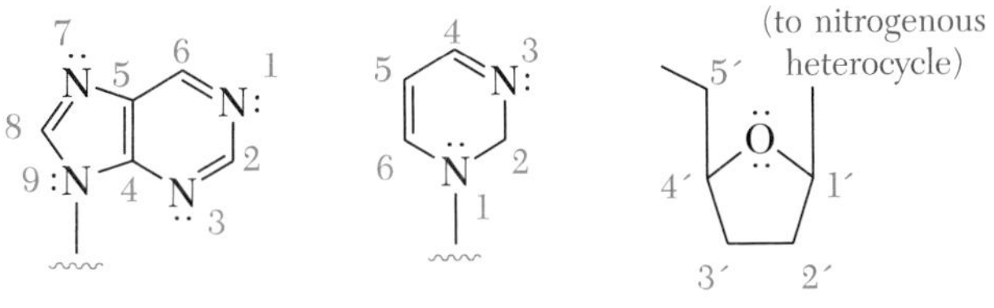

(to nitrogenous heterocycle)

PROBLEM 28.3 Draw the structure of each of the following:

a. uridine-3′-monophosphate
b. adenosine-3′,5′-diphosphate
c. 5-chlorouridine-5′-monophosphate

NUCLEIC ACIDS

Nucleic acids are composed of nucleosides joined to each other by phosphate diester linkages. These linkages are commonly found between the 5′-position of one nucleoside and the 3′-position of another. If the number of nucleoside units coupled in this way is relatively small, we generally refer to the molecule as an **oligonucleotide.** A molecule containing a larger number of linked nucleoside units is called a nucleic acid or a **polynucleotide.** The structure of a simple trinucleotide (three nucleoside units coupled by two phosphate diester linkages) is shown in Figure 28.6.

The names of oligonucleotides like the one shown in Figure 28.6 use the name of each of the component nucleosides in order, starting from the end of the chain having the unesterified 5′-hydroxyl group (the top, as shown in Figure 28.6). To these names we add a notation indicating the ring positions that are joined by the phosphate diester linkages. The name for the structure shown in Figure 28.6 is thus adenylyl(3′ → 5′)adenylyl(3′ → 5′)adenosine. For simplicity, biochemists often abbreviate the name of such a nucleotide as

Figure 28.6 The structure of a trinucleotide composed of three adenosine units joined by two phosphate diester linkages.

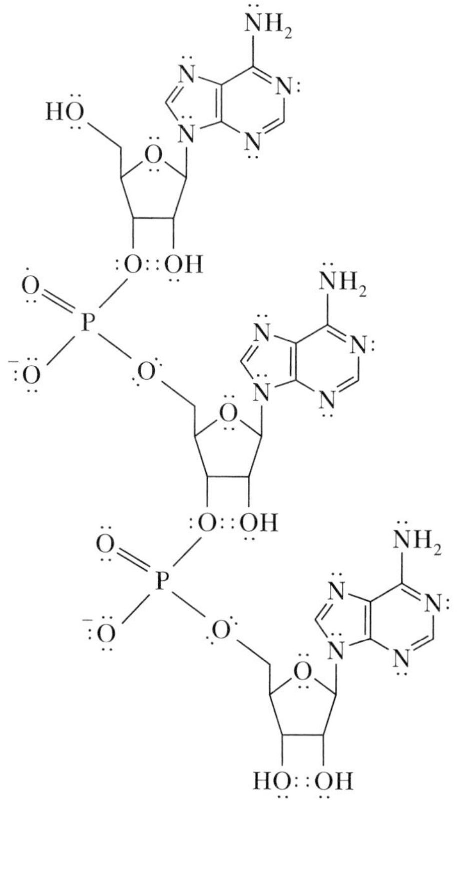

ApApA, where the symbol A represents the adenosine nucleoside and the symbol p indicates a phosphate diester linkage between the 3′-position of one nucleoside and the 5′-position of another.

PROBLEM 28.4 Draw the complete structure of each of the following oligonucleotides:

a. adenylyl(3′ → 5′)cytidylyl(3′ → 5′)uridine
b. uridylyl(3′ → 5′)guanylyl(3′ → 5′)adenosine
c. deoxythymidylyl(3′ → 5′)deoxyadenylyl(3′ → 5′)deoxyuridine
d. uridylyl(2′ → 5′)adenosine

PROBLEM 28.5 Name each of the following oligonucleotides:

a.

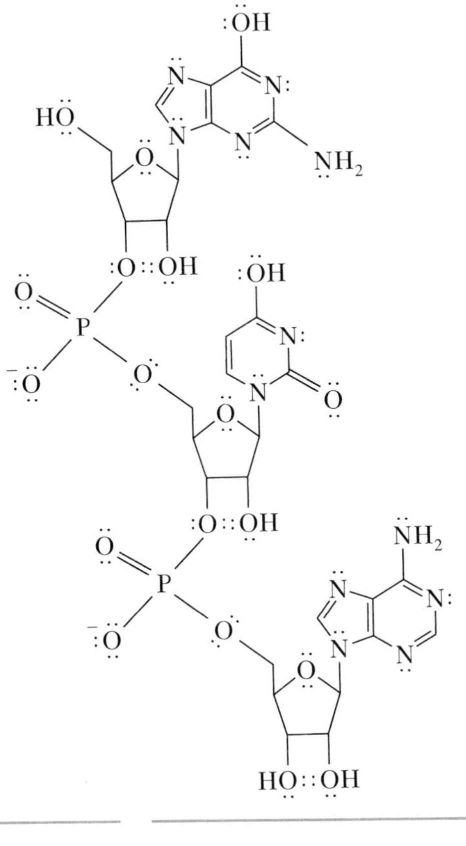

b.

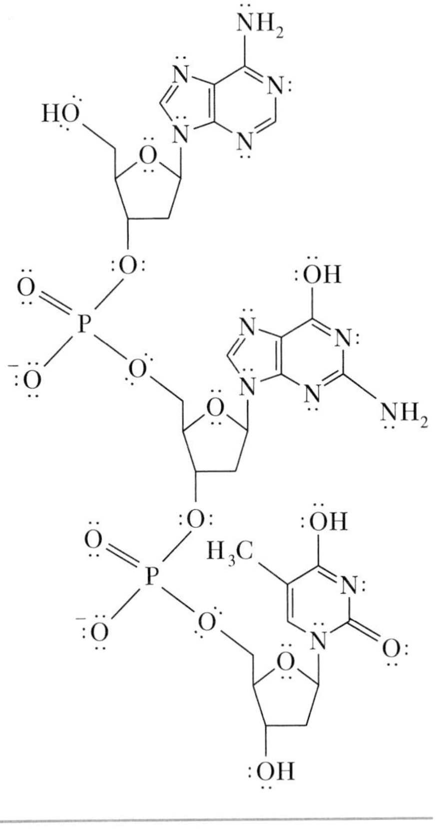

A nucleic acid (polynucleotide) in which all constituent nitrogenous heterocyclic components are the same is given a simplified name. For example, a ribonucleic acid bearing only adenine bases is called *polyadenylic acid* and abbreviated as $(Ap)_n$.

28.3 Nucleic Acid Function

DNA

General Function The biological function of DNA is to serve as the repository of genetic information for organisms. The structure of the DNA—the particular sequence of nitrogenous heterocycles along the DNA chain—constitutes this

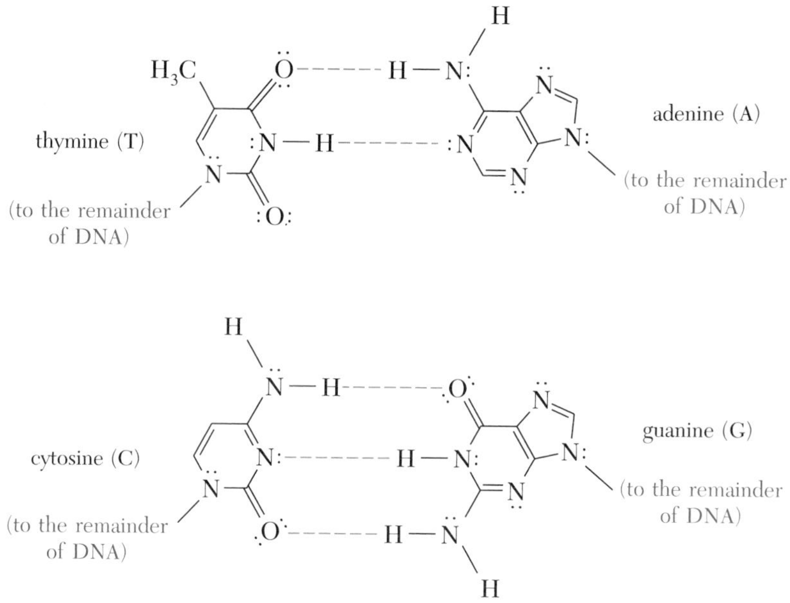

Figure 28.7 Hydrogen bonding between nitrogenous heterocycles of strands of DNA. This hydrogen bonding holds together complementary strands of DNA.

genetic information. All of the enzymes, the protein catalysts for biological processes (Chapter 26), that are present in an organism and allow it to perform its required metabolic processes are synthesized because the organism's DNA has a particular structure. The DNA of a given organism provides it with its biochemical uniqueness.

Double-Stranded Structure An important structural feature of DNA is that it is *double stranded.* Two chains of DNA bind to each other through hydrogen bonding (Chapter 3). The two strands are *complementary*—the sequence of nitrogenous heterocycles of one chain is matched by its sequence of hydrogen-bonding partners on the associated chain. Thymine (T) hydrogen bonds with adenine (A), and cytosine (C) hydrogen bonds with guanine (G). These hydrogen-bonded pairings are shown in Figure 28.7.

For a particular sequence of nitrogenous heterocycles in one strand of DNA (the *coding strand*), a complementary sequence exists along the second strand (the *template strand*), as is illustrated schematically in Figure 28.8, where the single-letter abbreviations for each of the bases are used.

Figure 28.8 is only a schematic illustration. It shows only the sequence of nitrogenous heterocycles along each chain and their particular associations. It does not show all the details of molecular structure, such as the carbohydrate and phosphate diester portions, nor does it show the conformation of the chains. The chain conformation is a point of particular importance.

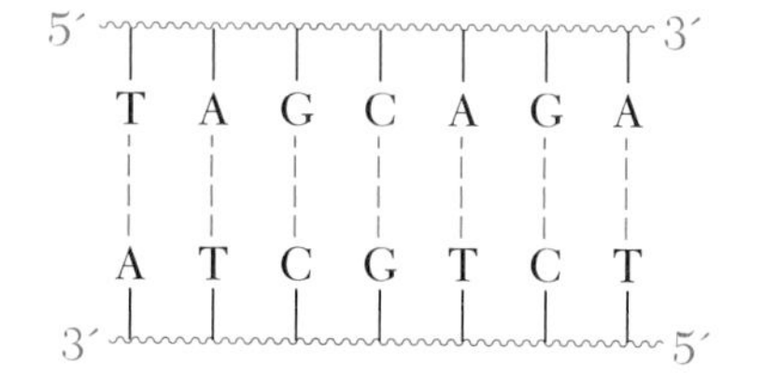

Figure 28.8 Complementary strands of DNA. The strand shown at the top (the coding strand), beginning with the free 5′-position at the left, has its complement (the template strand) in the strand shown at the bottom, whose free 5′-position is at the right.

PROBLEM 28.6 Give the complementary sequence for each of the following DNA base sequences:

a. GCAATGC **b.** CGTTATAG

Rather than lying beside each other linearly, as Figure 28.8 might seem to imply, the coding and template strands are arranged in a *double-helical* conformation, with both chains twisting about a common axis. The nitrogenous bases are directed inward along the double helix to allow hydrogen bonding between the chains, with the carbohydrate and phosphodiester portions directed toward the outside. The helix makes a complete turn every ten hydrogen-bonded **base pairs** along the chains. A model of the double-helical structure is shown in Figure 28.9.

Key:

Dark grey = Carbon
White = Hydrogen
Orange = Oxygen
Blue = Nitrogen
Green = Phosphorous

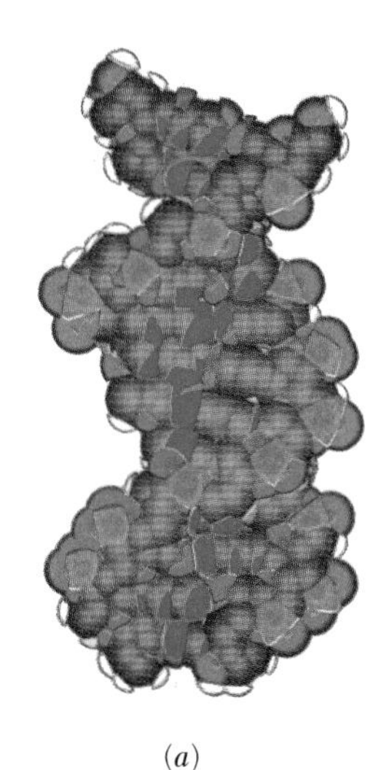

(*a*)

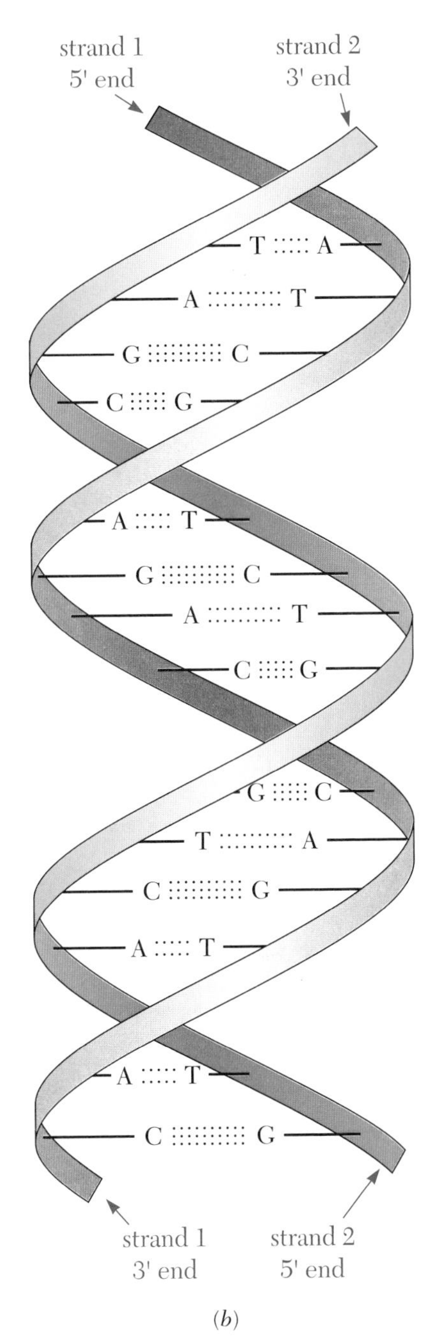

(*b*)

Figure 28.9 The double helical structure of DNA. (a) Space-filling model. Hydrogen bonds exist between complementary bases on the two helices. *Note*: Many hydrogen atoms have been deleted for simplicity. (b) Simplified version emphasizing the hydrogen bonds between complementary bases.

The double-stranded nature of DNA was deduced in 1953 by James Watson and Francis Crick, using X-ray diffraction photographs measured by Rosalind Franklin and Maurice Wilkins. The Nobel Prize was awarded to Watson and Crick in 1962 for their accomplishment.

The Genetic Code It is the *sequence* of nitrogenous bases along the DNA backbone of the coding strand that provides the instructions for the synthesis of enzymes in an organism. There are only four different nitrogenous bases present in DNA, but there are 20 fundamental α-amino acids in peptides. Thus the specification of an α-amino acid in the construction of an enzyme requires more than the presence of a single nitrogenous base. It has been determined that each of the naturally occurring α-amino acids (see Chapter 26) is specified by one or more **codons** (sequences of three bases) of the DNA. A particular sequence of three nucleosides in the nucleic acid chain specifies a particular α-amino acid to be introduced in the synthesis of enzymes. A particular series of codons thereby specifies a particular sequence of α-amino acids in the enzyme. The tabulation of these codons and the α-amino acids they specify is given in Table 28.1. The elucidation of this **genetic code** in the mid-1960s resulted in the awarding of the Nobel Prize to Har Gobind Khorana, Marshall W. Nirenberg, and Robert W. Holley in 1968. The code is universal for living species.

If the DNA of a cell of an organism (or *the* cell of a single-celled species) is damaged by the chance incorporation of the wrong nucleotide unit or by an

Table 28.1 Specification of α-Amino Acids by DNA Codon Triplets

The sequence of nitrogenous heterocycles is listed from the 5′-end to the 3′-end.

Codons	Amino acid	Codons	Amino acid	Codons	Amino acid	Codons	Amino acid	Codons	Amino acid
TTA, TTG, CTT, CTC, CTA, CTG	Leu	TCT, TCC, TCA, TCG, AGT, AGC	Ser	CGT, CGC, CGA, CGG, AGA, AGG	Arg				
GTT, GTC, GTA, GTG	Val	CCT, CCC, CCA, CCG	Pro	ACT, ACC, ACA, ACG	Thr	GCT, GCC, GCA, GCG	Ala	GGT, GGC, GGA, GGG	Gly
ATT, ATC, ATA	Ile	TAA, TAG, TGA	signal for termination of the peptide chain						
TTT, TTC	Phe	TAT, TAC	Tyr	CAT, CAC	His	CAA, CAG	Gln	AAT, AAC	Asn
AAA, AAG	Lys	GAT, GAC	Asp	GAA, GAG	Glu	TGT, TGC	Cys		
ATG	Met	TGG	Trp						

extraneous chemical reaction, the enzyme synthesis directed by that DNA will be changed. At times the change is so drastic that the cell simply does not survive to reproduce. At other times the change is so slight that it is not noticeable in ordinary observation of the species. At yet other times, such as with a cancerous cell, the cell may continue to live and reproduce but with significant changes in its nature since it has undergone a *mutation*.

In principle, a change in a single nucleotide in the DNA sequence can lead to significant modifications in the biological processes performed by a species. For example, the presence of a guanine where an adenine should be located could change the α-amino acid specification from arginine to glycine (GGA rather than AGA). Such a change would have a profound effect on the nature of the protein synthesized. This type of possibility is somewhat diminished because more than one codon can specify a given α-amino acid. That is, a similar change of guanine for adenine would have no effect in the specification of threonine, since the sequences ACA and ACG both specify threonine.

In addition to the codons specifying particular α-amino acids, three codons specify the termination of the peptide synthesis. But how is peptide synthesis initiated, and how does it occur? The answer to the first question is found in the presence of **promoter sequences.** Promoter sequences are groups of six base pairs located along the DNA chain between the 5′-end of the nucleic acid and the bases specifying the α-amino acid sequence.

The answer to the second question is more complex and requires consideration of another type of nucleic acid, RNA. DNA is not directly involved in peptide synthesis. Instead, it generates a specific RNA that in turn specifies the peptide synthesis. We need to consider two types of RNA; these are messenger RNA (mRNA) and transfer RNA (tRNA).

RNA

Messenger RNA **Messenger RNA** is synthesized by interaction of the template strand of DNA with ribonucleotides. At the promoter region of DNA, the two strands unwind and enzyme-facilitated synthesis (known as **transcription**) of an RNA complement of the DNA template begins. This mRNA complement of the DNA template strand has the same sequence of nitrogenous heterocycles (uracil replacing thymine) as the coding strand of the original DNA double helix. Thus a DNA coding strand sequence such as that shown in Figure 28.8 is transformed into a mRNA sequence, as illustrated schematically in Figure 28.10. This synthesis of mRNA starts at the free 5′-end of the chain and proceeds toward the free 3′-end of the chain.

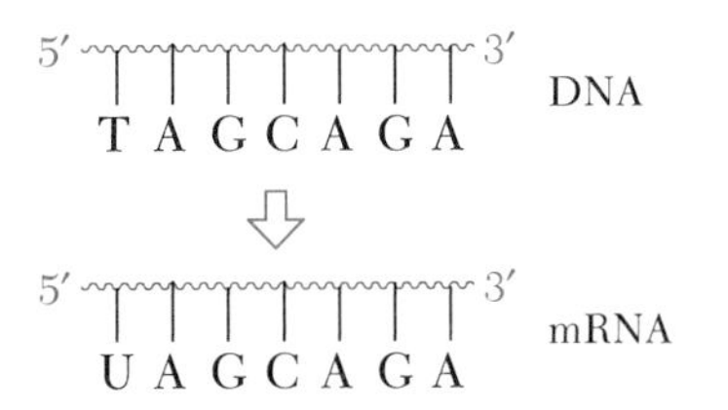

Figure 28.10 A section of a coding strand of DNA and its mRNA copy. The mRNA copy is synthesized from the template strand of the DNA double helix.

The mRNA serves as the site for the synthesis of peptides, with the sequence of nitrogenous heterocycles specifying the sequence of α-amino acids to be introduced. This synthesis process involves a *second* type of RNA that recognizes the mRNA codons and brings the proper α-amino acids to the coupling site.

PROBLEM 28.7 Give a sequence of mRNA nitrogenous heterocycles that would code for the following α-amino acid sequences:

a. Ala-Gln-Met-Phe **b.** Cys-Gly-His-Pro **c.** Lys-Ile-Asp

PROBLEM 28.8 Each of the peptide sequences in the previous problem could be coded by *several* mRNA sequences. How many different mRNA sequences could code each of them?

PROBLEM 28.9 Give the α-amino acid sequence that is coded by each of the following mRNA sequences:

a. CAAACAAAC b. GACTTGTGGCTA
c. TGCATAGTATAT d. ATGAAAAGGTCGTGCTGT

Transfer RNA **Transfer RNAs** (tRNA) are relatively short nucleic acids (< 100 ribonucleotides) that have a particular structure corresponding to each of the α-amino acids. In the activated form of tRNA, the α-amino acid is bound to its tRNA at the 3′-end. A recognition sequence within the tRNA is complementary to the specifying codon for that α-amino acid on the mRNA. Under the action of ribosomes and peptide-elongation enzymes, the specified activated tRNA species are temporarily bound to the mRNA and the synthesis of the peptide linkage occurs. (A ribosome is a complex of RNA and proteins that is involved in peptide synthesis.) The process is shown schematically in Figure 28.11. The process can be summarized by *DNA makes RNA, which makes protein.*

28.4 Genetic Engineering

In Chapter 26 we discussed the synthesis of polypeptides and proteins using standard chemical reactions. However, since the sequence of subunits in a nucleic acid constitutes a set of instructions for joining α-amino acids it follows

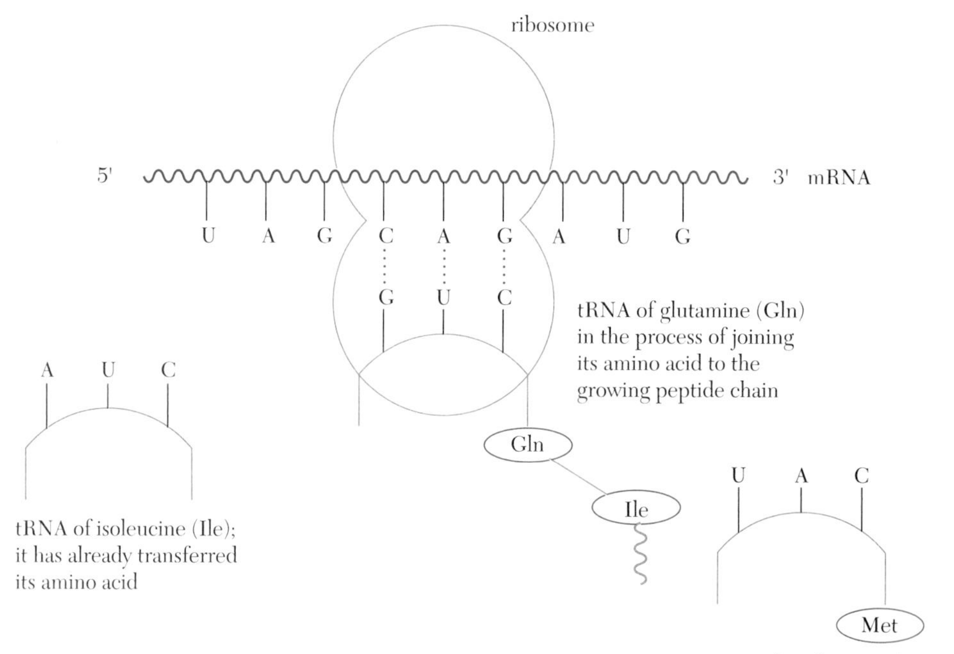

Figure 28.11 Schematic representation of the biological synthesis of proteins. The sequence of nitrogenous heterocycles in the mRNA chain specifies the sequence of amino acids to be introduced. The tRNA species, activated with their appropriate α-amino acids, bind to the mRNA under the influence of the ribosome (RNA/protein complex) and elongation enzymes to transfer their α-amino acids to the growing protein. In the diagram, the Gln tRNA is in the process of adding glutamine to the growing protein. In the preceding step, the Ile tRNA added isoleucine and was displaced to the solution. Following the addition of the unit of glutamine, the Met tRNA will bind to the mRNA, using its complementary sequence of nitrogenous heterocycles, and add methionine to the growing chain.

that specifying the nucleic acid composition should allow us to direct protein synthesis. If we can introduce a nucleic acid sequence with the proper order of subunits into a cell, we can generate a living factory for the synthesis of a protein of our choice.

In recent years great strides have been made in this area of technology, which has been referred to as *genetic engineering*. This directed production of specific enzymes depends on the universality of the genetic code. The genetic code is the same for bacteria such as *Escherichia coli* as it is for humans. It is possible to manipulate the DNA of such a bacterial cell and use it to produce enzymes needed in human biological processes.

Such DNA manipulation requires several steps. First, the bacterial DNA is removed from the bacterium and the chain is cut (hydrolyzed) in a specific manner using an enzyme known as a *restriction enzyme*. Then a new DNA sequence specifying a particular α-amino acid sequence is introduced into the bacterial DNA at the cut region. This step requires the use of another enzyme known as a *DNA ligase*. This procedure is referred to as a *recombinant DNA* technique. The modified DNA is reintroduced into the bacteria, which then synthesizes enzymes according to its modified DNA. When the bacteria multiply, the offspring also contain the modified DNA and in turn synthesize the desired enzyme. It has proven possible to modify bacterial DNA so that the bacteria synthesize medically useful proteins such as insulin.

28.5 Genetic Diseases

In Chapter 26 we mentioned that sickle-cell anemia is a disease caused by abnormal hemoglobin. A difference in *one* of the hundreds of α-amino acids in the hemoglobin structure results in a significant change in its physiological characteristics. This mistake in the hemoglobin structure can be traced to a single codon error in the DNA of the individual with the disease. Sickle-cell anemia is therefore a *genetic disease*. At some point a mutation occurred in the DNA of an individual (a codon was altered), and the resulting altered nucleic acid has been passed from generation to generation.

In 1990 the first attempt was made to treat a genetic disease using the recombinant DNA techniques discussed in the previous section. A portion of the individual's faulty DNA was removed and altered. In place of the faulty genetic material, a DNA chain with the proper sequence was introduced. The corrected material was copied and reinjected into the patient. It is anticipated that the correction of numerous genetic diseases and defects may be possible using this technique.

28.6 Other Roles of Nucleotides

In addition to their role as components of nucleic acids, nucleotides have other roles. Two of them will be discussed here.

NUCLEOTIDES CONTAINING REACTIVE LINKAGES

In Chapter 6 we first introduced biologically important molecules that, like the nucleotides, contain phosphate ester linkages. Nucleotides containing phosphorus *anhydride* linkages and phosphate *ester* linkages have been found to play a major role in the formation of these phosphate ester linkages.

Adenosine triphosphate (ATP) (**28.3**) is a common biological phosphorylating agent. ATP is formed in biological systems by oxidative phosphorylation of adenosine diphosphate (ADP) (**28.4**).

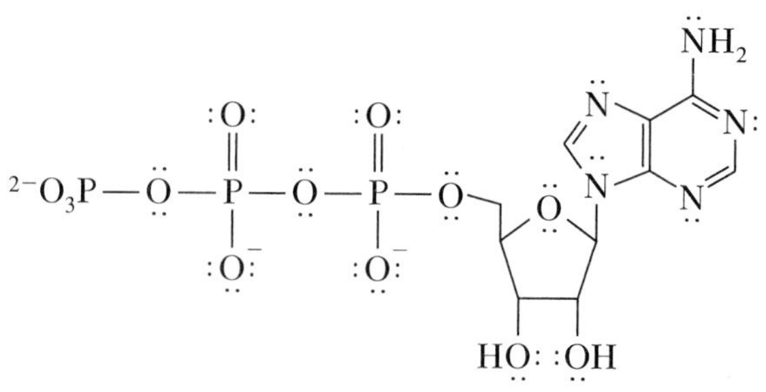

adenosine triphosphate (ATP)
28.3

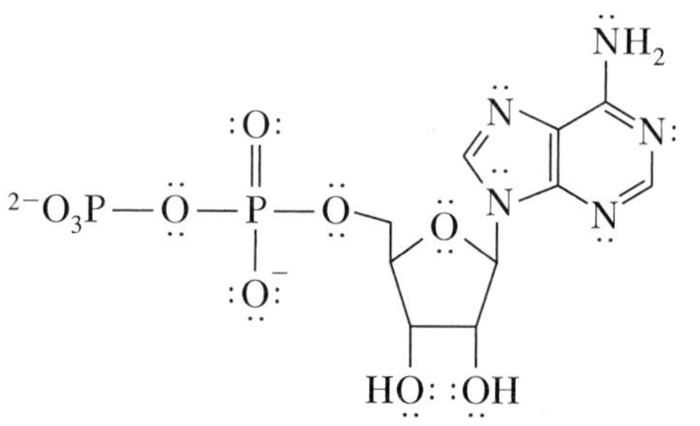

adenosine disphosphate (ADP)
28.4

Oxidative phosphorylation is a complex series of coupled reactions. In a set of coupled reactions, one reaction is either thermodynamically unfavorable or lacks a reagent generated in one of the other reactions. The particular reaction generating ATP from ADP is endoergic and thus requires the input of energy from another source (a coupled reaction). The formation of ATP from ADP is summarized in Figure 28.12.

The P-O-P linkage that is generated in the formation of ATP from ADP is an *anhydride* linkage (notice the extrusion of water between the reactants in the reaction in Figure 28.12). Like carboxylic anhydrides, phosphoric anhydrides are highly reactive and form esters in exoergic processes. When ATP reacts to form a phosphate ester or is hydrolyzed to ADP and inorganic phosphate, energy is released. Both of these energy-releasing processes may be coupled to other endoergic biological reactions, allowing them to occur efficiently.

Guanosine triphosphate (GTP) (**28.5**) is a species similar to ATP. Like ATP, GTP has *two* phosphoric anhydride linkages. While GTP does not have the ubiquitous role of ATP, which is involved in a wide range of biological processes, it is critical in protein synthesis. The exoergic hydrolysis of GTP to GDP is a critical coupled reaction in the protein elongation process using tRNA.

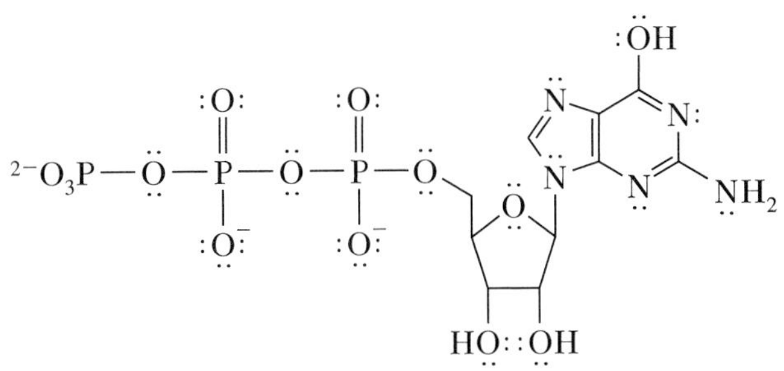

:ÖH
:O: :O: N N:
$^{2-}O_3P$—Ö—P—Ö—P—Ö N N NH_2
:Ö: :Ö: Ö
HÖ: :ÖH

guanosine triphosphate
28.5

Cyclic AMP (**28.6**) is another interesting nucleotide that is highly reactive and releases energy upon its hydrolysis. Cyclic AMP is a monophosphate, but it is also a *phosphodiester*, incorporating an additional ring into the AMP structure.

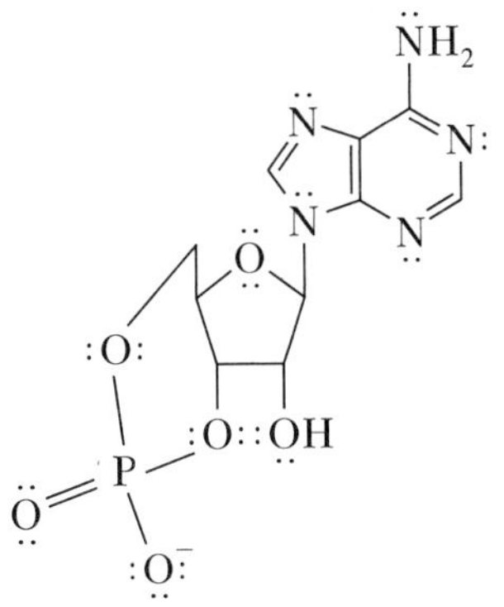

$\ddot{N}H_2$
N N:
N N
Ö
:O:
:O: :ÖH
Ö=P
:Ö:

cyclic AMP
28.6

Figure 28.12 Overall generation of ATP from ADP and phosphate. The reaction as written is endoergic by a significant amount. For the reaction to occur efficiently, energy input from other coupled reactions is required.

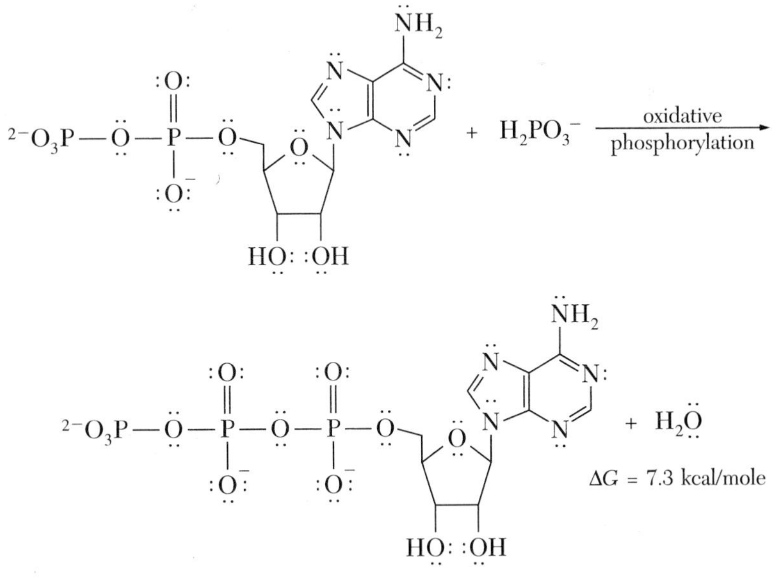

$\ddot{N}H_2$
:O: N N:
$^{2-}O_3P$—Ö—P—Ö Ö N N + $H_2PO_3^-$ —oxidative phosphorylation→
:Ö:
HÖ: :ÖH

$\ddot{N}H_2$
:O: :O: N N:
$^{2-}O_3P$—Ö—P—Ö—P—Ö Ö N N + $H_2\ddot{O}$
:Ö: :Ö:
ΔG = 7.3 kcal/mole
HÖ: :ÖH

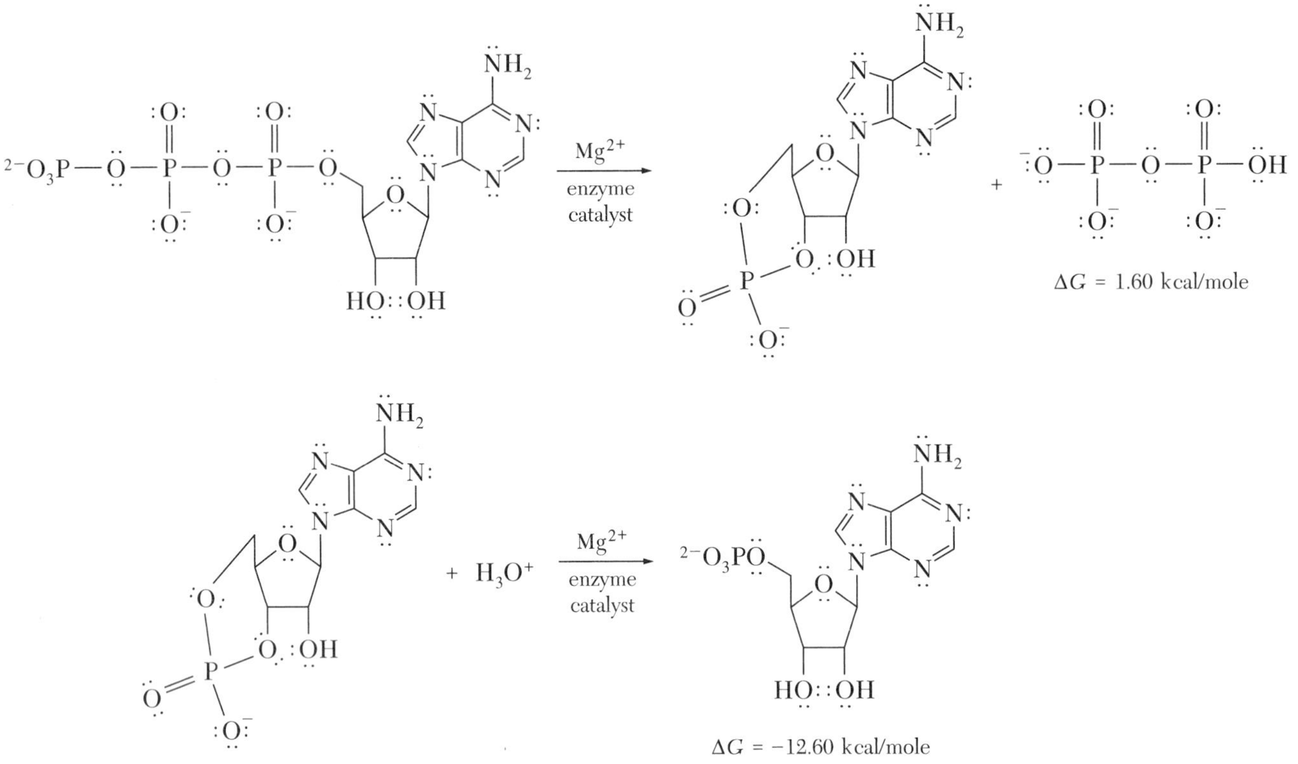

ΔG = 1.60 kcal/mole

ΔG = −12.60 kcal/mole

Figure 28.13 Formation and hydrolysis of cyclic AMP. The formation of cyclic AMP from ATP is endoergic by a small amount. This reaction becomes efficient when it is coupled to the hydrolysis of its by-product pyrophosphate. The hydrolysis of cyclic AMP to AMP is exoergic; this energy is used in coupling to other endoergic reactions in biological systems.

Cyclic AMP is formed from ATP in a coupled reaction process. The simple conversion of ATP to cyclic AMP is endoergic, requiring a coupled exoergic reaction in order to occur efficiently. Upon hydrolysis, which is coupled for reactions involving the activity of hormones (chemical messenger molecules in biological processes), cyclic AMP releases energy. These reactions are summarized in Figure 28.13.

Numerous other nucleotides containing reactive phosphoric anhydride (pyrophosphate) linkages or strained rings are found to be important components of biological processes. Our goal here is simply to introduce these species. We will now turn our attention to another type of nucleotide that plays important roles in biological systems.

NUCLEOTIDE REDOX REAGENTS

Earlier (Chapter 5) we briefly noted an important species involved in the biological oxidation of alcohols to carbonyl compounds. Nicotinamide adenine dinucleotide (NAD^+) (**28.7**) accepts the hydrogen (formally with a pair of electrons) from the hydroxyl-bearing carbon in the oxidation process. Both NAD^+ and its reduced form, NADH (**28.8**), are nucleotides that are structurally related to the molecules we have been considering.

In the oxidation of an alcohol in which NAD^+ serves as the oxidizing agent, a hydrogen with a pair of electrons is accepted onto a carbon of the nicotinamide

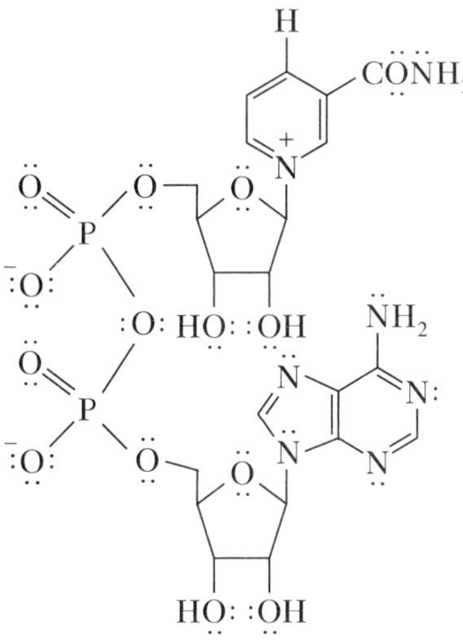

NAD^+
28.7

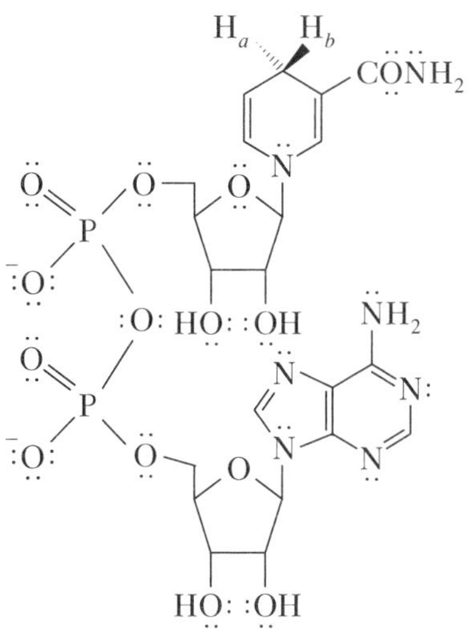

NADH
28.8

ring. In the reduced form (NADH), one carbon atom of the nicotinamide ring bears two hydrogens, designated H_a and H_b in structure **28.8**. These two hydrogens are *not* in identical positions—they exhibit different NMR signals (they are not magnetically equivalent) and are said to be **diastereotopic** hydrogens. That is, if we were to replace one of them (e.g., H_a) with some other substituent (e.g., Cl), we would have a diastereoisomer of the compound obtained by replacing H_b with Cl.

In any given biological oxidation reaction involving the NAD^+/NADH couple and a particular enzyme catalyst, the hydrogen transferred to NAD^+ is always transferred diastereospecifically. That is, the hydrogen coming from the substrate always attaches in either position H_a or H_b specifically, *never* attaching such that some hydrogen ends up in the H_a position and some in the H_b position. For example, in the oxidation of ethanol using enzymes from yeast with NAD^+, the hydrogen from the ethanol always ends up in the H_b position. However, in the oxidation of glucose using enzymes from liver with NAD^+, the hydrogen from the glucose always ends up in the H_a position.

Summary

- Nucleosides are derivatives of carbohydrates in which the anomeric position is bound into a full glycosidic-type linkage involving a molecule of a nitrogenous heterocycle instead of an alcohol.
- The most common carbohydrates involved in biological nucleosides are D-ribose and D-2-deoxyribose.
- Only a limited number of nitrogenous heterocycles serve as components of biological nucleosides. Three of these are derivatives of pyrimidine, and two are derivatives of purine.
- Nucleotides are nucleosides in which one or more of the hydroxyl groups of the carbohydrate component are bound into phosphate ester linkages.
- Nucleotides are the components of nucleic acids, complex molecules that retain and transmit genetic information in the continuing life of an organism, that

is, in the synthesis of proteins that serve as enzymes for its metabolic processes.

- Nucleotides also serve other roles in biological systems. Nucleotides bearing phosphoric anhydride linkages generate phosphate ester linkages and facilitate endoergic reactions in biological processes. Nucleotide-related materials also serve as redox couples for biological oxidations and reductions.

Terms to Remember

nucleic acid
deoxyribonucleic acid
ribonucleic acid
nucleoside
purine
pyrimidine
nucleotide
oligonucleotide
polynucleotide
base pair
codon
genetic code
promoter sequence
messenger RNA
transfer RNA
transcription
diastereotopic

29 CHAPTER Synthetic Polymers

29.1 Introduction

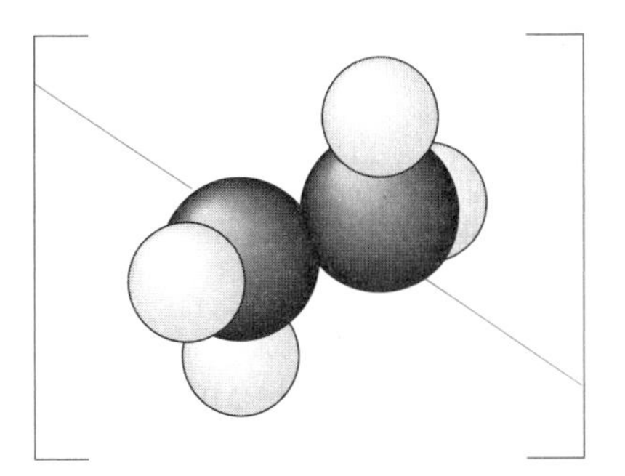

Polymers are high molecular weight compounds that consist of a large number of low molecular weight building blocks. Many important substances in the natural world are polymers, including polysaccharides (Chapter 24), proteins (Chapter 26), and DNA, the giant molecule responsible for the storage and transfer of hereditary information (Chapter 28). As we have seen in earlier chapters, each type of biologically important polymer is composed of building blocks of some basic structural type. For example, proteins are made up of combinations of individual α-amino acids, and polysaccharides are made up of combinations of pentoses or hexoses. For centuries, humans have made extensive practical use of natural polymers such as wood for building and silk, cotton, and wool for clothing. Rubber (Chapter 9) is another important natural polymer that has played a crucial role in the development of modern transportation systems.

One of the most spectacular industrial developments of the twentieth century has been the growth of the *synthetic* polymer industry. Synthetic polymers are often referred to as *plastics*, although strictly speaking, this term should be reserved for polymers that can be softened by heating and shaped by pressure. Some synthetic polymers consist of many units of a *single* building block known as a monomer. In this respect, these synthetic polymers are structurally much less complex than most natural polymers. Other synthetic polymers are composed of more than one building block. They are known as copolymers, and several types have been synthesized.

Hundreds of materials that we take for granted today are products of the synthetic polymer industry, and many chemists are still involved in the continuing effort to develop new polymers that can replace or improve upon conventional materials.

In this chapter we will survey some of the more common types of synthetic polymers, methods for their production, and their properties.

29.2 Polyethylene and Other Addition Polymers

Polymers formed from alkenes and their derivatives are referred to as **addition polymers.** The polymer-forming reaction involves the simple addition of monomer units to each other. There is no product other than the polymer.

The simplest and cheapest addition polymer is polyethylene. Equation 29.1 shows the structural relationship between ethylene and polyethylene.

Eqn. 29.1
$$n\left[\begin{array}{c}H\quad\quad H\\ \diagdown\quad\diagup\\ C{=}C\\ \diagup\quad\diagdown\\ H\quad\quad H\end{array}\right] \longrightarrow -\underset{H}{\overset{H}{\underset{|}{\overset{|}{C}}}}-\underset{H}{\overset{H}{\underset{|}{\overset{|}{C}}}}-\underset{H}{\overset{H}{\underset{|}{\overset{|}{C}}}}-\underset{H}{\overset{H}{\underset{|}{\overset{|}{C}}}}-\underset{H}{\overset{H}{\underset{|}{\overset{|}{C}}}}-\underset{H}{\overset{H}{\underset{|}{\overset{|}{C}}}}-\underset{H}{\overset{H}{\underset{|}{\overset{|}{C}}}}- \quad \text{or} \quad \left[-\underset{H}{\overset{H}{\underset{|}{\overset{|}{C}}}}-\underset{H}{\overset{H}{\underset{|}{\overset{|}{C}}}}-\right]_n$$

this unit is
repeated n times

Although the starting material for polyethylene is unsaturated, polyethylene itself is a saturated hydrocarbon. Polyethylene can be prepared as a thin film and is used extensively for packaging (e.g., plastic food wrap for fruits and vegetables, garbage can liners, and so forth). Some other common addition polymers are listed in Table 29.1.

The polymerization of alkenes can be effected in various ways. One important method is *free-radical polymerization,* which is a free-radical chain reaction. In this process, the alkene that is to serve as the monomer unit is heated in the presence of a material that can serve as a source of free radicals (e.g., a peroxide). The mechanism for the free-radical polymerization of styrene is shown below.

MECHANISM OF REACTION

Free-Radical Polymerization of Styrene

Step 1 Free radicals are formed by heating a suitable precursor such as a peroxide

$$(CH_3)_3C-\ddot{\underset{..}{O}}-\ddot{\underset{..}{O}}-C(CH_3)_3 \longrightarrow 2\ (CH_3)_3C-\ddot{\underset{..}{O}}\cdot$$

Step 2 A radical formed in the first step adds to a styrene molecule, producing a benzylic radical.

$$C_6H_5CH{=}CH_2 + \cdot\ddot{\underset{..}{O}}-C(CH_3)_3 \longrightarrow (CH_3)_3C-\ddot{\underset{..}{O}}-CH_2-\dot{C}H-C_6H_5$$

Step 3 The benzylic radical adds to another styrene molecule (monomer), producing a new benzylic radical.

$$(CH_3)_3C-\ddot{\underset{..}{O}}-CH_2\underset{\underset{C_6H_5}{|}}{\dot{C}H} + H_2C{=}CH-C_6H_5 \longrightarrow$$

$$(CH_3)_3C-\ddot{\underset{..}{O}}-CH_2\underset{\underset{C_6H_5}{|}}{CH}-CH_2-\underset{\underset{C_6H_5}{|}}{\dot{C}H}$$

Steps 4 to *n* The larger benzylic radical produced in the third step reacts with another styrene monomer, producing an even larger benzylic radical. The addition process repeats, with each addition reaction joining another monomer unit to the growing polymer chain.

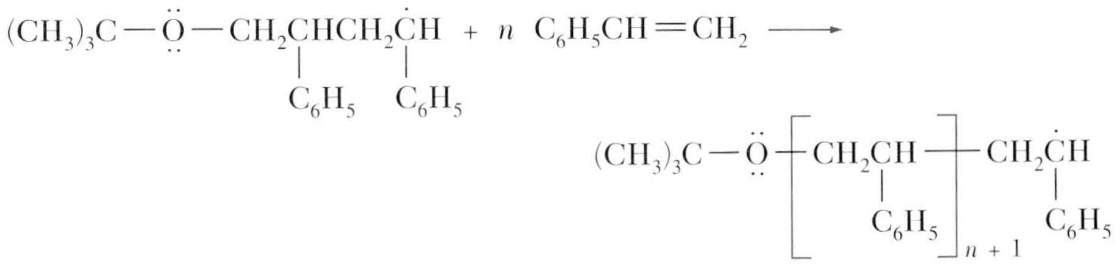

$$(CH_3)_3C-\ddot{\underset{..}{O}}-CH_2\underset{\substack{|\\C_6H_5}}{C}HCH_2\underset{\substack{|\\C_6H_5}}{\dot{C}}H + n\ C_6H_5CH{=}CH_2 \longrightarrow (CH_3)_3C-\ddot{\underset{..}{O}}-\left[CH_2\underset{\substack{|\\C_6H_5}}{C}H\right]_{n+1}-CH_2\underset{\substack{|\\C_6H_5}}{\dot{C}}H$$

Step *n* + 1 Eventually the polymer chain stops growing because a chain-terminating reaction takes place (see Chapter 13). Chain termination occurs when two radicals present in the reaction system react with one another rather than with an alkene molecule.

Depending on the mode of preparation of a polymer, the number of monomer subunits can vary greatly. Commercial synthetic polymers usually have between 100 and 1000 monomer subunits. Any given preparation produces a range of polymer molecules. (It is not possible to arrange that all the different chain reactions terminate after exactly the same number of cycles.) Rather than speaking of an exact molecular weight for a polymer, as we do for ordinary small molecules, we speak of the *average* molecular weight of the polymer produced. Synthetic commercial polymers generally have average molecular weights in the range 10^5–10^6 g/mole.

Notice that addition polymers produced as we have described have end groups derived from the radical initiator. Thus the end groups are different from the repeating unit in the rest of the molecule but are not significant in determining the overall chemical and physical properties of polymers.

PROBLEM 29.1 Soft contact lenses are made of the addition polymer having the repeating structure shown below. What monomer would you use to prepare this polymer?

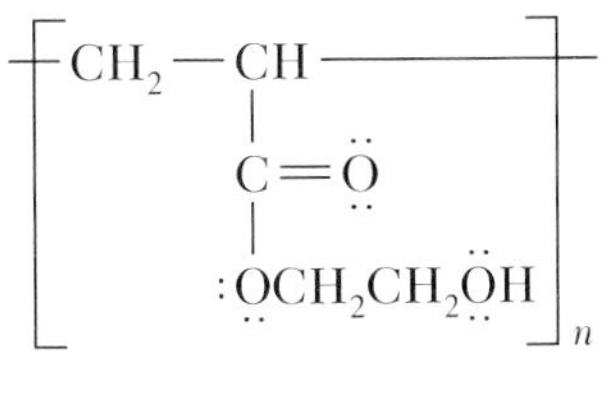

$$\left[CH_2-\underset{\substack{|\\C=\ddot{O}\\|\\:\ddot{O}CH_2CH_2\ddot{O}H}}{C}H\right]_n$$

PROBLEM 29.2 Consider the polymerization of styrene. Explain why the polymer always has the benzylic carbon atom of one monomer unit attached to the nonbenzylic carbon atom of the next monomer unit along the entire length of the chain.

Table 29.1 Some Common Addition Polymers

Name of Polymer	Structure	Common Uses
polypropylene	$\left[-\mathrm{CH(H)}-\mathrm{C(H)(CH_3)}- \right]_n$	indoor-outdoor carpeting, upholstery material
polystyrene	$\left[-\mathrm{CH(H)}-\mathrm{C(H)(C_6H_5)}- \right]_n$	molded housewares, toys, insulation, packaging filler
polyvinyl chloride (PVC)	$\left[-\mathrm{CH(H)}-\mathrm{C(H)(:\ddot{Cl}:)}- \right]_n$	plastic wrap, pipes for household plumbing, soles and heels of shoes
polytetrafluoro-ethylene (PTFE)	$\left[-\mathrm{C(:\ddot{F}:)(:\ddot{F}:)}-\mathrm{C(:\ddot{F}:)(:\ddot{F}:)}- \right]_n$	nonstick utensils, electrical insulation
polyacrylonitrile	$\left[-\mathrm{CH(H)}-\mathrm{C(H)(C{\equiv}N:)}- \right]_n$	fibers in the textile industry, yarns, wigs
polymethyl methacrylate	$\left[-\mathrm{CH(H)}-\mathrm{C(CH_3)(CO_2CH_3)}- \right]_n$	sheeting and tubing

It is possible to polymerize alkenes using cations instead of radicals. Cationic polymerization is commercially important for the preparation of polyisobutylene. The mechanism for cationic polymerization of isobutylene in the presence of H^+ (acid) is shown below. Notice that the general sequence is very similar to that involved in radical polymerization.

MECHANISM OF REACTION

Cationic Polymerization of Isobutylene

Step 1 Isobutene (2-methylpropene) is protonated by the acid to form the *tert*-butyl cation.

$$(CH_3)_2C{=}CH_2 + H^+ \longrightarrow (CH_3)_2\overset{+}{C}{-}CH_2{-}H$$

Step 2 Electrophilic attack of the *tert*-butyl cation on an isobutylene molecule occurs, producing a new and larger carbocation.

$$(CH_3)_2C{=}CH_2 + (CH_3)_3C^+ \longrightarrow (CH_3)_2\overset{+}{C}{-}CH_2{-}C(CH_3)_3$$

Steps 3 to *n* The cation from Step 2 reacts with another isobutylene molecule, forming a new and even larger cation. The process constantly repeats, building up the polymer chain with a cationic site near one end.

$$(CH_3)_2\overset{+}{C}{-}CH_2{-}C(CH_3)_3 \longrightarrow \longrightarrow \longrightarrow (CH_3)_2\overset{+}{C}{-}CH_2{-}\left[C(CH_3)_2{-}CH_2\right]_n{-}H$$

Step *n* + 1 Eventually, of course, the growth of the polymer stops when the supply of isobutylene monomer is depleted and the carbocation at the terminus either adds a nucleophile or loses a proton to form a double bond.

The reaction illustrated above was initiated by a Brønsted acid. Lewis acids such as boron trifluoride and aluminum trichloride are equally effective.

PROBLEM 29.3 In the polymerization of isobutylene, why do the monomer units become attached in a head-to-tail fashion all the way along the chain?

PROBLEM 29.4 It is possible to use anions, such as the amide ion, to initiate the polymerization of some α,β-unsaturated alkenes. Reaction begins with the amide ion attacking the alkene to form a resonance-stabilized carbanion. This carbanion in turn adds in a Michael fashion (Chapter 23) to another molecule of the alkene to produce a new and larger resonance-stabilized carbanion. The polymer chain is built up by a succession of additions of this type. Write a complete mechanism (use curved arrows) for the polymerization of acrylonitrile ($H_2C{=}CH{-}CN$) brought about by treatment with sodium amide.

A major advance in polymer chemistry was made in the 1950s by Karl Ziegler (Germany) and Giulio Natta (Italy), who were awarded the Nobel Prize in 1963 for their contributions. Their work focused on the use of transition metal catalysts to effect alkene polymerization. Ziegler and Natta found that with these catalysts they could control the polymerization of alkenes and substituted alkenes to a much greater degree than had been possible using earlier methods.

The **Ziegler-Natta catalysts** are complexes of transition metal halides and organometallic compounds. Triethylaluminum complexed with titanium tetrachloride is a common example of a Ziegler-Natta catalyst. The complexation results in the formation of a titanium species that can function as a Lewis acid toward the alkene molecule. We can think of the complexation as leading to an active center consisting of a titanium atom connected to an ethyl group, along with other groups that we will identify here only as X. That is, for simplicity we will represent the active catalyst as CH_3CH_2TiX, where X represents a group whose structure is not yet known precisely. (This is not unusual for industrial catalysts.)

In the polymerization process, the alkene monomer acts as a Lewis base, using its π electrons to form a bond to the transition metal, as shown in Equation 29.2.

Eqn. 29.2

$$CH_3CH_2TiX + H_2C{=}CH_2 \longrightarrow CH_3CH_2\underset{\displaystyle X}{\underset{|}{Ti}}-\begin{matrix} CH_2 \\ \| \\ CH_2 \end{matrix}$$

The next step is a rearrangement in which the original alkyl group migrates to one of the carbon atoms of the double bond, as shown in Equation 29.3.

Eqn. 29.3

$$CH_3CH_2\underset{\displaystyle X}{\underset{|}{Ti}}-\begin{matrix} CH_2 \\ \| \\ CH_2 \end{matrix} \longrightarrow CH_3CH_2CH_2CH_2TiX$$

The overall result is that an alkene monomer unit has inserted itself between the transition metal and its original alkene group, producing a species in which a new and larger alkyl group is attached to the metal. However, now a second alkene molecule can behave just as the first one did, again inserting itself between the metal and its attached alkyl group. After many cycles, the result is the polymer species of the type shown below (**29.1**).

$$CH_3CH_2\left[CH_2CH_2\right]_n TiX$$

29.1

Let us consider the advantages of polymers produced by the Ziegler-Natta process. To appreciate the issues involved, we need to consider a property known as the **crystallinity** of a polymer. The physical differences among polymers, even those prepared from the same monomers, can be quite profound. The polymer may take various forms, for example, a worthless gum (this was

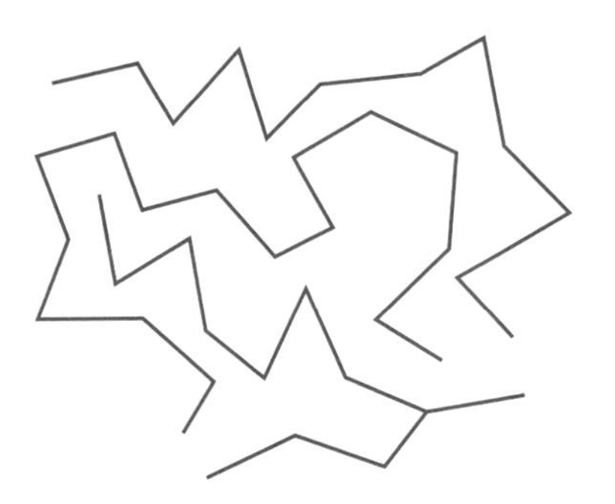

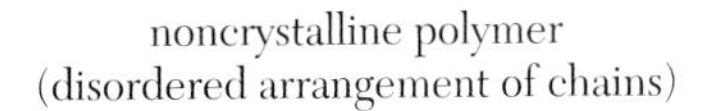

crystalline polymer
(ordered arrangement of chains)

Figure 29.1 Types of polymers. The crystallinity of a polymer correlates with the degree of order in the stacking of its chains.

the nature of polypropylene produced prior to the Ziegler-Natta method), a soft amorphous solid, or a harder, more crystalline material suitable for moldable plastics. One of the early successes of the Ziegler-Natta process was that it led to a usable polypropylene polymer.

The underlying factors leading to the formation of polymers with different crystallinities can be traced to the secondary structure of polymers. We used the term secondary structure previously in the context of polypeptides and proteins, and it is used in a similar way here. It refers to the way in which a polymer chain is oriented in space, how it coils and bends, and how any given chain interacts with other chains. These properties in turn depend on attractive interactions such as dipole-dipole, hydrogen-bonding, and van der Waals interactions. In general we find that the more orderly the fashion in which polymer chains stack together, the more crystalline the polymer (see Figure 29.1).

In this context, there is an important stereochemical factor that needs to be considered in the polymerization of polypropylene. The polymer contains many stereogenic carbon atoms. A typical carbon atom of the polymer chain is attached to four different groups, a hydrogen atom, a methyl group, and two generally nonequivalent (i.e., of different length) portions of the polymer chain (see Figure 29.2).

If the stereogenic centers are a random mix of *R* and S configurations, the polymer is said to **atactic** (without order). In an atactic polymer, the methyl groups are randomly arranged on the two sides of the stretched polymer chain, as shown in the bottom structure of Figure 29.3. Polypropylene produced by free-radical polymerization has this random arrangement of the methyl groups. Because of this randomness, the polymer is noncrystalline and is unsuited for widespread use because of its poor mechanical properties.

In contrast, the methyl groups of the polymer chain are oriented in an ordered fashion when the Ziegler-Natta method of polymerization is used. Two types of ordered arrangements are important. In the **isotactic** (same order) arrangement, all the methyl groups are on the same side of the chain, as shown

$$-\left[\begin{matrix} H & & H \\ | & & | \\ C & - & C \\ | & & | \\ CH_3 & & H \end{matrix}\right]_n - \begin{matrix} H \\ | \\ C \\ | \\ CH_3 \end{matrix} - \left[\begin{matrix} H & & H \\ | & & | \\ C & - & C \\ | & & | \\ H & & CH_3 \end{matrix}\right]_m -$$

Figure 29.2 Chirality in polypropylene. Every other carbon atom in a polypropylene chain is stereogenic, having four unlike groups attached to it. Each chain therefore contains *many* stereogenic carbon atoms.

Figure 29.3 Different arrangements of polypropylene.

Isotactic — all methyl groups same side

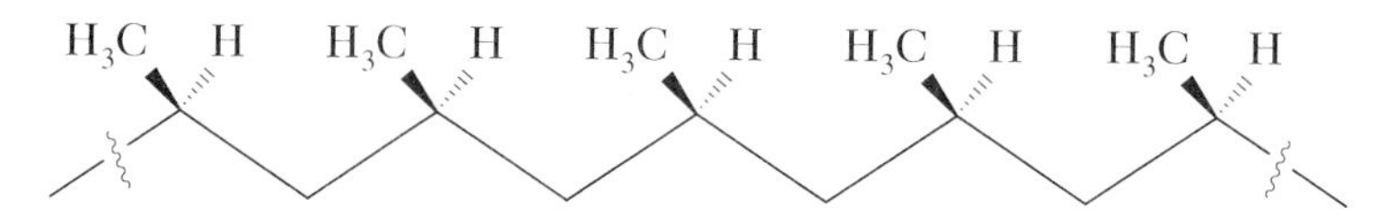

Syndiotactic — methyl groups alternate

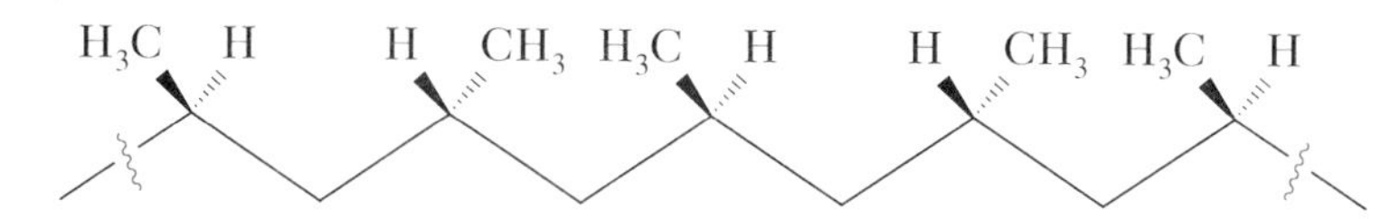

Atactic — methyl groups arranged randomly

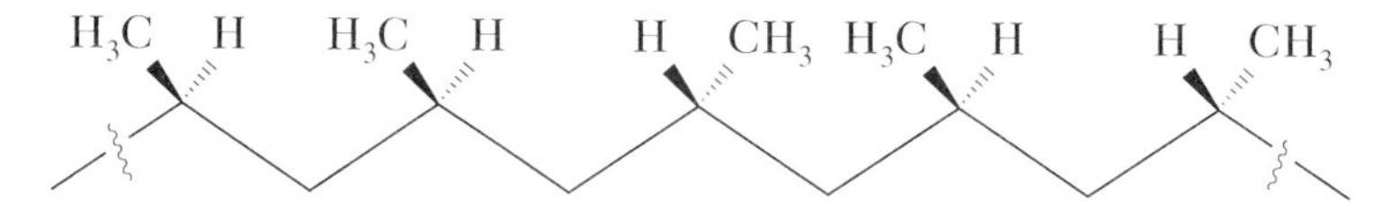

in the top structure of Figure 29.3. The isotactic form of polypropylene is a solid that melts at 175 °C. It has ideal properties for a variety of applications, and several billion pounds are produced each year. Another ordered arrangement is known as the **syndiotactic** form. In a syndiotactic ("two together") polymer the monomer units are arranged in repeating pairs so that the methyl groups alternate regularly between the two sides of the stretched chain, as shown at the center of Figure 29.3. The configurations of the stereogenic carbon atoms alternate along the chain.

The high degree of stereochemical control that is achieved with Ziegler-Natta catalysts presumably arises from preferred orientations for monomer units on the catalyst surface. However, many details of the mechanism of polymerization remain to be discovered.

PROBLEM 29.5 Would you expect any samples of polypropylene prepared by polymerization of propylene to be optically active? Explain your answer.

PROBLEM 29.6 Which of the following does *not* give rise to distinct isotactic, syndiotactic, and atactic polymers: vinyl chloride, $H_2C{=}CH{-}Cl$, or vinylidene chloride, $H_2C{=}CCl_2$? Explain why.

A final point of stereochemistry concerns the representation of isotactic polypropylene shown in Figure 29.3. The chain is pictured there in a stretched-out zigzag form to emphasize the stereochemical relationship of the pendant methyl groups. The actual preferred conformation for isotactic polypropylene is helical, as shown in Figure 29.4. This helical structure gives the best balance between the interatomic repulsive forces and the van der Waals attractive forces between the methyl groups. The isotactic chain makes one complete turn for every three monomer units.

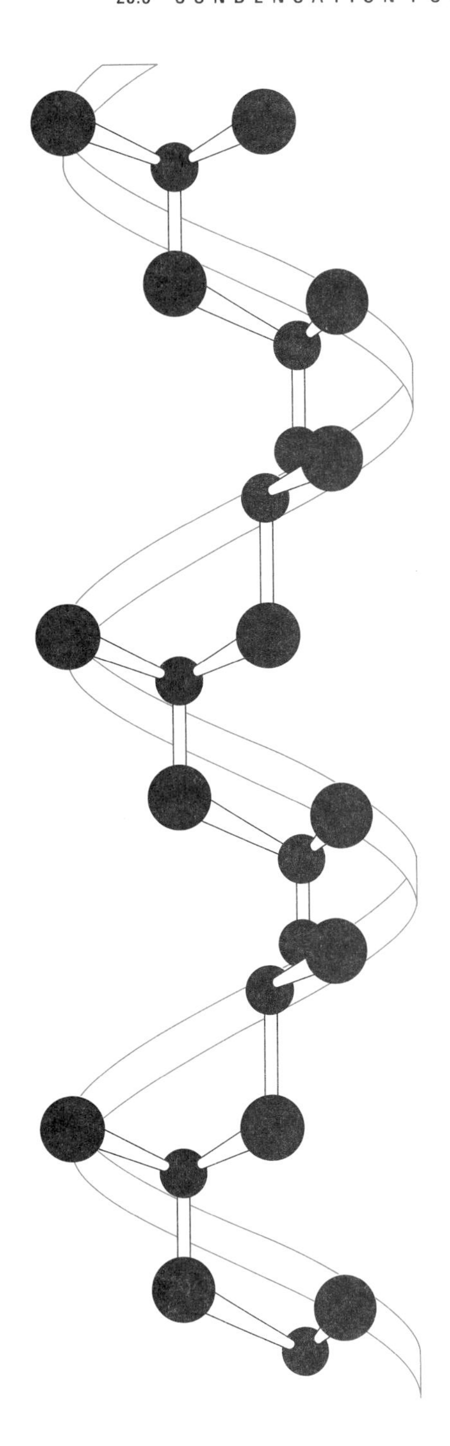

Figure 29.4 Preferred helical conformation for isotactic polypropylene.

29.3 Condensation Polymers

In Chapter 23 we defined condensation reactions as those in which two organic molecules combine to form a larger organic molecule along with a small molecule such as water, methanol, or ethanol. A **condensation polymer** is formed via a succession of condensation reactions between two appropriate monomers. Typical starting materials for the formation of condensation polymers are substituted at more than one position by some functional group that is reactive toward the

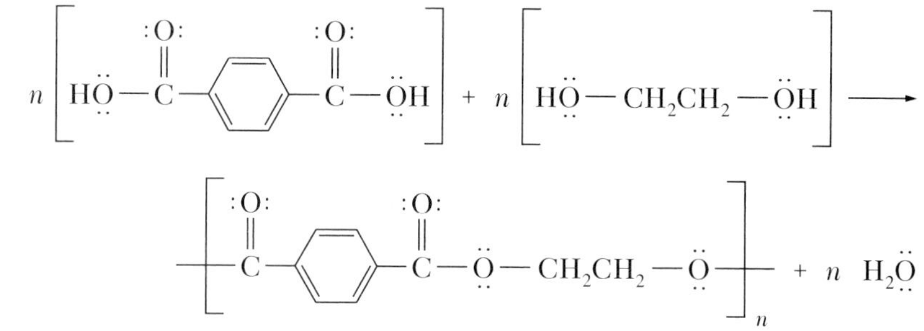

Figure 29.5 Formation of poly(ethylene terephthalate) from a dicarboxylic acid and a diol as the two building blocks.

$$n\left[HO-C(=O)-C_6H_4-C(=O)-OH\right] + n\left[HO-CH_2CH_2-OH\right] \longrightarrow \left[-C(=O)-C_6H_4-C(=O)-O-CH_2CH_2-O-\right]_n + n\ H_2O$$

functional group present in the *other* reactant. For example, the polyester poly(ethylene terephthalate) can be made from terephthalic acid and ethylene glycol, as shown in Figure 29.5.

The polymerization reaction begins with the formation of an ester linkage in a condensation reaction involving a carboxylic acid group of one starting material and the hydroxyl group of another, as shown in Equation 29.4.

$$HO-C(=O)-C_6H_4-C(=O)-OH + HO-CH_2CH_2-OH \longrightarrow HO-C(=O)-C_6H_4-C(=O)-O-CH_2CH_2-OH + H_2O \qquad \text{Eqn. 29.4}$$

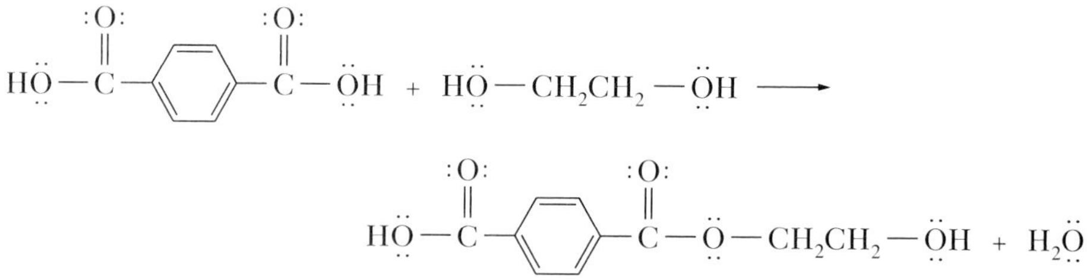

Notice that the product of Equation 29.4 has a free hydroxyl group at one end and a free carboxyl group at its other. Reaction with *additional* monomer units is possible at these sites, lengthening the polymer chain through the formation of new ester linkages. However, the product of such further reaction will *still* contain hydroxyl and carboxyl groups at its termini, so the chain of reactions leading to the final polymer can continue. This type of polymer is commonly known as a polyester.

The specific polyester shown in Figure 29.5 can be spun into fibers (known under the commercial names of Dacron and Terylene) or rolled into sheets (known as Mylar).

PROBLEM 29.7 How many different benzene dicarboxylic acids are there? Which one of these would you expect to produce the most crystalline polymer through reaction with ethylene glycol? Explain your answer.

PROBLEM 29.8 Many polyesters are efficiently prepared in a reaction known as a transesterification. Suggest how it would be possible to start with a diol and the dimethyl ester of a dicarboxylic acid to produce the polymer shown below in a transesterification reaction. (This polymer is known by its commercial name, Kodel.)

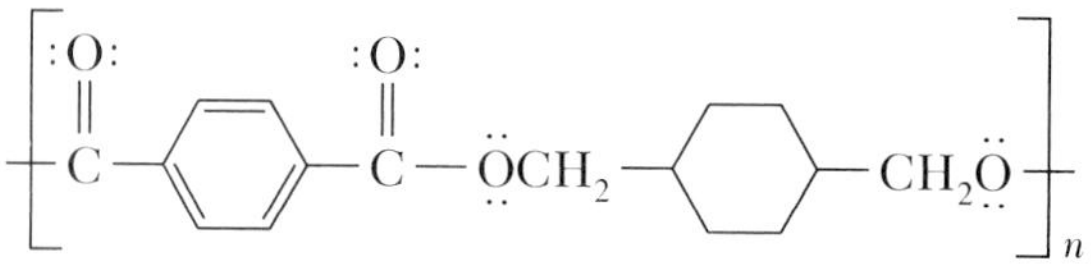

$$\left[-C(=O)-C_6H_4-C(=O)-OCH_2-C_6H_{10}-CH_2O-\right]_n$$

PROBLEM 29.9 A highly rigid polymer known as Glyptal can be prepared by reaction of phthalic anhydride and glycerol (1,2,3-propanetriol). The high rigidity of the polymer is associated with the **cross-linking** of polymer chains. In the first stages of the reaction, a *linear* polyester is formed because glycerol preferentially forms ester linkages through its more reactive terminal (primary) hydroxyl groups. Cross-linking then occurs as glycerol units of separate polymer chains form ester linkages between their less reactive central (secondary) hydroxyl groups. Show a representative portion of Glyptal, indicating the chemical nature of the cross-links.

Just as dicarboxylic acids and diols react to give polyesters, dicarboxylic acids and diamines react to give polyamides. The best known polyamide is nylon. There are several different types of nylon. The types vary according to the structures of the dicarboxylic acid and diamine used in the preparation. The most widely used type is nylon 66. The two 6s refer to the number of carbon atoms in the starting materials, as shown in Equation 29.5.

Eqn. 29.5

$$n\ HO{-}\overset{\overset{\displaystyle :O:}{\|}}{C}{-}(CH_2)_4{-}\overset{\overset{\displaystyle :O:}{\|}}{C}{-}OH + n\ H_2N{-}(CH_2)_6{-}NH_2 \longrightarrow \left[\overset{\overset{\displaystyle :O:}{\|}}{C}{-}(CH_2)_4{-}\overset{\overset{\displaystyle :O:}{\|}}{C}{-}NH{-}(CH_2)_6{-}NH \right]_n + (n-1)\ H_2O$$

Nylon 66 was first described in 1935 in a patent by Wallace Carothers, an organic chemist working at the Du Pont laboratories in Wilmington, Delaware. Stockings and other clothing made of nylon soon became commonplace.

29.4 Some Special Types of Polymers

COPOLYMERS

Copolymers are obtained when a mixture of monomers is used to achieve polymerization. An example of a copolymer of industrial importance is styrene-butadiene rubber (SBR), which is used for tires and electrical insulation. SBR is an addition polymer formed from 1,3,-butadiene and styrene. It has the general composition shown in Figure 29.6. The butadiene and styrene subunits are arranged randomly along the chain.

Another common copolymer, used in sheets as food wrapping, is prepared from vinylidene chloride ($CH_2{=}CCl_2$), the major component, and vinyl chloride, $CH_2{-}CHCl$.

Figure 29.6 Styrene butadiene rubber (SBR). This addition copolymer is made from a mixture of 1,3-butadiene and styrene. The monomer units are arranged randomly along the chain.

$$n\ H_2C{=}CH{-}CH{=}CH_2 + m\ C_6H_5CH{=}CH_2 \longrightarrow \left[CH_2CH{=}CHCH_2 \right]_n \left[\underset{\underset{\displaystyle C_6H_5}{|}}{CH}CH_2 \right]_m$$

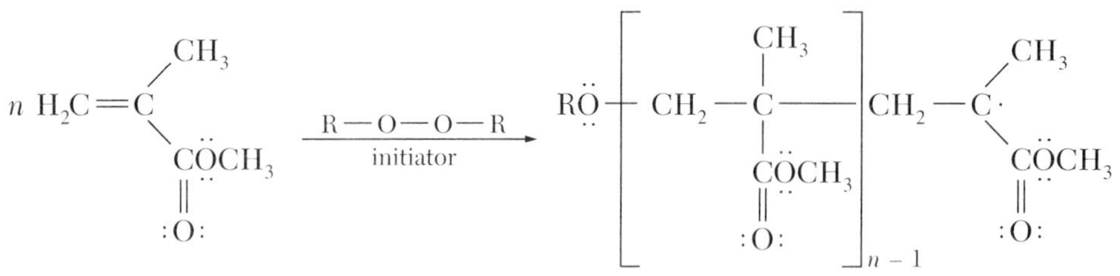

$$n\,H_2C{=}C(CH_3)(\ddot{C}(=\ddot{O}{:})\ddot{O}CH_3) \xrightarrow[\text{initiator}]{R-O-O-R} R\ddot{O}\left[CH_2-C(CH_3)(COCH_3{=}O)\right]_{n-1}CH_2-\dot{C}(CH_3)(COCH_3{=}O)$$

Figure 29.7 Beginning free-radical polymerization of methyl methacrylate.

BLOCK COPOLYMERS

Block copolymers are copolymers that contain alternating long sequences (or blocks) of different monomer subunits. For example, if we designate the subunits as I and II, a block copolymer could be represented as $\text{-(I)}_a\text{-(II)}_b\text{-(I)}_c\text{-(II)}_d\text{-}$. One method of preparing block copolymers is to use a condensation reaction to join two preformed polymer chains. Another method uses anionic polymerization.

GRAFT COPLYMERS

Graft copolymers are polymers in which a polymeric chain derived from one type of monomer is grafted (added) as a side chain onto the backbone chain of another polymer. The two polymer sections are synthesized from two different monomers. Graft copolymers can be made by carrying out the polymerization of one of the monomers in the presence of a preformed polymer of the other monomer.

For example, consider the polymerization of methyl methacrylate in the presence of polystyrene. A free-radical initiator is added to the mixture of methyl methacrylate and polystyrene, and the methyl methacrylate begins to polymerize (as discussed in Section 29.2). Each step of polymerization produces a radical, as shown in Figure 29.7. After each cycle of polymer growth, it is possible that the radical produced, instead of reacting with another methyl methacrylate molecule, will abstract a hydrogen atom from some position in a polystyrene molecule, as is shown in Figure 29.8.

Once a radical site is created on the polystyrene backbone, it can grow in the usual way by successive reactions with methyl methacrylate monomer. The result is a **graft copolymer.** A partial structure of this particular graft copolymer is shown in Figure 29.9.

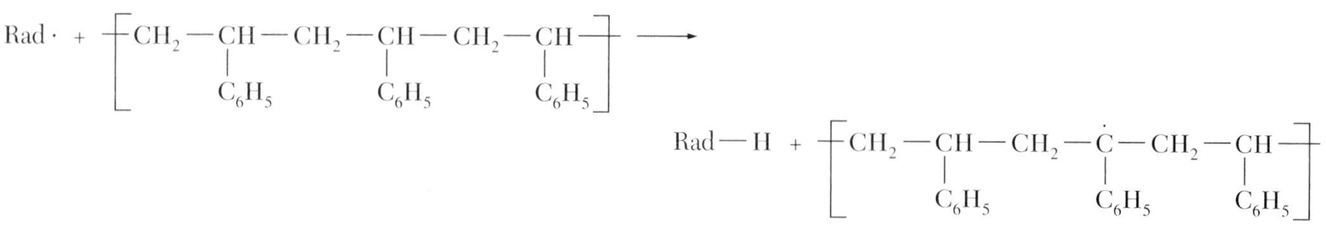

Figure 29.8 Second stage in the formation of a graft copolymer. The radical removing a hydrogen atom from the polystyrene was generated in the polymerization of methyl methacrylate, shown in Figure 29.7. The radical abstracts a hydrogen atom from the backbone of the polystyrene, producing a new active radical site at which further rounds of monomer addition can occur.

LIVING POLYMERS

It is sometimes possible to use anions to initiate polymerization (see Problem 29.4). In 1956, Michael Szwarc's studies of aspects of anionic polymerization

$$\text{Rad}\cdot + \left[CH_2-CH(C_6H_5)-CH_2-CH(C_6H_5)-CH_2-CH(C_6H_5)\right] \longrightarrow \text{Rad}-H + \left[CH_2-CH(C_6H_5)-CH_2-\dot{C}(C_6H_5)-CH_2-CH(C_6H_5)\right]$$

Figure 29.9 Portion of the structure of polystyrene–methyl methacrylate graft copolymer.

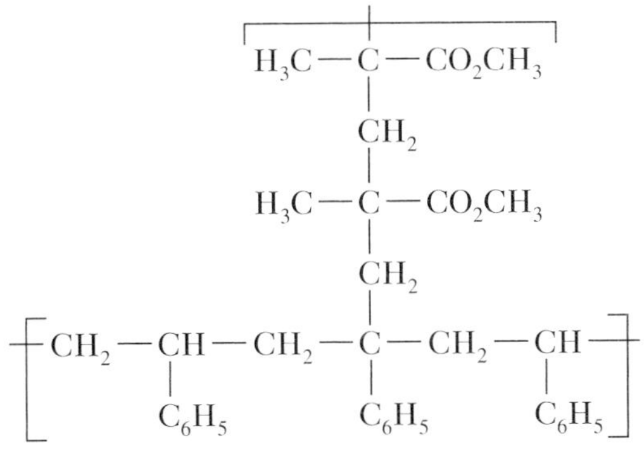

$$\left[CH_2-CH-CH_2-C(CH_2-C(CH_3)(CO_2CH_3)-CH_2-[C(CH_3)(CO_2CH_3)])-CH_2-CH \right]$$ (each CH/C on the backbone bearing C_6H_5)

led to the discovery of what are now known as living polymers. Szwarc was studying the polymerization of styrene upon exposure to sodium metal and naphthalene in tetrahydrofuran. The anionic initiator for the polymerization the radical anion of naphthalene, which is produced by transfer of an electron from sodium to naphthalene is shown in Equation 29.6.

Eqn. 29.6

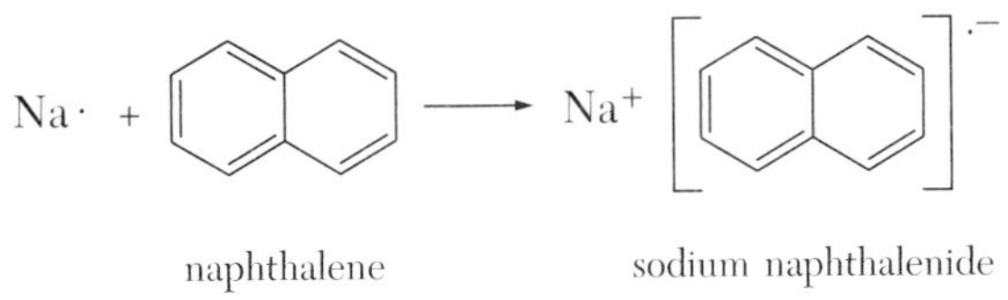

$$Na\cdot + C_{10}H_8 \longrightarrow Na^+ \left[C_{10}H_8\right]^{\cdot -}$$

naphthalene — sodium naphthalenide

In sodium naphthalenide, the electron added to the naphthalene component enters an antibonding molecular orbital of the aromatic system. This species is a potent base. The mechanism for the polymerization of the polystyrene using this radical anion is shown below.

MECHANISM OF REACTION

Polymerization of Styrene using the Naphthalene Radical Anion

Step 1 The naphthalene radical anion (represented here as $A\cdot^-$) transfers an electron to styrene, thus forming a radical anion of styrene.

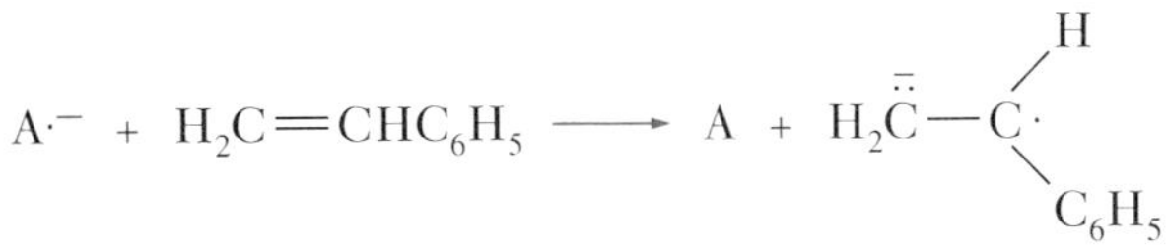

$$A\cdot^- + H_2C{=}CHC_6H_5 \longrightarrow A + H_2\ddot{C}^- - \dot{C}(H)(C_6H_5)$$

Step 2 Two styrene radical anions couple, forming a dianion.

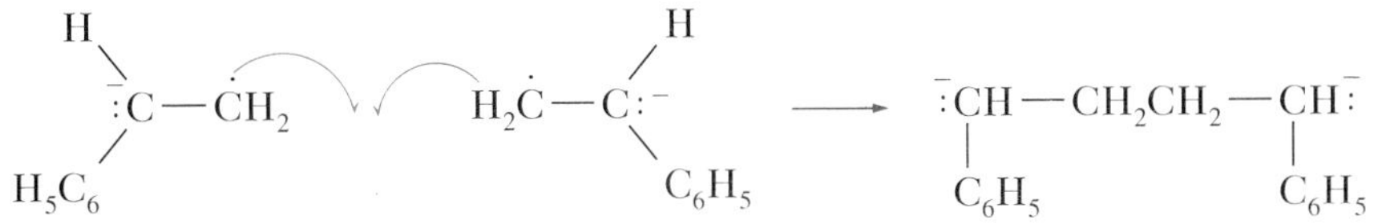

$$(H)(H_5C_6)\,{}^-\!:C-\dot{C}H_2 \;\; H_2\dot{C}-C:^-(H)(C_6H_5) \longrightarrow {}^-\!:CH(C_6H_5)-CH_2CH_2-CH(C_6H_5):^-$$

Steps 3 to *n* Each new anionic site can react with styrene monomer units, producing new anionic sites. A chain of reactions adding monomer units to both ends of the polymer is thereby set into motion.

$$\overset{-}{:}\underset{\displaystyle C_6H_5}{\underset{|}{C}}HCH_2CH_2\underset{\displaystyle C_6H_5}{\underset{|}{C}}H\overset{-}{:} \xrightarrow{n\ H_2C=\underset{\displaystyle C_6H_5}{\underset{|}{C}}H} \overset{-}{:}\underset{\displaystyle C_6H_5}{\underset{|}{C}}HCH_2-\left[\underset{\displaystyle C_6H_5}{\underset{|}{C}}HCH_2\right]_n-CH_2\underset{\displaystyle C_6H_5}{\underset{|}{C}}H\overset{-}{:}$$

There is a particularly novel aspect to this discovery. Szwarc treated some styrene with sodium and naphthalene, and after a rapid polymerization reaction took place, yielding polystyrene, he added some more styrene monomer. He found that it was taken up by the polystyrene, adding to its molecular weight. He also found that he could add other materials, such as butadiene, and that they were *also* taken up by the polystyrene. The latter reaction produced a block copolymer of styrene and butadiene. Put simply, Szwarc had discovered that he could get his polymer sample to grow if he "fed" it appropriate monomers, hence the term **living polymer.**

No such living polymers can be made through radical or cationic polymerization because of the existence of chain-terminating steps in radical and cationic polymerization processes, but these steps are lacking when anion polymerization is carried out under controlled conditions. The polystyrene produced by Szwarc was itself anionic, and therefore reactive, at its termini. The anionic sites are relatively stable compared to radical or cationic sites and thus persist for appreciable periods of time. If more monomer is added during the time the anionic sites are present, reaction will take place at these sites and the polymer will grow.

In radical and cationic polymerization, the growing polymer chain also has reactive sites at its termini. They are, in fact, responsible for the growth of the polymer, since successive monomer units are added at these sites. However, these cationic and radical sites are *highly* reactive. When the polymer chain stops growing, a chain-terminating step eliminates the positive charge or radical from the terminus of the polymer (see Section 29.2). If we add more monomer, no reaction can occur because the polymer no longer has a reactive site.

In controlled anionic polymerization, there is no chain-terminating step. Polymerization stops when the supply of monomer is consumed. The polymer so produced has negative charges at its termini and will accordingly react with an added monomer and continue to grow.

29.5 Expoxy Resins

Most people are familiar with epoxy resins as adhesives. Two components are mixed just before they are applied to the surfaces to be bonded. One of the components (the base resin or **epoxy resin**) is a polymer containing epoxide rings. The other component (the hardener) is a polyamine. The different amino groups of the polyamine act as nucleophiles toward epoxide rings of different chains, causing the polymer chains to become cross-linked (see Problem 29.8 for another example of the cross-linking of polymer chains). When the polymer is cross-linked, it becomes extremely hard and strong, accounting for the great bonding properties of this type of adhesive.

The most common of the epoxy resins is made by a polymerization reaction between *epichlorohydrin* (the common name given to the oxirane derived from 3-chloro-1-propene) and *bisphenol A* (the common name given to 2,2-bis(4'-hydroxyphenyl)propane), as shown in Equation 29.7.

Eqn. 29.7

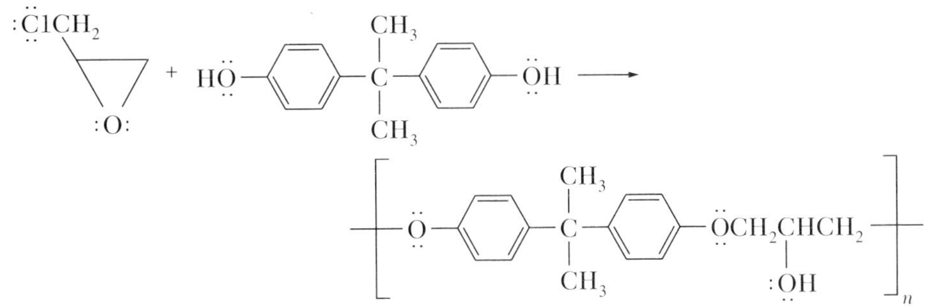

:ClCH₂ (oxirane, :O:) + HO—C₆H₄—C(CH₃)₂—C₆H₄—OH ⟶ [—O—C₆H₄—C(CH₃)₂—C₆H₄—OCH₂CH(OH)CH₂—]ₙ

An unopened oxirane ring remains at each end of the growing polymer chain. The hardener is a polyamine such as **29.2** or **29.3**; it reacts with the oxirane rings at the termini.

$(H_2NCH_2CH_2CH_2)_2NH$ **29.2**

$(H_2NCH_2CH_2CH_2)_3N$: **29.3**

Cross-linking begins with nucleophilic attack of the amino groups on oxirane rings of different polymer chains, as shown in Figure 29.10. Each time an oxirane ring is opened by nucleophilic attack of an amine group, a *new* nucleophilic hydroxyl group (an incipient alkoxide anion) is created that can attack the oxirane ring of another polymer chain. By a succession of such reactions, extensive cross-linking is established.

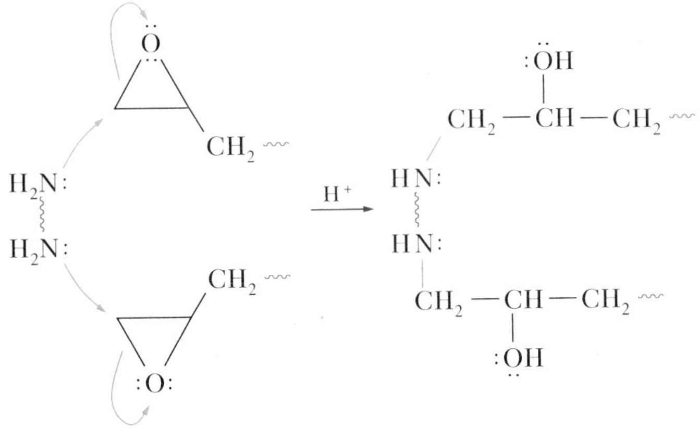

H₂N: ~ H₂N: + 2 oxirane—CH₂~ $\xrightarrow{H^+}$ HN(CH₂—CH(OH)—CH₂~) ~ HN(CH₂—CH(OH)—CH₂~)

Figure 29.10 The first step in the cross-linking of an epoxy resin with a polyamine hardener.

Summary

- Synthetic polymers are high molecular weight substances that find widespread use as plastics, fibers, adhesives, and construction materials.
- Addition polymers can be made by adding an appropriate initiator to a suitable monomer (i.e., an alkene or alkene derivative) to set into motion a chain reaction.
- Radicals, cations, anions, and organometallic reagents can be used to bring about addition polymerization reactions.
- In an isotactic polymer, all of the carbon atoms of the chain have the same configuration. In a syndiotactic polymer, the carbon atoms have alternating configurations. In an atactic polymer, there is no regularity to the arrangement of carbon atom configurations.
- The stereochemistry along a polymer chain has an important effect on the properties of the polymer. Different polymer chains of the structurally more ordered isotactic and syndiotactic polymers pack together better than do chains of atactic polymers. The result is a more crystalline and more useful polymer.
- The Ziegler-Natta catalysts provide a route to more crystalline isotactic addition polymers.
- A polymer made up of more than one kind of monomer is called a copolymer. Several sorts of copolymers have been synthesized. Among the more important are graft copolymers and block copolymers. Copolymers often have superior properties to more simple polymers.
- Condensation polymers are made by the reaction of a pair of monomers, each of which contains two (or more) functional groups that are reactive toward the functional groups of the other monomer. For example, diols and dicarboxylic acids react to form polyesters, and diamines and dicarboxylic acids react to form polyamides.
- Cross-linking of polymer chains produces a stronger polymer. A useful example is found with epoxy adhesives. The hardener used with these adhesives is a polyamine that creates the cross-links by nucleophilic attack on the oxirane rings of different polymer chains.

Terms to Remember

addition polymer	isotactic	block copolymer
Ziegler-Natta catalyst	syndiotactic	graft copolymer
crystallinity	condensation polymer	living polymer
atactic	cross-linking	epoxy resin

Additional Problems

29.10 We have often seen organic peroxides acting as initiators of radical chain reactions. Azobisisobutyronitrile (AIBN, shown below) can be used as an alternative to a peroxide. On heating, AIBN dissociates to yield nitrogen gas plus radicals. Use fishhook arrows to describe this decomposition. What end group will be present in an addition polymer produced using AIBN as the radical initiator?

$$:N{\equiv}C-\overset{\displaystyle CH_3}{\underset{\displaystyle CH_3}{\overset{|}{\underset{|}{C}}}}-\ddot{N}{=}\ddot{N}-\overset{\displaystyle CH_3}{\underset{\displaystyle CH_3}{\overset{|}{\underset{|}{C}}}}-C{\equiv}N:$$

AIBN

29.11 Give the structures of the monomers or polymers indicated *A–C:*

a. A (C_4H_5Cl) ⟶ $-[CH_2-C(Cl)=CH-CH_2]_n-$ neoprene: a synthetic rubber with excellent resistance to weather, oil, and heat

b. 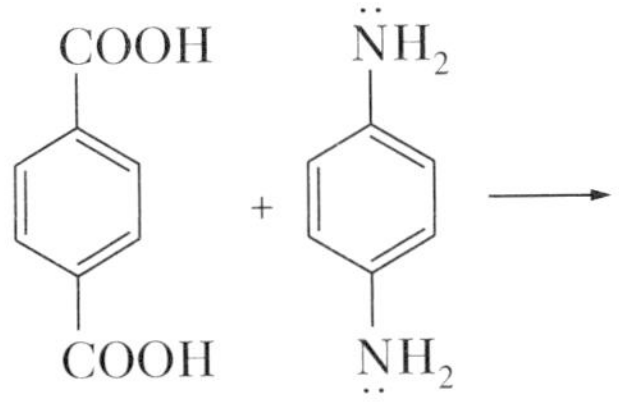 (p-HOOC–C_6H_4–COOH) + (p-H_2N–C_6H_4–NH_2) ⟶ *B* a polymer commonly known as Kevlar, used to make bulletproof vests

c. $Cl_2C=O$ (phosgene) + bisphenol A (see Section 29.5) ⟶ *C* a polycarbonate ester that is transparent and impact resistant, commonly known as Lexan

29.12 In a polymerization process initiated by free radicals, which experimental conditions would you choose to generate a polymer of higher molecular weight: an excess or a deficiency of the radical initiator? Explain your answer.

29.13 Poly(vinyl alcohol) is used for fibers and in adhesives. Give a structure for this polymer. It cannot be prepared by polymerization of vinyl alcohol. Why not? (*Hint:* Consult Figure 15.19 and the related discussion). How could you synthesize poly(vinyl alcohol) starting with vinyl acetate?

29.14 When each of the following is treated as indicated, a polymer forms. Show a mechanism for each reaction and deduce the repeating units in the polymer chains.

a. 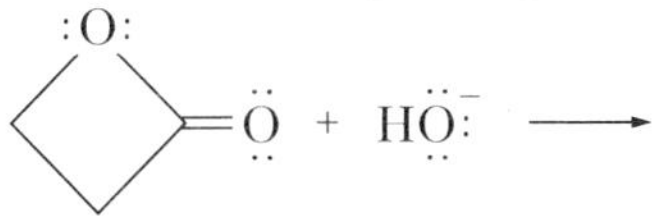 β-propiolactone + HO^- ⟶

b. 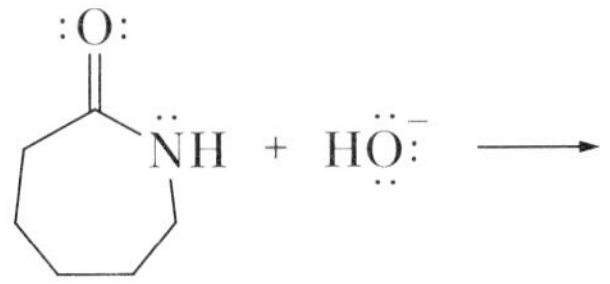 ε-caprolactam + HO^- ⟶

c.  maleic anhydride + $HOCH_2CH_2OH$ ⟶

29.15 Urethanes (general structure shown below) are made by the reaction of an isocyananate, $R-N=C=O$, with an alcohol, R′OH.

$$R-NH-C(=O)-OR'$$

Write a mechanism for the formation of a urethane using the curved-arrow formalism.

Polyurethanes are polymers with a variety of industrial uses. Which starting materials would you use to prepare a polyurethane? What is the repeating unit in the polymer chain?

29.16 A living polymer can be "killed" by adding water, that is, the polymer will no longer grow when fed monomer. Account for the role of water in killing the living polymer.

29.17 Polymerization of a substance of formula C_6H_{10} yields a polymer that on ozonolysis and workup under reductive conditions produces the compound shown below.

$$CH_3-\overset{\overset{:\ddot{O}:}{\|}}{C}-CH_2CH_2-\overset{\overset{:\ddot{O}:}{\|}}{C}-CH_3$$

Suggest a structure for the monomer, and show the repeating unit of the polymer.

30 CHAPTER Molecular Orbitals in Concerted Reactions

30.1 Introduction

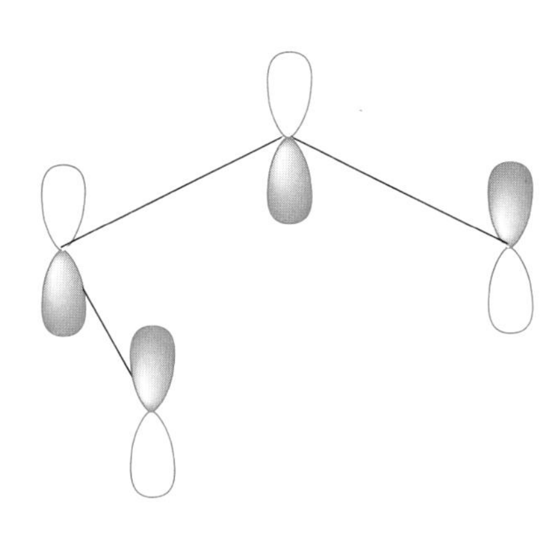

Organic chemists classify reactions according to similarities in their mechanisms. In this way, sets of reactions that may seem unrelated at first glance can be joined into families. A reaction mechanism was described earlier as a step-by-step listing of the processes through which reactants are converted into products. We have seen, however, that some reactions (e.g., an S_N2 reaction) proceed in a *single* reaction step. Such reactions are said to be **concerted reactions.** No reaction intermediates are involved. Instead, the reactants proceed to products via a single transition state. (See Chapter 10 to review the difference between intermediates and transition states.)

In this chapter we analyze a group of concerted **pericyclic reactions** (reactions with cyclic transition states). These reactions were poorly understood until the late Professor R. B. Woodward of Harvard University and Professor R. Hoffmann, currently of Cornell University, applied molecular orbital principles to gain an important new type of understanding of these reactions. Professor Hoffmann was rewarded in 1981 with the Nobel Prize in Chemistry, which he shared with Professor K. Fukui of Kyoto University, another pioneer in the application of molecular orbital methods to organic reactions. (Professor Woodward, who died in 1979, had already received a Nobel Prize in 1965 in recognition of his outstanding contributions to synthetic organic chemistry.)

We will begin by considering some examples of reactions that *do* occur and reactions that do *not* occur, to see how the puzzling contrasts set the stage for Woodward and Hoffmann to develop their model.

30.2 Experimental Results

CYCLOADDITIONS

The Diels-Alder reaction was introduced earlier in the text (Chapter 15). A further example of a Diels-Alder type of reaction is shown in Equation 30.1.

Eqn. 30.1

100 °C, 1 hr → CHO

100% yield

Diels-Alder reactions occur under conditions of thermal stimulation (i.e., upon heating). (Some Diels-Alder reactions actually occur at room temperature or below. They are still classified as thermal reactions.) The Diels-Alder reaction is a **cycloaddition** reaction—two separate open-chain entities combine to form a cyclic product. The reaction occurs in a single step. There is no evidence for intermediates such as radicals, carbocations, or carbanions.

While Diels-Alder reactions occur readily between dienes and dienophiles under thermal stimulation, the apparently similar cycloaddition depicted in Equation 30.2 *cannot* be effected by heating. However, it does occur under stimulation by light.

Eqn. 30.2

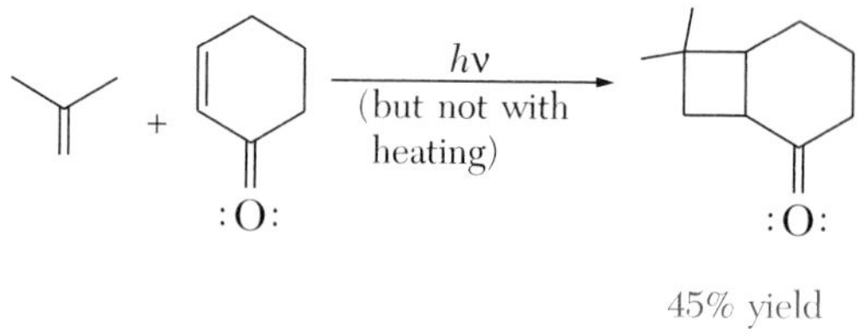

$h\nu$ (but not with heating)

:O: :O:

45% yield

In contrast, light energy cannot substitute for thermal energy in the Diels-Alder reaction. Shining light on a mixture of a diene and a dienophile does not cause a Diels-Alder reaction to occur (although a different type of reaction sometimes occurs under these conditions).

Many studies have demonstrated the generality of the observations just described. It is now helpful to introduce a classification system for considering these cycloadditions. Cycloadditions involving a diene component (a four π electron system) and an alkene component (a two π electron system) are known as $[\pi_4 + \pi_2]$ cycloadditions. Cycloadditions involving the union of two alkene components (each is a two π electron system) are referred to as $[\pi_2 + \pi_2]$ cycloadditions; this type of cycloaddition *requires* photochemical stimulation in order to occur.

ELECTROCYCLIC REACTIONS

In an **electrocyclic reaction,** a ring is formed by the generation of a new σ bond between the two ends of a conjugated π-electron system. Two examples of electrocyclic reactions involving the formation of six-membered rings are shown in Equations 30.3 and 30.4. Both reactions occur with the formation of a new σ bond between the termini of conjugated triene units. Notice, however, that while reaction is initiated under either thermal or photochemical conditions, *different* isomers result under the two sets of conditions.

Eqn. 30.3

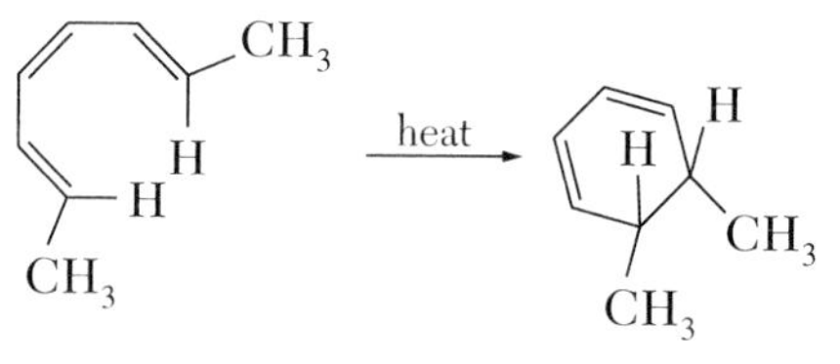

CH_3 H H CH_3 heat H H CH_3 CH_3

(2*E*,4*Z*,6*E*)-2,4,6-octatriene

cis-5,6-dimethyl-1,3-cyclohexadiene

Eqn. 30.4

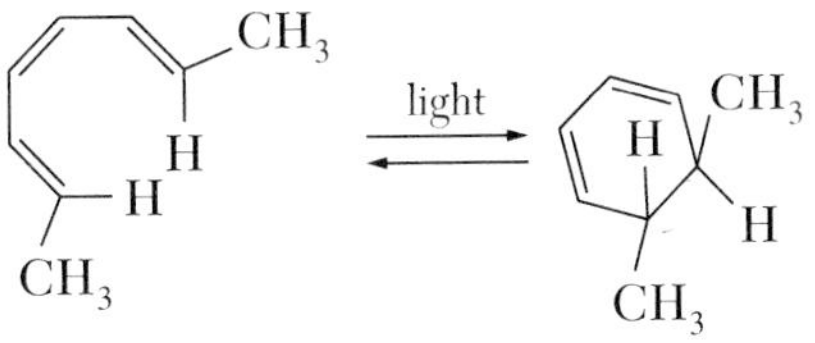

(2*E*,4*Z*,6*E*)-2,4,6-octatriene $\xrightarrow{\text{light}}$ *trans*-5,6-dimethyl-1,3-cyclohexadiene (racemic)

The reactions shown in Equations 30.5 and 30.6 illustrate electrocyclic processes that form four-membered rings by generation of a σ bond between the termini of diene components. Notice that the reactants differ *only* in the geometries about one of their double bonds. The two reactions give the same product, but the first requires thermal stimulation while the second requires photochemical stimulation.

Eqn. 30.5

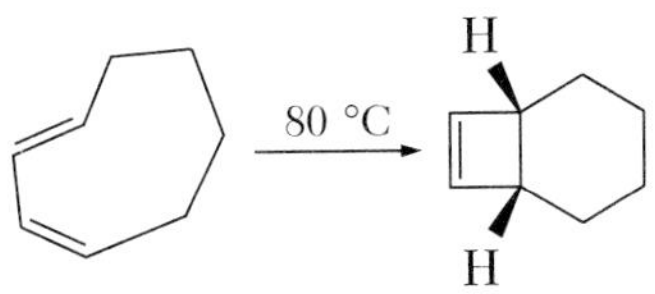

(*E*,*Z*)-1,3-cyclooctadiene $\xrightarrow{80\ °C}$ 100% yield

Eqn. 30.6

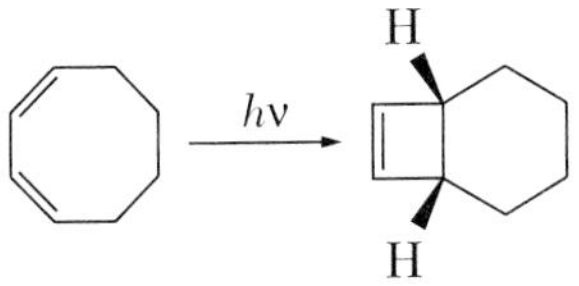

(*Z*,*Z*)-1,3-cyclooctadiene $\xrightarrow{h\nu}$ 41% yield

Finally, consider the two thermally induced electrocyclic reactions shown in Equations 30.7 and 30.8. Both involve the opening of cyclobutene rings, and both are *stereospecific*, that is, stereochemically different reactants give stereochemically different products.

Eqn. 30.7

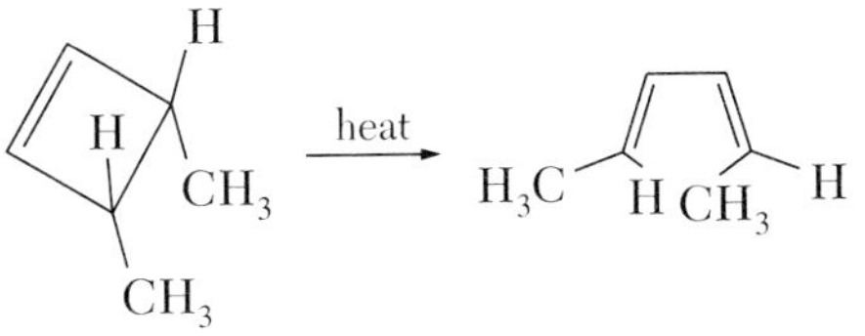

cis-3-4-dimethylcyclobutene $\xrightarrow{\text{heat}}$ (*E*,*Z*)-2,4-hexadiene

Eqn. 30.8

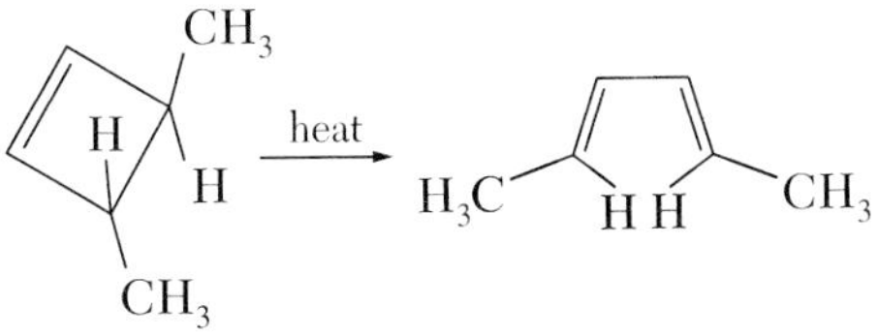

trans-3-4-dimethylcyclobutene $\xrightarrow{\text{heat}}$ (*E*,*E*)-2,4-hexadiene

Some patterns clearly exist in these reactions and in related reactions that we will meet later in this chapter. In particular, reactivity (or the lack of it) and the nature of the product depend critically on three factors:

1. the type of stimulation (thermal or photochemical)
2. the number of π electrons of the reactant
3. the stereochemistry of the reactant(s).

However, organic chemists were puzzled about the underlying theoretical basis of these observations. Could a model be developed that would satisfactorily rationalize all of the experimental observations and enable organic chemists to predict the conditions required to produce a particular stereochemical consequence? From Woodward's and Hoffmann's analysis emerged such a theoretical model. It will be the focus of our attention in the remainder of this chapter.

PROBLEM 30.1 Classify the following reactions as cycloadditions or electrocyclic reactions.

a. + $\xrightarrow{h\nu}$ CH_3 :O: :O:

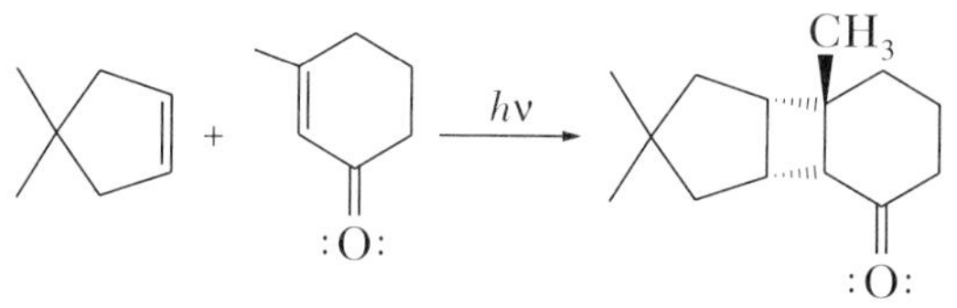

b. $\xrightarrow{100\ °C}$ H H

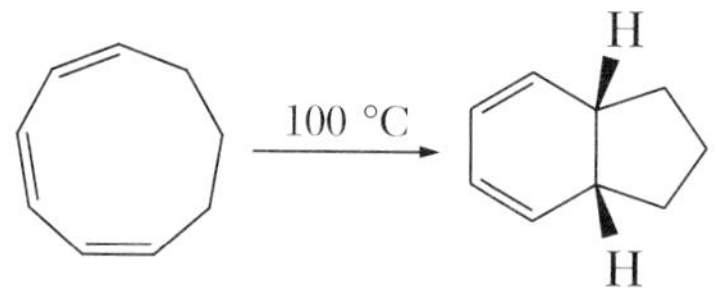

c. $\xrightarrow{h\nu}$

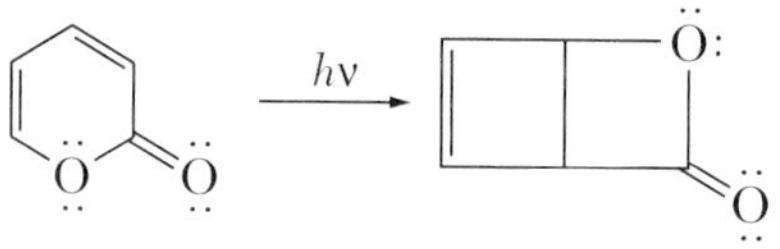

30.3 A Review of the Molecular Orbital Model

FUNDAMENTALS

According to the molecular orbital model, a set of orbitals (molecular orbitals), each with a characteristic shape and energy, is available to electrons in molecules (Chapter 16). The usual approach for obtaining a description of the molecular orbitals of a particular molecule is the *linear combination of atomic orbitals* (LCAO) method. The atomic orbitals of the constituent atoms provide the starting points in this method. Molecular orbitals are constructed by mathematically combining the participating atomic orbitals from the atoms in the molecule, following the guidelines outlined in Chapter 16 and elsewhere in the text. An important point is that a combination of n atomic orbitals always leads to n molecular orbitals.

Figure 30.1 Construction of molecular orbitals from atomic orbitals. Any molecular orbitals higher in energy than the starting atomic orbitals are antibonding; those lower in energy than the starting atomic orbitals are bonding molecular orbitals.

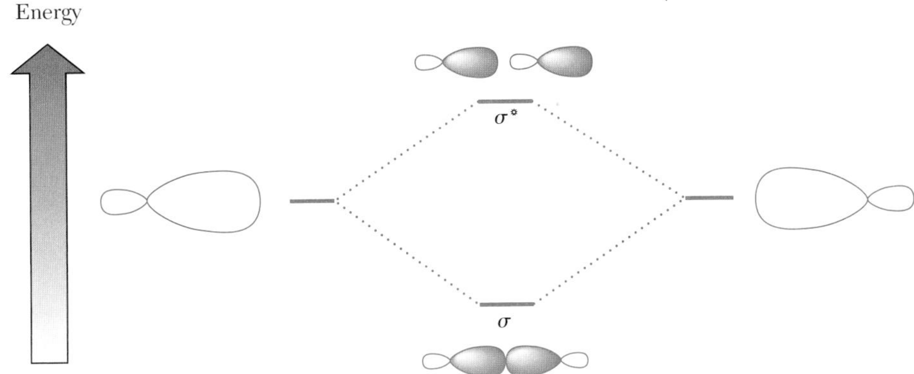

π molecular orbitals

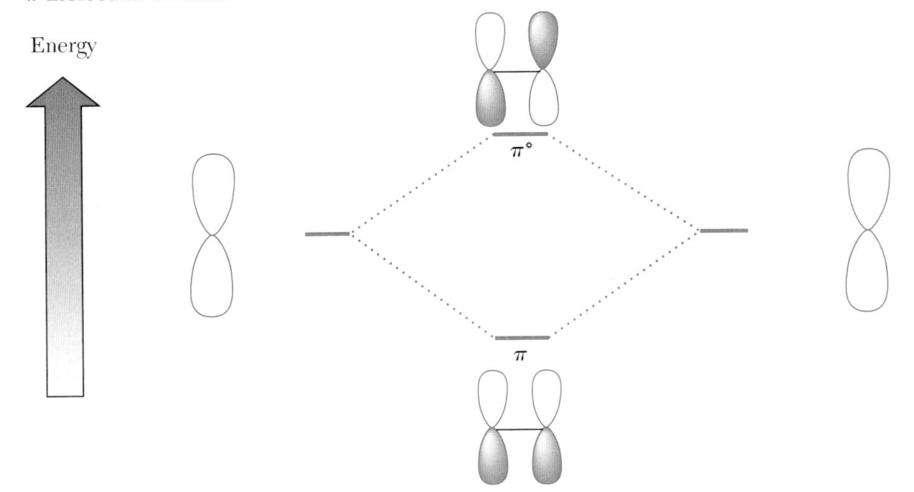

TYPES OF MOLECULAR ORBITALS

Examples of atomic orbital combinations that lead to σ and π molecular orbitals are shown in Figure 30.1. *End-on* interaction of s, p, or hybrid orbitals (or combinations thereof) leads to the generation of σ molecular orbitals, while *side-to-side* interaction leads to π molecular orbitals.

NODES, ENERGIES, AND SYMMETRY CORRECTNESS

A node is a region of a molecular orbital where the wave function has a value of zero. No electron density is present at a node. In Chapter 16 we introduced a useful correlation between the number of nodes and the energies of molecular orbitals created through interactions of atomic orbitals. Figure 30.2 reviews this correlation, using the π molecular orbitals of 1,3,5-hexatriene as an example.

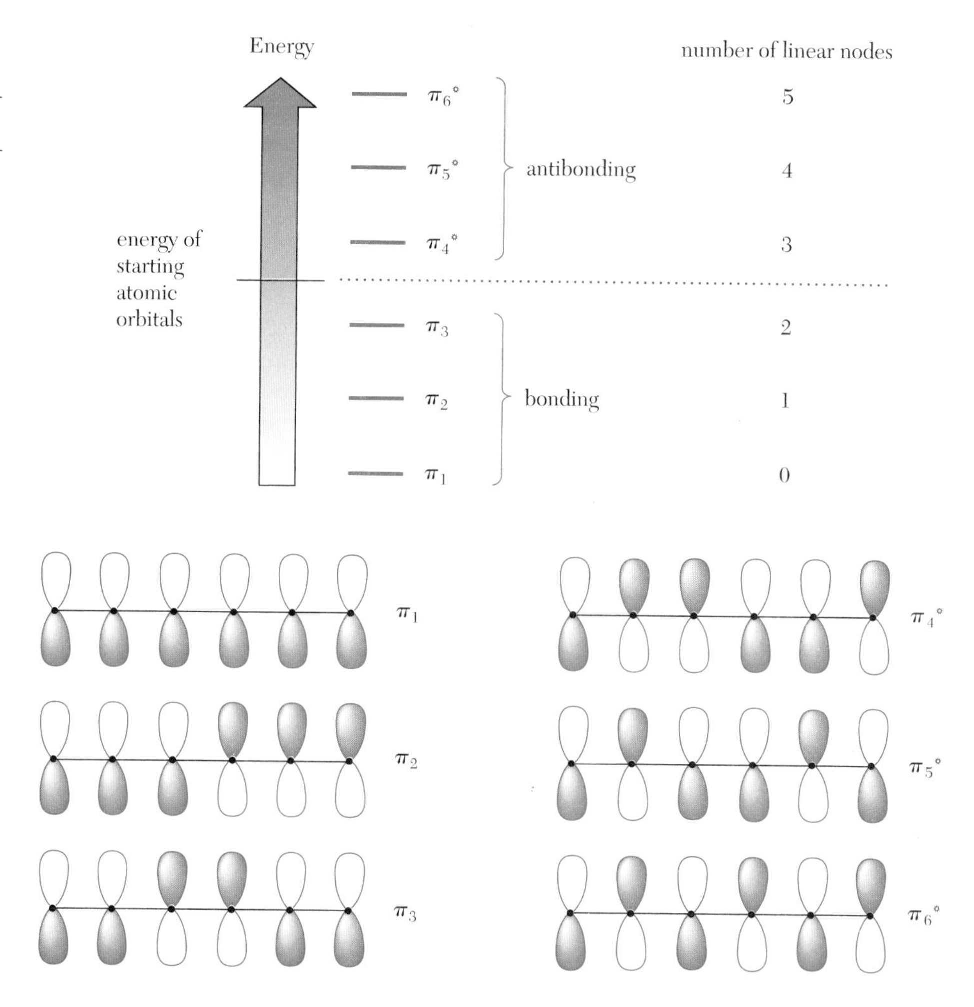

Figure 30.2 Relative energies and nodal characteristics of π molecular orbitals of the hexatriene system. The molecular orbitals increase in energy with increasing number of vertical (linear) nodes. The molecular orbitals are symmetrical in their energy distribution about the energy of the starting atomic orbitals.

Another important point to keep in mind in constructing molecular orbitals from atomic orbitals is that the molecular orbitals must be *symmetry correct*, that is, the molecular orbitals must be symmetric or antisymmetric with regard to the symmetry elements of the molecule in question (Chapter 16). For example, the single node of the π_2 molecular orbital of 1,3,5-hexatriene is midway between the third and fourth atoms of the chain.

FRONTIER MOLECULAR ORBITALS

A complete understanding of the reactivity of a molecule requires knowledge of *all* of its molecular orbitals. However, a useful simplification is to consider only the **frontier molecular orbitals,** that is, the highest occupied molecular orbital (HOMO) and the lowest unoccupied molecular orbital (LUMO). Often we can derive very useful information about the potential chemistry of a molecule through inspection of just its frontier molecular orbitals. If a pair of molecules are reacting with each other, we need to consider the frontier molecular orbitals of both molecules.

PROBLEM 30.2

a. Which π molecular orbitals of 1,3,5-hexatriene are symmetric and which are antisymmetric with regard to a plane bisecting the C3—C4 bond?
b. Which are the frontier molecular orbitals of a neutral, ground state molecule of 1,3,5-hexatriene?
c. Draw the molecular orbital representation for the HOMO and LUMO of 1,3,5,7-octatetraene.

30.4 The Transformation of Reactant to Product Molecular Orbitals

In a reaction, the molecular orbitals of the reactant(s) must be converted into the molecular orbitals of the product(s). Woodward and Hoffmann proposed that in *concerted* reactions a principle known as the **conservation of orbital symmetry** must hold. According to this principle, the molecular orbitals of the reactant(s) evolve smoothly into the molecular orbitals of the product(s). The essence of this model is that the orbitals of the reactants can evolve only into orbitals of products having the *same symmetry properties*.

In this chapter we will use the symmetry properties of frontier molecular orbitals to gain the types of insights that follow from the Woodward-Hoffmann approach. This is a *simplified form* of the application of orbital symmetry to concerted reactions (not *all* orbitals are considered), but it is extremely useful for its predictive abilities.

30.5 Contrasting Conditions for [$\pi_2 + \pi_2$] and [$\pi_4 + \pi_2$] Cycloadditions

Earlier in this chapter we pointed out that contrasting experimental conditions are necessary for the stimulation of different types of cycloaddition reactions. The specific examples we considered indicated that thermal stimulation was required for [$\pi_4 + \pi_2$] cycloadditions, while photochemical stimulation was required for [$\pi_2 + \pi_2$] cycloadditions. In this section we will analyze these reactions using frontier molecular orbital concepts. First, we will consider the orbital interactions that can occur under thermal stimulation for both types of cycloaddition reactions. We will then consider the same types of interactions under photochemical stimulation.

THERMAL STIMULATION

Under thermal stimulation, both reactants are present in their electronic ground states. None of the antibonding molecular orbitals are occupied. Therefore the frontier orbitals are the highest-energy bonding π molecular orbital of one reactant and the lowest-energy antibonding π molecular orbital of the other reactant. Looking at these interacting orbitals of the reactants, we now consider the new σ bonds that are created in the reaction (Figure 30.3).

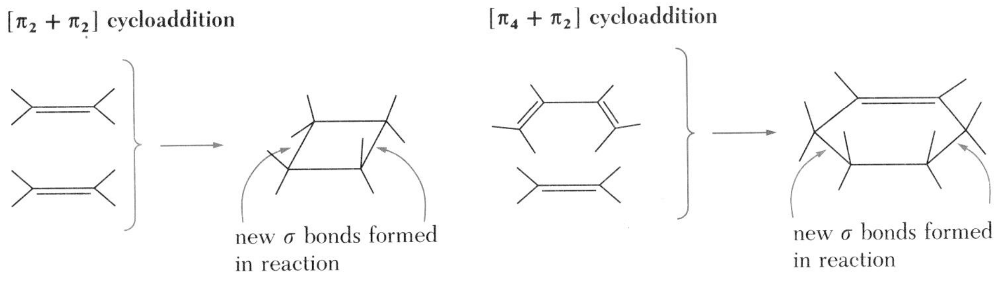

Figure 30.3 New bond formation in cycloaddition reactions. In both [$\pi_2 + \pi_2$] and [$\pi_4 + \pi_2$] cycloadditions, a pair of new σ bonds form. If the cycloaddition reaction is concerted, both new bonds must form simultaneously.

[$\pi_2 + \pi_2$] cycloaddition

new σ bonds formed in reaction

[$\pi_4 + \pi_2$] cycloaddition

new σ bonds formed in reaction

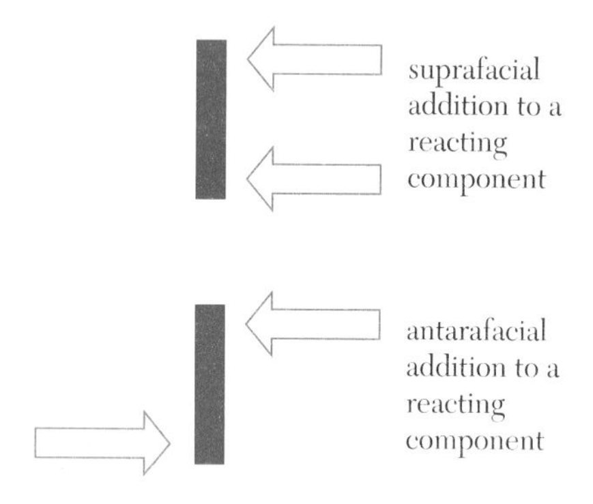

Figure 30.4 Suprafacial and antarafacial modes of addition. In a suprafacial addition, the two new bonds (illustrated by arrows) are formed to the same face of the substrate component. In an antarafacial addition, one new bond is formed to each of the two faces (opposite faces).

We see that in both reactions, two new σ bonds must form. If the reaction is concerted, both new σ bonds must form simultaneously, and this is possible only if the interaction of the frontier orbitals leads to the generation of two σ-bonding interactions at the same time. Before we consider the interaction of the frontier orbitals, we need to look at the geometric requirements of the reaction. In order for reaction to occur, the two components must approach so that the lobes of the reactant π orbitals interact in an end-on manner. If both new bonds form using the *same face* of a reaction component, the reaction is said to be **suprafacial** with regard to that component, as illustrated in Figure 30.4. If the two new bonds form to *opposite faces* of a reaction component, we say that the cycloaddition is **antarafacial** with regard to that reaction component. This geometry is also illustrated in Figure 30.4.

For simple $[\pi_2 + \pi_2]$ cycloadditions we need to consider only a mode of addition that is suprafacial with respect to *both* components. We classify such a reaction as a $[\pi_2 s + \pi_2 s]$ process. Another type of approach is possible *in principle*—a cycloaddition in which one component reacts in a suprafacial manner while the other reacts in an antarafacial manner. This type of reaction is classified as a $[\pi_2 s + \pi_2 a]$ process. Both types of processes are illustrated schematically in Figure 30.5.

Figure 30.5 Suprafacial-suprafacial and suprafacial-antarafacial cycloadditions. In the reaction illustrated on the left, both components interact in a suprafacial manner. In the reaction illustrated on the right, only one component interacts in a suprafacial manner while the other interacts in an antarafacial manner.

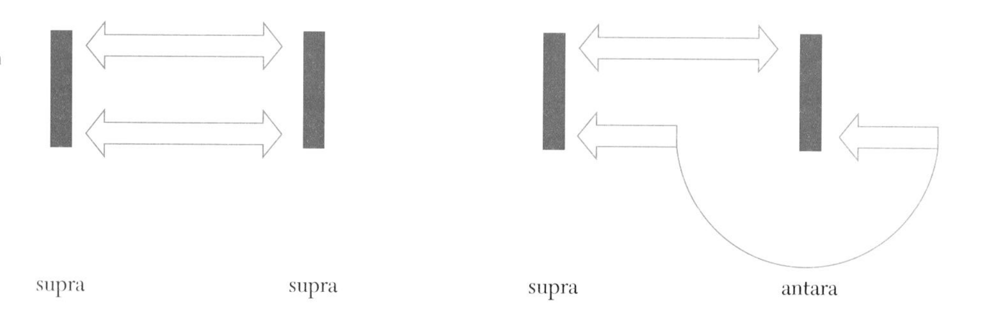

For simple $[\pi_2 + \pi_2]$ cycloadditions we generally only need to consider the $[\pi_2 s + \pi_2 s]$ process. The alternative $[\pi_2 s + \pi_2 a]$ process normally has too much strain associated with it. Thus, to assess the possibility of a *concerted* $[\pi_2 + \pi_2]$ cycloaddition, we normally need to consider only whether the simultaneous generation of two new σ bonds is possible through $[\pi_2 s + \pi_2 s]$ interaction of the frontier orbitals.

As is shown in Figure 30.6, the simultaneous generation of two new σ bonds is in fact *not* possible for a $[\pi_2 s + \pi_2 s]$ cycloaddition. When the HOMO of one alkene interacts with the LUMO of another alkene, only *one* new σ bonding interaction occurs. The approach of the remaining portions of the frontier orbitals yields an *antibonding* interaction. We thus say that the $[\pi_2 s + \pi_2 s]$ process is **symmetry forbidden.** (Notice that this analysis precludes only the possibility that a *concerted* reaction could occur—*stepwise* cycloaddition is *not* excluded. This frontier orbital analysis relates *only* to concerted processes.)

Figure 30.7 shows a frontier molecular orbital analysis for a $[\pi_4 s + \pi_2 s]$ cycloaddition of a diene and an alkene (Diels-Alder reaction). We could choose

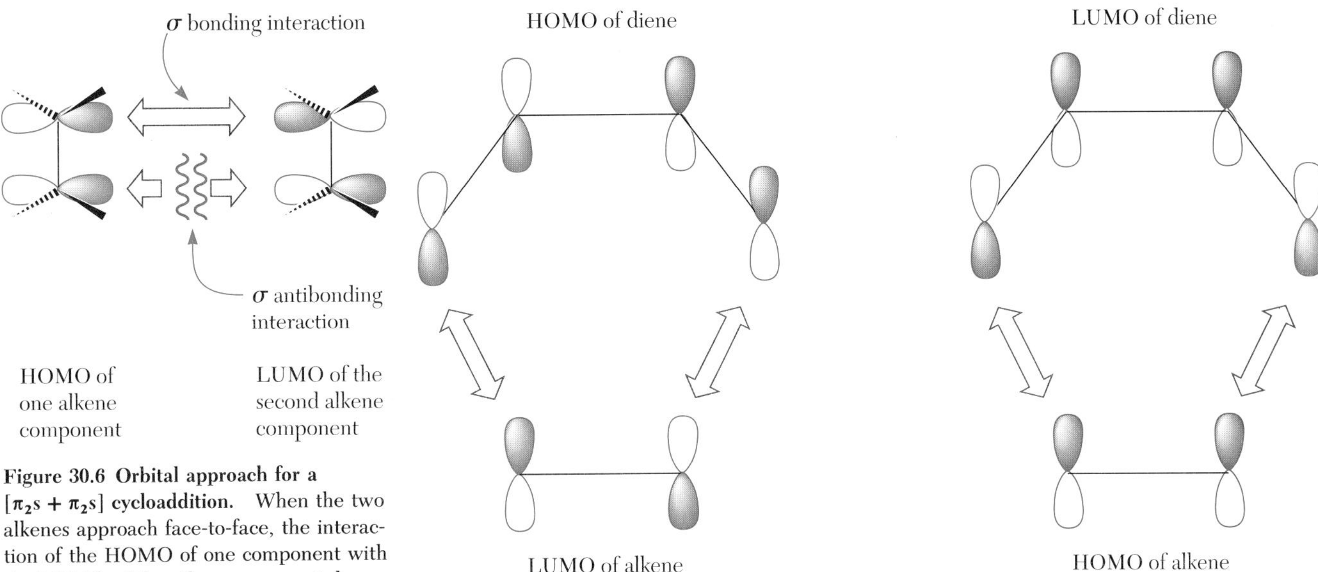

Figure 30.6 Orbital approach for a [π_2s + π_2s] cycloaddition. When the two alkenes approach face-to-face, the interaction of the HOMO of one component with the LUMO of the other component does *not* lead to the simultaneous formation of two new σ bonds. Thus *concerted* cycloaddition is not possible by a [π_2s + π_2s] process.

Figure 30.7 Frontier molecular orbital analysis of the suprafacial-suprafacial approach of a diene and an alkene under conditions of thermal stimulation. We can look at the interaction in two ways. The diagram on the left shows the interaction of the diene HOMO with the alkene LUMO, while the diagram on the right shows the interaction of the diene LUMO with the alkene HOMO. Each analysis leads to the conclusion that two simultaneous σ-bonding interactions can occur. This is consistent with the experimental result that concerted reaction (Diels-Alder reaction) *does* occur under thermal stimulation with these types of reagents.

two sets of frontier orbitals for this analysis, either diene HOMO/alkene LUMO, or diene LUMO/alkene HOMO. Regardless of the set we choose, we see that two simultaneous new σ-bonding interactions *do* occur. We thus say that a [π_4s + π_2s] cycloaddition is **symmetry allowed**—cycloaddition can occur in a concerted fashion.

A symmetry-allowed concerted pericyclic reaction generally occurs with relative ease. It has a significantly lower activation energy than does a symmetry-forbidden reaction, and its activation energy is lower than that for any stepwise process leading to the same products.

PHOTOCHEMICAL STIMULATION

Consider a [π_2s + π_2s] cycloaddition occurring under photochemical stimulation. (An example is the cyclodimerization of 2,3-dimethyl-2-butene, illustrated in Equation 30.9.)

Eqn. 30.9

2 (2,3-dimethyl-2-butene) $\xrightarrow{h\nu}$ (octamethylcyclobutane)

75% yield

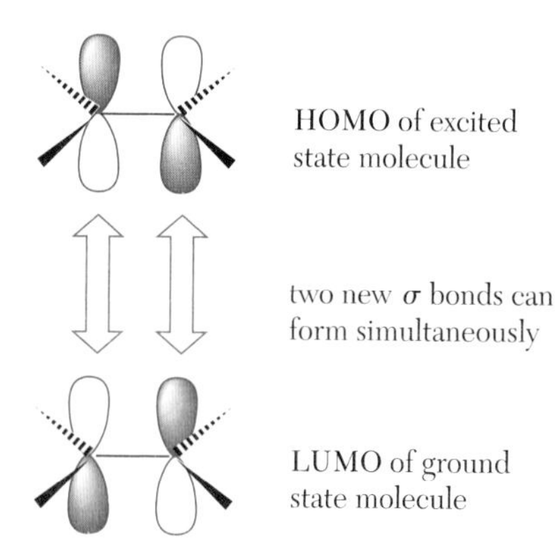

Figure 30.8 Frontier molecular orbital analysis of the cycloaddition of a ground state alkene molecule and an excited state alkene molecule. A concerted reaction is possible because the two required new σ bonds can form simultaneously.

If the excitation wavelength is properly chosen, *some* molecules will become excited. In these excited molecules one electron occupies an orbital that *was* the LUMO of the ground state molecule but is *now* the HOMO of the excited state species. Because the concentration of excited state molecules is very small compared to the concentration of ground state molecules, the most likely reaction is between an excited state molecule and a ground state molecule. A frontier molecular orbital analysis for such a reaction is shown in Figure 30.8. From this analysis we see that such a reaction is symmetry allowed, and thus frontier molecular orbital analysis provides an explanation for the experimental observation that concerted $[\pi_2s + \pi_2s]$ cycloadditions occur under photochemical (but not under thermal) conditions.

The frontier molecular orbital analysis for a $[\pi_4s + \pi_2s]$ cycloaddition under photochemical conditions is illustrated in Figure 30.9. One of the molecules (most likely the diene component) may be excited photochemically and may begin to interact with a ground state molecule of the other component. We see that regardless of which component is excited photochemically, the reaction is symmetry forbidden. This analysis provides a rationalization for the experimental observation that light does not substitute for heat in stimulating the Diels-Alder and related reactions.

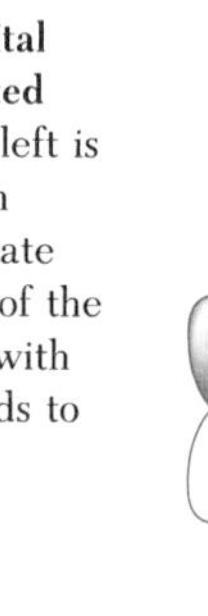

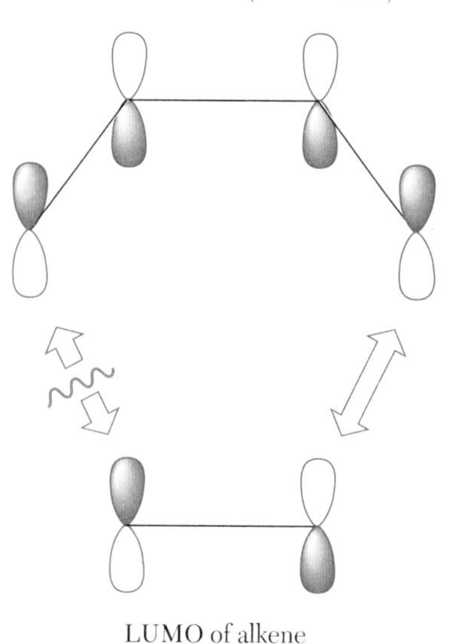

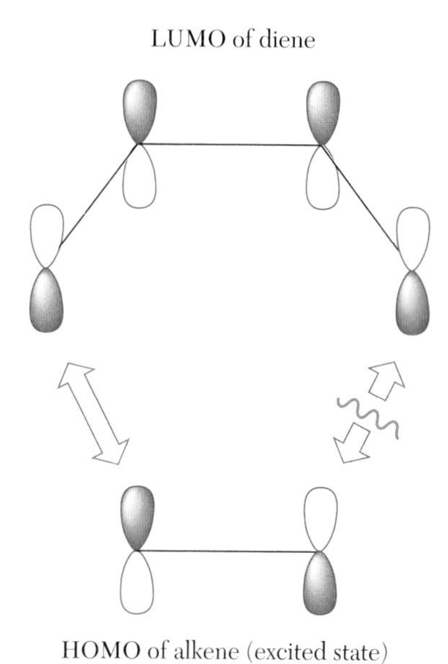

Figure 30.9 Frontier molecular orbital analysis of photochemically stimulated Diels-Alder type reaction. On the left is the analysis for the interaction of an excited state diene with a ground state alkene. On the right is the analysis of the interaction of a ground state diene with an excited state alkene. Neither leads to simultaneous formation of two new σ bonds.

PROBLEM 30.3

Determine whether each of the following cycloaddition processes is thermally allowed.

a. $[\pi_4s + \pi_2a]$ **b.** $[\pi_2s + \pi_2a]$ **c.** $[\pi_6s + \pi_2s]$ **d.** $[\pi_4s + \pi_4s]$

Steps to Solving the Problem

Solution to Problem 30.3a

1. Draw the HOMO of *one* of the components. In general, we can choose either of the reacting components as the HOMO contributor. For the present

problem, we will choose the four π-electron component as the HOMO. The HOMO of butadiene (a four π-electron system) has one node, as shown below.

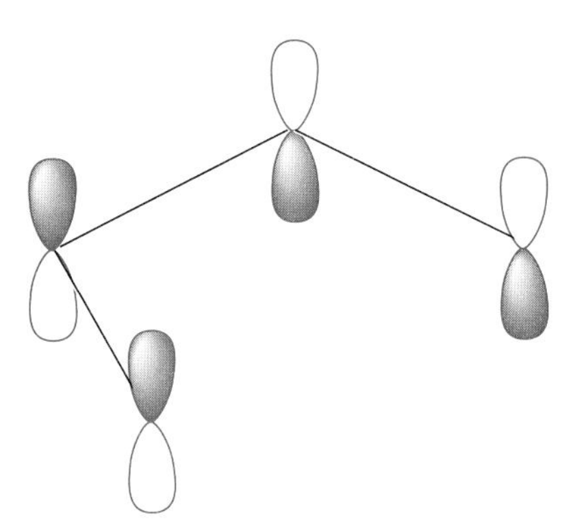

2. Draw the orbital phasing of the LUMO of the other component. The other component is a two π-electron system for which we can use the ethylene molecular orbitals. The LUMO of ethylene has one node. It is shown below.

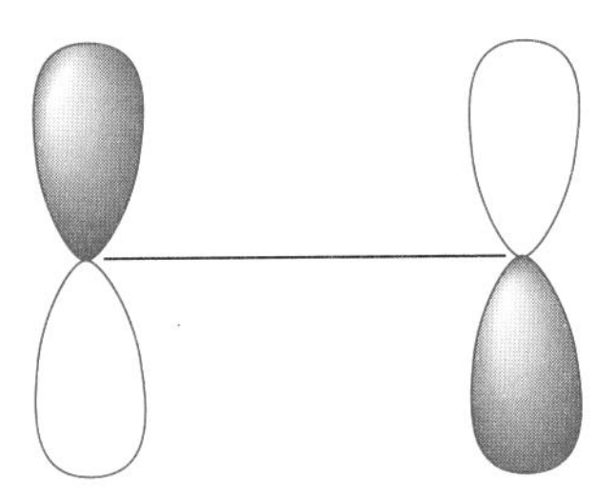

3. Consider the interaction of the two components with the given suprafacial/antarafacial orientation. It is illustrated below.

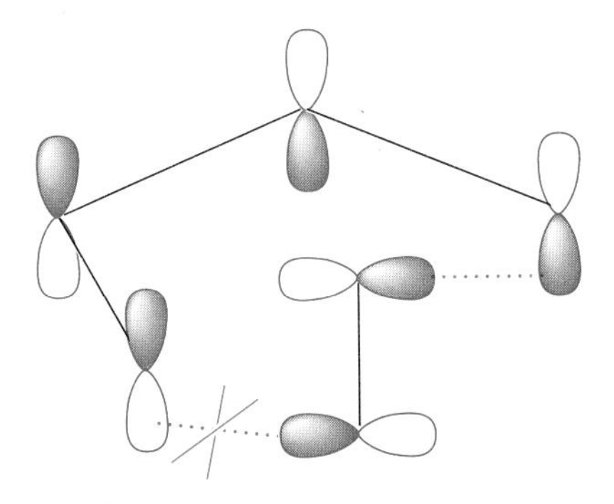

4. Determine whether the concerted reaction is thermally allowed or forbidden. As can be seen from the diagram above, two σ bonds cannot be formed simultaneously with this approach. Thus the thermal concerted [π_4s + π_2a] reaction is symmetry forbidden.

PROBLEM 30.4 Consider the symmetry-allowed or symmetry-forbidden status of the cycloaddition processes listed in Problem 30.3 under *photochemical* stimulation.

30.6 Concerted Electrocyclic Reactions

BASIC PRINCIPLES OF RING CLOSURES

Electrocyclic reactions (introduced earlier in this chapter) involve the intramolecular cyclization of a polyene or the reverse process, the ring opening of a cyclic alkene to an open-chain polyene. In this section we will apply the molecular orbital model toward an understanding of these reactions.

We will use the reactions depicted in Equations 30.3 and 30.4 to illustrate a simple approach for analyzing this type of reaction. Both of these reactions (Equations 30.3 and 30.4) employ (2*E*,4*Z*,6*E*)-2,4,6-octatriene (**30.1**) as a starting material. Under thermal stimulation this species is converted to *cis*-5,6-dimethyl-1,3-cyclohexadiene (**30.2**), but under photochemical stimulation the isomeric compound, *trans*-5,6-dimethyl-1,3-cyclohexadiene (**30.3**), is formed. Using molecular orbital theory to analyze these different reaction routes involves considering the HOMO of the open-chain polyene.

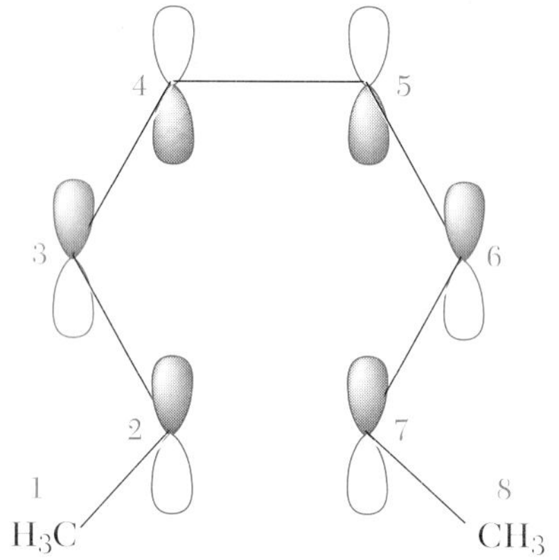

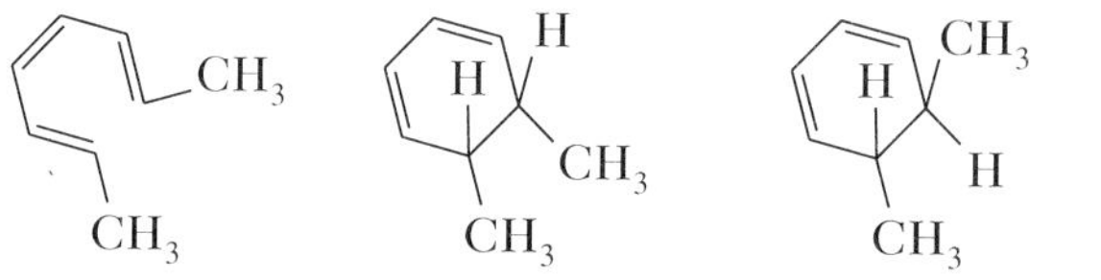

(2*E*,4*Z*,6*E*)-2,4,6-octatriene **30.1** | *cis*-5,6-dimethyl-1,3-cyclohexadiene **30.2** | *trans*-5,6-dimethyl-1,3-cyclohexadiene **30.3**

Figure 30.10 HOMO of ground state (2*E*,4*Z*,6*E*)-2,4,6-octatriene.

If we wish to consider the cyclization of **30.1** under thermal conditions, we need to look at the HOMO shown in Figure 30.10. Cyclization requires formation of a new σ bond between C2 and C7 of the chain. The formation of such a bond using the HOMO of the polyene requires a 90° rotation of the lobes of each of the orbital components on C2 and C7. Given the phasing of the lobes in the HOMO, formation of a σ bond requires that these orbital components rotate in *opposite* directions, as is shown in Figure 30.11. We refer to such rotation of the component lobes in opposite directions as a **disrotatory process.**

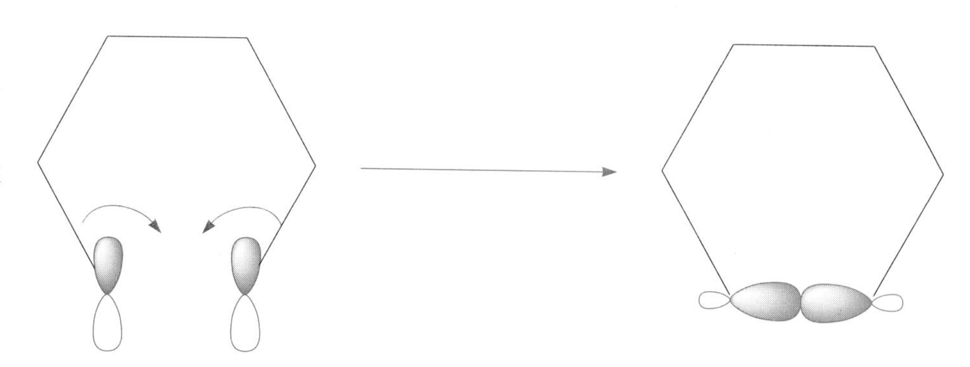

Figure 30.11 Disrotatory closure in an electrocyclic reaction. Rotation of the HOMO component lobes at C2 and C7 of a linear conjugated triene in a disrotatory manner leads to formation of a new σ bond. The remaining lobes of the involved orbitals are omitted for clarity. In a disrotatory closure process, the termini of the polyene rotate in opposite directions.

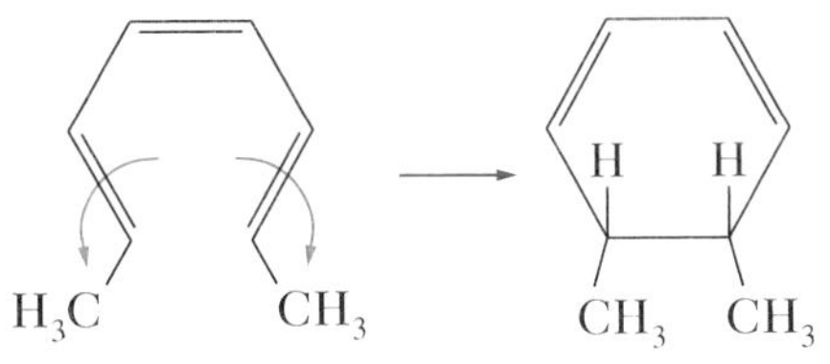

Figure 30.12 Disrotatory ring closure of (2*E*,4*Z*,6*E*)-2,4,6-octatriene to yield *cis*-5,6-dimethyl-1,3-cyclohexadiene.

When the termini of the polyene function rotate, the groups attached to those termini also rotate. In this case, disrotatory closure results in the two methyl groups having a *cis* relationship in the cyclized material, as is shown in Figure 30.12 (this is also the experimentally observed result).

If we irradiate (2*E*,4Z,6*E*)-2,4,6-octatriene with light of a suitable wavelength, an electron is promoted from the original HOMO to the original LUMO, which becomes the HOMO of the excited state molecule. The HOMO of the excited state molecule is shown in Figure 30.13. With this molecular orbital, the termini of the polyene linkage must rotate in the *same* direction if a new σ bond is to form between C2 and C7 of the chain. We refer to this rotation as a **conrotatory process.** It leads to the methyl groups of the cyclized product assuming a *trans* relationship, as is observed experimentally in the photochemical cyclization.

The analysis of electrocyclizations given here is a simplified version of that devised by Woodward and Hoffmann in that it does not consider the transformation of *all* of the involved reactant orbitals into product orbitals. However, this simplified method provides a quick, reliable method for predicting the outcomes of such reactions.

The reasoning introduced here can also be extended in a straightforward fashion to the formation of bicyclic molecules from monocyclic polyenes. For example, thermal stimulation of (*E*,Z)-1,3-cyclooctadiene (Equation 30.5) and photochemical stimulation of (Z,Z)-1,3-cyclooctadiene (Equation 30.6) lead to the same bicyclic product. These results are consistent with a symmetry-allowed thermal conrotatory ring closure of the (*E*,Z)-1,3-cyclooctadiene and a symmetry-allowed photochemical disrotatory closure of the (Z,Z)-1,3-cyclooctadiene. These closures are further illustrated in Figure 30.14.

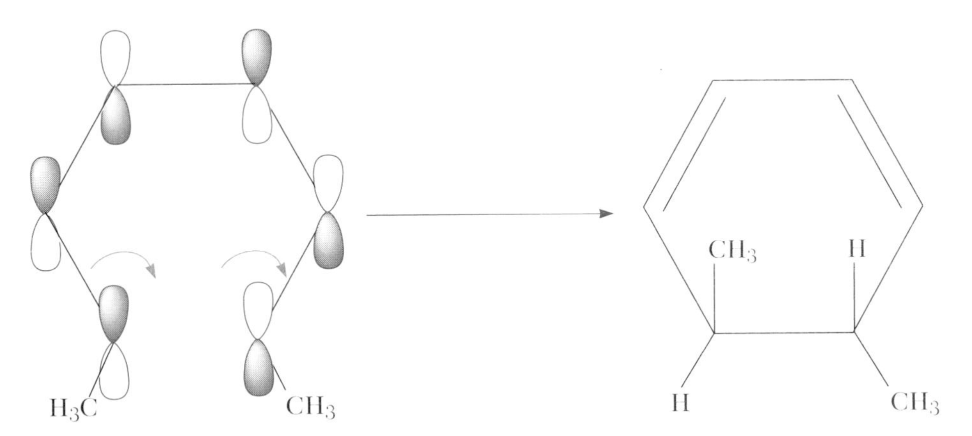

Figure 30.13 Conrotatory closure of (2*E*,4*Z*,6*E*)-2,4,6-octatriene under photochemical stimulation. The HOMO of the excited state of **30.1** requires a conrotatory process for the formation of a new σ bond between the termini of the polyene linkage.

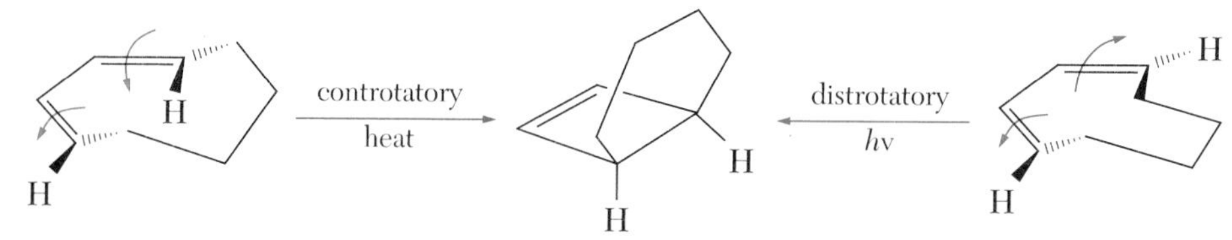

Figure 30.14 Symmetry-allowed electrocyclic closures of 1,3-cyclooctadienes.

PROBLEM 30.5 Draw the HOMO of the excited state of (Z,Z)-1,3-cyclooctadiene and use it to confirm that the photochemical ring closure of Equation 30.6 is disrotatory.

PROBLEM 30.6 Notice that the efficiency of Equation 30.5 (100% yield) is considerably greater than the efficiency of Equation 30.6 (41% yield). In fact, the first reaction has a larger driving force than the second because the strain is greater in the first reactant (Equation 30.5). What is the source of the strain in the reactant in Equation 30.5?

ELECTROCYCLIC RING OPENINGS: THE PRINCIPLE OF MICROSCOPIC REVERSIBILITY

The reactions discussed in the previous section are ring-forming electrocyclic processes. We can also consider concerted ring-*opening* reactions. The most common examples of ring-opening reactions involve cyclobutene derivatives. Two examples given earlier (Equations 30.7 and 30.8) are typical. The open-chain diene products are favored at equilibrium because of the strain associated with four-membered rings.

How can we apply molecular orbital theory to such ring-opening reactions? We could consider the molecular orbitals of the cyclic molecule and determine whether conrotatory or disrotatory ring opening would be in accord with orbital symmetry requirements. To do so, we would need to draw the σ molecular orbitals of the cyclic molecule, a task that is not as straightforward as drawing the π molecular orbitals of the polyenes.

However, we can also deduce the nature of the electrocyclic ring-opening reactions by invoking the principle of **microscopic reversibility.** This principle states that the most efficient route for the regeneration of reactants from products is the exact reversal of the steps involved in the forward reaction (the conversion of reactants into products). All concerted electrocyclic reactions occur in one step through a single transition state, and the transition state for the forward reaction is the same as that for the reverse reaction. Any conclusions we need to make regarding the conrotatory or disrotatory nature of the ring-opening reaction can be inferred from the ring-closing reaction. A disrotatory ring-closure process will reverse in a disrotatory manner, and a conrotatory ring closure will reverse in a conrotatory manner.

Suppose, for example, we wish to know which isomer of 2,4-hexadiene will result from the concerted, thermally-stimulated ring opening of *cis*-3,4-dimethylcyclobutene. To make this determination on an orbital symmetry basis, we need only to apply the frontier orbital considerations to the reverse reaction, that is, the ring-closure process. As shown in Figure 30.15, the thermal ring-closure process leading from a 1,3-butadiene to a cyclobutene is conro-

ring closure

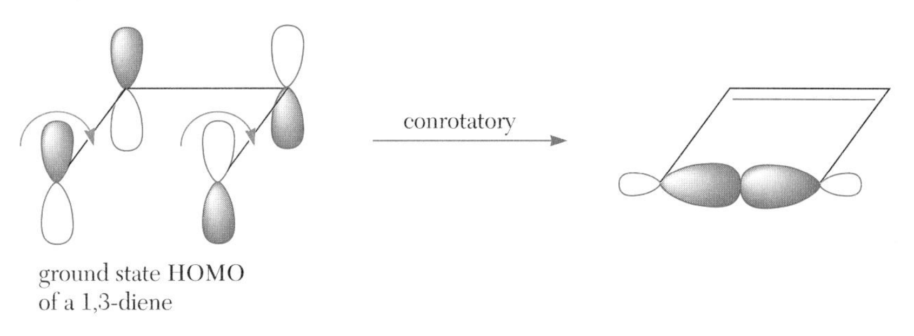

ring opening

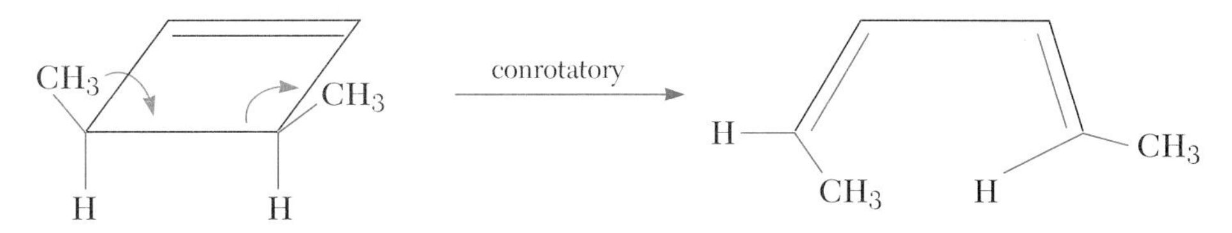

Figure 30.15 Application of the frontier molecular orbital model to electrocyclic ring-opening reactions. At the top is shown the molecular orbital analysis of the electrocyclic ring-closure process for the diene/cyclobutene system. A conrotatory process is required for the concerted thermal reaction. At the bottom is shown the ring-opening process. According to the principle of microscopic reversibility, this reaction should also proceed via a conrotatory route. Conrotatory ring opening leads from the *cis*-3,4-dimethyl-cyclobutene to the (*E*,*Z*)-2,4-hexadiene.

tatory. Thus, it follows that the ring opening is also conrotatory and that (*E*,*Z*)-2,4-hexadiene would form in the thermally stimulated ring-opening of *cis*-3,4-dimethylcyclobutene.

THE SPECIAL KINETIC STABILITY OF DEWAR BENZENE

Dewar benzene is the common name given to the compound bicyclo[2.2.0]-2,5-hexadiene (**30.4**). Dewar benzene is a highly strained isomer of benzene. It was first synthesized in 1963, although substituted derivatives had been prepared earlier. The most remarkable property of Dewar benzene is its great *kinetic* stability, which stands in striking contrast to its relatively great *thermodynamic* instability.

bicyclo[2.2.0]-2,5-hexadiene
"Dewar benzene"
30.4

Consider the conversion illustrated in Equation 30.10.

Eqn. 30.10

The reactant in Equation 30.10 is extremely strained and therefore thermodynamically unstable relative to the product (benzene), which has *aromatic* stabilization. We expect (and find) there to be a very large thermodynamic driving force for the conversion of Dewar benzene to benzene. The experimental value is > 70 kcal/mole.

With such a large thermodynamic driving force for the reaction, we might expect that Dewar benzene would rapidly isomerize to benzene. That is, we might expect it to be kinetically unstable as well as thermodynamically unstable. However, the reaction is rather slow. The half-life of Dewar benzene is about two days at room temperature.

Molecular orbital symmetry considerations provide an insight into the reason for the kinetic stability of Dewar benzene. The isomerization of Dewar benzene to benzene requires opening one of the cyclobutene rings. We have seen that for such a process to occur in a concerted manner under thermal stimulation, the ring opening must be *conrotatory*. However, conrotatory opening of a cyclobutene ring of Dewar benzene does *not* lead to benzene. Rather, it leads to an impossibly strained benzene isomer containing a *trans* double bond in a six-membered ring, as shown in Figure 30.16.

Figure 30.16 Concerted thermal ring opening of Dewar benzene. A concerted thermal ring opening of Dewar benzene must occur in a conrotatory manner because of molecular orbital symmetry requirements. Such a ring opening would lead not to benzene but rather to the highly strained (Z,Z,*E*)-1,3,5-cyclohexatriene, a molecule that has a *trans* double bond in a small ring and does not even form.

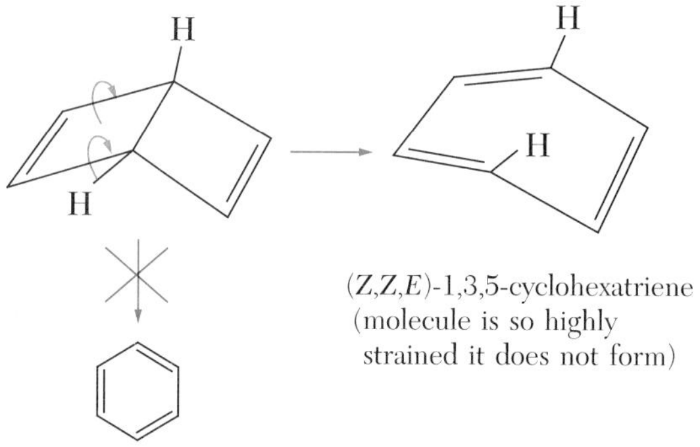

H
H
H
H
(Z,Z,*E*)-1,3,5-cyclohexatriene
(molecule is so highly
strained it does not form)

A disrotatory ring-opening of Dewar benzene would be required for the generation of benzene. However, this route is symmetry forbidden for a thermally stimulated process. The experimental result, a slow isomerization of Dewar benzene to benzene, is consistent with a stepwise rather than a concerted process.

PROBLEM 30.7 Which of the isomers shown below, *A* or *B*, would you expect to form (2*E*,4Z,6Z,8*E*)-2,4,6,8-decatetraene upon heating? Explain your answer.

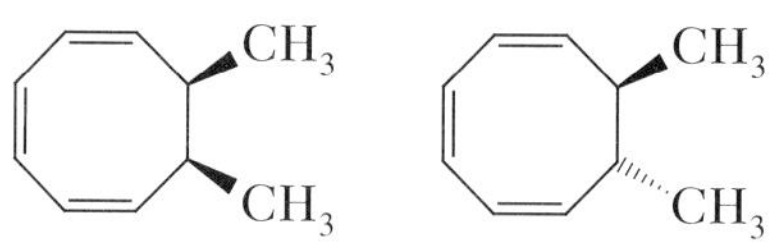

CH_3
CH_3
CH_3
CH_3
A
B

PROBLEM 30.8 Compound *C* undergoes thermal ring opening of its cyclobutene ring much less readily than does compound *D*. Suggest a reason for this difference in the behavior of the two compounds.

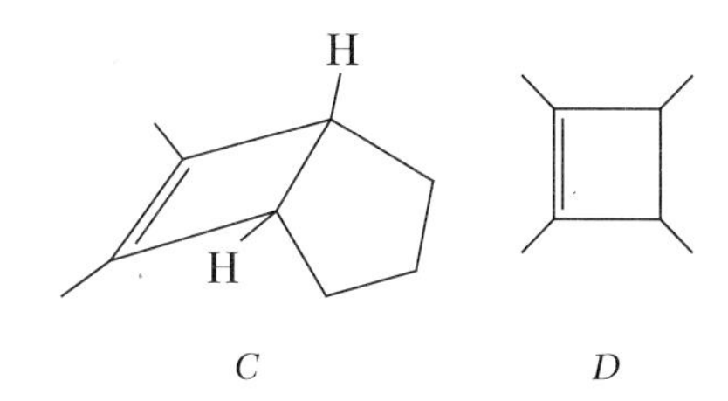

C *D*

PROBLEM 30.9 Tell which of the following electrocyclic closures are symmetry allowed under photochemical conditions. Explain each answer.

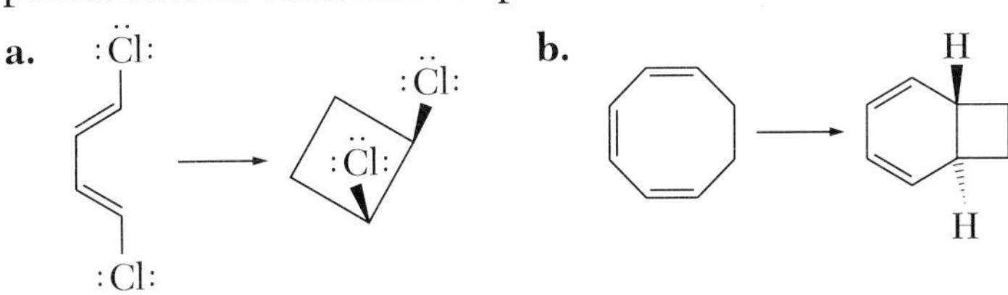

c.

H
H

PROBLEM 30.10 Predict the product in each of the following electrocyclic ring-closure reactions.

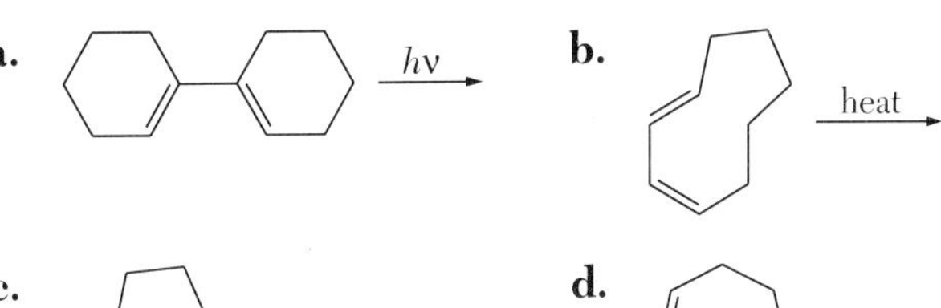

c. hν

d. :O: hν
:Cl:

PROBLEM 30.11 The reaction

:Cl:
H H heat
:Cl:

gives a *major* and a *minor* product through concerted ring-opening reactions. What are these products?

PROBLEM 30.12 Predict the product of each of the following electrocyclic ring-opening reactions.

a. 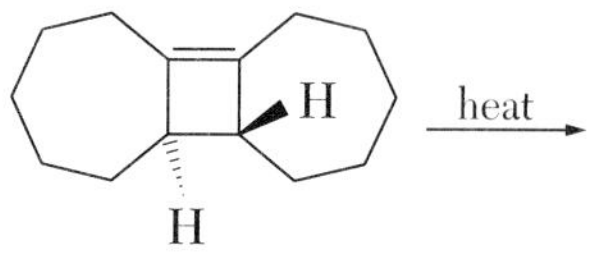

b. 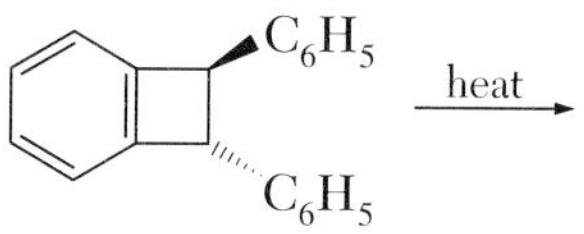

c. 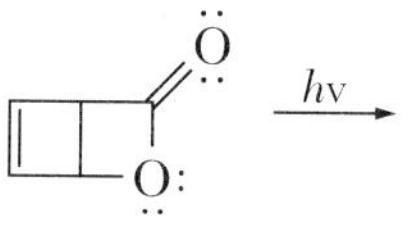

30.7 Sigmatropic Reactions

We will now consider another important class of concerted reactions, those known as **sigmatropic reactions.** In sigmatropic reactions a σ bond migrates from one position to another along a polyene chain, accompanied by a shift of the polyene π bonds.

A notation consisting of two numbers in a square bracket is used to classify sigmatropic reactions. Two examples, along with explanation of the notation, are shown in Figure 30.17.

Figure 30.17 Classification of sigmatropic reactions.

An example of an overall sigmatropic reaction is:

To designate the nature of this reaction, we begin numbering the chain in each direction from the site at which the original bond is broken, working toward the site at which the new bond is formed.

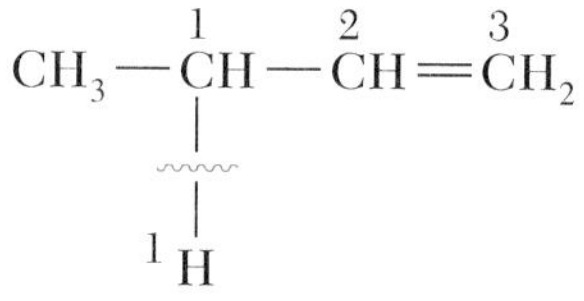

We now look for the site at which the new bond is formed. The new bond joins atom 3 of one group and atom 1 (the hydrogen atom) of the other group. We thus refer to this reaction as a [1,3] sigmatropic reaction.

A second example is provided by the reaction shown below.

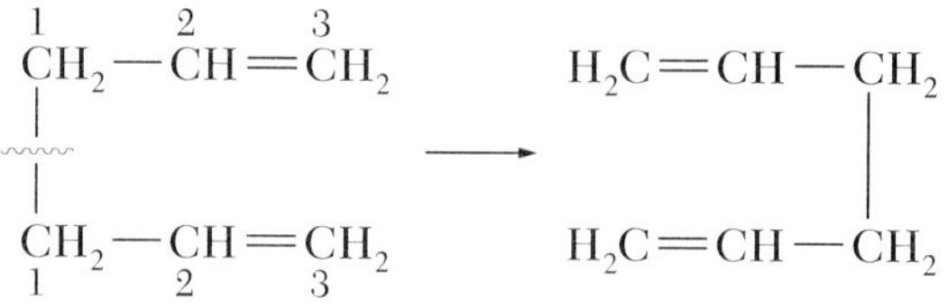

This reaction is known as a [3,3] sigmatropic reaction.

$$\mathrm{R{-}\overset{H}{\overset{|}{C}H}{-}CH{=}CH_2 \xrightarrow{[1,3]} R{-}CH{=}CH{-}\overset{H}{\overset{|}{C}H_2}}$$

$$\mathrm{R{-}\overset{H}{\overset{|}{C}H}{-}CH{=}CH{-}CH{=}CH_2 \xrightarrow{[1,5]} R{-}CH{=}CH{-}CH{=}CH{-}\overset{H}{\overset{|}{C}H_2}}$$

Figure 30.18 Sigmatropic reactions of the [1,3] and [1,5] type involving the transfer of hydrogen.

suprafacial

antarafacial

Figure 30.19 Suprafacial and antarafacial sigmatropic reactions.

Some sigmatropic reactions occur readily under thermal stimulation, while others require photochemical stimulation. Molecular orbital theory provides insights and gives useful predictive guidelines for these reactions. Consider, for example, the rearrangements shown in Figure 30.18. In the first reaction shown in Figure 30.18, a hydrogen is transferred in a [1,3] manner, while in the second reaction the hydrogen is transferred in a [1,5] manner. Both reactions involve the transfer of a hydrogen from one end of the molecule to the other. The molecular orbital model allows us to predict whether such reactions can be concerted and to analyze the geometrical requirements of such transfers. There are two geometrical possibilities—suprafacial and antarafacial reactions—as shown in Figure 30.19.

For [1,3] and [1,5] hydrogen sigmatropic reactions we need to consider only the suprafacial mode, in which the hydrogen moves across one face of the molecule. Antarafacial shifts in these small systems would require an unreasonable amount of twisting strain on the π framework in the transition state.

The critical molecular orbital analysis concerning the transition state for such reactions can be made in a rather simple way. The transition state is viewed as an association of the migrating group with the remainder of the molecule. For example, for the [1,3] rearrangement of Figure 30.18 we consider a hydrogen atom migrating along an allyl radical chain, as shown in Figure 30.20.

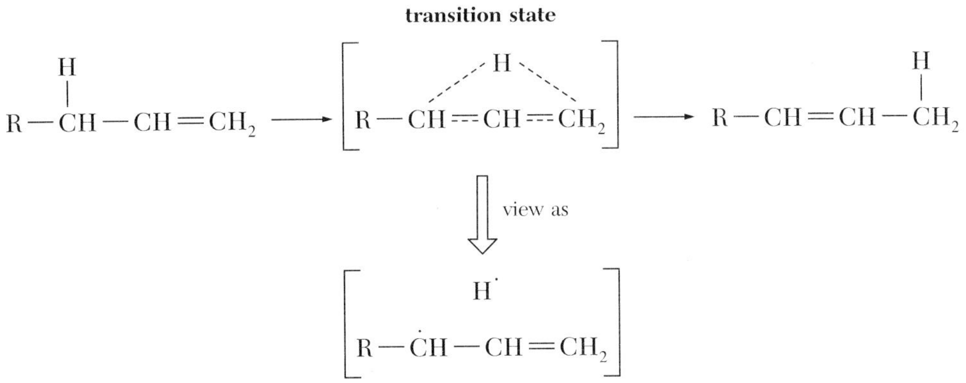

transition state

$$\mathrm{R{-}\overset{H}{\overset{|}{C}H}{-}CH{=}CH_2 \longrightarrow \left[R{-}CH{\overset{...}{=}}CH{\overset{...}{=}}CH_2 \;(\cdots H \cdots)\right] \longrightarrow R{-}CH{=}CH{-}\overset{H}{\overset{|}{C}H_2}}$$

view as

$$\left[\mathrm{H^{\cdot} \quad R{-}\dot{C}H{-}CH{=}CH_2}\right]$$

Figure 30.20 A [1,3] sigmatropic hydrogen transfer. We consider the concerted reaction proceeding through a single transition state as involving a hydrogen atom migrating along an allyl radical chain.

Figure 30.21 Allylic radical π molecular orbitals with the ground state electronic configuration.

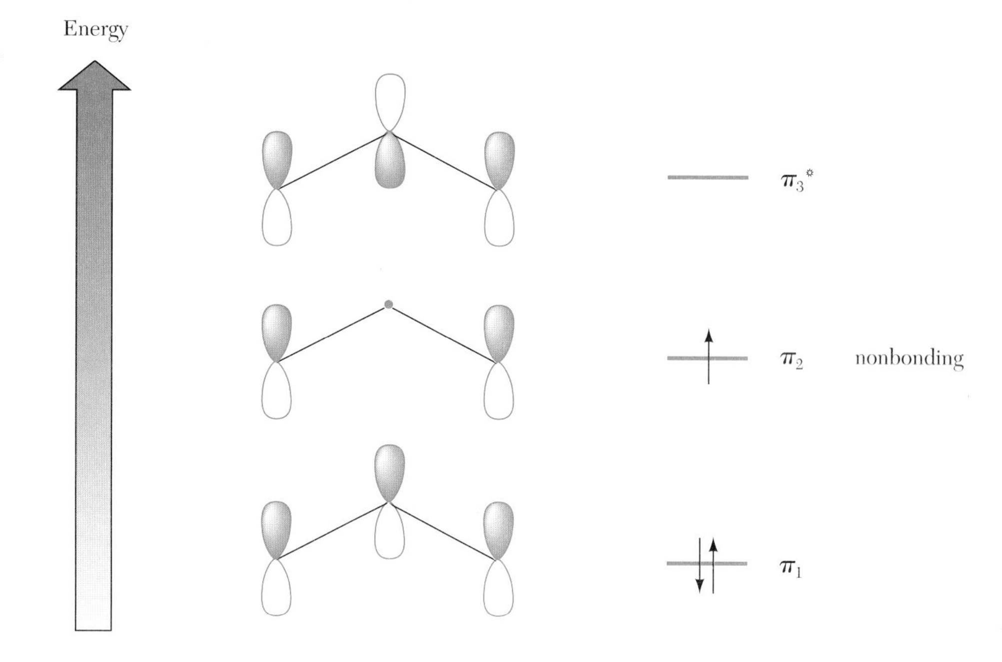

The hydrogen atom has its single electron in the 1*s* orbital and uses that orbital to bond to the allyl radical. To determine whether this process occurs in a concerted manner, we need to look at the way in which the 1*s* orbital of the hydrogen atom and the singly occupied molecular orbital of the allyl radical interact. The π orbitals of the allyl radical are shown in Figure 30.21 (see Chapter 16 for a discussion of these orbitals).

For a *thermal* concerted reaction, we need to consider the way in which the π_2 molecular orbital interacts with the 1*s* orbital of the hydrogen atom. For a *photochemical* reaction, however, we need to consider the *excited state*, in which the π_3* orbital is singly occupied. First consider an attempt at reaction under thermal conditions. For a suprafacial transfer the hydrogen atom *cannot* bond simultaneously with both termini of the π system (Figure 30.22), and thus the reaction cannot be concerted. However, the reaction is predicted to be

Figure 30.22 Molecular orbital analysis of the transition states for thermal and photochemical suprafacial [1,3] sigmatropic reaction involving hydrogen transfer.

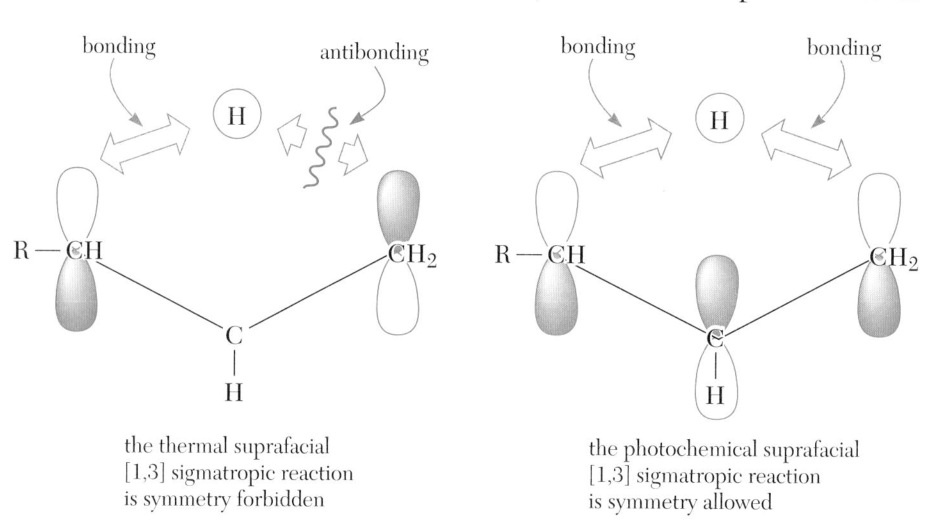

concerted if it is performed under photochemical conditions. Under these conditions the hydrogen atom *can* bind simultaneously to the two termini of the π system (Figure 30.22). This analysis matches the experimental observation that concerted [1,3] sigmatropic reactions involving the transfer of hydrogen occur only under photochemical stimulation.

PROBLEM 30.13 Consider suprafacial [1,5] sigmatropic reactions of the type:

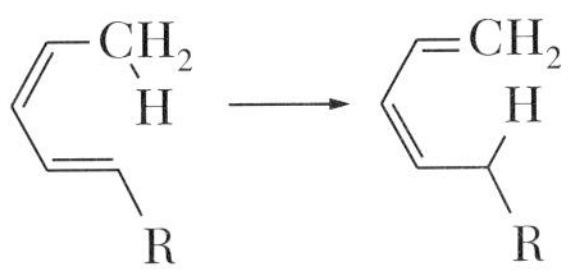

CH_2 H R → CH_2 H R

By viewing the transition state as an association of a hydrogen atom and a pentadienyl radical, predict whether the reaction is symmetry allowed or symmetry forbidden under thermal and under photochemical conditions.

Although [1,3] sigmatropic reactions involving hydrogen transfer are symmetry forbidden under thermal conditions, similar rearrangements involving transfer of a methyl (or other alkyl group) are not forbidden because a carbon atom can use different lobes of a 2*p* orbital to bind simultaneously to both termini of the allyl radial, as shown in Figure 30.23.

It follows from the analysis of Figure 30.23 that the migrating group in a sigmatropic reaction must bind to its attachment site in the product using a different lobe of its 2*p* orbital than was used to bind to its attachment site in

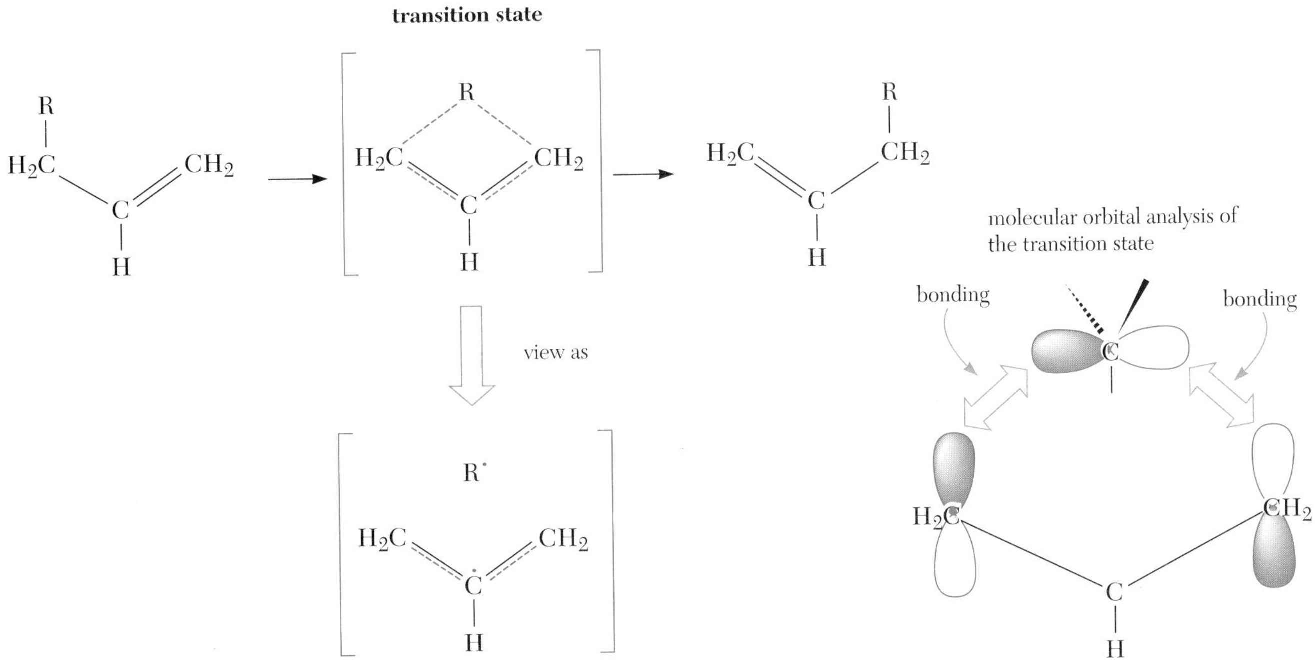

Figure 30.23 Thermal [1,3] sigmatropic reaction involving an alkyl group transfer. This reaction is symmetry allowed. Carbon can use both lobes of a 2*p* orbital to bind simultaneously with the two termini of the allylic system.

transition state

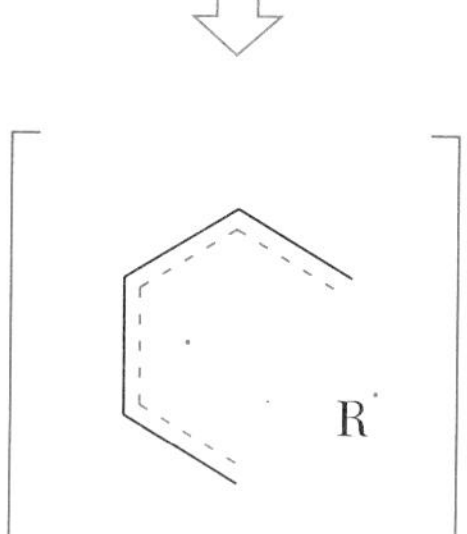

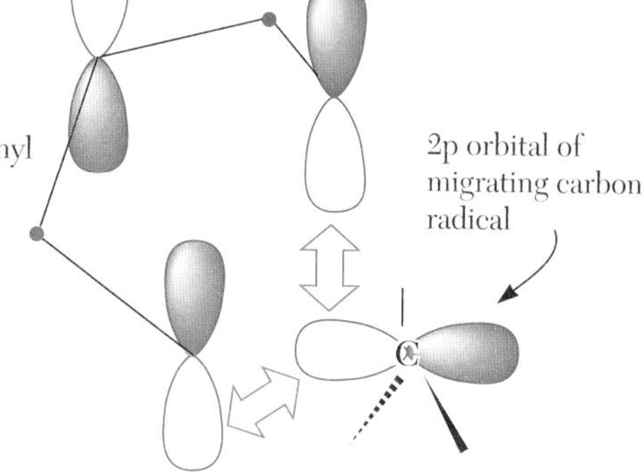

Figure 30.24 Suprafacial migration of an alkyl group in a thermal [1,5] sigmatropic reaction.

the reactant. We predict that if the migrating site is *stereogenic*, an inversion of configuration will accompany the [1,3] sigmatropic reaction. Such inversions have been observed experimentally. Again, the molecular orbital analysis provides an understanding of the experimental observation.

If the orbital symmetry of a reacting system is appropriate, a migrating carbon site could use the same lobe of its $2p$ orbital to bind to the two involved sites in the transition state of a sigmatropic reaction. The transition state of a suprafacial [1,5] sigmatropic reaction involving an alkyl shift is shown in Figure 30.24.

The final category of sigmatropic reactions we will consider here are processes of the type shown in Equations 30.11 and 30.12. We refer to them as [3,3] sigmatropic rearrangements.

Eqn. 30.11

CN NC 130 °C CN NC

80% yield

Eqn. 30.12

H Ö: 50 °C Ö

95% yield

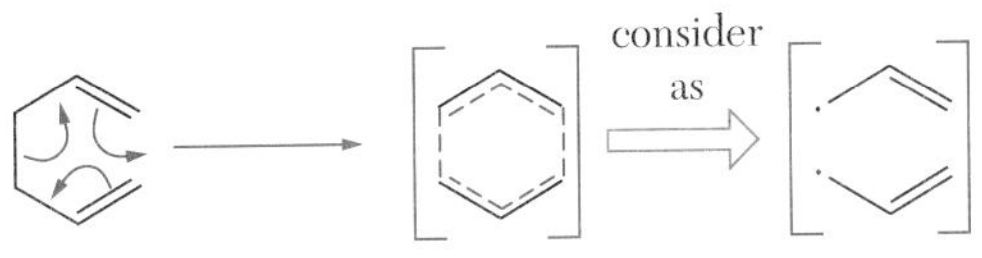

consider as

transition state

Figure 30.25 Transition state of a [3,3] sigmatropic reaction. It is convenient to view the transition state of a [3,3] sigmatropic reaction as an association of two allylic radicals.

Following the approach we have been using for sigmatropic reactions, we can analyze the transition states of these reactions in terms of the association between the migrating group and the remainder (substrate). Both the migrating group *and* the substrate can be viewed as allylic radicals, as shown in Figure 30.25.

Molecular orbital analysis of the system shows that this type of concerted [3,3] sigmatropic reaction is symmetry allowed under thermal conditions, as shown in Figure 30.26.

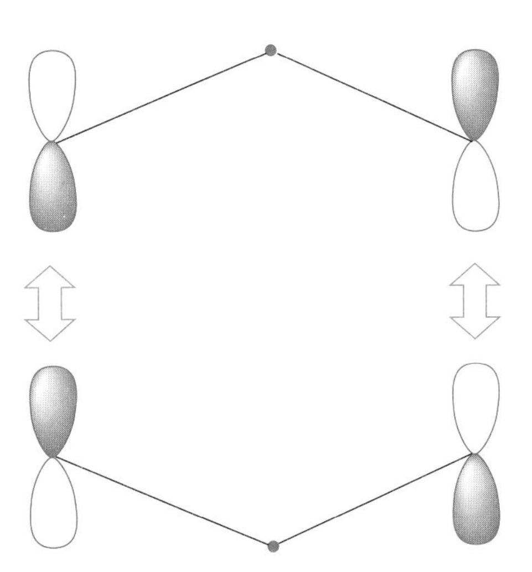

Figure 30.26 Orbital interactions in the transition state of a [3,3] sigmatropic reaction.

PROBLEM 30.14 What product would you expect to form upon [3,3] sigmatropic reaction of the following compound?

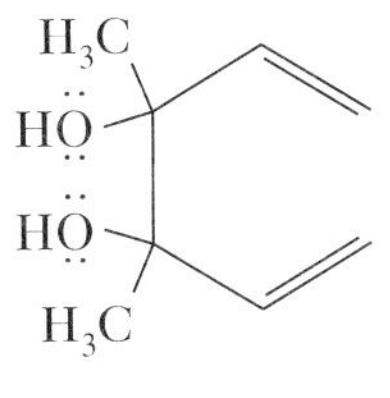

H_3C

HO

HO

H_3C

The observed product exhibits an IR absorption at $\sim 1715\ cm^{-1}$. Is this consistent with a [3,3] sigmatropic reaction having taken place?

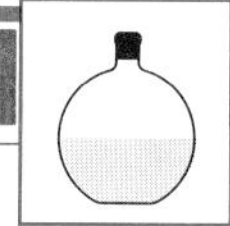

COMPOUND CAPSULE

Bullvalene

Bullvalene is one of a number of compounds that undergo rapid sigmatropic reactions at room temperature. When bullvalene undergoes such reactions it is transformed not into a new product, but rather into another molecule of itself, as is shown below.

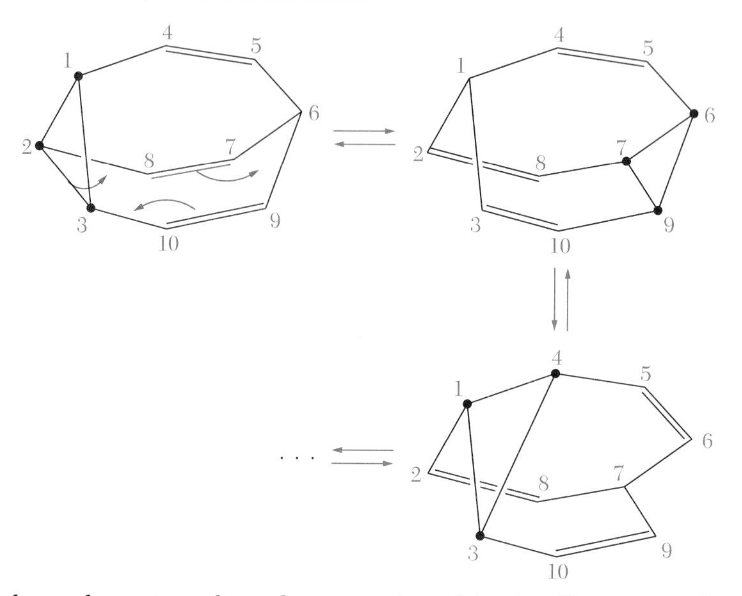

The carbon atoms have been numbered in the illustration above to indicate the changing bonding about the individual carbon sites. More than three thousand such sigmatropic reactions occur each second when bullvalene is at room temperature. However, in the process of undergoing this reaction, the carbon and hydrogen atoms change their individual environments. For example, in the first structure shown above, carbon atoms 1, 2, and 3 define the cyclopropane ring (the cyclopropane ring is emphasized by the use of large dots for the carbon atoms). After the first rearrangement of bullvalene, the product molecule is *still bullvalene*, but carbon atoms 6, 7, and 9 now constitute the cyclopropane ring. After a second rearrangement, carbon atoms 1, 3, and 4 define the cyclopropane ring. You should note that the product of this second rearrangement is *still bullvalene*—the positions of individual atoms have simply been shuffled— and is capable of undergoing further rearrangement. We say that bullvalene undergoes a *degenerate* rearrangement.

When bullvalene is heated, the rearrangement occurs so rapidly that the NMR spectrometer is not able to distinguish the different carbon or hydrogen atom positions. Only an identical average environment for each is detected. For example, at 100 °C the proton NMR spectrum exhibits a single peak (δ 4.2) reflecting the average environment. On cooling, the reaction slows and the individual environments of different hydrogens (or carbons) can be detected in the NMR spectra.

PROBLEM 30.15 Use the curved-arrow formalism to illustrate the second sigmatropic rearrangement of bullvalene in the diagram shown above.

PROBLEM 30.16 By writing out continuing sigmatropic rearrangements of bullvalene, verify that *all* of its carbon atoms eventually occupy equivalent positions.

Summary

- Concerted reactions proceed in a single mechanistic step without the formation of distinct chemical intermediates.
- Molecular orbital theory proves useful in analyzing pericyclic concerted reactions, that is, reactions that take place via a cyclic transition state. The three major classes of pericyclic reactions are cycloadditions, electrocyclic ring closures and openings, and sigmatropic reactions.
- The molecular orbital analysis of cycloaddition reactions involves an inspection of the HOMO of one component and the LUMO of the other component. The reaction is symmetry allowed if the interaction of this HOMO and LUMO results in two simultaneous new σ-bonding interactions, and it is symmetry forbidden if it does not.
- For electrocyclic reactions, we need to determine whether conrotatory or disrotatory ring opening or closure occurs. We determine this by inspection of the symmetry properties of the HOMO of the open-ring polyene that is either the reactant or the product of the reaction. The decision between conrotatory or disrotatory is made on the basis of the direction in which the terminal lobes of the polyene HOMO must rotate to generate a new σ bonding interaction between them.
- When applying molecular orbital theory to sigmatropic reactions, we find it convenient to view the transition state as an association between a migrating group and the remainder of the molecule (substrate). To decide whether a particular reaction is symmetry allowed, we determine whether the migrating group is able to bind simultaneously to both termini of the substrate portion in the transition state of the reaction.

Terms to Remember

concerted reaction
pericyclic reaction
cycloaddition
electrocyclic reaction
frontier molecular orbitals
conservation of orbital symmetry
suprafacial
antarafacial
symmetry forbidden
symmetry allowed
disrotatory process
conrotatory process
microscopic reversibility
sigmatropic reaction

Additional Problems

30.17 Deduce whether the following concerted cycloadditions are symmetry allowed under thermal or under photochemical stimulation:

a. $[\pi_6 s + \pi_2 s]$ **b.** $[\pi_4 s + \pi_4 s]$ **c.** $[\pi_8 s + \pi_2 s]$
d. $[\pi_6 s + \pi_4 s]$ **e.** $[\pi_6 s + \pi_2 a]$ **f.** $[\pi_{14} a + \pi_2 s]$

30.18 Predict whether the following concerted reactions require thermal or photochemical stimulation:

a.

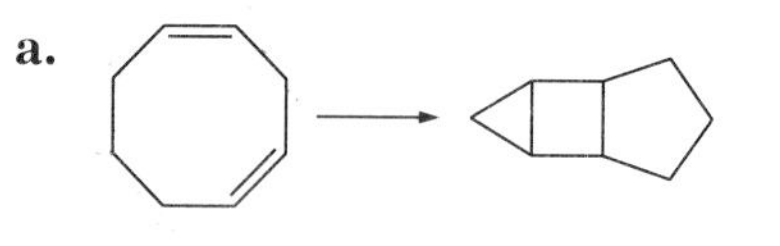

b.

c.

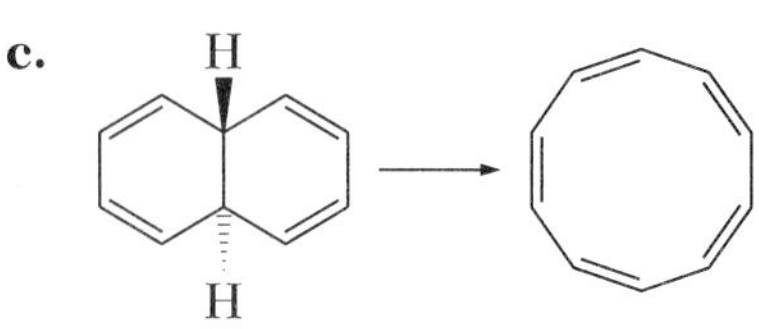

d.

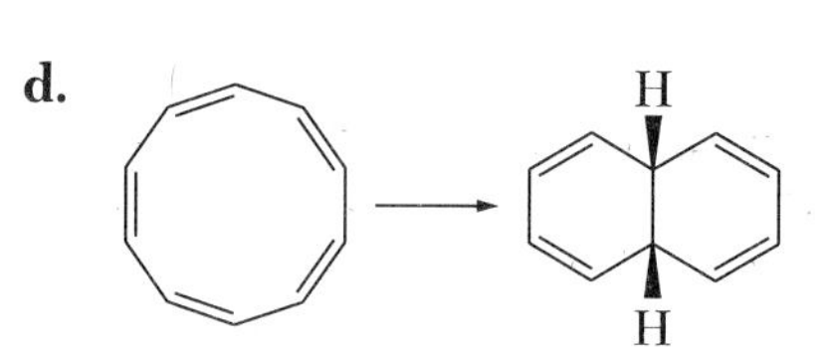

e.

30.19 Predict the products of each of the following pericyclic reactions:
a. (2*E*,4*Z*,6*Z*,8*E*)-2,4,6,8-decatetraene on heating to form a cyclic triene
b. *cis*-5,6-dimethylcyclohexa-1,3-diene on heating to yield an open-chain triene
c. (2*E*,4*E*)-2,4-hexadiene on irradiation with light to form a cyclobutene derivative
d. *cis*-3-ethyl-4-methylcyclobutene on heating to yield an open-chain diene

30.20 Bicyclo[2.1.0]pentane can be prepared by a photochemical ring-forming reaction. What compound would be used as the starting material for this reaction? In spite of its strained structure, bicyclo[2.1.0]pentane has a relatively high kinetic stability (half-life = 2 hours at room temperature). Offer an explanation for this kinetic stability.

30.21 In contrast to most cyclobutenes, the compound shown below undergoes opening of the cyclobutene ring only under extreme thermal conditions (> 380 °C). Explain this stability.

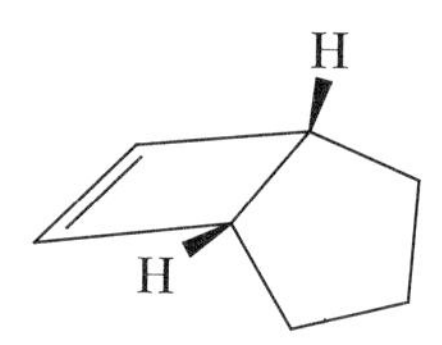

30.22 Give the molecular orbital designation for each of the following reactions. For each, tell whether thermal or photochemical initiation would be required.

a.

b.

c.

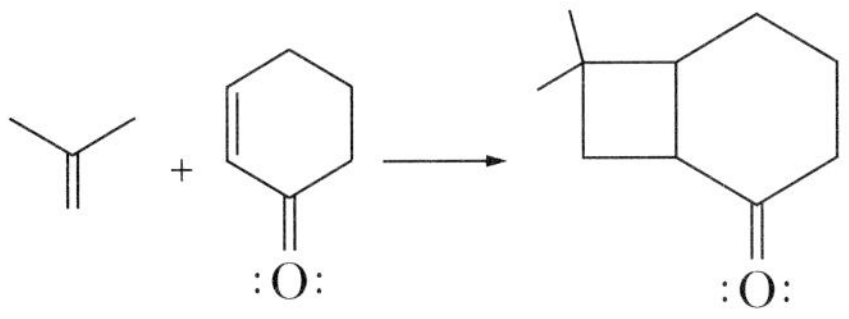

:O: :O:

d. C_6H_5 C_6H_5 CH_3 H_3C → C_6H_5 C_6H_5 CH_3 H_3C

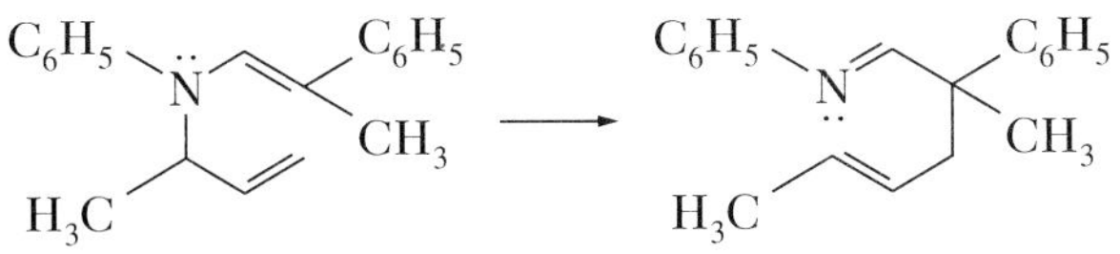

30.23 Consider the allyl anion. In principle, would you expect it to be able to add to a simple alkene or a conjugated diene in a concerted pericyclic reaction under thermal conditions? Explain your answer.

30.24 When compound *U* is heated, it undergoes partial isomerization to *one* of the species *V*–*X*. Tell which species is formed and explain what happens.

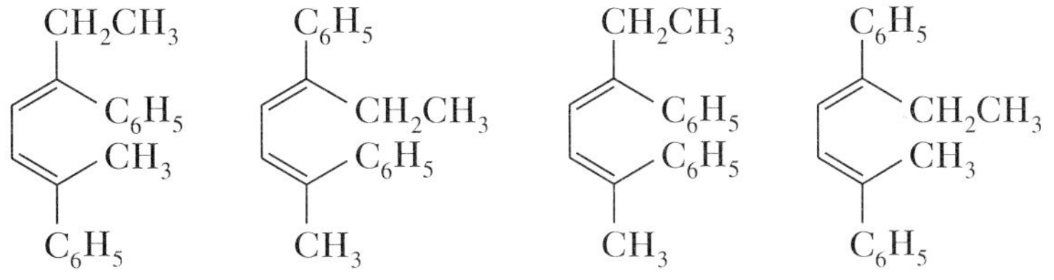

CH_2CH_3 C_6H_5 CH_3 C_6H_5 — *U*

C_6H_5 CH_2CH_3 C_6H_5 CH_3 — *V*

CH_2CH_3 C_6H_5 C_6H_5 CH_3 — *W*

C_6H_5 CH_2CH_3 CH_3 C_6H_5 — *X*

30.25 *meso*-3,4-Dimethyl-1,5-hexadiene undergoes rearrangement almost exclusively (>99.5%) to *cis,trans*-2,6-octadiene at 225 °C. What type of pericyclic reaction is this? Is the stereochemistry of this reaction consistent with a boat or a chair conformation for the transition state?

30.26 Which of the following undergoes symmetry-allowed thermally stimulated disrotatory cyclization to the indicated product?

a. pentadienyl cation to the cyclopentenyl cation
b. pentadienyl anion to the cyclopentenyl anion

30.27 Both of the conversions shown below produce an aromatic ring, but in the gas phase only one occurs easily via a concerted reaction. Which one occurs readily in the gas phase? Explain your answer.

a. CH_2 → CH_3 b.

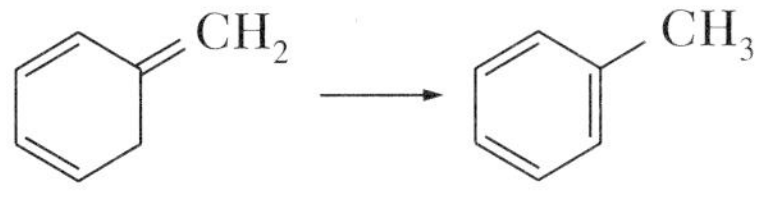

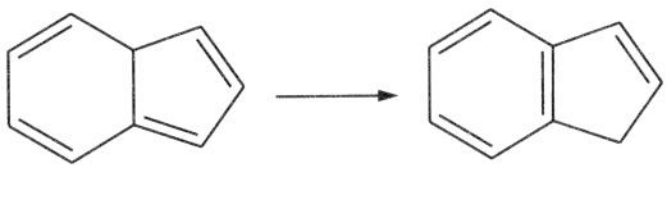

30.28 One of the following isomers undergoes ring opening of the cyclobutene ring at 90 °C, while the other undergoes reaction only above 250 °C. Which isomer is which? Explain your answer.

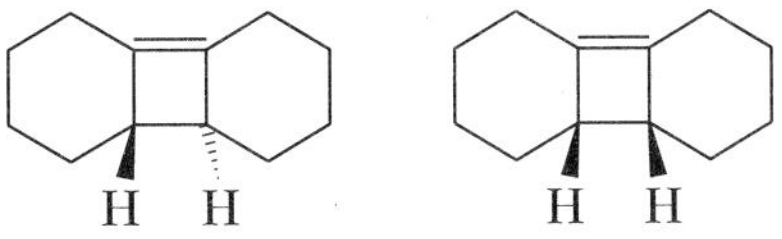

H H   H H

30.29 Suggest structures for compounds *E* and *F* in the following reaction scheme.

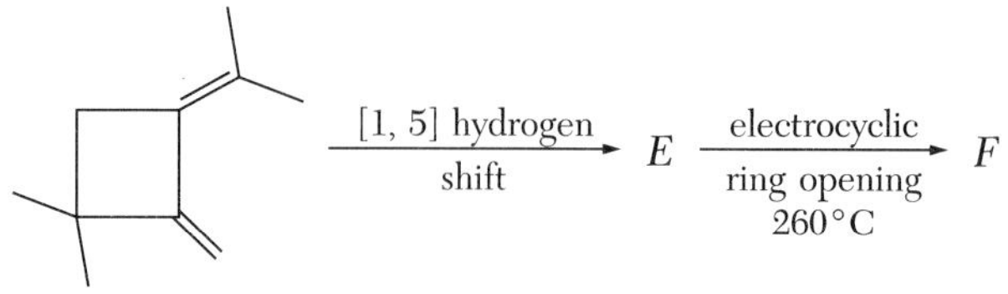

$$\xrightarrow[\text{shift}]{\text{[1, 5] hydrogen}} E \xrightarrow[\text{ring opening, } 260^\circ\text{C}]{\text{electrocyclic}} F$$

Index

Numbers following entries reference pages. The character *f* denotes figure; the character *t* denotes table; the character *s* denotes structure. Bold page references indicate pages where the definition of a *Term to Remember* is found.

A

B

D

F

G

H

I

N

O

Q

R

S

W

X

Z